Full pronun... ...y

The pronunciation of each word is shown just after the word, in this way:
ab·bre·vi·ate (ə brē′vē āt).

The letters and signs used are pronounced as in the words below.

The mark ′ is placed after a syllable with primary or heavy accent, as in the example above.

The mark ′ after a syllable shows a secondary or lighter accent, as in
ab·bre·vi·a·tion (ə brē′vē ā′shən).

a	hat, cap	**p**	paper, cup
ā	age, face	**r**	run, try
ä	father, far	**s**	say, yes
		sh	she, rush
		t	tell, it
b	bad, rob	**th**	thin, both
ch	child, much	**ŦH**	then, smooth
d	did, red		
		u	cup, butter
e	let, best	**u̇**	full, put
ē	equal, be	**ü**	rule, move
ėr	term, learn		
		v	very, save
f	fat, if	**w**	will, woman
g	go, bag	**y**	young, yet
h	he, how	**z**	zero, breeze
		zh	measure, seizure
i	it, pin		
ī	ice, five		
j	jam, enjoy	**ə**	represents:
k	kind, seek		a in about
l	land, coal		e in taken
m	me, am		i in pencil
n	no, in		o in lemon
ng	long, bring		u in circus
o	hot, rock		
ō	open, go		
ô	order, all		
oi	oil, voice		
ou	house, out		

Scott, Foresman
Beginning Dictionary

by E.L.Thorndike/Clarence L.Barnhart

Scott, Foresman and Company

Editorial Offices: Glenview, Illinois

Regional Offices: Sunnyvale, California ·
Tucker, Georgia · Glenview, Illinois ·
Oakland, New Jersey · Dallas, Texas

ISBN: 0-673-12387-1

5678910-RRW-9998979695

Contents

Author's Preface

The millions of children who have used the Thorndike dictionaries over the last fifty years owe their dictionaries to the idea of one man, Dr. E. L. Thorndike. He believed that the facts about words arranged in dictionaries should be in language that the pupils could understand. This unique idea of the 1920s, originating from studies in the psychology of language, was applied to the problems of dictionary-making in a lecture Dr. Thorndike gave to graduate students at Teacher's College, Columbia University. As an example of his work, in explaining *anecdote,* Dr. Thorndike wrote this definition: "a short account of some interesting incident or event. *Many anecdotes are told about Abraham Lincoln.*" All words used in this explanation are simpler than the word *anecdote* that is being defined; any words that were not easier and more frequent, such as "instructive," were not used; words that were misleading, such as "story," were not used because they are too vague and imply a plot. Dr. Thorndike tested every meaning so that he would not use words that were too hard or too vague; in order to do this satisfactorily he prepared three manuscripts before he sent the final one to his publisher, Scott, Foresman, in 1929.

Not only were the definitions in Dr. Thorndike's dictionaries carefully edited but great care was taken by the author and the Scott, Foresman editorial staff to provide illustrative sentences that complemented the definitions. The sentences are often written so that they force the meaning home to the pupil. Under *antagonize,* Dr. Thorndike used this sentence: *"Her unkind remarks antagonized people who had been her friends."* Whenever possible Dr. Thorndike gave pupils a sentence which teaches them how to use the word—a unique feature of his dictionaries.

The editor-in-chief asked me to check the manuscript back against other dictionaries to see if Dr. Thorndike had been successful in preparing understandable definitions. His claim of explaining meanings in language the ordinary child could understand was on the whole followed, and most of his manuscript was able to stand without changes.

There were so many opportunities for error, however, that an editorial staff of twenty or more editors and their assistants checked the manuscript of the author's work in detail. *Abrupt* was one of the words checked and commented on: in the third definition Dr. Thorndike used the word "unexpected": "short, sudden, or unexpected in speech or manner." The Scott, Foresman staff commented that an abrupt remark was not necessarily "unexpected." Dr. Thorndike agreed and suggested "blunt" instead, which was acceptable. The staff made over 50,000 such comments to Dr. Thorndike over a period of five years; about half were accepted, a fourth modified, and another fourth rejected. Certainly this experience of working through the English language to explain difficult terms in easier language was unique and has proven itself to be of lasting value. I have always been proud that I had a part in the adaptation of the science of psychology to the making of the Thorndike dictionaries.

Clarence L. Barnhart

Introduction

Children love using words, both in their conversation and in their writing activities, and they have a natural interest in learning about words. This latest revision of the Beginning Dictionary, in continuous publication since 1945, encourages this interest. For more than fifty years, millions of children have used dictionaries originally compiled and prepared by E. L. Thorndike and Clarence L. Barnhart, edited and published by Scott, Foresman. This dictionary maintains that tradition and combines with it a fresh design and carefully chosen illustrations. The result is a book that young people will want to browse through and will find rewarding when they do so.

To prepare this edition, a wide variety of contemporary children's textbooks and other literature was read to check for new words and new meanings. Current word frequency counts were reviewed to ensure that the dictionary contains the words and meanings most likely to be encountered by its users. This reading is backed by Scott, Foresman's citation files, which contain about one and a quarter million examples of words in use, collected from newspapers, children's and general magazines, books, and other publications.

Every dictionary entry was reexamined for simplicity and clarity by a staff of editors long experienced in writing dictionaries for young people. Many definitions and sentences showing words in use have been rewritten. Throughout this process, every effort has been made to carry out the original precept of Dr. Thorndike, that information be presented in a form suitable to the learner.

Word histories for selected entries are included in this dictionary, and are printed in blue type. In some cases, especially interesting word histories are featured, enclosed in a frame with a blue bar at the top. In addition, the foreign ancestry of selected groups of words is indicated at the word entries for such foreign language names as French, German, and Japanese.

Great care has been taken to make the dictionary visually attractive to its users. The purpose of the improved format is to stimulate young people to notice and retain interesting facts and impressions about words. The variety of illustrations—color (nearly 75%) and black-and-white photographs, drawings, cartoons, movie stills, collages—encourages browsing and incidental learning in which the user absorbs more than the specific information being sought. Fine art, such as paintings, sculpture, and etchings, provides an introduction to the arts, exposing young people to cultural values without obviously emphasizing them. Picture captions give the size of animals both in the customary way and in the metric system.

Words that express feelings, ideas, and actions deserve to be illustrated as much as words for things. Art can be very effective when called on to express *melancholy, forbidding, gleeful, imaginative, competition, breathtaking, lithe,* and similar words. Dramatizing such words broadens and deepens young people's conversational and written vocabulary. This new approach to dictionary illustration was pioneered in the Beginning Dictionary published a decade ago.

This book was specifically designed so that the user can readily find the information being sought. The type was chosen for its readability. Large guide words make entries easy to find. A short, easy-to-use pronunciation key appears at the top of each right-hand page. In addition, the varying line length on the right-hand margin of each column helps guide the user's attention to the entry words at the left, allows even spacing between words, and eliminates hyphens at the end of lines in order to make the text easier to read.

To help develop basic skills in dictionary use, self-teaching lessons are included in the front of the book. These colorfully illustrated lessons, prepared with the help of classroom teachers as consultants, are designed to appeal to young people, and involve actual practice in individual use of the dictionary. Stories, puzzles, games, and riddles teach the fundamentals of dictionary use—how to find a word, how to find and understand a definition, how to use the pronunciation symbols to pronounce a word, and the other skills that a child must learn in order to be able to derive the greatest benefit from a dictionary. An answer key for the lesson section begins on page 53, directly following the lessons.

Throughout the Beginning Dictionary, pictures and sentences showing words in use have been carefully chosen to reflect the richness and diversity of our world. Girls and boys and men and women of many cultures appear in a wide variety of occupations and activities.

Factual information of a different but collateral kind, relating to school curriculum subjects, has been included in the Student's Reference Section, beginning on page 737. Historical information concerning the nation's presidents and the individual states is presented, as well as important representative facts chosen from pupils' textbooks in reading and language arts, science, mathematics, social studies, and health and safety.

The Beginning Dictionary is truly a basic dictionary. Scott, Foresman continues to offer it as the best possible book of its kind for young people.

The Editors

How to Use This Dictionary

A dictionary is a book that lists words in alphabetical order. It is filled with information about these words—how they are spelled, how they are pronounced, what they mean, where they came from, and more.

Sometimes, in school or at home, you may hear a word you don't understand or read a word you can't pronounce. You may want to write a word that you're not sure how to spell, or you may wonder how a word came to be. The dictionary helps you find the answers to these questions, because the dictionary is packed full of information about words.

Meaning

Now I know what incredulous means— not ready to believe, doubting. I'm incredulous whenever my brother offers to help me.

I'm incredulous whenever anyone around here offers to feed me.

Spelling

How do I spell...?

Ah, here it is— p-u-f-f-i-n.

That's easy, now how do you spell—?

Pronunciation

My pen pal lives in Saskatchewan. I wonder how you say that?

...sa skach′ə won...

I'm glad my pen pal lives in Denver.

Word History

How interesting! The word unicorn can be traced back to two Latin words meaning 'one horn' Unicorn...one horn.

Now let's look up guppy.

The boys and girls in the cartoons above are learning many different things by reading the dictionary. You can, too. The lessons on the following pages will help you understand all the things the dictionary can help you with. Read each lesson and answer all the questions. Not only will you learn a lot, but you will have fun while doing it.

The Parts of a Dictionary Entry

The entry word shows how the word is spelled and how it may be divided in writing.

ki·mo·no (kə mō′nə), **1** a loose outer garment held in place by a sash, worn by both men and women in Japan. **2** a woman's loose robe. *noun, plural* **ki·mo·nos.**

kin (kin), **1** a family or relatives: *All our kin came to the family reunion.* **2** family relationship: *What kin is she to you? noun.*

The homograph number appears when two or more entry words have the same spelling.

kind① (kīnd), **1** friendly; doing good rather than harm: *A kind person tries to help others. Sharing your lunch was a kind thing to do.* **2** gentle: *Be kind to animals. adjective.*

kind² (kīnd), **1** a sort; type: *I like many kinds of food. A kilt is a kind of skirt.* **2** a natural group: *The wolf hunted with others of its kind. noun.*

kind of, nearly; almost; somewhat: *The room was kind of dark.*

of a kind, of the same sort: *The cakes were all of a kind—chocolate.*

The pronunciation tells how to say the word. Each letter or other symbol stands for a certain sound. These symbols are explained in the pronunciation key.

kin·der·gar·ten (kin′dər gärt′n), a school for children from about 4 to 6 years old that educates them by games, toys, and pleasant activities. *noun.*

[*Kindergarten* was borrowed from a German word meaning "children's garden."]

kind·heart·ed (kīnd′här′tid), having or showing a kind heart; kindly; sympathetic. *adjective.*

The definition of a word tells its meaning. A word with more than one meaning has numbered definitions, one for each meaning.

kin·dle (kin′dl), **1** to set on fire or catch fire; light: *I used a match to kindle the wood.* **2** to stir up; arouse: *The unfairness of the punishment kindled my anger. verb,* **kin·dles, kin·dled, kin·dling.**

kin·dling (kind′ling), small pieces of wood for starting a fire. *noun.*

kind·ness (kīnd′nis), **1** a kind nature; being kind: *We admire his kindness.* **2** a kind act: *They showed me many kindnesses. noun, plural* **kind·ness·es.**

A sentence or phrase to show how the word may be used is printed in slanted type following the definition.

kin·dred (kin′drid), like; similar; related: *We are studying about dew, frost, and kindred facts of nature. adjective.*

king·fish·er (king′fish′ər), a bright-colored bird with a large head and a strong beak. Kingfishers eat fish and insects. *noun.*

A picture helps to show what a word means. Some pictures have captions that give additional information or show how the word can be used in a sentence.

kingfisher—14 inches (36 centimeters) long

The pronunciation key is on each right-hand page.

a hat	i it	oi oil	ch child	⎧ a in about
ā age	ī ice	ou out	ng long	⎪ e in taken
ä far	o hot	u cup	sh she	ə = ⎨ i in pencil
e let	ō open	u̇ put	th thin	⎪ o in lemon
ē equal	ô order	ü rule	ᵺ then	⎩ u in circus
ėr term			zh measure	

knight (nīt), **1** (in the Middle Ages) a man raised to an honorable military rank and pledged to do good deeds. After serving as a page and squire, a man was made a knight by the king or a lord. **2** (in modern times) a man raised to an honorable rank because of great achievement or service. A man named John Smith becomes Sir John Smith, or Sir John, as a knight. **3** to raise to the rank of knight: *He was knighted by the queen.* **4** one of the pieces in the game of chess. 1,2,4 *noun,* 3 *verb.*

The part-of-speech label tells the part of speech of the entry word. When the word is used as more than one part of speech, definition numbers appear before each label.

knob (nob), **1** a rounded lump: *Grandfather's cane has a large knob at the top.* **2** a handle, object, or part often shaped like a rounded lump: *the knobs on a bureau drawer, the knob on the dial of a television set. noun.*

knob·by (nob′ē), **1** covered with knobs: *the knobby trunk of a tree.* **2** rounded like a knob: *the knobby, gold head of a cane. adjective,* knob·bi·er, knob·bi·est.

Word endings and special forms of entry words are given whenever their spelling might cause you trouble.

knock (nok), **1** to give a hard blow or blows to with the fist, knuckles, or anything hard; hit: *The ball knocked me on the head.* **2** a hit: *That knock on my head really hurt.* **3** to hit and cause to fall: *The speeding car knocked over a sign.* **4** to hit with a noise: *She knocked on the door.* **5** a hit with a noise: *I did not hear the knock on the door.* **6** to make a noise, especially a rattling or pounding noise: *The engine is knocking.* **7** the sound caused by loose parts or improper burning of fuel: *a knock in an engine.* 1,3,4,6 *verb,* 2,5,7 *noun.*

Idioms are word combinations having special definitions that cannot be understood from the meanings of the individual words. Each idiom starts a new line.

knock down, to take apart: *We knocked down the bookcases and packed them in the car.*

knock out, to hit so hard as to make helpless or unconscious: *She was knocked out by a blow on the head.*

kum·quat (kum′kwot), a yellow or orange fruit that is somewhat like a small orange. It has a sour pulp, and is used in candy, jam, and preserves. *noun.*

The word history tells what language the English word came from and what the word meant in that language. Word histories appear in blue type or in a box with a blue bar.

Word History

kumquat *Kumquat* comes from Chinese words meaning "golden orange."

How to Find a Word

Using the Color Bars

Close your dictionary and hold it so that the pages are facing you. You will see that there are three bars on the ends of these pages, one each in red, blue and green. Each of these color bars includes ⅓ of the alphabetical listings in the dictionary.

The first ⅓ is the red section, which marks the beginning letters: A, B, C, D, E, and F.

The second ⅓ is the blue section, which marks the middle letters: G, H, I, J, K, L, M, N, O, and P.

The last ⅓ is the green section, which marks the last letters of the dictionary: Q, R, S, T, U, V, W, X, Y, and Z.

Knowing which letters are contained in each of these three sections will help you find a word quickly, just as the words listed in the yellow box name things that help you get where you're going more quickly. Answer the questions below in order to practice what you have learned.

automobile
bicycle
clipper
glider
gondola
helicopter
jet
motorcycle
roller skate
train

Teach Yourself

1. Which of the words at the left will you find in the red section of your dictionary?
2. Now open your dictionary to the words beginning with *g*. What color is the section you are now in?
3. Which of the words at the left will you find in the blue section of your dictionary?
4. Which of the words will you find in the green section of your dictionary?

Exercise

The colored boxes below represent the color bars on your dictionary. The words in them are words that appear in this book. Some of these words would appear in the section of the dictionary indicated by the colored box they are in, but some would not. Number a piece of paper from 1 through 12. Write yes if the word would appear in that section and no if it would not.

1 bus	5 hydroplane	9 stroller
2 streetcar	6 ice skate	10 blimp
3 carriage	7 scooter	11 taxicab
4 canoe	8 sleigh	12 truck

Entry Words

The words that a dictionary explains are called entry words. Each entry word in this dictionary is printed in heavy black type. Some entry words are made up of more than one word—*disk jockey,* for example. All entries are listed in alphabetical order no matter how many words are used for the entry—*diskette* comes before *disk jockey,* for instance.

Below are nine entries from this dictionary. After you read them, answer questions 1 through 9 that follow.

dark·room (därk′rüm′), a room cut off from all outside light and arranged for developing photographs. It usually has a very dim, colored light. *noun.*

day-care center (dā′ker′ or dā′kar′), a place where small children are cared for during the day while their parents are at work.

dis-, a prefix meaning: **1** not; the opposite of; lack of: Dishonest means *not* honest, or *the opposite of* honest. Discomfort means the *lack of* comfort. **2** to do the opposite of: Disconnect means *to do the opposite of* connect.

dis·as·ter (də zas′tər), an event that causes much suffering or loss; great misfortune. A flood, fire, shipwreck, earthquake, or great loss of money is a disaster. *noun.*

disk·ette (dis ket′), a small, bendable, plastic disk used to store information and instructions for computers; floppy disk. *noun.*

disk jockey, an announcer for a radio program that consists chiefly of recorded popular music.

dis·like (dis līk′), **1** to not like; object to; have a feeling against: *He dislikes studying and would rather play football.* **2** a feeling of not liking; a feeling against: *I have a dislike of rain and fog.* **1** *verb,* **dis·likes, dis·liked, dis·lik·ing; 2** *noun.*

District of Columbia, a district in the southeastern United States that is entirely occupied by the city of Washington, the capital of the United States. *Abbreviation:* D.C. or DC

Dr., Doctor: *Dr. W. H. Smith.*

Teach Yourself

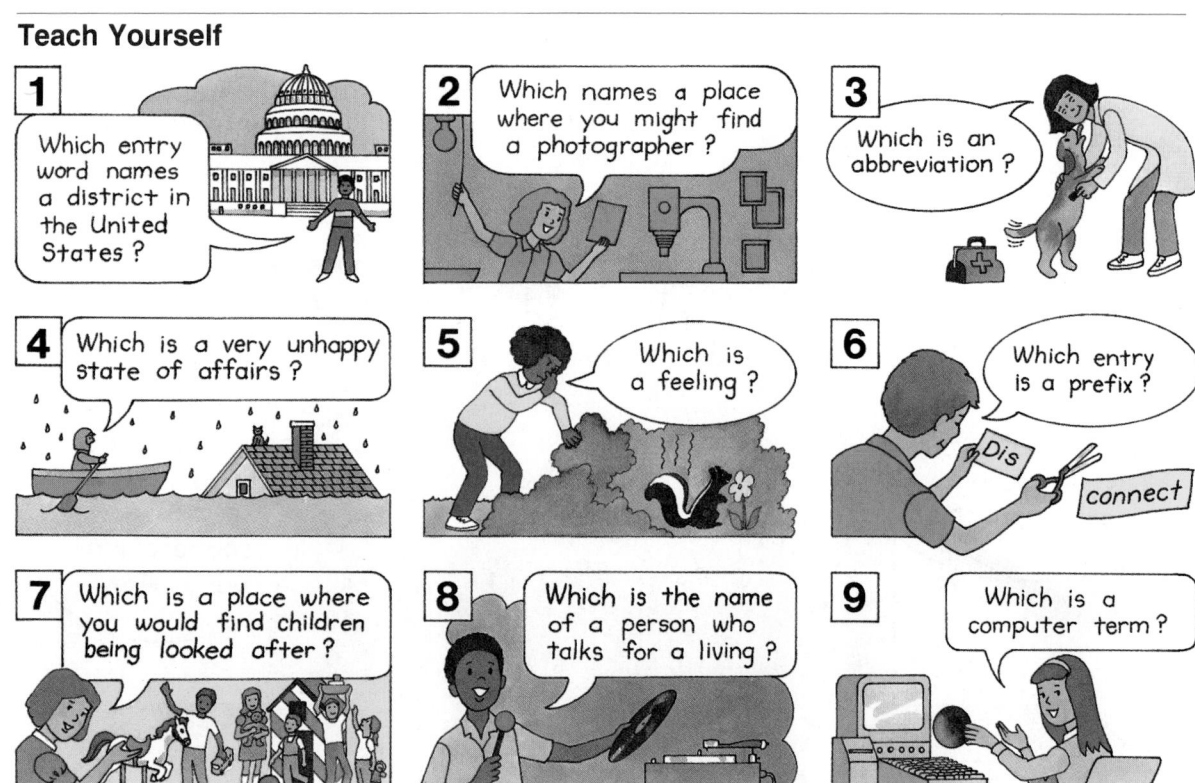

1 Which entry word names a district in the United States?

2 Which names a place where you might find a photographer?

3 Which is an abbreviation?

4 Which is a very unhappy state of affairs?

5 Which is a feeling?

6 Which entry is a prefix?

7 Which is a place where you would find children being looked after?

8 Which is the name of a person who talks for a living?

9 Which is a computer term?

Alphabetical Order

You have learned that your dictionary is divided into three sections—A through F, G through P, and Q through Z. You also know that all the entry words in this book are listed alphabetically from A through Z. Now is a good time to practice putting words in alphabetical order.

Teach Yourself

Amy
Peter
Flo
Zak
Ben
Chris
Viv
Will
John
Sam
Matt

A. Amy has ten brothers and sisters. One day they were all arguing about who would be the first to use the new computer. Amy said, "Let's take turns according to the first letter of our names. I'll go first."

1. Look at the names at the left and write them in alphabetical order from 1 to 11.
2. Who do you think was the least happy about this arrangement?

B. The next day Zak had an idea. "This time let's take turns according to the *last* letter of our names," said Zak.

1. Why do you think Zak said this?
2. Who would be the least happy about *this* arrangement?

Exercise

Zak and Amy are discussing their computer problem in the cartoon below, but their words are scrambled. Arrange the words in alphabetical order and you will be able to follow their conversation.

More about Alphabetizing

Suppose you wanted to look up *potato, peach,* and *picnic* in your dictionary. All these words begin with the letter *p.* You know you will find them with the words beginning with *p* in your dictionary. But which word comes first?

To find out, you must look at the second letter in each word. Words that have the same first letter are put in alphabetical order by their second letters. Now you know that *peach* will come first, then *picnic,* and then *potato.*

Teach Yourself

1. Look at list A on the right. It is part of a list of things Beth and her family are bringing on a picnic. What are the first and second letters in all the words?
2. What letter in each word must you look at to alphabetize the words?
3. Are the words listed in alphabetical order?
4. Look at list B on the right. What are the first three letters of each word?
5. What letter must you look at to alphabetize these words?
6. On a piece of paper, write the words in alphabetical order.
7. Add *salty* to the alphabetical list. What letter of the word must you look at to put it in alphabetical order?

A
beans
beef
benches
berries

B
salt
salad
salmon

Exercise

The words listed and numbered below are part of a list of things Beth's family brought to the picnic. They are in alphabetical order, but some items have been left out. At the side are the words left out of the list. Put each of these words in its place in the alphabetical list below. On a piece of paper, write each number that has no word after it; then write the word that fits alphabetically in that place.

1. charcoal
2. cheese
3. _____
4. _____
5. chicken
6. _____
7. chocolates
8. cider
9. _____
10. _____
11. clams
12. cocoa
13. _____
14. _____
15. cookies
16. _____
17. cornbread
18. _____
19. _____
20. crackers

citrus
coffee
chili
cherries
crabs
corn
crab apples
chewing gum
cola
cinnamon

Guide Words

What do you see at the very top of each page of your dictionary? Look, and you will see two words printed in large, very dark type. They are called guide words.

The first guide word is the same as the first entry word on the page. The second guide word is the same as the last entry word on the page. They can help you find the word you need easily and fast.

Teach Yourself

Suppose your need to look up the word *deface*. Turn to the first page in your dictionary that has words beginning with *de-*. It is page 156.

1. What are the guide words on the page?
2. Does *deface* come between these guide words in alphabetical order?
3. Would *deface* be found on this page?

Continue looking at the guide words of each page that has words beginning with *de-*. Stop when you come to the page that lists *deface*.

4. What are the guide words on the page?
5. What are the first and last entry words on the page?

photographer
pianist
picnicker
pharmacist
physician
performer
pilot
physicist
philosopher
picket
pilgrim
philanthropist

Exercise

At the left is a list of passengers ready to board their planes at the airport. The guide words show them which plane is theirs. Passengers who do not fit into any of the planes have had their flights canceled. Write the number of each airplane, and after it list the passengers who will fly in that plane. If any passengers do not fit in, list them at the end.

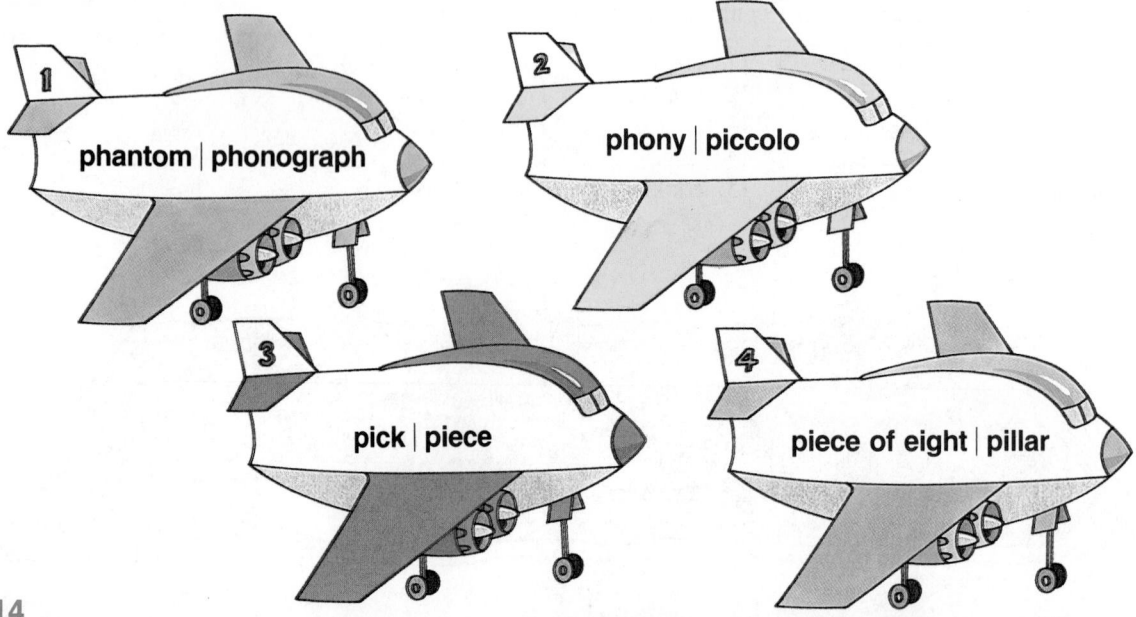

phantom | phonograph

phony | piccolo

pick | piece

piece of eight | pillar

Words That Aren't Entry Words

Many words that end in *s, es, ed, ing, er,* and *est* are not entry words in your dictionary. To find the meaning of such a word, you usually have to look up the word that the ending was added to.

To find the meaning of *mopes, moped,* or *moping,* you look up *mope.*
To find the meaning of *dinghies,* you look up *dinghy.*
To find the meaning of *grimier* or *grimiest,* you look up *grimy.*
To find the meaning of *drabber* or *drabbest,* you look up *drab.*

mope (mōp), to be dull, silent, and sad: *He has been moping indoors all afternoon. verb,* **mopes, moped, mop·ing.**

din·ghy (ding′ē), a small rowboat. *noun, plural* **din·ghies.**

grim·y (grī′mē), covered with grime; very dirty: *grimy hands. adjective,* **grim·i·er, grim·i·est.**

drab (drab), dull; not attractive: *The smoky mining town was full of drab houses. adjective,* **drab·ber, drab·best.**

Teach Yourself

1. What letter is dropped from *mope* before *ed* and *ing* are added?
2. What letter of *dinghy* changes when *es* is added?
3. What change is made in the spelling of *grimy* before *er* and *est* are added?
4. What letter of *drab* is doubled before *er* and *est* are added?

In each of these words—*mope, dinghy, grimy,* and *drab*—the spelling is changed before endings are added. Any time there is a change in the spelling of a word when an ending is added, the forms of the word are shown in dark type after the definition.

Exercise

Which entry word would you look up in your dictionary to find the meaning of each numbered word below? On a piece of paper, write each number and after it write the entry word. Use your dictionary to check your work.

1. coaches
2. dragged
3. prairies
4. fascinating
5. quicker
6. smuggling
7. heaviest
8. enemies
9. sturdier
10. transferring

Test Yourself

A. Knowing how to alphabetize will help you answer the following riddles. Read the questions, then write the words below in alphabetical order to get the answers.

1. What's red and goes up and down?

   full   elevator   of
   tomatoes   an   ripe

2. What do you get when you cross a hippopotamus with a groundhog?

   holes   yard   big   the   in

3. What makes a library so noble?

   have   titles   all   books

4. Why do dragons rest during the day?

   fight   knights   nights
   most   because   dragons

5. What did the teddy bear take on his trip?

   traveling   for   well
   bear   all   essentials

B. Here are more riddles with alphabetical answers. Remember, when words begin with the same letter, you must alphabetize by the second letter, or the third letter, and so on.

1. What do you have when you put six ducks in a crate?

   big   quackers   box   of   a

2. What keeps a theater cool?

   seats   fans   fill   most

3. What did the diet expert see at the restaurant?

   going   food   waist
   fattening   to   delicious

4. Why did the ghost have to leave the cafeteria?

   don't   spirits   because
   cafeterias   ever   serve

5. Why does the beaver have a fur coat?

   look   silly   beavers   winter
   weighty   wearing   woolens

C. The boys and girls on the next page were told to list some of their favorite things in alphabetical order. Can you help them? Write each of their names at the top of a piece of paper, and list the special interests they tell about alphabetically below their names. *Remember, if a word has a hyphen or if two separate words are used, think of them as one word when alphabetizing.*

Beth: My favorite *B*'s are
my *bicycle*, the beautiful
black-eyed Susan growing in my yard,
delicious *blackberry* pie,
my tame *blackbird*,
and a *black-eyed pea* sandwich.

Matt: I'd like to make a *motion picture*,
see a *mountain goat*,
climb to a *mountaintop*,
find some *mother-of-pearl*, and
walk along a *mountainside*.
But not in that order.

Flo: I am studying *French,* and I plan to
visit *France*. I love to eat *French toast*,
French fries, and a
frankfurter or two. I play
the *French horn*.

Sam: I enjoy taking my pet *sea gull*
to the *seashore*, where I eat
lots of *seafood*. I collect *seaweed*
from the *sea*. I'd love to
have a pet *sea lion*.

D. Like the fox at the right, the animals listed below do not add the usual *s* to their names when more than one is being talked about. Write the name of each animal on a piece of paper, numbered from 1 through 12. Look up each animal in your dictionary to find the correct plural form for each, then write it down also.

1. pony
2. butterfly
3. calf
4. ox
5. wolf
6. sheep
7. husky
8. goose
9. swordfish
10. canary
11. flamingo
12. ostrich

E. The words listed below are not entry words in your dictionary, but you know that you can find their meanings just the same. Number your paper 1 through 10 and write the entry word that you would look under to find the meaning of each. *Remember, just look up the base word, the word that the ending has been added to.*

1. thrushes
2. fiercest
3. animals
4. grazing
5. rhinoceroses
6. aviaries
7. grizzlier
8. caged
9. swimming
10. hibernated

F. Each of the boys and girls named below is from a different state in the U.S. Look at the names of each and find the guide words to the right that each would come between. Then open your book to those guide words and you will find the name of each one's state also. Alan has done the first one for you.

1. Alan   **agitation | ain't**   **air | alarm**   **alarm clock | alive**
2. Caleb   **C | cafe**   **cafeteria | call**   **caller | Canadian**
3. Connie   **congregate | consecrate**   **consecutive | consonant**   **conspicuous | consumer**
4. Flora   **flaunt | flicker**   **flied | flop**   **floppy | fluorine**
5. Geoff   **generator | geranium**   **gerbil | get**   **geyser | gin**
6. Hazel   **harness | harvester**   **harvest moon | have**   **haven | head**
7. Ian   **I | idea**   **ideal | ignition**   **ignorance | I'm**
8. Kestra   **K | keep**   **keeper | khan**   **kick | kilt**
8. Martha   **marina | maroon**   **maroon | mascot**   **masculine | mat**
10. Terry   **temptation | tepee**   **tepid | terribly**   **terrier | that**

How to Find a Meaning

Understanding What You Read and Hear

Jane could not imagine living in a world without cars or airplanes. She wondered how people traveled before the age of machines. In the library she found a book about Marco Polo, an Italian born around 1254, who was known for his travels.

The book told how Marco grew up in Venice, a city built on small islands. He went around the city in a gondola.

Jane had never heard of a gondola. She decided to look up the word in her dictionary. This is what she found:

> **gon·do·la** (gon′dl ə), **1** a long, narrow boat with a high peak at each end, used on the canals of Venice. **2** a car that hangs under a dirigible and holds the motors, passengers, and instruments. *noun.*

The part of the entry that describes a gondola is called the definition, or meaning. The word *gondola* has two meanings. The first one was what Jane needed. Also, a picture showed her exactly what a gondola looks like.

The book told how Marco went to China with his father and uncle. He was 17 when they left Venice. They survived storms at sea, attacks by bandits, and desert sandstorms. Finally, more than three years later, they reached China. "Although the perilous journey frightened them at times, they never thought of turning back," the book said.

Jane had never seen the word *perilous* before, but she did not think she needed to look it up. The words used with it made its meaning clear to her. *Perilous* seemed to refer to the dangerous and scary things that happened on the trip.

Here is the entry for *perilous* in your dictionary. You can see that Jane was right.

> **per·il·ous** (per′ə ləs), dangerous: *They survived a perilous crossing of the ocean in a tiny boat.* *adjective.*

Later, Jane read this sentence: "The Polos were the first medieval travelers to reach China from Europe." She did not know what *medieval* meant, and nothing in the rest of the sentence gave her a clue. She needed to look up the word in her dictionary.

gondola (definition 1)

Teach Yourself

Look up *medieval* and read its definition.

1. Does the word have to do with the past, present, or future?
2. Tell what *medieval* means in your own words.
3. Now write a sentence using the word *medieval*.

Exercise

The sentences below tell some of the things Jane learned from her book. Read each sentence. Then try to guess the meaning of each underlined word by using clues given by the words used with it. Write each number, and after it write the letter of the meaning you think is right. You can check your answers by looking up the underlined words in your dictionary.

1. Marco Polo, his father, and his uncle began their long and arduous journey by crossing the stormy Mediterranean Sea in a small sailing ship.

   a. pleasant   b. easy   c. hard

2. They continued overland through regions whose topography was unknown, and Marco stored up information about the deserts, mountains, lakes, and valleys.

   a. mountains   b. surface features   c. people

3. The journey seemed interminable, and in fact took more than three years.

   a. endless   b. fast   c. boring

4. When they reached the splendid palace of the Mongol ruler, or khan, Marco was amazed at the gold and silver decorations and the sumptuous beauty of the rooms.

   a. simple   b. costly   c. tasteful

5. He became proficient in the language of the Mongols, who ruled all China at that time, and was able to converse with people and learn many things.

   a. skilled   b. studious   c. profitable

6. He learned that the khan traveled in an ingenious wooden room which was fully furnished and attached to the backs of four elephants.

   a. not smart   b. ugly   c. cleverly made

7. He was astonished at the fortitude of the messengers who brought news to the khan by riding more than 200 miles a day, changing horses every 25 miles.

   a. courage   b. laziness   c. speed

8. After 17 years he left China, and wrote a book about his travels that gave Europeans the first valid description of Chinese people and customs.

   a. valued   b. true   c. false

9. Crestfallen when people refused to believe that his book told the truth, Marco Polo wrote no more.

   a. poor   b. lazy   c. discouraged

10. Years later, when asked to admit that his preposterous stories were made up, he answered, "I did not tell half of what I saw."

    a. foolish   b. early   c. written

Sentences and Phrases That Help Meaning

Sentences and phrases help you to understand what a word means by showing how the word is used. They are an important part of the definition of many words in this dictionary.

> **con·coct** (kon kokt′), to prepare; make up: *She concocted a drink made of grape juice and ginger ale. He concocted an excuse to explain his lateness.* verb.

Read the two sentences at the end of the definition of *concoct*. They help you to understand what *concoct* means and how it is used.

> **mag·nif·i·cent** (mag nif′ə sənt), richly colored or decorated; grand; stately; splendid: *a magnificent palace, a magnificent view of the mountains.* adjective.

The two phrases in the definition of *magnificent* help you to understand its meaning by showing how it is used.

Exercise

courtly

invincible

irksome

momentous

rumple

Look up the definition of each word at the left. Then choose the sentence that illustrates the use of the word. Write each number. Then copy the sentence, filling in the blank with the missing word.

1. After winning five games, the team seemed _____.
2. The war caused _____ changes in people's lives.
3. The prince's _____ manners impressed everyone.
4. Packing clothes in a suitcase can _____ them.
5. It is _____ to watch a boring TV show.

Using Definitions

Jane read the following sentence in a book about explorers:

It took an *intrepid* person to attempt to reach the North Pole.

She looked up *intrepid* in her dictionary, and found:

in·trep·id (in trep′id), fearless; very brave: *an intrepid mountain climber. adjective.*

Jane tried using the definition in the sentence in place of the word she didn't know. The definition has two parts, separated by a semicolon. Each part means almost the same thing. Each could be used in place of *intrepid* in the sentence above, like this:

It took a *fearless* person to attempt to reach the North Pole.
It took a *very brave* person to attempt to reach the North Pole.

Jane had learned two more ways to say the idea of the sentence.

Teach Yourself

Look up *precarious* and read its definition. Then read this sentence:

Explorers live through many *precarious* situations.

1. How many parts does the definition of *precarious* have?
2. On a piece of paper, rewrite the sentence using another word with the same meaning as *precarious*.

Exercise

Look up the underlined word in each sentence in your dictionary. Then choose which of the meanings listed is correct. On a piece of paper write the number of each sentence, and the letter of the correct meaning.

1. A powerful earthquake can <u>devastate</u> a large area.

   a. destroy   b. cover   c. surprise

2. When <u>ominous</u> clouds appeared, we called off our picnic.

   a. huge   b. very old   c. threatening

3. She was not a bit <u>intimidated</u> at going down the rapids on a raft.

   a. shy   b. brave   c. frightened

4. The sailboat's captain and crew were <u>jubilant</u> when they ended their 2000-mile trip.

   a. famous   b. joyful   c. sick

5. The robot had an <u>innovative</u> design.

   a. one of a kind   b. beautiful   c. new and different

6. The weather grew <u>perceptibly</u> worse when we reached the mountains.

   a. badly   b. noticeably   c. completely

Words with More than One Meaning

Last week Tom saw a television program about cataracts in the Nile
River. Today he saw a magazine article with the title "Cataracts
Need Medical Care." Tom might wonder why waterfalls need a
doctor. It's time for him to go to his dictionary.

Here is the dictionary entry for *cataract*:

> **cat·a·ract** (kat′ə rakt′), **1** a large, steep waterfall.
> **2** a violent rush or downpour of water; flood:
> *Cataracts of rain flooded the streets.* **3** a disease of
> the eye in which the lens develops a cloudy film.
> A cataract makes a person partly or entirely blind.
> *noun.*

Each definition has a number to make it easier for you to find the
meaning you're looking for. Be sure to read the whole definition,
including the sentence in italic type. It shows you how the word is
used in that particular sense.

Teach Yourself

Here are three sentences using the word *cataract*. Write the letters *a,*
b, and *c.* Then write which definition is used in each sentence.

a. The streets turned into raging torrents as cataracts of water
   poured down.
b. My grandmother went to the hospital to have a cataract removed.
c. People travel many miles to see the famous cataracts.

Exercise

On a piece of paper write the numbers 1 through 9. Look up in your
dictionary the underlined words in the following sentences. For each
underlined word write the number of the definition that makes sense
in the sentence.

1. It was September 1783, and the king of France had come to view
   an unusual happening.
2. The first balloon to carry living creatures was due to be launched
   soon.
3. It was under the direction of the Montgolfier brothers, who had
   sent up the first working balloon a few months before.
4. It was a large linen bag lined with paper, 35 feet around, inflated
   with hot air made by burning charcoal on a pan below.
5. Now, for this later ascent, they decided to place a duck, a sheep,
   and a rooster in a basket fastened under the balloon.
6. The audience gasped as the balloon started to rise—such a sight
   had not been seen there before.
7. The animals landed safely after a flight of eight minutes that took
   them two miles from their starting point.
8. The inventors next began to plan for a person to make an ascent.
9. Two months later the king's historian and a friend made a flight
   lasting 25 minutes over the city of Paris at a height of 300 feet.

Homographs: Different Words with the Same Spelling

In the cartoon at the right, Amy does not know that there are two different words that are both spelled *j-u-n-k*. Such words are called homographs. This dictionary shows that words such as *junk* are two different words by entering them separately.

Amy, look at that junk.

> **junk**[1] (jungk), trash; old paper, metal, and other
> rubbish. *noun.*
> **junk**[2] (jungk), a Chinese sailing ship. *noun.*

The small raised number after the entry word is a homograph number. It tells you that at least one other word has the same spelling. If the first word is not the one you want, the number reminds you to look at the next entry word.

Teach Yourself

Read the entries for the words spelled *j-u-n-k* again.

1. Which junk was Amy's father talking about, junk[1] or junk[2]?
2. Which junk did Amy think he meant?

Where, Dad? This place looks pretty clean to me.

Words like junk[1] and junk[2] are different because they have different word histories. You will learn more about word histories later in these lessons.

Exercise

Each of the words underlined below is a homograph. Decide which homograph is being used in each sentence. Do it this way: 1. bound[4].

1. About 1100 years ago, junks <u>bound</u> for India sailed from China.
2. By the year 1200, junks regularly left <u>port</u> to trade in Indonesia and along the coast of Africa.
3. The junk is a very efficient <u>kind</u> of sailing ship.
4. It can carry a great deal of cargo in its <u>hold</u>.
5. A junk's <u>bow</u> thrusts out sharply so it can be put ashore easily in shallow water.
6. The <u>stern</u> is high and there is no keel.
7. The sails are made up of a series of sheets, each stiffened by a bamboo <u>pole</u>. The sails can fold up like a paper fan.
8. An important feature <u>found</u> in a junk is its watertight compartments.
9. Many junks now have motors, and are no longer dependent only on the <u>wind</u> to move across the water.
10. The skipper often lives on board with his wife and a <u>band</u> of children.

No, Amy. Look at that ship down in the harbor. That's the kind of junk I mean.

A. Answer the following questions about your dictionary on a piece of paper.
   1. What do you call the two large words printed in dark type at the top of each page?

basset | batter

   2. What do you call the very first word in a dictionary entry?

> **bas·set** (bas′it), a dog with short legs and a long body. It is like a dachshund, but larger and heavier. *noun.*

   3. What do you call the words that tell you what the word you are looking up means?

> **bas·soon** (bə sün′), a deep-toned wind instrument with a doubled wooden body and a curved metal pipe to which a double reed is attached. *noun.*

   4. What do the small raised numbers after some words mean?

> **baste**[1] (bāst), to drip or pour melted fat or butter on meat, fish, or poultry while roasting: *Baste the turkey to keep it from drying out.* verb, **bastes, bast·ed, bast·ing.**
> **baste**[2] (bāst), to sew with long, loose stitches. These stitches are usually removed after the final sewing. *verb*, **bastes, bast·ed, bast·ing.**

   5. In what order are all the words in your dictionary entered?

B. Look up each of the underlined words below and answer the questions about them. *Give reasons for your answers.*
   1. Should a person swat a piñata?
   2. Is the money you have saved inexhaustible?
   3. Would you rather eat a kumquat or a whirligig?
   4. Would you call your best friend amigo or monsieur?
   5. Can an auk swim?
   6. Does a family tree grow in a yard?
   7. Would you rather see crabgrass or cowslips in your garden?
   8. Does an optometrist examine tummies?
   9. Does an equilateral triangle have three equal sides?
   10. Are the Himalayas and the Alps both mountains in Asia?

C. Each of the underlined words on the next page is an entry word with the same spelling as another entry word. Look up each underlined word and decide which one is being used in each sentence. Do it this way: 1. a. jerky[2].

1. a. While hiking in the woods I munched a stick of <u>jerky</u>.
   b. The rickety old wagon gave us a <u>jerky</u> ride.

2. a. I thought I heard the telephone <u>ring</u>.
   b. The children held hands and formed a <u>ring</u>.

3. a. I need a <u>yard</u> of fabric to cover this chair.
   b. The kitten was playing in the <u>yard</u>.

4. a. I jumped on the <u>scale</u> to check my weight.
   b. We must <u>scale</u> the fish before eating it.
   c. On a <u>scale</u> of one to ten, that movie was a two.

5. a. You must <u>till</u> the soil before planting the seeds.
   b. I stayed at school <u>till</u> five.
   c. He reached into the <u>till</u> and give me change for a dollar.

If you need help with this puzzle, look up the clue word in your dictionary. Where the clue is more than one word, look up the word in heavy type. The answer will be found in the definition. *Remember, for some words you may have to check several definitions.*

Across

1	part of the **face**
4	in
8	bird that can **hoot**
9	organ
10	dictate
12	past tense of **be**
13	distributes
16	dine
18	fateful
20	article
22	cereal
24	enemy
25	person
26	slumped
27	repair

Down

1	neither
2	is **indebted**
3	smack
5	necessity
6	covers with **tar**
7	found in **mining**
11	nightmare
12	rain
14	consume
15	formal
17	expend
18	sense
19	coin
21	digit
23	tin

How to Use the Pronunciations

Symbols That Stand for Sounds

In this dictionary, the pronunciation of a word comes right after its entry word, like this:

pronunciation

cliff (klif), a very steep slope of rock or clay. *noun.*

In pronunciations, letters of the alphabet are used to stand for sounds. Letters used in pronunciations are called pronunciation symbols. Below are some words followed by their pronunciations.

jam (jam)	nut (nut)	vest (vest)	pot (pot)
bed (bed)	flag (flag)	yak (yak)	zip (zip)
wisp (wisp)	drum (drum)	golf (golf)	hunt (hunt)

If you are able to pronounce the words above, you already know 23 pronunciation symbols. In this dictionary, 23 letters of the alphabet are used as pronunciation symbols. Each has the sound that the letter usually spells.

If all words were pronounced just as they are spelled, however, a dictionary would not have to give pronunciations. Below are some more words with their pronunciations. Notice how much easier the pronunciation of each word is than its spelling.

edge (ej)   knock (nok)   crumb (krum)   wrap (rap)

Teach Yourself

laugh
fun
phone
life
not
knot
knit
bend
wren

1. Say the words to the left. Which of the words have the (f) sound?
2. Which of the words have the (n) sound?
3. Which word at the left is pronounced (laf)?
4. Which word is pronounced (nit)?
5. Which word is pronounced (ren)?

Now can you read some of the words in the comic strip above? Which ones?

The Pronunciation Key

You may not remember what sound every pronunciation symbol stands for. You don't have to. If you open your dictionary to the front or back cover you will see the full pronunciation key. This is a list of all the pronunciation symbols used in this dictionary along with words that show how they are pronounced.

You already know 23 pronunciation symbols. They are the same as the letters of the alphabet. *Remember that the symbol always has the same sound that it has in the words that are listed beside it.* For example, (a) has the sound you hear when you say h**a**t or c**a**p, and (b) has the sound you hear when you say **b**ad or ro**b**. The (h) sound is the sound you hear in **h**e and **h**ow.

Teach Yourself

1. Look at the symbol (e). Pronounce its key words *let* and *best*. Which of the following words has the sound (e) in it?

   bat   bet   but   bit

2. Look at the symbol (j). Pronounce its key words *jam* and *enjoy*. Which of the following words has the sound (j) in it?

   ridge   rig   rug

You may not always want to turn to the front or back cover for the full pronunciation key. That is why this dictionary has a short pronunciation key at the top of each right-hand page. This key also shows pronunciation symbols, but with a single key word. It does not include the symbols that you already know, only those that you may need help remembering. If you forget what a pronunciation symbol stands for, *remember to look at the top of the right-hand page.*

Short pronunciation key

a hat	**i** it	**oi** oil	**ch** child	a in about
ā age	**ī** ice	**ou** out	**ng** long	e in taken
ä far	**o** hot	**u** cup	**sh** she	ə = { i in pencil
e let	**ō** open	** u̇** put	**th** thin	o in lemon
ē equal	**ô** order	**ü** rule	**ᴛʜ** then	u in circus
ėr term			**zh** measure	

Exercise

The sound at the left can be heard in only one of the words at the right. Write that word on a piece of paper for each of the seven sounds. If you do it right, you will receive a message.

1. (g) pigeons   big
2. (f) laughs   have
3. (k) can   knee
4. (l) calm   light
5. (u) dupe   up
6. (i) little   tiny
7. (s) faces   cruises

Vowels with Special Marks

As you have learned, the vowel letters *a, e, i, o,* and *u* without marks over them are used as pronunciation symbols. These stand for the short vowel sounds. Four vowel letters with marks over them are used as pronunciation symbols for the long vowel sounds. These are (ā) as in *age,* (ē) as in *equal,* (ī) as in *ice,* and (ō) as in *open.* You can see these words in the pronunciation key below. Say the words and listen for the long sounds.

a hat	**i** it	**oi** oil	**ch** child	⎡ a in about
ā age	**ī** ice	**ou** out	**ng** long	⎮ e in taken
ä far	**o** hot	**u** cup	**sh** she	ə = ⎨ i in pencil
e let	**ō** open	**u̇** put	**th** thin	⎮ o in lemon
ē equal	**ô** order	**ü** rule	**ᴛʜ** then	⎣ u in circus
ėr term			**zh** measure	

Exercise A

Kate has made a list of things she needs for a weekend visit to her grandmother. Two words are underlined in each sentence of Kate's list. Match the sound of the symbol on the left with the correct word. Write the correct words on a piece of paper.

1. (ī) A <u>nice</u> present and a <u>big</u> card for Grandma.
2. (ā) My favorite <u>bathrobe</u>, my <u>radio</u>, and my teddy bear.
3. (ō) <u>Socks</u>, pajamas, and a change of <u>clothes</u>.
4. (ē) Swimsuit, <u>beach</u> towel, and <u>sweat</u> shirt.

Four other pronunciation symbols are vowel letters with marks over them. They are (ä) as in *far,* (ô) as in *order,* (u̇) as in *put* and (ü) as in *rule.* One other important pronunciation is (yü) as in *mule.* The pronunciation of *u* in the word *mule* is actually a combination of two sounds, (y) and (ü). The symbols (yü) together always stand for this pronunciation.

Exercise B

David is very interested in robots. He is keeping a journal that tells about the various things robots can do. Two words are underlined in each sentence of David's observations. Match the sound of the symbol on the left with the correct word. Write that word.

1. (ô) One small robot can sweep, wash, and buff a <u>floor</u> a <u>lot</u> faster than a person can.
2. (ä) Another robot <u>has</u> trowels for feet and does the <u>hard</u> job of smoothing moist concrete.
3. (yü) This <u>unit</u> works three times as <u>quick</u> as a person would.
4. (ü) Yet another robot paints the <u>outside</u> of buildings without having to <u>fool</u> with ladders or scaffolds.
5. (u̇) This robot stays inside the building, <u>but</u> can <u>put</u> its long arms outside to do the job.

Test Yourself

The clues for this puzzle are the pronunciations of common words.
Copy the puzzle, or get a copy from your teacher. Fill in the spaces
with the words that the pronunciations stand for.

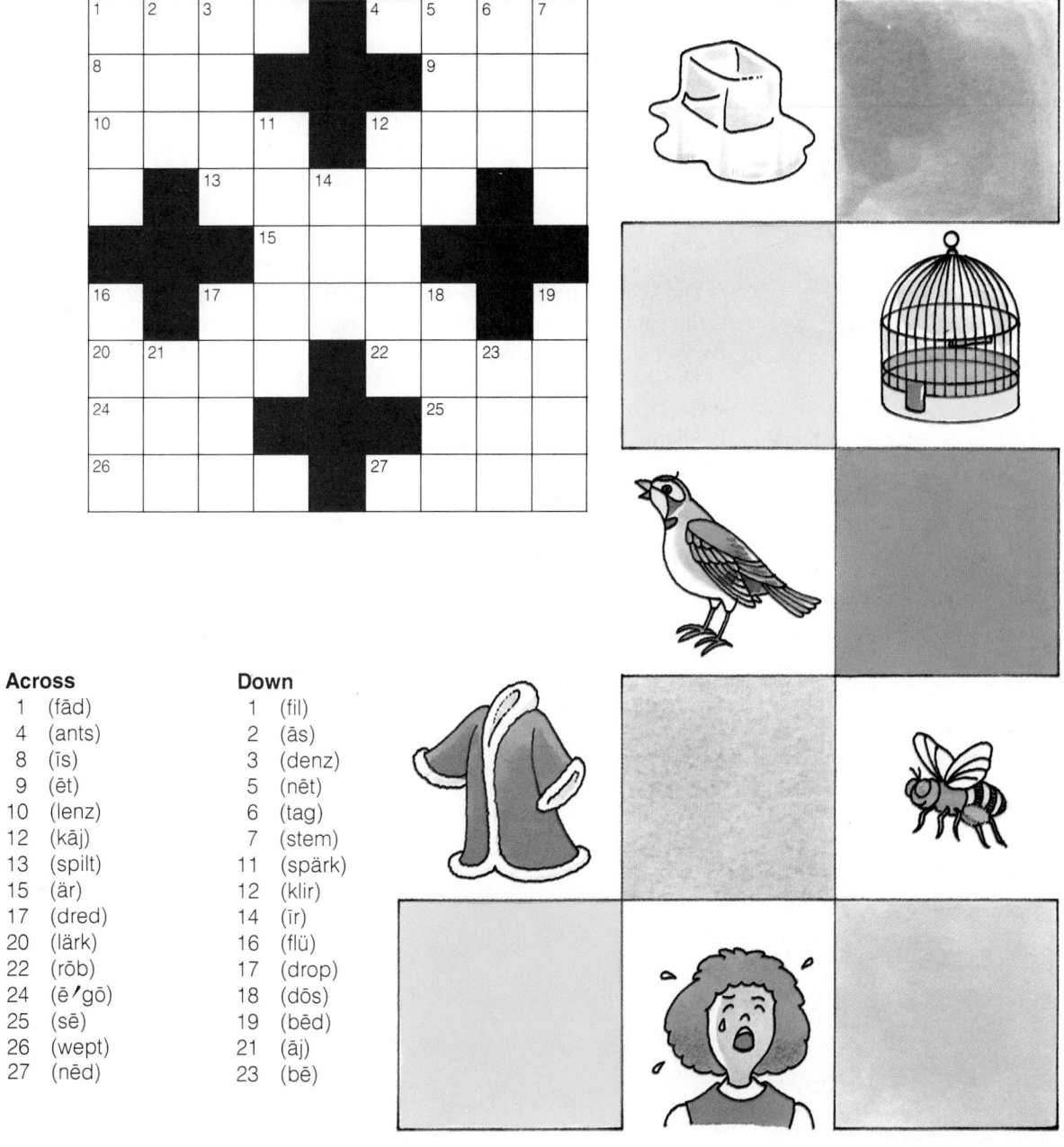

Across

1 (fād)
4 (ants)
8 (īs)
9 (ēt)
10 (lenz)
12 (kāj)
13 (spilt)
15 (är)
17 (dred)
20 (lärk)
22 (rōb)
24 (ē′gō)
25 (sē)
26 (wept)
27 (nēd)

Down

1 (fil)
2 (ās)
3 (denz)
5 (nēt)
6 (tag)
7 (stem)
11 (spärk)
12 (klir)
14 (īr)
16 (flü)
17 (drop)
18 (dōs)
19 (bēd)
21 (āj)
23 (bē)

(oi)
(ou)
(ėr)
(ng)
(ch)
(sh)
(zh)
(th)
(ŦH)

Two-letter symbols

All but one of the remaining pronunciation symbols are made up of two letters. These two-letter symbols are shown in the margin at the left. Two of them are for vowel sounds. The sound (oi) is the sound you hear in the words *oil* and *voice*. The sound (ou) is the sound you hear in *house* and *out*.

mē ou'

Teach Yourself

1. Which one of the following words has the sound (oi) in it?

   toy   toe   town

2. Which one of the following words has the sound (ou) in it?

   coal   cow   core

pėr

chēp

hongk

    The symbol (ėr) stands for the sound you hear in *term* and *learn*. It is the sound you hear in the words *fir, fur, word,* and *journey,* too. As you can see, the sound (ėr) is spelled many ways.

    The symbol (ng) stands for the sound that the letters *ng* usually spell. It is the sound you hear in *long* and *bring.*

    The letters *ch* and the letters *sh* often appear together in words. The symbol (ch) stands for the sound the combined letters usually spell, the sound you hear in *child* and *much.* The symbol (sh) stands for the sound *sh* usually spells, the sound you hear in *she* and *rush.*

    The sound (zh) is very close to (sh). The word *mesh* has the sound (sh) in it. The word *measure* has the sound (zh) in it. Say these two words and see if you can hear the difference between these sounds.

Teach Yourself

1. Say the words in the list below. Which have the sound (sh) in them?

   vision   she   carnation   garage   tissue

2. Which words in the list have the sound (zh) in them?

    The symbol (th) stands for the sound you hear in *thin* and *both.* The symbol (ŦH) stands for the closely related sound you hear in *then* and *smooth.*

bōŦH thin

Teach Yourself

1. Which words in the list below have the sound (th) in them?

   thank   breathe   breath   those   bath

2. Which words in the list have the sound (ᴛʜ) in them?

Exercise

For each of the following sentences, there is a two-letter symbol printed at the right. Write the number before each sentence. Then say the sentence aloud, and write down each word that has the sound represented by that symbol.

1. A large and noisy group of loyal admirers attended the concert of the boys' choir.   (oi)

2. I think these leather boots are more comfortable than those boots made of synthetic materials.   (ᴛʜ)

3. He used to be a chemist, but he changed his job and is now chief of police.   (ch)

4. She is going to the bank to make a change in her checking account.   (ng)

5. The kitten was pure white, and its purr showed that it was perfectly content.   (ėr)

6. She groaned when the new brown bowl fell to the ground.   (ou)

7. A television interviewer must think quickly, be able to make decisions, and have a casual manner.   (zh)

8. Those clouds look threatening, and I think that a thunderstorm will start soon.   (th)

9. A mishap in fashion design class ruined my latest creation.   (sh)

Syllables and Accent

Each part of a word that has one vowel sound in it is called a syllable.

may (mā)   **may·be** (mā′bē)

The word *may* has one vowel sound, (ā). *May* has one syllable. The word *maybe* has two vowel sounds, (ā) and (ē). *Maybe* has two syllables.

A

part (pärt)
tax (taks)
straight (strāt)

B

hand·ful (hand′fùl)
dai·sy (dā′zē)
car·toon (kär tün′)

C

o·ri·ole (ôr′ē ōl)
des·ig·nate (dez′ig nāt)
ba·by·ish (bā′bē ish)

Teach Yourself

Say each word at the left and look at its pronunciation:

1. How many syllables do the words in list A have?
2. How many syllables do the words in list B have?
3. How many syllables do the words in list C have?

If you look at the way the entry word is written, you can tell how many syllables a word has. There is a dot between the syllables.

Look again at the words in lists B and C. In the pronunciations you see either a space between syllables or an accent mark (′). An accent mark comes after an accented syllable. This is a syllable you say with more force than the other syllables.

There are two kinds of accent marks. The one used in the words above is called a primary accent mark. Now look at these words:

count·down (kount′doun′)   **mead·ow·lark** (med′ō lärk′)

The mark after the last syllable in the pronunciation of *countdown* and *meadowlark* is a secondary accent mark. A secondary accent mark comes after a syllable you say with more force than a syllable with no accent mark, but with less force than a syllable with a primary accent mark.

Teach Yourself

pre·his·to·ric (prē′hi stôr′ik)

1. Which syllable of *prehistoric* has a primary accent?
2. Which syllable of *prehistoric* has a secondary accent?

Exercise

Roger and his friends went to the park. People were enjoying games and sports. Below are the entry words and pronunciations of some of them. Write each number, and after it write the number of syllables in the word. Then tell which syllable or syllables are accented.

1. **hop·scotch** (hop′skoch′)
2. **bas·ket·ball** (bas′kit bôl′)
3. **ten·nis** (ten′is)
4. **cro·quet** (krō kā′)
5. **ju·do** (jü′dō)
6. **base·ball** (bās′bôl′)
7. **Fris·bee** (friz′bē)

The Schwa

One pronunciation symbol has not yet been introduced. This symbol is called the schwa (shwä) and looks like this (ə). It represents a vowel sound heard only in unaccented syllables. In fact, the sound represented by (ə) is the most common sound in the English language.

  As you can see from its key words listed at the right, the sound (ə) is spelled many different ways.

a in **a·bout** (ə bout′)
e in **tak·en** (tā′kən)
i in **pen·cil** (pen′səl)
o in **lem·on** (lem′ən)
u in **cir·cus** (sėr′kəs)

Teach Yourself

1. Pronounce the word **health·ful** (helth′fəl). What letter is used to spell the schwa sound?
2. Sometimes the sound (ə) is spelled with more than one letter. Now pronounce **bar·gain** (bär′gən). What letters spell the schwa sound?
3. How is the schwa sound spelled in **fa·mous** (fā′məs)?

Exercise

Below is a list of things found in the park. Write each word, then pronounce it, and circle the letter or letters used to spell the schwa sound. When you have finished, you will have found ten ways the sound can be spelled.

1. locust
2. sycamore
3. enormous
4. chrysanthemum
5. snapdragon
6. authority
7. hickory
8. tortoise
9. marigold
10. pigeon

NO DOGS
by authority
of Park Board
of Trustees

Pronunciation and Meaning

Sometimes when the meaning of a word changes, the pronunciation changes too.

> **per·mit** (pər mit′ *for 1;* pėr′mit *for 2*), **1** to let; allow: *My parents will not permit me to stay up late. The law does not permit smoking in this store.* **2** a license or written order giving permission to do something: *Have you a permit to fish in this lake?* 1 *verb,* **per·mits, per·mit·ted, per·mit·ting;** 2 *noun.*

The pronunciation tells you that *permit* is pronounced (pər mit′) when you use it with the first meaning. It tells you that *permit* is pronounced (pėr′mit) when you use it with the second meaning.

Teach Yourself

How is *permit* pronounced in the following sentence?

a. (pər mit′)   b. (pėr′mit)

My parents signed a permit so that I could go on the field trip.

Exercise

The pronunciation of each of the words in italics changes when its meaning changes. Read each sentence and decide which of the pronunciations listed at the side is correct. You can check your answers in your dictionary. Write each number, and after it write the letter of the correct pronunciation.

a. (ek skyüs′)
b. (ek skyüz′)

1. The teacher will excuse your lateness if you have a good *excuse.*

a. (reb′əl)
b. (ri bel′)

2. I *rebel* at being called a rebel.

a. (kom′bat)
b. (kəm bat′)

3. If he combats me, I'll engage him in *combat.*

a. (ō′vər flō′)
b. (ō′vər flō′)

4. The river is going to *overflow*, and the overflow will cause damage.

a. (pri zent′)
b. (prez′nt)

5. She plans to present her parents with a beautiful *present.*

a. (sus′pekt)
b. (sə spekt′)

6. The police suspect that the *suspect* is lying.

a. (pėr′fikt)
b. (pər fekt′)

7. It is not perfect yet, but we are trying to *perfect* it.

a. (prə gres′)
b. (prog′res)

8. We have made great *progress* in spelling, and hope to progress more.

Which Way Do You Say It?

Both people in the cartoon above think that their pronunciations are
correct. And they are both right!

Some English words have more than one correct pronunciation.
This is shown in your dictionary by listing the different
pronunciations like this:

>**creek** (krēk *or* krik)
>**to·ma·to** (tə mā′tō *or* tə mä′tō)

When you see more than one pronunciation listed for a word, you
know that either one is correct.

Exercise

The following words can be pronounced more than one way. Write
down the number before each word. Then write down the letter that
appears before the pronunciation you use.

1. adult   a. (ə dult′)   b. (ad′ult)
2. coyote   a. (kī ō′tē)   b. (kī′ōt)
3. juvenile   a. (jü′və nəl)   b. (jü′və nīl)
4. tune   a. (tün)   b. (tyün)
5. Colorado   a. (kol′ə rad′ō)   b. (kol′ə rä′dō)
6. route   a. (rüt)   b. (rout)
7. pecan   a. (pi cän′)   b. (pi can′)
8. advertisement   a. (ad′vər tīz′mənt)   b. (ad ver′tis mənt)

Test Yourself

After each number below is a pronunciation. Pronounce each word from the symbols given. Find the word in the word list and write it in the correct space.

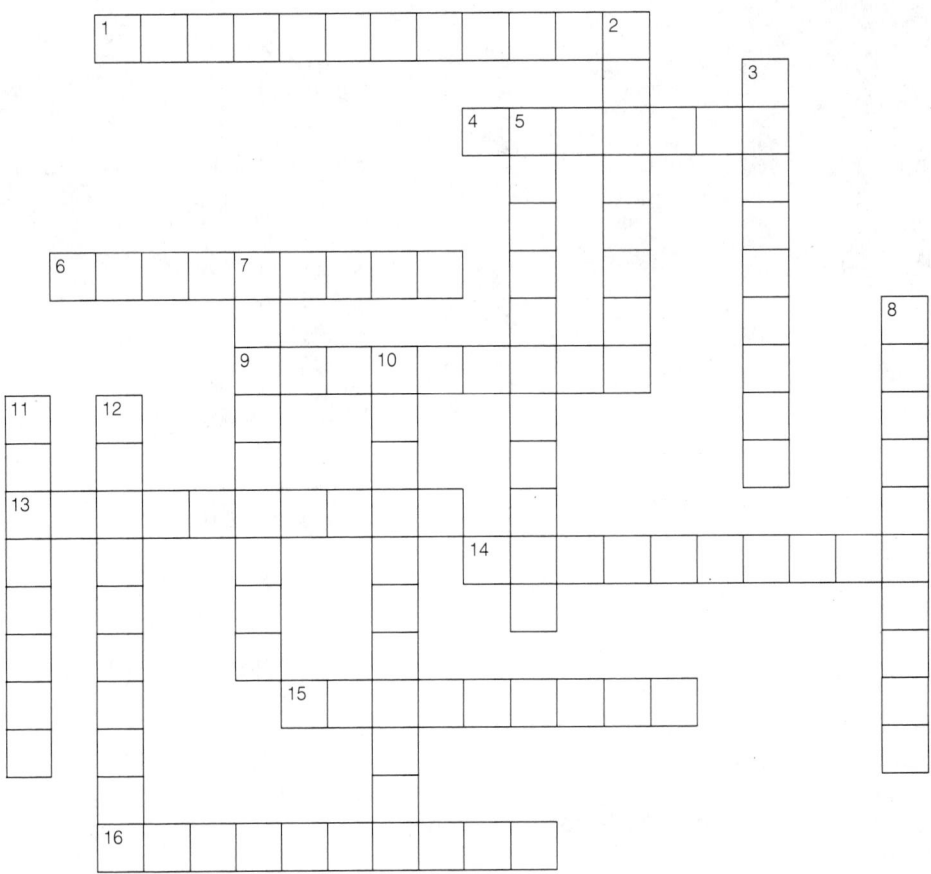

Word List

authorized
automobile
autopsies
boundaries
cauliflower
cautioned
communicable
dialogue
discourage
education
enunciation
equation
exhaustion
inoculate
pneumonia
sequoia

Across

1 (kə myü′nə kə bəl)
4 (si kwoi′ə)
6 (ô′top sēz)
9 (ej′ə kā′shən)
13 (ô′tə mə bēl′)
14 (boun′dər ēz)
15 (in ok′yə lāt)
16 (dis kėr′ij)

Down

2 (i kwā′zhən)
3 (kô′shənd)
5 (i nun′sē ā′shən)
7 (nü mō′nyə)
8 (eg zôs′chən)
10 (kô′lə flou′ər)
11 (dī′ə lôg)
12 (ô′thə rīzd′)

More about Meaning

Idioms: Phrases with Special Meanings

In the cartoon at right, Anna is using a few of her favorite idioms. An idiom is a phrase that cannot be understood from the usual meaning of the words in it. Idioms are listed in the dictionary under their most important word. For example, **let off steam** would be found under the entry **steam** in your dictionary. Below are two of the many idioms found in this book.

cat (kat), **1** a small, furry animal, often kept as a pet or for catching mice and rats. **2** any animal of the group including cats, lions, tigers, leopards, and jaguars. *noun.*

idiom listed
alphabetically
in black type

let the cat out of the bag, to tell a secret.
rain cats and dogs, to pour down rain very hard.

Exercise A

Some of the following phrases found in this dictionary are idioms. Others are not. Use your dictionary to help you decide which phrases are idioms. Write sentences on a piece of paper, using each idiom.

1. crossword puzzle
2. point of view
3. beat around the bush
4. by the skin of one's teeth
5. shape up
6. Brussels sprouts

Exercise B

Read the idioms below. Look up each one by determining the most important word in it. On a piece of paper, write each number, the word under which the idiom is listed, and the letter of its meaning (a, b, or c). Do it this way: 1. tell, b.

1. I was so mad I wanted to **tell** him **off.**

   a. I was so mad I wanted to ignore him.
   b. I was so mad I wanted to scold him.
   c. I was so mad I wanted to explain to him.

2. It is 10 miles **as the crow flies**.

   a. It is 10 miles if you go fast.
   b. It is 10 miles in an airplane.
   c. It is 10 miles in a straight line.

3. I was so tired I was about to **drop off**.

   a. I was so tired I was about to go to sleep.
   b. I was so tired I was about to fall over.
   c. I was so tired I was about to leave my place.

4. Nan wanted to **get even with** me.

   a. Nan wanted to shorten my skirt.
   b. Nan wanted to be beside me.
   c. Nan wanted to have revenge against me.

5. Don't **pass up** a great chance.

   a. Don't be unaware of a great chance.
   b. Don't take a great chance.
   c. Don't give up a great chance.

6. I didn't want to go **at any rate**.

   a. I didn't want to go for any amount of money.
   b. I didn't want to go anyway.
   c. I didn't want to go at any time.

Prefixes and Suffixes

Many words with prefixes and suffixes are entry words in your dictionary.

> **re·read** (rē rēd′), to read again: *to reread a good
> book. verb,* **re·reads, re·read** (rē red′),
> **re·read·ing.**

> **read·er** (rē′dər), **1** a person who reads. **2** a book
> for learning and practicing reading. *noun.*

Some words with prefixes and suffixes are not entered in your dictionary. However, you can find out what these words mean. Suppose you need to know the meaning of the word *nonessential* in the following sentence:

> It is silly to bring *nonessential* things on a camping trip.

Nonessential is not listed in your dictionary. However, the prefix *non-* is there.

repay
payer
payment
prepay
prepayment
payable
nonpayment
overpay
underpay

> **non-,** a prefix meaning: **1** not; not a: *Non*breakable
> means *not* breakable. *Non*member means *not a*
> member. **2** the opposite of; lack of: *Non*agreement
> means *the opposite of* or *lack of* agreement.

If you then look up *essential*, you will find the following entry:

> **es·sen·tial** (ə sen′shəl), **1** absolutely necessary;
> very important: *Good food is essential to good
> health.* **2** an absolutely necessary element or
> quality: *Learn the essentials first; then learn the
> details.* **1** *adjective,* **2** *noun.*

By putting the meaning of the prefix together with the meaning of the word it is added to, you can figure out that *nonessential* means "not necessary."

You can find out the meaning of a word with a suffix in the same way.

Teach Yourself

1. The word *wielder* is not in your dictionary. If you didn't know the meaning of *wielder*, what word would you look up?
2. What suffix would you look up?
3. On a piece of paper, write your own definition of the word *wielder*.

Exercise

The underlined words in the sentences below are not entry words in your dictionary. You can find the meaning of each word by looking up the meaning of the prefix or suffix used, and the meaning of the word to which the prefix or suffix is added. On a piece of paper write each number, and after it write the meaning of the sentence in your own words.

1. He <u>overreacted</u> to my remark, and lost his temper.
2. We were <u>forewarned</u> that a snowstorm was expected, but went skiing anyway.
3. She became bored with the <u>noncreative</u> jobs she was given.
4. We had to <u>rewring</u> the towels, as they were still dripping wet.
5. <u>Ungracious</u> behavior will not make you any friends.
6. She explained her theory <u>lucidly</u>.
7. He was dressed in a <u>darkish</u> suit.
8. We returned from our hike with <u>zesty</u> appetites.
9. This jacket does not fit well, but it is <u>alterable</u>.
10. We tried to improve the <u>legibleness</u> of our handwriting.

over-
fore-
non-
re-
un-
-ly
-ish
-y
-able
-ness

pain**ful**

nonstop

power**ful**

deep**ly**   **un**lock

wealth**y**

preschool

danger**ous**

Word Histories

Just as you have a family background, the words in our language have a history, too. You and many of your classmates may have parents or grandparents who came to America from such places as Germany, Spain, Egypt, Japan, Turkey, and other countries. Well, many of the words we speak in America came from foreign lands, also. Some started as English words spelled just as they are now, but many others came from French, German, Dutch, or other non-English words. Often, these words are spelled differently than they were originally. Below are some examples of word histories you will find in this dictionary.

con·spic·u·ous (kən spik′yü əs), **1** easily seen: *A traffic light should be placed where it is conspicuous.* **2** remarkable; attracting notice: *conspicuous bravery. adjective.*

Word History

conspicuous *Conspicuous* comes from a Latin word meaning "to catch sight of" or "to look at."

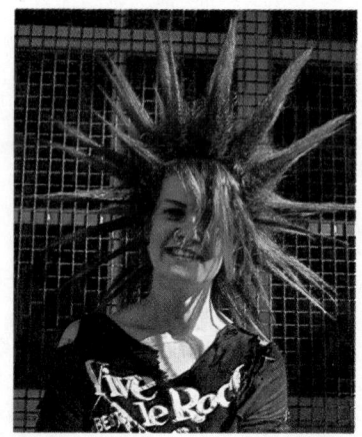

conspicuous
(definition 2)
Do you think my hair is too **conspicuous** like this?

gup·py (gup′ē), a very small fish of tropical fresh water, often kept in aquariums. The male is brightly colored. The female gives birth to live young instead of laying eggs. *noun, plural* **gup·pies.**
[*Guppy* was named for Robert Guppy. He was a British scientist of the West Indies, who sent the first samples of this fish to London in the 1800's.]

ham·burg·er (ham′bėr′gər), **1** ground beef, usually shaped into round flat cakes and fried or broiled. **2** a sandwich made with hamburger, usually in a roll or bun. *noun.*
[*Hamburger* comes from a German word meaning "of Hamburg." Hamburg is a city in West Germany.]

skel·e·ton (skel′ə tən), **1** the framework of bones inside the body that supports the muscles and organs of any animal having a backbone. **2** a frame: *the steel skeleton of a building. noun.*
[*Skeleton* comes from a Greek word meaning "dried up." The Greeks used this same word to mean "a mummy" or "a skeleton."]

As you can see, most word histories appear in brackets at the end of the entry in blue type. Some especially interesting word histories, however, are featured in a blue frame along with a picture, like the one above. These featured word histories are almost always found right after their entry.

Exercise

Read the sentences on the following page. Look up each underlined word and read the word history. On a piece of paper numbered from 1 to 10, write the language the word came from.

1. I was reading a <u>magazine</u> at breakfast one day.
2. All of a sudden, our <u>poodle</u> leaped onto the kitchen table.
3. The dog began attacking my cereal bowl, his foot in the <u>marmalade</u>.
4. <u>Tea</u> flowed everywhere, as well as juice and milk.
5. I took out my <u>kerchief</u> and began mopping up the mess.
6. I wanted to give that clumsy mutt a <u>karate</u> chop.
7. Then I noticed the dog staring at a big, green <u>insect</u> on the table.
8. The bug sat amidst my cereal, as large as a <u>moose</u>.
9. My alert pup had saved me from an <u>ugly</u> eating encounter.
10. I carried my pal to the <u>piano</u>, and we played a romantic duet.

How many different languages do you have written down?

Word Sources

The word histories at each entry tell you where a specific word came from, but where would you look if you wanted to know what other words also came from that same language? You would look for the bright red heading containing these words: Word Source . Word sources appear under the language you are interested in learning more about. Below is an example.

Por·tu·guese (pôr'chə gēz'), **1** of Portugal, its people, or their language. **2** a person born or living in Portugal. **3** the language of Portugal. **1** *adjective*, **2,3** *noun*, *plural* **Por·tu·guese** for 2.

Word Source

Portuguese is also the chief language of Brazil. The following words came into English from Portuguese:

cobra	dodo	jaguar	mango	teak
coco	flamingo	junk	pagoda	zebra

This word source gives you an idea of the number of words that came into English from Portugese, as well as information as to where else Portuguese is spoken. You will find similar word sources at the entries for *Arabic, French, Dutch, Latin,* and 11 other languages.

Exercise

1. Look up the entry *Dutch* and read it. Next, read the word source found below the entry *Dutch*. Answer the following questions:

   a. Who speaks Dutch?
   b. Is *pickle* a word that came into English from Dutch?

2. Where would you look to find a list of words that came into English from Greek?

   a. Do you find the word *astronaut* there?
   b. Do you find the word *clock* there?

3. Look up the word source at *Spanish*.

   a. Do you find the word *burro* there?
   b. Write two words that came from Mexican Spanish.

Test Yourself

A. The girls and boys in the cartoon below are all using the special phrases called idioms. Write each idiom on a piece of paper, followed by the word you would look under in your dictionary to find the idiom. Rewrite each of the sentences using your own words instead of the idioms.

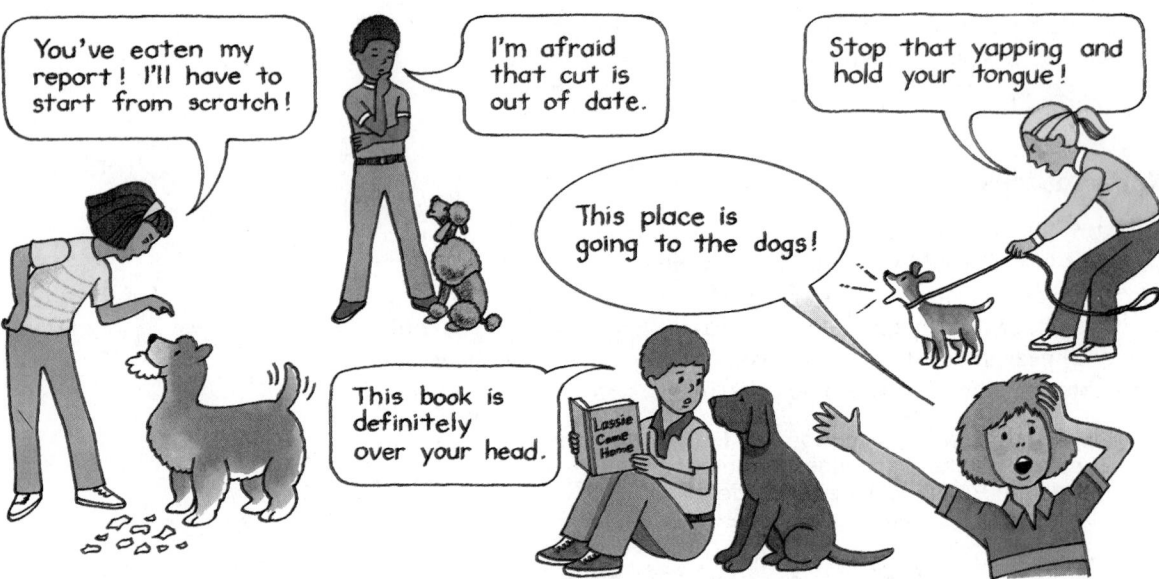

1. disentangle
2. unfancy
3. nonrigid
4. blackish
5. restack

B. The words at the left are not entry words in your dictionary. To find their meanings, you must look up the prefix or suffix that is part of each. You may also have to look up the meaning of the base word. Write each word, its prefix or suffix, and its meaning.

C. The questions below are about word histories and word sources found in your dictionary. Number your paper from 1 through 8 and answer the questions.

1. Where do you find word histories in your dictionary?
2. Look up the entry *lava.* What language does *lava* come from?
3. Nat has a *tulip,* a *magnolia,* and an *aster* in his hand. Which of these flowers is named for a person?
4. Melissa loves her old *teddy bear.* She even knows how he got his name. Do you? How?
5. Which of the following animal names are from American Indian words: **a** porpoise **b** raccoon **c** crocodile **d** moose **e** caribou.
6. Just about everybody owns a pair of jeans, but do you know where the word *jeans* came from? Tell where.
7. Where would you look to find a list of words that came into English from Italian?
8. Do you find the names of any musical instruments on the list of words that came from Italian? If so, what are they?

Challenge Puzzle

By writing in the correct answers to the clues, you will travel from
the outside of the wheel to its center. Each numbered clue is an
idiom. The answer will be found in the definition of this idiom in
your dictionary. The last letter of each answer is the first letter of the
next answer.

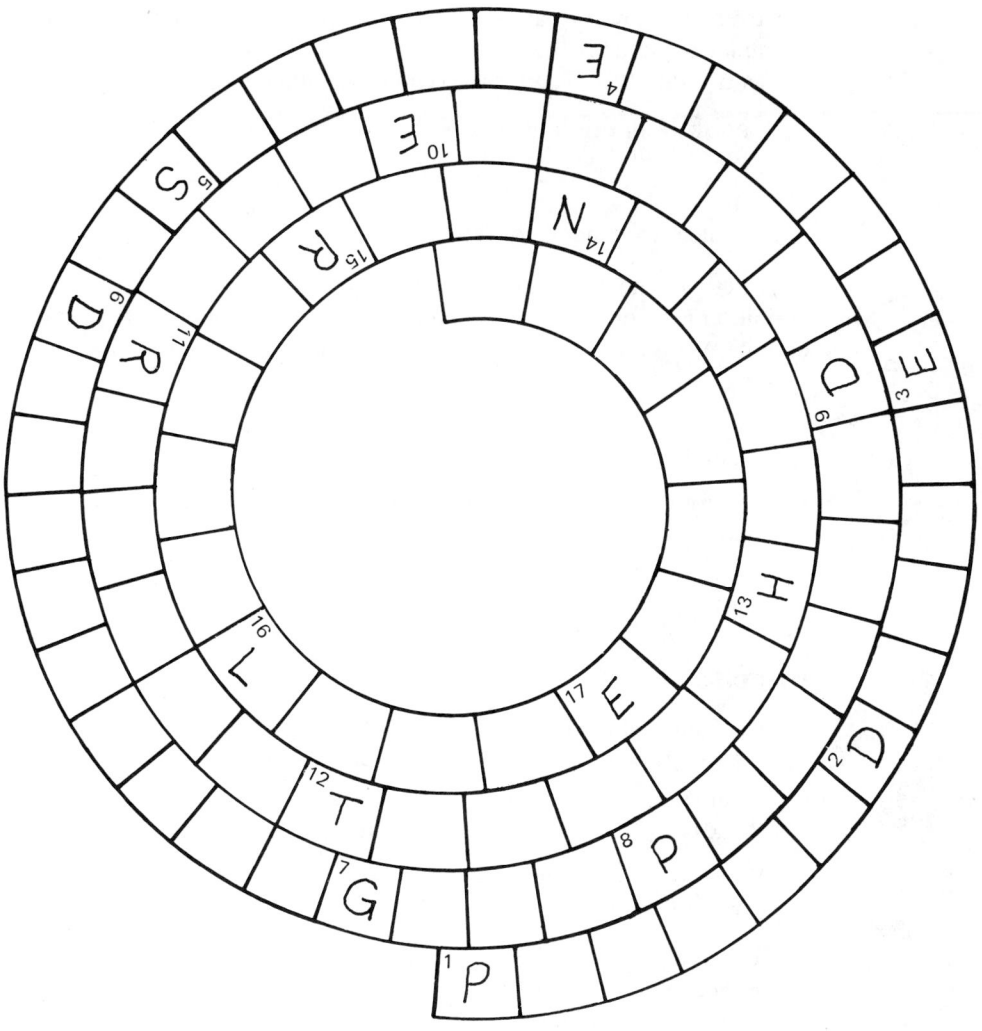

1	at a loss	10	come in
2	make up one's mind	11	look up to
3	set off	12	by means of
4	set forth	13	come about
5	out of spirits	14	on hand
6	at odds	15	bring out
7	lay hold of	16	go off
8	make believe	17	look over
9	look down on		

Spelling and Writing

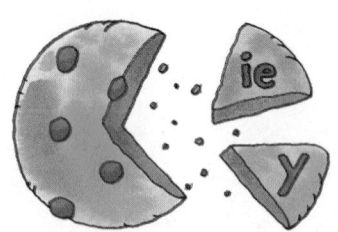

Words That Can Be Spelled More than One Way

Most words are correctly spelled in only one way. A few words, however, have more than one correct spelling—*cookie* or *cooky,* for example. Sometimes the spellings are entered together and defined as one entry, like this. The more common spelling is the first one.

> **cook·ie** or **cook·y** (kůk′ē), a small, flat, sweet cake. *noun, plural* **cook·ies.**
> [The words *cookie* and *cooky* look as if they come from the word *cook.* Actually they come from a Dutch word meaning "little cake."]

Sometimes the spellings are entered separately, like these. The definition is given at the more common spelling. Notice that after the definition come the words "Also spelled" followed by the other spelling.

> **co·sy** (kō′zē). See **cozy.** *adjective,* **co·si·er, co·si·est.**

> **co·zy** (kō′zē), warm and comfortable; snug: *The cat lay in a cozy corner near the fireplace. adjective,* **co·zi·er, co·zi·est.** Also spelled **cosy.**

Exercise

A. Use your dictionary to find another correct spelling for each of the words below. Write your answers on a piece of paper.

1. ameba	3. catalog	5. gray	7. playoff
2. adz	4. enclose	6. a.m.	8. doggie bag

B. Which of the spellings given for each of the words below is more common? Your dictionary will tell you.

1. adviser or advisor	5. pickax or pickaxe
2. cocoanut or coconut	6. quartet or quartette
3. Braille or braille	7. skilful or skillful
4. hooray, hurray, or hurrah	8. sirup or syrup

If it's named for me why don't I ever get the contents?

Using This Dictionary for Spelling

Your dictionary can help you spell just about any word you want to write. Sometimes, however, you may feel very confused when trying to spell a word . . . you can't quite figure out how to find the word you can't spell. Here are a few hints that may help.

1. Say the word slowly and carefully to yourself. Listen for the sounds. What are the sounds in the first syllable?

2. Look up the word according to the letters that usually spell its first few sounds. If you can't find the word, think of other ways it could be spelled.

3. If you are still having trouble, look at the Spellings of English Sounds chart on pages 46 and 47 of this dictionary. This chart helps you find words that you are having trouble looking up.

   Suppose you want to spell out the number 8. You would say the word to yourself—(āt)—and possibly try looking up the word in the *a*'s in your dictionary. But it wouldn't be there. The next thing to do would be to look at the spelling chart under the sound (ā). There you see the various ways the (ā) sound can be spelled. One of them is **eigh,** as in **eight.**

Teach Yourself

Turn to pages 46 and 47. Read the instructions for using the chart. Answer the following questions on a piece of paper.

1. How many ways can the (f) sound be spelled? What are they?
2. How is the (ch) sound spelled in the word pronounced (woch)?
3. How is the (b) sound spelled in the word pronounced (rab′it)?
4. How is the (zh) sound spelled in the word pronounced (trezh′ər)?

Exercise

In the exercise below, some of the words have missing parts for which a pronunciation symbol has been substituted. Use the spelling chart on the next two pages to help you spell the words correctly.

Prov(ėr)bs from (ə)round the W(ėr)ld

1. Time pa(s)es away, but s(ā)ings remain.
2. It is a bad worker who blames the t(ü)ls.
3. It is one thing to ca(k)le and another to lay an e(g).
4. Don't jump into the w(ô)ter to escape the r(ā)n.
5. Every man thinks his g(ē)se are sw(o)ns.
6. It is (ē)sier to tear down a (h)ole village than to b(i)ld (wu)ne house.
7. H(u)ney ca(ch)es more flies than vinegar.
8. (hw)en in dou(t), don't do it.
9. What is r(ī)t for one sh(u̇)d be r(ī)t for all.
10. It is not enou(f) to have mon(ē); one must kn(ō) h(ou) to spend it.

Spellings of English Sounds

This chart shows you the different sounds of the English language and ways of spelling those sounds. It can help you find out where to look in your dictionary for words you know how to say but do not know how to spell.

At the left-hand side of the chart you see pronunciation symbols that are used in this dictionary. Each symbol represents a different sound. Following each symbol are words showing different ways the sound may be spelled. The letters used to spell the sound are printed in heavy black type. Common spellings are listed first.

Some of the words used as examples are in more than one list. This is because the words are pronounced in more than one way.

Sound	Spelling and Examples
a	**a**t, pl**ai**d, h**a**lf, l**au**gh, **a**erial, pr**ay**er, th**ei**r, p**ea**r, **h**eir
ā	**a**ge, **ai**d, s**ay**, caf**e**, **eigh**t, v**ei**n, th**ey**, br**ea**k, bouqu**et**, str**aigh**t, g**au**ge
ä	f**a**ther, h**ea**rt, s**e**rgeant, **ah**, c**a**lm
b	**b**ad, ra**bb**it
ch	**ch**ild, fu**t**ure, wa**tch**, ques**ti**on, **c**ello, **Cz**echoslovakia
d	**d**id, fille**d**, a**dd**
e	**e**nd, br**ea**d, **a**ny, a**e**rial, s**ai**d, fr**ie**nd, l**eo**pard, s**ay**s, h**ei**fer, b**u**ry, h**ei**r
ē	**e**qual, happ**y**, **ea**ch, b**ee**, sk**i**, bel**ie**ve, c**ei**ling, k**ey**, alg**ae**, Ph**oe**nix, p**eo**ple
ėr	st**er**n, t**ur**n, f**ir**st, w**or**d, **ear**th, j**our**ney, m**yr**tle, p**urr**, h**er**b, w**or**ry, col**o**nel
f	**f**at, e**ff**ort, **ph**rase, lau**gh**
g	**g**o, e**gg**, lea**gu**e, **gu**est, **gh**ost
gz	e**x**act, e**x**hibit
h	**h**e, **w**ho
hw	**wh**eat
i	**i**n, **e**nough, myst**e**ry, man**a**ge, **ear**, bu**i**ld, s**ie**ve, b**u**sy, marr**ia**ge, b**ee**n, w**o**men, w**ei**rd
ī	**i**ce, sk**y**, l**ie**, h**igh**, r**ye**, **eye**, **i**sland, st**ei**n, h**eigh**t, b**uy**, kay**a**k, a**i**sle, **aye**, g**ey**ser, c**oy**ote
j	**g**em, lar**ge**, **j**am, bri**dge**, re**gi**on, gra**du**al, ba**dg**er, sol**di**er, e**xagg**erate

Sound	Spelling and Examples
k	coat, kind, back, school, account, excite, quit, antique, mosquito, acquire, khaki, biscuit, ache
ks	tax, tactics
l	land, tell
m	me, common, climb, autumn
n	no, manner, knife, gnaw, pneumonia
ng	ink, long, tongue, handkerchief
o	odd, watch, honest, knowledge, yacht
ō	old, oak, own, soul, toe, brooch, though, folk, bureau, oh, chauffeur, owe, sew
ô	order, all, auto, awful, oar, ought, walk, taught, cough, Utah
oi	oil, boy, buoy
ou	out, owl, bough, hour
p	pay, happy
r	run, carry, wrong, rhythm
s	say, cent, tense, dance, miss, scent, listen, psychology, pizza, sword
sh	nation, she, special, mission, tension, machine, conscience, issue, ocean, schwa, sugar
t	tell, button, stopped, doubt, two, receipt, pizza
th	thin
ŦH	then, breathe
u	under, other, trouble, flood, does
u̇	full, good, your, wolf, should
ü	food, rule, move, soup, threw, blue, fruit, shoe, maneuver, through, lieutenant, buoy
v	very, have, of
w	will, quick, choir
wu	one
y	opinion, yes
yü	use, few, feud, argue, view, beauty, yule
yu̇	uranium, Europe
z	has, zero, buzz, scissors, xylophone, raspberry, asthma
zh	division, measure, garage, azure
ə	occur, about, April, moment, cautious, circus, oxygen, bargain, gaiety, dungeon, authority

Spelling Hints

On this page and the next is a list of words that girls and boys your age often misspell. Look them over and try to learn their correct spellings. A number of spelling hints are included to help you remember how to spell these difficult words.

Words That Are Often Misspelled

about
address
again
all right
almost
always
another
answer
around
aunt

balloon
beautiful
because
been
bought
brought
building
buy

caught
children
clothes
color
come
could
country
cousin

didn't
dinner
doctor
does
doesn't
dollar
done
drink

early
easy
enough
every

Spelling Hint
When spelling **aunt**, remember this clue.
She can't be your a**u**nt without **u**!

Not without u!

Are U my aunt?

Spelling Hint
Be sure to **c a use** in **because**.

Why? Because you want to be a good speller!

Spelling Hint
If spelling **color** is something you dread, just remember
crayons **o**ffer **l**avender, **o**range, **r**ed.

Spelling Hint
Remember this when you spell **address**.
I saw an **ad** for a **dress** at this **ad**dress.

Dress for sale 427 High Street Lemon, MO 63025

Spelling Hint
Here's a tip for spelling **building**.
U and **I** are next-door neighbors in b**ui**lding.

Spelling Hint
Think of this when you spell **children**
The **child** reads **e**very **n**ight.

family
February
finally
first
finish
friend

Spelling Hint
Need a hint for spelling **friend**?
F.R. and **I** will be pals till the **end**.

ghost
goes
gone
great
ground
guess

Spelling Hint
Don't be afraid when spelling **ghost**.
Within each g**host** is a friendly **host**.

Spelling Hint
To spell **great** right every time,
remember the letters in this sign:

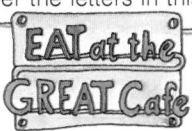
EAT at the GREAT Cafe

half
happened
have
hear
hour
hungry

it's

Spelling Hint
Here's a clue
for making **heard** clear.
You couldn't have h**ear**d
if you hadn't an **ear**!

knew
know

lady
laugh
little
loose

many
maybe
mean
money
morning
mountain

Spelling Hint
When spelling **mountain**
don't forget to put the **a in**.

next

Spelling Hint
To be a ruler of the high sea
Don't spell **ocean** without a **c**.

ocean
o'clock
off
once

people
piece
pretty
principal

Spelling Hint
Spelling **piece** is as easy as pie.
Write **pie**, add **ce**. Now give it a try.

raise
really
recess
remember
right

school

Spelling Hint
Open your eyes and use this tool.
Remember to **c** the **h** in **school**.

said
school
since
some
son
straight
sudden
sugar

SUN

Spelling Hint
How can you tell the words
son and **sun** apart?
The **son** yawns as the **sun** rises.

teacher
their
there
they
threw
tired
together
tomorrow
too
tried
two

Spelling Hint
Do you want to spell **together**?
Never fear.
Remember: We all went **to get her**.

upon
used

very
voice

wanted
wasn't
wear
were
weren't
when
where
which
would
write

Spelling Hint
Do you need help when you spell **where**?
Always look **here** to find **where**.

where

yesterday
your

Dividing Words in Writing

Sometimes when you are writing a report or a letter, you come to the end of a line and find that the next word will not fit. You have to write part of the word on one line and the rest on the next line. But where do you divide the word? You divide the word between syllables, and this dictionary shows you how to do it.

in·vite   **oc·cu·py**   **write**   **stead·y**

The words above are all entry words in your dictionary. The black dot between letters divides the word into syllables. *Invite* has two syllables—*in* and *vite*—and it can only be divided this way: *in-vite*. *Occupy* has three syllables and can be divided two ways: *oc-cupy* or *occu-py*. *Write* cannot be divided—it has only one syllable. *Steady* cannot be divided either, although it has two syllables, because you cannot divide a word if only one letter will be separated from the rest of the word. Below are four rules to remember when dividing words.

Rules for Dividing Words	Examples		
1. Check words in the dictionary and divide between syllables.	rein- deer	an- imal	ani- mal
2. Don't divide words the dictionary does not divide.	flight	through	
3. A word with a hyphen should be divided only at the hyphen.	good- natured	baby- sitter	
4. Don't separate a single letter from the rest of the word.	adult	idea	

Exercise

Use your dictionary and the rules above to help you divide the following words correctly. Write your answers on paper numbered from 1 to 10. Do it this way: 1. sales-person, salesper-son. Remember, some words should not be divided.

1. salesperson
2. android
3. zillion
4. floppy
5. caribou
6. old-timer
7. gripe
8. hatchery
9. limeade
10. idle

Proofreader's Marks

☰	Make a capital letter.
⊙	Write a period.
⑦	Write a question mark.
⑴	Write an exclamation point.
∧	Put in a letter or word.
ℓ	Take out a letter or word.
⑤⑨	Correct the spelling.
¶	Indent or start a new paragraph.
⌄⌄	Put in quotes.
⌃	Put in a comma.
/	Make a small letter.

On tuesday I went home.

The next day I left again⊙

When did you arrive⑦

Put that down⑴

You shouldn't ∧be rude.

The same goes double for you.

Why are you smileing⑤⑨?

¶ *He was only eight.*

Mother said, ⌄⌄Certainly you may.⌄⌄

John said, ⌃"No⌃you can't."

I'll ask my Dad.

Proofreader's Checklist

As you look over your written work, ask yourself each of these questions:

· Does each sentence begin with a capital letter?
· Does each sentence end with the correct punctuation mark (. ? !)?
· Do all proper nouns begin with a capital letter?

· Are all words spelled correctly?
· Is each new paragraph indented?
· Does each sentence tell one complete thought?

If you can answer yes to all these questions, you're on your way to being a superwriter!

Exercise

David wrote the report below for his health class. It is only the first draft, however, so there are a number of errors in it. The proofreader's marks on the right are lettered from A through G. The mistakes in David's report are numbered from 1 through 12. On a separate piece of paper, match the mistake to the correction, and write the correct answer. Do it this way: 1. D. It's

1.
it's important to take good care of youre teeth if you don't wont cavatees.
2. **3.** **4.**

5.
Brush your teeth at lest three times a day try not to eat too many sweets.
6. **7.**

8.
Use Dental floss every day. Be sure to eat healthy foods such as fruit,

9. **10.** **11.**
milk bread, and vegetables. Each meals should include foods the four food

12.
groups

A	⊙
B	ℓ
C	∧
D	☰
E	⌃
F	/
G	⑤⑨

51

Test Yourself

A. The musicians below have gotten their instruments mixed up. Each one is asking for his or her own instrument in pronunciation symbols. Match the person with the instrument being asked for. Do it this way: 1. Cary—cymbal

1. Cary says: I need my other (sim′bəl).
2. Beth says: Where's my (bə sün′)?
3. Luke asks: May I have my (līr)?
4. Otto says: Pass the (ō′bō).
5. Frank says: Give me the (flüt).
6. Charlotte says: (chel′ō), please.
7. Pam asks: Who has my (pik′ə lō)?
8. Henry says: Hand me my (härp).
9. Do you notice anything interesting about the musicians and the instruments they play?

B. Pictured below are things that can be spelled more than one way. One spelling is given for you. On a piece of paper numbered 1 through 4, write the other spelling for each.

1. raccoon   2. eerie   3. axe   4. wolverine

1. forever
2. length
3. condition
4. musician
5. father-in-law
6. highway
7. prove
8. better

C. Use your dictionary to divide the words listed at the right. Do it this way: 1. for-ever, forev-er

D. Kate remembers how to spell the word *skate* by adding *s* to her name, like this: s + Kate = skate. Do you have a spelling hint you can share with your classmates?

Answer Key

Page 10 **Teach Yourself**

1. automobile
   bicycle
   clipper
2. blue

3. glider
   gondola
   helicopter
   jet
   motorcycle

4. roller skate
   train

Exercise

1. yes
2. no
3. yes
4. yes

5. yes
6. yes
7. no
8. no

9. yes
10. no
11. yes
12. yes

Page 11 **Teach Yourself**

1. District of Columbia
2. darkroom
3. Dr.

4. disaster
5. dislike
6. dis-

7. day-care center
8. disk jockey
9. diskette

Page 12 **Teach Yourself**

A. 1. Amy   Peter
      Ben   Sam
      Chris   Viv
      Flo   Will
      John   Zak
      Matt

   2. Zak

B. 1. He would be first.
   2. Amy

Exercise

Girl: A brother can't fool his own sister this way.
Boy: Don't ever forget I'm more sneaky than you.
Girl: Could I make neat programs with you, Zak.
Boy: Amy, cooperation instead of quarreling serves us well.

Page 13 **Teach Yourself**

1. be
2. the third letter
3. yes
4. sal

5. the fourth letter
6. salad, salmon, salt
7. the fifth letter

Exercise

3. cherries
4. chewing gum
6. chili
9. cinnamon

10. citrus
13. coffee
14. cola

16. corn
18. crab apples
19. crabs

Page 14 **Teach Yourself**
1. **dazzling** | **debate**
2. no
3. no
4. **deduction** | **defiance**
5. first, deduction, last, defiance

Exercise
1. pharmacist, philanthropist, philosopher
2. photographer, physician, physicist, pianist
3. picket, picnicker
4. pilgrim
Do not fit: performer, pilot

Page 15 **Teach Yourself**
1. e
2. y changes to i
3. y changes to i
4. b

Exercise
1. coaches—coach
2. dragged—drag
3. prairies—prairie
4. fascinating—fascinate
5. quicker—quick
6. smuggling—smuggle
7. heaviest—heavy
8. enemies—enemy
9. sturdier—sturdy
10. transferring—transfer

Page 16 **Test Yourself**
A. 1. an elevator full of ripe tomatoes
2. big holes in the yard
3. all books have titles
4. because dragons fight knights most nights
5. all bear essentials for traveling well

B. 1. a big box of quackers
2. fans fill most seats
3. delicious fattening food going to waist
4. because cafeterias don't ever serve spirits
5. beavers look silly wearing weighty winter woolens

Page 17 C.
Beth:	Matt:
bicycle	mother-of-pearl
blackberry	motion picture
blackbird	mountain goat
black-eyed pea	mountainside
black-eyed Susan	mountaintop

Flo:	Sam:
France	sea
frankfurter	seafood
French	sea gull
French fries	sea lion
French horn	seashore
French toast	seaweed

D. 1. ponies 5. wolves 9. swordfish or swordfishes
  2. butterflies 6. sheep 10. canaries
  3. calves 7. huskies 11. flamingos or flamingoes
  4. oxen 8. geese 12. ostriches

E. 1. thrush 5. rhinoceros 9. swim
  2. fierce 6. aviary 10. hibernate
  3. animal 7. grizzly
  4. graze 8. cage

F. 1. air | alarm, Alabama
  2. cafeteria | call, California
  3. congregate | consecrate, Connecticut
  4. floppy | fluorine, Florida
  5. generator | geranium, Georgia
  6. haven | head, Hawaii
  7. I | idea, Idaho
  8. keeper | khan, Kentucky
  9. maroon | mascot, Maryland
  10. terrier | that, Texas

Page 18 Teach Yourself
1. the past. 2. Answers will vary. 3. Answers will vary.

Page 19 Exercise
1. c 6. c
2. b 7. a
3. a 8. b
4. b 9. c
5. a 10. a

Page 20 Exercise
1. invincible
2. momentous
3. courtly
4. rumple
5. irksome

Page 21 Teach Yourself
1. four
2. any of the following:
Explorers live through many uncertain situations.
Explorers live through many situations that are not
safe. Explorers live through many situations that are not
secure. Explorers live through many dangerous
situations.

Exercise
1. a 4. b
2. c 5. c
3. c 6. b

Page 22 **Teach Yourself**
a. 2　　　　b. 3　　　　c. 1

Exercise
1. 3　　　4. 1　　　7. 4
2. 2　　　5. 10　　8. 2
3. 1　　　6. 3　　　9. 4

Page 23 **Teach Yourself**
1. junk^2　　　　　2. junk^1

Exercise
1. bound^4　　　6. stern^2
2. port^1　　　　7. pole^1
3. kind^2　　　　8. found^1
4. hold^2　　　　9. wind^1
5. bow^3　　　10. band^1

Page 24 **Test Yourself**
A. 1. guide words
2. the entry word
3. the definition
4. They are homograph numbers, and mean that there is more than one word with this spelling.
5. alphabetical order

B. 1. Yes, you are supposed to hit it with a stick.
2. No, it can be used up.
3. A kumquat, because it is a fruit. A whirligig is not something to eat.
4. Amigo, because it means friend. Monsieur means Mr.
5. yes
6. No, it is a chart that shows one's ancestors.
7. Cowslips, because crabgrass is a weed.
8. No, an optometrist examines eyes.
9. yes
10. No, the Himalayas are in Asia but the Alps are in Europe.

C. 1. a. jerky^2　　　4. a. scale^1
　　b. jerky^1　　　　b. scale^2
2. a. ring^2　　　　　c. scale^3
　　b. ring^1　　　5. a. till^2
3. a. yard^2　　　　b. till^1
　　b. yard^1　　　　c. till^3

Crossword Puzzle

¹N	²O	³S	E		⁴I	⁵N	⁶T	⁷O

(Crossword solution grid)

Row 1: N O S E · · I N T O
Row 2: O W L · · · E A R
Row 3: R E A D · W E R E
Row 4: · S P R E A D S ·
Row 5: S · E A T · · S
Row 6: T · F A T E D · P
Row 7: I T E M · R I C E
Row 8: F O E · · M A N
Row 9: F E L L · M E N D

Page 26 **Teach Yourself**
1. laugh, fun, phone, life
2. fun, phone, not, knot, knit, bend, wren
3. laugh
4. knit
5. wren
   yes, Crumbs, best, hot, in, some

Page 27 **Teach Yourself**
1. bet
2. ridge

Exercise
1. big
2. laughs
3. can
4. light
5. up
6. little
7. faces

Page 28 **Exercise A**
1. nice
2. radio
3. clothes
4. beach

Exercise B
1. floor
2. hard
3. unit
4. fool
5. put

Page 29 **Test Yourself**

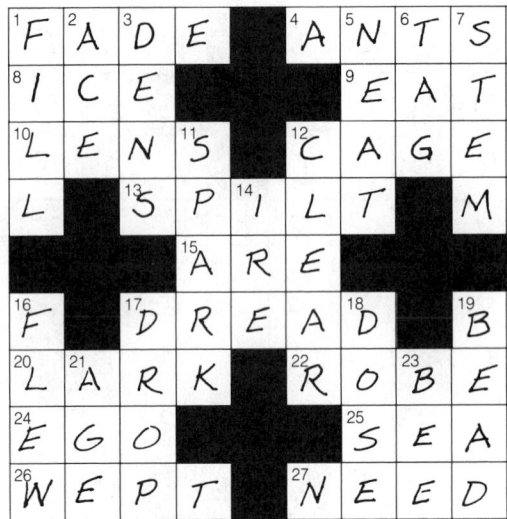

Page 30 **Teach Yourself, top**
1. toy   2. cow

Teach Yourself, bottom
1. she, carnation, tissue   2. vision, garage

Page 31 **Teach Yourself**
1. thank, breath, bath   2. breathe, those

Exercise
1. noisy, loyal, boys'
2. these, leather, than, those
3. changed, chief
4. going, bank, checking
5. purr, perfectly
6. brown, ground
7. television, decisions, casual
8. threatening, think, thunderstorm
9. fashion, creation

Page 32 **Teach Yourself, top**
1. one   2. two   3. three

Teach Yourself, bottom
1. the third   2. the first

Exercise
1. two; first has primary accent, second has secondary
2. three; first has primary accent, third has secondary
3. two; first
4. two; second
5. two; first
6. two; first has primary accent, second has secondary
7. two; first

Page 33 **Teach Yourself**
1. u   2. ai   3. ou

Exercise
1. loc**u**st   6. a**u**thority
2. syc**a**more   7. hick**o**ry
3. enorm**ou**s   8. tort**oi**se
4. chr**y**santhemum   9. mar**i**gold
5. snapdrag**o**n   10. pig**eo**n

Page 34 **Teach Yourself**
Answer: b

Exercise
1. a   5. b
2. b   6. a
3. a   7. b
4. b   8. b

Page 35 **Exercise**
Answers will vary.

Page 36 **Test Yourself**

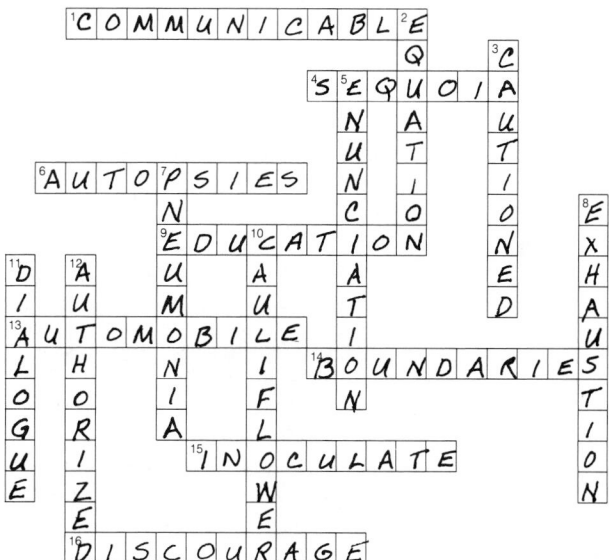

Page 37 **Exercise A**
1. not an idiom
2. not an idiom
3. Don't beat around the bush, just tell me the truth. (or similar answer)
4. I escaped by the skin of my teeth. (or similar answer)
5. You'd better shape up or you will fail this class. (or similar answer)
6. not an idiom

Exercise B
1. tell, b
2. crow, c
3. drop, a
4. even, c
5. pass, c
6. rate, b

Page 38 **Teach Yourself**
1. wield
2. -er
3. a person who holds and uses; a person who controls (or similar wording)

Page 39 **Exercise**
Answers will vary.

Pages
40–41 **Exercise**

1. Arabic	6. Japanese
2. German	7. Latin
3. Greek	8. American Indian
4. Chinese	9. Scandinavian
5. French	10. Italian

There are 10 different languages used.

Page 41 **Exercise**
1. a. People in the Netherlands speak Dutch. (or the Dutch, or people in Holland)
   b. yes.
2. a. at the entry *Greek*
   b. yes
   c. no
3. a. yes
   b. any two of the following: *bronco, cafeteria, chaps, mustang, stampede,* and *taco*

Page 42 **Test Yourself**
A. 1. *scratch* I'll have to start from the beginning.
    2. *date* I'm afraid that cut is old-fashioned.
    3. *head* That book is definitely too hard for you to understand.
    4. *tongue* Stop that yapping and keep quiet (or be silent).
    5. *dog* This place is being ruined (or going to ruin).

B. 1. disentangle dis-, do the opposite of getting twisted up
    2. unfancy un-, not decorated; plain; simple
       or not unusual, not high quality, not too high; not fancy
    3. nonrigid non-, not stiff or firm; not bending; *or* not strict; not rigid
    4. blackish -ish, somewhat black
    5. restack re-, to pile again; arrange in a stack again

C. 1. at the end of the entry
    2. Latin
    3. magnolia—named for Pierre Magnol
    4. from Theodore Roosevelt, because he refused
       to shoot a bear cub. Stuffed bears were then
       made and sold as teddy bears.
    5. b. raccoon; d. moose; and e. caribou
    6. Genoa, a city in Italy
    7. at the entry *Italian*
    8. yes; oboe, piano, and trombone

Page 43 **Challenge Puzzle**

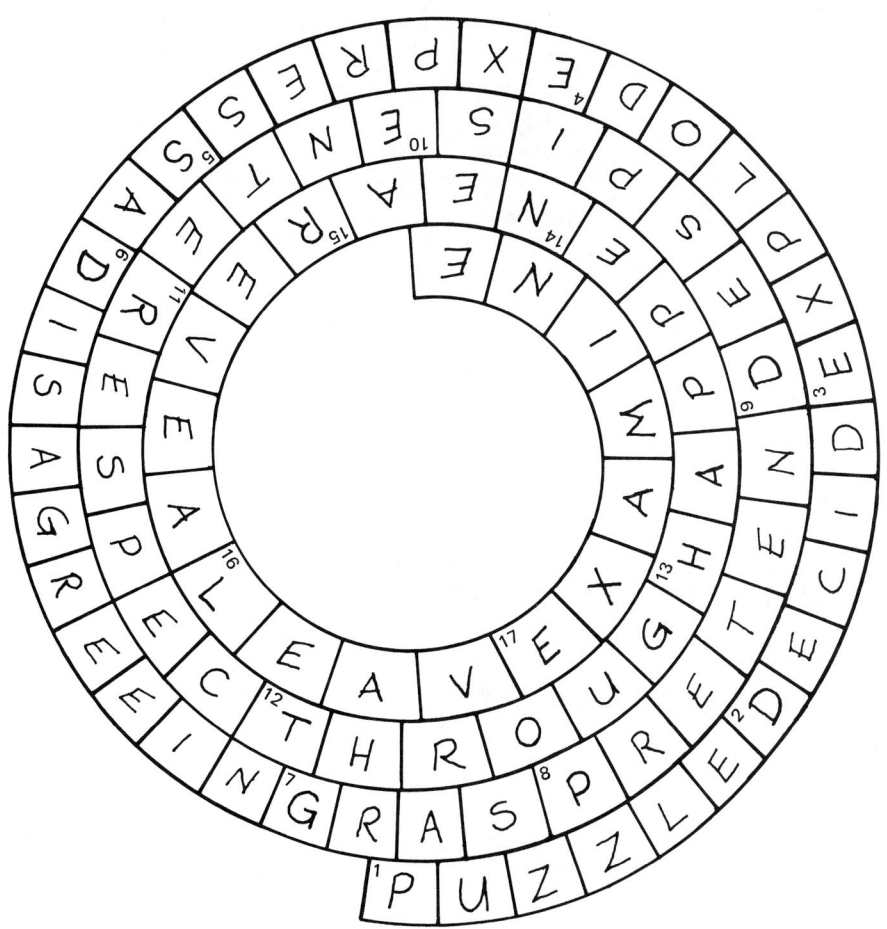

Page 44 **Exercise**

A. 1. amoeba   3. catalogue   5. grey   7. play-off
    2. adze   4. inclose   6. A.M.   8. doggy bag

B. 1. adviser   3. Braille   5. pickax   7. skillful
    2. coconut   4. hurrah   6. quartet   8. syrup

Page 45 **Teach Yourself**
1. 4; f, ff, ph, and gh
2. tch
3. bb
4. s

Exercise

Proverbs, around, World

1. passes, sayings
2. tools
3. cackle, egg
4. water, rain
5. geese, swans
6. easier, whole, build, one
7. honey, catches
8. when, doubt
9. right, should, right
10. enough, money, know, how

Page 50 **Exercise**
1. sales-person, salesper-son
2. an-droid
3. zil-lion
4. flop-py
5. car-ibou, cari-bou
6. old-timer
7. gripe—can't divide
8. hatch-ery
9. lime-ade
10. idle—can't divide

Page 51 **Exercise**
1. D. It's
2. B. your
3. G. want
4. G. cavities
5. G. least
6. A. day.
7. D. Try
8. F. dental
9. E. milk,
10. B. meal
11. C. from
12. A. groups.

Page 52 **Test Yourself**
A.
1. Cary—cymbal
2. Beth—bassoon
3. Luke—lyre
4. Otto—oboe
5. Frank—flute
6. Charlotte—cello
7. Pam—piccolo
8. Henry—harp
9. The name of the musician and the instrument he or she plays start with the same letter.

B.
1. racoon
2. eery
3. ax
4. wolverene

C.
1. for-ever, forev-er
2. length (cannot be divided)
3. con-dition, condi-tion
4. mu-sician, musi-cian
5. father-in-law (only at hyphens)
6. high-way
7. prove (cannot be divided)
8. bet-ter

D. Answers will vary.

A a

a hat	**i** it	**oi** oil	**ch** child		a in about
ā age	**ī** ice	**ou** out	**ng** long		e in taken
ä far	**o** hot	**u** cup	**sh** she	**ə =**	i in pencil
e let	**ō** open	**u̇** put	**th** thin		o in lemon
ē equal	**ô** order	**ü** rule	**ŦH** then		u in circus
ėr term			**zh** measure		

A or **a**[1] (ā), the first letter of the English alphabet. *noun, plural* **A's** or **a's.**

a[2] (ə *or* ā), **1** any: *Is there a pencil in the box?* **2** one: *Buy a dozen eggs.* **3** every: *Thanksgiving comes once a year.* **4** one kind of: *Chemistry is a science. adjective* or *indefinite article.*

aard·vark (ärd′värk), an animal with a snout like a pig's, a long, sticky tongue, and very strong claws. It eats ants and termites. *noun.*

Word History

aardvark Two South African words meaning "earth" and "pig" were combined to form *aardvark.* The animal was called this because it digs a burrow in which it lives underground.

aardvark—about 6 feet (2 meters) long with the tail

a·back (ə bak′). **taken aback,** surprised; confused: *I was taken aback by her insult. adverb.*

ab·a·cus (ab′ə kəs), a frame with rows of beads or counters that slide back and forth. Abacuses are used for counting in China, Japan, and some other countries. *noun, plural* **ab·a·cus·es.**

abacus—When the beads are pushed toward the middle bar, the top ones count as 5 and the bottom ones as 1 each. The number shown is 964,708.

ab·a·lo·ne (ab′ə lō′nē), a shellfish with a large, rather flat shell that has a pearly lining. Abalones are good to eat. *noun.*
[*Abalone* comes from a Mexican Spanish word for this shellfish. Spanish settlers in California got the word from the name that local American Indians used for this shellfish.]

a·ban·don (ə ban′dən), **1** to give up entirely: *We abandoned the idea of a picnic because of the rain.* **2** to leave without intending to return to; desert: *The crew abandoned the sinking ship. verb.*

a·ban·doned (ə ban′dənd), deserted: *The children played in the abandoned house. adjective.*

a·bate (ə bāt′), to make or become less: *The storm has abated. verb,* **a·bates, a·bat·ed, a·bat·ing.**

ab·bess (ab′is), a woman who is the head of an abbey of nuns. *noun, plural* **ab·bess·es.**

ab·bey (ab′ē), **1** the building or buildings where monks or nuns live a religious life. **2** the monks or nuns living there. *noun, plural* **ab·beys.**

ab·bot (ab′ət), a man who is the head of an abbey of monks. *noun.*

ab·bre·vi·ate (ə brē′vē āt), to make shorter: *We can abbreviate "hour" to "hr." and "week" to "wk." verb,* **ab·bre·vi·ates, ab·bre·vi·at·ed, ab·bre·vi·at·ing.**

ab·bre·vi·a·tion (ə brē′vē ā′shən), a shortened form: *"Dr." is an abbreviation for "Doctor." noun.*

A·B·C's (ā′bē′sēz′), **1** the alphabet: *Before you can read, you must learn your ABC's.* **2** the facts or skills to be learned first; basic rules: *I'm learning the ABC's of soccer. noun plural.*

ab·di·cate (ab′də kāt), to give up office, power, or authority; resign: *When the king abdicated his throne, his brother became king. verb,* **ab·di·cates, ab·di·cat·ed, ab·di·cat·ing.**

ab·do·men (ab′də mən), **1** the part of the body that contains the stomach, the intestines, and other digestive organs; belly. **2** the last of the three parts of the body of an insect. *noun.*

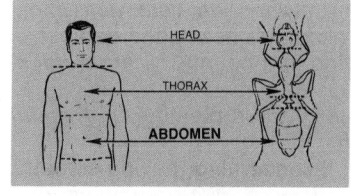

abdomen
(definitions 1 and 2)

ab·dom·i·nal (ab dom′ə nəl), of the abdomen: *abdominal muscles. adjective.*

ab·duct (ab dukt′), to kidnap: *The bank president was abducted and held for ransom. verb.*

ab·hor (ab hôr′), to shrink away from with horror; feel disgust for; hate very much: *He abhors snakes. verb,* **ab·hors, ab·horred, ab·hor·ring.**

a·bide (ə bīd′), to put up with; endure: *I can't abide their always being late. verb,* **a·bides, a·bid·ed, a·bid·ing.**
abide by, to accept and carry out; obey: *Both teams will abide by the umpire's decision.*

a·bil·i·ty (ə bil′ə tē), **1** a power: *Dogs have the ability to hear sounds that people cannot.* **2** a skill or talent: *He has great ability in making jewelry. Musical ability often shows itself early in life.* noun, plural **a·bil·i·ties.**

ab·ject (ab′jekt), so unhappy as to be hopeless; miserable: *Many people live in abject poverty.* adjective.

a·blaze (ə blāz′), on fire; blazing: *The forest was set ablaze by lightning.* adjective.

a·ble (ā′bəl), **1** having enough power, skill, or means: *A cat is able to see in the dark.* **2** having more power or skill than usual; skillful: *She is an able teacher.* adjective, **a·bler, a·blest.**

-able, a suffix meaning: **1** that can be _____ed: An enjoy*able* party means a party *that can be* enjoyed. **2** able, liable, or likely to _____: Break*able* means *liable to* break.

a·bly (ā′blē), in an able manner; with skill; well: *She did her job ably.* adverb.

ab·nor·mal (ab nôr′məl), very different from the ordinary conditions; unusual: *We've had an abnormal amount of rain.* adjective.

a·board (ə bôrd′), on board; in or on a ship, train, bus, or airplane: *"All aboard!" shouted the conductor. We had to be aboard the ship by noon.* adverb, preposition.

a·bode (ə bōd′), a place to live in; dwelling; house: *A simple hut was their abode.* noun.

a·bol·ish (ə bol′ish), to do away with; put an end to: *Many wish that nations would abolish war.* verb.

ab·o·li·tion (ab′ə lish′ən), a putting an end to; abolishing: *The abolition of slavery in the United States occurred in 1865.* noun.

ab·o·li·tion·ist (ab′ə lish′ə nist), a person who wishes to abolish something. The people who wished to put an end to slavery in the United States were called **Abolitionists.** noun.

A-bomb (ā′bom′), an atomic bomb. noun.

a·bom·i·na·ble (ə bom′ə nə bəl), **1** hateful; disgusting: *Kidnapping is an abominable act.* **2** very unpleasant: *The weather for the picnic was abominable—rainy, windy, and cold.* adjective.

ab·o·rig·i·nes (ab′ə rij′ə nēz′), the earliest known people living in a country or area. noun plural.

a·bound (ə bound′), to be plentiful: *Fish abound in the ocean.* verb.

a·bout (ə bout′), **1** concerning; having something to do with: *"Black Beauty" is a story about a horse.* **2** approximately; roughly: *He weighs about 100 pounds.* **3** approximately at: *We arrived about 6:00 p.m.* **4** nearly; almost: *She has about finished her work.* **5** all round; around: *A collar goes about the neck. Look about and tell me what you see.* **6** ready; going: *The plane is about to take off.* **1,3,5** preposition, **2,4,5** adverb, **6** adjective.

a·bove (ə buv′), **1** in a higher place; overhead: *The sky is above.* **2** higher than; over: *She kept her head above water. A captain is above a sergeant.* **3** more than: *Our club has above thirty members— thirty-five, to be exact.* **1** adverb, **2,3,** preposition.

ab·ra·ca·dab·ra (ab′rə kə dab′rə), a word supposed to have magic power. noun.

a·breast (ə brest′), **1** side by side: *The band members marched six abreast.* **2** up with; alongside of: *I like to keep abreast of the news.* adverb, adjective.

a·bridge (ə brij′), to make shorter, especially by using fewer words: *A long story can be abridged by leaving out unimportant parts.* verb, **a·bridg·es, a·bridged, a·bridg·ing.**

a·broad (ə brôd′), **1** outside one's country: *She is going abroad next year to study in Italy.* **2** far and wide; widely: *The news of the tornado damage was quickly spread abroad.* adverb.

a·brupt (ə brupt′), **1** sudden: *The driver made an abrupt turn to avoid another car.* **2** very steep: *The road made an abrupt rise up the hill.* **3** short, blunt, or sudden in speech or manner: *She answered me with an abrupt remark and left.* adjective.

ab·scess (ab′ses), a collection of pus in the tissues of some part of the body. An abscess results from an infection and is usually painful. noun, plural **ab·scess·es.**

ab·sence (ab′səns), **1** a being away: *My absence from school was caused by illness.* **2** a time of being away: *I returned to school after an absence of two days.* **3** a being without; lack: *Darkness is the absence of light.* noun.

ab·sent (ab′sənt), **1** away; not present: *Three members of the class are absent.* **2** lacking: *Catfish are covered with skin; scales are absent.* adjective.

ab·sen·tee (ab′sən tē′), a person who is away or stays away. noun.

ab·sent-mind·ed (ab′sənt mīn′did), forgetful; not paying attention to what is going on: *The absent-minded man put salt in his coffee and sugar on his egg.* adjective.

ab·so·lute (ab′sə lüt), **1** complete; entire: *That is the absolute truth.* **2** not limited in any way: *The dictator had absolute power.* adjective.

ab·so·lute·ly (ab′sə lüt′lē), **1** completely: *My broken bicycle was absolutely useless.* **2** without doubt; certainly: *This is absolutely the best cake I've ever eaten.* adverb.

ab·sorb (ab sôrb′), **1** to take in and hold: *The sponge absorbed the spilled milk. Rugs absorb sounds and make a house quieter.* **2** to take up all the attention of; interest very much. verb.

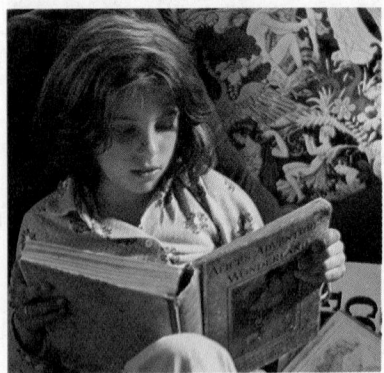

absorb (definition 2)
She was **absorbed** in reading a good book most of the afternoon.

ab·sorb·ent (ab sôr′bənt), able to take in moisture, light, or heat: *Absorbent paper is used to dry the hands.* adjective.

ab·sorb·ing (ab sôr′bing), extremely interesting: *I watched an absorbing program about dolphins on TV last night.* adjective.

ab·sorp·tion (ab sôrp′shən), 1 the ability to take in moisture, light, or heat: *A blotter dries ink by absorption.* 2 great interest: *The children's absorption in their game was so complete that they did not hear the doorbell.* noun.

ab·stain (ab stān′), to do without something; hold oneself back: *If you want to lose weight, abstain from eating candy and rich foods.* verb.

ab·sti·nence (ab′stə nəns), partly or entirely giving up certain pleasures, food, or drink: *Abstinence from candy and desserts helped my father lose weight.* noun.

ab·stract (ab′strakt), 1 thought of apart from any object or real thing: *Sweetness is abstract; a lump of sugar is concrete.* 2 hard to understand; difficult: *The atomic theory of matter is so abstract that it can be fully understood only by advanced students.* adjective.

ab·surd (ab sėrd′), plainly not true or sensible; foolish; ridiculous: *The idea that the number 13 brings bad luck is absurd.* adjective.

ab·surd·i·ty (ab sėr′də tē), 1 a lack of sense; foolishness: *I could see the absurdity of his superstitions.* 2 something foolish or ridiculous. noun, plural **ab·surd·i·ties.**

absurdity (definition 2)
I thought the fur-covered dishes were an **absurdity.**

a·bun·dance (ə bun′dəns), great plenty; quantity that is more than enough: *There is an abundance of apples this year.* noun.

a·bun·dant (ə bun′dənt), more than enough; very plentiful: *The trapper had an abundant supply of food for the winter.* adjective.

a·buse (ə byüz′ for 1 and 3; ə byüs′ for 2 and 4), 1 to make bad or wrong use of: *Don't abuse the privilege of using the library by talking too loud.* 2 a bad or wrong use: *The people hated the wicked king for his abuse of power.* 3 to treat cruelly or roughly: *The children abused the dog by throwing rocks at it.* 4 cruel or rough treatment: *I stopped their abuse of the dog.* 1,3 verb, **a·bus·es, a·bused, a·bus·ing;** 2,4 noun.

a·byss (ə bis′), a bottomless or very great depth;

a hat	i it	oi oil	ch child	a in about
ā age	ī ice	ou out	ng long	e in taken
ä far	o hot	u cup	sh she	ə = i in pencil
e let	ō open	ú put	th thin	o in lemon
ē equal	ô order	ü rule	ᴛʜ then	u in circus
ėr term			zh measure	

abyss

a very deep crack in the earth: *They stood at the edge of a cliff overlooking an abyss four thousand feet deep.* noun, plural **a·byss·es.**

a.c. or **A.C.,** alternating current.

a·cad·e·my (ə kad′ə mē), 1 a private high school. 2 a school where some special subject can be studied: *West Point is a military academy.* noun, plural **a·cad·e·mies.**

ac·cel·e·rate (ak sel′ə rāt′), to speed up: *The car accelerated as it went down the steep hill. Rest often accelerates a person's recovery from illness.* verb, **ac·cel·e·rates, ac·cel·e·rat·ed, ac·cel·e·rat·ing.**

ac·cel·e·ra·tion (ak sel′ə rā′shən), a speeding up: *The rapid acceleration of the rocket made it soon disappear from view.* noun.

ac·cel·e·ra·tor (ak sel′ə rā′tər), a thing that causes an increase in the speed of anything. The pedal or lever that controls the speed of an engine by regulating the flow of fuel to the engine is an accelerator. noun.

ac·cent (ak′sent), 1 the greater force or stronger tone of voice given to certain syllables or words: *In "letter," the accent is on the first syllable.* 2 a mark (′) written or printed to show the spoken force of a syllable, as in *to·day* (tə dā′). Some words have two accents, a stronger accent (′) and a weaker accent (′), as in *ac·cel·e·ra·tor* (ak sel′ə rā′tər). 3 to pronounce or mark with an accent: *Is "acceptable" accented on the first or second syllable?* 4 a different way of pronouncing heard in different parts of the same country, or in the speech of a person speaking a language not his or her own: *My father was born in Germany and speaks English with a German accent.* 5 stress; importance: *In our English class, considerable accent is given to grammar.* 1,2,4,5 noun, 3 verb.

ac·cept (ak sept′), 1 to take what is offered or

given to one; agree to take: *The teacher accepted our gift.* **2** to agree to; say yes to: *I accepted her invitation to the party.* **3** to take as true or satisfactory; believe: *The teacher accepted our excuse.* **4** to receive with liking and approval: *They soon accepted the new student as a friend. verb.*

ac·cept·a·ble (ak sep′tə bəl), **1** likely to be gladly received; agreeable: *Flowers are an acceptable gift.* **2** good enough but not outstanding; satisfactory: *I got an acceptable grade. adjective.*

ac·cept·ance (ak sep′təns), **1** the taking of what is offered or given to one: *The teacher's acceptance of the flowers they brought delighted the children.* **2** a being accepted: *She was excited by the acceptance of her story by the magazine. noun.*

ac·cess (ak′ses), **1** the right to enter or use: *All students have access to the library during the afternoon.* **2** an approach to places, things, or persons: *Access to mountain towns is often difficult because of poor roads. noun.*

ac·ces·si·ble (ak ses′ə bəl), easy to get at; easy to reach: *A telephone should be put where it will be accessible. adjective.*

ac·ces·sor·y (ak ses′ər ē), **1** a thing added to help something of more importance: *Her new car has many accessories, including an air conditioner.* **2** a person who has helped in a crime: *By not reporting the theft she became an accessory. noun, plural* **ac·ces·sor·ies.**

ac·ci·dent (ak′sə dənt), **1** something harmful or unlucky that happens unexpectedly: *She was hurt in an automobile accident.* **2** something that happens without being planned or known in advance: *A series of lucky accidents led the scientists to the discovery. noun.*

by accident, by chance; not on purpose: *I met an old friend by accident.*

ac·ci·den·tal (ak′sə den′tl), happening by chance: *Breaking the lamp was accidental; I did not do it on purpose. adjective.*

ac·ci·den·tal·ly (ak′sə den′tl ē), without being planned; by chance; not on purpose: *I accidentally stepped on the dog's tail. adverb.*

ac·claim (ə klām′), **1** to welcome with loud approval; praise highly; applaud: *The crowd acclaimed the winning team.* **2** a shout or show of approval; applause: *The astronaut was welcomed with great acclaim.* **1** *verb,* **2** *noun.*

ac·com·mo·date (ə kom′ə dāt), **1** to hold; have room for: *This airplane is large enough to accommodate 120 passengers.* **2** to help out; oblige: *I wanted change for five dollars, but no one could accommodate me.* **3** to supply with a place to sleep or live for a time: *Tourists are accommodated here. verb,* **ac·com·mo·dates, ac·com·mo·dat·ed, ac·com·mo·dat·ing.**

ac·com·mo·dat·ing (ə kom′ə dā′ting), helpful; obliging: *My teacher was accommodating enough to lend me a dollar. adjective.*

ac·com·mo·da·tion (ə kom′ə dā′shən), **1** a help, favor, or convenience: *It will be an accommodation to me if you will meet me tomorrow instead of today.* **2 accommodations,** a place to sleep or live for a time: *Can we find accommodations at a motel for tonight? noun.*

ac·com·pa·ni·ment (ə kum′pə nē mənt), anything that goes along with something else: *The rain was an unpleasant accompaniment to our ride. We sang with piano accompaniment. noun.*

ac·com·pa·ny (ə kum′pə nē), **1** to go along with: *May we accompany you on your walk? She accompanied the singer on the piano.* **2** to be or happen along with: *A high wind accompanied the rain. verb,* **ac·com·pa·nies, ac·com·pa·nied, ac·com·pa·ny·ing.**

ac·com·plice (ə kom′plis), a person who aids another in committing a crime: *The thief had an accomplice inside the building who unlocked the door. noun.*

ac·com·plish (ə kom′plish), to do; carry out: *Did you accomplish your purpose? She can accomplish more in a day than anyone else in class. verb.*

ac·com·plished (ə kom′plisht), **1** done; carried out: *With their work accomplished the children went out to play.* **2** expert; skilled: *Only an accomplished dancer can perform this ballet. adjective.*

ac·com·plish·ment (ə kom′plish mənt), **1** something that has been done with knowledge, skill, or ability: *The teacher was proud of her pupils' accomplishments.* **2** a special skill: *She was a woman of many accomplishments; she was a respected composer, a fine painter, and an excellent teacher.* **3** a doing; carrying out: *Accomplishment of his purpose took two months. noun.*

ac·cord (ə kôrd′), agreement: *Most people are in accord in their desire for peace. noun.*

of one's own accord, without being asked or without suggestion from anyone else: *We didn't ask for help; they helped of their own accord.*

ac·cord·ance (ə kôrd′ns), agreement: *What she did was in accordance with what she said. noun.*

ac·cord·ing·ly (ə kôr′ding lē), **1** in agreement with something that has been stated: *These are the rules; you can act accordingly or leave the club.* **2** therefore: *I was told to speak briefly; accordingly I cut short my talk. adverb.*

ac·cord·ing to (ə kôr′ding tü), **1** in agreement with: *He paid his debt according to his promise.* **2** in proportion to: *You will be paid according to the work you do.* **3** on the authority of: *According to the weather report, it is going to rain today.*

ac·cor·di·on (ə kôr′dē ən), a musical wind instrument with a bellows, metal reeds, and keys. *noun.*

accordion

4

A

ac·count (ə kount′), **1** a statement telling in detail about an event or thing; explanation: *She gave her parents an account of everything that happened on the class trip.* **2** value or importance: *She thought their ideas were out of date and of little account.* **3** a statement of money received and spent; record of business dealings: *I decided to keep a written account of the way I spend my allowance. All stores, banks, and factories keep accounts. noun.*
account for, 1 to tell what has been done with; answer for: *The treasurer of the club had to account for the money paid to her.* **2** to explain: *Can you account for your absence from class?* **3** to be the cause of: *Late frosts accounted for the poor fruit crop.*
on account of, because of; for the reason of: *The game was called off on account of rain.*
on one's account, for one's sake: *Don't wait on my account; I may be late.*
take into account, to make allowance for; consider: *You must take into account the wishes of all the class in planning a picnic.*
ac·count·ant (ə koun′tənt), a person who examines or manages business accounts. *noun.*
ac·count·ing (ə koun′ting), the method or practice of keeping and analyzing business accounts. *noun.*
ac·cu·mu·late (ə kyü′myə lāt), to pile up; collect: *Dust and cobwebs had accumulated in the empty house. verb,* **ac·cu·mu·lates, ac·cu·mu·lat·ed, ac·cu·mu·lat·ing.**
ac·cu·mu·la·tion (ə kyü′myə lā′shən), **1** material collected; mass: *Their accumulation of old papers filled the attic.* **2** a collecting: *The accumulation of useful knowledge is one result of reading. noun.*
ac·cu·ra·cy (ak′yər ə sē), exactness; correctness; being without errors or mistakes: *This watch is noted for its accuracy. noun.*
ac·cu·rate (ak′yər it), exactly right; correct: *You must be accurate in arithmetic. An airplane pilot must have an accurate watch. adjective.*
ac·cu·sa·tion (ak′yə zā′shən), a charge of doing something bad: *The accusation against them was that they had cheated on the exam. noun.*
ac·cuse (ə kyüz′), to charge with doing something bad: *The driver was accused of speeding. verb,* **ac·cus·es, ac·cused, ac·cus·ing.**
ac·cus·er (ə kyü′zər), a person who accuses another. *noun.*
ac·cus·tom (ə kus′təm), to make familiar by use or habit: *You can accustom yourself to almost any kind of food. verb.*
ac·cus·tomed (ə kus′təmd), usual: *By Monday I was well again and was back in my accustomed seat in class. adjective.*
accustomed to, used to; in the habit of: *I am accustomed to getting up early.*
ace (ās), **1** a playing card with a single large heart, club, spade, or diamond in the middle. It is the highest card in most card games. **2** a person who is an expert at something: *She is an ace at baseball.* **3** very skilled; expert: *He is an ace mechanic.* **1,2** *noun,* **3** *adjective.*

a hat	i it	oi oil	ch child	a in about
ā age	ī ice	ou out	ng long	e in taken
ä far	o hot	u cup	sh she	ə = i in pencil
e let	ō open	u̇ put	th thin	o in lemon
ē equal	ô order	ü rule	ᴛʜ then	u in circus
ėr term			zh measure	

ache (āk), **1** a continuous pain: *My cousin ate too much candy and got a stomach ache.* **2** to suffer continuous pain; be in pain; hurt: *My arm aches.* **3** to be eager; wish very much: *During the hot days of August we all ached to go swimming.* **1** *noun,* **2,3** *verb,* **aches, ached, ach·ing.**
a·chieve (ə chēv′), **1** to do; accomplish: *Did you achieve all that you expected to?* **2** to reach by one's own efforts: *She achieved fame as a swimmer. verb,* **a·chieves, a·chieved, a·chiev·ing.**
a·chieve·ment (ə chēv′mənt), **1** a thing achieved; some plan or action carried out with courage or with unusual ability. **2** an achieving: *the achievement of good grades, the achievement of success. noun.*

achievement (definition 1)
Landing astronauts on the moon was a great **achievement.**

ac·id (as′id), **1** a chemical substance that unites with a base to form a salt. The water solution of an acid turns blue litmus paper red. **2** sour; sharp or biting to the taste: *Lemons are an acid fruit.* **3** sharp in manner or temper: *My teacher made an acid comment about my frequent tardiness.* **1** *noun,* **2,3** *adjective.*
acid rain, rain containing small amounts of certain acids, caused by the burning of fuels such as oil and coal.
ac·knowl·edge (ak nol′ij), **1** to admit to be true: *He acknowledges his own faults.* **2** to recognize the authority or claims of; accept: *Everyone in the chorus acknowledged the twins to be the best singers.* **3** to make known that one has received a favor, service, or message: *She acknowledged the*

gift with a pleasant letter. verb, **ac·knowl·edg·es, ac·knowl·edged, ac·knowl·edg·ing.**

ac·knowl·edg·ment (ak nol′ij mənt), **1** something given or done to show that one has received a favor, service, or message: *The winner waved in acknowledgment of the cheers.* **2** an admitting that something is true: *I made acknowledgment of my mistake. noun.*

ac·ne (ak′nē), a skin disease in which the oil glands in the skin become clogged, sore, and swollen. It often causes pimples. *noun.*

a·corn (ā′kôrn), the nut of an oak tree. *noun.*

ac·quaint (ə kwānt′), to make aware; let know; inform: *Let me acquaint you with the work we do here. verb.*

be acquainted with, to be familiar with or know: *I have heard about your friend, but I am not acquainted with him.*

ac·quaint·ance (ə kwān′təns), **1** a person known to you, but not a close friend: *We have many acquaintances in our neighborhood.* **2** a knowledge of something gained from experience: *I have some acquaintance with French, but I do not know it well. noun.*

ac·quire (ə kwīr′), to gain or get as one's own; get: *I acquired a strong liking for sports at camp. verb,* **ac·quires, ac·quired, ac·quir·ing.**

ac·qui·si·tion (ak′wə zish′ən), **1** the act of acquiring or getting as one's own: *He spent hundreds of hours in the acquisition of skill at the piano.* **2** something acquired or gained: *The museum's new acquisitions included two very old vases. noun.*

ac·quit (ə kwit′), to declare not guilty: *Both of the prisoners accused of the robbery were acquitted. verb,* **ac·quits, ac·quit·ted, ac·quit·ting.**

acquit oneself, to do one's part; behave: *You acquitted yourself well during the game.*

a·cre (ā′kər), a unit of area equal to 160 square rods or 43,560 square feet. Land is measured in acres. *noun.*

acre—An acre is smaller than a football field. The green part of this football field is an **acre.**

a·cre·age (ā′kər ij), a number of acres: *The acreage of this park is over 800. noun.*

ac·rid (ak′rid), sharp, bitter, or stinging: *Smoke from a bonfire feels acrid when you breathe it in. The quarrelsome man made acrid comments. adjective.*

ac·ro·bat (ak′rə bat), a person who can swing on a trapeze, turn handsprings, walk a tightrope, or do other feats of bodily skill and strength. *noun.*

ac·ro·bat·ic (ak′rə bat′ik), of or like an acrobat: *He flipped backward with acrobatic skill. adjective.*

a·cross (ə krôs′), **1** from one side to the other of;

over: *The cat walked across the street.* **2** from one side to the other: *What is the distance across?* **3** on the other side of; beyond: *The woods are across the river.* **1,3** *preposition,* **2** *adverb.*

act (akt), **1** something done; deed: *Sharing the candy with your friends was a generous act.* **2** doing: *I was caught in the act of hiding the presents.* **3** to do something: *The firemen acted promptly and saved the burning house.* **4** to have effect: *The medicine failed to act.* **5** to behave: *I'm sorry I acted badly in school today.* **6** to perform on the stage, in motion pictures, on television, or over the radio; play a part: *He acts the part of a doctor in a TV series.* **7** a main division in a play or opera: *This play has three acts.* **8** one of several performances on a program: *We stayed to see the trained dog's act.* **9** a law. An act of Congress is a bill that has been passed by Congress. **10** a false display; pretending: *He's not really angry; it's just an act.* **1,2,7-10** *noun,* **3-6** *verb.*

act on, 1 to follow; obey: *I will act on your suggestion.* **2** to have an effect or influence on: *Yeast acted on the dough and made it rise.*

act up, to behave badly: *The children began to act up when the teacher left the room.*

ac·tion (ak′shən), **1** doing something: *The quick action of the firemen saved the building from being burned down.* **2** something done; act: *Finding the lost dog's owner was a kind action.* **3** a way of working: *A child can push our lawn mower, because it has such an easy action.* **4** a battle; part of a battle: *My uncle was wounded in action.* **5 actions,** conduct or behavior: *Her actions revealed her thoughtfulness. noun.*

ac·ti·vate (ak′tə vāt), to make active; cause to act: *To activate the alarm, you just push this button. verb,* **ac·ti·vates, ac·ti·vat·ed, ac·ti·vat·ing.**

ac·tive (ak′tiv), **1** showing much action; moving rather quickly much of the time; lively: *Most children are more active than grown people.* **2** acting; working: *An active volcano may erupt at any time. adjective.*

ac·tiv·i·ty (ak tiv′ə tē), **1** a being active; use of power; movement: *Children engage in a good deal of physical activity.* **2** an action: *The activities of groups of interested citizens have brought about many new laws.* **3** a thing to do: *Jogging is a popular outdoor activity. noun, plural* **ac·tiv·i·ties.**

ac·tor (ak′tər), a person who acts on the stage, in motion pictures, on television, or over the radio. *noun.*

ac·tress (ak′tris), a woman or girl who acts on the stage, in motion pictures, on television, or over the radio. *noun, plural* **ac·tress·es.**

ac·tu·al (ak′chü əl), real; existing as a fact: *What he told us was not a dream but an actual happening. adjective.*

ac·tu·al·ly (ak′chü ə lē), really; in fact: *Are you actually going to Europe? adverb.*

a·cute (ə kyüt′), **1** sharp and severe: *A toothache can cause acute pain.* **2** keen; sharp: *Dogs have an acute sense of smell. adjective.*

6

ACUTE ANGLE   RIGHT ANGLE

a hat	i it	oi oil	ch child	⌈ a in about
ā age	ī ice	ou out	ng long	e in taken
ä far	o hot	u cup	sh she	ə = ⎨ i in pencil
e let	ō open	u̇ put	th thin	o in lemon
ē equal	ô order	ü rule	ŦH then	⌊ u in circus
ėr term			zh measure	

acute angle, an angle less than a right angle.

ad (ad), an advertisement. *noun.*

A.D., after the birth of Christ. A.D. 100 is 100 years after the birth of Christ.

[The abbreviation A.D. stands for the Latin words *Anno Domini,* meaning "in the year of the Lord."]

ad·a·mant (ad′ə mənt), not willing to give in; firm; unyielding: *He was adamant in his refusal to give up. adjective.*

Ad·am's ap·ple (ad′əmz ap′əl), the slight lump in the front of a person's neck. It is formed by tough, elastic tissue in the upper end of the windpipe.

a·dapt (ə dapt′), to change to fit different conditions; adjust: *The children adapted the barn for use by the club. Polar bears are well adapted for living in cold climates. verb.*

a·dapt·a·ble (ə dap′tə bəl), easily changed or changing easily to fit different conditions: *I have an adaptable schedule; I can see you at any time. She is an adaptable person. adjective.*

ad·ap·ta·tion (ad′ap tā′shən), **1** a changing to fit different conditions: *She made a good adaptation to her new school. Adaptation is a way that a species can survive in new environments.* **2** something made by changing to fit different conditions: *A motion picture is often an adaptation of a novel. noun.*

add (ad), **1** to find the sum of: *Add 3 and 4 and you have 7.* **2** to say further; go on to say or write: *She said good-by and added that she had had a pleasant visit.* **3** to join one thing to another: *Add a stone to the pile. verb.*

add to, to make greater: *The fine day added to our pleasure.*

add up, to make the correct total: *These figures don't add up.*

add up to, to amount to: *What do your sales add up to?*

ad·dend (ad′end *or* ə dend′), a number to be added to another: *In 2 + 3 + 4 = 9, the addends are 2, 3, and 4. noun.*

ad·der (ad′ər), a kind of snake. The African and European adders are poisonous; the North American adder is not. *noun.*

ad·dict (ad′ikt), a person who is a slave to a habit: *A drug addict finds it almost impossible to stop using drugs. noun.*

ad·dict·ed (ə dik′tid), made a slave by a habit or by regular use: *People addicted to alcohol need help to stop drinking. adjective.*

ad·dic·tion (ə dik′shən), the condition of being a slave to a habit: *She spoke about the harmful effects of drug addiction. noun.*

ad·dic·tive (ə dik′tiv), causing or tending to cause addiction: *Alcohol can be addictive. adjective.*

ad·di·tion (ə dish′ən), **1** the operation of adding one number to another: *2 + 3 = 5 is a simple addition.* **2** the adding of one thing to another: *The addition of flour will thicken gravy.* **3** a thing added: *Cream is a tasty addition to many desserts.* **4** a part added to a building: *We hope to put on a new addition. noun.*

in addition or **in addition to,** besides: *In addition to her work in school, our teacher gives music lessons after school hours.*

ad·di·tion·al (ə dish′ə nəl), extra; more: *Can you give me the additional help I need? adjective.*

ad·di·tive (ad′ə tiv), a substance added to another substance to keep it from spoiling or make it more effective. *noun.*

ad·dress (ə dres′; *also* ad′res *for 3*), **1** a speech, especially one given to a large audience: *The President gave an address to the nation over television.* **2** to speak to or write to: *The king was addressed as "Your Majesty."* **3** the place to which mail is directed: *Write your name and address on this envelope.* **4** to write on an envelope or package where it is to be sent: *Please address this letter for me.* 1,3 *noun, plural* **ad·dress·es;** 2,4 *verb.*

adder
This African adder is about 5½ feet (1½ meters) long.

ad·e·noids (ad′n oidz), the growths in the upper part of the throat, just back of the nose. Adenoids can swell up and make breathing and speaking difficult. *noun plural.*

adept
This woman is **adept** at carrying jugs of water on her head.

a·dept (ə dept′), very skillful; expert. *adjective.*

ad·e·quate (ad′ə kwit), enough; sufficient; as much as is needed: *An adequate diet includes a variety of foods. adjective.*

ad·here (ad hir′), to stick tight: *Mud adheres to your shoes. He adhered to his plan even though others thought it foolish. verb,* **ad·heres, ad·hered, ad·her·ing.**

ad·he·sive (ad hē′siv), **1** glue, paste, or other substance for sticking things together. **2** holding tight; sticky: *I put an adhesive label on the package.* **1** *noun,* **2** *adjective.*

adhesive tape, a strip of cloth or plastic that is sticky on one side, used to hold bandages in place.

a·di·os (ä′dē ōs′ *or* ad′ē ōs′), good-by. *interjection, noun.*

ad·ja·cent (ə jā′snt), near; adjoining; next: *The house adjacent to ours has been sold. adjective.*

ad·jec·tive (aj′ik tiv), a word that describes more fully a person, place, or thing. In "a tiny brook," "The day is warm," "great happiness," and "this pencil," *tiny, warm, great,* and *this* are adjectives. *noun.*

ad·join (ə join′), to be next to; be close to; be side by side: *His yard adjoins ours. verb.*

ad·journ (ə jėrn′), to put off until a later time; stop for a time: *The meeting was adjourned until two o'clock. verb.*

ad·just (ə just′), **1** to arrange; set just right; change to make fit: *A music stand can be adjusted to different heights.* **2** to get used to; become accustomed to: *Some wild animals never adjust to life in the zoo. verb.*

ad·just·a·ble (ə jus′tə bəl), able to be adjusted: *This adjustable lamp can be placed in many different positions. adjective.*

ad·just·ment (ə just′mənt), **1** a changing to make fit; means of setting right: *All TVs have an adjustment for volume control.* **2** the act of getting used to something: *They were pleased with their daughter's adjustment to the new school. noun.*

ad·lib (ad lib′), to make up as one goes along: *The actor forgot some of his lines and had to adlib his part. verb,* **ad·libs, ad·libbed, ad·lib·bing.**

ad·min·is·ter (ad min′ə stər), **1** to manage; direct: *The mayor administers the city government.* **2** to give out; apply: *The coach administered first aid to the injured player. Judges administer justice and punishment. verb.*

ad·min·is·tra·tion (ad min′ə strā′shən), **1** the managing of a business or an office; management: *The administration of a big business requires skill in dealing with people.* **2** the group of persons in charge: *The principal and teachers are part of the administration of the school.* **3 the Administration,** the people in charge of running the government of the United States. The Administration includes the President, the cabinet appointed by the President, and the departments of the government headed by cabinet members. **4** the time during which a government holds office: *Franklin D. Roosevelt's administration lasted longer than that of any other president. noun.*

ad·min·is·tra·tor (ad min′ə strā′tər), a person who administers; manager. *noun.*

ad·mir·a·ble (ad′mər ə bəl), worth admiring; very good; excellent: *The doctor took admirable care of the patient. adjective.*

ad·mir·al (ad′mər əl), an officer having the highest rank in the navy. *noun.*

ad·mi·ra·tion (ad′mə rā′shən), a feeling of wonder, pleasure, and approval: *I expressed my admiration for the artist's beautiful painting. noun.*

ad·mire (ad mīr′), **1** to look at or think of with wonder, pleasure, and approval: *We all admired the beautiful painting.* **2** to think highly of; respect: *Everyone admired the explorer's courage. verb,* **ad·mires, ad·mired, ad·mir·ing.**

ad·mir·er (ad mī′rer), a person who thinks highly of someone or something. *noun.*

ad·mir·ing·ly (ad mī′ring lē), with admiration: *I looked at the new bicycle admiringly. adverb.*

ad·mis·sion (ad mish′ən), **1** an allowing to enter: *His admission into the hospital was delayed for lack of beds.* **2** the price paid for the right to enter: *Admission to the show is one dollar.* **3** an admitting to be true; confession: *Their admission that they were to blame kept others from being punished. noun.*

ad·mit (ad mit′), **1** to say something is real or true; confess; acknowledge: *I admit now that I made a mistake.* **2** to allow to enter: *She was admitted to law school. verb,* **ad·mits, ad·mit·ted, ad·mit·ting.**

ad·mit·tance (ad mit′ns), the right to enter; permission to enter: *There is no admittance to the park after 10 p.m. noun.*

ad·mon·ish (ad mon′ish), to warn or advise about a fault in order to encourage improvement: *The policeman admonished him not to drive so fast. The teacher admonished the students for their careless work. verb.*

a·do (ə dü′), action; stir; fuss: *There was much ado about the party by all the family. noun.*

adobe (definition 2)—adobe buildings and ovens

a hat	i it	oi oil	ch child	a in about
ā age	ī ice	ou out	ng long	e in taken
ä far	o hot	u cup	sh she	ə = i in pencil
e let	ō open	u̇ put	th thin	o in lemon
ē equal	ô order	ü rule	ᴛʜ then	u in circus
ėr term			zh measure	

A

a·do·be (ə dō′bē), **1** a brick made of clay baked in the sun. **2** built or made of adobe: *Our friends in Arizona live in an adobe house.* **3** a building made of adobe. **1,3** *noun,* **2** *adjective.*

ad·o·les·cence (ad′l es′ns), the period of growth from childhood to adulthood; youth. *noun.*

ad·o·les·cent (ad′l es′nt), a person growing up from childhood to adulthood, especially a person from about 12 to about 20 years of age. *noun.*

a·dopt (ə dopt′), **1** to take for your own or as your own choice: *I liked your idea and adopted it.* **2** to take a child of other parents and bring up as one's own: *The judge permitted the family to adopt the child.* **3** to accept or approve: *The members of the club voted to adopt the new rules. verb.*

a·dop·tion (ə dop′shən), **1** an adopting: *Our club voted for the adoption of some new rules.* **2** a being adopted: *The children were offered for adoption. noun.*

a·dor·a·ble (ə dôr′ə bəl), attractive; delightful: *What an adorable kitten! adjective.*

ad·o·ra·tion (ad′ə rā′shən), **1** the highest love and admiration. **2** worship. *noun.*

a·dore (ə dôr′), **1** to love and admire very greatly: *She adores her mother.* **2** to like very much: *I just adored that movie!* **3** to worship: *"O! Come, let us adore Him," sang the choir. verb,* **a·dores, a·dored, a·dor·ing.**

a·dorn (ə dôrn′), to add beauty to; decorate. *verb.*

a·drift (ə drift′), drifting; floating without being guided: *During the storm our boat was adrift on the lake. adjective.*

a·droit (ə droit′), skillful: *Monkeys are adroit climbers. A good teacher is adroit in asking questions. adjective.*

a·dult (ə dult′ *or* ad′ult), **1** full-grown; grown-up; having full size and strength: *an adult person.* **2** a grown-up person. **3** a living thing grown to full size and strength. **1** *adjective,* **2,3** *noun.*

a·dult·hood (ə dult′hu̇d), the condition or time of being an adult. *noun.*

ad·vance (ad vans′), **1** to move forward: *The angry crowd advanced toward the building.* **2** a forward movement; progress: *The army's advance was very slow.* **3** to help forward: *The President's speech advanced the cause of peace.* **4** to promote: *The colonel advanced him from lieutenant to captain.* **5** to pay money before it is due: *The company advanced the salesman money for expenses.* **6** money paid before it is due: *May I have an advance on next week's allowance?* **7 advances,** a personal approach made to gain something: *My sister made the first advances toward making up our quarrel.* **1,3-5** *verb,* **ad·vanc·es, ad·vanced, ad·vanc·ing; 2,6,7** *noun.*

in advance, ahead of time: *I paid for my ticket in advance.*

ad·vanced (ad vanst′), **1** ahead of most others in knowledge, skill, or progress: *an advanced class in science, an advanced aircraft design.* **2** very old: *Her grandmother lived to the advanced age of ninety years. adjective.*

ad·vance·ment (ad vans′mənt), **1** a moving forward; improvement: *Advancements in the science of medicine have saved many lives.* **2** promotion: *Good work won her advancement to a higher position. noun.*

ad·van·tage (ad van′tij), anything that is a benefit or a help in getting something wanted: *He had the advantage of a good education. noun.*

take advantage of, 1 to use to help or benefit oneself: *We took advantage of the beautiful day by working in our garden.* **2** to use unfairly: *He was so good-natured that people often took advantage of him.*

ad·van·ta·geous (ad′vən tā′jəs), favorable;

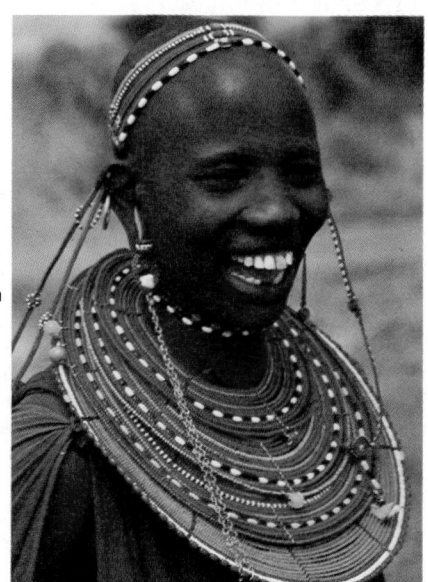

adorn
an African woman
adorned with
bead jewelry

helpful: *The agreement was advantageous to both of us. adjective.*

ad·ven·ture (ad ven′chər), **1** an unusual or exciting experience: *The trip to Alaska was quite an adventure for her.* **2** a bold and difficult undertaking, usually exciting and somewhat dangerous: *Sailing across the Pacific on a raft was a daring adventure. noun.*

ad·ven·tur·er (ad ven′chər ər), a person who has or seeks adventures. *noun.*

ad·ven·tur·ous (ad ven′chər əs), **1** fond of adventures; ready to take risks: *The adventurous family sailed around the world in a small boat.* **2** full of danger: *Sailing around the world in a small boat is an adventurous thing to do. adjective.*

ad·verb (ad′vėrb′), a word that tells how, when, or where something happens. In "He walked slowly," "He came late," "I saw her there," and "She sings well," *slowly, late, there,* and *well* are adverbs. Adverbs also tell how much or how little is meant. In "This soup is very good" and "I am rather tired," *very* and *rather* are adverbs. *noun.*

ad·ver·sar·y (ad′vər ser′ē), a person or group on the other side in a contest or fight; opponent or enemy: *The two football teams were adversaries for the championship. The countries were adversaries during the war. noun, plural* **ad·ver·sar·ies.**

ad·verse (ad′vėrs′ *or* ad vėrs′), **1** unfriendly in purpose; hostile: *Their adverse criticism discouraged me.* **2** unfavorable; harmful: *A poor diet and lack of sleep had an adverse effect on his health. adjective.*

ad·ver·si·ty (ad vėr′sə tē), misfortune; hardship; distress: *The pioneers faced many adversities. noun, plural* **ad·ver·si·ties.**

ad·ver·tise (ad′vər tīz), **1** to give public notice of; announce: *Stores often advertise in newspapers.* **2** to ask for by public notice: *He advertised for a job. verb,* **ad·ver·tis·es, ad·ver·tised, ad·ver·tis·ing.**

ad·ver·tise·ment (ad′vər tīz′mənt *or* ad vėr′tis mənt), a public announcement; printed notice: *The furniture store has an advertisement in the newspaper of a special sale. noun.*

ad·vice (ad vīs′), an opinion about what should be done: *My advice is that you study more. noun.*

ad·vis·a·ble (ad vī′zə bəl), wise; sensible; suitable: *It is not advisable for you to go to school while you are still sick. adjective.*

ad·vise (ad vīz′), **1** to give advice to: *He advised me to put my money in the bank.* **2** to inform: *We were advised that a storm was approaching, so we didn't go sailing. verb,* **ad·vis·es, ad·vised, ad·vis·ing.**

ad·vis·er *or* **ad·vi·sor** (ad vī′zər), a person who gives advice. *noun.*

ad·vo·cate (ad′və kāt *for 1;* ad′və kit *for 2*), **1** to speak in favor of; recommend publicly; support: *The mayor advocates using the land along the river for a public park.* **2** a person who speaks in favor of something; supporter: *She is an advocate of equal rights for all people.* 1 *verb,* **ad·vo·cates, ad·vo·cat·ed, ad·vo·cat·ing;** 2 *noun.*

adz

adz *or* **adze** (adz), a tool somewhat like an ax, used for shaping heavy timbers. The blade is set across the end of the handle and curves inward. *noun, plural* **adz·es.**

aer·i·al (er′ē əl *or* ar′ē əl), **1** the antenna of a radio or television set. **2** in or from the air: *This is an aerial photograph of the city.* 1 *noun,* 2 *adjective.*

aer·o·bics (er′ō′biks *or* ar′ō′biks), exercises that cause the body to use more oxygen and improve the heart, lungs, and circulation. Walking, jogging, swimming, and riding a bicycle are **aerobic exercises** if they are done steadily for twenty or thirty minutes or more. *noun.*

aer·o·nau·tics (er′ə nô′tiks *or* ar′ə nô′tiks), the science that deals with the design, manufacture, and operation of aircraft. *noun.*

aer·o·sol (er′ə sol *or* ar′ə sol), **1** very small particles of a solid or a liquid floating in air or in some other gas. Smoke and fog are aerosols. **2** a product that is mixed with gas and packed under pressure so that it comes out of its can as a spray. *noun.*

aer·o·space (er′ō spās *or* ar′ō spās), the earth's atmosphere and the space beyond it, especially the space in which rockets, satellites, and other spacecraft operate. *noun.*

a·far (ə fär′). **from afar,** from far off; from a distance: *I saw them from afar. adverb.*

af·fa·ble (af′ə bəl), easy to talk to; courteous and pleasant; friendly: *She is an affable person, well-liked by everyone. adjective.*

af·fair (ə fer′ *or* ə far′), **1** a thing to do; job; business: *Their lawyer looked after their affairs while they were gone.* **2** any thing, matter, or happening: *The costume party was a delightful affair. noun.*

af·fect[1] (ə fekt′), **1** to produce a result on; have an effect on; influence: *The small amount of rain last year affected the growth of crops.* **2** to touch the heart of; stir the feelings of: *The sad story affected me deeply. verb.*

af·fect[2] (ə fekt′), to pretend to have or feel: *She affected ignorance of the fight, but we knew that she had seen it. verb.*

a hat	i it	oi oil	ch child	a in about
ā age	ī ice	ou out	ng long	e in taken
ä far	o hot	u cup	sh she	ə = { i in pencil
e let	ō open	u̇ put	th thin	o in lemon
ē equal	ô order	ü rule	₮H then	u in circus
ėr term			zh measure	

affection
She showed her
affection for her
baby brother.

af·fec·tion (ə fek′shən), a friendly feeling; fondness; love. *noun.*

af·fec·tion·ate (ə fek′shə nit), loving; fond; showing affection: *an affectionate hug. adjective.*

af·firm (ə fėrm′), to say firmly; declare to be true; assert: *The prisoner affirmed his innocence. verb.*

af·firm·a·tive (ə fėr′mə tiv), saying yes; affirming: *Her answer to my question was affirmative. adjective.*

af·fix (ə fiks′ *for 1;* af′iks *for 2*), **1** to stick on; fasten; attach: *She affixed a stamp to the envelope.* **2** a sound or group of sounds added to a word to change its meaning or use. Affixes are either prefixes like *un-* and *re-* or suffixes like *-ly, -ness, -s,* or *-ed.* **1** *verb,* **2** *noun, plural* **af·fix·es.**

af·flict (ə flikt′), to cause pain to; trouble very much; distress: *She is afflicted with arthritis. verb.*

af·flic·tion (ə flik′shən), **1** a condition of pain, trouble, or distress; misery: *The country suffered from the affliction of war.* **2** a cause of pain, trouble, or distress; misfortune: *Blindness is an affliction. noun.*

af·flu·ent (af′lü ənt), having wealth; rich: *In that affluent community most of the homes have a swimming pool. adjective.*

af·ford (ə fôrd′), **1** to have the money, means, or time: *Can we afford to buy a new car? He cannot afford to waste time.* **2** to give; yield: *Reading this story will afford pleasure. verb.*

af·front (ə frunt′), **1** a deliberate insult: *To be called a coward is an affront.* **2** to insult deliberately: *I was affronted when they called me names.* **1** *noun,* **2** *verb.*

Af·ghan·i·stan (af gan′ə stan), a country in southwestern Asia. *noun.*

a·field (ə fēld′), away; away from home: *She wandered far afield in foreign lands. adverb.*

a·fire (ə fīr′), on fire; burning: *The lightning struck the building and set it afire. adverb, adjective.*

a·flame (ə flām′), in flames; on fire. *adverb, adjective.*

a·float (ə flōt′), floating on the water or in the air: *It took two of us to get the heavy rowboat afloat. adverb, adjective.*

a·foot (ə fu̇t′), **1** on foot; by walking: *The explorers abandoned their jeep and traveled afoot through the jungle.* **2** going on; in progress: *Dinner preparations were afoot in the kitchen. adverb, adjective.*

a·fraid (ə frād′), **1** frightened; feeling fear: *afraid of the dark, afraid of heights.* **2** sorry to have to say: *I'm afraid you are wrong about that. adjective.*

Af·ri·ca (af′rə kə), the continent south of Europe and east of the Atlantic Ocean. Only one other continent, Asia, is larger than Africa. Egypt and Tanzania are countries in Africa. *noun.*

Af·ri·can (af′rə kən), **1** of Africa; having something to do with Africa or its people; from Africa. **2** a person born or living in Africa. **1** *adjective,* **2** *noun.*

Af·ri·can-A·mer·i·can (af′rə kən ə mer′ə kən), **1** an American of African descent. **2** of or having something to do with Americans of African descent. **1** *noun,* **2** *adjective.*

African violet, a tropical plant with violet, white, or pink flowers. It is often grown as a house plant.

African violet

Af·ro (af′rō), a bushy hairdo like that worn in parts of Africa. *noun.*

Af·ro-A·mer·i·can (af′rō ə mer′ə kən), African-American. *noun, adjective.*

aft (aft), at or toward the rear of a ship, boat, or aircraft. *adverb.*

af·ter (af′tər), **1** later in time than: *After dinner we can go.* **2** following: *I ran so hard I panted for five minutes after. Day after day I waited for a letter from my friend.* **3** behind: *You come after me in the line. Jill came tumbling after.* **4** in search of; in pursuit of: *The dog ran after the rabbit.* **5** later than

aftermath | agitate

the time that: *After he goes, we shall eat.*
1-4 *preposition,* 2,3 *adverb,* 5 *conjunction.*

af·ter·math (af′tər math), a result, especially of something destructive: *The aftermath of the war was hunger and disease. noun.*

af·ter·noon (af′tər nün′), the part of the day between noon and evening. *noun.*

af·ter·thought (af′tər thôt′), a second or later thought or explanation: *I ordered toast, and as an afterthought asked for it without butter. noun.*

af·ter·ward (af′tər wərd), afterwards; later. *adverb.*

af·ter·wards (af′tər wərdz), later: *The bud was small at first, but afterwards it became a large flower. adverb.*

a·gain (ə gen′), another time; once more: *Come again to play. Say that again. adverb.*

a·gainst (ə genst′), 1 in opposition to: *Our team will play against yours. It is against the rules of the game.* 2 upon or toward; in the opposite direction to: *Rain beat against the window. We sailed against the wind.* 3 in contact with: *The ladder is leaning against the tree.* 4 in preparation for: *Squirrels store up nuts against the winter.* 5 so as to defend or protect from: *An umbrella is protection against rain. preposition.*

ag·ate (ag′it), 1 a kind of quartz with colored stripes or cloudy colors. 2 a marble used in games that looks like agate. *noun.*

agate (definition 1)
a polished **agate**

age (āj), 1 time of life: *His age is ten.* 2 the length of life: *Turtles live to a great age.* 3 a particular period of life: *She has reached old age.* 4 a period in history: *We live in the age of jet planes.* 5 **ages,** a long time: *I haven't seen you for ages!* 6 to grow old: *He is aging fast.* 7 to make old: *Worry can age a person.* 1-5 *noun,* 6,7 *verb,* **ag·es, aged, ag·ing** or **age·ing.**
of age, at the time of life when a person is considered legally an adult, usually 18 years old.

a·ged (ā′jid *for 1;* ājd *for 2*), 1 old; having lived a long time: *an aged woman.* 2 of the age of: *Children aged six must go to school. adjective.*

a·gen·cy (ā′jən sē), 1 the office or business of some person or company that acts for another: *An agency rented our house for us. Employment agencies help people to get jobs.* 2 a special department of the government: *The agency which deals with pollution in the United States is the*

Environmental Protection Agency. *noun, plural* **a·gen·cies.**

a·gent (ā′jənt), 1 a person or company that acts for another: *She is a real estate agent and can help you sell your house.* 2 something that produces an effect by its action: *Yeast is an agent that causes bread to rise. noun.*

ag·gra·vate (ag′rə vāt), 1 to make worse; make more severe: *His headache was aggravated by all the noise.* 2 to annoy; irritate: *She aggravated me by asking so many questions. verb,* **ag·gra·vates, ag·gra·vat·ed, ag·gra·vat·ing.**

ag·gre·gate (ag′rə git *for 1;* ag′rə gāt *for 2*), 1 a total: *The aggregate of all the gifts was over $100.* 2 to amount to: *The money collected will aggregate $1000.* 1 *noun,* 2 *verb,* **ag·gre·gates, ag·gre·gat·ed, ag·gre·gat·ing.**

ag·gres·sion (ə gresh′ən), the first step in an attack or a quarrel: *A country that sends its army to seize another country is guilty of aggression. noun.*

ag·gres·sive (ə gres′iv), 1 taking the first step in an attack or a quarrel; attacking: *The aggressive nation invaded two neighboring countries.* 2 forceful; energetic: *The police are waging an aggressive campaign against driving too fast. adjective.*

ag·gres·sor (ə gres′ər), one that begins an attack or a quarrel, especially a nation that starts a war. *noun.*

a·ghast (ə gast′), struck with surprise or horror: *I was aghast when I saw the destruction caused by the earthquake. adjective.*

ag·ile (aj′əl), able to move quickly and easily; nimble: *An acrobat has to be agile. You need an agile mind to solve puzzles. adjective.*

agile dancers

a·gil·i·ty (ə jil′ə tē), the ability to move quickly and easily: *He has the agility of a monkey. noun.*

ag·i·tate (aj′ə tāt), 1 to move or shake violently: *A sudden wind agitated the surface of the river.* 2 to disturb or upset very much: *He was agitated by the*

12

news of his friend's serious illness. verb, **ag·i·tates, ag·i·tat·ed, ag·i·tat·ing.**

ag·i·ta·tion (aj′ə tā′shən), **1** a violent moving or shaking: _The agitation of the sea almost turned over the little boat._ **2** a disturbed, upset, or troubled condition: _Because of her agitation, she could not sleep. noun._

ag·i·ta·tor (aj′ə tā′tər), **1** a person who stirs up public feeling for or against something. **2** a device or machine for shaking or stirring. Some washing machines have agitators. _noun._

a·glow (ə glō′), shining with light or color: _The Christmas tree was aglow with colored lights and tinsel. adjective._

a·go (ə gō′), **1** gone by; past: _I met her two years ago._ **2** in the past: _He lived here long ago._ **1** _adjective,_ **2** _adverb._

ag·o·niz·ing (ag′ə nī′zing), causing very great pain or suffering: _the agonizing loss of a child. adjective._

ag·o·ny (ag′ə nē), very great suffering of body or mind: _Nobody can stand for long the agony of a severe toothache. noun, plural_ **ag·o·nies.**

a·gree (ə grē′), **1** to have the same feeling or opinion: _We all agree on that subject. I agree that we should try to be more careful._ **2** to be in harmony; be the same as: _Your story agrees with mine._ **3** to say that one is willing; consent: _He agreed to go with us. verb,_ **a·grees, a·greed, a·gree·ing.**

agree with, to have a good effect on: _This food does not agree with me; it makes me sick._

a·gree·a·ble (ə grē′ə bəl), **1** pleasant; pleasing: _The boy had an agreeable manner._ **2** willing: _If she is agreeable, we can all meet tonight. adjective._

a·gree·ment (ə grē′mənt), **1** an understanding reached by two or more persons, groups of persons, or nations. Nations make treaties; certain persons make contracts. Both are agreements. **2** harmony in feeling or opinion: _There was perfect agreement between the two friends. noun._

ag·ri·cul·tur·al (ag′rə kul′chər əl), having something to do with farming; of agriculture: _The Middle West is an important agricultural region. adjective._

ag·ri·cul·ture (ag′rə kul′chər), farming; cultivating the soil to make crops grow; the raising of crops and farm animals. _noun._

a·ground (ə ground′), stranded on the shore or on the bottom in shallow water: _The ship ran aground and stuck in the sand. adverb, adjective._

ah (ä), an exclamation of pain, sorrow, regret, pity, admiration, surprise, joy, dislike, or contempt. _interjection._

a·ha (ä hä′), an exclamation of triumph, satisfaction, surprise, or joy. _interjection._

a·head (ə hed′), **1** in front; before: _Walk ahead of me. Road repairs ahead!_ **2** forward: _Go ahead with this work for another week._ **3** in advance: _He was ahead of his class in reading. adverb._

be ahead, to be winning: _Our team is ahead by 6 points._

a hat	i it	oi oil	ch child	(a in about
ā age	ī ice	ou out	ng long	e in taken
ä far	o hot	u cup	sh she	ə = { i in pencil
e let	ō open	u̇ put	th thin	o in lemon
ē equal	ô order	ü rule	ŦH then	(u in circus
ėr term			zh measure	

get ahead, to succeed: _I worked hard at my job in the hope that I would get ahead._

get ahead of, to do or be better than: _She worked hard and got ahead of the others in her class._

a·hoy (ə hoi′), a call used by sailors to attract attention. Sailors say, "Ship, ahoy!" when they call to a ship. _interjection._

aid (ād), **1** to give support to; help: _The Red Cross aids flood victims._ **2** help; assistance: _When my arm was broken, I could not dress without aid._ **3** a person or thing that helps; helper: _A dishwasher is an aid to housework._ **1** _verb,_ **2,3** _noun._

aide (ād), a helper; assistant: _a nurse's aide, a teacher's aide. noun._

ail (āl), **1** to be the matter with; trouble: _What ails the child?_ **2** to be ill; feel sick: _She has been ailing for a week. verb._

ai·le·ron (ā′lə ron′), a hinged, movable part on the rear edge of an airplane wing. It is used to balance the aircraft and to help it turn. _noun._

AILERON

AILERON

ail·ment (āl′mənt), an illness; sickness: _He has a serious heart ailment. noun._

aim (ām), **1** to point or direct something in order to hit: _She aimed carefully at the target._ **2** the act of pointing or directing at something: _She hit the target because her aim was good._ **3** to direct words or acts so as to influence a certain person or action: _The teacher's talk was aimed at the students who cheated on the test._ **4** to try: _He aimed to please his teachers._ **5** a purpose: _Her aim was to become a lawyer._ **1,3,4** _verb,_ **2,5** _noun._

aim·less (ām′lis), without purpose; pointless. _adjective._

ain't (ānt), **1** am not; is not. **2** are not. **3** have not; has not. Careful speakers and writers do not use _ain't._

air (er *or* ar), **1** the mixture of gases that surrounds the earth. Air has no smell, taste, or color. It consists of nitrogen, oxygen, hydrogen, and other gases. *We breathe air.* **2** the space overhead; sky: *Birds fly in the air.* **3** fresh air: *I opened the window to let some air into the stuffy room.* **4** to let fresh air in: *Open the windows and air the room.* **5** airline; airplane: *We traveled by air on our vacation.* **6** to make known: *Don't air your troubles too often.* **7** a simple melody or tune. **8** way; look; manner: *an air of importance.* **9** airs, unnatural or showy manners: *Your friends will laugh if you put on airs.* 1-3,5,7-9 *noun*, 4,6 *verb*.
off the air, not broadcasting: *We used to watch that show, but it's off the air now.*
on the air, broadcasting: *Is that radio show still on the air?*
air base, a headquarters and airfield for military aircraft.
air·borne (er′bôrn′ *or* ar′bôrn′), **1** off the ground: *Within seconds the plane was airborne.* **2** carried in aircraft: *airborne troops. adjective.*
air-con·di·tioned (er′kən dish′ənd *or* ar′kən dish′ənd), having air conditioning. *adjective.*
air conditioner, a device for the air conditioning of a building, room, car, or other place. Air conditioners usually cool the air and remove moisture and dust from it.
air conditioning, a means of controlling the temperature and humidity of air and of cleaning it.
air·craft (er′kraft′ *or* ar′kraft′), a machine for flying in the air. Airplanes, airships, helicopters, and balloons are aircraft. *noun, plural* **air·craft.**
air·field (er′fēld′ *or* ar′fēld′), the landing field of an airport. *noun.*
air force, the part of the armed forces that uses aircraft.
air·line (er′līn′ *or* ar′līn′), a company that carries passengers and freight by aircraft from one place to another. *noun.*
air·lin·er (er′lī′nər *or* ar′lī′nər), a large passenger airplane. *noun.*
air·mail (er′māl′ *or* ar′māl′), **1** mail sent by aircraft. **2** a system of sending mail by aircraft. *noun.*
air·man (er′mən *or* ar′mən), an enlisted man or woman of the lowest rank in the air force. *noun, plural* **air·men.**
air·plane (er′plān′ *or* ar′plān′), an aircraft heavier than air, that has wings and is driven by a propeller or jet engine. *noun.*
air pocket, a current or condition in the air which causes an airplane to drop suddenly.
air·port (er′pôrt′ *or* ar′pôrt′), an area used by aircraft to land and take off. An airport has buildings for passengers and for keeping and repairing aircraft. *noun.*
air pressure, the pressure caused by the weight of the air. Although we do not feel it, the air presses down on everything on earth all the time.
air sac, one of the tiny pouches in the lungs.

When you breathe, oxygen passes through the air sac into the blood and carbon dioxide is removed.
air·ship (er′ship′ *or* ar′ship′), a kind of balloon that can be steered; dirigible. An airship is filled with a gas that is lighter than air. *noun.*
air·sick (er′sik′ *or* ar′sik′), sick as a result of the motion of aircraft. *adjective.*
air·strip (er′strip′ *or* ar′strip′), a paved or cleared area on which aircraft land and take off. *noun.*
air·tight (er′tīt′ *or* ar′tīt′), **1** so tight that no air or other gases can get in or out: *The food was packed in airtight containers so it would not spoil.* **2** having no weak points open to attack: *She presented an airtight argument which convinced us she was right. adjective.*
air·y (er′ē *or* ar′ē), breezy; with air moving through it: *an airy room. adjective,* **air·i·er, air·i·est.**
aisle (īl), a passage between rows of something, such as seats in a theater, shelves in a library, or counters in a store. *noun.*
a·jar (ə jär′), slightly open: *Please leave the door ajar. adjective.*
AK, Alaska (used with postal Zip Code).
a·kim·bo (ə kim′bō), with the hands on the hips and the elbows bent outward. *adjective.*

akimbo
She stood with
her arms **akimbo.**

a·kin (ə kin′), **1** alike; similar: *His tastes in music seem akin to mine.* **2** belonging to the same family; related: *Your cousins are akin to you. adjective.*
AL, Alabama (used with postal Zip Code).
Ala., Alabama.
Al·a·bam·a (al′ə bam′ə), one of the south central states of the United States. *Abbreviation:* Ala. or AL *Capital:* Montgomery. *noun.*
[*Alabama* was named for an American Indian tribe that once lived in the area. The tribe's name came from Indian words meaning "I clear the thicket."]
à la mode or **a la mode** (ä′ lə mōd′ *or* al′ ə mōd′), served with ice cream: *pie à la mode.*
a·larm (ə lärm′), **1** sudden fear; excitement caused by fear of danger: *The deer darted off in alarm.* **2** to make afraid; frighten: *The breaking of a branch under my foot alarmed the deer.* **3** a warning of approaching danger: *The alarm went out that a tornado was approaching.* **4** a bell or other device that makes a noise to warn or waken people: *a fire alarm.* 1,3,4 *noun*, 2 *verb*.

alarm clock, a clock that can be set to ring or sound at a chosen time.

a·las (ə las′), a word expressing sorrow, grief, regret, pity, or dread. *interjection.*

Alas., Alaska.

A·las·ka (ə las′kə), one of the Pacific states of the United States, in the northwestern part of North America. *Abbreviation:* Alas. or AK *Capital:* Juneau. *noun.*
[*Alaska* got its name from a word used by people living on nearby islands. The word meant "mainland."]

Al·ba·ni·a (al bā′nē ə), a country in southeastern Europe. *noun.*

Al·ba·ny (ôl′bə nē), the capital of New York State. *noun.*

al·ba·tross (al′bə trôs), a very large sea bird that has webbed feet and can fly long distances. *noun, plural* **al·ba·tross·es.**
[*Albatross* comes from an Arabic word meaning "the sea eagle."]

Al·ber·ta (al bėr′tə), a province in western Canada. *Capital:* Edmonton. *noun.*

al·bum (al′bəm), **1** a book with blank pages for holding things like photographs, pictures, and stamps. **2** one or more phonograph records packaged together: *Have you heard that singer's new album? noun.*

al·co·hol (al′kə hôl), a colorless liquid in wine, beer, whiskey, gin, rum, and vodka. Alcohol can make people drunk. Alcohol in different forms is used in medicines, in manufacturing, and as a fuel. *noun.*

al·co·hol·ic (al′kə hô′lik), **1** of or containing alcohol: *Whiskey and gin are alcoholic liquors.* **2** a person who drinks too much alcoholic liquor. **1** *adjective,* **2** *noun.*

al·co·hol·ism (al′kə hô liz′əm), a disease in which too much alcoholic liquor is drunk. *noun.*

al·cove (al′kōv), a small room opening out of a larger room. *noun.*

al·der (ôl′dər), a tree or shrub somewhat like a birch. Alders usually grow in wet land. *noun.*

ale (āl), a strong beer made from malt and hops. *noun.*

a·lert (ə lėrt′), **1** watchful; wide-awake: *The dog was alert to every sound.* **2** a signal warning of an attack by approaching enemy aircraft, a hurricane, or other danger. **3** to make alert; warn: *The siren alerted the town that a tornado had been sighted.* **1** *adjective,* **2** *noun,* **3** *verb.*
on the alert, ready at any instant for what is coming; watchful: *A driver must be on the alert.*

al·fal·fa (al fal′fə), a plant with leaves like clover, deep roots, and bluish-purple flowers. Alfalfa is grown as food for horses and cattle. *noun,*

al·gae (al′jē), a group of living things, usually found in water, that can make their own food. Algae contain chlorophyll but lack true stems, roots, or leaves. Some algae can move about. Certain algae form scum on rocks; others, such as the seaweeds, are very large. *noun plural of* **al·ga** (al′gə).

a hat	i it	oi oil	ch child	⎧ a in about
ā age	ī ice	ou out	ng long	e in taken
ä far	o hot	u cup	sh she	ə = ⎨ i in pencil
e let	ō open	u̇ put	th thin	o in lemon
ē equal	ô order	ü rule	̵FH then	⎩ u in circus
ėr term			zh measure	

al·ge·bra (al′jə brə), the branch of mathematics that deals with the relations between quantities. Algebra uses letters as symbols that can stand for many different numbers. *noun.*

Al·ger·i·a (al jir′ē ə), a country in northern Africa. *noun.*

a·li·as (ā′lē əs), **1** a name other than a person's real name, used to hide who he or she is: *The spy's real name was Haines, but she went by the alias of Gray.* **2** otherwise called: *The police arrested a man named Jones, alias Brown.* **1** *noun, plural* **a·li·as·es;** **2** *adverb.*

al·i·bi (al′ə bī), **1** the claim that an accused person was somewhere else when a crime was committed: *The gang's alibi was that they were in another city when the bank was robbed.* **2** an excuse: *What is your alibi for failing to do your homework? noun, plural* **al·i·bis.**

al·ien (ā′lyən), **1** a person who is not a citizen of the country in which he or she lives. **2** of another country; foreign: *French is an alien language to Americans.* **3** entirely different; not in agreement; strange: *Cruelty is alien to his nature.* **1** *noun,* **2,3** *adjective.*

al·ien·ate (ā′lyə nāt), to make someone unfriendly, so that the person's feelings turn from fondness to indifference or dislike: *Her unkindness alienated me and ended our friendship. verb,* **al·ien·ates, al·ien·at·ed, al·ien·at·ing.**

a·light (ə līt′), **1** to get down; get off: *She alighted from the bus.* **2** to come down from the air; come down from flight: *The bird alighted on our windowsill. verb.*

a·lign (ə līn′), to bring into line; arrange in a straight line: *A mechanic aligned the front wheels of our car. verb.*

a·like (ə līk′), **1** in the same way: *She and her sister think alike.* **2** like one another; similar: *The children in that family look alike.* **1** *adverb,* **2** *adjective.*

al·i·men·tar·y ca·nal (al′ə men′tər ē kə nal′), the parts of the body through which food passes while it is being digested. The alimentary canal is a tube which begins at the mouth and ends where solid waste leaves the body.

al·i·mo·ny (al′ə mō′nē), the money paid in regular installments to a person's former wife or husband after a divorce. The amount of alimony is fixed by a court. *noun.*

a·live (ə līv′), **1** having life; living: *Was the snake alive or dead?* **2** active: *Although our team played badly in the first half of the game, we kept alive our hopes of winning. adjective.*
alive with, full of; swarming with: *The streets were alive with people.*

all (ôl), **1** every one of: *All the children came. You all know the teacher.* **2** everyone: *All of us are going.* **3** everything: *All is well.* **4** the whole of: *The mice ate all the cheese.* **5** the whole amount: *All of the bread has been eaten.* **6** wholly; entirely: *The cake is all gone.* **7** each; apiece: *The score was even at three all.* 1,4 *adjective,* 2,3,5 *pronoun,* 6,7 *adverb.*

after all, nevertheless; when everything has been considered: *It was cloudy, but we decided to have the picnic after all.*

all but, nearly; almost: *This job is all but done.*

all in all, when everything has been considered: *All in all, I think you did a good job.*

all over, everywhere: *There were toys all over.*

at all, in any way: *Maybe he won't be able to go at all. She was not at all upset by the change in plan.*

in all, counting every person or thing; altogether: *There were 100 people in all.*

Al·lah (al′ə *or* ä′lə), the Moslem name for God. *noun.*

all-A·mer·i·can (ôl′ə mer′ə kən), **1** chosen as the best of the year at a particular position, from among all high school or college players of a team sport in the United States. **2** a player that is chosen as all-American. 1 *adjective,* 2 *noun.*

all-a·round (ôl′ə round′), able to do many things; useful in many ways: *He is an all-around football player—he runs, passes, and punts. adjective.*

al·lege (ə lej′), to declare; state: *Although he has no proof, this man alleges that the janitor stole his watch. verb,* **al·leg·es, al·leged, al·leg·ing.**

Al·le·ghe·ny Moun·tains (al′ə gā′nē moun′tənz), a mountain range of the Appalachian Mountain system, in Pennsylvania, Maryland, Virginia, and West Virginia.

al·le·giance (ə lē′jəns), devotion to someone or something; loyalty: *I pledge allegiance to the flag. We owe our friends our allegiance. noun.*

al·ler·gic (ə lėr′jik), **1** having an allergy: *People who are allergic to milk sometimes break out in a rash if they drink it.* **2** caused by an allergy: *Hay fever is an allergic reaction to a kind of pollen. adjective.*

al·ler·gy (al′ər jē), an unusual bodily reaction to certain things such as particular kinds of pollen, food, hair, or cloth. Hay fever, asthma, headaches, and hives are common signs of allergy. *noun, plural* **al·ler·gies.**

al·ley (al′ē), **1** a narrow street behind buildings in a city or town. **2** a long, narrow wooden floor along which the ball is rolled in bowling; lane. **3** a building having a number of lanes for bowling. *noun, plural* **al·leys.**

al·ley·way (al′ē wā′), **1** an alley in a city or town. **2** a narrow passageway. *noun.*

al·li·ance (ə lī′əns), a union of persons, groups, or nations formed by agreement for some special purpose or benefit. *noun.*

al·lied (ə līd′ *or* al′īd), united by agreement: *France, Great Britain, Russia, and the United States were allied nations during World War II. adjective.*

al·li·ga·tor (al′ə gā′tər), a large reptile with a rather thick skin. It is like the crocodile but has a shorter and flatter head. Alligators live in the rivers and marshes of the warm parts of America and China. *noun.*

Word History

alligator *Alligator* comes from Spanish words meaning "the lizard." Spanish explorers were not familiar with this animal. They referred to it by their word for "lizard," an animal similar in shape if not in size.

alligator—about 10 feet (3 meters) long

al·lot (ə lot′), to give to as a share; assign: *Each class was allotted a part in the school program. verb,* **al·lots, al·lot·ted, al·lot·ting.**

al·low (ə lou′), **1** to let someone do something; permit: *My parents won't allow us to swim in the river.* **2** to let have; give: *My parents allowed me a dollar to spend as I wish.* **3** to add or subtract to make up for something: *The trip will cost only $20; but you ought to allow $5 more for expenses. verb.*

allow for, to take into consideration: *I buy my jeans a little large to allow for shrinking.*

al·low·ance (ə lou′əns), **1** a sum of money given regularly to someone: *My parents let me have a weekly allowance of $1.* **2** a discount; amount subtracted: *The salesman offered us an allowance of $400 for our old car; so we got a $6000 car for $5600. noun.*

make allowance for, to take into consideration; allow for: *We made allowance for the heavy traffic by leaving half an hour early.*

al·loy (al′oi), a metal made by melting and mixing two or more metals. An alloy may be harder, lighter, and stronger than the metals of which it is made. Brass is an alloy of copper and zinc. *noun.*

all-pur·pose (ôl′pėr′pəs), able to be used for any purpose: *All-purpose flour is as suitable for baking cakes as it is for baking bread. adjective.*

all right, 1 without error; correct: *The answers were all right.* **2** satisfactory: *The work was not done very well, but it was all right.* **3** in good condition; free from harm or illness: *I dropped the bag, but the eggs are all right.* **4** yes: *"Will you come with me?" "All right."*

all-round (ôl′round′), all-around. *adjective.*

all-star (ôl′stär′), made up of the best players or

performers: *Two of our players have been named to the all-star team. adjective.*

al·lude (ə lüd′), to refer indirectly; mention slightly: *Don't tell them about our plan; don't even allude to it. verb,* **al·ludes, al·lud·ed, al·lud·ing.**

al·lur·ing (ə lur′ing), very attractive; tempting: *On a hot day, a cold drink is an alluring idea. adjective.*

al·lu·sion (ə lü′zhən), a slight mention; indirect reference: *Don't make any allusion to the surprise party while he is present. noun.*

al·ly (al′ī *or* ə lī′ *for 1;* ə lī′ *for 2),* **1** a person, group, or nation united with another for some special purpose: *England and France were allies in some wars and enemies in others.* **2** to combine for some special purpose; unite by agreement. Small nations sometimes ally themselves with larger ones for protection. 1 *noun, plural* **al·lies;** 2 *verb,* **al·lies, al·lied, al·ly·ing.**

al·ma·nac (ôl′mə nak), **1** a book published every year which has tables of facts and figures and brief information on many subjects. **2** a booklike calendar that also gives information about the sun, moon, stars, tides, church days, and other facts, sometimes with weather predictions. *noun.*

al·might·y (ôl mī′tē), **1** possessing all power. **2 the Almighty,** God. 1 *adjective,* 2 *noun.*

al·mond (ä′mənd), the oval-shaped nut of the peachlike fruit of a tree growing in warm regions. Almonds are good to eat and are used to make flavoring for other foods. *noun.*

al·most (ôl′mōst), nearly: *It is almost ten o'clock. I almost missed the train. adverb.*

alms (ämz), money or gifts to help the poor: *The beggar asked for alms. noun singular or plural.*

a·loft (ə lôft′), **1** far above the earth; high up. **2** high up among the sails and masts of a ship: *The sailor went aloft to get a better view of the distant shore. adverb.*

aloft (definition 1)—tennis played **aloft**

a·lo·ha (ə lō′ə *or* ä lō′hä), a Hawaiian word meaning: **1** greetings; hello. **2** good-by; farewell. *noun, interjection.*

[The original meaning of the Hawaiian word *aloha* was "love."]

a hat	i it	oi oil	ch child	⎧ a in about
ā age	ī ice	ou out	ng long	e in taken
ä far	o hot	u cup	sh she	ə = ⎨ i in pencil
e let	ō open	u̇ put	th thin	o in lemon
ē equal	ô order	ü rule	ŦH then	⎩ u in circus
ėr term			zh measure	

a·lone (ə lōn′), **1** without other persons or things: *After my friends left, I was alone. One tree stood alone on the hill.* **2** without help from others: *I solved the problem alone.* **3** only; but not anyone else: *She alone can do this work, so it must wait till she returns.* 1,3 *adjective,* 1,2 *adverb.*

leave alone *or* **let alone,** not bother; not meddle with: *Let her alone so she can get her homework done.*

a·long (ə lông′), **1** from one end to the other end of: *Trees are planted along the street.* **2** forward; onward: *March along quickly.* **3** together with someone or something: *We took our dog along.* 1 *preposition,* 2,3 *adverb.*

all along, all the time: *He knew the answer all along.*

get along, 1 to manage: *Can you get along without our help?* **2** to agree: *They get along with each other.*

a·long·side (ə lông′sīd′), **1** at the side; side by side: *They were sitting in the car when a truck pulled up alongside.* **2** by the side of; side by side with: *The boat was alongside the wharf.* 1 *adverb,* 2 *preposition.*

a·loof (ə lüf′), **1** away; apart: *One boy stood aloof from all the others.* **2** tending to keep to oneself; not interested; indifferent: *Her aloof manner kept her from making many friends.* 1 *adverb,* 2 *adjective.*

a·loud (ə loud′), loud enough to be heard; not in a whisper: *She read the story aloud to me. adverb.*

al·pha·bet (al′fə bet), the letters of a language arranged in their usual order, not as they are in words. The English alphabet is: a b c d e f g h i j k l m n o p q r s t u v w x y z. *noun.*

[*Alphabet* comes from the names of the first two letters of the Greek alphabet: *alpha* A and *beta* B.]

al·pha·bet·i·cal (al′fə bet′ə kəl), arranged by letters in the order of the alphabet: *Dictionary entries are listed in alphabetical order. adjective.*

al·pha·bet·i·cal·ly (al′fə bet′ik lē), in the usual order of the letters of the alphabet. *adverb.*

al·pha·bet·ize (al′fə bə tīz), to arrange in the order of the letters of the alphabet: *The names in a telephone book have been alphabetized. verb,* **al·pha·bet·iz·es, al·pha·bet·ized, al·pha·bet·iz·ing.**

Alps (alps), a group of high mountains in southern Europe. The Alps are in Switzerland, France, Austria, and several other countries. *noun plural.*

al·read·y (ôl red′ē), before this time; by this time; even now: *You are half an hour late already. adverb.*

al·so (ôl′sō), too; in addition: *I like summer but I enjoy winter also. adverb.*

altar (definition 1)—a Buddhist altar

al·tar (ôl′tər), a table or stand used in religious worship in a church or temple: *The priest knelt in prayer before the altar.* noun.

al·ter (ôl′tər), to make or become different; change: *If this coat is too large, a tailor can alter it to fit you.* verb.

al·ter·a·tion (ôl′tə rā′shən), a change: *We put in new cabinets and made other alterations in our kitchen.* noun.

al·ter·nate (ôl′tər nāt *for 1,2;* ôl′tər nit *for 3-6*), **1** to happen or be arranged by turns, first one and then the other. Squares and circles alternate in this row: □ ○ □ ○ □ ○. **2** to take turns: *My brother and I will alternate in setting the table.* **3** first one and then the other by turns: *The United States flag has alternate stripes of red and white.* **4** every other: *My friends and I go bowling on alternate Thursdays.* **5** able to take the place of another: *If it rains tomorrow, the fair will be held on an alternate day.* **6** a substitute: *We have several alternates on our debating team.* **1,2** verb, **al·ter·nates, al·ter·nat·ed, al·ter·nat·ing;** **3-5** adjective, **6** noun.

al·ter·nate·ly (ôl′tər nit lē), by turns. adverb.

alternating current, an electric current that reverses its direction at regular intervals.

al·ter·na·tive (ôl tėr′nə tiv), **1** a choice from among two or more things: *She had the alternative of going to summer school or finding a summer job.* **2** one of the things to be chosen from: *She chose the first alternative and went to summer school.* **3** giving or requiring a choice from among two or more things: *I offered the alternative plans of having a picnic or taking a trip on a boat.* **1,2** noun, **3** adjective.

al·though (ôl ŦHō′), in spite of the fact that; though: *Although it rained all day, they went on the hike.* conjunction.

al·tim·e·ter (al tim′ə tər), an instrument for measuring altitude. Altimeters are used in aircraft to indicate height above the earth's surface. noun.

al·ti·tude (al′tə tüd *or* al′tə tyüd), **1** height above the earth's surface: *What altitude did the airplane reach?* **2** height above sea level: *The altitude of Denver is 5300 feet.* noun.

al·to (al′tō), **1** the lowest singing voice in women and boys. **2** a singer with such a voice. **3** an instrument with a range like that of the alto voice. noun, plural **al·tos.**

al·to·geth·er (ôl′tə geŦH′ər), **1** completely; entirely: *The house was altogether destroyed by fire.* **2** on the whole: *Altogether, he was pleased.* **3** all included: *Altogether there were 14 books.* adverb.

al·um (al′əm), a mineral that contains aluminum and is used in medicine and in dyeing fabrics. noun.

a·lu·mi·num (ə lü′mə nəm), a very light, silver-white metal that does not tarnish easily. Aluminum is a chemical element. It is used as foil and for making pots and pans, cans, and aircraft parts. noun.

al·ways (ôl′wiz), **1** every time; in each case: *Night always follows day.* **2** all the time; constantly: *Their home is always open to their friends.* **3** forever: *There will always be stars in the sky.* adverb.

am (am *or* əm). *Am* is a form of **be.** *I am at school. I am tired. I am going to school. I am frightened by loud noises.* verb.

a.m. or **A.M.,** before noon; in the time from midnight to noon: *School begins at 9 a.m.* [The abbreviations *a.m.* and *A.M.* stand for the Latin words *ante meridiem,* meaning "before noon."]

a·mass (ə mas′), to heap together; pile up; accumulate: *She invested her money wisely and amassed a fortune.* verb.

am·a·teur (am′ə chər *or* am′ə tər), **1** a person who does something for pleasure, not for money: *Only amateurs can compete in college sports.* **2** a person who does something rather poorly: *This painting is the work of an amateur; it shows very little skill.* **3** of amateurs; by amateurs: *Our town has an amateur orchestra.* **1,2** noun, **3** adjective. [*Amateur* was borrowed from a French word. Its original meaning in both English and French was "one who loves or is fond of."]

a·maze (ə māz′), to surprise greatly; strike with sudden wonder: *She was amazed at how different the strand of hair looked under a microscope.* verb, **a·maz·es, a·mazed, a·maz·ing.**

a·maze·ment (ə māz′mənt), great surprise; sudden wonder: *I was filled with amazement when I first saw the ocean.* noun.

a·maz·ing (ə mā′zing), very surprising. adjective.

Am·a·zon (am′ə zon), a river in northern South America. It is the largest river in the world. noun.

am·bas·sa·dor (am bas′ə dər), a representative of the highest rank sent by one government or ruler to another: *The U.S. ambassador to France lives in Paris and speaks and acts for the government of the United States.* noun.

am·ber (am′bər), **1** a hard, clear, yellow or yellowish-brown substance used for jewelry.

Amber is the resin of ancient pine trees that has become a fossil. **2** yellow or yellowish-brown: *a black cat with amber eyes.* 1 *noun,* 2 *adjective.*

am·big·u·ous (am big′yü əs), having more than one possible meaning. The sentence "After John hit Dick he ran away" is ambiguous because we cannot tell which boy ran away. *adjective.*

am·bi·tion (am bish′ən), **1** a strong desire for fame or success; a longing for a high position or for power: *Because he was filled with ambition, he worked after school and on Saturdays to earn money for college.* **2** a thing for which one has a strong desire: *Her ambition is to be a doctor. noun.*

am·bi·tious (am bish′əs), **1** having ambition; full of ambition: *She was ambitious to become a senator and campaigned long and hard for votes.* **2** showing ambition: *an ambitious plan. adjective.*

am·ble (am′bəl), **1** an easy, slow pace in walking. **2** to walk at an easy, slow pace. 1 *noun,* 2 *verb,* **am·bles, am·bled, am·bling.**

am·bu·lance (am′byə ləns), a vehicle equipped to carry sick or wounded persons. *noun.*
[*Ambulance,* which was borrowed from a French word, originally meant "a moving hospital accompanying an army." It came from two French words actually meaning "walking hospital."]

am·bush (am′bush), **1** a surprise attack on an approaching enemy from some hiding place. **2** a concealed position; a hiding place: *The soldiers lay in ambush, waiting for the signal to open fire.* **3** to attack from a hiding place: *The bandits ambushed the stagecoach.* 1,2 *noun, plural* **am·bush·es;** 3 *verb.*

a·me·ba (ə mē′bə), a very simple living thing having only one cell. Amebas are so small that they cannot be seen without a microscope. Many amebas live in water; others live as parasites in animals. Amebas move by flowing. *noun.* Also spelled **amoeba.**
[*Ameba* comes from a Greek word meaning "change." It was called this by an early biologist who saw it under a microscope, and noticed that its shape was always changing.]

a·men (ā′men′ *or* ä′men′), so be it; may it become true. *Amen* is said after a prayer, a wish, or a statement with which one agrees. *interjection.*

a·mend (ə mend′), **1** to change: *The Constitution of the United States was amended so that no one can be elected President more than twice.* **2** to change for the better; improve: *It is time you amended your poor table manners. verb.*

a·mend·ment (ə mend′mənt), **1** a change: *The Constitution of the United States has over twenty amendments.* **2** a change for the better; improvement. *noun.*

a·mends (ə mendz′), something given or paid to make up for a wrong or an injury done; payment for loss; compensation: *I bought my friend a new book to make amends for the one I lost. noun singular or plural.*

A·mer·i·ca (ə mer′ə kə), **1** the United States of America. **2** North America. **3** North America and

a hat	**i** it	**oi** oil	**ch** child	a in about
ā age	**ī** ice	**ou** out	**ng** long	e in taken
ä far	**o** hot	**u** cup	**sh** she	ə = { i in pencil
e let	**ō** open	**ù** put	**th** thin	o in lemon
ē equal	**ô** order	**ü** rule	**ᴛʜ** then	u in circus
ėr term			**zh** measure	

South America. The two continents are sometimes called **the Americas.** *noun.*
[The name *America* was made up by a German map maker in 1507 from the name *Americus* Vespucius. He was an Italian navigator who lived from 1451 to 1512. He claimed to have explored the Atlantic coast of South America.]

A·mer·i·can (ə mer′ə kən), **1** of the United States; having something to do with the United States or its people; from the United States. **2** a person born or living in the United States. **3** of North America and South America; having something to do with North America and South America or their people; from North America and South America. **4** a person born or living in North America or South America. 1,3 *adjective,* 2,4 *noun.*

American Indian, one of the people who have lived in North and South America from long before the time of the first European settlers.

am·e·thyst (am′ə thist), a purple or violet kind of quartz, used for jewelry. *noun.*

a·mi·a·ble (ā′mē ə bəl), good-natured and friendly; pleasant and agreeable: *She is an amiable girl who gets along with everyone. adjective.*

a·mid (ə mid′), in the middle of; among: *A small house stood amid the tall buildings. preposition.*

a·midst (ə midst′), amid. *preposition.*

a·mi·go (ə mē′gō), a friend. *noun, plural* **a·mi·gos.**

a·miss (ə mis′), wrong; not the way it should be; out of order: *We knew something was amiss when we saw that the window had been forced open. adverb, adjective.*

am·mo·nia (ə mō′nyə), **1** a colorless gas, consisting of nitrogen and hydrogen, that has a strong smell. **2** this gas dissolved in water. Ammonia is very useful for cleaning. *noun.*

am·mu·ni·tion (am′yə nish′ən), bullets, shells, grenades, and bombs that can be exploded or fired from guns or other weapons; military explosives and missiles. *noun.*

am·ne·sia (am nē′zhə), loss of memory caused by injury to the brain, or by disease or shock. *noun.*

a·moe·ba (ə mē′bə). See ameba. *noun.*

a·mong (ə mung′), **1** one of; in the group of: *The United States is among the largest countries in the world.* **2** with; in the company of: *to spend time among friends.* **3** surrounded by: *There is a house among the trees.* **4** with a portion for each of: *Divide the fruit among all of us.* **5** within the group of: *She had to choose from among the several law schools that accepted her application.* **6** throughout:

Talk of revolution spread among the crowd. preposition.

a·mongst (ə mungst′), among. *preposition.*

a·mount (ə mount′), **1** the total sum: *What is the amount of the bill for the groceries?* **2** a quantity or number of something: *No amount of coaxing would make the dog leave its owner.* **3** to reach; add up: *The loss from the flood amounts to ten million dollars.* **4** to be equal: *Keeping what belongs to another amounts to stealing.* 1,2 *noun,* 3,4 *verb.*

am·pere (am′pir), a unit for measuring the amount of an electric current. Ordinary light bulbs take from ½ to 1 ampere. *noun.*
[The *ampere* was named for André M. Ampère, who lived from 1775 to 1836. He was a French scientist who studied the nature of electric current.]

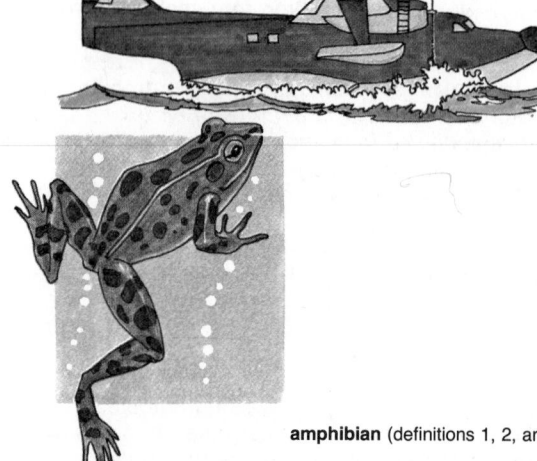

am·phib·i·an (am fib′ē ən), **1** one of a group of cold-blooded animals having a backbone and moist skin without scales. Their young usually have gills and live in water until they develop lungs for living on land. Frogs and toads are amphibians. **2** an aircraft that can take off from and land on either land or water. **3** a tank, truck, or other vehicle able to travel across land or water. *noun.*
[*Amphibian* is from a Greek word meaning "living in two ways." The word was used of this group of animals because they can live both on land and in water.]

amphibian (definitions 1, 2, and 3)

am·phib·i·ous (am fib′ē əs), able to live both on land and in water: *Frogs are amphibious. adjective.*

am·phi·the·a·ter (am′fə thē′ə tər), a circular or oval building with rows of seats around a central open space. Each row is higher than the one in front of it. *noun.*

am·ple (am′pəl), **1** more than enough: *We had ample time to catch our train, so we stopped for a soda.* **2** enough: *My allowance is ample for carfare and lunches.* **3** large; roomy: *This house has ample closets. adjective,* **am·pler, am·plest.**

am·pli·fi·er (am′plə fī′ər), an electronic device that makes sound louder or electrical current stronger. *noun.*

am·pli·fy (am′plə fī), **1** to make greater; make stronger: *When sound is amplified, it is louder.* **2** to add to; expand; enlarge: *Please amplify your description of the accident by giving us more details. verb,* **am·pli·fies, am·pli·fied, am·pli·fy·ing.**

am·ply (am′plē), in an ample manner: *We were amply supplied with food. adverb.*

am·pu·tate (am′pyə tāt), to cut off all or part of an arm or leg. *verb,* **am·pu·tates, am·pu·tat·ed, am·pu·tat·ing.**

Am·trak (am′trak), a public business that receives money from the government to provide railroad passenger service on certain routes in the United States. *noun.*

a·muse (ə myüz′), **1** to cause to laugh or smile: *The clown's jokes and antics amused everyone.* **2** to keep pleasantly interested; cause to feel cheerful or happy; entertain: *We amused ourselves on that rainy day by dressing up and acting out a play. verb,* **a·mus·es, a·mused, a·mus·ing.**

a·muse·ment (ə myüz′mənt), **1** the condition of being amused: *The boy's amusement was so great that we all had to laugh with him.* **2** anything that amuses: *My parents' favorite amusement is going to the theater. noun.*

amusement park, an outdoor place of entertainment with booths for games, various rides, and other amusements.

an (ən *or* an). *An* is used in place of *a* before words that begin with vowels or that sound as if they begin with vowels. **1** any: *Is there an apple in the box?* **2** one: *I had an egg for breakfast.* **3** every: *He earns two dollars an hour.* **4** one kind of: *Painting is an art. adjective* or *indefinite article.*

an·a·con·da (an′ə kon′də), a very large South

anaconda—This one is almost 30 feet (9 meters) long.

American snake that kills its prey by squeezing. Anacondas live in tropical forests and rivers and are the longest snakes in America. *noun.*

a·nal·y·sis (ə nal′ə sis), **1** separation of anything into its parts or elements to find out what it is made of. A chemical analysis of table salt shows that it is made up of two elements, sodium and chlorine. **2** an examination made with care and in detail. An analysis can be made of a book or a person's character. *noun, plural* **a·nal·y·ses** (ə nal′ə sēz′).

an·a·lyze (an′l īz), **1** to separate anything into its parts or elements to find out what it is made of: *The chemistry teacher analyzed water into two colorless gases, oxygen and hydrogen.* **2** to examine carefully and in detail: *The reporter analyzed the results of the election. verb,* **an·a·lyz·es, an·a·lyzed, an·a·lyz·ing.**

an·ar·chy (an′ər kē), **1** the absence of a system of government and law. **2** disorder and confusion; chaos. *noun.*

a·nat·o·my (ə nat′ə mē), **1** the science of the structure of living things. Anatomy is a part of biology. **2** the structure of a living thing: *The anatomy of an earthworm is much simpler than that of a human being. noun, plural* **a·nat·o·mies.**

an·ces·tor (an′ses′tər), a person from whom one is directly descended. Your grandfathers, your grandmothers, and so on back, are your ancestors. *noun.*

an·ces·tral (an ses′trəl), **1** of ancestors: *England was the ancestral home of the Pilgrims.* **2** inherited from ancestors: *Black hair is an ancestral trait in that family. adjective.*

an·ces·try (an′ses′trē), ancestors: *Many early settlers in California had Spanish ancestry. noun, plural* **an·ces·tries.**

an·chor (ang′kər), **1** a heavy piece of iron or steel fastened to a chain or rope and dropped from a ship to the bottom of the water to hold the ship in place: *The anchor caught in the mud at the bottom of the lake and kept the boat from drifting.* **2** to hold in place with an anchor: *Can you anchor the boat in this storm?* **3** to stay in place by using an anchor: *The ship anchored in the bay.* **4** to fasten in place; fix firmly: *The campers anchored their tent to the ground.* **5** a thing for holding something else in place: *The anchors of these cables are set in concrete.* **6** something that makes a person feel safe and secure: *My family home was an anchor for me during my years of travel.* **1,5,6** *noun,* **2-4** *verb.*

an·chor·age (ang′kər ij), a place to anchor. *noun.*

an·chor·man (ang′kər man′), a person on a television or radio program who reports the news and introduces the work of other reporters. *noun, plural* **an·chor·men.**

an·cient (ān′shənt), **1** belonging to times long past: *In Egypt, we saw the ruins of an ancient temple built six thousand years ago.* **2** of great age; very old: *Rome is an ancient city.* **3** the ancients, people who lived long ago, such as the ancient

Greeks, Romans, and Egyptians. **1,2** *adjective,* **3** *noun.*

and (ənd *or* and), **1** as well as; also: *Yesterday we went to the beach and to the zoo.* **2** added to; with: *4 and 2 make 6. I like ham and eggs.* **3** in addition; then; while: *I washed the dishes and my brother dried them. conjunction.*

An·des (an′dēz), a group of high mountains in western South America. *noun plural.*

and·i·ron (and′ī′ərn), one of a pair of metal supports for wood in a fireplace. *noun.*

andirons

an·droid (an′droid), a robot that resembles a human being. *noun.*

an·ec·dote (an′ik dōt), a short account of some interesting incident or event: *Many anecdotes are told about Abraham Lincoln. noun.*

a·ne·mi·a (ə nē′mē ə), a lack of red cells in the blood. Anemia often causes people to feel weak and tired. *noun.*

a·ne·mic (ə nē′mik), having anemia. *adjective.*

an·e·mom·e·ter (an′ə mom′ə tər), an instrument for measuring the speed of wind. *noun.*

anemometer
Wind catches the cups and moves them around, causing the shaft to turn. The speed of the wind is shown on an indicator.

a hat	i it	oi oil	ch child	a in about
ā age	ī ice	ou out	ng long	e in taken
ä far	o hot	u cup	sh she	ə = { i in pencil
e let	ō open	ů put	th thin	o in lemon
ē equal	ô order	ü rule	ŦH then	u in circus
ėr term			zh measure	

a·nem·o·ne (ə nem′ə nē), **1** a plant with a slender stem and small white or colored cup-shaped flowers. **2** the sea anemone, a flowerlike sea animal. *noun.*

an·es·thet·ic (an′əs thet′ik), a substance that causes a loss of feeling in all or part of the body. Dentists and surgeons use anesthetics so that patients will feel no pain. *noun.*

a·new (ə nü′ *or* ə nyü′), again; once more: *I made so many mistakes I had to begin my work anew. adverb.*

an·gel (ān′jəl), **1** a messenger from God. Angels are usually pictured as human figures with wings, dressed in white. **2** a person who is good, kind, or beautiful. *noun.*

an·gel·fish (ān′jəl fish′), any of several brightly colored tropical fishes with long, pointed fins. *noun, plural* **an·gel·fish** *or* **an·gel·fish·es.**

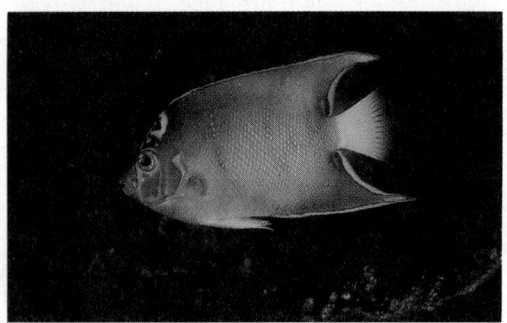

angelfish—about 6 inches (15 centimeters) long

angel food cake, a fluffy white cake made with beaten egg whites, flour, and sugar.

an·gel·ic (an jel′ik), like an angel; good, kind, or beautiful: *The little baby had an angelic face. adjective.*

an·ger (ang′gər), **1** the feeling that one has toward someone or something that hurts or annoys; a strong dislike or wish to harm: *In a moment of anger, I hit my friend.* **2** to cause to feel this way: *The girl's disobedience angered her parents.* **1** *noun,* **2** *verb.*

an·gle¹ (ang′gəl), **1** the space between two lines or surfaces that meet. **2** the figure formed by two such lines or surfaces. **3** to move or bend at an angle: *The road angles to the right here.* **4** a corner: *We took a picture of the northeast angle of the school.* **5** a point of view: *We are treating the problem from a new angle.* **1,2,4,5** *noun,* **3** *verb,* **an·gles, an·gled, an·gling.**

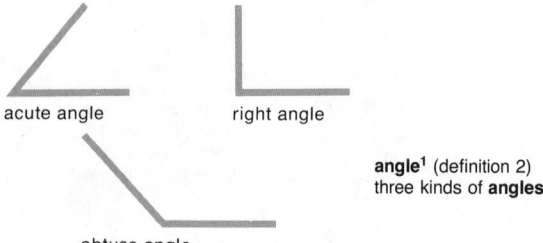

acute angle   right angle

angle¹ (definition 2)
three kinds of **angles**

obtuse angle

an·gle² (ang′gəl), **1** to fish with a hook and line. **2** to try to get something by using tricks or schemes: *They angled for an invitation to dinner by flattering the cook. verb,* **an·gles, an·gled, an·gling.**

an·gler (ang′glər), a person who fishes with a hook and line, especially one who does so for sport. *noun.*

an·gle·worm (ang′gəl wėrm′), an earthworm. *noun.*

An·go·la (ang gō′lə), a country in southwest Africa. *noun.*

an·gri·ly (ang′grə lē), in an angry manner. *adverb.*

an·gry (ang′grē), **1** feeling or showing anger: *My parents were very angry when I disobeyed them. My friend's angry words hurt my feelings.* **2** suggesting anger; stormy or threatening: *The angry waves pounded the beach.* **3** red, painful, and often swollen: *The cut on my little finger has become infected and looks angry. adjective,* **an·gri·er, an·gri·est.**

an·guish (ang′gwish), very great pain or grief: *He was in anguish until the doctor set his broken leg. noun.*

an·gu·lar (ang′gyə lər), having angles; having sharp corners: *I cut my hand on an angular piece of rock. adjective.*

an·i·mal (an′ə məl), **1** any living thing that is made up of many cells, can move about, and usually has a nervous system. Animals cannot make their own food from sunlight as plants do. A human being, a dog, a bird, a fish, a snake, a fly, and a worm are animals. **2** an animal other than a human being. *noun.*

an·i·mat·ed (an′ə mā′tid), **1** lively; full of life and spirit: *The children had an animated discussion about their trip.* **2** made to move or appear to move: *an animated cartoon. adjective.*

an·i·mos·i·ty (an′ə mos′ə tē), hatred; dislike; ill will: *There was violent animosity between the feuding neighbors. noun.*

an·kle (ang′kəl), the joint that connects the foot with the leg. *noun.*

an·klet (ang′klit), a short sock reaching just above the ankle. *noun.*

An·na·po·lis (ə nap′ə lis), the capital of Maryland. *noun.*

an·nex (ə neks′ *for* 1; an′eks *for* 2), **1** to join or add a smaller thing to a larger thing: *The United States annexed Texas in 1845.* **2** something annexed; an added part, especially to a building: *We are building an annex to the school.* **1** *verb,* **2** *noun, plural* **an·nex·es.**

an·nex·a·tion (an′ek sā′shən), an annexing; being annexed: *The annexation of Texas enlarged the United States. noun.*

an·ni·hi·late (ə nī′ə lāt), to destroy completely; wipe out of existence: *An avalanche annihilated the village. verb,* **an·ni·hi·lates, an·ni·hi·lat·ed, an·ni·hi·lat·ing.**

an·ni·ver·sar·y (an′ə vėr′sər ē), the yearly return of a special date: *Your birthday is an*

anniversary you like to have remembered. noun,
plural **an·ni·ver·sar·ies.**

an·nounce (ə nouns′), **1** to give public or formal notice of: *The teacher announced that there would be no school tomorrow.* **2** to make known the presence or arrival of: *The loudspeaker announced each airplane as it landed at the airport. verb,*
an·nounc·es, an·nounced, an·nounc·ing.

an·nounce·ment (ə nouns′mənt), a public or formal notice: *The principal made an announcement at the assembly. noun.*

an·nounc·er (ə noun′sər), a person who introduces programs, reads news, or describes sports events on radio or television. *noun.*

an·noy (ə noi′), to make somewhat angry; disturb: *I asked them to turn off the radio because it was annoying me. verb.*

an·noy·ance (ə noi′əns), **1** a feeling of slight anger or of being disturbed: *He showed his annoyance at us by slamming the door.* **2** something that annoys: *The heavy traffic on our street is an annoyance. noun.*

an·nu·al (an′yü əl), **1** coming once a year: *Your birthday is an annual event.* **2** in a year; for a year: *For the last two years her annual salary has been $12,000.* **3** living but one year or season: *Corn and beans are annual plants.* **4** a plant that lives but one year or season. 1-3 *adjective,* 4 *noun.*

an·nu·al·ly (an′yü ə lē), yearly; each year; year by year: *The parade is held annually. adverb.*

a·noint (ə noint′), to put oil on a person, especially as part of a religious ceremony: *The bishop anointed the new king. verb.*

a·non·y·mous (ə non′ə məs), **1** by or from a person whose name is not known or given: *I immediately hang up whenever I receive an anonymous phone call.* **2** unknown: *This book was written by an anonymous author. adjective.*

an·oth·er (ə nuŦH′ər), **1** one more: *Have another glass of milk. She ate a piece of candy and then asked for another.* **2** a different: *Show me another kind of hat.* **3** a different one: *I don't like this book; give me another.* 1,2 *adjective,* 1,3 *pronoun.*

an·swer (an′sər), **1** to speak or write in return to a question: *When I asked her a question, she answered right away.* **2** the words spoken or written in return to a question: *The boy gave a quick answer.* **3** an act or movement done in return: *A nod was her only answer.* **4** to act in return to a call or signal; respond: *I knocked on the door, but no one answered. I answered the phone.* **5** the solution to a problem: *What is the correct answer to this arithmetic problem?* **6** to be responsible: *The bus driver must answer for the safety of the children in the bus.* **7** to agree with; correspond: *The police questioned the man who answered to the description of the bank robber.* 1,4,6,7 *verb,* 2,3,5 *noun.*

ant (ant), a small insect that lives in tunnels in the ground or in wood. Ants live together in large groups called colonies. *noun.*

an·tag·o·nism (an tag′ə niz′əm), active opposition; hostility: *During the argument, the boy's antagonism showed plainly in his face. noun.*

a hat	i it	oi oil	ch child	a in about
ā age	ī ice	ou out	ng long	e in taken
ä far	o hot	u cup	sh she	ə = { i in pencil
e let	ō open	ủ put	th thin	o in lemon
ē equal	ô order	ü rule	ŦH then	u in circus
ėr term			zh measure	

an·tag·o·nist (an tag′ə nist), a person who fights, struggles, or competes against another; opponent: *The knight defeated each antagonist who came against him. noun.*

an·tag·o·nis·tic (an tag′ə nis′tik), acting against each other; opposing; conflicting: *Cats and dogs are antagonistic. adjective.*

an·tag·o·nize (an tag′ə nīz), to make an enemy of; arouse dislike in: *Her unkind remarks antagonized people who had been her friends. verb,*
an·tag·o·niz·es, an·tag·o·nized,
an·tag·o ·niz·ing.

ant·arc·tic (ant′ärk′tik *or* ant′är′tik), **1** Also, **Antarctic.** at or near the South Pole; of the south polar region. **2 the Antarctic,** the south polar region. 1 *adjective,* 2 *noun.*

Ant·arc·ti·ca (ant′ärk′tə kə *or* ant′är′tə kə), the continent around the South Pole. Only two other continents, Europe and Australia, are smaller than Antarctica. It is almost totally covered by ice. *noun.*

Antarctic Ocean, the ocean of the south polar region.

ant·eat·er (ant′ē′tər), an animal with a long, sticky tongue, that eats ants and termites. Anteaters have no teeth but use their very long claws to dig into anthills. *noun.*

anteater—about 6 feet (2 meters) long with the tail

antelope (definition 1)—up to 5 feet (1½ meters) at the shoulder

an·te·lope (an′tl ōp), **1** an animal of Africa and Asia that chews its cud and has hoofs. It is like the deer in appearance, grace, and speed but is related to goats and cows. **2** an animal like this, found on the plains of western North America;

pronghorn. *noun, plural* **an·te·lope** or **an·te·lopes.**

an·ten·na (an ten′ə), **1** one of the long, slender feelers on the heads of insects, crabs, lobsters, and shrimp. **2** a long wire or set of wires or rods used in television or radio for sending out or receiving sounds and pictures; aerial. *noun, plural* **an·ten·nae** (an ten′ē) or **an·ten·nas** for 1, **an·ten·nas** for 2.

antenna (definition 1)—**antennae** of a grasshopper

an·them (an′thəm), **1** a song of praise or patriotism: *"The Star-Spangled Banner" is the national anthem of the United States.* **2** a piece of sacred music, usually with words from some passage in the Bible. *noun.*

an·ther (an′thər), the top part of the stamen of a flower. The anthers produce the pollen. *noun.*

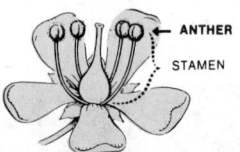

ant·hill (ant′hil′), a heap of earth piled up by ants around the entrance to their tunnels. *noun.*

an·thol·o·gy (an thol′ə jē), a collection of poems, stories, or other writings, usually from various authors. *noun, plural* **an·thol·o·gies.**

an·thra·cite (an′thrə sīt), a kind of coal that burns with very little smoke and flame; hard coal. *noun.*

an·thro·pol·o·gist (an′thrə pol′ə jist), a person who is an expert in anthropology. *noun.*

an·thro·pol·o·gy (an′thrə pol′ə jē), the science that studies the origin and development of human beings. It includes the study of their customs, cultures, and beliefs. *noun.*
[*Anthropology* comes from two Greek words meaning "discussion of a human being."]

anti-, a prefix meaning against: *Anti*aircraft means *against* aircraft. *Anti*slavery means *against* slavery.

an·ti·air·craft (an′tē er′kraft′ or an′tē ar′kraft′), used in defense against enemy aircraft. *adjective.*

an·ti·bi·ot·ic (an′ti bī ot′ik), a substance produced by bacteria or molds that destroys or weakens germs. Penicillin is an antibiotic useful in treating many infections. *noun.*

an·ti·bod·y (an′ti bod′ē), a substance in the blood that destroys or weakens germs and other harmful matter that enter the body. Antibodies help prevent infection. *noun, plural* **an·ti·bod·ies.**

an·tic·i·pate (an tis′ə pāt), **1** to look forward to; expect: *We are anticipating a good time at your party.* **2** to take care of ahead of time; consider in advance: *He anticipated all his guests' wishes by providing several flavors of ice cream. verb,* **an·tic·i·pates, an·tic·i·pat·ed, an·tic·i·pat·ing.**

an·tic·i·pa·tion (an tis′ə pā′shən), the act of anticipating; looking forward to; expectation: *In anticipation of a cold winter, the farmer cut more firewood than usual. noun.*

an·tics (an′tiks), funny gestures or actions: *The antics of the clown amused the audience. noun plural.*

an·ti·dote (an′ti dōt), a medicine that acts against the harmful effects of a poison; remedy: *Milk is an antidote for some poisons. noun.*

an·ti·freeze (an′ti frēz′), a substance added to the water in an automobile radiator, to prevent it from freezing. *noun.*

an·tique (an tēk′), **1** of times long ago; from times long ago. **2** something made long ago: *This carved chest is a genuine antique.* **1** *adjective,* **2** *noun.*

antique (definition 1)—an **antique** automobile

an·ti·sep·tic (an′tə sep′tik), a substance that prevents the growth of germs that cause infection. Iodine and alcohol are antiseptics. *noun.*

an·ti·slav·er·y (an′ti slā′vər ē), against slavery: *Antislavery leaders were active in the early history of the United States. adjective.*

an·ti·tox·in (an′ti tok′sən), **1** a kind of antibody that can prevent certain diseases, cure them, or make them milder. **2** a serum that contains an antitoxin. It is injected into people to protect them from a disease. *noun.*

ant·ler (ant′lər), a bony, hornlike growth on the head of a male deer, elk, or moose. Antlers grow in pairs and usually have one or more branches. They are shed once a year and grow back again during the next year. *noun.*

a	hat	i	it	oi	oil	ch	child		a in about
ā	age	ī	ice	ou	out	ng	long		e in taken
ä	far	o	hot	u	cup	sh	she	ə =	i in pencil
e	let	ō	open	u̇	put	th	thin		o in lemon
ē	equal	ô	order	ü	rule	ŦH	then		u in circus
ėr	term					zh	measure		

Word History

antler *Antler* comes from two Latin words meaning "before the eye." Our word was originally the name of the lowest branch of a stag's horn, which is closest to its eye. The word was later applied to the entire horn.

antlers of a deer

an·to·nym (an′tə nim), a word that means the opposite of another word. "True" is the antonym of "false"; "up" is the antonym of "down." *noun.*

an·vil (an′vəl), an iron or steel block on which metals are hammered and shaped. Blacksmiths use anvils. *noun.*

anx·i·e·ty (ang zī′ə tē), 1 uneasy thoughts or fears about what may happen; troubled, worried, or uneasy feeling: *The passengers were filled with anxiety when the airplane was caught in the storm.* 2 eager desire: *Her anxiety to succeed led her to work hard. noun, plural* **anx·i·e·ties.**

anx·ious (angk′shəs), 1 uneasy because of thoughts or fears of what may happen; troubled; worried: *I felt anxious about my final exams. The week of the flood was an anxious time for all of us.* 2 wishing very much; eager: *They were anxious to start their vacation. adjective.*

anx·ious·ly (angk′shəs lē), 1 uneasily: *Relatives of passengers on the missing plane were anxiously waiting for more news.* 2 eagerly: *The children anxiously opened their Christmas presents. adverb.*

an·y (en′ē), 1 one out of many: *Choose any book you like from the books on the shelf.* 2 some: *Have you any fresh fruit? We haven't any.* 3 every: *Any child knows that.* 4 at all: *Has my singing improved any?* 1-3 *adjective,* 2 *pronoun,* 4 *adverb.*

an·y·bod·y (en′ē bod′ē), any person; anyone: *Has anybody been here? pronoun.*

an·y·how (en′ē hou), 1 in any case; at any rate; anyway: *I can see as well as you can, anyhow.* 2 in any way whatever: *The answer is wrong anyhow you look at it. adverb.*

an·y·more (en′ē môr′), now; at present: *He doesn't smoke anymore. I seldom see her anymore. adverb.*

an·y·one (en′ē wun), any person; anybody: *Can anyone go to this movie or is it just for adults? pronoun.*

an·y·place (en′ē plās), anywhere: *Put the book down anyplace. adverb.*

an·y·thing (en′ē thing), 1 any thing: *Do you have anything to eat?* 2 at all: *My bike isn't anything like yours.* 1 *pronoun,* 2 *adverb.*

an·y·time (en′ē tīm), at any time: *You are welcome to visit us anytime. adverb.*

an·y·way (en′ē wā), in any case: *I am coming anyway, no matter what you say. adverb.*

an·y·where (en′ē hwer), in, at, or to any place: *I'll meet you anywhere you say. adverb.*

a·or·ta (ā ôr′tə), the main artery that carries the blood from the left side of the heart to all parts of the body except the lungs. *noun.*

A·pach·e (ə pach′ē), a member of a tribe of American Indians living in the southwestern United States. *noun, plural* **A·pach·e** or **A·pach·es.**

a·part (ə pärt′), 1 to pieces; in pieces; in separate parts: *She took the watch apart to see how it runs.* 2 away from each other: *Keep the dogs apart.* 3 to one side; aside: *He sets some money apart for a vacation each year. adverb.*
apart from, besides: *Apart from its cost, the plan was a good one.*
tell apart, to see any difference between: *I can't tell the twins apart.*

a·part·ment (ə pärt′mənt), a room or group of rooms to live in; flat: *Our apartment is on the second floor of that building. noun.*

apartment house, a building with a number of apartments in it.

ap·a·thy (ap′ə thē), a lack of interest or feeling; indifference: *Because of apathy, few people voted in the election. noun.*

ape (āp), 1 a large, tailless monkey with long arms. Apes can stand almost erect and walk on two feet. Chimpanzees, gorillas, orangutans, and gibbons are apes. 2 to imitate; mimic: *The children aped the way the TV star talked.* 1 *noun,* 2 *verb,* **apes, aped, ap·ing.**

ap·er·ture (ap′ər chər), an opening; gap; hole. A shutter regulates the size of the aperture through which light passes into a camera. *noun.*

a·phid (ā′fid *or* af′id), a very small insect that lives by sucking juices from plants. *noun.*

a·piece (ə pēs′), for each one; each: *These apples cost ten cents apiece. adverb.*

a·pol·o·get·ic (ə pol′ə jet′ik), making an excuse; expressing regret: *He sent an apologetic note saying he could not come to the party. adjective.*

a·pol·o·gize (ə pol′ə jīz), to make an apology; say one is sorry; offer an excuse: *I apologized for being so late. verb,* **a·pol·o·giz·es, a·pol·o·gized, a·pol·o·giz·ing.**

a·pol·o·gy (ə pol′ə jē), words saying one is sorry for an offense, fault, or accident; explanation asking pardon: *I made an apology to my teacher for being late. noun, plural* **a·pol·o·gies.**

a·pos·tle or **A·pos·tle** (ə pos′əl), one of the twelve special followers of Jesus. He chose them to go out and spread His teachings everywhere. *noun.*

a·pos·tro·phe (ə pos′trə fē), a sign (′) used: **1** to show the omission of one or more letters in contractions, as in *isn't* for *is not*, *tho'* for *though*. **2** to show the possessive forms of nouns, as in *Lee's book, the lions' den*. **3** to form plurals of letters and numbers: *There are two o's in apology and four 9's in 959,990. noun.*

Ap·pa·la·chian Moun·tains (ap′ə lā′chən moun′tənz), a group of mountains in the eastern United States and Canada.

ap·pall (ə pôl′), to fill with horror or fear; dismay; terrify: *They were appalled when they saw the destruction caused by the tornado. verb.*

ap·pa·ra·tus (ap′ə rā′təs *or* ap′ə rat′əs), anything necessary to carry out a purpose or for a particular use. Tools, special instruments, and machines are apparatus. Test tubes and beakers are apparatus; so are a grocer's scales and the equipment in a gymnasium. *noun, plural* **ap·pa·ra·tus** *or* **ap·pa·ra·tus·es.**

ap·par·el (ə par′əl), clothing; dress: *Does this store sell children's apparel? noun.*

ap·par·ent (ə par′ənt *or* ə per′ənt), **1** plain to see or understand; so plain that one cannot help seeing or understanding it: *It was apparent from the way she walked that she was very tired. It is apparent that she enjoys her work.* **2** seeming; appearing to be: *With half the votes counted, he was the apparent winner. adjective.*

ap·par·ent·ly (ə par′ənt lē *or* ə per′ənt lē), as far as one can judge by appearances; seemingly: *Their lights are not on; apparently they are not home. adverb.*

ap·pa·ri·tion (ap′ə rish′ən), a ghost: *The apparition, clothed in a white robe, glided through the wall. noun.*

ap·peal (ə pēl′), **1** to make an earnest request; ask for help or sympathy: *When the children were in trouble they appealed to their parents for help.* **2** an earnest request; call for help or sympathy: *The residents made an appeal to the school board not to close their neighborhood school. An appeal for aid for the flood victims was broadcast over TV.* **3** to ask that a case be taken to a higher court or judge to be heard again: *When the judge ruled against them, they decided to appeal.* **4** a request to have a case heard again before a higher court or judge: *Their appeal was granted.* **5** to be attractive, interesting, or enjoyable: *Blue and red appeal to me but I don't like gray or yellow.* **6** an attraction or interest: *Television has a great appeal for most young people.* **1,3,5** *verb,* **2,4,6** *noun.*

ap·pear (ə pir′), **1** to be seen; come in sight: *One by one the stars appear.* **2** to seem; look: *The apple appeared sound on the outside, but it was rotten inside.* **3** to be published: *Her latest book appeared a year ago.* **4** to show or present oneself in public: *The singer will appear on television today. verb.*

ap·pear·ance (ə pir′əns), **1** the act of coming in sight: *His sudden appearance in the doorway startled me.* **2** coming before the public: *The singer made her first appearance in a concert in San Francisco.* **3** the way a person or thing looks: *I knew from his appearance that he was ill. noun.*

ap·pease (ə pēz′), **1** to satisfy: *A good dinner will appease your hunger.* **2** to make calm; quiet: *I tried to appease the crying child by giving him candy. verb,* **ap·peas·es, ap·peased, ap·peas·ing.**

ap·pen·di·ci·tis (ə pen′də sī′tis), a soreness and swelling of the appendix. *noun.*

ap·pen·dix (ə pen′diks), **1** an addition at the end of a book or document. **2** a slender, closed tube growing out of the large intestine. *noun, plural* **ap·pen·dix·es, ap·pen·di·ces** (ə pen′də sēz′).

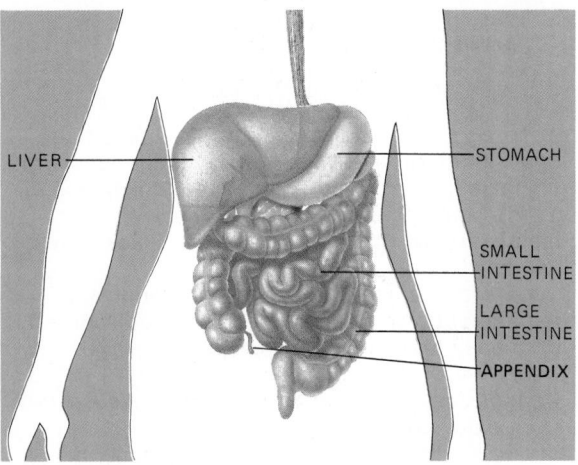

appendix (definition 2)

ap·pe·tite (ap′ə tīt), **1** a desire for food: *Swimming seems to increase my appetite.* **2** a desire: *The lively children had a great appetite for adventure. noun.*

ap·pe·tiz·er (ap′ə tī′zər), something that arouses the appetite, usually served before a meal. Pickles and olives are appetizers. *noun.*

ap·pe·tiz·ing (ap′ə tī′zing), arousing or exciting the appetite; pleasing to the taste: *Appetizing food always smells delicious. adjective.*

ap·plaud (ə plôd′), **1** to show approval by clapping hands or shouting: *The audience applauded at the end of the play.* **2** to approve; praise: *Her parents applauded her decision to study medicine. verb.*

ap·plause (ə plôz′), approval shown by clapping the hands or shouting: *Applause for the singer's good performance rang out from the audience. noun.*

ap·ple (ap′əl), the firm, fleshy, somewhat round fruit of a tree that is widely grown. Apples have red, yellow, or green skin, and are eaten either raw or cooked. *noun.*

ap·ple·sauce (ap′əl sôs′), apples cut in pieces

and cooked with sugar, spices, and water until soft. *noun.*

ap·pli·ance (ə plī′əns), a machine designed for a particular use, especially one which makes household work easier. A can opener is an appliance for opening tin cans. Vacuum cleaners, washing machines, and refrigerators are household appliances. *noun.*

ap·pli·ca·ble (ap′lə kə bəl), able to be applied; suitable; appropriate: *The rule "Look before you leap" is almost always applicable. adjective.*

ap·pli·cant (ap′lə kənt), a person who applies for a job, money, position, or help. *noun.*

ap·pli·ca·tion (ap′lə kā′shən), **1** a putting to use; use: *The application of what you know will help you solve new problems.* **2** an applying; putting on: *The painter's careless application of paint spattered the floor.* **3** a request made in person or in writing: *I put in an application for a job at the supermarket. noun.*

ap·ply (ə plī′), **1** to put on: *He applied two coats of paint to the table.* **2** to use: *I know the rule but I don't know how to apply it.* **3** to be useful or suitable; fit: *When does this rule apply?* **4** to ask: *He is applying for a job as clerk.* **5** to set to work and stick to it: *She applied herself to learning to play the piano. verb,* **ap·plies, ap·plied, ap·ply·ing.**

ap·point (ə point′), to name for an office or position; choose: *The mayor appointed two new members to the school board. verb.*

ap·point·ment (ə point′mənt), **1** the act of naming for an office or position; choosing: *The appointment of a new secretary of state was announced.* **2** an office or position: *The lawyer was offered a high government appointment.* **3** a meeting with someone at a certain time and place; engagement: *I have an appointment to see the doctor at four o'clock. noun.*

ap·praise (ə prāz′), **1** to estimate the value, amount, or quality of: *An employer should be able to appraise an employee's work.* **2** to set a price on; fix the value of: *The jeweler appraised the diamond ring at $1000. verb,* **ap·prais·es, ap·praised, ap·prais·ing.**

ap·pre·ci·ate (ə prē′shē āt), **1** to think highly of; recognize the worth or quality of; value; enjoy: *Almost everybody appreciates good food.* **2** to be thankful for: *We appreciate your help.* **3** to have an opinion of the value, worth, or quality of; estimate: *Most of us appreciate the importance of exercise for good health. verb,* **ap·pre·ci·ates, ap·pre·ci·at·ed, ap·pre·ci·at·ing.**

ap·pre·ci·a·tion (ə prē′shē ā′shən), **1** a valuing highly; recognizing or understanding the worth of: *She has no appreciation of modern art.* **2** thankfulness; gratitude: *He showed his appreciation of her help by sending a letter of thanks. noun.*

ap·pre·cia·tive (ə prē′shə tiv), having appreciation; showing appreciation; recognizing the value: *The appreciative audience applauded the performer. adjective.*

ap·pre·hend (ap′ri hend′), to arrest; seize: *The burglars were apprehended by the police. verb.*

ap·pre·hen·sion (ap′ri hen′shən), **1** fear; dread: *The roar of the hurricane filled us with apprehension.* **2** a seizing or being seized; arrest: *The appearance of the suspect's picture in all the papers led to her apprehension. noun.*

ap·pre·hen·sive (ap′ri hen′siv), afraid, anxious, or worried: *I felt apprehensive before taking my first airplane trip. adjective.*

ap·pren·tice (ə pren′tis), **1** a person who is learning a trade or an art by working with a skilled worker. In former times, apprentices worked for little or no pay. **2** to bind or take as an apprentice: *Benjamin Franklin's father apprenticed him to a printer.* **1** *noun,* **2** *verb,* **ap·pren·tic·es, ap·pren·ticed, ap·pren·tic·ing.**

ap·proach (ə prōch′), **1** to come near or nearer: *Walk softly as you approach the baby's crib. Winter is approaching.* **2** the act of coming near or nearer: *Sirens warned us of the approach of the fire truck.* **3** a way by which a place or person can be reached; access: *The approach to the house was a narrow path. Our best approach to the senator is through a mutual friend.* **4** a method of starting work on a task or problem: *She seems to have a good approach to the problem.* **5** to speak to about a plan or request: *We approached our teacher about having a class party.* **1,5** *verb,* **2-4** *noun, plural* **ap·proach·es.**

ap·proach·a·ble (ə prō′chə bəl), **1** able to be approached: *The house on the mountain is approachable only on foot.* **2** easy to approach and talk to: *No matter how busy the teacher was, she was always approachable. adjective.*

ap·pro·pri·ate (ə prō′prē it *for 1;* ə prō′prē āt *for 2),* **1** suitable; proper: *Plain, simple clothes are appropriate for school wear.* **2** to set apart for some special use: *The state appropriated money for a new road into our town.* **1** *adjective,* **2** *verb,* **ap·pro·pri·ates, ap·pro·pri·at·ed, ap·pro·pri·at·ing.**

ap·pro·pri·a·tion (ə prō′prē ā′shən), **1** a sum of money set apart: *Our town received a state appropriation of $12,000 for a new playground.* **2** a setting apart for some special use: *The appropriation of the land made it possible to have a park. noun.*

ap·prov·al (ə prü′vəl), **1** a favorable opinion; praise: *We all like others to show approval of what we do.* **2** permission; consent: *I have my parents' approval to go on the trip. noun.*

on approval, so that the customer can inspect the item and decide whether to buy or return it: *We bought the television set on approval.*

ap·prove (ə prüv′), **1** to think well of; be pleased with: *The teacher looked at her work and approved it. I do not approve of what you plan to do.* **2** to consent to: *The school board approved the budget for next year.* verb, **ap·proves, ap·proved, ap·prov·ing.**

ap·prox·i·mate (ə prok′sə mit *for 1;* ə prok′sə māt *for 2*), **1** nearly correct: *The approximate length of this room is 12 feet; the exact length is 12 feet 3 inches.* **2** to come near to; approach: *The crowd approximated a thousand people.* 1 adjective, 2 verb, **ap·prox·i·mates, ap·prox·i·mat·ed, ap·prox·i·mat·ing.**

ap·prox·i·mate·ly (ə prok′sə mit lē), nearly; about: *We are approximately 200 miles from home.* adverb.

ap·prox·i·ma·tion (ə prok′sə mā′shən), a nearly correct amount: *25,000 miles is an approximation of the circumference of the earth.* noun.

Apr., April.

a·pri·cot (ā′prə kot *or* ap′rə kot), **1** a round, pale, orange-colored fruit that grows on a tree. Apricots are smaller than peaches and have a smoother skin. They are good to eat. **2** pale orange-yellow. 1 noun, 2 adjective.

A·pril (ā′prəl), the fourth month of the year. It has 30 days. noun.
[*April* may have come from the Latin name of the Greek goddess of love and beauty.]

April Fools' Day, April 1, a day on which tricks and jokes are played on people.

a·pron (ā′prən), a garment worn over the front part of the body to cover or protect clothes: *a kitchen apron, a carpenter's apron.* noun.

apt (apt), **1** likely; inclined: *A careless person is apt to make mistakes.* **2** right for the occasion; suitable; fitting: *His apt reply to the question showed that he had understood it very well.* **3** quick to learn: *She is an apt student and does well in school.* adjective.

ap·ti·tude (ap′tə tüd *or* ap′tə tyüd), a natural tendency or talent; ability; capacity: *He had a remarkable aptitude for mathematics.* noun.

aq·ua (ak′wə), **1** a light bluish green. **2** light bluish-green. 1 noun, 2 adjective.
[The words *aqua, aquanaut, aquarium, aquatic,* and *aqueduct* all come from a Latin word *aqua,* meaning "water." The English word *aqua* refers to the color of water. The idea of water occurs in the other four words, although their endings are different, and they have different meanings.]

Aqua-Lung (ak′wə lung′), a trademark for an underwater breathing device used in skin diving; scuba. noun.

aq·ua·naut (ak′wə nôt), an underwater explorer. noun.

a·quar·i·um (ə kwer′ē əm), **1** a tank or glass bowl in which living fish or other water animals and water plants are kept. **2** a building used for showing collections of living fish, water animals, and water plants. noun.

a·quat·ic (ə kwat′ik), **1** growing or living in water: *Water lilies are aquatic plants.* **2** taking place in or on water: *Swimming and sailing are aquatic sports.* adjective.

aq·ue·duct (ak′wə dukt), an artificial channel or large pipe for bringing water from a distance. noun.

AR, Arkansas (used with postal Zip Code).

Ar·ab (ar′əb), **1** a person born or living in Arabia. **2** a member of a people living in southwestern and southern Asia and northern Africa. **3** of or having something to do with the Arabs or Arabia. 1,2 noun, 3 adjective.

A·ra·bi·a (ə rā′bē ə), a large peninsula in southwestern Asia. noun.

A·ra·bi·an (ə rā′bē ən), **1** of or having something to do with Arabia or the Arabs. **2** a person born or living in Arabia; Arab. 1 adjective, 2 noun.

Ar·a·bic (ar′ə bik), **1** the language of the Arabs. **2** of the Arabs or their language. 1 noun, 2 adjective.

Word Source

Arabic is spoken by many people in the Middle East and north Africa. The following words came into English from Arabic:

admiral	hazard	mattress	sheik
albatross	jar[1]	mummy	sofa
gazelle	lime[2]	racket[2]	sugar
genie	magazine	sash[1]	syrup
giraffe	massage	satin	zero

Arabic numerals, the figures 1, 2, 3, 4, 5, 6, 7, 8, 9, 0. They are called Arabic because they were first made known to Europeans by Arabian scholars.

ar·a·ble (ar′ə bəl), fit for plowing: *There is no arable land on a rocky mountain.* adjective.

ar·bi·trar·y (är′bə trer′ē), based on one's own wishes, notions, or will; not going by any rule or law: *The judge tried to be fair and did not make arbitrary decisions.* adjective.

ar·bi·trate (är′bə trāt), to give a decision in a dispute; settle by arbitration: *The teacher arbitrated between the two girls in the quarrel. The two nations finally agreed to arbitrate their dispute, and war was avoided.* verb, **ar·bi·trates, ar·bi·trat·ed, ar·bi·trat·ing.**

ar·bi·tra·tion (är′bə trā′shən), a settlement of a dispute by someone chosen to judge both sides: *Arbitration prevented the two nations from going to war.* noun.

ar·bor (är′bər), a shaded place formed by trees or shrubs or by vines growing on a wooden frame. noun.

arc (ärk), any part of the curved line of a circle or of any curve. noun.

ar·cade (är kād′), a store in which customers pay to play games, especially video games. noun.

arch[1] (ärch), **1** a curved structure that bears the weight of the material above it. Arches often form the tops of doors, windows, and gateways. **2** to bend into an arch; curve: *The cat arched its back and hissed at the barking dog.* **3** the lower part of arch¹ (definition 1)—The building has a row of **arches.**

a hat	**i** it	**oi** oil	**ch** child	a in about
ā age	**ī** ice	**ou** out	**ng** long	e in taken
ä far	**o** hot	**u** cup	**sh** she	ə = { i in pencil
e let	**ō** open	**u̇** put	**th** thin	o in lemon
ē equal	**ô** order	**ü** rule	**ᴛʜ** then	u in circus
ėr term			**zh** measure	

the foot which makes a curve between the heel and the toes: *Fallen arches cause flat feet.* 1,3 *noun, plural* **arch·es;** 2 *verb.*

arch² (ärch), **1** playfully mischievous: *The little boy gave his mother an arch look and ran away.* **2** chief; principal; leading: *The arch villain of the story was a pirate. adjective.*

ar·chae·ol·o·gist (är′kē ol′ə jist), a person who is an expert in archaeology. Archaeologists study buildings, tools, pottery, weapons, and other objects of ancient times. *noun.* Also spelled **archeologist.**

ar·chae·ol·o·gy (är′kē ol′ə jē), the study of the people, customs, and life of ancient times. *noun.* Also spelled **archeology.**

ar·che·ol·o·gist (är′kē ol′ə jist). See **archaeologist.**

ar·che·ol·o·gy (är′kē ol′ə jē). See **archaeology.** *noun.*

arch·bish·op (ärch′bish′əp), a bishop having the highest rank. *noun.*

arch·er (är′chər), a person who shoots with a bow and arrow. *noun.*

arch·er·y (är′chər ē), the skill or sport of shooting with a bow and arrow. *noun.*

ar·chi·pel·a·go (är′kə pel′ə gō), **1** a group of many islands. **2** a sea having many islands in it. *noun, plural* **ar·chi·pel·a·gos** or **ar·chi·pel·a·goes.**

ar·chi·tect (är′kə tekt), a person who designs and makes plans for buildings and sees that these plans are followed by the people who actually put up the buildings. *noun.*

ar·chi·tec·ture (är′kə tek′chər), **1** the science or art of planning and designing buildings. **2** a style or special manner of building: *Greek architecture made much use of columns. noun.*

arch·way (ärch′wā′, **1** an entrance or passageway with an arch above it. **2** an arch covering a passageway. *noun.*

arc·tic (ärk′tik *or* är′tik), **1** Also, **Arctic.** at or near the North Pole; of the north polar region: *They explored the great arctic wilderness of northern Canada.* **2 the Arctic,** the north polar region. The Arctic has an extremely cold winter. 1 *adjective,* 2 *noun.*

Arctic Ocean, the ocean of the north polar region.

ar·dent (ärd′nt), very enthusiastic; eager: *He is an ardent scout. adjective.*

ar·dor (är′dər), great enthusiasm; eagerness: *The reporter spoke with ardor about her work. noun.*

ar·du·ous (är′jü əs), hard to do; requiring much effort; difficult: *an arduous lesson. adjective.*

are (är *or* ər). *Are* is a form of *be. You are right. We are ready. They are waiting. We are going to school. We are impressed by their skill. verb.*

ar·e·a (er′ē ə *or* ar′ē ə), **1** the amount of surface; extent: *The area of this floor is 600 square feet.* **2** a range of knowledge or interest: *Our science teacher is familiar with the areas of physics and chemistry.* **3** a region: *The Rocky Mountain area is very mountainous.* **4** a level, open space: *a playground area. noun.*

area code, a combination of three numbers used to dial directly by telephone from one region of a country to another.

a·re·na (ə rē′nə), **1** a space or building in which certain contests or sports are held. **2** a building in which indoor sports are played. *noun.*

aren't (ärnt), are not.

Ar·gen·ti·na (är′jən tē′nə), a country in southern South America. *noun.*

ar·gue (är′gyü), **1** to discuss with someone who disagrees: *He argued with his sister about who should wash the dishes.* **2** to give reasons for or against something: *One side argued for building a new school, and the other side argued against it. verb,* **ar·gues, ar·gued, ar·gu·ing.**

ar·gu·ment (är′gyə mənt), **1** a discussion by persons who disagree; dispute: *She won the*

architect and construction worker

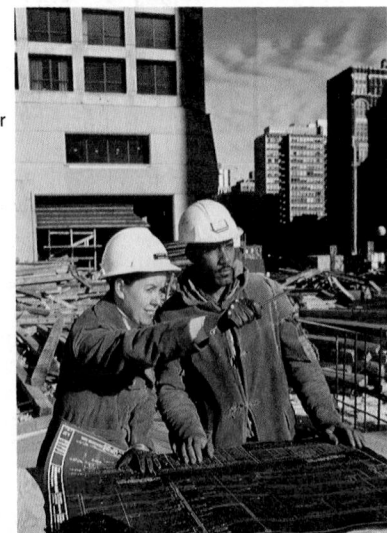

argument by producing facts to prove her point. **2** a reason or reasons offered for or against something: *Their arguments for a new school are convincing. noun.*

ar·id (ar′id), having very little rainfall; dry: *Desert lands are arid. adjective.*

a·rise (ə rīz′), **1** to rise up; get up: *They arose to greet us when we came in.* **2** to move upward: *Smoke arises from the chimney.* **3** to come into being; come about: *A great wind arose. Accidents often arise from carelessness. verb,* **a·ris·es, a·rose, a·ris·en** (ə riz′n), **a·ris·ing.**

ar·is·toc·ra·cy (ar′ə stok′rə sē), **1** a class of people having a high position in society because of birth, rank, or title. Earls, duchesses, and princes belong to the aristocracy. **2** a class of people considered superior because of intelligence, culture, or wealth. **3** a government in which the nobles rule. *noun, plural* **ar·is·toc·ra·cies.**

a·ris·to·crat (ə ris′tə krat), **1** a person who belongs to the aristocracy; a noble. **2** a person who has the tastes, opinions, and manners of a noble. *noun.*

a·ris·to·crat·ic (ə ris′tə krat′ik), **1** belonging to the upper classes; considered superior because of birth, intelligence, culture, or wealth. **2** of or like the aristocracy or aristocrats. *adjective.*

a·rith·me·tic (ə rith′mə tik), **1** the branch of mathematics that deals with adding, subtracting, multiplying, and dividing numbers. **2** the act of adding, subtracting, multiplying, or dividing numbers; calculation. *noun.*

Ariz., Arizona.

Ar·i·zo·na (ar′ə zō′nə), one of the southwestern states of the United States. *Abbreviation:* Ariz. or AZ *Capital:* Phoenix. *noun.*
[*Arizona* got its name from an American Indian word meaning "place of the small spring."]

ark (ärk), **1** (in the Bible) the large boat in which Noah saved himself, his family, and a pair of each kind of animal from the Flood. **2** a cabinet in a synagogue for keeping the scrolls of the Torah when it is not being used in worship. *noun.*

Ark., Arkansas.

Ar·kan·sas (är′kən sô), one of the south central states of the United States. *Abbreviation:* Ark. or AR *Capital:* Little Rock. *noun.*
[*Arkansas* was named for an American Indian tribe that once lived in the area. This name came from an Indian word meaning "downstream people."]

arm[1] (ärm), **1** the part of the body between the shoulder and the hand. **2** something shaped or used like an arm. An armchair has two arms. An inlet is an arm of the sea. *noun.*

arm[2] (ärm), **1 arms,** weapons of any kind. Guns, swords, axes, or sticks—any of these might be arms for defense or attack. **2** to supply with weapons: *During the American Revolutionary War the French helped arm the colonists.* **3** to supply with any means of defense or attack: *The lawyer entered court armed with the evidence to support his case.* **4** to take up weapons; prepare for war: *The*

soldiers armed for battle. **1** *noun plural,* 2-4 *verb.*

ar·ma·da (är mä′də), **1** a large fleet of warships. **2** a large fleet of airplanes. *noun.*

ar·ma·dil·lo (är′mə dil′ō), a small, burrowing animal that has a very hard shell like armor. Armadillos are found in South America and some parts of southern North America. *noun, plural* **ar·ma·dil·los.**

Word History

armadillo *Armadillo* comes from a Spanish word meaning "armed." Early Spanish explorers thought that the animal's very hard shell of bony plates served as a kind of armor.

armadillo—2½ feet (76 centimeters) long with the tail

ar·ma·ment (är′mə mənt), **1** the weapons, ammunition, and equipment used by the military; war equipment and supplies. **2** the guns on a naval vessel, a tank, or an airplane. *noun.*

arm·chair (ärm′cher′ *or* ärm′char′), a chair with pieces at the side to support a person's arms or elbows. *noun.*

Ar·me·ni·a (är mē′nē ə), a country in southwestern Asia. *noun.*

armed forces, all the army, navy, marine, and air forces of a country.

arm·ful (ärm′fùl), as much as one or both arms can hold: *I carried an armful of groceries. noun, plural* **arm·fuls.**

ar·mi·stice (är′mə stis), a stop in warfare; temporary peace; truce. *noun.*

arm·load (ärm′lōd′), an armful. *noun.*

ar·mor (är′mər), **1** a covering, usually of metal or leather, worn to protect the body in fighting. **2** any kind of protective covering. The steel plates of a warship are armor. *noun.*

ar·mored (är′mərd), covered or protected with armor: *The king rode in an armored car. adjective.*

ar·mor·y (är′mər ē), **1** a place where weapons are kept or manufactured. **2** a building with offices and an area for drill, used by the militia. *noun, plural* **ar·mor·ies.**

arm·pit (ärm′pit′), the hollow place under the arm at the shoulder. *noun.*

arms (ärmz), **1** See **arm**[2] (definition 1). **2** fighting;

war: *The colonists were quick to answer the call to arms. noun plural.*

ar·my (är′mē), **1** a large, organized group of soldiers trained and armed for war. **2** any group of people organized for a purpose: *an army of research scientists.* **3** a very large number; multitude: *an army of ants. noun, plural* **ar·mies.**

a·ro·ma (ə rō′mə), a fragrance; spicy odor: *Just smell the aroma of the cake baking in the oven. noun.*

a·rose (ə rōz′). See **arise.** *She arose from her chair. verb.*

a·round (ə round′), **1** in a circle about: *She has traveled around the world.* **2** in a circle: *The top spun around.* **3** in circumference: *The tree measures four feet around.* **4** on all sides of: *Woods lay around the house.* **5** on the far side of: *The store is just around the corner.* **6** here and there; about: *We walked around to see the town. Don't leave your books around the house.* **7** somewhere about; near: *We waited around for an hour.* **8** through a round of time: *Summer will soon come around again.* **9** near in amount, number, or time to; about: *That shirt cost around fifteen dollars. I'll be home around six o'clock.* **10** in the opposite direction: *Turn around! You are going the wrong way.* **1,4-6,9** *preposition,* **2,3,6-8,10** *adverb.*

a·rouse (ə rouz′), **1** to stir to action; excite: *The mystery story aroused my imagination.* **2** to awaken: *The barking dog aroused me from my sleep. verb,* **a·rous·es, a·roused, a·rous·ing.**

ar·range (ə rānj′), **1** to put in a certain order: *Please arrange the books on the library shelf. She arranged her business so that she could take a vacation in September.* **2** to plan; form plans: *Can you arrange to meet me this evening?* **3** to adapt; fit: *This music for the violin is also arranged for the piano. verb,* **ar·rang·es, ar·ranged, ar·rang·ing.**

ar·range·ment (ə rānj′mənt), **1** a putting or a being put in a certain order: *Careful arrangement of books in a library makes them easier to find.* **2** the way or order in which things or persons are put: *You can make six arrangements of the letters A, B, and C.* **3** something arranged in a particular way: *a beautiful flower arrangement. This piece of music for the piano also has an arrangement for the violin.* **4 arrangements,** plans; preparations: *We made arrangements for our trip to Chicago. noun.*

ar·ray (ə rā′), **1** order: *The troops were formed in battle array.* **2** to put in order: *The general arrayed his troops for the battle.* **3** a display or collection of persons or things: *The team had an impressive array of fine players.* **1,3** *noun,* **2** *verb.*

ar·rest (ə rest′), **1** to take to jail or court by authority of the law: *The police arrested the burglar.* **2** a stopping; seizing: *We saw the arrest of the burglar.* **3** to stop; check: *Filling a tooth arrests decay.* **1,3** *verb,* **2** *noun.*

ar·riv·al (ə rī′vəl), **1** the act of arriving; coming: *She is waiting for the arrival of the plane.* **2** a person or thing that arrives: *We greeted the new arrivals at the door. noun.*

a hat	i it	oi oil	ch child	a in about
ā age	ī ice	ou out	ng long	e in taken
ä far	o hot	u cup	sh she	ə = i in pencil
e let	ō open	u̇ put	th thin	o in lemon
ē equal	ô order	ü rule	ᴛʜ then	u in circus
ėr term			zh measure	

ar·rive (ə rīv′), **1** to come to a place: *We arrived in Boston a week ago.* **2** to come: *Summer finally arrived. verb,* **ar·rives, ar·rived, ar·riv·ing.**
arrive at, to come to; reach: *You should arrive at school before nine o'clock.*

ar·ro·gance (ar′ə gəns), too great pride in oneself and too much scorn for others: *He was a talented actor, but his arrogance made him unpopular. noun.*

ar·ro·gant (ar′ə gənt), too proud of oneself and too scornful of others: *Early success had made her vain and arrogant. adjective.*

ar·row (ar′ō), **1** a slender, pointed stick which is shot from a bow. **2** a sign (→) used to show direction or position in maps, on road signs, and in writing. *noun.*

ar·row·head (ar′ō hed′), the head or tip of an arrow. *noun.*

ar·roy·o (ə roi′ō), the dry bed of a stream, in the southwestern United States. *noun, plural* **ar·roy·os.**

ar·se·nal (är′sə nəl), a building for storing or manufacturing weapons and ammunition for an army or navy. *noun.*

ar·se·nic (är′sə nik), a white, tasteless powder that is a violent poison. It is used to make insecticides, weed killers, and certain medicines. Arsenic is a chemical element. *noun.*

ar·son (är′sən), the crime of intentionally setting fire to a building or other property. *noun.*

art (ärt), **1** painting, drawing, and sculpture: *I am studying art and music.* **2** paintings, sculptures, and other works of art: *We went to an exhibit at the museum of art.* **3** a branch of learning that depends more on special practice than on general principles. Writing is an art; botany is a science. The fine arts include painting, drawing, sculpture, architecture, music, and dancing. **4** a set of principles or methods gained by experience; skill: *She understands the art of making friends. noun.*

ar·ter·y (är′tər ē), **1** one of the blood vessels that carry blood from the heart to all parts of the body. **2** a main road; important channel: *Main Street and Broadway are the two arteries of traffic in our city. noun, plural* **ar·ter·ies.**

ar·te·sian well (är tē′zhən wel′), a deep, drilled well, especially one from which water gushes up without pumping.

art·ful (ärt′fəl), **1** slyly clever; crafty; deceitful: *A swindler uses artful tricks to get people's money away from them.* **2** skillful; clever: *Her artful handling of the situation prevented an argument. adjective.*

ar·thri·tis (är thrī′tis), soreness and swelling of a joint or joints of the body. *noun.*

artichoke

ar·ti·choke (är′tə chōk), the flower bud of a plant that looks somewhat like a thistle with large, prickly leaves. Artichokes are cooked and eaten as a vegetable. *noun.*

ar·ti·cle (är′tə kəl), **1** a written composition that is part of a magazine, newspaper, or book: *This is a good article on gardening.* **2** a clause in a contract, treaty, or law: *The original Constitution of the United States contained seven articles.* **3** a particular thing; item: *Gloves are articles of clothing.* **4** one of the words *a, an,* or *the,* as in *a book, an egg, the boy. A* and *an* are **indefinite articles;** *the* is the **definite article.** *noun.*

ar·ti·fact (är′tə fakt), anything made by human skill or work, especially a tool or weapon: *Archaeologists study ancient artifacts. noun.*

ar·ti·fice (är′tə fis), **1** a clever device; trick: *The child used every artifice to avoid going to the dentist.* **2** trickery; craft: *His conduct is free from artifice. noun.*

ar·ti·fi·cial (är′tə fish′əl), **1** made by human skill or labor; not natural: *artificial flowers. Plastics are artificial substances that do not occur in nature.* **2** put on; pretended: *When nervous, he had an artificial laugh. adjective.*

artificial respiration, a way of restoring normal breathing to a person who has stopped breathing. Air is alternately forced into and out of the lungs.

ar·til·ler·y (är til′ər ē), **1** large guns that are carried on wheels or wheeled vehicles. **2** the part of an army that uses and manages such large guns. *noun.*

ar·ti·san (är′tə zən), a person skilled in a craft or trade; craftsman. Carpenters, masons, plumbers, and electricians are artisans. *noun.*

art·ist (är′tist), **1** a person who paints pictures. **2** a person who is skilled in any of the fine arts, such as sculpture, music, or literature. **3** a public performer, especially an actor or singer. *noun.*

ar·tis·tic (är tis′tik), **1** of art or artists: *Our museum has many artistic treasures.* **2** done with skill and good taste: *That actress gave an artistic performance.* **3** having or showing appreciation of beauty: *artistic tastes. adjective.*

as (az *or* əz), **1** to the same degree; equally: *I am as tall as you.* **2** doing the work of: *Who will act as*

teacher? **3** while; when: *As they were walking, it began to rain.* **4** in the same way that: *Treat others as you wish them to treat you.* **5** for example: *Some animals, as dogs and cats, eat meat.* **6** because: *As she was a skilled worker, she received good wages.* **7** like: *They treat him as an equal.* **8** that: *Do the same thing as I do.* **9** a fact that: *As you know, he is not here today because he is sick.* **1,5** *adverb,* **2,7** *preposition,* **3,4,6** *conjunction,* **8,9** *pronoun.*

as for, about; concerning: *As for baseball, it isn't my favorite sport.*

as if or **as though,** the way it would be if: *You sound as if you were angry.*

as is, in the present condition: *If we buy the house as is, it won't cost us very much.*

as·bes·tos (as bes′təs), a kind of mineral which does not burn. Asbestos separates into fibers that can be made into fireproof clothing. *noun.*

as·cend (ə send′), to go up; rise; climb: *We watched a group of climbers ascend the mountainside. verb.*

as·cent (ə sent′), a going up; rising; climbing: *The ascent of Mount Everest is difficult. noun.*

as·cer·tain (as′ər tān′), to find out: *The detective tried to ascertain the facts about the robbery. verb.*

ash[1] (ash), what remains of a thing after it has been thoroughly burned: *He flicked his cigarette ash into the fireplace. noun, plural* **ash·es.**

ash[2] (ash), a kind of shade tree that has silver-gray bark and tough wood. *noun, plural* **ash·es.**

a·shamed (ə shāmd′), **1** feeling shame; disturbed or uncomfortable because one has done something wrong, bad, or silly: *I was ashamed of the lies I had told.* **2** unwilling because of fear of shame: *I was ashamed to tell my parents I had failed math. adjective.*

ash·es (ash′iz), what remains of a thing after it has thoroughly burned: *I removed the ashes from the fireplace. noun plural.*

a·shore (ə shôr′), on or to the shore or land: *The ship's passengers went ashore. Some of the crew had not been ashore for months. adverb.*

ash·tray (ash′trā′), a small, flat holder to put tobacco ashes in. *noun.*

A·sia (ā′zhə), the largest continent, east of Europe and west of the Pacific Ocean. China, India, and Israel are countries in Asia. *noun.*

A·sian (ā′zhən), **1** of Asia; having something to do with Asia or its people; from Asia. **2** a person born or living in Asia. **1** *adjective,* **2** *noun.*

a·side (ə sīd′), on one side; to one side; away: *He stepped aside to let me pass. adverb.*

aside from, except for: *Aside from arithmetic, I have finished my homework.*

ask (ask), **1** to try to find out by words: *Why don't you ask? She asked about our health. Ask the way.* **2** to seek the answer to: *Ask any questions you wish.* **3** to put a question to: *Ask him how old he is.* **4** to try to get by words: *Ask them to sing. Ask for help if you need it.* **5** to invite: *I asked ten people to my party.* **6** to demand: *They were asking too high a price for their house. verb.*

I once knew a man named Calvin Crew,
Whose hat and tie were always **askew**,
To say he was careless is surely true,
Since on his right foot he wore a left shoe!

askew

a hat	**i** it	**oi** oil	**ch** child	a in about
ā age	**ī** ice	**ou** out	**ng** long	e in taken
ä far	**o** hot	**u** cup	**sh** she	**ə** = i in pencil
e let	**ō** open	**u̇** put	**th** thin	o in lemon
ē equal	**ô** order	**ü** rule	**ŦH** then	u in circus
ėr term			**zh** measure	

a·skew (ə skyü′), to one side; turned or twisted the wrong way; out of the proper position: *The wind blew my hat askew. Isn't that picture askew? adverb, adjective.*

a·sleep (ə slēp′), **1** not awake; sleeping: *The cat is asleep.* **2** into a state of sleep: *The tired children fell asleep.* **3** numb: *My foot is asleep.* **1,3** *adjective,* **2** *adverb.*

as·par·a·gus (ə spar′ə gəs), the tender, green shoots of a plant with scalelike leaves. Asparagus is eaten as a vegetable. *noun.*

as·pect (as′pekt), **1** one side or part or view of a subject: *We must consider each aspect of this plan before we decide.* **2** a look; appearance: *Before the storm, the sky had a gray, gloomy aspect. noun.*

as·pen (as′pən), a kind of poplar tree whose leaves tremble and rustle in the slightest breeze. *noun.*

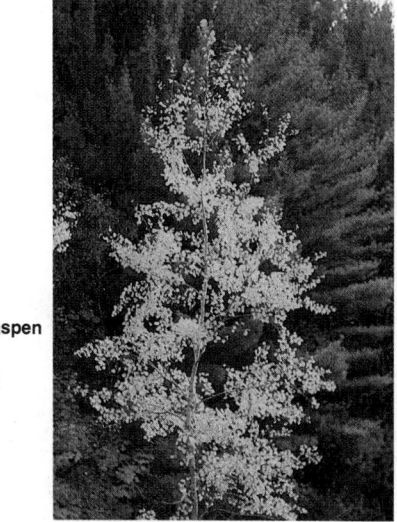

aspen

as·phalt (as′fôlt), **1** a dark substance much like tar, found in various parts of the world or obtained by refining petroleum. **2** a smooth, hard mixture of this substance with crushed rock or sand. Asphalt is used to pave roads. *noun.*

as·pi·ra·tion (as′pə rā′shən), an earnest desire; longing; ambition: *She has aspirations to be a doctor. noun.*

as·pire (ə spīr′), to have an ambition for something; desire earnestly; seek: *He aspired to be captain of the team.* verb, **as·pires, as·pired, as·pir·ing.**

as·pir·in (as′pər ən), a drug used to relieve pain and reduce fever. *noun.*

ass (as), **1** donkey. **2** a stupid, silly, or stubborn person; fool. *noun, plural* **ass·es.**

as·sail (ə sāl′), to attack with violence: *The soldiers assailed the enemy fort. verb.*

as·sail·ant (ə sā′lənt), a person who attacks: *The injured man did not know who his assailant was. noun.*

as·sas·sin (ə sas′n), a murderer; one who kills a well-known person by a sudden attack or from ambush. *noun.*

as·sas·si·nate (ə sas′n āt), to murder, especially a well-known person, by a sudden attack or from ambush: *President Kennedy was assassinated in 1963.* verb, **as·sas·si·nates, as·sas·si·nat·ed, as·sas·si·nat·ing.**

as·sas·si·na·tion (ə sas′n ā′shən), a murdering by a sudden attack or from ambush. *noun.*

as·sault (ə sôlt′), **1** a sudden, vigorous attack: *The soldiers made an assault on the enemy fort.* **2** to make an attack on: *My friend barely escaped from the gang that tried to assault him.* **1** *noun,* **2** *verb.*

as·sem·ble (ə sem′bəl), **1** to gather or come together: *The principal assembled all the students in the auditorium.* **2** to put together; fit together: *Will you help me assemble my model airplane?* verb, **as·sem·bles, as·sem·bled, as·sem·bling.**

as·sem·bly (ə sem′blē), **1** a group of people gathered together for some purpose; meeting: *The principal addressed the school assembly.*
2 Assembly, the lower branch of the state legislature of some states of the United States.
3 a putting together; fitting together: *In Detroit we saw the assembly of the parts which make up an automobile.* **4** all the parts necessary to put something together: *The bicycle had a complicated gear assembly. noun, plural* **as·sem·blies.**

as·sent (ə sent′), **1** to agree; express agreement; consent: *Everyone assented to the plans for the picnic.* **2** an agreement; acceptance of a proposal or statement: *She smiled her assent to the plan.* **1** *verb,* **2** *noun.*

as·sert (ə sėrt′), **1** to state positively; declare firmly: *She asserts that her story is absolutely true.* **2** to defend or insist on a right or claim: *Assert your independence. verb.*
assert oneself, to insist on one's rights; demand recognition: *Her salary was not raised until she asserted herself and demanded a promotion.*

as·ser·tion (ə sėr′shən), **1** a very strong statement; firm declaration: *His assertion of innocence was believed by the jury.* **2** an insisting on a right or claim: *She moved away from home as an assertion of her independence. noun.*

A

as·sess (ə ses′), **1** to estimate the value of property or income for taxation; value: *The property was assessed at $10,000.* **2** to charge as a tax or fee: *The library assessed several dollars in fines for the overdue books.* verb.

as·sess·ment (ə ses′mənt), an estimation of the value of property or income. noun.

as·ses·sor (ə ses′ər), a person who estimates the value of property or income for taxation. noun.

as·set (as′et), **1** a valuable quality or possession; advantage: *Ability to get along with people is an asset.* **2 assets,** things of value; property, such as a house, a car, stocks, bonds, or jewelry. noun.

as·sign (ə sīn′), **1** to give as a task to be done: *The teacher assigned the next ten problems.* **2** to appoint: *We were assigned to decorate the room.* **3** to fix; set: *The judge assigned a day for the trial.* **4** to give out; distribute: *The scoutmasters assigned a different tent area to each troop.* verb.

as·sign·ment (ə sīn′mənt), **1** something assigned: *Today's assignment in arithmetic consists of ten examples.* **2** an assigning or a being assigned: *Room assignments were made on the first day of school.* noun.

as·sist (ə sist′), to help: *She assisted the science teacher with the experiment.* verb.

as·sist·ance (ə sis′təns), a help; aid: *I need your assistance.* noun.

as·sist·ant (ə sis′tənt), **1** a helper: *I was her assistant in the library.* **2** helping; assisting: *He is an assistant teacher.* **1** noun, **2** adjective.

as·so·ci·ate (ə sō′shē āt *for 1 and 3;* ə sō′shē it *for 2 and 4*), **1** to connect in thought: *We associate turkey with Thanksgiving.* **2** joined with another or others: *I am an associate editor of the school paper.* **3** to join as a companion, partner, or friend: *She is associated with her brothers in business.* **4** a companion, partner, or friend: *She is an associate in a law firm.* **1,3** verb, **as·so·ci·ates, as·so·ci·at·ed, as·so·ci·at·ing; 2** adjective, **4** noun.

as·so·ci·a·tion (ə sō′sē ā′shən), **1** a group of people joined together for some purpose: *Will you join the young people's association at our church?* **2** companionship or friendship: *They had enjoyed a close association over many years.* **3** an idea connected with another idea in thought: *Many people make the association of the color red with anger.* noun.

as·sort·ed (ə sôr′tid), selected so as to be of different kinds; various: *They served assorted cakes.* adjective.

assorted—assorted fruit

as·sort·ment (ə sôrt′mənt), a collection of various kinds: *These scarfs come in an assortment of colors.* noun.

as·sume (ə süm′), **1** to take for granted without proof; suppose: *He assumed that the train would be on time.* **2** to take upon oneself; undertake: *She assumed the leadership of the project.* **3** to take for oneself: *The king's brother tried to assume the throne in the king's absence.* **4** to pretend: *Although she was afraid, she assumed a confident manner.* verb, **as·sumes, as·sumed, as·sum·ing.**

as·sump·tion (ə sump′shən), **1** the act of assuming: *The country celebrated the new president's assumption of office.* **2** the thing assumed: *His assumption that he would win the prize proved incorrect.* noun.

as·sur·ance (ə shùr′əns), **1** a statement intended to make a person more sure: *We gave her our assurance that we would not play in her yard again.* **2** confidence in one's own ability: *His careful preparation gave him assurance in taking the test.* noun.

as·sure (ə shùr′), **1** to tell positively: *They assured us that the plane would be on time.* **2** to make sure: *I assured myself that I had all my books before leaving for school.* verb, **as·sures, as·sured, as·sur·ing.**

as·sur·ed·ly (ə shùr′id lē), **1** surely; certainly: *I will assuredly come.* **2** confidently; boldly. adverb.

as·ter (as′tər), a common plant having daisylike flowers with white, pink, or purple petals around a yellow center. noun.

Word History

aster *Aster* comes from a Greek word meaning "star." The plant was called this because its petals look like rays.

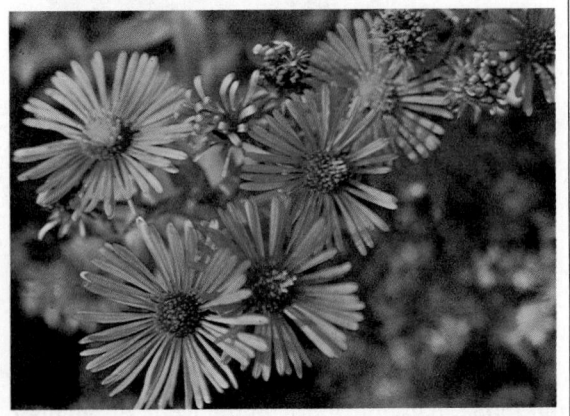

as·ter·isk (as′tə risk′), a star-shaped mark (*) used in printing and writing to tell a reader that there is more information at another place on the page. It is also used to tell a computer to multiply two numbers. noun.

a·stern (ə stėrn′), at or toward the rear of a ship or boat: *The captain went astern.* adverb.

as·ter·oid (as′tə roid′), any of the thousands of

very small planets that revolve about the sun, chiefly between the orbits of Mars and Jupiter. *noun.*

asth·ma (az′mə), a disease that makes breathing difficult and causes wheezing and coughing. *noun.*

a·stir (ə stėr′), in motion; up and about: *Although it was midnight, the whole family was astir.* *adjective.*

as·ton·ish (ə ston′ish), to surprise greatly; amaze: *We were astonished at the force of the wind during the hurricane.* *verb.*

as·ton·ish·ment (ə ston′ish mənt), great surprise; sudden wonder; amazement. *noun.*

as·tound (ə stound′), to surprise greatly; amaze: *She was astounded by the news that she had won the contest.* *verb.*

a·stray (ə strā′), **1** out of the right way or place; wandering: *The gate is open and all the cows have gone astray.* See picture. **2** in or into error: *We reached the theater late because a mistake in the newspaper ad led us astray.* *adjective, adverb.*

a·stride (ə strīd′), with one leg on each side of: *to sit astride a horse.* *preposition.*

as·trol·o·gy (ə strol′ə jē), the study of the influence that some people believe the sun, moon, stars, and planets have on lives and events here on earth. *noun.*

as·tro·naut (as′trə nôt), a member of the crew of a spacecraft. *noun.*
[*Astronaut* comes from two Greek words meaning "star" and "sailor."]

as·tron·o·mer (ə stron′ə mər), a person who is an expert in astronomy. *noun.*

as·tro·nom·i·cal (as′trə nom′ə kəl), **1** having something to do with astronomy: *A telescope is an astronomical instrument.* **2** enormous; very great: *an astronomical sum of money.* *adjective.*

as·tron·o·my (ə stron′ə mē), the science that deals with the sun, moon, planets, stars, and other heavenly bodies. *noun.*

a·sun·der (ə sun′dər), in pieces; into separate parts; apart: *Lightning split the tree asunder.* See picture. *adverb.*

a·sy·lum (ə sī′ləm), **1** an institution for the support and care of the mentally ill, the blind, orphans, or other people who need care. **2** a refuge; shelter. Asylum is sometimes given by one nation to persons of another nation. *noun.*

at (at, ət, *or* it), **1** in; on; by; near: *I will be at the store. There is someone at the front door.* **2** in the direction of; to; toward: *I aimed at the target.* **3** on or near the time of: *She goes to bed at nine o'clock.* **4** in a condition of: *England and France were at war.* **5** for: *We bought two books at a dollar each.* *preposition.*

ate (āt). See **eat**. *We ate our dinner.* *verb.*

a·the·ist (ā′thē ist), a person who believes that there is no God. *noun.*

ath·lete (ath′lēt′), a person trained in sports and exercises of physical strength, speed, and skill. Baseball players and swimmers are athletes. *noun.*

A BULL FROM THE FIELDS WENT ASTRAY,

CHINA

WANDERING INTO A SHOP ONE FINE DAY,

WITH HOOFBEATS LIKE THUNDER KNOCKING TEACUPS ASUNDER

WHICH FRIGHTENED THE PATRONS AWAY.

athlete's foot, a very contagious skin disease of the feet, caused by a fungus.

ath·let·ic (ath let′ik), **1** of an athlete; like or suited to an athlete: *athletic skills*. **2** having something to do with active games and sports: *He joined an athletic association*. **3** strong and active: *She is an athletic girl. adjective.*

ath·let·ics (ath let′iks), sports and exercises that require physical strength and skill. Athletics include baseball and tennis. *noun plural.*

At·lan·ta (at lan′tə), the capital of Georgia. *noun.*

At·lan·tic (at lan′tik), **1** the ocean east of North and South America. It extends to Europe and Africa. **2** of, on, or near the Atlantic Ocean: *New York is on the Atlantic coast of North America.* **1** *noun,* **2** *adjective.*

at·las (at′ləs), a book of maps. A big atlas has maps of every country. *noun, plural* **at·las·es.**
[The word *atlas* comes from the name of Atlas, a giant in Greek myths. According to one story, he had to hold up the sky on his shoulders as a punishment. A picture showing this appeared as a first page in early books of maps. People began to call a book of maps an *atlas*.]

at·mo·sphere (at′mə sfir), **1** the air that surrounds the earth. **2** the mass of gases that surrounds any heavenly body: *The atmosphere of Venus is cloudy.* **3** the air in any given place: *Plants grow rapidly in the moist atmosphere of a jungle.* **4** surrounding influence: *The peaceful atmosphere in the library helped me to study. noun.*

at·mo·spher·ic (at′mə sfir′ik), of, in, or having something to do with the atmosphere: *Atmospheric conditions often prevent observations of the stars. adjective.*

at·oll (at′ol), a coral island or group of islands forming a ring around a shallow lagoon. *noun.*

atoll

at·om (at′əm), **1** one of the tiny particles which make up all the matter in the universe. An atom is the smallest particle of a chemical element that has the characteristics of that element. An atom is made up of protons and neutrons in a central nucleus surrounded by electrons. A molecule of water consists of two atoms of hydrogen and one atom of oxygen. **2** a tiny bit: *There is not an atom of truth in his whole story. noun.*

atom bomb, an atomic bomb.

a·tom·ic (ə tom′ik), **1** of or having something to do with atoms: *atomic research.* **2** using or run by atomic energy: *an atomic submarine. adjective.*

atomic bomb, a bomb in which the splitting of atoms results in an explosion of tremendous force and heat, accompanied by a blinding light; A-bomb.

atomic energy, the energy that exists inside the nucleus of an atom; nuclear energy. Atomic energy can be released by splitting or combining the centers of some kinds of atoms.

a·tone (ə tōn′), to make up; make amends: *She atoned for her unkindness to her sister by taking her to the movies. verb,* **a·tones, a·toned, a·ton·ing.**

a·top (ə top′), on the top of: *He had a hat atop his head. preposition.*

a·tri·um (ā′trē əm), either of the two upper chambers of the heart. An atrium receives blood from the veins and forces it into a lower chamber. *noun, plural* **a·tri·a** (ā′trē ə) or **a·tri·ums.**

a·tro·cious (ə trō′shəs), **1** very cruel or brutal: *Kidnapping is an atrocious crime.* **2** very unpleasant: *The weather has been simply atrocious. adjective.*

a·troc·i·ty (ə tros′ə tē), a very cruel or brutal act: *Many atrocities are committed in war. noun, plural* **a·troc·i·ties.**

at·tach (ə tach′), **1** to fasten: *I attached a rope to my sled.* **2** to bind by affection: *She is very attached to her cousin.* **3** to give; think of as belonging to: *I did not attach much importance to what he said. verb.*

at·tach·ment (ə tach′mənt), **1** an attaching or being attached; connection: *The attachment of a rope to the sled took less than a minute.* **2** anything attached, such as an additional device. Vacuum cleaners often have attachments for cleaning drapes and furniture. **3** affection; devotion: *The children have a great attachment to their dog. noun.*

at·tack (ə tak′), **1** to set upon to hurt; begin fighting against: *The dog attacked the cat. The enemy attacked at dawn.* **2** to talk or write against: *The candidate attacked his opponent's record as mayor.* **3** to go at with vigor: *attack a hard lesson. The hungry hikers attacked dinner as soon as it was ready.* **4** an attacking: *The enemy attack took us by surprise.* **5** to act harmfully on: *Locusts attacked the crops.* **6** a sudden occurrence of illness or discomfort: *an attack of flu, an attack of sneezing.* **1-3,5** *verb,* **4,6** *noun.*

at·tack·er (ə tak′ər), a person or thing that attacks: *They fought with their attackers. noun.*

at·tain (ə tān′), **1** to arrive at: *Grandfather has attained the age of 80.* **2** to gain by effort; accomplish: *She attained her goal. verb.*

at·tain·ment (ə tān′mənt), an attaining: *Her main goal was the attainment of a medical degree. noun.*

at·tempt (ə tempt′), **1** to try. **2** a try; effort: *They made an attempt to climb the mountain.* **3** an attack:

a hat	i it	oi oil	ch child		a in about
ā age	ī ice	ou out	ng long		e in taken
ä far	o hot	u cup	sh she	ə =	i in pencil
e let	ō open	u̇ put	th thin		o in lemon
ē equal	ô order	ü rule	ᴛʜ then		u in circus
ėr term			zh measure		

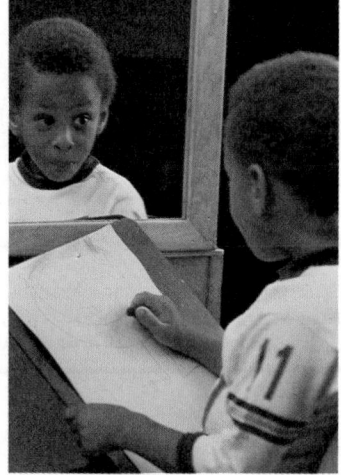

attempt (definition 1)
He **attempted** to draw a picture of himself.

An assassin made an attempt upon the king's life.
1 *verb,* 2,3 *noun.*

at·tend (ə tend′), **1** to be present at: *My little sister attends kindergarten.* **2** to give care and thought; pay attention to: *Attend to your work.* **3** to go with; accompany: *Noble ladies attended the queen.* **4** to wait on; care for; tend: *Nurses attend the sick. verb.*

at·tend·ance (ə ten′dəns), **1** the act of being present at a place; attending: *Our class had perfect attendance today.* **2** the number of people present; persons attending: *The attendance at the meeting was over 200. noun.*

at·tend·ant (ə ten′dənt), **1** a person who waits on another: *The airliner had several flight attendants to care for the passengers.* **2** going with as a result; accompanying: *Coughing is one of the attendant discomforts of a cold.* 1 *noun,* 2 *adjective.*

at·ten·tion (ə ten′shən), **1** careful thinking, looking, or listening: *Give me your attention while I explain this math problem.* **2** notice; power of attending: *She called my attention to the problem.* **3** care and thoughtfulness; consideration: *The children showed their grandparents much attention.* **4** standing very straight with the arms at the sides, the heels together, and the eyes looking ahead: *The soldiers stood at attention during the inspection. noun.*

at·ten·tive (ə ten′tiv), **1** paying attention; observant: *The attentive pupil is most likely to learn.* **2** courteous; polite: *Good hosts are attentive to their guests. adjective.*

at·test (ə test′), to give proof of; testify to: *Your good work attests the care you have taken. The handwriting expert attested to the genuineness of the signature. verb.*

at·tic (at′ik), the space in a house just below the roof and above the other rooms. *noun.*
[*Attic* comes from the words *attic story,* meaning "the top story of a building." It was called this because people used to build the top stories of their houses to look like the buildings of Attica, a district of ancient Greece.]

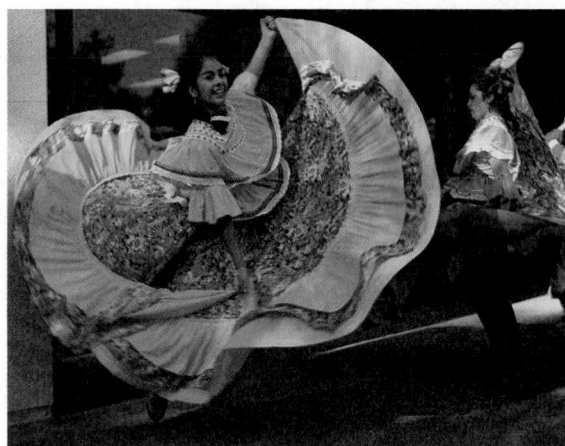

attire (definition 1)
The dancers wore colorful **attire.**

at·tire (ə tīr′), **1** clothing or dress. **2** to clothe or dress: *The king was attired in a cloak trimmed with ermine.* 1 *noun,* 2 *verb,* **at·tires, at·tired, at·tir·ing.**

at·ti·tude (at′ə tüd *or* at′ə tyüd), **1** a way of thinking, acting, or feeling: *I used to dislike that teacher but I've changed my attitude.* **2** a position of the body: *He raised his fists in the attitude of a boxer ready to fight. noun.*

at·tor·ney (ə tėr′nē), a lawyer. *noun, plural* **at·tor·neys.**

at·tract (ə trakt′), **1** to draw to itself or oneself: *The magnet attracted the iron filings. The famous actor attracted a crowd.* **2** to be pleasing to; win the attention and liking of: *Bright colors attract children. verb.*

at·trac·tion (ə trak′shən), **1** a thing that delights or attracts people: *The elephants were the chief attraction at the circus.* **2** the act or power of attracting: *The iron filings were drawn to the magnet by attraction. Sports have no attraction for me. noun.*

at·trac·tive (ə trak′tiv), winning attention and liking; pleasing: *an attractive young couple. adjective.*

at·trib·ute (ə trib′yüt *for 1 and 2;* at′rə byüt *for 3*), **1** to think of as caused by: *She attributes her good health to a proper diet.* **2** to think of as belonging to or appropriate to: *We attribute courage to the lion and cunning to the fox.* **3** a quality thought of as belonging to a person or thing; characteristic: *Patience is a necessary attribute of a good teacher.* 1,2 *verb,* **at·trib·utes, at·trib·ut·ed, at·trib·ut·ing;** 3 *noun.*

at·tune (ə tün′ *or* ə tyün′), to adjust; get used to: *Our ears became attuned to the noise of the city.* *verb,* **at·tunes, at·tuned, at·tun·ing.**

au·burn (ô′bərn), reddish-brown. *adjective.*

auc·tion (ôk′shən), **1** a public sale in which each thing is sold to the person who offers the most money for it. **2** to sell at an auction. **1** *noun,* **2** *verb.*

auc·tion·eer (ôk′shə nir′), a person whose business is conducting auctions. *noun.*

au·da·cious (ô dā′shəs), **1** having the courage to take risks; bold; daring: *an audacious explorer.* **2** too bold; impudent: *The audacious waiter demanded a larger tip. adjective.*

au·di·ble (ô′də bəl), loud enough to be heard; able to be heard: *Without a microphone the speaker was barely audible. adjective.*

au·di·ence (ô′dē əns), **1** a group of people that sees or hears something: *The audience at the theater enjoyed the play. That television program has a large audience.* **2** a formal interview with a person of high rank: *The ambassador was granted an audience with the queen. noun.*

au·di·o (ô′dē ō), having to do with sound: *The audio part of the program was off for several minutes because of problems at the TV station. adjective.*

au·di·tion (ô dish′ən), **1** a hearing to test the ability of a singer, actor, or other performer. **2** to perform at or give such a hearing: *to audition for a part in a play. The director auditioned ten actors.* **1** *noun,* **2** *verb.*

au·di·to·ri·um (ô′də tôr′ē əm), **1** a large room for an audience in a theater, school, or the like; large hall. **2** a building especially designed for public meetings, concerts, and lectures. *noun.*

au·di·to·ry (ô′də tôr′ē), having to do with hearing or the organs of hearing. The **auditory nerve** goes from the ear to the brain. *adjective.*

Aug., August.

au·ger (ô′gər), a tool for boring holes in wood. *noun.*

auger

aug·ment (ôg ment′), to increase: *He augmented his income by working overtime three nights a week. verb.*

au·gust (ô gust′), inspiring respect and admiration; majestic: *The august beauty of the mountains filled them with wonder. adjective.*

Au·gust (ô′gəst), the eighth month of the year. It has 31 days. *noun.*
[*August* was named for Augustus, the first emperor of Rome. He lived from 63 B.C. to A.D. 14.]

Au·gus·ta (ô gus′tə), the capital of Maine. *noun.*

auk (ôk), a sea bird found in arctic regions, with legs set so far back that it stands like a penguin. It has short wings used chiefly as paddles in swimming. *noun.*

Word History

auk These birds are common in Iceland. The word *auk* comes from an old name for them used in Iceland and nearby arctic regions.

auk—about 16 inches (41 centimeters) tall

aunt (ant), **1** a sister of one's father or mother. **2** the wife of one's uncle. *noun.*

aunt·ie or **aunt·y** (an′tē), aunt. *noun, plural* **aunt·ies.**

au·ra (ôr′ə), something that seems to come from or surround a person or thing as an atmosphere: *There was an aura of mystery about the stranger. noun.*

au·ri·cle (ôr′ə kəl), either of the two upper chambers of the heart; atrium. *noun.*

au·ro·ra (ô rôr′ə), streamers or bands of light that appear in the sky at night, especially in polar regions. *noun.*

aus·pi·cious (ô spish′əs), with signs of success; favorable: *The popularity of his first book was an auspicious beginning for his career. adjective.*

A

a hat	i it	oi oil	ch child	a in about
ā age	ī ice	ou out	ng long	e in taken
ä far	o hot	u cup	sh she	ə = { i in pencil
e let	ō open	ù put	th thin	o in lemon
ē equal	ô order	ü rule	ŦH then	u in circus
ėr term			zh measure	

austere (definition 1)
They look very **austere**.

Grant Wood, "American Gothic," Courtesy of The Art Institute of Chicago

aus·tere (ô stir′), **1** stern; harsh: *My father was a silent, austere man, very strict with us.* **2** strict in morals: *Some ideas of the Puritans seem too austere to us.* **3** severely simple: *The tall, plain columns stood against the sky in austere beauty. adjective.*

Aus·tin (ô′stən), the capital of Texas. *noun.*

Aus·tral·ia (ô strā′lyə), the smallest continent, located southeast of Asia between the Pacific and Indian oceans. The country of Australia covers the whole continent. *noun.*

Aus·tral·ian (ô strā′lyən), **1** of Australia; having something to do with Australia or its people; from Australia. **2** a person born or living in Australia. **1** *adjective,* **2** *noun.*

Aus·tri·a (ô′strē ə), a country in central Europe. *noun.*

au·then·tic (ô then′tik), **1** reliable: *We read an authentic account of the plane crash given by one of the survivors.* **2** genuine; real: *That is her authentic signature, not a forgery. adjective.*

au·thor (ô′thər), **1** a person who writes books, poems, stories, or articles; writer: *My little sister's favorite author is Dr. Seuss.* **2** a person who creates or begins anything: *Are you the author of this scheme? noun.*
[*Author* comes from a Latin word meaning "one who creates or builds."]

au·thor·i·ta·tive (ə thôr′ə tā′tiv), **1** having authority: *An authoritative source in the government stated that there would be no food shortage.* **2** commanding: *In authoritative tones the policeman shouted to us, "Keep back."* **3** that can be believed because it comes from expert knowledge: *A doctor's statement concerning the cause of an illness is considered authoritative. adjective.*

au·thor·i·ty (ə thôr′ə tē), **1** the power or right to give commands and enforce obedience: *Parents have authority over their children. The police have the authority to arrest speeding drivers.* **2** the **authorities,** the officials in control: *The authorities at city hall received many complaints about unrepaired streets.* **3** a source of information or advice: *A good dictionary is an authority on the meanings of words.* **4** an expert on some subject: *She is an authority on the Revolutionary War. noun, plural* **au·thor·i·ties.**

au·thor·i·za·tion (ô′thər ə zā′shən), giving the power or right to: *The authorization of the police to give tickets to jaywalkers reduced the number of accidents. noun.*

au·thor·ize (ô′thə rīz′), **1** to give power or right to: *The committee authorized us to proceed with our plan.* **2** to approve: *The mayor authorized the spending of money for better public transportation. verb,* **au·thor·iz·es, au·thor·ized, au·thor·iz·ing.**

au·to (ô′tō), an automobile. *noun, plural* **au·tos.**

au·to·bi·og·ra·phy (ô′tə bī og′rə fē), the story of a person's life written by that person. *noun, plural* **au·to·bi·og·ra·phies.**

au·to·graph (ô′tə graf), **1** a person's signature: *Many people collect the autographs of celebrities.* **2** to write one's name in or on: *The movie star autographed pictures for her fans.* **1** *noun,* **2** *verb.*

Autoharp

Au·to·harp (ô′tō härp′), a trademark for a stringed musical instrument that is like a small harp. An Autoharp produces chords when the strings are plucked. *noun.*

au·to·mat·ic (ô′tə mat′ik), **1** able to work by itself: *We have an automatic dishwasher in our kitchen.* **2** done without thought or attention: *Breathing and swallowing are usually automatic.* **3** a gun that throws out the empty shell and reloads by itself. An automatic continues to fire until the pressure on the trigger is released. **1,2** *adjective,* **3** *noun.*

au·to·mat·i·cal·ly (ô′tə mat′ik lē), in an automatic manner: *Supermarket doors usually open automatically.* adverb.

au·to·ma·tion (ô′tə mā′shən), the use of automatic controls in the operation of a machine or group of machines. In automation, machines do many of the tasks formerly performed by people. *noun.*

au·to·mo·bile (ô′tə mə bēl′), a passenger vehicle for traveling on roads and streets. Most automobiles are powered by gasoline engines that drive the rear or front wheels. *noun.*
[*Automobile* comes from a Greek word meaning "self" and a Latin word meaning "movable."]

au·top·sy (ô′top sē), a medical examination of a dead body to find the cause of death: *The autopsy showed that the patient died of a heart attack. noun,* plural **au·top·sies.**

au·tumn (ô′təm), **1** the season of the year between summer and winter; fall. **2** of, for, or coming in autumn: *autumn leaves.* **1** *noun,* **2** *adjective.*

aux·il·iar·y (ôg zil′yər ē), **1** helping; assisting: *Some sailboats have auxiliary engines.* **2** a person or thing that helps; aid: *The microscope is a useful auxiliary to the human eye.* **1** *adjective,* **2** *noun,* plural **aux·il·iar·ies.**

a·vail (ə vāl′), **1** help; use; benefit: *Matches are of no avail if they are wet.* **2 avail oneself of,** to take advantage of; make use of: *While traveling in France, he availed himself of the opportunity to learn a little French.* **1** *noun,* **2** *verb.*

a·vail·a·ble (ə vā′lə bəl), **1** able to be used: *She is not available for the job; she has other work now.* **2** able to be had or obtained: *All available tickets were sold.* adjective.

av·a·lanche (av′ə lanch), a large mass of snow and ice, or of dirt and rocks, rapidly sliding or falling down the side of a mountain. *noun.*

av·ar·ice (av′ər is), too great a desire to acquire money or property; greed for wealth. *noun.*

Ave., Avenue.

a·venge (ə venj′), to get revenge for: *They fought to avenge the enemy's invasion of their country.* *verb,* **a·veng·es, a·venged, a·veng·ing.**

av·e·nue (av′ə nü *or* av′ə nyü), **1** a street, sometimes wide or bordered with trees. **2** a way of approach: *Hard work is one avenue to success.* *noun.*

av·er·age (av′ər ij), **1** the quantity found by dividing the sum of all the quantities by the number of quantities. The average of 3 and 5 and 10 is 6 (because 3 + 5 + 10 = 18, and 18 ÷ 3 = 6). **2** to find the average of: *Will you average those numbers for me?* **3** obtained by averaging: *The average temperature for the week was 82.* **4** to have as an average; amount on the average to: *The cost of our lunches at school averaged three dollars a week.* **5** the usual sort or amount: *The amount of rain this year has been below average.* **6** usual; ordinary: *The average person likes TV.* **1,5** *noun,* **2,4** *verb,* **av·er·ag·es, av·er·aged, av·er·ag·ing;** **3,6** *adjective.*

a·verse (ə vėrs′), opposed; unwilling: *I am averse to smoking.* adjective.

a·ver·sion (ə vėr′zhən), a strong dislike: *He has an aversion to beef liver. noun.*

a·vert (ə vėrt′), **1** to keep from happening; prevent; avoid: *The driver averted an accident by a quick turn of the steering wheel.* **2** to turn away; turn aside: *I averted my eyes from the automobile accident.* verb.

a·vi·ar·y (ā′vē er′ē), a place where many birds, especially wild birds, are kept. *noun,* plural **a·vi·ar·ies.**

a·vi·a·tion (ā′vē ā′shən), **1** the science of flying and navigating aircraft: *You must study aviation to become a pilot.* **2** the designing and manufacturing of aircraft: *Aviation is an important industry. noun.*
[*Aviation* comes from a Latin word meaning "bird." The English words *aviary* and *aviator* also come from this same Latin word.]

a·vi·a·tor (ā′vē ā′tər), a person who flies an aircraft; pilot. *noun.*

av·id (av′id), extremely eager: *He was an avid reader who often read several books a week.* adjective.

av·o·ca·do (av′ə kä′dō), the fruit of a tree that grows in warm regions. Avocados are shaped like pears and have a dark-green or almost black skin and a very large seed. Their yellow-green pulp is used in salads. *noun,* plural **av·o·ca·dos.**

avocado

av·o·ca·tion (av′ə kā′shən), something that a person likes to do in addition to a regular job; hobby: *She is a lawyer, but writing stories is her avocation. noun.*

a·void (ə void′), to keep away from; keep out of the way of: *We avoided driving through large cities on our trip. verb.*

a·void·ance (ə void′ns), a keeping away from: *Her avoidance of me made me think she was angry with me. noun.*

a·wait (ə wāt′), **1** to wait for; look forward to: *We anxiously awaited the arrival of the plane.* **2** to be ready for; be in store for: *Many pleasures await you on your trip. verb.*

a·wake (ə wāk′), **1** to wake up; arouse: *I awoke from a sound sleep. The alarm clock awoke me.* **2** roused from sleep; not asleep: *She is always awake early.* **1** *verb,* **a·wakes, a·woke** or

a·waked, a·waked, a·wak·ing; 2 *adjective.*

a·wak·en (ə wā′kən), to wake up; stir up; arouse: *The sun was shining when he awakened. I was awakened early this morning. verb.*

a·ward (ə wôrd′), **1** to give after careful consideration; grant: *A medal was awarded to the best speller.* **2** something given after careful consideration; prize: *That painting won the highest award at the art show.* **3** to decide upon or settle by law: *The court awarded damages of $5000 to each injured person.* 1,3 *verb,* 2 *noun.*

a·ware (ə wer′ *or* ə war′), having knowledge; realizing; conscious: *I was too sleepy to be aware how cold it was. She was not aware of her danger. adjective.*

a·wash (ə wosh′), **1** covered with water: *The beach was awash with the flowing tide.* **2** carried about by water; floating: *The rising water set everything awash. adjective.*

a·way (ə wā′), **1** from a place; to a distance: *Stay away from the fire.* **2** at a distance; a way off: *The travelers were far away from home. His home is miles away.* **3** absent; gone: *My friend is away today.* **4** out of one's possession, notice, or use: *He gave his boat away.* **5** out of existence: *The sounds died away.* **6** in another direction; aside: *She turned her car away to avoid an accident.* **7** without stopping: *She worked away at her job.* **8** without delay; at once: *Fire away!* 1,2,4-8 *adverb,* 2,3 *adjective.*

awe (ô), **1** great fear and wonder; fear and great respect: *The sight of the great waterfall filled us with awe. The child stood in awe before the queen.* **2** to cause to feel awe; fill with awe: *The majesty of the mountains awed us.* 1 *noun,* 2 *verb,* **awes, awed, aw·ing.**

awe·some (ô′səm), causing great fear or wonder: *The fire was an awesome sight. adjective.*

aw·ful (ô′fəl), **1** causing fear; dreadful; terrible: *An awful storm with thunder and lightning came up.* **2** very great: *I had an awful lot of work to do.* **3** very bad: *I have an awful headache.* **4** very: *I was awful mad.* 1-3 *adjective,* 4 *adverb.*

aw·ful·ly (ô′flē *or* ô′fə lē), **1** dreadfully; terribly: *The broken leg hurt awfully.* **2** very: *I'm awfully sorry that I hurt your feelings. adverb.*

a·while (ə hwīl′), for a short time: *I usually read awhile before going to bed. adverb.*

awk·ward (ôk′wərd), **1** clumsy; not graceful or skillful in movement: *Seals are very awkward on land, but graceful in the water.* **2** not easily used or managed: *The handle of this pitcher is an awkward shape. This is an awkward package to carry.* **3** embarrassing: *He asked me such an awkward question that I did not reply. adjective.*

awl (ôl), a pointed tool used for making small holes in leather or wood. *noun.*

awn·ing (ô′ning), a piece of canvas, metal, or other material that forms a rooflike covering over a door, window, or porch. Awnings are used for protection from the sun or rain. *noun.*

a·woke (ə wōk′). See **awake.** *I awoke them at seven. We awoke early. verb.*

a hat	**i** it	**oi** oil	**ch** child	a in about	
ā age	**ī** ice	**ou** out	**ng** long	e in taken	
ä far	**o** hot	**u** cup	**sh** she	ə = { i in pencil	
e let	**ō** open	**ů** put	**th** thin	o in lemon	
ē equal	**ô** order	**ü** rule	**ŦH** then	u in circus	
ėr term			**zh** measure		

a·wry (ə rī′), **1** with a twist or turn to one side: *My hat was blown awry by the wind.* **2** wrong; out of order: *Our plans have gone awry. adverb.*

ax or **axe** (aks), a tool with a flat, sharp blade fastened on a handle, used for chopping, splitting, and shaping wood. *noun, plural* **ax·es.**

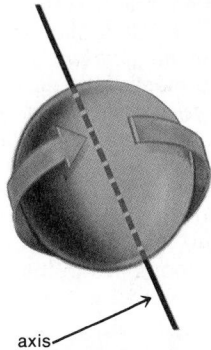

axis

ax·is (ak′sis), a straight line about which an object turns or seems to turn. The axis of the earth is an imaginary line through the North Pole and the South Pole. *noun, plural* **ax·es** (ak′sēz′).

ax·le (ak′səl), a bar or shaft on which a wheel turns. Some axles turn with the wheel. *noun.*

aye or **ay** (ī), **1** yes: *Aye, aye, sir.* **2** a vote or voter in favor of something: *The ayes won when the vote was taken.* 1 *adverb,* 2 *noun.*

AZ, Arizona (used with postal Zip Code).

azalea

a·zal·ea (ə zā′lyə), a shrub bearing many showy flowers. *noun.*

A·zer·bai·jan (ä′zər bī jän′), a country in southeastern Europe. *noun.*

Az·tec (az′tek), a member of an American Indian people of central Mexico. The Aztecs had a highly developed culture and ruled a large empire over 400 years ago. *noun, plural* **Az·tec** or **Az·tecs.**

az·ure (azh′ər), blue; blue like the sky. *adjective.*

B b

B or **b** (bē), the second letter of the English alphabet. *noun, plural* **B's** or **b's.**

baa (bä), **1** the sound a sheep makes; bleat. **2** to make this sound; bleat. 1 *noun,* 2 *verb.*

bab·ble (bab/əl), **1** to make sounds like a baby: *My baby brother babbles and coos in his crib.* **2** talk that cannot be understood: *A confused babble filled the room.* **3** to talk foolishly: *They babbled on and on without saying anything serious.* **4** foolish talk. **5** to talk too much; tell secrets: *He babbled all about the surprise party we had planned.* **6** to make a murmuring sound: *The little brook babbled away just behind our tent.* 1,3,5,6 *verb,* **bab·bles, bab·bled, bab·bling;** 2,4 *noun.*

babe (bāb), a baby. *noun.*

ba·boon (ba bün/), a large, fierce monkey with a doglike face. Baboons live in the rocky hills of Africa and Arabia. *noun.*

Word History

baboon *Baboon* comes from an earlier French word meaning "stupid person." The features of the animal were thought to look like a person's funny face.

baboon—about 3½ feet (1 meter) long with the tail

ba·by (bā/bē), **1** a very young child. **2** the youngest of a family or group. **3** young; small: *There were six baby hamsters in the cage.* **4** of or for a baby: *baby shoes, a baby bottle.* **5** like that of a baby; childish: *baby talk.* **6** a person who acts like a baby: *Don't be a baby.* **7** to treat as a baby: *You are too old to be babied.* 1,2,6 *noun, plural* **ba·bies;** 3-5 *adjective,* 7 *verb,* **ba·bies, ba·bied, ba·by·ing.**

ba·by·ish (bā/bē ish), like a baby; childish: *His round face and bald head gave him a babyish appearance. adjective.*

ba·by-sit (bā/bē sit/), to take care of a child or children while the parents are away for a while. *verb,* **ba·by-sits, ba·by-sat** (bā/bē sat/), **ba·by-sit·ting.**

ba·by-sit·ter (bā/bē sit/ər), a person who takes care of a child or children while the parents are away for a while. *noun.*

baby teeth, the first set of teeth.

bach·e·lor (bach/ə lər), a man who has not married. *noun.*

back (bak), **1** the part of a person's body opposite to the face or to the front part of the body. **2** the upper part of an animal's body from the neck to the end of the backbone. **3** the backbone; spine: *She fell from the ladder and broke her back.* **4** the side of anything away from the front; the rear or farther part: *I had a bruise on the back of my hand. Put the suitcase in the back of the closet.* **5** at the back: *the back seat of the car.* **6** the part of a chair, couch, bench, or the like, which supports the back of a person sitting down. **7** to support or help: *Her friends backed her plan.* **8** to move or cause to move backward: *I backed the car out of the driveway.* **9** behind in space or time: *Please walk back three steps. Have you read the back issues of this magazine?* **10** in return: *They paid back what they borrowed.* **11** in the place from which something or someone came: *Put the books back.* **12** a football player whose position is behind the line. 1-4,6,12 *noun,* 5,9 *adjective,* 7,8 *verb,* 9-11 *adverb.*

back and forth, first one way and then the other: *The dog ran back and forth across the field.*

back down, to give up an attempt or claim; withdraw: *I said I would go swimming, but I backed down when I found out how cold the water was.*

back of, in the rear of; behind: *The barn is back of the house.*

back out or **back out of,** to withdraw from an undertaking: *The village backed out of building a pool when the cost got too high.*

back·ache (bak/āk/), a continuous pain in the back. *noun.*

back·board (bak/bôrd/), the upright surface of wood, glass, or plastic to which the basket on a basketball court is fastened. *noun.*

back·bone (bak/bōn/), **1** the main bone along the middle of the back in human beings, horses, birds, snakes, frogs, fish, and many other animals; spine. The backbone consists of many separate bones, called vertebrae, held together by muscles and tendons. **2** the most important part: *The Constitution is the backbone of our legal system.* **3** strength of character: *It took backbone to tell the neighbors that you had accidentally broken their window. noun.*

back·field (bak/fēld/), the football players whose position is behind the line. *noun.*

back·fire (bak/fīr/), **1** an explosion of gas occurring at the wrong time or in the wrong place in a gasoline engine. **2** to explode in this way. **3** to have a result opposite to the expected result: *His* *plan backfired, and instead of getting rich he lost his money.* 1 *noun,* 2,3 *verb,* **back·fires, back·fired, back·fir·ing.**

back·gam·mon (bak′gam′ən), a game for two played on a special board with 12 spaces on each side. Each player has 15 pieces, which are moved according to the throw of the dice. *noun.*

back·ground (bak′ground′), 1 the part of a picture or scene toward the back: *The cottage stands in the foreground with the mountains in the background.* 2 the surface against which a thing or person is placed or shown: *The curtains had blue flowers on a white background.* 3 earlier conditions or events that help to explain some later condition or event: *This book gives the background of the Revolutionary War.* 4 past experience, knowledge, and training: *His early background included living on a farm. noun.*

in the background, out of the way; not involved: *I stayed in the background during their argument because I didn't want to get involved.*

back·hand (bak′hand′), a stroke in tennis and other games made with the back of the hand turned outward. *noun.*

backhand

back·pack (bak′pak′), 1 a pack, often supported by a frame, that is worn on the back by hikers and campers to carry food, clothes, and equipment. 2 to go hiking or camping while carrying a backpack. 1 *noun,* 2 *verb.*

back·stage (bak′stāj′), in the part of a theater not seen by the audience: *We went backstage after the play to congratulate the actors. adverb, adjective.*

back·stroke (bak′strōk′), a swimming stroke made while lying on one's back. *noun.*

back talk, rude or bold answers, especially by a younger person to an older one.

back·track (bak′trak′), to go back over a course or path. *verb.*

back·ward (bak′wərd), 1 with the back first: *He tumbled over backward.* 2 toward the back: *I looked backward. She gave a backward look as she left the room.* 3 opposite to the usual way: *Can you count backward?* 4 from better to worse: *In some towns living conditions improved; in some they went backward.* 5 slow in development: *a backward country.* 1-4 *adverb,* 2,5 *adjective.*

a hat	**i** it	**oi** oil	**ch** child	a in about
ā age	**ī** ice	**ou** out	**ng** long	e in taken
ä far	**o** hot	**u** cup	**sh** she	ə = { i in pencil
e let	**ō** open	**ù** put	**th** thin	o in lemon
ē equal	**ô** order	**ü** rule	**ŦH** then	u in circus
ėr term			**zh** measure	

back·wards (bak′wərdz), backward (definitions 1-4). *adverb.*

back·woods (bak′wùdz′), uncleared forests or wild regions far away from towns. *noun plural.*

back·yard (bak′yärd′), the piece of ground behind a house or building. *noun.*

ba·con (bā′kən), salted and smoked meat from the back and sides of a pig. *noun.*

bac·te·ri·a (bak tir′ē ə), very tiny and simple living things, so small that they can usually be seen only through a microscope. Certain bacteria cause diseases such as pneumonia; others do useful things, such as turning cider into vinegar. *noun plural of* **bac·te·ri·um** (bak tir′ē əm).

Word History

bacteria *Bacteria* comes from a Greek word meaning "a little rod." Bacteria were called this because some of them are rod-shaped.

bacteria
bottom, three types of **bacteria;**
top, the rod type as seen through a microscope

bad (bad), 1 not good; not as it ought to be: *Reading in dim light is bad for your eyes. The repair job on our car was bad, and it soon broke down again.* 2 evil; wicked: *Murder is a bad crime.* 3 not friendly; cross; unpleasant: *a bad temper.* 4 causing pain or sorrow: *We were all upset by the bad news.* 5 naughty; not behaving well: *My sister was bad when she ate my candy.* 6 unfavorable: *You came at a bad time.* 7 severe: *A bad thunderstorm delayed the airplane.* 8 rotten; spoiled: *Don't use that egg; it's bad.* 9 sorry: *I feel* *bad about losing your baseball.* **10** sick: *Her cold made her feel bad.* **11** incorrect: *a bad guess. adjective,* **worse, worst.**

bade (bad). See **bid.** *They bade her remain. verb.*

badge (baj), something worn to show that a person belongs to a certain occupation, school, class, club, or society. *noun.*

badg·er (baj′ər), **1** a hairy, gray animal that feeds at night and digs a hole to live in. **2** to keep on annoying or teasing: *They badgered me with endless questions.* **1** *noun,* **2** *verb.*

Word History

badger The word *badger* probably comes from *badge,* meaning "an identifying mark." The white streak along the badger's face and neck apparently was seen as a badge, or identifying mark.

badger (definition 1)—about 2 feet (60 centimeters) long

bad·ly (bad′lē), **1** in a bad manner: *She sings badly.* **2** very much: *We need help badly. adverb.*

bad·min·ton (bad′min tən), a game in which two or four players use light rackets to hit a small cork and plastic object back and forth over a high net. *noun.*

[*Badminton* was named for an estate in England. The game came from India and was first played in England in 1873.]

bad-tem·pered (bad′tem′pərd), having a bad temper; cross; irritable: *A bad-tempered person is hard to live with. adjective.*

baf·fle (baf′əl), to be too hard for a person to understand or solve; bewilder: *This puzzle baffles me. verb,* **baf·fles, baf·fled, baf·fling.**

bag (bag), **1** a container made of paper, cloth, or other soft material: *Fresh vegetables are sometimes sold in plastic bags.* **2** something like a bag in its use. A suitcase or a purse is a bag. **3** to hang loosely: *These pants bag at the knees.* **4** to kill in hunting: *The hunter bagged a duck.* **1,2** *noun,* **3,4** *verb,* **bags, bagged, bag·ging.**

ba·gel (bā′gəl), a hard roll made of raised dough, shaped into a ring. It is simmered in water, then baked. *noun.*

bag·gage (bag′ij), trunks, bags, or suitcases packed for traveling. *noun.*

bag·gy (bag′ē), hanging loosely: *The clown had baggy pants. adjective,* **bag·gi·er, bag·gi·est.**

bagpipe

bag·pipe (bag′pīp′), a musical instrument made of a tube to blow through, a leather bag for air, and four pipes. Bagpipes produce shrill tones and are used especially in Scotland and Ireland. *noun.*

bah (bä), an exclamation used to express scorn, dislike, disgust, or impatience. *interjection.*

bail[1] (bāl), **1** the money left with a court of law in order to free a person from jail until a trial is held: *They put up bail for their friend, who was accused of stealing.* **2** to set a person free by offering this money: *They bailed their friend out of jail.* **1** *noun,* **2** *verb.*

bail[2] (bāl), to throw water out of a boat with a bucket, pail, or any other container: *We bailed water from our sinking rowboat. verb.*

bail out, to jump from an airplane by parachute: *When the plane caught fire, the pilot bailed out.*

bait (bāt), **1** anything, especially food, used to attract fish or other animals so that they may be caught. **2** to put bait on a hook or in a trap: *I baited my fishhook.* **3** a thing used to tempt or attract a person to do something. **4** to torment or worry by unkind or annoying remarks: *A noisy group kept baiting the speaker.* **1,3** *noun,* **2,4** *verb.*

bake (bāk), **1** to cook by the dry heat of an oven: *I bake every Saturday.* **2** to dry or harden by heat: *Bricks are baked out of clay. verb,* **bakes, baked, bak·ing.**

bak·er (bā′kər), a person who makes or sells bread, pies, and cakes. *noun.*

bak·er·y (bā′kər ē), a place where bread, pies, and cakes are made or sold. *noun, plural* **bak·er·ies.**

baking powder, a mixture of chemicals used instead of yeast to cause biscuits or cakes to rise.

baking soda, a white powder used in cooking and medicine.

bal·ance (bal′əns), **1** an instrument for weighing. **2** to weigh two things against each other on scales, in one's hands, or in one's mind to see which is heavier or more important: *She balanced a trip to the mountains against a chance to go to a summer camp.* **3** the condition of being equal in weight or amount: *The two sides of the scale were in balance.* **4** a steady condition or position: *I lost my balance and fell off the ladder.* **5** to put or keep in a steady condition or position: *Can you balance a coin on its edge?* **6** the part that is left over;

balance (definitions 1 and 2)
The guinea pig is **balanced** by a 1000 gram weight.
Therefore, the guinea pig weighs 1000 grams (about 2 pounds).

a hat	**i** it	**oi** oil	**ch** child	⎧ a in about
ā age	**ī** ice	**ou** out	**ng** long	⎪ e in taken
ä far	**o** hot	**u** cup	**sh** she	ə = ⎨ i in pencil
e let	**ō** open	**u̇** put	**th** thin	⎪ o in lemon
ē equal	**ô** order	**ü** rule	**ᴛʜ** then	⎩ u in circus
ėr term			**zh** measure	

B

remainder: *I will be away for the balance of the week.* 1,3,4,6 *noun,* 2,5 *verb,* **bal·anc·es, bal·anced, bal·anc·ing.**

in the balance, undecided: *The outcome of the game was in the balance until the last inning.*

bal·co·ny (bal′kə nē), **1** an outside platform, enclosed by a railing, that sticks out from an upper floor of a building. **2** an upper floor in a theater or hall, that sticks out part way over the other floor. *noun, plural* **bal·co·nies.**

bald (bôld), **1** wholly or partly without hair on the head. **2** without its natural covering: *A mountain with no trees or grass is bald. adjective.*

bald eagle, a large, powerful, North American eagle with white feathers on its head, neck, and tail.

bald eagle—about 3 feet (1 meter) from head to tail

bale (bāl), **1** a large bundle of material securely wrapped or bound for shipping or storage: *a bale of cotton.* **2** to make into bales: *We saw a big machine bale hay.* **1** *noun,* **2** *verb,* **bales, baled, bal·ing.**

balk (bôk), **1** to stop short and stubbornly refuse to go on: *My horse balked at the fence.* **2** to prevent from going on; hinder: *The police balked the robber's plans. verb.*

ball¹ (bôl), **1** a round or somewhat oval object that is thrown, batted, kicked, rolled, or carried in various games. Different sizes and types of balls

are used in tennis, baseball, football, and soccer. Balls may be either hollow or solid. **2** a game in which some kind of ball is thrown, hit, or kicked, especially baseball. **3** anything round or roundish; something that is somewhat like a ball: *I have a ball of string. I have a blister on the ball of my foot.* **4** a baseball pitched too high, too low, or not over the plate, that the batter does not strike at. **5** a round, solid object shot from a gun or cannon: *a musket ball, a cannon ball. noun.*

ball² (bôl), a large, formal party with dancing. *noun.*

bal·lad (bal′əd), **1** a poem that tells a story. Ballads are often sung. **2** a romantic popular song. *noun.*

bal·last (bal′əst), something heavy carried in a ship to steady it. *noun.*

ball bearing, 1 a part of a machine in which a metal bar turns upon a number of freely moving steel balls. Ball bearings are used to reduce friction. **2** one of these steel balls.

bal·le·ri·na (bal′ə rē′nə), a woman ballet dancer. *noun.*

bal·let (bal′ā), **1** an elaborate dance by a group on a stage. A ballet usually tells a story through the movements of the dancing and the music. **2** the dancers: *The Royal Ballet will soon perform in our city. noun.*

bal·loon (bə lün′), **1** an airtight bag filled with some gas lighter than air, so that it will rise and float in the air. Some balloons have a basket or container for carrying persons or instruments high up in the air. **2** a child's toy made of thin rubber filled with air or some gas lighter than air. **3** to ride in a balloon. **4** to swell out like a balloon: *The sails of the boat ballooned in the wind.* **1,2** *noun,* **3,4** *verb.*

bal·loon·ist (bə lü′nist), a person who goes up in balloons. *noun.*

bal·lot (bal′ət), **1** a piece of paper or other object used in voting: *Have you cast your ballot?* **2** to vote or decide by using ballots: *We will now ballot for president of the club.* **1** *noun,* **2** *verb.*

ball·point pen (bôl′point′ pen′), a pen that writes with a tiny hard ball at the point. The ball turns inside the end of a thin tube that holds the ink.

ball·room (bôl′rüm′), a large room for dancing. *noun.*

balm·y (bä′mē), mild; gentle: *A balmy breeze blew across the lake. adjective,* **balm·i·er, balm·i·est.**

ba·lo·ney (bə lō′nē), a large sausage usually made of beef, veal, and pork; bologna. *noun.*

bal·sa (bôl′sə), the strong, lightweight wood of a

tropical American tree, used in making airplane models. *noun.*

bal·sam (bôl′səm), a kind of fir tree. *noun.*

Bal·tic Sea (bôl′tik sē′), a sea in northern Europe.

Bal·ti·more (bôl′tə môr), a city in Maryland. *noun.*

bam·boo (bam bü′), a woody, treelike grass with a very tall, stiff, hollow stem that has hard, thick joints. Bamboo grows in warm regions. Its stems are used for making canes, fishing poles, furniture, and even houses. *noun, plural* **bam·boos.**
[*Bamboo* comes from a Malay word for this grass. Dutch explorers learned the name and brought it back to Europe.]

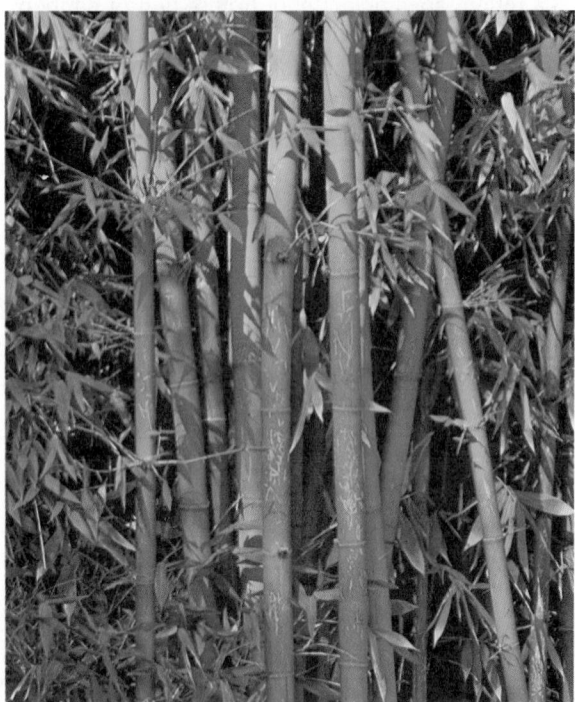

bamboo

ban (ban), **1** to forbid; prohibit: *Swimming is banned in this lake.* **2** the forbidding of an act or speech by authority: *The city has a ban on parking cars in this busy street.* 1 *verb,* **bans, banned, ban·ning;** 2 *noun.*

ba·nan·a (bə nan′ə), a slightly curved, yellow tropical fruit with firm, creamy pulp. Bananas grow in large bunches on a plant like a tree. *noun.*

band[1] (band), **1** a number of persons joined or acting together: *A band of robbers held up the train.* **2** to unite in a group: *The children banded together to buy a present for their teacher.* **3** a group of musicians performing together: *The school band played several marches.* 1,3 *noun,* 2 *verb.*

band[2] (band), **1** a thin, flat strip of material for binding, trimming, or some other purpose: *The oak box was strengthened with bands of iron.* **2** to put a band on: *Students of birds often band them*

in order to identify them later. **3** a stripe: *The white cup has a gold band.* 1,3 *noun,* 2 *verb.*

band·age (ban′dij), **1** a strip of cloth or other material used to wrap or cover a wound or injury. **2** to wrap or cover with a bandage. 1 *noun,* 2 *verb,* **band·ag·es; band·aged, band·ag·ing.**

Band-Aid (band′ād′), a trademark for a small bandage, used to cover minor wounds. *noun.*

ban·dan·na or **ban·dan·a** (ban dan′ə), a large, colored handkerchief. *noun.*

ban·dit (ban′dit), a robber or thief, especially one of a gang of outlaws. *noun.*

bang (bang), **1** a sudden, loud noise or blow: *We heard the bang of firecrackers.* **2** to make a sudden, loud noise: *The door banged as it blew shut.* **3** to hit with violent and noisy blows: *The baby was banging the pan with a spoon.* **4** a thrill: *I get a bang out of riding the roller coaster.* 1,4 *noun,* 2,3 *verb.*

Ban·gla·desh (bäng′glə desh′), a country in southern Asia. *noun.*

bangs (bangz), hair cut short and worn over the forehead. *noun plural.*

ban·ish (ban′ish), **1** to force to leave a country: *The king banished some of his enemies.* **2** to force to go away; drive away: *The children banished her from their game for cheating.* *verb.*

ban·ish·ment (ban′ish mənt), **1** the act of banishing: *The queen ordered the banishment of her enemies.* **2** the condition of being banished: *Their banishment was for twenty years. noun.*

ban·is·ter (ban′ə stər), a handrail of a staircase and its row of supports. *noun.*

ban·jo (ban′jō), a musical instrument having four or five strings, played by plucking the strings with the fingers or a pick. *noun, plural* **ban·jos.**
[This word probably comes from a west African name used for a musical instrument that resembled the banjo.]

banjo

bank[1] (bangk), **1** a long pile or heap: *a bank of snow.* **2** to pile up; heap up: *Tractors banked the snow by the roadside.* **3** the ground bordering a river or lake; shore: *We fished from the bank.* **4** a

a hat	i it	oi oil	ch child	a in about
ā age	ī ice	ou out	ng long	e in taken
ä far	o hot	u cup	sh she	ə = { i in pencil
e let	ō open	ů put	th thin	o in lemon
ē equal	ô order	ü rule	ŦH then	u in circus
ėr term			zh measure	

shallow place in a body of water; shoal: *The fishing banks of Newfoundland are famous.* 1,3,4 *noun,* 2 *verb.*

bank[2] (bangk), **1** a place of business for keeping, lending, exchanging, and issuing money. **2** to keep or put money in a bank: *We bank at the First National.* **3** a small container with a slot through which coins can be dropped to save money. **4** any place where reserve supplies are kept: *a blood bank.* 1,3,4 *noun,* 2 *verb.*

bank·er (bang′kər), a person who runs a bank. *noun.*

bank·ing (bang′king), the business of a bank or banker. *noun.*

bank·rupt (bang′krupt), **1** a person who is declared by a court of law to be unable to pay his or her debts. **2** unable to pay one's debts. **3** to make bankrupt: *Foolish expenditures will bankrupt him.* 1 *noun,* 2 *adjective,* 3 *verb.*

ban·ner (ban′ər), **1** a flag: *Banners of the world's nations fly outside the headquarters of the United Nations.* **2** a piece of cloth with some design or words on it: *Our scout troop has a banner which we carry in parades.* **3** leading or outstanding: *This has been a banner year for apples.* 1,2 *noun,* 3 *adjective.*

ban·quet (bang′kwit), **1** a large meal with many courses, prepared for a special occasion or for many people; feast: *a wedding banquet.* **2** a formal dinner with speeches. *noun.*

ban·ter (ban′tər), **1** a playful teasing; joking: *There was much banter going on at the party.* **2** to tease playfully; talk in a joking way: *The two friends bantered as they walked.* 1 *noun,* 2 *verb.*

bap·tism (bap′tiz əm), a ceremony in which a person is dipped in water or sprinkled with water, as a sign of washing away sin and of admission to the Christian church. *noun.*

bap·tize (bap tīz′), **1** to dip a person into water or sprinkle with water as a sign of washing away sin and of admission into the Christian church. **2** to give a first name to a person at baptism; christen: *She was baptized Maria. verb,* **bap·tiz·es, bap·tized, bap·tiz·ing.**

bar (bär), **1** an evenly shaped piece of some solid, longer than it is wide or thick: *a bar of soap, a chocolate bar.* **2** a rod or pole put across an opening to close it off: *The windows of the prison have iron bars.* **3** to put bars across; fasten or shut off: *Bar the door.* **4** anything that blocks the way or prevents progress: *A bar of sand kept boats out of the harbor.* **5** to block; obstruct: *Fallen trees bar the road.* **6** to keep out: *Dogs are barred from that store.* **7** a band of color; stripe. **8** a unit of rhythm in music. The regular accent falls on the first note of each bar. **9** the dividing line between two such units on a musical staff. **10** a counter or place where drinks and sometimes food are served to customers. **11** the whole group of practicing lawyers: *After passing her law examinations, she was admitted to the bar.* **12** a court of law: *to try a case at the bar.* 1,2,4,7-12 *noun,* 3,5,6 *verb,* **bars, barred, bar·ring.**

BARB

barb (bärb), a point sticking out and curving backward from the main point of an arrow or fishhook. *noun.*

bar·bar·i·an (bär ber′ē ən *or* bär bar′ē ən), **1** a member of a primitive, uncivilized people. **2** not civilized; cruel and coarse: *barbarian customs.* 1 *noun,* 2 *adjective.*

bar·be·cue (bär′bə kyü), **1** an outdoor meal in which meat is cooked over an open fire. **2** a grill or open fireplace for cooking meat, fish, or fowl, usually over charcoal. **3** meat cooked over an open fire. **4** to cook over an open fire or hot charcoal. **5** to cook meat, fish, or fowl in a highly flavored sauce. 1-3 *noun,* 4,5 *verb,* **bar·be·cues, bar·be·cued, bar·be·cu·ing.**
[*Barbecue* comes from a Spanish word meaning "framework for roasting meat." The Spanish word was taken from a Central American Indian word.]

barbed (bärbd), having a barb or barbs. A fishhook is barbed. *adjective.*

barbed wire, wire with sharp points on it every few inches, used for fences.

bar·ber (bär′bər), a person whose work is cutting hair and shaving or trimming beards. *noun.*
[*Barber* comes from a French word meaning "beard."]

bar·ber·shop (bär′bər shop′), the place where a barber works. *noun.*

bar·bit·ur·ate (bär bich′ər it), a drug used in medicine to produce sleep. *noun.*

bar code, a set of short upright lines that have differing lengths and differing amounts of space between them. Printed on any item, these lines can be read by a machine which turns them into numbers that stand for a price, an address, or similar information.

bar code

bare (ber *or* bar), **1** without covering; not clothed; naked: *The sun burned his bare shoulders.* **2** empty; not furnished: *a room bare of furniture.* **3** just enough and no more: *She earns only a bare living.* **4** to uncover; reveal: *to bare one's feelings. The dog bared its teeth.* 1-3 *adjective,* **bar·er, bar·est;** 4 *verb,* **bares, bared, bar·ing.**

bare·back (ber′bak′ *or* bar′bak′), without a saddle; on a horse's bare back. *adverb, adjective.*

bare·foot (ber′fut′ *or* bar′fut′), wearing nothing on the feet: *The children ran barefoot around the yard. adjective, adverb.*

bare·foot·ed (ber′fut′id *or* bar′fut′id), barefoot. *adjective, adverb.*

bare·head·ed (ber′hed′id *or* bar′hed′id), wearing nothing on the head: *You shouldn't be bareheaded in such cold weather. adjective.*

bare·ly (ber′lē *or* bar′lē), with nothing to spare; only just: *I barely had time to catch my bus. adverb.*

bar·gain (bär′gən), **1** an agreement to trade or exchange: *You can't back out on our bargain.* **2** something offered for sale cheap or bought cheap: *This hat is a bargain.* **3** to try to get good terms; try to make a good deal: *I bargained with the shopkeeper and bought the book for $2 instead of $5.* 1,2 *noun,* 3 *verb.*
bargain for, to be prepared for or expect: *He hadn't bargained for rain and had left his umbrella at home.*

barge (bärj), **1** a large, strongly built, flat-bottomed boat for carrying freight on rivers and canals. **2** to move clumsily like a barge: *He barged into the table and knocked the lamp over.* **3** to push oneself rudely: *Don't barge in where you're not wanted.* 1 *noun,* 2,3 *verb,* **barg·es, barged, barg·ing.**

bar graph, a graph that shows amounts by parallel bars which differ in length in proportion to the difference in amount.

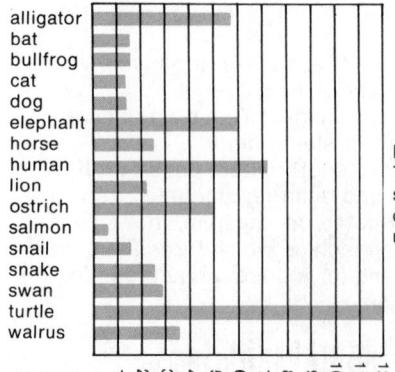

bar graph
This **bar graph** shows how long certain animals usually live.

bar·i·tone (bar′ə tōn), **1** a man's singing voice between tenor and bass. **2** a singer with such a voice. *noun.*

bark[1] (bärk), **1** the tough outside covering of the trunk and branches of trees. **2** to scrape the skin from: *I fell down the steps and barked my shins.* 1 *noun,* 2 *verb.*

bark[2] (bärk), **1** the short, sharp sound that a dog makes. **2** to make this sound: *The dog barked when I came in.* **3** to speak gruffly or sharply: *The policeman barked out his order.* 1 *noun,* 2,3 *verb.*

bar·ley (bär′lē), the grain of a kind of cereal grass, or the plant that it grows on. Barley grows in cool climates and is used as food for people and farm animals. *noun.*

bar mitz·vah (bär′ mits′və), **1** the ceremony or celebration held when a Jewish boy becomes thirteen years old. It means he has reached the age of religious responsibility. **2** the boy himself.

barn (bärn), a building for storing hay and grain and for sheltering farm animals. *noun.*

bar·na·cle (bär′nə kəl), a small, saltwater animal with a shell. It fastens itself to rocks, the timbers of wharves and docks, and the bottoms of ships. *noun.*

barn·yard (bärn′yärd′), the piece of ground around a barn. *noun.*

ba·rom·e·ter (bə rom′ə tər), an instrument for measuring the pressure of air. It is used to predict changes in the weather. *noun.*

barometer

bar·on (bar′ən), a nobleman of the lowest rank. *noun.*

bar·on·ess (bar′ə nis), **1** the wife or widow of a baron. **2** a woman whose rank is equal to that of a baron. *noun, plural* **bar·on·ess·es.**

bar·racks (bar′əks), a building or group of buildings for soldiers to live in, usually in a fort or camp. *noun plural or singular.*

bar·ra·cu·da (bar′ə kü′də), a long, narrow fish with sharp teeth, found in salt water. It sometimes attacks swimmers. *noun, plural* **bar·ra·cu·das** *or* **bar·ra·cu·da.**

barracuda—up to 6 feet (2 meters) long

bar·rel (bar'əl), **1** a container with a round, flat top and bottom and sides that curve out slightly. Barrels are usually made of boards held together by hoops. **2** the amount that a barrel can hold: *They picked a barrel of apples.* **3** a metal tube, such as the part of a gun from which a bullet is fired. *noun.*

bar·ren (bar'ən), **1** not able to bear seeds, fruit, or young: *a barren fruit tree, a barren animal.* **2** not able to produce much: *a barren desert. adjective.*

bar·rette (bə ret'), a pin with a clasp for holding the hair in place. *noun.*

bar·ri·cade (bar'ə kād'), **1** a rough, hastily made barrier for defense: *The soldiers cut down trees to make a barricade across the road.* **2** to block or obstruct with a barrier: *The road was barricaded by fallen trees.* **1** *noun,* **2** *verb,* **bar·ri·cades, bar·ri·cad·ed, bar·ri·cad·ing.**

bar·ri·er (bar'ē ər), **1** something that stands in the way; something that stops progress or prevents approach: *The landslide created a barrier across the road.* **2** something that separates or keeps apart: *Our argument had created a barrier between us. noun.*

bar·ri·o (bär'ē ō), the part of a city where mainly Spanish-speaking people live. *noun, plural* **bar·ri·os.**

bar·ter (bär'tər), **1** to trade by exchanging one kind of goods for other goods without using money; exchange: *The trapper bartered furs for supplies.* **2** the exchange of goods: *Nations sometimes trade by barter instead of paying money for the things they need.* **1** *verb,* **2** *noun.*

ba·salt (bə sôlt'), a hard, dark-colored rock of volcanic origin. *noun.*

base[1] (bās), **1** the part on which anything stands or rests; bottom: *This big machine has a wide steel base.* **2** a starting place; headquarters: *an army base. The base for our hike was the cabin.* **3** to use as a base or basis for: *This novel is based on the lives of famous people.* **4** the main or most important part of something: *This paint has an oil base.* **5** the place that is a goal in certain games, such as baseball or hide-and-seek: *A home run doesn't count if you fail to touch a base.* **6** a chemical substance that unites with an acid to form a salt. The water solution of a base turns red litmus paper blue. **7** the form of a word that word endings may be added to. *Barge is the base of barges, barged,* and *barging.* **1,2,4-7** *noun,* **3** *verb,* **bas·es, based, bas·ing.**

base[2] (bās), **1** mean; selfish and cowardly: *To betray a friend is a base action.* **2** having little value when compared with something else; inferior: *Iron and lead are base metals; gold and silver are precious metals. adjective,* **bas·er, bas·est.**

base·ball (bās'bôl'), **1** a game played with bat and ball by two teams of nine players each, on a field with four bases. A player who touches all the bases, under the rules, scores a run. **2** the ball used in this game. *noun.*

base·ment (bās'mənt), the lowest story of a building, partly or wholly below ground. *noun.*

base word, a word from which other words are made. *Baby* is the base word of *babies, babied,* and *babying.*

bash (bash), to strike with a smashing blow. *verb.*

bash·ful (bash'fəl), uneasy in the presence of others; easily embarrassed; shy: *The child was too bashful to greet us. adjective.*

ba·sic (bā'sik), forming the basis or main part; fundamental: *Addition, subtraction, multiplication, and division are the basic processes of arithmetic. adjective.*

BA·SIC (bā'sik), a simple language used to give instructions to computers. *noun.*
[BASIC comes from the words *beginner's all-purpose symbolic instruction code.* It was formed by using the first letter of each of these words.]

ba·si·cal·ly (bā'sik lē), chiefly; fundamentally: *Although I have had a few colds, I am basically healthy. adverb.*

ba·sin (bā'sn), **1** a wide, shallow bowl for holding liquids. **2** the amount that a basin can hold: *They have used up a basin of water.* **3** a shallow area containing water: *Part of the harbor is a basin for yachts.* **4** all the land drained by a river and the streams that flow into the river: *The Mississippi basin extends from the Appalachians to the Rockies. noun.*

ba·sis (bā'sis), the main part; foundation: *The basis of their friendship was a common interest in sports. noun, plural* **ba·ses** (bā'sēz').

bask (bask), to warm oneself pleasantly: *The cat basks before the fire. verb.*

bas·ket (bas'kit), **1** a container made of twigs, grasses, fibers, plastic, or strips of wood woven together: *a clothes basket.* **2** the amount that a basket holds: *We ate a basket of peaches.* **3** anything that looks like or is shaped like a basket: *I bought a metal wastepaper basket.* **4** a metal hoop with an open net hanging from it, used as a goal in basketball. **5** a score made in basketball. *noun.*

bas·ket·ball (bas'kit bôl'), **1** a game played with a large, round ball between two teams of five players each. The players score points by tossing the ball through baskets hanging at either end of the court. **2** the ball used in this game. *noun.*

bas mitz·vah (bäs' mits'və), bat mitzvah.

bass[1] (bās), **1** the lowest singing voice of a man. **2** a singer with such a voice. **3** a part sung by such a voice. **4** an instrument playing such a part. *noun, plural* **bass·es.**

bass[2] (bas), any of several North American freshwater or saltwater fish used for food. *noun, plural* **bass** or **bass·es.**

basset—about 14 inches (36 centimeters) at the shoulder

bas·set (bas′it), a dog with short legs and a long body. It is like a dachshund, but larger and heavier. *noun.*

bas·soon (bə sün′), a deep-toned wind instrument with a doubled wooden body and a curved metal pipe to which a double reed is attached. *noun.*

bass vi·ol (bās vī′əl), a double bass.

baste[1] (bāst), to drip or pour melted fat or butter on meat, fish, or poultry while roasting: *Baste the turkey to keep it from drying out. verb,* **bastes, bast·ed, bast·ing.**

baste[2] (bāst), to sew with long, loose stitches. These stitches are usually removed after the final sewing. *verb,* **bastes, bast·ed, bast·ing.**

bat[1] (bat), **1** a stout wooden stick or club, used to hit the ball in baseball, cricket, and similar games. **2** to hit with a bat; hit: *He bats well. I batted the balloon with my hand.* **3** a turn at batting: *Who goes to bat first?* 1,3 *noun,* 2 *verb,* **bats, bat·ted, bat·ting.**

at bat, in position to bat; having a turn at batting: *Our side is at bat.*

bat[2] (bat), a flying mammal with a body like that of a mouse and wings covered by thin skin. Bats fly at night. Most of them eat insects but some live on fruit and a few suck the blood of other mammals. *noun.*

bat[2]—wingspread about 15 inches (38 centimeters)

batch (bach), **1** a quantity of something made at the same time: *a batch of cookies, a batch of candy.* **2** a number of persons or things taken together: *She caught a fine batch of fish. noun, plural* **batch·es.**

[*Batch* comes from an old English word meaning "to bake."]

bath (bath), **1** a washing of the body: *I took a hot bath.* **2** water in a tub for a bath: *Your bath is ready.* **3** a room for bathing; bathroom: *The house*

had two baths. *noun, plural* **baths** (baᴛHz).

bathe (bāᴛH), **1** to take a bath or give a bath to: *I bathe regularly. We bathed our dog.* **2** to apply water or other liquid to: *She bathed her sore feet.* **3** to go swimming; go into a river, lake, or ocean for pleasure or to get cool. **4** to cover or surround: *The valley was bathed in light. verb,* **bathes, bathed, bath·ing.**

bathing suit, clothing worn for swimming.

bath·robe (bath′rōb′), a loose garment worn before and after a bath, or when resting or lounging. *noun.*

bath·room (bath′rüm′), **1** a room fitted out for taking baths, usually with a sink and a toilet. **2** a room containing a toilet. *noun.*

bath·tub (bath′tub′), a tub to bathe in. *noun.*

bassoon

bat mitz·vah (bät′ mits′və), **1** the ceremony or celebration held when a Jewish girl becomes thirteen years old. It means she has reached the age of religious responsibility. **2** the girl herself. Also spelled **bas mitzvah.**

ba·ton (ba ton′), **1** a light stick used by the leader of an orchestra, chorus, or band to indicate the beat and direct the performance. **2** a hollow metal rod that is twirled by a drum major or majorette for display. *noun.*

Bat·on Rouge (bat′n rüzh′), the capital of Louisiana.

bat·tal·ion (bə tal′yən), any large part of an army organized to act together. Two or more companies make a battalion. *noun.*

bat·ter[1] (bat′ər), to strike with repeated blows so as to bruise, break, or get out of shape; pound: *The fireman battered down the door with an ax. verb.*

bat·ter[2] (bat′ər), a liquid mixture of flour, milk, and eggs that becomes solid when cooked. Cakes and muffins are made from batter. *noun.*

bat·ter[3] (bat′ər), a player whose turn it is to bat in baseball, cricket, and similar games. *noun.*

bat·tered (bat′ərd), damaged by hard use: *I found a battered old book in the office. adjective.*

battering ram, a heavy wooden beam with a metal striking end. Battering rams were used in ancient warfare for battering down walls and gates.

bat·ter·y (bat′ər ē), **1** a single electric cell: *Most flashlights work on two batteries.* **2** a set of two or more electric cells that produce electric current. Batteries provide the current that starts automobile and truck engines. **3** any set of similar or connected things: *The mayor spoke before a battery of television cameras.* **4** a set of big guns for combined action in attack or defense: *Four batteries began firing. noun, plural* **bat·ter·ies.**

bat·tle (bat′l), **1** a fight between armies, air forces, or navies: *The battle for the island lasted six months.* **2** any fight or contest: *The candidates fought a battle of words during the campaign.* **3** to take part in a battle; fight; struggle: *The swimmer had to battle a strong current.* **1,2** *noun,* **3** *verb,* **bat·tles, bat·tled, bat·tling.**

battle-ax

bat·tle-ax or **bat·tle-axe** (bat′l aks′), an ax with a broad blade, formerly used as a weapon in battle. *noun, plural* **bat·tle-ax·es.**

bat·tle·field (bat′l fēld′), the place where a battle is fought or has been fought. *noun.*

bat·tle·ground (bat′l ground′), a battlefield. *noun.*

bat·tle·ment (bat′l mənt), a low wall for defense at the top of a tower or wall, built with open places to shoot through. *noun.*

battlement

a hat	i it	oi oil	ch child		a in about
ā age	ī ice	ou out	ng long		e in taken
ä far	o hot	u cup	sh she	ə =	i in pencil
e let	ō open	u̇ put	th thin		o in lemon
ē equal	ô order	ü rule	ŦH then		u in circus
ėr term			zh measure		

bat·tle·ship (bat′l ship′), a very large warship having the heaviest armor and the most powerful guns. The last battleships were built during World War II. *noun.*

baux·ite (bôk′sīt), a mineral from which aluminum is obtained. *noun.*

bawl (bôl), **1** to weep loudly: *The baby dropped his toy and began to bawl.* **2** to shout or cry out in a noisy way: *The lost calf was bawling for its mother. "Attention!" bawled the sergeant. verb.*

bawl out, to scold loudly: *She bawled me out for denting her bicycle.*

bay[1] (bā), a part of a sea or lake extending into the land. A bay is usually smaller than a gulf and larger than a cove. *noun.*

bay[2] (bā), **1** a long, deep barking, especially by a large dog: *We heard the distant bay of the hounds.* **2** to bark with long, deep sounds: *Dogs sometimes bay at the moon.* **1** *noun,* **2** *verb.*

bay[3] (bā), **1** reddish-brown. **2** a reddish-brown horse with black mane and tail. **1** *adjective,* **2** *noun.*

bay·o·net (bā′ə nit), a knife attached to the front end of a rifle. *noun.*
[*Bayonet* was named for Bayonne, a city in southern France. Bayonets were first made in this city.]

bay·ou (bī′ü), a marshy, slow-moving stream that flows out of a lake, river, or gulf in the southern United States. *noun.*
[*Bayou* was a word used by French colonists in Louisiana. This word came from an American Indian word meaning "creek."]

bay window, a window or set of windows that sticks out beyond an outside wall to form a small space in a room.

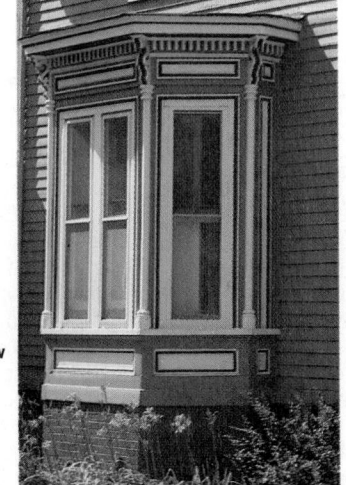

bay window

ba·zaar (bə zär′), **1** a street or streets full of small shops and booths in Oriental countries. **2** a sale of things given for some special purpose: *I bought this scarf at the church bazaar.* noun.

B.C., before Christ. The abbreviation B.C. is used for dates before the birth of Christ. The abbreviation A.D. is used for dates after the birth of Christ. 350 B.C. is 100 years earlier than 250 B.C. From 20 B.C. to A.D. 50 is 70 years.

be (bē). *Be* is a very common verb that has several different forms. We say: I *am,* you (we, they) *are,* he (she, it) *is,* I (he, she, it) *was,* you (we, they) *were.* **1** to live; exist: *Dinosaurs came to be many years ago.* **2** to have a place or position: *The new bookcase is going to be in the bedroom.* **3** to happen; take place: *Will the meeting be at your house?* **4** to go or come: *Has he ever been to New York?* **5** to belong to the group of: *Whales are mammals.* **6** *Be* is used as a linking verb: *Can this jacket be yours? No, mine is yellow. Who is the librarian?* **7** *Be* is used to begin a request or a question: *Be careful. Is that so?* **8** *Be* is used as a helping verb to show that action is taking place: *Can he be sleeping this late? We are leaving.* **9** *Be* is used as a helping verb to show that action is happening to someone or something: *Can he be coaxed to come with us? The room was painted last year.* verb, **am, are, is; was, were; been; be·ing.**

beach (bēch), **1** an almost flat shore of sand or pebbles along the edge of a sea, lake, or big river. **2** to run ashore; pull up on the shore: *We beached the boat on the island.* 1 noun, plural **beach·es;** 2 verb.

beach ball, a large, lightweight ball that is filled with air, often used at the beach.

bea·con (bē′kən), **1** a fire or light used as a signal to guide or warn. **2** a radio signal for guiding aircraft and ships through fogs and storms. noun.

bead (bēd), **1** a small ball or bit of glass, metal, or plastic with a hole through it, so that it can be strung on a thread with others like it. **2 beads, a** a string of beads. **b** a string of beads for keeping count in saying prayers; rosary. **3** to put beads on; ornament with beads. **4** any small, round object like a drop or bubble: *Beads of sweat covered his forehead.* 1,2,4 noun, 3 verb.

bead·y (bē′dē), small, round, and shiny: *The parakeet has beady eyes.* adjective, **bead·i·er, bead·i·est.**

bea·gle (bē′gəl), a small hunting dog with smooth hair, short legs, and drooping ears. noun.

beak (bēk), **1** the bill of a bird. Eagles and hawks have strong, hooked beaks that are useful in striking or tearing. **2** anything shaped like a beak, such as the spout of a pitcher. noun.

beak·er (bē′kər), a thin glass or metal container used in laboratories. A beaker has a flat bottom, no handle, and a small lip for pouring. noun.

beam (bēm), **1** a large, long piece of timber, iron, or steel. A beam is used as the main horizontal support of a building or ship. **2** a ray of light: *The beam of the flashlight revealed a kitten in the tree.* **3** to send out rays of light; shine: *The sun was beaming brightly.* **4** to look or smile brightly: *Her face beamed with delight.* **5** a radio signal directed in a straight line, used to guide aircraft or ships. 1,2,5 noun, 3,4 verb.

bean (bēn), **1** the smooth, somewhat flat seed of a bush or vine, eaten as a vegetable. **2** the long green or yellow pod containing such seeds, also used as a vegetable. **3** any seed shaped somewhat like a bean. Coffee beans are seeds of the coffee plant. noun.

bean·bag (bēn′bag′), a small bag partly filled with dry beans, used to toss in play. noun.

bean·stalk (bēn′stôk′), the stem of a bean plant. noun.

bear[1] (ber *or* bar), **1** to carry or support; hold up: *The hikers were bearing heavy packs. The ice is too thin to bear your weight.* **2** to put up with; endure: *He cannot bear any more pain.* **3** to bring forth; produce: *This tree bears fine apples.* **4** to give birth to: *She was born on May 15. Our cat will soon bear kittens.* verb, **bears, bore, borne** or **born, bear·ing.**

bear down, to press down: *The lead will break if you bear down too hard on your pencil.*

bear[2] (ber *or* bar), a large animal with thick, coarse fur and a very short tail. A bear walks flat on the soles of its feet. noun.

beard (bird), **1** the hair growing on a man's chin and cheeks. **2** something like this. The long hair on the chin of a goat is a beard; so are the stiff hairs on the heads of plants like oats, barley, and wheat. noun.

bear·ing (ber′ing *or* bar′ing), **1** a way of standing, sitting, walking, or behaving; manner: *She had the graceful bearing of a dancer.* **2** a connection in thought or meaning; relation: *Do not ask questions that have no bearing on our discussion.* **3 bearings,** position in relation to other things; direction: *We had no compass, so we got our bearings from the stars.* **4** a part of a machine on which another part moves. A bearing supports the moving part and reduces friction by turning with the motion. noun.

beast (bēst), **1** any four-footed animal. Lions, bears, cows, and horses are beasts. A **beast of burden** is an animal used for carrying loads. **2** a cruel or brutal person. noun.

beagle—about 14 inches (36 centimeters) at the shoulder

beast·ly (bēst′lē), **1** like a beast; cruel or brutal. **2** unpleasant: *I have a beastly headache. adjective,* **beast·li·er, beast·li·est.**

beat (bēt), **1** to strike again and again: *The baby beat the floor with the toy hammer.* **2** a stroke or blow made again and again: *We heard the beat of a drum.* **3** to get the better of; defeat; overcome: *Their team beat ours by a huge score.* **4** to make flat; shape with a hammer: *The jeweler beat gold into thin strips.* **5** to mix by stirring rapidly with a fork, spoon, or other utensil: *I helped make the cake by beating the eggs.* **6** a sound made by the regular action of the heart as it pumps blood. **7** to throb: *My heart beat fast with joy.* **8** to move up and down; flap: *The bird beat its wings.* **9** the unit of time or accent in music: *A waltz has three beats to a measure.* **10** a regular round or route taken by a police officer or guard: *The officers were friendly with the people on their beat.* **11** tired; worn out: *I was beat after running the race.* 1,3-5,7,8 *verb,* **beats, beat, beat·en** or **beat, beat·ing;** 2,6,9,10 *noun,* 11 *adjective.*

beat·en (bēt′n), **1** whipped; struck: *The beaten dog ran away from its owner.* **2** much walked on or traveled: *The children had worn a beaten path across the grass.* **3** defeated; overcome: *a beaten team.* **4** shaped by blows of a hammer: *This bowl is made of beaten silver.* **5** See **beat.** *Our team was beaten in football on Saturday.* 1-4 *adjective,* 5 *verb.*

beat·er (bē′tər), a utensil for beating eggs, cream, and similar things. *noun.*

beat-up (bēt′up′), worn out from long or hard use: *a beat-up car. adjective.*

beau·ti·ful (byü′tə fəl), very pleasing to see or hear; delighting the mind or senses: *a beautiful park, beautiful music. adjective.*

beau·ti·fy (byü′tə fī), to make beautiful: *Flowers beautify a room. verb,* **beau·ti·fies, beau·ti·fied, beau·ti·fy·ing.**

beau·ty (byü′tē), **1** good looks: *The child had beauty and intelligence.* **2** the quality that pleases in flowers, pictures, or music: *There is beauty in a fine painting.* **3** something or someone beautiful: *the beauties of nature. noun, plural* **beau·ties.**

beauty shop, a place where women can have their hair, skin, and nails cared for.

bea·ver (bē′vər), **1** an animal with soft fur, a

beaver (definition 1)—about 3½ feet (1 meter) long with the tail

a hat	**i** it	**oi** oil	**ch** child	(a in about
ā age	**ī** ice	**ou** out	**ng** long	e in taken
ä far	**o** hot	**u** cup	**sh** she	**ə** = ⟨ i in pencil
e let	**ō** open	**u̇** put	**th** thin	o in lemon
ē equal	**ô** order	**ü** rule	**ŦH** then	u in circus
ėr term			**zh** measure	

broad, flat tail, webbed hind feet for swimming, and large front teeth. Beavers live both in water and on land. They gnaw down trees and build dams and nests in streams. **2** its soft brown fur. *noun.*

be·came (bi kām′), See **become.** *The seed became a plant. verb.*

be·cause (bi kôz′), for the reason that; since: *Because we were late, we ran the whole way home. conjunction.*

because of, by reason of; on account of: *The game was called off because of rain.*

beck·on (bek′ən), to signal to a person by motion of the head or hand: *She beckoned me to follow her. verb.*

be·come (bi kum′), **1** to come to be; grow to be: *It is becoming colder. I became tired and fell asleep.* **2** to look well on; suit: *That blue sweater becomes you. verb,* **be·comes, be·came, be·come, be·com·ing.**

become of, to happen to: *What has become of the box of candy?*

be·com·ing (bi kum′ing), **1** fitting; suitable: *the kindness and patience becoming to a teacher.* **2** pleasant to look at; attractive: *a very becoming new coat. adjective.*

bed (bed), **1** anything to sleep or rest on. A bed is usually a frame that holds up a mattress covered with sheets and blankets. **2** any place where people or animals sleep or rest: *The cat made its bed by the fireplace.* **3** to provide with a bed; put to bed; go to bed: *She bedded the horse in the barn.* **4** a flat base on which anything rests; foundation: *The tall flagpole was set in a bed of concrete.* **5** the ground under a body of water: *The creek bed was soft and muddy.* **6** a piece of ground in a garden in which plants are grown: *We planted a bed of tulips.* 1,2,4-6 *noun,* 3 *verb,* **beds, bed·ded, bed·ding.**

bed down, to go to bed; lie down to sleep: *We bedded down for the night.*

bed·bug (bed′bug′), a small, flat, reddish-brown insect that sucks blood. It is found in houses, most often in beds, and its bite is painful. *noun.*

bed·clothes (bed′klōz′), sheets, blankets, or quilts. *noun plural.*

bed·ding (bed′ing), **1** bedclothes. **2** material for beds: *Straw is used as bedding for cows and horses. noun.*

bed·lam (bed′ləm), uproar; confusion. *noun.*

be·drag·gled (bi drag′əld), wet or soiled, and hanging limp: *I tried to comb my bedraggled hair. adjective.*

bed·rock (bed′rok′), the solid rock under the soil and under looser rocks. *noun.*

B

bed·room (bed′rüm′), a room to sleep in. *noun.*

bed·side (bed′sīd′), the side of a bed: *The nurse sat by the patient's bedside. noun.*

bed·spread (bed′spred′), a cover for a bed that is spread over the blankets. *noun.*

bed·stead (bed′sted′), the wooden or metal framework of a bed. *noun.*

bed·time (bed′tīm′), the time to go to bed: *Her regular bedtime is nine o'clock. noun.*

bee (bē), **1** an insect with four wings and, usually, a stinger. Bees gather pollen and nectar from flowers, and they make honey from the nectar. Some bees live in large groups, and these bees produce wax. **2** a gathering for work or amusement: *The teacher let us have a spelling bee in class today. noun.*

beech (bēch), **1** a tree with smooth, gray bark and glossy leaves. It bears a sweet nut which is good to eat. **2** its wood. *noun, plural* **beech·es** or **beech** for 1.

beef (bēf), meat from a steer, cow, or bull. *noun.*

beef·steak (bēf′stāk′), a slice of beef for broiling or frying; steak. *noun.*

bee·hive (bē′hīv′), **1** a hive or house for bees. **2** a busy, swarming place: *The school was a beehive of activity on visiting day. noun.*

bee·keep·er (bē′kē′pər), a person who raises bees for their honey. *noun.*

bee·line (bē′līn′), the straightest way between two places, like the flight of a bee to its hive: *At noon we made a beeline for the cafeteria. noun.*

been (bin). *Been* is a form of **be.** *I have been sick. The book has been read by everyone in the class. verb.*

beer (bir), an alcoholic drink made from malted barley flavored with hops. *noun.*

bees·wax (bēz′waks′), the wax made by bees, from which they make their honeycomb. *noun.*

beet (bēt), the thick, fleshy root of a garden plant. Red beets are eaten as a vegetable. Sugar is made from white beets. *noun.*

bee·tle (bē′tl), an insect that has two hard, shiny front wings that cover and protect the delicate rear wings when it is not flying. *noun.*

be·fall (bi fôl′), to happen or happen to: *They feared that harm had befallen their friend. verb,* **be·falls, be·fell** (bi fel′), **be·fall·en** (bi fô′lən), **be·fall·ing.**

be·fore (bi fôr′), **1** earlier than: *Come before noon.* **2** earlier: *Come at five o'clock, not before.* **3** until now; in the past: *You were never late before.* **4** in front of; ahead of: *Walk before me.* **5** in front; ahead: *The scout went before to see if the trail was safe.* **6** rather than; sooner than: *I'd starve before giving in.* **7** earlier than the time when: *I would like to talk to you before you go.* **1,4** *preposition,* **2,3,5** *adverb,* **6,7** *conjunction.*

be·fore·hand (bi fôr′hand′), ahead of time: *Get everything ready beforehand. adverb, adjective.*

be·friend (bi frend′), to act as a friend to; help: *The children befriended the stray dog. verb.*

beg (beg), **1** to ask for food, money, or clothes as a charity: *The old woman was so poor that she had to beg for food.* **2** to ask a favor; ask earnestly or humbly: *The children begged for a ride on the pony.* **3** to ask politely and courteously: *I beg your pardon. verb,* **begs, begged, beg·ging.**

be·gan (bi gan′). See **begin.** *Snow began to fall. verb.*

beg·gar (beg′ər), **1** a person who lives by begging. **2** a very poor person. *noun.*

be·gin (bi gin′), **1** to do the first part; start: *When shall we begin? I began reading the book yesterday.* **2** to come into being: *The club began years ago.* **3** to be near; come near: *Your big brother's suit wouldn't even begin to fit you. verb,* **be·gins, be·gan, be·gun, be·gin·ning.**

be·gin·ner (bi gin′ər), a person who is doing something for the first time; person who lacks skill and experience: *You skate well for a beginner. noun.*

be·gin·ning (bi gin′ing), **1** a start: *I was anxious to make a good beginning at the new school.* **2** the time when anything begins: *The beginning of winter is usually on December 21st.* **3** the first part: *I enjoyed this book from beginning to end.* **4** the starting point; source; origin: *The idea of the airplane had its beginning in the flight of birds. noun.*

be·gone (bi gôn′), **1** go away! *"Begone!" said the prince.* **2** to go away: *The princess bade the witch begone.* **1** *interjection,* **2** *verb.*

be·go·nia (bi gō′nyə), a tropical plant often grown for its large, colorful leaves and bright flowers. *noun.*

begonia

be·gun (bi gun′). See **begin.** *It has begun to rain. verb.*

be·half (bi haf′), side, interest, or favor: *A friend will act in my behalf while I'm away. noun.*
in behalf of or **on behalf of,** in the interest of; for: *I am speaking in behalf of my friend.*

be·have (bi hāv′), **1** to act; conduct oneself: *The children behaved as if they were hungry. The ship behaves well even in a storm.* **2** to act properly; do what is right: *If you behave today, we can come here again. verb,* **be·haves, be·haved, be·hav·ing.**

be·hav·ior (bi hā′vyər), a way of acting; conduct; actions: *Her sullen behavior showed that she was angry. noun.*

B

be·head (bi hed′), to cut off the head of. *verb.*
be·held (bi held′). See **behold**. *The little child beheld the approaching storm with fear. verb.*
be·hind (bi hīnd′), **1** at the back of: *I hid behind a bush.* **2** at the back: *The dog's tail hung down behind.* **3** supporting: *Don't give up, we're all behind you.* **4** farther back: *The rest of the hikers are still quite a way behind.* **5** later than: *The milkman is behind his usual time.* **6** not on time; late: *The class is behind in its work.* **7** less advanced than: *I am behind my class because I missed two weeks of school.* **8** in the place that has been or is being left: *When my family went to New York, I stayed behind.* 1,3,5,7 *preposition,* 2,4,6,8 *adverb.*
be·hold (bi hōld′), **1** to look at; see; observe: *They wanted to behold the sunrise.* **2** look! see! *Behold! the queen!* 1 *verb,* **be·holds, be·held, be·hold·ing;** 2 *interjection.*
beige (bāzh), pale-brown. *adjective.*
be·ing (bē′ing). **1** *Being* is a form of *be. The dog is being fed.* **2** a person; living creature: *a human being.* **3** life; existence: *The world came into being long ago.* 1 *verb,* 2,3 *noun.*
Bel·a·rus (bel′ə rüs), Byelarus. *noun.*
be·lat·ed (bi lā′tid), happening or coming late; delayed: *Your belated letter has arrived at last. adjective.*
belch (belch), **1** to throw out gas noisily from the stomach through the mouth. **2** to throw out with force: *The volcano belched fire and smoke.* **3** an act of belching. 1,2 *verb,* 3 *noun, plural* **belch·es.**
bel·fry (bel′frē), **1** a tower for a bell or bells. **2** a space in a tower in which a bell or bells may be hung. *noun, plural* **bel·fries.**
Bel·gium (bel′jəm), a country in western Europe. *noun.*
be·lief (bi lēf′), **1** what is held to be true or real; thing believed: *It was once a common belief that the earth is flat.* **2** acceptance as true or real: *His belief in ghosts makes him afraid of the dark.* **3** faith; trust: *She expressed her belief in people. noun.*
be·liev·a·ble (bi lē′və bəl), able to be believed: *His excuse for being late was not believable. adjective.*
be·lieve (bi lēv′), **1** to think something is true or real: *Who doesn't believe that the earth is round?* **2** to think somebody tells the truth: *I believe you.* **3** to have faith; trust: *We believe in our friends.* **4** to think; suppose: *I believe we are going to have a test soon. verb,* **be·lieves, be·lieved, be·liev·ing.**
be·lit·tle (bi lit′l), to make seem little or unimportant: *They belittled your success because they were jealous. verb,* **be·lit·tles, be·lit·tled, be·lit·tling.**
bell (bel), **1** a hollow metal object shaped like a cup, that makes a musical sound when struck by a clapper or hammer. **2** anything that makes a ringing sound as a signal: *I heard the bell ring, and ran to open the door.* **3** the stroke or sound of a bell: *Our teacher dismissed us five minutes before the bell.* **4** the stroke of a bell used on shipboard

a hat	i it	oi oil	ch child	a in about
ā age	ī ice	ou out	ng long	e in taken
ä far	o hot	u cup	sh she	ə = i in pencil
e let	ō open	u̇ put	th thin	o in lemon
ē equal	ô order	ü rule	ᴛʜ then	u in circus
ėr term			zh measure	

to indicate a half hour of time. **5** anything shaped like a bell: *the bell of a trumpet. noun.*
bell·boy (bel′boi′), a person whose work is carrying baggage and doing errands for the guests of a hotel or club. *noun.*
bel·lig·er·ent (bə lij′ər ənt), **1** fond of fighting; warlike: *a belligerent neighborhood gang.* **2** at war; engaged in war; fighting: *Great Britain and Germany were belligerent powers in 1941. adjective.*
bel·low (bel′ō), **1** to make a loud, deep noise; roar: *He bellowed at the children who were trampling his flowers. The bull bellowed.* **2** a loud, deep noise; roar. 1 *verb,* 2 *noun.*
bel·lows (bel′ōz), a device for producing a strong current of air. A bellows is used to supply more air to a fire to make it burn hotter. An accordion receives air from a bellows. *noun singular or plural.*

bellows

bel·ly (bel′ē), **1** the lower front part of the body, below the chest; abdomen. It contains the stomach and intestines. **2** the under part of an animal's body. **3** the stomach: *I couldn't eat another bite; my belly is full.* **4** the bulging part of anything, or the hollow in it: *the belly of a sail. The damaged plane skidded on its belly.* **5** to swell out; bulge: *The sails bellied in the wind.* 1-4 *noun, plural* **bel·lies;** 5 *verb,* **bel·lies, bel·lied, bel·ly·ing.**
be·long (bi lông′), to have one's or its proper place: *That book belongs on this shelf. verb.*
belong to, 1 to be the property of: *Does this cap belong to you?* **2** to be a part of: *That top belongs to this box.* **3** to be a member of: *She belongs to the team.*
be·long·ings (bi lông′ingz), things that belong to a person; possessions. *noun plural.*
be·lov·ed (bi luv′id *or* bi luvd′), **1** dearly loved; dear: *After many years, he was able to return to his beloved homeland.* **2** a person who is loved. 1 *adjective,* 2 *noun.*

be·low (bi lō′), **1** in or to a lower place: *From the airplane we could see the fields below.* **2** on a lower floor or deck; downstairs: *The ship's cargo is stored below.* **3** lower than; under: *My brother's room is below mine.* **4** less than: *It is four degrees below freezing.* **5** below zero: *The temperature is five below today.* **1,2,5** *adverb*, **3,4** *preposition*.

belt (belt), **1** a strip of leather or cloth, fastened around the waist to hold in or support clothes, tools, or weapons. **2** to hit suddenly and hard: *She belted the ball over the fence.* **3** a region having some special feature: *The cotton belt is where most of our cotton is grown.* **4** an endless band that transfers motion from one wheel or pulley to another: *A belt connected to the motor moves the fan in an automobile.* **1,3,4** *noun*, **2** *verb*.

belt (definition 4)
belts used to transmit power in different directions

bench (bench), **1** a long seat, usually of wood or stone. **2** a strong, heavy table used by a carpenter, or by any person who works with tools and materials; workbench. **3** the judge or group of judges sitting in a court of law: *Bring the prisoner before the bench.* **4** position as a judge: *The attorney was appointed to the bench.* **5** to take a player out of a game. **1-4** *noun, plural* **bench·es;** **5** *verb*.

bend (bend), **1** a part that is not straight; curve; turn: *There is a sharp bend in the road here.* **2** to make or become crooked; curve: *bend a wire. The branch began to bend as I climbed along it.* **3** to turn or move in a certain direction; direct: *His steps were bent toward home now.* **4** to stoop; bow: *She bent down and picked up a stone.* **1** *noun*, **2-4** *verb*, **bends, bent, bend·ing.**

be·neath (bi nēth′), **1** in a lower place; below; underneath; under: *The apple fell to the ground beneath. The dog sat beneath the tree.* **2** not worthy of: *Your insulting remarks are beneath notice.* **1** *adverb*, **1,2** *preposition*.

be·ne·dic·tion (ben′ə dik′shən), the asking of God's blessing at the end of a religious service. *noun.*
[*Benediction* comes from two Latin words meaning "to speak well."]

ben·e·fac·tor (ben′ə fak′tər), a person who has given money or kindly help. *noun.*

ben·e·fi·cial (ben′ə fish′əl), favorable; helpful; producing good: *Daily exercise is beneficial to your health. adjective.*

ben·e·fit (ben′ə fit), **1** anything which is for the good of a person or thing; advantage: *Good roads are of great benefit to travelers.* **2** to do good to; be good for: *Rest will benefit a sick person.* **3** to receive good; profit: *He benefited from the medicine.* **1** *noun*, **2,3** *verb*.

be·nev·o·lence (bə nev′ə ləns), **1** good will; kindly feeling. **2** an act of kindness; something good that is done. *noun.*

be·nev·o·lent (bə nev′ə lənt), kindly; charitable: *Giving money to help the hospital is a benevolent act. adjective.*

bent (bent), **1** See **bend**. *He bent the wire.* **2** not straight; crooked; curved: *It is hard to hammer a bent nail into wood.* **3** determined: *He is bent on being a doctor.* **1** *verb*, **2,3** *adjective*.

be·queath (bi kwēth′), **1** to give or leave by means of a will when one dies: *She bequeathed her fortune to her children.* **2** to hand down; pass along: *One age bequeaths its knowledge to the next. verb.*

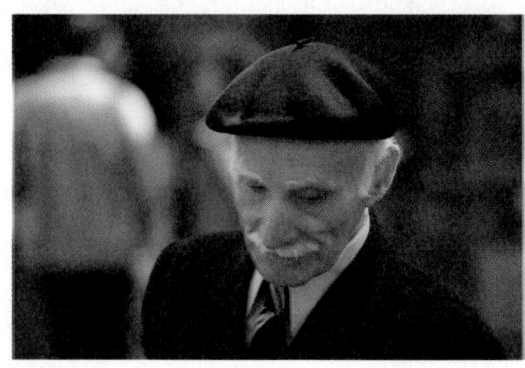

beret

be·ret (bə rā′), a soft, flat, round cap of wool or felt. *noun.*

Ber·lin (bər lin′), the capital of Germany. From 1949 to 1990 it was divided into East Berlin, the capital of East Germany, and West Berlin, a part of West Germany. *noun.*

ber·ry (ber′ē), any small, juicy fruit with many seeds. Strawberries and raspberries are berries. *noun, plural* **ber·ries.**

berth (bérth), **1** a place to sleep on a ship or a railroad sleeping car. **2** a ship's place at a wharf. *noun.*

be·seech (bi sēch′), to ask earnestly; beg: *I beseech you to listen to me. verb,* **be·seech·es, be·sought** or **be·seeched, be·seech·ing.**

be·set (bi set′), to attack; attack from all sides: *We were beset by mosquitoes in the swamp. verb,* **be·sets, be·set, be·set·ting.**

be·side (bi sīd′), by the side of; close to; near: *Grass grows beside the fence. preposition.*
beside oneself, very upset; greatly distressed: *They're beside themselves with worry over their son.*

be·sides (bi sīdz′), **1** more than that; moreover: *I won't go to the movies; besides, I have no money.* **2** in addition to: *Others came to the picnic besides our class.* **3** in addition; also: *We tried two other ways besides.* **4** other than; except: *They spoke of no one besides you.* **1,3** *adverb*, **2,4** *preposition*.

be·siege (bi sēj′), **1** to try for a long time to take a place by armed force; surround and try to capture: *Enemy soldiers besieged the fortified town all winter.* **2** to crowd around: *Hundreds of admirers*

besieged the movie star. verb, **be·sieg·es,
be·sieged, be·sieg·ing.**

be·sought (bi sôt′). See **beseech.** *She besought
them to listen to her.* verb.

best (best), **1** of the most valuable, excellent, or
desirable quality: *My work is good; your work is
better; but her work is best. I want to be one of the
best students in the class.* **2** in the most excellent
way: *Who reads best?* **3** in or to the greatest
degree: *I like this book best.* **4** a person or thing
that is best: *He is the best in the class.* **5** the most
that is possible: *I did my best to finish the work on
time.* **1** *adjective, superlative of* **good;** 2,3 *adverb,
superlative of* **well¹;** 4,5 *noun.*

get the best of, to defeat: *They got the best of us
in the game.*

make the best of, to do as well as possible with:
*We didn't enjoy the weather, but we tried to make
the best of it.*

be·stow (bi stō′), to give something as a gift;
give: *The millionaire bestowed a large sum of
money on the university.* verb.

bet (bet), **1** a promise between two people or
groups that the one who guesses wrong will give
something of value to the one who guesses right:
*We made a 25-cent bet on who would win the
game.* **2** to promise something of value to another
if you are wrong: *I bet her a candy bar that my
team would win.* **3** the money or thing promised:
My bet on the game was 25 cents. **4** to make a bet:
Which team did you bet on? **5** to be very sure: *I
bet you are wrong about that.* **1,3** *noun,* 2,4,5 *verb,*
bets, bet or **bet·ted, bet·ting.**

be·tray (bi trā′), **1** to hand over to the power of
an enemy: *The traitor betrayed the plans for the
new naval base to the enemy agent.* **2** to be
unfaithful or disloyal to: *She betrayed her promise.*
verb.

be·tray·al (bi trā′əl), an act of betraying. noun.

bet·ter (bet′ər), **1** more valuable, excellent, or
desirable than another: *She drew a better picture
than her friend.* **2** in a more satisfactory way: *Try
to read better next time.* **3** in a greater degree: *I
know my old friend better than I know anyone else.*
4 a person or thing that is better: *Which is the
better of these two dresses?* **5** to make better;
improve: *We can better that work by being more
careful next time.* **6** improved in health: *The sick
child is better today.* **1,6** *adjective, comparative of*
good; 2,3 *adverb, comparative of* **well¹;** 4 *noun,*
5 *verb.*

better off, in a better condition: *He is better off
now that he has a new job.*

get the better of, to be superior to; defeat: *Their
team got the better of our team in yesterday's game.*

had better, ought to; should: *I had better go now.*

be·tween (bi twēn′), **1** in the space or time
separating two objects or places: *The valley lay
between two mountains. We don't go to school
between Friday and Monday.* **2** in the range of: *She
earned between ten and twelve dollars.*
3 connecting; joining: *There is a good highway
between Chicago and Detroit.* **4** having to do with;

a hat	i it	oi oil	ch child	ə =	a in about
ā age	ī ice	ou out	ng long		e in taken
ä far	o hot	u cup	sh she		i in pencil
e let	ō open	ů put	th thin		o in lemon
ē equal	ô order	ü rule	₮H then		u in circus
ėr term			zh measure		

involving: *A war between two countries can affect
the whole world.* **5** either one or the other of: *We
must choose between the two books.* **6** by the joint
action of: *They caught twelve fish between them.*
1-6 *preposition,* 1 *adverb.*

in between, in the middle: *I planted peas and
carrots with lettuce in between.*

bev·er·age (bev′ər ij), a liquid used or prepared
for drinking. Milk, fruit juice, coffee, and tea are
beverages. noun.

be·ware (bi wer′ or bi war′), to be on your guard
against; be careful of: *You must beware of
swimming in a strong current.* verb.

be·wil·der (bi wil′dər), to confuse completely;
puzzle: *I was bewildered by the confusing
instructions.* verb.

be·witch (bi wich′), **1** to put under a spell; use
magic on: *The wicked fairy bewitched the princess
and made her fall into a long sleep.* **2** to charm;
delight very much: *They were bewitched by their
bright little grandchild.* verb.

be·yond (bi yond′), **1** on or to the farther side of:
I live beyond those trees. **2** farther on than: *I fell
asleep on the bus and rode beyond my stop.*
3 farther away: *Your ball did not fall here; look
beyond.* **4** later than; past: *I stayed up beyond my
usual bedtime.* **5** out of the limit or understanding
of: *This wilted plant is beyond help. The poem's
meaning is beyond me.* **6** more than: *The trip was
beyond all we had hoped.* **1,2,4-6** *preposition,*
3 *adverb.*

bi·as (bī′əs), **1** a tendency to favor or oppose a
person or thing without real cause: *An umpire
should have no bias in favor of either side.* **2** to give
a bias to; influence, usually unfairly: *Judges
cannot let their feelings bias their decisions.* **1** *noun,
plural* **bi·as·es;** 2 *verb,* **bi·as·es, bi·ased** or
bi·assed, bi·as·ing or **bi·as·sing.**

bi·ased (bī′əst), favoring or opposing a person or
thing without real cause: *a biased opinion.*
adjective.

bib (bib), a cloth worn under the chin by babies
and small children to protect their clothing during
meals. noun.

Bi·ble (bī′bəl), **1** the book of sacred writings of
the Christian religion containing the Old
Testament and the New Testament. **2** the Old
Testament, sacred to Jews. **3** the book of the
sacred writings of any religion. The Koran is the
Bible of the Moslems. noun.
[*Bible* comes from a Greek word meaning
"books."]

bib·li·cal or **Bib·li·cal** (bib′lə kəl), of the Bible;
having something to do with the Bible: *the biblical
story of Adam and Eve.* adjective.

BICEPS

bi·ceps (bī′seps), the large muscle in the front part of the upper arm. If you move your fist up to your shoulder, the biceps will stick out. *noun*, *plural* **bi·ceps.**

bick·er (bik′ər), to take part in a noisy quarrel about something unimportant; squabble: *The children bickered about which television program to watch. verb.*

bi·cus·pid (bī kus′pid), a double-pointed tooth that tears and grinds food. Adult human beings have eight bicuspids. *noun.*

bi·cy·cle (bī′sik′əl), **1** a light vehicle with two wheels, one behind the other. The wheels support a metal frame on which there is a seat. The rider pushes two pedals that move the back wheel and steers with handlebars. **2** to ride a bicycle. 1 *noun*, 2 *verb*, **bi·cy·cles, bi·cy·cled, bi·cy·cling.**

bi·cy·clist (bī′sik′list), a person who rides a bicycle. *noun.*

bid (bid), **1** to tell someone what to do or where to go; command: *We were bidden to stay in our seats until the bus stopped.* **2** to say; tell: *His friends bade him good-by.* **3** to offer to pay a certain price: *She bid $5 for the table.* **4** an offer to pay a certain price: *She made a bid on the table.* **5** the amount offered or stated: *My bid was $7.* 1-3 *verb*, **bids, bade** or **bid, bid·den** or **bid, bid·ding;** 4,5 *noun.*

bid·den (bid′n). See **bid**. *The class was bidden to remain seated until the bell rang. verb.*

bid·ding (bid′ing), **1** a command; order: *The servant awaited the queen's bidding.* **2** the act of offering money for something: *The bidding at the auction was slow.* **3** See **bid**. *We are bidding him good-by.* 1,2 *noun*, 3 *verb.*

bide (bīd), to continue; wait; abide: *Bide here awhile. verb*, **bides, bid·ed, bid·ing.**

bi·fo·cal (bī fō′kəl), **1** having two focuses. The lenses of bifocal glasses have two sections, the upper part for distant vision, the lower part for close vision. **2 bifocals**, *plural*, a pair of glasses with bifocal lenses. 1 *adjective*, 2 *noun.*

big (big), **1** great in amount or size: *Rabbits are bigger than squirrels. The growth and distribution of food is a big business.* **2** important; great: *The election of the President is big news. adjective*, **big·ger, big·gest.**

big·horn (big′hôrn′), a wild, grayish-brown sheep of the Rocky Mountains, with large, curving horns. *noun, plural* **big·horns** or **big·horn.**

bike (bīk), **1** a bicycle. **2** to ride a bicycle. 1 *noun*, 2 *verb*, **bikes, biked, bik·ing.**

bile (bīl), a bitter, greenish-yellow liquid produced by the liver. It aids digestion in the small intestine. *noun.*

bill[1] (bil), **1** a statement of money owed for work done or things supplied: *The store sent me a $135 bill for clothing I had charged.* **2** to send a bill to: *The telephone company bills us each month.* **3** a piece of paper money: *a dollar bill.* **4** a written or printed public notice, such as an advertisement or poster. **5** a written or printed statement; list of items. A **bill of rights** lists the basic rights belonging to the citizens of a country. **6** a proposed law presented to a lawmaking group for its approval: *The tax bill will be voted on by the Senate today.* 1,3-6 *noun*, 2 *verb.*

bill[2] (bil), the hard, horny part of the mouth of a bird; beak. *noun.*

bill·board (bil′bôrd′), a large board, usually outdoors, on which to display advertisements. *noun.*

bill·fold (bil′fōld′), a small, flat case for carrying paper money or cards in one's pocket; wallet. *noun.*

bil·liards (bil′yərdz), a game played with three hard balls on a special table with a raised, cushioned edge. A long stick called a cue is used to hit the balls. *noun.*

bil·lion (bil′yən), one thousand millions; 1,000,000,000. *noun, adjective.*

bil·low (bil′ō), **1** a great, swelling wave. **2** any great wave or swelling mass of smoke, flame, or sound: *Billows of smoke rose from the chimney.* **3** to rise or roll in big waves: *Smoke billowed from the burning building.* **4** to swell out; bulge: *Sheets on a line billow in the wind.* 1,2 *noun*, 3,4 *verb.*

bil·ly goat (bil′ē gōt′), a male goat.

bin (bin), a box or enclosed place for holding or storing grain, coal, and similar things. *noun.*

bi·nar·y sys·tem (bī′nər ē sis′təm), a system of writing numbers in which any amount can be written using only the figures 1 and 0. The binary system is used by electronic computers, because 1 and 0 can easily be represented by a closed or open circuit.

bighorn—about 3½ feet (1 meter) at the shoulder

bind (bīnd), **1** to tie together; hold together; fasten: *She bound the package with string.* **2** to fasten sheets of paper into a cover; put a cover on a book: *The loose pages were bound into a book.* **3** to hold by a promise, duty, or law: *He wanted to stay longer, but felt bound by his promise to his parents that he would return early.* **4** to put a bandage on: *bind up a wound.* **5** to fit too tightly: *This new shirt binds across the shoulders. verb,* **binds, bound, bind·ing.**

bin·go (bing′gō), a game in which players cover numbers on cards as the numbers are called out. The first player to cover a row of numbers in any direction wins. *noun.*

bi·noc·u·lars (bə nok′yə lərz), a double telescope made for use with both eyes. Binoculars make distant things appear nearer and larger. *noun plural.*

Word History

binoculars *Binoculars* comes from two Latin words meaning "two at a time" and "eye."

bi·o·de·grad·a·ble (bī′ō di grā′də bəl), that can be removed from the environment by the action of bacteria and other living things. A biodegradable detergent does not pollute water. *adjective.*

bi·o·graph·i·cal (bī′ə graf′ə kəl), **1** of a person's life: *The book gives many biographical details about the explorer.* **2** having to do with biography. *adjective.*

bi·og·ra·phy (bī og′rə fē), the written story of a person's life. *noun, plural* **bi·og·ra·phies.**

bi·o·log·i·cal (bī′ə loj′ə kəl), **1** of living things: *He is engaged in biological studies.* **2** having to do with biology. *adjective.*

bi·ol·o·gist (bī ol′ə jist), a person who is an expert in biology. *noun.*

bi·ol·o·gy (bī ol′ə jē), the science of living things; study of all forms of life. Biology deals with the origin, structure, activities, and distribution of living things. Botany, zoology, and ecology are branches of biology. *noun.*

bi·on·ic (bī on′ik), having electronic parts that replace parts of the body. *adjective.*
[*Bionic* was formed by joining parts of the words *biology* and *electronic.*]

a hat	**i** it

a hat	**i** it	**oi** oil	**ch** child	a in about
ā age	**ī** ice	**ou** out	**ng** long	e in taken
ä far	**o** hot	**u** cup	**sh** she	ə = i in pencil
e let	**ō** open	**ù** put	**th** thin	o in lemon
ē equal	**ô** order	**ü** rule	**ŦH** then	u in circus
ėr term			**zh** measure	

biplane

bi·plane (bī′plān′), an airplane having two wings on each side of the body, one above the other. *noun.*

birch (bėrch), a tree having hard wood, often used in making furniture. Its smooth bark may be peeled off in thin layers. *noun, plural* **birch·es.**

bird (bėrd), one of a group of warm-blooded animals that have a backbone, feathers, two legs, and wings. Birds lay eggs; most birds can fly. A **bird of prey** eats flesh. Eagles, hawks, vultures, and owls are birds of prey. *noun.*

birth (bėrth), **1** a coming into life; being born: *At birth, the baby weighed 6 pounds, 8 ounces.* **2** a beginning; origin: *the birth of a nation.* **3** family; descent: *a person of Spanish birth. noun.*
give birth to, to bring forth; bear: *The dog gave birth to four puppies.*

birth·day (bėrth′dā′), **1** the day on which a person was born or on which something began. **2** the anniversary of this day. *noun.*

birth·mark (bėrth′märk′), a mark on the skin that was there at birth. *noun.*

birth·place (bėrth′plās′), **1** the place where a person was born. **2** the place of origin: *Philadelphia is the birthplace of the United States. noun.*

birth·right (bėrth′rīt′), a right or privilege that a person is entitled to by birth: *Freedom of speech is a birthright in the United States. noun.*

bis·cuit (bis′kit), a soft bread dough baked in small portions. *noun.*

bish·op (bish′əp), **1** a clergyman of high rank in some Christian churches. **2** one of the pieces in the game of chess. A bishop can move diagonally across empty squares. *noun.*

Bis·marck (biz′märk), the capital of North Dakota. *noun.*

bi·son (bī′sn *or* bī′zn), a wild animal of North America, related to cattle, with a big shaggy head

bison—about 5½ feet (1½ meters) at the shoulder

and a hump above the shoulders; buffalo. *noun, plural* **bi·son.**

bit¹ (bit), **1** a small piece; small amount: *A pebble is a bit of rock.* **2** a short time: *Stay a bit.* **3** 12½ cents. A quarter is two bits. *noun.*
a bit, a little; slightly: *I am a bit tired.*

bit² (bit). See **bite.** *Our dog bit the dog next door. The other dog was bit on the leg. verb.*

bit³ (bit), **1** a tool for boring or drilling that fits into a handle called a brace or into a drill. **2** the part of a bridle that goes in a horse's mouth. *noun.*

Word History

bit³ *Bit*³ comes from an earlier English word meaning "to bite." The tool bites into wood as it bores holes. The kind of bit used in a horse's mouth fits where the horse bites.

bit³ (definition 1)

bit⁴ (bit), the smallest unit of information in a computer. *noun.*
[*Bit*⁴ was formed from the first two letters of *binary* (as in *binary system*) and the last letter of *digit.*]

bite (bīt), **1** to seize, cut into, or cut off with the teeth: *She bit into the apple.* **2** a cutting or seizing with the teeth; nip: *The dog gave a bite or two at the bone.* **3** a piece bitten off; mouthful: *Eat the whole apple, not just a bite.* **4** a light meal; snack: *Have a bite with me now or you'll get hungry later.* **5** to wound with teeth, fangs, or a sting: *My dog never bites. A mosquito bit me.* **6** a wound made by biting or stinging: *Mosquito bites itch.* **7** a sharp, smarting pain: *We felt the bite of the wind.* **8** to cause a sharp, smarting pain to: *The icy wind bit her nose and ears.* **9** to take a bait; be caught: *The fish are biting well today.* 1,5,8,9 *verb,* **bites, bit, bit·ten** or **bit, bit·ing;** 2-4,6,7 *noun.*

bit·ing (bī′ting), causing pain or distress: *Dress warmly before you go out in that biting wind. Biting remarks hurt people's feelings. adjective.*

bit·ten (bit′n). See **bite.** *Finish the apple, now that you have bitten into it. verb.*

bit·ter (bit′ər), **1** having a sharp, harsh, unpleasant taste: *This coffee is so strong it tastes bitter.* **2** causing pain or grief; hard to admit or bear: *The death of his father was a bitter loss.* **3** showing pain or grief: *The lost child shed bitter tears.* **4** harsh or cutting: *a bitter remark.* **5** very cold: *The bitter winter killed our apple tree. adjective.*

bi·tu·mi·nous coal (bə tü′mə nəs kōl′), a coal that burns with much smoke and flame; soft coal.

black (blak), **1** the color of coal or the ink this sentence is printed in. **2** having this color: *a black sweater.* **3** without any light; very dark: *The room was black as night.* **4** sullen; angry: *She gave her brother a black look.* **5** Also, **Black, a** having dark skin; Negro. **b** a person who has dark skin; Negro. 1,5b *noun,* 2-5a *adjective.*

black-and-blue (blak′ən blü′), discolored from a bruise. *adjective.*

black·ber·ry (blak′ber′ē), a small, dark-purple fruit growing on certain thorny bushes and vines. It is sweet and juicy. *noun, plural* **black·ber·ries.**

blackbird
about 9 inches
(23 centimeters) long

black·bird (blak′bėrd′), any of various American birds, the male of which is mostly black. *noun.*

black·board (blak′bôrd′), a smooth, hard surface, used for writing or drawing on with chalk. *noun.*

blacken (definition 1)
The storm clouds gathered and the sky **blackened.**

a hat	i it	oi oil	ch child	⎧ a in about
ā age	ī ice	ou out	ng long	e in taken
ä far	o hot	u cup	sh she	ə = ⎨ i in pencil
e let	ō open	u̇ put	th thin	o in lemon
ē equal	ô order	ü rule	ᴛʜ then	⎩ u in circus
ėr term			zh measure	

black·en (blak′ən), **1** to make or become black: *Soot blackened the snow.* **2** to speak evil of: *Enemies blackened his character with false rumors.* *verb.*

black eye, a dark-purple bruise around an eye.

black-eyed pea (blak′īd′ pē′), the seed of a plant related to peas and beans, grown in the southern United States as a vegetable.

black-eyed Su·san (blak′īd′ sü′zn), a yellow, daisylike flower with a black center.

black-eyed Susan

black·head (blak′hed′), a small, black-tipped mass of dead cells and oil plugging a pore of the skin. *noun.*

black·mail (blak′māl′), **1** to get or try to get money from someone by threatening to reveal something which that person wishes to keep secret. **2** an attempt to get money by such threats. **1** *verb,* **2** *noun.*

black·out (blak′out′), the going out of all the lights of a city or district. This may happen when the electrical power goes off. *noun.*

black·smith (blak′smith′), a person who makes things out of iron by heating it in a forge and hammering it into shape on an anvil. Blacksmiths mend tools and shoe horses. *noun.*

black·top (blak′top′), **1** an asphalt mixed with crushed rock, used as pavement for highways and driveways. **2** to pave a surface with blacktop. **1** *noun,* **2** *verb,* **black·tops, black·topped, black·top·ping.**

black widow, a spider, the female of which is poisonous and has a glossy, black body with a reddish mark in the shape of an hourglass on its underside.

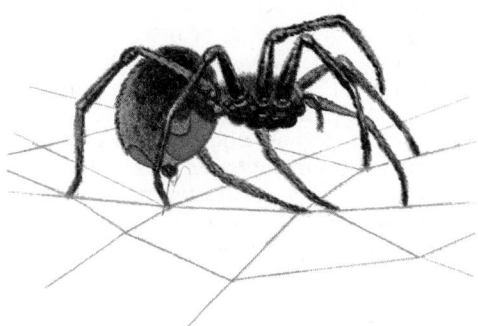

black widow—about 1½ inches (4 centimeters) when legs are extended

blad·der (blad′ər), a soft, thin bag in the body that stores urine from the kidneys until it is released by the body. *noun.*

blade (blād), **1** the cutting part of anything like a knife or sword: *A carving knife should have a very sharp blade.* **2** a leaf of grass. **3** the flat, wide part of anything. An oar or a paddle has a blade at one end of the shaft. *noun.*

blame (blām), **1** to hold responsible for something bad or wrong: *The driver blamed the fog for the accident.* **2** responsibility for something bad or wrong: *I won't take the blame for something I didn't do.* **3** to find fault with: *I don't blame her for wanting a better bicycle.* **1,3** *verb,* **blames, blamed, blam·ing; 2** *noun.*

bland (bland), mild; soothing; not irritating: *a bland manner, a bland diet of baby food. adjective.*

blank (blangk), **1** a space left empty or to be filled in: *Leave a blank if you can't answer the question.* **2** not written or printed on: *blank paper.* **3** a paper with spaces to be filled in: *Fill out this application blank and return it at once.* **4** with spaces left for filling in: *Here is a blank form for you to fill in and return.* **5** empty; vacant: *There was a blank look on his face.* **6** a cartridge containing gunpowder but no bullet. **1,3,6** *noun,* **2,4,5** *adjective.*

blan·ket (blang′kit), **1** a soft, heavy covering woven from wool, cotton, nylon, or other material, used to keep people or animals warm. **2** anything like a blanket: *A blanket of snow covered the ground.* **3** to cover with a blanket: *The snow blanketed the ground.* **1,2** *noun,* **3** *verb.*

blare (bler *or* blar), **1** to make a loud, harsh

sound: *The trumpets blared.* **2** a loud, harsh sound. **1** *verb,* **blares, blared, blar·ing; 2** *noun.*

blast (blast), **1** a strong, sudden rush of wind or air: *Last night we felt the icy blasts of winter.* **2** a sound made by blowing a trumpet, horn, or whistle: *The warning blast of a bugle aroused the camp.* **3** to blow up with dynamite or other explosives: *The big boulders were blasted to clear the way for a new road.* **4** an explosion: *We heard the blast a mile away.* **5** to ruin: *The bad news blasted our hopes.* **1,2,4** *noun,* **3,5** *verb.*

blast off, to take off into flight propelled by rockets: *The spacecraft blasts off tomorrow morning.*

blast·off (blast′ôf′), a taking off into rocket-propelled flight. *noun.*

blaze[1] (blāz), **1** a bright flame or fire: *We could see the blaze of the campfire across the beach.* **2** to burn with a bright flame: *A fire was blazing in the fireplace.* **3** a glow of brightness; glare: *the blaze of the noon sun.* **4** to show bright colors or lights: *On New Year's Eve the big house blazed with lights.* **5** a bright display: *The tulips made a blaze of color.* **6** to burst out in anger or excitement: *She blazed at the insult.* **1,3,5** *noun,* **2,4,6** *verb,* **blaz·es, blazed, blaz·ing.**

blaze[2] (blāz), **1** a mark made on a tree by cutting off a piece of bark, to indicate a trail or boundary in a forest. **2** to mark a tree, trail, or boundary by cutting off bark. **1** *noun,* **2** *verb,* **blaz·es, blazed, blaz·ing.**

bleach (blēch), **1** to make white by exposing to sunlight or by using chemicals: *animal skulls bleached by the desert sun. We bleached the linen napkins in the wash.* **2** any chemical used in bleaching: *She used bleach along with the detergent to wash the white sheets.* **1** *verb,* **2** *noun, plural* **bleach·es.**

bleach·ers (blē′chərz), a section of benches for people attending baseball games or other outdoor events. Bleachers are not roofed, and are the lowest priced seats. *noun.*

bleak (blēk), **1** swept by winds; bare: *The rocky peaks of high mountains are bleak.* **2** chilly; cold: *a bleak winter wind.* **3** cheerless and depressing; dismal: *A prisoner's life is bleak. adjective.*

bleat (blēt), **1** the cry made by a sheep, goat, or calf. **2** to make a sound like this. **1** *noun,* **2** *verb.*

bled (bled). See **bleed.** *The cut bled for ten minutes. verb.*

bleed (blēd), **1** to lose blood: *The cut on your leg is bleeding.* **2** to lose sap or juice from a surface that has been cut or scratched: *Trees bleed if they are pruned when the sap is rising in the spring.* **3** to feel pity, sorrow, or grief: *My heart bleeds for the earthquake victims. verb,* **bleeds, bled, bleed·ing.**

blem·ish (blem′ish), **1** something that spoils beauty; defect; flaw: *A pimple is a blemish on the skin.* **2** to injure; mar: *The scandal blemished his reputation.* **1** *noun, plural* **blem·ish·es; 2** *verb.*

blend (blend), **1** to mix together; mix or become mixed so thoroughly that the things mixed cannot be distinguished or separated: *Blend the butter*

and the sugar before adding the other ingredients of the cake. **2** to shade into each other, little by little: *The colors of the rainbow blend into one another.* **3** to go well together; harmonize. **4** a mixture of several kinds: *This coffee is a blend.* **5** two or more consonants that begin a syllable. *Sp* in *spell* and *pl* in *replace* are blends. **1-3** *verb,* **4,5** *noun.*

blend·er (blen′dər), an electric kitchen appliance for grinding, mixing, or beating various foods. *noun.*

bless (bles), **1** to make holy or sacred: *The bishop blessed the new church.* **2** to ask God's favor for: *Bless these little children.* **3** to wish good to; feel grateful to: *She blessed him for his kindness.* **4** to make happy or fortunate: *I have always been blessed with good health.* **5** to praise: *to bless the Lord. verb,* **bless·es, blessed** or **blest, bless·ing.**

bless·ed (bles′id *or* blest), holy; sacred. *adjective.*

bless·ing (bles′ing), **1** a prayer asking God's favor. **2** a wish for happiness or success: *When I left home, I received my family's blessing.* **3** anything that makes one happy and contented: *A good temper is a great blessing. noun.*

blest (blest). See **bless.** *She was blest with good fortune. verb.*

blew (blü). See **blow**[2]. *The wind blew. verb.*

blight (blīt), **1** a disease that causes plants or parts of plants to wither and die: *The apple crop was wiped out by blight.* **2** anything that destroys or ruins: *The garbage dump is a blight on the neighborhood. noun.*

blimp

blimp (blimp), a kind of balloon that can be steered. A blimp is filled with a gas that is lighter than air. *noun.*

blind (blīnd), **1** not able to see: *The man with the white cane is blind.* **2** to make unable to see: *The bright lights blinded me for a moment.* **3** hard to see; hidden: *Several accidents took place at that blind curve because the drivers could not see the oncoming traffic.* **4** by means of instruments instead of the eyes: *the blind flying of an aircraft at night. We flew blind through the storm.* **5** without thought, judgment, or good sense: *She was in a blind fury.* **6** to take away the power to understand or judge: *His strong opinions blinded him to the facts.* **7** something that keeps out light or hinders sight. A window shade or shutter is a blind. **8** with only one opening. A blind alley is a passageway closed at one end. 1,3-5,8 *adjective,* 2,6 *verb,* 4 *adverb,* 7 *noun.*

blind·fold (blīnd′fōld′), **1** to cover the eyes of: *We blindfolded her.* **2** with the eyes covered: *He walked the line blindfold.* **3** a thing covering the eyes. 1 *verb,* 2 *adjective,* 3 *noun.*

blind·man's buff (blīnd′manz buf′), a game in which a blindfolded person tries to catch and name one of several other players.

blink (blingk), **1** to look with the eyes opening and shutting: *She blinked at the sudden light.* **2** to open and shut the eyes; wink: *We blink every few seconds.* **3** to shine with an unsteady light: *A little lantern blinked through the darkness. verb.*

blink·er (bling′kər), a device with flashing lights used as a warning signal: *When her car broke down, the driver left the blinkers flashing. noun.*

bliss (blis), great happiness; perfect joy: *What bliss it is to plunge into the waves on a hot day! noun.*

bliss·ful (blis′fəl), very happy; joyful. *adjective.*

blis·ter (blis′tər), **1** a small area of skin that puffs out into a bubble. Blisters fill with a clear watery liquid from the skin underneath. They are often caused by burns or by rubbing. *My new shoes have made blisters on my heels.* **2** a bubble on the surface of a plant, on metal, on painted wood, or in glass. **3** to form or cause to form blisters: *Sunburn blistered my back.* 1,2 *noun,* 3 *verb.*

blithe (blīŦH), happy and cheerful; joyful: *a blithe spirit. adjective,* **blith·er, blith·est.**

bliz·zard (bliz′ərd), a blinding snowstorm with a very strong wind and very great cold. *noun.*

bloat (blōt), to swell up; puff up: *Overeating bloated the cow's stomach. verb.*

blob (blob), a small, soft drop; sticky lump: *Blobs of wax covered the candlestick. noun.*

block (blok), **1** a solid piece of wood, stone, metal, or ice: *The ancient Egyptians used blocks of stone to build huge pyramids.* **2** to fill up so as to prevent passage or progress: *The country roads were blocked with snow.* **3** to get in the way of; hinder: *Mother's illness blocked my plans for her birthday party.* **4** anything or any group of persons that keeps something from being done: *A block in traffic kept our car from moving on.* **5** the space in a city or town enclosed by four streets; square. **6** the length of one side of a block in a city or town: *Walk one block east.* **7** a holder in which a pulley or pulleys are mounted. 1,4-7 *noun,* 2,3 *verb.*

block·ade (blo kād′), **1** the blocking of a place by an army or navy to control who or what goes into or out of it. **2** to put under blockade. 1 *noun,* 2 *verb,* **block·ades, block·ad·ed, block·ad·ing.**

block·house (blok′hous′), a small fort or building with loopholes to shoot from. *noun, plural* **block·hous·es** (blok′hou′ziz).

blond or **blonde** (blond), **1** light in color: *blond hair, blond furniture.* **2** having yellow or light-brown hair. **3** a person having this color hair.

a hat	**i** it	**oi** oil	**ch** child	(a in about
ā age	**ī** ice	**ou** out	**ng** long	e in taken
ä far	**o** hot	**u** cup	**sh** she	ə = { i in pencil
e let	**ō** open	**ù** put	**th** thin	o in lemon
ē equal	**ô** order	**ü** rule	**ŦH** then	u in circus
ėr term			**zh** measure	

A man or boy of this sort is usually called a blond. A woman or girl of this sort is usually called a blonde. 1,2 *adjective,* 3 *noun.*

blood (blud), **1** the red liquid in the veins and arteries; the red liquid that flows from a cut. Blood is pumped by the heart. It carries oxygen and digested food to all parts of the body and carries away waste materials. **2** family; parentage; descent: *We are related by blood.* **3** a temper; state of mind: *There was bad blood between them. noun.* **in cold blood,** cruelly or on purpose: *The bandits shot down three men in cold blood.*

blood bank, a place where blood for use in transfusions is kept.

blood·hound (blud′hound′), a large dog with a keen sense of smell. *noun.*

bloodhound
about 26 inches
(66 centimeters)
at the shoulder

blood pressure, the pressure of the blood against the inner walls of the arteries. Blood pressure varies with physical activity, excitement, health, and age.

blood·shed (blud′shed′), the shedding of blood; slaughter. *noun.*

blood·shot (blud′shot′), red and inflamed from broken or swollen blood vessels: *bloodshot eyes. adjective.*

blood·stream (blud′strēm′), the blood as it flows through the body. *noun.*

blood·thirst·y (blud′ŦHėr′stē), eager for bloodshed; cruel and murderous: *a bloodthirsty pirate. adjective.*

blood vessel, any tube in the body through which the blood circulates. Arteries and veins are blood vessels.

blood·y (blud′ē), **1** covered with blood; bleeding: *a bloody nose.* **2** accompanied by much killing: *a bloody battle. adjective,* **blood·i·er, blood·i·est.**

bloom (blüm), **1** to have flowers; open into flowers; blossom: *Many plants bloom in the spring.* **2** a flower; blossom. **3** the condition or time of flowering: *violets in bloom.* **4** the condition or time of greatest health, vigor, or beauty: *the bloom of youth.* **5** to be in the condition or time of greatest health, vigor, or beauty; flourish: *Water makes the desert bloom.* 1,5 *verb,* 2-4 *noun.*

blos·som (blos′əm), **1** a flower, especially of a plant that produces fruit: *apple blossoms.* **2** the condition or time of flowering: *pear trees in blossom.* **3** to have flowers; open into flowers: *Orchards blossom in spring.* **4** to open out; develop: *The shy child blossomed into an outgoing teenager.* 1,2 *noun,* 3,4 *verb.*

blot (blot), **1** a spot of ink or stain of any kind. **2** to make blots on; stain; spot: *My pen slipped and blotted the paper.* **3** to dry something written in ink with absorbent paper: *He wrote with a fountain pen, and was careful to blot each page.* **4** a blemish; disgrace: *The field of rusting cars was a blot on the landscape.* 1,4 *noun,* 2,3 *verb,* **blots, blot·ted, blot·ting.**

blot out, 1 to cover up entirely; hide: *He blotted out the mistake with ink.* **2** to wipe out; destroy: *When the dam broke, an entire village was blotted out.*

blotch (bloch), **1** a large, irregular spot or stain. **2** a place where the skin is red or broken out. *noun, plural* **blotch·es.**

blot·ter (blot′ər), a soft paper used to dry writing by soaking up ink. *noun.*

blouse (blous), **1** a loose upper garment worn by women and children as a part of their outer clothing. **2** a loosely fitting garment for the upper part of the body: *The sailor wore a wool blouse as part of his uniform. noun.*

blow[1] (blō), **1** a hard hit; knock; stroke: *The boxer struck his opponent a blow that knocked him down.* **2** a sudden happening that causes misfortune or loss; severe shock: *His mother's death was a great blow to him. noun.*

blow[2] (blō), **1** to send forth a strong current of air: *Blow on the fire or it will go out.* **2** to move rapidly or with power: *The wind blew in gusts.* **3** to drive or carry by a current of air: *The wind blew the curtain.* **4** to force a current of air into, through, or against: *She blew her nose.* **5** to form or shape by air; swell with air: *to blow bubbles.* **6** to make a sound by a current of air or steam: *The whistle blows at noon.* **7** to break by an explosion: *The dynamite blew the wall to bits.* **8** to melt: *The short circuit caused the fuse to blow.* **9** a gale of wind: *Last night's big blow brought down several trees.* 1-8 *verb,* **blows, blew, blown, blow·ing;** 9 *noun.*

blow out, 1 to put out or be put out by a current of air: *The candle blew out.* **2** to have or cause a blowout in: *The worn tire blew out.*

blow up, 1 to explode: *The ammunition ship blew up and sank when it hit the rocks.* **2** to fill with air: *to blow up a bicycle tire.* **3** to become very angry: *She blew up at me for keeping her waiting for two hours.* **4** to become stronger; arise: *A storm blew up suddenly.*

blow·er (blō′ər), a fan or other machine for

forcing air into a building, furnace, mine, or other enclosed area. *noun.*

blow·hole (blō′hōl′), a hole for breathing, in the top of the head of whales, porpoises, and dolphins. *noun.*

blowhole
A plume of water is blown from the whale's **blowhole.**

blown (blōn). See **blow**[2]. *My hat was blown away by the wind. verb.*

blow·out (blō′out′), the bursting of a tire: *A blowout caused the driver to lose control of the car. noun.*

blow·torch (blō′tôrch′), a device that shoots out a very hot flame. A blowtorch is used to melt metal and burn off paint. *noun, plural* **blow·torch·es.**

blub·ber (blub′ər), **1** the fat of whales and some other sea animals. Oil obtained from whale blubber was burned in lamps. **2** to weep noisily. 1 *noun,* 2 *verb.*

blue (blü), **1** the color of the clear sky in daylight. **2** having this color. **3** having a dull-bluish color: *My hands were blue from cold.* **4** sad; discouraged: *She felt blue when her best friend moved away.* 1 *noun,* 2-4 *adjective,* **blu·er, blu·est.**

out of the blue, completely unexpectedly: *Her visit came out of the blue.*

blue·bell (blü′bel′), a plant with blue bell-shaped flowers. *noun.*

blue·ber·ry (blü′ber′ē), a small, round, sweet, blue berry that grows on a shrub. *noun, plural* **blue·ber·ries.**

bluebird
about 7 inches (18 centimeters) long

blue·bird (blü′bėrd′), a small songbird of North America. The male usually has a bright blue back and wings and a chestnut-brown breast. *noun.*

blue·grass (blü′gras′), a grass with bluish-green stems. It is valuable as food for horses and cattle, and is used for lawns. *noun.*

blue jay—about 12 inches (30 centimeters) long

a hat	i it	oi oil	ch child	⎧ a in about
ā age	ī ice	ou out	ng long	⎪ e in taken
ä far	o hot	u cup	sh she	ə = ⎨ i in pencil
e let	ō open	ů put	th thin	⎪ o in lemon
ē equal	ô order	ü rule	ŦH then	⎩ u in circus
ėr term			zh measure	

B

blue jay, a North American bird with a crest and a blue back.

blue jeans, jeans, usually made of blue denim.

blue·print (blü′print′), a photographic print that shows white outlines on a blue background. Blueprints are copies of original drawings of building plans or maps. *noun.*

blues (blüz), **1** a slow, sad song with jazz rhythm. **2 the blues,** low spirits: *A rainy day always gives me the blues.* 1 *noun,* 2 *noun plural.*

blue whale, a blue-gray whale that sometimes grows to be 100 feet (30 meters) in length. It is the largest living animal.

bluff[1] (bluf), a high, steep slope or cliff. *noun.*

bluff[2] (bluf), **1** to fool or mislead by pretending confidence: *She bluffed the robbers by telling them that the police were on the way.* **2** something said or done to fool or mislead others: *During the card game she acted as if she were winning, but it was only a bluff.* 1 *verb,* 2 *noun.*

blu·ish (blü′ish), somewhat blue. *adjective.*

blun·der (blun′dər), **1** a stupid mistake: *Misspelling the title of a book is a silly blunder to make in a book report.* **2** to make a stupid mistake: *Someone blundered in sending you to the wrong address.* **3** to move as if blind; stumble: *I blundered through the dark room.* 1 *noun,* 2,3 *verb.*

blun·der·buss (blun′dər bus), a short gun with a wide muzzle, formerly used to shoot balls or slugs a very short distance without exact aim. *noun,* plural **blun·der·buss·es.**

blunt (blunt), **1** without a sharp edge or point; dull: *a blunt knife.* **2** to make less sharp; make less keen: *Cutting the cardboard blunted my scissors.* **3** saying what one thinks very frankly, without trying to be polite; outspoken: *When I asked her if she liked my painting, her blunt answer was "No."* 1,3 *adjective,* 2 *verb.*

blur (blėr), **1** to make or become less clear in form or outline: *Mist blurred the hills.* **2** a thing seen dimly or indistinctly: *When I don't have my glasses on, your face is just a blur.* **3** to smear; smudge: *I blurred my painting by touching it before the paint was dry.* 1,3 *verb,* **blurs, blurred, blur·ring;** 2 *noun.*

blur·ry (blėr′ē), dim; indistinct: *The blurry outline of the tall buildings could be seen through the fog.* *adjective,* **blur·ri·er, blur·ri·est.**

blurt (blėrt), to say suddenly or without thinking: *In his excitement he blurted out the secret.* *verb.*

blush (blush), **1** to become red in the face because of shame, confusion, or excitement: *The little boy blushed when everyone laughed at his mistake.* **2** a reddening of the face caused by confusion, shame, or excitement. **3** to be ashamed: *I blushed at my sister's bad table manners.* **4** a rosy color: *the blush of dawn.* 1,3 *verb,* 2,4 *noun,* plural **blush·es.**

blus·ter (blus′tər), **1** to storm noisily; blow violently: *The wind blustered around the corner of the house.* **2** stormy noise and violence: *We could hear the bluster of the wind, and knew the snow would pile up in drifts.* **3** to talk noisily and violently: *When he first heard my plan, he blustered for a while, but he finally agreed to try it.* **4** noisy and violent talk: *angry bluster.* 1,3 *verb,* 2,4 *noun.*

boa constrictor—up to 15 feet (4½ meters) long

bo·a con·stric·tor (bō′ə kən strik′tər), a large snake which is not poisonous, but kills its prey by crushing with its coils. Boa constrictors are found in the tropical parts of America.

boar (bôr), **1** a male pig or hog. **2** a wild pig or hog. *noun.*

boar (definition 2)
2½ feet (76 centimeters) high at the shoulder

board (bôrd), **1** a broad, thin piece of wood for use in building: *We used boards 10 inches wide, 1 inch thick, and 3 feet long for shelves.* **2** to cover with such pieces of wood: *We board up the windows of our summer cottage in the fall.* **3** a flat piece of wood or other material used for one special purpose: *an ironing board, a drawing board.* **4** meals provided for pay: *The cost of going away to college includes room and board.* **5** to give or get meals, or room and meals, for pay: *You will have to board elsewhere.* **6** a group of persons managing something; council: *a school board, a board of directors.* **7** to get on a ship, train, bus, or airplane: *We board the school bus at the corner.* 1,3,4,6 *noun,* 2,5,7 *verb.*
on board, on a ship, train, bus, or airplane: *When everybody was on board, the ship sailed.*

board·er (bôr′dər), a person who pays for meals, or for room and meals, at another's house. *noun.*

board·ing·house (bôr′ding hous′), a house where meals, or room and meals, are provided for pay. *noun, plural* **board·ing·hous·es** (bôr′ding hou′ziz).

boarding school, a school with buildings where the pupils live during the school term.

boast (bōst), **1** to speak too highly of oneself or what one owns: *He boasts about his grades in school.* **2** a statement speaking too highly of oneself or what one owns; boasting words: *I don't believe her boast that she can run faster than I can.* **3** to have something to be proud of: *Our town boasts a beautiful new high school.* 1,3 *verb,* 2 *noun.*

boast·ful (bōst′fəl), fond of boasting: *It is hard to listen very long to a boastful person. adjective.*

boat (bōt), **1** a small, open vessel, such as a motorboat or a rowboat. **2** a large vessel, such as a freighter, passenger liner, or oil tanker; ship. **3** to go in a boat. 1,2 *noun,* 3 *verb.*

boat·house (bōt′hous′), a house or shed for sheltering a boat or boats. *noun, plural* **boat·hous·es** (bōt′hou′ziz).

bob[1] (bob), **1** to move up and down, or to and fro, with short, quick motions: *The pigeon bobbed its head as it picked up crumbs.* **2** a short, quick motion up and down, or to and fro. 1 *verb,* **bobs, bobbed, bob·bing;** 2 *noun.*

bob[2] (bob), **1** a child's or woman's haircut that is fairly short all around the head. **2** to cut hair short. **3** a float for a fishing line. 1,3 *noun,* 2 *verb,* **bobs, bobbed, bob·bing.**

bob·bin (bob′ən), a reel or spool for holding thread, yarn, and the like. Bobbins are used in spinning, weaving, machine sewing, and making lace. *noun.*

bob·by pin (bob′ē pin′), a small, thin piece of metal with prongs that close tightly on the hair and hold it in place. Bobby pins are used by women and girls.

bob·cat (bob′kat′), a small wildcat of North America. It has a reddish-brown coat with black spots. *noun.*

bob·o·link (bob′ə lingk), a common North American songbird that lives in fields and meadows. *noun.*

bob·sled (bob′sled′), a long sled with two sets of runners. It has a steering wheel and brakes. *noun.*

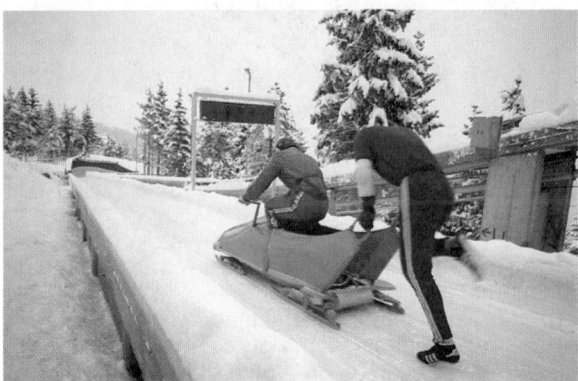

bobsled
The riders have to jump into the **bobsled** after pushing it to start.

bob·white (bob′whīt′), an American quail that has a grayish body with brown and white markings. Its call sounds like its name. *noun.*

bode (bōd), to be a sign of: *The rumble of thunder boded rain. verb,* **bodes, bod·ed, bod·ing.**

bod·i·ly (bod′l ē), **1** of the body; in the body: *Athletes have bodily strength.* **2** in person: *Although she cannot be with us bodily, she is here in spirit.* 1 *adjective,* 2 *adverb.*

bod·y (bod′ē), **1** the whole material or physical part of a person or animal: *I exercise to keep my body strong and healthy.* **2** the main part of an animal, not the head, limbs, or tail. **3** the main part of anything. **4** a group of persons or things: *The student body of our school gathered for an assembly.* **5** a dead person or animal. **6** a mass: *A lake is a body of water. The moon, the sun, and the stars are heavenly bodies. noun, plural* **bod·ies.**

bod·y·guard (bod′ē gärd′), a person or persons

bobcat—23 inches (58 centimeters) high at the shoulder

who guard someone: *A bodyguard usually accompanies the President. noun.*

bog (bog), **1** soft, wet, spongy ground; marsh; swamp. **2 bog down,** to sink in or get stuck so that one cannot get out without help: *I am bogged down with all this homework.* **1** *noun,* **2** *verb,* **bogs, bogged, bog·ging.**

bo·gey·man (bō′gē man′ or bug′ē man′), a frightening imaginary creature. *noun, plural* **bo·gey·men.**

boil¹ (boil), **1** to bubble up and give off steam: *Water boils when heated.* **2** to cause a liquid to boil by heating it: *Boil some water for tea.* **3** to cook by boiling: *We boil eggs four minutes.* **4** to have its contents boil: *The pot is boiling.* **5** to be very excited; be stirred up: *He boiled with anger.* **6** a boiling condition: *to heat water to a boil.* **1-5** *verb,* **6** *noun.*

boil² (boil), a painful, red swelling on the skin caused by infection. A boil has a hard core and is filled with pus. *noun.*

boil·er (boi′lər), a tank for making steam to heat buildings or drive engines. *noun.*

boiling point, the temperature at which a liquid boils. The boiling point of water at sea level is 212 degrees Fahrenheit or 100 degrees Celsius.

Boi·se (boi′sē), the capital of Idaho. *noun.*

bois·ter·ous (boi′stər əs), **1** noisily cheerful: *The room was filled with boisterous laughter.* **2** rough and noisy: *a boisterous child. adjective.*

bold (bōld), **1** without fear; having or showing courage; brave: *a bold knight. A circus lion tamer must be bold and fearless.* **2** rude; impudent: *The bold child made faces at us as we passed.* **3** sharp and clear to the eye; striking: *The mountains stood in bold outline against the sky. adjective.*

bold·face (bōld′fās′), **1** a heavy printing type that stands out clearly. **This sentence is in boldface. 2** of or having to do with this type: *boldface headlines.* **1** *noun,* **2** *adjective.*

Bo·liv·i·a (bə liv′ē ə), a country in western South America. *noun.*

boll (bōl), the seed pod of a plant like cotton or flax. *noun.*

boll weevil, a small beetle with a long snout whose larva is hatched in young cotton bolls and does great damage to them.

boll weevil—about 1/5 inch (5 millimeters) long

a hat	**i** it	**oi** oil	**ch** child	a in about
ā age	**ī** ice	**ou** out	**ng** long	e in taken
ä far	**o** hot	**u** cup	**sh** she	ə = { i in pencil
e let	**ō** open	**u̇** put	**th** thin	o in lemon
ē equal	**ô** order	**ü** rule	**ᴛʜ** then	u in circus
ėr term			**zh** measure	

bo·lo·gna (bə lō′nē *or* bə lō′nə), a large sausage usually made of beef, veal, and pork. *noun.* [*Bologna* was named for Bologna, a city in Italy. Bologna sausage was first made in this city.]

bol·ster (bōl′stər), **1** a long pillow or cushion for a couch or bed. **2** to keep from falling; support; prop: *Her faith bolstered my confidence.* **1** *noun,* **2** *verb.*

bolt (definitions 1, 2, 5, 6, and 8)

bolt (bōlt), **1** a slender, round piece of metal with a head at one end and a screw thread for a nut at the other. Bolts are used to fasten things together or hold something in place. **2** a sliding fastening for a door or gate. **3** the part of a lock moved by a key. **4** to fasten with a bolt: *Bolt the doors.* **5** a flash of lightning. **6** a sudden start; a running away: *The rabbit saw the fox and made a bolt for safety.* **7** to dash off; run away: *The horse bolted at the sight of the car.* **8** a roll of cloth or wallpaper. **1-3,5,6,8** *noun,* **4,7** *verb.*

bolt upright, stiff and straight: *Awakened by a noise, I sat bolt upright in bed.*

bomb (bom), **1** a container filled with an explosive. A bomb is set off by a fuse or by the force with which it hits something. **2** to hurl bombs at; drop bombs on. **1** *noun,* **2** *verb.*

bom·bard (bom bärd′), **1** to attack with bombs or heavy fire from big guns: *The artillery bombarded the enemy all day.* **2** to keep attacking forcefully: *The lawyer bombarded the witness with one question after another. verb.*

Bom·bay (bom bā′), a city in India. *noun.*

bomb·er (bom′ər), an aircraft used to drop bombs. *noun.*

bond (bond), **1** anything that ties, binds, or unites: *the bonds of slavery. There is a bond of affection between the two sisters.* **2** a certificate issued by a government or private company which promises to pay back with interest the money borrowed from the buyer of the certificate: *The city issued bonds to raise money for a new park. noun.*

bond·age (bon′dij), the lack of freedom; slavery. *noun.*

bone (bōn), **1** one of the pieces of the skeleton of an animal with a backbone: *the bones of the hand.* **2** to take bones out of: *We boned the fish before eating it.* 1 *noun,* 2 *verb,* **bones, boned, bon·ing.**

bon·fire (bon′fīr′), a fire built outdoors: *We had to sit around the bonfire to keep warm. noun.* [*Bonfire* comes from the words *bone* and *fire.* It was called this because in the past a fire was made to burn old bones.]

bon·go (bong′gō), a small drum played with flattened hands. Bongos usually come in pairs and are held between the knees. *noun, plural* **bon·gos.**

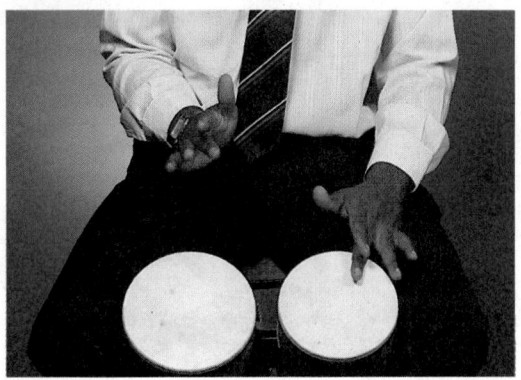

bongos

bon·net (bon′it), **1** a covering for the head usually tied under the chin with strings or ribbons, worn by women and children. **2** a headdress of feathers worn by North American Indians. *noun.*

bo·nus (bō′nəs), something extra, given in addition to what is due: *The company gave each worker a bonus of $200. noun, plural* **bo·nus·es.**

bon·y (bō′nē), **1** of bone: *the bony structure of the skull.* **2** full of bones: *a bony fish.* **3** having bones that stick out; very thin: *bony hands, an old horse with bony hips. adjective,* **bon·i·er, bon·i·est.**

boo (bü), **1** a sound made to show dislike or contempt, or to frighten: *They were frightened when I jumped from behind the door and shouted, "Boo!"* **2** to make such a sound; shout "boo" at: *He sang so badly that the audience booed him.* 1 *noun, plural* **boos;** 1 *interjection,* 2 *verb,* **boos, booed, boo·ing.**

book (bùk), **1** sheets of paper, either blank or printed, bound together between covers: *I read the first two chapters of that book last night.* **2** anything like a book: *a book of matches.* **3** a main division of a book: *Genesis is the first book of the Old Testament.* **4** to make reservations to get tickets or to engage service: *He had booked passage by airplane from New York to London.* **5** to write down an accusation against a person in a police record: *At the police station an officer booked the suspect.* 1-3 *noun,* 4,5 *verb.*

book·case (bùk′kās′), a piece of furniture with shelves for holding books. *noun.*

book·end (bùk′end′), a prop or support placed at the end of a row of books to hold them upright. *noun.*

book·keep·er (bùk′kē′pər), a person who keeps a record of business accounts. *noun.*

book·let (bùk′lit), a little book; thin book. Booklets often have paper covers. *noun.*

book·mark (bùk′märk′), a strip of cloth, paper, or the like, put between the pages of a book to mark the reader's place. *noun.*

book·mo·bile (bùk′mə bēl′), a truck that serves as a traveling branch of a library. *noun.*

book·shelf (bùk′shelf′), a shelf for holding books. *noun, plural* **book·shelves.**

book·worm (bùk′wėrm′), a person who is very fond of reading and studying. *noun.*

boom[1] (büm), **1** a deep hollow sound like the roar of cannon or of big waves: *We listened to the boom of the pounding surf.* **2** to make a deep hollow sound: *His voice boomed out above the rest.* **3** a rapid growth: *A recent boom doubled the size of the town.* **4** to grow rapidly: *Business is booming.* 1,3 *noun,* 2,4 *verb.*

boom[2] (büm), a long pole or beam. A boom is used to extend the bottom of a sail or as the lifting pole of a derrick. *noun.*

boo·me·rang (bü′mə rang′), a curved piece of wood, used as a weapon by the original people of Australia. Certain boomerangs can be thrown so that they return to the thrower. *noun.*

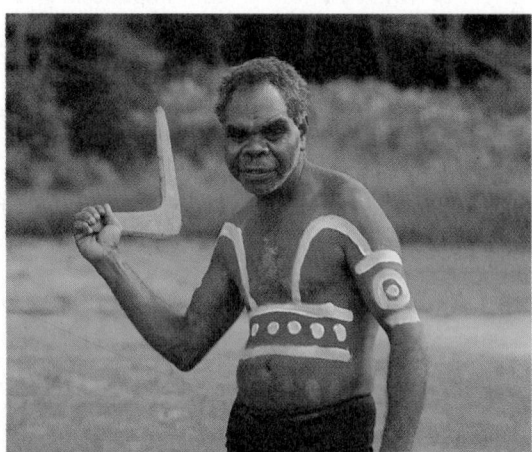

boomerang—man demonstrating the use of a **boomerang**

boon (bün), a great benefit; blessing: *Those warm boots were a boon to me in the cold weather. noun.*

boost (büst), **1** a lift or push that helps a person up or over something: *a boost over the fence.* **2** to lift or push from below: *Her friend boosted her to the lowest branch of the tree so she could pick the apples.* 1 *noun,* 2 *verb.*

boost·er (bü′stər), **1** a rocket or an engine that propels a missile, spacecraft, or the like. **2** a booster shot. *noun.*

booster shot, an additional injection of a

vaccine or serum to continue the effect of a previous injection.

boot (büt), **1** a leather or rubber covering for the foot and lower part of the leg. **2** a kick: *She gave the ball a boot.* **3** to give a kick to. 1,2 *noun,* 3 *verb.*

boot·ee (bü′tē), a baby's soft shoe, often knitted. *noun.*

booth (büth), **1** a place where goods are sold or shown at a fair, market, or convention. **2** a small enclosed or partly enclosed place: *a telephone booth, a voting booth, a booth in a restaurant.* *noun, plural* **booths** (büŦHz *or* büths).

boo·ty (bü′tē), things taken by force; plunder: *The pirates fought over how to divide the booty from the captured ship. noun.*

bor·der (bôr′dər), **1** the side, edge, or boundary of anything, or the part near it: *We pitched our tent on the border of the lake.* **2** to touch at the edge or boundary: *Canada borders on the United States.* **3** a strip on the edge of anything for strength or ornament: *a lace border.* **4** to put a border on: *to border a lawn with shrubs.* 1,3 *noun,* 2,4 *verb.*

bor·der·line (bôr′dər līn′), **1** a dividing line; boundary. **2** in between; uncertain: *a borderline case of mumps.* 1 *noun,* 2 *adjective.*

bore[1] (bôr), **1** to make a hole by means of a revolving tool: *Bore through the handle of that brush so we can hang it up.* **2** to make a hole by digging, chewing, or pushing: *Moles bore tunnels in lawns. verb,* **bores, bored, bor·ing.**

bore[2] (bôr), **1** to make weary by being uninteresting: *This book bores me, so I shall not finish it.* **2** a dull, tiresome person or thing: *It is a bore to wash dishes.* 1 *verb,* **bores, bored, bor·ing;** 2 *noun.*

bore[3] (bôr). See **bear**[1]. *She bore her loss bravely. verb.*

bore·dom (bôr′dəm), weariness caused by uninteresting people or events: *Her boredom was evident during the mayor's dull speech. noun.*

born (bôrn), **1** brought into life; brought forth: *a newly born calf.* **2** by birth; by nature: *She could swim and skate at such an early age, we believed she was a born athlete.* **3** See **bear**[1]. *He was born on December 30, 1900.* 1,2 *adjective,* 3 *verb.*

borne (bôrn), See **bear**[1]. *I have borne the pack for three miles. She has borne three children. verb.*

bor·ough (bėr′ō), **1** a town with certain powers of government. **2** one of the five divisions of New York City. *noun.*

bor·row (bor′ō), **1** to get something from another person with the understanding that it must be returned: *I borrowed the book and promised to return it to him in a week.* **2** to take and use as one's own; adopt; take: *The English word "kindergarten" was borrowed from German. verb.*

Bos·ni·a-Her·ze·go·vi·na (boz′nē ə hėr′tsə gə vē′nə), a country in southeastern Europe. *noun.*

bos·om (bůz′əm), the upper, front part of the human body; breast: *She clasped the child to her bosom. noun.*

boss (bôs), **1** a person who hires workers or tells

a hat	**i** it	**oi** oil	**ch** child	⎧ a in about
ā age	**ī** ice	**ou** out	**ng** long	⎪ e in taken
ä far	**o** hot	**u** cup	**sh** she	ə = ⎨ i in pencil
e let	**ō** open	**ů** put	**th** thin	⎪ o in lemon
ē equal	**ô** order	**ü** rule	**ŦH** then	⎩ u in circus
ėr term			**zh** measure	

them what to do; foreman; manager. **2** to be the boss of; direct; control: *He complained that you were trying to boss him.* 1 *noun, plural* **boss·es;** 2 *verb.*

[*Boss* comes from a Dutch word meaning "master." Dutch colonists in New York City used this word for a master craftsman who taught young apprentice workers.]

boss·y (bô′sē), fond of telling others what to do and how to do it: *Bossy people are seldom popular. adjective,* **boss·i·er, boss·i·est.**

Bos·ton (bô′stən), the capital of Massachusetts. *noun.*

bo·tan·i·cal (bə tan′ə kəl), having to do with the study of plants. *adjective.*

bot·a·nist (bot′n ist), a person who is an expert in botany. *noun.*

bot·a·ny (bot′n ē), the science of plants; the study of plants and plant life. Botany is a branch of biology. *noun.*

both (bōth), **1** the two; the one and the other: *Both houses are white.* **2** the two together: *Both belong to her.* **3** together; alike; equally: *He sings and dances both at once. She is both strong and healthy.* 1 *adjective,* 2 *pronoun,* 3 *adverb, conjunction.*

both·er (boŦH′ər), **1** much fuss or worry; trouble: *What a lot of bother about nothing!* **2** to take trouble; concern oneself: *Don't bother to cook; we'll eat out.* **3** a person or thing that causes worry, fuss, or trouble: *A door that will not shut is a bother.* **4** to annoy: *Hot weather bothers me.* 1,3 *noun,* 2,4 *verb.*

both·er·some (boŦH′ər səm), causing worry or fuss; troublesome: *Being sick at Thanksgiving was bothersome. adjective.*

Bot·swa·na (bot swä′nə), a country in southern Africa. *noun.*

bot·tle (bot′l), **1** a container without handles for holding liquids, usually made of glass or plastic. Most bottles have narrow necks which can be closed with caps or stoppers. **2** the amount that a bottle can hold: *He drank a bottle of ginger ale.* **3** to put into bottles: *Wine makers bottle wine for sale.* 1,2 *noun,* 3 *verb,* **bot·tles, bot·tled, bot·tling.**

bottle up, to hold in; control: *I bottled up my anger.*

bot·tom (bot′əm), **1** the lowest part: *These berries at the bottom of the basket are crushed.* **2** the part on which anything rests; base: *The bottom of that glass is wet.* **3** the ground under water: *Many wrecks lie at the bottom of the sea.* **4 bottoms,** the low land along a river. **5** a seat: *This chair needs a new bottom.* **6** a basis; foundation; origin: *We will* *get to the bottom of the mystery.* **7** lowest or last: *I see a robin on the bottom branch of that tree.* 1-6 *noun,* 7 *adjective.*

bot·tom·less (bot′əm lis), **1** without a bottom: *The old pail was bottomless.* **2** very, very deep: *a bottomless lake. adjective.*

bough (bou), one of the main branches of a tree. *noun.*

bought (bôt). See **buy.** *We bought apples at the market. I have bought two new pencils. verb.*

boul·der (bōl′dər), a large rock, rounded or worn by the action of water and weather. *noun.*

boul·e·vard (bùl′ə värd), a broad street, often with a line of trees planted along its sides, or down the center. *noun.*

bounce (bouns), **1** to spring into the air like a ball: *The baby likes to bounce up and down on the bed.* **2** to cause to bounce: *Bounce the ball to me.* **3** a springing back: *I caught the ball on the first bounce.* 1,2 *verb,* **bounc·es, bounced, bounc·ing;** 3 *noun.*

bounc·y (boun′sē), **1** lively; eager: *She was bouncy and full of life.* **2** that bounces back; springy: *He walked with a bouncy step. adjective,* **bounc·i·er, bounc·i·est.**

bound[1] (bound), **1** under some obligation; obliged: *I feel bound by my promise.* **2** certain; sure: *Everyone is bound to make a mistake sooner or later.* **3** See **bind.** *She bound the package with string. They have bound my hands.* **4** that has been put in a cover: *a bound book.* 1,2,4 *adjective,* 3 *verb.*

bound[2] (bound), **1** to leap or spring lightly along; jump: *Mountain goats can bound from rock to rock.* **2** a jump: *With one bound the deer went into the woods.* 1 *verb,* 2 *noun.*

bound[3] (bound), **1 bounds,** a boundary; limiting line; limit: *Stay within the bounds of the schoolyard. Keep your hopes within bounds.* **2** to form the boundary of; limit: *Canada bounds the United States on the north.* 1 *noun,* 2 *verb.*

bound[4] (bound), on the way; going: *The weary traveler was homeward bound at last. adjective.*

bound·ar·y (boun′dər ē), a limiting line or thing; limit; border: *Lake Superior forms part of the boundary between Canada and the United States. noun, plural* **bound·ar·ies.**

bound·less (bound′lis), not limited: *Outer space is boundless. She has boundless energy. adjective.*

boun·ti·ful (boun′tə fəl), more than enough; plentiful; abundant: *We put in so many plants that we have a bountiful supply of tomatoes. adjective.*

boun·ty (boun′tē), a reward: *The state government used to give a bounty for killing coyotes. noun, plural* **boun·ties.**

bou·quet (bō kā′ *or* bü kā′), a bunch of flowers. *noun.*

bout (bout), **1** a trial of strength; contest: *Those are the two boxers who will appear in the main bout.* **2** a length of time; spell: *I have just had a long bout of illness. noun.*

bow[1] (bou), **1** to bend the head or body in greeting, respect, worship, or obedience: *The*

people bowed before the queen. **2** a bending of the head or body in this way: *The men made a bow to the queen.* **3** to bend; bend by weight: *The trees were bowed down with heavy snow.* **4** to give in; yield: *The boy bowed to his parents' wishes.* 1,3,4 *verb,* 2 *noun.*

bow[2] (bō), **1** a weapon for shooting arrows. A bow usually consists of a strip of flexible wood bent by a string. **2** a slender rod with horsehairs stretched on it, for playing a violin or cello. **3** a knot that has loops: *The package had a bow on top. noun.*

bow[3] (bou), the front part of a ship or boat. *noun.*

bow·els (bou′əlz), **1** the tube in the body into which food passes from the stomach; intestines. **2** the inner part of anything: *Miners dig for coal in the bowels of the earth. noun plural.*

bow·ie knife (bō′ē nīf′ *or* bü′ē nīf′), a long, single-edged hunting knife carried in a sheath. [The *bowie knife* was named for Colonel James Bowie, who lived from 1799 to 1836. He was an American pioneer who made the knife popular.]

bowl[1] (bōl), **1** a hollow, rounded dish, usually without handles: *a mixing bowl.* **2** the amount that a bowl can hold: *She had a bowl of soup for lunch.* **3** the hollow, rounded part of anything: *The bowl of a pipe holds the tobacco.* **4** a structure shaped somewhat like a bowl: *The Yale Bowl is a stadium used for football and other sports.* **5** a special football game played when the season is over: *We flew to Miami, Florida, to see the Orange Bowl. noun.*

bowl[2] (bōl), **1** to play the game of bowling. **2** to roll or throw a ball in bowling: *You can bowl after me. verb.*

bowl over, to strike with sudden wonder or great surprise, or to shock: *I was bowled over by the bad news.*

bow·leg·ged (bō′leg′id), having the legs curved outward: *a bowlegged cowboy. adjective.*

bowl·ing (bō′ling), a game played indoors, in which balls are rolled down an alley at bottle-shaped wooden pins. *noun.*

bow·man (bō′mən), a person who shoots with a bow and arrow; archer. *noun, plural* **bow·men.**

bow·string (bō′string′), a strong cord stretched from the ends of a bow, pulled back by the archer to send the arrow forward. *noun.*

box[1] (boks), **1** a container, usually with four sides, a bottom, and a lid, to pack or put things in: *We packed the boxes full of books.* **2** the amount that a box can hold: *I bought a box of soap.* **3** to pack in a box; put into a box: *She boxed the candy before she sold it.* **4** an enclosed space, often with seats: *a jury box, a theater box.* 1,2,4 *noun, plural* **box·es;** 3 *verb.*

box[2] (boks), **1** a blow with the open hand or fist: *A box on the ear hurts.* **2** to strike with such a blow: *I will box your ears if you yell at me again.* **3** to fight with the fists as a sport: *He had not boxed since he left school.* 1 *noun, plural* **box·es;** 2,3 *verb.*

box·car (boks′kär′), a railroad freight car enclosed on all sides. Most boxcars are loaded and unloaded through a sliding door on either side. *noun.*

box·er (bok′sər), **1** a person who fights with the fists as a sport, usually in padded gloves and according to special rules. **2** a medium-sized dog with a smooth brown coat. It has a short nose like that of a bulldog. *noun.*

boxer (definition 2)—about 2 feet (60 centimeters) at the shoulder

box·ing (bok′sing), the act or sport of fighting with the fists, usually while wearing padded leather gloves. *noun.*

box office, the office or booth where tickets of admission are sold, as in a theater, hall, or stadium.

boy (boi), a male child from birth to about eighteen. *noun.*

boy·cott (boi′kot), **1** to join together against and agree not to buy from, sell to, or associate with a person, business, or nation. People boycott in order to force a change or to punish. **2** the act of boycotting. **1** *verb,* **2** *noun.*

boy·friend (boi′frend′), **1** a girl's sweetheart or steady male companion. **2** a male friend. *noun.*

boy·hood (boi′hùd), the time of being a boy. *noun.*

boy·ish (boi′ish), **1** of a boy. **2** like a boy. **3** like a boy's; suitable for a boy. *adjective.*

boy scout, a member of the Boy Scouts.

Boy Scouts, an organization for boys that seeks to develop character, citizenship, usefulness to others, and various skills.

brace (definition 1)

brace (brās), **1** a thing that holds parts together or in place, such as a timber used to strengthen a building or to support a roof. **2** a medical device used to support or straighten a part of the body, as a weak back or broken ankle. **3** **braces,** metal wires and bands used to straighten crooked teeth.

a hat	i it	oi oil	ch child		a in about
ā age	ī ice	ou out	ng long		e in taken
ä far	o hot	u cup	sh she	ə =	i in pencil
e let	ō open	ù put	th thin		o in lemon
ē equal	ô order	ü rule	ᴛʜ then		u in circus
ėr term			zh measure		

4 to give strength or firmness to; support: *We braced the roof with four poles.* **5** to prepare oneself: *He braced himself for the crash.* **6** the handle for a tool or drill used for boring. 1-3,6 *noun,* 4,5 *verb,* **brac·es, braced, brac·ing.**

brace·let (brās′lit), a band or chain worn for ornament around the wrist or arm. *noun.*

brac·ing (brā′sing), giving strength and energy; refreshing: *We enjoyed the day skiing in the bracing mountain air. adjective.*

brack·et (brak′it), **1** a flat piece of stone, wood, or metal attached to a wall to hold up something, such as a shelf. **2** either of these signs [ ], used to enclose words or figures. The word histories in this dictionary are enclosed in brackets. **3** to enclose within brackets: *The teacher bracketed the mistakes in my work.* **4** any group thought of or mentioned together: *I am the fastest swimmer in the 8-to-10 age bracket.* 1,2,4 *noun,* 3 *verb.*

bracket (definition 1)
a shelf supported by **brackets**

brag (brag), to speak too highly of oneself or what one owns; boast: *They bragged about their new car. verb,* **brags, bragged, brag·ging.**

braid (brād), **1** a band formed by weaving together three or more strands of hair, ribbon, yarn, or the like: *She wore her hair in braids.* **2** to weave or twine together three or more strands of hair, ribbon, yarn, or the like: *She can braid her own hair.* 1 *noun,* 2 *verb.*

Braille or **braille** (brāl), a system of writing and printing for blind people. In Braille, letters and numbers are represented by different arrangements of raised dots and are read by touching them. *noun.*

[*Braille* was named for Louis Braille, a blind Frenchman who lived from 1809 to 1852. He invented this system while he was teaching the blind.]

brain (brān), **1** a soft mass of nerve cells and nerve fibers enclosed in the skull or head of persons and animals. With the brain we can learn, think, and remember. **2** to hit on the head: *If you don't return my ball, I'll brain you.* **3** **brains,** intelligence: *A dog has more brains than a worm.* 1,3 *noun,* 2 *verb.*

brain·storm (brān′stôrm′), a sudden idea or inspiration: *I've had a brainstorm; to make money let's put on a play and charge admission. noun.*

brake¹ (brāk), **1** anything used to slow or stop the motion of a wheel or vehicle by pressing or scraping or by rubbing against. **2** to slow or stop by using a brake: *The driver braked the speeding* car and it slid to a stop. **1** *noun,* **2** *verb,* **brakes, braked, brak·ing.**

brake² (brāk), a thick growth of bushes; thicket. *noun.*

brake·man (brāk′mən), a member of a train crew who helps the conductor. *noun, plural* **brake·men.**

bram·ble (bram′bəl), a shrub with slender, drooping branches covered with little thorns that prick. Blackberry and raspberry plants are brambles. *noun.*

bran (bran), the outer covering of grains like wheat and rye. When flour is made from these grains, the bran is often separated from the inner part. Bran is used in cereal and bread, and as food for farm animals. *noun.*

branch (branch), **1** a part of a tree growing out from the trunk; any large, woody part of a tree above the ground except the trunk. A bough is a large branch. A twig is a very small branch. **2** a division; part: *a branch of a river, a branch of a family. Biology is a branch of science.* **3** to divide into branches: *The road branches at the bottom of the hill.* **1,2** *noun, plural* **branch·es;** **3** *verb.*

brand (brand), **1** a certain kind, grade, or make: *Do you like this brand of flour?* **2** a name or mark that a company uses to distinguish its goods from the goods of others. **3** a mark made by burning the skin with a hot iron: *The cattle on this big ranch have a brand which shows who owns them.* **4** to mark by burning the skin with a hot iron. **5** a mark of disgrace: *He could never rid himself of the brand of coward.* **6** to put a mark of disgrace on: *She has been branded as a traitor.* **1-3,5** *noun,* **4,6** *verb.*

brand (definition 4)—**branding** a calf

branding iron, an iron instrument that is used to burn a mark on cattle or other animals.

brand-new (brand′nü′ *or* brand′nyü′), very new; entirely new: *Someone stole my brand-new bicycle. adjective.*

bran·dy (bran′dē), a strong alcoholic drink made from wine or fermented fruit juice. *noun, plural* **bran·dies.**

brash (brash), **1** showing lack of respect; impudent: *That brash boy is rude to everyone.* **2** hasty; rash: *It is best to avoid brash actions. adjective,* **brash·er, brash·est.**

brass (bras), **1** a yellowish metal that is made of copper and zinc. **2** anything made of brass, such as an ornament or a dish: *I polished all the brass.* **3** Also, **brasses.** musical instruments made of metal. The trumpet, trombone, and French horn are brasses. *noun, plural* **brass·es.**

brat (brat), a rude, annoying, or unpleasant child. *noun.*

brave (brāv), **1** without fear; having courage; showing courage: *The brave girl went into the burning house to save a baby.* **2** a brave people: *The United States has been called "the land of the free and the home of the brave."* **3** to meet without fear; defy: *The early settlers braved the hardships of life in a new land.* **4** an American Indian warrior. **1** *adjective,* **brav·er, brav·est;** **2,4** *noun,* **3** *verb,* **braves, braved, brav·ing.**

brav·er·y (brā′vər ē), courage; being brave: *They owed their lives to the bravery of the firefighters. noun.*

bra·vo (brä′vō), **1** well done! fine! excellent! **2** a cry of "bravo!" **1** *interjection,* **2** *noun, plural* **bra·vos.**

brawl (brôl), **1** a noisy quarrel. **2** to quarrel in a noisy way. **1** *noun,* **2** *verb.*

brawn·y (brô′nē), strong; muscular: *The wrestler had brawny arms. adjective,* **brawn·i·er, brawn·i·est.**

bray (brā), the loud, harsh cry or noise made by a donkey. *noun.*

bra·zen (brā′zn), having no shame; shameless: *The brazen girl told lie after lie. adjective.*

Bra·zil (brə zil′), a country in central South America. *noun.*

breach (brēch), **1** an opening made by breaking down something solid; gap: *Cannon fire had made a breach in the wall of the fort.* **2** to break through; make an opening in: *The wall had been breached in several places.* **3** a breaking or neglect: *For me to leave now would be a breach of duty.* **1,3** *noun, plural* **breach·es;** **2** *verb.*

bread (bred), **1** a food made of flour or meal mixed with milk or water and baked. **2** the things necessary for keeping alive, such as food: *How will you earn your daily bread? noun.*

bread·fruit (bred′früt′), the large, round, starchy fruit of a tropical tree, much used for food. When baked, the fruit tastes somewhat like bread. *noun.*

breadfruit

breadth (bredth), how broad a thing is; distance across; width: *He has traveled the length and the breadth of this land.* noun.

break (brāk), **1** to come apart or make come apart; smash: *The plate broke into pieces when it fell on the floor. I broke the window with a ball.* **2** a broken place; crack: *There was a break in the wall. The X ray showed a break in my leg.* **3** to damage: *She broke her watch by winding it too tightly.* **4** to crack the bone of: *He fell and broke his arm.* **5** to fail to keep or obey: *One should try not to break a promise. People who break the law are punished.* **6** to force a way: *The lion broke out of its cage. The robbers broke into the warehouse.* **7** a forcing a way out: *The prisoners made a break for freedom.* **8** to come suddenly: *The storm broke within ten minutes.* **9** to change suddenly: *The spell of rainy weather has broken.* **10** a sudden change: *a break in the weather.* **11** a short interruption in work or practice: *The coach told us to take a break for five minutes.* **12** to make less; lessen: *The bushes broke her fall from the tree.* **13** to make or become very sad: *The little boy's heart broke when his puppy died.* **14** to dawn; appear: *The day is breaking.* **15** to put an end to; stop: *After not eating for three days she broke her fast. It is difficult to break the habit of smoking.* **16** to train to obey; tame: *to break a colt.* **17** to go beyond; do better than: *The speed of the new plane has broken all records.* **18** to make known; reveal: *Someone must break the news of the girl's accident to her parents.* **19** a stroke of luck; fortune; chance: *Finding that money was a lucky break.*
1,3-6,8,9,12-18 *verb,* **breaks, broke, bro·ken, break·ing;** 2,7,10,11,19 *noun.*

break down, 1 to go out of order; fail suddenly: *The car's engine broke down.* **2** to begin to cry: *He broke down when he heard the bad news.* **3** to separate or divide into bits or parts: *When food is digested, it is broken down into simpler forms that the body can use.*

break in, 1 to prepare or train: *Let's take a walk so I can break in my new shoes. The manager is breaking in a new salesperson.* **2** to interrupt: *He broke in with a remark while the teacher was reading to us.*

break into, 1 to begin suddenly: *When it started to rain, we broke into a run.* **2** to interrupt: *He rudely broke into their conversation.*

break out, 1 to start suddenly; begin: *A fire broke out in the garage.* **2** to have pimples or rashes appear on the skin: *The child broke out with measles.*

break up, 1 to scatter; separate into parts: *The fog is breaking up. The crowd broke up after the game and went home.* **2** to come or bring to an end: *The committee broke up its meeting early. Their marriage is breaking up.* **3** to laugh or cause to laugh: *The audience broke up at the comedian's jokes.*

break·a·ble (brā′kə bəl), able to be broken: *Be careful! Those glasses are breakable.* adjective.

break·down (brāk′doun′), **1** a failure to work:

a hat	i it	oi oil	ch child	a in about
ā age	ī ice	ou out	ng long	e in taken
ä far	o hot	u cup	sh she	ə = { i in pencil
e let	ō open	ù put	th thin	o in lemon
ē equal	ô order	ü rule	ŦH then	u in circus
ėr term			zh measure	

Lack of oil caused a breakdown in the motor. **2** a loss of health; collapse: *If you don't stop worrying, you will have a breakdown.* noun.

break·er (brā′kər), a wave that breaks into foam on the beach or on rocks. noun.

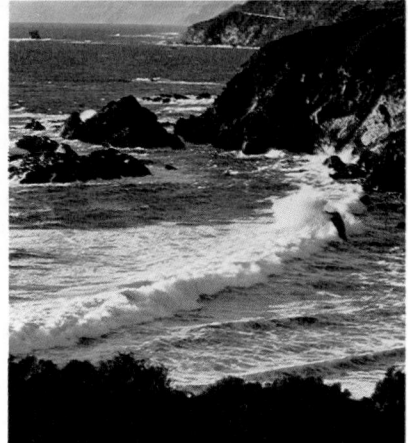
breaker

break·fast (brek′fəst), **1** the first meal of the day. **2** to eat breakfast: *I like to breakfast alone.* **1** *noun,* **2** *verb.*
[*Breakfast* comes from the phrase *break* (one's) *fast,* meaning "to end a period of not eating."]

break·through (brāk′thrü′), a discovery that solves a problem: *Vaccination was an important breakthrough in helping prevent disease.* noun.

breast (brest), **1** the upper, front part of the body between the shoulders and the stomach; chest. **2** a gland of females that gives milk. noun.
make a clean breast of, to confess completely: *When he was shown proof that he broke the window, he made a clean breast of it.*

breast·bone (brest′bōn′), the thin, flat bone in the front of the chest to which the ribs are attached. noun.

breast·plate (brest′plāt′), a piece of armor worn over the chest. noun.

breast·stroke (brest′strōk′), a stroke in swimming in which the swimmer lies face downward, draws both arms at one time from in front of the head to the sides, and kicks like a frog. noun.

breath (breth), **1** the air drawn into and forced out of the lungs. **2** breathing: *Hold your breath a moment.* **3** the ability to breathe easily: *Running so fast made me lose my breath.* **4** a slight movement in the air: *Not a breath of air was stirring.* noun.
catch one's breath, to stop for breath; rest:

After the race we sat down to catch our breath.
out of breath, short of breath; breathless: *At the end of the race the winner was out of breath.*
under one's breath, in a whisper: *She was talking under her breath so no one could hear.*
breathe (brēⱦH), 1 to draw air into the lungs and force it out. You breathe through your nose or through your mouth. 2 to say softly; whisper: *Don't breathe a word of this to anyone. verb,* **breathes, breathed, breath·ing.**
breath·less (breth′lis), 1 out of breath: *Running fast made me breathless.* 2 unable to breathe freely because of fear, interest, or excitement: *The beauty of the scenery left her breathless. adjective.*
breath·tak·ing (breth′tā′king), thrilling; exciting: *We took a breathtaking ride on the roller coaster. We saw a breathtaking sunset over the ocean from the top of the cliff. adjective.*
bred (bred). See **breed.** *They bred cattle for market. They have bred many prize-winning dogs. verb.*
breech·es (brich′iz), 1 short trousers fastened below the knees. 2 trousers. *noun plural.*

breeches (definition 1)

breed (brēd), 1 to produce young: *Rabbits breed rapidly.* 2 to raise or grow: *This farmer breeds cattle for market.* 3 to produce; be the cause of: *Careless driving breeds accidents.* 4 to bring up; train: *The princess was born and bred to one day be queen.* 5 a group of animals or plants looking much alike and having the same type of ancestors: *Collies and German shepherds are breeds of dogs.* 1-4 *verb,* **breeds, bred, breed·ing;** 5 *noun.*
breed·ing (brē′ding), bringing up; training; behavior; manners: *Politeness is a sign of good breeding. noun.*
breeze (brēz), 1 a light, gentle wind. 2 to move easily or briskly: *She breezed through her homework.* 1 *noun,* 2 *verb,* **breez·es, breezed, breez·ing.**
breez·y (brē′zē), 1 with light winds blowing: *It was a breezy day.* 2 lively and jolly: *We like his breezy, joking manner. adjective,* **breez·i·er, breez·i·est.**

brev·i·ty (brev′ə tē), shortness; briefness: *The brevity of such an exciting story disappointed the children. noun.*
brew (brü), 1 to make beer or ale by soaking, boiling, and fermenting malt and hops. 2 to make a drink by soaking or boiling in water: *I brewed a pot of tea.* 3 a drink that is brewed: *The last brew of beer tasted bad.* 4 to plan; plot: *The group whispering in the corner are brewing some mischief.* 5 to begin to form; gather: *Dark clouds show that a storm is brewing.* 1,2,4,5 *verb,* 3 *noun.*
brew·er·y (brü′ər ē), a place where beer and ale are made. *noun, plural* **brew·er·ies.**
bri·ar (brī′ər). See **brier.** *noun.*
bribe (brīb), 1 anything given or offered to get someone to do something wrong: *The thief offered the policemen a bribe to let him go.* 2 a reward for doing something that a person does not want to do: *The stubborn child needed a bribe to go to bed.* 3 to give or offer a bribe to: *A gambler bribed one of the boxers to lose the fight.* 1,2 *noun,* 3 *verb,* **bribes, bribed, brib·ing.**
[*Bribe* comes from an early French word meaning "bit of bread given to a beggar."]
brib·er·y (brī′bər ē), the giving or taking of a bribe: *The dishonest detective was arrested for bribery. noun.*
brick (brik), 1 a block of clay baked by sun or fire. Bricks are used to build walls or houses and pave walks. 2 these blocks used as building material: *Chimneys are usually built of brick.* 3 anything shaped like a brick: *Cheese is often sold in bricks.* 4 to build or pave with bricks; cover or fill in with bricks: *The old window had been bricked up for many years.* 1-3 *noun,* 4 *verb.*
brick·lay·er (brik′lā′ər), a person whose work is building with bricks. *noun.*
brid·al (brī′dl), of or having to do with a bride or a wedding: *a bridal shop, bridal gowns. adjective.*
bride (brīd), a woman just married or about to be married. *noun.*
bride·groom (brīd′grüm′), a man just married or about to be married; groom. *noun.*
brides·maid (brīdz′mād′), a woman who attends the bride at a wedding. *noun.*
bridge¹ (brij), 1 something built over a river, road, or railroad so that people, cars, or trains can get across. 2 to build a bridge over: *The engineers bridged the river.* 3 a platform above the deck of a ship for the officer in command: *The captain directed the course of the ship from the bridge.* 4 the upper, bony part of the nose. 1,3,4 *noun,* 2 *verb,* **bridg·es, bridged, bridg·ing.**
bridge² (brij), a card game for two pairs of players played with 52 cards. *noun.*
bri·dle (brī′dl), 1 the part of a harness that fits around a horse's head, including the bit and reins which control the animal. 2 to put a bridle on: *I saddled and bridled my horse.* 1 *noun,* 2 *verb,* **bri·dles, bri·dled, bri·dling.**
bridle path, a path for people riding horses.
brief (brēf), 1 lasting only a short time: *The meeting was brief. A brief shower fell in the*

afternoon. **2** using few words: *She made a brief announcement.* **3** to give detailed information to: *The forest ranger briefed the campers on fire prevention.* 1,2 *adjective,* 3 *verb.*

bri·er (brī′ər), a thorny or prickly plant or bush. The blackberry plant and the wild rose are often called briers. *noun.* Also spelled **briar.**

brig (brig), **1** a ship with two masts and square sails. **2** a prison on a ship. *noun.*

bri·gade (bri gād′), **1** a part of an army, usually made up of two or more regiments. **2** any group of persons organized for some purpose. A fire brigade puts out fires. *noun.*

bright (brīt), **1** giving much light; shining: *The stars are bright, but sunshine is brighter.* **2** very light or clear: *It is a bright day. Dandelions are bright yellow.* **3** clever; intelligent: *A bright student learns quickly. She can always think of a bright idea.* **4** lively or cheerful: *There was a bright smile on his face.* **5** favorable: *There is a bright outlook for the future.* **6** in a bright manner: *The fire shines bright.* 1-5 *adjective,* 6 *adverb.*

bright·en (brīt′n), to make or become bright or brighter: *The good news brightened my day. verb.*

bril·liance (bril′yəns), **1** great brightness; sparkle: *the brilliance of a fine diamond.* **2** great ability: *His brilliance as a pianist was known all over the world. noun.*

bril·liant (bril′yənt), **1** shining brightly; sparkling: *brilliant jewels, brilliant sunshine.* **2** splendid; magnificent: *The singer gave a brilliant performance.* **3** having great ability: *She is a brilliant musician. adjective.*

brim (brim), **1** an edge or a border; rim: *The glass was full to the brim. Don't go near the brim of the canyon.* **2** to fill to the brim; be full to the brim: *The pond was brimming with water after the heavy rain.* **3** an edge that sticks out from the bottom part of a hat: *The hat's wide brim shaded my eyes from the sun.* 1,3 *noun,* 2 *verb,* **brims, brimmed, brim·ming.**

brin·dle (brin′dl), **1** brindled. **2** a brindled color. **3** a brindled animal. 1 *adjective,* 2,3 *noun.*

brin·dled (brin′dld), gray, tan, or tawny with darker streaks and spots. *adjective.*

brindled
a **brindled** dog

brine (brīn), very salty water. Some pickles are kept in brine. *noun.*

bring (bring), **1** to come with or carry some thing or person from another place: *Bring me a clean plate and take the dirty one away. The bus brought us home.* **2** to cause to come: *What brings you into town today?* **3** to sell for: *Tomatoes bring a high price in winter. verb,* **brings, brought, bring·ing.**

bring about, to cause; cause to happen: *The flood was brought about by a heavy rain.*

bring forth, to give birth to: *In spring the cows brought forth their young.*

bring on, to cause; cause to happen: *My headache was brought on by a cold.*

bring out, 1 to reveal; show: *The lawyer brought out new evidence at the trial.* **2** to offer to the public: *The company is bringing out a new product.*

bring up, 1 to care for in childhood: *My grandparents brought up four children.* **2** to educate or train: *His good manners showed he was well brought up.* **3** to suggest for action or discussion; mention: *Please bring your plan up at the meeting.*

brink (bringk), **1** the edge at the top of a steep place: *the brink of the cliff.* **2** edge: *Their business is on the brink of ruin. noun.*

brisk (brisk), **1** quick and active; lively: *a brisk walk.* **2** keen; sharp: *a brisk wind. adjective.*

bristle (definition 1)—The walrus has **bristles.**

bris·tle (bris′əl), **1** one of the short, stiff hairs of some animals or plants. Hog bristles are often used in making brushes. **2** a substitute for an animal bristle, often made of nylon. **3** to stand up straight: *The dog growled and its hair bristled.* **4** to have one's hair stand up straight: *The frightened kitten bristled when it saw the dog.* **5** to show that one is angry and ready to fight: *The insult made*

him bristle. 1,2 *noun,* 3-5 *verb,* **bris·tles,
bris·tled, bris·tling.**

Brit·ain (brit′n), England, Scotland, and Wales;
Great Britain. *noun.*

britch·es (brich′iz), pants; trousers. *noun plural.*

Brit·ish (brit′ish), **1** of or having something to do
with Great Britain or its people. **2** the people of
Great Britain. **1** *adjective,* **2** *noun plural.*

British Columbia, a province in southwestern
Canada, on the Pacific. *Capital:* Victoria.

brit·tle (brit′l), very easily broken; breaking with
a snap; apt to break: *Thin glass is brittle. adjective.*

broach (brōch), to begin to talk about: *I didn't
want to broach the subject because I knew it would
upset them. verb.*

broad (brôd), **1** wide; large across: *Many cars can
go on that broad, new road.* **2** large; not limited or
narrow; of wide range: *Our teacher has had broad
experience with children.* **3** including only the most
important parts; general: *Give the broad outlines
of today's lesson.* **4** clear; full: *The theft was made
in broad daylight. adjective.*

broad·cast (brôd′kast′), **1** something sent out
by radio or television; radio or television program
of speech, music, and the like: *The President's
broadcast was televised from Washington, D.C.* **2** to
send out by radio or television: *His speech to the
nation was broadcast at 9 p.m. Some stations
broadcast twenty-four hours a day.* **3** to make
widely known: *Don't broadcast gossip.* **1** *noun,*
2,3 *verb,* **broad·casts, broad·cast** or
broad·cast·ed, broad·cast·ing.

broad·en (brôd′n), to make or become broad or
broader; widen: *The river broadens at its mouth.
Travel broadens a person's experience. verb.*

broad·side (brôd′sīd), the firing of all the guns
on one side of a ship at the same time. *noun.*

bro·cade (brō kād′), an expensive cloth with
raised designs woven into it. *noun.*

broc·co·li (brok′ə lē), a vegetable with green,
branching stems and flower heads. *noun, plural*
broc·co·li.

broil (broil), **1** to cook directly over heat on a rack
or under heat in a pan: *We often broil steaks.* **2** to
be very hot: *You will broil in this hot sun. verb.*

broil·er (broi′lər), a pan or rack for broiling.
noun.

broke (brōk), **1** See **break.** *She broke her glasses.*
2 without money: *When we returned from vacation
we were broke.* **1** *verb,* **2** *adjective.*

bro·ken (brō′kən), **1** See **break.** *The window
was broken by a ball.* **2** separated into parts by a
break; in pieces: *a broken cup.* **3** not in working
condition; damaged: *a broken watch.* **4** not kept: *a
broken promise.* **5** imperfectly spoken: *The French
girl speaks broken English.* **1** *verb,* 2-5 *adjective.*

bro·ken-down (brōk′kən doun′), ruined; not fit
for use: *Someone should repair this old,
broken-down chair. adjective.*

bro·ken·heart·ed (brō′kən här′tid), crushed by
sorrow or grief; heartbroken: *I was brokenhearted
when we moved from the farm into the city.
adjective.*

bro·ker (brō′kər), a person who buys and sells
such things as stocks, bonds, grain, and cotton
for other people. *noun.*

bron·chi·al (brong′kē əl), having to do with the
bronchial tubes: *a bronchial infection. adjective.*

bronchial tubes, the two main branches of the
windpipe, one going to each lung, and their many
branches.

bron·chi·tis (brong kī′tis), soreness and
swelling of the mucous membrane that lines the
bronchial tubes. Bronchitis usually causes a deep
cough. *noun.*

bron·co (brong′kō), a wild or partly tamed horse
of the western United States. *noun, plural*
bron·cos.

brocade

Word History

bronco *Bronco* was borrowed from a Mexican Spanish
word used in the Southwest. In Spanish, the word
originally meant "rough."

bronco
cowgirl riding a **bronco**

bron·to·sau·rus (bron′tə sôr′əs), a huge, prehistoric, plant-eating dinosaur with a long neck and tail and a small head. *noun, plural* **bron·to·sau·ri** (bron′tə sôr′ī) or **bron·to·sau·rus·es.**

Word History

brontosaurus *Brontosaurus* comes from two Greek words meaning "thunder" and "lizard." Because of its great size, the animal was thought of as making noise as loud as thunder when it moved around.

brontosaurus
about 60 feet
(18 meters) long;
about 14 feet
(4 meters) tall

a hat	**i** it	**oi** oil	**ch** child	a in about	
ā age	**ī** ice	**ou** out	**ng** long	e in taken	
ä far	**o** hot	**u** cup	**sh** she	**ə =** i in pencil	
e let	**ō** open	**ů** put	**th** thin	o in lemon	
ē equal	**ô** order	**ü** rule	**ŦH** then	u in circus	
ėr term			**zh** measure		

B

bronze (bronz), **1** a dark yellowish-brown metal made of copper and tin. **2** made of this metal: *He won a bronze medal in swimming.* **3** dark yellowish-brown. **4** to make or become a dark yellowish brown: *The lifeguard was bronzed by the sun.* 1 *noun*, 2,3 *adjective*, 4 *verb*, **bronz·es, bronzed, bronz·ing.**

brooch (brōch *or* brüch), an ornamental pin having the point fastened by a catch. Brooches are often made of gold, silver, or jewels. *noun, plural* **brooch·es.**

brooch

brood (brüd), **1** the young birds hatched at one time in the nest or cared for together: *a brood of chicks.* **2** the children in one family: *Our neighbors have a brood of twelve.* **3** to sit on eggs in order to hatch. Hens and other birds brood till the young are hatched. **4** to think or worry a long time about some one thing: *The boy brooded over his lost dog.* 1,2 *noun*, 3,4 *verb.*

brook (brůk), a small stream. *noun.*

broom (brüm), **1** a brush with a long handle for sweeping. **2** a bush with slender branches, small leaves, and yellow flowers. *noun.*

broom·stick (brüm′stik′), the long handle of a broom. *noun.*

broth (brôth), a thin soup made from water in which meat, fish, or vegetables have been boiled. *noun, plural* **broths** (brôŦHz *or* brôths).

broth·er (bruŦH′ər), **1** the son of the same parents. A boy is a brother to the other children of his parents. **2** male member of the same group, club, union, or religious organization. *noun.*

broth·er·hood (bruŦH′ər hůd), **1** the bond between brothers; feeling of brother for brother: *Soldiers who are fighting together often have a strong feeling of brotherhood.* **2** an association of men with some common aim, interest, or profession. *noun.*

broth·er-in-law (bruŦH′ər in lô′), **1** the brother of one's husband or wife. **2** the husband of one's sister. *noun, plural* **broth·ers-in-law.**

broth·er·ly (bruŦH′ər lē), of or like a brother; friendly; kindly: *The older boys gave me some brotherly advice. adjective.*

brought (brôt). See **bring.** *She brought her lunch yesterday. I was brought to school in a bus. verb.*

brow (brou), **1** the part of the face above the eyes; forehead: *a wrinkled brow.* **2** the arch of hair over the eye; eyebrow: *He has heavy brows. noun.*

brown (broun), **1** the color of coffee and toast. **2** having this color: *Many people have brown hair.* **3** to make or become brown: *He browned the onions in hot oil.* 1 *noun*, 2 *adjective*, 3 *verb.*

brown·ie (brou′nē), **1** a good-natured elf or fairy, especially one supposed to help secretly at night. **2 Brownie,** a member of the junior division of the Girl Scouts. **3** a small, flat, sweet chocolate cake, often containing nuts. *noun.*

brown·ish (brou′nish), somewhat brown. *adjective.*

brown·out (broun′out′), a partial lowering of electric power that causes lights to dim. *noun.*

brown·stone (broun′stōn′), a house with outer walls built of reddish-brown sandstone. *noun.*

browse (brouz), **1** to feed on growing grass or leaves by nibbling and eating here and there; graze: *The sheep browsed in the meadow.* **2** to read or look here and there, as in a book, library, or store: *She browsed through her new schoolbooks. They spent the afternoon browsing in the shops on Main Street. verb,* **brows·es, browsed, brows·ing.**

bruise (brüz), **1** an injury to the body, caused by a fall or a blow, that does not break the skin: *The bruise turned black and blue.* **2** an injury to the outside of a fruit, vegetable, or plant. **3** to injure or be injured on the outside: *Rough handling bruised the apples. My legs bruise easily.* **4** to hurt; injure: *Their harsh words bruised her feelings.* 1,2 *noun*, 3,4 *verb*, **bruis·es, bruised, bruis·ing.**

bru·nette *or* **bru·net** (brü net′), **1** having dark-brown or black hair. **2** a person having this color hair. 1 *adjective*, 2 *noun.*

brush[1] (brush), **1** a tool for sweeping, scrubbing, smoothing, or painting. A brush is made of bristles, hair, or wire set in a stiff back or fastened to a handle. **2** to sweep, scrub, smooth, or paint with a brush; use a brush on: *I brushed my hair until it was shiny.* **3** a brushing: *I gave my hair a quick brush.* **4** to wipe away; remove: *The child brushed the tears from his eyes.* **5** to touch lightly in passing: *No harm was done—your bumper just brushed our fender.* **6** a short, brisk fight or quarrel: *The police had a brush with the demonstrators.* 1,3,6 *noun, plural* **brush·es;** 2,4,5 *verb.*

brush up on or **brush up,** to refresh one's knowledge of: *I brushed up on fractions before taking the arithmetic test.*

brush[2] (brush), **1** the branches broken or cut off: *After chopping down the tree, we carted off the wood and burned the brush.* **2** the shrubs, bushes, and small trees growing thickly in the woods. *noun.*

Brus·sels sprouts (brus′əlz sprouts′), a vegetable that looks like small heads of cabbage. The heads grow close together along the stalk of the plant.

Brussels sprouts—about 2½ feet (76 centimeters) tall

bru·tal (brü′tl), cruel; inhuman: *a brutal beating.* *adjective.*

bru·tal·i·ty (brü tal′ə tē), **1** cruelty; brutal conduct. *noun.*

brute (brüt), **1** an animal without power to reason. **2** a cruel or coarse person. *noun.*

bu., bushel or bushels.

bub·ble (bub′əl), **1** a round, thin film of liquid enclosing air or gas. When water boils, it is full of bubbles which come to the top and break. **2** a round space filled with air or gas in a liquid or solid. Sometimes there are bubbles in ice or in glass. **3** to send up or rise in bubbles; make sounds like water boiling: *Water bubbled up between the stones.* 1,2 *noun,* 3 *verb,* **bub·bles, bub·bled, bub·bling.**

buc·ca·neer (buk′ə nir′), a pirate. *noun.*

buck[1] (buk), **1** a male deer, goat, hare, or rabbit. **2** to jump into the air with the back curved and come down with the front legs stiff: *My horse began to buck, but I managed to stay on.* **3** to throw by bucking: *The cowboy was bucked off the bronco.* **4** to fight against; work against: *I have to*

buck heavy traffic every Friday after work. 1 *noun,* 2-4 *verb.*

buck[2] (buk), a dollar. *noun.*

buck·et (buk′it), **1** a container for carrying liquids, sand, or the like; pail. **2** bucketful: *Pour in about four buckets of water. noun.*

buck·et·ful (buk′it fùl), the amount that a bucket can hold. *noun, plural* **buck·et·fuls.**

bucket seat, a small, low, single seat with a rounded back, used in some cars and small airplanes.

buck·eye (buk′ī′), a tree or shrub with clusters of white flowers, large divided leaves, and large brown seeds. *noun.*

buck·le (buk′əl), **1** a catch or clasp used to hold together the ends of a belt, strap, or ribbon. **2** to fasten together with a buckle: *She buckled her belt.* **3** to bend; wrinkle: *The heavy snowfall caused the roof of the shed to buckle.* **4** a bend or wrinkle. 1,4 *noun,* 2,3 *verb,* **buck·les, buck·led, buck·ling.**

buckle down to, to work hard at: *I buckled down to my studies before the test.*

buck·saw (buk′sô′), a saw set in a light frame and held with both hands. *noun.*

bucksaw

buck·shot (buk′shot′), a large lead shot used to shoot large game, such as deer. *noun.*

buck·skin (buk′skin′), a strong, soft leather, yellowish or grayish in color, made from the skins of deer or sheep. *noun.*

buck·tooth (buk′tüth′), an upper front tooth that sticks out beyond the other teeth: *The child needed braces to correct buckteeth. noun, plural* **buck·teeth.**

buck·toothed (buk′tütht′), having upper front teeth that stick out beyond the other teeth. *adjective.*

buck·wheat (buk′hwēt′), **1** a plant with black or gray triangular seeds and fragrant white flowers. **2** the flour made from the seeds of this plant, often used for pancakes. *noun.*

bud (bud), **1** a small swelling on a plant that will grow into a flower, leaf, or branch: *Buds on the trees are a sign of spring.* **2** a partly opened flower or leaf. **3** to put forth buds: *The rosebush has budded.* **1,2** *noun,* **3** *verb,* **buds, bud·ded, bud·ding.**

Bud·dha (bü′də), the founder of Buddhism. The name means "The Enlightened One." *noun.*

Bud·dhism (bü′diz əm), a religion based on the teachings of Buddha. *noun.*

Bud·dhist (bü′dist), **1** a person who believes in and follows the teachings of Buddha. **2** of Buddha, his followers, or the religion founded by him: *a Buddhist temple.* **1** *noun,* **2** *adjective.*

bud·ding (bud′ing), showing signs of becoming; developing: *She is a budding scientist. adjective.*

bud·dy (bud′ē), a close friend; comrade; pal. *noun, plural* **bud·dies.**

budge (buj), to move even a little: *The stone was so heavy that we couldn't budge it. verb,* **budg·es, budged, budg·ing.**

budg·et (buj′it), **1** a plan that helps make the best use of money. Governments, companies, schools, and families make budgets. **2** to make a plan for spending: *She budgeted her allowance so that she could save money for a tennis racket.* **1** *noun,* **2** *verb.*

Bue·nos Ai·res (bwā′nəs er′ēz *or* bwā′nəs ar′ēz), the capital of Argentina. *noun.*

buff (buf), **1** dull-yellow. **2** a strong, soft, dull-yellow leather. **3** to polish; shine: *I buffed my shoes with a soft cloth.* **1** *adjective,* **2** *noun,* **3** *verb.*

buf·fa·lo (buf′ə lō), **1** a wild animal of North America, with a great, shaggy head and a large hump over the shoulders; bison. **2** any of several kinds of large animals related to cattle. The tame water buffalo is found in many parts of Asia; the wild buffalo of Africa is very fierce and dangerous. *noun, plural* **buf·fa·loes, buf·fa·los,** *or* **buf·fa·lo.**

buf·fet (bu fā′), **1** a piece of dining-room furniture with a flat top for dishes and with shelves or drawers for holding silver and table linen. **2** a meal at which guests serve themselves from food laid out on a table. *noun.*

bug (bug), **1** a crawling insect with a pointed beak for piercing and sucking. **2** any insect somewhat like a true bug. Ants, spiders, beetles, and flies are often called bugs. **3** a disease germ: *the flu bug.* **4** a defect in the operation of a machine: *My car is running better now, but there are still a few bugs in it.* **5** a mistake in the instructions given to a computer: *It took all day to find the bugs that kept the computer from working.* **6** a very small microphone hidden within a room, telephone, or other place for overhearing conversation. **7** to hide a small microphone within a room, telephone, or other place for overhearing conversation: *The spy bugged enemy headquarters.* **8** to annoy; irritate: *His constant grumbling bugs me.* **1-6** *noun,* **7,8** *verb,* **bugs, bugged, bug·ging.**

bug·gy (bug′ē), **1** a light carriage with or without a top, pulled by one horse and having a single

a hat	i it	oi oil	ch child	a in about
ā age	ī ice	ou out	ng long	e in taken
ä far	o hot	u cup	sh she	ə = { i in pencil
e let	ō open	ů put	th thin	o in lemon
ē equal	ô order	ü rule	ŦH then	u in circus
ėr term			zh measure	

B

large seat. **2** a baby carriage. *noun, plural* **bug·gies.**

bu·gle (byü′gəl), a musical instrument like a small trumpet, made of brass or copper. Bugles are used in the army and navy to sound certain signals, including reveille and taps. *noun.*

bu·gler (byü′glər), a person who blows a bugle. *noun.*

build (bild), **1** to make by putting materials together: *People build houses, bridges, ships, and machines. Birds build nests.* **2** to produce gradually; develop: *to build a business. A lawyer's case should be built on facts.* **3** a bodily shape: *a person with a heavy build.* **1,2** *verb,* **builds, built, build·ing; 3** *noun.*

build·er (bil′dər), a person whose business is constructing buildings. *noun.*

build·ing (bil′ding), **1** a thing built. Barns, stores, factories, houses, and hotels are all buildings. **2** the business or process of making houses, stores, bridges, ships, and similar things. *noun.*

build·up (bild′up′), an increase in the strength or size of: *There was a sudden buildup of pressure in the boiler. noun.*

built (bilt). See **build.** *The bird built a nest. It was built of twigs. verb.*

built-in (bilt′in′), not movable; put in as part of: *All the apartments have built-in dishwashers. adjective.*

bulb (bulb), **1** a round, underground part from which certain plants grow. Onions, tulips, and lilies grow from bulbs. **2** any object with a rounded end or swelling part: *an electric light bulb. noun.*

Bul·gar·i·a (bul ger′ē ə), a country in southeastern Europe. *noun.*

bulge (bulj), **1** to swell outward: *His pockets bulged with candy.* **2** an outward swelling: *The wallet made a bulge in his pocket.* **1** *verb,* **bulg·es, bulged, bulg·ing; 2** *noun.*

bulk (bulk), **1** size, especially large size: *An elephant has great bulk.* **2** the largest part of: *The oceans form the bulk of the earth's surface. noun.*
in bulk, lying loose in heaps, not in packages: *Some markets sell fresh fruit in bulk.*

bulk·y (bulk′kē), large; hard to handle: *She was carrying a bulky package of curtain rods. adjective,* **bulk·i·er, bulk·i·est.**

bull (bul), **1** the full-grown male of cattle. **2** the male of the whale, elephant, seal, and other large animals. *noun.*

bull·dog (bul′dôg′), a heavy, muscular dog of medium height. It has a large head, very short nose, strong jaws, and short hair. *noun.*

bull·doz·er (bul′dō′zər), a powerful tractor with a wide steel blade that pushes rocks and earth

bulldozer

and knocks down trees. Bulldozers are used to make rough ground level and to help build roads.

bul·let (bùl'it), a piece of metal shaped to be fired from a pistol or rifle. *noun.*

bul·le·tin (bùl'ə tən), **1** a short statement of news: *Sports bulletins and weather bulletins are published in most newspapers.* **2** a small magazine or newspaper appearing regularly: *Our club publishes a bulletin each month. noun.*

bulletin board, a board on which notices are placed.

bull·fight (bùl'fīt'), a public entertainment in which men perform a series of complex, dangerous acts with a bull, usually killing it at last with a sword. Bullfights are popular in Spain, Portugal, Mexico, and parts of South America. *noun.*

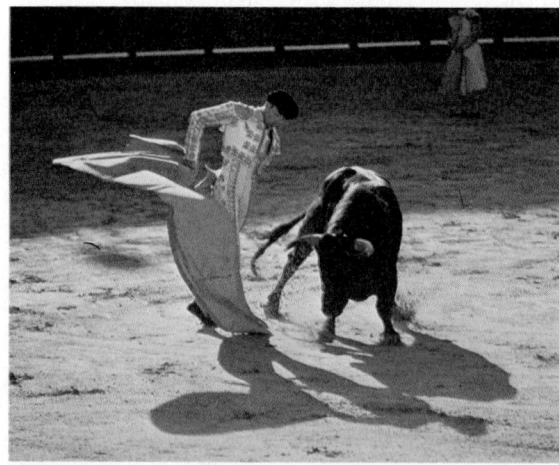

bullfight

bull·finch (bùl'finch'), a European songbird with a blue and gray back and light-red breast, and a short, stout bill. *noun, plural* **bull·finch·es.**

bull·frog (bùl'frog'), a large frog that makes a loud, croaking noise. *noun.*

bull's-eye (bùlz'ī'), **1** the center of a target. **2** a shot that hits it. *noun.*

bul·ly (bùl'ē), **1** a person who teases, threatens, or hurts smaller or weaker people. **2** to frighten into doing something: *Stop trying to bully me into doing what you want.* **1** *noun, plural* **bul·lies;** **2** *verb,* **bul·lies, bul·lied, bul·ly·ing.**

bum (bum), **1** an idle person; tramp. **2** to beg: *We tried to bum a ride.* **3** of poor quality; worthless. **1** *noun,* **2** *verb,* **bums, bummed, bum·ming;** **3** *adjective,* **bum·mer, bum·mest.**

bum·ble (bum'bəl), to act in a clumsy or awkward way: *They bumbled around as though they had never been in a restaurant before. verb,* **bum·bles, bum·bled, bum·bling.**

bum·ble·bee (bum'bəl bē'), a large bee with a thick, hairy body, usually banded with gold. Bumblebees make a loud, buzzing sound. *noun.*

bump (bump), **1** to hit or strike against something solid or heavy: *The truck bumped our car.* **2** a heavy blow: *The bump knocked our car forward a few feet.* **3** to move with jolts or jerks: *Our car bumped along the dirt road.* **4** a swelling caused by a blow: *I had a bump on my head from getting hit by a baseball.* **5** a ridge or raised surface: *Avoid the bump in the road.* **1,3** *verb,* **2,4,5** *noun.*

bump·er (bum'pər), **1** a bar or bars across the front and back of a car, truck, or bus that protect it from being damaged if bumped. **2** unusually large: *There was a bumper crop of wheat last year.* **1** *noun,* **2** *adjective.*

bump·y (bum'pē), rough or uneven; having or causing bumps: *We drove over the bumpy road. adjective,* **bump·i·er, bump·i·est.**

bun (bun), **1** a small roll. Buns are often slightly sweetened and may contain spice or raisins. **2** hair coiled at the back of the head in a knot. *noun.*

bunch (bunch), **1** a group of things of the same kind growing, fastened, placed, or thought of together: *a bunch of grapes, a bunch of sheep.* **2** a group of people: *They are a friendly bunch.* **3** to come together in one place: *The sheep were all bunched in the shed to keep warm.* **1,2** *noun, plural* **bunch·es;** **3** *verb.*

bun·dle (bun'dl), **1** a number of things tied or wrapped together: *a bundle of old newspapers.* **2** a parcel; package: *My arms were so full of bundles that I had trouble opening the door.* **3** to tie or wrap together; make into a bundle: *We bundled all our old newspapers for the school's paper drive.* **1,2** *noun,* **3** *verb,* **bun·dles, bun·dled, bun·dling.**

bundle up, to dress warmly: *You should bundle up on cold winter mornings.*

bun·ga·low (bung'gə lō), a small one-story house. *noun.*

[*Bungalow* comes from a word of northern India, meaning "of Bengal." Bungalows were called this because such houses were common in the Bengal region of northeastern India.]

bun·gle (bung'gəl), to do or make in a clumsy, unskilled way: *I tried to make a clay pot but I* bungled the job. verb, **bun·gles, bun·gled, bun·gling.**

bunk (bungk), **1** a narrow bed, often stacked one above another: *I sleep in the top bunk.* **2** to sleep: *We bunked in the barn.* **1** *noun,* **2** *verb.*

bunk·house (bungk′hous′), a rough building with sleeping quarters or bunks, especially one provided for workers on a ranch. *noun, plural* **bunk·hous·es** (bungk′hou′ziz).

bun·ny (bun′ē), a rabbit. *noun, plural* **bun·nies.**

Bun·sen burn·er (bun′sən bėr′nər), a gas burner with a very hot, blue flame, used in laboratories.

Bunsen burner

bunt (bunt), **1** to bat a pitched baseball so lightly that the ball goes only a short distance into the infield. **2** a baseball hit in this way. **1** *verb,* **2** *noun.*

buoy (boi *or* bü′ē), **1** an anchored object floating on the water to warn against hidden rocks or shallows or to show the safe part of a channel. **2** a ring, belt, or vest used as a life preserver. *noun.*
buoy up, 1 to hold up; keep from sinking: *His life preserver buoyed him up until rescuers came.* **2** to support or encourage: *Hope can buoy you up, even when something goes wrong.*

bur (bėr), **1** a prickly, clinging seedcase or flower of some plants. Burs stick to cloth and fur. **2** a plant that has burs. *noun.* Also spelled **burr.**

bur·den (bėrd′n), **1** something carried; load of things, care, work, duty, or sorrow: *A light burden was laid on the mule's back. Everyone in my family shares the burden of housework.* **2** a load too heavy to carry easily; heavy load: *Her debts are a burden that will bankrupt her.* **3** to put a burden on; load too heavily: *The mule was burdened with heavy bags of ore.* **1,2** *noun,* **3** *verb.*

bur·den·some (bėrd′n səm), hard to bear; very heavy; wearying: *The President's many duties are burdensome. adjective.*

bur·eau (byùr′ō), **1** a piece of furniture with drawers for clothes and usually a mirror; dresser. **2** a business office, especially one at which facts of various kinds are available: *We asked about the airplane fares at the travel bureau.* **3** a division within a government department: *The Forest*

a hat	**i** it	**oi** oil	**ch** child	a in about
ā age	**ī** ice	**ou** out	**ng** long	e in taken
ä far	**o** hot	**u** cup	**sh** she	ə = { i in pencil
e let	**ō** open	**ù** put	**th** thin	o in lemon
ē equal	**ô** order	**ü** rule	**ŦH** then	u in circus
ėr term			**zh** measure	

Service is a bureau of the Department of Agriculture. noun.

bur·glar (bėr′glər), a person who breaks into a house or other building to steal something. *noun.*

bur·glar·y (bėr′glər ē), a breaking into a house or other building to steal something. *noun, plural* **bur·glar·ies.**

bur·i·al (ber′ē əl), the act of putting a dead body in a grave, in a tomb, or in the sea; burying: *The sailor was given a burial at sea. noun.*

bur·ied (ber′ēd). See **bury.** *The dog buried the bone. Many nuts were buried under the leaves. verb.*

bur·lap (bėr′lap), a coarse fabric made from jute or hemp. Burlap is used to make sacks, curtains, wall coverings, and upholstery. *noun.*

Bur·ma (bėr′mə), the former name of **Myanmar.** *noun.*

burn (bėrn), **1** to be on fire; set on fire; be or cause to be very hot: *The campfire burned all night. They burned wood in the fireplace.* **2** to destroy by fire: *Please burn those old papers.* **3** to injure by fire or heat: *The flame from the candle burned her finger.* **4** an injury caused by fire or heat; burned place: *When I spilled the hot spaghetti sauce, it caused a bad burn on my hand.* **5** to make by fire or heat: *A spark from the fireplace burned a hole in the rug. She burned designs on wood to make a picture.* **6** to feel hot; give a feeling of heat to: *His forehead burns with fever.* **7** to give light: *Lamps were burning in every room.* **8** to use to produce heat: *Our furnace burns oil.* **1-3,5-8** *verb,* **burns, burned** *or* **burnt, burn·ing;** **4** *noun.*

burn·er (bėr′nər), the part of a lamp, stove, or furnace where the flame or heat is produced. *noun.*

burnt (bėrnt), burned. See **burn.** *I don't like burnt toast. verb.*

burp (bėrp), belch. *noun, verb.*

burr (bėr). See **bur.** *noun.*

bur·ro (bėr′ō), a donkey. This word is used mainly in the southwestern United States. *noun, plural* **bur·ros.**

bur·row (bėr′ō), **1** a hole dug in the ground by an animal for shelter or protection. Rabbits live in burrows. **2** to dig a hole in the ground: *The mole quickly burrowed out of sight.* **3** to search: *She burrowed in the back files for a missing report.* **1** *noun,* **2,3** *verb.*

burst (bėrst), **1** to open or be opened suddenly: *They burst the lock. The trees had burst into bloom.* **2** to fly apart suddenly with force; explode: *The balloon burst when he stuck a pin into it.* **3** to go, come, or do by force or suddenly: *Don't burst* *into the room without knocking.* **4** to be very full: *The barns were bursting with grain.* **5** a sudden release; outbreak: *In a burst of speed, he won the race at the last minute.* 1-4 *verb,* **bursts, burst, burst·ing;** 5 *noun.*

bur·y (ber′ē), **1** to put a dead body in the earth, in a tomb, or in the sea: *The children buried the dead bird.* **2** to cover up; hide: *Ancient treasures were discovered in the ruins where they had been buried long ago. verb,* **bur·ies, bur·ied, bur·y·ing.**

bus (bus), **1** a large motor vehicle with seats. Buses carry passengers from one place to another along a certain route. **2** to take or go by bus: *The city bused the children to school.* 1 *noun, plural* **bus·es** or **bus·ses;** 2 *verb,* **bus·es, bused, bus·ing** or **bus·ses, bussed, bus·sing.**

[*Bus* is short for *omnibus,* an older English word for the vehicle. This word was borrowed from a Latin word meaning "for everyone." The vehicle was called this because it was considered large enough for everyone making the trip.]

bush (bush), **1** a woody plant smaller than a tree, often with many separate branches starting from or near the ground. Some bushes are used as hedges; others are grown for their fruit. **2** open forest or wild land. *noun, plural* **bush·es.**
beat around the bush, to avoid coming straight to the point: *Tell me the truth right now; don't beat around the bush.*

bushed (busht), very tired; exhausted: *The hikers were bushed after being out on the trail all day. adjective.*

bush·el (bush′əl), **1** a unit of measure for grain, fruit, vegetables, and other dry things, equal to 4 pecks. **2** a container that holds a bushel. *noun.*

bush·y (bush′ē), spreading out like a bush; growing thickly: *a bushy beard. adjective,* **bush·i·er, bush·i·est.**

bus·i·ly (biz′ə lē), in a busy manner; actively: *Bees were busily collecting nectar in the clover. adverb.*

busi·ness (biz′nis), **1** work done to earn a living; occupation: *A carpenter's business is building.* **2** a matter; affair: *I am tired of the whole business.* **3** buying and selling; trade: *This hardware store does a lot of business in tools.* **4** a store, factory, or other place that makes or sells goods and services: *They sold the bakery business. noun, plural* **busi·ness·es** for 4.

busi·ness·like (biz′nis līk′), well managed; practical: *She runs her life in a businesslike fashion. adjective.*

busi·ness·man (biz′nis man′), a man who is in business or runs a business. *noun, plural* **busi·ness·men.**

busi·ness·wom·an (biz′nis wum′ən), a woman who is in business or runs a business. *noun, plural* **busi·ness·wom·en.**

bus·ing (bus′ing), sending students by bus from one neighborhood to another in order to achieve racial balance in schools. *noun.*

bus·ses (bus′iz), **1** a plural of **bus. 2** See **bus.** *He busses five miles to work every day.* 1 *noun,* 2 *verb.*

bust[1] (definition 1)

bust[1] (bust), **1** a statue of a person's head, shoulders, and upper part of the chest. **2** a woman's breasts. *noun.*

bust[2] (bust), to burst; break: *He dropped his watch and busted it. verb.*

bus·tle (bus′əl), **1** to be noisily busy and in a hurry: *The children bustled to get ready for the party.* **2** a noisy or excited activity: *There was a great bustle as the children got ready for the party.* 1 *verb,* **bus·tles, bus·tled, bus·tling;** 2 *noun.*

bus·y (biz′ē), **1** having plenty to do; working; active: *The principal of our school is a busy person.* **2** full of work or activity: *Main Street is a busy place.* **3** to make busy; keep busy: *The children busied themselves with drawing pictures.* **4** in use: *The phone was busy.* 1,2,4 *adjective,* **bus·i·er, bus·i·est;** 3 *verb,* **bus·ies, bus·ied, bus·y·ing.**

bus·y·bod·y (biz′ē bod′ē), a person who meddles in the affairs of others; meddler. *noun, plural* **bus·y·bod·ies.**

but (but), **1** on the other hand: *You may go, but you must come home at six o'clock.* **2** except: *I went swimming every day this week but Tuesday.* **3** unless; except that: *It never rains but it pours.* **4** nevertheless; yet: *I wanted to go but I couldn't.* **5** only: *The child was but two years old.* **6** yet: *The story was strange, but true.* 1,3,4 *conjunction,* 2 *preposition,* 5,6 *adverb.*

butch·er (buch′ər), **1** a person who cuts up and sells meat. **2** to kill animals for food. **3** to kill needlessly, cruelly, or in large numbers. 1 *noun,* 2,3 *verb.*
[*Butcher* comes from an early French word meaning "person who kills and sells male goats."]

but·ler (but′lər), the head male servant in a household. *noun.*

butt[1] (but), **1** the thicker end of a weapon: *the butt of a gun.* **2** the end that is left; stub or stump: *a cigar butt. noun.*

butt[2] (but), a person who is a target of fun or ridicule: *The new boy in school was the butt of jokes for several weeks. noun.*

butt[3] (but), **1** to strike or push by knocking hard with the head or horns: *A goat butts.* **2** a push or

blow with the head or horns. 1 *verb*, 2 *noun*.
butt in, to busy oneself with or in another person's affairs without being asked.
butte (byüt), a steep hill that has a flat top and stands alone. A butte is usually smaller than a mesa and not as steep. *noun.*

a hat	i it	oi oil	ch child	a in about
ā age	ī ice	ou out	ng long	e in taken
ä far	o hot	u cup	sh she	ə = { i in pencil
e let	ō open	ů put	th thin	o in lemon
ē equal	ô order	ü rule	ŦH then	u in circus
ėr term			zh measure	

buttes

but·ter (but′ər), 1 the solid yellowish fat separated from cream by churning. 2 to put butter on: *Please butter my bread.* 3 a food that is cooked or ground fine so that it spreads like butter: *peanut butter, apple butter.* 1,3 *noun*, 2 *verb.*
but·ter·cup (but′ər kup′), a common plant with bright yellow flowers shaped like cups. *noun.*
but·ter·fly (but′ər flī′), an insect with a slender body and two pairs of large, usually brightly colored, wings. Butterflies fly mostly in the daytime. *noun, plural* **but·ter·flies.**
but·ter·milk (but′ər milk′), the salty liquid left after butter has been made from cream. *noun.*
but·ter·nut (but′ər nut′), an oily kind of walnut that grows on a North American tree. Butternuts are good to eat. *noun.*
but·ter·scotch (but′ər skoch′), a candy or flavoring made from brown sugar and butter. *noun.*
but·tocks (but′əks), the part of the body on which a person sits; rump. *noun plural.*
but·ton (but′n), 1 a round, flat piece of plastic, metal, or the like, sewn onto clothes as fasteners or for decoration. 2 to fasten the buttons of: *Button your coat.* 3 a knob pushed to make something work: *an elevator button.* 1,3 *noun*, 2 *verb.*
but·ton·hole (but′n hōl′), 1 a hole or slit through which a button is passed. 2 to hold in conversation or force to listen, as if holding someone by the buttonhole of his coat. 1 *noun*, 2 *verb*, **but·ton·holes, but·ton·holed, but·ton·hol·ing.**
but·tress (but′ris), 1 a support built against a wall or building to strengthen it. 2 to support and strengthen: *The committee buttressed its report with facts and figures.* 1 *noun, plural* **but·tress·es;** 2 *verb.*
buy (bī), 1 to get for money; purchase: *You can buy a pencil for ten cents.* 2 a bargain: *That book

was a real buy.* 1 *verb*, **buys, bought, buy·ing;** 2 *noun.*
buy·er (bī′ər), a person who buys. *noun.*
buzz (buz), 1 the humming sound made by flies, mosquitoes, or bees. 2 the low, humming sound of many people talking quietly: *The buzz of whispers stopped when the teacher entered the room.* 3 to make a steady, humming sound; hum loudly: *The radio should be fixed; it buzzes when you turn it on.* 4 to signal with a buzzer. 5 to talk with enthusiasm or excitement: *The whole class buzzed with the news of the holiday.* 6 to fly an airplane very fast and low over a place or person: *The pilot buzzed the treetops.* 1,2 *noun*, 3-6 *verb.*
buz·zard (buz′ərd), 1 a kind of vulture. 2 any of several kinds of hawk. *noun.*
buzz·er (buz′ər), an electrical device that makes a buzzing sound as a signal. *noun.*
by (bī), 1 near; beside: *The garden is by the house. Sit by me.* 2 along; over; through: *They went by the main road.* 3 through the means, use, or action of: *We traveled by airplane. The house was destroyed by fire. The story was written by our teacher's older sister.* 4 in the measure of: *They sell eggs by the dozen.* 5 as soon as; not later than: *Be here by six o'clock.* 6 during: *The sun shines by day.* 7 past: *The Pilgrims lived in days gone by. A car raced by. We ran by the cemetery.* 8 aside or away: *She puts money by every week to save for a new bicycle.* 9 according to: *It's more fun to play by the rules.* 10 combined with in arithmetic or measurement: *a room 4 feet by 9 feet.* 11 taken as steps in a series: *week by week.* 12 with a difference of: *We won by ten points.* 1-7,9-12 *preposition*, 7,8 *adverb.*
by and by, after a while; before long; soon: *Summer vacation will come by and by.*
Byel·a·rus (byel′ə rüs′), a country in eastern Europe. Also spelled **Belarus.** *noun.*
by·gone (bī′gôn′), 1 gone by; past; former: *The ancient Romans lived in bygone days.* 2 **bygones,** what is gone by and past: *Let bygones be forgotten.* 1 *adjective*, 2 *noun.*
by·pass (bī′pas′), 1 a road, channel, or pipe providing a secondary passage to be used instead of the main passage: *Drivers use the bypass to avoid the city.* 2 to go around: *The highway bypasses the city.* 1 *noun, plural* **by·pass·es;** 2 *verb.*
by-prod·uct (bī′prod′əkt), something of value produced as the result of making something else: *Molasses is a by-product of sugar refining.* *noun.*
by·stand·er (bī′stan′dər), a person who stands near or looks on but does not take part; onlooker. *noun.*
by·way (bī′wā′), a side path or road; way that is little used. *noun.*

C c

C or **c** (sē), the third letter of the English alphabet. *noun, plural* **C's** or **c's.**

c or **c.,** 1 centimeter or centimeters. 2 cubic.

C or **C.,** Celsius.

c. or **c,** 1 cent or cents. 2 cup or cups.

CA, California (used with postal Zip Code).

cab (kab), 1 an automobile that can be hired with its driver; taxicab. 2 a carriage that can be hired, pulled by one horse. 3 the covered part of a railroad engine, truck, tractor, or other machine where the driver or operator sits. *noun.*

cab·bage (kab′ij), a vegetable with thick, green or reddish-purple leaves closely folded into a firm, round head. *noun.*

cab·in (kab′ən), 1 a small, roughly built house; hut: *a cabin in the woods.* 2 a bedroom on a ship: *The 500 passengers occupied 200 cabins.* 3 the place for passengers in an aircraft or spacecraft. *noun.*

cab·i·net (kab′ə nit), 1 a piece of furniture with shelves or drawers, used to hold articles such as dishes, jewels, or letters for use or display. 2 a group of advisers chosen by the head of a nation to direct certain departments of the government. *noun.*

cable (definition 2)

ca·ble (kā′bəl), 1 a strong, thick rope, usually made of wires twisted together: *A suspension bridge hangs from strong steel cables.* 2 a protected bundle of wires which carries an electric current. Cables carry telegraph messages, telephone conversations, and television signals. 3 a message sent under the ocean by cable. 4 to send a message under the ocean by cable. 1-3 *noun,* 4 *verb,* **ca·bles, ca·bled, ca·bling.**

cable car, a car pulled by a moving cable that is operated by an engine.

cable television, a system of bringing television programs by cable directly to television sets.

ca·boose (kə büs′), a small railroad car, usually the last car of a freight train. Several of the train crew ride and work in the caboose. *noun.*

ca·ca·o (kə kā′ō), a tropical American tree having large seeds from which cocoa and chocolate are made. *noun, plural* **ca·ca·os.**

cacao

cack·le (kak′əl), 1 the loud clucking sound that a hen makes, especially after laying an egg. 2 to make such a sound: *The hens started to cackle early in the morning.* 3 to laugh in a loud, harsh way: *The old man cackled at his own joke.* 1 *noun,* 2,3 *verb,* **cack·les, cack·led, cack·ling.**

cac·tus (kak′təs), a plant with a thick, fleshy stem that usually has spines but no leaves. Most cactuses grow in very hot, dry regions of America and have brightly colored flowers. *noun, plural* **cac·tus·es, cac·ti** (kak′tī).

cad·die or **cad·dy** (kad′ē), 1 a person who helps a golf player by carrying golf clubs or finding a lost ball. 2 to help a golf player in this way. 1 *noun, plural* **cad·dies;** 2 *verb,* **cad·dies, cad·died, cad·dy·ing.**

ca·det (kə det′), a person in training for service as an officer in the army, navy, or air force. *noun.*

ca·fe or **ca·fé** (ka fā′), a place to buy and eat a meal; restaurant. *noun.*
[*Cafe* comes from a French word, which also means "coffee." The word *caffeine* also comes from the same French word.]

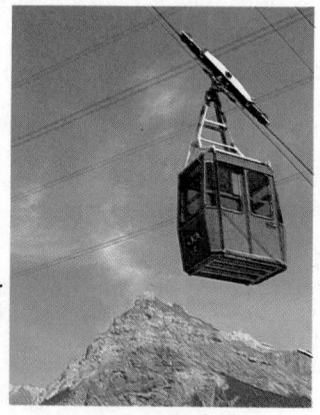

cable car

caf·e·ter·i·a (kaf′ə tir′ē ə), a restaurant where people are served at a counter but carry their food to tables themselves. *noun.*
[*Cafeteria* comes from a Mexican Spanish word meaning "coffee shop."]

caf·feine (kaf′ēn′), a slightly bitter, stimulating drug found in coffee, tea, and cola drinks. *noun.*

cage (kāj), **1** a frame or place closed in with wires, iron bars, or wood. Birds and wild animals are kept in cages. **2** a thing shaped or used like a cage. Bank tellers or movie cashiers sometimes work in a cage. **3** to put or keep in a cage: *After the lion was caught, it was caged.* 1,2 *noun,* 3 *verb,* **cag·es, caged, cag·ing.**

Cai·ro (kī′rō), the capital of Egypt. *noun.*

cake (kāk), **1** a baked mixture of flour, sugar, eggs, flavoring, and other things: *I baked a chocolate cake with white frosting for my sister's birthday.* **2** a flat, thin mass of dough baked or fried; pancake. **3** a shaped mass of food or other substance: *That restaurant makes good fish cakes. I carved a cake of soap into the shape of a dog.* **4** to form into a solid mass; harden: *Mud cakes as it dries.* 1-3 *noun,* 4 *verb,* **cakes, caked, cak·ing.**

cal or **cal.,** calorie or calories.

ca·lam·i·ty (kə lam′ə tē), a great misfortune such as a flood, a fire, the loss of one's sight, or the loss of much money; disaster. *noun, plural* **ca·lam·i·ties.**

cal·ci·um (kal′sē əm), a soft, white metal. Calcium is a chemical element. It is a part of limestone, chalk, milk, bone, shells, teeth, and many other things. Calcium is needed to grow strong, healthy bones. *noun.*

cal·cu·late (kal′kyə lāt), **1** to find out by adding, subtracting, multiplying, or dividing: *They calculated the cost of building a house.* **2** to find out beforehand by any process of reasoning; estimate: *Calculate the day of the week on which New Year's Day will fall.* **3** to plan or intend: *That remark was calculated to make me angry.* *verb,* **cal·cu·lates, cal·cu·lat·ed, cal·cu·lat·ing.**

cal·cu·la·tion (kal′kyə lā′shən), **1** the act or process of calculating to find a result. **2** the result found by calculating. *noun.*

cal·cu·la·tor (kal′kyə lā′tər), an electronic device that can do arithmetic and can solve some types of mathematical problems. A calculator has buttons with numbers and symbols on them and a display screen that shows the numbers entered and the answers. Most calculators are small enough to hold in one hand. *noun.*

cal·en·dar (kal′ən dər), **1** a chart showing the months, weeks, and days of the year. A calendar shows the day of the week on which each day of the month falls. **2** a list or schedule: *The newspaper has a calendar of community events on page three. noun.*

calf[1] (kaf), **1** a young cow or bull. **2** a young deer, elephant, whale, or seal. **3** calfskin: *The gloves are made of calf. noun, plural* **calves** for 1 and 2.

calf[2] (kaf), the thick, muscular part of the back of the leg below the knee. *noun, plural* **calves.**

a hat	i it	oi oil	ch child	a in about
ā age	ī ice	ou out	ng long	e in taken
ä far	o hot	u cup	sh she	ə = i in pencil
e let	ō open	u̇ put	th thin	o in lemon
ē equal	ô order	ü rule	ŦH then	u in circus
ėr term			zh measure	

calf·skin (kaf′skin′), the leather made from the skin of a calf. *noun.*

cal·i·co (kal′ə kō), **1** a cotton cloth that usually has colored patterns printed on one side. **2** spotted in colors: *a calico cat.* 1 *noun, plural* **cal·i·coes** or **cal·i·cos;** 2 *adjective.*

Calif., California.

Cal·i·for·nia (kal′ə fôr′nyə), one of the Pacific states of the United States. *Abbreviation:* Calif. or CA *Capital:* Sacramento. *noun.*
[*California* probably got its name from the name of an island in a Spanish adventure story written about 1500. Spanish explorers thought that Lower California was an island.]

call (kôl), **1** to speak or say in a loud voice; shout or cry out: *He called from downstairs.* **2** a loud sound or shout: *I heard the swimmer's call for help.* **3** the special noise or cry an animal or bird makes: *The call of a moose came from the forest.* **4** to make such a noise or cry: *The crows called to each other from the trees around the meadow.* **5** to command or ask to come: *I called my dog with a loud whistle.* **6** an invitation or command: *Many people answered the mayor's call for volunteer workers in the campaign.* **7** to give a name to; name: *They called the new baby "Leslie."* **8** to read over aloud: *The teacher called the class roll.* **9** to talk to by telephone; communicate by telephone: *I called my parents to say I would be late. Did anyone call today?* **10** talk or communication by telephone: *Were there any calls for me while I was out?* **11** to make a short visit or stop: *The girl scouts called yesterday selling cookies.* **12** a short visit or stop: *The rabbi made six calls.* **13** to consider; estimate: *Everyone called the party a success.* **14** to make a spoken judgment about: *The umpire called the long fly a foul ball.* **15** to end; stop: *The umpires called the game because it began to pour.* 1,4,5,7-9,11,13-15 *verb,* 2,3,6,10,12 *noun.*

call for, 1 to go and get; stop and get: *The cab called for her at the hotel.* **2** to need; require: *This recipe calls for two eggs.* **3** to request; appeal: *The mayor called for an investigation of the warehouse fire.*

call off, 1 to do away with; cancel: *We called off our trip.* **2** to say or read over aloud in succession: *The teacher called off the names on the roll.*

call on or **call upon, 1** to pay a short visit to: *We must call on our new neighbors.* **2** to appeal to: *They called upon their friends for help.*

call up, to telephone to: *I called her up at her office.*

on call, ready or available: *Doctors are expected to be on call day and night.*

C

call·er (kô′lər), **1** a person who makes a short visit: *The doctor said that the patient was now able to receive callers.* **2** a person who calls out names or steps at a square dance. *noun.*

call number, a number put on a library book to help the user to identify and find it.

cal·lus (kal′əs), a hard, thickened place on the skin. *noun, plural* **cal·lus·es.**

calm (käm), **1** quiet; still; not stormy or windy: *In fair weather, the sea is usually calm.* **2** not stirred up; peaceful: *Although she was frightened, she tried to answer with a calm voice.* **3** quietness; stillness: *There was a sudden calm as the wind dropped.* **4** to make or become calm: *The crying baby soon calmed down.* 1,2 *adjective,* 3 *noun,* 4 *verb.*

cal·or·ie (kal′ər ē), **1** a unit for measuring the amount of heat energy. **2** a unit 1000 times the size of this, to measure the energy supplied by food. An ounce of sugar will produce about one hundred calories. *noun.*

calves (kavz), more than one calf. *noun plural.*

ca·lyx (kā′liks), the sepals of a flower. *noun, plural* **ca·lyx·es.**

Cam·bo·di·a (kam bō′dē ə), a country in southeastern Asia. *n.*

came (kām). See **come.** *He came early. verb.*

cam·el (kam′əl), a large, four-footed animal with a long neck, used as a beast of burden in the desert. The camel of northern Africa has one hump; the camel of central Asia has two humps. Camels can go for a long time without drinking water. *noun.*

cam·er·a (kam′ər ə), a machine for taking photographs or motion pictures. A camera lens focuses light rays through the dark inside part of the camera onto film which is sensitive to light. **2** a machine which changes images into electronic signals for television broadcasting. *noun.*

Cam·er·oon or **Cam·er·oun** (kam′ə rün′), a country in west central Africa. *noun.*

cam·ou·flage (kam′ə fläzh), **1** a disguise or appearance that makes a person or animal look much like its surroundings. **2** the act of giving soldiers or equipment an appearance that helps hide them from view. **3** to give something an appearance that makes it hard to see; disguise: *The hunters were camouflaged with shrubbery so they blended with the landscape.* 1,2 *noun,* 3 *verb,* **cam·ou·flag·es, cam·ou·flaged, cam·ou·flag·ing.** [See Word History.]

camp (kamp), **1** a group of tents, huts, or other shelters where people live for a time: *We hiked six miles before we made camp.* **2** to live away from home for a time outdoors or in a tent or hut: *The scout troop camped at the foot of the mountain for two weeks.* **3** a place where one lives in a tent or hut or outdoors: *Last year I spent a week at summer camp.* **4** to live simply, as one does in a tent: *We camped in the empty house until our furniture arrived.* 1,3 *noun,* 2,4 *verb.*

cam·paign (kam pān′), **1** a number of connected military operations in a war which are aimed at some special purpose: *The general planned a campaign to capture the enemy's most important city.* **2** a number of connected activities to do or get something: *a campaign to raise money for a new hospital.* **3** to take part or serve in a campaign: *She campaigned for mayor by giving speeches.* 1,2 *noun,* 3 *verb.*

camp·er (kam′pər), **1** a person who camps. **2** a motor vehicle built for camping. *noun.*

camp·fire (kamp′fīr′), a fire in a camp used for cooking, warmth, or social gatherings. *noun.*

camp·ground (kamp′ground′), a place for camping, especially a public park with campsites and fireplaces for cooking. *noun.*

cam·phor (kam′fər), a white substance with a strong odor. It is used in medicine and to protect clothes from moths. *noun.*

camp·site (kamp′sīt′), a place where people camp. *noun.*

cam·pus (kam′pəs), the buildings and grounds of a college, university, or school. *noun, plural* **cam·pus·es.**

can[1] (kan *or* kən), **1** to be able to: *You can run fast.* **2** to know how to: *She can speak Spanish.* **3** to have the right to: *Anyone can cross the street here.* **4** may: *Can I go now? verb, past tense* **could.**

can[2] (kan), **1** an airtight metal container in which food is stored: *a can of peaches.* **2** a container of metal, usually with a cover or lid: *a paint can, a trash can.* **3** the amount that a can holds: *Add three cans of water to make the orange juice.* **4** to put in an airtight can or jar to preserve: *We are going to can tomatoes.* 1-3 *noun,* 4 *verb,* **cans, canned, can·ning.**

Can·a·da (kan′ə də), a country in North America, north of the United States. *noun.*

Ca·na·di·an (kə nā′dē ən), **1** of or having something to do with Canada or its people. **2** a

Word History

camouflage *Camouflage* comes from a Latin word meaning "to disguise."

camouflage (definition 1)—The chipmunk's coloring is a natural **camouflage** which keeps it from being easily seen.

person born or living in Canada. 1 *adjective*, 2 *noun*.

ca·nal (kə nal/), 1 a waterway dug across land for ships or small boats to go through or to carry water to places that need it. 2 a tube in the body of a person or animal that carries food, liquid, or air. The food that a person eats goes through his or her alimentary canal. *noun*.

ca·nar·y (kə ner/ē), 1 a small, yellow songbird, often kept as a pet. 2 light-yellow. 1 *noun, plural* **ca·nar·ies;** 2 *adjective*.

can·cel (kan/səl), 1 to put an end to, set aside, or withdraw; do away with; stop: *She canceled her appointment with the dentist.* 2 to cross out; mark, stamp, or punch so that it cannot be used again: *The post office cancels the stamp on a letter. verb*.

can·cer (kan/sər), a very harmful growth in the body. Cancer tends to spread and destroy the healthy tissues and organs of the body. *noun*.

can·did (kan/did), 1 free in expressing one's real thoughts, opinions, and feelings; sincere: *Please be candid with me.* 2 not posed: *a candid photograph of children playing. adjective*.

can·di·date (kan/də dāt), a person who seeks, or is suggested by others for, some office or honor: *There are three candidates for president of our club. noun*.

can·died (kan/dēd), cooked in sugar; coated with sugar: *candied sweet potatoes, candied apples. adjective*.

can·dle (kan/dl), a stick of wax or tallow with a wick in it, burned to give light. Long ago, before there was gas or electric light, people burned candles to see by. *noun*.

can·dle·light (kan/dl līt/), the light of a candle or candles. *noun*.

can·dle·stick (kan/dl stik/), a holder for a candle. *noun*.

can·dy (kan/dē), 1 a sweet food made of sugar or syrup often mixed with chocolate, fruit, nuts, or flavorings. 2 a piece of this: *Take a candy from the box.* 3 to cook or preserve by boiling in sugar: *She candied the peaches before canning them.* 1,2 *noun, plural* **can·dies;** 3 *verb,* **can·dies, can·died, can·dy·ing.**

[*Candy* comes from a Persian word meaning "sugar." In early English, candy was called sugar candy.]

cane (kān), 1 a slender stick used as an aid in walking. 2 a long, jointed stem, such as that of the bamboo, often used in making furniture. 3 a plant having such stems. Sugarcane and bamboo are canes. *noun*.

ca·nine tooth (kā/nīn tüth/), one of the four pointed teeth next to the incisors.

[The word *canine* comes from a Latin word meaning "dog." The tooth was called this because it looks like the pointed tooth of a dog.]

can·is·ter (kan/ə stər), a small box or can, especially for tea, coffee, flour, or sugar. *noun*.

canned (kand), put in a can; preserved by being put in airtight cans or jars: *canned peaches. adjective*.

a hat	**i** it	**oi** oil	**ch** child	a in about
ā age	**ī** ice	**ou** out	**ng** long	e in taken
ä far	**o** hot	**u** cup	**sh** she	**ə =** i in pencil
e let	**ō** open	**u̇** put	**th** thin	o in lemon
ē equal	**ô** order	**ü** rule	**ŦH** then	u in circus
ėr term			**zh** measure	

can·ner·y (kan/ər ē), a factory where food is canned. *noun, plural* **can·ner·ies.**

can·ni·bal (kan/ə bəl), 1 a person who eats human flesh. 2 an animal that eats others of its own kind: *Some fish are cannibals. noun*.

can·non (kan/ən), a big gun supported by wheels or a flat base. *noun, plural* **can·nons** or **can·non.**

can·non·ball (kan/ən bôl/), a large iron or steel ball, that used to be fired from cannons. *noun*.

can·not (kan/ot *or* ka not/), can not. *verb*.

ca·noe (kə nü/), 1 a light, narrow boat pointed at both ends and moved with a paddle. 2 to paddle a canoe; go in a canoe. 1 *noun,* 2 *verb,* **ca·noes, ca·noed, ca·noe·ing.**

canoe
(definition 1)

canopy

can·o·py (kan/ə pē), a covering fixed over a bed, throne, or entrance, or carried on poles over a person. *noun, plural* **can·o·pies.**

can't (kant), can not.

can·ta·loupe (kan/tl ōp), a kind of melon with a

hard, rough rind and sweet, juicy, orange-colored flesh. *noun.*

can·teen (kan tēn′), **1** a small container for carrying water or other drinks. **2** a store in a school, camp, factory, or hospital where food, drinks, and other articles are sold, often from vending machines. *noun.*

can·ter (kan′tər), **1** a gait of a horse, like a slow gallop. **2** to ride at a canter: *I cantered my horse down the road.* **1** *noun,* **2** *verb.*
[In the Middle Ages, English pilgrims used to travel to *Canterbury,* a city in England. It was their habit to ride at a slow pace. By shortening *Canterbury* to *canter,* people coined a new word for riding at such a pace.]

can·tor (kan′tər), a person who sings and leads the music in a synagogue. *noun.*

can·vas (kan′vəs), **1** a strong cloth with a coarse weave often made of cotton. It is used to make tents, sails, and certain articles of clothing, and for painting on. **2** something made of canvas: *The artist prepared a canvas for painting on the next day.* **3** a picture painted on canvas; oil painting: *The beautiful canvas was hanging in the art gallery. noun, plural* **can·vas·es.**

can·yon (kan′yən), a narrow valley with high, steep sides, usually with a stream at the bottom. *noun.*
[*Canyon* comes from a Mexican Spanish word meaning "narrow passage." Spanish settlers in New Mexico used the word for the deep valleys which they found there.]

cap (kap), **1** a soft, close-fitting covering for the head, having no brim or only a visor. **2** anything that covers or forms the top of something. The stopper or top of a jar, bottle, tube, marker, or pen is a cap. **3** to put a cap on; cover the top of: *Snow capped the mountain peaks.* **4** a small amount of explosive in a wrapper: *This toy gun uses caps.* **1,2,4** *noun,* **3** *verb,* **caps, capped, cap·ping.**

ca·pa·bil·i·ty (kā′pə bil′ə tē), the ability to learn or do; power or fitness; capacity: *A computer has the capability of solving mathematical problems very quickly. noun, plural* **ca·pa·bil·i·ties.**

ca·pa·ble (kā′pə bəl), able; having fitness, power, or ability: *He was such a capable student that everyone had great hopes for his future. adjective.*
capable of, having ability, power, or fitness for: *an airplane capable of going 2000 miles an hour.*

ca·pac·i·ty (kə pas′ə tē), **1** the amount of space inside; largest amount that can be held by a container: *A gallon can has a capacity of 4 quarts.* **2** the ability to learn or do; power or fitness: *A bright student has a capacity for learning.* **3** position: *She is here in the capacity of teacher. noun, plural* **ca·pac·i·ties.**

cape¹ (kāp), a piece of outer clothing, without sleeves, worn falling loosely from the shoulders and often fastened at the neck. *noun.*

cape² (kāp), a point of land that sticks out into an ocean, bay, or other body of water. *noun.*

ca·per (kā′pər), a prank; trick. *noun.*

cap·il·lar·y (kap′ə ler′ē), a very slender blood vessel with a tiny opening. Capillaries join the ends of arteries to the beginnings of veins. *noun, plural* **cap·il·lar·ies.**

cap·i·tal (kap′ə təl), **1** a city where the government of a country, state, or province is located. Washington is the capital of the United States. Each state of the United States has a capital. **2** A, B, C, D, or any other large letter. **3** very important; leading; chief: *The invention of the telephone was a capital advance in communication.* **4** punishable by death: *Murder is a capital crime in many countries.* **5** the amount of money or property that a company or a person uses in carrying on a business: *The Smith Company has a capital of $3,000,000.* **1,2,5** *noun,* **3,4** *adjective.*

cap·i·tal·ism (kap′ə tə liz′əm), an economic system in which private individuals or groups of individuals own land, factories, and other means of production. Using the hired labor of other persons, owners produce goods and services in competition for profits. *noun.*

cap·i·tal·i·za·tion (kap′ə tə lə zā′shən), a writing or printing with a capital letter. *noun.*

cap·i·tal·ize (kap′ə tə līz), to write or print with a capital letter: *You always capitalize your name. verb,* **cap·i·tal·iz·es, cap·i·tal·ized, cap·i·tal·iz·ing.**

Cap·i·tol (kap′ə təl), **1** the building at Washington, D.C., in which Congress meets. **2** Also, **capitol.** the building in which a state legislature meets. *noun.*

cap·size (kap sīz′), to turn bottom side up; upset; overturn: *The sailboat nearly capsized in the high wind. verb,* **cap·siz·es, cap·sized, cap·siz·ing.**

cap·sule (kap′səl), **1** a tiny container. Medicine often comes in gelatin capsules made to be swallowed. The seeds of some plants grow in capsules. **2** the enclosed front section of a rocket made to carry instruments or astronauts into space. In flight the capsule can separate from the rest of the rocket and go into orbit or be directed back to earth. *noun.*

cap·tain (kap′tən), **1** the head of a group; leader or chief: *the captain of a basketball team.* **2** the commander of a ship. **3** an army, air force, or marine officer ranking below a major. **4** a navy officer ranking below a rear admiral. **5** to lead or command as captain: *She will captain the softball team next season.* **1-4** *noun,* **5** *verb.*

cap·tion (kap′shən), a title or words next to a picture that tell what it is. *noun.*

cap·tive (kap′tiv), **1** a person or animal captured and held unwillingly; prisoner: *The pirates took many captives during raids along the coast.* **2** made a prisoner; held against one's will: *The enemy released the captive soldiers.* **1** *noun,* **2** *adjective.*

cap·tiv·i·ty (kap tiv′ə tē), the condition of being held unwillingly: *Some animals cannot bear captivity, and die after a few weeks in a cage. noun.*

cap·tor (kap′tər), a person who takes or holds a prisoner. *noun.*

cap·ture (kap′chər), **1** to make a prisoner of; take by force; seize: *We captured butterflies with a net.* **2** a capturing or a being captured: *The capture of this ship took place on July 6.* **3** to attract and hold; catch and keep: *The story of Alice in Wonderland captures the imagination.* 1,3 *verb,* **cap·tur·es, cap·tured, cap·tur·ing;** 2 *noun.*

car (kär), **1** an automobile. **2** any vehicle that moves on its wheels along tracks: *a subway car, a railroad car.* **3** the part of an elevator used to carry passengers or cargo. *noun.*

car·a·mel (kar′ə məl *or* kär′məl), **1** sugar browned or burned over heat, used for coloring and flavoring food. **2** a chewy candy flavored with this sugar. *noun.*

car·at (kar′ət), **1** a unit of weight for precious stones, equal to 200 milligrams. **2** See **karat.** *noun.*

car·a·van (kar′ə van), a group of merchants, pilgrims, tourists, or the like, often traveling together for safety through difficult or dangerous country: *A caravan of Arab merchants and camels, carrying spices and silks, moved across the desert. noun.*

car·bo·hy·drate (kär′bō hī′drāt), a substance made from carbon dioxide and water by green plants in sunlight. Carbohydrates are made up of carbon, hydrogen, and oxygen. Sugar and starch are carbohydrates. *noun.*

car·bon (kär′bən), a very common substance that is in all living things. Carbon is a chemical element. Coal and charcoal are mostly carbon. Diamonds and graphite are pure carbon in the form of crystals. *noun.*

car·bon·at·ed (kär′bə nā′tid), containing carbon dioxide. Carbonated soft drinks bubble and fizz. *adjective.*

car·bon di·ox·ide (kär′bən dī ok′sīd), a heavy, colorless, odorless gas, present in the atmosphere or formed when any fuel containing carbon is burned. The air that is breathed out of an animal's lungs contains carbon dioxide. Plants absorb it from the air and use it to make plant tissue. Carbon dioxide is used in soda water, in fire extinguishers, and in other ways.

car·bon mon·ox·ide (kär′bən mo nok′sīd), a colorless, odorless, very poisonous gas, formed when carbon burns with too little air. It is part of the exhaust gases of automobile engines.

car·bu·re·tor (kär′bə rā′tər), a device for mixing air with a liquid fuel to produce an explosive mixture. A carburetor is part of the gasoline engine of many automobiles. *noun.*

car·cass (kär′kəs), a body of a dead animal: *Steak is cut from a beef carcass. noun, plural* **car·cass·es.**

card¹ (kärd), **1** a flat piece of stiff paper, thin cardboard, or plastic: *a birthday card, a library card, a report card, a credit card.* **2** one of a pack of cards used in playing games. *noun.*

card² (kärd), to clean and straighten the fibers of wool, cotton, or flax with a special tool. *verb.*

card·board (kärd′bôrd′), a stiff material made of layers of paper pressed together, used to make cards and boxes. *noun.*

card catalog, a list of items in a library, entered on cards arranged alphabetically in a filing cabinet.

car·di·nal (kärd′n əl), **1** one of the high officials of the Roman Catholic Church, appointed by the Pope and ranking next below him. Cardinals wear red robes and red hats. **2** a North American songbird. The male has bright-red feathers marked with black. **3** a bright, rich red. **4** of first importance; chief; principal: *The cardinal value of the plan is that it is simple.* 1,2 *noun,* 3,4 *adjective.*

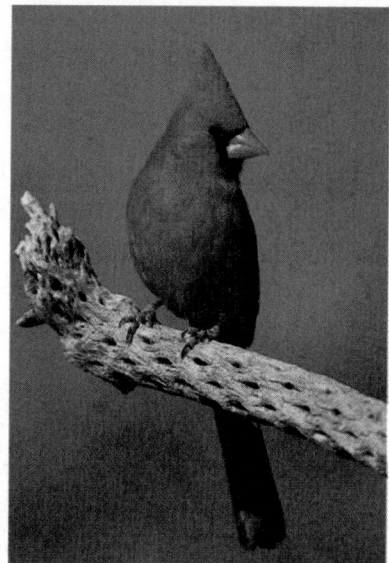

cardinal
(definition 2)
9 inches
(23 centimeters) long

cards (kärdz), **1** a pack of playing cards. **2** a game or games played with playing cards. *noun plural.*

care (ker *or* kar), **1** worry: *I haven't a care in the world.* **2** attention: *A pilot's work requires great care.* **3** to feel interest: *Musicians care about music.* **4** safekeeping; protection: *The little girl was left in her older brother's care.* **5** to like; want; wish: *I don't care to go to that movie.* **6** to mind; object to: *Do you care if I leave early?* 1,2,4 *noun,* 3,5,6 *verb,* **cares, cared, car·ing.**

care for, 1 to be fond of; like: *I don't care for her friends.* **2** to want; wish: *I don't care for any dessert.* **3** to take charge of: *The nurse will care for him now.*

take care, to be careful: *Take care to be accurate.*

take care of, 1 to take charge of; attend to: *A baby-sitter is expected to take care of children. She took care of the party arrangements.* **2** to be careful with: *Take care of your money.*

ca·reer (kə rir′), an occupation or profession: *I plan to make law my career.* noun.

care·free (ker′frē′ or kar′frē′), without worry; happy; gay: *The children spent a carefree summer sailing and swimming at the seashore.* adjective.

care·ful (ker′fəl or kar′fəl), **1** thinking about what you say or do; watchful; cautious: *He is careful to tell the truth at all times. Be careful with my new bicycle!* **2** showing care; done with thought or effort; exact; thorough: *Arithmetic requires careful work.* adjective.

care·less (ker′lis or kar′lis), **1** not thinking about what you say or do; not careful: *I was careless and broke the cup.* **2** done without enough thought or effort; not exact or thorough: *careless work.* **3** not caring or troubling; indifferent: *Some people are careless about their appearance.* adjective.

ca·ress (kə res′), **1** a touch showing affection; tender embrace or kiss. **2** to touch or stroke tenderly; embrace or kiss. **1** noun, plural **ca·ress·es; 2** verb.

care·tak·er (ker′tā′kər or kar′tā′kər), a person who takes care of someone else's house or other property. noun.

car·fare (kär′fer′ or kär′far′), the money paid for riding on a bus or subway, in a taxicab, or in other passenger vehicles. noun.

car·go (kär′gō), the load of goods carried by a ship, plane, or truck: *The freighter had docked to unload a cargo of wheat.* noun, plural **car·goes** or **car·gos.**

Car·ib·be·an Sea (kar′ə bē′ən or kə rib′ē ən), a sea bordered by Central America, the West Indies, and South America.

car·i·bou (kar′ə bü), a large deer with branching antlers that lives in northern North America. Caribou living in Europe and Asia are called reindeer. noun, plural **car·i·bou** or **car·i·bous.**
[We borrowed the name of this animal from the French of Canada. They got it from the word that the North American Indians used for the animal.]

car·na·tion (kär nā′shən), **1** a red, white, or pink flower with a spicy fragrance, grown in gardens and greenhouses. **2** rosy-pink. **1** noun, **2** adjective.

car·ni·val (kär′nə vəl), a place of amusement or a traveling show having merry-go-rounds, games, and shows. noun.

car·niv·or·ous (kär niv′ər əs), meat-eating; feeding chiefly on flesh. Cats, dogs, lions, tigers, and bears are carnivorous animals. adjective.

car·ob (kar′əb), **1** a powder made by grinding the sweet pulp of the pod of the carob tree. It is used as a substitute for chocolate. **2** made of or flavored with carob: *carob ice cream.* **1** noun, **2** adjective.

car·ol (kar′əl), **1** a hymn or song of joy sung at Christmas. **2** to sing carols: *At Christmas the children went from house to house, caroling.* **1** noun, **2** verb.

car·ou·sel (kar′ə sel′ or kar′ə sel), a merry-go-round. noun. Also spelled **carrousel.**

carp[1] (kärp), to find fault; complain. verb.

carp[2] (kärp), a bony, freshwater fish which lives in ponds and slow streams. It feeds mostly on plants and sometimes grows quite large. noun, plural **carp** or **carps.**

car·pen·ter (kär′pən tər), a person whose work is building and repairing the wooden parts of houses, barns, and ships. noun.

car·pet (kär′pit), **1** a heavy, woven fabric used for covering floors and stairs. **2** anything like a carpet: *a carpet of grass.* **3** to cover with a carpet: *The ground was carpeted with leaves.* **1,2** noun, **3** verb.

car pool, an arrangement made by a group of persons to take turns driving themselves or others to and from a place: *The parents formed a car pool to take their children to school.*

car·port (kär′pôrt′), a shelter for automobiles, usually attached to a house and open on at least one side. noun.

car·riage (kar′ij), **1** a vehicle that moves on wheels. Some carriages are pulled by horses and are used to carry people. Baby carriages are small and light, and can often be folded. **2** a frame on wheels that supports a gun. **3** a moving part of a machine that supports some other part: *a typewriter carriage.* noun.

car·ri·er (kar′ē ər), a person or thing that carries something. A postman is a mail carrier. Railroads, airlines, bus systems, and truck companies are carriers. noun.

car·rot (kar′ət), the long, tapering, orange-red root of a garden plant. Carrots are eaten as a vegetable, either cooked or raw. noun.

car·rou·sel (kar′ə sel′ or kar′ə sel). See **carousel.** noun.

car·ry (kar′ē), **1** to take a thing or person from one place to another: *Railroads carry coal from the mines to the factories. The man carried the child home. This story will carry your thoughts back to last winter.* **2** to have with one: *I carry an umbrella whenever it looks like rain.* **3** to transmit from one to another; spread: *Rats carry disease.* **4** to hold up; support: *Rafters carry the weight of the roof.* **5** to hold one's body and head in a certain way: *The ballet dancer carries himself gracefully.* **6** to capture or win: *Our side carried the election.* **7** to continue; extend: *He carries his practical jokes too far.* **8** to cover the distance: *The singer's voice carries to the last row of the theater.* **9** to sing a melody or part with correct pitch: *I can't carry a tune.* **10** to keep in stock: *This store carries toys and games.* **11** to transfer a number from one place or column in the sum to the next: *A 10 in the 1's column must be carried to the 10's column.* verb, **car·ries, car·ried, car·ry·ing.**

carry away, to arouse strong feeling in; influence beyond reason: *Have you ever been so carried away by a sad movie that you began to cry?*

carry on, 1 to do; manage; conduct: *She carried on a successful business.* **2** to keep going; not stop; continue: *We must carry on in our effort to establish world peace.* **3** to behave wildly or foolishly: *The children carried on at the party.*

carry out, to get done; do; complete: *They carried out the job well.*

Car·son Cit·y (kär′sən sit′ē), the capital of Nevada.

cart (kärt), **1** a strong vehicle with two wheels, used in farming and for carrying heavy loads. Horses, donkeys, and oxen are often used to draw carts. **2** a small vehicle on wheels, moved by hand: *a grocery cart.* **3** to carry in or as if in a cart: *Cart away this rubbish.* 1,2 *noun,* 3 *verb.*

car·ti·lage (kär′tl ij), a tough, elastic substance forming parts of the skeleton of animals with a backbone. Cartilage is more flexible than bone and not as hard. The outer part of the ear is made of cartilage and skin. *noun.*

car·ton (kärt′n), **1** a box made of pasteboard or cardboard: *a candy carton. Pack the books in large cartons.* **2** the amount that a carton holds: *The children drink a carton of milk at each meal. noun.*

car·toon (kär tün′), **1** a drawing which interests or amuses us by showing people or things in an exaggerated way. Cartoons are often found in magazines and newspapers. **2** a comic strip. **3** a motion picture made up of a series of drawings, each one slightly different, that are put on film and seem to move when shown through a projector. *noun.*

car·toon·ist (kär tü′nist), a person who draws cartoons. *noun.*

car·tridge (kär′trij), **1** a case made of metal, plastic, or cardboard for holding gunpowder and a bullet or shot. **2** a container which holds a supply of material, made to be easily put into a larger device. Film, ink, and magnetic tape come in cartridges. **3** a small device with a plastic case and electronic circuits inside it. A cartridge put into a computer, a calculator, or an electronic games machine allows these machines to work in particular ways. *noun.*

cart·wheel (kärt′hwēl′), **1** a wheel of a cart. **2** a sideways handspring with the legs and arms kept straight. *noun.*

carve (kärv), **1** to cut into slices or pieces: *I carved the meat at the dinner table.* **2** to make by cutting; cut: *Statues are often carved from marble, stone, or wood. verb,* **carves, carved, carv·ing.**

carv·ing (kär′ving), **1** a carved work; carved decoration: *a wood carving.* **2** See **carve.** *I am carving the meat for dinner.* 1 *noun,* 2 *verb.*

cas·cade (ka skād′), **1** a small waterfall. **2** something like a waterfall: *When he sneezed while carrying a stack of dishes, they fell in a cascade.* **3** fall, pour, or flow in a cascade: *The dishes went cascading to the floor.* 1,2 *noun,* 3 *verb,* **cas·cades, cas·cad·ed, cas·cad·ing.**

case[1] (kās), **1** an example or instance: *A case of chicken pox kept me away from school. Any case of cheating will be punished.* **2** the actual condition; real situation: *She said the work was done, but that was not the case.* **3** a person who has an injury or illness; patient: *I was the first case of poison ivy at camp.* **4** a matter for a court of law to decide: *The case will be brought before the court tomorrow. noun.*

in any case, no matter what happens: *In any*

a hat	**i** it	**oi** oil	**ch** child	⎡a in about
ā age	**ī** ice	**ou** out	**ng** long	e in taken
ä far	**o** hot	**u** cup	**sh** she	ə = ⎨ i in pencil
e let	**ō** open	**ù** put	**th** thin	o in lemon
ē equal	**ô** order	**ü** rule	**ᴛʜ** then	⎣u in circus
ėr term			**zh** measure	

case, you should prepare for the worst.

in case, it should happen that; if; supposing: *In case it rains, bring your umbrella.*

in case of, if there should be: *In case of fire walk quietly to the nearest door.*

case[2] (kās), **1** a thing to hold or cover something: *a typewriter case.* **2** a box: *There is a big case full of books in the hall.* **3** the amount that a case can hold: *The children drank a case of ginger ale at the party. noun.*

cash (kash), **1** money in the form of coins and bills. **2** money paid at the time of buying something: *Do you want to pay cash for the clothes or charge them?* **3** to give or get cash for: *The bank will cash your check.* 1,2 *noun,* 3 *verb,* **cash·es, cashed, cash·ing.**

cash·ew (kash′ü), the small nut of a tropical American tree. Cashews are good to eat. *noun.* [Portuguese settlers who came to Brazil got the word for this nut from the native Indian name for the cashew tree.]

cashews

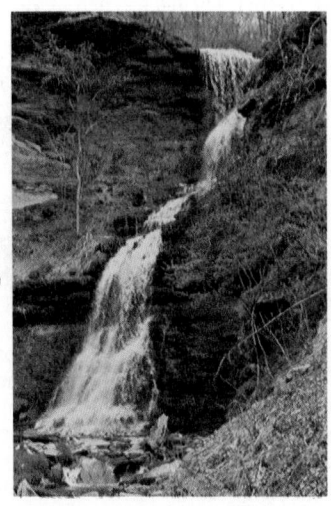

cascade
(definition 1)

cash·ier (ka shir′), a person who has charge of money in a bank, or in any business. *noun*.

cash·mere (kash′mir), a fine, soft wool, used in making sweaters or scarves. The finest cashmere is obtained from a breed of long-haired goats of Asia. *noun*.

cask (kask), 1 a barrel. A cask may be large or small, and is usually made to hold liquids. 2 the amount that a cask holds. *noun*.

cas·ket (kas′kit), 1 a coffin. 2 a small box or chest, often fine and beautiful, used to hold jewels and letters. *noun*.

cas·se·role (kas′ə rōl′), 1 a covered baking dish in which food can be both cooked and served. 2 food cooked and served in such a dish. *noun*.

cas·sette (kə set′), 1 a container holding plastic tape for recording and playing back pictures, sound, or computer information. 2 a cartridge for film. *noun*.

cast (kast), 1 to throw: *cast a stone, cast a fishing line. She was cast into the water when the railing of the bridge broke.* 2 to throw off; cause to fall: *The snake cast its skin. The setting sun cast long shadows.* 3 the distance a thing is thrown; throw: *The fisherman made a long cast with his line.* 4 to direct or turn: *She cast a glance of surprise at me.* 5 to put on record: *I cast my vote for President of the United States.* 6 to shape by pouring or squeezing into a mold to harden. Metal is first melted and then cast. 7 a thing shaped in a mold: *The sculptor made a cast of Queen Elizabeth.* 8 a mold used to shape or support: *My cousin's broken arm is in a plaster cast.* 9 to select for a part in a play: *The director cast her in the role of the heroine.* 10 actors in a play: *The cast was listed on the program.* 11 an outward form or look; appearance: *His face had a gloomy cast.* 12 a slight amount of color; tinge: *a white shirt with a pink cast.* 1,2,4-6,9 *verb*, **casts, cast, cast·ing;** 3,7,8,10-12 *noun*.

cast down, to make sad or discouraged: *He was cast down by the bad news.*

cast off, 1 to let loose; set free: *to cast off a boat from its moorings.* 2 to abandon or discard: *She cast off her old friends when she moved.*

castanets

cas·ta·net (kas′tə net′), one of a pair of wooden or plastic instruments held in the hand and clicked together in time to music. *noun*.

cast iron, a hard, brittle form of iron shaped by pouring into a mold to harden.

cas·tle (kas′əl), 1 a large building or group of buildings with thick walls, towers, and other defenses against attack. Most castles were built during the Middle Ages and were surrounded by water-filled ditches, or moats, for protection. 2 a large and impressive residence. 3 one of the pieces in the game of chess; rook. A castle can move in a straight line across any number of empty squares. *noun*.

cas·u·al (kazh′ü əl), 1 happening by chance; not planned or expected; accidental: *Our long friendship began with a casual meeting at a party.* 2 without plan or method; careless: *I didn't read the newspaper but gave it only a casual glance.* 3 informal: *We dressed in casual clothes for the picnic. Her casual behavior was sometimes mistaken for rudeness.* *adjective*.

cas·u·al·ty (kazh′ü əl tē), 1 a soldier, sailor, or other member of the armed forces who has been wounded, killed, or captured: *The war produced many casualties.* 2 a person injured or killed in an accident: *If drivers were more careful, there would be fewer casualties on the highways.* *noun, plural* **cas·u·al·ties.**

cat (kat), 1 a small, furry animal, often kept as a pet or for catching mice and rats. 2 any animal of the group including cats, lions, tigers, leopards, and jaguars. *noun*.

let the cat out of the bag, to tell a secret.

rain cats and dogs, to pour down rain very hard.

cat·a·log (kat′l ôg), 1 a list. A library usually has a catalog of its books, arranged in alphabetical order. Some companies print catalogs showing pictures and prices of the things that they have to sell. 2 to make a list of; enter in the proper place in a list: *to catalog an insect collection.* 1 *noun*, 2 *verb*.

cat·a·logue (kat′l ôg). See **catalog.** *noun, verb,* **cat·a·logues, cat·a·logued, cat·a·logu·ing.**

catapult (definition 1)—By means of ropes, ancient soldiers drew this very heavy bow. It could send an arrow a great distance.

cat·a·pult (kat′ə pult), 1 a weapon used in ancient times for shooting stones or arrows. 2 a device for launching an airplane from the deck of a ship. 3 to throw; hurl: *He stopped his bicycle so suddenly that he was catapulted over the handlebars.* 1,2 *noun*, 3 *verb*.

cat·a·ract (kat′ə rakt′), 1 a large, steep waterfall. 2 a violent rush or downpour of water; flood: *Cataracts of rain flooded the streets.* 3 a disease of the eye in which the lens develops a cloudy film. A cataract makes a person partly or entirely blind. *noun.*

ca·tas·tro·phe (kə tas′trə fē), a sudden, terribly bad or horrifying thing that happens; very great misfortune. An earthquake, tornado, flood, or big fire is a catastrophe. *noun.*

cat·bird (kat′bėrd′), a North American songbird with gray feathers. It can make a sound like a cat mewing. *noun.*

catch (kach), **1** to take and hold something moving; seize: *Catch the ball with both hands. The children chased the puppy and caught it.* **2** to attract: *The bright display caught my attention.* **3** to take or get: *Paper catches fire easily. Put on a warm coat or you will catch cold. I caught a glimpse of my grandmother waving as her plane took off.* **4** to reach or get to in time: *You have just five minutes to catch your train.* **5** to see, hear, or understand: *He spoke so rapidly that I didn't catch the meaning of what he said.* **6** to become hooked or fastened: *My sweater caught in the door.* **7** to come upon suddenly; surprise: *Mother caught me just as I was hiding her birthday present.* **8** to act as catcher in baseball: *He catches for our team.* **9** the act of catching: *She made a fine catch with one hand.* **10** a thing that fastens: *The catch on that door is broken.* **11** a thing caught: *A dozen fish is a good catch.* **12** a game of throwing and catching a ball: *The children played catch on the lawn.* **13** a hidden or tricky condition: *There is a catch to that question.* 1-8 *verb,* **catch·es, caught, catch·ing;** 9-13 *noun, plural* **catch·es.**

catch on, 1 to get the idea; understand: *The second time the teacher explained the problem, I caught on.* **2** to be widely used or accepted: *That new song caught on quickly.*

catch up on, to bring up to date: *I've got to catch up on my homework.*

catch up with, to come up even with a person or thing while going the same way; overtake: *I was late, and had to run to catch up with my friends.*

catch·er (kach′ər), **1** a person or thing that catches. **2** a baseball player who stands behind the batter to catch the ball thrown by the pitcher. *noun.*

catch·ing (kach′ing), **1** spread by infection; contagious: *Colds are catching.* **2** likely to spread from one person to another: *Enthusiasm is catching. adjective.*

catch·y (kach′ē), pleasing and easy to remember: *a catchy new song. adjective,* **catch·i·er, catch·i·est.**

cat·e·chism (kat′ə kiz′əm), **1** a book of questions and answers about religion. **2** a set of questions and answers about any subject. *noun.*

cat·e·go·ry (kat′ə gôr′ē), a group or general division in classification; class: *The library arranges books according to categories. noun, plural* **cat·e·go·ries.**

ca·ter (kā′tər), **1** to provide food and supplies, and sometimes service: *They run a restaurant and also cater for weddings and parties.* **2** to provide

what is needed or wanted: *The new store caters to tourists by selling souvenirs. verb.*

cat·er·pil·lar (kat′ər pil′ər), the wormlike larva of a butterfly or a moth. Caterpillars are often colorful, and many are furry or have bristles. *noun.*

catfish—20 inches (50 centimeters) long

cat·fish (kat′fish′), a fish without scales and with long, slender growths around the mouth that look somewhat like a cat's whiskers. *noun, plural* **cat·fish** or **cat·fish·es.**

ca·the·dral (kə thē′drəl), **1** the official church of a bishop. **2** a large or important church. *noun.*

Cath·o·lic (kath′ə lik), **1** of the Christian church governed by the pope; Roman Catholic. **2** a member of this church. 1 *adjective,* 2 *noun.*

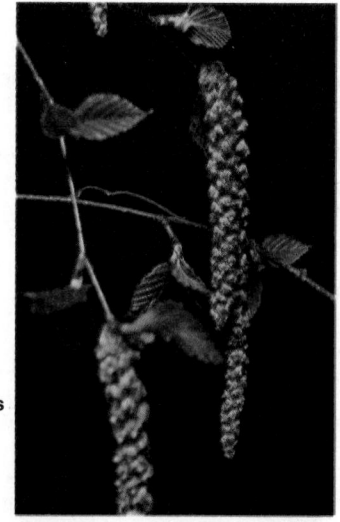

catkins

cat·kin (kat′kən), the soft, downy or scaly, pointed flower, without petals, that grows on willow or birch trees. *noun.*

cat·sup (kech′əp *or* kat′səp), a thick sauce made of tomatoes, onions, salt, sugar, and spices. *noun.* Also spelled **ketchup.**
[*Catsup* comes from a Malay word for a kind of fish sauce.]

cattails

cat·tail (kat′tāl′), a tall marsh plant with a long, furry, brown spike and long, pointed leaves. *noun.*

cat·tle (kat′l), animals that chew their cud, have hoofs, and are raised for meat, milk, and hides; cows, bulls, and steers. *noun, plural.*

cat·tle·man (kat′l mən), a person who raises or takes care of cattle. *noun, plural* **cat·tle·men.**

caught (kôt). See **catch.** *I caught the ball. The mouse was caught in a trap. verb.*

cau·li·flow·er (kô′lə flou′ər), a vegetable having a solid white head with leaves around it. *noun.*

cause (kôz), **1** a person, thing, or event that makes something happen: *The flood was the cause of much damage.* **2** to make happen; bring about: *The fire caused much damage. A loud noise caused me to jump.* **3** a reason or occasion for action: *Winning the contest was a cause for celebration. You have no cause to complain.* **4** something in which many people are interested and to which they give their support: *World peace is the cause she works for.* **1,3,4** *noun,* **2** *verb,* **caus·es, caused, caus·ing.**

cau·tion (kô′shən), **1** great care; unwillingness to take chances: *Use caution in crossing streets.* **2** to urge to be careful; warn: *I cautioned them against playing in the street.* **1** *noun,* **2** *verb.*

cau·tious (kô′shəs), very careful; not taking chances: *A cautious driver never drives too fast. adjective.*

cav·al·cade (kav′əl kād′), a long, continuous line of persons riding on horses, in carriages, or in automobiles. *noun.*

cav·al·ry (kav′əl rē), soldiers fighting on horseback or from tanks and other armored vehicles. *noun.*

cave (kāv), **1** a hollow space underground, especially one with an opening in the side of a hill or mountain. **2 cave in,** to fall in; sink: *The weight of the snow caused the roof of the cabin to cave in.* **1** *noun,* **2** *verb,* **caves, caved, cav·ing.**

cave-in (kāv′in′), **1** a caving in; collapse: *a tunnel cave-in, the cave-in of a mine.* **2** a place where something has caved in. *noun.*

cave man, a person who lived in a cave in prehistoric times.

cav·ern (kav′ərn), a large cave. *noun.*

cav·i·ty (kav′ə tē), a hollow place; hole. Cavities in teeth are caused by decay. *noun, plural* **cav·i·ties.**

caw (kô), **1** the harsh cry made by a crow or raven. **2** to make this cry. **1** *noun,* **2** *verb.*

cc or **c.c.,** cubic centimeter or cubic centimeters.

cease (sēs), to stop: *The music ceased suddenly. verb,* **ceas·es, ceased, ceas·ing.**

cease·less (sēs′lis), going on all the time; never stopping; continual: *the ceaseless roar of the waterfall. adjective.*

ce·dar (sē′dər), an evergreen tree with widely spreading branches. Its fragrant, durable, reddish wood is used for making chests, pencils, posts, and shingles. *noun.*

ceil·ing (sē′ling), **1** the inside, top covering of a room. **2** the distance between the earth and the lowest clouds: *The weather report said that the ceiling was only 300 feet.* **3** top limit: *There is a ceiling on the amount candidates can spend for election campaigns. noun.*

cel·e·brate (sel′ə brāt), **1** to observe a special time or day with festive activities: *We celebrated my birthday with a party and cake and ice cream.* **2** to perform publicly with the proper ceremonies and rites: *The priest celebrates Mass in church. verb,* **cel·e·brates, cel·e·brat·ed, cel·e·brat·ing.**

cel·e·brat·ed (sel′ə brā′tid), famous; well-known; much talked about: *a celebrated poet. adjective.*

cel·e·bra·tion (sel′ə brā′shən), **1** special services or activities in honor of a particular person, act, time, or day: *A Fourth of July celebration often includes a display of fireworks.* **2** the act of celebrating: *celebration of a birthday. noun.*

ce·leb·ri·ty (sə leb′rə tē), a famous person; person who is well known or much talked about: *I collect the autographs of celebrities. noun, plural* **ce·leb·ri·ties.**

cel·er·y (sel′ər ē), a vegetable with long, crisp stalks which are sometimes covered as they grow to whiten them. Celery is eaten raw or cooked. *noun.*

ce·les·tial (sə les′chəl), of the sky; having something to do with the sky: *The sun, moon, planets, and stars are celestial bodies. adjective.*

cell (sel), **1** a small room in a prison, convent, or monastery. **2** any small, hollow place: *Bees store honey in the cells of a honeycomb.* **3** the extremely small unit of living matter of which all living things are made. Most cells consist of protoplasm, have a nucleus near the center, and are enclosed by a very thin membrane. The body has blood cells, nerve cells, and muscle cells. **4** a device for producing electricity. Some cells are containers holding materials which produce electricity by chemical action. A battery is one or more such cells. Other cells turn sunlight into electricity. *noun.*

cel·lar (sel′ər), an underground room or rooms, usually under a building and often used for storage. *noun.*

cel·lo (chel′ō), a musical instrument like a violin, but very much larger and with a lower tone. It is held between the knees while being played. *noun, plural* **cel·los.**

cello

cel·lo·phane (sel′ə fān), a transparent material somewhat like paper, made from cellulose. It is used as a wrapping to keep things fresh. *noun.*

cel·lu·lose (sel′yə lōs), a substance that forms the walls of plant cells; the woody part of trees and plants. Wood, cotton, flax, and hemp are largely cellulose. Cellulose is used to make paper, rayon, plastics, and explosives. *noun.*

cell wall, the hard outer covering that surrounds every plant cell, made of a substance that is not alive. Animal cells do not have cell walls.

Cel·si·us (sel′sē əs). On the **Celsius thermometer,** 0 degrees is the temperature at which water freezes, and 100 degrees is the temperature at which water boils. *adjective.* [*Celsius* was named for Anders Celsius, who lived from 1701 to 1744. He was a Swedish scientist who invented this thermometer.]

ce·ment (sə ment′), **1** a fine, gray powder made by burning clay and limestone. Cement mixed with water and such materials as sand and gravel becomes hard like stone when it dries. It is used to make concrete for sidewalks, streets, floors, and walls. Cement, sand, and water form mortar used to hold stones and bricks together in the walls of buildings. **2** any soft substance which when it hardens makes things stick together: *rubber cement.* **3** to fasten or repair with cement:

a hat	**i** it	**oi** oil	**ch** child	⎧ a in about
ā age	**ī** ice	**ou** out	**ng** long	⎪ e in taken
ä far	**o** hot	**u** cup	**sh** she	ə = ⎨ i in pencil
e let	**ō** open	**ù** put	**th** thin	⎪ o in lemon
ē equal	**ô** order	**ü** rule	**ŦH** then	⎩ u in circus
ėr term			**zh** measure	

A cracked wall can be cemented. **4** to spread cement over: *to cement a floor.* **1,2** *noun,* **3,4** *verb.*

cem·e·ter·y (sem′ə ter′ē), a place for burying the dead. *noun, plural* **cem·e·ter·ies.**

cen·sor (sen′sər), **1** a person who examines books, motion pictures, and the like in order to find and remove anything thought to be wrong or offensive. **2** to examine books, motion pictures, and the like in order to find and remove anything thought to be wrong or offensive: *Two scenes in the movie had been censored for having too much violence.* **1** *noun,* **2** *verb.*

cen·sure (sen′shər), **1** an expression of unfavorable opinion; criticism: *Censure is sometimes harder to bear than punishment.* **2** to find fault with; criticize: *I was censured by the club for not paying my dues.* **1** *noun,* **2** *verb,* **cen·sures, cen·sured, cen·sur·ing.**

cen·sus (sen′səs), an official count of the people of a country or district. It is taken to find out the number of people, their age, sex, what they do to make a living, and many other facts about them. *noun, plural* **cen·sus·es.**

cent (sent), a coin of the United States and Canada; penny. One hundred cents make one dollar. *noun.*

cen·ten·ni·al (sen ten′ē əl), **1** having to do with the 100th anniversary. **2** a 100th anniversary: *The town is celebrating its centennial.* **1** *adjective,* **2** *noun.*

cen·ter (sen′tər), **1** a point within a circle or sphere equally distant from all points of the circumference or surface. **2** the middle point, place, or part: *the center of a room.* **3** a person, thing, or group that is the central point of attraction: *The Egyptian mummy was the center of the exhibit.* **4** a place to which people or things go for a particular purpose: *The family went skating at the recreation center.* **5** to place in or at a center: *The bowl of fruit was centered on the table.* **6** to collect at a center: *The guests centered around the table.* **7** a player who has a position at the center of a team in football, basketball, hockey, and some other sports. **1-4,7** *noun,* **5,6** *verb.*

cen·ti·grade (sen′tə grād), divided into 100 degrees. On the **centigrade thermometer,** 0 degrees is the temperature at which water freezes, and 100 degrees is the temperature at which water boils. *adjective.*

cen·ti·me·ter or **cen·ti·me·tre** (sen′tə mē′tər), a unit of length equal to 1/100 of a meter. *noun.*

cen·ti·pede (sen′tə pēd′), a flat, wormlike animal with many pairs of legs. Centipedes vary

centipede—1 inch (2½ centimeters) long

in length from an inch or so to nearly a foot. The bite of some centipedes is painful. *noun.*

cen·tral (sen′trəl), **1** of the center; forming the center: *The sun is central in the solar system.* **2** at the center; near the center: *The park is in the central part of the city.* **3** main; chief; principal: *The central library sends books to its branches. adjective.*

Central African Republic, a country in central Africa.

Central America, the part of North America between Mexico and South America.

cen·tral·ly (sen′trə lē), at or near the center: *The business district is centrally located. adverb.*

cen·tur·y (sen′chər ē), **1** each 100 years, counting from some special time, such as the birth of Christ. The first century is 1 through 100; the nineteenth century is 1801 through 1900; the twentieth century is 1901 through 2000. **2** a period of 100 years. From 1824 to 1924 is a century. *noun, plural* **cen·tur·ies.**

ce·ram·ic (sə ram′ik), of pottery or porcelain. *adjective.*

ce·ram·ics (sə ram′iks), the art of making pottery or porcelain. *noun.*

cer·e·al (sir′ē əl), **1** any grass that produces grain which is used as a food. Wheat, rice, corn, oats, and barley are cereals. **2** the grain. **3** a food made from the grain. Oatmeal and cornmeal are cereals. **4** of or having something to do with grain: *cereal crops, cereal products.* 1-3 *noun,* 4 *adjective.*
[*Cereal* comes from a Latin word meaning "of Ceres." She was the Roman goddess of agriculture and the harvest.]

cer·e·mo·ni·al (ser′ə mō′nē əl), **1** of or having something to do with ceremony: *ceremonial costumes.* **2** very formal: *The ambassador receives guests in a ceremonial way. adjective.*

cer·e·mo·ni·ous (ser′ə mō′nē əs), very formal; extremely polite: *a ceremonious bow. adjective.*

cer·e·mo·ny (ser′ə mō′nē), **1** a special act or set of acts to be done on special occasions such as weddings, funerals, graduations, or holidays: *The graduation ceremony was held in the school auditorium.* **2** very polite conduct; way of conducting oneself that follows all the rules of polite social behavior: *Dinner was served with a great deal of ceremony. noun, plural* **cer·e·mo·nies.**

cer·tain (sert′n), **1** sure: *I am certain that these are the facts.* **2** some; particular: *Certain plants will not grow in this country.* **3** settled: *She works a*

certain number of hours each day. **4** known to be true; definite: *I have certain information that school will end a day earlier this year. adjective.*

cer·tain·ly (sert′n lē), without a doubt; surely: *I will certainly be at the party. adverb.*

cer·tain·ty (sert′n tē), **1** freedom from doubt; being certain: *The man's certainty was amusing, for we could all see that he was wrong.* **2** something certain; a sure fact: *The coming of spring and summer is a certainty. noun, plural* **cer·tain·ties.**

cer·tif·i·cate (sər tif′ə kit), a written or printed statement that may be used as proof of some fact. Your birth certificate gives the date and place of your birth and the names of your parents. *noun.*

cer·ti·fy (sèr′tə fī), **1** to declare something true or correct by an official spoken, written, or printed statement: *This diploma certifies that you have completed high school.* **2** to guarantee the quality or value of: *The fire inspector certified the school building as fireproof. verb,* **cer·ti·fies, cer·ti·fied, cer·ti·fy·ing.**

Chad (chad), a country in central Africa. *noun.*

chafe (chāf), to rub so as to make or become sore: *The new collar chafed his neck. verb,* **chafes, chafed, chaf·ing.**

chaff (chaf), **1** the tough outer skin of wheat, oats, or rye. Chaff is separated from grain by threshing. **2** worthless stuff. *noun.*

chain (chān), **1** a row of links joined together: *The dog is fastened to a post by a chain.* **2** a series of things linked together: *a chain of mountains, a chain of restaurants, a chain of events.* **3** to fasten with a chain: *The dog was chained to a post.* **4** anything that binds or restrains: *the chains of duty.* 1,2,4 *noun,* 3 *verb.*

chain store, one of a group of stores owned and operated by the same company.

chair (cher *or* char), **1** a seat that has a back and legs and, sometimes, arms, usually for one person. **2** the position or authority of a person who has a certain rank or dignity: *Professor Smith has the chair of astronomy at this college.* **3** a chairman or chairwoman. *noun.*

chair·man (cher′mən *or* char′mən), **1** a person who is in charge of a meeting. **2** a person at the head of a committee. *noun, plural* **chair·men.**

chair·per·son (cher′pèr′sən *or* char′pèr′sən), **1** a person who is in charge of a meeting. **2** a person at the head of a committee. *noun.*

chair·wom·an (cher′wùm′ən *or* char′wùm′ən), **1** a woman in charge of a meeting. **2** a woman at the head of a committee. *noun, plural* **chair·wom·en.**

chal·ice (chal′is), a cup or goblet. *noun.*

chalice
This **chalice** was used in religious ceremonies more than 1000 years ago.

chalk (chôk), **1** a soft, white mineral used for writing or drawing. Chalk is made up mostly of very small fossil seashells. **2** a white or colored substance like chalk, used for writing or drawing on a blackboard or chalkboard. **3** to mark, write, or draw with chalk. 1,2 *noun,* 3 *verb.*

chalk up, 1 to write down; record: *You learned your lesson the hard way and you can chalk it up to experience.* **2** to score: *The team chalked up 10 points.*

chalk·board (chôk′bôrd′), a smooth, hard surface, used for writing or drawing on with chalk. *noun.*

chalk·y (chô′kē), **1** of chalk; containing chalk. **2** like chalk; white as chalk: *The clown's face was chalky. adjective,* **chalk·i·er, chalk·i·est.**

chal·lenge (chal′ənj), **1** a call or invitation to a game, contest, or fight: *The champions accepted our team's challenge.* **2** to call or invite to a game, contest, or fight: *The knight challenged his rival to fight a duel.* **3** to stop and question a person about an action: *When I tried to enter the building, the guard at the door challenged me.* **4** to doubt; demand proof before one will accept: *The teacher challenged my statement that Montana is a coastal state.* **5** anything that claims or commands effort, interest, or feeling: *Fractions are a real challenge to me.* **6** to claim or command effort, interest, or feeling: *She was challenged by the responsibilities of being governor.* 1,5 *noun,* 2-4,6 *verb,* **chal·leng·es, chal·lenged, chal·leng·ing.**

chal·leng·er (chal′ən jər), a person who challenges another or others. *noun.*

cham·ber (chām′bər), **1** a room, especially a bedroom. **2** a hall where lawmakers meet: *the council chamber.* **3** a group of lawmakers: *The Congress of the United States has two chambers, the Senate and the House of Representatives.* **4** an enclosed space in the body of a living thing, or in some kinds of machinery. The heart has four chambers. The part of a gun that holds the bullet is called the chamber. *noun.*

cham·ber·lain (chām′bər lən), the person who manages the household of a king or great noble. *noun.*

cha·me·le·on (kə mē′lē ən), a small lizard that can change the color of its skin to blend with the surroundings. *noun.*

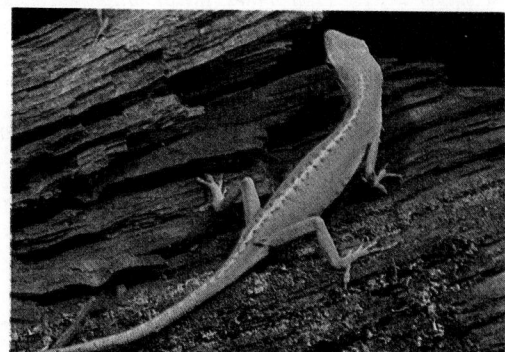
chameleon—up to 1 foot (30 centimeters) long

a hat	i it	oi oil	ch child	⎧ a in about
ā age	ī ice	ou out	ng long	e in taken
ä far	o hot	u cup	sh she	ə = i in pencil
e let	ō open	u̇ put	th thin	o in lemon
ē equal	ô order	ü rule	ŦH then	⎩ u in circus
ėr term			zh measure	

champ (champ), a champion. *noun.*

cham·pi·on (cham′pē ən), a person, animal, or thing that wins first place in a game or contest: *a swimming champion. Her steer was the champion at the county fair last year. noun.*

cham·pi·on·ship (cham′pē ən ship), the position of a champion; first place: *Our school won the championship in baseball. noun.*

chance (chans), **1** a favorable time; opportunity: *I saw a chance to earn some money selling newspapers.* **2** a possibility: *There's a good chance that you will be well enough to return to school next week.* **3** fate, fortune, or luck: *Chance led to the finding of gold in California.* **4** to happen: *I chanced to meet an old friend today.* **5** a risk: *You will be taking a chance if you try to swim that wide river.* **6** to take the risk of: *Don't chance driving in this blizzard.* **7** not expected or planned; accidental: *We had a chance visit from Grandmother last week.* **8** a ticket in a lottery: *She bought two chances on a car at the bazaar.* 1-3,5,8 *noun,* 4,6 *verb,* **chanc·es, chanced, chanc·ing;** 7 *adjective.*

chan·cel·lor (chan′sə lər), a very high official. Chancellor is the title used for a very high official in some governments, courts of law, and universities. *noun.*

chanc·y (chan′sē), uncertain; risky: *a chancy undertaking. adjective,* **chanc·i·er, chanc·i·est.**

chan·de·lier (shan′də lir′), a holder with branches for lights that hangs from the ceiling. *noun.*

chandelier

change (chānj), **1** to make different; become different: *She changed the decoration of the room by painting the walls green.* **2** to put something in place of another; take in place of; exchange: *Can you change a dollar bill for ten dimes?* **3** a passing from one form or place to a different one: *Vacationing in the country is a pleasant change from city life.* **4** something to be used in place of another of the same kind: *a change of sheets.* **5** the money returned to you when you have given a larger amount than the price of what you buy: *I handed the clerk a dollar for the candy bar, and he gave me fifty cents in change.* **6** small coins: *He always carries a pocketful of change.* **7** to put different clothes on: *After swimming we went to the cabin and changed.* 1,2,7 *verb*, **chang·es, changed, chang·ing;** 3-6 *noun.*

change·a·ble (chān′jə bəl), able or likely to change; varying: *changeable weather. adjective.*

chan·nel (chan′l), **1** the deeper part of a waterway: *There is shallow water on both sides of the channel in this river.* **2** the bed of a stream or river: *Rivers cut their own channels to the sea.* **3** a body of water joining two larger bodies of water: *The English Channel lies between the North Sea and the Atlantic Ocean.* **4** a passage for liquids; groove; duct: *Gutters are channels to carry off water.* **5** the means by which something moves or is carried: *The information came through secret channels.* **6** to form a channel in; wear or cut into a channel: *The river had channeled its way through the rocks.* **7** a television station: *If you don't like this program, change to another channel.* **8** a narrow band of frequencies that carries the programs of a television or radio station. 1-5,7,8 *noun*, 6 *verb.*

chant (chant), **1** a song in which several words or syllables are sung on one tone. Chants are sometimes used in religious services. **2** to sing: *to chant a prayer.* **3** a calling or shouting of words again and again. **4** to call over and over again: *The football fans chanted, "Go, team, go!"* 1,3 *noun*, 2,4 *verb.*

cha·os (kā′os), complete disorder; very great confusion: *The tornado left the town in chaos. noun.*

chap[1] (chap), to crack open; make or become rough: *My lips often chap in cold weather. verb,* **chaps, chapped, chap·ping.**

chap[2] (chap), a fellow; man or boy: *He's a nice-looking chap. noun.*

chap·el (chap′əl), **1** a building for worship, not as large as a church. **2** a small place for worship in a larger building: *a hospital chapel. noun.*

chap·e·ron (shap′ə rōn), **1** an older person who is present at a party or other social activity of young people and is responsible for their behavior. **2** to act as a chaperon to. 1 *noun*, 2 *verb*, **chap·e·rons, chap·e·roned, chap·e·ron·ing.**

chap·lain (chap′lən), a member of the clergy serving a special group or place: *a hospital chaplain, a prison chaplain. noun.*

chaps—cowboys wearing **chaps**

chaps (shaps *or* chaps), strong leather trousers without a back, worn over other trousers by cowboys. *noun plural.*

chap·ter (chap′tər), **1** a main division of a book, dealing with a particular part of the story or subject. **2** a local division of an organization, which holds its own meetings; branch of a club. *noun.*

char (chär), **1** to burn to charcoal. **2** to burn enough to blacken; scorch: *After the fire a carpenter replaced the badly charred floor. verb,* **chars, charred, char·ring.**

char·ac·ter (kar′ik tər), **1** all the qualities or features of anything; kind; sort; nature: *The soil on the prairies is of a different character from that in the mountains.* **2** personality. The special way in which you think, feel, and act makes up your character. *She has an honest, dependable character.* **3** moral strength: *Her courage in the face of suffering showed her character.* **4** a person or animal in a play, poem, story, book, or motion picture: *My favorite character in "Charlotte's Web" is Wilbur, the pig.* **5** a person who attracts attention by being different or odd: *Ever since he painted his house plaid, people have thought of him as a real character.* **6** a letter, number, mark, or sign: *There are 52 characters in our alphabet, consisting of 26 small letters and 26 capital letters. noun.*

char·ac·ter·is·tic (kar′ik tə ris′tik), **1** special; distinguishing a certain person or thing from others: *Bananas have their own characteristic smell.* **2** a special quality or feature; whatever distinguishes one person or thing from others: *Cheerfulness is a characteristic that we admire in people. An elephant's trunk is its most noticeable characteristic.* 1 *adjective*, 2 *noun.*

char·ac·ter·ize (kar′ik tə rīz′), **1** to describe the special qualities or features of a person or thing: *The story of "Red Riding Hood" characterizes the wolf as a cunning and savage beast.* **2** to distinguish; make different from others: *A camel is characterized by the humps on its back and its ability to go without water for several days.* verb, **char·ac·ter·iz·es, char·ac·ter·ized, char·ac·ter·iz·ing.**

cha·rades (shə rādz′), a game in which one player acts out a word or phrase and the other players try to guess what it is. *noun singular or plural.*

char·coal (chär′kōl′), a black, brittle mineral made by partly burning wood in a place from which the air is shut out. Charcoal is used for fuel, filters, and drawing. It is a form of carbon. *noun.*

charge (chärj), **1** to ask as a price; put a price of: *The grocer charged 75 cents a dozen for eggs.* **2** a price; expense: *The charge for delivery is $3.* **3** to ask to pay; request payment from: *A doctor charges a patient for treatment.* **4** to put on record as a debt to be paid later: *We charged the table, so its cost will be included in our monthly bill from the department store.* **5** the amount needed to load or fill something; load. A gun is fired by exploding the charge of powder and shot. **6** to put an amount of electricity on or into: *Our car battery ran down and needed to be charged.* **7** an amount of electricity gathered in one place. **8** to give a task or duty to: *My parents charged me with taking care of the baby.* **9** care; management: *Doctors and nurses have charge of sick people.* **10** to accuse; blame: *The driver was charged with speeding.* **11** an accusation: *He admitted the truth of the charge and paid a fine.* **12** to rush at; attack: *The captain gave the order to charge the fort.* **13** an attack: *The charge drove the enemy back.* 1,3,4,6,8,10,12 *verb,* **charg·es, charged, charg·ing;** 2,5,7,9,11,13 *noun.*

in charge, in command; responsible: *The mate is in charge when the captain leaves the ship.*

in charge of, having the care or management of; in command of; responsible for: *My mother is in charge of her company's art department.*

charge account, a record kept at a store of things bought by a person on credit. A customer with a charge account can buy something and use it before paying for it.

charg·er (chär′jər), **1** a horse ridden in war. **2** a device that gives an electrical charge to storage batteries. *noun.*

char·i·ot (char′ē ət), a two-wheeled carriage

chariot—Roman chariot

pulled by horses. The chariot was used in ancient times for fighting and racing. *noun.*

char·i·ta·ble (char′ə tə bəl), **1** generous in giving to poor, sick, or helpless people: *He was a charitable man who used his wealth to help others.* **2** of charity; for charity: *The Salvation Army is a charitable organization.* **3** kindly in judging people and their actions: *Grandparents are usually charitable toward the mistakes of their grandchildren.* *adjective.*

char·i·ty (char′ə tē), **1** a generous giving to the poor, or to organizations which look after the sick, the poor, and the helpless: *The charity of our citizens enabled the hospital to purchase new beds.* **2** a fund or organization for helping the sick, the poor, and the helpless: *She gives money regularly to the Salvation Army and other charities.* **3** kindness in judging people's faults. *noun, plural* **char·i·ties.**

Charles·ton (chärlz′tən), the capital of West Virginia. *noun.*

Char·lotte·town (shär′lət toun), the capital of Prince Edward Island, Canada. *noun.*

charm (chärm), **1** the power of delighting or fascinating: *The child's charm won our hearts.* **2** to please greatly; delight: *They were charmed by the seaside cottage.* **3** a small ornament or trinket worn on a watch chain or bracelet. **4** a word, verse, act, or thing supposed to have magic power to help or harm people. **5** to affect or overcome by the power to please: *She charmed her grandparents into letting her stay with them for another week.* 1,3,4 *noun,* 2,5 *verb.*

charm·ing (chär′ming), very pleasing; delightful; fascinating: *They are a charming couple.* *adjective.*

chart (chärt), **1** a map used by sailors to show the coasts, rocks, and shallow places of the sea. The course of a ship is marked on a chart. **2** an arrangement of information in a form that makes it easy to understand, such as a picture, diagram, or table. **3** to make a map or chart of: *The navigator charted the course of the ship.* 1,2 *noun,* 3 *verb.*

char·ter (chär′tər), **1** an official written statement that grants certain rights to people or a company: *The proposed new airline must obtain a government charter.* **2** to give a charter to: *The government chartered the new airline.* **3** to hire: *Our school chartered a bus to take the class to the zoo.* 1 *noun,* 2,3 *verb.*

chase (chās), **1** to run after to catch or kill: *The cat chased the mouse.* **2** to drive; drive away: *The blue jay chased the squirrel from its nest.* **3** to follow; pursue: *The children chased the ball as it rolled downhill.* **4** the act of running after to catch or kill: *The police caught up with the fleeing robbers after a long chase.* 1-3 *verb,* **chas·es, chased, chas·ing;** 4 *noun.*

chasm (kaz′əm), **1** a deep opening or crack in the earth. **2** a wide difference of feeling or interests between two persons, two groups, or two parties: *The chasm between England and the American colonies grew until it finally resulted in the Revolutionary War. noun.*

chat (chat), **1** easy, friendly talk: *We had a pleasant chat about old times.* **2** to talk in an easy, friendly way: *We sat chatting by the fire after supper.* 1 *noun,* 2 *verb,* **chats, chat·ted, chat·ting.**

chat·ter (chat′ər), **1** to talk constantly and quickly, often about unimportant things: *The children chattered about the circus.* **2** constant, quick talk, often about unimportant things: *The pupils′ chatter disturbed the classroom.* **3** to make quick, indistinct sounds: *Monkeys chatter.* **4** quick, indistinct sounds: *She was awakened at dawn by the chatter of sparrows.* **5** to rattle together: *Cold makes your teeth chatter.* 1,3,5 *verb,* 2,4 *noun.*

chat·ty (chat′ē), fond of easy, friendly talk. *adjective,* **chat·ti·er, chat·ti·est.**

chauf·feur (shō′fər *or* shō fėr′), a person whose work is driving an automobile. *noun.*

cheap (chēp), **1** costing little: *Potatoes are cheap at this time of year.* **2** costing less than it is worth: *My clothes are cheap, because I make them myself.* **3** charging low prices: *I bought the shoes at a very cheap store.* **4** of low value; worth little: *My shoes were so cheap they wore out in a few months.* **5** unwilling to spend money; stingy: *Although he had the money, he was too cheap to replace his worn suit with a new one. adjective.*

cheap·en (chēp′ən), to make cheap; lower the value of. *verb.*

cheap·ly (chēp′lē), at a low price; without spending much money or effort. *adverb.*

cheap·skate (chēp′skāt′), a person who is very stingy. *noun.*

cheat (chēt), **1** to deceive or trick; do business or play in a way that is not honest: *I hate to play games with someone who cheats.* **2** a person who is not honest and does things to deceive and trick others. 1 *verb,* 2 *noun.*

check (chek), **1** to stop suddenly: *The boys checked their steps.* **2** a sudden stop: *The storm warning put a check to our plans for a picnic.* **3** to hold back; control: *to check one′s anger.* **4** a holding back; control: *It is often hard to keep a quick temper in check.* **5** to examine or compare in order to prove true or right: *Check your watch with the school clock.* **6** a proving or proof by comparing: *My work will be a check on yours.* **7** to seek information and advice from; consult: *I checked the dictionary to find out what the word meant.* **8** a mark (√) to show that something has been looked at or compared. Often it shows that the thing looked at was found to be true or right. *I put a check beside the correct answers.* **9** to mark, often with a check: *The teacher checked the correct*

answers in red. **10** a ticket or token given in return for a coat, hat, baggage, or package to show the right to claim again later: *You will need this check to get your suitcase at the Chicago airport.* **11** to leave or take for safekeeping: *We checked our suitcases at the airport.* **12** a written order directing a bank to pay money to the person named: *My parents pay most of their bills by check.* **13** a written statement of the amount owed in a restaurant: *After we finished eating, the waiter brought the check to our table.* **14** a pattern made of squares: *Do you want a check or a stripe for your new shirt?* **15** a single one of these squares: *The checks in this dress are big.* 1,3,5,7,9,11 *verb,* 2,4,6,8,10,12-15 *noun.*

check in, to arrive and register at a hotel, motel, or the like: *When did you check in?*

check out, 1 to pay the bill when leaving: *We checked out of the hotel before noon.* **2** to inspect or examine: *I checked out the apartment before deciding to rent it.* **3** to borrow from a library: *I checked out several books about skiing.*

check·book (chek′bük′), a book of blank checks from a bank. *noun.*

check·er[1] (chek′ər), a cashier in a self-service store or market. *noun.*

check·er[2] (chek′ər), one of the pieces used in the game of checkers. *noun.*

check·er·board (chek′ər bôrd′), a board marked in a pattern of 64 squares of two alternating colors, used in playing checkers or chess. *noun.*

check·ered (chek′ərd), marked in a pattern of squares of different colors: *a checkered tablecloth. adjective.*

check·ers (chek′ərz), a game played by two people, each with 12 flat, round pieces to move on a checkerboard. *noun.*

check·out coun·ter (chek′out′ koun′tər), a counter in a store where a cashier collects payment for purchases.

check·up (chek′up′), **1** a careful examination: *The mechanic gave my car a checkup to prepare it for the winter.* **2** a thorough physical examination: *I went to the doctor for a checkup. noun.*

cheek (chēk), the side of the face below either eye. *noun.*

cheek·bone (chēk′bōn′), the bone just below either eye. *noun.*

cheep (chēp), **1** to make a noise like a young bird; chirp; peep. **2** a young bird′s cry. 1 *verb,* 2 *noun.*

cheer (chir), **1** a shout of encouragement and support or praise: *Give three cheers for the players who won the game.* **2** to show praise and approval by cheers: *We all cheered loudly.* **3** to urge on with cheers: *Everyone cheered our team.* **4** good spirits; hope; gladness: *The warmth of the fire and a good meal brought us cheer.* **5** to give joy to; make glad; comfort: *It cheered me to have my friends visit me while I was sick.* 1,4 *noun,* 2,3,5 *verb.*

cheer up, to be or make glad; raise one′s spirits: *Cheer up, perhaps we′ll win next time.*

cheer·ful (chir′fəl), **1** full of cheer; joyful; glad:

raised for food; hen or rooster. **2** the flesh of a chicken used for food: *fried chicken.* **3** afraid of risk: *She didn't want them to think she was chicken.* 1,2 *noun,* 3 *adjective.*

chick·en pox (chik′ən poks′), a mild disease most often of children that causes a rash on the skin. You can catch chicken pox if you are around someone who has it.

chide (chīd), to find fault with; blame; scold: *She chided the little girl for behaving badly.* *verb,* **chides, chid·ed** or **chid** (chid), **chid·ing.**

chief (chēf), **1** the head of a tribe or group; leader; person highest in rank or authority: *a chief of police.* **2** at the head; leading: *the chief engineer of a building project.* **3** most important; main: *the chief town in the country.* 1 *noun,* 2,3 *adjective.*

chief·ly (chēf′lē), **1** mainly; mostly: *This juice is made chiefly of tomatoes.* **2** first of all; especially: *We visited Washington chiefly to see the Capitol and the White House.* *adverb.*

chief·tain (chēf′tən), the head of a clan or group; leader: *a Scottish chieftain.* *noun.*

Chihuahuas—about 7 inches (18 centimeters) at the shoulder

Chi·hua·hua (chē wä′wä), a very small dog of an old Mexican breed. *noun.*
[Our name for this dog was borrowed from the Mexican Spanish word *Chihuahua,* which came from the name of a state and a city in Mexico. The modern breed was discovered there, where it is thought to have originated more than 500 years ago.]

child (chīld), **1** a young boy or girl. **2** a son or daughter. **3** a baby. *noun, plural* **chil·dren.**

child·hood (chīld′húd), the time during which one is a child. *noun.*

child·ish (chīl′dish), **1** of or like a child: *She spoke in a high, childish voice.* **2** not proper for a grown person; silly: *Crying for things you can't have is childish.* *adjective.*

child·proof (chīld′prüf′), not able to be opened, used, or damaged by a child because of its design: *childproof containers.* *adjective.*

chil·dren (chil′drən), **1** young boys and girls. **2** sons and daughters: *Two of their children are still in school.* *noun plural.*

chil·e (chil′ē). See **chili.** *noun.*

Chil·e (chil′ē), a country in southwestern South America. *noun.*

chil·i (chil′ē), **1** a hot-tasting pod of red pepper, used to flavor food. **2** a highly seasoned dish of chopped meat and often beans, flavored with red peppers. *noun, plural* **chil·ies** for 1. Also spelled **chile.**

chill (chil), **1** an unpleasant coldness: *There's a chill in the air today.* **2** unpleasantly cold: *A chill wind blew across the lake.* **3** to make or become cold: *The icy wind chilled us to the bone. My blood chilled as I read the horror story.* **4** a sudden coldness of the body with shivering: *I had a chill yesterday and still feel ill.* 1,4 *noun,* 2 *adjective,* 3 *verb.*

chill·y (chil′ē), **1** cold; unpleasantly cool: *It is a rainy, chilly day.* **2** cold in manner; unfriendly: *She has been chilly to me since our quarrel.* *adjective,* **chill·i·er, chill·i·est.**

chime (chīm), **1** a set of bells, pipes, or pieces of glass or metal that make a musical sound when struck or moved. **2** the musical sound produced by such an instrument. **3** to ring out musically: *The bells chimed at midnight.* 1,2 *noun,* 3 *verb,* **chimes, chimed, chim·ing.**

chime in, to join in a conversation, especially to express one's agreement: *When my friends and I are talking, my little sister likes to chime in.*

chim·ney (chim′nē), **1** an upright structure of brick or stone, connected with a fireplace or furnace, to make a draft and carry away smoke. **2** a glass tube placed around the flame of a lamp. *noun, plural* **chim·neys.**

chimney sweep, a person whose work is cleaning out chimneys.

chimp (chimp), a chimpanzee. *noun.*

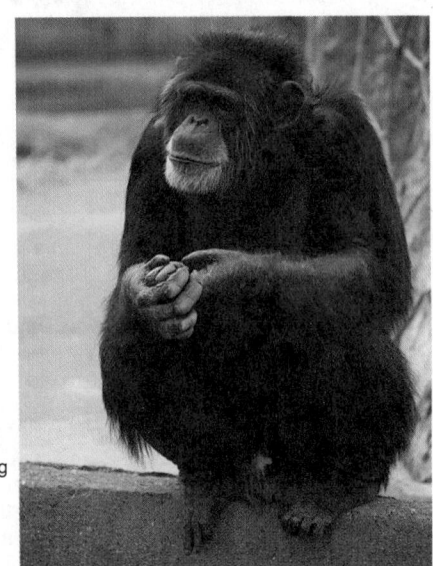
chimpanzee
up to 4½ feet
(1½ meters)
tall when standing

chim·pan·zee (chim′pan zē′ *or* chim pan′zē), an African ape smaller than a gorilla. Chimpanzees are very intelligent. *noun.*
[The chimpanzee was first found in west Africa. Explorers got the word for this animal from the people who lived there.]

chin (chin), **1** the front of the lower jaw below the mouth. **2 chin oneself,** to hang by the hands from an overhead bar and pull up until the chin is even with or above the bar. 1 *noun,* 2 *verb,* **chins, chinned, chin·ning.**

chi·na (chī′nə), **1** a fine, white pottery made of clay baked by a special process, first used in China. Colored designs can be baked into china. **2** dishes, vases, or other things made of china. *noun.*

Chi·na (chī′nə), a large country in eastern Asia. *noun.*

chinchilla—up to 15 inches (38 centimeters) long without the tail

chin·chil·la (chin chil′ə), a small South American animal that looks somewhat like a squirrel. It has very valuable soft, bluish-gray fur. *noun.*

Chi·nese (chī nēz′), **1** of or having something to do with China, its people, or their language. **2** a person born or living in China. **3** the language of China. 1 *adjective,* 2,3 *noun,* plural **Chi·nese** for 2.

Word Source

Chinese is spoken by more people than any other language. Kumquat, sampan, tea, and typhoon are words that have come into English from Chinese.

chink (chingk), a narrow opening; crack: *The chinks in the log cabin let in wind and snow. noun.*

chip (chip), **1** a small, thin piece that has been cut or broken off: *They used chips of wood to light a fire.* **2** a place where a small, thin piece has been cut or broken off: *This plate has a chip on the edge.* **3** to cut or break off in small, thin pieces: *I chipped off the old paint. These cups chip if they are not handled carefully.* **4** a small, thin piece of food or candy: *potato chips, chocolate chips.* **5** a small, thin piece that holds a very complicated set of tiny electronic devices. Chips are usually made of silicon. They are used in computers, video games, televisions, and other electronic machines. A chip can control thousands of electric signals in a space smaller than your fingernail. 1,2,4,5 *noun,* 3 *verb,* **chips, chipped, chip·ping.**
chip in, to join with others in giving money or help: *We all chipped in to buy our teacher a gift.*
chip·munk (chip′mungk), a small, striped North

American animal somewhat like a squirrel. It lives in a burrow in the ground. *noun.*

chirp (chėrp), **1** the short, sharp sound made by some small birds and insects: *the chirp of a sparrow.* **2** to make a chirp: *The crickets chirped outside the house.* 1 *noun,* 2 *verb.*

chis·el (chiz′əl), **1** a tool with a sharp edge at the end of a strong blade. Chisels are used for cutting and shaping wood, stone, or metal. **2** to cut or shape with a chisel: *The sculptor was at work chiseling a statue.* 1 *noun,* 2 *verb.*

chiv·al·ry (shiv′əl rē), the qualities of an ideal knight in the Middle Ages; skill in fighting with arms, bravery, honor, protection of the weak, respect for women, and fairness to an enemy. *noun.*

chives (chīvz), the long, slender leaves of a plant related to the onion, used as seasoning. *noun plural.*

chlo·rine (klôr′ēn′), a greenish-yellow, bad-smelling, poisonous gas. Chlorine is very irritating to the nose and throat. It is a chemical element, used in bleach and disinfectants. *noun.*

chlo·ro·phyll (klôr′ə fil), the substance in green plants that gives them their color. Plants use chlorophyll and light to make sugar from water and carbon dioxide. *noun.*

choc·o·late (chôk′lit *or* chôk′ə lit), **1** a substance made by roasting and grinding cacao seeds. It has a strong, rich flavor and much value as food. **2** a drink made of chocolate with hot milk or water and sugar. **3** a candy made of chocolate. **4** made of or flavored with chocolate: *chocolate cake.* **5** dark-brown. 1-3 *noun,* 4,5 *adjective.*
[The name for the drink was borrowed from a Mexican Spanish word. Spanish settlers got it from the American Indian name for the food.]

chip (definition 5)

choice (chois), **1** the act of choosing; selection: *She was careful in her choice of friends.* **2** the power or chance to choose: *I have my choice between a radio and a camera for my birthday.* **3** a person or thing chosen: *This camera is my choice.*

4 a quantity and variety to choose from: *We found a wide choice of vegetables in the market.*
5 excellent; of fine quality: *The choicest fruit had the highest price.* 1-4 *noun,* 5 *adjective,* **choic·er, choic·est.**

choir (kwīr), a group of singers who sing together, often in a church service. *noun.*

choke (chōk), **1** to stop the breath of an animal or person by squeezing or blocking the throat: *The smoke from the burning building almost choked the firefighters.* **2** to be unable to breathe: *I choked when a piece of meat stuck in my throat.* **3** to kill or injure a plant by depriving it of air and light or of room to grow: *Weeds choked the flowers.* **4** to fill up or block: *Sand is choking the river.* *verb,* **chokes, choked, chok·ing.**
choke back, to hold back, control, or suppress: *I choked back a sharp reply.*

chol·er·a (kol′ər ə), a painful disease of the stomach and intestines that causes cramps and vomiting. *noun.*

cho·les·te·rol (kə les′tə rol′), a white, fatty substance found in the blood and tissues of the body. Foods such as eggs and meat contain cholesterol. *noun.*

chomp (chomp), to bite and chew noisily: *The horse chomped the carrots.* *verb.*

choose (chüz), **1** to pick out; select from a group: *Choose a book. She chose wisely.* **2** to prefer and decide; think fit: *I did not choose to go out in the rain today.* *verb,* **choos·es, chose, cho·sen, choos·ing.**

choos·y (chü′zē), hard to please; fussy: *They are so choosy about their food that they seldom eat out.* *adjective,* **choos·i·er, choos·i·est.**

chop[1] (chop), **1** to cut by hitting with something sharp: *You can chop wood with an ax. I chopped down the dead tree.* **2** to cut into small pieces: *to chop up cabbage.* **3** a cutting blow or stroke: *He split the log with one chop of his ax.* **4** a slice of meat, especially of lamb, veal, or pork that usually contains a piece of bone. 1,2 *verb,* **chops, chopped, chop·ping;** 3,4 *noun.*

chop[2] (chop), a jaw: *The cat licked the milk off its chops. noun.*

chop·py (chop′ē), **1** jerky: *The speaker made nervous, choppy gestures.* **2** moving in short, irregular, broken waves: *The strong west wind made the water very choppy. adjective,* **chop·pi·er, chop·pi·est.**

chop·sticks (chop′stiks′), a pair of small, slender sticks used to lift food to the mouth. The Chinese, Japanese, and other Asians use chopsticks. *noun plural.*

chord (kôrd), a combination of two or more notes of music sounded at the same time. *noun.*

chore (chôr), **1** a small task or easy job, usually done regularly: *Feeding my pets is my daily chore.* **2** a difficult or disagreeable thing to do: *Painting the house is a real chore. noun.*

cho·re·og·ra·pher (kôr′ē og′rə fər), a person who plans, creates, or directs dances in a ballet, motion picture, or musical play. *noun.*

chor·tle (chôr′tl), **1** to chuckle or snort with glee: *He chortled at the joke.* **2** a gleeful chuckle or snort. 1 *verb,* **chor·tles, chor·tled, chor·tling;** 2 *noun.*
[This word was formed by joining parts of the words *chuckle* and *snort. Chortle* was originally made up by Lewis Carroll, the English author of *Alice in Wonderland,* who lived from 1832 to 1898.]

cho·rus (kôr′əs), **1** a group of singers who sing together, such as a choir: *Our school chorus gave a concert at the town hall.* **2** the repeated part of a song coming after each verse: *Everybody knew the chorus by heart.* **3** to sing or speak all at the same time: *When asked if they wanted to play, the children chorused, "Yes!"* **4** a group of singers and dancers. 1,2,4 *noun, plural* **cho·rus·es;** 3 *verb.*

chose (chōz). See **choose.** *She chose the red dress. verb.*

cho·sen (chō′zn), **1** See **choose.** *Have you chosen a book from the library?* **2** picked out; selected from a group: *Six chosen scouts marched in front of the parade.* 1 *verb,* 2 *adjective.*

chow (chou), food: *I'd rather eat at the place where we get the best chow. noun.*

chow·der (chou′dər), a thick soup usually made of clams or fish with potatoes and other vegetables. *noun.*

Christ (krīst), Jesus, the founder of the Christian religion. *noun.*

chris·ten (kris′n), **1** to give a first name to a person at baptism: *The child was christened Maria.* **2** to give a name to: *The new ship was christened before it was launched.* **3** to baptize as a Christian. *verb.*

chris·ten·ing (kris′n ing), baptism; act or ceremony of baptizing and naming. *noun.*

Chris·tian (kris′chən), **1** a person who believes in Christ and follows His teachings. **2** believing in or belonging to the religion of Christ: *the Christian church, Christian countries.* **3** showing a gentle, humble, helpful spirit: *Christian kindness.* **4** of Christ, His teachings, or His followers: *the Christian faith.* 1 *noun,* 2-4 *adjective.*

Chris·ti·an·i·ty (kris′chē an′ə tē), the religion based on the teachings of Christ as they appear in the Bible. *noun.*

Christ·mas (kris′məs), the yearly celebration of the birth of Christ; December 25. *noun, plural* **Christ·mas·es.**

Christ·mas·time (kris′məs tīm′), the Christmas season: *We visit my grandparents at Christmastime. noun.*

Christmas tree, a real or artificial evergreen tree hung with decorations at Christmastime.

chrome (krōm), chromium. *noun.*

chro·mi·um (krō′mē əm), a grayish, hard, brittle metal that does not rust easily. Chromium is a chemical element. It is used mixed with other metals and is also used widely to make a shiny, silvery coating on parts of automobiles, toasters, and other things. *noun.*

chro·mo·some (krō′mə sōm), one of the many

rod-shaped objects in the nucleus of a cell that become visible when the cell divides. Chromosomes pass from a living thing to its offspring, and they control the characteristics of each living thing. *noun.*

chron·ic (kron′ik), lasting a long time: *He suffered for twenty years from chronic heart disease. adjective.*

chron·i·cle (kron′ə kəl), a record of happenings in the order in which they happened; history; story: *Columbus kept a chronicle of his voyages. noun.*

chro·nom·e·ter (krə nom′ə tər), a clock or watch that keeps very accurate time. *noun.*

chrys·a·lis (kris′ə lis), **1** a stage in the development of a butterfly from a caterpillar. The caterpillar sheds its skin and develops a hard shell around itself. During the time inside the shell, the caterpillar changes into a butterfly. **2** the shell in which this occurs. *noun, plural* **chrys·a·lis·es.**

a hat	**i** it	**oi** oil	**ch** child	a in about
ā age	**ī** ice	**ou** out	**ng** long	e in taken
ä far	**o** hot	**u** cup	**sh** she	ə = i in pencil
e let	**ō** open	**u̇** put	**th** thin	o in lemon
ē equal	**ô** order	**ü** rule	**ᴛʜ** then	u in circus
ėr term			**zh** measure	

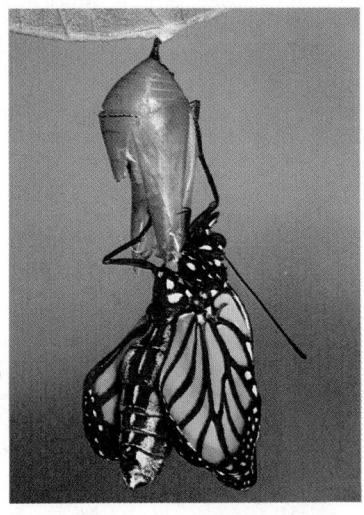

chrysalis (definition 2) a monarch butterfly emerging from its **chrysalis**

chry·san·the·mum (krə san′thə məm), a round flower with many petals, which blossoms in the fall. *noun.*

chub·by (chub′ē), round and plump: *The baby had chubby cheeks. adjective,* **chub·bi·er, chub·bi·est.**

chuck (chuk), **1** to give a slight tap; pat: *He chucked the baby under the chin.* **2** a slight tap: *He gave the baby a chuck under the chin.* **3** to throw or toss: *She chucked the stones into the pond.* **4** a throw or toss. *1,3 verb, 2,4 noun.*

chuck·le (chuk′əl), **1** to laugh softly or quietly: *She chuckled to herself.* **2** a soft laugh; quiet laughter. *1 verb,* **chuck·les, chuck·led, chuck·ling;** *2 noun.*

chuck wag·on (chuk′ wag′ən), (in the western United States) a wagon or truck that carries food and cooking equipment for cowhands or harvest workers.

chug (chug), **1** a short, loud burst of sound: *We heard the chug of a steam engine.* **2** to make such sounds. *1 noun, 2 verb,* **chugs, chugged, chug·ging.**

chum (chum), **1** a very close friend. **2** to be on very friendly terms: *They chummed around together in school.* *1 noun, 2 verb,* **chums, chummed, chum·ming.**

chum·my (chum′ē), like a chum; very friendly: *I like my cousin, but we're not really chummy. adjective,* **chum·mi·er, chum·mi·est.**

chunk (chungk), a thick piece or lump: *I ate two large chunks of candy. noun.*

chunk·y (chung′kē), short and thick or stout: *The child had a chunky build. adjective,* **chunk·i·er, chunk·i·est.**

church (chėrch), **1** a building for public Christian worship: *The church was full on Sunday morning.* **2** public worship of God in a church: *Don't be late for church.* **3** Usually, **Church.** a group of Christians with the same beliefs and under the same authority: *the Methodist Church, the Roman Catholic Church. noun, plural* **church·es.**
[*Church* comes from a Greek word meaning "the Lord's." It was shortened from two Greek words meaning "the Lord's house."]

church·yard (chėrch′yärd′), the ground around a church. Part of a churchyard is sometimes used as a burial ground. *noun.*

churn (chėrn), **1** a container or machine in which butter is made from cream by beating and shaking. **2** to beat and shake cream in a churn. **3** to move as if beaten and shaken: *The water churns in the rapids.* *1 noun, 2,3 verb.*

churn (definition 1)

chute (shüt), a steep slide or passageway down. There are chutes for carrying mail, soiled clothes, and coal to a lower level. A toboggan slide is called a chute. *noun.*

ci·der (sī′dər), the juice pressed out of apples, used as a drink and in making vinegar. *noun.*

ci·gar (sə gär′), a tight roll of tobacco leaves for smoking. *noun.*

cig·a·rette (sig′ə ret′), a small roll of finely cut tobacco enclosed in a thin sheet of paper for smoking. *noun.*

cil·i·a (sil′ē ə), the very small, hairlike parts growing from certain cells. Cilia in the nose, throat, and lungs help move mucus, dust, and germs away from the lungs. Some microscopic animals use cilia to move themselves. *noun plural of* **cil·i·um** (sil′ē əm).

cinch (sinch), **1** a strong strap for fastening a saddle or pack on a horse. **2** to fasten on with a cinch; bind firmly. **3** something sure and easy: *It's a cinch to ride a bike once you know how.* **1,3** *noun, plural* **cinch·es; 2** *verb.*

cin·der (sin′dər), **1** a piece of wood or coal partly burned and no longer flaming. **2 cinders,** burned-up wood or coal; ashes: *I removed the cinders from the fireplace. noun.*

cin·e·ma (sin′ə mə), **1** a motion picture. **2** a motion-picture theatre. *noun.*

cin·na·mon (sin′ə mən), **1** a spice made from the inner bark of a tropical tree. **2** light reddish-brown: *a cinnamon bear.* **1** *noun,* **2** *adjective.*

cir·cle (sėr′kəl), **1** a round line. Every point on a circle is the same distance from the center. **2** a figure bounded by such a line. **3** anything shaped like a circle; ring: *We sat in a circle around the teacher.* **4** to go around in a circle: *The plane circled until the fog lifted and it was able to land.* **5** to form or make a circle around; encircle: *A ring of trees circled the clearing. I circled the wrong answer.* **6** a group of people held together by the same interests: *a circle of friends.* **1-3,6** *noun,* **4,5** *verb,* **cir·cles, cir·cled, cir·cling.**

cir·cuit (sėr′kit), **1** a going around; a moving around: *The earth takes a year to make its circuit of the sun.* **2** the route over which a person or group makes repeated journeys at certain times: *Some judges make a circuit, stopping at certain towns along the way to hold court.* **3** the path over which an electric current flows. *noun.*

circuit breaker, a switch that automatically breaks an electric circuit when the current gets too strong.

cir·cu·lar (sėr′kyə lər), **1** round like a circle: *The full moon has a circular shape.* **2** moving in a circle: *The hands of a clock follow a circular path.* **3** a letter, notice, or advertisement sent to each of a number of people. **1,2** *adjective,* **3** *noun.*

cir·cu·late (sėr′kyə lāt), **1** to go around or to send around: *Water circulates in the pipes of a building. Money circulates as it goes from person to person.* **2** to flow from the heart through the arteries and veins back to the heart: *Blood circulates. verb,* **cir·cu·lates, cir·cu·lat·ed, cir·cu·lat·ing.**

cir·cu·la·tion (sėr′kyə lā′shən), **1** a going around; circulating: *Open windows increase the circulation of air in a room.* **2** the flow of the blood from the heart through the arteries and veins and back to the heart. **3** a sending around of books, papers, or news from person to person or place to place. *noun.*

cir·cu·la·to·ry (sėr′kyə lə tôr′ē), having something to do with circulation. The **circulatory system** of the human body includes the heart and the blood vessels. It moves blood through the body. *adjective.*

cir·cum·fer·ence (sər kum′fər əns), **1** the boundary line of a circle. Every point on the circumference of a circle is the same distance from the center. **2** the distance around a circle: *The circumference of the earth at the equator is almost 25,000 miles. noun.*

cir·cum·nav·i·gate (sėr′kəm nav′ə gāt), to sail around: *Magellan's ship circumnavigated the earth completely. verb,* **cir·cum·nav·i·gates, cir·cum·nav·i·gat·ed, cir·cum·nav·i·gat·ing.**

cir·cum·stance (sėr′kəm stans), **1** a condition that accompanies an act or event: *What were the circumstances that made you change your mind?* **2** a fact or event: *It was a lucky circumstance that she found her money.* **3 circumstances,** financial condition: *A rich person is in good circumstances; a poor person is in bad circumstances. noun.*

cir·cus (sėr′kəs), a traveling show of acrobats, clowns, horses, riders, and wild animals. The performers who give the show and the show that they give are both called the circus. *noun, plural* **cir·cus·es.**

cir·rus cloud (sir′əs), a cloud formation made up of thin, featherlike white clouds of ice crystals formed very high in the air.

cirrus cloud

cit·a·del (sit′ə del), **1** a fortress overlooking a city. **2** a strongly fortified place; stronghold. *noun.*

ci·ta·tion (sī tā′shən), **1** honorable mention for bravery in war: *The soldier received a citation from the President.* **2** a quotation. *noun.*

cite (sīt), **1** to quote, especially to quote as an authority: *She cited the United States Constitution to prove her statement.* **2** to refer to; mention; bring up as an example: *Can you cite another case like this one? verb,* **cites, cit·ed, cit·ing.**

cit·i·zen (sit′ə zən), **1** a person who by birth or

choice is a member of a nation. A citizen owes loyalty to that nation and is given certain rights by it. *Many immigrants have become citizens of the United States.* **2** an inhabitant of a city or town. *noun.*

cit·i·zen·ry (sit/ə zən rē), citizens as a group. *noun.*

cit·i·zen·ship (sit/ə zən ship), the duties, rights, and privileges of a citizen. *noun.*

cit·rus (sit/rəs), any tree bearing lemons, limes, oranges, grapefruit, or similar fruits. *noun, plural* **cit·rus·es.**

cit·y (sit/ē), **1** a large, important center of population and business activity. New York, Buenos Aires, London, Cairo, and Shanghai are major world cities. **2** the people living in a city: *The city was alarmed by the great fire.* **3** of the city; in the city: *He loved the city lights.* **1,2** *noun, plural* **cit·ies; 3** *adjective.*

civ·ic (siv/ik), **1** of a city: *She is interested in civic affairs and will be a candidate for mayor.* **2** of citizens or citizenship. A person's civic duties include such things as obeying the laws, voting, and paying taxes. *adjective.*

civ·ics (siv/iks), the study of the duties, rights, and privileges of citizens. *noun.*

civ·il (siv/əl), **1** of a citizen or citizens; having something to do with citizens: *Voting and paying taxes are civil duties.* **2** not connected with the military, the navy, or the church: *The accused soldier was tried in a civil rather than in a military court. The bride and groom had both a civil and a religious marriage ceremony.* **3** polite; courteous: *It was hard for me to give a civil answer to their rude question. adjective.*

ci·vil·ian (sə vil/yən), **1** a person who is not a member of any of the armed forces. **2** of civilians; not military or naval: *Soldiers on leave usually wear civilian clothes.* **1** *noun,* **2** *adjective.*

civ·i·li·za·tion (siv/ə lə zā/shən), **1** civilized condition. **2** the ways of living of a people or nation: *There are differences between Chinese civilization and that of the United States. noun.*

civ·i·lize (siv/ə līz), to change from a primitive way of life. Civilized people usually have a written language and an advanced knowledge of agriculture, the sciences, and the arts. *verb,* **civ·i·liz·es, civ·i·lized, civ·i·liz·ing.**

civ·i·lized (siv/ə līzd), **1** advanced in social customs, art, and science: *The ancient Greeks were a civilized people.* **2** well-bred; showing culture and good manners: *civilized behavior, a civilized attitude toward one's neighbors. adjective.*

civil rights, the rights of every citizen of the United States, of whatever race, color, religion, or sex.

civil service, the branch of government service concerned with affairs not military, naval, legislative, or judicial. It includes all civilian government workers who are appointed rather than elected. Forest rangers and postal service employees belong to the United States civil service.

a hat	i it	oi oil	ch child		a in about
ā age	ī ice	ou out	ng long		e in taken
ä far	o hot	u cup	sh she	ə =	i in pencil
e let	ō open	ů put	th thin		o in lemon
ē equal	ô order	ü rule	₮H then		u in circus
ėr term			zh measure		

civil war, 1 a war between opposing groups of citizens of one nation. **2 Civil War,** the war between the northern and southern states of the United States from 1861 to 1865.

clack (klak), **1** to make a short, sharp sound: *The train clacked over the rails.* **2** a short, sharp sound: *We could hear the clack of typewriters in the office next to us.* **1** *verb,* **2** *noun.*

clad (klad), clothed. See **clothe.** *He was clad all in green. verb.*

claim (klām), **1** to demand as one's own or one's right: *The settlers claimed the land as theirs. Does anyone claim this pencil?* **2** a demand as one's own or one's right: *Both drivers filed claims for repairs to their cars after the accident.* **3** a right or title to something: *She has a legal claim to the property. There are too many claims on my time.* **4** a piece of land which someone claims: *The miner worked his claim, but found little gold.* **5** to require; call for; deserve: *This homework claims all of my attention.* **6** to declare as a fact; say strongly: *She claimed that her answer was correct.* **7** a declaration of something as true: *Careful study showed that the claims that the vaccine would prevent polio were correct.* **1,5,6** *verb,* **2-4,7** *noun.*

clam (klam), **1** a shellfish with a soft body and a shell in two hinged halves. Clams burrow in sand along the seashore, or at the edges of rivers and lakes. Many kinds are good to eat. **2** to go out after clams; dig for clams. **1** *noun,* **2** *verb,* **clams, clammed, clam·ming.**

clam·bake (klam/bāk/), a picnic where clams are baked or steamed. *noun.*

clam·ber (klam/bər), to climb, using both hands and feet; scramble: *We clambered up the cliff. verb.*

clam·my (klam/ē), cold and damp: *The walls of the cellar were clammy. adjective,* **clam·mi·er, clam·mi·est.**

clam·or (klam/ər), **1** a loud noise, especially of voices; continuous uproar: *The clamor of the crowd filled the air.* **2** to make a loud noise or continuous uproar. **3** a noisy demand: *the clamor for better housing.* **4** to demand or ask for noisily: *The children were clamoring for candy.* **1,3** *noun,* **2,4** *verb.*

clamp (klamp), **1** a device for holding things tightly together: *I used a clamp to hold the arm on the chair until the glue dried.* **2** to fasten together with a clamp; fix in a clamp; strengthen with clamps: *A picture frame must be clamped together while the glue is drying.* **1** *noun,* **2** *verb.*

clamp down, to become more strict: *The police clamped down on speeders.*

clan (klan), a group of related families that claim

to be descended from a common ancestor. *noun.*

clang (klang), **1** a loud, harsh, ringing sound like metal being hit: *The clang of the fire bell aroused the town.* **2** to make or cause to make a loud, harsh, ringing sound: *The fire bell clanged. I clanged the dinner bell.* 1 *noun,* 2 *verb.*

clank (klangk), **1** a sharp, harsh sound like the rattle of a heavy chain: *The clank of heavy machinery filled the factory.* **2** to make or cause to make a sharp, harsh sound: *The steel door clanked shut.* 1 *noun,* 2 *verb.*

clap (klap), **1** to strike together loudly: *clap one's hands.* **2** to applaud by striking the hands together: *When the show was over, we all clapped.* **3** a sudden noise, such as a single burst of thunder, the sound of the hands struck together, or the sound of a loud slap. **4** to slap lightly, but without anger: *My friend clapped me on the back.* **5** a light slap, not given in anger: *a clap on the shoulder.* 1,2,4 *verb,* **claps, clapped, clap·ping;** 3,5 *noun.*

clap·per (klap/ər), the movable part inside a bell that strikes against and rings the outer part. *noun.*

clar·i·fy (klar/ə fī), to make clearer; explain: *The teacher's explanation clarified the difficult instructions. verb,* **clar·i·fies, clar·i·fied, clar·i·fy·ing.**

clar·i·net (klar/ə net/), a wooden wind instrument played by means of holes and keys. *noun.*

clarinet

clar·i·ty (klar/ə tē), clearness: *He expresses his ideas with great clarity. noun.*

clash (klash), **1** a loud, harsh sound like that of two things running into each other, of striking metal, or of bells rung together but not in tune: *As the band approached, we heard the clash of cymbals.* **2** to make or cause to make a loud, harsh sound: *The metal gate clashed shut.* **3** a strong disagreement; a conflict: *There were many clashes of opinion between the opposing candidates.* **4** to disagree strongly; come into conflict: *The children clashed over whose turn it was. Your red shirt and purple pants clash with each other.* 1,3 *noun, plural* **clash·es;** 2,4 *verb.*

clasp (klasp), **1** a thing to fasten two parts or pieces together. A buckle on a belt is one kind of clasp. **2** to fasten together with a clasp. **3** to hold closely with the arms; embrace: *She clasped the kitten tenderly.* **4** a close hold with the arms: *The dog escaped from the clasp of the bear.* **5** to grip firmly with the hand; grasp: *I clasped the railing as I climbed the stairs.* **6** a firm grip with the hand: *He gave my hand a warm clasp.* 1,4,6 *noun,* 2,3,5 *verb.*

class (klas), **1** a group of persons or things alike in some way; kind; sort: *Pet owners make up a large class of people in this country.* **2** a group of pupils taught together: *The art class meets in room 202.* **3** a meeting of such a group: *She was absent and missed a great many classes.* **4** a group of pupils entering a school together and graduating in the same year: *The class of 1982 graduated in 1982.* **5** a rank of society: *the upper class, the middle class, the lower class.* **6** to put in a class; classify: *She is classed among the best swimmers in the school.* **7** grade or quality: *The travel guide described hotels of various classes.* 1-5,7 *noun, plural* **class·es;** 6 *verb.*

clas·sic (klas/ik), **1** an author or an artist of great excellence: *Shakespeare is a classic.* **2** a fine book or painting produced by such a person: *"Alice in Wonderland" is a classic.* **3** of the highest rank or quality; excellent: *"Lassie Come-Home" is a classic children's story.* **4 the classics,** the literature of ancient Greece and Rome. 1,2,4 *noun,* 3 *adjective.*

clas·si·cal (klas/ə kəl), **1** of or having to do with the literature, art, and life of ancient Greece and Rome: *Classical languages include ancient Greek and the Latin of the ancient Romans.* **2** excellent; first-class: *Shakespeare is one of the classical authors of the English language.* **3** of high musical quality. Symphonies, concertos, and operas are considered classical music. *adjective.*

clas·si·fi·ca·tion (klas/ə fə kā/shən), arrangement in classes or groups; grouping according to some system: *The classification of books in a library helps you to find the books you want. noun.*

clas·si·fy (klas/ə fī), to arrange in groups or classes: *In the post office mail is classified according to the places where it is to go. verb,* **clas·si·fies, clas·si·fied, clas·si·fy·ing.**

class·mate (klas/māt/), a member of the same class in school. *noun.*

class·room (klas/rüm/), a room in which classes are held; schoolroom. *noun.*

clat·ter (klat/ər), **1** a confused noise like that of many plates being struck together: *The clatter in the school cafeteria made it hard to hear one another talk.* **2** to move or fall with confused noise; make a confused noise: *The horse's hoofs clattered over the stones.* 1 *noun,* 2 *verb.*

clause (klôz), **1** a part of a sentence having a subject and a verb. In the sentence "They came before we left," both "They came" and "before we left" are clauses. **2** a single paragraph or division of a contract, deed, will, or any other written agreement: *There is a clause in our lease that says we may not keep a dog in this building.* *noun.*

claw (klô), **1** a sharp, hooked nail on a bird's or animal's foot. **2** the pincers of a lobster or crab. **3** anything like a claw. The part of a hammer used for pulling nails is the claw. **4** to scratch, tear, seize, or pull with claws or hands: *The kitten was clawing the screen door.* 1-3 *noun,* 4 *verb.*

clay (klā), a sticky kind of earth that can be easily shaped when wet and hardens when it is dried or baked. Bricks and dishes are made from various kinds of clay. *noun.*

clean (klēn), **1** free from dirt or filth; not soiled or stained: *clean clothes. Soap and water make us clean.* **2** innocent; without guilt; free from wrong: *He served in politics for many years and had a clean record.* **3** having habits that keep one free of dirt: *Cats are clean animals.* **4** to make something free from dirt or filth: *I'm going to clean the house today.* **5** even or regular: *a clean cut with no ragged edges, the clean features of a handsome face.* **6** complete; entire; total: *After he lost his job, he made a clean break with the friends he had at work.* **7** completely; entirely; totally: *The horse jumped clean over the brook.* 1-3,5,6 *adjective,* 4 *verb,* 7 *adverb.*

clean up, to make clean by removing dirt, rubbish or clutter: *Let's clean up this room before we go.*

clean·er (klē′nər), **1** a person whose work is keeping buildings, windows, or other objects clean. **2** anything that removes dirt, grease, or stains. *noun.*

clean·li·ness (klen′lē nis), a being clean; cleanness: *Cleanliness is good for health.* *noun.*

clean·ly[1] (klen′lē), clean: *A cat is a cleanly animal.* *adjective,* **clean·li·er, clean·li·est.**

clean·ly[2] (klēn′lē), in a clean manner: *The butcher's knife cut cleanly through the meat.* *adverb.*

cleanse (klenz), to make clean: *to cleanse a wound before bandaging.* *verb,* **cleans·es, cleansed, cleans·ing.**

cleans·er (klen′zər), a substance for cleaning, especially a powder for scrubbing: *Use cleanser to clean the bathtub.* *noun.*

clean·up (klēn′up′), a cleaning up: *The cleanup of the classroom took an hour.* *noun.*

clear (klir), **1** not cloudy, misty, or hazy; bright; light: *A clear sky is free of clouds.* **2** easy to see through; transparent: *I looked through the clear glass.* **3** easily heard, seen, or understood; plain: *The witness gave a clear account of the accident.* **4** to make clean and free; get clear: *After dinner, we cleared the table. She cleared her throat.* **5** to become clear: *It rained and then it cleared.* **6** to pass by or over without touching: *The horse cleared the fence.* **7** free from blame or guilt; innocent: *The man knew nothing of the crime and had a clear conscience.* **8** in a clear manner; completely; entirely: *We could see clear to the*

a hat	**i** it	**oi** oil	**ch** child	a in about
ā age	**ī** ice	**ou** out	**ng** long	e in taken
ä far	**o** hot	**u** cup	**sh** she	ə = { i in pencil
e let	**ō** open	**u̇** put	**th** thin	o in lemon
ē equal	**ô** order	**ü** rule	**ᴛʜ** then	u in circus
ėr term			**zh** measure	

bottom of the lake. 1-3,7 *adjective,* 4-6 *verb,* 8 *adverb.*

clear up, 1 to make or become clear: *Stay indoors until the weather clears up.* **2** to explain: *She cleared up our problem by showing us what we had done wrong.*

clear·ance (klir′əns), **1** the act of clearing: *Clearance of the theater was quick during the fire.* **2** a clear space: *There was only a foot of clearance between the top of the truck and the roof of the tunnel.* *noun.*

clear·ing (klir′ing), an open space of cleared land in a forest. *noun.*

cleat (klēt), **1** a strip of wood or iron fastened across anything for support or for sure footing: *The gangplank had cleats to keep the passengers from slipping.* **2** a piece of metal, wood, stiff leather, or plastic fastened to the sole or heel of a shoe to prevent slipping. *noun.*

cleave (klēv), to cut or split open: *A blow of the whale's tail caused the whaling boat to cleave in two.* *verb,* **cleaves, cleft** or **cleaved** or **clove, cleft** or **cleaved** or **clo·ven, cleav·ing.**

cleav·er (klē′vər), a butcher's tool with a heavy blade and a short handle, used for cutting through meat or bone. *noun.*

cleaver

clef

clef (klef), a sign in music that shows the pitch of the notes on a staff. *noun.*

cleft (kleft), **1** to cut. See **cleave.** *A blow of the ax cleft the log in two.* **2** split; divided: *a cleft stick.* **3** a space or opening made by splitting; crack: *a cleft in the rocks.* 1 *verb,* 2 *adjective,* 3 *noun.*

clem·en·cy (klem/ən sē), **1** mercy: *The judge showed clemency to the prisoner.* **2** mildness: *The clemency of the weather allowed them to live outdoors. noun, plural* **clem·en·cies.**

clench (klench), **1** to close tightly together: *She clenched her teeth and refused to take the medicine. The angry man shook his clenched fist at us.* **2** to grasp firmly: *I clenched the bat and swung at the ball. verb.*

cler·gy (klėr/jē), persons appointed to do religious work, such as ministers, priests, and rabbis. *noun.*

cler·gy·man (klėr/jē mən), a member of the clergy; a minister, priest, or rabbi. *noun, plural* **cler·gy·men.**

cler·i·cal (kler/ə kəl), of a clerk or clerks: *Keeping records and typing letters are clerical jobs in an office. adjective.*

clerk (klėrk), **1** a person employed to sell goods in a store or shop. **2** a person employed in an office to file records or keep accounts. **3** to work as a clerk: *I clerk in a drugstore after school.* **1,2** *noun,* **3** *verb.*

clev·er (klev/ər), **1** bright; intelligent; having a quick mind: *She is the cleverest person in our class.* **2** skillful in doing some particular thing: *My friend is clever at working with wood.* **3** showing skill or intelligence: *The magician did a clever trick. His answer to the riddle was clever. adjective.*

click (klik), **1** a short, sharp sound like that of a key turning in a lock: *I heard a click as the dime went down the coin slot.* **2** to make such a sound: *The key clicked in the lock.* **1** *noun,* **2** *verb.*

cli·ent (klī/ənt), **1** a person for whom a lawyer, accountant, or other professional person acts. **2** a customer. *noun.*

cliff (klif), a very steep slope of rock or clay. *noun.*

cli·mate (klī/mit), **1** the kind of weather a place has. Climate includes conditions of heat and cold, moisture and dryness, clearness and cloudiness, wind and calm. **2** a region with certain conditions of heat and cold, rainfall, wind, or sunlight: *We went to a warmer climate on our winter vacation. noun.*

cli·max (klī/maks), the highest point of interest; the most exciting part: *A visit to the Grand Canyon was the climax of our trip. noun, plural* **cli·max·es.**

climb (klīm), **1** to go up, especially by using the hands or feet, or both: *She climbed the stairs quickly.* **2** to go in any direction, especially with the help of the hands: *to climb over a fence, to climb down a ladder.* **3** to grow upward. A vine climbs by twining about a support of some kind. **4** the act of going up: *Our climb took two hours.* **5** to move upward; rise: *Smoke climbed slowly from the chimney. The price of sugar climbed last year.* **6** a place to be climbed: *The path ended in a difficult climb.* **1-3,5** *verb,* **4,6** *noun.*

clime (klīm), **1** a region. **2** a climate. *noun.*

clinch (klinch), **1** to hammer flat the pointed end of a nail that sticks through a board or plank. **2** to

settle definitely: *A deposit of five dollars clinched the bargain.* **3** to hold on to each other tightly in boxing or wrestling. **4** the act of clinching in boxing or wrestling. **1-3** *verb,* **4** *noun, plural* **clinch·es.**

cling (kling), to stick or hold fast: *A vine clings to its support. Wet clothes cling to the body. Some people cling to old-fashioned ideas. verb,* **clings, clung, cling·ing.**

clin·ic (klin/ik), a place where people can receive medical treatment, sometimes at a reduced cost. A clinic is often connected with a hospital or medical school: *an eye clinic, a dental clinic. noun.* [The word *clinic* comes from a Greek word meaning "a physician who visits patients who are sick in bed."]

clink (klingk), **1** a light, sharp, ringing sound, like that of glasses hitting together. **2** to make such a sound: *The spoon clinked in the glass.* **1** *noun,* **2** *verb.*

clip¹ (klip), **1** to cut; cut short; trim with shears, scissors, or clippers: *A sheep's fleece is clipped off to get wool.* **2** to trim: *The hedge in front of the house needs to be clipped.* **3** to cut out of a newspaper or magazine: *She clipped the cartoon and passed it around the class.* **4** a fast pace or speed: *The bus passed at quite a clip.* **1-3** *verb,* **clips, clipped, clip·ping;** **4** *noun.*

clip² (klip), **1** to hold tight; fasten: *I clipped the papers together.* **2** something used for clipping things together. A paper clip is made of a piece of bent wire. **1** *verb,* **clips, clipped, clip·ping;** **2** *noun.*

clip·board (klip/bôrd/), a board with a heavy clip at one end for holding papers while writing. *noun.*

clip·per (klip/ər), **1** a tool for cutting: *hair clippers, a nail clipper.* **2** a fast sailing ship: *American clippers used to sail all over the world. noun.*

clipper (definition 2)

clip·ping (klip/ing), a piece cut out of a newspaper or magazine. *noun.*

clique (klēk *or* klik), a small, exclusive group of people within a larger group. *noun.*

cloak (klōk), **1** a long, loose piece of clothing for

outdoor wear, usually without sleeves. **2** anything that covers or hides: *They hid their dislike of us behind a cloak of friendship.* **3** to cover up; conceal: *I cloaked my fear by pretending to be unafraid.* **1,2** *noun,* **3** *verb.*

clob·ber (klob'ər), to hit hard or beat severely: *A falling tree limb clobbered me on the head. verb.*

clock (klok), **1** an instrument for measuring and showing time. A clock is not made to be carried about as a watch is. **2** to measure the time or speed of: *I clocked the runners with a stopwatch to see who was the fastest.* **1** *noun,* **2** *verb.*
[*Clock* comes from a Latin word meaning "bell." It was called this because bells were used to mark the hours before the invention of modern clocks.]

clock radio, a radio with a built-in clock that can be set to turn the radio or an alarm on or off.

clock·wise (klok'wīz'), in the direction in which the hands of a clock move; from left to right: *Turn the key clockwise to unlock the door. adverb, adjective.*

clock·work (klok'wèrk'), the machinery of a clock or like that of a clock. Toys that move are often run by clockwork. *noun.*

clod (klod), **1** a lump of earth. **2** a stupid person. *noun.*

clog (klog), **1** to fill up; choke up: *Grease clogged the drain.* **2** to hold back; hinder: *An accident clogged traffic.* **3** a shoe with a thick, wooden sole. **1,2** *verb,* **clogs, clogged, clog·ging; 3** *noun.*

clois·ter (kloi'stər), a covered walk along the wall of a building, with a row of pillars on the open side. A cloister is often built around the courtyard of a monastery, church, or college building. *noun.*

clone (klōn), **1** a living thing produced from one parent, often from a single cell. A clone and its parent are always exactly alike. **2** to produce from a single parent. **1** *noun,* **2** *verb,* **clones, cloned, clon·ing.**

clop (klop), **1** a sharp, hard sound such as that made by a horse's hoof on a paved road. **2** to make such a sound: *The horse clopped down the road.* **1** *noun,* **2** *verb,* **clops, clopped, clop·ping.**

close¹ (klōz), **1** to shut: *Close the door. The sleepy child's eyes are closing.* **2** to bring or come together: *I closed my arms around the dog and picked it up.* **3** to come or bring to an end: *The meeting closed with a speech by the president.* **4** an end: *She spoke at the close of the meeting.* **1-3** *verb,* **clos·es, closed, clos·ing; 4** *noun.*

close² (klōs), **1** with little space between; near together; near: *These two houses are close. That cloth has a close weave.* **2** tight; narrow: *They live in very close quarters.* **3** known very well, or near in relationship: *a close friend, a close relative.* **4** careful; strict: *Pay close attention to what I say.* **5** having little fresh air: *With the windows shut, the room was hot and close.* **6** nearly equal: *The last game was a close contest. adjective,* **clos·er, clos·est.**

close call, a narrow escape: *We had a close call when our car skidded and just missed a truck.*

close·ly (klōs'lē), **1** with little difference; to a

a hat	**i** it	**oi** oil	**ch** child	⌠a in about
ā age	**ī** ice	**ou** out	**ng** long	⎪e in taken
ä far	**o** hot	**u** cup	**sh** she	**ə** = ⎨i in pencil
e let	**ō** open	**ů** put	**th** thin	⎪o in lemon
ē equal	**ô** order	**ü** rule	**ⱦH** then	⌡u in circus
ėr term			**zh** measure	

close degree; greatly: *She closely resembles her sister.* **2** snugly; tightly: *My coat fits closely.* **3** carefully; with strict attention: *Watch closely while I do a magic trick. adverb.*

clos·et (kloz'it), a small room used for storing clothes or household supplies. *noun.*

close-up (klōs'up'), a picture taken with a camera at close range. *noun.*

clos·ing (klō'zing), the word or words that come before the signature at the end of a letter. "Sincerely" and "Yours truly" are closings. *noun.*

clot (klot), **1** a half-solid lump: *A blood clot formed in the cut and stopped the bleeding.* **2** to form into clots: *Blood clots when it is exposed to the air.* **1** *noun,* **2** *verb,* **clots, clot·ted, clot·ting.**

cloth (klôth), **1** a woven or knitted material made from wool, cotton, silk, rayon, or other fiber. Cloth is used for clothing, curtains, bedding, and many other purposes. **2** a piece of cloth used for a special purpose: *I bought a new cloth for the kitchen table. noun, plural* **cloths** (klôⱦHz or klôths).

clothe (klōⱦH), **1** to put clothes on; cover with clothes; dress: *I clothed the child warmly in a heavy sweater and pants.* **2** to provide with clothes: *It takes a lot of money to feed and clothe a large family.* **3** to cover: *The sun clothes the earth with light. verb,* **clothes, clothed** or **clad, cloth·ing.**

clothes (klōz), coverings for the body: *I bought a jacket, jeans, and other clothes. noun plural.*

clothes·line (klōz'līn'), a rope or wire to hang clothes on to dry or air them. *noun.*

clothes·pin (klōz'pin'), a wooden or plastic clip to hold clothes on a line. *noun.*

cloth·ing (klō'ⱦHing), coverings for the body: *This store sells men's clothing. noun.*

cloud (kloud), **1** a white or gray or almost black mass in the sky, made up of tiny drops of water or ice crystals: *Sometimes when it rains, the sky is covered with dark clouds.* **2** a mass of smoke or dust in the air. **3** to cover with a cloud or clouds: *A mist clouded our view.* **4** to grow cloudy: *My eyes clouded with tears.* **5** a great number of things moving close together: *a cloud of insects.* **6** to make dark; become gloomy: *His face clouded with anger.* **1,2,5** *noun,* **3,4,6** *verb.*

cloud·burst (kloud'bèrst'), a sudden, heavy rain. *noun.*

cloud·less (kloud'lis), without a cloud; clear and bright; sunny: *a cloudless sky. adjective.*

cloud·y (klou'dē), **1** covered with clouds; having clouds in it: *a cloudy sky.* **2** not clear: *The stream is cloudy with mud. adjective,* **cloud·i·er, cloud·i·est.**

clout (klout), to hit: *I clouted the ball. verb.*

clove[1] (klōv), a strong, fragrant spice, made from the dried flower buds of a tropical tree. *noun.*

clove[2] (klōv), a small, separate section of a plant bulb. Cloves of garlic are often used to flavor salads and cooked foods. *noun.*

clove[3] (klōv). See **cleave**. *With one blow of the ax I clove the log in two. verb.*

clo·ven (klō′vən), **1** cleft. See **cleave**. **2** split; divided into two parts: *Cows have cloven hoofs.* 1 *verb,* 2 *adjective.*

clo·ver (klō′vər), a plant with leaves made up of three leaflets. It has sweet-smelling red, white, or purple flowers in rounded heads. Clover is grown as food for livestock and to make the soil richer. *noun.*

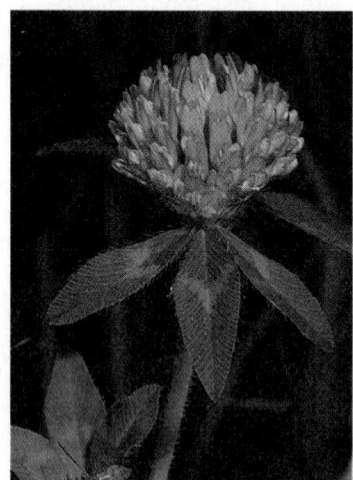

clover

clown (kloun), **1** a performer who makes people laugh by wearing funny costumes and makeup and by playing tricks and jokes: *The clowns in the circus were very funny.* **2** to act like a clown; play tricks and jokes; act silly: *Quit clowning and be serious.* **3** a person who acts like a clown; silly person. 1,3 *noun,* 2 *verb.*

club (klub), **1** a heavy stick of wood, thicker at one end, used as a weapon. **2** a stick or bat used to hit a ball in some games: *golf clubs.* **3** to beat or hit with a club or something similar. **4** a group of people joined together for some special purpose: *My parents belong to a tennis club.* **5** the building or rooms used by a club: *We had dinner at the yacht club.* **6** a figure shaped like this: ♣. **7** a playing card with one or more figures shaped like this. 1,2,4-7 *noun,* 3 *verb,* **clubs, clubbed, club·bing.**

club·house (klub′hous′), **1** a building used by a club. **2** a shack, room, or other place used by children for meetings and play: *The children built a clubhouse out of crates and cardboard boxes. noun, plural* **club·hous·es** (klub′hou′ziz).

cluck (kluk), **1** the sound that a hen makes when calling to her chicks. **2** to make such a sound. 1 *noun,* 2 *verb.*

clue (klü), something which helps to solve a mystery or a problem: *The police could find no fingerprints or other clues to help them in solving the robbery. noun.*

clump (klump), **1** a number of things of the same kind growing or grouped together; cluster: *I hid in a clump of trees.* **2** a lump or mass: *a clump of earth.* **3** to walk in a heavy, clumsy, noisy manner: *The hiker clumped along in heavy boots.* 1,2 *noun,* 3 *verb.*

clum·si·ly (klum′zə lē), in a clumsy manner; awkwardly: *Because of my sore foot I walk clumsily. adverb.*

clum·sy (klum′zē), **1** awkward in moving: *The cast on my broken leg made me clumsy.* **2** not well-shaped or well-made: *Our boat was a clumsy thing made out of scrap wood. adjective,* **clum·si·er, clum·si·est.**

clung (klung). See **cling**. *The child clung to his sister. Mud had clung to my boots. verb.*

clunk (klungk), a dull sound like that of something hard striking the ground; thump. *noun.*

clus·ter (klus′tər), **1** a number of things of the same kind growing or grouped together: *a little cluster of houses in the valley.* **2** to be in a bunch; gather in a group: *The children clustered around their teacher.* 1 *noun,* 2 *verb.*

cluster (definition 1)—**clusters** of grapes

clutch (kluch), **1** to grasp tightly: *I clutched the railing to keep from falling.* **2** a tight grasp: *I kept a clutch on the railing to keep from falling.* **3** to snatch; seize eagerly: *I clutched at a branch as I fell from the tree.* **4** a grasping claw, paw, or hand: *The fish wiggled out of the hungry bear's clutches.* **5** a device in a machine for connecting or disconnecting the engine or motor that makes it go. 1,3 *verb,* 2,4,5 *noun, plural* **clutch·es.**

clut·ter (klut′ər), **1** litter; confusion; disorder: *It was hard to find the lost pen in the clutter of his room.* **2** to litter with things: *Her desk was cluttered with papers and books.* 1 *noun,* 2 *verb.*

cm or **cm.,** centimeter or centimeters.

CO, Colorado (used with postal Zip Code).

coach (kōch), **1** a large, closed carriage with seats inside and often on top. In former times, most coaches carried passengers along a regular run, stopping for meals and fresh horses. **2** a passenger car of a railroad train. **3** a bus. **4** a kind of passenger seating and service on an airplane that is cheaper than traveling first-class. **5** a person who teaches or trains an athlete, a performer, or athletic teams: *a swimming coach.* **6** to train or teach: *She coaches swimmers.* **1-5** *noun, plural* **coach·es; 6** *verb.*

coach·man (kōch′mən), a person who drives a coach or carriage for a living. *noun, plural* **coach·men.**

co·ag·u·late (kō ag′yə lāt), to change from a liquid to a thickened mass; thicken: *Cooking coagulates the whites of eggs. verb,* **co·ag·u·lates, co·ag·u·lat·ed, co·ag·u·lat·ing.**

coal (kōl), **1** a black mineral that is mostly carbon. Coal is formed from partly decayed vegetable matter under great pressure in the earth. It burns and is used as fuel. **2** a piece of burning wood or coal: *The big log had burned down to a few glowing coals. noun.*

coarse (kôrs), **1** not fine; made up of fairly large parts: *coarse sand.* **2** rough: *Burlap is a coarse cloth.* **3** not delicate; crude; vulgar: *She ate noisily and showed other signs of coarse manners. adjective.* **coars·er, coars·est.**

coars·en (kôr′sən), to make or become coarse: *Her skin was coarsened by wind and sun. verb.*

coast (kōst), **1** the land along the sea; seashore: *Many ships were wrecked on that rocky coast.* **2** to slide down a hill or ride without using effort or power: *You can coast downhill on a sled. He shut off the engine and the car coasted into the driveway.* **1** *noun,* **2** *verb.*

coast·al (kō′stl), at the coast; along a coast; near a coast: *The Coast Guard patrols coastal waters. adjective.*

coast·er (kō′stər), **1** a sled to coast on. **2** a small tray or mat placed under a glass or bottle. A coaster protects surfaces of furniture from moisture. *noun.*

coast guard, a group whose work is protecting lives and property and preventing smuggling along the coast of a country.

Coast Guard, the government organization that guards the coasts of the United States. It rescues ships and boats in distress and prevents goods from entering the country illegally.

coast·line (kōst′līn′), the outline of a coast: *From their spacecraft, the astronauts could see the coastline of Africa. noun.*

coat (kōt), **1** a piece of outer clothing with long sleeves: *It is cold enough today for your winter coat. Father wears a coat and tie to work.* **2** any outer covering: *a dog's coat of hair.* **3** a thin layer: *a coat of paint.* **4** to cover with a thin layer: *The floor is coated with varnish. This pill is coated with sugar.* **1-3** *noun,* **4** *verb.*

coat·ing (kō′ting), a layer of any substance spread over a surface: *There was a coating of dust on the furniture. noun.*

coat of arms, a design or pattern, usually on a shield, that in former times was a symbol for a knight or lord. Some families, schools, and other groups now have coats of arms. *plural* **coats of arms.**

coax (kōks), to persuade by soft words; influence

a hat	**i** it	**oi** oil	**ch** child	a in about
ā age	**ī** ice	**ou** out	**ng** long	e in taken
ä far	**o** hot	**u** cup	**sh** she	ə = i in pencil
e let	**ō** open	** u̇** put	**th** thin	o in lemon
ē equal	**ô** order	**ü** rule	**ᴛʜ** then	u in circus
ėr term			**zh** measure	

by pleasant ways: *She coaxed me into letting her use my bike. I coaxed a smile from the baby. verb.*

cob (kob), the part of an ear of corn on which the grains grow; corncob. *noun.*

co·balt (kō′bôlt), a silver-white metal used in making steel or paint. Cobalt is a chemical element. *noun.*

cob·bler[1] (kob′lər), a person whose work is mending or making shoes. *noun.*

cob·bler[2] (kob′lər), a fruit pie baked in a deep dish, usually with a crust only on top. *noun.*

cob·ble·stone (kob′əl stōn′), a rounded stone that was formerly much used in paving. *noun.*

co·bra (kō′brə), a very poisonous snake of Asia and Africa. When excited, a cobra can flatten its neck so that its head seems to have a hood. *noun.*

Word History

cobra *Cobra* comes from a Portuguese phrase meaning "snake with a hood." Later, the phrase was shortened to the single word *cobra,* meaning "snake."

cobra
about 6 feet
(2 meters) long

coat of arms—Each colored shield is the **coat of arms** of a different family.

cob·web (kob′web′), a spider's web, or the stuff it is made of. *noun.*

cock[1] (kok), **1** a male chicken; a rooster. **2** the male of other birds: *a turkey cock.* **3** to pull back the hammer of a gun so that it is ready to fire: *There was a click as the sheriff cocked his revolver.* **1,2** *noun,* **3** *verb.*

cock[2] (kok), to stick up, or tilt to one side: *The puppy cocked its ears at the strange sound. verb.*

cock·a·too (kok′ə tü′), a large parrot of Australia with a crest which it can raise or lower. *noun, plural* **cock·a·toos.**

cockatoo
about 18 inches
(46 centimeters) long

cock·le (kok′əl), **1** a small shellfish that is good to eat. **2** its heart-shaped shell. *noun.*

cock·pit (kok′pit′), **1** the place where the pilot sits in an airplane or spacecraft. **2** the small, open place in a small boat where the pilot or passengers sit. *noun.*

cock·roach (kok′rōch′), a brown insect with a flattened body. It is often found in kitchens and around water pipes. Cockroaches usually come out at night to feed. *noun, plural* **cock·roach·es.**

cock·tail (kok′tāl′), **1** a chilled alcoholic drink made of gin, whiskey, or the like mixed with fruit juice or a flavored wine. **2** shellfish or mixed fruits usually served before a meal: *a shrimp cocktail, fruit cocktail. noun.*

cock·y (kok′ē), too sure of oneself; conceited: *He was a cocky fellow who thought he knew everything. adjective,* **cock·i·er, cock·i·est.**

co·coa (kō′kō), **1** a powder made by roasting, grinding, and removing some of the fat from the seeds of the cacao tree. **2** a drink made from this powder with sugar and milk or water. *noun.*

co·co·nut or **co·coa·nut** (kō′kə nut′), the large, round, brown, hard-shelled fruit of the coconut palm. Coconuts have a white lining that is good to eat and a white liquid called **coconut**

milk. The white lining is cut up into shreds and used for cakes, puddings, and pies. *noun.*

coconut palm, a tall, tropical palm tree on which coconuts grow.

co·coon (kə kün′), the silky case spun by caterpillars to live in while they are turning into adult insects: *In the spring a moth came out of the cocoon the caterpillar had spun. noun.*

cod (kod), a large fish much used for food. It is found in the cold parts of the northern Atlantic Ocean. **Cod-liver oil** is an oil taken from the livers of cod; it is rich in vitamins. *noun, plural* **cod** or **cods.**

cod·dle (kod′l), to treat tenderly; pamper: *They coddled their sick child. verb,* **cod·dles, cod·dled, cod·dling.**

code (kōd), **1** an arrangement of words or figures to keep a message short or secret; system of secret writing: *The army tried to figure out the code that the enemy used to write messages.* **2** to change into a code: *The spy coded a message to headquarters.* **3** a collection of laws or rules: *The building code requires the inspection of electrical wiring.* **4** a system of signals for sending messages. Flags or blinking lights are used to send messages between ships. **5** any set of signals or symbols used with computers or other machines. **1,3-5** *noun,* **2** *verb,* **codes, cod·ed, cod·ing.**

cod·fish (kod′fish′), cod. *noun, plural* **cod·fish** or **cod·fish·es.**

co·erce (kō ėrs′), to compel; force: *The prisoner was coerced into confessing the crime. verb,* **co·erc·es, co·erced, co·erc·ing.**

cof·fee (kô′fē), **1** a dark-brown drink made from the roasted and ground seeds of a tall, tropical shrub. **2** the seeds, called **coffee beans,** from which the drink is made. *noun.*

cof·fee·pot (kô′fē pot′), a container for making or serving coffee. *noun.*

cof·fin (kô′fən), a box into which a dead person is put to be buried. *noun.*

cog (kog), one of a series of teeth on the edge of a gear. *noun.*

cogs on gears

co·ho (kō′hō), a small Pacific salmon that has been brought into freshwater lakes. Coho are good for food. *noun, plural* **co·ho** or **co·hos.**

coil (koil), **1** to wind around and around into a pile, a tube, or a curl: *The snake coiled itself around the branch. The wire spring was evenly coiled.*

coil (definition 2)
a **coil** of rope

a hat	**i** it	**oi** oil	**ch** child		a in about
ā age	**ī** ice	**ou** out	**ng** long		e in taken
ä far	**o** hot	**u** cup	**sh** she	ə =	i in pencil
e let	**ō** open	**u̇** put	**th** thin		o in lemon
ē equal	**ô** order	**ü** rule	**ᴛʜ** then		u in circus
ėr term			**zh** measure		

C

2 anything that is coiled. One wind or turn of a coil is a single coil. 1 *verb*, 2 *noun*.

coin (koin), **1** a piece of metal issued by the government for use as money. Pennies, nickels, dimes, and quarters are coins. **2** to make money by stamping metal: *The mint coins millions of nickels and dimes each year.* **3** to make up; invent: *We often coin new words to name new products. Alfred Nobel coined the word "dynamite."* 1 *noun*, 2,3 *verb*.

coin·age (koi′nij), **1** the making of coins: *The United States mint is in charge of coinage.* **2** coins; metal money. **3** a making up or inventing: *Travel in outer space has led to the coinage of many new words. noun.*

co·in·cide (kō′in sīd′), **1** to occupy the same place in space. If these triangles △△ were placed one on top of the other, they would coincide. **2** to occupy the same time: *The working hours of the two friends coincide.* **3** to be just alike; correspond exactly: *Her answers are correct and coincide with the answers in the book. verb,* **co·in·cides, co·in·cid·ed, co·in·cid·ing.**

co·in·ci·dence (kō in′sə dəns), the happening by chance of two things at the same time or place in such a way as to seem remarkable or planned: *It was just a coincidence that we both went to the same place on vacation. noun.*

coke (kōk), a fuel made from coal that has been heated in an oven from which most of the air has been shut out. Coke burns with much heat and is used in industry to melt metals. *noun.*

co·la (kō′lə), a soft drink flavored with a nut from a tropical tree. *noun.*

cold (kōld), **1** much less warm than the body: *Snow and ice are cold.* **2** less warm than it usually is: *The weather is cold for April.* **3** feeling cold or chilly: *Put on a sweater, or you will be cold.* **4** coldness; being cold: *Warm clothes protect against the cold of winter.* **5** a common sickness that causes a runny nose, a sore throat, coughing, and sneezing. **6** not kind and cheerful; unfriendly: *Since our argument she has been cold to me.* 1-3,6 *adjective*, 4,5 *noun*.

catch cold, to become sick with a cold.

cold-blood·ed (kōld′blud′id), **1** having blood that is about the same temperature as the air or water around the animal. The blood of such animals is colder in winter than in summer. Turtles are cold-blooded; dogs are warm-blooded. **2** lacking in feeling; cruel: *a cold-blooded murderer. adjective.*

cold sore, a blister near or on the mouth, caused by a germ that infects the skin.

cole·slaw (kōl′slô′), a salad made of finely shredded raw cabbage. *noun.*

col·lage (kə läzh′), a picture made by pasting on a background such things as parts of photographs and newspapers, fabric, and string. *noun.*
[The word *collage* comes from a French word meaning "glue." The parts of a collage are glued onto a flat surface.]

col·lapse (kə laps′), **1** to fall down or cave in: *The building suddenly collapsed under the heavy snow.* **2** a falling down or caving in: *A heavy flood caused the collapse of the bridge.* **3** to break down; fail suddenly: *The business collapsed because it was run poorly.* **4** a breakdown; failure: *Overwork can cause the collapse of a person's health.* **5** to fold together: *This table collapses so that it can be stored easily.* 1,3,5 *verb,* **col·laps·es, col·lapsed, col·laps·ing;** 2,4 *noun.*

col·lar (kol′ər), **1** the part of a coat, a dress, or a shirt that makes a band around or just below the neck. **2** a leather or plastic band or a metal chain for the neck of a dog or other pet animal. **3** a leather roll for a horse's neck to bear the weight of the loads it pulls. **4** any of the various kinds of rings, bands, or pipes in machinery. Sometimes a collar is a short pipe connecting two other pipes. **5** to seize by the collar; capture. 1-4 *noun*, 5 *verb*.

collar (definition 5)—She **collared** the muddy boy and tried to wash him under the pump.

col·lar·bone (kol′ər bōn′), the bone connecting the breastbone and the shoulder blade. *noun.*

col·league (kol′ēg′), an associate; fellow worker: *His colleagues taught his classes while he was ill. noun.*

col·lect (kə lekt′), **1** to bring together; come together; gather together: *I collect stamps as a hobby. A crowd soon collected at the scene of the accident.* **2** to ask for and receive payment for something: *My scout troop collects dues each week. verb.*

col·lect·ed (kə lek′tid), not confused or disturbed; calm: *Throughout all the excitement she remained cool and collected. adjective.*

col·lec·tion (kə lek′shən), **1** a bringing together; coming together: *The collection of these stamps took ten years.* **2** a group of things gathered from many places and belonging together: *Our library has a large collection of books.* **3** the money gathered from people: *A church takes up a collection to help pay its expenses.* **4** a mass or heap: *a collection of dust under the bed. noun.*

col·lec·tor (kə lek′tər), **1** a person or thing that collects: *I am a stamp collector.* **2** a person hired to collect money owed: *a tax collector. noun.*

col·lege (kol′ij), **1** a school attended after high school that gives degrees or diplomas: *After I finish high school, I plan to go to college to become a teacher.* **2** a school for special training: *I went to business college to learn to be a bookkeeper. noun.*

col·lide (kə līd′), to crash; hit or strike hard together: *Two ships collided in the harbor and sank. verb,* **col·lides, col·lid·ed, col·lid·ing.**

col·lie (kol′ē), a large, intelligent, long-haired dog. Collies are used for tending sheep and as pets. *noun.*

col·li·sion (kə lizh′ən), a crash; hitting or striking hard together: *The car was badly damaged in the collision. noun.*

Colo., Colorado.

Co·lom·bi·a (kə lum′bē ə), a country in northwestern South America. *noun.*

co·lon[1] (kō′lən), a mark (:) of punctuation. Colons are used before explanations, lists, and long quotations to set them off from the rest of the sentence. *noun.*

co·lon[2] (kō′lən), the lower part of the large intestine. *noun.*

colo·nel (kėr′nl), an army, air force, or marine officer ranking above a major and below a general. *noun.*

co·lo·ni·al (kə lō′nē əl), **1** of or having to do with a colony or colonies: *colonial government.* **2** having something to do with the thirteen British colonies which became the United States of America. *adjective.*

col·o·nist (kol′ə nist), a person who lives in a colony; settler: *Early colonists in New England suffered from cold and hunger. noun.*

col·o·ni·za·tion (kol′ə nə zā′shən), the setting up of a colony or colonies: *The story was about the colonization of other planets by space travelers. noun.*

col·o·nize (kol′ə nīz), to set up a colony or colonies in: *The English colonized New England. verb,* **col·o·niz·es, col·o·nized, col·o·niz·ing.**

col·o·ny (kol′ə nē), **1** a group of people who leave their own country and go to settle in another land, but who still remain citizens of their own country: *The Pilgrim colony came from England to America in 1620.* **2** the settlement made by such a group of people: *The Pilgrims founded a colony at Plymouth, Massachusetts.* **3** the Colonies, the thirteen British colonies that became the United States of America; New Hampshire, Massachusetts, Rhode Island, Connecticut, New York, New Jersey, Pennsylvania, Delaware, Maryland, Virginia, North Carolina, South Carolina, and Georgia. **4** a territory distant from the country that governs it: *Hong Kong is a British colony.* **5** a group of people of one country or occupation living in their own part of a city: *The city had a colony of artists.* **6** a group of living things of the same kind that grow or live together: *We found two colonies of ants under the steps. noun, plural* **col·o·nies.**

col·or (kul′ər), **1** red, yellow, blue, or any combination of them. Green is a combination of yellow and blue; purple is a combination of red and blue. **2** to give color to; put color on; change the color of: *I colored a picture with crayons.* **3** a paint; stain; dye: *Sunlight faded the colors of the bedspread.* **4** the appearance of the skin; complexion: *She has a healthy color.* **5** the colors, the flag: *Salute the colors.* **1,3-5** *noun,* **2** *verb.*

Col·o·rad·o (kol′ə rad′ō or kol′ə rä′dō), **1** one of the western states of the United States. *Abbreviation:* Colo. or CO *Capital:* Denver. **2** a river in the western United States and Mexico. *noun.*

[The state of *Colorado* was named for the Colorado River, which flows through it. The river got its name from a Spanish word meaning "colored" or "reddish." It was called this because the water looked reddish as it flowed through canyons of red stone.]

col·or-blind (kul′ər blīnd′), unable to tell certain colors apart; unable to see certain colors. Some color-blind people may see both red and green as the same shade of brown. *adjective.*

col·ored (kul′ərd), **1** having color; not black or white: *This book has colored pictures.* **2** of the black race or any race other than white. This meaning of *colored* is often considered offensive. **3** See color. *He colored the sky blue.* **1,2** *adjective,* **3** *verb.*

col·or·ful (kul′ər fəl), **1** full of color; having many or bright colors: *She bought a colorful red and yellow scarf.* **2** interesting or exciting: *Her letters describe her colorful travels. adjective.*

col·or·ing (kul′ər ing), **1** the way in which a person or thing is colored: *Our cat has a tan coloring.* **2** a substance used to color: *I added some yellow food coloring to the cake frosting. noun.*

col·or·less (kul′ər lis), **1** without color: *Pure water* *is colorless.* **2** not interesting: *They lived in a colorless town where there was little to see or do.* *adjective.*

co·los·sal (kə los′əl), huge; gigantic; vast: *Skyscrapers are colossal buildings. adjective.*

colt (kōlt), a young horse, donkey, or zebra. A male horse until it is four or five years old is a colt. *noun.*

Co·lum·bi·a (kə lum′bē ə), the capital of South Carolina. *noun.*

Co·lum·bus (kə lum′bəs), the capital of Ohio. *noun.*

col·umn (kol′əm), **1** a tall, slender structure somewhat like a large post; pillar. Columns are usually made of stone, wood, or metal, and used as supports or ornaments to a building. **2** anything that seems tall and slender like a column: *A column of smoke rose from the fire. You add a*

a hat	**i** it	**oi** oil	**ch** child	a in about
ā age	**ī** ice	**ou** out	**ng** long	e in taken
ä far	**o** hot	**u** cup	**sh** she	ə = { i in pencil
e let	**ō** open	**ů** put	**th** thin	o in lemon
ē equal	**ô** order	**ü** rule	**ŦH** then	u in circus
ėr term			**zh** measure	

column of figures. **3** a line of persons or things following one behind another. **4** a narrow division of a page reading from top to bottom, kept separate by lines or by blank spaces. This page has two columns. **5** a part of a newspaper used for a special subject or written by a special writer: *the sports column. noun.*

co·ma (kō′mə), a long period of deep unconsciousness. A coma may be caused by disease, injury, or poison. *noun.*
[*Coma* comes from a Greek word meaning "deep sleep."]

comb (kōm), **1** a piece of plastic, metal, or other material with teeth, used to arrange the hair or to hold it in place. **2** anything shaped or used like a comb. One kind of comb cleans and takes out the tangles in wool or flax. **3** to take out tangles in; arrange with a comb: *You should comb your hair every morning.* **4** to search through: *We had to comb the neighborhood before we found our lost dog.* **5** the red, fleshy piece on the top of the head of chickens and some other fowls. **6** a honeycomb. 1,2,5,6 *noun,* 3,4 *verb.*

com·bat (kəm bat′ *or* kom′bat *for 1;* kom′bat *for 2 and 3*), **1** to fight against; struggle with: *The whole town turned out to combat the fire.* **2** a fight with weapons; battle: *The soldier was wounded in combat.* **3** any fight or struggle. 1 *verb,* 2,3 *noun.*

com·bi·na·tion (kom′bə nā′shən), **1** one whole made by combining two or more different things: *The color purple is a combination of red and blue.* **2** a series of numbers or letters used in opening a certain kind of lock: *Do you know the combination of the safe?* **3** a combining or being combined; union: *The combination of flour and water makes paste. noun.*

com·bine (kəm bīn′ *for 1;* kom′bīn *for 2*), **1** to join two or more things together; unite: *to combine work and play. Our club combined the offices of secretary and treasurer. Two atoms of hydrogen combine with one of oxygen to form water.* **2** a machine for harvesting and threshing grain. 1 *verb,* **com·bines, com·bined, com·bin·ing;** 2 *noun.*

com·bus·ti·ble (kəm bus′tə bəl), capable of taking fire and burning; easy to burn: *Gasoline is highly combustible. adjective.*

com·bus·tion (kəm bus′chən), the act or process of burning. We sometimes heat houses by the combustion of oil. *noun.*

come (kum), **1** to move toward: *Come this way. One boy came toward me; the other boy went away from me.* **2** to arrive: *The girls will come home tomorrow. The train comes at noon.* **3** to reach; extend: *The drapes come to the floor.* **4** to take

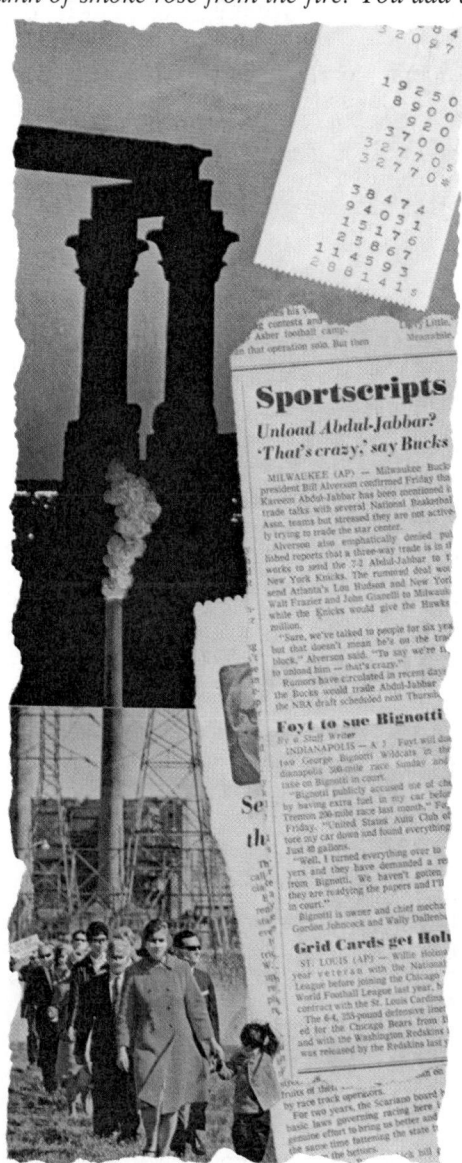

column (definitions 1, 2, 3, and 5)

place; happen: *Snow comes in winter.* **5** to be born; be from: *She comes from a musical family. The word "coma" comes from a Greek word.* **6** to turn out to be; become: *My wish came true.* **7** to be available or be sold: *This bathrobe comes in only one size.* **8** to be equal; amount: *The bill comes to five dollars.* verb, **comes, came, come, com·ing.**

come about, 1 to take place; happen: *Many changes have come about in the past year.* **2** to turn around: *The sailboat came about, heading back to the dock.*

come across, to meet or find by chance: *I came across my old teddy bear while cleaning my closet.*

come at, to rush toward; attack.

come back, to return: *Come back home.*

come in, to arrive: *When did you come in this morning?*

come off, 1 to take place; happen: *The rocket launching comes off next week.* **2** to turn out: *Our first meeting did not come off as I had expected.*

come out, 1 to take place in the end; result: *The ball game came out in our favor.* **2** to be offered to the public: *The singer's new recording will come out next fall.* **3** to put in an appearance; turn out: *How many people came out to cheer the team?*

come to, to become conscious again: *He came to slowly after the accident.*

come up, to arise; develop: *A storm came up suddenly. The question is not likely to come up.*

co·me·di·an (kə mē′dē ən), **1** a person who amuses others with funny talk and actions. **2** an actor in comedies. *noun.*

com·e·dy (kom′ə dē), **1** an amusing play or show having a happy ending. **2** an amusing happening. *noun, plural* **com·e·dies.**

come·ly (kum′lē), pleasant to look at; attractive: *a comely girl. adjective,* **come·li·er, come·li·est.**

com·et (kom′it), a heavenly body that looks like a star with a cloudy tail of light. Comets are made up of ice and dust, and they shine by reflecting sunlight. They move around the sun in large orbits that take many years to complete. *noun.*

Word History

comet *Comet* comes from a Greek word meaning "long-haired star." It was called this because the tail of a comet looks like long, flowing hair.

comet

comfort (definition 1)
The policeman **comforted** the frightened child.

com·fort (kum′fərt), **1** to ease the grief or sorrow of. **2** a person or thing that lessens trouble or sorrow or makes life easier: *You were a great comfort to me while I was sick. The fire was a comfort to the cold campers.* **3** ease; freedom from hardship: *It's nice to have enough money to live in comfort.* **1** *verb,* **2,3** *noun.*

com·fort·a·ble (kum′fər tə bəl), **1** giving comfort: *A soft, warm bed is comfortable.* **2** in comfort; free from pain or hardship: *We felt comfortable in the warm house after a cold day outdoors. adjective.*

com·fort·a·bly (kum′fər tə blē), in a comfortable manner; easily: *You can work more comfortably here where it is warm and quiet. adverb.*

com·fort·er (kum′fər tər), a padded or quilted covering used on a bed for warmth. *noun.*

com·ic (kom′ik), **1** causing laughter or smiles; amusing; funny: *I enjoy writing comic poems for my friends.* **2** a comedian. **3** of comedy; in comedies: *a comic actor.* **4 comics,** comic strips. **5** containing comic strips: *As soon as the newspaper arrived, he opened it to the comic page.* **1,3,5** *adjective,* **2,4** *noun.*

com·i·cal (kom′ə kəl), amusing; funny: *You look comical in that battered old hat. adjective.*

comic book, a magazine containing comic strips.

comic strip, a group of drawings, sometimes funny, that often tell a story or an adventure.

com·ing (kum′ing), **1** an approach; arrival: *the coming of summer.* **2** approaching; next: *this coming spring.* **1** *noun,* **2** *adjective.*

com·ma (kom′ə), a mark (,) of punctuation, usually used where a pause would be made in speaking a sentence aloud. Commas are used to separate ideas, parts of a sentence, or things in a series. *noun.*

com·mand (kə mand′), **1** to give an order to; order; direct: *The queen commanded the admiral to set sail at once.* **2** order; direction: *The admiral obeyed the queen's command.* **3** to be in control of; have power or authority over: *A captain commands a ship.* **4** control; power; authority: *When the fire started, she took command and led* *everyone to safety.* **5** the soldiers or ships or a region under a person who has the right to command them: *The captain knew every man in his command.* **6** the ability to have and use: *She has an excellent command of English and speaks it very well.* **1,3** *verb,* **2,4-6** *noun.*

com·mand·er (kə man′dər), **1** a person who commands or is in charge: *The commander of the rebel forces led a daring raid.* **2** an officer in the navy, ranking next below a captain. *noun.*

com·mand·ment (kə mand′mənt), **1** (in the Bible) one of the ten rules for living and for worship, called the **Ten Commandments,** given by God to the Jews. "Thou shalt not kill" is one of the Ten Commandments. **2** any law or command. *noun.*

com·mem·o·rate (kə mem′ə rāt), to preserve or honor the memory of. *verb,* **com·mem·o·rates, com·mem·o·rat·ed, com·mem·o·rat·ing.**

Word History

commemorate *Commemorate* comes from a Latin word meaning "to bring to mind." The English word *memory* comes from the same Latin root.

Lexington & Concord 1775 by Sandham

US Bicentennial 10cents

commemorate
This stamp **commemorates** the beginning of the Revolutionary War at Lexington and Concord in 1775.

---

com·mence (kə mens′), to begin; start: *The play will commence at ten o'clock.* *verb,* **com·menc·es, com·menced, com·menc·ing.**

com·mence·ment (kə mens′mənt), **1** beginning; start: *We are eagerly waiting for the end of winter and the commencement of spring.* **2** the ceremony during which colleges and schools give diplomas to persons who have completed their studies; day of graduation. *noun.*

com·mend (kə mend′), to praise: *The teacher commended the pupils who did well on the test.* *verb.*

com·ment (kom′ent), **1** a note or remark that explains, praises, or finds fault with a book, a person, or a thing: *The teacher had written helpful comments on the last page of my composition.* **2** to make notes or remarks: *Everyone commented on my new coat.* **1** *noun,* **2** *verb.*

a hat	i it	oi oil	ch child	a in about
ā age	ī ice	ou out	ng long	e in taken
ä far	o hot	u cup	sh she	ə = i in pencil
e let	ō open	u̇ put	th thin	o in lemon
ē equal	ô order	ü rule	ŦH then	u in circus
ėr term			zh measure	

com·men·ta·tor (kom′ən tā′tər), a person who reports and comments on news, sporting events, concerts, and the like: *I watch the sports commentator on a TV news program every night.* *noun.*

com·merce (kom′ərs), trade; buying and selling of goods in large amounts between different places: *The United States has much commerce with other countries.* *noun.*

com·mer·cial (kə mėr′shəl), **1** having something to do with trade or business: *a store or other commercial establishment.* **2** an advertising message on radio or television, broadcast between or during programs. **1** *adjective,* **2** *noun.*

com·mis·sion (kə mish′ən), **1** a written order giving certain powers, rights, and duties. In the army a person who is appointed to the rank of lieutenant or higher receives a commission. **2** to give a person the right, the power, or the duty to do something: *They commissioned a real estate agent to sell their house.* **3** a group of people appointed or elected with authority to do certain things: *The mayor appointed a commission to investigate the rise in crime.* **4** doing; committing: *He was arrested for the commission of a series of crimes.* **5** the money paid to a salesperson for the amount of business done: *She gets a commission of 10 percent on all the sales that she makes.* **6** working order; service; use: *A flat tire put my bicycle out of commission.* **7** to put into active service; make ready for use: *A new ship is commissioned when it has the officers, crew, and supplies needed for a trip.* **1,3-6** *noun,* **2,7** *verb.*

com·mis·sion·er (kə mish′ə nər), an official in charge of some department of a government: *a police commissioner, a health commissioner.* *noun.*

com·mit (kə mit′), **1** to do or perform, usually something wrong: *A person who steals commits a crime.* **2** to put under the care or control of another: *Mentally ill people are sometimes committed to mental hospitals.* **3** to bind or involve oneself; pledge: *I have committed myself now and must keep my promise.* *verb,* **com·mits, com·mit·ted, com·mit·ting.**

com·mit·tee (kə mit′ē), a group of persons appointed or elected to do some special thing: *Our teacher appointed a committee of five pupils to plan the class picnic.* *noun.*

com·mod·i·ty (kə mod′ə tē), anything that is bought and sold: *Groceries are commodities.* *noun, plural* **com·mod·i·ties.**

com·mon (kom′ən), **1** belonging equally to all: *The house is the common property of the three brothers.* **2** general; of all; from all; by all: *By common consent of the class, she was chosen for*

president. **3** often met with; usual; familiar: *Snow is common in cold countries.* **4** without rank; having no special position: *A private is a common soldier; a sergeant is not.* **5** coarse; vulgar: *a common person.* **6** belonging to the entire community; public: *It is in the common interest to clean up pollution.* **7** Also, **commons.** land owned or used by all the people of a village or town.
1-6 *adjective,* 7 *noun.*

in common, equally with another or others; owned, used, or done by both or all: *The two sisters have many interests in common.*

common denominator, a number that can be divided, without a remainder, by the denominators of two or more fractions: *15 is a common denominator of ⅗ and ⅔ because 15 can be divided by both 5 and 3 without a remainder. When ⅗ and ⅔ are written using this common denominator, they become ⁹⁄₁₅ and ¹⁰⁄₁₅.*

com·mon·ly (kom′ən lē), usually; generally: *Arithmetic is commonly taught in elementary schools. adverb.*

common noun, a noun used as the name of any one of a class or group of persons, places, or things. *Boy* and *city* are common nouns. *Carlos* and *Boston* are proper nouns.

com·mon·place (kom′ən plās′), ordinary; not new or interesting: *The plots of television movies are often commonplace. adjective.*

common sense, good sense in everyday affairs; practical intelligence: *He was not a good student, but he had a lot of common sense.*

com·mon·wealth (kom′ən welth′), **1** a nation in which the people have the right to make the laws; republic: *Brazil, Australia, the United States, and West Germany are commonwealths.* **2** any state of the United States, especially Kentucky, Massachusetts, Pennsylvania, and Virginia. **3** a group of nations united by some common interest: *Great Britain, Canada, Australia, and India are members of the Commonwealth of Nations. noun.*

com·mo·tion (kə mō′shən), a violent movement; confusion; disturbance: *Their fight caused quite a commotion in the hall. noun.*

com·mu·ni·ca·ble (kə myü′nə kə bəl), able to be transferred or passed along to others: *Chicken pox is a communicable disease. adjective.*

com·mu·ni·cate (kə myü′nə kāt), to give or exchange information or news: *Since my brother is away at school, I communicate with him by telephone every weekend. She communicated her wishes to me in a letter. verb,* **com·mu·ni·cates, com·mu·ni·cat·ed, com·mu·ni·cat·ing.**

com·mu·ni·ca·tion (kə myü′nə kā′shən), **1** giving information or news: *People who are deaf often use sign language as a means of communication.* **2** the information or news given; letter or message which gives information or news: *Your communication came in time to change all my plans.* **3 communications,** a system of communicating by telephone, telegraph, radio, or television: *A network of communications links all parts of the civilized world. noun.*

com·mun·ion (kə myü′nyən), **1** a sharing or exchange of thoughts and feelings; fellowship: *There was a close communion among the families of the neighborhood.* **3 Communion,** a Christian church service in which bread and wine are blessed in memory of Christ's last supper. *noun.*

com·mu·nism (kom′yə niz′əm), a system in which most or all property is owned by the state and is shared by all. *noun.*

com·mu·nist (kom′yə nist), a person who favors or supports communism. *noun.*

com·mu·ni·ty (kə myü′nə tē), **1** all the people living in the same place; the people of any district or town: *This lake provides water for six communities.* **2** a neighborhood; the place, district, or area where people live: *There are a few stores and a post office in our community, but not a theater.* **3** a group of people living together or sharing common interests: *a community of monks, the scientific community.* **4** all the living things in any one place. *noun, plural* **com·mu·ni·ties.**

community center, a building where the people of a community meet for social, educational, and other purposes: *Twice a week I play volleyball at the community center.*

com·mute (kə myüt′), to travel regularly to and from work by train, bus, automobile, or other transportation. *verb,* **com·mutes, com·mut·ed, com·mut·ing.**

com·mut·er (kə myü′tər), a person who travels regularly to and from work by train, bus, automobile, or other transportation. *noun.*

com·pact¹ (kəm pakt′ or kom′pakt for 1,2; kom′pakt for 3,4), **1** closely and firmly packed together: *The leaves of a cabbage are folded into a compact head.* **2** having the parts neatly or tightly arranged within a small space: *a compact portable TV.* **3** a small case containing face powder or rouge. **4** an automobile smaller than most models. 1,2 *adjective,* 3,4 *noun.*

com·pact² (kom′pakt), an agreement: *The United Nations is a result of a compact among nearly all nations of the world. noun.*

com·pan·ion (kəm pan′yən), one who often goes along with or accompanies another; one who shares in what another is doing: *The twins were companions in work and play.*
[*Companion* comes from a Latin word meaning "one who eats bread with another."]

com·pan·ion·a·ble (kəm pan′yə nə bəl), friendly; agreeable; pleasant as a companion: *The people I work with are very companionable. adjective.*

com·pan·ion·ship (kəm pan′yən ship), a being a companion; fellowship: *I enjoy the companionship of my friends. noun.*

com·pa·ny (kum′pə nē), **1** a group of people joined together for some purpose: *a company of tourists, a company of actors.* **2** a business firm: *I work for a company that makes furniture.* **3** a companion or companions: *You are known by the company you keep.* **4** companionship: *Her dog provided the old woman with company during the* long winters. **5** a guest or guests; visitor or visitors: *We are having company for dinner tonight.* **6** the part of an army commanded by a captain. Two or more platoons make a company. *noun, plural* **com·pa·nies.**

keep company, stay with for companionship: *My dog kept me company while you were away.*

com·pa·ra·ble (kom′pər ə bəl), **1** able to be compared; similar: *The two students are of comparable ability.* **2** worthy or fit to be compared: *A small car is not comparable to a larger one for comfort. adjective.*

com·par·a·tive (kəm par′ə tiv), **1** that compares; involving comparison: *He made a comparative study of bees and wasps.* **2** measured by comparison with something else; relative: *Although they have lived next door to us for several years, they are comparative strangers.* **3** a form of a word or a combination of words to show a greater degree or amount than others. *Faster* is the comparative of *fast. Better* is the comparative of *good. More quickly* is the comparative of *quickly.* **1,2** *adjective,* **3** *noun.*

a hat	i it	oi oil	ch child	⎧ a in about
ā age	ī ice	ou out	ng long	e in taken
ä far	o hot	u cup	sh she	ə = ⎨ i in pencil
e let	ō open	ù put	th thin	o in lemon
ē equal	ô order	ü rule	₮H then	⎩ u in circus
ėr term			zh measure	

no comparison between these two cameras; one is much better than the other. noun.

in comparison with, compared with: *Even a large lake is small in comparison with an ocean.*

com·part·ment (kəm pärt′mənt), a separate division set off by walls or partitions: *The kitchen drawer has different compartments for knives, forks, and spoons. noun.*

com·pass (kum′pəs), **1** an instrument for showing directions, having a needle that always points to the north. **2** an instrument for drawing circles and measuring distances. *noun, plural* **com·pass·es.**

compass (definition 1)   compass (definition 2)

com·pas·sion (kəm pash′ən), pity; feeling for another's sorrow or hardship that leads to help; sympathy: *Compassion for the earthquake victims caused many people to make contributions. noun.*

com·pas·sion·ate (kəm pash′ə nit), pitying; wishing to help those that suffer: *The compassionate doctor gave free treatment to the poor. adjective.*

com·pat·i·ble (kəm pat′ə bəl), able to exist or get on well together; agreeing; in harmony: *My new roommate and I are quite compatible. adjective.*

com·pel (kəm pel′), to force: *The rain compelled us to stop our ball game. verb,* **com·pels, com·pelled, com·pel·ling.**

com·pen·sate (kom′pən sāt), **1** to give something to in order to make up for something else: *We compensated our neighbor for the window we broke by replacing it.* **2** to balance by equal weight or power; make up for: *Skill sometimes compensates for lack of strength.* **3** to pay: *The company always compensated her for her extra work. verb,* **com·pen·sates, com·pen·sat·ed, com·pen·sat·ing.**

comparative (definition 3)—Shorter is the **comparative** of short. Shortest is the superlative of short.

com·par·a·tive·ly (kəm par′ə tiv lē), by comparison; relatively; somewhat: *Mountains are comparatively free from mosquitoes. adverb.*

com·pare (kəm per′ *or* kəm par′), **1** to find out or point out how persons or things are alike and how they are different: *I compared my answers with the teacher's and found I had made a mistake.* **2** to say something is like something else; liken: *The fins of a fish may be compared to the legs of a dog; both are used in moving.* **3** to be considered like or equal: *Canned fruit cannot compare with fresh fruit. verb,* **com·pares, com·pared, com·par·ing.**

com·par·i·son (kəm par′ə sən), **1** the act of comparing; finding out the likenesses and the differences: *The teacher's comparison of the heart to a pump helped the students to understand how the heart works.* **2** a likeness; similarity: *There is*

com·pen·sa·tion (kom/pən sā/shən),
1 something given to make up for something else;
something which makes up for something else:
*He gave me a new knife as compensation for the
one of mine he lost.* **2** pay: *The same compensation
should be given to men and women for the same
work.* noun.

com·pete (kəm pēt/), to try hard to win or gain
something wanted by others; take part in a
contest: *She competed against many fine athletes
for the gold medal. Will you compete in the final
race?* verb, **com·petes, com·pet·ed,
com·pet·ing.**

com·pe·tent (kom/pə tənt), able; skilled: *He is a
competent driver who has never caused an accident.*
adjective.

com·pe·ti·tion (kom/pə tish/ən), **1** a trying hard
to win or gain something wanted by others. **2** a
contest. noun.

competition (definition 1)
The **competition** among the racers was very intense.

com·pet·i·tive (kəm pet/ə tiv), decided by
competition; using competition: *Tennis and
baseball are competitive sports.* adjective.

com·pet·i·tor (kəm pet/ə tər), a person who tries
hard to win or gain something wanted by others;
rival: *There are many competitors for the golf
championship.* noun.

com·pile (kəm pīl/), to collect and bring together
in one list or account: *I compiled a list of books
written on the subject of glaciers.* verb, **com·piles,
com·piled, com·pil·ing.**

com·pla·cent (kəm plā/snt), pleased or satisfied
with oneself: *The winner's complacent smile
annoyed the loser.* adjective.

com·plain (kəm plān/), **1** to say that something is
wrong, troublesome, or painful; find fault: *We
complained that the room was too cold. He is
always complaining about his health.* **2** to make an
accusation or charge: *I complained to the police
about the barking of my neighbor's dog.* verb.

com·plaint (kəm plānt), **1** a complaining; finding
fault: *Her letter is filled with complaints about the
food at camp.* **2** an accusation; charge: *The judge
heard the complaint and ordered an investigation.*
3 a cause for complaining: *Her main complaint is
that she has too much work to do.* noun.

com·ple·ment (kom/plə mənt *for 1 and 2;*
kom/plə ment *for 3*), **1** something that completes
or makes perfect: *The teacher considers homework
a necessary complement to classroom work.* **2** the
number required to complete or make perfect:
*The plane had its full complement of passengers; all
seats were taken.* **3** to make complete: *This dessert
complements a fine dinner.* 1,2 noun, 3 verb.

com·plete (kəm plēt/), **1** with all the parts; whole;
entire: *We have a complete set of garden tools.* **2** to
make whole or perfect; make up the full number
or amount of: *I completed the set of dishes by
buying the cups and saucers.* **3** perfect; thorough:
The birthday party was a complete surprise to me.
4 finished; done: *My homework is complete.* **5** to
finish: *She completed her homework early in the
evening.* 1,3,4 adjective, 2,5 verb, **com·pletes,
com·plet·ed, com·plet·ing.**

com·plete·ly (kəm plēt/lē), **1** entirely; wholly:
*The film was completely ruined when I held it up to
the light.* **2** thoroughly; perfectly: *The birthday
party completely surprised me.* adverb.

com·ple·tion (kəm plē/shən), **1** a finishing; act of
completing: *After the completion of the job, she
went home.* **2** the condition of being completed:
The work is near completion. noun.

com·plex (kəm pleks/ *or* kom/pleks), **1** made up
of a number of parts: *A watch is a complex device.*
2 hard to understand: *The instructions for building
the radio were so complex we could not follow
them.* adjective.

com·plex·ion (kəm plek/shən), **1** the color,
quality, and general appearance of the skin,
particularly of the face: *The child has a healthy
complexion.* **2** the general appearance; nature;
character: *the complexion of the little farm town
changed when two big factories were built nearby.*
noun.

com·plex·i·ty (kəm plek/sə tē), a complex quality
or condition: *The complexity of the road map
puzzled him.* noun, plural **com·plex·i·ties.**

com·pli·cate (kom/plə kāt), to make hard to
understand or to settle; mix up; confuse: *Too
many rules complicate a game.* verb,
com·pli·cates, com·pli·cat·ed, com·pli·cat·ing.

com·pli·cat·ed (kom/plə kā/tid), **1** hard to
understand: *Many airplane models have very
complicated directions for putting them together.*
2 made up of many parts; complex: *An automobile
engine is a complicated machine.* adjective.

com·pli·ca·tion (kom/plə kā/shən), something
that makes matters difficult, worse, or confusing:
Various complications delayed the start of our trip.
noun.

com·pli·ment (kom/plə mənt *for 1;* kom/plə ment
for 2), **1** something good said about you;
something said in praise of your work: *She*

received many compliments on her science project. **2** to pay a compliment to; congratulate: *The principal complimented the boy on his good grades.* **1** *noun,* **2** *verb.*

com·pli·men·tar·y (kom′plə men′tər ē), **1** expressing a compliment; praising: *It is nice to receive complimentary remarks about one's work.* **2** given free: *Mother received two complimentary tickets to the circus. adjective.*

com·ply (kəm plī′), to act in agreement with a request or a command: *I will comply with your orders. verb,* **com·plies, com·plied, com·ply·ing.**

com·pose (kəm pōz′), **1** to make up: *The ocean is composed of salt water. Our party was composed of three grown-ups and four children.* **2** to put together. To compose a story or poem is to construct it from words. To compose a piece of music is to invent the tune and write down the notes. To compose a picture is to get an artistic arrangement of the things in it. **3** to make calm: *Stop crying and compose yourself. verb,* **com·pos·es, com·posed, com·pos·ing.**

com·pos·er (kəm pō′zər), a person who writes musical compositions. *noun.*

com·pos·ite (kəm poz′it), made up of various parts: *The photographer made a composite picture by putting together parts of several others. adjective.*

com·po·si·tion (kom′pə zish′ən), **1** the makeup of anything; what is in it: *The composition of this candy includes sugar, chocolate, and milk.* **2** a putting together of a whole. Writing sentences, making pictures, and setting type in printing are all forms of composition. **3** a thing composed. A symphony, poem, or painting is a composition. **4** a short essay written as a school exercise: *I wrote a composition about my dog. noun.*

com·post (kom′pōst), a mixture of decaying leaves, grass, manure, or other such matter for fertilizing soil. *noun.*

com·po·sure (kəm pō′zhər), calmness; quietness; self-control: *She always keeps her composure, even during a crisis. noun.*

com·pound (kom′pound *for 1-4;* kom pound′ *for 5),* **1** having more than one part: *A clover leaf is a compound leaf.* **2** a mixture: *Many medicines are compounds.* **3** a word made up of two or more words. *Steamship* is a compound made up of the two words *steam* and *ship.* **4** a substance formed by chemical combination of two or more elements: *Water is a compound of hydrogen and oxygen.* **5** to mix; combine: *The druggist compounded several medicines to fill the prescription.* **1** *adjective,* **2-4** *noun,* **5** *verb.*

com·pre·hend (kom′pri hend′), to understand: *If you can use a word correctly, you comprehend it. verb.*

com·pre·hen·sion (kom′pri hen′shən), the act or power of understanding: *Arithmetic is beyond the comprehension of a baby. noun.*

com·pre·hen·sive (kom′pri hen′siv), including much: *The month's schoolwork ended with a comprehensive review. adjective.*

com·press (kəm pres′ *for 1;* kom′pres *for 2),* **1** to

squeeze together; make smaller by pressure: *Cotton is compressed into bales.* **2** a pad of cloth applied to a part of the body to stop bleeding or to lessen soreness and swelling: *I put a cold compress on my forehead to relieve my headache.* **1** *verb,* **2** *noun, plural* **com·press·es.**

com·prise (kəm prīz′), to consist of; include: *The United States comprises 50 states. verb,* **com·pris·es, com·prised, com·pris·ing.**

com·pro·mise (kom′prə mīz), **1** to settle a quarrel or difference of opinion by agreeing that each side will give up part of what it demands: *Since they both wanted the apple, they compromised by sharing it.* **2** a settlement of a quarrel or a difference of opinion by a partial yielding on both sides: *They both wanted the apple; their compromise was to share it.* **1** *verb,* **com·pro·mis·es, com·pro·mised, com·pro·mis·ing;** **2** *noun.*

com·pul·sion (kəm pul′shən), a compelling; use of force; force: *A contract signed under compulsion is not legal. noun.*

com·pul·sor·y (kəm pul′sər ē), compelled; required: *Attendance at school is compulsory for children over seven years old. adjective.*

com·pu·ta·tion (kom′pyə tā′shən), a figuring out; calculation. Addition and subtraction are forms of computation. *noun.*

com·pute (kəm pyüt′), to do by arithmetic; calculate; figure out: *We computed the cost of our trip. verb,* **com·putes, com·put·ed, com·put·ing.**

com·put·er (kəm pyü′tər), an electronic machine that can store, recall, or process information. A computer performs these tasks according to instructions which can easily be changed, so it is able to do many different kinds of work. Computers keep files, play games, solve mathematical problems, and control the operations of other machines. *noun.*

com·rade (kom′rad), a close companion and friend, especially one who shares in what another is doing. *noun.*

con[1] (kon), **1** against: *The two groups argued the question pro and con.* **2** a reason against. The pros and cons of a question are the arguments for and against it. **1** *adverb,* **2** *noun.*

con[2] (kon), **1** to swindle someone after gaining his or her confidence; trick: *Don't let anyone con you out of your lunch money.* **2** a swindle; trick: *Because of a sales con my brother paid far too much for that used car.* **1** *verb,* **cons, conned, con·ning;** **2** *noun.*

con·cave (kon kāv′), hollow and curved in like the inside of a circle or sphere: *The palm of one's hand is slightly concave. adjective.*

con·ceal (kən sēl′), to put or keep out of sight; hide: *He concealed the ball behind his back. verb.*

con·ceal·ment (kən sēl′mənt), a hiding or keeping secret: *The witness's concealment of facts prevented a fair trial. noun.*

con·cede (kən sēd′), to admit; admit as true: *I conceded that I had made a mistake. The candidate conceded defeat in the election. verb,* **con·cedes, con·ced·ed, con·ced·ing.**

con·ceit (kən sēt′), too high an opinion of oneself or of one's ability to do things. *noun.*

conceit

con·ceit·ed (kən sē′tid), having too high an opinion of oneself or of one's ability to do things; vain: *The conceited young man thought he knew more than the teacher. adjective.*

con·ceiv·a·ble (kən sē′və bəl), able to be thought of; imaginable: *I looked for my lost watch in every conceivable place. adjective.*

con·ceive (kən sēv′), **1** to form in the mind; think up; imagine: *The Wright brothers conceived the design of the first successful powered airplane.* **2** to have an idea or feeling; think: *Young children cannot conceive of life without automobiles and television. verb,* **con·ceives, con·ceived, con·ceiv·ing.**

con·cen·trate (kon′sən trāt), **1** to bring or come together in one place: *A magnifying glass can concentrate enough sunlight to scorch paper. The audience at the music festival concentrated around the stage.* **2** to pay close attention: *I concentrated on my reading so that I would understand the story.* **3** to make stronger. *A concentrated solution of acid is one which has a lot of acid in it. verb,* **con·cen·trates, con·cen·trat·ed, con·cen·trat·ing.**

con·cen·tra·tion (kon′sən trā′shən), **1** close attention: *When he gave the problem his full concentration, he figured out the answer.* **2** a concentrating: *By a concentration of effort our class won the election.* **3** a group brought together in one place: *There is a large concentration of fish in the lake. noun.*

con·cept (kon′sept), a thought; general notion or idea: *I believe in the concept that a person is innocent until proven guilty. noun.*

con·cep·tion (kən sep′shən), a thought; notion; idea: *Her conception of the problem was different from mine. noun.*

con·cern (kən sėrn′), **1** to have to do with; belong to: *This letter is private and concerns nobody but me.* **2** anything that has to do with one's work or one's interests: *The party decorations are my concern; you pay attention to refreshments.* **3** a troubled interest; worry: *Their concern over their sick child kept them awake all night.* **4** to cause to worry; trouble: *We didn't want to concern you with the bad news.* **5** a business company; firm: *We wrote to two big concerns for their catalogs.* **1,4** *verb,* **2,3,5** *noun.*

con·cerned (kən sėrnd′), **1** troubled; worried; anxious: *The father of the sick child had a concerned look on his face.* **2** interested: *Concerned citizens make use of their right to vote. adjective.*

con·cern·ing (kən sėr′ning), having to do with; about: *The reporter asked many questions concerning the accident. preposition.*

con·cert (kon′sərt), a musical performance in which one or more musicians take part: *The school orchestra gave a free concert. noun.*
in concert, all together; in agreement: *The class worked in concert to put on the play.*

con·cer·to (kən cher′tō), a piece of music to be played by one or more principal instruments, such as a violin or piano, accompanied by an orchestra. *noun, plural* **con·cer·tos.**

con·ces·sion (kən sesh′ən), **1** anything granted or yielded: *The teacher made a special concession and postponed the test.* **2** a right or space leased for a specific purpose: *The park has a concession to sell food and drinks. Our concession at the fair sold hot dogs and soda pop. noun.*

conch (kongk *or* konch), **1** a shellfish with a large, spiral shell. **2** its shell. *noun, plural* **conchs** (kongks), **conch·es** (kon′chiz).

conch (definition 2)—8 to 12 inches (20 to 30 centimeters) long

con·cil·i·ate (kən sil′ē āt), to win over; soothe: *I conciliated the angry child with a candy bar.* verb, **con·cil·i·ates, con·cil·i·at·ed, con·cil·i·at·ing.**

con·cise (kən sīs′), expressing much in few words; brief but full of meaning: *He gave a concise report of the meeting.* adjective.

con·clude (kən klüd′), **1** to end: *The play concluded with a happy ending and the curtain came down.* **2** to reach certain decisions or opinions by reasoning: *From the tracks we saw, we concluded that the animal must have been a deer.* **3** to settle; arrange: *The two countries concluded a trade agreement.* verb, **con·cludes, con·clud·ed, con·clud·ing.**

con·clu·sion (kən klü′zhən), **1** to end: *I couldn't wait to read the conclusion of the story.* **2** a decision or opinion reached by reasoning: *She came to the conclusion that she would have to work harder to finish on time.* **3** a settlement; arrangement: *The government leaders met for the conclusion of a peace treaty between their countries.* noun.

con·clu·sive (kən klü′siv), final; settling something beyond question: *The evidence against the burglar was conclusive.* adjective.

con·coct (kon kokt′), to prepare; make up: *She concocted a drink made of grape juice and ginger ale. He concocted an excuse to explain his lateness.* verb.

con·coc·tion (kon kok′shən), a thing prepared or made up. noun.

concoction
The chocolate sundae was a magnificent **concoction**.

con·cord (kon′kôrd), agreement; peace; harmony: *concord between friends.* noun.

Con·cord (kong′kərd), the capital of New Hampshire. noun.

con·crete (kon′krēt′ *or* kon krēt′), **1** real; existing as an actual object: *A painting is concrete, but its beauty is not.* **2** a mixture of cement, sand or gravel, and water that hardens as it dries. Concrete is used for foundations, buildings, sidewalks, roads, dams, and bridges. **1** adjective, **2** noun.

con·cur (kən kėr′), to agree; be of the same opinion: *The judges all concurred in giving her the prize.* verb, **con·curs, con·curred, con·cur·ring.**

con·cus·sion (kən kush′ən), **1** a violent shaking;

a hat	**i** it	**oi** oil	**ch** child	a in about
ā age	**ī** ice	**ou** out	**ng** long	e in taken
ä far	**o** hot	**u** cup	**sh** she	ə = { i in pencil
e let	**ō** open	**u̇** put	**th** thin	o in lemon
ē equal	**ô** order	**ü** rule	**ŦH** then	u in circus
ėr term			**zh** measure	

shock: *The concussion caused by the explosion broke many windows.* **2** an injury to the brain from a blow, fall, or other shock. noun.

con·demn (kən dem′), **1** to express strong disapproval of: *We condemn cruelty to animals.* **2** to declare guilty of crime or wrong: *The accused man was condemned by the jury.* **3** to give a punishment to; sentence: *The spy was condemned to death.* **4** to declare not sound or suitable for use: *This bridge was condemned because it is no longer safe.* verb.

con·dem·na·tion (kon′dem nā′shən), a condemning or a being condemned: *the condemnation of an unsafe bridge.* noun.

con·den·sa·tion (kon′den sā′shən), **1** a changing from a gas or a vapor to a liquid. The condensation of steam into water occurs when warm, moist air touches a cold surface. **2** something changed from a gas or a vapor to a liquid. A cloud is a condensation of water vapor in the atmosphere. **3** something that has been shortened: *The magazine printed a condensation of the book.* noun.

con·dense (kən dens′), **1** to make denser; become more compact: *Milk is condensed by removing much of the water from it.* **2** to change from a gas or a vapor to a liquid. If warm air touches a cold surface, it condenses into tiny drops of water. **3** to say briefly; put into fewer words: *A long story can often be condensed.* verb, **con·dens·es, con·densed, con·dens·ing.**

con·de·scend (kon′di send′), to come down willingly to the level of one's inferiors in rank: *The king condescended to eat with the beggars.* verb.

con·di·tion (kən dish′ən), **1** the state in which a person or thing is: *My room is in a messy condition.* **2** good condition; good health: *People who take part in sports must keep in condition.* **3** to put in good condition: *Exercise conditions your muscles.* **4 conditions,** set of circumstances: *Icy roads cause bad driving conditions.* **5** a thing on which something else depends; thing without which something else cannot be: *One condition of the peace treaty was the return of all prisoners.* **6** to accustom or train: *This dog was conditioned to expect food when it heard a bell.* **1,2,4,5** noun, **3,6** verb.

on condition that, if: *I'll go on condition that you will too.*

con·di·tion·al (kən dish′ə nəl), depending on something else: *"I will come if the sun is shining" is a conditional promise.* adjective.

con·di·tion·er (kən dish′ə nər), a substance that is used to improve something: *Since my hair is dry, I use a conditioner after I shampoo it.* noun.

con·do·min·i·um (kon′də min′ē əm), **1** an

apartment house in which each apartment is owned rather than rented. **2** an apartment in a building like this. *noun.*

con·dor (kon′dər), a large vulture with a bare neck and head. Condors live on high mountains in South America and California. *noun.*

condor—4 feet (1 meter) long; wingspread up to 10 feet (3 meters)

con·duct (kon′dukt *for 1;* kən dukt′ *for 2-5*), **1** way of acting; behavior thought of as good or bad: *Her conduct was rude.* **2** to act in a certain way; behave: *When company comes, the children usually conduct themselves well.* **3** to manage; direct: *to conduct an orchestra, to conduct a business.* **4** to guide or lead: *I will conduct you to her office.* **5** to transmit: *Metals conduct heat and electricity.* **1** *noun,* **2-5** *verb.*

con·duc·tion (kən duk′shən), the movement of heat or electricity through a substance by the transfer of energy directly from one particle to another. *noun.*

con·duc·tor (kən duk′tər), **1** a guide or leader; person who is conducting. The conductor of an orchestra or chorus trains the performers to work together, beats time for them, and selects the music to be used. **2** a person in charge of a train or a bus and its passengers. The conductor usually collects tickets or fares. **3** a thing that transmits heat, electricity, light, or sound: *Copper wire is used as a conductor of electricity. noun.*

cone (kōn), **1** a solid object that has a flat, round base and narrows to a point at the top. **2** anything shaped like a cone: *an ice-cream cone, the cone of a volcano.* **3** the part that bears the seeds on pine, cedar, and other evergreen trees. *noun.*

Con·es·to·ga wag·on (kon′ə stō′gə wag′ən), a covered wagon with broad wheels, used by the American pioneers for traveling on soft ground or on the prairie.

con·fed·er·a·cy (kən fed′ər ə sē), **1** a union of countries or states; group of people joined together for a special purpose. **2** the

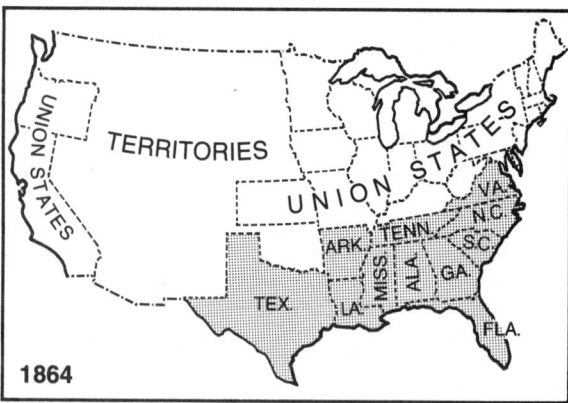

1864

the **Confederacy** (definition 2)—the darker area

Confederacy, the group of eleven southern states that left the United States in 1860 and 1861. *noun, plural* **con·fed·er·a·cies.**

con·fed·er·ate (kən fed′ər it), **1** a person or country joined with another for a special purpose; ally: *The thief and his confederates escaped to another city.* **2** joined together for a special purpose; allied. **3 Confederate, a** of or belonging to the Confederacy. **b** a person who lived in, supported, or fought for the Confederacy. **1,3b** *noun,* **2,3a** *adjective.*

con·fed·er·a·tion (kən fed′ə rā′shən), **1** a joining together of countries, groups, or states for a special purpose: *The conference devised a plan for a confederation of the colonies.* **2** a group joined together for a special purpose: *The United States of America was originally a confederation of thirteen colonies. noun.*

con·fer (kən fėr′), **1** to talk things over; consult together; exchange ideas: *His parents conferred with the teacher about his schoolwork.* **2** to give; bestow: *The university conferred an honorary degree on the scientist. verb,* **con·fers, con·ferred, con·fer·ring.**

con·fer·ence (kon′fər əns), **1** a meeting of interested persons to discuss a particular subject: *Conferences between parents and teachers will be held next Tuesday evening.* **2** a group of athletic teams, churches, or clubs, joined together for some special purpose: *My brother's college won*

cone (definition 1)

cone (definition 3)

CLOSED   OPEN

the football championship in their conference. noun.

con·fess (kən fes′), **1** to admit; acknowledge; own up: *I confessed to eating all the cake. I confess you are right on one point.* **2** to admit one's guilt: *The guilty person confessed.* **3** to tell one's sins to a priest in order to obtain forgiveness. verb.

con·fes·sion (kən fesh′ən), **1** an owning up; telling one's mistakes: *The guilty person made a full confession.* **2** the telling of one's sins to a priest in order to obtain forgiveness. noun.

con·fet·ti (kən fet′ē), bits of colored paper thrown about at weddings, parades, or other celebrations: *We threw confetti at the bride and groom as they left the church.* noun.

con·fide (kən fīd′), **1** to tell as a secret: *He confided his troubles to his sister.* **2** to show trust by telling secrets: *She always confided in her friend.* verb, **con·fides, con·fid·ed, con·fid·ing.**

con·fi·dence (kon′fə dəns), **1** a firm belief or trust: *I have complete confidence in his honesty.* **2** a firm belief in oneself and one's abilities: *Years of experience at his work have given him great confidence.* **3** trust that a person will not tell others what is said: *The secret was told to me in strict confidence.* **4** a thing told as a secret: *I would never reveal a confidence.* noun.

con·fi·dent (kon′fə dənt), firmly believing; certain; sure: *I feel confident that our team will win.* adjective.

con·fi·den·tial (kon′fə den′shəl), spoken or written as a secret: *This story is confidential; you must never repeat it.* adjective.

con·fine (kən fīn′ *for 1;* kon′fīn *for 2*), **1** to keep in; hold in: *A cold confined her to the house.* **2** a boundary; limit: *These people have never been beyond the confines of their own valley.* 1 *verb,* **con·fines, con·fined, con·fin·ing;** 2 *noun.*

con·fine·ment (kən fīn′mənt), a confining; being confined: *confinement indoors because of a cold.* noun.

con·firm (kən fėrm′), **1** to prove to be true or correct; make certain: *The rumor that the war had ended was confirmed by a news broadcast.* **2** to make more certain; place beyond all doubt: *The airline office telephoned to confirm the plane reservation I had made last week.* **3** to approve; agree to: *The Senate confirmed the President's appointments to the cabinet.* **4** to admit to full membership in a church or synagogue after required study and preparation. verb.

con·fir·ma·tion (kon′fər mā′shən), **1** a making sure by more information or evidence: *I telephoned the theater for confirmation of the starting time of the movie.* **2** a thing that confirms; proof: *Don't believe rumors that lack confirmation.* **3** the ceremony of admitting a person to full membership in a church or synagogue after required study and preparation. noun.

con·firmed (kən fėrmd′), **1** firmly established; proved: *a confirmed rumor.* **2** settled; habitual: *a confirmed bachelor.* adjective.

con·fis·cate (kon′fə skāt), to take or seize by

a hat	i it	oi oil	ch child	a in about
ā age	ī ice	ou out	ng long	e in taken
ä far	o hot	u cup	sh she	ə = i in pencil
e let	ō open	u̇ put	th thin	o in lemon
ē equal	ô order	ü rule	ŦH then	u in circus
ėr term			zh measure	

authority: *The teacher confiscated several comic books.* verb, **con·fis·cates, con·fis·cat·ed, con·fis·cat·ing.**

con·flict (kon′flikt *for 1 and 2;* kən flikt′ *for 3*), **1** a fight or struggle, especially a long one: *The conflict between the two nations lasted for ten years.* **2** a strong disagreement; clash: *A conflict of opinion arose over where to go for the picnic.* **3** to disagree strongly; clash: *Her report of the accident conflicted with mine.* 1,2 *noun,* 3 *verb.*

con·form (kən fôrm′), **1** to act according to law or rule; be in agreement with generally accepted standards: *Members must conform to the rules of our club.* **2** to agree; be the same as: *Her choice of programs rarely conforms with mine, so we seldom watch TV together.* verb.

con·front (kən frunt′), **1** to face boldly; meet courageously: *Once she confronted her problems, she was able to solve them easily.* **2** to bring face to face; make directly aware: *The teacher confronted me with my failing grade.* verb.

con·fuse (kən fyüz′), **1** to throw into disorder; mix up: *So many people talking at once confused me.* **2** to be unable to tell apart; mistake one thing or person for another: *People often confuse this girl with her twin sister.* verb, **con·fus·es, con·fused, con·fus·ing.**

con·fu·sion (kən fyü′zhən), **1** a confused condition; disorder: *In the confusion after the accident, I forgot to get the name of the witness.* **2** a mistaking one thing or person for another: *The confusion of some colors is a problem for those who are color-blind.* noun.

con·geal (kən jēl′), **1** to harden or make solid by cold; freeze. **2** thicken; stiffen: *The blood around the wound had congealed.* verb.

con·gest (kən jest′), **1** to fill too full; overcrowd: *The streets of this city are often congested with traffic.* **2** to fill with blood or mucus. In pneumonia the lungs become congested. verb.

Con·go (kong′gō), a country in west central Africa. noun.

con·grat·u·late (kən grach′ə lāt), to express pleasure at the happiness or good fortune of: *Everyone congratulated the winner of the race.* verb, **con·grat·u·lates, con·grat·u·lat·ed, con·grat·u·lat·ing.**

con·grat·u·la·tion (kən grach′ə lā′shən), **1** the expressing of pleasure at another's happiness or good fortune. **2 congratulations, a** pleasure at another's happiness or good fortune: *The spectators shouted their congratulations to the winning team.* **b** a word used to express such pleasure: *Congratulations on your high grades.* 1,2a *noun,* 2b *interjection.*

con·gre·gate (kong′grə gāt), to come together into a crowd or group. *verb*, **con·gre·gates, con·gre·gat·ed, con·gre·gat·ing.**

congregate *Congregate* comes from a Latin word meaning "to flock together." Animals often group themselves together into a flock or a herd. The idea here is that people often do the same thing by choice.

congregate—People began to **congregate** to hear the musicians.

con·gre·ga·tion (kong′grə gā′shən), **1** a gathering of people or things; assembly. **2** a group of people gathered together for religious worship or instruction. *noun.*

con·gress (kong′gris), **1** the lawmaking body of a nation, especially of a republic. **2 Congress,** the national lawmaking body of the United States, consisting of the Senate and the House of Representatives, with members elected from every state. *noun, plural* **con·gress·es.**

con·gres·sion·al (kən gresh′ə nəl), **1** of a congress. **2 Congressional,** of Congress. *adjective.*

con·gress·man or **Con·gress·man** (kong′gris mən), a member of the United States Congress, especially of the House of Representatives. *noun, plural* **con·gress·men** or **Con·gress·men.**

con·gress·wom·an or **Con·gress·wom·an** (kong′gris wùm′ən), a woman member of Congress, especially of the House of Representatives. *noun, plural* **con·gress·wom·en** or **Con·gress·wom·en.**

con·gru·ent (kən grü′ənt), having the same size and shape: *congruent triangles. adjective.*

con·i·fer (kon′ə fər *or* kō′nə fər), a tree or shrub that has cones. The pine, spruce, hemlock, and larch are conifers. *noun.*

con·junc·tion (kən jungk′shən), **1** a word that connects words, phrases, clauses, or sentences. *And, but, or, though,* and *if* are conjunctions. **2** a joining together; union; combination: *Our school, in conjunction with two other schools, will hold an art fair next week. noun.*

con·jure (kon′jər *or* kun′jər), to cause to appear or happen as if by magic: *Grandmother conjured up a bag of old-fashioned toys from the attic for us to play with. verb,* **con·jures, con·jured, con·jur·ing.**

Conn., Connecticut.

con·nect (kə nekt′), **1** to join one thing to another; fasten together; link: *Connect the hose to a faucet.* **2** to think of one thing with another: *We usually connect spring with sunshine and flowers. verb.*

Con·nect·i·cut (kə net′ə kət), one of the northeastern states of the United States. *Abbreviation:* Conn. or CT *Capital:* Hartford. *noun.*

[*Connecticut* was named for the Connecticut River, which flows through the state. The river got its name from an American Indian word meaning "at the long tidal river."]

con·nec·tion (kə nek′shən), **1** the act of connecting: *The connection of a trailer to our car was a difficult job.* **2** the state of being connected: *A trailer is hard to move except in connection with an automobile.* **3** a thing that connects; connecting part: *The connection between the radiator and the furnace is a pipe that comes through the floor.* **4** any kind of relation; association: *I had no connection with that prank.* **5** the meeting of trains, ships, buses, or airplanes so that passengers can change from one to the other without delay: *The bus arrived late at the airport and we missed our airplane connection. noun.*

con·quer (kong′kər), **1** to overcome; get the better of: *His desire to be an actor conquered his shyness.* **2** to win in war; get by fighting: *Napoleon conquered much of Europe. verb.*

con·quer·or (kong′kər ər), a person who conquers. *noun.*

con·quest (kon′kwest), **1** the act of conquering: *to gain a country by conquest.* **2** a thing conquered: *Mexico and Peru were important Spanish conquests. noun.*

con·science (kon′shəns), the sense of right and wrong; ideas and feelings within you that tell you when you are doing right and warn you of what is wrong. *noun.*

con·sci·en·tious (kon′shē en′shəs), done with care to make it right: *Conscientious work is careful and exact. adjective.*

con·scious (kon′shəs), **1** having knowledge; aware: *I was conscious of a sharp pain.* **2** aware of what one is doing; awake: *About five minutes after fainting he became conscious again.* **3** done on purpose; intentional: *She made a conscious effort to improve her handwriting. adjective.*

con·scious·ness (kon′shəs nis), **1** being conscious; awareness: *The injured woman lost consciousness.* **2** all the thoughts and feelings of a person. *noun.*

con·se·crate (kon′sə krāt), **1** to set apart as sacred; make holy: *A church is consecrated to worship.* **2** to set apart for a purpose; dedicate: *She consecrated her life to helping the sick. verb,*

con·se·crates, con·se·crat·ed, con·se·crat·ing.

con·sec·u·tive (kən sek′yə tiv), following one right after another: *Monday, Tuesday, and Wednesday are consecutive days of the week.* *adjective.*

con·sent (kən sent′), **1** to agree; give approval or permission: *My parents would not consent to my staying out overnight.* **2** agreement; permission: *We received the owner's consent before we went swimming in his pond.* **1** *verb,* **2** *noun.*

con·se·quence (kon′sə kwens), **1** a result: *He was always late and, as a consequence, he lost his job.* **2** importance: *His opinions are of little consequence to her, so she ignores them.* *noun.*

take the consequences, to accept what happens because of one's action: *She felt that she had to admit her mistake and take the consequences.*

con·se·quent (kon′sə kwent), resulting; following as an effect: *My illness and consequent absence put me behind in my schoolwork.* *adjective.*

con·se·quent·ly (kon′sə kwent′lē), as a result; therefore: *He overslept and, consequently, he was late.* *adverb.*

con·ser·va·tion (kon′sər vā′shən), protection from loss or from being used up; avoidance of waste; preservation: *Conservation of energy saves fuel.* **2** the official protection and care of forests, rivers, and other natural resources. *noun.*

con·ser·va·tion·ist (kon′sər vā′shə nist), a person who wants to preserve and protect the forests, rivers, and other natural resources of a country. *noun.*

con·serv·a·tive (kən sér′və tiv), **1** inclined to keep things as they are or were in the past: *A conservative person distrusts and opposes change and too many new ideas.* **2** a person opposed to change. **3** not inclined to take risks; cautious: *This old, reliable company has conservative business methods.* **1,3** *adjective,* **2** *noun.*

con·serve (kən sérv′), to keep from harm or decay; protect from loss or from being used up; preserve: *to conserve natural resources. Try to conserve your strength for the end of the race.* *verb,* **con·serves, con·served, con·serv·ing.**

con·sid·er (kən sid′ər), **1** to think about in order to decide: *Before you suggest an answer, take time to consider the problem.* **2** to think to be; regard as: *I consider him a very able student.* **3** to allow for; take into account: *This watch runs very well, when you consider how old it is.* **4** to be thoughtful of others and their feelings: *A kind person considers the feelings of others.* *verb.*

con·sid·er·a·ble (kən sid′ər ə bəl), large; important: *$500 is a considerable sum of money.* *adjective.*

con·sid·er·a·bly (kən sid′ər ə blē), much; a good deal: *The boy was considerably older than he looked.* *adverb.*

con·sid·er·ate (kən sid′ər it), thoughtful of others and their feelings: *It was considerate of you to call and let me know that you would be late.* *adjective.*

con·sid·er·a·tion (kən sid′ə rā′shən), **1** careful thought about things in order to decide: *Give*

a hat	i it	oi oil	ch child	a in about
ā age	ī ice	ou out	ng long	e in taken
ä far	o hot	u cup	sh she	ə = { i in pencil
e let	ō open	u̇ put	th thin	o in lemon
ē equal	ô order	ü rule	₮H then	u in circus
ėr term			zh measure	

careful consideration to these questions before answering them. **2** something thought of as a reason: *Price and quality are two considerations in buying anything.* **3** thoughtfulness for others and their feelings: *Playing the radio loud at night shows a lack of consideration for the neighbors.* *noun.*

in consideration of, 1 because of: *In consideration of my bad cold, the teacher let me leave school early.* **2** in return for: *The neighbor gave the girl a dollar in consideration of her help.*

take into consideration, to take into account; consider; make allowance for: *The teacher took my illness into consideration and gave me more time to finish my report.*

under consideration, being thought about: *Her request for a higher salary is under consideration.*

con·sid·er·ing (kən sid′ər ing), taking into account; making allowance for: *Considering her age, the little girl reads very well.* *preposition.*

con·sign (kən sīn′), **1** to hand over; deliver: *His will consigned his property to his sister.* **2** to send: *We will consign the goods to you by express.* *verb.*

con·sist (kən sist′), to be made up: *A week consists of seven days.* *verb.*

con·sist·en·cy (kən sis′tən sē), **1** a degree of firmness or stiffness: *Frosting for a cake must be of the right consistency to spread easily without dripping.* **2** a keeping to the same principles or course: *You show very little consistency if you are always changing your mind.* *noun, plural* **con·sist·en·cies.**

con·sist·ent (kən sis′tənt), **1** thinking or acting today in agreement with what you thought yesterday; keeping to the same principles and habits. **2** harmonious; in agreement: *Driving very fast on a rainy night is not consistent with safety.* *adjective.*

con·so·la·tion (kon′sə lā′shən), **1** comfort. **2** a comforting person, thing, or event. *noun.*

con·sole[1] (kən sōl′), to comfort: *The policeman consoled the lost child by promising to find his parents.* *verb,* **con·soles, con·soled, con·sol·ing.**

con·sole[2] (kon′sōl), a radio, television, or phonograph cabinet made to stand on the floor. *noun.*

con·sol·i·date (kən sol′ə dāt), to unite; combine: *The three banks consolidated and formed a single large bank.* *verb,* **con·sol·i·dates, con·sol·i·dat·ed, con·sol·i·dat·ing.**

con·so·nant (kon′sə nənt), **1** any letter of the alphabet that is not a vowel. *B, c, d,* and *f* are consonants. **2** a sound represented by such a letter or combination of letters. The two consonants in *ship* are spelled by the letters *sh* and *p. noun.*

conspicuous | consumer

con·spic·u·ous (kən spik′yü əs), **1** easily seen: *A traffic light should be placed where it is conspicuous.* **2** remarkable; attracting notice: *conspicuous bravery. adjective.*

conspicuous
(definition 2)
Do you think my hair
is too **conspicuous**
like this?

con·spir·a·cy (kən spir′ə sē), a secret planning with others to do something wrong or unlawful; plot: *a conspiracy to overthrow the government. noun, plural* **con·spir·a·cies.**

con·spir·a·tor (kən spir′ə tər), a person who conspires; one who joins in a plot: *A group of conspirators planned to overthrow the dictator. noun.*

con·spire (kən spīr′), to plan secretly with others to do something wrong or unlawful; plot: *The spies conspired to steal secret government documents. verb,* **con·spires, con·spired, con·spir·ing.**

con·sta·ble (kon′stə bəl *or* kun′stə bəl), a police officer; member of the police. *noun.*

con·stant (kon′stənt), **1** continuous; never stopping: *The clock makes a constant ticking sound.* **2** always the same; not changing: *The ship held a constant course due north. adjective.*

con·stant·ly (kon′stənt lē), **1** always; in every case: *He is constantly late.* **2** without stopping: *If a clock is kept wound it runs constantly.* **3** often: *She has to be reminded constantly to clean her room. adverb.*

con·stel·la·tion (kon′stə lā′shən), a group of stars that forms a recognized pattern. There are 88 constellations in the sky. *noun.*

con·ster·na·tion (kon′stər nā′shən), dismay; alarm: *To our consternation the child darted out in front of the speeding car. noun.*

con·stit·u·ent (kən stich′ü ənt), **1** a part of a whole; necessary part: *Sugar is the main constituent of candy.* **2** one of the voters represented by an elected official: *Senators are eager to hear from their constituents. noun.*

con·sti·tute (kon′stə tüt *or* kon′stə tyüt), **1** to make up; form: *Seven days constitute a week.* **2** to set up; establish: *Schools are constituted by law to teach boys and girls. verb,* **con·sti·tutes, con·sti·tut·ed, con·sti·tut·ing.**

con·sti·tu·tion (kon′stə tü′shən *or* kon′stə tyü′shən), **1** the way in which a person or thing is formed; nature; makeup: *A person with a good constitution is strong and healthy.* **2** the fundamental principles according to which a country, a state, or a society is governed: *Many clubs have written constitutions.* **3** the **Constitution,** the written set of fundamental principles by which the United States is governed. *noun.*

con·sti·tu·tion·al (kon′stə tü′shə nəl *or* kon′stə tyü′shə nəl), **1** of or in the constitution of a person or thing: *A constitutional weakness makes him catch a cold easily.* **2** of or according to the constitution of a nation, state, or group: *The Supreme Court must decide whether this law is constitutional. adjective.*

con·struct (kən strukt′), to put together; fit together; build: *We constructed a raft of logs fastened with rope. verb.*

con·struc·tion (kən struk′shən), **1** the act of constructing; building; putting together: *The construction of the bridge took nearly a year.* **2** the way in which a thing is put together: *Cracks and leaks are signs of poor construction.* **3** something built or put together: *The dolls' house was a construction of wood and cardboard. noun.*

construction paper, a kind of heavy paper, often brightly colored, used to make things especially in schools.

con·struc·tive (kən struk′tiv), helping to improve; useful: *During my report the teacher gave some constructive suggestions that helped me think of ideas I had overlooked. adjective.*

con·sul (kon′səl), an officer appointed by a government to live in some foreign city in order to look after its business interests and to protect its citizens who are traveling or living there. *noun.*

con·sult (kən sult′), **1** to seek information or advice from: *You can consult travelers, books, or maps for help in planning a trip abroad.* **2** to exchange ideas; talk things over: *She consulted with her lawyer before signing the contract. verb.*

con·sult·ant (kən sult′nt), a person hired to provide technical or professional advice. *noun.*

con·sume (kən süm′), **1** to use up; spend: *Rockets consume large quantities of fuel when they take off.* **2** to eat or drink up: *We will each consume at least two sandwiches on our hike.* **3** to destroy; burn up: *A huge fire consumed the forest. verb,* **con·sumes, con·sumed, con·sum·ing.**

con·sum·er (kən sü′mər), **1** a person who buys and uses food, clothing, or anything grown or made by someone else: *A low price for wheat should reduce the price of flour to the consumer.* **2** a living thing that has to eat in order to stay alive. Animals are consumers, but plants make their own food. *noun.*

con·sump·tion (kən sump′shən), **1** the act of using up; use: *We took along some food for our consumption on the trip.* **2** the amount used up: *The consumption of gasoline on our driving trip was about 20 gallons per day. noun.*

con·tact (kon′takt), **1** the condition of touching; touching together: *A magnet will draw iron filings into contact with it.* **2** a connection: *The control tower lost radio contact with the airplane pilot.* **3** to get in touch with; make a connection with: *I've been trying to contact you for two days.* **1,2** *noun,* **3** *verb.*

contact lens, a very small, thin, plastic lens fitted on the front of the eyeball to improve vision.

con·ta·gious (kən tā′jəs), **1** catching; spreading by infection: *Mumps is a contagious disease.* **2** easily spreading from one to another: *Yawning is often contagious. adjective.*

con·tain (kən tān′), **1** to have within itself; hold as contents: *My wallet contains two dollars. Books contain information.* **2** to be equal to: *A pound contains 16 ounces.* **3** to hold back; control one's feelings: *She could not contain her excitement over winning the contest. verb.*

con·tain·er (kən tā′nər), a box, can, jar, carton, or anything used to contain something. *noun.*

con·tam·i·nate (kən tam′ə nāt), to make impure by contact or by mixing; pollute: *The water was contaminated by sewage. verb,* **con·tam·i·nates, con·tam·i·nat·ed, con·tam·i·nat·ing.**

con·tem·plate (kon′təm plāt), **1** to look at or think about for a long time: *I will contemplate your offer. We contemplated the beautiful mountain landscape.* **2** to have in mind; expect; intend: *She is contemplating a trip to Europe. verb,* **con·tem·plates, con·tem·plat·ed, con·tem·plat·ing.**

con·tem·pla·tion (kon′təm plā′shən), the act of looking at or thinking about something for a long time; deep thought. *noun.*

contemplation
She seemed lost
in **contemplation.**

con·tem·po·rar·y (kən tem′pə rer′ē), **1** belonging to the same period of time: *The telephone and the phonograph were contemporary inventions.* **2** a person who belongs to the same period of time as another: *Abraham Lincoln and Robert E. Lee were contemporaries.* **3** of the present time; modern: *The book had contemporary children's stories in addition to the old fairy tales.* **1,3** *adjective,* **2** *noun, plural* **con·tem·po·rar·ies.**

a hat	**i** it	**oi** oil	**ch** child	a in about
ā age	**ī** ice	**ou** out	**ng** long	e in taken
ä far	**o** hot	**u** cup	**sh** she	ə = { i in pencil
e let	**ō** open	**ù** put	**th** thin	o in lemon
ē equal	**ô** order	**ü** rule	**ŦH** then	u in circus
ėr term			**zh** measure	

con·tempt (kən tempt′), **1** scorn; feeling that a person or act is shameful and disgraceful: *to feel contempt for a cheat.* **2** the condition of being despised; disgrace: *The traitor was held in contempt. noun.*

con·tempt·i·ble (kən temp′tə bəl), deserving contempt or scorn: *Cruelty is contemptible. adjective.*

con·tend (kən tend′), **1** to fight; struggle: *The first settlers in New England had to contend with harsh winters, sickness, and lack of food.* **2** to take part in a contest: *Five runners were contending in the first race.* **3** to declare to be true; state: *Most doctors contend that cigarette smoking is dangerous to one's health. verb.*

con·tent[1] (kon′tent), **1 a contents,** what is contained in anything; all the things inside: *An old chair, a desk, and a bed were the only contents of the room.* **b** chapters or sections in a book. A **table of contents** gives a list of these. **2** what is written in a book; what is said in a speech: *I didn't understand the content of his speech.* **3** the amount contained: *Maple syrup has a high sugar content. noun.*

con·tent[2] (kən tent′), **1** to satisfy; please: *Nothing contents me when I am sick.* **2** satisfied; pleased: *Will you be content to wait till tomorrow?* **3** contentment; satisfaction: *The cat lay beside the fire in sleepy content.* **1** *verb,* **2** *adjective,* **3** *noun.*

con·tent·ed (kən ten′tid), satisfied: *A contented person is happy with things as they are. adjective.*

con·ten·tion (kən ten′shən), **1** a statement or point that one has argued for: *Columbus's contention that the earth was round turned out to be correct.* **2** an arguing; disputing; quarreling: *There was some contention about choosing a captain for the baseball team. noun.*

con·tent·ment (kən tent′mənt), satisfaction; being pleased; happiness. *noun.*

con·test (kon′test), **1** a trial of skill to see which can win. A game or race is a contest. **2** a dispute; struggle; fight: *The contest for control of the country ended when the rebel leaders were killed in battle. noun.*

con·test·ant (kən tes′tənt), a person who takes part in a contest: *My sister was a contestant in the 100-yard dash. noun.*

con·text (kon′tekst), the part directly before and after a word or sentence that influences its meaning. You can often tell the meaning of a word from its use in context. *noun.*

[*Context* comes from a Latin word meaning "to weave together." The context of a word was thought of as a kind of fabric or woven structure around it.]

con·ti·nent (kon′tə nənt), one of the seven great masses of land on the earth. The continents are North America, South America, Europe, Africa, Asia, Australia, and Antarctica. *noun.*

con·ti·nent·al (kon′tə nen′tl), of a continent; like a continent. *adjective.*

con·tin·u·al (kən tin′yü əl), 1 never stopping: *the continual flow of the river.* 2 repeated many times; very frequent: *I can't study with these continual interruptions. adjective.*

con·tin·u·al·ly (kən tin′yü ə lē), 1 always; without stopping: *A doctor is continually on call.* 2 again and again; very frequently: *I am continually losing my gloves. adverb.*

con·tin·u·ance (kən tin′yü əns), a continuing; going on: *We disagree so much that there is no point in the continuance of this talk. noun.*

con·tin·u·a·tion (kən tin′yü ā′shən), 1 the act of going on with a thing: *Continuation of my reading was hard after so many interruptions.* 2 anything by which a thing is continued; added part: *The continuation of the story will be seen on next week's program. noun.*

con·tin·ue (kən tin′yü), 1 to keep on; not stop; last; cause to last: *The road continues for miles.* 2 to go on after stopping: *The story will be continued next week.* 3 to stay; remain; last: *She will continue as class president next year. verb,* **con·tin·ues, con·tin·ued, con·tin·u·ing.**

con·ti·nu·i·ty (kon′tə nü′ə tē *or* kon′tə nyü′ə tē), a going on without stopping; continuing without interruption: *The continuity of his story was broken when the telephone rang. noun.*

con·tin·u·ous (kən tin′yü əs), connected; unbroken; without a stop: *a continuous sound, a continuous line of cars. adjective.*

con·tor·tion (kən tôr′shən), 1 a twisting out of shape. 2 a twisted condition. *noun.*

contortion (definition 2)
The **contortions** of the dancer were amazing.

con·tour (kon′tùr), 1 an outline: *The contour of the Atlantic coast of America is very irregular.* 2 following natural ridges and hollows to avoid erosion: *Contour plowing allows farmers to grow crops on the sides of steep hills.* 1 *noun,* 2 *adjective.*

con·tract (kən trakt′ *for 1-3;* kon′trakt *for 4;* kon′trakt *or* kən trakt′ *for 5),* 1 to draw together; make or become shorter or smaller: *The earthworm contracted its body. A balloon contracts when the air is let out of it.* 2 to shorten a word or phrase by omitting some of the letters or sounds: *In talking and writing we often contract "do not" to "don't."* 3 to bring on oneself; get; form: *Bad habits, once contracted, are hard to get rid of.* 4 an agreement, often in writing, by which two or more people promise to do or not to do certain things. A contract can be enforced by law. 5 to make a contract: *The builder contracted to build a new house for a certain price.* 1-3,5 *verb,* 4 *noun.*

con·trac·tion (kən trak′shən), 1 a shrinking; drawing together: *The contraction of mercury by cold makes it go down in thermometers.* 2 something contracted; a shortened form: *"Can't" is a contraction of "cannot." noun.*

con·trac·tor (kon′trak tər *or* kən trak′tər), a person who agrees to supply materials or to do a piece of work for a certain price: *My family hired a contractor to build our new house. noun.*

con·tra·dict (kon′trə dikt′), 1 to say that a statement is not true; deny: *I contradicted the rumor that I was moving to another town.* 2 to say the opposite of what a person has said: *Not only did she contradict him, she said that he was not telling the truth.* 3 to be opposite to; disagree with: *Your story and her story contradict each other. verb.*

con·tra·dic·tion (kon′trə dik′shən), 1 a denying what has been said: *The expert spoke without fear of contradiction by his listeners.* 2 a statement that contradicts another; denial. 3 a disagreement. *noun.*

con·tra·dic·tor·y (kon′trə dik′tər ē), contradicting; in disagreement; saying the opposite: *Reports of what had happened were so contradictory that we didn't know what to believe. adjective.*

con·tral·to (kən tral′tō), 1 the lowest singing voice of a woman. 2 a singer with such a voice. *noun, plural* **con·tral·tos.**

con·trap·tion (kən trap′shən), a device or gadget. *noun.*

contraption
This **contraption** helps the dog walk even though it has two broken legs.

con·tra·ry (kon′trer ē *for 1 and 2;* kən trer′ē *for 3*), **1** opposed; opposite; completely different: *Her taste in music is contrary to mine.* **2** the opposite: *After promising to come early, she did the contrary and came late.* **3** opposing others; stubborn: *The contrary boy often refused to do what was suggested.* **1,3** *adjective,* **2** *noun.*

on the contrary, exactly opposite to what has been said: *He is not stingy; on the contrary, no one could be more generous.*

contrast
(definition 1)

con·trast (kon′trast *for 1 and 2;* kən trast′ *for 3 and 4*), **1** a difference; a great difference: *There is a clear contrast between life now and life years ago.* **2** a person, thing, or event that shows differences when put side by side with another: *Her dark hair is a sharp contrast to her brother's light hair.* **3** to compare two things so as to show their differences: *She contrasted the advantages of her plan with the weaknesses of mine.* **4** to be different from something else when placed in comparison: *Her interest in sports contrasts with her brother's liking for books.* **1,2** *noun,* **3,4** *verb.*

in contrast, by comparison; as opposed to: *In contrast to yours, my grades are not good.*

con·trib·ute (kən trib′yüt), **1** to give money or help: *Will you contribute to the Red Cross? Everyone was asked to contribute suggestions for the party.* **2** to write articles or stories for a newspaper or magazine. *verb,* **con·trib·utes, con·trib·ut·ed, con·trib·ut·ing.**

contribute to, to help bring about: *A poor diet contributed to the child's bad health.*

con·tri·bu·tion (kon′trə byü′shən), **1** the act of contributing; giving money or help: *Contribution to worthy causes is her favorite activity.* **2** the money or help contributed; gift: *Our contribution to the picnic was the lemonade.* **3** something written for a newspaper or magazine. *noun.*

con·trite (kən trīt′ *or* kon′trīt), **1** sorry for doing something wrong; repentant: *I felt contrite after losing my temper and hitting my friend.* **2** showing deep regret: *I wrote a contrite apology. adjective.*

a hat	i it	oi oil	ch child	⎧ a in about
ā age	ī ice	ou out	ng long	e in taken
ä far	o hot	u cup	sh she	ə = ⎨ i in pencil
e let	ō open	ů put	th thin	o in lemon
ē equal	ô order	ü rule	ŦH then	⎩ u in circus
ėr term			zh measure	

con·triv·ance (kən trī′vəns), a thing invented; mechanical device: *A can opener is a handy contrivance. noun.*

con·trive (kən trīv′), to invent; design: *The inventor had contrived a new engine. verb,* **con·trives, con·trived, con·triv·ing.**

con·trol (kən trōl′), **1** to have power or authority over; direct: *The government controls the printing of money.* **2** power; authority; direction: *Children are under their parents' control.* **3** to hold back; keep down: *I was so upset by the accident that I couldn't control my tears.* **4** the ability to keep back or hold down; restraint: *Try not to lose control of your temper.* **5** a device on or connected to a machine that starts, stops, or adjusts its operation: *This control starts the dishwasher.* **6** the **controls,** the instruments and devices by which an airplane, car, or other machine is operated. **1,3** *verb,* **con·trols, con·trolled, con·trol·ling;** **2,4-6** *noun.*

control tower, a tower at an airfield for controlling the taking off and landing of aircraft.

con·tro·ver·sial (kon′trə vėr′shəl), open to argument or dispute: *The possibility of closing a school is a controversial topic in our town. adjective.*

con·tro·ver·sy (kon′trə vėr′sē), a dispute; a long dispute; argument: *The controversy between the company and the union ended after the strike was settled. noun, plural* **con·tro·ver·sies.**

con·va·lesce (kon′və les′), to recover health and strength after illness: *I convalesced at home for a week after my operation. verb,* **con·va·lesc·es, con·va·lesced, con·va·lesc·ing.**

con·va·les·cent (kon′və les′nt), **1** recovering health and strength after illness. **2** a person recovering after illness. **1** *adjective,* **2** *noun.*

con·vec·tion (kən vek′shən), the transfer of heat from one place to another by the movement of heated particles of a gas or a liquid. *noun.*

con·vene (kən vēn′), to gather together; assemble: *Congress convenes at least once a year. verb,* **con·venes, con·vened, con·ven·ing.**

con·ven·ience (kən vē′nyəns), **1** a being convenient: *The convenience of packaged goods increases their sale.* **2** comfort; advantage: *Many national parks have camping places for the convenience of tourists.* **3** anything handy or easy to use; thing that saves trouble or work: *We find our folding table a great convenience. noun.*

at your convenience, when it is convenient for you: *Come by to pick me up at your convenience.*

con·ven·ient (kən vē′nyənt), **1** suitable; saving trouble; well arranged; easy to use: *to take a convenient bus, to live in a convenient house.*

2 easily done; not troublesome: *Will it be convenient for you to bring your lunch to school?* **3** within easy reach; handy: *to meet at a convenient place. adjective.*

con·vent (kon′vent), **1** a group of nuns living together. **2** the building or buildings in which they live. *noun.*

con·ven·tion (kən ven′shən), **1** a meeting arranged for some particular purpose: *The Democratic and Republican parties hold conventions every four years to choose candidates for President.* **2** a custom or practice approved by general agreement: *Using the right hand to shake hands is a convention. noun.*

con·ven·tion·al (kən ven′shə nəl), **1** according to conventions; customary: *"Good morning" is a conventional greeting.* **2** acting or behaving according to commonly accepted and approved ways: *The people living next door are quiet, conventional people. adjective.*

conventional (definition 1)—It used to be **conventional** for everyone to do the laundry on Monday morning.

con·ver·sa·tion (kon′vər sā′shən), a friendly talk; exchange of thoughts by talking informally together. *noun.*

con·verse (kən vėrs′), to talk together in an informal way. *verb,* **con·vers·es, con·versed, con·vers·ing.**

con·ver·sion (kən vėr′zhən), **1** a turning; a change: *Heat causes the conversion of water into steam.* **2** a change from one belief to another or from lack of belief to faith. *noun.*

con·vert (kən vėrt′ *for 1 and 2;* kon′vėrt′ *for 3*), **1** to change; turn: *The generators at the dam convert water power into electricity. One last effort converted defeat into victory.* **2** to cause to change from one belief to another or from lack of belief to faith: *Missionaries tried to convert the villagers.* **3** a person who has been converted to a different belief or faith. **1,2** *verb,* **3** *noun.*

con·vert·i·ble (kən vėr′tə bəl), **1** capable of being converted: *A dollar bill is convertible into ten dimes.* **2** an automobile with a folding top. **1** *adjective,* **2** *noun.*

con·vex (kon veks′ *or* kon′veks), curved out, like the outside of a sphere or circle: *The lens of an automobile headlight is convex on the outside. adjective.*

con·vey (kən vā′), **1** to carry: *A bus conveyed the passengers to the airport. A wire conveys an electric current.* **2** to make known; communicate: *Do the author's words convey any meaning to you? verb.*

con·vey·or belt or **con·vey·er belt** (kən vā′ər belt′), a broad belt with its ends joined together that revolves on rollers and carries things from place to place in a factory, store, or other place of business.

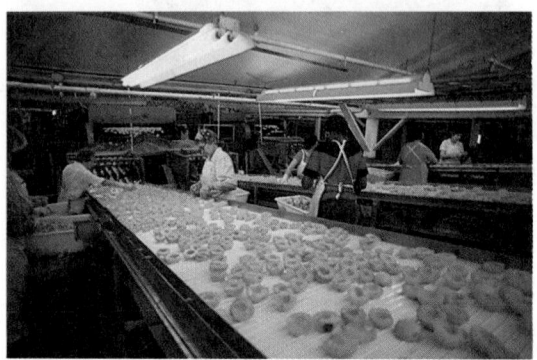

conveyor belt—The workers are sorting peaches that are moving on a **conveyor belt.**

con·vict (kən vikt′ *for 1;* kon′vikt *for 2*), **1** to prove or declare guilty: *The jury convicted the accused woman of stealing.* **2** a person serving a prison sentence for some crime. **1** *verb,* **2** *noun.*

con·vic·tion (kən vik′shən), **1** a proving or declaring guilty: *The trial resulted in the conviction of the accused man.* **2** a firm belief: *It is my conviction that you are right. noun.*

con·vince (kən vins′), to make a person feel sure; cause to believe; persuade firmly: *The mistakes she made convinced me that she had not studied her lesson. verb,* **con·vinc·es, con·vinced, con·vinc·ing.**

con·voy (kən voi′ *or* kon′voi *for 1;* kon′voi *for 2 and 3*), **1** to go with in order to protect; escort: *Armed guards convoyed the gold to the bank.* **2** a group of ships or motor vehicles traveling together for protection or convenience. **3** the warships or soldiers that convoy. **1** *verb,* **2,3** *noun.*

con·vulse (kən vuls′), **1** to shake violently: *An earthquake convulsed the island, damaging many of the buildings.* **2** to throw into fits of laughter; cause to shake with laughter: *The clown's funny antics convulsed the audience. verb,* **con·vuls·es, con·vulsed, con·vuls·ing.**

con·vul·sion (kən vul′shən), a violent disturbance: *An earthquake is a convulsion of the earth. noun.*

coo (kü), **1** the soft, murmuring sound made by doves or pigeons. **2** to make this sound. **3** to murmur softly: *to coo to a baby.* **1** *noun, plural* **coos;** **2,3** *verb,* **coos, cooed, coo·ing.**

cook (kůk), **1** to prepare food by using heat. Boiling, frying, broiling, roasting, and baking are forms of cooking. **2** to undergo cooking; be cooked: *Let the meat cook slowly.* **3** a person who cooks. 1,2 *verb,* 3 *noun.*

cook up, to make up or prepare, especially something false: *We cooked up an excuse for being late.*

cook·book (kůk′bůk′), a book of directions for cooking various kinds of food; book of recipes. *noun.*

cook·ie or **cook·y** (kůk′ē), a small, flat, sweet cake. *noun, plural* **cook·ies.**

[The words *cookie* and *cooky* look as if they come from the word *cook.* Actually they come from a Dutch word meaning "little cake."]

cook·out (kůk′out′), a picnic where the food is cooked outdoors on a grill. *noun.*

cool (kül), **1** somewhat cold; more cold than hot: *a cool day.* **2** allowing or giving a cool feeling: *a cool, thin shirt.* **3** not excited; calm: *Everyone kept cool when paper in the wastebasket caught fire.* **4** having little enthusiasm or interest; not cordial: *My former friend gave me a cool greeting.* **5** something cool; cool part, place, or time: *in the cool of the evening.* **6** to make or become cool: *Ice cools water. The ground cools off after the sun goes down.* **7** very good; excellent: *That movie was so cool that it was worth seeing twice.* **8** calmness; presence of mind: *He was so upset by the accident that he lost his cool completely.* 1-4,7 *adjective,* 5,8 *noun,* 6 *verb.*

coon (kün), a raccoon. *noun.*

coop (küp), **1** a small cage or pen for chickens, rabbits, or other small animals. **2** to keep in a coop; confine in a small place: *The children were cooped up in the house by the rain.* 1 *noun,* 2 *verb.*

co·op·e·rate (kō op′ə rāt′), to work together. *verb,* **co·op·e·rates, co·op·e·rat·ed, co·op·e·rat·ing.**

cooperate—They **cooperated** and got the job done quickly.

co·op·e·ra·tion (kō op′ə rā′shən), working together; united effort or labor: *Cooperation can accomplish what no individual could do alone. noun.*

co·op·er·a·tive (kō op′ər ə tiv *or* kō op′ə rā′tiv), wanting or willing to work together with others. *adjective.*

co·or·di·nate (kō ôrd′n āt), to work or cause to work together in the proper way; fit together: *Coordinating the movements of the arms and legs is the hardest part of learning to swim. verb,* **co·or·di·nates, co·or·di·nat·ed, co·or·di·nat·ing.**

co·or·di·na·tion (kō ôrd′n ā′shən), acting or working together in a smooth way: *Muscular coordination is important to an athlete. noun.*

cope (kōp), to struggle and not fail; struggle with some chance of success; deal successfully: *She was busy but was still able to cope with the extra work. verb,* **copes, coped, cop·ing.**

co·pi·lot (kō′pī′lət), the assistant or second pilot in an aircraft. *noun.*

co·pi·ous (kō′pē əs), more than enough; plentiful; abundant: *a copious harvest. adjective.*

cop·per (kop′ər), **1** a reddish-brown metal, easy to work with. Copper is a chemical element. It is an excellent conductor of heat and electricity. **2** made of this metal: *a copper kettle.* **3** reddish-brown: *She had copper hair.* 1 *noun,* 2,3 *adjective.*

cop·per·head (kop′ər hed′), a poisonous snake of North America. It has a copper-colored head. *noun.*

cop·y (kop′ē), **1** a thing made to be just like another. A written page, a picture, a dress, or a piece of furniture can be an exact copy of another. **2** to make a copy of: *Copy this page. I copied the painting.* **3** to be a copy of; follow as an example; imitate: *to copy someone's way of dressing.* **4** one of a number of books, magazines, newspapers, or pictures made at the same printing: *Please get six copies of today's newspaper.* 1,4 *noun, plural* **cop·ies;** 2,3 *verb,* **cop·ies, cop·ied, cop·y·ing.**

cop·y·cat (kop′ē kat′), a person who imitates another. *noun.*

co·ral (kôr′əl), **1** a hard substance made up of the skeletons of tiny sea animals. Red, pink, and white coral is often used for jewelry. **2** deep-pink; red. 1 *noun,* 2 *adjective.*

coral
(definition 1)

coral snake
about 18 inches to 4 feet (46 centimeters to 1 meter) long

coral snake, a small, poisonous American snake whose body has alternate rings of red, yellow, and black.

cord (kôrd), **1** a thick string; very thin rope: *He tied the package with a cord.* **2** a length of flexible electrical wire, covered with plastic or cloth, with a plug at one end, that connects an appliance to an outlet. **3** a structure like a cord in an animal body. The spinal cord is in the backbone. **4** a unit for measuring cut wood equal to 128 cubic feet. A pile of wood 4 feet wide, 4 feet high, and 8 feet long is a cord. *noun.*

cor·dial (kôr′jəl), sincere; hearty; warm; friendly: *My friends gave me a cordial welcome. adjective.*

cor·di·al·i·ty (kôr′jē al′ə tē), a cordial quality; cordial feeling; heartiness; warm friendliness: *The cordiality of his welcome made me feel at home. noun.*

cor·du·roy (kôr′də roi′), a thick cotton or rayon cloth with close, raised ribs or ridges that run lengthwise along the cloth. *noun.*

core (kôr), **1** the hard, central part containing the seeds of fruits like apples and pears: *After eating the apple he threw the core away.* **2** the central or most important part: *She is honest to the core. The core of the senator's speech was that we must not waste natural resources.* **3** the central or innermost part of the earth. **4** to take out the core of fruit: *We cored the apples.* **1-3** *noun,* **4** *verb,* **cores, cored, cor·ing.**

cork (kôrk), **1** the light, thick, outer bark of a kind of oak tree. Cork is used for bottle stoppers, floats for fishing lines, filling for some kinds of life preservers, and some floor coverings. **2** a bottle stopper made of cork or other material. **3** to stop up with a cork: *Fill and cork these bottles.* **1,2** *noun,* **3** *verb.*

cork·screw (kôrk′skrü′), a tool that can be screwed into corks to remove them from bottles. A corkscrew is a long, twisted piece of metal with a sharp point and a handle. *noun.*

corn[1] (kôrn), the grain of a kind of cereal grass, or the plant that it grows on. Corn grows on large ears. Corn is used as food for people and farm animals. Also called **maize** or **Indian corn.** *noun.*

corn[2] (kôrn), a hard, shiny thickening of the skin, usually on a toe. Shoes that rub or fit too tightly can cause painful corns. *noun.*

corn·bread (kôrn′bred′), a bread made of cornmeal. *noun.*

corn·cob (kôrn′kob′), the central, woody part of an ear of corn, on which the kernels grow. *noun.*

cor·ne·a (kôr′nē ə), the transparent part of the outer coat of the eyeball. It covers the iris and the pupil. *noun.*

corned (kôrnd), preserved with strong salt water or dry salt: *corned beef. adjective.*

cor·ner (kôr′nər), **1** the place where two lines or surfaces meet; angle: *the corner of a room. I watched what she was doing out of the corner of my eye.* **2** the place where two streets meet: *There is a traffic light at the corner.* **3** at a corner: *a corner house.* **4** for a corner: *a corner cupboard.* **5** a region; part; place that is far away: *People have searched in all corners of the earth for gold.* **6** a difficult place: *His enemies had driven him into a corner.* **7** to force into an awkward or difficult position; drive into a corner: *This question cornered him. Workers at the zoo cornered the lion in the alley and returned it to its cage.* **1,2,5,6** *noun,* **3,4** *adjective,* **7** *verb.*

cor·net (kôr net′), a wind instrument like a trumpet, usually made of brass. *noun.*

cornet

corn·field (kôrn′fēld′), a field in which corn is grown. *noun.*

corn·flakes (kôrn′flāks′), a dry breakfast cereal made of crisp flakes of corn, usually served cold in a bowl with milk and sugar. *noun plural.*

corn·meal (kôrn′mēl′), coarsely ground dried corn. *noun.*

corn·stalk (kôrn′stôk′), a stalk of corn. *noun.*

corn·starch (kôrn′stärch′), a starchy flour made from corn, used to thicken puddings, gravies, and other foods. *noun.*

corn·y (kôr′nē), outdated, sentimental, or commonplace: *a corny movie. No one laughed at his corny jokes. adjective,* **corn·i·er, corn·i·est.**

co·ro·na·tion (kôr′ə nā′shən), the ceremony of crowning a king, queen, emperor, or empress. *noun.*

cor·po·ral[1] (kôr′pər əl), of the body: *Spanking someone is corporal punishment. adjective.*

cor·po·ral[2] (kôr′pər əl), the lowest ranking officer in the army. A corporal is higher than a private and lower than a sergeant. *noun.*

cor·po·ra·tion (kôr′pə rā′shən), a group of persons who obtain a charter giving them as a group certain rights and privileges. A corporation can buy and sell, own property, and manufacture and ship products as if its members were a single person. *noun.*

corps (kôr), **1** a group of soldiers, trained for special military service: *the Medical Corps, the Signal Corps.* **2** a group of people with special training, organized for working together: *A large hospital has a corps of nurses. noun, plural* **corps** (kôrz).

corpse (kôrps), a dead human body. *noun.*

cor·pu·lent (kôr′pyə lənt), large or bulky of body; fat. *adjective.*

cor·pus·cle (kôr′pus′əl), any of the cells that form a large part of blood. Red corpuscles carry oxygen from the lungs to various parts of the body; some white corpuscles destroy disease germs. *noun.*

cor·ral (kə ral′), **1** a pen for horses, cattle, and other animals. **2** to drive into or keep in a corral: *The cowhands corralled the herd of wild ponies.* **3** to hem in; surround; capture: *The reporters corralled the mayor and began asking questions.* **1** *noun,* **2,3** *verb,* **cor·rals, cor·ralled, cor·ral·ling.**

cor·rect (kə rekt′), **1** free from mistakes; true; right: *She gave the correct answer.* **2** agreeing with an accepted standard of good behavior; proper: *correct manners.* **3** to mark the mistakes in or remove the mistakes from: *The teacher corrected our tests and returned them to us.* **4** to change to what is right or what agrees with some standard: *I wear braces to correct my crooked teeth.* **5** to set right by punishing; find fault with to improve: *to correct a child for misbehaving.* **1,2** *adjective,* **3-5** *verb.*

cor·rec·tion (kə rek′shən), **1** a correcting; setting right: *The correction of all my mistakes took nearly an hour.* **2** something put in place of an error or mistake: *Write in your corrections neatly so I can read them. noun.*

cor·re·spond (kôr′ə spond′), **1** to agree; be the same as: *Her answers correspond with mine.* **2** to be similar: *The fins of a fish correspond to the wings of a bird.* **3** to exchange letters; write letters to one another: *Will you correspond with me while I am away? verb.*

cor·re·spond·ence (kôr′ə spon′dəns), **1** agreement: *Your account of the accident has little correspondence with the story the other witness told.* **2** an exchange of letters; letter writing: *The boy kept up a correspondence with his friend in Europe.* **3** letters: *Bring me the correspondence concerning that order. noun.*

cor·re·spond·ent (kôr′ə spon′dənt), **1** a person who exchanges letters with another: *My cousin and I are correspondents.* **2** a person employed to send news from a distant place: *There was a report on the news tonight from the correspondent in China. noun.*

cor·ri·dor (kôr′ə dər), a long hallway; passage in

a large building into which rooms open: *Our classroom is at the end of a corridor. noun.*

cor·rode (kə rōd′), to eat away gradually: *Moisture corrodes iron. verb,* **cor·rodes, cor·rod·ed, cor·rod·ing.**

cor·ru·gat·ed (kôr′ə gā′tid), bent or shaped into wavy folds or ridges: *The carton was made of corrugated cardboard. adjective.*

cor·rupt (kə rupt′), **1** influenced by bribes; dishonest: *a corrupt judge.* **2** to influence by bribes; make dishonest; bribe: *That judge cannot be corrupted.* **3** wicked: *He became a thief and led a corrupt life.* **4** to make evil or wicked: *Bad companions may corrupt a person.* **1,3** *adjective,* **2,4** *verb.*

cor·rup·tion (kə rup′shən), a being influenced by bribes; dishonesty: *The police force must be kept free from corruption. noun.*

cor·sage (kôr säzh′), a small bouquet to be worn on the waist or shoulder of a woman's clothes, or on her wrist. *noun.*

corsage

cor·set (kôr′sit), a stiff, close-fitting piece of underwear worn about the waist and hips to support or shape the body. *noun.*

cos·met·ic (koz met′ik), a preparation for beautifying the skin or hair. Powder and rouge are cosmetics. *noun.*

cos·mic (koz′mik), **1** having to do with the whole universe: *Cosmic forces produce stars and planets.* **2** vast: *a cosmic explosion. adjective.*

cos·mos (koz′məs), the universe thought of as an orderly, harmonious system. *noun.*

cost (kôst), **1** the price paid: *The cost of this watch was $10.* **2** to be obtained at the price of: *This watch costs $10.* **3** a loss; sacrifice: *The fox escaped from the trap at the cost of a leg.* **4** to cause the loss or sacrifice of: *A thoughtless remark almost cost me a friend.* **1,3** *noun,* **2,4** *verb,* **costs, cost, cost·ing.**

Cos·ta Ri·ca (kos′tə rē′kə), a country in Central America.

cost·ly (kôst′lē), **1** of great value: *costly jewels.* **2** costing much: *He made a costly mistake and had to do his work over.* adjective, **cost·li·er, cost·li·est.**

cos·tume (kos′tüm *or* kos′tyüm), **1** a way of dressing, including the way the hair is worn: *The kimono is part of the national costume of Japan.* **2** clothing worn on the stage, or for fun: *a Halloween costume. The actors wore colonial costumes.* noun.

co·sy (kō′zē). See **cozy.** adjective, **co·si·er, co·si·est.**

cot (kot), a narrow bed, sometimes made of canvas stretched on a frame that folds together. noun.

cot·tage (kot′ij), **1** a small house. **2** a house at a summer resort. noun.

cottage cheese, a soft, white cheese made from the curds of sour skim milk.

cot·ton (kot′n), **1** a plant that produces soft, white fibers in a fluffy mass around its seeds. The fibers are used in making fabrics or thread. **2** a cloth made of cotton: *I like to wear cotton in hot weather.* noun.

cotton (definition 1)

cot·ton·mouth (kot′n mouth′), a poisonous American snake; water moccasin. noun, plural **cot·ton·mouths** (kot′n mouŦHZ′).

cot·ton·tail (kot′n tāl′), a common American wild rabbit with a fluffy, white tail. noun.

cot·ton·wood (kot′n wůd′), **1** a kind of American poplar tree with tufts that look like cotton on its seeds. **2** the soft wood of this tree. noun.

couch (kouch), a long seat, usually upholstered and having a back and arms; sofa. noun, plural **couch·es.**

cou·gar (kü′gər), a puma. noun.

cough (kôf), **1** to force air from the lungs with sudden effort and noise. **2** the act or sound of coughing. **3** a condition of repeated coughing: *I had a bad cough.* **1** verb, **2,3** noun.

could (kůd), **1** was able; was able to: *She could ski very well.* See **can**[1]. **2** might be able to: *Perhaps I could go with you tomorrow.* verb.

could·n't (kůd′nt), could not.

coun·cil (koun′səl), **1** a group of people called together to give advice and to discuss or settle questions. **2** a group of people elected by citizens to make laws for and manage a city or town. noun.

coun·ci·lor or **coun·cil·lor** (koun′sə lər), a member of a council. noun.

coun·sel (koun′səl), **1** advice: *A wise person gives good counsel.* **2** a lawyer or group of lawyers: *Each side of a case in a court of law has its own counsel.* **3** to give advice to; advise: *My teacher counseled me to join the school band.* **1,2** noun, **3** verb, **coun·sels, coun·seled, coun·sel·ing.**

coun·se·lor (koun′sə lər), **1** a person who gives advice; adviser. **2** a lawyer. **3** an instructor or leader in a summer camp. noun.

count[1] (kount), **1** to name numbers in order: *The child can count from one to ten.* **2** to add up; find the number of: *I counted the books and found there were fifty.* **3** an adding up; finding out how many: *The count showed more than 5000 votes had been cast.* **4** the total number; amount: *The exact count was 5170 votes.* **5** to include or be included in the total number; take or be taken into account: *Your first race is only for practice; it won't count.* **6** to have an influence; be of account or value: *Every vote counts in an election. Every penny counts.* **7** to depend; rely: *We count on your help.* **1,2,5-7** verb, **3,4** noun.

count on, to expect; allow for: *I hadn't counted on your coming so early; I'm not ready yet.*

count[2] (kount), a European nobleman about equal in rank to an English earl. noun.

count·down (kount′doun′), the calling out of the minutes or seconds left before the launching of a missile, rocket, or the like. This is done by counting backwards from a certain time to zero. noun.

coun·te·nance (koun′tə nəns), **1** the expression of the face. **2** a face; features: *a person with a noble countenance.* noun.

countenance (definition 1) The general was a man of stern **countenance.**

count·er[1] (koun′tər), **1** a long, flat, raised surface on which food is prepared or eaten, goods are displayed and sold, money is counted, and the like. **2** a thing used for counting. noun.

coun·ter[2] (koun′tər), **1** opposed; contrary; in the opposite way: *Your plans are counter to ours.* **2** to act or go against; oppose: *He countered my plan with one of his own.* **1** *adverb, adjective,* **2** *verb.*

coun·ter·act (koun′tər akt′), to act against; hinder: *A hot bath will sometimes counteract a chill. verb.*

coun·ter·clock·wise (koun′tər klok′wīz′), in the direction opposite to that in which the hands of a clock go; from right to left. *adverb, adjective.*

coun·ter·feit (koun′tər fit), **1** to copy something in order to deceive: *They were arrested for counterfeiting twenty-dollar bills.* **2** something copied and passed as genuine: *This twenty-dollar bill looks genuine, but it is a counterfeit.* **3** not genuine: *a counterfeit stamp.* **1** *verb,* **2** *noun,* **3** *adjective.*

coun·ter·part (koun′tər pärt′), a person or thing closely resembling another: *She is the counterpart of her twin sister. noun.*

count·ess (koun′tis), **1** the wife or widow of a count or an earl. **2** a woman whose rank is equal to that of a count or an earl. *noun, plural* **count·ess·es.**

count·less (kount′lis), too many to count: *The sky is filled with countless stars. adjective.*

coun·try (kun′trē), **1** land; region: *The country out beyond the river is rough and hilly.* **2** the land of a group of people united under the same government and usually speaking the same language: *France is a country in Europe.* **3** the land where a person was born or where he or she is a citizen: *The United States is my country.* **4** the people of a nation: *The country rejoiced when the war ended.* **5** the land outside of cities and towns: *She likes the farms and fields of the country.* **6** of the country; in the country: *He likes hearty country food and fresh country air.* **1-5** *noun, plural* **coun·tries; 6** *adjective.*

coun·try·man (kun′trē mən), a person of one's own country. *noun, plural* **coun·try·men.**

coun·try·side (kun′trē sīd′), the land outside of cities and towns: *I saw many cows in the countryside. noun.*

coun·ty (koun′tē), **1** one of the districts into which a state or country is divided for purposes of government. The county officers collect taxes, hold court, keep county roads in repair, and maintain county schools. **2** the people or the officials of a county. *noun, plural* **coun·ties.**

cou·ple (kup′əl), **1** two things of the same kind that go together; pair: *She bought a couple of tires*

for her bicycle. **2** a man and woman who are married, engaged, or partners in a dance. **3** a small number; a few: *I'll be gone for a couple of days.* **4** to join together: *The brakeman coupled the freight cars.* **1-3** *noun,* **4** *verb,* **cou·ples, cou·pled, cou·pling.**

cou·pon (kü′pon *or* kyü′pon), a small piece of paper or part of a package or advertisement that gives the person who holds it certain rights: *I saved coupons from boxes of cereal and got a free toy. noun.*

cour·age (kėr′ij), bravery; meeting danger without fear: *The pioneers faced the hardships of their westward journey with courage. noun.*

cou·ra·geous (kə rā′jəs), brave; fearless; full of courage. *adjective.*

cour·i·er (kėr′ē ər *or* kùr′ē ər), a messenger sent in haste. *noun.*

course (kôrs), **1** onward movement: *Our history book traces the course of human development from the cave to modern city living.* **2** the direction taken: *Our course was straight to the north.* **3** a line of action; way of doing: *The only sensible course was to go home.* **4** a way; path; track; channel: *the winding course of a stream.* **5** a series of classes on a particular subject: *Each course in mathematics lasts one year.* **6** a part of a meal served at one time: *The first course was chicken soup.* **7** a place for races or games: *a golf course.* **8** to run or flow rapidly: *Tears coursed down the unhappy child's cheeks.* **1-7** *noun,* **8** *verb,* **cours·es, coursed, cours·ing.**

of course, 1 surely; certainly: *Of course you can go!* **2** naturally; as should be expected: *She gave me a gift, and, of course, I accepted it.*

course·ware (kôrs′wer′ *or* kôrs′war′), lessons that have been written to be used on a computer or with a computer: *The arithmetic courseware includes a computer game and a book of problems. noun.*

court (kôrt), **1** a place where legal cases are decided or where trials are held. **2** officials, including a judge or judges, and often a jury, who hear and decide legal cases or questions. **3** a ruler and his or her advisers, followers, and household: *The court of Queen Elizabeth I was noted for its splendor.* **4** an assembly held by a king, queen, or other ruler: *The queen held court to hear from her advisers.* **5** a space partly or wholly enclosed by walls or buildings: *The four apartment houses were built around a court of grass.* **6** a short street: *I live at 39 Plymouth Court.* **7** a place marked off for a game: *a tennis court, a basketball court.* **8** to seek the favor of; try to please: *The nobles courted the king to get positions*

a hat / ā age / ä far / e let / ē equal / ėr term / i it / ī ice / o hot / ō open / ô order / oi oil / ou out / u cup / ù put / ü rule / ch child / ng long / sh she / th thin / ŦH then / zh measure / ə = a in about, e in taken, i in pencil, o in lemon, u in circus

139

of power. **9** to try to win the love of; pay loving attention to in order to marry: *He courted her by bringing her flowers every day.* 1-7 *noun,* 8,9 *verb.*

cour·te·ous (kėr′tē əs), polite: *The clerks are courteous at this store. adjective.*

cour·te·sy (kėr′tə sē), **1** polite behavior; thoughtfulness for others: *It is a sign of courtesy to give one's seat to an old person on a bus.* **2** a kindness; act of consideration; polite act: *Thanks for all your courtesies. noun, plural* **cour·te·sies.**

court·house (kôrt′hous′), **1** a building in which courts of law meet. **2** a building used for the government of a county. *noun, plural* **court·hous·es** (kôrt′hou′ziz).

cour·ti·er (kôr′tē ər), a person often present at a royal court. *noun.*

court·ly (kôrt′lē), having manners fit for a royal court; polite; elegant: *a courtly old gentleman. adjective,* **court·li·er, court·li·est.**

court·room (kôrt′rüm′), a room in which courts of law meet. *noun.*

court·ship (kôrt′ship), the condition or time of courting in order to marry: *Their brief courtship was a very happy one. noun.*

court·yard (kôrt′yärd′), a space enclosed by walls, in or near a large building. *noun.*

cous·in (kuz′n), a son or daughter of one's uncle or aunt. First cousins have the same grandparents; second cousins have the same great-grandparents. *noun.*

cove (kōv), a small, sheltered bay. *noun.*

cov·er (kuv′ər), **1** to put something over: *I covered the child with a blanket.* **2** to be over; spread over: *Snow covered the ground.* **3** anything that is put over, protects, or hides: *the cover of a book. A thicket makes good cover for animals to hide in.* **4** to hide: *I tried to cover my mistake by pretending it was a joke.* **5** to defend from attack; protect: *One soldier ran for the fort, while the others covered him by firing at the enemy.* **6** protection; shelter: *The burglar escaped under cover of darkness.* **7** to go over; travel: *On our trip we covered 400 miles a day by car.* **8** to include; take in: *The math review covers everything we've studied.* **9** to report or photograph an event, meeting, or the like: *A reporter covered the football game for the newspaper.* 1,2,4,5,7-9 *verb,* 3,6 *noun.*

cover up, 1 to cover completely. **2** to hide; conceal.

covered wagon, a wagon having a canvas cover that can be taken off.

cov·er·ing (kuv′ər ing), anything that covers: *A blanket is a bed covering. noun.*

cov·et (kuv′it), to desire eagerly, especially something that belongs to another: *Her friends coveted her new bicycle. verb.*

cow[1] (kou), **1** the full-grown female of domestic cattle that gives milk. **2** the female of the buffalo, moose, and other large animals that nurse their young: *an elephant cow. noun.*

cow[2] (kou), to make afraid; frighten: *I was cowed by their threats and stayed out of their sight. verb.*

cow·ard (kou′ərd), a person who lacks courage or is easily made afraid; one who runs from danger. *noun.*

cow·ard·ice (kou′ər dis), a lack of courage; being easily made afraid: *to be guilty of cowardice in the presence of danger. noun.*

cow·ard·ly (kou′ərd lē), without courage; like a coward. *adjective.*

cow·bird (kou′bėrd′), a small North American blackbird that often lays its eggs in the nests of other birds. *noun.*

cow·boy (kou′boi′), a man who works on a cattle ranch or at rodeos. *noun.*

cow·er (kou′ər), to crouch in fear or shame: *The dog cowered under the table after being scolded. verb.*

cow·girl (kou′gėrl′), a woman who works on a cattle ranch or at rodeos. *noun.*

cow·hand (kou′hand′), a person who works on a cattle ranch. *noun.*

cow·hide (kou′hīd′), **1** the hide of a cow. **2** leather made from it. *noun.*

cowl (koul), **1** a monk's cloak with a hood. **2** the hood itself. *noun.*

co-work·er (kō′wėr′kər), a person who works with another: *You should try very hard to get along with your co-workers. noun.*

cow·punch·er (kou′pun′chər), a cowhand. *noun.*

cow·slip (kou′slip), a wild plant with bright, yellow flowers that bloom in early spring. *noun.*

coy (koi), acting more shy than one really is. *adjective.*

coy·o·te (kī ō′tē *or* kī′ōt), a small wolflike animal living mostly on the prairies of western North America. *noun, plural* **coy·o·tes** *or* **coy·o·te.**

coyote—about 21 inches (53 centimeters) high at the shoulder

co·zi·ly (kō′zə lē), in a snug and comfortable manner. *adverb.*

co·zy (kō′zē), warm and comfortable; snug: *The cat lay in a cozy corner near the fireplace. adjective,* **co·zi·er, co·zi·est.** Also spelled **cosy.**

crab (krab), **1** a shellfish with eight legs, two claws, and a broad, flat shell covering. Many kinds of crabs are good to eat. **2** to find fault; complain; criticize: *Don't crab so much about the weather.* **1** noun, **2** verb, **crabs, crabbed, crab·bing.**

crab apple, a small, sour kind of apple used to make jelly.

crab·by (krab/ē), bad-tempered, cross, or grouchy. *adjective,* **crab·bi·er, crab·bi·est.**

crab·grass (krab/gras/), a rough grass that spreads rapidly and spoils lawns. *noun.*

crack (krak), **1** a split or opening made by breaking without separating into parts: *There is a crack in this cup.* **2** to break without separating into parts: *You have cracked the window.* **3** a narrow opening: *I can see between the cracks in the old wood floor.* **4** a sudden, sharp noise like that made by loud thunder, by a whip, or by something breaking. **5** to make or cause to make a sudden, sharp noise: *The stagecoach driver cracked the whip.* **6** to break with a sudden, sharp noise: *We cracked the nuts.* **7** a hard, sharp blow: *The falling branch gave me a crack on the head.* **8** to hit with a hard, sharp blow: *The falling branch cracked me on the head.* **9** a funny or clever remark; joke: *If you make another crack about my singing, you'll be sorry.* **10** to tell or say something funny or clever: *She cracked a joke.* 1,3,4,7,9 *noun,* 2,5,6,8,10 *verb.*

crack up, 1 to crash or smash: *The driver skidded off the road and cracked up his car against a tree.* **2** to suffer a mental or physical collapse: *She was in danger of cracking up under the strain of overwork.*

crack·er (krak/ər), a thin, crisp wafer. *noun.*

crack·le (krak/əl), **1** to make slight, sharp sounds: *A fire crackled in the fireplace.* **2** a slight, sharp sound, such as paper makes when it is crushed. 1 *verb,* **crack·les, crack·led, crack·ling;** 2 *noun.*

crack·up (krak/up/), **1** a crash; smash: *That fast driver has been in more than one automobile crackup.* **2** a mental or physical collapse. *noun.*

cra·dle (krā/dl), **1** a small bed for a baby, usually mounted on rockers. **2** to hold as in a cradle: *I cradled the baby in my arms.* **3** a place where anything begins its growth: *The sea is thought to have been the cradle of life.* **4** any kind of framework looking like or used as a cradle. The part of a telephone that supports the receiver is a cradle. 1,3,4 *noun,* 2 *verb,* **cra·dles, cra·dled, cra·dling.**

craft (kraft), **1** a special skill: *The carpenter shaped and fitted the wood into a cabinet with great craft.* **2** a trade or art requiring skilled work: *Carpentry is a craft.* **3** skill in deceiving others; slyness; sly tricks: *By craft the gambler tricked them out of all their money.* **4** to work, make, or finish with skill or art: *The woodwork in our house was crafted by expert carpenters.* **5** boats, ships, or aircraft: *Craft of all kinds come into New York every day.* 1-3,5 *noun,* 4 *verb.*

crafts·man (krafts/mən), a person skilled in a craft or trade. *noun, plural* **crafts·men.**

a hat	i it	oi oil	ch child	a in about
ā age	ī ice	ou out	ng long	e in taken
ä far	o hot	u cup	sh she	ə = i in pencil
e let	ō open	u̇ put	th thin	o in lemon
ē equal	ô order	ü rule	ᴛʜ then	u in circus
ėr term			zh measure	

craft·y (kraf/tē), skillful in deceiving others: *The crafty girl tricked her brother into doing all her chores. adjective,* **craft·i·er, craft·i·est.**

crag (krag), a steep, rugged rock rising above others. *noun.*

cram (kram), **1** to force into; force down; stuff: *I crammed all my clothes into a suitcase.* **2** to fill too full; crowd: *The bus was crammed, with many people standing.* **3** to try to learn a lot in a short time: *As he hasn't studied during the year, he has to cram for his final tests. verb,* **crams, crammed, cram·ming.**

cramp (kramp), **1** a sudden, painful contracting or pulling together of muscles, often from chill or strain: *The swimmer was seized with a cramp and had to be helped from the pool.* **2** to shut in a small space; limit: *In only three rooms, the family was cramped for space.* 1 *noun,* 2 *verb.*

cran·ber·ry (kran/ber/ē), a firm, sour, dark-red berry that grows on low shrubs in marshes. Cranberries are used in making sauce, juice, and jelly. *noun, plural* **cran·ber·ries.**

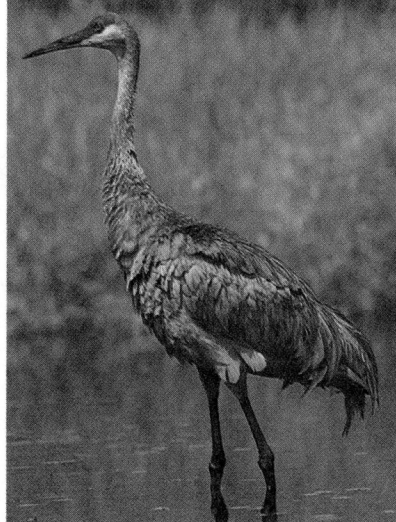

crane (definition 2) about 3 feet (1 meter) tall

crane (krān), **1** a machine with a long, swinging arm, for lifting heavy objects. **2** a large wading bird with long legs, neck, and bill. **3** to stretch the neck as a crane does, in order to see better. 1,2 *noun,* 3 *verb,* **cranes, craned, cran·ing.**

cra·ni·um (krā/nē əm), **1** the skull. **2** the part of the skull enclosing the brain. *noun.*

crank (krangk), **1** a part or handle of a machine connected at right angles to another part to set it in motion: *I turned the crank of the sharpener to sharpen my pencil.* **2** to work or start by means of a crank. **3** a cross or ill-tempered person. **4** an odd person; person who has strange ideas or habits. 1,3,4 *noun,* 2 *verb.*

crank·y (krang′kē), cross; bad-tempered; irritable. *adjective,* **crank·i·er, crank·i·est.**

crash (krash), **1** a sudden, loud noise like many dishes falling and breaking: *The lightning was followed by a crash of thunder.* **2** to make a sudden, loud noise: *The thunder crashed loudly.* **3** to fall, hit, or break with force and a loud noise: *The airplane lost power and crashed.* **4** a falling, hitting, or breaking with force and a loud noise: *The skillful pilot brought down the damaged airplane without a crash.* **5** the violent striking of one solid thing against another: *There was a crash of two cars at the corner.* **6** sudden ruin; severe failure in business: *Many people lost all their savings in the stock market crash.* **7** to go to a party or dance without being invited. 1,4,5,6 *noun,* 2,3,7 *verb.*

crate (krāt), **1** a large frame or box made of strips of wood, for shipping glass, china, fruit, or furniture. **2** to pack in a crate: *to crate a mirror for moving.* 1 *noun,* 2 *verb,* **crates, crat·ed, crat·ing.**

cra·ter (krā′tər), **1** the opening at the top of a volcano. **2** a hole in the ground shaped like a bowl: *The meteor crashed to earth and formed a huge crater. noun.*

Word History

crater *Crater* comes from a Greek word meaning "a mixing bowl."

crater (definition 2)—a **crater** on the moon

crave (krāv), to long for; desire very much: *The thirsty hiker craved water. verb,* **craves, craved, crav·ing.**

crav·ing (krā′ving), a longing; yearning; strong desire: *I had a craving for something sweet. noun.*

craw·fish (krô′fish′), crayfish. *noun, plural* **craw·fish** or **craw·fish·es.**

crawl (krôl), **1** to move slowly with the body close to the ground, or on the hands and knees: *Babies crawl before they begin to walk. Worms, snakes, and lizards crawl. We crawled through a hole in the fence.* **2** to move slowly: *The heavy traffic crawled*

through the narrow tunnel. **3** a slow movement: *Traffic had slowed to a crawl.* **4** to swarm with crawling things: *The ground was crawling with ants.* **5** to feel as if things were creeping over the skin: *My flesh crawled at the thought of the huge black snakes.* **6** a fast way of swimming by overarm strokes and rapid kicking of the feet. 1,2,4,5 *verb,* 3,6 *noun.*

crawl·y (krô′lē), **1** feeling as if things are crawling over one's skin; creepy: *Just to look at a spider makes me feel crawly.* **2** crawling: *Some people hate spiders and other crawly things. adjective,* **crawl·i·er, crawl·i·est.**

cray·fish (krā′fish′), a freshwater shellfish looking much like a small lobster. *noun, plural* **cray·fish** or **cray·fish·es.**

cray·on (krā′on *or* krā′ən), a stick of a waxlike colored substance, used for drawing or writing. *noun.*

craze (krāz), a short-lived, eager interest in doing some one thing: *The craze for flying kites was replaced by another for roller-skating. noun.*

cra·zy (krā′zē), **1** mentally ill; insane. **2** foolish: *It was crazy to jump out of such a high tree.* **3** very enthusiastic: *crazy about horses. adjective,* **cra·zi·er, cra·zi·est.**

creak (krēk), **1** to squeak loudly: *The hinges on the door creaked because they needed oiling.* **2** a loud squeaking noise: *The creak of the stairs in the old house was spooky.* 1 *verb,* 2 *noun.*

creak·y (krē′kē), likely to squeak; squeaking: *creaky floors. adjective,* **creak·i·er, creak·i·est.**

cream (krēm), **1** the oily, yellowish part of milk. Cream rises to the top when milk as it comes from the cow is allowed to stand. Butter is made from cream. **2** to make into a smooth mixture like cream: *I creamed butter and sugar for the cake.* **3** any preparation like cream that is put on the skin: *shaving cream.* **4** yellowish-white. **5** the best part of anything: *The cream of a class is made up of the best students.* 1,3,5 *noun,* 2 *verb,* 4 *adjective.*

cream cheese, a soft, white cheese made from cream, or milk and cream.

cream·y (krē′mē), **1** like cream; smooth and soft. **2** having much cream in it: *pie with a rich, creamy filling. adjective,* **cream·i·er, cream·i·est.**

crease (krēs), a line produced by folding or wrinkling; fold; ridge: *Her slacks have a sharp crease down the front. noun.*

cre·ate (krē āt′), to make a thing which has not been made before; cause to be: *Composers create music. The noise created a disturbance. verb,* **cre·ates, cre·at·ed, cre·at·ing.**

cre·a·tion (krē ā′shən), **1** a creating; act of making a thing which has not been made before: *The gasoline engine led to the creation of the modern automobile.* **2** all things that have been created; the world; the universe: *They thought their house by the ocean was the nicest spot in all creation.* **3** a thing produced by intelligence or skill, usually something important or original: *A poem is a creation of the imagination.* **4 the Creation,** the creating of the universe by God:

The Bible says the Creation took six days. noun.

cre·a·tive (krē ā′tiv), having the power to create; inventive; productive: *He has a very creative mind, always full of new ideas. adjective.*

cre·a·tor (krē ā′tər), **1** a person who creates. **2 the Creator,** God. *noun.*

crea·ture (krē′chər), **1** any living person or animal: *We fed the lost dog because the poor creature was starving.* **2** a monster; imaginary, frightening being: *I dreamed I was captured by creatures from Mars. noun.*

cred·it (kred′it), **1** belief in the truth of something; faith; trust: *I put great credit in what he says.* **2** to believe; have faith in; trust: *I can credit all that you are telling me.* **3** a trust in a person's ability and intention to pay: *This store will extend credit to you by opening a charge account in your name.* **4** one's reputation in money matters: *If you pay your bills on time, your credit will be good.* **5** praise; honor: *The person who does the work should get the credit.* **1,3-5** *noun,* **2** *verb.*

on credit, on a promise to pay later: *He bought a new car on credit.*

cred·it·a·ble (kred′ə tə bəl), bringing praise or honor: *She has a creditable record as a senator. adjective.*

credit card, a plastic card that allows a person to charge the cost of goods or services instead of paying cash.

cred·i·tor (kred′ə tər), a person to whom a debt is owed. *noun.*

creed (krēd), **1** a brief statement of the main points of religious belief of some church. **2** any statement of faith, belief, or opinion: *"Honesty is the best policy" was their creed in all their business dealings. noun.*

creek (krēk *or* krik), a small stream. *noun.*

creep (krēp), **1** to move slowly with the body close to the ground or floor; crawl: *The cat was creeping toward the mouse. Babies creep on their hands and knees before they begin to walk.* **2** to move slowly: *The traffic crept over the narrow bridge.* **3** to grow along the ground or on a wall: *Ivy had crept up the wall of the old house.* **4** to feel as if things were creeping over the skin: *It made my flesh creep to hear the wolves howl.* **5** an unpleasant or annoying person. **6 the creeps,** a feeling of fear or horror, as if things were creeping over one's skin. **1-4** *verb,* **creeps, crept, creep·ing;** **5,6** *noun.*

creep·y (krē′pē), causing a feeling of horror, as if things were creeping over one's skin; scary: *The wind howling through the old house was creepy. adjective,* **creep·i·er, creep·i·est.**

crepe (krāp), a very thin pancake, usually served folded around a filling. *noun.*

crepe paper (krāp′ pā′pər), a thin, crinkled tissue paper used for making decorations.

crept (krept). See **creep.** *The cat crept toward the mouse. We had crept up on them without their seeing us. verb.*

cres·cent (kres′nt), **1** the shape of the moon when it is small and thin. **2** anything that curves in a similar way. *noun.*

a hat	**i** it	**oi** oil	**ch** child	⎧ a in about
ā age	**ī** ice	**ou** out	**ng** long	e in taken
ä far	**o** hot	**u** cup	**sh** she	**ə =** ⎨ i in pencil
e let	**ō** open	**ů** put	**th** thin	o in lemon
ē equal	**ô** order	**ü** rule	**ŦH** then	⎩ u in circus
ėr term			**zh** measure	

crest (definition 1)—This bird has a colorful **crest.**

crest (krest), **1** a tuft or comb on the head of a bird or animal. **2** the top part: *the crest of a wave, the crest of the hill. noun.*

crest·fall·en (krest′fô′lən), dejected; discouraged: *The students who had failed the test were crestfallen. adjective.*

cre·vasse (krə vas′), a deep crack or split in the ice of a glacier, or in the ground after an earthquake. *noun.*

crevasse—The climbers approached a **crevasse.**

crescent (definition 1)

crev·ice (krev′is), a narrow split or crack: *Tiny ferns grew in crevices in the stone wall.* noun.

crew (krü), a group of people who work together: *It takes a crew of ten to sail that ship. A train crew runs a railroad train.* noun.

crew cut, a kind of very short haircut for men and boys.

crib (krib), **1** a small bed with high sides to keep a baby from falling out. **2** a rack or manger for horses and cows to eat from. **3** a building or bin for storing grain: *Rats damaged much of the corn in the crib.* noun.

crick·et[1] (krik′it), a black insect related to the grasshopper. A male cricket makes a chirping noise by rubbing its front wings together. noun.

crick·et[2] (krik′it), an English outdoor game played by two teams of eleven players each, with a ball, bats, and wickets. noun.

cri·er (krī′ər), (in former times) an official who shouted out public announcements. noun.

crime (krīm), **1** a very wrong deed that is against the law: *Murder is a crime.* **2** a violation of law: *Police forces combat crime.* **3** an evil or wrong act: *It is a crime to let people live without food and clothing and do nothing to help them.* noun.

crim·i·nal (krim′ə nəl), **1** a person who has committed a crime: *The criminal was sentenced to prison for theft.* **2** of or having to do with crime or its punishment: *A criminal court hears criminal cases.* **3** like crime; wrong: *It is criminal to neglect a pet.* **1** noun, **2,3** adjective.

crim·son (krim′zən), deep-red. adjective.

cringe (krinj), to crouch in fear; shrink from danger or pain: *The kitten cringed when it saw the dog come into the yard.* verb, **cring·es, cringed, cring·ing.**

crin·kle (kring′kəl), **1** to wrinkle; ripple. **2** to rustle: *Paper crinkles when it is crushed.* verb, **crin·kles, crin·kled, crin·kling.**

Word History

crinkle *Crinkle* comes from an older English word meaning "to bend."

crinkle (definition 1)
Aluminum foil **crinkles** easily.

crin·kly (kring′klē), full of wrinkles: *Crepe paper is crinkly.* adjective, **crin·kli·er, crin·kli·est.**

crip·ple (krip′əl), **1** a person or animal that cannot use an arm or leg properly because of injury or deformity; lame person or animal. **2** to make a cripple of: *He has been crippled since he broke his hip.* **3** to damage; weaken: *The ship was crippled by the storm.* **1** noun, **2,3** verb, **crip·ples, crip·pled, crip·pling.**

cri·sis (krī′sis), **1** a time of difficulty and of anxious waiting: *A scarcity of oil could produce an energy crisis.* **2** the point at which a change must come, either for the better or for the worse: *The election was a crisis in the senator's career.* **3** the turning point in a disease, toward life or death: *After the fever broke, the doctor said the patient had passed the crisis and would recover.* noun, plural **cri·ses** (krī′sēz′).

crisp (krisp), **1** hard and thin; breaking easily with a snap: *Dry toast is crisp. Fresh celery is crisp.* **2** fresh; sharp and clear; bracing: *The fresh air was cool and crisp.* **3** quick and to the point: *"Sit down!" was her crisp command.* adjective.

crisp·y (kris′pē), crisp: *We had crispy bacon for breakfast.* adjective, **crisp·i·er, crisp·i·est.**

criss·cross (kris′krôs′), **1** to mark or cover with crossed lines: *Little cracks crisscrossed the wall.* **2** to come and go across: *Buses and cars crisscross the city.* **3** made or marked with crossed lines: *Plaids have a crisscross pattern.* **4** a pattern of crossed lines: *The messy paper was a crisscross of lines and scribbles.* **1,2** verb, **3** adjective, **4** noun, plural **criss·cross·es.**

crit·ic (krit′ik), **1** a person whose job is to say what is good or bad about books, music, pictures, plays, or acting: *We read what the critics in the newspapers had to say about the new play.* **2** a person who disapproves or finds fault: *I tried to please him, but he was my worst critic.* noun.

crit·i·cal (krit′ə kəl), **1** inclined to find fault or disapprove: *She was so critical of people's mistakes that no one liked her.* **2** coming from one who is skilled as a critic: *Would you give me your critical opinion of my story?* **3** of a crisis; being important to the outcome of a situation: *Help arrived at the critical moment.* **4** full of danger or difficulty: *The patient was in a critical condition.* adjective.

crit·i·cism (krit′ə siz′əm), unfavorable remarks or judgments; finding fault: *I could not let their rudeness pass without criticism.* noun.

crit·i·cize (krit′ə sīz), **1** to blame; find fault with: *Do not criticize her until you know the facts.* **2** to judge as a critic: *He criticized the novel favorably.* verb, **crit·i·ciz·es, crit·i·cized, crit·i·ciz·ing.**

crit·ter (krit′ər), a creature. noun.

croak (krōk), **1** the deep, hoarse sound made by a frog, a crow, or a raven. **2** to make this sound. **1** noun, **2** verb.

Cro·a·tia (krō ā′shə), a country in southeastern Europe. noun.

cro·chet (krō shā′), to make sweaters, lace, and other things by looping thread or yarn into links with a single hooked needle. Crocheting is similar

to knitting. *verb*, **cro·chets** (krō shāz′),
cro·cheted (krō shād′), **cro·chet·ing**
(krō shā′ing).

crock (krok), a pot or jar made of baked clay.
noun.

croc·o·dile (krok′ə dīl), a large reptile with a long
body, four short legs, a thick skin, a pointed
snout, and a long tail. Crocodiles live in the rivers
and marshes of the warm parts of Africa, Asia,
Australia, and America. *noun.*

Word History

crocodile *Crocodile* comes from a Greek word meaning
"lizard." The animal was called this because it was
thought to look like a very large lizard.

crocodiles—up to 30 feet (9 meters) long

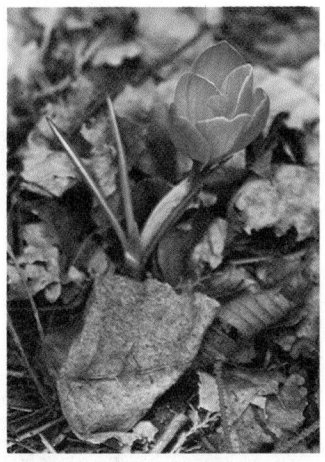

crocus

cro·cus (krō′kəs), a small plant that blooms very
early in the spring and has white, yellow, or
purple flowers. *noun, plural* **cro·cus·es.**

cro·ny (krō′nē), a very close friend; chum. *noun,
plural* **cro·nies.**

crook (krùk), **1** to make a hook or curve in; bend:
*I crooked my leg around the branch to keep from
falling.* **2** a hooked, curved, or bent part: *I carry
my books in the crook of my arm.* **3** a shepherd's

a hat	i it	oi oil	ch child	⌈ a in about
ā age	ī ice	ou out	ng long	e in taken
ä far	o hot	u cup	sh she	ə = ⟨ i in pencil
e let	ō open	ù put	th thin	o in lemon
ē equal	ô order	ü rule	ᴛʜ then	⌊ u in circus
ėr term			zh measure	

hooked staff. **4** a dishonest person; thief or
swindler: *The crook stole all my money.* **1** *verb,*
2-4 *noun.*

crook·ed (krùk′id), **1** not straight; bent; curved;
twisted: *The picture on the wall was crooked, so I
straightened it. The crooked road twisted and turned
through the hills.* **2** not honest: *a crooked scheme.*
adjective.

croon (krün), to hum, sing, or murmur in a low
tone: *I crooned a lullaby to the baby. verb.*

crop (krop), **1** plants grown or gathered by people
for their use: *Wheat, corn, and cotton are three
main crops of the United States.* **2** the amount of
any grain, fruit, or vegetable which is grown in
one season: *The drought made the state's potato
crop very small this year.* **3** to cut or bite off the top
of: *Sheep had cropped the grass very short.* **4** to clip
or cut short: *to crop a horse's tail.* **5** a baglike
swelling of a bird's food passage. In the crop,
food is prepared for digestion. **6** a short whip with
a loop instead of a lash. **1,2,5,6** *noun,* **3,4** *verb,*
crops, cropped, crop·ping.

crop up, to turn up unexpectedly: *All sorts of
difficulties cropped up.*

cro·quet (krō kā′), a lawn game played by
knocking wooden balls through small wire arches
with mallets. *noun.*

cross (krôs), **1** a stick or post with another across
it like a T, an X, or a +. **2 the Cross,** the cross on
which Jesus died. **3** anything shaped like this. A
cross is a symbol of the Christian religion. A
person who cannot write makes a cross instead of
a signature. **4** to draw a line across: *In writing you
cross the letter "t." She crossed out the wrong
word.* **5** to put or lay one over another: *He crossed
his arms.* **6** to move from one side to another; go
across: *He crossed the street. The bridge crosses
the river.* **7** to lie across; intersect: *Main Street
crosses Market Street.* **8** lying or going across;
crossing: *I saw you standing at the intersection of
the cross streets.* **9** to make the sign of the cross on
or over: *She crossed herself as she went into the
church.* **10** to act against; get in the way of;
oppose: *If anyone crosses him, he gets very angry.*
11 in a bad temper: *People are often cross when
they don't feel well.* **12** to mix kinds or breeds of:
*A new plant is sometimes made by crossing two
others.* **13** a mixing or mixture of kinds or breeds:
My dog is a cross between a collie and a poodle.
1-3,13 *noun, plural* **cross·es;** **4-7,9,10,12** *verb,*
8,11 *adjective.*

cross·bar (krôs′bär′), a bar, line, or stripe going
crosswise. *noun.*

cross·bones (krôs′bōnz′), two bones placed
crosswise, usually below a skull, to mean death:

crossbones
skull and
crossbones

Poisonous medicines are sometimes marked with a skull and crossbones. noun plural.

cross·bow (krôs′bō′), an old-time weapon for shooting arrows, consisting of a bow fixed across a wooden stock with a groove in it to direct the arrows. *noun.*

cross·coun·try (krôs′kun′trē), **1** across fields or open country: *Do you enjoy cross-country skiing?* **2** across an entire country: *She took a cross-country flight from Maine to Oregon. adjective.*

cross-eyed (krôs′īd′), having one or both eyes turned toward the nose, and unable to focus on the same point. *adjective.*

cross·ing (krô′sing), **1** the place where lines or tracks cross: *"Railroad crossing! Stop! Look! Listen!"* **2** the place at which a street or river may be crossed: *White lines mark the crossing.* **3** a going across, especially a voyage across water: *The ship's crossing took two weeks. noun.*

cross-leg·ged (krôs′leg′id), with one leg over the other. *adjective, adverb.*

cross·piece (krôs′pēs′), a piece of wood or metal that is placed across something. *noun.*

cross·ref·er·ence (krôs′ref′ər əns), a reference from one part of a book or index to another part. *noun.*

cross·road (krôs′rōd′), **1** a road that crosses another. **2 crossroads,** place where roads cross: *At the crossroads we stopped and read the signs. noun.*

cross section, 1 the act of cutting anything across: *I sliced the tomatoes by making a series of cross sections.* **2** a piece cut in this way. **3** a sample; small selection of people, animals, or things with the same qualities as the entire group.

cross·walk (krôs′wôk′), an area marked with lines, used by people walking across a street. *noun.*

cross·ways (krôs′wāz′), crosswise. *adverb.*

cross·wise (krôs′wīz′), across: *The tree fell crosswise over the stream. adverb.*

cross·word puz·zle (krôs′wėrd′ puz′əl), a puzzle with sets of numbered squares to be filled in with words, one letter in each square. The words may be read both across and down. Clues are given with numbers matching the numbers of the squares.

crotch (kroch), a forked piece or part: *The nest was in the crotch of a tree. noun, plural* **crotch·es.**

crouch (krouch), **1** to stoop low with bent legs: *The cat crouched in the corner, waiting for the mouse to come out of its hole.* **2** a crouching position. 1 *verb,* 2 *noun, plural* **crouch·es.**

crossbow—soldiers using **crossbows**

croup (krüp), a children's disease of the throat and windpipe that causes a cough and difficult breathing. *noun.*

crow[1] (krō), **1** the loud cry of a rooster. **2** to make this cry: *The cock crowed as the sun rose.* **3** to make a happy sound: *The baby crowed with delight when it saw its new toy.* **4** to boast; show one's happiness and pride: *The winning team crowed over its victory.* 1 *noun,* 2-4 *verb.*

crow[2] (krō), a large, glossy, black bird with a harsh cry. *noun.*

as the crow flies, in a perfectly straight line.

cross sections (definition 2)

eat crow, to be forced to do something very disagreeable.

crow·bar (krō′bär′), a bar of iron or steel used to lift things or pry them apart. *noun.*

crowd (kroud), **1** a large number of people together: *A crowd gathered at the scene of the fire.* **2** a set; group: *Our crowd wasn't invited to the party.* **3** to collect in large numbers: *The children crowded around the edge of the swimming pool to hear the instructor.* **4** to fill; fill too full: *Christmas shoppers crowded the store.* **5** to push; shove: *The big man crowded the child out of his way.* **6** to press forward; force one's way: *She crowded into the subway car.* 1,2 *noun,* 3-6 *verb.*

crown (kroun), **1** a head covering of precious metal and jewels, worn by a king or queen. **2** the **Crown,** royal power; supreme governing power in a country ruled by a king or queen: *The Crown granted lands in colonial America to William Penn.* **3** to make king or queen: *The prince was crowned in London.* **4** a wreath for the head: *The winner of the race received a crown.* **5** to honor; reward: *Her hard work was crowned with success.* **6** the top; highest part: *the crown of a hat, the crown of a mountain.* **7** to be on top of; cover the highest part of: *A fort crowns the hill.* **8** to hit someone on the head. **9** the part of a tooth which appears beyond the gum, or an artificial substitute for it. 1,2,4,6,9 *noun,* 3,5,7,8 *verb.*

crow's-nest (krōz′nest′), a platform for the lookout, near the top of a ship's mast. *noun.*

cru·cial (krü′shəl), very important; critical; decisive: *This was the crucial game that would decide the championship. adjective.*

cru·ci·fix (krü′sə fiks), a cross with the figure of the crucified Jesus on it. *noun, plural* **cru·ci·fix·es.**

cru·ci·fix·ion (krü′sə fik′shən), **1** crucifying. **2** the Crucifixion, the putting to death of Jesus on the Cross. *noun.*

cru·ci·fy (krü′sə fī), to put to death by nailing or binding the hands and feet to a cross. *verb,* **cru·ci·fies, cru·ci·fied, cru·ci·fy·ing.**

crude (krüd), **1** in a natural or raw state. Crude oil is oil as it is pumped from the wells before it is refined and prepared for use. **2** rough; coarse: *The boys made a crude chair out of a box.* **3** lacking grace, taste, or refinement: *I cannot stand someone with crude manners. adjective,* **crud·er, crud·est.**

cru·el (krü′əl), **1** ready to give pain to others or to delight in their suffering; hardhearted: *The cruel man kicked his dog.* **2** causing pain or suffering: *The cruel wind brought tears to my eyes. adjective.*

cru·el·ty (krü′əl tē), **1** readiness to give pain to others or to delight in their suffering. **2** a cruel act or acts: *That organization seeks to prevent cruelty to animals. noun, plural* **cru·el·ties.**

cruise (krüz), **1** to sail about from place to place: *We cruised to Bermuda on our vacation. Freighters and tankers cruise the oceans of the world.* **2** a voyage for pleasure: *We went for a cruise on the Great Lakes last summer.* **3** to travel or journey from place to place: *The taxicab cruised the city streets in search of passengers.* 1,3 *verb,* **cruis·es, cruised, cruis·ing;** 2 *noun.*

cruis·er (krü′zər), **1** a warship with less armor and more speed than a battleship. **2** a motorboat having a cabin so that people can live on board. **3** a police car. *noun.*

crumb (krum), **1** a very small piece of bread or cake broken from a larger piece: *I fed crumbs to the birds.* **2** a little bit: *When my friend moved away, it was a crumb of comfort to learn that he could visit me in the summer. noun.*

crum·ble (krum′bəl), **1** to break into small pieces or crumbs: *Do not crumble your bread on the table.* **2** to fall to pieces; decay: *The old wall was crumbling away at the edges. verb,* **crum·bles, crum·bled, crum·bling.**

crum·bly (krum′blē), tending to crumble; easily crumbled: *These cookies are very crumbly. adjective,* **crum·bli·er, crum·bli·est.**

crum·my (krum′ē), having little value or quality: *We were all disappointed by that crummy movie. adjective,* **crum·mi·er, crum·mi·est.**

crum·ple (krum′pəl), **1** to crush together; wrinkle: *She crumpled the paper into a ball.* **2** to fall down: *He crumpled to the floor in a faint. verb,* **crum·ples, crum·pled, crum·pling.**

crunch (krunch), **1** to crush noisily with the teeth: *She crunched a carrot.* **2** to make such a sound: *The hard snow crunched under our feet.* **3** the act or sound of crunching. 1,2 *verb,* 3 *noun, plural* **crunch·es.**

crunch·y (krun′chē), brittle and crackling: *crunchy candy. adjective,* **crunch·i·er, crunch·i·est.**

cru·sade (krü sād′), **1** any one of the Christian military expeditions between the years 1096 and 1272 to take the Holy Land from the Moslems. **2** a vigorous movement against a public evil or in favor of some new idea: *Everyone was asked to join the crusade against cancer.* **3** to take part in a crusade: *to crusade against smoking.* 1,2 *noun,* 3 *verb,* **cru·sades, cru·sad·ed, cru·sad·ing.**

cru·sad·er (krü sā′dər), a person who takes part in a crusade. *noun.*

crush (krush), **1** to squeeze together violently so as to break or bruise: *The car door slammed and crushed her fingers.* **2** to wrinkle or crease by pressure or rough handling: *My suitcase was so full that my clothes were crushed.* **3** to break into fine pieces by grinding, pounding, or pressing: *The ore is crushed between steel rollers.* **4** to subdue; overcome: *The revolt was crushed. He was crushed when he failed to get a part in the play.* **5** a sudden, strong liking for a person: *I once had*

a hat	i it	oi oil	ch child	a in about
ā age	ī ice	ou out	ng long	e in taken
ä far	o hot	u cup	sh she	ə = i in pencil
e let	ō open	u̇ put	th thin	o in lemon
ē equal	ô order	ü rule	ŦH then	u in circus
ėr term			zh measure	

a crush on my third-grade teacher. 1-4 *verb*, 5 *noun, plural* **crush·es.**

crust (krust), **1** the hard outside part of bread. **2** a piece of the crust; any hard, dry piece of bread. **3** a rich dough rolled out thin and baked for pies. **4** any hard outside covering: *The crust of the snow was thick enough to walk on.* **5** the solid outside part of the earth. **6** to cover with a crust; form into a crust; become covered with a crust: *By the next day the snow had crusted over.* 1-5 *noun*, 6 *verb.*

crus·ta·cean (krus′tā′shən), any of a group of animals with hard shells that mostly live in water. Crabs, lobsters, and shrimp are crustaceans. *noun.*

crustaceans

crutch (kruch), a support to help a lame or injured person walk. It is a stick with a padded crosspiece at the top that fits under a person's arm and supports part of the weight in walking. *noun, plural* **crutch·es.**

cry (krī), **1** to call loudly: *The drowning man cried, "Help!"* **2** a loud call; shout: *a cry of rage. We heard his cry for help.* **3** to shed tears: *My little sister cried when she broke her favorite toy.* **4** a time of shedding tears; fit of weeping: *Sometimes you feel much better after a good cry.* **5** a noise or call of an animal: *The dogs fell silent when they heard the cry of the wolf.* **6** to make such a noise: *The crows cried to one another from the treetops.* 1,3,6 *verb*, **cries, cried, cry·ing**; 2,4,5 *noun, plural* **cries.**

cry·ba·by (krī′bā′bē), a person who cries easily or pretends to be hurt. *noun, plural* **cry·ba·bies.**

crys·tal (kris′tl), **1** a clear, transparent mineral that looks like ice. It is a kind of quartz. **2** clear and transparent like crystal: *crystal water.* **3** very

transparent glass from which drinking glasses, vases, and other things are made: *They have a collection of fine crystal.* **4** the transparent glass or plastic over the face of a watch. **5** one of the regularly shaped pieces with angles and flat surfaces into which many substances solidify. Snow is water vapor that has frozen into crystals. 1,3-5 *noun*, 2 *adjective.*

crys·tal·line (kris′tl ən), **1** made of crystals: *Sugar and salt are crystalline.* **2** clear and transparent like crystal: *A crystalline sheet of ice covered the pond. adjective.*

crys·tal·lize (kris′tl īz), to form into crystals. Water vapor crystallizes as snow. *verb*, **crys·tal·liz·es, crys·tal·lized, crys·tal·liz·ing.**

CT, Connecticut (used with postal Zip Code).

cu. or **cu,** cubic.

cub (kub), a young bear, fox, or lion. *noun.*

Cu·ba (kyü′bə), an island country in the West Indies, south of Florida. *noun.*

cube (kyüb), **1** a solid object with 6 square sides. **2** anything shaped like a cube: *ice cubes, a cube of sugar.* **3** to make or form into the shape of a cube: *The beets were cubed instead of sliced.* **4** the sum when a number is multiplied by itself twice: *8 is the cube of 2, because $2 \times 2 \times 2 = 8$.* 1,2,4 *noun*, 3 *verb*, **cubes, cubed, cub·ing.**

cube (definition 1)

cu·bic (kyü′bik), **1** shaped like a cube: *The block of ice had a cubic form.* **2** having length, width, and thickness. A cubic foot is the volume of a cube whose edges are each one foot long. *adjective.*

cub scout, a member of the junior division of the Boy Scouts.

cuck·oo (kü′kü), **1** a bird whose call sounds much like its name. The European cuckoo lays its eggs in the nests of other birds instead of hatching them itself. The American cuckoo builds its own nest and has a call less like the name. **2** crazy; silly. 1 *noun, plural* **cuck·oos;** 2 *adjective.*

cu·cum·ber (kyü′kum bər), a long, green vegetable with firm flesh. Cucumbers grow on vines and are eaten usually in thin slices as a salad, or used to make pickles. *noun.*

cud (kud), a mouthful of food brought back from the first stomach of cattle or similar animals for a slow second chewing in the mouth. *noun.*

cud·dle (kud′l), **1** to hold closely and lovingly in one's arms or lap: *I cuddled the kitten.* **2** to lie close and comfortably; curl up: *The two puppies cuddled together in front of the fire. verb*, **cud·dles, cud·dled, cud·dling.**

cue[1] (kyü), **1** a signal to an actor, musician, or other performer that it is time to do something. **2** a hint as to what should be done: *Take your cue from me at the party about when it is time to leave.* noun.

cue² (kyü), a long stick used for striking the ball in the game of billiards or pool. *noun.*

cuff¹ (kuf), **1** a band of material attached to a sleeve and worn around the wrist. **2** the turned-up fold around the bottom of a leg of a pair of trousers. *noun.*

cuff² (kuf), **1** to hit with the hand; slap. **2** a hit with the hand; slap. **1** *verb,* **2** *noun.*

cull (kul), to pick out; select: *We culled the berries, discarding the bad ones. verb.*

cul·prit (kul′prit), an offender; person guilty of a fault or crime: *Someone broke the window; are you the culprit? noun.*

cul·ti·vate (kul′tə vāt), **1** to prepare and use land to raise crops by plowing it, planting seeds, and taking care of the growing plants. **2** to help plants grow by labor and care. **3** to loosen the ground around growing plants to kill weeds. **4** to improve or develop by study or training: *She cultivated her mind by reading good books. verb,* **cul·ti·vates, cul·ti·vat·ed, cul·ti·vat·ing.**

cul·ti·va·tion (kul′tə vā′shən), **1** a preparing land and growing crops by plowing, planting, and necessary care: *Better cultivation of soil will result in better crops.* **2** an improving or developing by study or training: *The cultivation of good study habits can lead to better grades. noun.*

cul·ti·va·tor (kul′tə vā′tər), a tool or machine used to loosen the ground and destroy weeds. A cultivator is pulled or pushed between rows of growing plants. *noun.*

cultivator

cul·tur·al (kul′chər əl), having to do with culture: *I enjoy going to symphony concerts, ballets, plays, and other cultural events. adjective.*

cul·ture (kul′chər), **1** fineness of feelings, thoughts, tastes, or manners; the result of good education and surroundings: *A person of culture appreciates art, music, and literature.* **2** the customs, arts, and tools of a nation or people at a certain time: *She spoke on the culture of the ancient Egyptians.* **3** a training of the mind or of the

a hat	**i** it	**oi** oil	**ch** child	⎧ a in about
ā age	**ī** ice	**ou** out	**ng** long	⎪ e in taken
ä far	**o** hot	**u** cup	**sh** she	ə = ⎨ i in pencil
e let	**ō** open	**u̇** put	**th** thin	⎪ o in lemon
ē equal	**ô** order	**ü** rule	**ᴛʜ** then	⎩ u in circus
ėr term			**zh** measure	

body: *He enjoyed lifting weights and other forms of physical culture. noun.*

cul·tured (kul′chərd), having a good education and fine manners: *a cultured person. adjective.*

cul·vert (kul′vərt), a pipe or channel which carries water under a road or railroad. *noun.*

cum·ber·some (kum′bər səm), hard to manage; clumsy; troublesome: *The armor worn by knights was often so cumbersome they had to be helped onto their horses. adjective.*

cu·mu·lus cloud (kyü′myə ləs), a fluffy white cloud with a flat bottom, seen in fair weather.

Word History

cumulus cloud Such a cloud is made up of rounded masses heaped upon one another. Therefore it was called by the Latin word *cumulus,* meaning "a heap."

cumulus cloud

cun·ning (kun′ing), **1** clever in deceiving; sly: *The cunning fox outwitted the dogs and got away.* **2** skillful or sly ways of getting what one needs or wants, or of escaping one's enemies: *The fox has a great deal of cunning.* **1** *adjective,* **2** *noun.*

cup (kup), **1** a hollow, rounded dish to drink from. Most cups have handles. **2** as much as a cup holds: *She drank a cup of milk.* **3** a unit of measure used in cooking equal to 8 fluid ounces. **4** anything shaped like a cup: *A silver cup was awarded to the winner of the race.* **5** to shape like a cup: *He cupped his cold hands around the mug of hot chocolate to warm them.* **1-4** *noun,* **5** *verb,* **cups, cupped, cup·ping.**

cup·board (kub′ərd), a cabinet with shelves for dishes and food supplies. *noun.*

cup·cake (kup′kāk′), a small cake about the same size and shape as a cup. *noun.*

cup·ful (kup′fu̇l), as much as a cup can hold. *noun, plural* **cup·fuls.**

Cu·pid (kyü′pid), **1** the Roman god of love, son of Venus. Cupid is usually shown as a winged boy with bow and arrows. **2 cupid,** a winged baby used as a symbol of love: *cupids on a valentine.* *noun.*

cur (kėr), a dog of mixed breed; mongrel. *noun.*

cur·ate (kyùr′it), an assistant clergyman; helper of a pastor or rector. *noun.*

cu·ra·tor (kyü rā′tər), a person in charge of all or part of a museum, library, art gallery, or zoo. *noun.*

curb (kėrb), **1** a raised border of concrete or stone along the edge of a pavement or sidewalk: *The driver parked the car close to the curb.* **2** to hold back; check: *I curbed my hunger by eating a piece of cheese.* **3** a holding back; check: *Put a curb on your temper.* **1,3** *noun,* **2** *verb.*

curd (kėrd), the thick part of milk that separates from the watery part when the milk sours. Cheese is made from curds. *noun.*

cur·dle (kėr′dl), to form into curds: *Milk curdles when it is kept too long in a warm place.* *verb,* **cur·dles, cur·dled, cur·dling.**

cure (kyùr), **1** to bring back to health; make well: *The medicine cured the sick child.* **2** to get rid of: *to cure a cold. Only great determination can cure a bad habit like smoking.* **3** something that removes or relieves a disease or a bad condition; remedy: *The scientist hoped to find a cure for the common cold.* **4** to keep bacon or other meat from spoiling by drying, salting, or other means. **1,2,4** *verb,* **cures, cured, cur·ing; 3** *noun.*

cur·few (kėr′fyü), a fixed time in the evening when certain people are required to be off the streets or at home: *Children in this town must be home before curfew.* *noun.*
[The word *curfew* comes from old French words meaning "to cover the fire." In the Middle Ages fires were put out at night, in order to reduce the danger to wooden houses. Night was also the time for people to be off the streets, safe at home. The word *curfew* was used to express both these ideas.]

cur·i·os·i·ty (kyùr′ē os′ə tē), **1** an eager desire to know: *Curiosity got the better of me, and I opened the unmarked box.* **2** a strange, unusual, or rare object: *One of the curiosities we saw was a spoon made of the horn of a deer.* *noun, plural* **cur·i·os·i·ties.**

cur·i·ous (kyùr′ē əs), **1** eager to know: *Small children are very curious, and they ask many questions.* **2** strange; odd; unusual: *I found a curious old box in the attic.* *adjective.*

curl (kėrl), **1** to twist into rings: *to curl someone's hair. The baby's hair curls naturally.* **2** to curve or twist out of shape: *Paper curls as it burns.* **3** a curled lock of hair: *The little girl had long curls.* **4** anything curled or bent into a curve: *Curls of smoke rose from the fire.* **1,2** *verb,* **3,4** *noun.*
curl up, to draw up one's legs: *I curled up in bed.*

curl·y (kėr′lē), **1** curling; wavy: *curly hair.* **2** having curls or curly hair: *a curly head. adjective,* **curl·i·er, curl·i·est.**

cur·rant (kėr′ənt), **1** a small raisin without seeds made from certain small, sweet grapes. Currants are used in puddings, cakes, and buns. **2** a small and sour red, black, or white berry, which grows on a bush and is used for jelly. *noun.*

cur·ren·cy (kėr′ən sē), **1** the money in actual use in a country: *Coins and paper money are currency in the United States.* **2** widespread use or acceptance: *Words such as "ye" and "thou" have little currency now. noun, plural* **cur·ren·cies.**

cur·rent (kėr′ənt), **1** a flow; stream. Running water or moving air makes a current. *The current swept the stick down the river. The draft created a current of cold air over my feet.* **2** a flow of electricity through a wire: *The current went off when lightning hit the power lines.* **3** the course or movement of events or of opinions: *Newspapers influence the current of public opinion.* **4** of the present time. The current issue of a magazine is the latest one published. *We discuss current events in our social studies class.* **5** widespread or generally accepted: *Long ago the belief was current that the earth was flat.* **6** passing from person to person: *A rumor is current that school will close tomorrow.* **1-3** *noun,* **4-6** *adjective.*

cur·rent·ly (kėr′ənt lē), at the present time; now: *The flu is currently going around school and many people are absent. adverb.*

cur·ry¹ (kėr′ē), to rub and clean a horse with a currycomb. *verb,* **cur·ries, cur·ried, cur·ry·ing.**

cur·ry² (kėr′ē), **1** a peppery sauce or powder. Curry is a popular seasoning in India. **2** a food flavored with it. *noun, plural* **cur·ries.**

cur·ry·comb (kėr′ē kōm′), a flat, round comb with rows of short teeth, made of metal or rubber. Currycombs are used to rub and clean horses. *noun.*

currycomb

curse (kėrs), **1** to ask God or a powerful spirit to bring evil or harm on: *The wicked witch cursed the prince.* **2** the words that a person says when cursing in this way: *The witch uttered a long curse with many strange words in it.* **3** to bring evil or harm on; trouble greatly; torment: *The farmers were cursed with dry weather and dust storms.* **4** trouble; harm: *My quick temper is a curse to me.* **5** to swear; say bad words: *I cursed when I shut* *the door on my finger.* **6** the words used in swearing: *Their talk was full of curses.* 1,3,5 *verb,* **curs·es, cursed, curs·ing;** 2,4,6 *noun.*

cur·sive (kėr′siv), written with the letters joined together. Most people use cursive letters when signing their name. *adjective.*

cur·sor (kėr′sər), a movable mark on a computer screen. It shows where the next letter or number can be made to appear on the screen. *noun.* [Our word was borrowed from the Latin word *cursor,* meaning "a runner."]

curt (kėrt), rudely brief; short; abrupt: *The impatient clerk gave a curt reply. adjective.*

cur·tail (kėr′tāl′), to cut short; stop part of; reduce: *My parents curtailed my allowance. verb.*

cur·tain (kėrt′n), **1** a cloth hung across a window or other space to shut out light, to give privacy, or for decoration. **2** a hanging screen or cloth which separates the stage of a theater from the part where the audience sits. **3** to provide with a curtain; hide by a curtain: *The children took two sheets and curtained off a space in the corner.* 1,2 *noun,* 3 *verb.*

curt·sy (kėrt′sē), **1** a bow of respect or greeting by women and girls, made by bending the knees and lowering the body slightly. **2** to make a curtsy: *The actress curtsied when the audience applauded.* 1 *noun, plural* **curt·sies;** 2 *verb,* **curt·sies, curt·sied, curt·sy·ing.**

curtsy (definition 1)

curve (kėrv), **1** a line that has no straight part. A circle is a closed curve. **2** a bend in a road: *The automobile had to slow down to go around the curves.* **3** to bend so as to form a line that has no straight part: *The highway curved to the right in a sharp turn.* **4** a baseball thrown to swerve just before it reaches the batter. 1,2,4 *noun,* 3 *verb,* **curves, curved, curv·ing.**

cush·ion (kush′ən), **1** a soft pillow or pad used to sit, lie, or kneel on: *The couch had cushions on the seat and along the back.* **2** anything that is like a

a hat	**i** it	**oi** oil	**ch** child	a in about
ā age	**ī** ice	**ou** out	**ng** long	e in taken
ä far	**o** hot	**u** cup	**sh** she	ə = i in pencil
e let	**ō** open	** u̇** put	**th** thin	o in lemon
ē equal	**ô** order	**ü** rule	**ŦH** then	u in circus
ėr term			**zh** measure	

cushion by being soft: *I fell on a cushion of deep snow.* **3** to supply with a cushion: *The chair seat was cushioned with foam rubber.* **4** to soften or ease the effects of: *Nothing could cushion the shock of my friend's death.* 1,2 *noun,* 3,4 *verb.*

cus·tard (kus′tərd), a baked, boiled, or frozen mixture of eggs, milk, and sugar. Custard is used as a dessert or as a food for sick persons. *noun.*

cus·to·di·an (ku stō′dē ən), **1** a person in charge; keeper; guardian: *He is the custodian of the library's collection of rare books.* **2** a janitor: *a school custodian. noun.*

cus·to·dy (kus′tə dē), the keeping; care: *Parents have the custody of their young children. noun.* **in custody,** in prison or in the care of the police: *The person accused of the robbery is now in custody.*

cus·tom (kus′təm), **1** any usual action; habit: *It was her custom to rise early.* **2** a long-established or accepted way of doing things: *The social customs of many countries differ from ours.* **3** made specially for one customer: *He wore custom suits made for him by an expert tailor.* **4 customs, a** taxes paid to the government on things brought in from a foreign country: *I paid $4 in customs on the $100 Swiss watch.* **b** an office at a seaport, airport, or border-crossing point where imported goods are checked. 1,2,4 *noun,* 3 *adjective.*

cus·tom·ar·y (kus′tə mer′ē), usual: *My customary bedtime is ten o'clock. adjective.*

cus·tom·er (kus′tə mər), a person who buys goods or services: *Just before the holidays the store was full of customers. noun.*

cut (kut), **1** to divide, separate, open, or remove with something sharp: *The butcher cut the meat with a knife. We cut a branch from the tree.* **2** to pierce or wound with something sharp: *She cut her finger on the broken glass.* **3** an opening made by a knife or sharp-edged tool: *I put a bandage on my leg to cover the cut.* **4** a place that has been made by cutting: *The train went through a deep cut in the side of the mountain.* **5** a piece that has been cut off or cut out: *A leg of lamb is a tasty cut of meat.* **6** to make by cutting: *He cut a hole through the wall with an ax.* **7** to have teeth grow through the gums: *The baby is cutting her first tooth.* **8** to make less; reduce; decrease: *We must cut our expenses to save money.* **9** to cut short; trim: *The barber cut my hair.* **10** a shortening or making less; reduction: *The speech was too long, so cuts were made. Cuts in prices helped sales.* **11** to go by a shortcut: *She cut across the field to save time.* **12** to cross: *A brook cuts through that field.* **13** to hit or strike sharply: *The cold wind cut me to the bone.* **14** to stop: *Cut the kidding and be serious.* **15** to act

151

as if one does not know a person: *After our fight, she cut me whenever we met.* **16** to stay away from on purpose: *The principal called my parents when I cut two classes.* 1,2,6-9,11-16 *verb,* **cuts, cut, cut·ting;** 3-5,10 *noun.*

cute (kyüt), **1** pretty and dear: *a cute baby.* **2** handsome; good-looking: *Most girls in the class thought the new boy was cute.* **3** clever; shrewd: *She used all sorts of cute tricks to avoid doing homework. adjective,* **cut·er, cut·est.**

cu·ti·cle (kyü′tə kəl), the hard skin around the sides and base of a fingernail or toenail. *noun.*

cut·lass (kut′ləs), a short, heavy, slightly curved sword. *noun, plural* **cut·lass·es.**

cut·out (kut′out′), a shape or design to be cut out. Some books for children have cutouts. *noun.*

cut·ter (kut′ər), **1** a person who cuts: *A garment cutter cuts out pieces of fabric to be made into clothes.* **2** a tool or machine for cutting: *The blade of a meat cutter is very sharp.* **3** a small, armed ship of the Coast Guard, used to patrol coastal waters. *noun.*

cut·ting (kut′ing), **1** a small shoot cut from a plant to grow a new plant. **2** a newspaper clipping. **3** able to cut; sharp: *Keep the cutting edge of the knife turned away from you.* **4** hurting the feelings: *He was offended by her cutting remark.* 1,2 *noun,* 3,4 *adjective.*

cut·worm (kut′werm′), a caterpillar that cuts off the stalks of young plants. *noun.*

cy·cle (sī′kəl), **1** any series of events which repeats itself in the same order again and again. The seasons of the year—spring, summer, autumn, and winter—make a cycle. **2** to ride a bicycle, tricycle, or motorcycle. 1 *noun,* 2 *verb,* **cy·cles, cy·cled, cy·cling.**

cy·clone (sī′klōn), a very violent windstorm with circular winds; tornado. *noun.*

[The word *cyclone* comes from a Greek word meaning "a wheel," or "a circle." The winds of a cyclone blow in a circle. From the same Greek word come the words *bicycle, motorcycle, tricycle,* and *unicycle.* These words all refer to vehicles with wheels.]

cyl·in·der (sil′ən dər), **1** a hollow or solid object shaped like a round pole or tube. Tin cans and rollers are cylinders. **2** a part of an automobile engine that contains a piston. *noun.*

cy·lin·dri·cal (sə lin′drə kəl), shaped like a

cylinder. Cans of fruit, candles, and water pipes are usually cylindrical. *adjective.*

cym·bal (sim′bəl), a round brass plate used as a musical instrument. Cymbals are often used in pairs and make a loud, ringing noise when struck against each other. *noun.*

cymbals

cy·press (sī′prəs), **1** an evergreen tree with small, dark-green leaves like scales. **2** a similar tree that loses its leaves each autumn. The wood of this cypress is used for boards and shingles. *noun, plural* **cy·press·es.**

Cy·prus (sī′prəs), an island country in the Mediterranean Sea. *noun.*

czar (zär), an emperor. When Russia had an emperor, his title was czar. *noun.*

cza·ri·na (zä rē′nə), **1** the wife of a czar. **2** a Russian ruler; empress. *noun.*

Czech·o·slo·va·ki·a (chek′ə slō vä′kē ə), a country in central Europe. *noun.*

cylinders
(definition 1)

Dd

a hat	i it	oi oil	ch child	a in about
ā age	ī ice	ou out	ng long	e in taken
ä far	o hot	u cup	sh she	ə = { i in pencil
e let	ō open	u̇ put	th thin	o in lemon
ē equal	ô order	ü rule	ᴛʜ then	u in circus
ėr term			zh measure	

D or **d** (dē), the fourth letter of the English alphabet. *noun, plural* **D's** or **d's.**

dab (dab), **1** to touch lightly; tap: *I dabbed my lips with a napkin.* **2** a pat or tap: *The cat made a dab at the butterfly.* **3** to put on with light strokes: *She dabbed paint on the canvas.* **4** a small, soft or moist mass: *dabs of butter.* **5** a little bit: *Put a dab of paint on this spot you missed.* 1,3 *verb,* **dabs, dabbed, dab·bing;** 2,4,5 *noun.*

dab·ble (dab'əl), **1** to dip in and out of water; splash: *We sat and dabbled our feet in the pool.* **2** to work at a little: *He dabbled at painting but soon gave it up.* *verb,* **dab·bles, dab·bled, dab·bling.**

dachs·hund (däks'hu̇nt'), a small dog with a long body, drooping ears, and very short legs. *noun.*

[Dachshunds were originally bred to chase animals that burrow into the earth, especially badgers. Their short, strong legs help them to do this. The name of the breed comes from two German words meaning "badger dog."]

dachshund
about 8 inches (20 centimeters) high at the shoulder

dad (dad), father. *noun.*

dad·dy (dad'ē), father. *noun, plural* **dad·dies.**

dad·dy-long·legs (dad'ē lông'legz'), an insect that looks much like a spider, but does not bite. It has a small body and long, thin legs. *noun, plural* **dad·dy-long·legs.**

daf·fo·dil (daf'ə dil), a plant with long, slender leaves and yellow flowers that bloom in the spring. Daffodils grow from bulbs. *noun.*

dag·ger (dag'ər), a small weapon with a short, pointed blade, used for stabbing. *noun.*

dai·ly (dā'lē), **1** done, happening, or appearing every day: *a daily visit. She reads a daily paper to keep up with the news.* **2** every day; day by day: *She rides her bike daily.* **3** a newspaper printed every day, or every day but Sunday. 1 *adjective,* 2 *adverb,* 3 *noun, plural* **dai·lies.**

dain·ti·ly (dān'tl ē), in a dainty way. *adverb.*

dain·ty (dān'tē), **1** fresh, delicate, and pretty: *She wore a dainty cotton dress.* **2** hard to please; particular: *A person who is dainty about eating may like only certain foods.* **3** good to eat; delicious: *The royal cook prepared many dainty dishes.* *adjective,* **dain·ti·er, dain·ti·est.**

dair·y (der'ē), **1** a place where milk and cream are kept and made into butter and cheese. **2** a store or company that sells milk, cream, butter, cheese, yogurt, ice cream, and the like. **3** having to do with milk and products made from milk: *dairy cattle, dairy farming, the dairy industry.* 1,2 *noun, plural* **dair·ies;** 3 *adjective.*

da·is (dā'is), a raised platform at one end of a hall or large room. A throne, seats of honor, or a desk may be set on a dais. *noun, plural* **da·is·es.**

dai·sy (dā'zē), a wildflower having white, pink, or yellow petals around a yellow center. *noun, plural* **dai·sies.**

[*Daisy* comes from two earlier English words meaning "day's eye." The flower was called this because its petals open in the morning and close in the evening.]

dale (dāl), a valley. *noun.*

Dal·las (dal'əs), a city in Texas. *noun.*

dally (definition 1)
He **dallied** along the way and was late for school.

dal·ly (dal'ē), **1** to linger idly; loiter. **2** to waste time: *He dallied the afternoon away looking out the window and daydreaming.* *verb,* **dal·lies, dal·lied, dal·ly·ing.**

Dal·ma·tian (dal mā'shən), a large, short-haired dog, usually white with black spots. *noun.*

dam (dam), **1** a wall built to hold back the water of

a stream, creek, or river. **2** to put up a dam; block up with a dam: *Beavers had dammed the stream.* **1** *noun,* **2** *verb,* **dams, dammed, dam·ming.**

dam·age (dam′ij), **1** harm or injury that lessens value or usefulness: *The accident did some damage to the car.* **2** to harm or injure so as to lessen value or usefulness; hurt: *An early fall frost damaged the apple crops.* **1** *noun,* **2** *verb,* **dam·ag·es, dam·aged, dam·ag·ing.**

dame (dām), **Dame,** a title for a woman raised to the same rank as a knight because of great achievement or service: *Dame Edith Evans.* *noun.*

damn (dam), **1** to declare something to be bad; condemn: *Several people who reviewed the new book damned it.* **2** to swear or swear at by saying "damn"; curse. *verb.*

damp (damp), **1** slightly wet; moist: *This house is damp in rainy weather.* **2** moisture: *When it's foggy you can feel the damp in the air.* **1** *adjective,* **2** *noun.*

damp·en (dam′pən), **1** to make damp; become damp: *He sprinkled water over the clothes to dampen them before ironing.* **2** to cast a chill over; depress; discourage: *The sad news dampened our spirits.* *verb.*

dam·sel (dam′zəl), a maiden; young girl. *noun.*

dance (dans), **1** to move in time with music: *She can dance very well.* **2** a movement in time with music: *Ballet is a well-known form of dance.* **3** some special group of steps: *The waltz is a well-known dance.* **4** a party where people dance: *My older brother is going to the high-school dance.* **5** one period of dancing: *May I have the next dance?* **6** to jump up and down; move in a lively way: *The children danced with delight.* **1,6** *verb,* **danc·es, danced, danc·ing; 2-5** *noun.*

danc·er (dan′sər), a person who dances. *noun.*

dan·de·li·on (dan′dl ī′ən), a plant that grows as a weed. It has deeply notched leaves and bright-yellow flowers. *noun.*

[*Dandelion* comes from three French words meaning "lion's tooth." The plant was called this because its toothed leaves were thought to look like the teeth of a lion.]

dan·druff (dan′drəf), small, whitish flakes of dead skin from the scalp. *noun.*

dan·dy (dan′dē), **1** a man very careful of his dress and appearance. **2** an excellent or first-rate thing: *That new bike is a dandy.* **3** excellent; first-rate: *I got a dandy new bike.* **1,2** *noun, plural* **dan·dies; 3** *adjective,* **dan·di·er, dan·di·est.**

Dane (dān), a person born or living in Denmark. *noun.*

dan·ger (dān′jər), **1** a chance of harm; nearness to harm; risk; peril: *The trip through the jungle was full of danger.* **2** a thing that may cause harm: *Hidden rocks are a danger to ships.* *noun.*

dan·ger·ous (dān′jər əs), likely to cause harm; not safe; risky: *Shooting off firecrackers can be dangerous.* *adjective.*

dan·gle (dang′gəl), **1** to hang and swing loosely: *The mountain climber dangled from a rope.* **2** to hold or carry a thing so that it swings loosely: *The*

cat played with the string I dangled in front of it. *verb,* **dan·gles, dan·gled, dan·gling.**

Dan·ish (dā′nish), **1** of Denmark, its people, or their language. **2** the people of Denmark. **3** the language of Denmark. **1** *adjective,* **2** *noun plural,* **3** *noun singular.*

dap·ple (dap′əl), dappled. *adjective.*

dap·pled (dap′əld), marked with spots; spotted. *adjective.*

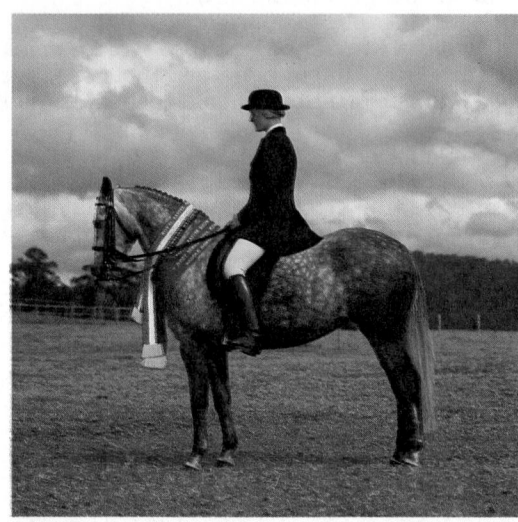

dappled
a **dappled** gray horse

dare (der *or* dar), **1** to be bold; be bold enough: *The children dared to explore the haunted house.* **2** to have courage to try; be bold enough for; not be afraid of: *The pioneers dared the dangers of a strange land.* **3** to challenge: *I dare you to jump the puddle.* **4** a challenge: *I took his dare to jump.* **1-3** *verb,* **dares, dared, dar·ing; 4** *noun.*

dare·dev·il (der′dev′əl *or* dar′dev′əl), **1** a reckless person. **2** recklessly daring: *The motorist's daredevil driving caused an accident.* **1** *noun,* **2** *adjective.*

dar·ing (der′ing *or* dar′ing), **1** boldness; courage to take risks: *The lifeguard's daring saved a swimmer's life.* **2** bold; fearless: *At the circus we saw people perform a daring trapeze act.* **1** *noun,* **2** *adjective.*

dark (därk), **1** without light: *A night without a moon is dark.* **2** nearly black in color: *Her eyes are brown and very dark.* **3** gloomy: *It was a dark day, rainy and cold.* **4** darkness: *Don't be afraid of the dark.* **5** night; nightfall: *The dark comes on early in the winter.* **1-3** *adjective,* **4,5** *noun.*

in the dark, in ignorance: *He said nothing, leaving me in the dark about his plans.*

dark·en (där′kən), to make dark or darker; become dark or darker: *We darkened the room by drawing the shades.* *verb.*

dark·ness (därk′nis), the quality or state of being dark: *It was hard to see anything in the darkness of the closet.* *noun.*

dark·room (därk′rüm′), a room cut off from all

outside light and arranged for developing photographs. It usually has a very dim, colored light. *noun.*

dar·ling (där′ling), **1** a person very dear to another; person much loved: *You are a darling.* **2** very dear; much loved: *"My darling daughter,"* her letter began. **3** pleasing or attractive: *What a darling little puppy!* **1** *noun,* **2,3** *adjective.*

darn (därn), to mend by making rows of stitches back and forth across a hole. *verb.*

dart (därt), **1** a slender, pointed object usually thrown by hand. **2 darts,** an indoor game in which darts are thrown at a target. **3** a sudden, swift movement. **4** to move suddenly and swiftly: *The deer saw us and darted away.* **5** to send suddenly: *The girl darted an angry glance at her younger sister.* **1-3** *noun,* **4,5** *verb.*

dash (dash), **1** to strike or send with force, often so as to break: *I was so angry I dashed the glass to bits on the tile floor.* **2** to rush: *They dashed by in a hurry.* **3** a rush: *She made a dash for safety.* **4** to ruin: *Our hopes were dashed by the bad news.* **5** a small amount: *Put in just a dash of pepper.* **6** a short race: *the fifty-yard dash.* **7** a mark (—) used in writing or printing. A dash shows that there is a break in thought. **1,2,4** *verb,* **3,5-7** *noun, plural* **dash·es.**

dash·board (dash′bôrd′), a panel below the windshield of a motor vehicle. It contains the speedometer and instruments that indicate whether the vehicle is working properly. *noun.*

dash·ing (dash′ing), **1** full of energy and spirit; lively: *a dashing young couple.* **2** showy: *The band members wore bright, dashing uniforms. adjective.*

da·ta (dā′tə *or* dat′ə), facts; facts known or granted; information: *Names, ages, and other data about the class are written in the teacher's book. noun plural.*

date[1] (dāt), **1** the time when something happens or happened: *July 4, 1776, is the date of the signing of the Declaration of Independence.* **2** a statement of time: *There is a date stamped on every piece of United States money.* **3** to mark the time of; put a date on: *Please date your letter.* **4** to find out the date of; give a date to: *The scientist was unable to date the fossil.* **5** to belong to a certain period of time; have its origin: *The oldest house in town dates from the 1780's.* **6** an appointment for a certain time: *Don't forget to keep your Monday morning date with the dentist.* **7** to go out with for friendship or companionship: *They have been dating one another for several weeks.* **8** a person of the opposite sex one goes out with: *He was her date for the school dance last Friday.* **1,2,6,8** *noun,* **3-5,7** *verb,* **dates, dat·ed, dat·ing.**

out of date, old-fashioned: *I refused to wear the suit because it was out of date.*

up to date, 1 in fashion; modern: *Their clothes are always up to date.* **2** up to the present time: *The teacher entered our latest grades on our report cards to bring them up to date.*

date[2] (dāt), the sweet fruit of a kind of palm tree. *noun.*

a hat	i it	oi oil	ch child	a in about
ā age	ī ice	ou out	ng long	e in taken
ä far	o hot	u cup	sh she	ə = i in pencil
e let	ō open	u̇ put	th thin	o in lemon
ē equal	ô order	ü rule	ŦH then	u in circus
ėr term			zh measure	

daub (dôb), **1** to cover with plaster, clay, mud, or any soft material that will stick: *She filled the cracks in the wall by daubing them with cement.* **2** to apply something without skill: *I wore a clown costume and daubed paint on my face. verb.*

daugh·ter (dô′tər), a female child. A girl or woman is the daughter of her father and mother. *noun.*

daugh·ter-in-law (dô′tər in lô′), the wife of one's son. *noun, plural* **daugh·ters-in-law.**

daunt (dônt), to frighten; discourage: *Rain did not daunt the campers. verb.*

daunt·less (dônt′lis), brave; not to be frightened or discouraged: *a dauntless explorer. adjective.*

daw·dle (dô′dl), to waste time; be idle; loiter: *Don't dawdle so long over your work. verb,* **daw·dles, daw·dled, daw·dling.**

dawn (dôn), **1** the beginning of day; the first light in the east. **2** the beginning: *Dinosaurs roamed the earth before the dawn of human life.* **3** to grow light in the morning: *It was dawning when I awoke.* **4** to grow clear to the eye or mind: *When the dog kept barking, it dawned on me that it wanted to go out.* **1,2** *noun,* **3,4** *verb.*

day (dā), **1** the time of light between sunrise and sunset: *Days are longer in summer than in winter.* **2** the 24 hours of day and night. **3** hours for work or other activity: *a school day. An eight-hour working day is common.* **4** a time; period: *the present day, in days of old. noun.*

day·break (dā′brāk′), dawn; time when it first begins to get light in the morning. *noun.*

day-care center (dā′ker′ *or* dā′kar′), a place where small children are cared for during the day while their parents are at work.

day·dream (dā′drēm′), **1** dreamy thinking about pleasant things. **2** to think about pleasant things in a dreamy way. **1** *noun,* **2** *verb.*

day·light (dā′līt′), **1** the light of day: *It is easier to read by daylight than by lamplight.* **2** daytime. **3** dawn; daybreak: *He was up at daylight. noun.*

day·time (dā′tīm′), the time when it is day and not night: *The baby sleeps even in the daytime. noun.*

daze (dāz), **1** to make unable to think clearly; bewilder; stun: *A blow on the head dazed him so that he could not keep playing.* **2** a dazed condition: *She was in a daze after falling from her horse and could not understand what was happening.* **1** *verb,* **daz·es, dazed, daz·ing; 2** *noun.*

daz·zle (daz′əl), **1** to hurt the eyes with too bright light, or quick-moving lights: *It dazzles the eyes to look straight at the sun.* **2** to amaze; impress deeply: *We were dazzled by the richness of the palace. verb,* **daz·zles, daz·zled, daz·zling.**

D

dazzling

At night, the bright lights of the city street were **dazzling**.

daz·zling (daz′ling), brilliant or splendid: *The magician gave us a dazzling display of skill.* *adjective.*

DC, District of Columbia (used with postal Zip Code).

d.c., direct current.

D.C., 1 direct current. **2** District of Columbia.

de-, a prefix meaning: **1** to do the opposite of: *Desegregate means to do the opposite of* segregate. **2** down; lower: *Depress means to press down.* **3** to take away; remove: *Defrost means to remove the frost.*

DE, Delaware (used with postal Zip Code).

dea·con (dē′kən), **1** an officer of a church who helps the minister in church duties not connected with preaching. **2** a member of the clergy next below a priest or minister in rank. *noun.*

dead (ded), **1** not alive; no longer living: *The flowers in my garden are dead.* **2 the dead,** persons not living any more: *We remember the dead of our wars on Memorial Day.* **3** without life: *The surface of the moon is dead.* **4** dull; quiet; not active: *This beach is crowded now, but in the winter it's dead.* **5** without force or activity: *The car won't start because the battery is dead.* **6** having no feeling or sensation; numb: *After the race, his legs felt dead.* **7** very tired; exhausted: *I was dead when I finished the six-mile hike.* **8** sure; certain: *a dead shot with a rifle.* **9** complete: *There was dead silence in the library.* **10** completely; absolutely: *I was dead tired after the long hike.* **11** directly; straight: *A floating log lay dead ahead of our canoe.* **12** the time when there is the least life stirring: *A loud noise woke us in the dead of night.* 1,3-9 *adjective,* 2,12 *noun,* 10,11 *adverb.*

dead·en (ded′n), to make dull or weak; lessen the force of: *Some medicines deaden pain. Thick walls deaden the noises from the street.* *verb.*

dead end, a street that is closed at one end.

dead·line (ded′līn′), the latest possible time to do something: *The teacher made Friday afternoon the deadline for handing in all book reports.* *noun.*

dead·ly (ded′lē), **1** causing death; likely to cause death; fatal: *a deadly disease, deadly toadstools.* **2** filled with hatred: *deadly enemies.* **3** extremely:

"Washing dishes is deadly dull," she said. 1,2 *adjective,* **dead·li·er, dead·li·est;** 3 *adverb.*

deaf (def), **1** not able, or only partly able, to hear: *A deaf person can learn to read people's lips.* **2** not willing to hear: *He is deaf to any criticism of his work.* *adjective.*

deaf·en (def′ən), to make deaf, especially for a short time: *A sudden explosion deafened us for a moment.* *verb.*

deaf-mute (def′myüt′), a person who is unable to hear and speak, usually because of deafness from birth or from early childhood. *noun.*

deal (dēl), **1** to have to do: *Arithmetic deals with numbers.* **2** to act; behave: *Deal kindly with them so you don't hurt their feelings.* **3** to handle or manage; take action concerning: *When the faucet broke, Mother dealt with it until the plumber came.* **4** to carry on business; buy and sell: *This garage deals in gasoline, oil, and tires.* **5** a bargain: *He got a good deal on a television set.* **6** to give: *One fighter dealt the other a hard blow.* **7** to give out: *It's my turn to deal the cards.* **8** an arrangement; plan: *I have a deal to trade some old books with her.* 1-4,6,7 *verb,* **deals, dealt, deal·ing;** 5,8 *noun.*

a good deal or **a great deal,** a large part, portion, or amount: *A great deal of her money goes for rent.*

deal·er (dē′lər), **1** a person who makes a living by buying and selling: *a used-car dealer.* **2** a person who deals out the cards in a card game. *noun.*

deal·ing (dē′ling), a way of acting or doing business: *The judge is known for her fair dealing.* *noun.*

dealt (delt). See **deal.** *The principal's talk dealt with fire drills. The cards have been dealt.* *verb.*

dear (dir), **1** much loved; precious: *His sister was very dear to him.* **2** a darling; dear one: *"Come, my dear,"* said her grandfather. **3** much valued; highly respected. *Dear Sir* or *Dear Madam* is a polite way to begin a letter. **4** an exclamation of surprise or trouble: *Oh, dear! I lost my pencil.* 1,3 *adjective,* 2 *noun,* 4 *interjection.*

dear·ly (dir′lē), very much: *We love our parents dearly.* *adverb.*

death (deth), **1** dying; the ending of life: *The old man's death was calm and peaceful.* **2** any ending that is like dying: *the death of an empire, the death of one's hopes.* *noun.*

death·less (deth′lis), lasting forever; eternal: *deathless fame.* *adjective.*

death·ly (deth′lē), **1** like death: *a deathly paleness, deathly pale.* **2** extremely: *He is deathly afraid of deep water.* 1 *adjective,* 1,2 *adverb.*

de·bate (di bāt′), **1** to consider; think over: *I am debating buying a camera.* **2** a discussion, often public, of reasons for and against something: *There has been much debate about building a new school.* **3** to discuss a question or topic: *The two candidates debated building a new expressway.* 1,3 *verb,* **de·bates, de·bat·ed, de·bat·ing;** 2 *noun.*

de·bris (də brē′), scattered fragments; ruins; rubbish. *noun.*

debt (det), **1** something owed to another: *Having borrowed money a few times, he had debts to pay back to several people.* **2** the condition of owing: *She is in debt to the bank for her new car. noun.*

debt·or (det′ər), a person who owes something to another: *If I borrow a dollar from you, I am your debtor. noun.*

de·bug (dē bug′), to find and correct the mistakes in a computer program. *verb,* **de·bugs, de·bugged, de·bug·ging.**

de·but (dā′byü *or* dā byü′), a first public appearance: *Last night was the young actor's debut on the stage. noun.*

Dec., December.

dec·ade (dek′ād), ten years. From 1900 to 1910 was a decade. Two decades ago means twenty years ago. *noun.*

de·caf·fein·at·ed (di kaf′ə nā′tid), having the caffeine removed: *Some people drink decaffeinated coffee. adjective.*

de·cal (dē′kal *or* di kal′), a design or picture that will stick fast when it is put on glass, wood, plastic, or metal. *noun.*

de·cant·er (di kan′tər), a glass bottle with a stopper, used for serving wine or other liquids. *noun.*

de·cay (di kā′), **1** to become rotten; rot: *The old apples got moldy and decayed.* **2** a rotting: *The decay in the tree trunk proceeded so rapidly the tree fell over in a year.* **3** to grow less in power, strength, wealth, or beauty: *Many nations have grown great and then decayed.* **4** a growing less in power, strength, wealth, or beauty: *the decay of a nation's strength.* **1,3** *verb,* **2,4** *noun.*

de·ceased (di sēst′), **1** dead: *a deceased writer.* **2 the deceased,** a particular dead person or persons: *The deceased had been a famous writer.* **1** *adjective,* **2** *noun.*

de·ceit (di sēt′), **1** a deceiving; lying; cheating; making a person believe as true something that is false: *He was a truthful person, incapable of deceit.* **2** the quality that makes a person tell lies or cheat: *The dishonest trader was full of deceit. noun.*

de·ceit·ful (di sēt′fəl), ready or willing to deceive or lie: *a deceitful person. adjective.*

de·ceive (di sēv′), to make a person believe as true something that is false; mislead: *The magician deceived her audience into thinking she had really pulled a rabbit from a hat. verb,* **de·ceives, de·ceived, de·ceiv·ing.**

de·cel·e·rate (dē sel′ə rāt′), to decrease the speed of; slow down: *By putting on the brake, the driver decelerated the car. verb,* **de·cel·e·rates, de·cel·e·rat·ed, de·cel·e·ra·ting.**

De·cem·ber (di sem′bər), the 12th and last month of the year. It has 31 days. *noun.*
[*December* came from a Latin word meaning "ten." In the ancient Roman calendar, December was the tenth month of the year, which began in March.]

a hat	i it	oi oil	ch child	⎧ a in about
ā age	ī ice	ou out	ng long	e in taken
ä far	o hot	u cup	sh she	ə = ⎨ i in pencil
e let	ō open	u̇ put	th thin	o in lemon
ē equal	ô order	ü rule	ᴛH then	⎩ u in circus
ėr term			zh measure	

de·cen·cy (dē′sn sē), being decent; proper behavior: *Common decency requires that you pay for the window you broke. noun.*

de·cent (dē′snt), **1** respectable; proper and right: *The decent thing to do is to pay for the damage you have done.* **2** good enough; not wonderful and not very bad: *I usually get decent marks at school. adjective.*

de·cen·tral·ize (dē sen′trə līz), to spread or distribute authority or power among more groups or local governments. *verb,* **de·cen·tral·izes, de·cen·tral·ized, de·cen·tral·iz·ing.**

de·cep·tion (di sep′shən), **1** a misleading or a being misled; deceiving: *The twins' deception in exchanging places fooled everybody.* **2** a trick meant to deceive; fraud; sham: *The scheme is all a deception to cheat people out of their money. noun.*

de·cep·tive (di sep′tiv), deceiving or misleading: *Travelers on the desert are often fooled by the deceptive appearance of water where there is none. adjective.*

dec·i·bel (des′ə bəl), a unit for measuring the loudness of sounds. *noun.*

de·cide (di sīd′), **1** to settle a question or dispute: *Fighting is not the best way to decide an argument.* **2** to make up one's mind; resolve: *She decided to be a scientist. verb,* **de·cides, de·cid·ed, de·cid·ing.**

de·cid·ed (di sī′did), definite; unquestionable: *There was a decided change in the temperature. adjective.*

de·cid·ed·ly (di sī′did lē), clearly; definitely; without question: *One painting was decidedly better than the others. It was a decidedly warm morning. adverb.*

dec·i·mal (des′ə məl), **1** a fraction like .04 or ⁴⁄₁₀₀, .2 or ²⁄₁₀. **2** a number like 75.24, 3.062, .7, or .091. **3** of or based on the number 10; counting by tens: *United States money has a decimal system.* **1,2** *noun,* **3** *adjective.*

decimal point, a period placed before a decimal fraction, as in 2.03 or .623.

decimal system, a system of numbering which is based on units of 10.

dec·i·me·ter (des′ə mē′tər), a unit of length equal to ¹⁄₁₀ of a meter. *noun.*

de·ci·pher (di sī′fər), **1** to make out the meaning of something puzzling: *We couldn't decipher his handwriting.* **2** to change something in code into ordinary language: *The spy deciphered the secret message. verb.*

de·ci·sion (di sizh′ən), **1** a deciding; judgment; making up one's mind: *I have not yet come to a decision about buying a coat.* **2** firmness and determination: *She is a woman of decision who* *makes up her mind what to do and then does it.* noun.

de·ci·sive (di sī′siv), **1** having or giving a clear result; settling something beyond question: *The team won by 20 points, which was a decisive victory.* **2** having or showing decision: *When I asked for a decisive answer, he finally said, "No."* adjective.

deck (dek), **1** one of the floors of a ship that divide it into different levels. **2** a part or floor that resembles a ship's deck: *Carpenters built a deck on the back of our house.* **3** a pack of playing cards: *He shuffled the deck and dealt the cards.* **4** to decorate; trim: *Deck the halls with holly.* 1-3 noun, 4 verb.
[*Deck* comes from an early Dutch word meaning "roof" or "covering." The change in meaning from roof or covering to floor took place in English. The deck of a ship is a covering over the space below and also serves as a floor.]

dec·la·ra·tion (dek′lə rā′shən), **1** a declaring: *The soldiers rejoiced at the declaration of a truce.* **2** a public statement; official announcement: *The royal declaration was announced in every city and town.* noun.

Declaration of Independence, the statement made on July 4, 1776, declaring that the Colonies were independent of Great Britain.

de·clare (di kler′ *or* di klar′), **1** to announce officially or formally: *Only Congress has the power to declare war.* **2** to say openly or strongly: *I declared that I would never do anything so foolish again.* verb, **de·clares, de·clared, de·clar·ing.**

de·cline (di klīn′), **1** to turn away from doing; refuse to do or accept something: *They declined to do as they were told.* **2** to grow less in power, strength, wealth, or beauty: *Great nations have risen and declined.* **3** a growing worse: *Lack of money for books and equipment led to a decline in the condition of the school.* **4** a falling to a lower level; sinking: *a decline in prices.* 1,2 verb, **de·clines, de·clined, de·clin·ing;** 3,4 noun.

de·code (dē kōd′), to translate secret writing from code into ordinary language. verb, **de·codes, de·cod·ed, de·cod·ing.**

de·com·pose (dē′kəm pōz′), to decay; rot: *Lettuce and oranges decompose quickly in the heat.* verb, **de·com·pos·es, de·com·posed, de·com·pos·ing.**

dec·o·rate (dek′ə rāt′), **1** to make beautiful; trim; adorn: *We decorated the Christmas tree.* **2** to paint or paper a room: *The old rooms looked like new after they had been decorated.* **3** to give a badge, ribbon, or medal to: *The general decorated the soldier for his brave act.* verb, **dec·o·rates, dec·o·rat·ed, dec·o·rat·ing.**

dec·o·ra·tion (dek′ə rā′shən), **1** a thing used to decorate; ornament: *We put pictures and other decorations up in the classroom.* **2** a decorating: *Decoration of the gymnasium took most of the day before the dance.* **3** a badge, ribbon, or medal given as an honor. noun.

dec·o·ra·tive (dek′ə rā′tiv), decorating;

ornamental; helping to make beautiful: *Wallpaper gives a decorative effect to a room.* adjective.

dec·o·ra·tor (dek′ə rā′tər), a person who decorates. An **interior decorator** plans and arranges the furnishings and decorations for a house or other building. noun.

de·coy (di koi′ *for* 1; dē′koi *or* di koi′ *for* 2 and 3), **1** to lead or tempt by trickery; entice: *The bird decoyed us away from her nest by dragging a drooping wing.* **2** an artificial bird used to lure birds into a trap or near the hunter. **3** any person or thing used to lead or tempt into danger; lure. 1 verb, 2,3 noun.

decoy (definition 2)

de·crease (di krēs′ *for* 1; dē′krēs *for* 2 and 3), **1** to make or become less: *The driver decreased the speed of the car.* **2** a growing less: *Toward night there was a decrease in temperature.* **3** the amount by which a thing becomes less or is made less: *The decrease in temperature was 10 degrees.* 1 verb, **de·creas·es, de·creased, de·creas·ing;** 2,3 noun.

de·cree (di krē′), **1** an official decision; law; order: *The new state holiday was declared by a decree of the Governor.* **2** to order or settle by authority: *The city government decreed that all dogs must be licensed.* 1 noun, 2 verb, **de·crees, de·creed, de·cree·ing.**

ded·i·cate (ded′ə kāt), to set apart for a purpose: *The doctor dedicated her life to serving the poor. The library was dedicated to the memory of a great writer.* verb, **ded·i·cates, ded·i·cat·ed, ded·i·cat·ing.**

ded·i·ca·tion (ded′ə kā′shən), a setting apart for a purpose; being set apart for a purpose: *the dedication of a park.* noun.

de·duct (di dukt′), to take away; subtract: *When I broke the window, my parents deducted its cost from my allowance.* verb.

decoration (definition 3)
He wore seven **decorations.**

de·duc·tion (di duk′shən), **1** the act of taking away; subtraction: *When I broke the window, my parents made a deduction from my allowance to pay for it.* **2** the amount deducted: *There was a deduction of $20 from the price of the chair because it was damaged. noun.*

deed (dēd), **1** something done; an act; an action: *To feed the hungry is a good deed.* **2** a written or printed statement of ownership. The buyer of land receives a deed to the property from the former owner. **3** to transfer by means of a deed: *She deeded the land to her son.* 1,2 *noun,* 3 *verb.*

deep (dēp), **1** going a long way down from the top or surface: *The pond is deep in the middle.* **2** far down; far on: *They dug deep before they found water.* **3** far down or back: *I had a deep cut on my finger.* **4** going a long way back from the front: *Our house stands on a deep lot.* **5** low in pitch: *the low tones of Father's deep voice.* **6** hard to understand; needing much time for thought: *It takes a lot of study to understand a deep subject.* **7** strong; great; intense; extreme: *She fell into a deep sleep after the game. Deep feeling is hard to put into words.* **8** rich and dark in color: *The deep red roses are beautiful.* **9** in depth: *The lot on which our house stands is 100 feet deep.* **10** with the mind fully taken up: *He was deep in thought about what to do next.* **11 the deep,** the sea: *Long ago, frightened sailors thought they saw monsters from the deep.* 1,3-10 *adjective,* 2 *adverb,* 11 *noun.*

deep·en (dē′pən), to make or become deeper: *We deepened the hole. verb.*

deer (dir), a swift, graceful animal that has hoofs and chews the cud. The male deer has antlers which are shed and grow again every year. *noun, plural* **deer.**
[*Deer comes from an earlier English word meaning "a wild animal."*]

deer·skin (dir′skin′), **1** leather made from the skin of a deer. **2** clothing made of this leather. *noun.*

de·face (di fās′), to spoil the appearance of; damage; disfigure. *verb,* **de·fac·es, de·faced, de·fac·ing.**

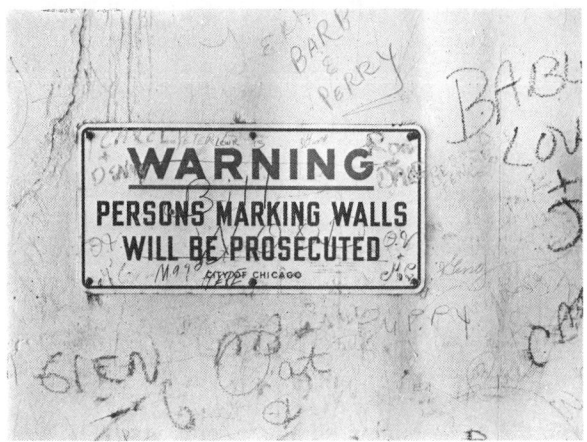

deface—Many people had **defaced** the wall with their scribbling.

a hat	**i** it	**oi** oil	**ch** child		a in about
ā age	**ī** ice	**ou** out	**ng** long		e in taken
ä far	**o** hot	**u** cup	**sh** she	**ə** =	i in pencil
e let	**ō** open	** u̇** put	**th** thin		o in lemon
ē equal	**ô** order	**ü** rule	**ᴛʜ** then		u in circus
ėr term			**zh** measure		

de·feat (di fēt′), **1** to overcome; win a victory over: *to defeat the enemy in battle, to defeat another school in basketball.* **2** to cause to fail; make useless: *to defeat someone's plans.* **3** an overcoming: *The crowd cheered their team's defeat of the visiting team.* **4** a being overcome: *We were unhappy about our team's defeat.* 1,2 *verb,* 3,4 *noun.*

de·fect (dē′fekt *or* di fekt′), a fault; blemish; imperfection: *The cloth had holes and other defects. noun.*

de·fec·tive (di fek′tiv), not complete; not perfect; faulty: *This watch is defective; it does not keep the correct time. adjective.*

de·fend (di fend′), **1** to keep safe; guard from attack or harm; protect: *The soldiers defended the fort.* **2** to act, speak, or write in favor of: *The newspapers defended the governor's action. Lawyers are hired to defend people who are charged with crimes. verb.*

de·fense (di fens′ *for 1 and 2;* di fens′ *or* dē′fens *for 3*), **1** any thing or act that defends, guards, or protects: *A wall around a city was a defense against enemies. A warm coat is a defense against cold weather.* **2** a guarding against attack or harm; protecting: *The army, navy, and air force are responsible for the defense of the country.* **3** the team or team members who try to keep their opponents from making points: *Our football team has a good defense. noun.*

de·fense·less (di fens′lis), having no defense; helpless against attack; not protected: *a defenseless village, a defenseless child. adjective.*

de·fen·sive (di fen′siv), of or for protection; intended to defend: *Knights wore defensive armor in battle. adjective.*
on the defensive, ready to defend, apologize, or explain: *When his work was criticized he was put on the defensive.*

de·fer[1] (di fėr′), to put off; delay: *The test was deferred because so many students were sick. verb,* **de·fers, de·ferred, de·fer·ring.**

de·fer[2] (di fėr′), to yield in opinion or judgment: *The children deferred to their parents' wishes. verb,* **de·fers, de·ferred, de·fer·ring.**

def·er·ence (def′ər əns), respect for the opinion, judgment, or wishes of another: *People often show deference to others who are older and wiser. noun.*

de·fi·ance (di fī′əns), a defying; standing up against authority and refusing to recognize or obey it: *She refused to obey the rules and was punished for her defiance. noun.*
in defiance of, without regard for; in spite of: *The driver failed to stop at the red light in defiance of the law.*

de·fi·ant (di fī′ənt), showing defiance; openly resisting; disobedient: *She told us in a defiant manner that she was against our plans. adjective.*

de·fi·cien·cy (di fish′ən sē), **1** a lack or absence of something needed: *A deficiency of calcium in your diet can cause soft bones and teeth.* **2** the amount by which a thing falls short or is too small: *If a bill to be paid is $10 and you have only $6, the deficiency is $4. noun, plural* **de·fi·cien·cies.**

de·fi·cient (di fish′ənt), lacking something needed; not complete: *My knowledge of science is deficient. His diet was deficient in calcium. adjective.*

de·fine (di fīn′), **1** to make clear the meaning of; explain: *A dictionary defines words.* **2** to make clear; make distinct: *The shape of the building was defined against the dark sky.* **3** to fix or mark the limits of: *The boundary between the United States and Canada is defined by treaty. verb,* **de·fines, de·fined, de·fin·ing.**

def·i·nite (def′ə nit), **1** clear; exact; not vague: *Say "Yes" or "No," or give me some definite answer.* **2** certain; without doubt: *Is it definite that they are moving? adjective.*

def·i·nite·ly (def′ə nit lē), **1** in a definite manner; exactly: *Say definitely what you have in mind.* **2** certainly: *I am definitely not going. adverb.*

def·i·ni·tion (def′ə nish′ən), an explaining or making clear the meaning of a word or phrase. One definition of "home" is "the place where a person or family lives." *noun.*

de·flate (di flāt′), to let air or gas out of a balloon, tire, football, or the like: *A nail had deflated the tire. verb,* **de·flates, de·flat·ed, de·flat·ing.**

de·form (di fôrm′), to spoil the shape or appearance of: *Shoes that are too tight may deform the feet. Rage deformed the man's face. verb.*

de·form·i·ty (di fôr′mə tē), **1** a part of the body that is not properly formed. **2** the condition of being improperly formed: *Many deformities can be corrected. noun, plural* **de·form·i·ties.**

de·fraud (di frôd′), to take something away from by being dishonest; cheat: *The company defrauded the public by making false claims about its product. verb.*

de·frost (di frôst′), to remove frost or ice from; thaw: *We defrosted the refrigerator. verb.*

deft (deft), quick and skillful in action: *The fingers of a violinist must be deft. adjective.*

de·fy (di fī′), **1** to set oneself openly against authority; resist boldly: *The American Colonies defied many British laws.* **2** to challenge a person to do or prove something: *I defy you to do that again. verb,* **de·fies, de·fied, de·fy·ing.**

de·grade (di grād′), to make lower in the eyes of others; bring shame upon; dishonor: *Students who cheat degrade themselves. verb,* **de·grades, de·grad·ed, de·grad·ing.**

de·gree (di grē′), **1** a step in a series; stage in a process: *By degrees I became better at swimming.* **2** an amount; extent: *To what degree are you interested in reading?* **3** a unit for measuring temperature: *The freezing point of water is 32 degrees (32°) Fahrenheit.* **4** a unit for measuring an angle or a part of a circle. There are 90 degrees in a right angle and 360 degrees in the circumference of a circle. **5** a rank or title given by a college or university to a student who graduates or to a famous person as an honor. *noun.*

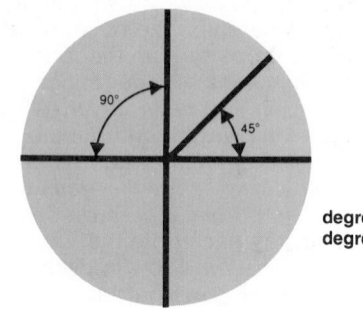

degree (definition 4)
degrees in two angles

de·hy·drate (dē hī′drāt), to take water or moisture from; dry: *High fever dehydrates the body. verb,* **de·hy·drates, de·hy·drat·ed, de·hy·drat·ing.**

de·i·ty (dē′ə tē), a god or goddess: *The ancient Romans had many deities. noun, plural* **de·i·ties.**

de·ject·ed (di jek′tid), sad; discouraged. *adjective.*

dejected—The people waiting in the employment office looked tired and **dejected.**

Del., Delaware.

Del·a·ware (del′ə wer *or* del′ə wär), one of the southeastern states of the United States. *Abbreviation:* Del. or DE *Capital:* Dover. *noun.* [*Delaware* was named for the Delaware River. The river was named for Baron De La Warr, who lived from 1577 to 1618. He was the first governor of the colony of Virginia.]

de·lay (di lā′), **1** to put off till a later time: *We will delay the party for a week and hold it next Saturday.* **2** a putting off till a later time: *The delay upset our plans.* **3** to make late; keep waiting;

hinder the progress of: *The accident delayed the train for two hours.* **4** to go slowly; stop along the way: *Do not delay on this errand.* **5** a stopping or a being stopped along the way: *We were so late that we could afford no further delay.* 1,3,4 *verb,* 2,5 *noun.*

del·e·gate (del′ə git *or* del′ə gāt *for 1;* del′ə gāt *for 2*), **1** a person given power or authority to act for others; a representative: *Our club sent two delegates to the meeting.* **2** to appoint or send a person as a representative: *Her team delegated her to buy the new baseball bat.* 1 *noun,* 2 *verb,* **del·e·gates, del·e·gat·ed, del·e·gat·ing.**

del·e·ga·tion (del′ə gā′shən), **1** a delegating. **2** a group of delegates: *Each club sent a delegation to the meeting. noun.*

del·i (del′ē), a delicatessen. *noun, plural* **del·is.**

de·lib·er·ate (di lib′ər it *for 1-3;* di lib′ə rāt′ *for 4 and 5*), **1** intended; done on purpose; thought over beforehand: *Their excuse was a deliberate lie.* **2** slow and careful in deciding what to do: *Deliberate persons do not make up their minds quickly.* **3** slow; not hurried: *The old man walked with deliberate steps.* **4** to think over carefully; consider: *I am deliberating where to put up my new picture.* **5** to talk over reasons for and against; debate: *Congress deliberated the question of raising taxes.* 1-3 *adjective,* 4,5 *verb,* **de·lib·er·ates, de·lib·er·at·ed, de·lib·er·at·ing.**

de·lib·er·ate·ly (di lib′ər it lē), **1** on purpose. **2** slowly. *adverb.*

de·lib·e·ra·tion (di lib′ə rā′shən), **1** careful thought: *After long deliberation, he decided not to go.* **2** a talking about reasons for or against an action: *The deliberations of Congress over raising taxes.* **3** slowness and care: *She drove the car over the icy bridge with great deliberation. noun.*

del·i·ca·cy (del′ə kə sē), **1** fineness of weave, quality, or make: *the delicacy of lace, the delicacy of a flower.* **2** thought for the feelings of others; tact: *His refusal required delicacy; he did not wish to hurt his friend's feelings.* **3** a choice kind of food. Nuts and candy are delicacies. *noun, plural* **del·i·ca·cies.**

del·i·cate (del′ə kit), **1** pleasing to the taste; mild or soft: *delicate foods, delicate colors.* **2** of fine weave, quality, or make; thin; easily torn. **3** requiring care, skill, or tact: *When my friends asked me to settle their argument, I knew it could be a delicate situation.* **4** very quickly responding to slight changes of condition; sensitive: *The surgeon used delicate instruments for the eye operation.* **5** easily hurt or made ill: *a weak and delicate child. adjective.*

del·i·ca·tes·sen (del′ə kə tes′n), a store that sells prepared foods, such as cooked meats, smoked fish, cheese, salads, and sandwiches. *noun.*

de·li·cious (di lish′əs), very pleasing or satisfying; delightful, especially to the taste or smell: *a delicious cake. adjective.*

de·light (di līt′), **1** great pleasure; joy: *The children took great delight in their toys.* **2** to please

greatly: *The circus delighted us.* 1 *noun,* 2 *verb.*

de·light·ed·ly (di lī′tid lē), in a very pleased way: *When we gave her the gift, she smiled delightedly. adverb.*

de·light·ful (di līt′fəl), giving joy; very pleasing: *a delightful visit from an old friend. adjective.*

de·lir·i·ous (di lir′ē əs), **1** out of one's senses for a short time; raving: *The patient with the high fever was delirious.* **2** wildly excited: *The students were delirious with joy when their team won the tournament. adjective.*

de·lir·i·um (di lir′ē əm), **1** a sickness of the mind that may come during fevers, insanity, or drunkenness, and lasts only a short time. People in delirium are often restless and excited. They sometimes talk wildly and see or hear things that aren't there. **2** wild excitement. *noun.*

de·liv·er (di liv′ər), **1** to carry and give out; distribute: *The mail carrier delivers our mail in the morning.* **2** to give forth in words: *She delivered a talk on her travels in Africa. The jury delivered its verdict.* **3** to strike; throw: *The boxer delivered a blow.* **4** to set free; rescue; save: *Deliver us from temptation.* **5** to help a woman give birth to a child. *verb.*

de·liv·er·ance (di liv′ər əns), a setting free or a being set free; rescue; release: *The shipwrecked passengers rejoiced at their deliverance. noun.*

de·liv·er·y (di liv′ər ē), **1** a carrying and giving out: *There is one delivery of mail a day in our city.* **2** a manner of speaking or singing: *The speaker had an excellent delivery.* **3** the act or way of striking or throwing: *That pitcher has a fast delivery.* **4** a giving birth to a child. *noun, plural* **de·liv·er·ies.**

dell (del), a small, sheltered valley, usually with trees in it. *noun.*

a hat	i it	oi oil	ch child	(a in about
ā age	ī ice	ou out	ng long	e in taken
ä far	o hot	u cup	sh she	ə = { i in pencil
e let	ō open	u̇ put	th thin	o in lemon
ē equal	ô order	ü rule	ŦH then	u in circus
ėr term			zh measure	

D

delicate (definition 2)—A spider web is very **delicate**.

delta
a satellite
view of the
Nile **delta**

del·ta (del′tə), a deposit of earth and sand that collects at the mouth of some rivers and is usually three-sided. *noun.*

de·lude (di lüd′), to mislead; deceive: *He deluded me into thinking he was on my side. verb,* **de·ludes, de·lud·ed, de·lud·ing.**

del·uge (del′yüj), **1** a great flood: *After the dam broke, the deluge washed away the bridge.* **2** a heavy fall of rain: *We were caught in a deluge.* **3** to overwhelm: *The singer was deluged with requests for her autograph.* 1,2 *noun,* 3 *verb,* **del·ug·es, del·uged, del·ug·ing.**

de·lu·sion (di lü′zhən), a false belief or opinion: *She was under the delusion that she could pass any test without studying for it. noun.*

delve (delv), to search carefully for information: *The scholar delved in many libraries for facts to support her theory. verb,* **delves, delved, delv·ing.**

de·mand (di mand′), **1** to ask for with authority or as a right: *The teacher demanded silence. The landlord demanded payment of the overdue rent.* **2** to call for; require; need: *Training a puppy demands patience.* **3** a claim: *Parents have many demands upon their time.* **4** the desire and ability to buy: *Because of the large crop, the supply of apples is greater than the demand this year.* 1,2 *verb,* 3,4 *noun.*

in demand, wanted: *She is always in demand as a babysitter.*

de·mer·it (di mer′it), a mark against a person's record for bad behavior or poor work. *noun.*

de·moc·ra·cy (di mok′rə sē), **1** a government that is run by the people who live under it. In a democracy either the people rule through meetings that all may attend, such as a town meeting in New England, or they elect representatives to take care of the business of government. **2** a country or town in which the government is a democracy. *noun, plural* **de·moc·ra·cies.**

Dem·o·crat (dem′ə krat), a member of the Democratic Party. *noun.*

dem·o·crat·ic (dem′ə krat′ik), **1** of a democracy; like a democracy. **2 Democratic,** of the Democratic Party. *adjective.*

Democratic Party, one of the two main political parties in the United States.

de·mol·ish (di mol′ish), to pull or tear down; destroy. *verb.*

demolish—The old building was being **demolished** to make room for a new one.

dem·o·li·tion (dem′ə lish′ən), a destroying; destruction: *We watched the demolition of the old building. noun.*

de·mon (dē′mən), **1** a devil; evil spirit; fiend. **2** a person with great energy: *My music teacher is a demon for practicing. noun.*

dem·on·strate (dem′ən strāt), **1** to show clearly; prove: *The pianist demonstrated her musical skill.* **2** to explain by the use of examples: *The coach demonstrated how to dribble a basketball.* **3** to show or make known the quality of: *The saleswoman played a record to demonstrate the stereo to us.* **4** to take part in a parade or meeting to protest or to make demands: *An angry crowd demonstrated in front of the mayor's office demanding better police protection. verb,* **dem·on·strates, dem·on·strat·ed, dem·on·strat·ing.**

dem·on·stra·tion (dem′ən strā′shən), **1** clear proof: *The ease with which he solved the hard problem was a demonstration of his ability in*

demonstration (definition 4)
a civil rights **demonstration** in Washington

arithmetic. **2** an explaining by the use of examples: *A compass was used in a demonstration of the earth's magnetism.* **3** a showing or making known the quality of something: *The saleswoman gave me a demonstration of the vacuum cleaner.* **4** a parade or meeting to protest or make demands. *noun.*

de·mon·stra·tive (di mon′strə tiv), showing affection freely and openly. *adjective.*

demonstrative
Children are often **demonstrative**.

dem·on·stra·tor (dem′ən strā′tər), **1** a person or thing that demonstrates. **2** a person who takes part in a parade or meeting to protest or make demands. *noun.*

de·mote (di mōt′), to put back to a lower grade; reduce in rank: *The student who had trouble doing fourth grade work was demoted to third grade.* *verb,* **de·motes, de·mot·ed, de·mot·ing.**

de·mure (di myür′), seeming more modest and proper than one really is: *the demure smile of a flirt. adjective,* **de·mur·er, de·mur·est.**

den (den), **1** a wild animal's home or resting place: *The bear's den was in a cave.* **2** a private room for reading and work, usually small and cozy. **3** a group of from two to ten cub scouts. *noun.*

de·ni·al (di nī′əl), **1** a saying that something is not true: *a denial of the existence of ghosts.* **2** a refusing: *Their quick denial of our request was very rude. noun.*

den·im (den′əm), **1** a heavy, coarse cotton cloth used for jeans, skirts, and other clothing. **2 denims,** pants or overalls made of this cloth. *noun.*

Den·mark (den′märk), a country in northwestern Europe. *noun.*

de·nom·i·na·tion (di nom′ə nā′shən), **1** a religious group or sect: *Methodists and Baptists are two large Protestant denominations.* **2** a class or kind of units: *Changing 5/12, 1/3, and 1/6 to the same denomination gives 5/12, 4/12, and 2/12. noun.*

de·nom·i·na·tor (di nom′ə nā′tər), the number below or to the right of the line in a fraction: *In 3/4, 4 is the denominator, and 3 is the numerator. noun.*

de·note (di nōt′), **1** to indicate; be the sign of: *A*

fever usually denotes sickness. **2** to mean: *The word "density" denotes thickness. verb,* **de·notes, de·not·ed, de·not·ing.**

de·nounce (di nouns′), to speak against; express strong disapproval of; condemn: *The mayor denounced crime in the streets. verb,* **de·nounc·es, de·nounced, de·nounc·ing.**

dense (dens), **1** closely packed together; thick: *We could not see through the dense fog.* **2** stupid. *adjective,* **dens·er, dens·est.**

den·si·ty (den′sə tē), **1** closeness; compactness; thickness: *The density of the forest prevented us from seeing more than a little way ahead.* **2** the amount of matter in a unit of volume: *The density of lead is greater than the density of wood. noun, plural* **den·si·ties.**

dent (dent), **1** a hollow made by a blow or pressure: *When my bicycle fell over, it put a dent in the fender.* **2** to make or get a dent or dents: *The movers dented the table. Soft wood dents easily.* **1** *noun,* **2** *verb.*

den·tal (den′tl), **1** of or for the teeth: *For healthy teeth, practice good dental care.* **2** of or for a dentist's work: *I heard the buzz of the dental drill. adjective.*

dental floss, a strong, often waxed thread for cleaning between the teeth.

dental hygienist, a person who helps a dentist by examining and cleaning patients' teeth and by taking X rays.

den·tin (den′tən), the hard, bony material beneath the enamel of a tooth. It forms the main part of a tooth. *noun.*

den·tist (den′tist), a doctor whose work is the care of teeth. A dentist fills cavities in teeth, cleans, straightens, or pulls them, and supplies artificial teeth. *noun.*

den·tist·ry (den′tə strē), the work of a dentist. *noun.*

den·ture (den′chər), a set of artificial teeth. *noun.*

Den·ver (den′vər), the capital of Colorado. *noun.*

de·ny (di nī′), **1** to say something is not true: *The prisoners denied the charges against them.* **2** to refuse: *I could not deny the stray cat some milk. verb,* **de·nies, de·nied, de·ny·ing.**

de·o·dor·ant (dē ō′dər ənt), a substance that destroys bad odors. *noun.*

de·part (di pärt′), **1** to go away; leave: *The train departs at 6:15.* **2** to turn away; change: *We departed from our usual routine and went out to dinner.* **3** to die. *verb.*

de·part·ment (di pärt′mənt), a separate part of some whole; special branch; division: *the toy department of a store. Our city government has a*

D

fire department and a police department. noun.

department store, a large store that sells many different kinds of articles in separate departments.

de·par·ture (di pär′chər), **1** the act of going away; act of leaving: *His departure was very sudden.* **2** a turning away; change: *a departure from our old custom.* noun.

de·pend (di pend′), **1** to be controlled by something else; be a result of: *The success of our picnic will depend on the weather.* **2** to have as a support; get help from: *Children depend on their parents for food and clothing.* **3** to rely; trust: *I depend on my alarm clock to wake me in time for school.* verb.

de·pend·a·ble (di pen′də bəl), able to be depended on; reliable; trustworthy: *My friend works hard and is dependable.* adjective.

de·pend·ence (di pen′dəns), **1** the condition of being controlled by something else: *We learned about the dependence of crops on good weather.* **2** a trusting or relying on another for support or help: *I am going to work so that I can end my dependence on my parents.* noun.

de·pend·ent (di pen′dənt), **1** trusting to or relying on another person or thing for support or help: *A child is dependent on its parents.* **2** a person who is supported by another. **3** possible if something else takes place: *Good crops are dependent on the right amount of sunshine and rainfall.* 1,3 adjective, 2 noun.

de·pict (di pikt′), to represent by drawing, painting, or describing; portray: *The artist tried to depict the splendor of the sunset.* verb.

de·plore (di plôr′), to be very sorry about; express great sorrow for: *We deplore the accident.* verb, **de·plores, de·plored, de·plor·ing.**

de·port (di pôrt′), to force to leave; banish. When an alien is deported he or she is sent back to his or her native land. verb.

de·pos·it (di poz′it), **1** to put down; lay down; leave lying: *She deposited her bundles on the table. The flood deposited a layer of mud in the streets.* **2** any material laid down or left lying by natural means: *There is often a deposit of sand and mud at the mouth of a river.* **3** to put in a place to be kept safe: *Deposit your money in the bank.* **4** something put in a certain place to be kept safe: *Money put in the bank is a deposit.* **5** money paid as a pledge to do something or to pay more later: *I put down a $25 deposit on the coat, and I will pay the remaining $50 next month.* **6** a mass of some mineral in rock or in the ground: *deposits of coal.* 1,3 verb, 2,4-6 noun.

de·pos·i·tor (di poz′ə tər), a person who deposits: *Depositors in savings banks may receive interest on the money deposited.* noun.

de·pot (dē′pō), a railroad or bus station. noun.

de·pre·ci·ate (di prē′shē āt), to lessen in value: *Usually, the longer an automobile is driven, the more it depreciates.* verb, **de·pre·ci·ates, de·pre·ci·at·ed, de·pre·ci·at·ing.**

de·press (di pres′), **1** to make sad or gloomy: *I was depressed by the bad news.* **2** to press down; lower: *When you play the piano, you depress the keys.* **3** to make less active; weaken: *Some medicines depress the action of the heart.* verb.

de·pres·sant (di pres′nt), a drug that slows down the activity of the body: *Alcohol is a depressant.* noun.

de·pres·sion (di presh′ən), **1** a low place; hollow: *Rain formed puddles in the depressions in the ground.* **2** low spirits; sadness: *Failure usually brings on a feeling of depression.* **3** a time when business activity is very slow and many people are out of work. noun.

de·prive (di prīv′), to keep from having or doing; take away from: *Worrying deprived them of sleep. Children should never be deprived of an education.* verb, **de·prives, de·prived, de·priv·ing.**

depth (depth), **1** the distance from the top to the bottom: *The depth of the lake was so great we could not see the bottom.* **2** the distance from front to back: *The depth of our playground is 250 feet.* **3** the deepest or most central part of anything: *in the depths of the earth, in the depths of one's heart.* **4** a deep quality; deepness: *They admired their teacher's depth of understanding.* noun.

dep·u·ty (dep′yə tē), a person appointed to do the work or take the place of another: *The sheriff appointed deputies to help him enforce the law.* noun, plural **dep·u·ties.**

de·rail (dē rāl′), to run or cause to run off the rails: *The train derailed just north of Springfield.* verb.

der·by (dėr′bē), **1** an important horse race or other competition. **2** a stiff hat with a rounded crown and narrow brim. noun, plural **der·bies.**

derby (definition 2)

de·rive (di rīv′), to get; receive; obtain: *She derives much pleasure from reading adventure stories.* verb, **de·rives, de·rived, de·riv·ing.**

de·rog·a·to·ry (di rog′ə tôr′ē), unfavorable: *We don't like to hear derogatory remarks about our school.* adjective.

der·rick (der′ik), **1** a machine for lifting and moving heavy objects. A derrick has a long arm that swings at an angle from the base of an

derrick
(definition 1)

a hat	i it	oi oil	ch child	⎧a in about
ā age	ī ice	ou out	ng long	e in taken
ä far	o hot	u cup	sh she	ə = ⎨ i in pencil
e let	ō open	u̇ put	th thin	o in lemon
ē equal	ô order	ü rule	ᴛ͡ʜ then	⎩u in circus
ėr term			zh measure	

upright post or frame. **2** a towerlike framework over an oil well that holds the drilling and hoisting machinery. *noun.*

de·scend (di send′), **1** to go or come down from a higher to a lower place: *I descended the stairs to the basement. The river descends from the mountains to the sea.* **2** to be handed down from parent to child: *This land has descended from my grandfather to my mother and now to me. verb.*

de·scend·ant (di sen′dənt), **1** a person born of a certain family or group: *a descendant of the Pilgrims.* **2** an offspring; child, grandchild, great-grandchild, and so on. You are a direct descendant of your parents, grandparents, and great-grandparents. *noun.*

de·scent (di sent′), **1** a coming or going down from a higher to a lower place: *The descent of the balloon was more rapid than its rise had been.* **2** a downward slope: *We climbed down a steep descent.* **3** a family line; ancestors: *They are of Italian descent. noun.*

de·scribe (di skrīb′), to tell in words how a person looks, feels, or acts, or how a place, a thing, or an event looks; tell or write about: *The reporter described the accident in detail. verb,* **de·scribes, de·scribed, de·scrib·ing.**

de·scrip·tion (di skrip′shən), **1** a telling in words how a person looks, feels, or acts, or how a place, a thing, or an event looks; a describing: *They gave a description of the missing child.* **2** a composition or account that describes or gives a picture in words: *The vivid description of the hotel fire made me feel as if I had seen it.* **3** kind; sort: *There were people of every description at the airport. noun.*

de·scrip·tive (di skrip′tiv), using words to give a picture; describing: *A descriptive booklet tells about the places to be seen on the trip. adjective.*

de·seg·re·gate (dē seg′rə gāt), to bring about desegregation. *verb,* **de·seg·re·gates, de·seg·re·gat·ed, de·seg·re·gat·ing.**

de·seg·re·ga·tion (dē seg′rə gā′shən), the doing away with the practice of separating people of different races, especially in schools, restaurants, and other public places. *noun.*

des·ert[1] (dez′ərt), **1** a region without water and trees. It is usually sandy. *In northern Africa there is a great desert called the Sahara.* **2** having no people: *They were shipwrecked on a desert island.* **1** *noun,* **2** *adjective.*

de·sert[2] (di zėrt′), to go away and leave a person, or a place, especially one that should not be left; forsake: *A husband should not desert his family. A soldier who deserts is punished. verb.*

de·sert[3] (di zėrt′), what one deserves; suitable reward or punishment: *The reckless driver got his just deserts; he was fined and his driver's license was suspended. noun.*

de·sert·ed (di zėr′tid), abandoned; forsaken: *They were afraid to enter the deserted house. adjective.*

de·sert·er (di zėr′tər), a person who deserts, especially from military duty. *noun.*

Desert Storm, the Persian Gulf War.

de·serve (di zėrv′), to have a right to; have a claim to; be worthy of: *A hard worker deserves good pay. Reckless drivers deserve to have their licenses taken away. verb,* **de·serves, de·served, de·serv·ing.**

de·sign (di zīn′), **1** a drawing, plan, or sketch made to serve as a pattern from which to work: *The design showed how to build the machine.* **2** the arrangement of details, form, and color in painting, weaving, or building: *We chose a wallpaper design with tan and white stripes.* **3** to make a first sketch of; plan out; arrange the form and color of: *My mother designed my coat and my grandmother made it.* **4** to set apart; intend; plan: *This room was designed to be a study.* **1,2** *noun,* **3,4** *verb.*

des·ig·nate (dez′ig nāt), **1** to point out; mark; show: *Red lines designate main roads on this map.* **2** to select; appoint: *She has been designated by the mayor as superintendent of schools. verb,* **des·ig·nates, des·ig·nat·ed, des·ig·nat·ing.**

designated hitter, in baseball, a player who does not play in the field but is designated at the start of a game to bat in place of the pitcher.

de·sign·ing (di zī′ning), scheming; plotting: *A designing person is a false friend. adjective.*

de·sir·a·bil·i·ty (di zī′rə bil′ə tē), a desirable quality; condition to be wished for: *Nobody doubts the desirability of good health. noun.*

de·sir·a·ble (di zī′rə bəl), worth wishing for; worth having; pleasing; good: *The creek valley was a desirable location for the state park. adjective.*

D

de·sire (di zīr′), **1** a wish: *My desire is to travel.* **2** to wish earnestly for: *The people in the warring nations desired peace.* **3** to ask for: *The principal desires your presence in his office.* **1** *noun,* **2,3** *verb,* **de·sires, de·sired, de·sir·ing.**

de·sist (di zist′), to stop; cease: *Desist at once!* *verb.*

desk (desk), a piece of furniture with a flat or sloping top on which to write or to rest books for reading. *noun.*

Des Moines (də moin′), the capital of Iowa.

des·o·late (des′ə lit), **1** destroyed; ruined: *We visited the desolate ruins.* **2** not lived in; deserted: *a desolate house.* **3** unhappy; forlorn: *The lost child looked desolate. adjective.*

des·o·la·tion (des′ə lā′shən), **1** destruction; ruin: *The people mourned the desolation of their town by a tornado.* **2** sadness; lonely sorrow: *A person feels desolation at the loss of loved ones. noun.*

de·spair (di sper′ *or* di spar′), **1** the loss of hope; being without hope; a dreadful feeling that nothing good can happen to you: *Despair seized us as we felt the boat sinking.* **2** to lose hope; be without hope: *The doctors despaired of saving the patient's life.* **1** *noun,* **2** *verb.*

des·per·ate (des′pər it), **1** not caring what happens because hope is gone: *Suicide is a desperate act.* **2** ready to try anything; ready to run any risk: *He hadn't worked in a year and was desperate for a job.* **3** having little chance for hope or cure; very dangerous: *a desperate illness. adjective.*

des·pe·ra·tion (des′pə rā′shən), a hopeless and reckless feeling; readiness to try anything: *In desperation he jumped out the window when he saw the stairs were on fire. noun.*

de·spise (di spīz′), to look down upon; hate very much; scorn: *They were despised for their cruelty. verb,* **de·spis·es, de·spised, de·spis·ing.**

de·spite (di spīt′), in spite of: *We went for a walk despite the rain. preposition.*

de·spond·ent (di spon′dənt), having lost heart, courage, or hope; discouraged; dejected: *He was despondent because he lost his job. adjective.*

des·sert (di zėrt′), a course of pie, cake, ice cream, cheese, fruit, or the like served at the end of a meal. *noun.*

des·ti·na·tion (des′tə nā′shən), the place to which a person or thing is going or is being sent. *noun.*

des·tine (des′tən), to intend; set apart for a special purpose or use: *The prince was destined from birth to be a king. verb,* **des·tines, des·tined, des·tin·ing.**
destined for, intended to go to; bound for: *The ships were destined for England.*

des·ti·ny (des′tə nē), what becomes of a person or thing; one's fate or fortune: *She felt it was her destiny to be a writer. noun, plural* **des·ti·nies.**

des·ti·tute (des′tə tüt *or* des′tə tyüt), lacking necessary things such as food, clothing, and shelter: *The destitute family needed help. adjective.*

de·stroy (di stroi′), **1** to spoil; ruin; do away with: *A tornado destroyed the farmhouse. The rain destroyed all hope of a picnic.* **2** to kill: *The horse was so sick it had to be destroyed. verb.*

de·stroy·er (di stroi′ər), a small, fast warship with guns, torpedoes, and other weapons. *noun.*

destroyer

de·struc·tion (di struk′shən), **1** a destroying: *A bulldozer was used in the destruction of the old barn.* **2** great damage; ruin: *The storm left destruction behind it. noun.*

de·struc·tive (di struk′tiv), **1** destroying; causing destruction: *Fires and earthquakes are destructive.* **2** not helpful; damaging: *Destructive criticism shows things to be wrong, but does not show how to correct them. adjective.*

de·tach (di tach′), to unfasten; loosen and remove; separate: *I detached a key from the chain. verb.*

de·tached (di tacht′), **1** not attached; standing apart; separate: *Our house has a detached garage.* **2** not taking sides; not influenced by others; aloof: *When my friends argue, I usually remain detached. adjective.*

de·tach·ment (di tach′mənt), **1** a lack of interest: *He watched the dull motion picture with detachment.* **2** troops or ships sent away on some special duty. *noun.*

de·tail (di tāl′ *or* dē′tāl), **1** a small or unimportant part: *Her report was complete; it did not leave out a single detail.* **2** a dealing with small things one by one: *I do not enjoy the details of housekeeping.* **3** to tell fully; tell even the small and unimportant parts: *Our neighbors detailed to us all the things they had done on their vacation.* **4** a small group sent on some special duty: *A detail of six scouts was sent out to find firewood.* **5** to send on special duty: *Several police officers were detailed to direct traffic after the big game.* **1,2,4** *noun,* **3,5** *verb.*

de·tain (di tān′), **1** to keep from going ahead; hold back; delay: *The heavy traffic detained us for almost an hour.* **2** to hold as a prisoner; keep in custody: *Police detained the suspected thief for questioning. verb.*

de·tect (di tekt′), to find out; make out; discover; catch: *Could you detect any odor in the room?* verb.

de·tec·tion (di tek′shən), a finding out; discovery: *Early detection is important in treating many diseases.* noun.

de·tec·tive (di tek′tiv), a member of a police force or other person whose work is finding information secretly and solving crimes. *noun.*

de·tec·tor (di tek′tər), a person or thing that discovers: *Every home should have a smoke detector. noun.*

de·ten·tion (di ten′shən), a being held back or delayed: *Detention after hours is a punishment in our school. noun.*

de·ter (di tėr′), to prevent; keep back; discourage: *The barking dog deterred me from crossing the neighbor's yard. verb,* **de·ters, de·terred, de·ter·ring.**

de·ter·gent (di tėr′jənt), a substance used for cleansing. Many detergents are chemical compounds that act like soap. *noun.*

de·te·ri·o·rate (di tir′ē ə rāt′), to make or become worse: *The severe winter caused the roads to deteriorate. verb,* **de·te·ri·o·rates, de·te·ri·o·rat·ed, de·te·ri·o·rat·ing.**

de·ter·mi·na·tion (di tėr′mə nā′shən), **1** great firmness in carrying out a purpose: *The boy's determination was not weakened by the difficulties he met.* **2** a deciding; settling beforehand: *The determination of what things we needed to take on our camping trip took a long time. noun.*

de·ter·mine (di tėr′mən), **1** to make up one's mind very firmly: *He determined to become the best scout in his troop.* **2** to find out exactly: *The pilot determined how far she was from the airport.* **3** to be the deciding fact in reaching a certain result; settle: *The number of answers you get right determines your mark on this test. Tomorrow's weather will determine whether we go to the beach or stay home.* **4** to fix or settle beforehand; decide: *Can we now determine the date for our party? verb,* **de·ter·mines, de·ter·mined, de·ter·min·ing.**

de·ter·mined (di tėr′mənd), firm; with the mind made up: *Her determined look showed that she had decided what to do. adjective.*

de·ter·min·er (di tėr′mə nər), a word that points out the person, animal, or thing named. In "a hat," "the big house," and "every little thing," *a, the,* and *every* are determiners. *noun.*

de·test (di test′), to dislike very much; hate: *Many people detest snakes. verb.*

de·test·a·ble (di tes′tə bəl), deserving to be detested; hateful: *Murder is a detestable crime. adjective.*

de·throne (di thrōn′), to remove from a throne or a high position: *The rebels dethroned the king. verb,* **de·thrones, de·throned, de·thron·ing.**

de·tour (dē′tùr), **1** a road that is used when the main or direct road cannot be traveled: *Our bus had to take a detour because the road was blocked.* **2** to use a detour: *We detoured around the bridge that had been washed out.* **1** *noun,* **2** *verb.*

a hat	**i** it	**oi** oil	**ch** child	⎧ a in about
ā age	**ī** ice	**ou** out	**ng** long	⎪ e in taken
ä far	**o** hot	**u** cup	**sh** she	ə = ⎨ i in pencil
e let	**ō** open	**ù** put	**th** thin	⎪ o in lemon
ē equal	**ô** order	**ü** rule	**ŦH** then	⎩ u in circus
ėr term			**zh** measure	

de·tract (di trakt′), to remove some of the quality or worth: *The ugly frame detracts from the beauty of the picture. verb.*

De·troit (di troit′), a city in Michigan. *noun.*

dev·as·tate (dev′ə stāt), to destroy; make unfit to live in: *A long war devastated the country. verb,* **dev·as·tates, dev·as·tat·ed, dev·as·tat·ing.**

de·vel·op (di vel′əp), **1** to grow; bring or come into being or activity: *Plants develop from seeds. Scientists have developed many new drugs to fight disease. He developed an interest in collecting stamps.* **2** to work out in greater and greater detail: *Gradually we developed our plans for the club.* **3** to use chemicals on a photographic film or plate to bring out the picture. *verb.*

de·vel·op·ment (di vel′əp mənt), **1** a process of developing; growth: *We watched the development of the seeds into plants.* **2** a new event or happening: *The newspaper gave news about the latest developments in the elections.* **3** a group of similar houses or apartment buildings built in one area and usually by the same builder. **4** a working out in greater and greater detail: *The development of plans for a flight to the moon took many years. noun.*

de·vice (di vīs′), **1** something invented or made for a particular use or special purpose. A can opener is a device. *Our gas stove has a device for lighting it automatically.* **2** a plan, scheme, or trick: *In order to stay outside she used the device of pretending not to hear her mother calling her. noun.*
leave to one's own devices, to leave to do as one thinks best: *The teacher left us to our own devices in choosing the books for our reports.*

dev·il (dev′əl), **1** the Devil, in the Jewish and Christian religions, the supreme evil spirit; Satan. **2** any evil spirit. **3** a wicked or cruel person. *noun.*

dev·iled (dev′əld), prepared with seasonings, such as salt, pepper, and spices: *deviled eggs. adjective.*

dev·il·ish (dev′ə lish), **1** very bad; evil; like a devil: *His temper exploded in devilish fury.* **2** daring; mischievous: *The children played devilish pranks on Halloween. adjective.*

devil's food cake, a rich, dark, chocolate cake.

de·vise (di vīz′), to think out; plan; contrive; invent: *The kids are trying to devise a scheme of earning money during vacation. verb,* **de·vis·es, de·vised, de·vis·ing.**

de·vote (di vōt′), to give one's money, time, effort, or self to some person or purpose: *She devoted herself to her studies. Many people devoted their efforts to cleaning up the neighborhood. verb,* **de·votes, de·vot·ed, de·vot·ing.**

D

de·vot·ed (di vō′tid), very loyal; faithful: *Dogs are often devoted companions. adjective.*

de·vo·tion (di vō′shən), **1** deep, steady affection; loyalty: *the devotion of parents to their children.* **2 devotions,** worship, prayers, or praying. *noun.*

de·vour (di vour′), **1** to eat hungrily or greedily: *The lion devoured the zebra. The hungry girl devoured her dinner.* **2** to consume; destroy: *The raging fire devoured the forest. verb.*

de·vout (di vout′), **1** religious; active in worship and prayer: *a devout Moslem, a devout Christian.* **2** earnest; sincere; hearty: *You have our devout thanks for bringing back our lost child. adjective.*

dew (dü or dyü), the moisture from the air that collects in small drops on cool surfaces during the night: *In the early morning, the grass is often wet with dew. noun.*

dew·drop (dü′drop′ or dyü′drop′), a drop of dew. *noun.*

dex·ter·i·ty (dek ster′ə tē), skill in using the hands, body, or mind: *A good surgeon works with dexterity. noun.*

di·a·be·tes (dī′ə bē′tis), a disease in which a person's body cannot properly absorb normal amounts of sugar and starch. *noun.*

di·a·crit·i·cal mark (dī′ə krit′ə kəl märk′), a mark like ·· ^ – put over or under a letter to indicate pronunciation or accent. See the diacritical marks in the short key in the upper right corner of page 169.

di·ag·nose (dī′əg nōs′), to find out by tests or examination: *The doctor diagnosed the disease as measles. verb,* **di·ag·nos·es, di·ag·nosed, di·ag·nos·ing.**

di·ag·no·sis (dī′əg nō′sis), a finding out what disease a person or animal has by examination and careful study of the symptoms: *The doctor used X rays and blood samples in her diagnosis. noun, plural* **di·ag·no·ses** (dī′əg nō′sēz′).

di·ag·o·nal (dī ag′ə nəl), **1** a straight line that cuts across in a slanting direction, often from corner to corner. **2** taking the direction of a diagonal; slanting: *My blue tie has red diagonal stripes.* **1** *noun,* **2** *adjective.*

di·a·gram (dī′ə gram), **1** a drawing or sketch showing important parts of a thing. A diagram may be a plan, a drawing, a chart, or any combination of these, made to show clearly what a thing is or how it works. A plan of a house or an airplane is a diagram. **2** to put on paper or on a chalkboard in the form of a drawing or sketch; make a diagram of: *Our teacher diagramed how we should leave the building during a fire drill.* **1** *noun,* **2** *verb.*

di·al (dī′əl), **1** the front surface or face of a measuring instrument. A dial has numbers, letters, or marks over which a pointer moves. The pointer indicates amount, speed, pressure, time, direction, or the like. The face of a clock, a compass, a thermostat, or a pressure gauge on a water tank is a dial. **2** a knob or other device of a radio or television set with numbers and letters on it for tuning in to a radio or television station. **3** the round, movable part of some telephones used in making telephone calls. **4** to call or tune in by means of a dial: *She dialed the wrong number the first time she tried to call us.* **1,2,3** *noun,* **4** *verb.*

di·a·lect (dī′ə lekt), a form of a language spoken in a certain district or by a certain group of people: *The Scottish dialect of English has many words and pronunciations that Americans do not use. A dialect of French is spoken in southern Louisiana by descendants of French Canadians. noun.*

di·a·logue (dī′ə lôg), a conversation, spoken or written out: *That book has a good plot and much clever dialogue. noun.*

dial tone, a humming sound heard on a telephone, which indicates that a number may be dialed.

di·am·e·ter (dī am′ə tər), **1** a straight line that goes from one side through the center of a circle or sphere to the other side. **2** the length of such a line; width; thickness: *The diameter of the earth is about 8000 miles. The tree trunk was almost 2 feet in diameter. noun.*

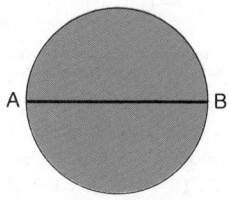

diameter (def. 1)
Line AB is a diameter.

dia·mond (dī′mənd), **1** a precious stone, usually colorless, that is formed of pure carbon in crystals. Diamond is the hardest substance known. **2** a figure shaped like this: ◇. **3** a playing card with one or more figures shaped like this. **4** the space inside the lines that connect the bases in baseball; infield. *noun.*

dia·per (dī′pər), a piece of cloth or other soft material folded and used as underpants for a baby. *noun.*

di·a·phragm (dī′ə fram), a layer of muscles and

Word History

diagonal *Diagonal* comes from a Greek word meaning "from angle to angle."

diagonal (definition 2)

tendons separating the cavity of the chest from the cavity of the abdomen. *noun.*

di·ar·y (dī′ər ē), **1** an account, written down each day, of what has happened to one, or what one has done or thought, during that day: *I kept a diary while I was on vacation.* **2** a book for keeping such a daily account. It has a blank space for each day of the year. *noun, plural* **di·ar·ies.**

dice (dīs), **1** small cubes with a different number of spots (one to six) on each side. Dice are used in playing some games. **2** to cut into small cubes: *Carrots are sometimes diced before being cooked.* **1** *noun plural;* **2** *verb,* **dic·es, diced, dic·ing.**

di·cot (dī′kot), a flowering plant with seeds that have two seed leaves. Dicots have petals in groups or four or five. Roses, almonds, peas, and elm trees are dicots. *noun.*

dic·tate (dik′tāt), **1** to say or read something aloud for another person to write down, or for a machine to record: *The teacher dictated a list of books to the students.* **2** to make others do what one says; give orders: *Big nations sometimes dictate to little ones.* **3** a command or order that is to be carried out or obeyed: *The people followed the dictates of their leaders.* **1,2** *verb,* **dic·tates, dic·tat·ed, dic·tat·ing; 3** *noun.*

dic·ta·tion (dik tā′shən), the words said or read aloud to another person who writes them down, or to a machine that records them: *The secretary took the dictation in shorthand and typed it out later. noun.*

dic·ta·tor (dik′tā tər), a person who rules, using complete authority: *The dictator seized control of the government and took complete power over the people of the country. noun.*

dic·ta·tor·ship (dik′tā tər ship), a country ruled by a dictator. *noun.*

dic·tion·ar·y (dik′shə ner′ē), a book that explains the words of a language. It is arranged alphabetically. You can use this dictionary to find out the meaning, pronunciation, or spelling of a word. *noun, plural* **dic·tion·ar·ies.**

did (did). See **do.** *Did he go to school yesterday? Yes, he did. verb.*

did·n't (did′nt), did not.

die¹ (dī), **1** to stop living; become dead: *The flowers in the garden died from frost.* **2** to lose force or strength; come to an end; stop: *My sudden anger died. The motor sputtered and died.* **3** to want very much: *I was dying for an ice-cream cone. verb,* **dies, died, dy·ing.**

die away or **die down,** to stop or end little by little: *The music died away. The noise died down.*

die² (dī), a carved metal block or plate. Different kinds of dies are used for coining money, for raising letters up from the surface of paper, and for giving a certain shape to articles made by forging and cutting. *noun.*

die·sel en·gine (dē′zəl en′jən), an engine that burns oil with heat produced by compressing air. [The *diesel engine* was named for Rudolf Diesel, who lived from 1858 to 1913. He was a German engineer who invented it.]

a hat	**i** it	**oi** oil	**ch** child	(a in about
ā age	**ī** ice	**ou** out	**ng** long	e in taken
ä far	**o** hot	**u** cup	**sh** she	**ə =** { i in pencil
e let	**ō** open	**ù** put	**th** thin	o in lemon
ē equal	**ô** order	**ü** rule	**ŦH** then	(u in circus
ėr term			**zh** measure	

di·et (dī′ət), **1** the usual kind of food and drink: *My diet is made up of meat, fish, vegetables, fruits, water, and milk. Grass is a large part of a cow's diet.* **2** any special selection of food eaten during sickness, or in order to lose or gain weight: *While I was sick I was on a liquid diet.* **3** to eat special food as a part of a doctor's treatment, or in order to lose or gain weight. **1,2** *noun,* **3** *verb.*

di·e·ti·tian (dī′ə tish′ən), a person trained to plan meals that have the right amount of various kinds of food. Many hospitals and schools employ dietitians. *noun.*

dif·fer (dif′ər), **1** to be unlike; be different: *My answer to the problem differed from hers.* **2** to hold or express a different opinion; disagree: *The two of us differ about what to buy Mom. verb.*

dif·fer·ence (dif′ər əns), **1** a being unlike; a being different: *There are few differences between baseball and softball.* **2** an amount or manner of being different; way in which people or things are different: *The only difference between the twins is that John weighs five pounds more than Bob.* **3** what is left after subtracting one number from another: *The difference between 6 and 15 is 9.* **4** a quarrel; dispute: *We had a difference over a name for the puppy. noun.*

make a difference, to be important; matter: *Whether we go or not doesn't make a difference to me.*

dif·fer·ent (dif′ər ənt), **1** not alike; not like: *People have different names. A boat is different from an automobile.* **2** not the same; separate; distinct: *She won three different swimming contests.* **3** unusual: *That story was really different; I've never read one like it. adjective.*

dif·fi·cult (dif′ə kult), **1** hard to do or understand: *Arithmetic is difficult for some pupils.* **2** hard to deal with or get along with; not easy to please: *My cousins are difficult and always want their own way. adjective.*

dif·fi·cul·ty (dif′ə kul′tē), **1** the condition of being difficult; degree to which something is difficult: *The difficulty of the job kept us from finishing it on time.* **2** hard work; much effort: *I finished the long arithmetic problem with difficulty.* **3** something which stands in the way of getting things done; thing that is hard to do or understand: *Lack of time and lack of money were two difficulties we had to overcome.* **4** trouble: *Some children have difficulty learning how to spell. noun, plural* **dif·fi·cul·ties.**

dif·fu·sion (di fyü′zhən), a mixing caused by spreading out. If milk is poured into water, diffusion causes the water to become equally cloudy throughout. *noun.*

D

dig (dig), **1** to use a shovel, spade, hands, claws, or snout to make a hole or turn over soil: *Dogs bury bones and dig for them later.* **2** to make by digging: *The workers dug a cellar.* **3** to make a way by digging: *They dug through the mountain to build a tunnel.* **4** to get by digging: *to dig potatoes, to dig clams.* **5** to make a thrust or stab into: *The cat dug its claws into my hand.* **6** a thrust or poke: *I gave my friend a dig in the ribs.* 1-5 *verb,* **digs, dug, dig·ging;** 6 *noun.*

dig up, to get or find, especially by a careful search or by study: *You can probably dig up the information you need for your report in the school library.*

di·gest (də jest′ *for 1 and 2;* dī′jest *for 3*), **1** to change food in the stomach and intestines, so that the body can use it: *The body digests fat slowly.* **2** to think over something until you understand it clearly, or until it becomes a part of your own thought: *It often takes a long time to digest new ideas.* **3** a brief statement or a shortened form of what is in a longer book or article. 1,2 *verb,* 3 *noun.*

di·ges·tion (də jes′chən), the digesting of food: *Proper digestion is necessary for good health. noun.*

di·ges·tive (də jes′tiv), having something to do with digestion: *Saliva is one of the digestive juices. adjective.*

digestive system, the system of the body that digests food. It includes the mouth, stomach, intestine, and other organs.

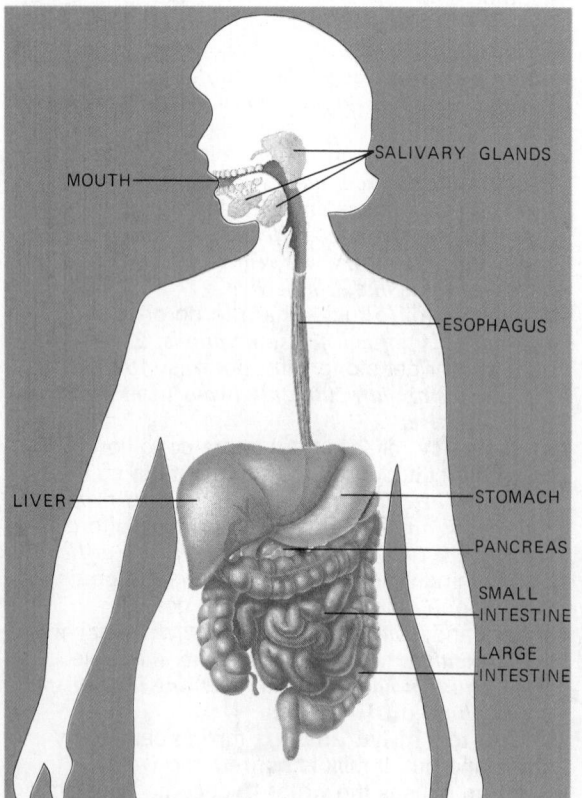

digestive system

dig·ger (dig′ər), **1** a person or thing that digs. **2** a tool or machine for digging. *noun.*

dig·it (dij′it), **1** any of the figures 0, 1, 2, 3, 4, 5, 6, 7, 8, 9. Sometimes 0 is not called a digit. **2** a finger or toe. *noun.*

dig·i·tal (dij′ə təl), showing time, temperature, or other information by digits alone, rather than by other means such as hands on a dial or mercury in a tube: *a digital computer. adjective.*

digital—a digital clock

dig·ni·fied (dig′nə fīd), having dignity; noble; stately: *The queen has a dignified manner. adjective.*

dig·ni·tar·y (dig′nə ter′ē), a person who has a position of honor: *We saw several foreign dignitaries when we visited the United Nations. noun, plural* **dig·ni·tar·ies.**

dig·ni·ty (dig′nə tē), **1** proud and self-respecting manner or appearance: *The candidate kept her dignity during the noisy debate.* **2** a quality of character or ability that wins the respect and high opinion of others: *A judge should maintain the dignity of his or her position. noun.*

dike (dīk), a bank of earth or a dam built as a defense against flooding by a river or the sea. *noun.* Also spelled **dyke.**

di·lap·i·dat·ed (də lap′ə dā′tid), falling to pieces; partly ruined or decayed through neglect: *No one had lived in the dilapidated old house for years. adjective.*

di·late (dī lāt′), to make or become larger or wider: *The pupil of the eye dilates when the light gets dim. verb,* **di·lates, di·lat·ed, di·lat·ing.**

What a dilemma!

dilemma

di·lem·ma (də lem′ə), a situation requiring a choice between two evils; a difficult choice: *She was faced with the dilemma of either staying up late to rewrite her paper or getting a poor grade on it. noun.*

dil·i·gence (dil′ə jəns), a working hard; careful effort; ability to work steadily: *The student's diligence was rewarded with high marks. noun.*

dil·i·gent (dil′ə jənt), hard-working; industrious; not lazy: *The diligent student kept on working until he had finished his homework. adjective.*

dill (dil), a plant whose seeds or leaves are used to flavor pickles. *noun.*

dil·ly·dal·ly (dil′ē dal′ē), to loiter; waste time; trifle: *Let's not dillydally over such unimportant matters. verb,* **dil·ly·dal·lies, dil·ly·dal·lied, dil·ly·dal·ly·ing.**

di·lute (də lüt′), to make weaker or thinner by adding water or some other liquid: *I diluted the frozen orange juice with several cups of water. verb,* **di·lutes, di·lut·ed, di·lut·ing.**

dim (dim), **1** not bright; without much light: *With the shades drawn, the room was dim.* **2** not clearly seen, heard, or understood: *We could see only the dim outline of the mountain in the distance.* **3** not seeing, hearing, or understanding clearly: *My eyesight is getting dimmer.* **4** to make or become less bright: *She dimmed the car's headlights as the other car approached.* 1-3 *adjective,* **dim·mer, dim·mest;** 4 *verb,* **dims, dimmed, dim·ming.**

dime (dīm), a coin of the United States and Canada equal to 10 cents. Ten dimes make one dollar. *noun.*

di·men·sion (də men′shən), a measurement of length, width, or thickness: *I need wallpaper for a room of the following dimensions: 16 feet long, 12 feet wide, and 8 feet high. noun.*

di·min·ish (də min′ish), to make or become smaller in size, amount, or importance: *A sound diminishes as you get farther and farther away from it. verb.*

di·min·u·tive (də min′yə tiv), very small; tiny. *adjective.*

diminutive
The **diminutive** child was no larger than a butterfly.

dim·mer (dim′ər), a device that dims an electric light. *noun.*

dim·ple (dim′pəl), **1** a small hollow place, usually in the cheek or chin. **2** to form dimples: *He dimples whenever he smiles.* 1 *noun,* 2 *verb,* **dim·ples, dim·pled, dim·pling.**

din (din), **1** a loud, confused noise that lasts: *The din of the cheering crowd was deafening.* **2** to say one thing over and over: *Our boss is always*

a hat	i it	oi oil	ch child	a in about
ā age	ī ice	ou out	ng long	e in taken
ä far	o hot	u cup	sh she	ə = { i in pencil
e let	ō open	u̇ put	th thin	o in lemon
ē equal	ô order	ü rule	ᵺ then	u in circus
ėr term			zh measure	

dinning into our ears the importance of hard work. 1 *noun,* 2 *verb,* **dins, dinned, din·ning.**

dine (dīn), to eat dinner: *We dine at six o'clock. verb,* **dines, dined, din·ing.**

din·er (dī′nər), **1** a person who is eating dinner. **2** a railroad car in which meals are served. **3** a small eating place that often looks like a railroad car. *noun.*

di·nette (dī net′), a small dining room. *noun.*

din·ghy (ding′ē), a small rowboat. *noun, plural* **din·ghies.**

din·gy (din′jē), dirty-looking; lacking brightness or freshness; dull: *Dingy curtains covered the windows of the dusty old room. adjective,* **din·gi·er, din·gi·est.**

dining room, a room in which dinner and other meals are served.

din·ner (din′ər), **1** the main meal of the day: *In the city we have dinner at night, but in the country we have dinner at noon.* **2** a formal meal in honor of some person or occasion: *The city officials gave the mayor a dinner to celebrate his reelection. noun.*

din·ner·time (din′ər tīm′), the time at which dinner is served: *Is it dinnertime yet? noun.*

di·no·saur (dī′nə sôr), one of a group of extinct reptiles that lived many millions of years ago. Some dinosaurs were bigger than elephants. Some were smaller than cats. *noun.*

Word History

dinosaur The great size of some dinosaurs can be seen from their bones, a number of which have been dug up over the years. A British naturalist of the 1800s used Greek words meaning "terrible lizard" in naming the dinosaur.

dinosaur

di·o·cese (dī′ə sis), the church district over which a bishop has authority. *noun.*

dip (dip), **1** to put under water or any liquid and lift quickly out again: *He dipped his hand into the pool to see how cold the water was.* **2** a plunge into and out of water; short swim: *She felt cool after a dip in the ocean.* **3** a liquid in which to dip something for cleaning, coloring, or other purposes: *The sheep were driven through a dip to disinfect their coats.* **4** to make a candle by putting a wick into hot tallow or wax. **5** something that is taken out with a scoop; scoop: *Please give me two dips of vanilla ice cream.* **6** a creamy mixture of foods eaten by dipping it up with a cracker, potato chip, or the like: *a cheese dip.* **7** to lower and raise again quickly: *The ship's flag was dipped as a salute.* **8** to sink or drop down: *The bird dipped low over the water in its flight.* **9** a sudden drop: *The dip in the road made the car bounce.* 1,4,7,8 *verb,* **dips, dipped, dip·ping;** 2,3,5,6,9 *noun.*

diph·ther·i·a (dif thir′ē ə), an often fatal disease of the throat that attacks children especially. Unless you have been vaccinated against diphtheria, you can catch the disease if you are around someone who has it. *noun.*

diph·thong (dif′thông), a vowel sound made up of two vowel sounds pronounced in one syllable, such as *oi* in *noise* or *ou* in *out. noun.*

di·plo·ma (də plō′mə), a written or printed paper, given by a school or college, which says that a person has completed certain courses, or has been graduated after a certain amount of work. *noun.*

dip·lo·mat (dip′lə mat), **1** a person whose work is to handle the relations of his or her country with other nations. **2** a person who is skillful in dealing with people. *noun.*

dip·lo·mat·ic (dip′lə mat′ik), **1** having to do with the management of relations between nations: *Ambassadors are members of the diplomatic service.* **2** skillful in dealing with people; tactful: *I gave a diplomatic answer to avoid hurting my friend's feelings. adjective.*

dip·per (dip′ər), **1** a long-handled cup or larger container for lifting water or other liquids. **2** The **Big Dipper** and **Little Dipper** are two groups of stars in the northern sky somewhat resembling the shape of a dipper. *noun.*

dipper (definition 2)—The pointers of the Big Dipper point to the North Star in the Little Dipper.

dire (dīr), dreadful; causing great fear or suffering: *We fear the dire results of a nuclear war. adjective,* **dir·er, dir·est.**

di·rect (də rekt′), **1** to manage or guide; control: *The teacher directs the work of the pupils.* **2** to order; command: *The policeman directed the traffic to stop.* **3** to tell or show the way: *We turned left where the signpost directed.* **4** to point or aim: *The firefighters directed the hose at the flames.* **5** straight; without a stop or turn: *The freeway crosses the county in almost a direct line.* **6** in an unbroken line: *They are direct descendants of the founder of this town.* **7** truthful; frank; plain: *She gave direct answers to all the questions.* **8** directly: *This airplane goes to Los Angeles direct, without stopping between here and there.* 1-4 *verb,* 5-7 *adjective,* 8 *adverb.*

direct current, an electric current that flows in one direction. The current from all batteries is direct current.

di·rec·tion (də rek′shən), **1** management; guidance; control: *The school is under the direction of the principal.* **2** an order; command: *It was at the teacher's direction that I prepared an oral report.* **3** **directions,** a knowing or telling what to do, how to do, or where to go; instructions: *He needs directions to the lake.* **4** a course along which something moves: *The town shows improvement in many directions.* **5** any way in which one may face or point. North, south, east, and west are directions: *Our school is in one direction and the post office is in another. noun.*

di·rect·ly (də rekt′lē), **1** in a direct line or manner; straight: *This road runs directly into the center of town.* **2** exactly; absolutely: *That is directly opposite to what I meant.* **3** immediately; at once: *Come home directly. adverb.*

di·rec·tor (də rek′tər), a manager; person who directs. A person who directs the performance of a play, a motion picture, or a show on television or radio is called a director. *noun.*

di·rec·tor·y (də rek′tər ē), a book or list of names and addresses. A telephone book is a directory with telephone numbers. *noun, plural* **di·rec·tor·ies.**

dir·i·gi·ble (dir′ə jə bəl *or* də rij′ə bəl), a kind of balloon that is driven by an engine and can be steered. A dirigible has a rigid inner framework and is filled with a gas that is lighter than air. *noun.*

dirigible

dirk (dėrk), a dagger: *Scottish warriors used to fight with dirks. noun.*

dirt (dėrt), **1** anything that makes something unclean, such as mud, grease, or dust. Dirt soils skin, clothing, houses, or furniture. **2** earth; soil: *Before I planted my garden I had to take lots of stones out of the dirt.* *noun.*

dirt·i·ness (dėr′tē nis), a dirty condition. *noun.*

dirt·y (dėr′tē), **1** not clean; soiled by mud, grease, dust, or anything like them: *I got dirty while I was cleaning out the garage.* **2** not fair, decent, or acceptable: *To say that you would meet me and then not show up was a dirty trick.* **3** to make dirty; soil: *You will dirty your new clothes if you play outside on the muddy ground.* **1,2** *adjective,* **dirt·i·er, dirt·i·est; 3** *verb,* **dirt·ies, dirt·ied, dirt·y·ing.**

dis-, a prefix meaning: **1** not; the opposite of; lack of: *Dishonest means* not *honest, or* the opposite of honest. *Discomfort means the* lack of *comfort.* **2** to do the opposite of: *Disconnect means* to do the opposite of *connect.*

dis·a·bil·i·ty (dis′ə bil′ə tē), **1** a lack of ability or power: *The player's disability was due to illness.* **2** something that disables: *Deafness is a disability for a musician.* *noun, plural* **dis·a·bil·i·ties.**

dis·a·ble (dis ā′bəl), to make unfit for use; cripple: *A sprained wrist disabled the tennis player for three weeks.* *verb,* **dis·a·bles, dis·a·bled, dis·a·bling.**

dis·ad·van·tage (dis′əd van′tij), **1** a lack of advantage; unfavorable condition: *Her shyness was a disadvantage in company.* **2** a loss; injury: *The candidate's opponents spread rumors to his disadvantage.* *noun.*

dis·a·gree (dis′ə grē′), **1** to fail to agree; be different: *Your account of the accident disagrees with hers.* **2** to have unlike opinions; differ: *Doctors sometimes disagree about the proper method of treating a patient.* **3** to quarrel; dispute: *The two neighbors never spoke to each other again after they disagreed about their boundary line.* **4** to have a bad effect; be harmful: *I can't eat strawberries because they disagree with me.* *verb,* **dis·a·grees, dis·a·greed, dis·a·gree·ing.**

dis·a·gree·a·ble (dis′ə grē′ə bəl), **1** not to one's liking; not pleasant: *A headache is disagreeable.* **2** not friendly; bad-tempered; cross: *People often become disagreeable when they are tired.* *adjective.*

dis·a·gree·ment (dis′ə grē′mənt), **1** a failure to agree; difference of opinion: *The disagreement that existed among members of the town council caused a postponement of the meeting.* **2** a quarrel; dispute: *Their disagreement led to blows.* **3** a difference; lack of agreement: *There is a disagreement between her account of the accident and mine.* *noun.*

dis·ap·pear (dis′ə pir′), **1** to pass from sight: *The little dog disappeared around the corner.* **2** to pass from existence; stop being: *When spring comes, the snow disappears.* **3** to become lost: *Our kitten disappeared while we were away from home, and it did not return for three days.* *verb.*

dis·ap·pear·ance (dis′ə pir′əns), the act of disappearing: *The disappearance of the airplane brought about a search of the area.* *noun.*

dis·ap·point (dis′ə point′), **1** to fail to satisfy one's desire, wish, or hope: *The circus*

a hat	**i** it	**oi** oil	**ch** child		a in about
ā age	**ī** ice	**ou** out	**ng** long		e in taken
ä far	**o** hot	**u** cup	**sh** she	**ə** =	i in pencil
e let	**ō** open	**u̇** put	**th** thin		o in lemon
ē equal	**ô** order	**ü** rule	**ᴛʜ** then		u in circus
ėr term			**zh** measure		

disappointed him, for there was no elephant. **2** to fail to keep a promise to: *You said you would help; do not disappoint me.* *verb.*

dis·ap·point·ment (dis′ə point′mənt), **1** a being disappointed; the feeling you have when you do not get what you expected or hoped for: *When she did not get a new bicycle, her disappointment was very great.* **2** a person or thing that causes disappointment: *The movie was a disappointment to me because it wasn't exciting.* *noun.*

dis·ap·prov·al (dis′ə prü′vəl), an opinion or feeling against; expressing an opinion against; dislike: *Hisses from the audience showed its disapproval of the speaker's remarks.* *noun.*

dis·ap·prove (dis′ə prüv′), to consider not good or not suitable; have or express an opinion against: *My parents disapproved of our playing rough games in the house.* *verb,* **dis·ap·proves, dis·ap·proved, dis·ap·prov·ing.**

dis·arm (dis ärm′), **1** to take weapons away from: *The police captured the robbers and disarmed them.* **2** to stop having armed forces or to reduce their size: *The nations agreed to disarm.* **3** to make harmless: *The soldiers disarmed the bomb by removing the fuse.* *verb.*

dis·ar·ma·ment (dis är′mə mənt), the reduction or removal of a country's armed forces or their weapons. *noun.*

dis·as·ter (də zas′tər), an event that causes much suffering or loss; great misfortune. A flood, fire, shipwreck, earthquake, or great loss of money is a disaster. *noun.*

dis·as·trous (də zas′trəs), bringing disaster; causing much suffering or loss: *A disastrous hurricane struck the city.* *adjective.*

dis·band (dis band′), to break up; dismiss: *After most of the members quit, the club was disbanded.* *verb.*

dis·be·lief (dis′bi lēf′), a lack of belief; refusal to believe: *When we heard the shocking rumor, we immediately expressed disbelief.* *noun.*

disc (disk). See **disk.** *noun.*

dis·card (dis kärd′ *for 1;* dis′kärd *for 2*), **1** to throw aside; give up as useless or worn out. You can discard clothes, ways of doing things, or beliefs. **2** a thing or things thrown aside as useless or not wanted: *That worn-out old book is a discard from the library.* **1** *verb,* **2** *noun.*

dis·cern (də zėrn′ *or* də sėrn′), to see clearly; recognize the difference between two or more things: *They discerned a road zigzagging up the mountain. There are too many different opinions for me to discern the truth.* *verb.*

dis·charge (dis chärj′), **1** to unload cargo or passengers from a ship, train, bus, or airplane:

The ship discharged its passengers at the dock. **2** to fire off; shoot: *The policeman discharged his gun at the fleeing robbers.* **3** to release; let go; dismiss: *to discharge a patient from a hospital, to discharge a lazy worker.* **4** a release; letting go; dismissing: *I expect my discharge from the hospital in a few days.* **5** to give off; let out: *The infection discharged pus.* **6** a giving off; letting out: *Lightning is a discharge of electricity from thunderclouds.* **7** a thing given off or let out: *the watery discharge from an eye.* 1-3,5 *verb,* **dis·charg·es, dis·charged, dis·charg·ing;** 4,6,7 *noun.*

dis·ci·ple (də sī′pəl), **1** a believer in the thought and teaching of any leader; follower. **2** (in the Bible) one of the followers of Jesus. *noun.*

dis·ci·pline (dis′ə plin), **1** training, especially training of the mind or character: *Children who have had no discipline are often hard to teach.* **2** a trained condition of order and obedience; order kept among school pupils, soldiers, or members of any group: *When the fire broke out, the pupils showed good discipline.* **3** to train; bring to a condition of order and obedience; bring under control: *An officer must know how to discipline troops.* **4** punishment: *A little discipline would do them good.* **5** to punish: *They have never disciplined their children unfairly.* 1,2,4 *noun,* 3,5 *verb,* **dis·ci·plines, dis·ci·plined, dis·ci·plin·ing.**

disc jockey. See **disk jockey.**

dis·claim (dis klām′), to refuse to recognize as one's own; deny connection with: *The motorist disclaimed responsibility for the accident.* *verb.*

dis·close (dis klōz′), to make known; reveal: *This letter discloses a secret.* *verb,* **dis·clos·es, dis·closed, dis·clos·ing.**

dis·col·or (dis kul′ər), to change or spoil the color of; stain: *Smoke had discolored the building.* *verb.*

dis·com·fort (dis kum′fərt), **1** uneasiness; lack of comfort: *Embarrassing questions cause discomfort.* **2** a thing that causes discomfort: *Mud and cold were the discomforts the campers minded most.* *noun.*

dis·con·nect (dis′kə nekt′), to separate; unfasten; undo or break the connection of: *I disconnected the electric fan by pulling out the plug.* *verb.*

dis·con·tent (dis′kən tent′), dissatisfaction; dislike of what one has and a desire for something different: *Low pay and long hours of work caused discontent among the factory workers.* *noun.*

dis·con·tent·ed (dis′kən ten′tid), not contented; not satisfied; disliking what one has and wanting something different: *The discontented workers went on strike.* *adjective.*

dis·con·tin·ue (dis′kən tin′yü), to stop; give up; put an end or stop to: *The 10 o'clock bus to Boston has been discontinued. I discontinued my piano lessons.* *verb,* **dis·con·tin·ues, dis·con·tin·ued, dis·con·tin·u·ing.**

dis·cord (dis′kôrd), **1** a difference of opinion;

disputing: *Constant argument caused angry discord that spoiled the meeting.* **2** (in music) a lack of harmony in notes sounded at the same time. *noun.*

dis·count (dis′kount), **1** to take off a certain amount from a price: *The store discounts all clothes ten percent.* **2** the amount taken off from a price: *We bought the new TV set on sale at a 20 percent discount.* **3** selling goods at prices below those suggested by manufacturers: *a discount store.* **4** to believe only part of; allow for exaggeration in: *You must discount some of what he tells you, because he likes to make up stories.* 1,4 *verb,* 2 *noun,* 3 *adjective.*

dis·cour·age (dis kėr′ij), **1** to take away the courage of; destroy the hopes of: *Failing again and again discourages anyone.* **2** to try to prevent by disapproving: *All her friends discouraged her from such a dangerous swim.* **3** to prevent or hinder: *The chill of coming winter soon discouraged our picnics.* *verb,* **dis·cour·ag·es, dis·cour·aged, dis·cour·ag·ing.**

dis·cour·age·ment (dis kėr′ij mənt), a loss of hope or courage; act or condition of being discouraged: *My discouragement over failing grades made me dislike school.* *noun.*

dis·course (dis′kôrs for 1 and 2; dis kôrs′ for 3), **1** a long written or spoken discussion of some subject: *Sermons and lectures are discourses.* **2** a talk; conversation. **3** to talk; converse. 1,2 *noun,* 3 *verb,* **dis·cours·es, dis·coursed, dis·cours·ing.**

dis·cour·te·ous (dis kėr′tē əs), not courteous; not polite; rude: *It is discourteous to interrupt someone who is talking.* *adjective.*

dis·cour·te·sy (dis kėr′tə sē), a lack of courtesy; impoliteness; rudeness: *Their discourtesy in pushing into line ahead of us annoyed me.* *noun,* plural **dis·cour·te·sies.**

dis·cov·er (dis kuv′ər), to find out; see or learn of for the first time: *Madame Curie discovered the element radium in 1898. I discovered their secret.* *verb.*

dis·cov·er·y (dis kuv′ər ē), **1** a finding out; seeing or learning of something for the first time: *Balboa's discovery of the Pacific Ocean occurred in 1513.* **2** a thing found out: *One of Benjamin Franklin's discoveries was that lightning is electricity.* *noun,* plural **dis·cov·er·ies.**

dis·cred·it (dis kred′it), **1** to cast doubt on; destroy belief, faith, or trust in: *The lawyer discredited the witnesses by proving that they both had lied.* **2** a loss of belief, faith, or trust; doubt: *This newspaper story throws discredit on your account of the trip.* **3** to refuse to believe: *We discredit her account because she has lied so often.* **4** to do harm to the good name or standing of; give a bad reputation to: *His cheating during tests discredited him among his classmates.* **5** the loss of good name or standing: *The player who took a bribe brought discredit upon the team.* 1,3,4 *verb,* 2,5 *noun.*

dis·creet (dis krēt′), very careful in speech and

action; showing good judgment: *A discreet person does not spread gossip. "Perhaps" is a discreet answer. adjective.*

dis·cre·tion (dis kresh′ən), good judgment; care in speech and action; caution: *She rushed across the street in front of a car, but I showed more discretion by waiting for it to pass. noun.*

dis·crim·i·nate (dis krim′ə nāt), **1** to make or see a difference between; distinguish: *People who are color-blind usually cannot discriminate between red and green.* **2** to show an unfair difference in treatment: *It is wrong to discriminate against people because of their race, religion, nationality, or sex.* *verb,* **dis·crim·i·nates, dis·crim·i·nat·ed, dis·crim·i·nat·ing.**

dis·crim·i·na·tion (dis krim′ə nā′shən), **1** the ability to make good choices; good judgment: *I think they showed lack of discrimination when they painted their house a bright purple.* **2** a showing of an unfair difference in treatment: *Racial or religious discrimination in hiring employees is against the law. noun.*

dis·cuss (dis kus′), to talk over; consider from various points of view: *The class discussed several problems. Congress is discussing taxes. verb.*

dis·cus·sion (dis kush′ən), talk; talk about the reasons for and against; discussing things: *After hours of discussion, we came to a decision. noun.*

dis·dain (dis dān′), **1** to consider to be lower; look down on; scorn: *Now that they live in a new neighborhood, they disdain their old friends.* **2** a feeling that someone or something is beneath oneself: *The older students tended to treat the younger ones with disdain, and wouldn't have much to do with them.* **1** *verb,* **2** *noun.*

dis·dain·ful (dis dān′fəl), proud and scornful. *adjective.*

disdainful
She gave the children a **disdainful** look.

dis·ease (də zēz′), a sickness; illness; condition in which a bodily organ, system, or part does not work properly: *People, animals, and plants can all suffer from disease. Cleanliness helps prevent disease. noun.*

a	hat	i	it	oi	oil	ch	child		a in about
ā	age	ī	ice	ou	out	ng	long		e in taken
ä	far	o	hot	u	cup	sh	she	ə =	i in pencil
e	let	ō	open	ů	put	th	thin		o in lemon
ē	equal	ô	order	ü	rule	ŦH	then		u in circus
ėr	term					zh	measure		

dis·eased (də zēzd′), having a disease: *A diseased lung may be removed by an operation. adjective.*

dis·fa·vor (dis fā′vər), a feeling of not liking; dislike; disapproval: *The factory workers looked with disfavor on any attempt to lower their wages. noun.*

dis·fig·ure (dis fig′yər), to spoil the appearance of; hurt the beauty of: *A scar may disfigure a person's face. verb,* **dis·fig·ures, dis·fig·ured, dis·fig·ur·ing.**

dis·grace (dis grās′), **1** the loss of honor or respect; shame: *The disgrace of being sent to prison was hard for them to bear.* **2** to cause disgrace to; bring shame upon: *The traitor disgraced his family and friends.* **3** a person or thing that causes dishonor or shame: *The slums in many cities are a disgrace.* **1,3** *noun,* **2** *verb,* **dis·grac·es, dis·graced, dis·grac·ing.**

dis·grace·ful (dis grās′fəl), shameful; causing dishonor or loss of respect: *Their rude behavior was disgraceful. adjective.*

dis·guise (dis gīz′), **1** to make changes in one's clothes or appearance so as to look like someone else: *On Halloween I disguised myself as a ghost.* **2** the clothes or actions used to hide or deceive: *Glasses and a wig formed the spy's disguise.* **3** to hide what a thing really is; make a thing seem like something else: *The pirates disguised their ship as a trading vessel. She disguised her handwriting by writing with her left hand.* **1,3** *verb,* **dis·guis·es, dis·guised, dis·guis·ing;** **2** *noun.*

dis·gust (dis gust′), **1** a strong dislike; sickening dislike: *We feel disgust for bad odors or tastes.* **2** to cause a feeling of disgust in: *The smell of rotten eggs disgusts many people.* **1** *noun,* **2** *verb.*

dis·gust·ed (dis gus′tid), filled with dislike or displeasure: *When I struck out again, the coach gave me a disgusted look. adjective.*

dish (dish), **1** anything to serve food in. Plates, platters, bowls, cups, and saucers are all dishes. **2** the amount served in a dish: *I ate two dishes of ice cream.* **3** food served: *Sliced peaches with cream is the dish I like best.* **4** to put food into a dish for serving at the table: *You may dish up the dinner now.* **1-3** *noun, plural* **dish·es;** **4** *verb.*

dis·heart·en (dis härt′n), to discourage; depress: *Long illness is disheartening. verb.*

dis·hon·est (dis on′ist), not honest; ready to cheat: *A person who lies or steals is dishonest. adjective.*

dis·hon·es·ty (dis on′ə stē), a lack of honesty: *People who lie or cheat can't be trusted because of their dishonesty. noun.*

dis·hon·or (dis on′ər), **1** disgrace; shame; loss of

reputation or standing: *Cheating brought dishonor to the team.* **2** to bring disgrace or shame upon: *The player who cheated dishonored the entire team.* **1** *noun,* **2** *verb.*

dis·hon·or·a·ble (dis on′ər ə bəl), without honor; disgraceful; shameful: *The police officer was accused of taking bribes and other dishonorable conduct. adjective.*

dish·pan (dish′pan′), a pan, now usually made of plastic, in which to wash dishes. *noun.*

dish·wash·er (dish′wosh′ər), a person or machine that washes dishes, pots, and glasses. *noun.*

dis·in·fect (dis′in fekt′), to destroy the disease germs in: *The dentist disinfected his instruments. verb.*

dis·in·fect·ant (dis′in fek′tənt), a substance used to destroy disease germs. Alcohol and iodine are disinfectants. *noun.*

dis·in·her·it (dis′in her′it), to keep from inheriting; take away an inheritance from: *She disinherited her son by leaving him out of her will. verb.*

dis·in·te·grate (dis in′tə grāt), to break up; separate into small parts or bits: *The old papers had disintegrated into a pile of dust. verb,* **dis·in·te·grates, dis·in·te·grat·ed, dis·in·te·grat·ing.**

dis·in·ter·est·ed (dis in′tər ə stid), **1** free from selfish reasons for acting; fair: *An umpire makes disinterested decisions.* **2** not interested: *During her illness she was disinterested in food. adjective.*

disk (disk), **1** a flat, thin, round object shaped like a coin. **2** a phonograph record. **3** an object like a phonograph record, made of metal or plastic and with a magnetic surface, used to store information and instructions for computers. *noun.* Also spelled **disc.**

disk drive, an electronic device that transfers information and instructions back and forth between a computer and magnetic storage disks.

disk·ette (dis ket′), a small, bendable, plastic disk used to store information and instructions for computers; floppy disk. *noun.*

disk jockey, an announcer for a radio program that consists chiefly of recorded popular music.

dis·like (dis līk′), **1** to not like; object to; have a feeling against: *He dislikes studying and would rather play football.* **2** a feeling of not liking; a feeling against: *I have a dislike of rain and fog.* **1** *verb,* **dis·likes, dis·liked, dis·lik·ing;** **2** *noun.*

dis·lo·cate (dis′lō kāt), to put out of joint: *He dislocated his shoulder when he fell. verb,* **dis·lo·cates, dis·lo·cat·ed, dis·lo·cat·ing.**

dis·lodge (dis loj′), to drive or force out of a place or position: *She used a crowbar to dislodge a heavy stone. verb,* **dis·lodg·es, dis·lodged, dis·lodg·ing.**

dis·loy·al (dis loi′əl), not loyal; unfaithful: *He was disloyal to his friends, often talking about them behind their backs. adjective.*

dis·loy·al·ty (dis loi′əl tē), unfaithfulness. *noun, plural* **dis·loy·al·ties.**

dismal (definition 1)—It was a **dismal** afternoon.

dis·mal (diz′məl), **1** dark; gloomy. **2** miserable: *Sickness or bad luck often makes a person feel dismal. adjective.*

dis·man·tle (dis man′tl), to pull down; take apart: *We had to dismantle the bookcases in order to move them. verb,* **dis·man·tles, dis·man·tled, dis·man·tling.**

dis·may (dis mā′), **1** a sudden loss of courage because of fear of what is about to happen or what has happened: *I was filled with dismay when the basement began to flood.* **2** to trouble greatly; make afraid: *The thought that she might fail the test dismayed her.* **1** *noun,* **2** *verb.*

dis·miss (dis mis′), **1** to send away; allow to go: *At noon the teacher dismissed the class for lunch.* **2** to remove from office or service; not allow to keep a job: *We dismissed the painters because their work was so poor.* **3** to put out of mind; stop thinking about: *Dismiss your troubles. verb.*

dis·miss·al (dis mis′əl), **1** the act of dismissing: *The dismissal of those five workers caused a strike.* **2** the condition or fact of being dismissed: *The company refused to announce the reason for the workers' dismissal. noun.*

dis·mount (dis mount′), to get off something, such as a horse or a bicycle: *She dismounted and led her horse across the stream. verb.*

dis·o·be·di·ence (dis′ə bē′dē əns), refusal to obey; failure to obey: *The children were punished for disobedience. noun.*

dis·o·be·di·ent (dis′ə bē′dē ənt), failing to follow orders or rules; refusing to obey: *The disobedient child would not go to bed when her parents told her to. adjective.*

dis·o·bey (dis′ə bā′), to refuse to obey; fail to obey: *The student who disobeyed the teacher was punished. verb.*

dis·or·der (dis ôr′dər), **1** a lack of order; confusion: *The room was in disorder after the birthday party.* **2** to disturb the regular order or working of; throw into confusion: *A series of accidents disordered traffic.* **3** a public disturbance; riot: *The police needed help from the army to end the disorder in the streets.* **4** a sickness; disease: *Eating the wrong food can cause a stomach disorder.* **1,3,4** *noun,* **2** *verb.*

dis·or·der·ly (dis ôr′dər lē), **1** not orderly; untidy; confused: *I can never find anything in this disorderly closet.* **2** causing disorder; making a disturbance; breaking rules; unruly: *The disorderly crowd pushed and shoved to get on the bus.* *adjective.*

a hat	i it	oi oil	ch child	a in about
ā age	ī ice	ou out	ng long	e in taken
ä far	o hot	u cup	sh she	ə = { i in pencil
e let	ō open	ù put	th thin	o in lemon
ē equal	ô order	ü rule	ᴛʜ then	u in circus
ėr term			zh measure	

ORDERLY

DISORDERLY

dis·or·gan·ize (dis ôr′gə nīz), to throw into confusion or disorder: *Heavy snowstorms delayed all flights and disorganized the airline schedule.* *verb,* **dis·or·gan·iz·es, dis·or·gan·ized, dis·or·gan·iz·ing.**

dis·own (dis ōn′), to refuse to recognize as one's own; cast off: *They disowned their daughter.* *verb.*

dis·patch (dis pach′), **1** to send off to some place or for some purpose: *The captain dispatched a boat to bring a doctor on board ship.* **2** a sending off: *Please hurry the dispatch of this telegram.* **3** a written message, such as special news or government business: *The correspondent in Paris rushed news dispatches to her newspaper in New York.* **4** promptness in doing anything; speed: *This boy works with neatness and dispatch.* **1** *verb,* **2,3,4** *noun, plural* **dis·patch·es.**

dis·pel (dis pel′), to make go away; drive away and scatter: *Talking with the pilot helped dispel my fear of flying.* *verb,* **dis·pels, dis·pelled, dis·pel·ling.**

dis·pense (dis pens′), **1** to give out; distribute: *The Red Cross dispensed food and clothing to the flood victims.* **2** to prepare and give out: *Druggists must dispense medicine with the greatest care.* *verb,* **dis·pens·es, dis·pensed, dis·pens·ing.**
dispense with, to do without: *I shall dispense with these crutches as soon as my leg heals.*

dis·perse (dis pėrs′), to spread in different directions; scatter: *The crowd dispersed when it began raining.* *verb,* **dis·pers·es, dis·persed, dis·pers·ing.**

dis·place (dis plās′), **1** to take the place of; put something else in the place of: *The automobile has displaced the horse and buggy.* **2** to put out of place; move from the usual place or position: *The war displaced thousands of people.* *verb,* **dis·plac·es, dis·placed, dis·plac·ing.**

dis·play (dis plā′), **1** to show; exhibit: *He displayed his good nature by patiently answering the same question several times.* **2** a showing; exhibit: *a display of bad temper. The store window has a display of new books.* **3** a showing off: *A fondness for display led her to buy a flashy car.* **1** *verb,* **2,3** *noun.*

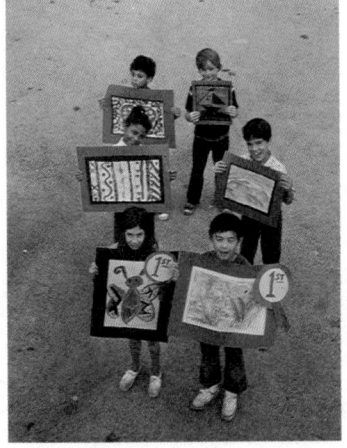

display (definition 1) The children **displayed** their drawings.

dis·please (dis plēz′), to annoy or anger somewhat; not please: *The teacher was displeased by the number of students who were late for class.* *verb,* **dis·pleas·es, dis·pleased, dis·pleas·ing.**

dis·pleas·ure (dis plezh′ər), the feeling of being annoyed or somewhat angry: *She expressed her displeasure at being interrupted by refusing to continue talking.* *noun.*

dis·pos·a·ble (dis pō′zə bəl), made to be thrown away after use: *disposable diapers. adjective.*

dis·pos·al (dis pō′zəl), **1** the act of getting rid of something: *The city takes care of the disposal of garbage.* **2** dealing with; settling: *His disposal of the difficulty pleased everybody. noun.*
at one's disposal, ready for one's use or service at any time: *I will put my room at your disposal.*

dis·pose (dis pōz′). **dispose of, 1** to get rid of: *Dispose of that rubbish.* **2** to give away or sell: *The owner disposed of her house for $35,000.* **3** to arrange; settle: *The committee disposed of all its business in an hour.* verb, **dis·pos·es, dis·posed, dis·pos·ing.**

dis·po·si·tion (dis′pə zish′ən), one's natural way of acting toward others: *His cheerful disposition made him popular.* noun.

dis·prove (dis prüv′), to prove false or incorrect: *She disproved my claim that I had less candy by weighing both boxes.* verb, **dis·proves, dis·proved, dis·prov·ing.**

dis·pute (dis pyüt′), **1** to argue angrily or quarrel: *They disputed over the last piece of cake.* **2** an angry argument or quarrel: *There is a dispute over where to build the new school.* **3** to say that something is false or doubtful; disagree with: *The insurance company disputed his claim for damages to his car.* 1,3 verb, **dis·putes, dis·put·ed, dis·put·ing;** 2 noun.

dis·qual·i·fy (dis kwol′ə fī), **1** to make unable to do something: *Her broken leg disqualified her from all sports.* **2** to declare unfit or unable to do something: *Students with low grades were disqualified from acting in the school play.* verb, **dis·qual·i·fies, dis·qual·i·fied, dis·qual·i·fy·ing.**

dis·re·gard (dis′ri gärd′), **1** to pay no attention to; take no notice of: *We disregarded the cold weather and went camping as planned.* **2** lack of attention; neglect: *Her disregard of traffic signs caused her to have an accident.* 1 verb, 2 noun.

dis·re·pair (dis′ri per′ or dis′ri par′), bad condition; need of repair: *The house was in disrepair.* noun.

dis·rep·u·ta·ble (dis rep′yə tə bəl), having a bad reputation; not respectable: *a disreputable gang.* adjective.

dis·re·spect (dis′ri spekt′), rudeness; lack of respect: *I meant no disrespect by my hasty remark.* noun.

dis·re·spect·ful (dis′ri spekt′fəl), rude; impolite: *Making fun of your elders is disrespectful.* adjective.

dis·rupt (dis rupt′), to break up or cause disorder in: *The storm disrupted telephone service throughout the area.* verb.

dis·sat·is·fac·tion (dis′sat i sfak′shən), discontent; displeasure: *Low pay caused dissatisfaction among the workers.* noun.

dis·sat·is·fied (dis sat′i sfīd), discontented; displeased: *When we do not get what we want, we are dissatisfied.* adjective.

dis·sect (di sekt′), to cut apart something that was once alive so as to examine or study its structure. verb.

dis·sen·sion (di sen′shən), a disputing; quarreling; hard feeling caused by a difference in opinion: *The club broke up because of dissension among its members.* noun.

dis·sent (di sent′), **1** to disagree; think differently; express a different opinion from others: *Two of the judges dissented from the decision of the other three.* **2** a disagreement; difference of opinion: *Dissent among the members broke up the club.* 1 verb, 2 noun.

dis·sim·i·lar (di sim′ə lər), unlike; different. adjective.

dis·si·pate (dis′ə pāt), to scatter; spread in different directions: *The fog is beginning to dissipate.* verb, **dis·si·pates, dis·si·pat·ed, dis·si·pat·ing.**

dis·solve (di zolv′), **1** to make liquid; become liquid, especially by putting or being put into a liquid: *You can dissolve sugar in water.* **2** to break up; end: *They dissolved the partnership over a quarrel.* verb, **dis·solves, dis·solved, dis·solv·ing.**

dis·suade (di swād′), to persuade not to do something: *I dissuaded her from quitting the swimming team.* verb, **dis·suades, dis·suad·ed, dis·suad·ing.**

dis·tance (dis′təns), **1** the space in between: *The distance from the farm to the town is five miles.* **2** a place far away: *She saw a light in the distance.* noun.

at a distance, a long way: *The farm is at a distance from the railroad.*

keep at a distance, to refuse to be friendly or familiar with; treat coldly: *The teacher kept the students at a distance.*

dis·tant (dis′tənt), **1** far away in space: *The sun is distant from the earth.* **2** away: *The town is three miles distant.* **3** far apart in time: *We plan a trip to Europe in the distant future.* **4** not closely related: *A third cousin is a distant relative.* **5** not friendly: *After our quarrel he was distant.* adjective.

dis·taste (dis tāst′), dislike: *His distaste for carrots showed clearly on his face.* noun.

dis·taste·ful (dis tāst′fəl), unpleasant; disagreeable; offensive: *Cleaning out the garbage cans is a distasteful task.* adjective.

dis·tem·per (dis tem′pər), a disease of dogs and other animals that causes a cough, fever, and weakness. noun.

dis·till (dis til′), to make a liquid pure by heating it and turning it into a vapor and then cooling it into liquid form again: *Water is distilled to remove minerals and other impurities. Gasoline is distilled from crude oil.* verb.

dis·til·la·tion (dis′tl ā′shən), the act or process of distilling: *Fresh water can be obtained by the distillation of salt water.* noun.

dis·tinct (dis tingkt′), **1** not the same; separate; different: *She asked me about it three distinct times. Mice are distinct from rats.* **2** clear; easily seen, heard, or understood: *Large, distinct print is easy to read.* **3** unmistakable; definite: *A tall player has a distinct advantage in a basketball game.* adjective.

dis·tinc·tion (dis tingk′shən), **1** making a difference: *They treated all their children alike without distinction.* **2** difference: *The distinction between hot and cold is easily noticed.* **3** honor: *The judge served on the court for many years with distinction.* **4** excellence; superiority: *Prizes were awarded to scientists and authors of great distinction.* noun.

dis·tinc·tive (dis tingk′tiv), clearly showing a

a hat	i it	oi oil	ch child		a in about
ā age	ī ice	ou out	ng long		e in taken
ä far	o hot	u cup	sh she	ə =	i in pencil
e let	ō open	u̇ put	th thin		o in lemon
ē equal	ô order	ü rule	ᵀH then		u in circus
ėr term			zh measure		

D

distinctive—Each kind of butterfly has distinctive markings.

difference from others; special: *The police wear a distinctive uniform. adjective.*

dis·tin·guish (dis ting′gwish), **1** to see the differences in; tell apart: *Can you distinguish cotton cloth from wool?* **2** to see or hear clearly; make out plainly: *On a clear, bright day you can distinguish things far away.* **3** to make different; be a special quality or feature of: *The elephant's trunk distinguishes it from all other animals.* **4** to make famous or well-known: *He distinguished himself by winning three prizes at the science fair. verb.*

dis·tin·guished (dis ting′gwisht), famous or well-known because of excellence: *The distinguished artist had paintings displayed in many museums. adjective.*

dis·tort (dis tôrt′), **1** to pull or twist out of shape; make crooked or ugly. **2** to change from the truth: *The driver distorted the facts of the accident to escape blame. verb.*

Word History

distort *Distort* comes from a Latin word meaning "to twist."

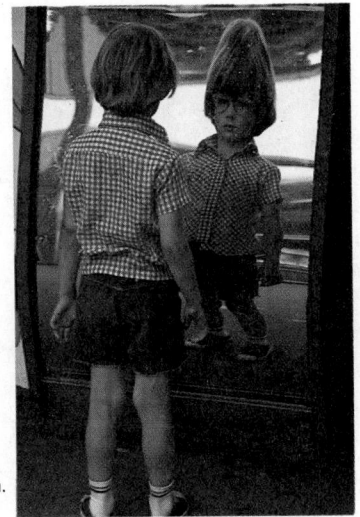

distort (definition 1) The trick mirror **distorts** his reflection.

dis·tract (dis trakt′), to draw away the mind or attention: *Noise distracts me when I am trying to study. verb.*

dis·trac·tion (dis trak′shən), something that draws away the mind or attention: *Noise is a distraction when you are trying to study. noun.*

dis·tress (dis tres′), **1** great pain or sorrow; anxiety; trouble: *The loss of our kitten caused us much distress.* **2** to cause pain or sorrow to; make unhappy: *Your tears distress me.* **3** a dangerous condition; difficult situation: *A burning or sinking ship is in distress.* **1,3** *noun,* **2** *verb.*

dis·trib·ute (dis trib′yüt), **1** to give some to each; deal out: *I distributed the candy among my friends.* **2** to spread; scatter: *A painter should distribute the paint evenly over the wall.* **3** to divide or arrange into groups; sort: *A mail clerk distributes mail by putting each letter into the proper bag. verb,* **dis·trib·utes, dis·trib·ut·ed, dis·trib·ut·ing.**

dis·tri·bu·tion (dis′trə byü′shən), the act of distributing: *After the contest the distribution of prizes to the winners took place. noun.*

dis·trict (dis′trikt), **1** a part of a larger area; region: *The leading farming district of the United States is in the Middle West.* **2** a part of a country, a state, or a city, marked off for a special purpose, such as providing schools and electing certain government officers: *a school district. noun.*

District of Columbia, a district in the southeastern United States that is entirely occupied by the city of Washington, the capital of the United States. *Abbreviation:* D.C. or DC

dis·trust (dis trust′), **1** to have no confidence in; not trust; doubt: *Everyone should distrust shaky ladders.* **2** lack of trust; lack of belief in the goodness of: *I could not explain my distrust of the stranger.* **1** *verb,* **2** *noun.*

dis·turb (dis tėrb′), **1** to bother someone by talking or by being noisy; interrupt: *Please do not disturb her while she's studying.* **2** to put out of order: *Someone has disturbed my books; I can't find the one I want.* **3** to make uneasy; trouble: *He was disturbed to hear of his friend's illness. verb.*

dis·turb·ance (dis tėr′bəns), **1** a disturbing or being disturbed: *Nightmares often cause disturbances in sleep.* **2** a thing that disturbs: *Turn off the television, so it won't be a disturbance.* **3** confusion; disorder: *The police were called to quiet the disturbance at the street corner. noun.*

ditch (dich), **1** a long, narrow hole dug in the earth. Ditches are usually used to carry off water. **2** to get rid of: *The robber ditched the gun in a sewer.* **1** *noun, plural* **ditch·es; 2** *verb.*

dive (dīv), **1** to plunge headfirst into water. **2** the act of diving: *We applauded his graceful dive.* **3** to

179

plunge suddenly into something: *She dived into her pockets and brought out a dollar. I dived into my homework and soon had it done.* **4** to plunge downward at a steep angle: *The hawk dived straight at the field mouse.* **5** a downward plunge at a steep angle: *The submarine made a dive toward the bottom.* 1,3,4 *verb,* **dives, dived** or **dove, dived, div·ing;** 2,5 *noun.*

div·er (dī′vər), **1** a person who dives. **2** person whose occupation is to work under water. **3** a diving bird, such as a penguin. *noun.*

di·verse (də vèrs′), different; completely unlike: *A great many diverse opinions were expressed at the meeting. adjective.*

di·ver·sion (də vèr′zhən), **1** a turning aside: *A magician's talk creates a diversion of our attention so that we do not see how the tricks are done.* **2** a relief from work or care; amusement; entertainment; pastime: *Watching TV is a popular diversion. noun.*

di·ver·si·ty (də vèr′sə tē), a difference; variety: *The diversity of food on the table made it hard for us to choose. noun.*

di·vert (də vèrt′), **1** to turn aside: *A ditch diverted water from the stream into the fields. The siren of the fire engine diverted the audience's attention from the play.* **2** to amuse; entertain: *We were diverted by the clown's tricks. verb.*

di·vide (də vīd′), **1** to separate into parts: *A brook divides the field. The road divides and forms two roads.* **2** to separate into equal parts: *When you divide 8 by 2, you get 4.* **3** to give some of to each; share: *We divided the candy.* **4** to disagree; separate in feeling or opinion: *The school divided on the question of a shorter lunch hour.* **5** a ridge of land between the regions drained by two different river systems: *The Rocky Mountains form part of the Continental Divide.* 1-4 *verb,* **di·vides, di·vid·ed, di·vid·ing;** 5 *noun.*

div·i·dend (div′ə dend), **1** a number to be divided by another: *In 728 ÷ 16, 728 is the dividend.* **2** the money earned as profit by a company and divided among the owners of the company and people who own stock in it. *noun.*

di·vine (də vīn′), **1** of God or a god: *The Bible describes the creation of the world as a divine act.* **2** given by or coming from God: *The king believed that his power to rule was a divine right.* **3** to or for God; sacred; holy: *Services for divine worship were held daily.* **4** excellent; unusually good or great: *Oh, what a divine vacation we had! adjective.*

di·vin·i·ty (də vin′ə tē), **1** a divine being; god or goddess. **2** divine nature or quality. *noun, plural* **di·vin·i·ties.**

di·vis·i·ble (də viz′ə bəl), able to be divided: *In arithmetic 12 is divisible by 4. adjective.*

di·vi·sion (də vizh′ən), **1** a dividing; being divided: *the division of land into lots for houses.* **2** a sharing; giving some to each: *The making of automobiles in large numbers is made possible by a division of labor, in which each worker has a certain part of the work to do.* **3** the operation of dividing one number by another: *26 ÷ 2 = 13 is a*

simple division. **4** a thing that divides: *This fence is the division between your property and mine.* **5** one of the parts into which a thing is divided; group; section. Two or more regiments make a division of the army. *noun.*

di·vi·sor (də vī′zər), a number by which another is divided: *In 728 ÷ 16, 16 is the divisor. noun.*

di·vorce (də vôrs′), **1** the legal ending of a marriage. **2** to end legally a marriage between: *They were divorced last year.* 1 *noun,* 2 *verb,* **di·vorc·es, di·vorced, di·vorc·ing.**

di·vulge (də vulj′), to tell; reveal; make known: *The traitor divulged secret plans to the enemy. verb,* **di·vulg·es, di·vulged, di·vulg·ing.**

diz·zi·ness (diz′ē nis), dizzy condition. *noun.*

diz·zy (diz′ē), **1** likely to fall, stagger, or spin around; not steady: *When you spin round and round, and stop suddenly, you feel dizzy.* **2** confused; bewildered: *The noise and crowds of the city streets made the little boy dizzy.* **3** likely to make dizzy; causing dizziness: *The airplane climbed to a dizzy height. adjective,* **diz·zi·er, diz·zi·est.**

do (dü), **1** to carry through to an end any action or piece of work; carry out; perform: *Do your work well.* **2** to take care of: *Who does the dishes at your house?* **3** to act; behave: *You did very well today.* **4** to be satisfactory: *That hat will do.* **5** *Do* is used: **a** to ask questions: *Do you like milk?* **b** to make what one says stronger: *I do want to go. Do come, please.* **c** to stand for another word already used: *My dog goes where I do. Her brother walks just as she does.* **d** in expressions that contain *not: People talk; animals do not. verb,* **does, did, done, do·ing.**

do up, to wrap up: *Please do up this package for me.*

Do·ber·man pin·scher (dō′bər mən pin′shər), a large slender dog with short, dark hair.
[This dog was named for Ludwig *Doberman*, a German dog breeder who was the first to develop the breed. He lived in the 1800's. *Pinscher* was borrowed from the German word meaning "terrier."]

Doberman pinscher
24 to 28 inches (61 to 71 centimeters) high at the shoulder

doc·ile (dos′əl), easily trained or managed; obedient: *People who are just starting to ride should use a docile horse. adjective.*

dock[1] (dok), **1** a platform built on the shore or out from the shore; wharf; pier. Ships load and unload beside a dock. **2** a platform for loading and unloading trucks or railroad cars. **3** to bring a ship to dock: *The crew docked the ship and began to unload it.* **4** to join two spacecraft to each other while in space. 1,2 *noun*, 3,4 *verb*.

dock[2] (dok), **1** to cut off a part of: *The company docks the workers' wages if they come to work late.* **2** to cut short; cut off the end of. Dogs' tails are sometimes docked. *verb*.

doc·tor (dok′tər), **1** a person who is trained to treat diseases. A doctor must have a license to practice medicine. Physicians, surgeons, dentists, and veterinarians are doctors. **2** to treat disease in: *My mother doctored me when I had a cold.* 1 *noun*, 2 *verb*.

doc·trine (dok′trən), what is taught as true by a church, nation, or group; belief: *religious doctrine. The Constitution states the doctrine of freedom of speech. noun.*

doc·u·ment (dok′yə mənt), something written or printed that gives information and can be used as proof of some fact; any object used as evidence. Letters, maps, and pictures are documents. *noun.*

dodge (doj), **1** to move or jump quickly to one side: *As I looked, he dodged behind a bush.* **2** to move quickly in order to get away from a person, a blow, or something thrown: *She dodged the bicycle as it came at her.* **3** a sudden movement to one side: *With a sudden dodge to the left, she caught the ball.* **4** to get away from by some trick: *She dodged our question by changing the subject.* 1,2,4 *verb*, **dodg·es, dodged, dodg·ing;** 3 *noun*.

dodge·ball (doj′bôl′), a children's game in which players stand in a circle or in two opposite lines, and try to hit other players inside the circle or in the other line with a large, soft rubber ball. *noun.*

do·do (dō′dō), a large, clumsy bird that could not fly. Dodos lived on several islands in the Indian Ocean until the last ones died about 300 years ago. *noun, plural* **do·dos** or **do·does.**

Word History

dodo The name for this bird comes from a Portuguese word meaning "fool." It was called this because of its clumsy appearance.

dodo
about 4 feet (1 meter) long

a hat	**i** it	**oi** oil	**ch** child	⎧ a in about
ā age	**ī** ice	**ou** out	**ng** long	⎪ e in taken
ä far	**o** hot	**u** cup	**sh** she	ə = ⎨ i in pencil
e let	**ō** open	**ù** put	**th** thin	⎪ o in lemon
ē equal	**ô** order	**ü** rule	**ŦH** then	⎩ u in circus
ėr term			**zh** measure	

doe (dō), a female deer, antelope, rabbit, or hare. *noun.*

does (duz). See **do.** *She does all her work. Does he sing well? verb.*

does·n't (duz′nt), does not.

doff (dof), to take off; remove. *verb.*

Word History

doff *Doff* was shortened from the words *do off*, an old expression meaning "to take off."

doff—He **doffed** his hat.

dog (dôg), **1** a four-legged animal used as a pet, for hunting, and for guarding property. **2** to hunt or follow like a dog: *The police dogged the suspected thief until they caught him.* 1 *noun*, 2 *verb*, **dogs, dogged, dog·ging.**

go to the dogs, be ruined; go to ruin: *The house was not cared for and soon went to the dogs.*

dog·ged (dô′gid), stubborn; not giving up: *Her dogged determination helped her win the race. adjective.*

dog·gie (dô′gē), **1** a little dog. **2** an affectionate name for a dog. *noun.* Also spelled **doggy.**

doggie bag or **doggy bag,** a small bag given by a restaurant to a customer, in which uneaten food can be carried home.

dog·gy (dô′gē), **1** like a dog: *The rug had a doggy smell.* **2** See **doggie**. 1 *adjective*, **dog·gi·er, dog·gi·est;** 2 *noun, plural* **dog·gies.**

dog·house (dôg′hous′), a small shelter for a dog. *noun, plural* **dog·hous·es** (dôg′hou′ziz).
in the doghouse, in trouble; out of favor: *I'm in the doghouse with my parents for coming home so late.*

do·gie (dō′gē), a calf without a mother, on the range or in a herd. *noun.*

dog·wood (dôg′wůd′), a tree with large white or pinkish flowers in the spring and red berries in the fall. *noun.*

doi·ly (doi′lē), a small piece of linen, lace, paper, or plastic used under a dish or vase as a decoration or to protect the surface beneath it. *noun, plural* **doi·lies.**

do·ings (dü′ingz), things done; actions; events: *There were dances, parties, and lots of doings over the holidays. noun plural.*

dole (dōl), to give in small portions: *I doled out a few peanuts to each child. verb,* **doles, doled, dol·ing.**

doll (dol), a child's toy made to look like a baby, a child, or a grown person. *noun.*

dol·lar (dol′ər), a unit of money in the United States and Canada equal to 100 cents. $1.00 means one dollar. *noun.*

doll·house (dol′hous′), a toy house for children to use in playing with dolls. *noun, plural* **doll·hous·es** (dol′hou′ziz).

dol·phin (dol′fən), a sea mammal much like a small whale. It has a snout like a beak and remarkable intelligence. *noun.*

dolphins—about 10 feet (3 meters) long

dolt (dōlt), a dull, stupid person. *noun.*
do·main (dō mān′), the lands under the control of one ruler or government: *The brave knight was given the best land in the queen's domain. noun.*
dome (dōm), **1** a large, rounded roof on a circular or many-sided base. **2** a thing shaped like a dome: *the rounded dome of a hill. noun.*
do·mes·tic (də mes′tik), **1** of the home, the household, or family affairs: *We share cooking, cleaning, and other domestic duties.* **2** not wild; tame. Horses, dogs, cats, cows, and pigs are domestic animals. **3** of one's own country; not

foreign: *Most newspapers publish both domestic and foreign news. adjective.*

do·mes·ti·cate (də mes′tə kāt), to tame; change animals and plants from a wild to a tame state. *verb,* **do·mes·ti·cates, do·mes·ti·cat·ed, do·mes·ti·cat·ing.**

dom·i·nant (dom′ə nənt), ruling; governing; controlling; most influential: *The principal was the dominant person at the meeting. Football is the dominant sport in the fall. adjective.*

dom·i·nate (dom′ə nāt), to control or rule by strength or power: *She was very outspoken and tended to dominate our club meetings. verb,* **dom·i·nates, dom·i·nat·ed, dom·i·nat·ing.**

dom·i·na·tion (dom′ə nā′shən), control; rule; dominating: *British domination of the seas lasted over 200 years. noun.*

dom·i·neer·ing (dom′ə nir′ing), inclined to dominate; arrogant; overbearing: *A bully has a domineering attitude. adjective.*

do·min·ion (də min′yən), the lands under the control of one ruler or government. *noun.*

dom·i·no (dom′ə nō), one of a set of small, flat pieces of wood or plastic marked with spots. **Dominoes** is the game played with them. *noun, plural* **dom·i·noes** or **dom·i·nos.**

don (don), to put on clothing: *The knight donned his armor. verb,* **dons, donned, don·ning.**
[*Don* was shortened from the words *do on,* an old expression meaning "put on."]

do·nate (dō′nāt), to give money or help; contribute: *I donated ten dollars to charity. verb,* **do·nates, do·nat·ed, do·nat·ing.**

do·na·tion (dō nā′shən), a gift of money or help; contribution: *a donation to charity. noun.*

done (dun), **1** finished; completed; ended: *She is done with her homework.* **2** cooked: *The steak was done just right.* **3** See **do**. *Have you done all your chores?* **1,2** *adjective,* **3** *verb.*

dome (definition 1)—**dome** of the United States Capitol

don·key (dong′kē), an animal somewhat like a small horse but with longer ears and a shorter mane. *noun, plural* **don·keys.**

do·nor (dō′nər), a person who gives; giver. *noun.*

don't (dōnt), do not.

doo·dle (dü′dl), to draw or make marks in an absent-minded way while talking or thinking. *verb,* **doo·dles, doo·dled, doo·dling.**

doom (düm), **1** a terrible fate; ruin; death: *As the ship sank, the voyagers faced their doom.* **2** to sentence to an unhappy or terrible fate: *The prisoner was doomed to death.* **3** to make a bad or unwelcome outcome certain: *The weather doomed our hopes of a picnic.* 1 *noun,* 2,3 *verb.*

door (dôr), **1** a movable part to close an opening in a wall, cabinet, vehicle, or the like. A door turns on hinges or slides open and shut. **2** a doorway: *He walked into the room through the door. noun.*

door·bell (dôr′bel′), a bell to be rung as a signal that someone wishes to have the door opened. *noun.*

door·knob (dôr′nob′), a handle on a door. *noun.*

door·step (dôr′step′), a step leading from an outside door to the ground. *noun.*

door·way (dôr′wā′), an opening in a wall where a door is. *noun.*

dope (dōp), **1** a narcotic or other drug, such as heroin or marijuana. **2** a very stupid person. **3** a thick varnish or similar liquid applied to a fabric to strengthen or waterproof it. Dope is sometimes used on model airplanes. *noun.*

dope·y (dō′pē), **1** drowsy; sluggish: *The hot, stuffy room made me feel dopey.* **2** stupid: *I was always doing dopey things like leaving my homework on the bus. adjective,* **dop·i·er, dop·i·est.**

dor·mant (dôr′mənt), not active: *Many volcanoes are dormant. Bears and other animals that hibernate are dormant during the winter. adjective.*

dor·mer (dôr′mər), a part of a roof that sticks out from a sloping roof and has a window. *noun.*

dormer

dor·mi·to·ry (dôr′mə tôr′ē), a building with many rooms to live in. Many colleges have dormitories for students whose homes are somewhere else. *noun, plural* **dor·mi·to·ries.**

a hat	i it	oi oil	ch child	⎧ a in about
ā age	ī ice	ou out	ng long	⎪ e in taken
ä far	o hot	u cup	sh she	ə = ⎨ i in pencil
e let	ō open	u̇ put	th thin	⎪ o in lemon
ē equal	ô order	ü rule	ᴛʜ then	⎩ u in circus
ėr term			zh measure	

D

dormouse
about 5 inches
(13 centimeters)
long with the tail

dor·mouse (dôr′mous′), a small animal somewhat like a mouse and somewhat like a squirrel. It sleeps during cold weather. *noun, plural* **dor·mice** (dôr′mīs′).

do·ry (dôr′ē), a rowboat with a narrow, flat bottom and high sides, often used in fishing. *noun, plural* **do·ries.**

dose (dōs), **1** the amount of a medicine to be taken at one time: *a dose of cough medicine.* **2** to give medicine to: *The doctor dosed the sick child with penicillin.* 1 *noun,* 2 *verb,* **dos·es, dosed, dos·ing.**

dot (dot), **1** a tiny, round mark; point: *Put a dot over each i.* **2** a small spot: *a blue necktie with white dots.* **3** to mark with a dot or dots: *Dot your i's and j's.* **4** to be here and there in: *Dandelions dotted the lawn.* 1,2 *noun,* 3,4 *verb,* **dots, dot·ted, dot·ting.**

dote (dōt). **dote on,** to be foolishly fond of; be too fond of: *They dote on their grandchildren, giving them too many presents. verb,* **dotes, dot·ed, dot·ing.**

dou·ble (dub′əl), **1** twice as much, as large, or as strong: *They were given double pay for working on Sunday.* **2** twice: *He was paid double by mistake.* **3** a number or amount that is twice as much: *Four is the double of two.* **4** to make or become twice as much or twice as many: *They doubled their money in ten years by investing it wisely.* **5** made of two like parts; in a pair: *double doors.* **6** having two meanings or characters. The spelling *b-e-a-r* has a double meaning: *to carry* and *a certain animal.* **7** two instead of one: *The blow on the head made him see double. It is dangerous to ride double on a bicycle.* **8** a person or thing just like another: *Her twin sister is her double.* **9** to fold over: *She* *doubled the slice of bread to make a sandwich.* **10** to close tightly together; clench: *They doubled their fists and began to fight.* **11** to bend or turn sharply backward: *The fox doubled on its track and escaped the dogs.* **12** a hit by which a batter gets to second base in baseball. **13** to make such a hit in baseball. 1,5,6 *adjective,* 2,7 *adverb,* 3,8,12 *noun,* 4,9-11,13 *verb,* **dou·bles, dou·bled, dou·bling.**

double bass (dub/əl bās/), a musical instrument shaped like a violin and having a very deep tone. The double bass is so large that the player must stand or sit on a high stool.

double bass

dou·ble-cross (dub/əl krôs/), to promise to do one thing and then do another. *verb.*

dou·ble·head·er (dub/əl hed/ər), two games played one after another on the same day. *noun.*

double play, in baseball, a play in which two runners are put out.

dou·bloon (du blün/), a former Spanish gold coin. *noun.*

dou·bly (dub/lē), twice as; twice: *Be doubly careful crossing busy streets. adverb.*

doubt (dout), **1** to feel uncertain; not believe; not be sure: *She doubted if we would arrive on time.* **2** a lack of belief; feeling of uncertainty: *My doubts about her ability to run fast vanished when she won the race.* **3** an uncertain state of mind: *We were in doubt as to the right road.* 1 *verb,* 2,3 *noun.*

no doubt, certainly: *No doubt we will win.*

doubt·ful (dout/fəl), full of doubt; not sure; not certain: *We are doubtful about the weather for tomorrow. adjective.*

doubt·less (dout/lis), without doubt; surely: *Since the autumn has been so cold, winter will doubtless come early. adverb.*

dough (dō), **1** a soft, thick mixture of flour, liquid, and other things from which bread, biscuits, cake, and pie crust are made. **2** money. *noun.*

dough·nut (dō/nut/), a small cake of sweetened dough cooked in deep fat. A doughnut is usually made in the shape of a ring. *noun.*

douse (dous), **1** to throw water over; drench: *She quickly doused the flames.* **2** to put out: *Douse the lights. verb,* **dous·es, doused, dous·ing.**

dove[1] (duv), a bird with a thick body and short legs; pigeon. The dove is often a symbol of peace. *noun.*

dove[1]—about 13 inches (33 centimeters) long

dove[2] (dōv), dived. See **dive.** *The diver dove deep into the water after the sunken treasure. verb.*

Do·ver (dō/vər), the capital of Delaware. *noun.*

down[1] (doun), **1** from a higher to a lower place: *They ran down the hill. The temperature has gone down.* **2** in a lower place: *Down in the valley the fog still lingers. The sun is down.* **3** from an earlier time to a later time: *The story has come down through many years.* **4** down along: *You can ride down a hill, sail down a river, or walk down a street.* **5** going or pointed down: *We waited for a down elevator.* **6** to put down: *He was downed in a fight. She downed the medicine with one swallow.* **7** sick; ill: *She is down with a cold.* **8** in cash when bought: *You can pay $10 down and the rest later. We made a down payment on a new car.* **9** in football, a play that begins when the center passes the ball to a back. 1-3,8 *adverb,* 4 *preposition,* 6 *verb,* 2,5,7,8 *adjective,* 9 *noun.*

down[2] (doun), **1** soft feathers: *the down of a young bird.* **2** soft hair or fluff: *The down on a boy's chin develops into a beard. noun.*

down·cast (doun/kast/), **1** turned downward: *She stood with downcast eyes, avoiding my look.* **2** dejected; sad; discouraged: *After all our plans failed, we felt very downcast. adjective.*

downcast (definition 2)

down·draft (doun′draft′), a downward movement of air: *The aircraft was caught in a sudden downdraft during a thunderstorm. noun.*

down·fall (doun′fôl′), a bringing to ruin; sudden overthrow: *the downfall of a government. Lack of practice caused the team's downfall, as they lost the championship. noun.*

down·heart·ed (doun′här′tid), discouraged; dejected; depressed. *adjective.*

down·hill (doun′hil′), **1** down the slope of a hill; downward: *I ran downhill.* **2** going or sloping downward: *a downhill race.* **1** *adverb,* **2** *adjective.*

down·pour (doun′pôr′), a heavy rainfall. *noun.*

down·right (doun′rīt′), **1** thorough; complete: *a downright fool, a downright lie.* **2** thoroughly; completely: *They were downright rude to me.* **1** *adjective,* **2** *adverb.*

down·stage (doun′stāj′), toward or at the front of the stage in a theater. *adverb, adjective.*

down·stairs (doun′sterz′ or doun′starz′), **1** down the stairs: *I hurried downstairs.* **2** on or to a lower floor: *Look downstairs for my glasses. The downstairs rooms are dark.* **3** the lower floor or floors: *The entire downstairs was flooded after the heavy rain.* **1,2** *adverb,* **2** *adjective,* **3** *noun.*

down·stream (doun′strēm′), with the current of a stream; down a stream: *It is easy to swim or row downstream. adverb, adjective.*

down·town (doun′toun′), to or in the main part or business part of a town or city: *My parents went downtown shopping. adverb, adjective.*

down·ward (doun′wərd), toward a lower place or position: *The bird swooped downward. The downward trip was a lot faster than the climb. adverb, adjective.*

down·wards (doun′wərdz), downward. *adverb.*

down·y (dou′nē), covered with soft feathers; like soft feathers: *a downy chick. adjective,* **down·i·er, down·i·est.**

dow·ry (dou′rē), the money or property that a woman brings to the man she marries. *noun, plural* **dow·ries.**

doz., dozen.

doze (dōz), to sleep lightly; be half asleep: *The old cat dozed by the fire. verb,* **doz·es, dozed, doz·ing.**

doz·en (duz′n), 12; group of 12: *We had to have dozens of chairs for the party. We will need three dozen eggs and a dozen rolls. noun, plural* **doz·ens** or *(after a number)* **doz·en.**

Dr., Doctor: *Dr. W. H. Smith.*

drab (drab), dull; not attractive: *The smoky mining town was full of drab houses. adjective,* **drab·ber, drab·best.**

draft (draft), **1** a current of air: *Close the window; there is a draft.* **2** a device for controlling a current of air: *Opening the draft of the furnace causes the fire to burn faster.* **3** a rough copy, plan, or sketch: *She made two different drafts of her book report before she handed it in in final form.* **4** to make a rough copy, plan, or sketch of: *Three members of the club drafted a set of rules to be voted on.* **5** the selection of persons for some special purpose.

a hat	i it	oi oil	ch child	a in about
ā age	ī ice	ou out	ng long	e in taken
ä far	o hot	u cup	sh she	ə = { i in pencil
e let	ō open	u̇ put	th thin	o in lemon
ē equal	ô order	ü rule	ᴛʜ then	u in circus
ėr term			zh measure	

Men needed as soldiers are supplied to the army by draft. **6** to select for some special purpose: *If no one volunteers, I will draft someone for the job.* **7** for pulling loads. A draft horse is used for pulling wagons and plows. **1-3,5** *noun,* **4,6** *verb,* **7** *adjective.* Also spelled **draught.**

draft·ee (draf tē′), a person who is drafted by law for military service. *noun.*

drafts·man (drafts′mən), a person who draws plans for buildings and machines. *noun, plural* **drafts·men.**

draft·y (draf′tē), in a current of air: *The room was drafty, so I closed the window. adjective,* **draft·i·er, draft·i·est.**

drag (drag), **1** to pull or move along heavily or slowly; pull or draw along the ground: *A team of horses dragged the big log out of the forest.* **2** to trail on the ground: *The little girl's blanket dragged behind her as she went downstairs.* **3** to go too slowly: *Time drags when you are bored.* **4** to pull a net or hook over or along for some purpose: *Police dragged the river searching for the missing swimmer.* **5** a boring person or situation: *You're a real drag—you never want to have any fun.* **1-4** *verb,* **drags, dragged, drag·ging; 5** *noun.*

drag·net (drag′net′), **1** a net pulled over the bottom of a river, pond, or lake, or along the ground. Dragnets are used to catch fish and small birds. **2** a means of catching or gathering in: *All kinds of criminals were caught in the police dragnet. noun.*

drag·on (drag′ən), a huge, fierce animal in old stories, supposed to look like a winged lizard with scales and claws, and often supposed to breathe out fire and smoke. *noun.*

dragonfly—about life-size

drag·on·fly (drag′ən flī′), a large, harmless insect with a long, slender body and two pairs of wings. It flies about very rapidly to catch flies, mosquitoes, and other insects. *noun, plural* **drag·on·flies.**

drain (drān), **1** to draw off or flow off slowly: *The water drains into the river.* **2** to draw water or other liquid from; empty or dry by draining: *The farmers drained the swamps to get more land for crops. Set the dishes here to drain.* **3** a channel or pipe for carrying off water or waste of any kind: *The drain in the sink was clogged.* **4** to take away from slowly; use up little by little: *The country's large population drained it of food, fuel, and other resources.* **5** a slow taking away; using up little by little: *A long illness can be a drain on your strength.* 1,2,4 *verb,* 3,5 *noun.*

drain·age (drā′nij), a draining; drawing off water: *The drainage of swamps improved the land near the river. noun.*

drake (drāk), a male duck. *noun.*

dra·ma (drä′mə *or* dram′ə), **1** a play such as one sees in a theater; a story written to be performed by actors. **2** the art of writing and producing plays: *He is studying drama.* **3** a part of real life that seems to have been planned like a story: *The history of America is a great and thrilling drama. noun.*

dra·mat·ic (drə mat′ik), like a drama; exciting; full of action or feeling: *The runner scored a dramatic win in a close race. adjective.*

dra·mat·i·cal·ly (drə mat′ik lē), in a dramatic manner. *adverb.*

dram·a·tist (dram′ə tist), a writer of plays. *noun.*

dram·a·tize (dram′ə tīz), **1** to arrange or present in the form of a play: *The children dramatized the story of Rip Van Winkle.* **2** to make seem exciting and thrilling: *The speaker dramatized her story with her hands and voice. verb,* **dram·a·tiz·es, dram·a·tized, dram·a·tiz·ing.**

drank (drangk). See **drink.** *I drank four glasses of milk yesterday. verb.*

drape (drāp), **1** to cover or hang with cloth falling loosely in folds, especially as a decoration: *The buildings were draped with red, white, and blue cloth.* **2** to arrange to hang loosely in folds: *I draped the cape around my shoulders.* **3** a cloth hung in folds; draperies: *There are drapes on the large windows in the living room.* 1,2 *verb,* **drapes, draped, drap·ing;** 3 *noun.*

dra·per·y (drā′pər ē), window curtains arranged in folds: *The draperies in the living room are bright red. noun, plural* **dra·per·ies.**

dras·tic (dras′tik), extreme; very forceful or harsh: *During the drought the city took the drastic step of turning the water off at certain times. adjective.*

drat (drat), to damn; condemn: *Drat that dog—he dug another hole in the yard. verb,* **drats, drat·ted, drat·ting.**

draught (draft). See **draft.** *noun, verb, adjective.*

draw (drô), **1** to pull; drag; haul: *The horses draw the wagon.* **2** to pull out; pull up; cause to come out; take out; get: *Draw a pail of water from this well. She drew ten dollars from the bank. Until you hear both sides of the argument, draw no conclusions.* **3** the act of pulling out or taking out: *She was a good marksman and was very quick on*

the draw. **4** to move: *The car drew near.* **5** to attract: *A parade always draws crowds.* **6** to make a picture or likeness of anything with pen, pencil, or chalk: *Draw a circle.* **7** to make a current of air to carry off smoke: *The chimney does not draw well.* **8** to breathe in; inhale: *Draw a deep breath.* **9** a tie. A game is a draw when neither side wins. **10** to make longer; stretch: *to draw out a rubber band.* **11** a kind of valley: *The rancher found the stray cattle grazing in a draw.* 1,2,4-8,10 *verb,* **draws, drew, drawn, draw·ing;** 3,9,11 *noun.*

draw up, 1 to write out in proper form: *Our family lawyer drew up my parents' wills.* **2** to stop: *A car drew up in front of the house.*

draw·back (drô′bak′), a disadvantage; anything which makes a situation or experience less complete or satisfying: *Our trip was interesting, but the rainy weather was a drawback. noun.*

draw·bridge (drô′brij′), a bridge that can be entirely or partly lifted, lowered, or moved to one side. In old castles drawbridges were lifted to keep out enemies. A drawbridge over a river is lifted to let boats pass. *noun.*

drawer (drôr), a box with handles, built to slide in and out of a table, desk, or bureau: *He kept his shirts in the dresser drawer. noun.*

draw·ing (drô′ing), **1** a picture, sketch, plan, or design done with pen, pencil, or crayon. **2** the making of such a sketch, plan, or design: *She is good at drawing and painting.* **3** the choosing of a ticket that awards the owner a prize: *The drawing for the bicycle will be tonight. noun.*

drawl (drôl), **1** to talk in a slow way, drawing out the vowels. **2** the speech of a person that talks in such a slow way. 1 *verb,* 2 *noun.*

drawn (drôn). See **draw.** *That old horse has drawn many loads. verb.*

draw·string (drô′string′), a string or cord threaded through the folded edge of a bag, jacket, or the like, so that it can be tightened or loosened. *noun.*

dread (dred), **1** to fear greatly what is to come; dislike to experience: *I dreaded my visits to the dentist. Cats dread water.* **2** fear, especially fear of something that will happen, or may happen: *They lived in dread of another great earthquake.* **3** causing fear; frightening: *The dread day of the trial was approaching.* 1 *verb,* 2 *noun,* 3 *adjective.*

dread·ful (dred′fəl), **1** causing dread; terrible; fearful: *The fairy tale was about a dreadful dragon.* **2** very bad; very unpleasant: *I have a dreadful cold. adjective.*

dream (drēm), **1** something thought, felt, or seen during sleep: *I had a bad dream last night.* **2** something like a dream; daydream; wish: *Sometimes I sit at my desk and have dreams of becoming a famous scientist.* **3** to think, feel, hear, or see during sleep; have dreams: *The little boy dreamed that he was flying.* **4** to imagine; think of as possible: *The sky was so clear, I never dreamed it would rain. For years she dreamed she would someday be famous.* 1,2 *noun,* 3,4 *verb,* **dreams, dreamed** or **dreamt, dream·ing.**

dream·er (drē′mər), **1** a person who has dreams. **2** a person whose ideas do not fit real conditions. *noun.*

dreamt (dremt), dreamed. See **dream.** *verb.*

dream·y (drē′mē), **1** like a dream; vague; dim: *His wonderful week at the seashore soon became just a dreamy recollection.* **2** wonderful; exciting; attractive: *They moved into a dreamy new house with a swimming pool and a tennis court. adjective,* **dream·i·er, dream·i·est.**

drear·y (drir′ē), dull; without cheer; gloomy: *A cold, rainy day is dreary. adjective,* **drear·i·er, drear·i·est.**

dredge (drej), **1** a machine with a scoop or a suction pipe for cleaning out or deepening a harbor or channel. **2** to clean out or deepen with a dredge. **1** *noun,* **2** *verb,* **dredg·es, dredged, dredg·ing.**

dregs (dregz), any small bits that settle to the bottom of a liquid: *After pouring the tea I rinsed the dregs out of the teapot. noun plural.*

drench (drench), to wet thoroughly; soak: *A heavy rain drenched the campers. verb.*

dress (dres), **1** a piece of clothing worn by women and girls. A dress is a top and skirt made as one piece or sewed together. **2** clothes; clothing: *They went to the dance in formal dress.* **3** to put clothes on: *Please dress the baby.* **4** to wear clothes properly and attractively: *Some people don't know how to dress.* **5** to make ready for use: *The butcher dressed the chicken by pulling out the feathers, cutting off the head and feet, and taking out the insides.* **6** to care for. To dress a cut or sore is to treat it with medicine and bandages. **1,2** *noun, plural* **dress·es; 3-6** *verb,* **dress·es, dressed, dress·ing.**

dress up, 1 to put on your best clothes: *They dressed up for the party.* **2** to put on a costume or unusual clothes: *I dressed up like a pirate for Halloween.*

dress·er (dres′ər), a piece of furniture with drawers for clothes and sometimes a mirror; bureau. *noun.*

dress·ing (dres′ing), **1** a medicine or a bandage, put on a wound or sore. **2** a mixture of bread crumbs and seasoning used to stuff chickens or turkeys. **3** a sauce for salads or other foods. *noun.*

dress·mak·er (dres′mā′kər), a person whose work is making women's or children's clothing. *noun.*

dress rehearsal, a rehearsal of a play with costumes and scenery just as for a regular performance.

dress·y (dres′ē), fancy and suited to special occasions such as parties and dances: *I'm going to wear something dressy for the piano recital. adjective,* **dress·i·er, dress·i·est.**

drew (drü). See **draw.** *She drew a picture. verb.*

drib·ble (drib′əl), **1** to flow or let flow in drops or small amounts; trickle: *That faucet dribbles.* **2** to drip from the mouth: *Babies dribble on their bibs.* **3** a dropping; dripping; trickle: *There's a dribble of*

milk running down your chin. **4** to move a ball along by bouncing it or giving it short kicks: *to dribble a basketball, to dribble a soccer ball.* **1,2,4** *verb,* **drib·bles, drib·bled, drib·bling; 3** *noun.*

dried (drīd). See **dry.** *I dried my hands. verb.*

dri·er (drī′ər), more dry: *This towel is drier than that one. adjective, comparative of* **dry.**

dries (drīz). See **dry.** *Dad dries the dishes. verb.*

dri·est (drī′ist), most dry: *Which is the driest towel? adjective, superlative of* **dry.**

drift (drift), **1** to carry or be carried along by currents of air or water: *A raft drifts if it is not steered.* **2** to go along without knowing or caring where one is going: *Some people have a purpose in life, but others just drift.* **3** the movement caused by currents of air or water: *the drift of an iceberg.* **4** to heap or be heaped up by the wind: *The wind is so strong it's drifting the snow.* **5** snow or sand heaped up by the wind: *After the heavy snow there were deep drifts in the yard.* **1,2,4** *verb,* **3,5** *noun.*

drift·wood (drift′wu̇d′), wood carried along by water or washed ashore from the water. *noun.*

driftwood

drill (dril), **1** a tool or machine for boring holes. **2** to bore a hole with a drill; use a drill: *I drilled a hole in the wall. Several wells were drilled before oil was found.* **3** to teach by having the learner do a thing over and over: *The sergeant drilled the new soldiers.* **4** a teaching or training by having the learners do a thing over and over for practice: *The teacher gave the class plenty of drill in arithmetic.* **1,4** *noun,* **2,3** *verb.*

drink (dringk), **1** to swallow anything liquid, such as water or milk: *A person must drink water to stay alive.* **2** a liquid swallowed or to be swallowed: *Water is a good drink to quench one's thirst.* **3** a portion of a liquid: *Please give me a drink of milk.*

4 to suck up; absorb: *The dry soil drank up the rain.* **5** alcoholic liquor. **6** to drink alcoholic liquor. 1,4,6 *verb*, **drinks, drank, drunk, drink·ing;** 2,3,5 *noun.*

drink in, to take in with eagerness and pleasure: *Our ears drank in the music.*

drip (drip), **1** to fall or let fall in drops: *Rain drips from an umbrella.* **2** a falling in drops: *the drip of water from a leaky faucet.* **3** to be so wet that drops fall: *My forehead was dripping with sweat.* 1,3 *verb*, **drips, dripped, drip·ping;** 2 *noun.*

drive (drīv), **1** to make go: *Drive the dog away. Drive the nails into the board. The wind drives the windmill. The noise of the drums almost drove me mad.* **2** to control the movement of an automobile or other vehicle: *Are you old enough to drive? I'd like to drive a truck.* **3** to go or carry in an automobile or other vehicle: *We want to drive through the mountains on the way home. She drove us to the station.* **4** a trip in an automobile or other vehicle: *On Sunday we took a drive in the country.* **5** a road: *He built a drive from the street to his house.* **6** to force; urge on: *Hunger drove them to steal.* **7** a strong force; push; pressure: *She has a drive to succeed.* **8** to bring about or obtain by cleverness or force: *He drove a good bargain at the store.* **9** a special effort: *The town had a drive to get money for charity.* **10** to work hard or compel to work hard: *The workers said their boss drove them too hard.* **11** a very hard, fast hit: *The batter's drive went over the fence.* 1-3,6,8,10 *verb*, **drives, drove, driv·en, driv·ing;** 4,5,7,9,11 *noun.*

drive-in (drīv′in′), **1** arranged and equipped so that customers may drive in and be served or entertained while staying in their cars: *a drive-in restaurant, a drive-in bank.* **2** a place arranged and equipped this way. 1 *adjective*, 2 *noun.*

driv·en (driv′ən). See **drive.** *Mom has just driven to work. verb.*

driv·er (drī′vər), a person who drives an automobile or other vehicle. *noun.*

drive·way (drīv′wā′), a road leading from a house or garage to the street. *noun.*

driz·zle (driz′əl), **1** to rain gently, in very small drops like mist. **2** very small drops of rain like mist. 1 *verb*, **driz·zles, driz·zled, driz·zling;** 2 *noun.*

droll (drōl), odd and amusing; laughable: *We smiled at the monkey's droll tricks. adjective.*

drom·e·dar·y (drom′ə der′ē), a swift camel with one hump, used for riding in Arabia and northern Africa. *noun, plural* **drom·e·dar·ies.** See Word History.

drone (drōn), **1** a male bee that fertilizes the queen. Drones have no stings, and do no work. **2** to make a deep, continuous humming sound: *Bees droned among the flowers.* **3** a deep, continuous humming sound: *the drone of mosquitoes, the drone of a far-off motorboat.* **4** to talk or say with the same dull voice: *Several people in the audience fell asleep as the speaker droned on.* 1,3 *noun*, 2,4 *verb*, **drones, droned, dron·ing.**

drool (drül), to let saliva run from the mouth as a baby does. *verb.*

droop (drüp), to hang down; bend down: *Flowers soon droop if they are not put in water. His eyelids drooped with fatigue. verb.*

drop (drop), **1** a small amount of liquid in a round shape: *a drop of rain, a drop of blood.* **2** a small amount of something shaped like a drop: *a cough drop.* **3** **drops,** liquid medicine given in drops: *eye drops, nose drops.* **4** to fall or let fall: *Rain dropped from the trees. Did you drop this package?* **5** a sudden fall: *a drop in temperature, a drop in prices.* **6** the distance down; a sudden fall in level; length of a fall: *From the top of the cliff to the water is a drop of 200 feet.* **7** to cause to fall: *He dropped his attacker with a single punch.* **8** to fall or cause to fall dead, wounded, or tired out: *The hunter dropped the deer with a single shot. After working all day I was ready to drop.* **9** to lower: *His voice dropped to a whisper.* **10** to let go; dismiss: *Members who do not pay their dues will be dropped from the club.* **11** to leave out; omit: *Drop the "e" in "drive" before adding "ing."* **12** to stop; end: *The matter is not important; let it drop.* **13** to send: *Drop me a note from camp.* **14** to let out from an automobile, ship, or carriage: *Drop me at the corner of Main Street.* 1-3,5,6 *noun*, 4,7-14 *verb*, **drops, dropped, drop·ping.**

drop in, to visit informally: *Drop in and see me.*

drop off, to go to sleep: *I dropped off soon after going to bed.*

drop out, to leave school before completing a course or term.

drop·let (drop′lit), a tiny drop. *noun.*

drop·out (drop′out′), a student who leaves school or college before completing a course or a term. *noun.*

drop·per (drop′ər), a narrow glass or plastic tube

Word History

dromedary *Dromedary* comes from a Greek word meaning "running." This word was used to describe a certain kind of very swift camel.

dromedary—7½ feet (2½ meters) high at the hump

open at one end with a hollow rubber cap at the other end. It is used to put drops of liquid into the eyes, nose, or throat. *noun.*

drought (drout), a long period of dry weather; continued lack of rain. *noun.*

drought

a hat	**i** it	**oi** oil	**ch** child		a in about
ā age	**ī** ice	**ou** out	**ng** long		e in taken
ä far	**o** hot	**u** cup	**sh** she	ə =	i in pencil
e let	**ō** open	**u̇** put	**th** thin		o in lemon
ē equal	**ô** order	**ü** rule	**ᵮH** then		u in circus
ėr term			**zh** measure		

drouth (drouth), a drought. *noun.*

drove[1] (drōv). See **drive.** *We drove two hundred miles today. verb.*

drove[2] (drōv), **1** a group of cattle, sheep, or hogs moving or driven along together; herd; flock: *The rancher sent a drove of cattle to market.* **2** many people moving along together; crowd: *People rushed to the main square in droves. noun.*

drown (droun), **1** to die under water or other liquid because of lack of air to breathe: *We almost drowned when our boat overturned.* **2** to kill by keeping under water or other liquid: *The flood drowned many cattle in the lowlands.* **3** to be stronger than; keep from being heard: *The boat's whistle drowned out what she was trying to tell us. verb.*

drowse (drouz), to be half asleep: *She drowsed, but did not quite fall asleep. verb,* **drows·es, drowsed, drows·ing.**

drow·sy (drou′zē), **1** sleepy; half asleep: *Sitting at my desk after a big lunch, I began to feel drowsy.* **2** making one sleepy: *It was a warm, quiet, drowsy afternoon. adjective,* **drow·si·er, drow·si·est.**

drudge (druj), a person who does hard, tiresome, or disagreeable work. *noun.*

drudg·er·y (druj′ər ē), any work that is hard, without interest, or disagreeable: *I think that washing dishes is drudgery. noun.*

drug (drug), **1** a substance used to treat, prevent, or cure disease. Penicillin and aspirin are drugs. **2** a substance taken for its effect and not for medical reasons. Such drugs speed up or slow down the activity of the body or affect the senses. Heroin and alcohol are drugs. **3** to give drugs to, often drugs that are harmful or cause sleep: *The spy drugged the guard and then stole the secret code.* 1,2 *noun,* 3 *verb,* **drugs, drugged, drug·ging.**

drug·gist (drug′ist), **1** a person who is trained to fill doctors' prescriptions; pharmacist. **2** a person who sells drugs or other things in a drugstore. *noun.*

drug·store (drug′stôr′), a store that sells drugs and other medicines and often such things as soft drinks, cosmetics, and magazines. *noun.*

drum (drum), **1** a musical instrument that makes a sound when it is beaten. A drum is hollow with a cover stretched tight over the ends. **2** a sound made by, or as if by, a drum: *I heard the drum of rain on the roof.* **3** to play the drum: *I drum in the school band.* **4** to beat, tap, or strike again and again: *Stop drumming on the table with your fingers.* **5** to teach or drive into one's head by repeating over and over: *Arithmetic had to be drummed into me because I couldn't understand it.* **6** a container or other thing shaped somewhat like a drum: *an oil drum.* 1,2,6 *noun,* 3-5 *verb,* **drums, drummed, drum·ming.**

drum major

drum major, a man who leads a marching band, often twirling a baton.

drum ma·jor·ette (drum′ mā′jə ret′), a girl or woman who leads parades, twirling a baton.

drum·mer (drum′ər), a person who plays a drum. *noun.*

drum·stick (drum′stik′), **1** a stick for beating a drum. **2** the lower half of the leg of a cooked chicken or turkey. *noun.*

drunk (drungk), **1** having had too many alcoholic drinks. People who are drunk may have trouble speaking, thinking, or acting normally. **2** a person who is drunk. **3** See **drink.** *He has drunk several glasses of milk already.* 1 *adjective,* 2 *noun,* 3 *verb.*

drunk·ard (drung′kərd), a person who is often drunk; person who drinks too much alcoholic liquor. *noun.*

drunk·en (drung′kən), **1** drunk: *A drunken person should not drive a car.* **2** caused by being drunk: *a drunken argument. adjective.*

dry (drī), **1** not wet; not moist: *Dust is dry. The paint is dry now.* **2** to make or become dry: *We washed and dried the dishes after dinner. Clothes dry in the sun.* **3** having little or no rain: *Arizona has a dry climate.* **4** empty of water or other liquid: *That pond is dry in the summer.* **5** thirsty; wanting a drink: *I am dry after that hike.* **6** not under, in, or on water: *He was glad to be on dry land and away from the swamp.* **7** not interesting; dull: *A book full of facts and figures is dry.* 1,3-7 *adjective,* **dri·er, dri·est;** 2 *verb,* **dries, dried, dry·ing.**

dry cell, an electric cell in which the chemicals producing the electric current are made into a paste. A flashlight battery is a dry cell.

dry-clean (drī′klēn′), to clean clothes with a chemical cleaning fluid instead of water. *verb.*

dry·er (drī′ər), a machine that removes water by heat or air: *a clothes dryer, a hair dryer. noun.*

dry goods, cloth, ribbons, laces, and the like.

dry ice, a very cold, white solid formed when carbon dioxide is greatly compressed and then cooled. It is used for keeping ice cream and other things cold, because it changes from a solid back to a gas without becoming liquid.

du·al (dü′əl *or* dyü′əl), consisting of two parts; double; twofold: *The car had dual controls, one set for the learner and one for the teacher. adjective.*

du·bi·ous (dü′bē əs *or* dyü′bē əs), doubtful; uncertain. *adjective.*

dubious—She was **dubious** about the way she looked in the new hat.

duch·ess (duch′is), **1** the wife or widow of a duke. **2** a woman whose rank is equal to that of a duke. *noun, plural* **duch·ess·es.**

duck¹ (duk), **1** a wild or tame swimming bird with a flat bill, short neck, short legs, and webbed feet. **2** a female duck. The male is called a drake. **3** the flesh of a duck used for food: *roast duck. noun.*

duck² (duk), **1** to dip or plunge suddenly under water and out again: *The children in the pool were ducking each other.* **2** to lower the head or bend the body quickly to keep from being hit or seen: *She ducked to avoid a low branch.* **3** a sudden lowering of the head or bending of the body to keep from being hit or seen. 1,2 *verb,* 3 *noun.*

duck·ling (duk′ling), a young duck. *noun.*

duct (dukt), **1** a tube, pipe, or channel for carrying liquid or air. **2** a tube in the body for carrying a bodily fluid: *tear ducts. noun.*

duds (dudz), clothes: *We packed our duds and left the camp. noun plural.*

due (dü *or* dyü), **1** owed as a debt; owing; to be paid as a right: *The money due her for her work was paid today. Respect is due to older people.* **2** a person's right; what is owed to a person: *Courtesy is his due while he is your guest.* **3 dues,** the amount of money it costs to be a member of a club; fee or tax for some purpose: *Members who do not pay dues will be suspended from the club.* **4** looked for; expected; promised to come or to do: *The train is due at noon. Your report is due tomorrow.* **5** straight; exactly; directly: *The ship sailed due west.* 1,4 *adjective,* 2,3 *noun,* 5 *adverb.*

due to, 1 caused by: *The accident was due to the driver's carelessness.* **2** because of: *The game was called off due to rain.*

du·el (dü′əl *or* dyü′əl), **1** a formal fight to settle a quarrel. Duels are fought with pistols or swords between two persons in the presence of two others called seconds. **2** any fight or contest between two opponents: *The lawyers fought a duel of wits in the court of law.* **3** to fight a duel. 1,2 *noun,* 3 *verb.*

du·et (dü et′ *or* dyü et′), **1** a piece of music for two voices or instruments. **2** two singers or players performing together. *noun.*

duf·fel bag (duf′əl bag′), **1** a large canvas sack for carrying clothing and other belongings, used by campers and soldiers. **2** any small bag made of a tough material.
[*Duffel* was borrowed from a Dutch word meaning "a coarse, woolen cloth." The cloth was called this because it was first made in Duffel, a town in Belgium.]

duffel bag (definition 1) The soldier carried his belongings in a **duffel bag.**

dug (dug). See **dig**. *The dog dug a hole in the ground. The potatoes have all been dug.* verb.

dug·out (dug′out′), **1** a rough shelter or dwelling formed by digging into the side of a hill or trench. During war, soldiers use dugouts for protection against bullets and bombs. **2** a small shelter at the side of a baseball field, used by players not on the field. **3** a boat made by hollowing out a large log. noun.

duke (dük *or* dyük), a nobleman ranking just below a prince. noun.

dull (dul), **1** not sharp or pointed: *It is hard to cut with a dull knife.* **2** not bright or clear: *dull eyes, a dull color, a dull day.* **3** slow in understanding; stupid: *a dull mind. A dull person often fails to get the meaning of a joke.* **4** not felt sharply: *the dull pain of a bruise.* **5** not interesting; tiresome; boring: *a dull book.* **6** not active: *The fur coat business is usually dull in summer.* **7** to make or become dull: *Chopping wood dulled the blade of the ax.* 1-6 *adjective,* 7 *verb.*

dul·ly (dul′ē), in a dull manner. adverb.

du·ly (dü′lē *or* dyü′lē), properly; as due; in a proper way; rightly; suitably: *The documents were duly signed before a lawyer.* adverb.

dumb (dum), **1** not able to speak: *Even intelligent animals are dumb.* **2** unwilling to speak; silent; not speaking. **3** not intelligent; stupid; silly: *Forgetting your homework is a dumb thing to do.* adjective.

dumb·bell (dum′bel′), a short bar of wood or iron with large, heavy, round ends. It is lifted or swung around to exercise the muscles of the arms or back. noun.

dumb·found (dum′found′). See **dumfound**. verb.

dum·found (dum′found′), to amaze and make unable to speak; confuse: *We were dumfounded by the complicated instructions.* verb. Also spelled **dumbfound**.

dum·my (dum′ē), **1** a life-size figure of a person, used to display clothing in store windows, to shoot at in rifle practice, to tackle in football, or in other ways. **2** a stupid person. **3** made to look like the real thing; imitation: *We had a sword fight with dummy swords made of wood.* 1,2 *noun, plural* **dum·mies;** 3 *adjective.*

dump (dump), **1** to empty out; throw down: *The truck dumped the coal on the sidewalk.* **2** a place for throwing rubbish: *Garbage is taken to the city dump.* **3** a dirty, shabby, or untidy place. 1 *verb,* 2,3 *noun.*

dump·ling (dump′ling), a rounded piece of dough, boiled or steamed and usually served with meat. noun.

dumps (dumps). **in the dumps,** feeling sad: *She was in the dumps because her bike was broken.* noun plural.

dunce (duns), a person who is stupid or slow to learn. noun.

dune (dün *or* dyün), a mound or ridge of loose sand heaped up by the wind. noun.

dune buggy, a motor vehicle with very large tires, used on sand.

a hat	**i** it	**oi** oil	**ch** child	a in about
ā age	**ī** ice	**ou** out	**ng** long	e in taken
ä far	**o** hot	**u** cup	**sh** she	ə = i in pencil
e let	**ō** open	**u̇** put	**th** thin	o in lemon
ē equal	**ô** order	**ü** rule	**ŦH** then	u in circus
ėr term			**zh** measure	

dun·ga·ree (dung′gə rē′), **1** a coarse cotton cloth, used for work clothes. **2 dungarees,** trousers or clothing made of this cloth. noun.

dun·geon (dun′jən), a dark underground room or cell to keep prisoners in. noun.

dunk (dungk), **1** to dip food into a liquid: *She likes to dunk doughnuts in coffee.* **2** (in basketball) to throw the ball down through the basket from above the rim. verb.

dupe (düp *or* dyüp), **1** a person easily deceived or tricked. **2** to deceive; trick: *The dishonest merchant tried to dupe us.* 1 *noun,* 2 *verb,* **dupes, duped, dup·ing.**

du·pli·cate (dü′plə kit *or* dyü′plə kit *for 1 and 2;* dü′plə kāt *or* dyü′plə kāt *for 3*), **1** exactly like something else: *We have duplicate keys for the front door.* **2** one of two things exactly alike; exact copy: *He mailed the letter, but kept a duplicate.* **3** to make an exact copy of; repeat exactly: *Duplicate the picture so that we may both have copies of it.* 1 *adjective,* 2 *noun,* 3 *verb,* **du·pli·cates, du·pli·cat·ed, du·pli·cat·ing.**

du·pli·ca·tion (dü′plə kā′shən *or* dyü′plə kā′shən), **1** a duplicating or being duplicated: *Duplication of effort is a waste of time.* **2** a duplicate copy: *Her answers were a duplication of her sister's.* noun.

dur·a·ble (dur′ə bəl *or* dyur′ə bəl), **1** able to withstand wear or decay: *Work clothes are made of durable fabric.* **2** lasting a long time: *Another war destroyed all hopes of a durable peace between the two nations.* adjective.

du·ra·tion (du̇ rā′shən *or* dyu̇ rā′shən), length of time; time during which anything continues: *The storm was sudden and of short duration.* noun.

dunes

dur·ing (dùr′ing *or* dyùr′ing), **1** through the whole time of: *We played during the afternoon.* **2** at some time in; in the course of: *Come sometime during the day.* preposition.

dusk (dusk), the time just before dark: *We saw the evening star at dusk.* noun.

dusk·y (dus′kē), **1** somewhat dark; dark-colored. **2** dim; obscure: *the dusky light of the late afternoon.* adjective, **dusk·i·er, dusk·i·est.**

dust (dust), **1** fine, dry earth: *Dust lay thick on the road.* **2** any fine powder: *The old papers had turned to dust.* **3** to get dust off; brush or wipe the dust from: *I dusted the furniture.* 1,2 *noun,* 3 *verb.*

dust·pan (dust′pan′), a wide, flat pan with a handle, onto which dust can be swept from the floor. noun.

dust·y (dus′tē), covered with dust; filled with dust: *He found some dusty old books in the attic.* adjective, **dust·i·er, dust·i·est.**

Dutch (duch), **1** of or having something to do with the Netherlands, its people, or their language. **2** the people of the Netherlands. **3** their language. 1 *adjective,* 2 *noun plural,* 3 *noun singular.*

go Dutch, to have each person pay his or her own bill: *When we stopped for ice cream, we went Dutch.*

Word Source

Dutch is the official language of the Netherlands. The following words have come into English from Dutch:

boss	dock[1]	pickle	slim	waffle
cookie	easel	skate	spook	wagon
cruise	gruff	sled	spool	walrus
deck	iceberg	sleigh	tub	yacht

du·ti·ful (dü′tə fəl *or* dyü′tə fəl), doing your duty; obedient: *They are dutiful children, always helping their parents with the housework.* adjective.

du·ty (dü′tē *or* dyü′tē), **1** the thing that is right to do; what a person ought to do: *It is your duty to obey the laws.* **2** an obligation: *A sense of duty sometimes makes people do what they think is right even when they don't want to do it.* **3** the thing that one must do in one's work: *Her duties at the post office are to sort and to weigh packages.* **4** a tax, especially on articles brought into a country: *There is a duty on perfume brought into the United States.* noun, plural **du·ties.**

on duty, working at one's job or position.

dwarf (dwôrf), **1** a person, animal, or plant much smaller than the usual size for its kind. **2** in fairy tales, an ugly little man with magic power. **3** to cause to seem small by contrast or by distance. 1,2 *noun,* plural **dwarfs, dwarves** (dwôrvz); 3 *verb.*

dwell (dwel), to live; make one's home: *They dwell in the country but work in the city.* verb, **dwells, dwelt** *or* **dwelled, dwell·ing.**

dwell on, to think, speak, or write about for a long time: *My mind dwelt on my pleasant day in the country.*

dwell·er (dwel′ər), a person who dwells or lives: *A city dweller lives in a city.* noun.

dwell·ing (dwel′ing), a house; place in which one lives. noun.

dwelt (dwelt). See **dwell.** *We dwelt there for a long time. We have dwelt in the country for years.* verb.

dwin·dle (dwin′dl), to become smaller and smaller; shrink: *During the storm the trapper's supply of food dwindled day by day.* verb, **dwin·dles, dwin·dled, dwin·dling.**

dye (dī), **1** a substance that can be mixed with water and used to color cloth, hair, and other things. **2** a color produced by such a substance: *A good dye will not fade.* **3** to color or stain: *I dyed my shirt red.* 1,2 *noun,* 3 *verb,* **dyes, dyed, dye·ing.**

dy·ing (dī′ing), **1** about to die; ceasing to live: *a dying old woman.* **2** coming to an end: *the dying year.* **3** of death; at death: *dying words.* **4** See **die**[1]. *The storm is dying down.* 1-3 *adjective,* 4 *verb.*

dyke (dīk). See **dike.** noun.

dy·nam·ic (dī nam′ik), active; forceful. *adjective.*

dy·na·mite (dī′nə mīt), **1** a powerful explosive most commonly used in blasting rocks. **2** to blow up with dynamite. 1 *noun,* 2 *verb,* **dy·na·mites, dy·na·mit·ed, dy·na·mit·ing.**

[*Dynamite* was made up from a Greek word meaning "force" by Alfred Nobel, a Swedish chemist who lived from 1833 to 1896. He invented the explosive.]

dy·na·mo (dī′nə mō), a machine that makes electricity; generator. *noun,* plural **dy·na·mos.**

dy·nas·ty (dī′nə stē), a series of rulers who belong to the same family. *noun,* plural **dy·nas·ties.**

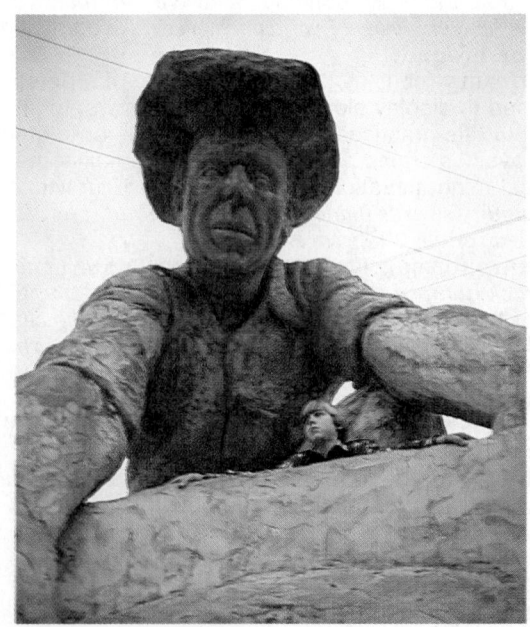

dwarf (definition 3)
The statue **dwarfs** the child.

E e

a hat	**i** it	**oi** oil	**ch** child		⎧ a in about
ā age	**ī** ice	**ou** out	**ng** long		⎪ e in taken
ä far	**o** hot	**u** cup	**sh** she	**ə** = ⎨ i in pencil
e let	**ō** open	**u̇** put	**th** thin		⎪ o in lemon
ē equal	**ô** order	**ü** rule	**ᴛʜ** then		⎩ u in circus
ėr term			**zh** measure		

E or **e** (ē), the fifth letter of the English alphabet. There are two *e*'s in *see*. *noun, plural* **E's** or **e's**.

E or **E.,** **1** east. **2** eastern.

each (ēch), **1** every: *Each child has a desk.* **2** every one: *Each of the students has a pencil.* **3** for each one; apiece: *These pens are a quarter each.* **1** *adjective,* **2** *pronoun,* **3** *adverb.*

each other, one another: *The two friends saw each other at the playground.*

ea·ger (ē′gər), wanting very much: *The children are eager to go the picnic. adjective.*

ea·gle (ē′gəl), a large bird that can see far and has powerful wings. The bald eagle is the symbol of the United States. *noun.*

ear[1] (ir), **1** the part of the body by which people and animals hear. **2** the sense of hearing: *Her voice is pleasing to the ear.* **3** the ability to hear small differences in sounds: *She has a good ear for music. noun.*

be all ears, to listen in a very eager way; pay careful attention: *The children were all ears while their teacher read them the exciting story.*

ear[1] (definition 1)

ear[2] (ir), the part of certain plants on which the grains grow. The grains of corn are formed on ears. *noun.*

ear·ache (ir′āk′), pain in the ear. *noun.*

ear·drum (ir′drum′), a thin, skinlike layer that stretches across the middle ear. It vibrates when sound waves strike it. *noun.*

earl (ėrl), a British nobleman. *noun.*

ear·ly (ėr′lē), **1** in the beginning; in the first part: *The sun is not hot early in the day.* **2** before the usual time: *We have an early dinner today. Please come early. adverb, adjective,* **ear·li·er, ear·li·est.**

ear·muffs (ir′mufs′), a pair of coverings worn over the ears in cold weather to keep them warm. *noun plural.*

earn (ėrn), **1** to get in return for work or service; be paid: *She earns $175 a week.* **2** to win; bring or get as deserved: *Her hard work earned her the respect of her teachers. verb.*

ear·nest (ėr′nist), strong and firm in purpose; eager and serious: *The earnest pupil tried very hard to do his best. adjective.*

in earnest, determined or sincere; serious: *She is in earnest about becoming a famous painter.*

earn·ings (ėr′ningz), money earned; wages; profits. *noun plural.*

ear·phone (ir′fōn′), a device placed over or in the ear to carry sound directly from a radio, phonograph, or the like. *noun.*

ear·ring (ir′ring′), jewelry for the ear. *noun.*

ear·shot (ir′shot′), the distance a sound can be heard; range of hearing: *We shouted, but he was out of earshot and could not hear our voices. noun.*

earth (ėrth), **1** Also, **Earth.** the planet on which we live. **2** ground: *The earth in the garden is soft. Our environment is made up of the earth, the sea, and the sky. noun.*

earth·en (ėr′thən), **1** made of baked clay: *Earthen jugs were dug up at the site of the ancient town.* **2** made of earth: *The old cabin had an earthen floor. adjective.*

earth·en·ware (ėr′thən wer′ or ėr′thən war′), dishes or containers made of baked clay. Pottery is earthenware. *noun.*

earth·ly (ėrth′lē), **1** on earth; not heavenly: *She left all her earthly goods to a niece.* **2** possible: *That junk is of no earthly use. adjective.*

earth·quake (ėrth′kwāk′), a shaking or sliding of the ground, caused by the sudden movement of rock far beneath the earth's surface. Earthquakes can cause great destruction. *noun.*

earthquake—houses damaged by the San Francisco **earthquake** in 1906

earth·worm (ėrth′wėrm′), a reddish-brown or grayish worm that lives in the soil; angleworm. Earthworms help loosen the soil. *noun.*

ease (ēz), **1** freedom from pain or trouble; comfort: *When school is out, I am going to live a life of ease for a whole week.* **2** to make free from pain or trouble: *Her kind words eased my worried mind.* **3** very little need to try hard: *You can do this lesson with ease.* **4** to make less; lighten: *Some medicines ease pain.* **5** to move slowly and carefully: *He eased the big box through the narrow door.* **1,3** *noun,* **2,4,5** *verb,* **eas·es, eased, eas·ing.**

ea·sel (ē′zəl), a stand for a picture or blackboard. *noun.*

Word History

easel *Easel* comes from a Dutch word meaning "donkey." It was called this because it has legs and serves as a support.

---

eas·i·ly (ē′zə lē), **1** in an easy manner; without trying hard: *The simple tasks were quickly and easily done.* **2** without pain or trouble; comfortably: *A few hours after the operation, the patient was resting easily.* **3** surely; without question: *He is easily the best player on the field.* **4** probably: *She is a good writer who works hard and may easily become famous. adverb.*

east (ēst), **1** the direction of the sunrise. **2** toward the east; farther toward the east: *Walk east to find the road.* **3** coming from the east: *an east wind.* **4** in the east: *the east wing of a house.* **5** the part of any country toward the east. **6 the East, a** the eastern part of the United States. **b** the countries in Asia: *China and Japan are in the East.* **1,5,6** *noun,* **3,4** *adjective,* **2** *adverb.*

east of, further east than: *Ohio is east of Indiana.*

Eas·ter (ē′stər), the yearly Christian celebration of Jesus' rising from the dead. Easter comes on a Sunday between March 22 and April 25. *noun.* [*Easter* was named for an ancient goddess of the dawn. Her festival was celebrated in the spring. Later on, the Christian celebration replaced the earlier festival, although the original name was kept.]

east·er·ly (ē′stər lē), **1** toward the east: *We walked in an easterly direction.* **2** from the east: *an easterly wind. adjective, adverb.*

east·ern (ē′stərn), **1** toward the east: *an eastern trip.* **2** from the east: *eastern tourists.* **3** of or in the east: *eastern schools.* **4 Eastern, a** of or in the eastern part of the United States. **b** of or in the countries in Asia. *adjective.*

East Germany, a former country in Europe.

East In·dies (ēst′ in′dēz), the islands off the coast of southeast Asia.

east·ward (ēst′wərd), toward the east; east: *to walk eastward, an eastward slope. adverb, adjective.*

east·wards (ēst′wərdz), eastward. *adverb.*

eas·y (ē′zē), **1** not hard to do or get: *Washing a few dishes was easy work.* **2** free from pain, difficulty, or worry; pleasant: *The wealthy family led an easy life.* **3** not strict or harsh: *We bought our new car on easy terms of payment. adjective,* **eas·i·er, eas·i·est.**

take it easy, to act calmly; move slowly and carefully: *She asked her busy friend to relax and take it easy.*

easy chair, a comfortable chair, usually having arms and cushions.

eas·y·go·ing (ē′zē gō′ing), taking matters easily; not worrying: *The new teacher is pleasantly easygoing and relaxed with the class. adjective.*

eat (ēt), **1** to chew and swallow food: *Cows eat grass and grain.* **2** to have a meal: *Where shall we eat?* **3** to destroy as if by eating: *Rust ate away part of the car's fender. Buying candy every day ate up our allowance. verb,* **eats, ate, eat·en, eat·ing.**

eat·en (ēt′n). See eat. *Have you eaten your dinner? verb.*

eaves (ēvz), the lower edge of a roof that stands out a little from the side of a building. *noun plural.*

EAVES

eaves·drop (ēvz′drop′), to listen to talk that you are not supposed to hear: *She could not help eavesdropping on the noisy conversation in the next room. verb,* **eaves·drops, eaves·dropped, eaves·drop·ping.** [*Eavesdrop* was formed from *eavesdropper,* in the earlier meaning "one who stands under the eaves to listen." The image is that of a person standing close to a house, under the eaves, listening to conversation inside.]

eaves·drop·per (ēvz′drop′ər), a person who eavesdrops. *noun.*

ebb (eb), **1** a flowing of the tide away from the

shore; fall of the tide. **2** to flow out; fall: *We waded farther out as the tide ebbed.* **3** to grow less or weaker; decline: *His courage began to ebb as he neared the haunted house.* **1** *noun,* **2,3** *verb.*

eb·on·y (eb′ə nē), a hard, black wood, used for the black keys of a piano and for ornamental woodwork. *noun.*

ec·cen·tric (ek sen′trik), **1** out of the ordinary; not usual; peculiar; odd: *Wearing a fur coat in hot weather is eccentric behavior.* **2** a person who behaves in an unusual manner. **1** *adjective,* **2** *noun.*

ech·o (ek′ō), **1** a repeated sound. You hear an echo when a sound you make bounces back from a distant hill or wall so that you hear it again. **2** to be heard again: *The gunshot echoed through the valley.* **3** to say or do what another says or does: *Small children sometimes echo their parents' words and actions.* **1** *noun, plural* **ech·oes;** **2,3** *verb.*

e·clipse (i klips′), **1** the blocking of light from one heavenly body by another heavenly body. An eclipse of the sun occurs when the moon passes between the sun and the earth. An eclipse of the moon occurs when the earth passes between the sun and the moon. **2** to cut off or dim the light from; darken. **1** *noun,* **2** *verb,* **e·clips·es, e·clipsed, e·clips·ing.**

e·col·o·gist (ē kol′ə jist), a person who is an expert in ecology. *noun.*

e·col·o·gy (ē kol′ə jē), the science that deals with the relation of living things to their environment and to each other. Ecology is a branch of biology. *noun.*

e·co·nom·ic (ē′kə nom′ik *or* ek′ə nom′ik), of or about economics: *Rising prices and growing unemployment caused serious economic problems. adjective.*

e·co·nom·i·cal (ē′kə nom′ə kəl *or* ek′ə nom′ə kəl), avoiding waste; thrifty; saving: *An economical shopper tries to buy things on sale. adjective.*

e·co·nom·ics (ē kə nom′iks *or* ek′ə nom′iks), the science of how people produce money, goods, and services, how they distribute them among themselves, and how they use them. *noun.*

e·con·o·mize (i kon′ə mīz), to be thrifty or economical: *We can economize on household expenses by turning off lights when we don't need them on. verb,* **e·con·o·miz·es, e·con·o·mized, e·con·o·miz·ing.**

e·con·o·my (i kon′ə mē), **1** a making the most of what one has; thrift; the use of something without any waste: *Because of our economy in buying food and clothes, we were able to save enough money for our vacation.* **2** the way a country, area, or business manages its resources: *Under the new administration, the country's economy improved greatly. noun, plural* **e·con·o·mies.**

ec·sta·sy (ek′stə sē), a feeling of very great joy; delightful thrill: *The little girl was speechless with ecstasy over her birthday present. noun, plural* **ec·sta·sies.**

ec·stat·ic (ek stat′ik), very joyful; full of delight:

a hat	**i** it	**oi** oil	**ch** child	a in about
ā age	**ī** ice	**ou** out	**ng** long	e in taken
ä far	**o** hot	**u** cup	**sh** she	ə = { i in pencil
e let	**ō** open	**u̇** put	**th** thin	o in lemon
ē equal	**ô** order	**ü** rule	**͋H** then	u in circus
ėr term			**zh** measure	

An ecstatic look of pleasure came over their faces. adjective.

Ec·ua·dor (ek′wə dôr), a country in northwestern South America. *noun.*

ed·dy (ed′ē), a small whirlpool or whirlwind; water, air, or smoke whirling around. *noun, plural* **ed·dies.**

edge (ej), **1** the line or place where something begins or ends: *A page of notebook paper has four edges.* **2** the thin side that cuts: *The knife had a very sharp edge.* **3** to put an edge on; form an edge on: *The gardener edged the path with white stones.* **4** to move little by little: *She edged her way through the crowd.* **1,2** *noun,* **3,4** *verb,* **edg·es, edged, edg·ing.**

edge·ways (ej′wāz′), with the edge forward; in the direction of the edge. *adverb.*

ed·i·ble (ed′ə bəl), fit to eat: *Toadstools are not edible. adjective.*

ed·it (ed′it), **1** to prepare for publication by correcting errors and checking facts: *The teacher is editing famous speeches for use in schoolbooks.* **2** to have charge of a publication and decide what will be printed in it: *Two girls were chosen to edit the school paper. verb.*

e·di·tion (i dish′ən), **1** all the copies of a book, newspaper, or magazine printed just alike and at or near the same time: *The second edition of the book corrected many errors found in the first edition.* **2** the form in which a book is printed: *This edition of "Alice in Wonderland" has large print and pictures. noun.*

ed·i·tor (ed′ə tər), a person who edits: *He is the editor of our school paper. noun.*

ed·i·to·ri·al (ed′ə tôr′ē əl), **1** an article in a newspaper or magazine giving the editor's or publisher's opinion on some subject. **2** a radio or television program giving the station manager's opinion on some subject. **3** of an editor: *editorial work.* **1,2** *noun,* **3** *adjective.*

Ed·mon·ton (ed′mən tən), the capital of Alberta, Canada. *noun.*

ed·u·cate (ej′ə kāt), to teach, train, or provide schooling for: *The job of teachers is to educate the people. verb,* **ed·u·cates, ed·u·cat·ed, ed·u·cat·ing.**

ed·u·ca·tion (ej′ə kā′shən), **1** training; schooling: *In the United States, public schools offer an education to all children.* **2** the knowledge and abilities gained through training: *A person with education knows how to speak, write, and read well. noun.* [*Education* comes from a Latin word meaning "a bringing up" or "a leading out."]

ed·u·ca·tion·al (ej′ə kā′shə nəl), **1** of education:

The educational goals of our school are high.
2 providing education: *Our science class saw an educational motion picture about wild animals.* adjective.

eel (ēl), a long, slippery fish shaped like a snake. *noun, plural* **eels** or **eel.**

eer·ie (ir′ē), strange; weird; causing fear: *A dark, eerie old house stood at the end of the driveway.* *adjective,* **eer·i·er, eer·i·est.**

eerie—an **eerie** face

ef·face (ə fās′), to rub out; blot out; do away with; destroy; wipe out: *The writing on many old monuments has been effaced by time.* verb, **ef·fac·es, ef·faced, ef·fac·ing.**

ef·fect (ə fekt′), **1** something made to happen by a person or thing; result: *The effect of the gale was to overturn several boats.* **2** to bring about; make happen: *Machines have effected many changes in the way we live.* **3** the power to produce results; force: *The medicine had the immediate effect of reducing pain.* **1,3** *noun,* **2** *verb.*

for effect, for show; to impress others: *He said that only for effect; he really didn't mean it.*

take effect, to operate; become active: *That pill takes effect as soon as you swallow it.*

ef·fec·tive (ə fek′tiv), **1** able to cause some desired result: *Several new drugs are effective in treating serious diseases.* **2** in operation; active: *A law passed by Congress becomes effective as soon as the President signs it.* adjective.

ef·fi·cien·cy (ə fish′ən sē), the ability to do things without waste of time or energy: *The skilled carpenter worked with great efficiency to finish the job quickly.* noun.

ef·fi·cient (ə fish′ənt), able to produce the effect wanted without waste of time or energy; capable: *An efficient worker makes good use of his or her skills, and of the materials used on the job.* adjective.

ef·fort (ef′ərt), **1** the use of energy and strength to do something; trying hard: *Climbing a steep hill takes effort.* **2** a hard try; strong attempt: *She did not win, but at least she made an effort.* noun.

egg¹ (eg), **1** the round or oval object which is laid by the female of birds, insects, many reptiles and

fish, and other types of animals. Young animals hatch from these eggs. **2** the contents of an egg, especially a hen's egg, used as food: *I like two boiled eggs for breakfast.* **3** an egg cell. noun.

egg² (eg), to urge: *We egged the team on to victory.* verb.

[*Egg²* comes from an old word used in Iceland to mean "edge." An early meaning of our word was "to sharpen" or "to give an edge to." When we egg someone on, we sharpen that person's willingness to do what we want.]

egg cell, cell in a female for producing young. After an egg cell combines with a sperm cell, a new organism starts to grow.

egg·nog (eg′nog′), a drink made of eggs beaten up with milk and sugar. noun.

egg·plant (eg′plant′), a large, egg-shaped vegetable with a purple skin. noun.

eggplant

egg roll, a small tube of egg dough, filled with a mixture of minced vegetables and roast pork, and fried.

egg·shell (eg′shel′), the shell covering an egg. noun.

E·gypt (ē′jipt), a country in northeastern Africa. noun.

E·gyp·tian (i jip′shən), **1** of or having something to do with Egypt or its people. **2** a person born or living in Egypt. **1** *adjective,* **2** *noun.*

eh (ā *or* e), an exclamation expressing doubt, surprise, or failure to hear exactly, or suggesting "Yes" for an answer: *Eh? What's that you said? That's a good joke, eh?* interjection.

eight (āt), one more than seven; 8. Four and four make eight. *noun, adjective.*

eight·een (ā′tēn′), eight more than ten; 18. *noun, adjective.*

eight·eenth (ā′tēnth′), **1** next after the 17th. **2** one of 18 equal parts. *adjective, noun.*

eighth (ātth), **1** next after the seventh. **2** one of eight equal parts. *adjective, noun.*

eight·i·eth (ā′tē ith), **1** next after the 79th. **2** one of 80 equal parts. *adjective, noun.*

eight·y (ā′tē), eight times ten; 80. *noun, plural* **eight·ies;** *adjective.*

ei·ther (ē′ᴛʜər *or* ī′ᴛʜər), **1** one or the other of two: *You may read either book. Either is all right to read. Either come in or go out.* **2** each of two:

There are fields of corn on either side of the river.
3 also; likewise: *If you don't go, I won't either.*
1 *adjective, pronoun, conjunction,* **2** *adjective,*
3 *adverb.*

e·ject (i jekt′), to throw out; turn out; drive out. *verb.*

eject—The volcano **ejected** lava and ashes.

el (el), an electric railroad raised above street level on a supporting frame, allowing traffic to pass underneath. *noun.*

e·lab·or·ate (i lab′ər it *for 1;* i lab′ə rāt′ *for 2*), **1** worked out with great care; having many details; complicated: *They made elaborate plans for the birthday party.* **2** to give added details; say or write more: *The witness was asked to elaborate on one of his statements.* **1** *adjective,* **2** *verb,* **e·lab·or·ates, e·lab·or·at·ed, e·lab·or·at·ing.**

e·lapse (i laps′), to pass; slip away; glide by: *Hours elapsed while he slept. verb,* **e·laps·es, e·lapsed, e·laps·ing.**

e·las·tic (i las′tik), **1** able to spring back to its original shape, after being pressed together or stretched out: *Rubber bands, sponges, and steel springs are elastic.* **2** a tape or cloth woven partly of an elastic material: *His trunks have a band of elastic at the top.* **1** *adjective,* **2** *noun.*

e·las·tic·i·ty (i las tis′ə tē), elastic quality: *Rubber has great elasticity. noun.*

e·late (i lāt′), to raise the spirits of; make joyful or proud: *Her success in the contest elated her. verb,* **e·lates, e·lat·ed, e·lat·ing.**

e·la·tion (i lā′shən), high spirits; joy or pride: *He was filled with elation at winning the first prize. noun.*

el·bow (el′bō), **1** the joint between the upper and lower arm. **2** any bend or corner having the same shape as a bent arm. A bent joint for connecting pipes or a sharp turn in a road or a river may be called an elbow. **3** to push with the elbow: *Don't elbow me off the sidewalk.* **1,2** *noun,* **3** *verb.*

eld·er (el′dər), **1** older: *my elder brother.* **2** an older person: *As an only child, she spent a lot of her time with her elders.* **3** an officer in some Christian churches. **1** *adjective,* **2,3** *noun.*

eld·er·ly (el′dər lē), somewhat old: *Several elderly people sat on the park bench. adjective.*

eld·est (el′dist), oldest: *Their eldest daughter graduated from high school last year. adjective.*

a hat	i it	oi oil	ch child	⎧ a in about
ā age	ī ice	ou out	ng long	e in taken
ä far	o hot	u cup	sh she	ə = ⎨ i in pencil
e let	ō open	ů put	th thin	o in lemon
ē equal	ô order	ü rule	ŦH then	⎩ u in circus
ėr term			zh measure	

e·lect (i lekt′), **1** to choose by voting: *Americans elect a President every four years.* **2** to choose: *She elected to take piano lessons. verb.*

e·lec·tion (i lek′shən), **1** a choosing by vote: *In our city we have an election for mayor every two years.* **2** a selection by vote: *The candidate's excellent campaign resulted in her election. noun.*

e·lec·tric (i lek′trik), **1** of electricity: *an electric current.* **2** containing or working by electricity: *an electric cell, electric lights. adjective.*

e·lec·tri·cal (i lek′trə kəl), electric: *electrical energy, an electrical storm. adjective.*

e·lec·tri·cian (i lek′trish′ən), a person who repairs or installs electric wiring, lights, or motors. *noun.*

e·lec·tric·i·ty (i lek′tris′ə tē), **1** a form of energy that can produce light, heat, or motion. Electricity flows from generators over wires to homes, offices, and factories. Electricity also comes from batteries and solar cells. Lightning is electricity. *Electricity makes light bulbs shine, radios and televisions play, cars start, and subways run.* **2** an electric current: *The storm damaged the wire carrying electricity to the house. noun.*

e·lec·tri·fy (i lek′trə fī), **1** to charge with electricity. **2** to equip for the use of electric power: *Some railroads once run by steam were later electrified.* **3** to excite; thrill: *She electrified us with ghost stories. verb,* **e·lec·tri·fies, e·lec·tri·fied, e·lec·tri·fy·ing.**

e·lec·tro·cute (i lek′trə kyüt), to kill by a strong electric shock. *verb,* **e·lec·tro·cutes, e·lec·tro·cut·ed, e·lec·tro·cut·ing.**

e·lec·tro·mag·net (i lek′trō mag′nit), a piece of iron that becomes a strong magnet when an electric current is passing through wire coiled around it. *noun.*

e·lec·tron (i lek′tron), a tiny particle having one unit of negative electricity. All atoms have one or more electrons revolving around a nucleus. A large number of electrons moving together form an electric current. *noun.*

e·lec·tron·ic (i lek′tron′ik), **1** working by electricity: *an electronic game.* **2** used in or produced by electronics: *an electronic device. adjective.*

e·lec·tron·ics (i lek′tron′iks), the branch of physics that deals with electrons in motion. Electronics has made possible the development of television, radio, radar, and computers. *noun.*

el·e·gance (el′ə gəns), good taste; grace and beauty that is combined with dignity: *We admired the elegance of the clothes worn to the formal dinner. noun.*

el·e·gant (el′ə gənt), showing good taste;

E

197

graceful; beautiful: *The palace had elegant furnishings. adjective.*

el·e·ment (el′ə mənt), **1** one of over 100 basic substances from which all other things are made. An element is formed of only one kind of atom. Elements combine to form more complicated substances. Gold, iron, oxygen, carbon, and tin are elements. **2** one of the parts of which anything is made up: *I like a story that has an element of surprise in it.* **3** a simple or necessary part: *We learn the elements of arithmetic before the seventh grade.* **4** **the elements,** the forces of the air, especially in bad weather: *The raging storm seemed to be a war of the elements. noun.*

el·e·men·tar·y (el′ə men′tər ē), introductory; dealing with the simpler parts: *We learned addition and subtraction in elementary arithmetic. adjective.*

elementary school, 1 a school of usually six grades for pupils from about six to twelve years of age, followed by junior high school. **2** a school of eight grades for pupils from about six to fourteen years of age, followed by a four-year high school.

el·e·phant (el′ə fənt), the largest land animal now living. It has a long snout called a trunk, and ivory tusks. *noun, plural* **el·e·phants** or **el·e·phant.**

Word History

elephant *Elephant* comes from a Greek word meaning "ivory." The animal was called this because its tusks are made of ivory.

elephants—11 feet (3½ meters) high at the shoulder; body 8 feet (2½ meters) long

el·e·vate (el′ə vāt), to raise; lift up: *The doctor told me to elevate my injured foot. The company elevated her to a position of assistant manager. verb,* **el·e·vates, el·e·vat·ed, el·e·vat·ing.**

el·e·va·tion (el′ə vā′shən), **1** a raised place; high place: *A hill is an elevation.* **2** height above sea level: *The elevation of that city is 5300 feet.* **3** a raising; lifting up: *The elevation of a clerk to store manager surprised us. noun.*

elevator
(definition 2)

el·e·va·tor (el′ə vā′tər), **1** a car or cage used to carry people or things up or down in a building or mine. **2** a building for storing grain. **3** a movable, flat piece on the tail of an airplane to cause it to go up or down. *noun.*

e·lev·en (i lev′ən), **1** one more than ten; 11. **2** a team of eleven football, soccer, or cricket players. **1,2** *noun,* **1** *adjective.*

e·lev·enth (i lev′ənth), **1** next after the tenth. **2** one of 11 equal parts. *adjective, noun.*

elf (elf), (in stories) a tiny being that is full of mischief; fairy. *noun, plural* **elves.**

el·i·gi·ble (el′ə jə bəl), fit to be chosen; qualified: *In this state a person must be 16 to be eligible for a driver's license. adjective.*

e·lim·i·nate (i lim′ə nāt), **1** to remove; get rid of: *Eliminate unnecessary details from your book report. verb,* **e·lim·i·nates, e·lim·i·nat·ed, e·lim·i·nat·ing.**

e·lim·i·na·tion (i lim′ə nā′shən), a removal; getting rid of: *elimination of wastes from the body. noun.*

elk (elk), **1** a large deer of Europe and Asia. It has antlers like a moose. **2** a large red deer of North America. *noun, plural* **elk** or **elks.**

elk (definition 2)
5 feet (1½ meters) high at the shoulder

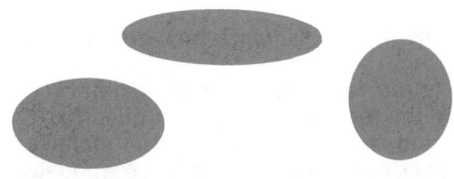

ellipse—three elipses

a hat	i it	oi oil	ch child	a in about
ā age	ī ice	ou out	ng long	e in taken
ä far	o hot	u cup	sh she	ə = { i in pencil
e let	ō open	ů put	th thin	o in lemon
ē equal	ô order	ü rule	ŧH then	u in circus
ėr term			zh measure	

el·lipse (i lips′), a figure shaped like an oval with both ends alike. *noun.*

elm (elm), **1** a tall shade tree with high, spreading branches. **2** its hard, heavy wood. *noun.*

e·lon·gate (i lông′gāt), to make or become longer; lengthen; extend; stretch. *verb,* **e·lon·gates, e·lon·gat·ed, e·lon·gat·ing.**

elongate—The cake Alice ate **elongated** her like a telescope.

e·lope (i lōp′), to run away to get married. *verb,* **e·lopes, e·loped, e·lop·ing.**

el·o·quence (el′ə kwəns), a flow of speech that has grace and force: *The jury was moved by the eloquence of the lawyer's words. noun.*

el·o·quent (el′ə kwənt), **1** having the power of expressing one's feelings or thoughts with grace and force: *an eloquent speaker.* **2** very expressive: *eloquent eyes. adjective.*

El Sal·va·dor (el sal′və dôr), a country in Central America.

else (els), **1** other; different: *Will somebody else speak? What else could I say?* **2** in addition; more: *The Browns are here; do you expect anyone else?* **3** differently: *How else can it be done?* **4** otherwise; if not; or: *Hurry, else you will be late.* **1,2** *adjective,* **3,4** *adverb.*

else·where (els′hwer or els′hwar), somewhere else; in or to some other place. *adverb.*

e·lude (i lüd′), to avoid or escape by quickness or cleverness; slip away from: *The sly fox eluded the dogs. verb,* **e·ludes, e·lud·ed, e·lud·ing.**

e·lu·sive (i lü′siv), **1** hard to describe or understand: *I had an idea that was too elusive to be put in words.* **2** tending to elude or escape: *The elusive fox got away. adjective.*

elves (elvz), more than one elf; fairies. *noun plural.*

e·man·ci·pate (i man′sə pāt), to set free from slavery of any kind; release: *Women have been emancipated from many old restrictions. verb,* **e·man·ci·pates, e·man·ci·pat·ed, e·man·ci·pat·ing.**

em·balm (em bäm′), to treat a dead body with chemicals to keep it from decaying. *verb.*

em·bank·ment (em bangk′mənt), a raised bank of earth or stones, used to hold back water or support a roadway. *noun.*

em·bark (em bärk′), **1** to go or put on board a ship or an aircraft: *We embarked for Hawaii at San Francisco.* **2** to set out; start: *After leaving college, the young woman embarked upon a business career. verb.*

em·bar·rass (em bar′əs), **1** to make uneasy and ashamed; make self-conscious: *She embarrassed me by asking me if I really liked her.* **2** to burden with debt: *The company was financially embarrassed and could not pay its employees last week. verb.*

em·bar·rass·ment (em bar′əs mənt), shame; an uneasy feeling: *I blushed in embarrassment at my stupid mistake. noun.*

em·bas·sy (em′bə sē), the residence and offices of an ambassador and his or her assistants in a foreign country. *noun, plural* **em·bas·sies.**

em·bed (em bed′), to fix or enclose in a surrounding substance: *Precious stones are often found embedded in rock. verb,* **em·beds, em·bed·ded, em·bed·ding.**

em·ber (em′bər), **1** a piece of wood or coal still glowing in the ashes of a fire. **2** embers, ashes in which there is still some fire: *He stirred the embers to make them blaze up again. noun.*

em·bez·zle (em bez′əl), to steal money entrusted to one's care: *The cashier embezzled $50,000 from the bank. verb,* **em·bez·zles, em·bez·zled, em·bez·zling.**

em·bit·ter (em bit′ər), to make bitter: *They were embittered by the loss of all their money. verb.*

em·blem (em′bləm), a symbol; sign that stands for an idea; token: *The dove is an emblem of peace. The white flag is the emblem of surrender. noun.*

em·bod·y (em bod′ē), to put into a form that can be seen: *A building embodies the idea of its architect. verb,* **em·bod·ies, em·bod·ied, em·bod·y·ing.**

em·boss (em bôs′), to decorate with a design or pattern that stands out from the surface: *Our coins are embossed with letters and figures. verb.*

em·brace (em brās′), **1** to hug; hold in the arms to show love or friendship: *I embraced my old friend.* **2** a hug: *My old friend gave me a fond* *embrace.* **3** to take up; accept: *He eagerly embraced the offer of a trip to Europe.* 1,3 *verb,* **em·brac·es, em·braced, em·brac·ing;** 2 *noun.*

em·broi·der (em broi′dər), **1** to decorate cloth or leather with a pattern of stitches: *I embroidered the shirt with a colorful design.* **2** to add imaginary details to; exaggerate: *They didn't exactly lie, but they did embroider their story.* *verb.*

em·broi·der·y (em broi′dər ē), ornamental designs sewn in cloth or leather with a needle. *noun.*

embroidery

embryo of a chicken

em·bry·o (em′brē ō), an animal or plant in the earlier stages of its development, before birth, hatching, or sprouting. The plant contained within a seed is an embryo. A chicken within an egg is an embryo. *noun, plural* **em·bry·os.**

em·er·ald (em′ər əld), **1** a bright-green precious stone or jewel. **2** bright-green. 1 *noun,* 2 *adjective.*

e·merge (i mėrj′), to come out; come up; come into view: *The sun emerged from behind a cloud. Many facts emerged as a result of a second investigation.* *verb,* **e·merg·es, e·merged, e·merg·ing.**

e·mer·gen·cy (i mėr′jən sē), **1** a sudden need for immediate action: *I keep a box of tools in my car for use in an emergency.* **2** for a time of sudden need: *The surgeon performed an emergency operation.* 1 *noun, plural* **e·mer·gen·cies;** 2 *adjective.*

em·er·y (em′ər ē), a hard, dark mineral which is used in the form of a powder for grinding, smoothing, and polishing metals or stones. *noun.*

em·i·grant (em′ə grənt), a person who leaves his or her own country to settle in another: *My grandparents were emigrants from Japan. noun.*

em·i·grate (em′ə grāt), to leave one's own country to settle in another: *My grandparents emigrated from Ireland to the United States.* *verb,* **em·i·grates, em·i·grat·ed, em·i·grat·ing.**

em·i·gra·tion (em′ə grā′shən), leaving one's own country to settle in another: *There has been much emigration from Italy to the United States. noun.*

em·i·nence (em′ə nəns), a rank or position above all or most others; greatness; fame: *The surgeon's eminence was due to his superior skill. noun.*

em·i·nent (em′ə nənt), above all others in rank; famous; outstanding: *an eminent poet. adjective.*

em·is·sar·y (em′ə ser′ē), a person sent on a mission or errand. *noun, plural* **em·is·sar·ies.**

e·mit (i mit′), to send out; give off: *The sun emits light and heat. Volcanoes emit lava. The trapped lion emitted roars of rage.* *verb,* **e·mits, e·mit·ted, e·mit·ting.**

e·mo·tion (i mō′shən), a strong feeling of any kind. Joy, grief, fear, hate, love, anger, and excitement are emotions. *noun.*

e·mo·tion·al (i mō′shə nəl), **1** of the emotions: *A person who is always afraid may be suffering from a serious emotional problem.* **2** with strong feeling; appealing to the emotions: *The speaker made an emotional plea for money to help handicapped children.* **3** easily excited: *Emotional people are likely to cry if they hear sad music or read sad stories. adjective.*

em·per·or (em′pər ər), a man who is the ruler of an empire. *noun.*

em·pha·sis (em′fə sis), **1** stress; importance: *That school puts emphasis on arithmetic and reading.* **2** greater vocal stress or accent put on particular words or syllables: *In reading, our teacher puts emphasis upon the most important words. noun, plural* **em·pha·ses** (em′fə sēz′).

em·pha·size (em′fə sīz), **1** to stress; give importance to: *The large number of automobile accidents emphasizes the need for careful driving.* **2** to put greater vocal stress or accent on: *He emphasized her name as he read the list of winners.* *verb,* **em·pha·siz·es, em·pha·sized, em·pha·siz·ing.**

em·phat·ic (em fat′ik), said or done with force; meant to stand out; clear; positive: *Her answer was an emphatic "No!" adjective.*

em·phat·i·cal·ly (em fat′ik lē), in an emphatic manner. *adverb.*

em·pire (em′pīr), **1** a group of nations or states under one ruler or government: *The Roman Empire lasted for hundreds of years.* **2** power; rule: *India was once under the empire of Great Britain. noun.*

em·ploy (em ploi′), **1** to give work and pay to: *That big factory employs many workers.* **2** service for pay; employment: *There are many workers in the employ of that big factory.* **3** to use: *You employ a knife, fork, and spoon in eating.* 1,3 *verb,* 2 *noun.*

em·ploy·ee (em ploi′ē), a person who works for some person or firm for pay. *noun.*

em·ploy·er (em ploi′ər), a person or firm that employs one or more persons. *noun.*

em·ploy·ment (em ploi′mənt), **1** work; job: *She had no difficulty finding employment.* **2** an employing or being employed: *A large office requires the employment of many people. noun.*

em·pow·er (em pou′ər), to give power or authority to: *The secretary was empowered to sign certain contracts. verb.*

em·press (em′pris), **1** the wife of an emperor. **2** a woman who is the ruler of an empire. *noun, plural* **em·press·es.**

emp·ti·ness (emp′tē nis), a being empty; lack of contents. *noun.*

emp·ty (emp′tē), **1** with nothing or no one in it: *The birds had gone, and their nest was left empty.* **2** to pour out or take out all that is in a thing; make empty: *He emptied his glass quickly.* **3** to become empty: *The hall emptied as soon as the meeting was over.* **4** to flow out: *The Mississippi River empties into the Gulf of Mexico.* **5** not real; without meaning: *An empty promise is one that you do not plan to keep.* 1,5 *adjective,* **emp·ti·er, emp·ti·est;** 2-4 *verb,* **emp·ties, emp·tied, emp·ty·ing.**

e·mul·sion (i mul′shən), mixture of liquids that do not dissolve in each other. In an emulsion one of the liquids contains tiny drops of the other evenly distributed throughout. *noun.*

en·a·ble (en ā′bəl), to make able; give ability, power, or means to: *Airplanes enable people to travel great distances rapidly. verb,* **en·a·bles, en·a·bled, en·a·bling.**

en·act (en akt′), **1** to make into law: *Congress enacted a bill to lower taxes.* **2** to act out; play: *He enacted the part of the hero very well. verb.*

e·nam·el (i nam′əl), **1** a glasslike substance melted and then cooled to make a smooth, hard surface. Different colors of enamel are used to cover or decorate metal, glass, or pottery. **2** a paint used to make a smooth, hard, glossy surface. **3** the smooth, hard, glossy outer layer that covers and protects a tooth. **4** to cover or decorate with enamel. 1-3 *noun,* 4 *verb.*

en·camp·ment (en kamp′mənt), **1** a forming a camp. **2** a place where a camp is; camp. *noun.*

en·case (en kās′), to cover completely; enclose: *A cocoon encased the caterpillar. verb,* **en·cas·es, en·cased, en·cas·ing.**

en·chant (en chant′), **1** to use magic on; put under a spell: *The witch had enchanted the princess.* **2** to delight greatly; charm: *The music enchanted us all. verb.*
[*Enchant* comes from a Latin word meaning "to chant or sing words having magic power."]

a hat	i it	oi oil	ch child		a in about
ā age	ī ice	ou out	ng long		e in taken
ä far	o hot	u cup	sh she	ə =	i in pencil
e let	ō open	u̇ put	th thin		o in lemon
ē equal	ô order	ü rule	╥H then		u in circus
ėr term			zh measure		

E

en·chant·ment (en chant′mənt), **1** the use of magic spells; spell or charm: *In "The Wizard of Oz" Dorothy finds herself at home again by the enchantment of the Good Witch.* **2** something that delights or charms: *We felt the enchantment of the moonlight on the lake. noun.*

en·cir·cle (en sėr′kəl), **1** to form a circle around; surround: *Trees encircled the pond.* **2** to go in a circle around: *The moon encircles the earth. verb,* **en·cir·cles, en·cir·cled, en·cir·cling.**

en·close (en klōz′), **1** to shut in on all sides; surround: *The little park was enclosed by tall apartment buildings.* **2** to put a wall or fence around: *We are going to enclose our backyard to keep dogs out.* **3** to put in an envelope along with a letter: *He enclosed a check when he mailed his order. verb,* **en·clos·es, en·closed, en·clos·ing.** Also spelled **inclose.**

en·clo·sure (en klō′zhər), **1** an enclosed place, as a pen or corral: *At the zoo the elephants and giraffes were kept in different enclosures.* **2** a thing that encloses. A wall or fence is an enclosure. **3** a thing enclosed: *The envelope contained a letter and $5 as an enclosure. noun.* Also spelled **inclosure.**

en·code (en kōd′), to put into code: *The spy encoded the message before sending it. verb,* **en·codes, en·cod·ed, en·cod·ing.**

en·com·pass (en kum′pəs), to go or reach all the way around; encircle: *The atmosphere encompasses the earth. verb.*

en·core (äng′kôr), **1** a call by the audience for an additional song or other performance from a performer or entertainer. **2** a demand, which an audience makes by shouting "Encore!" and by clapping, for a person or group to give an extra or a repeat performance: *The singer received several encores and many bouquets.* **3** an extra song or piece of music given in answer to the applause of the audience. *noun.*

en·coun·ter (en koun′tər), **1** to meet unexpectedly: *What if we should encounter a bear?* **2** an unexpected meeting: *A fortunate encounter*

encounter (definition 1)

We seem to have encountered a few difficulties.

brought the two friends together after a long separation. **3** to be faced with: *She encountered many difficulties before the job was done.* **4** to meet as an enemy: *He encountered the strange knight in direct combat.* **5** a meeting of enemies; fight; battle: *The two armies had a desperate encounter.* 1,3,4 *verb,* 2,5 *noun.*

en·cour·age (en kėr′ij), **1** to give hope, courage, or confidence to; urge on: *The cheers of the crowd encouraged the players to try to win.* **2** to give help to; be favorable to: *Sunlight encourages the growth of green plants. verb,* **en·cour·ag·es, en·cour·aged, en·cour·ag·ing.**

en·cour·age·ment (en kėr′ij mənt), **1** an urging on toward success: *Her encouragement was a great help to me.* **2** something that gives hope, courage, or confidence: *The teacher's praise of his drawings was his only encouragement. noun.*

en·croach (en krōch′), **1** to go beyond proper or usual limits: *The sea encroached upon the shore and covered the beach.* **2** to trespass upon the property or rights of another; intrude: *The cattle from the next farm have been encroaching on our land. verb.*

en·crust (en krust′), to cover with a crust or hard coating: *The inside of the kettle was encrusted with rust. verb.*

en·cy·clo·pe·di·a (en sī′klə pē′dē ə), a book or set of books giving information on all branches of knowledge, with its articles arranged alphabetically. *noun.*
[*Encyclopedia* comes from two Greek words meaning "general education."]

end (end), **1** the last part: *He read to the end of the book.* **2** the part where a thing begins or where it stops: *Every stick has two ends. Drive to the end of this road.* **3** to bring or come to its last part; finish: *Let us end this fight.* **4** a purpose; what is aimed at in doing something: *She had this end in mind—to do her work without a mistake.* **5** a result; outcome: *It is hard to tell what the end will be.* **6** a football player at either end of the line. 1,2,4-6 *noun,* 3 *verb.*

end up, to wind up; come out: *I spent all my allowance and ended up broke.*

in the end, finally; at last: *In the end, he confessed that he had made the mistake.*

en·dan·ger (en dān′jər), to cause danger to: *Fire endangered the hotel's guests. verb.*

en·dan·gered (en dān′jərd), liable to become extinct: *an endangered species. adjective.*

en·dear (en dir′), to make dear: *Their kindness endeared them to me. verb.*

en·deav·or (en dev′ər), **1** to try hard; make an effort; strive: *A runner endeavors to win a race.* **2** an effort; a strong attempt: *With each endeavor she did better.* 1 *verb,* 2 *noun.*

end·ing (en′ding), **1** the end; last part: *The story has a sad ending.* **2** a letter or syllable added to a word to change its meaning; suffix: *The common plural ending is "s" or "es." noun.*

end·less (end′lis), **1** having no end; never stopping; lasting or going on forever: *the endless*

revolution of the earth around the sun. **2** seeming to have no end: *Doing housework is an endless task.* **3** joined in a circle; without ends: *The chain that turns the back wheel of a bicycle is an endless chain. adjective.*

en·do·crine gland (en′dō krən gland′), any organ that produces chemicals and puts them directly into the bloodstream. Endocrine glands working together form the **endocrine system,** which controls growth and many other body activities.

en·dorse (en dôrs′), **1** to write one's name on the back of a check, note, or other document: *He had to endorse the check before the bank would cash it.* **2** to approve; support: *They endorsed the plan for a school playground. verb,* **en·dors·es, en·dorsed, en·dors·ing.**

en·dow (en dou′), **1** to give money or property to provide an income for: *Rich people sometimes endow the college they have attended.* **2** to give from birth: *Nature endowed him with good looks. verb.*

en·dow·ment (en dou′mənt), money or property given to a person or institution to provide an income: *This college has a large endowment. noun.*

end·point (end′point′), the point where a line segment begins or ends. *noun.*

en·dur·ance (en dûr′əns *or* en dyûr′əns), **1** the power to last or keep on: *A runner must have great endurance to run 30 miles in a day.* **2** the power to stand something without giving out; power to put up with something: *Her endurance of pain is remarkable. noun.*

en·dure (en dûr′ *or* en dyûr′), **1** to last; keep on: *Metal and stone endure for a long time.* **2** to put up with; bear; stand: *The pioneers endured many hardships. verb,* **en·dures, en·dured, en·dur·ing.**

end·ways (end′wāz′), **1** on end. **2** with the end forward. **3** lengthwise. **4** end to end. *adverb.*

en·e·my (en′ə mē), **1** a person or group that hates or tries to harm another; foe. Two countries fighting against each other are enemies. **2** anything that will harm: *Frost is an enemy of flowers. noun, plural* **en·e·mies.**

en·er·get·ic (en′ər jet′ik), full of energy; active; eager to work; full of force: *Cool autumn days make us feel energetic. adjective.*

en·er·get·i·cal·ly (en′ər jet′ik lē), with energy; vigorously. *adverb.*

en·er·gy (en′ər jē), **1** the will to work; vigor: *I was so full of energy that I could not keep still.* **2** the power to work or act; force: *All our energies were used in keeping the fire from spreading.* **3** the ability to do work, such as lifting or moving an object. Light, heat, and electricity are different forms of energy. Atomic energy is the energy released by some kinds of atoms when they are split or combined. *noun, plural* **en·er·gies.**

en·force (en fôrs′), to force obedience to; cause to be carried out: *The police will enforce the laws of the city. verb,* **en·forc·es, en·forced, en·forc·ing.**

en·force·ment (en fôrs′mənt), an enforcing:

Strict enforcement of the laws against speeding will reduce automobile accidents. noun.

en·gage (en gāj′), **1** to keep oneself busy; be active; take part: *They engaged in conversation.* **2** to keep busy; occupy: *Work engages much of his time.* **3** to take for use or work; hire: *We engaged two rooms in the hotel.* **4** to promise or pledge to marry: *He is engaged to my sister.* **5** to fit into; lock together. The teeth in one gear engage with those in another. **6** to start a battle against; attack: *Our soldiers engaged the enemy. verb,* **en·gag·es, en·gaged, en·gag·ing.**

a hat	i it	oi oil	ch child	⎧ a in about
ā age	ī ice	ou out	ng long	⎪ e in taken
ä far	o hot	u cup	sh she	ə = ⎨ i in pencil
e let	ō open	u̇ put	th thin	⎪ o in lemon
ē equal	ô order	ü rule	₮H then	⎩ u in circus
ėr term			zh measure	

E

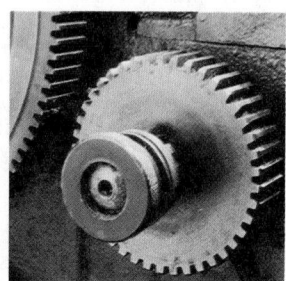

engage (definition 5)
gears **engaged**   gears not **engaged**

English horn

en·gaged (en gājd′), **1** pledged to marry: *The engaged woman wore a diamond ring.* **2** busy; occupied: *Engaged in conversation, they did not see us. adjective.*

en·gage·ment (en gāj′mənt), **1** a promise to marry: *Their parents announced the young couple's engagement.* **2** a meeting with someone at a certain time; an appointment: *My parents have a dinner engagement tonight. noun.*

en·gag·ing (en gā′jing), attractive; pleasing: *an engaging smile. adjective.*

en·gine (en′jən), **1** the part of a machine that uses energy to make the machine move or run. Engines use electricity, the heat from burning fuel, and other forms of energy. Automobiles and airplanes have engines. **2** a machine that pulls a railroad train; locomotive. *noun.*

en·gi·neer (en′jə nir′), **1** a person who takes care of or runs engines. The driver of a locomotive is an engineer. **2** a person who is an expert in engineering. **3** to guide; manage with skill: *She engineered the whole job from start to finish.* **1,2** *noun,* **3** *verb.*

en·gi·neer·ing (en′jə nir′ing), the science of planning and building engines, machines, roads, bridges, canals, and the like. *noun.*

Eng·land (ing′glənd), the largest division of Great Britain, in the southern part. *noun.*

Eng·lish (ing′glish), **1** of or having something to do with England, its people, or their language. **2** the people of England. **3** the language of England. English is spoken also in Ireland, Scotland, Canada, the United States, and many other places. **1** *adjective,* **2** *noun plural,* **3** *noun singular.*

English Channel, the strait between England and France.

English horn, a wooden musical instrument resembling an oboe, but larger and having a lower tone.

English sparrow, a small, brownish-gray bird, now very common in America.

en·grave (en grāv′), **1** to carve in; carve in an artistic way: *The jeweler engraved the boy's initials on the back of the watch.* **2** to cut a picture, design, or map in lines on wood, stone, metal, or glass plates for printing. *verb,* **en·graves, en·graved, en·grav·ing.**

en·grav·ing (en grā′ving), **1** the art or act of a person who engraves. **2** a picture made from an engraved plate; print. *noun.*

en·gross (en grōs′), to occupy wholly; fill the mind of. *verb.*

engross—The men were **engrossed** in watching the contest.

"Nearing the Issue at the Cockpit," Horace Bonham.
In the collection of The Corcoran Gallery of Art

en·gulf (en gulf′), to swallow up; overwhelm: *A wave engulfed the small boat.* verb.

en·hance (en hans′), to add to; make greater: *The growth of a city often enhances the value of land close to it.* verb, **en·hanc·es, en·hanced, en·hanc·ing.**

en·joy (en joi′), 1 to have or use with joy; be happy with; take pleasure in: *The children enjoyed their visit to the museum.* 2 to have as an advantage or benefit: *He enjoys good health.* verb. **enjoy oneself,** to be happy; have a good time: *Enjoy yourself at the party.*

en·joy·a·ble (en joi′ə bəl), giving joy; pleasant: *I had an enjoyable time at the party.* adjective.

en·joy·ment (en joi′mənt), 1 pleasure; joy; delight: *The children found great enjoyment in their visit to the museum.* 2 a having as an advantage or benefit; possession or use: *She has the enjoyment of good health.* noun.

en·large (en lärj′), to make or become larger: *The factory was enlarged to make room for more machinery.* verb, **en·larg·es, en·larged, en·larg·ing.**

en·large·ment (en lärj′mənt), 1 a making larger: *The enlargement of the factory took all summer.* 2 a photograph or other thing that has been made larger. noun.

en·light·en (en līt′n), to make clear; give truth and knowledge to; inform; instruct: *She found the lesson very enlightening.* verb.

en·list (en list′), 1 to join or get to join the army, navy, or some other branch of the armed forces: *He enlisted in the navy.* 2 to get the help of: *We enlisted my sister and her friends in building our new clubhouse.* verb.

en·liv·en (en lī′vən), to make lively, active, or cheerful: *Bright curtains enliven a dull room.* verb.

en·mi·ty (en′mə tē), the feeling that enemies have for each other; hatred. noun, plural **en·mi·ties.**

e·nor·mous (i nôr′məs), very, very large; huge: *Long ago enormous animals lived on the earth.* adjective.

e·nough (i nuf′), 1 as much or as many as needed or wanted; sufficient: *Are there enough seats for all?* 2 an amount needed or wanted: *Has he had enough to eat?* 3 until no more is needed or wanted; sufficiently: *Have you played enough?* 1 adjective, 2 noun, 3 adverb.

en·rage (en rāj′), to make very angry; make furious; madden: *The dog was enraged by the teasing.* verb, **en·rag·es, en·raged, en·rag·ing.**

en·rich (en rich′), to make rich or richer: *An education enriches your mind. Adding vitamins or minerals to food enriches it. Fertilizer enriches the soil.* verb.

en·roll (en rōl′), to make or become a member: *He enrolled his daughter and son in a music school.* verb, **en·rolls, en·rolled, en·roll·ing.**

en·roll·ment (en rōl′mənt), 1 an enrolling: *Enrollment took place in the fall.* 2 the number enrolled: *The school has an enrollment of 200 students.* noun.

en route (än rüt′), on the way: *We shall stop at Philadelphia en route from New York to Washington.*

en·sign (en′sən), 1 a flag or banner: *The ensign of the United States is the Stars and Stripes.* 2 an officer in the navy ranking next below a lieutenant junior grade. noun.

en·slave (en slāv′), to make a slave of; take away freedom from. verb, **en·slaves, en·slaved, en·slav·ing.**

en·sure (en shùr′), 1 to make sure or certain: *Careful planning and hard work ensured the success of the party.* 2 to make safe; protect: *A good map of the region ensured us against getting lost.* verb, **en·sures, en·sured, en·sur·ing.**

en·tan·gle (en tang′gəl), 1 to get twisted up and caught: *The fly was entangled in the spider's web.* 2 to involve; get into difficulty: *Do not entangle us in your schemes.* verb, **en·tan·gles, en·tan·gled, en·tan·gling.**

en·tan·gle·ment (en tang′gəl mənt), an entangling or being entangled: *The new nation kept out of entanglements with other countries.* noun.

en·ter (en′tər), 1 to go in; come in: *He entered the house. Let them enter.* 2 to join; become a part or member of: *She entered the contest.* 3 to cause to join or enter; enroll: *Parents enter their children in school.* 4 to write or print in a book or list: *Words are entered alphabetically in a dictionary.* 5 to make a record of: *The teller entered the deposit in my bank book.* verb. **enter into,** to take part in; join in: *Right after she joined us she entered into our conversation.*

en·ter·prise (en′tər prīz), a plan to be tried, especially one that is important, difficult, or dangerous: *A trip into space is a daring enterprise.* noun.

en·ter·pris·ing (en′tər prī′zing), likely to start projects; ready to face difficulties: *an enterprising young businessman.* adjective.

en·ter·tain (en′tər tān′), 1 to keep pleasantly interested; please or amuse: *The circus entertained the children.* 2 to have as a guest or have guests: *They entertained ten people at dinner. My parents entertain a lot.* 3 to take into the mind; consider: *I refuse to entertain such a foolish idea.* verb.

en·ter·tain·er (en′tər tā′nər), a singer, musician, or actor who performs in public. noun.

en·ter·tain·ing (en′tər tā′ning), interesting; pleasing or amusing. adjective.

en·ter·tain·ment (en′tər tān′mənt), 1 something that interests, pleases, or amuses, such as a show or a circus. 2 the act of entertaining: *We devoted ourselves to the entertainment of our guests.* 3 the condition of being entertained; amusement: *I played the piano for their entertainment.* noun.

en·thrall (en thrôl′), to enchant; fascinate; charm: *The pilot enthralled her audience with stories about stunt flying.* verb, **en·thralls, en·thralled, en·thrall·ing.**

en·thuse (en thüz′), to show or fill with

enthusiasm: *She enthused over the idea of going on a picnic.* verb, **en·thus·es, en·thused, en·thus·ing.**

en·thu·si·asm (en thü′zē az′əm), an eager interest: *Going swimming aroused our enthusiasm.* noun.

en·thu·si·ast (en thü′zē ast), a person who is filled with enthusiasm: *a baseball enthusiast.* noun.

en·thu·si·as·tic (en thü′zē as′tik), full of enthusiasm; eagerly interested: *My little brother is enthusiastic about going to kindergarten.* adjective.

en·thu·si·as·ti·cal·ly (en thü′zē as′tik lē), with enthusiasm: *The fans shouted enthusiastically when our team made a touchdown.* adverb.

en·tice (en tīs′), to attract; lead into something by raising hopes or desires; tempt: *The smell of food enticed the hungry children into the house.* verb, **en·tic·es, en·ticed, en·tic·ing.**

en·tire (en tīr′), whole; complete; having all the parts: *The entire class behaved very well on the trip.* adjective.

en·tire·ly (en tīr′lē), wholly; completely; fully: *He is entirely wrong.* adverb.

en·tire·ty (en tīr′tē), completeness; the whole. noun.
in its entirety, wholly; completely: *He enjoyed the concert in its entirety.*

en·ti·tle (en tī′tl), **1** to give someone a claim or right: *The one who wins is entitled to first prize.* **2** to give a book, play, or the like the title of; name: *I entitled my theme "Looking for Treasure."* verb, **en·ti·tles, en·ti·tled, en·ti·tling.**

en·trance[1] (en′trəns), **1** the act of entering: *The actor's entrance was greeted with applause.* **2** a place by which to enter; door or passageway: *The entrance to the hotel was blocked with baggage.* **3** the right to enter; permission to enter: *Entrance to the exhibit is on weekdays only.* noun.

en·trance[2] (en trans′), to delight; fill with joy: *From the first note the singer's voice entranced the audience.* verb, **en·tranc·es, en·tranced, en·tranc·ing.**

en·treat (en trēt′), to keep asking earnestly; beg and pray: *The prisoners entreated the governor to pardon them.* verb.

en·treat·y (en trē′tē), an earnest request: *My parents gave in to my entreaties.* noun, plural **en·treat·ies.**

en·trust (en trust′), to give the care of; hand over for safekeeping: *While traveling, they entrusted their child to her grandparents.* verb.

en·try (en′trē), **1** the act of entering: *His sudden entry startled me.* **2** a place by which to enter; way to enter. An entrance hall is an entry. **3** a thing written or printed in a book or list. Each word explained in a dictionary is an entry or **entry word. 4** a person or thing that takes part in a contest: *The car race had nine entries.* noun, plural **en·tries.**

en·twine (en twīn′), to twine together or around: *Two hearts were entwined on the valentine.* verb, **en·twines, en·twined, en·twin·ing.**

e·nu·me·rate (i nü′mə rāt′ or i nyü′mə rāt′), **1** to name one by one; list: *He enumerated the capitals of the 50 states.* **2** to find the number of; count. verb, **e·nu·me·rates, e·nu·me·rat·ed, e·nu·me·rat·ing.**

e·nun·ci·ate (i nun′sē āt), to speak or pronounce words: *Radio and television announcers must enunciate very clearly.* verb, **e·nun·ci·ates, e·nun·ci·at·ed, e·nun·ci·at·ing.**

e·nun·ci·a·tion (i nun′sē ā′shən), a manner of pronouncing words. noun.

en·vel·op (en vel′əp), to wrap, cover, or hide: *The baby was enveloped in blankets.* verb.

envelop—Fog began to **envelop** the trees.

en·ve·lope (en′və lōp), a paper cover in which a letter or anything flat can be mailed. It usually has a flap which can be folded over and sealed. noun.

en·vi·ous (en′vē əs), feeling or showing discontent because another person has what you want; full of envy: *He was envious of his brother's success in sports.* adjective.

en·vi·ron·ment (en vī′rən mənt), all of the surroundings that influence the growth, development, and well-being of a living thing: *A child's character is greatly influenced by the environment at home. A plant will often grow differently in a different environment.* noun.

en·vi·ron·men·tal (en vī′rən men′tl), having to do with environment: *the environmental sciences. Air pollution is an environmental problem.* adjective.

en·voy (en′voi), **1** a messenger. **2** a diplomat next below an ambassador in rank. noun.

en·vy (en′vē), **1** a feeling of discontent or dislike because another person has what you want: *All of us were filled with envy when we saw her new bicycle.* **2** a person or thing that causes you to feel envy: *Their new car was the envy of the neighborhood.* **3** to feel envy toward or because of: *He envied his friend's success.* 1,2 noun, 3 verb, **en·vies, en·vied, en·vy·ing.**

a hat	i it	oi oil	ch child	a in about
ā age	ī ice	ou out	ng long	e in taken
ä far	o hot	u cup	sh she	ə = i in pencil
e let	ō open	u̇ put	th thin	o in lemon
ē equal	ô order	ü rule	₮н then	u in circus
ėr term			zh measure	

E

e·on (ē′on), a very long period of time; many thousands of years: *Eons passed before life existed on earth.* noun.

ep·ic (ep′ik), **1** a long poem that tells the adventures of one or more great heroes. **2** of or like an epic; grand; heroic: *The first flight over the Atlantic was an epic deed.* 1 noun, 2 adjective.

ep·i·dem·ic (ep′ə dem′ik), the rapid spreading of a disease so that many people have it at the same time: *All the schools in the city were closed during the epidemic of measles.* noun.

ep·i·sode (ep′ə sōd), a single happening or group of happenings in real life or a story: *Being elected class president was an important episode in her life at school.* noun.

ep·och (ep′ək), a period of time in which striking things happened: *The years of the Civil War were an epoch in the United States.* noun.

e·qual (ē′kwəl), **1** the same in amount, size, number, value, or rank: *Ten dimes are equal to one dollar. All persons are considered equal before the law.* **2** to be the same as: *Four times five equals twenty.* **3** a person or thing that is equal: *In spelling she had no equal.* 1 adjective, 2 verb, 3 noun.

equal to, strong enough for: *One horse is not equal to pulling a load of five tons.*

e·qual·i·ty (i kwol′ə tē), the exact likeness in amount, size, number, value, or rank. noun.

e·qual·ize (ē′kwə līz), to make equal. verb, **e·qual·iz·es, e·qual·ized, e·qual·iz·ing.**

e·qual·ly (ē′kwə lē), in equal shares; in an equal manner; to an equal degree: *Divide the pie equally. My sister and brother are equally talented.* adverb.

e·qua·tion (i kwā′zhən), a statement that two quantities are equal. EXAMPLE: 4 + 5 = 9. noun.

e·qua·tor (i kwā′tər), an imaginary circle around the middle of the earth, halfway between the North Pole and the South Pole. The equator divides the earth into the Northern Hemisphere and the Southern Hemisphere. noun.

e·qua·to·ri·al (ē′kwə tôr′ē əl), **1** of or near the equator: *Ecuador is an equatorial country.* **2** like conditions at or near the equator: *The weather this week was hot and humid; it was almost equatorial.* adjective.

e·qui·lat·er·al tri·an·gle (ē′kwə lat′ər əl trī′ang′gəl), a triangle that has all sides equal.

e·qui·lib·ri·um (ē′kwə lib′rē əm), balance. noun.

e·qui·nox (ē′kwə noks), either of the two times in the year when day and night are of equal length everywhere on earth. An equinox occurs when the sun passes directly above the earth's equator, about March 22 and September 23. noun, plural **e·qui·nox·es.**

e·quip (i kwip′), to fit out; provide; supply with all that is needed: *The scouts equipped themselves with canteens and food for the hike.* verb, **e·quips, e·quipped, e·quip·ping.**

e·quip·ment (i kwip′mənt), **1** a fitting out; providing: *The equipment of the expedition took six months.* **2** an outfit; what one is equipped with; supplies: *We keep our camping equipment in order.* noun.

eq·ui·ta·ble (ek′wə tə bəl), fair; just: *It is equitable to pay a person good wages for work well done.* adjective.

e·quiv·a·lent (i kwiv′ə lənt), **1** equal: *Nodding your head is equivalent to saying yes.* **2** something equivalent: *Five pennies are the equivalent of a nickel.* 1 adjective, 2 noun.

-er[1], a suffix meaning a person or thing that _____s: Follow*er* means *a person or thing that follows.*

-er[2], a suffix meaning more: Soft*er* means *more soft.* Slow*er* means *more slow.*

er·a (ir′ə), **1** a period of time or history: *We live in the era of space exploration.* **2** a period of time starting from some important or significant happening or date: *We live in the 20th century of the Christian era.* noun.

e·rad·i·cate (i rad′ə kāt), to get rid of entirely; destroy completely: *Yellow fever has been eradicated in the United States but it still exists in some other countries.* verb, **e·rad·i·cates, e·rad·i·cat·ed, e·rad·i·cat·ing.**

e·rase (i rās′), to rub out; wipe out: *He erased the wrong answer and wrote in the right one.* verb, **e·ras·es, e·rased, e·ras·ing.**

e·ras·er (i rā′sər), something used to erase marks made with pencil, ink, or chalk: *His pencil had a worn-out eraser at the tip.* noun.

e·ra·sure (i rā′shər), **1** a rubbing out: *the erasure of a typing error.* **2** a place where a word or letter has been erased. noun.

ere (er *or* ar), an old word meaning before: *He will come ere long.* preposition, conjunction.

e·rect (i rekt′), **1** straight up; not tipping; not bending: *The athlete had an erect posture.* **2** to put straight up; set upright: *They erected a television antenna on the roof.* **3** to put up; build: *That house was erected forty years ago.* 1 adjective, 2,3 verb.

e·rec·tion (i rek′shən), a setting up; raising: *The erection of the tent took only a few minutes.* noun.

Er·ie (ir′ē), **Lake,** one of the five Great Lakes. noun.

er·mine (ėr′mən), **1** a weasel that is brown in summer but white with a black tip on its tail in

equilibrium—It is important for tightrope walkers to maintain their **equilibrium.**

ermine (definition 1)
11 inches (28 centimeters) long with the tail

winter. **2** its soft, white fur, used for coats and trimming. *noun, plural* **er·mines** or **er·mine.**

e·rode (i rōd′), to eat away; wear away: *Running water erodes soil and rock. verb,* **e·rodes, e·rod·ed, e·rod·ing.**

erosion
The cracks in the land are caused by **erosion.**

e·ro·sion (i rō′zhən), an eating away; being worn away little by little: *In geography, we study the erosion of the earth by wind and water. noun.*

err (ėr *or* er), **1** to go wrong; make a mistake: *Everyone errs at some time or other.* **2** to do wrong; sin: *To err is human; to forgive, divine. verb.*

er·rand (er′ənd), **1** a trip to do something: *She has gone on an errand to the store.* **2** what one is sent to do: *I did ten errands in one trip. noun.*

er·rat·ic (ə rat′ik), **1** uncertain; irregular: *An erratic clock is not dependable.* **2** unusual; odd: *erratic ideas. adjective.*

er·ro·ne·ous (ə rō′nē əs), mistaken; incorrect; wrong: *Years ago many people held the erroneous belief that the earth was flat. adjective.*

er·ror (er′ər), **1** a mistake; something done that is wrong; something that is not the way it ought to be: *I failed my test because of errors in spelling.* **2** in baseball, a fielder's mistake that either allows a batter to reach first, or a runner to advance one or more bases. *noun.*

e·rupt (i rupt′), to burst forth: *Lava and ashes erupted from the volcano. verb.*

e·rup·tion (i rup′shən), a bursting forth: *an eruption of lava. noun.*

es·ca·la·tor (es′kə lā′tər), a moving stairway: *The store had both an elevator and an escalator. noun.*

es·cape (e skāp′), **1** to get free; get out and away: *The bird escaped from its cage.* **2** to keep free or safe from: *We all escaped the measles.* **3** the act of escaping: *Their escape was aided by the thick fog.* **4** a way of escaping: *There was no escape from the trap.* **5** to fail to be noticed or remembered by: *I knew his face, but the name escaped me.* 1,2,5 *verb,* **es·capes, es·caped, es·cap·ing;** 3,4 *noun.*

es·cort (es′kôrt *for 1-3;* e skôrt′ *for 4*), **1** a person or group going with another person to give protection, or to show honor: *An escort of several city officials accompanied the famous visitor.* **2** one or more ships or airplanes serving as a guard: *During World War II destroyers often served as escorts to tankers.* **3** a man who goes on a date with a woman: *Her escort to the party was a tall young man.* **4** to go with as an escort: *Police cars escorted the governor during the parade. I enjoyed escorting my cousin to the movie.* 1-3 *noun,* 4 *verb.*

Es·ki·mo (es′kə mō), **1** a member of a people living in the arctic regions of North America and northeastern Asia. **2** the language of the Eskimos. **3** of or having to do with the Eskimos or their language. 1,2 *noun, plural* **Es·ki·mos** or **Es·ki·mo** *for* 1; 3 *adjective.*

e·soph·a·gus (ē sof′ə gəs), the passage for food from the throat to the stomach. *noun.*

es·pe·cial (e spesh′əl), special; more than others: *They are my especial friends. adjective.*

es·pe·cial·ly (e spesh′ə lē), more than others; particularly; principally; chiefly: *This book is especially designed for students. adverb.*

es·pi·o·nage (es′pē ə näzh *or* es′pē ə nij), spying; the use of spies. *Nations use espionage to find out other countries' secrets. noun.*

es·say (es′ā), a short composition on a particular subject. *noun.*

es·sence (es′ns), the most important or characteristic part of something: *Being thoughtful of others is the essence of politeness. noun.*

es·sen·tial (ə sen′shəl), **1** absolutely necessary; very important: *Good food is essential to good health.* **2** an absolutely necessary element or quality: *Learn the essentials first; then learn the details.* 1 *adjective,* 2 *noun.*

es·sen·tial·ly (ə sen′shə lē), in essence; in essentials; in an essential manner. *adverb.*

-est, a suffix meaning most: *Warmest means most warm. Slowest means most slow.*

es·tab·lish (e stab′lish), **1** to set up and keep going for a long time: *to establish a government, to* establish a business. *The English established colonies in America.* **2** to show beyond any doubt; prove: *He established his client's alibi by calling several witnesses. verb.*

es·tab·lish·ment (e stab′lish mənt), **1** an establishing or a being established: *The establishment of the business took several years.* **2** something established. A household or a business is called an establishment. *noun.*

es·tate (e stāt′), **1** a large piece of land, usually with a large house built on it. **2** the property of all kinds that a person owns: *When the rich woman died, she left an estate of two million dollars. noun.*

es·teem (e stēm′), **1** to think highly of: *We esteem courage.* **2** a very favorable opinion; high regard: *Courage is held in esteem.* **1** *verb,* **2** *noun.*

es·ti·mate (es′tə mit *for 1;* es′tə māt *for 2*), **1** a judgment or opinion about how much, how many, or how good: *Her estimate of the length of the fish was 15 inches.* **2** to form a judgment or opinion: *We estimate the job will take a day.* **1** *noun,* **2** *verb,* **es·ti·mates, es·ti·mat·ed, es·ti·mat·ing.**

es·ti·ma·tion (es′tə mā′shən), an opinion; judgment: *In my estimation, your plan will not work. noun.*

Es·to·ni·a (e stō′nē ə), a country in northern Europe. *noun.*

etc., et cetera. *Etc.* is usually read "and so forth." The definition of *etching* below uses *etc.* after the word *glass.* This means that *etching* can be done on other items similar to metal and glass.

et cet·er·a (et set′ər ə), and so forth; and so on; and the rest; and the like.
[*Et cetera* is a Latin phrase meaning "and all the other things."]

etch (ech), to engrave a design on a metal plate by acid that eats lines into it. Filled with ink, the lines of the design will reproduce a copy on paper. *verb.*

etch·ing (ech′ing), **1** a picture or design printed from an etched plate. **2** the process of engraving a drawing or design on metal, glass, etc., by means of acid. *noun.*

e·ter·nal (i tėr′nl), **1** without beginning or ending; lasting throughout all time. **2** seeming to go on forever: *When will we have an end to this eternal noise? adjective.*

e·ter·ni·ty (i tėr′nə tē), **1** all time; all the past and all the future. **2** a period of time that seems endless: *I waited in the dentist's office for an eternity. noun, plural* **e·ter·ni·ties.**

-eth, a suffix meaning: number _____ in order or position in a series. Sixti*eth* means *number* sixty *in order or position in a series.* The suffix *-th* is used to form numbers like *sixth.*

e·ther (ē′thər), a liquid that causes one to become unconscious when its fumes are inhaled. It is sometimes used in operations so that a person won't feel pain. *noun.*

E·thi·o·pi·a (ē′thē ō′pē ə), a country in eastern Africa. *noun.*

eth·nic (eth′nik), of or having to do with a group of people who have the same race, nationality, or culture: *ethnic festivals, ethnic foods. adjective.*

et·i·quette (et′ə ket), the usual rules for behavior in society: *Etiquette requires that we eat peas with a fork, not a knife. noun.*

et·y·mol·o·gy (et′ə mol′ə jē), an account or explanation of the origin and history of a word; word history. There is an etymology at the word **elephant.** *noun, plural* **et·y·mol·o·gies.**

eu·ca·lyp·tus (yü′kə lip′təs), a very tall tree that grows mainly in Australia. It is valued for its timber and for an oil made from its leaves, used in flavorings, perfumes, and drugs. *noun, plural* **eu·ca·lyp·tus·es.**

Eur·a·sia (yur ā′zhə), Europe and Asia, thought of as a single land mass or continent. *noun.*

Eur·ope (yur′əp), the continent west of Asia and east of the Atlantic Ocean. Only one continent, Australia, is smaller than Europe. France and Greece are countries in Europe. *noun.*

Eur·o·pe·an (yur′ə pē′ən), **1** of Europe; having something to do with Europe or its people; from Europe. **2** a person born or living in Europe. Frenchmen, Germans, and Spaniards are Europeans. **1** *adjective,* **2** *noun.*

European Community, an organization of 12 European countries with common economic and social policies. Its members are France, Germany, United Kingdom, Italy, Denmark, Belgium, the Netherlands, Ireland, Luxembourg, Greece, Spain, and Portugal.

e·vac·u·ate (i vak′yü āt), **1** to leave empty; withdraw from: *People quickly evacuated the burning building.* **2** to withdraw; remove: *Efforts were made to evacuate all civilians from the war zone. verb,* **e·vac·u·ates, e·vac·u·at·ed, e·vac·u·at·ing.**

e·vade (i vād′), to get away from by trickery; avoid by cleverness: *When my parents asked who broke the lamp, I tried to evade the question by saying, "I wonder who!" verb,* **e·vades, e·vad·ed, e·vad·ing.**

e·val·u·ate (i val′yü āt), to find out the value or the amount of: *An expert will evaluate the old furniture you wish to sell. verb,* **e·val·u·ates, e·val·u·at·ed, e·val·u·at·ing.**

e·vap·o·rate (i vap′ə rāt′), **1** to turn into a gas: *Boiling water evaporates rapidly.* **2** to vanish; disappear: *My good resolutions evaporated soon after New Year. verb,* **e·vap·o·rates, e·vap·o·rat·ed, e·vap·o·rat·ing.**

ethnic—The dancers wore **ethnic** costumes.

e·vap·o·ra·tion (i vap′ə rā′shən), an evaporating: *Wet clothes on a line become dry by evaporation of the water in them. noun.*

eve (ēv), the evening or day before some holiday or special day: *Christmas Eve. noun.*

e·ven (ē′vən), **1** level; flat; smooth: *The country is even, with no high hills.* **2** at the same level: *The snow was even with the window.* **3** keeping about the same; regular; uniform: *an even temper, an even motion, an even temperature.* **4** equal; no more or less than: *They divided the money in even shares.* **5** to make equal or level: *She evened the edges by trimming them.* **6** able to be divided by 2 without a remainder: *2, 4, 6, 8, and 10 are even numbers.* **7** neither more nor less; exact: *Twelve apples make an even dozen.* **8** just: *She left even as you came.* **9** indeed: *He is ready, even eager, to go.* **10** though one would not expect it; as one would not expect: *Even the weather service was surprised by the snowstorm.* **11** still; yet: *You can read even better if you try.* 1-4,6,7 *adjective,* 5 *verb,* 8-11 *adverb.*

even if, although: *I will come, even if it rains.*

get even, to have revenge: *I got even with him for telling lies about me.*

eve·ning (ēv′ning), the time between sunset and bedtime: *We spent the evening watching TV. noun.*

e·vent (i vent′), **1** a happening; important happening: *The discovery of America was a great event.* **2** an item or contest in a program of sports: *Running a mile was the last event. noun.*

in the event of, in the case of: *In the event of rain, the party will be held indoors.*

e·vent·ful (i vent′fəl), full of events; having many unusual events: *The class spent an eventful day touring the new zoo. adjective.*

e·ven·tu·al (i ven′chü əl), coming in the end: *After several failures, his eventual success surprised us. adjective.*

e·ven·tu·al·ly (i ven′chü ə lē), finally; in the end: *We searched a long time for the key but eventually we found it. adverb.*

ev·er (ev′ər), **1** at any time: *Is she ever at home?* **2** at all times; always: *She is ever ready to accept a new challenge.* **3** by any chance; at all: *What did you ever do to make him so angry? adverb.*

ever so, very: *The ocean is ever so deep.*

ev·er·glade (ev′ər glād), a large swamp or marsh. *noun.*

ev·er·green (ev′ər grēn′), **1** having green leaves all the year. **2** an evergreen plant. Pine, spruce, cedar, ivy, and rhododendrons are evergreens. **3** evergreens, evergreen twigs or branches used for decoration, especially at Christmas. 1 *adjective,* 2,3 *noun.*

ev·er·last·ing (ev′ər las′ting), **1** lasting forever; never stopping: *the everlasting beauty of nature.* **2** lasting too long; tiresome: *Their everlasting complaints annoyed me. adjective.*

eve·ry (ev′rē), each one of the entire number of: *Read every word on the page. Every student must have a book. adjective.*

every now and then, from time to time: *Every*

a hat	**i** it	**oi** oil	**ch** child	a in about
ā age	**ī** ice	**ou** out	**ng** long	e in taken
ä far	**o** hot	**u** cup	**sh** she	ə = i in pencil
e let	**ō** open	**u̇** put	**th** thin	o in lemon
ē equal	**ô** order	**ü** rule	**ᵀʜ** then	u in circus
ėr term			**zh** measure	

now and then we have a frost that ruins the crop.

every other, every second: *Every other day it's my turn to do the dishes.*

eve·ry·bod·y (ev′rə bud′ē or ev′rē bod′ē), every person: *Everybody likes the new principal. pronoun.*

eve·ry·day (ev′rē dā′), **1** of every day; daily: *Accidents are everyday occurrences.* **2** for every ordinary day; not for Sundays or holidays: *She wears everyday clothes to work. adjective.*

eve·ry·one (ev′rē wun or ev′rē wən), each one; everybody: *Everyone in the class is here. pronoun.*

eve·ry·thing (ev′rē thing), **1** every thing; all things: *She did everything she could to help her friend.* **2** something extremely important: *This news means everything to us.* 1 *pronoun,* 2 *noun.*

eve·ry·where (ev′rē hwer or ev′rē hwar), in every place; in all places or lands: *A smile is understood everywhere. adverb.*

ev·i·dence (ev′ə dəns), facts; proof; anything that shows or makes clear: *The jam on his face was evidence that he had been in the kitchen. noun.*

in evidence, easily seen or noticed: *The damage caused by the flood was much in evidence.*

ev·i·dent (ev′ə dənt), easy to see or understand; clear; plain: *It was evident that the shattered vase could never be repaired. adjective.*

e·vil (ē′vəl), **1** bad; wrong; causing harm: *an evil life, an evil character, an evil plan.* **2** something bad; evil quality or act: *Their thoughts were full of evil.* **3** a thing causing harm: *Crime and poverty are some of the evils of society.* 1 *adjective,* 2,3 *noun.*

ev·o·lu·tion (ev′ə lü′shən), **1** gradual development: *the evolution of transportation from horse and buggy to jet aircraft.* **2** the theory that all

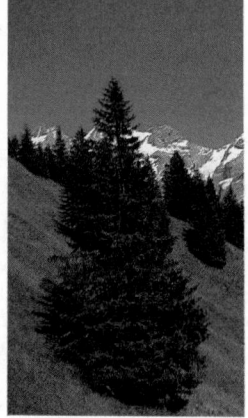

evergreen (definition 2)—**Evergreens** grow in many climates.

living things developed from a few simple forms of life. *noun.*

e·volve (i volv′), to unfold; develop gradually: *Buds evolve into flowers. The modern automobile evolved from the horse and buggy. She evolved a plan for earning money during her summer vacation. verb,* **e·volves, e·volved, e·volv·ing.**

ewe (yü), a female sheep. *noun.*

ex·act (eg zakt′), without any mistake; correct; accurate: *an exact measurement, the exact amount. adjective.*

ex·act·ing (eg zak′ting), 1 requiring much; hard to please: *An exacting teacher will not permit careless work.* 2 needing hard work, care, or attention: *Flying an airplane is exacting work. adjective.*

ex·act·ly (eg zakt′lē), 1 without any error; precisely. 2 just so; quite right. *adverb.*

ex·ag·ge·rate (eg zaj′ə rāt′), to say or think something is larger or greater than it is; go beyond the truth: *The little boy exaggerated when he said there were a million cats in the backyard. verb,* **ex·ag·ge·rates, ex·ag·ge·rat·ed, ex·ag·ge·rat·ing.**

[*Exaggerate* comes from a Latin word meaning "to heap up." Our word developed in meaning from "heap up," to "make large," to "make too large," and then to "go beyond the truth."]

ex·ag·ge·ra·tion (eg zaj′ə rā′shən), a statement that goes beyond the truth: *It is an exaggeration to say that you would rather die than touch a snake. noun.*

ex·alt (eg zôlt′), to make high in rank, honor, or power: *The queen exalted the landowner to the rank of earl. verb.*

ex·am (eg zam′), examination. *noun.*

ex·am·i·na·tion (eg zam′ə nā′shən), 1 an examining: *The doctor made a careful examination of my eyes.* 2 a test: *an examination in arithmetic. noun.*

ex·am·ine (eg zam′ən), 1 to look at closely and carefully: *The doctor examined the wound.* 2 to test; test the knowledge or ability of; ask questions of: *The lawyer examined the witness. verb.* **ex·am·ines, ex·am·ined, ex·am·in·ing.**

ex·am·ple (eg zam′pəl), 1 a sample; one thing taken to show what the others are like: *New York is an example of a busy city.* 2 a model; pattern: *Children often follow the example set by their parents.* 3 a problem in arithmetic: *She wrote the example on the chalkboard.* 4 a warning to others: *The principal made an example of the students who were tardy by making them come to school early for a week. noun.*

set an example, to give, show, or be a model of conduct.

ex·as·pe·rate (eg zas′pə rāt′), to irritate very much; annoy greatly; make angry: *The pupils' constant noise exasperated the teacher. verb,* **ex·as·pe·rates, ex·as·pe·rat·ed, ex·as·pe·rat·ing.**

ex·as·pe·ra·tion (eg zas′pə rā′shən), extreme annoyance; anger; irritation. *noun.*

excavate (definition 4)—The students were looking for evidence of ancient people when they **excavated** the site.

ex·ca·vate (ek′skə vāt), 1 to make hollow; hollow out: *The tunnel was made by excavating the side of a mountain.* 2 to make by digging; dig: *The builders excavated a basement for the new house.* 3 to dig out; scoop out: *Big machines excavated the dirt and loaded it into trucks.* 4 to uncover by digging. *verb,* **ex·ca·vates, ex·ca·vat·ed, ex·ca·vat·ing.**

ex·ca·va·tion (ek′skə vā′shən), 1 digging out; digging: *The excavation for the basement of our new house took three days.* 2 a hole made by digging: *The excavation for the new building was fifty feet across. noun.*

ex·ceed (ek sēd′), 1 to be more or greater than: *The sum of 5 and 7 exceeds 10. Lifting that heavy trunk exceeds my strength.* 2 to do more than; go beyond: *Drivers should not exceed the speed limit. verb.*

ex·ceed·ing·ly (ek sē′ding lē), very greatly; more than others; very: *Yesterday was an exceedingly hot day. adverb.*

ex·cel (ek sel′), to be better than others; do better than others: *She excels in arithmetic. verb,* **ex·cels, ex·celled, ex·cel·ling.**

ex·cel·lence (ek′sə ləns), a very high quality; being better than others: *His teacher praised him for the excellence of his report. noun.*

Ex·cel·len·cy (ek′sə lən sē), a title of honor used in speaking to or of a prime minister, governor, bishop, or other high official: *Your Excellency, His Excellency, Her Excellency. noun, plural* **Ex·cel·len·cies.**

ex·cel·lent (ek′sə lənt), very, very good; better than others: *Excellent work deserves high praise. adjective.*

ex·cept (ek sept′), 1 leaving out; other than: *He works every day except Sunday.* 2 to leave out: *Those who passed the first test were excepted from the second.* 3 only; but: *I would have had a perfect score except I missed the last question.* 1 *preposition,* 2 *verb,* 3 *conjunction.*

except for, 1 with the exception of; except: *They all came early except for her.* 2 if it were not for: *We could have gone today except for the rain.*

ex·cep·tion (ek sep′shən), 1 a leaving out; omission: *I like all my studies with the exception of* arithmetic. **2** a thing that is different from the rule: *He comes on time every day; today is an exception.* noun.

take exception, to object: *Several teachers and students took exception to the plan of having classes on Saturdays.*

ex·cep·tion·al (ek sep′shə nəl), unusual; out of the ordinary: *This warm weather is exceptional for January. She is an exceptional student.* adjective.

ex·cess (ek ses′ for 1; ek′ses for 2), **1** the part that is too much: *There was too much grease in the pan so I poured off the excess.* **2** extra: *Passengers must pay for excess baggage taken on an airplane.* **1** noun, plural **ex·ces·ses;** **2** adjective.

ex·ces·sive (ek ses′iv), too much; too great; extreme: *I did not buy her bicycle because the price she asked was excessive.* adjective.

ex·change (eks chānj′), **1** to give for something else; change: *He exchanged the tight coat for one that was a size larger.* **2** to give and take things of the same kind: *to exchange letters. They exchanged blows.* **3** a giving and taking: *Ten pennies for a dime is a fair exchange. During the truce there was an exchange of prisoners.* **4** a place where people buy, sell, or trade things. A stock exchange is a place to do business in stocks. **1,2** verb, **ex·chang·es, ex·changed, ex·chang·ing; 3, 4** noun.

ex·cit·a·ble (ek sī′tə bəl), easily excited. adjective.

ex·cite (ek sīt′), **1** to stir up the feelings of: *I was excited about going to summer camp.* **2** to bring out; arouse: *Plans for a field trip excited the students' interest.* verb, **ex·cites, ex·cit·ed, ex·cit·ing.**

ex·cit·ed (ek sī′tid), stirred up; aroused: *The excited mob rushed into the mayor's office.* adjective.

ex·cite·ment (ek sīt′mənt), **1** an excited condition: *The birth of twins caused great excitement in the family.* **2** something that excites: *Camping out in the high mountains was an excitement for us all.* noun.

ex·cit·ing (ek sī′ting), causing excitement; arousing; stirring: *We read an exciting story about pirates and buried treasure.* adjective.

ex·claim (ek sklām′), to cry out; speak suddenly in surprise or strong feeling: *"Here you are at last!" I exclaimed.* verb.

ex·cla·ma·tion (ek′sklə mā′shən), something said suddenly as the result of surprise or strong feeling. *Oh!, Hurrah!, Well!, Look!,* and *Listen!* are common exclamations. noun.

exclamation mark or **exclamation point,** a mark (!) used after a word, phrase, or sentence to show that it was exclaimed. EXAMPLE: *Hurrah! We are going to the circus.*

ex·clam·a·to·ry (ek sklam′ə tôr′ē), using, containing, or expressing exclamation. adjective.

ex·clude (ek sklüd′), to shut out; keep out: *The club's rules exclude from membership anyone who lives out of town.* verb, **ex·cludes, ex·clud·ed, ex·clud·ing.**

ex·clu·sion (ek sklü′zhən), **1** an excluding:

a hat	**i** it	**oi** oil	**ch** child	⎧ a in about
ā age	**ī** ice	**ou** out	**ng** long	⎪ e in taken
ä far	**o** hot	**u** cup	**sh** she	ə = ⎨ i in pencil
e let	**ō** open	**u̇** put	**th** thin	⎪ o in lemon
ē equal	**ô** order	**ü** rule	**ŦH** then	⎩ u in circus
ėr term			**zh** measure	

Swimmers asked for the exclusion of boats from one side of the lake. **2** a being excluded: *Their exclusion from the meeting hurt their feelings.* noun.

ex·clu·sive (ek sklü′siv), **1** not divided or shared with others; single; sole: *Inventors have an exclusive right for a certain number of years to make what they have invented and patented.* **2** limited to a single object: *Please give exclusive attention to these instructions.* **3** very particular about choosing friends, members, and so on: *It is hard to get admitted to an exclusive club.* adjective.

exclusive of, leaving out; not counting: *There are 26 days in that month, exclusive of Sundays.*

ex·clu·sive·ly (ek sklü′siv lē), with the exclusion of all others; only: *She is interested exclusively in sports.* adverb.

ex·cur·sion (ek skėr′zhən), a trip taken for interest or pleasure, often by a number of people together: *Our club went on an excursion to the mountains.* noun.

ex·cuse (ek skyüz′ for 1,3-5; ek skyüs′ for 2 and 6), **1** to offer an apology for; try to remove the blame of: *She excused her being upset yesterday as the result of a headache from too little sleep.* **2** a reason, real or pretended, that is given; explanation: *He had many excuses for coming late.* **3** to be a reason or explanation for: *Sickness excuses absence from school.* **4** to pardon; forgive: *Excuse me; I have to go now. Will you excuse my carelessness in spilling the milk?* **5** to free from duty; let off: *Those who passed the first test will be excused from the second one.* **6** a note saying that someone should be excused for something or from something: *The next time you are late for school, your parents will have to write you an excuse.* **1,3-5** verb, **ex·cus·es, ex·cused, ex·cus·ing; 2,6** noun.

excuse oneself, 1 to ask to be pardoned: *He*

exclamations

excused himself for bumping into me. **2** to ask permission to leave: *I excused myself from the table.*

ex·e·cute (ek′sə kyüt), **1** to carry out; do; complete: *The magician executed a difficult trick.* **2** to put into effect; enforce: *Congress makes the laws; the President executes them.* **3** to put to death according to law: *The murderer was executed.* *verb,* **ex·e·cutes, ex·e·cut·ed, ex·e·cut·ing.**

ex·e·cu·tion (ek′sə kyü′shən), **1** a carrying out; doing: *She was prompt in the execution of her duties.* **2** a putting into effect. **3** a putting to death according to law. *noun.*

ex·e·cu·tion·er (ek′sə kyü′shə nər), a person who puts criminals to death according to law. *noun.*

ex·ec·u·tive (eg zek′yə tiv), **1** having to do with management: *An executive job is a job managing something.* **2** having the duty and power of putting laws into effect: *The President is the head of the executive branch of government.* **3** a person who manages things and who decides or helps decide what should be done: *The president of a business is an executive.* **4** a person, group, or branch of government that has the duty and power of putting laws into effect: *The highest executive of a state is the governor.* **1,2** *adjective,* **3,4** *noun.*

ex·em·pli·fy (eg zem′plə fī), to show by example; be an example of: *The lifeguard exemplified courage.* *verb,* **ex·em·pli·fies, ex·em·pli·fied, ex·em·pli·fy·ing.**

ex·empt (eg zempt′), **1** to make free from a duty, obligation, or rule; release: *Students who get high marks all year are exempted from final examinations.* **2** freed from a duty, obligation, or rule: *School property is exempt from all taxes.* **1** *verb,* **2** *adjective.*

ex·er·cise (ek′sər sīz), **1** the active use of the body or mind for its improvement: *Physical exercise is good for the health.* **2** a using or practice: *Safety requires the exercise of caution.* **3** to make use of: *It is wise to exercise caution in crossing the street.* **4** something that gives skill: *I perform physical exercises each day to strengthen my body. Study the lesson, and then do the exercises at the end.* **5** to take exercise; go through exercises: *I exercise for ten minutes each morning.* **6** to give exercise to; train: *She exercises her horse after school every day.* **7** **exercises,** ceremony or program: *She gave the farewell address at the graduation exercises.* **1,2,4,7** *noun,* **3,5,6** *verb,* **ex·er·cis·es, ex·er·cised, ex·er·cis·ing.**

ex·ert (eg zėrt′), to use; put into use; use fully: *An athlete exerts both strength and skill. A ruler exerts authority.* *verb.*

exert oneself, to make an effort; try hard; strive: *You will really have to exert yourself to make up the work you missed.*

ex·er·tion (eg zėr′shən), an effort: *Our exertions kept the fire from spreading.* *noun.*

ex·hale (eks hāl′), to breathe out: *We exhale air from our lungs.* *verb,* **ex·hales, ex·haled, ex·hal·ing.**

ex·haust (eg zôst′), **1** to use up: *The dry summer nearly exhausted the city's supply of water.* **2** to tire out: *The long, hard climb up the hill exhausted us.* **3** a pipe through which gases escape from an engine. **4** the gases that escape from an engine: *The exhaust from an automobile engine is poisonous.* **1,2** *verb,* **3,4** *noun.*

ex·haust·ed (eg zô′stid), **1** used up: *The teacher's patience was exhausted by the students' jabbering.* **2** worn out; very tired: *The exhausted hikers stopped to rest after their long walk. adjective.*

ex·haus·tion (eg zôs′chən), **1** the act of exhausting. **2** the condition of being exhausted; great tiredness: *The hikers were suffering from extreme exhaustion. noun.*

ex·hib·it (eg zib′it), **1** to show: *Both of their children exhibit a talent for music. He exhibits interest whenever you talk about dogs.* **2** to show publicly; put on display: *She hopes to exhibit her paintings in New York.* **3** an exhibiting; public showing; exhibition: *Our school gave an exhibit of student science projects.* **4** a thing or things shown publicly. **1,2** *verb,* **3,4** *noun.*

exhibit (definition 3)
a museum **exhibit** of the first giraffes brought to England

ex·hi·bi·tion (ek′sə bish′ən), **1** a showing: *Pushing and shoving in line is an exhibition of bad manners.* **2** a public show: *The art school holds an exhibition of paintings every year.* **3** a thing or things shown publicly; exhibit. *noun.*

ex·hil·a·rate (eg zil′ə rāt′), to make lively; stimulate; refresh: *We were exhilarated by an early morning swim.* *verb,* **ex·hil·a·rates, ex·hil·a·rat·ed, ex·hil·a·rat·ing.**

ex·ile (eg′zīl *or* ek′sīl), **1** to make a person go from home or country, often by law as a punishment; banish: *The traitors were exiled from their country for life.* **2** a person who is banished: *She has been an exile for ten years.* **3** banishment: *He was sent into exile for life.* **1** *verb,* **ex·iles, ex·iled, ex·il·ing; 2,3** *noun.*

ex·ist (eg zist′), **1** to be: *The world has existed a* *long time.* **2** to be real: *She believes that ghosts exist.* **3** to live; have life: *A person cannot exist without air.* **4** to be found; occur: *The whooping crane exists only in North America. verb.*

ex·ist·ence (eg zis′təns), **1** the state or condition of being: *Dinosaurs disappeared from existence thousands of years ago.* **2** a being real: *Most people do not now believe in the existence of ghosts.* **3** life: *Drivers of racing cars lead a dangerous existence. noun.*

ex·it (eg′zit *or* ek′sit), **1** a way out: *The theater had six exits.* **2** an act of leaving; departure: *When the cat came in, the mice made a hasty exit.* **3** to go out; leave: *Please exit by the doors at the rear of the room.* **1,2** *noun,* **3** *verb.*

ex·or·bi·tant (eg zôr′bə tənt), very excessive; much too high: *One dollar is an exorbitant price for a pack of gum. adjective.*

ex·ot·ic (eg zot′ik), foreign; strange. *adjective.*

exotic—Have you ever seen such an **exotic** fish?

ex·pand (ek spand′), to spread out; open out; unfold; swell; make or grow larger: *A balloon expands when it is blown up. A bird expands its wings before flying. Our country has expanded many times. You can expand a short speech into a long one. verb.*

ex·panse (ek spans′), an open or unbroken stretch; wide, spreading surface: *The Pacific Ocean is a vast expanse of water. noun.*

ex·pan·sion (ek span′shən), an increase in size or volume: *The expansion of the factory made room for more machines. Heat causes the expansion of metal. noun.*

ex·pect (ek spekt′), **1** to think something will probably come or happen; look for: *We expect hot days in summer.* **2** to want or count on something because it is necessary or right: *I expect you to pay for the damage you did to my bicycle.* **3** to think; suppose; guess: *I expect you're right about that. verb.*

ex·pect·ant (ek spek′tənt), expecting something; thinking that something will happen or come: *She opened her package with an expectant smile. adjective.*

ex·pec·ta·tion (ek′spek tā′shən), an expecting or being expected; anticipation: *His expectations*

a hat	**i** it	**oi** oil	**ch** child	⎧ a in about
ā age	**ī** ice	**ou** out	**ng** long	e in taken
ä far	**o** hot	**u** cup	**sh** she	**ə =** ⎨ i in pencil
e let	**ō** open	**u̇** put	**th** thin	o in lemon
ē equal	**ô** order	**ü** rule	**ᴛʜ** then	⎩ u in circus
ėr term			**zh** measure	

of getting money for his invention failed to come true. noun.

ex·pe·di·tion (ek′spə dish′ən), **1** a journey for a special purpose, such as exploration or scientific study. **2** the people that make such a journey. *noun.*

expedition (definition 2)—The **expedition** made a camp at the base of the mountains.

ex·pel (ek spel′), to put out; dismiss: *A pupil who cheats or steals may be expelled from school.* verb, **ex·pels, ex·pelled, ex·pel·ling.**

ex·pend (ek spend′), to spend; use up: *He expended thought, work, and money on his project. verb.*

ex·pend·i·ture (ek spen′də chu̇r), **1** a spending; using up: *Building a sailboat requires the expenditure of much money, time, and effort.* **2** the amount of money, time, or effort spent; expense: *Her expenditures for Christmas presents were $23 and 14 hours of shopping. noun.*

ex·pense (ek spens′), **1** cost; charge: *The expense of the trip was small. The class traveled to the zoo at the school's expense.* **2** a cause of spending: *Supporting a child at college is an expense for parents. noun.*

ex·pen·sive (ek spen′siv), costly; high-priced: *He had a very expensive pen which cost $10. adjective.*

ex·per·i·ence (ek spir′ē əns), **1** what happens to a person: *We had several pleasant experiences on our trip. People learn by experience.* **2** practice; knowledge gained by doing or seeing things: *Have you had any experience in this kind of work?* **3** to feel; have happen to one: *to experience great pain.* **1,2** *noun,* **3** *verb,* **ex·per·i·enc·es, ex·per·i·enced, ex·per·i·enc·ing.**

ex·per·i·enced (ek spir′ē ənst), skillful or wise because of experience: *The job calls for a person experienced in teaching children. adjective.*

ex·per·i·ment (ek sper′ə mənt *for 1;* ek sper′ə mənt *for 2*), **1** to try in order to find out;

make trials or tests: *The painter is experimenting with different paints to get the color he wants.* **2 a** trial or test to find out something: *We made an experiment to discover the weight of the air in a basketball. Scientists test out theories by experiment.* 1 *verb,* 2 *noun.*

ex·per·i·men·tal (ek sper′ə men′tl), **1** based on experiments: *Chemistry is an experimental science.* **2** used for experiments: *A new variety of wheat was developed at the experimental farm.* **3** for testing or trying out: *The young bird made experimental attempts to fly. adjective.*

experimental (definition 3)—This is an **experimental** model of a car with three wheels.

ex·per·i·men·ta·tion (ek sper′ə men tā′shən), an experimenting: *Cures for disease are sometimes found by experimentation on animals. noun.*

ex·pert (ek′spėrt′ for 1; ek spėrt′ or ek′spėrt′ for 2 and 3), **1** a person who has much skill or who knows a great deal about some special thing: *She is an expert at fishing.* **2** having much skill; knowing a great deal about some special thing: *an expert painter.* **3** needing or showing special skill or knowledge: *We were amazed at the expert workmanship in the fine carving.* 1 *noun,* 2,3 *adjective.*

ex·pi·ra·tion (ek′spə rā′shən), a coming to an end: *We shall move at the expiration of our lease. noun.*

ex·pire (ek spīr′), **1** to come to an end: *You must obtain a new automobile license when your old one expires.* **2** to die. *verb,* **ex·pires, ex·pired, ex·pir·ing.**

ex·plain (ek splān′), **1** to make plain or clear; tell the meaning of; tell how to do: *The teacher explained multiplication to the class.* **2** to give reasons for; state the cause of: *Can somebody explain her absence? verb.*

ex·pla·na·tion (ek′splə nā′shən), **1** an explaining; making clear or giving reasons: *He did not understand the teacher's explanation of multiplication.* **2** something that explains: *This diagram is a good explanation of how an automobile engine works. noun.*

ex·plan·a·to·ry (ek splan′ə tôr′ē), helping to explain; helping to make clear: *Read the explanatory part of the lesson before you try to do the problems. adjective.*

ex·plic·it (ek splis′it), clearly expressed; distinctly stated; definite: *She gave such explicit directions that everyone understood them. adjective.*

ex·plode (ek splōd′), **1** to blow up; burst with a loud noise: *The building was destroyed when the defective boiler exploded.* **2** to cause to explode: *Some people explode firecrackers on the Fourth of July.* **3** to burst forth noisily: *The speaker's mistake was so funny the audience exploded with laughter.* *verb,* **ex·plodes, ex·plod·ed, ex·plod·ing.**

ex·ploit (ek′sploit for 1; ek sploit′ for 2 and 3), **1** a bold, unusual act; daring deed: *This book tells about the exploits of Robin Hood.* **2** to make use of; turn to practical account: *A mine is exploited for its minerals.* **3** to make unfair use of; use selfishly for one's own advantage: *Nations used to exploit their colonies, taking as much wealth out of them as they could.* 1 *noun,* 2,3 *verb.*

ex·plo·ra·tion (ek′splə rā′shən), **1** a traveling in little-known lands, seas, or in outer space for the purpose of discovery. **2** a going over carefully; looking into closely; examining. *noun.*

ex·plore (ek splôr′), **1** to travel over little-known lands, seas, or in outer space for the purpose of discovery: *Some day people may explore Mars and Venus.* **2** to go over carefully; examine: *to explore a subject thoroughly. The children explored the new house from attic to cellar. verb,* **ex·plores, ex·plored, ex·plor·ing.**

ex·plor·er (ek splôr′ər), a person who explores. *noun.*

ex·plo·sion (ek splō′zhən), **1** a blowing up; bursting with a loud noise: *The explosion of the bomb shook the whole neighborhood.* **2** a noisy bursting forth; outbreak: *explosions of anger.* **3** a sudden or rapid increase or growth: *The explosion of the world's population has created a shortage of food in many countries. noun.*

ex·plo·sive (ek splō′siv), **1** able to explode; likely to explode: *Gunpowder is explosive.* **2** a substance that is able or likely to explode: *Explosives are used in making fireworks.* **3** tending to burst forth noisily: *His explosive temper gets him into many arguments.* 1,3 *adjective,* 2 *noun.*

ex·port (ek spôrt′ or ek′spôrt for 1; ek′spôrt for 2 and 3), **1** to send goods out of one country for sale and use in another: *The United States exports automobiles.* **2** a thing exported: *Cotton is an important export of the United States.* **3** the act or fact of exporting: *the export of oil from the Arab nations.* 1 *verb,* 2,3 *noun.*

ex·pose (ek spōz′), **1** to lay open; uncover; leave without protection: *While we fished, we were exposed to the hot sun. The whole class has been exposed to the flu.* **2** to put in plain sight; display: *Goods are exposed for sale in a store.* **3** to make known; reveal: *They exposed the plot to the police.* **4** to allow light to reach and act on a photographic film or plate. *verb,* **ex·pos·es, ex·posed, ex·pos·ing.**

ex·po·si·tion (ek′spə zish′ən), a public show or exhibition. A world's fair is an exposition. *noun.*

ex·po·sure (ek spō′zhər), **1** an exposing; laying open; making known: *The exposure of the real criminal cleared the innocent suspect.* **2** a being exposed: *Exposure to the rain has ruined this machinery.* **3** position in relation to the sun and wind. A house with a southern exposure receives sun and wind from the south. **4** an allowing light to reach and form a picture on a photographic film. *noun.*

ex·press (ek spres′), **1** to put into words: *Try to express your idea clearly.* **2** to show by look, voice, or action: *A smile expresses joy.* **3** clear and definite: *It was his express wish that we should go without him.* **4** special; particular: *She came for the express purpose of seeing you.* **5** a quick or direct means of sending. Packages can be sent by express in trains or airplanes. **6** to send by some quick means: *express a package.* **7** a train, bus, or elevator that goes direct from one point to another without making intermediate stops. **8** for fast traveling: *The express train sped past the station without stopping.* **1,2,6** *verb,* **3,4,8** *adjective,* **5,7** *noun, plural* **ex·press·es** for **7.**

express oneself, to say what one thinks: *You must be able to express yourself clearly to become a good public speaker.*

ex·pres·sion (ek spresh′ən), **1** a putting into words: *the expression of an idea.* **2** a word or group of words with a particular meaning: *"Wise guy" is a slang expression.* **3** a showing by look, voice, or action: *A sigh is often an expression of sadness.* **4** a look that shows feeling: *The winners all had happy expressions on their faces.* **5** a bringing out the meaning or beauty of something spoken, sung, or played: *Try to read with more expression. noun.*

ex·pres·sive (ek spres′iv), having much feeling or meaning: *"The cat's skin hung on its bones" is a more expressive sentence than "The cat was very thin." adjective.*

ex·press·way (ek spres′wā′), a highway built for high-speed, long-distance travel. An expressway has a limited number of entrances and exits and a dividing strip between lanes of traffic going in opposite directions. *noun.*

ex·pul·sion (ek spul′shən), a forcing out or a being forced out: *Expulsion from school is a punishment for bad behavior. noun.*

ex·qui·site (ek′skwi zit), **1** very lovely; delicate; beautifully made: *The violet is an exquisite flower.* **2** of highest excellence; most admirable: *They have exquisite taste and manners. adjective.*

ex·tend (ek stend′), **1** to stretch out: *to extend one's hand, to extend a visit, a road that extends to New York.* **2** to give; grant: *This organization extends help to poor people. verb.*

ex·tend·ed fam·i·ly (ek sten′did fam′ə lē), a family of parents, children, and other near relatives of different generations and relationships, all living together.

ex·ten·sion (ek sten′shən), **1** a stretching out: *We are having such a good time that we have decided on an extension of our vacation for three more days.* **2** an addition: *The new extension to our school will make room for more students.* **3** a telephone connected with the main telephone or with a switchboard but in a different location. *noun.*

ex·ten·sive (ek sten′siv), far-reaching; large:

a hat	i it	oi oil	ch child		a in about
ā age	ī ice	ou out	ng long		e in taken
ä far	o hot	u cup	sh she	ə =	i in pencil
e let	ō open	u̇ put	th thin		o in lemon
ē equal	ô order	ü rule	ŦH then		u in circus
ėr term			zh measure		

extensive changes, an extensive park. adjective.

ex·tent (ek stent′), the size, space, length, amount, or degree to which a thing extends: *Airplanes carry people and goods through the whole extent of the country. The extent of a judge's power is limited by law. noun.*

ex·te·ri·or (ek stir′ē ər), **1** outside; outward appearance: *I saw only the exterior of the house, not the interior. Some people have a harsh exterior but a kind heart.* **2** outer: *The skin of an apple is its exterior covering.* **1** *noun,* **2** *adjective.*

ex·ter·mi·nate (ek stėr′mə nāt), to get rid of; destroy completely; kill: *This poison will exterminate rats. verb,* **ex·ter·mi·nates, ex·ter·mi·nat·ed, ex·ter·mi·nat·ing.**
[*Exterminate* comes from a Latin word meaning "to drive out." The original meaning in both Latin and English was "to drive beyond the boundaries," that is, "to banish" or "to exile."]

ex·ter·nal (ek stėr′nl), on the outside; outer: *An ear of corn has an external husk. adjective.*

ex·tinct (ek stingkt′), **1** no longer existing: *The dinosaur is an extinct animal.* **2** not active; gone out: *an extinct volcano. adjective.*

ex·tinc·tion (ek stingk′shən), a bringing to an end; wiping out; destruction: *Physicians are working for the extinction of diseases. noun.*

ex·tin·guish (ek sting′gwish), to put out: *Water extinguished the fire. verb.*

ex·tra (ek′strə), **1** beyond what is usual, expected, or needed: *extra pay, extra fine quality, extra fare.* **2** anything beyond what is usual, expected, or needed: *Their parents bought an expensive new car that had many extras.* **3** a special edition of a newspaper: *The paper published an extra to announce the end of the war.* **1** *adjective,* **1** *adverb,* **2,3** *noun.*

ex·tract (ek strakt′ *for 1;* ek′strakt *for 2*), **1** to draw out, usually with some effort; take out: *to extract oil from olives, to extract iron from the earth, to extract a tooth, to extract a confession.* **2** something drawn out or taken out: *He read several extracts from the poem. Vanilla extract is made from vanilla beans.* **1** *verb,* **2** *noun.*

ex·traor·di·nar·i·ly (ek strôr′də ner′ə lē), most unusually. *adverb.*

ex·traor·di·nar·y (ek strôr′də ner′ē), beyond what is ordinary; very unusual; remarkable; special: *Eight feet is an extraordinary height for a person. adjective.*

ex·trav·a·gance (ek strav′ə gəns), a careless and wasteful spending: *Their extravagance kept them always in debt. noun.*

ex·trav·a·gant (ek strav′ə gənt), spending carelessly and wastefully: *It is extravagant to buy*

extreme | eyewitness

a second television when you have not finished paying for the first one. adjective.

ex·treme (ek strēm′), **1** much more than usual; very great; very strong: *She drove with extreme caution during the snowstorm.* **2** at the very end; the farthest possible; last: *He lives in the extreme western part of town.* **3** two things that are as different as possible from each other: *Joy and grief are two extremes of feeling.* **1,2** *adjective,* **3** *noun.*

go to extremes, to do or say too much: *A person who owns twenty cats is going to extremes.*

ex·treme·ly (ek strēm′lē), much more than usual; very: *It is extremely cold in the Arctic. adverb.*

ex·trem·i·ty (ek strēm′ə tē), **1** the very end; the tip: *Florida is at the southeastern extremity of the United States.* **2** **extremities,** the hands and feet. *noun, plural* **ex·trem·i·ties.**

ex·tri·cate (ek′strə kāt), to release; set free from entanglements, difficulties, or embarrassing situations. *verb,* **ex·tri·cates, ex·tri·cat·ed, ex·tri·cat·ing.**

extricate—She rushed to **extricate** him from his perilous situation.

ex·ult (eg zult′), to be very glad; rejoice greatly: *The winners exulted in their victory. verb.*

ex·ult·ant (eg zult′nt), exulting; rejoicing greatly; triumphant: *The students gave an exultant shout when the teacher told them there would be no classes on Monday. adjective.*

eye (ī), **1** the part of the body by which people and animals see. **2** the colored part of the eye; iris: *She has brown eyes.* **3** the region surrounding the

eye (definition 1)

EYELID
CORNEA
PUPIL
IRIS
LENS
RETINA
OPTIC NERVE
EYELASHES

eye (definition 6)—The man **eyed** the fish and the fish **eyed** the man.

eye: *The blow gave him a black eye.* **4** the ability to see small differences in things: *An artist should have an eye for color.* **5** a look; glance: *I cast an eye over the books and quickly found one I liked.* **6** to watch; observe. **7** a way of thinking; view; opinion: *Stealing is a crime in the eye of the law.* **8** something like an eye or that suggests an eye. The little spots on potatoes, the hole in a needle, and the loop into which a hook fastens are all called eyes. **9** the calm, clear area at the center of a hurricane. **1-5,7-9** *noun,* **6** *verb,* **eyes, eyed, ey·ing** or **eye·ing.**

catch one's eye, to attract one's attention: *A bright red flower caught my eye.*

keep an eye on, to look after; watch carefully: *Keep an eye on the baby.*

see eye to eye, to agree entirely: *My parents and I do not see eye to eye on my weekly allowance.*

eye·ball (ī′bôl′), the eye without the surrounding lids and bony socket. *noun.*

eye·brow (ī′brou′), the hair that grows along the bony ridge just above the eye. *noun.*

eye·glass (ī′glas′), **1** a lens to aid poor vision. **2** **eyeglasses,** a pair of glass or plastic lenses set in a frame, used to help poor vision; glasses. *noun, plural* **eye·glass·es.**

eye·lash (ī′lash′), **1** one of the hairs on the edge of the eyelid. **2** the fringe of such hairs. *noun, plural* **eye·lash·es.**

eye·let (ī′lit), a small, round hole for a lace or cord to go through. *noun.*

eye·lid (ī′lid′), the movable cover of skin, upper or lower, by means of which we can shut and open our eyes. *noun.*

eye·sight (ī′sīt′), **1** the power of seeing; sight: *A hawk has keen eyesight.* **2** range of vision; view: *The water was within eyesight. noun.*

eye·tooth (ī′tüth′), an upper canine tooth. *noun, plural* **eye·teeth.**

eye·wit·ness (ī′wit′nis), a person who has actually seen something happen and so can tell about it. *noun.*

F f

a hat	i it	oi oil	ch child	⎧ a in about
ā age	ī ice	ou out	ng long	e in taken
ä far	o hot	u cup	sh she	ə = ⎨ i in pencil
e let	ō open	u̇ put	th thin	o in lemon
ē equal	ô order	ü rule	ᴛʜ then	⎩ u in circus
ėr term			zh measure	

F or **f** (ef), the sixth letter of the English alphabet. *noun, plural* **F's** or **f's.**

F or **F.,** Fahrenheit.

fa·ble (fā/bəl), **1** a story that is made up to teach a lesson. Fables are often about animals who can talk, such as *The Hare and the Tortoise.* **2** a story that is not true. *noun.*

fab·ric (fab/rik), a woven or knitted material; cloth. Velvet, denim, and linen are fabrics. *noun.*

fab·u·lous (fab/yə ləs), too extraordinary to seem possible; beyond belief; amazing: *The painting was sold for a fabulous price. adjective.*

face (fās), **1** the front part of the head. Your eyes, nose, and mouth are parts of your face. **2** a look; expression: *His face was sad.* **3** an ugly or funny look made by twisting the face: *The girl made a face at her brother.* **4** the front part; the right side; surface: *The face of a clock or watch has numbers on it.* **5** to have the face or front toward: *The house faces the street. The teacher asked the student to face the front of the room.* **6** to meet bravely or boldly: *face a challenge.* 1-4 *noun,* 5,6 *verb,* **fac·es, faced, fac·ing.**

face to face, a with faces toward each other: *The enemies stood face to face.* **b** in direct awareness of something: *The teacher brought me face to face with my poor grade.*

in the face of, 1 in the presence of: *No one wanted to surrender even in the face of invasion.* **2** in spite of: *She said she was right in the face of facts that proved she was wrong.*

fac·et (fas/it), one of the small, polished surfaces of a cut gem. *noun.*

fa·cial (fā/shəl), of or for the face: *We laughed at the facial expressions of the children as they watched the magician. She wiped off the lipstick with a facial tissue. adjective.*

fa·cil·i·tate (fə sil/ə tāt), to make easy; lessen the labor of; help: *Computers facilitate the solving of many problems. verb,* **fa·cil·i·tates, fa·cil·i·tat·ed, fa·cil·i·tat·ing.**

fa·cil·i·ty (fə sil/ə tē), **1** ease; absence of difficulty: *He swam the length of the pool with great facility.* **2** the power to do anything easily and quickly; skill in using the hands or mind: *She has the facility to become a fine composer.* **3 facilities,** something that makes an action easier or provides a special service; aid: *Laundry facilities for our apartment building are in the basement. noun, plural* **fa·cil·i·ties.**

fact (fakt), **1** a thing known to be true; thing known to have happened: *It is a fact that the Pilgrims sailed to America on the Mayflower in 1620.* **2** what is true; truth: *The fact is, I did not want to go to the dance.* **3** a thing said or supposed to be true or to have really happened: *We doubted his facts. noun.*

fac·tor (fak/tər), **1** any one of the causes that helps bring about a result; one element in a situation: *The low price was a factor in my decision to buy this car.* **2** any of the numbers that produce a given number when multiplied together: *The numbers 2 and 5 are factors of 10. noun.*

fac·to·ry (fak/tər ē), a building or group of buildings where things are made by machines or by hand. *noun, plural* **fac·to·ries.**

fac·tu·al (fak/chü əl), concerned with fact; consisting of facts: *I wrote a factual account of the field trip for the school newspaper. adjective.*

fac·ul·ty (fak/əl tē), **1** a power of the mind or body: *A bad explosion can harm one's faculty of hearing.* **2** the power or ability to do some special thing: *She has a great faculty for arithmetic.* **3** the teachers of a school, college, or university. *noun, plural* **fac·ul·ties.**

fad (fad), something everybody is very much interested in for a short time; fashion or craze. *noun.*

fad—Some years ago it was the **fad** to see how many people could pack themselves into an automobile.

fade (fād), **1** to become less bright; lose color: *My blue jeans faded after they were washed several times.* **2** to lose freshness or strength; wither: *The flowers in our garden faded at the end of the summer.* **3** to die away; disappear little by little: *The sound of the train faded after it went by. verb,* **fades, fad·ed, fad·ing.**

Fahr·en·heit (far/ən hīt). On the **Fahrenheit thermometer,** 32 degrees is the temperature at which water freezes, and 212 degrees is the temperature at which water boils. *adjective.*

[*Fahrenheit* was named for Gabriel D. Fahrenheit, who lived from 1686 to 1736. He was a German physicist who invented the mercury thermometer.]

fail (fāl), **1** to not succeed; not be able to do something: *He tried hard to learn to play the guitar, but he failed.* **2** to not do; neglect: *She failed to follow our advice.* **3** to be of no use to when needed: *When I needed their help, they failed me.* **4** to be missing; be not enough: *When our supplies failed, we had no food.* **5** to lose strength; grow weak; die away: *The patient's heart was failing.* **6** to be unable to pay what one owes; become bankrupt: *The company lost all its money and failed in business.* **7** to be unsuccessful in an examination: *You failed the test because you didn't study.* *verb.*

fail·ing (fā′ling), a fault; weakness; defect: *We all have our failings; none of us is perfect. noun.*

fail·ure (fā′lyər), **1** a lack of success: *My efforts to learn to play the guitar ended in failure.* **2** a not doing; neglecting: *Failure to follow directions may cause errors.* **3** the condition of not being enough; a falling short: *The failure of the wheat crop caused the price of bread to rise.* **4** losing strength; becoming weak: *heart failure.* **5** a being unable to pay what one owes; being or becoming bankrupt. **6** a person or thing that has failed: *The picnic was a failure because it rained. noun.*

faint (fānt), **1** not clear or plain; dim: *faint colors.* **2** weak; feeble: *a faint voice.* **3** to fall into a state of shock, in which a person is unconscious for a short time: *After the car accident the driver fainted.* **4** a state of fainting; brief loss of consciousness: *When the driver was walking away from the car after the accident, he fell down in a faint.* **5** ready to faint; dizzy and weak: *I felt faint.* 1,2,5 *adjective,* 3 *verb,* 4 *noun.*

fair¹ (fer *or* far), **1** honest; just; giving the same treatment to all: *Try to be fair, even to people you dislike.* **2** according to the rules: *It isn't fair to peek when you're playing hide-and-seek.* **3** in a fair manner; honestly: *The team played fair.* **4** not good and not bad; average: *That movie wasn't one of my favorites; it was only fair.* **5** light; not dark: *A blond person has fair hair and skin.* **6** clear; sunny; not cloudy or stormy: *fair weather.* **7** beautiful: *a fair lady.* **8** (in baseball) falling within the base lines; not being a foul: *a fair ball.* 1,2,4-8 *adjective,* 3 *adverb.*

fair² (fer *or* far), **1** a showing of farm products and goods of a certain region: *Prizes were given for the best livestock at the county fair.* **2** a gathering of buyers and sellers, often held at the same time and place every year: *a trade fair, an art fair.* **3** a sale of articles: *Our church held a fair to raise money for charity. noun.*

fair·ground (fer′ground′ *or* far′ground′), a place outdoors where fairs are held. *noun.*

fair·ly (fer′lē *or* far′lē), **1** in a fair manner; justly: *All contestants will be treated fairly.* **2** to a moderate degree; rather; somewhat: *She is a fairly good pupil, about average. adverb.*

fair·y (fer′ē *or* far′ē), (in stories) a tiny being, very lovely and delicate, who could help or harm human beings. *noun, plural* **fair·ies.**

fair·y·land (fer′ē land′ *or* far′ē land′), **1** a place

where the fairies are supposed to live. **2** an enchanting and pleasant place. *noun.*

fairy tale, **1** a story about fairies. **2** something said that is not true; lie.

faith (fāth), **1** belief without proof; trust; confidence: *We have faith in our friends.* **2** belief in God. **3** what a person believes. **4** a religion: *the Jewish faith, the Christian faith.* **5** a being loyal. *noun.*

in good faith, honestly; sincerely.

faith·ful (fāth′fəl), **1** worthy of trust; loyal: *A faithful friend will keep your secret. Several workers were given awards for long and faithful service.* **2** true to fact; accurate: *The witness gave a faithful account of what happened. adjective.*

faith·less (fāth′lis), not true to duty or to one's promises; not loyal: *a faithless traitor. adjective.*

fake (fāk), **1** something false: *The diamond ring was a fake.* **2** not real; false: *a fake fur, fake money.* **3** to make something false appear real in order to deceive; counterfeit: *fake someone else's signature. They faked the picture by pasting two photographs together.* **4** to pretend: *I wasn't really crying; I was only faking.* 1 *noun,* 2 *adjective,* 3,4 *verb,* **fakes, faked, fak·ing.**

fal·con (fôl′kən *or* fal′kən), a swift-flying hawk having a short, curved bill and long claws and wings. Falcons are sometimes trained to hunt and kill birds and small game. *noun.*

Word History

falcon The name of this bird comes from a Latin word meaning "sickle." It was called this because of its hooked talons.

falcon—about 17 inches (43 centimeters) long. **Falcons** are trained to perch on a glove or cover around the hand.

---

fall (fôl), **1** to drop or come down from a higher place: *Snow is falling fast. Her hat fell off. Leaves fall from the trees. The light falls on my book.* **2** a dropping from a higher place: *a fall from a horse.*

3 the amount that comes down: *a heavy fall of snow.* **4 falls,** a waterfall: *Niagara Falls. We enjoyed visiting the falls.* **5** to come down suddenly from a standing position: *A baby who is learning to walk often falls.* **6** a coming down suddenly from a standing position: *The child had a bad fall.* **7** ruin; destruction; downfall: *the fall of an empire.* **8** to lose position, power, or dignity: *The ruler fell from the people's favor.* **9** to be captured, overthrown, or destroyed: *The fort fell after the enemy's violent attack.* **10** to drop wounded or dead; be killed: *fall in battle.* **11** to pass into some condition or state: *He fell sick. The baby fell asleep. The boy and girl fell in love.* **12** to come by chance or luck: *Our choice fell on her.* **13** to happen; take place: *This year my birthday falls on a Monday.* **14** to become lower or less: *Prices are falling. The water in the river has fallen two feet.* **15** a becoming lower or less: *a fall in prices.* **16** a season of the year between summer and winter; autumn. **17** of, for, or coming in the fall: *fall clothes, fall plowing.* **18** to look sad or disappointed: *His face fell at the news.* 1,5,8-14,18 *verb,* **falls, fell, fall·en, fall·ing;** 2-4,6,7,15,16 *noun,* 17 *adjective.*

fall back on, turn to someone or something when other things fail.

fall behind, to fail to keep up with: *On the hike I fell behind the rest of the scouts. Some of the floats in the parade are falling behind.*

fall through, to fail: *Their plans fell through.*

fall·en (fôl′ən), **1** See **fall.** *Much rain has fallen.* **2** down on the ground; down flat: *a fallen tree.* 1 *verb,* 2 *adjective.*

fall·out (fôl′out′), the radioactive particles or dust that fall to the earth after a nuclear explosion. *noun.*

fal·low (fal′ō), plowed but not seeded for a season or more; uncultivated: *The north forty acres lay fallow last spring. adjective.*

false (fôls), **1** not true; not correct; wrong: *Witnesses to an accident should not make false statements in a court trial.* A **false note** is wrong in pitch. A **false step** is a stumble or a mistake. **2** not loyal; deceitful: *A person who tells another what you've said in secret is a false friend.* **3** used to deceive: *false advertising, false signals.* A ship sails under **false colors** when it raises the flag of another country than its own. **4** not real; artificial: *false teeth. adjective,* **fals·er, fals·est.**

false·hood (fôls′hùd), a false statement; a lie. *noun.*

fal·ter (fôl′tər), **1** to not go straight on; hesitate; waver; lose courage: *I faltered for a moment before making my decision.* **2** to become unsteady in movement; stumble; totter: *The horse faltered on the rocky lane. verb.*

fame (fām), the fact of being very well known; a having much said or written about one: *An athlete may win fame at the Olympic games. noun.*

famed (fāmd), famous; well-known: *The doctors at the clinic were famed for their medical discoveries. adjective.*

a hat	i it	oi oil	ch child	a in about
ā age	ī ice	ou out	ng long	e in taken
ä far	o hot	u cup	sh she	ə = i in pencil
e let	ō open	ù put	th thin	o in lemon
ē equal	ô order	ü rule	ŦH then	u in circus
ėr term			zh measure	

fa·mil·iar (fə mil′yər), **1** well-known; common: *a familiar face. French was as familiar to him as English.* **2** having a good or thorough knowledge of: *She is familiar with French and English.* **3** close; personal; intimate: *She spent her vacation visiting old and familiar friends. adjective.*

fa·mil·iar·i·ty (fə mil′yar′ə tē), a good or thorough knowledge: *Her familiarity with French was a great help to us when we visited Paris. noun.*

fam·i·ly (fam′ə lē), **1** a father, mother, and their children: *Our town has about a thousand families.* **2** the children of a father and mother; offspring: *They are raising a family.* **3** all of a person's relatives: *a family reunion.* **4** a group of related living things. Lions, tigers, and leopards belong to the cat family. *noun, plural* **fam·i·lies.**

family room, a usually large room for general family use, relaxation, or recreation. It often has a TV set and stereo.

family tree, a diagram showing how all the members and ancestors of a family are related.

fam·ine (fam′ən), lack of food in a place; a time of starving: *Many people died during the famine in India. noun.*

fam·ished (fam′isht), very hungry; starving: *We were famished after not eating anything for ten hours. adjective.*

fa·mous (fā′məs), very well known; noted: *The famous singer was greeted by a large crowd. adjective.*

fan[1] (fan), **1** a device made up of rotating blades turned by an electric motor. It is used to stir the air in order to cool a room, an engine, or one's body, or to remove odors. **2** a device, often made of stiff paper, held in the hand and waved back and forth to stir the air in order to cool one's face. Some fans can be folded up. **3** to stir, blow, or move air on or toward: *Fan the fire to make it burn faster. She fanned herself.* **4** anything that is flat and spread out like an open fan: *The peacock spread out its tail into a beautiful fan.* 1,2,4 *noun,* 3 *verb,* **fans, fanned, fan·ning.**

fan[2] (fan), a person extremely interested in some sport, the movies, the radio, or television: *A baseball fan would hate to miss the championship game. noun.*
[*Fan*[2] was shortened from the English word *fanatic.*]

fa·nat·ic (fə nat′ik), **1** a person who is carried away beyond reason because of feelings or beliefs: *My friend is a fanatic about fresh air and refuses to stay in a room with closed windows.* **2** enthusiastic beyond reason; too great or unreasonable: *He has a fanatic interest in professional sports.* 1 *noun,* 2 *adjective.*

fanciful (definition 1)
I read a **fanciful** story
about a rose and
a butterfly.

fan·ci·ful (fan′sə fəl), **1** imaginary; unreal.
2 having a good imagination: *The fanciful author
wrote a book of fairy tales. adjective.*

fan·cy (fan′sē), **1** to picture to oneself; imagine:
Can you fancy yourself on the moon? **2** the
imagination: *Dragons and giants are creatures of
fancy.* **3** an idea; notion; something imagined or
thought of: *I had a sudden fancy to go swimming.*
4 a liking: *They took a great fancy to each other.*
5 to like; be fond of: *She fancies bright colors, but
he prefers pastels.* **6** not plain or simple; decorated:
fancy needlework, a fancy dinner for guests. **7** of
high quality or an unusual kind: *The shop offered
a wide choice of fancy fruits for sale.* **8** much too
high: *She paid a fancy price for that car.* 1,5 *verb,*
fan·cies, fan·cied, fan·cy·ing; 2-4 *noun, plural*
fan·cies; 6-8 *adjective,* **fan·ci·er, fan·ci·est.**

fang (fang), a long, pointed tooth of a dog, wolf,
or snake. Poisonous snakes inject their poison
through fangs. *noun.*

fang
The snake showed
its **fangs.**

fan·tas·tic (fan tas′tik), **1** very odd; unreal;
strange and wild in shape or manner: *The firelight
cast weird, fantastic shadows on the walls.* **2** very
good, quick, or high: *That store charges fantastic
prices. The class prepared a fantastic science
exhibition. adjective.*

fan·ta·sy (fan′tə sē), **1** a product of the
imagination. Fairy tales are fantasies. **2** a picture
existing only in the mind: *I have a fantasy in which
I win a million dollars. noun, plural* **fan·ta·sies.**

far (fär), **1** a long way; a long way off: *She studied
far into the night.* **2** not near; distant: *They live in a
far country. The moon is far from the earth.* **3** more
distant: *We live on the far side of the hill.* **4** much:
It is far better to go by train. 1,4 *adverb,* **far·ther,**

far·thest or **fur·ther, fur·thest;** 2,3 *adjective,*
far·ther, far·thest or **fur·ther, fur·thest.**
as far as, to the distance, point, or degree that:
*Tall maples lined the road as far as I could see. As
far as I'm concerned, we can leave right now.*
by far, very much: *This is by far the best
restaurant in town.*
so far, 1 until now: *So far we've enjoyed fine
weather on our vacation.* **2** to this or that point: *I
had read just so far when the phone rang.*

far·a·way (fär′ə wā′), distant; far away: *He read
of faraway places in geography books. adjective.*

fare (fer *or* far), **1** the money that a person pays to
ride in a bus, taxi, subway, airplane, train, or ship.
2 food: *They dined on plain and simple fare.* **3** to
do; get on: *He is faring well in school.* 1,2 *noun,*
3 *verb,* **fares, fared, far·ing.**

Far East, China, Japan, and other parts of
eastern Asia.

fare·well (fer′wel′ *or* far′wel′), **1** good-by:
Farewell! Have a good trip! **2** good wishes at
parting: *We said our farewells at the station.*
3 parting; last: *a farewell kiss. The singer gave a
farewell performance.* 1 *interjection,* 2 *noun,*
3 *adjective.*

farm (färm), **1** a piece of land which a person
uses to raise crops or animals. **2** to raise crops or
animals either to eat or to sell: *Her parents farm
for a living.* **3** to cultivate land: *They farm fifty
acres.* 1 *noun,* 2,3 *verb.*

farm·er (fär′mər), a person who raises crops or
animals on a farm. *noun.*

farm·house (färm′hous′), a house to live in on
a farm. *noun, plural* **farm·hous·es**
(färm′hou′ziz).

farm·ing (fär′ming), the business of raising
crops or animals on a farm; agriculture. *noun.*

farm·land (färm′land′), the land used or
suitable for raising crops or grazing. *noun.*

farm·yard (färm′yärd′), the yard connected with
farm buildings or enclosed by them. *noun.*

far-off (fär′ôf′), distant; far away: *The writer
traveled to far-off countries to find ideas for a
novel. adjective.*

far-reach·ing (fär′rē′ching), having a wide
influence or effect; extending far: *The use of
atomic energy has far-reaching effects. adjective.*

far·sight·ed (fär′sī′tid), seeing distant things
more clearly than near ones. Some farsighted
people wear glasses to read. *adjective.*

far·ther (fär′ᴛʜər), **1** more distant: *Three miles is
farther than two.* **2** to a greater distance: *We
walked farther than we meant to.* **3** to a more
advanced point: *She has looked into the problem
farther than anyone else.* 1 *adjective, comparative of*
far; 2,3 *adverb, comparative of* **far.**

far·thest (fär′ᴛʜist), **1** most distant: *Ours is the
house farthest down the road.* **2** to or at the
greatest distance: *He hit the ball farthest.* **3** most:
Their ideas were the farthest advanced at that time.
1 *adjective, superlative of* **far;** 2,3 *adverb,
superlative of* **far.**

fas·ci·nate (fas′n āt), to charm; interest greatly:

The designs and colors in African art fascinated her. verb, **fas·ci·nates, fas·ci·nat·ed, fas·ci·nat·ing.**

fas·ci·na·tion (fas/n ā/shən), a very strong attraction; charm: *Studying a dictionary has a fascination for some people. noun.*

fash·ion (fash/ən), **1** the way a thing is shaped, made, or done; manner: *He walks in a peculiar fashion.* **2** the current custom in dress, manners, or speech; style: *the latest fashion in shoes.* **3** to make, shape, or form. **1,2** *noun,* **3** *verb.*

fashion (definition 3)
The boys and girls **fashioned** puppets from paper bags.

fash·ion·a·ble (fash/ə nə bəl), following the fashion; in fashion; stylish: *They replaced their old clothes with fashionable new outfits. adjective.*

fast[1] (fast), **1** quick; rapid; swift: *She is a fast runner.* **2** quickly; rapidly; swiftly: *Airplanes go fast.* **3** showing a time ahead of the real time: *That clock is fast.* **4** firm; secure; tight: *The painter kept a fast hold on the ladder.* **5** firmly: *He held fast as the sled went on down the hill.* **6** loyal; faithful: *They have been fast friends for years.* **7** not fading easily: *cloth dyed with fast color.* **8** thoroughly; sound: *The baby is fast asleep.* **1,3,4,6,7** *adjective,* **2,5,8** *adverb.*

fast[2] (fast), **1** to go without food; eat little or nothing; go without certain kinds of food. **2** the act or time of fasting. **1** *verb,* **2** *noun.*

fas·ten (fas/n), **1** to tie, lock, or make hold together in any way: *fasten a door, fastern a seat belt.* **2** to fix; direct: *The dog fastened its eyes on me. verb.*

fas·ten·er (fas/n ər), an attachment or device used to fasten something together. A zipper is a fastener. *noun.*

fast-food (fast/füd/), serving food that is prepared quickly, such as hamburgers, pizza, or fried chicken: *fast-food restaurants. adjective.*

fas·tid·i·ous (fa stid/ē əs), hard to please: *a fastidious dresser. adjective.*

fat (fat), **1** a white or yellow oily substance formed in the body of animals. Fat is also found in plants, especially in some seeds. **2** having much of this: *fat meat.* **3** having much flesh; plump: *a fat person.* **4** large or larger than usual; thick: *a fat book.* **1** *noun,* **2-4** *adjective,* **fat·ter, fat·test.**

fa·tal (fā/tl), **1** causing death: *Careless drivers cause many fatal accidents.* **2** causing destruction or ruin: *The loss of all our money was fatal to our plans. adjective.*

a hat	**i** it	**oi** oil	**ch** child	a in about
ā age	**ī** ice	**ou** out	**ng** long	e in taken
ä far	**o** hot	**u** cup	**sh** she	ə = { i in pencil
e let	**ō** open	**ů** put	**th** thin	o in lemon
ē equal	**ô** order	**ü** rule	**ŦH** then	u in circus
ėr term			**zh** measure	

fate (fāt), **1** the power that is supposed to decide and control what is to happen in the future. Fate is thought to be beyond anyone's control. *Many people don't believe in fate.* **2** what happens to a person or group; one's fortune: *History shows the fate of many nations. noun.*

fat·ed (fā/tid), controlled by fate: *The fortuneteller told me I was fated to become famous. adjective.*

fate·ful (fāt/fəl), **1** determining what is to happen; important; decisive: *a fateful battle.* **2** controlled by fate; fated. *adjective.*

fa·ther (fä/ŦHər), **1** a male parent. **2** a man who did important work as a maker or leader: *Washington is called the father of his country.* **3** a priest. **4** Father, God. *noun.*

fa·ther·hood (fä/ŦHər hůd), the condition of being a father. *noun.*

fa·ther-in-law (fä/ŦHər in lô/), the father of one's husband or wife. *noun, plural* **fa·thers-in-law.**

fa·ther·land (fä/ŦHər land/), one's native country; land of one's ancestors. *noun.*

fa·ther·less (fä/ŦHər lis), having no father: *a fatherless child. adjective.*

fa·ther·ly (fä/ŦHər lē), of or like a father; kindly: *a fatherly person, a fatherly smile. adjective.*

fath·om (faŦH/əm), a unit of length equal to 6 feet. It is used in measuring the depth of water and the length of the ropes and cables on ships. *noun.*

fa·tigue (fə tēg/), **1** a tired feeling caused by hard work or effort: *I felt extreme fatigue after studying for three hours.* **2** to make weary or tired: *Getting too little sleep will fatigue a person.* **1** *noun,* **2** *verb,* **fa·tigues, fa·tigued, fa·ti·guing.**

fat·ten (fat/n), **1** to make fat: *fatten pigs for market.* **2** to become fat: *The pigs fattened on corn. verb.*

fat·ty (fat/ē), of or containing fat: *One should avoid fatty foods. adjective,* **fat·ti·er, fat·ti·est.**

fau·cet (fô/sit), a device for turning on or off a flow of liquid from a pipe or a container holding it; tap. *noun.*

faucet—the inside of a **faucet** when the water is turned on. To stop the flow of water, the handle is turned until the round washer covers the circular hole.

fault (definition 3)—The **fault** can be seen clearly from an airplane.

fault (fôlt), **1** something that is not as it should be; failing: *Her dog has two faults; it eats too much, and it howls at night.* **2** a cause for blame; responsibility: *Whose fault was it?* **3** a break in the earth's crust, with the mass of rock on one side of the break pushed up, down, or sideways. *noun.*
find fault with, to object to or criticize: *My teacher is always finding fault with my homework.*
fault·less (fôlt′lis), without a single fault or defect; perfect: *The violinist gave a faultless performance. adjective.*
fault·y (fôl′tē), having faults; imperfect; defective: *The leak in the tire was caused by a faulty valve. adjective,* **fault·i·er, fault·i·est.**
faun (fôn), a minor god in Roman myths that lived in fields and woods and helped farmers and shepherds. A faun was supposed to look like a man, but to have the ears, horns, tail, and legs of a goat. *noun.*

faun

fa·vor (fā′vər), **1** an act of kindness: *Will you do me a favor?* **2** to show kindness to; oblige: *Favor us with a song.* **3** a liking; approval: *They will look with favor on your plan.* **4** to like; approve: *We favor his plan.* **5** more than fair treatment: *Parents should try not to show favor toward one of their children.* **6** to give more than is fair to: *The teacher favors you.* **7** to treat gently: *The dog favors its sore foot when it walks.* **8** a small gift given to every guest at a party or dinner: *Paper hats were used as favors at the birthday party.* **9** to look like: *That girl favors her mother a great deal.*
1,3,5,8 *noun,* **2,4,6,7,9** *verb.*
in favor of, 1 on the side of: *He argued in favor of her plan.* **2** to the advantage of: *The referee's decision was in favor of the other team.*

in one's favor, for one; to one's benefit: *The bank made an error in my favor.*
fa·vor·a·ble (fā′vər ə bəl), **1** favoring; approving: *"Yes" is a favorable answer to a request.* **2** being to one's advantage; helping: *A favorable wind made the boat go faster. adjective.*
fa·vor·a·bly (fā′vər ə blē), with consent or approval: *The teacher commented favorably on my book report. adverb.*
fa·vor·ite (fā′vər it), **1** liked better than others: *What is your favorite flower?* **2** the one liked better than others; person or thing liked very much: *He is a favorite with everybody.* **1** *adjective,* **2** *noun.*
fawn[1] (fôn), **1** a deer less than a year old. **2** light yellowish-brown. **1** *noun,* **2** *adjective.*
fawn[2] (fôn), to try to get favor or notice by slavish acts: *Many flattering relatives fawned on the rich old man. verb.*
fear (fir), **1** a feeling that danger or evil is near: *I have a fear of high places.* **2** to be afraid of: *Our cat fears big dogs.* **3** to feel fear; have an uneasy feeling or idea: *I fear that my friends are in danger. I fear that I am late.* **1** *noun,* **2,3** *verb.*
fear·ful (fir′fəl), **1** causing fear; terrible; dreadful: *a fearful dragon.* **2** feeling fear; frightened: *The child was fearful of the dark.* **3** very bad or unpleasant: *I have a fearful cold. adjective.*
fear·less (fir′lis), without fear; afraid of nothing; brave: *The fearless lion tamer was one of the stars of the circus. adjective.*
fear·some (fir′səm), causing fear; frightful: *The monster was a fearsome sight. adjective.*
feast (fēst), **1** a rich meal prepared for some special occasion and for a number of guests; banquet: *We went to the wedding feast.* **2** to eat a rich meal; eat well; have a feast: *We feast on turkey and pumpkin pie at Thanksgiving.* **1** *noun,* **2** *verb.*
feat (fēt), a great deed; act showing great skill, strength, or daring. *noun.*

feat—Twelve people riding on one bicycle is quite a **feat.**

feath·er (feŦH′ər), one of the light, thin growths that cover a bird's skin. Because feathers are soft and light, they are used to fill pillows. *noun.*

feather bed, a bed with a very soft mattress filled with feathers.

feath·er·y (feŦH′ər ē), like feathers; soft and light: *feathery clouds. adjective.*

fea·ture (fē′chər), **1** a part of the face. The eyes, nose, mouth, chin, and forehead are features. **2** a distinct part or quality; thing that stands out and attracts attention: *Your plan has many good features. The main features of southern California are the climate and the scenery.* **3** the main film shown at a motion-picture theather: *After the previews, we settled back in our seats for the feature.* **4** to give special attention to; make a feature of: *The local newspapers featured the mayor's speech.* 1-3 *noun,* 4 *verb.*

Feb., February.

Feb·ru·ar·y (feb′rü er′ē), the second month of the year. It has 28 days except in leap years, when it has 29. *noun.*
[*February* comes from the name of a Roman festival celebrated on February 15.]

fed (fed). See **feed.** *We fed the birds yesterday. Have they been fed today? verb.*

fed up, bored, impatient, or disgusted with something: *I became fed up with the static on the radio and turned it off.*

fed·er·al (fed′ər əl), **1** formed by an agreement between states setting up a central government: *The United States became a nation by federal union.* **2** of the central government of the United States, not of any state or city alone: *Coining money is a federal power. adjective.*

fed·e·ra·tion (fed′ə rā′shən), a league; a union by agreement, often a union of states or nations: *Each member of the federation controls its own affairs. noun.*

fee (fē), the money asked for or paid for some service or privilege; charge: *an admission fee. Doctors and lawyers receive fees for their services. noun.*

fee·ble (fē′bəl), weak: *A sick person is often feeble. A feeble attempt is liable to fail. adjective,* **fee·bler, fee·blest.**

feed (fēd), **1** to give food to: *We feed babies because they cannot feed themselves.* **2** to give as food: *Feed this grain to the chickens.* **3** to eat: *Our cows feed in a shed near the barn.* **4** food for animals: *Give the chickens their feed.* **5** to supply with material or something necessary: *Find some dry wood to feed the fire.* 1-3,5 *verb,* **feeds, fed, feed·ing;** 4 *noun.*

feed·er (fē′dər), a device for supplying food for an animal: *The bird feeder in our yard is filled with seed. noun.*

feel (fēl), **1** to touch: *Feel this cloth.* **2** the way something seems to the touch; feeling: *I like the feel of silk.* **3** to try to find or make one's way by touch: *He felt his way across the room when the lights went out.* **4** to find out by touching: *Feel how cold my hands are.* **5** to be aware of: *I felt the cool*

a hat	i it	oi oil	ch child	⎧ a in about
ā age	ī ice	ou out	ng long	e in taken
ä far	o hot	u cup	sh she	ə = ⎨ i in pencil
e let	ō open	u̇ put	th thin	o in lemon
ē equal	ô order	ü rule	ŦH then	⎩ u in circus
ėr term			zh measure	

breeze on my face. **6** to be; have the feeling of being: *He feels angry. We felt hot.* **7** to seem; give the feeling of being: *The air feels cold.* **8** to have in one's mind; experience: *They feel pity. I felt pain.* **9** to have a feeling: *Try to feel more kindly toward her. I feel that he will come.* **10** to have pity or sympathy: *We feel for those who suffer.* 1,3-10 *verb,* **feels, felt, feel·ing;** 2 *noun.*

feel like, to have a desire for; be in the mood for: *Even though it was raining, they felt like going out for a walk.*

feel·er (fē′lər), a special part of an animal's body for sensing by touch. Insects, crabs, lobsters, and shrimp have feelers on their heads. *noun.*

feel·ing (fē′ling), **1** the sense of touch. By feeling we tell what is hard from what is soft. **2** a sensation; condition of being aware: *She had no feeling in her leg.* **3** an emotion. Joy, sorrow, fear, and anger are feelings. *The loss of the ball game stirred up much feeling.* **4 feelings,** the tender or sensitive side of one's nature: *You hurt my feelings when you yelled at me.* **5** an opinion: *I have no feeling about the plan, one way or the other. noun.*

feet (fēt), more than one foot: *A dog has four feet. I am five feet tall. noun plural.*

feign (fān), to pretend: *She isn't sick; she is only feigning illness. verb.*

feint (fānt), **1** a movement made with the purpose of deceiving; pretended attack or blow: *The fighter made a feint at his opponent with his right hand and struck with his left.* **2** to make a feint: *The fighter feinted with his right hand and struck with his left.* 1 *noun,* 2 *verb.*

fell¹ (fel). See **fall.** *Snow fell last night. verb.*

fell² (fel), to cause to fall; knock, cut, or strike down: *They had to fell many trees to clear the land. verb.*

fel·low (fel′ō), **1** a male person; man or boy. **2** a person; anybody; one: *What can a fellow do?* **3** a companion; one of the same class; equal: *He was cut off from his fellows.* **4** being in a similar situation or group: *fellow classmates, fellow sufferers, fellow workers.* 1-3 *noun,* 4 *adjective.*

fel·low·ship (fel′ō ship), **1** companionship; friendliness: *I enjoy the fellowship of my classmates.* **2** a group of people having similar tastes or interests; brotherhood: *Our church fellowship is serving a fish dinner tonight. noun.*

felt¹ (felt). See **feel.** *I felt the cat's soft fur. It was felt that the picnic should be postponed. verb.*

felt² (felt), **1** a cloth that is not woven, but is made by rolling and pressing together fibers such as wool, nylon, or fur. **2** made of felt: *a felt hat.* 1 *noun,* 2 *adjective.*

F

fe·male (fē′māl), **1** a woman or girl. **2** of women or girls. **3** belonging to the sex that can give birth to young or lay eggs. Mares, cows, and hens are female animals. **4** an animal belonging to this sex. 1,4 *noun,* 2,3 *adjective.*

fem·i·nine (fem′ə nən), **1** of women or girls. **2** like a woman; womanly. *adjective.*

fence (fens), **1** a railing or wall put around a yard, garden, field, or farm to show where it ends or to keep people or animals out or in. Most fences are made of wood, wire, or metal. **2** to put a fence around. **3** to fight with long slender swords or foils. 1 *noun,* 2,3 *verb,* **fenc·es, fenced, fenc·ing.**

fenc·er (fen′sər), a person who knows how to fight with a sword or foil. *noun.*

fenc·ing (fen′sing), the art or sport of fighting with swords or foils. *noun.*

fencing

fend (fend), **1 fend for oneself,** to provide for oneself; get along by one's own efforts: *While traveling alone I had to fend for myself.* **2 fend off,** to keep off; ward off: *The boxer fended off several blows. verb.*

fend·er (fen′dər), a metal frame over the wheel of a car, truck, or bicycle. The fender protects the wheel and reduces splashing in wet weather. *noun.*

fer·ment (fər ment′ *for 1;* fėr′ment *for 2*), **1** to undergo or produce a gradual chemical change in which yeast or bacteria change sugar into alcohol and carbon dioxide. Grape juice ferments into wine. **2** excitement; unrest: *The school was in a ferment.* 1 *verb,* 2 *noun.*

fer·men·ta·tion (fėr′men tā′shən), the act or process of fermenting: *Fermentation causes milk to sour. noun.*

fern (fėrn), a kind of plant that has roots, stems, and feathery leaves, but no flowers or seeds. In the little brown dots on the backs of the leaves grow cells called spores, each of which can develop into a new plant. *noun.*

fe·ro·cious (fə rō′shəs), fierce; savage; very cruel: *I was frightened when I saw the ferocious-looking statue. adjective.*

fer·ret (fer′it), **1** a kind of weasel with black feet, found in western North America. **2** a white or yellowish-white European animal like a weasel, which people use for killing rats and driving rabbits from their holes. **3** to hunt; search: *It took the detectives over a year to ferret out the criminal.* 1,2 *noun,* 3 *verb.*

Word History

ferret The name of this animal comes from a Latin word meaning "thief." The European animal may have been called this because it hunts animals in their burrows like a thief breaking into people's homes.

ferret (definition 1)—about 20 inches (50 centimeters) long with the tail

Ferris wheel—The first **Ferris wheel** was built for the Chicago World's Fair in 1893.

Fer·ris wheel (fer′is hwēl′), a large revolving wheel with hanging seats, used in carnivals, amusement parks, and fairs.

fer·ry (fer′ē), **1** to carry people, vehicles, and goods across a river or narrow stretch of water. **2** a boat that carries people, vehicles, and goods; ferryboat. **3** a place where boats carry people, vehicles, and goods across a river or narrow stretch of water. **4** to go across in a ferryboat. **5** to carry back and forth in an airplane. 1,4,5 *verb,* **fer·ries, fer·ried, fer·ry·ing;** 2,3 *noun, plural* **fer·ries.**

fer·ry·boat (fer′ē bōt′), a boat that carries people, vehicles, and goods across a river or narrow stretch of water. *noun.*

fer·tile (fer′tl), **1** able to bear seeds, fruit, or young: *a fertile animal or plant.* **2** able to develop into a new individual; fertilized: *Chicks hatch from fertile eggs.* **3** able to produce much; producing crops easily: *Fertile soil yields good crops.* *adjective.*

fer·til·i·ty (fer til′ə tē), the state or condition of being fertile: *The fertility of the soil was increased by the use of manure. noun.*

fer·ti·li·za·tion (fer′tl ə zā′shən), **1** a making or a being made fertile. **2** the union of a male reproductive cell and a female reproductive cell to form a cell that will develop into a new individual. *noun.*

fer·ti·lize (fer′tl īz), **1** to make fertile: *A plant can produce seeds only when it has been fertilized with pollen.* **2** to make a thing start to grow. **3** to make the soil produce more by putting manure or other fertilizer into or on the soil. *verb,* **fer·ti·liz·es, fer·ti·lized, fer·ti·liz·ing.**

fer·ti·liz·er (fer′tl ī′zər), a substance put into or on the soil to make it produce more. *noun.*

fer·vent (fer′vənt), showing great emotion; very earnest: *She made a fervent plea for food and medicine for the earthquake victims. adjective.*

fer·vor (fer′vər), great emotion; enthusiasm; earnestness: *The patriot spoke with such fervor that his voice trembled. noun.*

fes·ti·val (fes′tə vəl), **1** a day or special time of rejoicing or feasting, often in memory of some great happening: *Christmas is a Christian festival; Hanukkah is a Jewish festival.* **2** a program of entertainment, often held annually: *a summer music festival. noun.*

fes·tive (fes′tiv), of or suitable for a feast or holiday; gay; merry: *A birthday is a festive occasion. adjective.*

fes·tiv·i·ty (fe stiv′ə tē), a rejoicing and feasting; merry party: *The wedding festivities were very gay. noun, plural* **fes·tiv·i·ties.**

fetch (fech), **1** to go and get; bring: *Please fetch me my glasses.* **2** to be sold for: *These eggs will fetch a good price. verb.*

fet·ter (fet′ər), **1** Usually, **fetters.** chains or shackles for the feet: *Fetters prevented the prisoner's escape.* **2** to bind with chains; chain the feet of. **1** *noun,* **2** *verb.*

feud (fyüd), **1** a long and deadly quarrel between families. Feuds are often passed down from generation to generation. **2** bitter hatred between two persons or groups. **3** to carry on a long and deadly quarrel: *Those tribes have feuded for years.* **1,2** *noun,* **3** *verb.*

fe·ver (fē′vər), **1** an unhealthy condition in which the body temperature is higher than normal (98.6 degrees Fahrenheit or 37.0 degrees Celsius in human beings). **2** any sickness that causes or is accompanied by fever: *scarlet fever, typhoid fever. noun.*

fe·ver·ish (fē′vər ish), **1** having fever. **2** having

some fever but not much. **3** excited; restless: *He packed his bags in feverish haste. adjective.*

few (fyü), **1** not many: *Few people came to the meeting because of the storm.* **2** a small number: *Winter in New England has not many warm days, only a few.* **1** *adjective,* **2** *noun.*

fez (fez), a felt cap, usually red and ornamented with a long black tassel. *noun, plural* **fez·zes.**

Word History

fez This hat was formerly the national headdress of Turkish men. It was named for Fez, a city in Morocco, where it was first made.

fez
man wearing a **fez**

fib (fib), **1** a lie about some small matter. **2** to tell such a lie. **1** *noun,* **2** *verb,* **fibs, fibbed, fib·bing.**

fib·ber (fib′ər), a person who fibs. *noun.*

fi·ber (fī′bər), **1** a thread; threadlike part. A muscle is made up of many fibers. **2** a substance made up of threads or threadlike parts: *Hemp fiber can be spun or woven.* **3** any part of food that cannot be digested and so speeds the movement of food and waste products through the intestines. The cellulose in vegetables is fiber. **4** character; nature: *A person of strong moral fiber can resist temptation. noun.*

fi·ber·glass (fī′bər glas′), very fine threads of glass used in insulating materials and in fabrics. Mixed with plastic, fiberglass is made into boat and car bodies. *noun.*

fick·le (fik′əl), changing; not constant; likely to change without reason: *a fickle friend. adjective.*

fic·tion (fik′shən), **1** a story that is not fact. Short stories and novels are fiction. "Robinson Crusoe" is fiction. **2** something made up: *She exaggerates*

F

her experiences so much that it is hard to separate fact from fiction. *noun.*

fid·dle (fid′l), **1** a violin. **2** to play on a violin. **3** to waste time: *He fiddled away the whole day doing absolutely nothing.* 1 *noun,* 2,3 *verb,* **fid·dles, fid·dled, fid·dling.**

fidg·et (fij′it), to move about restlessly: *Children sometimes fidget if they have to sit still too long.* *verb.*

field (fēld), **1** an open stretch of land without trees or shrubs, often used for crops or as pasture: *The fields surrounding the house were planted with corn and oats.* **2** a piece of land used for some special purpose: *a baseball field.* **3** a battlefield: *the field of Gettysburg.* **4** the land yielding some product: *the coal fields of Pennsylvania.* **5** a range of interest; area of activity or occupation: *the field of art. Her field is medicine.* **6** the space throughout which a force operates. A magnet has a magnetic field around it. **7** (in baseball) to stop or catch a batted ball. 1-6 *noun,* 7 *verb.*

field·er (fēl′dər), a baseball player who is stationed around or outside the diamond to stop or catch the ball. *noun.*

field glasses, small binoculars for use outdoors.

field goal, a play in football that scores three points, made by kicking the ball from the ground through the goal posts.

field trip, a trip away from school to give students an opportunity to learn by seeing things closely and at first hand: *The class went on a field trip to the zoo to observe animals they had read about.*

fiend (fēnd), **1** a devil; evil spirit. **2** a very wicked or cruel person. *noun.*

fiend·ish (fēn′dish), very cruel or wicked: *the fiendish laughter of a wicked witch. adjective.*

fierce (firs), **1** savage; wild: *A wounded lion can be fierce.* **2** very great or strong; intense: *fierce anger, a fierce wind. adjective,* **fierc·er, fierc·est.**

fie·ry (fī′rē), **1** like fire; very hot; glowing: *a fiery red, fiery heat.* **2** full of feeling or spirit: *The audience was excited by the fiery speech.* **3** easily aroused or excited: *a fiery temper. adjective,* **fie·ri·er, fie·ri·est.**

fi·es·ta (fē es′tə), a religious festival, especially in a Spanish-speaking country or area. *noun.* [*Fiesta* was borrowed from a Spanish word meaning "feast" or "festival."]

fife (fīf), a small, shrill musical instrument like a flute, played by blowing. Fifes are used with drums to make music for marching. *noun.*

fif·teen (fif′tēn′), five more than ten; 15. *noun, adjective.*

fif·teenth (fif′tēnth′), **1** next after the 14th. **2** one of 15 equal parts. *adjective, noun.*

fifth (fifth), **1** next after the fourth. **2** one of five equal parts. *adjective, noun.*

fif·ti·eth (fif′tē ith), **1** next after the 49th. **2** one of 50 equal parts. *adjective, noun.*

fif·ty (fif′tē), five times ten; 50. *noun, plural* **fif·ties;** *adjective.*

fig (fig), a small, soft, sweet fruit of a tree that grows in warm regions. Figs are sometimes eaten fresh or canned, but usually are dried like dates and raisins. *noun.*

fight (fīt), **1** a violent struggle; combat; contest: *A fight ends when one side gives up.* **2** an angry dispute; quarrel: *Their fights were always over money.* **3** to take part in a violent struggle, quarrel, or the like; have a fight: *When people fight they hit one another. Soldiers fight by shooting with guns. Countries fight with armies.* **4** to take part in a struggle against: *to fight disease, to fight one's fear of the dark.* **5** to carry on a struggle, conflict, or the like: *to fight a duel.* **6** to get or make by struggling: *She had to fight her way through the crowd.* **7** the power or will to struggle: *There was not much fight left in the losing team.* 1,2,7 *noun,* 3-6 *verb,* **fights, fought, fight·ing.**

fight·er (fī′tər), **1** a person that fights. **2** a professional boxer. *noun.*

fig·ur·a·tive (fig′yər ə tiv), using words out of their ordinary meaning. Much poetry is figurative. *adjective.*

fig·ure (fig′yər), **1** a symbol for a number. 1, 2, 3, 4, etc., are figures. **2** to use numbers to find out the answer to some problem: *Can you figure the cost of painting this room?* **3 figures,** arithmetic: *She is very good at figures.* **4** an amount or value given in figures; price: *The house was sold at a very high figure.* **5** a form partially or completely enclosing a surface or space. Squares, triangles, cubes, and other shapes are called figures. **6** a form or shape: *I could see the figure of a woman against the window.* **7** a person; character: *The governor is a well-known figure throughout the state.* **8** to stand out; appear: *The names of great leaders figure in the story of human progress.* **9** a picture; drawing; diagram; illustration: *This book has many figures to help explain words.* **10** a design or pattern: *the figures in the wallpaper.* **11** to think; consider: *I figured I should stop where I was.* 1,3-7,9,10 *noun,* 2,8,11 *verb,* **fig·ures, fig·ured, fig·ur·ing.**

figure out, to think out; understand: *Even the repairman couldn't figure out what had gone wrong with the washer.*

fig·ure·head (fig′yər hed′), **1** a person who is head in name only, without real authority. **2** a

fife—The soldiers marched to the sound of **fife** and drum.

a hat	i it	oi oil	ch child	(a in about
ā age	ī ice	ou out	ng long	e in taken
ä far	o hot	u cup	sh she	ə = { i in pencil
e let	ō open	ů put	th thin	o in lemon
ē equal	ô order	ü rule	ᴛʜ then	u in circus
ėr term			zh measure	

figurehead (definition 2)

figure placed for ornament on the bow of a ship. *noun.*

figure of speech, an expression in which words are used out of their ordinary meaning to add beauty or force. When we say someone has "the eye of an eagle," we are using a figure of speech.

fil·a·ment (fil′ə mənt), a very fine thread; very slender part that is like a thread. The wire that gives off light in an electric light bulb is a filament. The slender stem of the stamen of a flower is a filament. *noun.*

file[1] (fīl), **1** a container, drawer, or folder for keeping memorandums, letters, or other papers in order. **2** a set of papers kept in order: *a file of receipts.* **3** to put away in order: *Please file those letters.* **4** a row of persons or things one behind another: *a file of soldiers marching in time.* **5** to march or move in a file: *The pupils filed out of the room during the fire drill.* **6** to place among the records of a court, public office, or the like: *The deed to our house is filed with the county clerk.* 1,2,4 *noun,* 3,5,6 *verb,* **files, filed, fil·ing.**

file[2] (fīl), **1** a steel tool with many small ridges or teeth on it. Its rough surface is used to smooth rough materials or wear away hard substances. **2** to smooth or wear away with a file. 1 *noun,* 2 *verb,* **files, filed, fil·ing.**

fi·let (fi lā′ *or* fil′ā), a slice of fish or meat without bones or fat; fillet. *noun.*

fil·ings (fī′lingz), small pieces of iron or wood which have been removed by a file. *noun plural.*

fill (fil), **1** to make or become full: *Fill this bottle with water.* **2** to take up all the space in; spread throughout: *The crowd filled the hall. Smoke filled the room.* **3** to supply with all that is needed or wanted for: *The druggist filled the doctor's prescription.* **4** to stop up or close by putting something in: *The dentist filled my tooth.* **5** to hold and do the duties of a position or office: *We need*

someone to fill the office of vice-president. **6** something that fills. Earth or rock used to make uneven land level is called fill. 1-5 *verb,* 6 *noun.*

fill in, to put in to complete something: *She filled in the date on the application blank.*

fil·let (fi lā′ *or* fil′ā), **1** a slice of meat or fish without bones or fat. **2** to cut fish or meat into such slices. 1 *noun,* 2 *verb.*

fill·ing (fil′ing), a thing put in to fill something: *a filling in a tooth. noun.*

filling station, a place where gasoline and oil for motor vehicles are sold; gas station; service station.

fil·ly (fil′ē), a young female horse, donkey, or zebra. A mare until it is four or five years old is a filly. *noun, plural* **fil·lies.**

film (film), **1** a very thin surface or coating, often of liquid: *Oil on water will spread and make a film.* **2** a roll or sheet of thin material covered with a coating that is changed by light, used to take photographs: *He bought two rolls of film for his camera.* **3** a motion picture: *We saw a film about animals.* **4** to make a motion picture of: *They filmed "The Wizard of Oz."* 1-3 *noun,* 4 *verb.*

film·strip (film′strip′), a series of still pictures printed on a reel of film. *noun.*

fil·ter (fil′tər), **1** a device for passing water or other liquids, or air, through cloth, paper, sand, charcoal, or the like, in order to remove impurities. **2** a material through which the liquid or air passes in a filter. **3** to pass or flow very slowly: *Water filters through the sandy soil and into the well.* **4** to put through a filter: *We filter this water for drinking.* **5** to remove by a filter: *Filter the dirt out of the water.* 1,2 *noun,* 3-5 *verb.*

filth (filth), any foul, disgusting dirt: *The alley was filled with garbage and filth. noun.*

filth·y (fil′thē), very dirty; foul. *adjective,* **filth·i·er, filth·i·est.**

fil·tra·tion (fil trā′shən), the act or process of filtering: *water filtration. noun.*

fin (fin), **1** one of the movable winglike or fanlike parts of a fish's body. By moving its fins a fish can swim and balance itself in the water. **2** a thing shaped or used like a fin. Some aircraft have fins to help balance them when they move. *noun.*

fi·nal (fī′nl), **1** at the end; coming last: *The book was interesting from the first to the final chapter.* **2** deciding completely; settling the question: *The one with the highest authority makes the final decisions.* **3 finals,** the last or deciding set in a series of games or examinations. 1,2 *adjective,* 3 *noun.*

fi·na·le (fə nä′lē), the last part of a piece of music or a play. *noun.*

fi·nal·ly (fī′nl ē), at the end; at last: *The lost dog finally came home.* adverb.

fi·nance (fə nans′ *or* fī′nans), **1** the management or control of money matters, including banking and investments. **2 finances,** money; income; revenues: *New taxes were needed to increase the nation's finances.* **3** to provide money for: *A part-time job helped finance her college education.* 1,2 *noun,* 3 *verb.*

fi·nan·cial (fə nan′shəl *or* fī nan′shəl), having to do with money or the management of money: *My financial affairs are in good order.* adjective.

fin·an·cier (fin′ən sir′ *or* fī′nən sir′), a person who is skilled in managing and investing money. Bankers are financiers. *noun.*

finch (finch), a small songbird with a bill shaped like a cone. Sparrows, cardinals, and canaries are finches. *noun, plural* **finch·es.**

find (fīnd), **1** to meet with; come upon: *I found a dime on the sidewalk. They find friends everywhere.* **2** to look for and get: *Please find my hat for me.* **3** to learn; discover: *We found that he could not swim.* **4** to get; get the use of: *Can you find time to do this?* **5** to reach; arrive at: *The arrow found its mark.* **6** to decide and declare: *The jury found the woman guilty.* **7** something found. 1-6 *verb,* **finds, found, find·ing;** 7 *noun.* **find out,** to learn about; come to know; discover.

find·ing (fīn′ding), **1** the act of discovering; discovery: *The finding of a cure for the disease was a welcome event.* **2** a thing found; a find: *The buried bottle was an exciting finding for the collector.* *noun.*

fine[1] (fīn), **1** very good; excellent: *Everyone praised his fine singing. She is a fine student.* **2** very small or thin: *Thread is finer than rope. Sand is finer than gravel.* **3** sharp: *a tool with a fine edge.* **4** delicate: *fine linen.* **5** very well; excellently: *I'm doing fine.* 1-4 *adjective,* **fin·er, fin·est;** 5 *adverb.*

fine[2] (fīn), **1** a sum of money paid as a punishment for breaking a law or regulation. **2** to make pay such a sum: *The judge fined the driver twenty dollars for speeding.* 1 *noun,* 2 *verb,* **fines, fined, fin·ing.**

fin·er·y (fī′nər ē), showy clothes or ornaments. *noun.*

fin·ger (fing′gər), **1** one of the five end parts of the hand, especially the four besides the thumb. **2** anything shaped or used like a finger. **3** to touch or handle with the fingers; use the fingers on: *to finger the keyboard of a piano.* 1,2 *noun,* 3 *verb.*

fin·ger·nail (fing′gər nāl′), a hard layer of horn at the end of a finger. *noun.*

fin·ger·print (fing′gər print′), **1** a mark made by the fleshy tip of a finger. Your fingerprints can be used to identify you because no two fingers have the same pattern of lines on them. **2** to take the fingerprints of. 1 *noun,* 2 *verb.*

fin·ger·tip (fing′gər tip′), the tip of a finger. *noun.*

fin·ish (fin′ish), **1** to complete; bring to an end; reach the end of: *to finish one's dinner, to finish painting a picture.* **2** an end: *a fight to the finish.*

3 to use up completely: *to finish a bottle of milk.* **4** the way in which the surface is prepared: *a smooth finish on furniture.* **5** to prepare the surface of in some way: *to finish metal with a dull surface.* 1,3,5 *verb,* 2,4 *noun, plural* **fin·ish·es.**

fink (fingk), **1** someone who informs on or accuses someone else. **2** an undesirable or inferior person. *noun.*

Fin·land (fin′lənd), a country in northern Europe. *noun.*

fiord (fyôrd), a long, narrow bay bordered by steep cliffs. *noun.*

fiord We borrowed *fiord* from the word the Norwegians use for such a bay. There are hundreds of fiords along the rocky west coast of Norway.

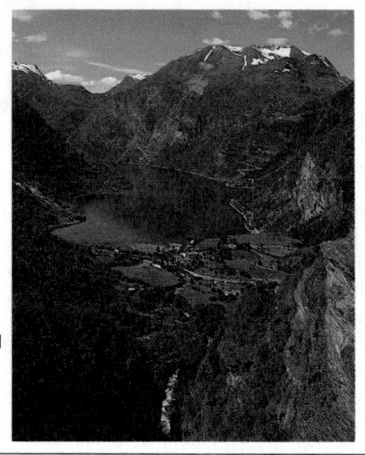

fiord

fir (fėr), an evergreen tree somewhat like a spruce. Small firs are often used for Christmas trees. Some firs are valued for their timber. *noun.*

fire (fīr), **1** the flame, heat, and light caused by something burning. **2** something burning: *There was a nice fire in the fireplace.* **3** destruction by burning: *A cigarette thrown into the woods in dry weather may start a fire.* **4** to make burn; set on fire. **5** to dry thoroughly with heat; bake: *Bricks are fired to make them hard.* **6** enthusiasm; readiness to act; excitement: *Their hearts were full*

fingerprint (definition 1)—the eight basic kinds of **fingerprints.** Almost all fingerprints can be classified by using these patterns.

of patriotic fire. **7** to arouse; excite; inflame: *Stories of adventure fire the imagination.* **8** the shooting or discharge of guns: *The enemy's fire forced the troops to take shelter in a ravine.* **9** to shoot: *I fired at the target.* **10** to dismiss from a job: *The manager fired two salesclerks last week.* 1-3,6,8 *noun,* 4,5,7,9,10 *verb,* **fires, fired, fir·ing.**

catch fire, to begin to burn.
on fire, 1 burning. **2** excited.
open fire, to begin shooting.
under fire, 1 exposed to shooting from the enemy's guns: *Soldiers are under fire in a battle.* **2** attacked; blamed.

fire·arm (fīr′ärm′), a weapon to shoot with. Pistols, rifles, and shotguns are firearms. *noun.*

fire·ball (fīr′bôl′), the great, glowing cloud of hot gases, water vapor, and dust produced by a nuclear explosion. *noun.*

fire·crack·er (fīr′krak′ər), a paper roll containing gunpowder and a fuse. Firecrackers explode with a loud noise. *noun.*

fire engine, a truck with equipment for pumping and spraying water to put out fires; fire truck.

fire escape, a stairway or ladder used when a building is on fire.

fire ex·tin·guish·er (fīr′ ek sting′gwish ər), a container filled with chemicals which are sprayed on a fire to put it out.

fire·fight·er (fīr′fī′tər), a person whose work is putting out fires. *noun.*

fire·fly (fīr′flī′), a small insect that gives off flashes of light when it flies at night. *noun, plural* **fire·flies.**

firefly
about two times
life size

fire·house (fīr′hous′), a building where fire engines are kept, and where firemen are on duty. *noun, plural* **fire·hous·es** (fīr′hou′ziz).

fire·light (fīr′līt′), the light from a fire. *noun.*

fire·man (fīr′mən), **1** a person whose work is putting out fires. **2** a person who looks after fires in engines or furnaces. *noun, plural* **fire·men.**

fire·place (fīr′plās′), a place built to hold a fire. An indoor fireplace is usually made of brick or stone, with a chimney leading up from it through the roof. *noun.*

fire·plug (fīr′plug′), a large water pipe that sticks up from the ground and has places where firefighters can connect hoses; hydrant. *noun.*

fire·proof (fīr′prüf′), **1** almost impossible to burn; very resistant to fire: *A building made*

a hat	i it	oi oil	ch child	(a in about
ā age	ī ice	ou out	ng long	e in taken
ä far	o hot	u cup	sh she	ə = { i in pencil
e let	ō open	ů put	th thin	o in lemon
ē equal	ô order	ü rule	ᴛʜ then	u in circus
ėr term			zh measure	

entirely of steel and concrete is fireproof. **2** to make fireproof: *to fireproof a theater curtain.* **1** *adjective,* **2** *verb.*

fire·side (fīr′sīd′), **1** the space around a fireplace or hearth. **2** home; hearth: *The weary travelers longed to be back at their own fireside. noun.*

fire truck, a fire engine.

fire·wood (fīr′wůd′), wood to make a fire. *noun.*

fire·works (fīr′wėrks′), firecrackers, skyrockets, and other things that make a loud noise or a brilliant display of light at night. *noun plural.*

firm¹ (fėrm), **1** not yielding when pressed: *firm flesh, firm ground.* **2** solid; fixed in place; not easily shaken or moved: *a tree firm in the earth.* **3** not easily changed; determined; positive: *a firm voice, a firm character, a firm belief.* **4** strong: *a firm handshake. adjective.*

firm² (fėrm), a company of two or more persons in business together. *noun.*

first (fėrst), **1** coming before all others: *He is first in his class.* **2** before all others; before anything else: *We eat first and then feed the cat.* **3** a person, thing, or place that is first: *We were the first to get here.* **4** the beginning: *At first I did not like school.* **5** for the first time: *When we first met, we were both in grade school.* **1** *adjective,* **2,5** *adverb,* **3,4** *noun.*

first aid, emergency treatment given to an injured or sick person before a doctor sees the person.

first-class (fėrst′klas′), **1** of the highest class or best quality; excellent: *a first-class teacher.* **2** by the best and most expensive passenger seating and service offered by ship, airplane, or train: *We could not afford to travel first-class.* **1** *adjective,* **2** *adverb.*

first·hand (fėrst′hand′), direct; from the original source: *firsthand information. adjective, adverb.*

first-rate (fėrst′rāt′), **1** of the highest class; excellent; very good: *a first-rate summer.* **2** well: *She did first-rate on the test.* **1** *adjective,* **2** *adverb.*

fish (fish), **1** one of a group of cold-blooded animals with a long backbone that live in water and have gills instead of lungs. Fish are usually covered with scales and have fins for swimming. Some kinds of fish lay eggs in the water; others produce living young. **2** the flesh of fish used for food. **3** to catch fish; try to catch fish. **4** to search: *I fished in my pocket for a dime.* **5** to find and pull: *She fished the map from the drawer.* **1,2** *noun, plural* **fish** or **fish·es;** **3-5** *verb.*

fish·er·man (fish′ər mən), a person who fishes, especially one who makes a living by catching fish. *noun, plural* **fish·er·men.**

fish·er·y (fish′ər ē), **1** a place for catching fish.

fishhook | flank

2 a place for breeding fish. *noun, plural* **fish·er·ies.**

fish·hook (fish′hùk′), a hook used for catching fish. *noun.*

fish·y (fish′ē), 1 like a fish in smell, taste, or shape. 2 doubtful; unlikely: *That story sounds fishy; I don't believe it. adjective,* **fish·i·er, fish·i·est.**

fis·sion (fish′ən), the splitting apart of atomic nuclei to produce tremendous amounts of energy. *noun.*

fist (fist), a tightly closed hand: *He shook his fist at me. noun.*

fit¹ (fit), 1 right and proper; suitable: *The spoiled food isn't fit to eat.* 2 healthy and strong: *Proper exercise and good food help to keep us fit.* 3 to be right, proper, or suitable for: *The role of the queen's friend fits you perfectly.* 4 to make right, proper, or suitable; suit: *She fitted the words to the music.* 5 to have the right size or shape; have the right size or shape for: *Does this glove fit?* 6 to make the right size or shape; adjust: *I had my new jacket fitted at the store.* 7 the way that something fits: *The coat was not a very good fit; it was too tight.* 8 to supply with everything needed; equip: *We fitted out our summer cabin with wooden furniture.* 1,2 *adjective,* **fit·ter, fit·test;** 3-6,8 *verb,* **fits, fit** or **fit·ted, fit·ting;** 7 *noun.*

fit² (fit), 1 a sudden, violent outburst of feeling: *In a fit of anger, she punched her brother.* 2 a short period of doing some one thing: *a fit of coughing, a fit of laughing. noun.*

by fits and starts, starting, stopping, beginning again, and so on; irregularly: *He does his homework by fits and starts instead of steadily.*

have a fit, to show great anger: *My parents had a fit when I spilled a gallon of paint.*

fit·ful (fit′fəl), irregular; going on and then stopping for a while: *I had a fitful sleep during the storm, waking up every few minutes. adjective.*

fit·ness (fit′nis), the state of being healthy and strong: *physical fitness. noun.*

fit·ting (fit′ing), right; proper; suitable. *adjective.*

five (fīv), one more than four; 5. *noun, adjective.*

fix (fiks), 1 to make firm: *I fixed the post in the ground.* 2 to set; put or place definitely: *It was not possible to fix the blame for the accident on either driver.* 3 to direct or hold steadily: *We fixed our eyes on the blackboard.* 4 to make ready; prepare: *We fixed our own breakfast this morning.* 5 to mend; repair: *to fix a watch.* 6 to pay someone money in advance to arrange the result of: *to fix a jury, to fix a race.* 7 a position hard to get out of: *Whoever took my bicycle is going to be in a fix.* 1-6 *verb,* 7 *noun, plural* **fix·es.**

fix·ture (fiks′chər), a thing put in place to stay: *light fixtures. noun.*

fizz (fiz), 1 to make a hissing sound. 2 a hissing sound; bubbling: *the fizz of soda water.* 1 *verb,* 2 *noun, plural* **fizz·es.**

FL, Florida (used with postal Zip Code).

Fla., Florida.

flab·ber·gast (flab′ər gast), to amaze; make speechless with surprise: *We were flabbergasted by the size of the fish. verb.*

flab·by (flab′ē), without firmness; soft; weak: *His muscles were flabby after he was sick in bed with the flu. adjective,* **flab·bi·er, flab·bi·est.**

flag¹ (flag), 1 a piece of cloth, usually with square corners, on which is the picture or pattern that stands for some country: *the flag of the United States, the British flag.* 2 a cloth or banner, often used as a signal: *a red flag of danger.* 3 to signal or stop a person, vehicle, or the like, especially by waving a flag: *The train was flagged at the bridge.* 1,2 *noun,* 3 *verb,* **flags, flagged, flag·ging.**

flag² (flag), to get tired; grow weak; droop: *My horse was flagging, but I urged it on. verb,* **flags, flagged, flag·ging.**

flag·pole (flag′pōl′), a pole from which a flag is flown. *noun.*

flail (flāl), to strike or beat; thrash: *The rider flailed the horse. verb.*

flair (fler *or* flar), a natural talent: *The poet had a flair for making clever rhymes. noun.*

flake (flāk), 1 a flat, thin piece, usually not very large: *a flake of snow, flakes of rust.* 2 to come off in flakes; separate into flakes: *Spots showed where the paint had flaked off.* 1 *noun,* 2 *verb,* **flakes, flaked, flak·ing.**

flame (flām), 1 one of the glowing tongues of light that rise or shoot up when a fire blazes up: *a candle's flame, the flames of a burning house.* 2 to rise up in flames; burn; blaze: *The dry logs flamed up in the fireplace.* 3 a burning with flames; blaze: *The dying fire suddenly burst into flame.* 4 to shine brightly; flash: *Her eyes flamed with rage.* 1,3 *noun,* 2,4 *verb,* **flames, flamed, flam·ing.**

flamingo
about 4½ feet
(1½ meters) tall

fla·min·go (flə ming′gō), a tropical wading bird with very long legs and neck, and feathers that vary from rosy-pink to bright red. *noun, plural* **fla·min·gos** or **fla·min·goes.**

flam·ma·ble (flam′ə bəl), easily set on fire; inflammable: *Paper is flammable. adjective.*

flank (flangk), 1 the side of an animal or a person between the ribs and the hip. 2 to be at the side

230

of: *A garage flanked the house.* **3** the far right or the far left side of an army, fort, or fleet. **4** to get around the far right or the far left side of an enemy's army. **5** to attack from or on the side. 1,3 *noun*, 2,4,5 *verb*.

flan·nel (flan′l), **1** a soft, warm, woolen or cotton cloth. **2** made of flannel: *flannel pajamas, a flannel shirt.* 1 *noun*, 2 *adjective*.

flap (flap), **1** to swing or sway about loosely and with some noise: *The sails flapped in the wind.* **2** to move the wings or arms up and down: *The goose flapped its wings but could not rise from the ground.* **3** a flapping motion; flapping noise: *the flap of banners, the flap of a bird's wing.* **4** to strike noisily with something broad and flat: *The clown's big shoes flapped along the ground.* **5** a piece hanging or fastened at one edge only: *The coat had flaps on the pockets. I sealed the flap on the envelope.* 1,2,4 *verb*, **flaps, flapped, flap·ping;** 3,5 *noun*.

flap·jack (flap′jak′), a pancake. *noun*.

flare (fler *or* flar), **1** to flame up briefly or unsteadily, sometimes with smoke: *The damp logs flared up briefly, then the fire went out.* **2** a blaze; bright, brief, unsteady flame: *In the flare of the match I was able to find the light switch.* **3** a device that produces a dazzling light that burns for a short time, used for signaling, lighting up an area, or as a warning: *The Coast Guard vessel responded to the flare sent up from the lifeboat.* **4** to burst out into open anger or violence: *Her temper flared at the insult.* **5** to spread out in the shape of a bell: *These pants flare at the bottom.* **6** a spreading out into a bell shape: *the flare of a skirt.* 1,4,5 *verb*, **flares, flared, flar·ing;** 2,3,6 *noun*.

flare up, to burst into sudden anger or violence.

flash (flash), **1** a sudden, brief light or flame: *a flash of lightning.* **2** to give out such a light or flame: *Lightning flashed across the sky.* **3** to come suddenly; pass quickly: *A train flashed by. A thought flashed across my mind.* **4** a sudden, short feeling or display: *a flash of hope.* **5** a very short time: *It all happened in a flash.* **6** to give out or send out like a flash: *Her eyes flashed defiance.* 1,4,5 *noun*, *plural* **flash·es;** 2,3,6 *verb*.

flash·back (flash′bak′), a break in the continuous series of events in a novel, motion picture, or the like, to introduce some earlier event or scene. *noun*.

flash·bulb (flash′bulb′), an electric bulb which gives out a brilliant flash of light for a very short time. It is used in taking photographs indoors or at night. *noun*.

flash·light (flash′līt′), a portable electric light, operated by batteries. *noun*.

flash·y (flash′ē), likely to attract attention; too bright or dazzling to be in good taste: *His coat was a little too flashy.* *adjective*, **flash·i·er, flash·i·est.**

flask (flask), a glass or metal bottle, especially one with a narrow neck. *noun*.

flat[1] (flat), **1** smooth and level; even: *flat land.*

a hat	i it	oi oil	ch child	(a in about
ā age	ī ice	ou out	ng long	e in taken
ä far	o hot	u cup	sh she	ə = { i in pencil
e let	ō open	ů put	th thin	o in lemon
ē equal	ô order	ü rule	ŦH then	u in circus
ėr term			zh measure	

2 horizontal; at full length: *The storm left the trees flat on the ground.* **3** the flat part: *The flat of one's hand is the palm.* **4** land that is smooth and level: *There were flats on both sides of the river.* **5** not very deep or thick: *A plate is flat.* **6** with little air in it: *A nail or sharp stone can cause a flat tire.* **7** a tire with little air in it: *Our car got a flat when we drove over a nail.* **8** positive; not to be changed: *A flat refusal is complete. We paid a flat rate with no extra charges.* **9** without much life, interest, or flavor; dull: *a flat voice. Without seasoning many foods would taste flat.* **10** not shiny or glossy: *We used flat paint on the walls and enamel on the woodwork.* **11** below the true pitch in music: *The singer's high notes were flat. Try not to sing flat.* **12** a tone one half step below natural pitch: *Play a B flat.* **13** the sign in music (♭) that shows this. **14** in a flat manner: *He fell flat on the floor.* 1,2,5,6,8-11 *adjective*, **flat·ter, flat·test;** 3,4,7,12,13 *noun*, 11,14 *adverb*.

flat[2] (flat), an apartment or set of rooms on one floor. *noun*.

flat·boat (flat′bōt′), a large boat with a flat bottom, formerly much used for floating goods down a river or canal. *noun*.

flat·car (flat′kär′), a railroad car without a roof or sides, used for hauling freight. *noun*.

flat·fish (flat′fish′), a fish having a flat body and swimming on one side. Halibut, flounder, and sole are kinds of flatfish. *noun*, *plural* **flat·fish** or **flat·fish·es.**

flatfish

flat·land (flat′land′), level land, not broken into hills and valleys. *noun*.

flat·ten (flat′n), to make flat; become flat: *Use a rolling pin to flatten the pie dough.* *verb*.

flat·ter (flat′ər), **1** to praise too much or beyond the truth in order to please: *Were you only flattering me when you said I sang well, or did you mean it?* **2** to show as more beautiful or better looking than what is true: *This picture flatters me.* *verb*.

flat·ter·y (flat′ər ē), words of praise, usually untrue or exaggerated: *Some people use flattery to get favors.* *noun*, *plural* **flat·ter·ies.**

flaunt (flônt), to show off: *They flaunted their expensive toys in front of their playmates. verb.*

fla·vor (flā′vər), **1** a taste: *Chocolate and vanilla have different flavors.* **2** to give added taste to; season: *We use salt, pepper, and spices to flavor food.* **3** a special quality: *Stories about ships and sailors have a flavor of the sea.* 1,3 *noun,* 2 *verb.*

fla·vor·ing (flā′vər ing), something used to give a particular taste to food or drink: *a chocolate flavoring. noun.*

flaw (flô), a slight defect; blemish; fault: *a flaw in a mirror. Her quick temper is a flaw in her character. noun.*

flaw·less (flô′lis), without a flaw; perfect: *a flawless diamond. The actor's performance was flawless. adjective.*

flax (flaks), **1** a slender, upright plant with narrow leaves and blue flowers. Linseed oil is made from its seeds and linen from its stems. **2** the threadlike parts into which the stems of this plant separate. Flax is spun into thread and woven into linen cloth. *noun.*

flax·en (flak′sən), **1** made of flax. **2** like flax; pale-yellow: *Flaxen hair is very light. adjective.*

flea (flē), a small, jumping insect without wings. Fleas live on the bodies of dogs, cats, and other animals, and feed on their blood. *noun.*

fleck (flek), **1** a small spot or patch; speck: *Freckles are brown flecks on the skin.* **2** to mark with spots of color or light: *The bird's breast is flecked with brown.* 1 *noun,* 2 *verb.*

fled (fled). See **flee.** *The enemy fled when we attacked. The prisoner has fled. verb.*

fledg·ling (flej′ling), **1** a young bird that has just grown feathers needed for flying. **2** a young, inexperienced person. *noun.*

flee (flē), **1** to run away: *The robbers tried to flee, but they were caught.* **2** to go quickly; move swiftly: *Vacation time was over and the summer days were fleeing. verb,* **flees, fled, flee·ing.**

fleece (flēs), **1** the wool that covers a sheep. The coat of wool cut off or shorn from one sheep is called a fleece. **2** to cut the fleece from. 1 *noun,* 2 *verb,* **fleec·es, fleeced, fleec·ing.**

fleec·y (flē′sē), like a fleece; soft and white: *fleecy clouds. adjective,* **fleec·i·er, fleec·i·est.**

fleet[1] (flēt), **1** a group of warships under one command: *the United States fleet.* **2** a group of ships, airplanes, automobiles, or the like, moving or working together: *a fleet of fishing boats, a fleet of trucks. noun.*

fleet[2] (flēt), swiftly moving; rapid: *The fleet horse won the race. adjective.*

fleet·ing (flē′ting), passing swiftly; soon gone: *He gave me a fleeting smile, and then waved good-by. adjective.*

flesh (flesh), **1** the soft substance of the body that covers the bones and is covered by skin. Flesh is made up mostly of muscles and fat. **2** meat: *Lions eat the flesh of zebras.* **3** the soft part of fruits or vegetables; the part of fruits that can be eaten: *The flesh of apples is white. noun.*

flesh and blood, family; relatives by birth.

flesh·y (flesh′ē), having much flesh; plump; fat. *adjective,* **flesh·i·er, flesh·i·est.**

flew (flü). See **fly**[2]. *The bird flew away. verb.*

flex (fleks), to bend: *She flexed her stiff arm slowly. verb.*

flex·i·ble (flek′sə bəl), **1** able to be bent without breaking; not stiff; easily bent in all directions: *Leather, rubber, and wire are flexible.* **2** able to change easily to fit different conditions: *My mother works from our home and her hours are very flexible. Our vacation plans are flexible, depending on the weather. adjective.*

flexible (definition 1) His arms and legs were as **flexible** as rubber.

flick (flik), **1** a sudden light blow or movement: *She threw the dart with a flick of the wrist.* **2** to strike lightly with a quick blow: *He flicked the dust from his shoes with a handkerchief.* **3** to make a sudden blow with: *The children flicked wet towels at each other.* 1 *noun,* 2,3 *verb.*

flick·er[1] (flik′ər), **1** to shine or burn with an unsteady, wavering light: *The firelight flickered on the walls.* **2** an unsteady, wavering light or flame: *the flicker of an oil lamp.* **3** to move lightly and quickly in and out, or back and forth: *We heard the birds flicker among the leaves.* **4** a quick, light movement: *I knew he was not sleeping by the flicker of his eyelids.* 1,3 *verb,* 2,4 *noun.*

flick·er[2] (flik′ər), a large, common woodpecker of

flicker[2]—about 12 inches (30 centimeters) long

North America, with yellow markings on the wings and tail, and a spotted breast. *noun.*

flied (flīd). See **fly**[2] (definition 9). *The batter flied to center field. verb.*

fli·er (flī′ər), **1** a person or thing that flies, such as a bird or insect: *That eagle is a high flier.* **2** a pilot of an airplane; aviator. *noun.* Also spelled **flyer.**

flies[1] (flīz), more than one fly: *There are many flies on the window. noun plural.*

flies[2] (flīz). See **fly**[2]. *A bird flies. He flies an airplane. verb.*

flight[1] (flīt), **1** the act or manner of flying: *the flight of a bird through the air.* **2** the distance a bird, bullet, airplane, or the like can fly: *The flight of the arrow was several hundred feet.* **3** a group of things flying through the air together: *a flight of pigeons.* **4** a trip in an aircraft: *We had an enjoyable flight.* **5** an airplane that makes a scheduled trip: *She took the three o'clock flight to Boston.* **6** a set of stairs from one landing or one story of a building to the next. *noun.*

flight[2] (flīt), a running away; escape: *The flight of the prisoners was discovered. noun.*

flight attendant, a person employed by an airline to look after passengers during an airplane flight.

flim·sy (flim′zē), **1** light and thin: *I accidentally tore the flimsy paper.* **2** weak: *Their excuse was so flimsy that no one believed it. adjective,* **flim·si·er, flim·si·est.**

flinch (flinch), to draw back from difficulty, danger, or pain; shrink: *She flinched when she touched the hot radiator. verb.*

fling (fling), **1** to throw; throw with force: *to fling a stone.* **2** a throw. **3** to rush; dash: *In a rage the child flung out of the room.* 1,3 *verb,* **flings, flung, fling·ing;** 2 *noun.*

flint (flint), a very hard stone, which makes a spark when struck against steel. *noun.*

flint·lock (flint′lok′), an old-fashioned gun in which a piece of flint striking against steel makes sparks that explode the gunpowder. *noun.*

flip (flip), **1** to cause to spin in the air: *to flip a coin. He flipped me over his shoulder, and I landed on my feet.* **2** to move with a snap or a jerk: *to flip the pages of a book. Please flip that light switch for me.* **3** to turn over: *to flip a record and play the other side. The cook flipped the pancake over in the frying pan.* **4** a spinning; a toss: *The winner was picked by the flip of a coin.* 1-3 *verb,* **flips, flipped, flip·ping;** 4 *noun.*

flip·pant (flip′ənt), too free in speech or action; not properly serious or respectful: *His flippant answer to my question annoyed me. adjective.*

flip·per (flip′ər), **1** one of the broad, flat body parts used for swimming by animals such as seals and walruses. **2** a molded rubber attachment for the human foot, used as an aid in swimming. *noun.*

flirt (flėrt), **1** to pay attention to someone in a romantic way without being serious about it. **2** a person who flirts. 1 *verb,* 2 *noun.*

a hat	**i** it	**oi** oil	**ch** child	a in about
ā age	**ī** ice	**ou** out	**ng** long	e in taken
ä far	**o** hot	**u** cup	**sh** she	ə = i in pencil
e let	**ō** open	**u̇** put	**th** thin	o in lemon
ē equal	**ô** order	**ü** rule	**ŦH** then	u in circus
ėr term			**zh** measure	

flit (flit), to move lightly and quickly: *Birds flitted from tree to tree. Many thoughts flitted through my mind as I sat daydreaming. verb,* **flits, flit·ted, flit·ting.**

float (flōt), **1** to stay on top of or be held up by air, water, or other liquid. A cork will float, but a stone sinks. **2** anything that stays up or holds up something else in water. A raft is a float. A cork on a fishline is a float. **3** to move on a liquid or in the air: *The boat floated out to sea. A balloon floated in the sky.* **4** a low, flat car that carries an exhibit in a parade: *The king of the parade rode on a beautiful float covered with flowers.* 1,3 *verb,* 2,4 *noun.*

flock (flok), **1** a group of animals of one kind keeping, feeding, or herded together: *a flock of sheep, a flock of geese, a flock of birds.* **2** a large number; crowd: *Visitors came in flocks to the zoo to see the new gorilla.* **3** to go in a group; crowd: *The sheep flocked together. The children flocked around the ice-cream stand.* **4** people of the same church group. 1,2,4 *noun,* 3 *verb.*

floe (flō), a field or sheet of floating ice. *noun.*

flog (flog), to beat or whip hard. *verb,* **flogs, flogged, flog·ging.**

flood (flud), **1** a great flow of water over what is usually dry land: *The heavy rains caused a serious flood near the river.* **2** to flow over; cover or fill with water: *The river flooded the fields.* **3 the Flood,** (in the Bible) the water that covered the earth in the time of Noah. **4** a great flow of anything: *She apologized in a flood of words.* **5** to fill, cover, or overcome like a flood: *In the morning, my room is flooded with sunlight.* 1,3,4 *noun,* 2,5 *verb.*

flood·light (flud′līt′), a lamp that gives a broad beam of light. *noun.*

floor (flôr), **1** the part of a room to walk on: *The floor of this room is made of wood.* **2** to put a floor in or on: *The carpenter will floor this room with oak.* **3** a flat surface at the bottom: *They dropped their net to the floor of the ocean.* **4** a level or story of a building: *They live on the fourth floor.* **5** the right to speak: *"You may have the floor," said the chairman.* **6** to knock down: *The boxer floored his opponent with one blow.* **7** to confuse; puzzle: *The last question on the test completely floored us.* 1,3-5 *noun,* 2,6,7 *verb.*

flop (flop), **1** to move loosely or heavily; flap around clumsily: *The fish flopped helplessly on the deck.* **2** to fall, drop, throw, or move heavily or clumsily: *The tired girl flopped down into a chair.* **3** a heavy, clumsy, or noisy fall or drop: *I threw myself on the bed with a flop.* **4** a failure: *The party was a flop.* **5** to fail: *Their first business venture*

flopped. 1,2,5 *verb,* **flops, flopped, flop·ping;**
3,4 *noun.*

flop·py (flop′ē), hanging loosely; flapping: *Our
dog has floppy ears. adjective,* **flop·pi·er,
flop·pi·est.**

floppy disk, a small, bendable plastic disk with
a magnetic surface, used to store instructions and
information for a computer; diskette.

flo·ral (flôr′əl), of flowers: *floral designs. adjective.*

Flo·ri·da (flôr′ə də), one of the southeastern
states of the United States. *Abbreviation:* Fla. or
FL *Capital:* Tallahassee. *noun.*
[*Florida* comes from a Spanish phrase meaning
"flowery Easter." The state was named this by
Ponce de León. He first sighted the land on
Easter Sunday of 1513, and named it after the
holiday.]

flo·rist (flôr′ist), a person who raises or sells
flowers. *noun.*

floss (flôs), **1** a shiny, silk or cotton thread that
has not been twisted. Floss is used for
embroidery. Dental floss is used for cleaning
between the teeth. **2** to use dental floss, or use
dental floss on: *I flossed my teeth this morning.*
1 *noun,* **2** *verb.*

floun·der[1] (floun′dər), **1** to struggle without
making much progress; plunge about: *After the
blizzard, we found cattle floundering in snowdrifts.*
2 to be clumsy or confused and make mistakes: *I
was so nervous I floundered through my speech.*
verb.

floun·der[2] (floun′dər), a flatfish that lives in salt
water and is much used for food. *noun, plural*
floun·der or **floun·ders.**

flour (flour), **1** the fine powder or meal made by
grinding and sifting wheat or other grain,
potatoes, soybeans, and so on. **2** to cover or
sprinkle with flour. **1** *noun,* **2** *verb.*

flour·ish (flėr′ish), **1** to grow or develop with
vigor; do well; thrive: *Your radishes are
flourishing. Their newspaper business grew and
flourished.* **2** to wave in the air: *She flourished the
letter at us.* **3** a waving about in the air: *The
magician removed his cape with a flourish.* **4** an
extra ornament or curve in handwriting. **1,2** *verb,*
3,4 *noun, plural* **flour·ish·es.**

flourish (definition 4)
John Hancock's signature has several **flourishes.**

flout (flout), to treat with contempt or scorn;
mock; scoff at: *You are foolish to flout good
advice. verb.*

flow (flō), **1** to run like water; move in a current or
stream: *Blood flows through our bodies.* **2** a
current; stream: *There is a constant flow of water*
from the spring. **3** to pour; move steadily: *The
crowd flowed out of the town hall and down the
main street.* **4** any smooth, steady movement: *The
police officer helped maintain the flow of traffic.*
5 to hang loose and waving: *The emperor's robes
flowed to the floor.* **6** the act of pouring out: *A
tight bandage should stop the flow of blood.* **7** the
rise of the tide. **1,3,5** *verb,* **2,4,6,7** *noun.*

flow·chart (flō′chärt′), a diagram that shows,
step by step, each thing a computer must do to
perform a certain job. *noun.*

flow·er (flou′ər), **1** a blossom; part of a plant or
tree that produces the seed. Flowers are often
beautifully colored or shaped. **2** a plant grown for
its blossoms. **3** to have flowers; produce flowers;
bloom: *Many fruit trees flower in the spring.*
1,2 *noun,* **3** *verb.*

PETAL
STAMEN
SEPAL
PISTIL

flower (definition 1)
the parts of a flower

flow·er·pot (flou′ər pot′), a pot to hold soil and
a plant. *noun.*

flow·er·y (flou′ər ē), **1** having many flowers. **2** full
of fine words and fanciful expressions: *a flowery
speech. adjective,* **flow·er·i·er, flow·er·i·est.**

flown (flōn). See **fly**[2]. *The bird has flown. The
flag is flown on all national holidays. verb.*

fl. oz. or **fl oz,** fluid ounce or fluid ounces.

flu (flü), a disease much like a very bad cold. It is
caused by a virus. *noun.*

flue (flü), a tube, pipe, or other enclosed passage
for smoke or hot air. A chimney has a flue. *noun.*

fluff (fluf), **1** soft, light, downy particles, such as
hair, tiny feathers, or bits of wool. **2** a soft, light,
downy mass: *The kitten looked like a fluff of fur.*
3 to shake or puff out into a soft, light mass: *I
fluffed my pillow.* **1,2** *noun,* **3** *verb.*

fluff·y (fluf′ē), **1** soft and light: *a fluffy scarf.
Whipped cream is fluffy.* **2** covered with soft, light
feathers or hair: *The baby chicks were fluffy.*
adjective, **fluff·i·er, fluff·i·est.**

flu·id (flü′id), **1** any liquid or gas; something that
will flow. Water, mercury, air, and oxygen are
fluids. **2** like a liquid or a gas; flowing: *We poured
the fluid mass of hot fudge into a pan to harden
into candy.* **1** *noun,* **2** *adjective.*

fluid ounce, a unit for measuring liquids. There
are 16 fluid ounces in 1 pint.

flung (flung). See **fling.** *I flung my coat on the
chair. The paper was flung into the fire. verb.*

flunk (flungk), to fail in schoolwork: *She flunked
the history examination. verb.*

fluor·ine (flür′ēn), a pale-yellow, bad-smelling,
poisonous gas that occurs naturally only in

combination with other substances. Fluorine is a chemical element. It is used in small amounts in water to prevent tooth decay. *noun.*

flur·ry (flėr′ē), **1** a sudden gust: *A flurry of wind upset the small sailboat.* **2** a light fall of rain or snow: *snow flurries.* **3** a sudden commotion: *There was a flurry of alarm when the fire broke out. noun, plural* **flur·ries.**

flush (flush), **1** to blush; glow: *Her face flushed when they laughed at her.* **2** a rosy glow or blush: *the flush of sunrise. A sudden flush showed his embarrassment.* **3** to rush suddenly: *I felt the blood flush to my cheeks.* **4** a sudden rush; rapid flow: *After using the toilet, please give it a flush.* **5** to send a sudden rush of water over or through to clean or empty: *to flush a toilet. The city streets were flushed to clean them.* **6** even; level: *Make that shelf just flush with this one.* 1,3,5 *verb,* 2,4 *noun, plural* **flush·es;** 6 *adjective.*

flus·ter (flus′tər), **1** to make nervous and excited; confuse: *The honking of horns flustered the driver, and he stalled his automobile.* **2** nervous excitement; confusion: *He was in a fluster before giving his speech.* 1 *verb,* 2 *noun.*

flute (flüt), a long, slender, pipelike musical instrument. A flute is played by blowing across a hole near one end. Different notes are made by covering different holes along its length with the fingers or with keys. *noun.*

flute

flut·ist (flü′tist), a person who plays a flute. *noun.*

flut·ter (flut′ər), **1** to wave back and forth quickly and lightly: *The flag fluttered in the breeze.* **2** to flap the wings; flap: *The chickens fluttered excitedly when they saw the dog.* **3** to move through the air with a wavy motion: *The falling leaves fluttered to the ground.* **4** to move restlessly: *They fluttered about, making preparations for the party.* **5** to beat a little faster than usual: *My heart fluttered when I rose to give my speech.* **6** a quick, light flapping movement: *the flutter of curtains in a breeze.* **7** excitement: *The appearance of the queen caused a great flutter in the crowd.* 1-5 *verb,* 6,7 *noun.*

fly¹ (flī), **1** any of a large group of insects that

fly¹ (definition 2)—The shape and movement of these **flies** in the water attract fish.

have two wings, especially the housefly. **2** a fishhook with feathers, silk, or tinsel on it to make it look like a fly. *noun, plural* **flies.**

fly² (flī), **1** to move through the air with wings: *These birds fly long distances.* **2** to float or wave in the air: *Our flag flies every day.* **3** to cause to float or wave in the air: *The children are flying kites.* **4** to travel by aircraft; to carry by aircraft: *We flew to Hawaii. The government flew food and supplies to the flooded city.* **5** to pilot an aircraft: *My cousin flies for an airline. He flies planes for a living.* **6** to rush; move swiftly: *When the phone rang, I flew to answer it.* **7** a flap to cover buttons or a zipper on clothing. **8** a baseball hit high in the air with a bat: *The batter hit a fly to left field.* **9** to bat a baseball high in the air: *The batter flied to the outfield.* 1-6,9 *verb,* **flies, flew, flown, fly·ing** for 1-6, **flies, flied, fly·ing** for 9; 7,8 *noun, plural* **flies.**

fly·catch·er (flī′kach′ər), a bird that catches insects while flying. *noun.*

fly·er (flī′ər). See flier. *noun.*

flying fish, a tropical sea fish that has fins like wings and can leap through the air.

flying fish—from 8 to 18 inches (20 to 46 centimeters) long

flying saucer, an undentified disklike object reported in the sky over many parts of the world; UFO.

fly·wheel (flī′hwēl′), a heavy wheel attached to a machine to keep it and its parts moving at an even speed. *noun.*

foal (fōl), a young horse, donkey, or zebra; colt or filly. *noun.*

foal—a **foal** beside its mother

foam (fōm), **1** a mass of very small bubbles. **2** to form or gather into a mass of bubbles: *The soda foamed over the glass.* **1** *noun,* **2** *verb.*

foam rubber, a soft, spongy rubber used for mattresses, pillows, and cushions.

focus (definition 1)—Rays of light are brought to a **focus** by the lens.

fo·cus (fō′kəs), **1** a point at which rays of light or heat meet after being reflected from a mirror or bent by a lens. **2** to bring rays of light or heat to a focus: *The lens focused the sun's rays on a piece of paper and burned a hole in it.* **3** the distance from a lens or mirror to the point where rays from it meet: *A near-sighted eye has a shorter focus than a normal eye.* **4** the correct adjustment of a lens, or of the eye, to make a clear image: *If the camera is not brought into focus, the photograph will be blurred.* **5** to adjust a lens or the eye to make a clear image: *A near-sighted person cannot focus accurately on distant objects.* **6** a central point of attraction, attention, or activity: *The baby was the focus of attention.* **7** to concentrate; direct: *I focused all my attention on the teacher.* **1,3,4,6** *noun, plural* **fo·cus·es; 2,5,7** *verb.*

fod·der (fod′ər), any coarse food for horses, cattle, and sheep. Hay and cornstalks are fodder. *noun.*

foe (fō), an enemy. *noun.*

fog (fog), **1** a cloud of fine drops of water just above the earth's surface; thick mist. **2** to cover with fog or something like fog: *The steam in the bathroom fogged the mirror.* **3** a confused or puzzled condition: *My mind was in a fog from lack of sleep.* **1,3** *noun,* **2** *verb,* **fogs, fogged, fog·ging.**

fog·gy (fog′ē), **1** having much fog; misty. **2** not clear; dim; blurred: *Their ideas are confused and rather foggy.* *adjective,* **fog·gi·er, fog·gi·est.**

fog·horn (fog′hôrn′), a horn that warns ships in foggy weather. *noun.*

foil[1] (foil), to outwit; prevent from carrying out plans: *Quick thinking by the bank clerk foiled the robbers, and they were captured.* *verb.* [An earlier English meaning of *foil*[1] was "to tread under foot" or "to trample." It was taken from an old French word meaning "to trample."]

foil[2] (foil), metal beaten, hammered, or rolled into a very thin sheet: *Candy is sometimes wrapped in foil to keep it fresh.* *noun.* [*Foil*[2] comes from a Latin word meaning "leaf."]

foil[3] (foil), a long, narrow sword with a flexible blade and a blunted point to prevent injury, used in fencing. *noun.*

fold[1] (fōld), **1** to bend or double over on itself: *to fold a letter.* **2** a mark or line made by folding: *Cut along this fold.* **3** to bend till close to the body: *She folded her arms. A bird folds its wings.* **4** to put the arms around and hold tenderly: *He folded the crying child to him.* **1,3,4** *verb,* **2** *noun.*

fold[2] (fōld), a pen to keep sheep in. *noun.*

fold·er (fōl′dər), **1** a holder for papers made by folding a piece of stiff paper once. **2** a pamphlet made of one or more folded sheets: *My Dad brought home folders about places to visit on our vacation.* *noun.*

fo·li·age (fō′lē ij), the leaves of a plant. *noun.*

folk (fōk), **1** people of a certain kind: *Most city folk know very little about farming.* **2** of or coming from the common people: *folk music, a folk singer.* **3** **folks, a** people: *Most folks enjoy eating.* **b** relatives: *Her folks are very nice.* **1,3** *noun, plural* **folk** or **folks; 2** *adjective.*

folk dance, 1 a dance originating and handed down among the common people. **2** the music for it.

folk·lore (fōk′lôr′), the beliefs, stories, legends, and customs of a people. *noun.*

folk song, a song originating and handed down among the common people.

folk tale, a story or legend originating and handed down among the common people.

fol·low (fol′ō), **1** to go or come after: *Sheep follow a leader. Night follows day. You lead and we'll follow.* **2** to result from; result: *Floods followed the heavy rain.* **3** to go along: *Follow this road to the corner.* **4** to use; obey; act according to; take as a guide: *Follow her advice.* **5** to watch closely; keep in view: *I followed the bird's flight.* **6** to keep the mind on; understand: *Could you explain that again? I couldn't follow it all.* verb.

follow up, to act upon with energy: *She followed up the suggestion for a field trip by making all the arrangements.*

fol·low·er (fol′ō ər), **1** a person or thing that follows: *That student is a leader, not a follower.* **2** a person who follows the ideas or beliefs of another: *Christians are followers of Christ.* noun.

fol·low·ing (fol′ō ing), **1** a group of followers or fans: *That team has quite a following.* **2** that follows; next after: *If that was Sunday, then the following day must have been Monday.* **1** noun, **2** adjective.

fol·ly (fol′ē), **1** a being foolish; lack of sense; unwise conduct: *It was folly to eat too much on the picnic.* **2** a foolish act, practice, or idea; something silly: *My biggest folly was trying to ride my bike down the front steps.* noun, plural **fol·lies.**

fond (fond), loving; liking: *She gave her daughter a fond look.* adjective.

fond of, having a liking for: *I am very fond of my uncle.*

fon·dle (fon′dl), to pet; caress: *They fondled the baby kittens.* verb, **fon·dles, fon·dled, fon·dling.**

font (font), **1** a basin holding water for baptism. **2** a basin for holy water. **3** a fountain; source. noun.

food (füd), **1** anything that living things eat or drink that makes them live and grow. **2** anything that causes growth: *Books are food for the mind.* noun.

food chain, several kinds of living things that are linked because each uses another as food. Cats, birds, caterpillars, and plants are a food chain because each eats the one named next.

fool (fül), **1** a person without sense; person who acts unwisely: *He's a fool to drive so recklessly.* **2** a clown formerly kept by a king, queen, or other noble to amuse people. **3** to joke, tease, or pretend: *I'm not really hurt; I was only fooling.* **4** to make a fool of; deceive; trick: *You can't fool me.* **1,2** noun, **3,4** verb.

[*Fool* comes from a Latin word that originally meant "a bellows," that is, an empty baglike device for blowing air onto a fire. Later on, the word was used to refer to a person who was like a bag of wind, one who talks a lot but says very little.]

fool with, to meddle foolishly with: *Stop fooling with that machine.*

fool·har·dy (fül′här′dē), foolishly brave; rash: *The man made a foolhardy attempt to go over Niagara Falls in a barrel.* adjective, **fool·har·di·er, fool·har·di·est.**

fool·ish (fü′lish), without sense; unwise: *It is foolish to cross the street without looking both ways.* adjective.

fool·proof (fül′prüf′), so safe, simple, or well made that anyone can use or do it: *This lock is foolproof. My plan is foolproof; nothing can go wrong.* adjective.

foot (fut), **1** the end part of a leg; part that a

a hat	i it	oi oil	ch child	a in about
ā age	ī ice	ou out	ng long	e in taken
ä far	o hot	u cup	sh she	ə = { i in pencil
e let	ō open	u̇ put	th thin	o in lemon
ē equal	ô order	ü rule	₮H then	u in circus
ėr term			zh measure	

person, animal, or thing stands on. **2** the part opposite the head of something: *the foot of a bed.* **3** the lowest part; the bottom; base: *the foot of a column, the foot of a hill, the foot of a page.* **4** a unit of length; 12 inches. 3 feet equal 1 yard. **5** to pay: *My parents footed the bill for the dinner.* **1-4** noun, plural **feet; 5** verb.

on foot, walking or running: *They traveled on foot.*

put one's foot down, to make up one's mind and act firmly: *If you don't go to bed right now, I'll have to put my foot down.*

foot·ball (fut′bôl′), **1** a game played with an oval leather ball which is to be kicked, thrown, or carried past the goal line at either end of the field. **2** a ball used in this game. noun.

foot·hill (fut′hil′), a low hill at the base of a mountain or mountain range. noun.

foot·hold (fut′hōld′), **1** a place to put a foot; support for the feet: *I climbed the steep cliff by getting footholds in cracks in the rocks.* **2** a firm footing or position: *It is hard to break a habit after it has a foothold.* noun.

foot·ing (fut′ing), **1** a firm placing or position of the feet: *She lost her footing and fell on the ice.* **2** a place or support for the feet: *The steep cliff gave us no footing.* **3** a condition; position; relationship: *The United States and Canada are on a friendly footing.* noun.

foot·lights (fut′līts′), a row of lights at the front of a stage. noun plural.

foot·man (fut′mən), a male servant who answers the bell, waits on table, and opens doors. noun, plural **foot·men.**

foot·note (fut′nōt′), a note at the bottom of a page about something on the page. noun.

foot·path (fut′path′), a path for people on foot only. noun, plural **foot·paths** (fut′pa₮Hz′ or fut′paths′).

foot·print (fut′print′), a mark made by a foot. noun.

foot·sore (fut′sôr′), having sore feet from much walking: *The hike left us footsore and hungry.* adjective.

foot·step (fut′step′), **1** a person's step: *a baby's first footsteps.* **2** the distance covered in one step: *The hall was only a few footsteps from the kitchen.* **3** the sound of steps coming or going: *I heard footsteps in the other room.* **4** the mark made by a foot; footprint. noun.

follow in someone's footsteps, to do as another has done.

foot·stool (fut′stül′), a low stool on which to place the feet when seated. noun.

foot·wear (fut′wer′), shoes, slippers, stockings, or the like. noun.

for (fôr *or* fər), **1** in place of: *We used boxes for chairs.* **2** in support of: *He stands for honest government.* **3** in return; in consideration of: *These apples are eight for a dollar. We thanked him for his kindness.* **4** with the object or purpose of: *He went for a walk.* **5** in order to become, have, keep, or get to: *He ran for his life. She is hunting for her cat. They left for New York yesterday.* **6** meant to belong to or be used with; suited to: *a box for gloves, books for children.* **7** meant to belong to: *This gift is for you.* **8** with a feeling toward: *We longed for home. She has an eye for beauty.* **9** with regard or respect to: *It is warm for April. Eating too much is bad for one's health.* **10** because of; by reason of: *They were punished for stealing.* **11** in honor of: *A party was given for her.* **12** as far as: *We walked for a mile.* **13** as long as: *We worked for an hour.* **14** as being: *They know it for a fact.* **15** to the amount of: *a check for $20. preposition.*

fo·rage (fôr′ij), **1** hay, grain, or other food for horses, cattle, or other domestic animals. **2** to hunt or search for food: *Rabbits forage in our garden.* **3** to hunt; search about: *We foraged for old lumber to build a tree house.* **1** *noun,* **2,3** *verb,* **fo·rag·es, fo·raged, fo·rag·ing.**

fo·ray (fôr′ā), a raid for plunder: *Bandits made forays on the villages and took away cattle. noun.*

for·bade *or* **for·bad** (fər bad′). See **forbid.** *My parents forbade me to stay out past ten o'clock. verb.*

for·bear (fôr ber′ *or* fôr bar′), **1** to hold back; keep from doing, saying, or using: *I forbore telling her the truth because I knew it would upset her.* **2** to be patient; control oneself. *verb,* **for·bears, for·bore, for·borne, for·bear·ing.**

for·bear·ance (fôr ber′əns *or* fôr bar′əns), patience; self-control. *noun.*

for·bid (fər bid′), to say one must not do; not allow; make a rule against: *The teacher forbade us to leave our seats. State law forbids picking wildflowers. verb,* **for·bids, for·bade** *or* **for·bad, for·bid·den** *or* **for·bid, for·bid·ding.**

for·bid·den (fər bid′n), **1** not allowed; against the law or the rules: *Eve ate the forbidden fruit.* **2** See **forbid.** *My parents have forbidden me to swim in that river.* **1** *adjective,* **2** *verb.*

for·bid·ding (fər bid′ing), causing fear or dislike; looking dangerous or unpleasant: *The coast was rocky and forbidding. adjective.*

for·bore (fôr bôr′). See **forbear.** *He forbore from showing his anger. verb.*

for·borne (fôr bôrn′). See **forbear.** *We have forborne from vengeance. verb.*

force (fôrs), **1** power; strength: *The speeding car struck the tree with great force.* **2** strength used against a person or thing; violence: *We had to use force to break open the locked trunk.* **3** to make act against one's will: *Give it to me at once, or I will force you to.* **4** to get or take by strength or violence: *He forced his way in.* **5** to break open; break through: *I had to force the lock to get into my suitcase.* **6** to make by an unusual or unnatural effort: *The unhappy child forced a smile.* **7** to hurry the growth or blossoming of: *We forced apple blossoms by cutting branches and placing them in water in our warm living room.* **8** a group of people who work together: *our office force, the police force.* **9 forces,** the armed services: *United States forces were stationed on the island during the war.* **10** any cause that produces, changes, or stops the motion of a body: *the force of gravitation. Magnetic force causes a compass needle to turn.* **1,2,8-10** *noun,* **3-7** *verb,* **for·ces, forced, forc·ing.**
in force, in use: *The old rules are still in force.*

forced (fôrst), **1** made or driven by force: *The work of slaves was forced labor.* **2** not natural; strained: *She hid her dislike with a forced smile. adjective.*

force·ful (fôrs′fəl), having much force; vigorous; strong: *I admired her frank and forceful manner. adjective.*

for·ceps (fôr′seps), small pincers or tongs used by surgeons or dentists for seizing and holding. *Dentists use forceps for pulling teeth. noun, plural* **for·ceps.**

for·ci·ble (fôr′sə bəl), made or done by force; using force: *a forcible entrance into a house. adjective.*

for·ci·bly (fôr′sə blē), in a forcible manner: *They had to remove the intruder forcibly. adverb.*

ford (fôrd), **1** a place where a river, stream, or other body of water is not too deep to cross by walking through the water. **2** to cross a river, stream, or other body of water by walking or driving through the water. **1** *noun,* **2** *verb.*

fore (fôr), at the front; toward the beginning or front; forward: *The fore section of a ship is the bow. adjective.*

fore-, a prefix meaning: **1** front: *Forefoot means a front foot.* **2** before; beforehand: *Foresee means to see beforehand.*

fore·arm (fôr′ärm′), the part of the arm between the elbow and the wrist. *noun.*

fore·cast (fôr′kast′), **1** to predict; tell what is

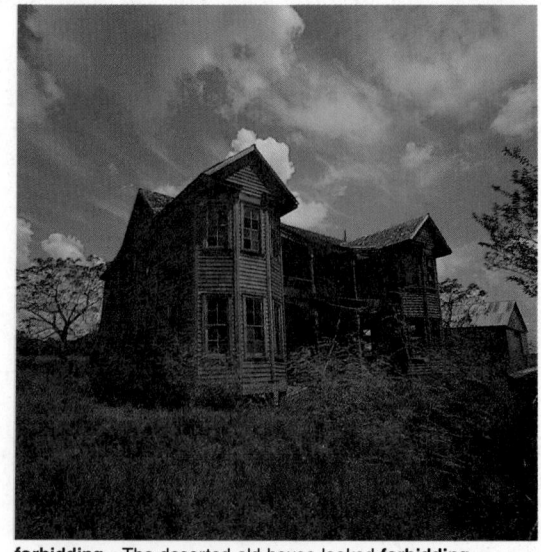

forbidding—The deserted old house looked **forbidding.**

coming: *Cooler weather is forecast for tomorrow.*
2 a prediction; a statement of what is coming:
What is the forecast for the weather today? 1 *verb,*
fore·casts, fore·cast or **fore·cast·ed,**
fore·cast·ing; 2 *noun.*

fore·fa·ther (fôr′fä′ᴛʜər), an ancestor: *My
forefathers were pioneers. noun.*

fore·fin·ger (fôr′fing′gər), the finger next to the
thumb; index finger. *noun.*

fore·foot (fôr′fut′), one of the front feet of an
animal having four or more feet. *noun, plural*
fore·feet.

fore·go·ing (fôr′gō′ing), preceding; going
before: *Read again the foregoing pages. adjective.*

fore·gone (fôr′gôn), known or decided
beforehand: *It was a foregone conclusion that the
popular mayor would run for reelection. adjective.*

fore·ground (fôr′ground′), the part of a picture
or scene nearest the observer; part toward the
front: *The cottage stands in the foreground with the
mountains in the background. noun.*

fore·hand (fôr′hand′), a stroke in tennis and
other games made with the palm of the hand
turned forward. *noun.*

forehand

fore·head (fôr′id *or* fôr′hed′), the part of the
face above the eyes. *noun.*

fo·reign (fôr′ən), **1** outside one's own country:
She has traveled a lot in foreign countries. **2** coming
from outside one's own country: *a foreign ship, a
foreign language, foreign money.* **3** having to do
with other countries: *foreign trade.* **4** not
belonging: *Sitting still all day is foreign to a healthy
child's nature. adjective.*

fo·reign·er (fôr′ə nər), a person from another
country; outsider. *noun.*

fore·leg (fôr′leg′), one of the front legs of an
animal having four or more legs. *noun.*

fore·man (fôr′mən), **1** a person in charge of a
group of workers; person in charge of the work in
some part of a factory. **2** a person at the head of a
jury. *noun, plural* **fore·men.**

a hat	i it	oi oil	ch child	(a in about
ā age	ī ice	ou out	ng long	e in taken
ä far	o hot	u cup	sh she	ə = { i in pencil
e let	ō open	u̇ put	th thin	o in lemon
ē equal	ô order	ü rule	ᴛʜ then	(u in circus
ėr term			zh measure	

fore·most (fôr′mōst), chief; leading: *He is
regarded as one of the foremost scientists of this
century. adjective.*

fore·noon (fôr′nün′), the time between early
morning and noon; part of the day from sunrise to
noon. *noun.*

fore·paw (fôr′pô′), a front paw: *Our cat's
forepaws are white. noun.*

fore·run·ner (fôr′run′ər), a person or thing that
is a sign or warning that something is coming:
*Black clouds and high winds are forerunners of a
storm. noun.*

fore·saw (fôr sô′). See **foresee.** *We foresaw that
we would be late and called to tell our friends. verb.*

fore·see (fôr sē′), to see or know beforehand:
*She could foresee that the job would take all day, so
she canceled her plans for the afternoon. verb,*
fore·sees, fore·saw, fore·seen, fore·see·ing.

fore·seen (fôr sēn′). See **foresee.** *Nobody could
have foreseen how cold it would be. verb.*

fore·sight (fôr′sīt′), the ability to see what is
likely to happen and prepare for it: *She had the
foresight to wear a warm coat. noun.*

fo·rest (fôr′ist), **1** thick woods; woodland, often
covering many miles. **2** of the forest: *Help prevent
forest fires.* 1 *noun,* 2 *adjective.*

fo·rest·ed (fôr′ə stid), covered with trees; thickly
wooded: *The lake was in the middle of a forested
area. adjective.*

fo·rest·er (fôr′ə stər), a person who is in charge
of planting and taking care of a forest. *noun.*

fo·rest·ry (fôr′ə strē), the science of planting and
taking care of forests. *noun.*

fore·tell (fôr tel′), to tell beforehand; predict;
prophesy: *Who can foretell what the future will be?
verb,* **fore·tells, fore·told, fore·tell·ing.**

fore·thought (fôr′thôt′), careful thought or
planning for the future: *A great deal of forethought
went into their trip. noun.*

fore·told (fôr tōld′). See **foretell.** *The weather
bureau foretold the cold wave. verb.*

for·ev·er (fər ev′ər), **1** for ever; without ever
coming to an end: *Nobody lives forever.* **2** always;
all the time: *My older brother is forever talking on
the phone. adverb.*

for·feit (fôr′fit), **1** to lose or have to give up by
one's own act, neglect, or fault: *Some of the
players didn't show up, so we had to forfeit the
game.* **2** a thing lost or given up because of some
act, neglect, or fault: *The forfeit of the game cost
us the championship.* 1 *verb,* 2 *noun.*

for·gave (fər gāv′). See **forgive.** *She forgave my
mistake. verb.*

forge[1] (fôrj), **1** a kind of small hearth or fireplace
where metal is heated very hot and then

forge¹ (definition 1)
a **forge** in a blacksmith's shop a hundred years ago

hammered into shape. **2** a blacksmith's shop. **3** to heat metal very hot and then hammer into shape: *The blacksmith forged a bar of iron into a big hook.* **4** to make; shape; form: *Leaders of the two governments forged an agreement to increase trade between their countries.* **5** to make or write something false to deceive; sign falsely: *You can be sent to jail for forging checks.* 1,2 *noun*, 3–5 *verb*, **forg·es, forged, forg·ing.**

forge² (fôrj), to move forward slowly but steadily: *One runner forged ahead of the others and won the race. verb*, **forg·es, forged, forg·ing.**

for·get (fər get′), **1** to be unable to remember; fail to recall: *I forgot my lines in the play.* **2** to fail to remember to do, take, or notice: *I forgot to call the dentist. He had forgotten his umbrella. verb*, **for·gets, for·got, for·got·ten** or **for·got, for·get·ting.**

for·get·ful (fər get′fəl), apt to forget; having a poor memory: *If I get too tired, I become forgetful. adjective.*

for·get-me-not (fər get′mē not′), a plant with clusters of small blue or white flowers. *noun.*

for·give (fər giv′), to pardon; excuse; give up the wish to punish: *She forgave me for breaking her tennis racket. Please forgive my mistake. verb*, **for·gives, for·gave, for·giv·en, for·giv·ing.**

for·giv·en (fər giv′ən). See **forgive.** *Your mistakes are forgiven, but be more careful. verb.*

for·give·ness (fər giv′nis), the act of forgiving; pardon. *noun.*

for·go (fôr gō′), to do without; give up: *She decided to forgo the movies and do her lessons. verb*, **for·goes, for·went, for·gone, for·go·ing.**

for·gone (fôr gôn′). See **forgo.** *verb.*

for·got (fər got′). See **forget.** *He was so busy that he forgot to eat his lunch. verb.*

for·got·ten (fər got′n). See **forget.** *I have forgotten many of the details of my summer vacation. verb.*

fork (fôrk), **1** a handle with two or more long points, with which to lift food. **2** a much larger kind with which to lift hay; pitchfork. **3** to lift, throw, or

dig with a fork: *fork hay into a wagon.* **4** anything shaped like a fork; any branching: *the fork of a tree, the fork of a road.* **5** one of the branches into which anything is divided: *Take the right-hand fork.* **6** to have forks; divide into forks: *There is a garage where the road forks.* 1,2,4,5 *noun*, 3,6 *verb.*

forked (fôrkt), divided into branches: *a forked stick, the forked tail of a bird. adjective.*

for·lorn (fôr lôrn′), left alone; neglected; miserable; hopeless. *adjective.*

forlorn
He felt **forlorn** because he wasn't included in the group.

form (fôrm), **1** a shape: *Circles are simple forms.* **2** to shape; make: *Bakers form dough into loaves.* **3** to take shape: *Clouds form in the sky.* **4** to become: *Water forms ice when it freezes.* **5** to make up: *Parents and children form a family.* **6** to develop: *She formed the good habit of doing her homework before watching television.* **7** a kind; sort: *Ice, snow, and steam are forms of water.* **8** a manner; method: *He is a fast runner, but his form in running is bad.* **9** a piece of printed paper with blank spaces to be filled in: *We filled out a form to get a license for our dog.* **10** any of the ways in which a word is spelled or pronounced to show its different meanings. *Toys is the plural form of toy.* 1,7-10 *noun*, 2-6 *verb.*

for·mal (fôr′məl), **1** stiff; not familiar and homelike: *a formal greeting. A judge has a formal manner in a court of law.* **2** according to set customs or rules: *The new ambassador paid a formal call on the President.* **3** done with or having authority; official: *A written contract is a formal agreement to do something.* **4** a dance, party, or other social affair at which women often wear long, fancy dresses and men wear elegant suits. **5** a long, fancy dress worn at such a social affair. 1-3 *adjective*, 4,5 *noun.*

for·mal·i·ty (fôr mal′ə tē), **1** a set way of doing something according to custom: *At a wedding there are many formalities.* **2** stiffness of manner, behavior, or arrangement: *The formality of the party made me uneasy. noun, plural* **for·mal·i·ties.**

for·ma·tion (fôr mā′shən), **1** the forming, making, or shaping of something: *Heat causes the formation of steam from water.* **2** the way in which something is arranged; arrangement; order: *Football players line up in various formations for their plays.* **3** a thing formed: *Clouds are formations of tiny drops of water in the sky.* noun.

for·mer (fôr′mər), **1** the first of two: *When she had a choice between a telescope and a camera, she chose the former because of her interest in astronomy.* **2** earlier; past; long past: *In former times, cooking was done in fireplaces instead of stoves.* adjective.

for·mer·ly (fôr′mər lē), in time past; some time ago: *Our teacher formerly taught elsewhere.* adverb.

for·mi·da·ble (fôr′mə də bəl), hard to overcome; hard to deal with; to be dreaded: *A long examination is more formidable than a short test.* adjective.

for·mu·la (fôr′myə lə), **1** a set of directions for preparing a mixture: *a formula for making soap. A formula is sometimes fed to babies in place of mother's milk.* **2** a combination of symbols used in chemistry to show what is in a compound: *The formula for water is H_2O.* **3** a combination of symbols used in mathematics to state a rule or principle: *The formula for the area of a rectangle is $A = lw$ (in which A stands for area and lw for length times width).* noun.

for·mu·late (fôr′myə lāt), to state definitely or exactly: *Our country formulates its laws according to its constitution.* verb, **for·mu·lates, for·mu·lat·ed, for·mu·lat·ing.**

for·sake (fôr sāk′), to give up; leave; leave alone: *He ran away, forsaking his home and friends.* verb, **for·sakes, for·sook, for·sak·en, for·sak·ing.**

for·sak·en (fôr sā′kən), **1** See forsake. *She has forsaken her old friends.* **2** deserted; abandoned; forlorn: *We found an old, forsaken graveyard out in the country.* **1** verb, **2** adjective.

for·sook (fôr sůk′). See forsake. *He forsook his family.* verb.

for·syth·i·a (fôr sith′ē ə), a shrub having many bell-shaped, yellow flowers in early spring before its leaves come out. noun.

[*Forsythia* was named for William Forsyth, an English botanist who lived from 1737 to 1804.]

forsythia

fort (fôrt), a strong building or place that can be defended against an enemy. noun.

forth (fôrth), **1** forward: *From this day forth I'll try to do better.* **2** out; into view: *The sun came forth from behind the clouds.* adverb.

and so forth, and so on; and the like: *This leather case can be used to carry books, papers, drawings, and so forth.*

forth·com·ing (fôrth′kum′ing), about to appear; approaching: *The forthcoming week will be busy.* adjective.

for·ti·eth (fôr′tē ith), **1** next after the 39th. **2** one of 40 equal parts. adjective, noun.

for·ti·fi·ca·tion (fôr′tə fə kā′shən), **1** making strong; adding strength to: *The general was responsible for the fortification of the town.* **2** a wall or fort built to make a place strong. noun.

for·ti·fy (fôr′tə fī), **1** to build forts or walls to protect a place against attack; strengthen against attack. **2** to give support to; strengthen: *They fortified themselves for a busy day by eating a big breakfast.* **3** to enrich with vitamins and minerals: *Some dairies fortify their milk.* verb, **for·ti·fies, for·ti·fied, for·ti·fy·ing.**

for·ti·tude (fôr′tə tüd or fôr′tə tyüd), courage in facing pain, danger, or trouble. noun.

fort·night (fôrt′nīt), two weeks. noun.

for·tress (fôr′tris), a place built with walls and defenses; large fort or fortification. noun, plural **for·tress·es.**

for·tu·nate (fôr′chə nit), having or bringing good luck; lucky: *You are fortunate in having such a fine family.* adjective.

for·tune (fôr′chən), **1** a great deal of money or property; riches; wealth: *The family made a fortune in oil.* **2** luck; chance; what happens: *Fortune was against us and we lost.* **3** what is going to happen to a person; fate: *I know someone who claims to be able to tell people's fortunes.* noun.

for·tune·tell·er (fôr′chən tel′ər), a person who claims to be able to tell what is going to happen to people. noun.

for·ty (fôr′tē), four times ten; 40. noun, plural **for·ties;** adjective.

fo·rum (fôr′əm), **1** the public square of an ancient Roman city, where business was done and courts and public assemblies were held. **2** a meeting to discuss questions of public interest: *An open forum was held to discuss the city budget.* noun.

for·ward (fôr′wərd), **1** onward; ahead: *Forward, march! From this time forward we shall be friends.* **2** to the front; near the front: *The magician asked for a helper from the audience to come forward. Our cabin was in the forward part of the ship.* **3** into consideration; out: *In her talk she brought forward* several new ideas. **4** to send on farther: *Please forward my mail to my new address.* **5** too sure of oneself; bold: *Don't be so forward as to interrupt the speaker.* **6** a player in basketball, soccer, and some other games who plays in the front line. 1,2,3 *adverb,* 2,5 *adjective,* 4 *verb,* 6 *noun.*

for·wards (fôr′wərdz), forward. *adverb.*

for·went (fôr went′). See **forgo.** *verb.*

fos·sil (fos′əl), the hardened remains or traces of something which lived in a former age. Fossils of dinosaurs that lived many millions of years ago have been found in North America and other continents. *noun.*

Word History

fossil *Fossil* comes from a Latin word meaning "to dig up." Fossils were called this because they are dug up out of the earth.

fossil —the **fossil** of a fish

fossil fuel, a fuel found in the earth and formed from the remains of things that lived millions of years ago. Coal, oil, and natural gas are fossil fuels.

fos·ter (fô′stər), **1** to help the growth or development of; encourage: *His parents fostered his interest in reading by giving him many books.* **2** in the same family, but not related by birth or adoption. A **foster child** is a child brought up by a person not his or her parent. A **foster father, foster mother,** and **foster parent** are persons who bring up the child of another. 1 *verb,* 2 *adjective.*

fought (fôt). See **fight.** *They fought for their rights. A battle was fought there. verb.*

foul (foul), **1** very dirty; nasty; smelly: *foul air.* **2** to make dirty; become dirty; soil: *Oil fouled the harbor.* **3** very wicked or cruel: *Murder is a foul crime.* **4** unfair; against the rules: *The boxer received a foul punch after the bell ended the round.* **5** (in football, basketball, and other sports) an unfair play; thing done against the rules. **6** a

baseball hit so that it falls outside the base lines. **7** to get tangled up with: *The rope they threw fouled our anchor chain.* **8** unfavorable; stormy: *Foul weather delayed us.* 1,3,4,8 *adjective,* 2,7 *verb,* 5,6 *noun.*

foul line, (in baseball) either one of the two straight lines that go from home plate through first base and third base to the end of the playing field.

found[1] (found). See **find.** *We found the treasure. The lost child was found. verb.*

found[2] (found), to establish: *The Pilgrims founded a colony at Plymouth. verb.*

foun·da·tion (foun dā′shən), **1** a part on which other parts rest or depend; base: *The foundation of a house is built first.* **2** a basis: *This report has no foundation in fact.* **3** a founding; establishing: *She was a leader in the foundation of schools for the blind. noun.*

found·er[1] (foun′dər), **1** to fill with water and sink: *A ship foundered in the storm.* **2** to fall down; stumble; break down: *Cattle foundered in the swamp. The business foundered and finally closed. verb.*

found·er[2] (foun′dər), a person who founds or establishes something. *noun.*

found·ling (found′ling), a baby or little child found deserted. *noun.*

found·ry (foun′drē), a place where metal is melted and molded; place where things are made of melted metal. *noun, plural* **found·ries.**

foun·tain (foun′tən), **1** water flowing or rising into the air in a spray. **2** the pipes through which the water is forced and the basin built to receive it. **3** a device from which a person can get a drink of water: *The school had a drinking fountain on each floor.* **4** a source: *My friend is a fountain of information about football. noun.*

fountain pen, a pen for writing in which the ink flows from a rubber or plastic tube inside.

four (fôr), one more than three; 4. *noun, adjective.* **on all fours, 1** on all four feet. **2** on hands and knees.

four-foot·ed (fôr′fut′id), having four feet: *A dog is a four-footed animal. adjective.*

Four-H clubs or **4-H clubs** (fôr′āch′ klubz), a group of clubs that teach farm and home skills to children, mainly in rural areas.

four·score (fôr′skôr′), four times twenty; 80. *adjective, noun.*

four·teen (fôr′tēn′), four more than ten; 14. *noun, adjective.*

four·teenth (fôr′tēnth′), **1** next after the 13th. **2** one of 14 equal parts. *adjective, noun.*

fourth (fôrth), **1** next after the third. **2** quarter; one of four equal parts. *adjective, noun.*

Fourth of July, a holiday in honor of the adoption of the Declaration of Independence on July 4, 1776; Independence Day.

fowl (foul), **1** any of several kinds of large birds used for food. Chickens, ducks, and turkeys are fowl. **2** a wild fowl. *noun, plural* **fowl** or **fowls.**

fox (foks), **1** a wild animal somewhat like a dog,

with a pointed snout and a bushy tail. In many stories the fox gets the better of other animals by its cleverness. **2** its fur. **3** a clever or sly person. *noun, plural* **fox·es** or (for definition 1) **fox.**

fox·hound (foks′hound′), a hound with a keen sense of smell, trained to hunt foxes. *noun.*

a hat	**i** it	**oi** oil	**ch** child	⎧ a in about
ā age	**ī** ice	**ou** out	**ng** long	⎪ e in taken
ä far	**o** hot	**u** cup	**sh** she	ə = ⎨ i in pencil
e let	**ō** open	**u̇** put	**th** thin	⎪ o in lemon
ē equal	**ô** order	**ü** rule	**ᴛʜ** then	⎩ u in circus
ėr term			**zh** measure	

foxhounds—up to 25 inches (64 centimeters) high at the shoulder

fox·y (fok′sē), sly; like a fox is considered to be. *adjective,* **fox·i·er, fox·i·est.**

fra·cas (frā′kəs), disorderly noise; a noisy quarrel or fight. *noun, plural* **fra·cas·es.**

frac·tion (frak′shən), **1** one or more of the equal parts of a whole. ½, ⅓, and ¾ are fractions; so are ⅘ and ¹⁰%. **2** a very small part; not all of a thing: *I had time to do only a fraction of my homework. noun.*

frac·ture (frak′chər), **1** a breaking of a bone or cartilage: *He suffered several fractures in the accident.* **2** a break; crack: *The fracture in the foundation is widening.* **3** to break; crack: *I fell from the tree and fractured my arm.* **1,2** *noun,* **3** *verb,* **frac·tures, frac·tured, frac·tur·ing.**

frag·ile (fraj′əl), easily broken; delicate; frail: *Be careful; that thin glass is fragile. adjective.*

frag·ment (frag′mənt), a part broken off; piece of something broken: *After I broke the vase, I tried to glue the fragments back together. noun.*

fra·grance (frā′grəns), a sweet smell; pleasing odor: *the fragrance of flowers or of perfume. noun.*

fra·grant (frā′grənt), sweet-smelling: *This rose is fragrant. adjective.*

frail (frāl), **1** slender and not very strong; weak: *a frail and sickly child.* **2** easily broken or giving way: *Be careful; those little branches are a very frail support. adjective.*

frail·ty (frāl′tē), **1** a weakness: *We were concerned about his frailty after his long illness.* **2** a fault caused by weakness: *No one is perfect; we all have our frailties. noun, plural* **frail·ties.**

frame (frām), **1** a support over which something is stretched or built: *the frame of a house.* **2** the body: *She is a slender person with a small frame.* **3** to make; put together; plan: *It took time to frame an answer to that difficult question.* **4** the border in which a thing is set: *The oil painting had a wide gold frame.* **5** to put a border around: *frame a*

picture. **6** to make seem guilty by some false arrangement: *The real criminal framed an innocent person by telling lies to the jury.* **1,2,4** *noun,* **3,5,6** *verb,* **frames, framed, fram·ing.**

frame of mind, way one is thinking or feeling; disposition; mood: *Don't criticize me when I'm already in a bad frame of mind.*

frame·work (frām′wėrk′), **1** a structure that gives shape or support: *The bridge had a steel framework.* **2** the way in which a thing is put together; structure; system: *the framework of government. noun.*

franc (frangk), a unit of money in France, Belgium, Switzerland, and some other countries. *noun.*

France (frans), a country in western Europe. *noun.*

fracas—Their argument ended in a **fracas.**

frank (frangk), free in expressing one's real thoughts and feelings; not afraid to say what one thinks: *She was frank in saying that she thought the plan would not work. adjective.*

Frank·fort (frangk′fərt), the capital of Kentucky. *noun.*

frank·furt·er (frangk′fər tər), a reddish sausage made of beef and pork, or of beef alone. Frankfurters are often called hot dogs. *noun.*
[*Frankfurter* comes from a German word meaning "of Frankfurt" or "from Frankfurt." This type of sausage is a specialty of Frankfurt, a city in West Germany.]

fran·tic (fran′tik), very much excited; wild with rage, fear, pain, or grief: *The trapped animal made frantic efforts to escape. adjective.*

fran·ti·cal·ly (fran′tik lē), in a frantic manner; with wild excitement. *adverb.*

fra·ter·nal (frə tėr′nl), brotherly. *adjective.*

fra·ter·ni·ty (frə tėr′nə tē), 1 a club or society of men or boys, especially at a college. *noun, plural* **fra·ter·ni·ties.**

fraud (frôd), 1 dishonest dealing; cheating; trickery: *The person who sold us a furnace that he knew would not work properly was charged with fraud.* 2 a person who is not what he or she pretends to be: *The fortuneteller was a fraud; she had no knowledge of the future. noun.*

fraught (frôt), loaded; filled: *The attempt to climb Mount Everest was fraught with danger. adjective.*

fray[1] (frā), to separate into threads; make or become ragged or worn along the edge: *Long wear had frayed the collar of his old shirt. verb.*

fray[2] (frā), a fight; noisy quarrel: *The boys leaped into the fray. noun.*

freak (frēk), 1 something very odd or unusual: *Snow in summer would be called a freak of nature.* 2 a living thing that has developed in an abnormal way. *noun.*

freak (definition 2)—This two-headed snake is a **freak.**

freck·le (frek′əl), one of the small, light-brown spots that some people have on the skin. *noun.*

Fred·er·ic·ton (fred′rik tən), the capital of New Brunswick, Canada. *noun.*

free (frē), 1 not under another's control; not a slave: *a free person, a free nation.* 2 loose; not fastened or shut up: *They set free the bear cub caught in the trap.* 3 not held back from acting or thinking as one pleases: *She was free to do as she liked.* 4 not busy: *The doctor will call you back as soon as she is free.* 5 to make free; let loose; let go: *We freed the bird from the cage. She freed her foot from a tangled vine.* 6 to clear: *The judge freed her of all charges.* 7 without anything to pay: *These tickets are free. We were admitted to the play free.* 1-4,7 *adjective,* **fre·er, fre·est;** 5,6 *verb,* **frees, freed, free·ing;** 7 *adverb.*

free from or **free of,** without: *free from fear, air free of dust.*

free·dom (frē′dəm), 1 the condition of being free: *The American colonists gained freedom from England.* 2 liberty; power to do, say, or think as one pleases: *freedom of speech, freedom of religion.* 3 free use: *We gave our guest the freedom of the house. noun.*

free·hand (frē′hand′), done by hand without using instruments or measurements: *freehand drawing. adjective.*

free·man (frē′mən), a person who is not a slave or a serf. *noun, plural* **free·men.**

free·way (frē′wā′), a highway for fast traveling on which no tolls are charged. *noun.*

freeze (frēz), 1 to harden by cold; turn into a solid: *The raindrops froze into ice crystals.* 2 to make or become very cold: *We froze at the football game.* 3 to kill or injure by frost; be killed or injured by frost: *A drop in temperature froze the tomato plants. The tip of my nose froze in the chill wind.* 4 to cover or become covered with ice; clog with ice: *Low temperatures at night froze the pond. The pipes froze.* 5 to fix or become fixed to something by freezing: *His fingers froze to the tray of ice cubes.* 6 a freezing or a being frozen: *An early freeze damaged many gardens.* 7 to become motionless: *I froze on the high diving board, afraid to jump into the water.* 1-5,7 *verb,* **freez·es, froze, fro·zen, freez·ing;** 6 *noun.*

freeze-dry (frēz′drī′), to dry food by freezing and evaporating the liquid content in a vacuum. Freeze-dried food keeps well without being refrigerated. *verb,* **freeze-dries, freeze-dried, freeze-dry·ing.**

freez·er (frē′zər), a refrigerator or a part of a refrigerator in which the temperature is well below the freezing point. Foods are frozen and kept from spoiling in freezers. *noun.*

freezing point, the temperature at which a liquid freezes. The freezing point of water at sea level is 32 degrees Fahrenheit or 0 degrees Celsius.

freight (frāt), 1 the goods that a train, truck, ship, or aircraft carries. 2 the carrying of goods on a train, ship, aircraft, or truck: *He sent the box by freight.* 3 a train for carrying goods. *noun.*

freight·er (frā′tər), a ship that carries mainly freight. *noun.*

French (french), 1 of or having something to do with France, its people, or their language. 2 the people of France. 3 the language of France. 1 *adjective,* 2 *noun plural,* 3 *noun singular.*

Word Source

French is also spoken in Belgium, Switzerland, Canada, and other countries. Here are some words that have come into English from French:

amateur	cafe	kerchief	reveille
ambulance	collage	lawn	spaniel
baboon	curfew	pansy	supper
barber	dandelion	plateau	turquoise
bribe	goblet	poach[2]	Vermont
butcher	grudge	restaurant	vinegar

French fries, potatoes cut into thin strips and fried in deep fat until crisp on the outside.

French horn, a brass wind instrument that has a mellow tone.

French horn

French toast, slices of bread dipped in a mixture of egg and milk and then fried in a small amount of fat.

fren·zied (fren′zēd), frantic; wild; very much excited. *adjective.*

fren·zy (fren′zē), **1** near madness; frantic condition: *They were in a frenzy after hearing that their child was missing.* **2** a very great excitement: *The crowd was in a frenzy after the home team scored the winning goal. noun, plural* **fren·zies.**

fre·quen·cy (frē′kwən sē), **1** the rate of occurrence: *The flashes of light came with a frequency of three per minute.* **2** frequent occurrence: *The frequency of their visits annoyed us.* **3** the number of vibrations per second of a radio wave or other electric wave. Different radio and television stations broadcast at different frequencies so that their signals can be received clearly. *noun, plural* **fre·quen·cies.**

fre·quent (frē′kwənt *for 1;* fri kwent′ *for 2*), **1** happening often, near together, or every little while: *In my part of the country, storms are frequent in March.* **2** to be often in; go to often: *Frogs frequent ponds, streams, and marshes.* **1** *adjective,* **2** *verb.*

fre·quent·ly (frē′kwənt lē), often: *They look so much alike that they are frequently mistaken for one another. adverb.*

fresh[1] (fresh), **1** newly made, grown, or gathered: *fresh footprints, fresh coffee, fresh flowers.* **2** new; recent: *Is there any fresh news from home?* **3** another: *After her failure she made a fresh start.* **4** not salty: *Rivers are usually made up of fresh water.* **5** not spoiled; not stale: *Is this milk fresh?* **6** clean; not soiled by use: *I put fresh sheets on my bed.* **7** not artificially preserved: *Fresh foods often*

have better flavor than canned foods. **8** not tired out; vigorous; lively: *Fresh horses pulled the stagecoach the last part of the trip.* **9** pure; cool; refreshing: *fresh air. adjective.*

fresh[2] (fresh), rude; too bold; disrespectful: *She often got into trouble for making fresh remarks to her teachers. adjective.*

fresh·en (fresh′ən), to make or become fresh: *The rest freshened me. verb.*

fresh·man (fresh′mən), a student in the first year of high school or college. *noun, plural* **fresh·men.**

fresh·wa·ter (fresh′wô′tər), of or living in water that is not salty: *The catfish is a freshwater fish. adjective.*

fret (fret), to be or cause to be cross, discontented, or worried: *Don't fret over your mistakes. The baby frets in hot weather. verb,* **frets, fret·ted, fret·ting.**

fret·ful (fret′fəl), cross, discontented, or worried; ready to fret: *My baby brother is fretful because he is cutting his teeth. adjective.*

Fri., Friday.

fri·ar (frī′ər), a man who belongs to one of certain religious brotherhoods of the Roman Catholic Church. *noun.*

fric·tion (frik′shən), **1** a rubbing of one thing against another: *Matches are lighted by friction.* **2** the resistance to motion of surfaces that touch: *Oil reduces friction. A sled moves more easily on smooth ice than on rough ground because there is less friction.* **3** a conflict of differing ideas or opinions; disagreement; clash: *Constant friction between the two nations brought them dangerously close to war. noun.*

Fri·day (frī′dē), the sixth day of the week; the day after Thursday. *noun.*

[*Friday* is from an earlier English word meaning "Frig's day." Frig is the name of the Norse goddess of love.]

fried (frīd), **1** cooked in hot fat: *fried eggs.* **2** See **fry.** *I fried the ham. The potatoes had been fried.* **1** *adjective,* **2** *verb.*

friend (frend), **1** a person who knows and likes another. **2** a person who favors and supports: *He was a generous friend of the art museum.* **3** a person who belongs to the same side or group: *Are you friend or enemy? noun.*

friend·less (frend′lis), without friends. *adjective.*

friend·li·ness (frend′lē nis), a friendly feeling or behavior. *noun.*

friend·ly (frend′lē), **1** like a friend; kind: *a friendly teacher.* **2** like a friend's: *a friendly greeting.* **3** on good terms: *After the war, the two countries worked to establish friendly relations. adjective,* **friend·li·er, friend·li·est.**

F

friend·ship (frend′ship), **1** the condition of being friends: *Our friendship lasted for many years.* **2** friendly feeling or behavior; friendliness: *We tried to be helpful and show friendship to the foreign visitors. noun.*

frieze (frēz), a band of decoration around a room, building, or mantel. *noun.*

frig·ate (frig′it), a fast, three-masted sailing warship of medium size. Frigates were much used from 1750 to 1850. *noun.*

fright (frīt), **1** a sudden fear; sudden terror: *The howl filled me with fright.* **2** a person or thing that is ugly, shocking, or ridiculous: *When I put on the wig, they laughed and said I looked like a fright. noun.*

fright·en (frīt′n), **1** to fill with fright; make afraid; scare: *Thunder frightened the puppy.* **2** to drive or force by terrifying: *The sudden noise frightened the deer away. verb.*

fright·ful (frīt′fəl), **1** causing fear or terror: *Being lost in the forest was a frightful experience.* **2** terrible to think about; shocking: *The frightful destruction caused by the fire stretched for many blocks.* **3** disagreeable; unpleasant: *There was a frightful smell in the air from the burning tar. adjective.*

frig·id (frij′id), **1** very cold: *Arctic regions have a frigid climate.* **2** cold in feeling or manner; stiff; chilling: *After our argument, he gave me a frigid stare whenever we met. adjective.*

frill (fril), **1** a ruffle: *I wore a dressy shirt with frills down the front.* **2** a thing added merely for show; useless ornament: *The car had no hood ornament or other frills. noun.*

fringe (frinj), **1** a border or trimming made of threads or cords, either loose or tied together in small bunches: *The knitted shawl had a fringe of yarn around the bottom.* **2** anything like this; border: *A fringe of hair hung over her forehead.* **3** to be a border for: *Bushes fringed the road.* **1,2** *noun,* **3** *verb,* **fring·es, fringed, fring·ing.**

Fris·bee (friz′bē), a trademark for a saucer-shaped disk of colored plastic for tossing back and forth in play. *noun.*

frisk (frisk), to run and jump about playfully; dance and skip joyously: *Our lively puppy frisks all over the house. verb.*

frisk·y (fris′kē), playful; lively: *The horse was so frisky that the rider could barely stay on it. adjective,* **frisk·i·er, frisk·i·est.**

friv·o·lous (friv′ə ləs), **1** lacking in seriousness or sense; silly: *Frivolous behavior is out of place in a courtroom.* **2** of little worth or importance: *Don't waste time on frivolous matters. adjective.*

fro (frō). **to and fro,** first one way and then back again; back and forth: *The lion paced to and fro in its cage. adverb.*

frock (frok), a woman's or girl's dress; gown. *noun.*

frog (frog), a small, leaping animal with webbed feet that lives in or near water. Frogs hatch from eggs as tadpoles and live in the water until they grow legs. Some frogs live in trees. *noun.*

frog·man (frog′man′), a person trained and equipped for working underwater. *noun, plural* **frog·men.**

frol·ic (frol′ik), to play about joyously; have fun together: *The children frolicked with the puppy. verb,* **frol·ics, frol·icked, frol·ick·ing.**

from (from, frum, *or* frəm), **1** out of: *take a quarter from one's pocket. Steel is made from iron.* **2** out of the possession of: *Take the book from her.* **3** starting at; beginning with: *We took a train from New York. I start two weeks from today.* **4** because of: *I am suffering from a cold.* **5** having its source in: *oil from Alaska, a word from Spanish.* **6** as distinguished from: *Anyone can tell apples from oranges.* **7** given, sent, or caused by: *a letter from a friend.* **8** off: *He took a book from the table. preposition.*

frond (frond), a leaf of a fern or palm. *noun.*

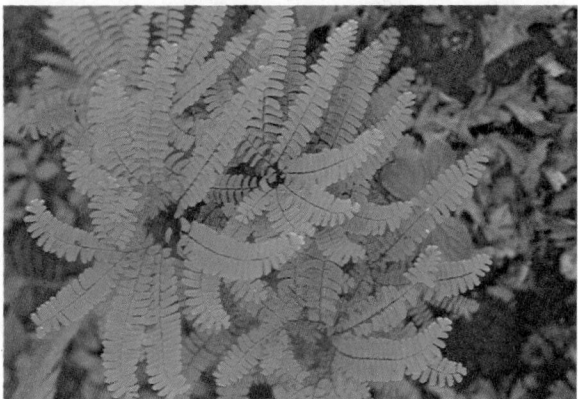
fronds of a fern

front (frunt), **1** the part that faces forward; forward part: *the front of a car, the front of a coat.* **2** the first part; beginning: *There is an introduction in the front of this book.* **3** the place where fighting is going on during a war: *Wounded soldiers were sent home from the front.* **4** the land facing a street or a body of water: *We have a house on the lake front.* **5** on or in the front; at the front: *a front door.* **6** to have the front toward; face: *My house fronts the park.* **7** the forward part of a great mass of air: *A cold front is moving toward this area from Canada.* **1-4,7** *noun,* **5** *adjective,* **6** *verb.*

fron·tier (frun tir′), **1** the last edge of settled country, where the wilds begin. **2** the part of one country that touches the edge of another; boundary line between two countries: *Border guards patrolled the frontier between the two countries.* **3** the farthest limits: *to explore the frontiers of science. noun.*

fron·tiers·man (frun tirz′mən), a person who lives on the frontier. *noun, plural* **fron·tiers·men.**

frost (frôst), **1** a freezing condition; very cold weather; temperature below the point at which water freezes: *Frost came early last winter.* **2** moisture frozen on or in a surface; feathery crystals of ice formed when water vapor in the air condenses at a temperature below freezing: *On cold fall mornings, there is frost on the grass.* **3** to cover with frost or something that suggests frost: *The cold during the night frosted the trees.* **4** to cover with frosting: *The cook frosted the cake.* **1,2** *noun,* **3,4** *verb.*

frost·bite (frôst′bīt′), an injury to a part of the body caused by freezing: *The victim's fingers and toes were numb from frostbite. noun.*

frost·bit·ten (frôst′bit′n), injured by freezing: *My ears were frostbitten. adjective.*

frost·ing (frô′sting), **1** a flavored mixture of sugar, butter or margarine, egg whites, and other things, used to cover cakes and other baked goods; icing. **2** a dull finish on glass or metal. *noun.*

frost·y (frô′stē), **1** cold enough for frost: *a frosty morning.* **2** covered with frost: *The glass is frosty.* **3** cold and unfriendly; with no warmth of feeling: *She spoke to us in a frosty manner after our quarrel. adjective,* **frost·i·er, frost·i·est.**

froth (frôth), **1** foam: *the froth on a chocolate soda.* **2** to give out froth; foam: *The soda frothed up and over the edge of the glass.* **1** *noun,* **2** *verb.*

frown (froun), **1** a wrinkling of the forehead to show disapproval or anger. **2** to wrinkle the forehead to show disapproval or anger; look displeased or angry: *My teacher frowned when I came in late.* **3** to look with disapproval: *The principal frowned on our plan for a picnic just before examinations.* **1** *noun,* **2,3** *verb.*

froze (frōz). See **freeze.** *The water in the pond froze last week. verb.*

fro·zen (frō′zn), **1** hardened with cold; turned into ice: *a river frozen over, frozen sherbet.* **2** very cold: *My hands are frozen; I need some gloves.* **3** kept from spoiling by freezing: *frozen foods.* **4** killed or injured by frost: *frozen flowers.* **5** covered or clogged with ice: *frozen water pipes.* **6** cold and without feeling: *a frozen heart, a frozen stare.* **7** too frightened or stiff to move: *frozen in horror.* **8** See **freeze.** *The water has frozen to ice.* **1-7** *adjective,* **8** *verb.*

fru·gal (frü′gəl), **1** without waste; not wasteful; saving; using things well: *A frugal person always shops for bargains.* **2** costing little; barely enough: *He ate a frugal supper of bread and milk. adjective.*

fruit (früt), **1** a juicy or fleshy product of a tree, bush, shrub, or vine, usually sweet and good to eat. Apples, oranges, bananas, and berries are fruit. **2** the part of a plant where the seeds are. Pea pods, acorns, and grains of wheat are fruits. **3** the result of anything: *This invention was the fruit of much effort. noun, plural* **fruit** or **fruits.**

fruit·ful (früt′fəl), having good results; bringing benefit or profit: *Our plan was fruitful. adjective.*

fruit·less (früt′lis), having no results; useless; unsuccessful: *Our search was fruitless; we could not find the lost book. adjective.*

fruit·y (frü′tē), tasting or smelling like fruit: *the fruity odor of jam. adjective,* **fruit·i·er, fruit·i·est.**

frus·trate (frus′trāt), to defeat; make useless or worthless; block: *Heavy rain frustrated our plans for a picnic. verb,* **frus·trates, frus·trat·ed, frus·trat·ing.**

frus·tra·tion (fru strā′shən), a defeating or being defeated; a making or becoming useless: *The frustration of his hopes to join the team made him feel sad. noun.*

fry (frī), to cook in hot fat: *We fried the potatoes in a deep pan. verb,* **fries, fried, fry·ing.**

frying pan, a shallow pan with a handle, used for frying; skillet.

ft., **1** foot or feet. **2** fort.

fudge (fuj), soft candy made of sugar, milk, chocolate, and butter. *noun.*

fu·el (fyü′əl), anything that can be burned to produce useful heat or power. Coal, wood, and oil are fuels. *noun.*

fu·gi·tive (fyü′jə tiv), **1** a person who is running away or has run away: *The robber became a fugitive from justice.* **2** running away; having run away: *a fugitive slave.* **1** *noun,* **2** *adjective.*

-ful, a suffix meaning: **1** full of _____: Cheer*ful* means *full of* cheer. **2** showing _____: Care*ful* means *showing* care. **3** enough to fill a _____: Cup*ful* means *enough to fill a* cup.

ful·crum (ful′krəm), the support on which a lever turns or is supported in moving or lifting something. *noun.*

fulcrum—The seesaw moves on a **fulcrum.**

ful·fill (ful fil′), **1** to keep or carry out a promise or an agreement: *The mechanic did not fulfill his promise to have our car fixed by Saturday.* **2** to perform or do a duty, command, or the like: *She fulfilled all the teacher's requests.* **3** to satisfy a requirement or condition: *This diet will fulfill your needs in food.* **4** to bring to an end; finish or complete: *fulfill a contract. verb,* **ful·fills, ful·filled, ful·fill·ing.**

ful·fill·ment (ful fil′mənt), a fulfilling; completion; accomplishment. *noun.*

full (fůl), **1** able to hold no more. Anything is full when it holds all that it is intended to hold. *This suitcase is full.* **2** complete; entire: *a full supply of clothes.* **3** completely: *Fill the pail full.* **4** plump; round; well filled out: *a full face.* **5** having wide folds or much cloth: *a full skirt.* 1,2,4,5 *adjective,* 3 *adverb.*

full of, filled with: *The child's room is full of toys.*
in full, to or for the complete amount: *They made payment in full for the furniture.*

full·back (fůl′bak′), **1** a football player whose position is behind the front line on offense. **2** a soccer player who plays near his own goal on defense. *noun.*

full-grown (fůl′grōn′), fully grown. *adjective.*

full moon, the moon seen from the earth as a whole circle.

full-time (fůl′tīm′), for the normal working day: *She is looking for a full-time job. adjective.*

ful·ly (fůl′ē), **1** completely; entirely: *I am fully satisfied.* **2** abundantly: *The gymnasium was fully equipped with ropes and rings.* **3** at least; no less than: *She has been gone fully an hour. adverb.*

fum·ble (fum′bəl), **1** to search awkwardly; feel or grope around clumsily: *I fumbled in the darkness for the doorknob.* **2** to handle awkwardly; let drop instead of catching and holding: *The quarterback fumbled the ball, and the other team recovered it.* **3** an awkward attempt to find or handle something: *The quarterback's fumble of the ball caused our team to lose the game.* 1,2 *verb,* **fum·bles, fum·bled, fum·bling;** 3 *noun.*

fume (fyüm), **1** Often, **fumes.** a gas, smoke, or vapor, especially if harmful or strong: *The fumes from the automobile exhaust nearly choked me.* **2** to give off gas, smoke, or vapor: *The candle fumed, sputtered, and went out.* **3** to let off one's rage in angry complaints: *She fumed about the slowness of the train.* 1 *noun,* 2,3 *verb,* **fumes, fumed, fum·ing.**

fu·mi·gate (fyü′mə gāt), to disinfect with fumes; expose to fumes: *They fumigated the building to kill the cockroaches. verb,* **fu·mi·gates, fu·mi·gat·ed, fu·mi·gat·ing.**

fun (fun), playfulness; merry play; amusement; joking: *They had a lot of fun at the party. noun.*

make fun of or **poke fun at,** to laugh at; ridicule: *The other students made fun of the hole in my pants.*

func·tion (fungk′shən), **1** proper work; purpose; use: *The function of the stomach is to digest food.* **2** to work; act: *One of the older students can function as teacher. This old fountain pen does not function very well.* **3** a formal public or social gathering for some purpose: *The hotel ballroom is often used for weddings and other functions.* 1,3 *noun,* 2 *verb.*

fund (fund), **1** a sum of money set aside for a special purpose: *Our school has a fund of $2000 to buy books with.* **2 funds,** money ready to use: *We took $10 from the club's funds to buy a flag.* **3** a stock or store ready for use: *There is a fund of information in our new library. noun.*

fun·da·men·tal (fun′də men′tl), **1** basic; essential; forming a basis: *Reading is a fundamental skill.* **2** something basic; essential part: *We are taught the fundamentals of grammar in English class. adjective.*

fu·ner·al (fyü′nər əl), the ceremonies held at the burial of a dead person. A funeral usually includes a religious service and taking the body to the place where it is buried or burned. *noun.*

fun·gi (fun′jī), more than one fungus. *noun plural.*

fun·gus (fung′gəs), any living thing that is like a plant but has no leaves, flowers, or green coloring matter, and cannot make its own food as plants do. Mushrooms, toadstools, molds, and yeast are fungi. Fungi reproduce by spores or by dividing. *noun, plural* **fun·gi** or **fun·gus·es.**

fungus—various kinds of **fungi**

fun·nel (fun′l), **1** a utensil that is like a narrow tube at the bottom and a cone with a wide mouth at the top. A funnel is used to pour liquid, powder, or grain into a small opening without spilling. **2** a smokestack or chimney on a steamship or steam engine. *noun.*

[*Funnel* comes from a Latin word meaning "to pour in."]

fun·nies (fun′ēz), comic strips. *noun plural.*

fun·ny (fun′ē), **1** causing laughter; amusing: *The clown told us funny jokes.* **2** strange; odd: *It's funny that they are so late. adjective,* **fun·ni·er, fun·ni·est.**

fur (fér), **1** the soft hair covering the skin of many animals. **2** skin with such hair on it. Fur is used to make, cover, trim, or line clothing. *noun.*

fur·i·ous (fyůr′ē əs), **1** very angry; full of wild, fierce anger: *The owner of the house was furious*

furl | -fy

when she learned of the broken window. **2** raging; violent: *A hurricane is a furious storm. adjective.*

furl (fėrl), to roll up; fold up: *furl a sail, furl a flag. verb.*

fur·lough (fėr′lō), a leave of absence: *The soldier has two weeks furlough. noun.*

fur·nace (fėr′nis), an enclosed space to make a very hot fire in. Furnaces are used to heat buildings, melt metals, and make glass. *noun.*

fur·nish (fėr′nish), **1** to supply; provide: *furnish an army with blankets. The sun furnishes heat.* **2** to supply a room, house, or office with furniture or equipment: *furnish a bedroom. verb.*

fur·nish·ings (fėr′ni shingz), furniture or equipment for a room, house, or office. *noun plural.*

fur·ni·ture (fėr′nə chər), movable articles needed in a room, house, or office. Beds, chairs, tables, and desks are furniture. *noun.*

fur·row (fėr′ō), **1** a long, narrow groove or track, as one cut in the earth by a plow. **2** a wrinkle: *a furrow in one's brow.* **3** to make wrinkles in: *The old woman's face was furrowed with age.* **1,2** *noun,* **3** *verb.*

furrow
(definition 1)

fur·ry (fėr′ē), **1** covered with fur: *Raccoons are furry animals.* **2** soft like fur: *The rock was covered with furry moss. adjective,* **fur·ri·er, fur·ri·est.**

fur·ther (fėr′ᵺər), **1** more distant: *on the further side.* **2** to a more advanced point: *Inquire further into the matter.* **3** more: *Do you need further help?* **4** to help forward: *Let us further the cause of peace.* **5** also; in addition: *My parents told me to clean my room and said further that I must wash the dishes.* **1,3** *adjective, comparative of* **far; 2,5** *adverb, comparative of* **far; 4** *verb.*

fur·ther·more (fėr′ᵺər môr), also; besides; moreover: *Be sure to arrive on time; furthermore, don't forget to bring your bathing suit. adverb.*

fur·ther·most (fėr′ᵺər mōst), furthest. *adjective.*

fur·thest (fėr′ᵺist), **1** most distant: *To make you unhappy was the furthest thing from my mind.* **2** to or at the greatest distance: *He hit the ball furthest.* **3** most: *Their ideas were the furthest advanced at*

that time. **1** *adjective, superlative of* **far; 2,3** *adverb, superlative of* **far.**

fur·tive (fėr′tiv), **1** done quickly and slyly; secret: *a furtive glance into the forbidden room.* **2** sly: *The thief had a furtive manner. adjective.*

fur·y (fyùr′ē), **1** a rage; wild, fierce anger: *She was in a fury because I'd dropped her camera.* **2** violence; fierceness: *the fury of a hurricane. noun, plural* **fur·ies.**

fuse¹ (fyüz), a slow-burning wick or other device used to set off a shell, bomb, or blast of gunpowder. *noun.*

fuse² (fyüz), **1** a wire or strip of metal in an electric circuit that melts and breaks the circuit if the current becomes dangerously strong. **2** to melt; join together by melting: *Copper and zinc are fused to make brass.* **3** to blend; unite: *The intense heat fused the rocks together.* **1** *noun,* **2,3** *verb,* **fus·es, fused, fus·ing.**

fu·se·lage (fyü′sə läzh *or* fyü′sə lij), the body of an airplane to which the wings and tail are fastened. The fuselage holds the passengers, crew, and cargo. *noun.*

fu·sion (fyü′zhən), **1** a fusing; melting; melting together: *Bronze is made by the fusion of copper and tin.* **2** the combining of atomic nuclei to produce tremendous amounts of energy. *noun.*

fuss (fus), **1** much bother about small matters; useless talk and worry; attention given to something not worth it: *My parents made a great fuss because I didn't telephone them that I'd be late.* **2** to make a fuss: *There's no need to fuss over the broken cup.* **1** *noun,* **2** *verb.*

fuss·y (fus′ē), hard to please; never satisfied: *A sick person is likely to be fussy about food. adjective,* **fuss·i·er, fuss·i·est.**

fu·tile (fyü′tl), useless; not successful: *He fell down after making futile attempts to keep his balance. adjective.*

fu·ture (fyü′chər), **1** time to come; what is to come: *You cannot change the past, but you can do better in the future.* **2** coming; that will be: *We hope your future years will all be happy.* **3** expressing something expected to happen or exist in time to come: *the future tense of a verb.* **1** *noun,* **2,3** *adjective.*

fuzz (fuz), loose, light fibers or hairs; fine down: *the fuzz on a caterpillar, the fuzz on a peach. noun.*

fuzz·y (fuz′ē), **1** like or covered with fuzz: *Peaches are fuzzy.* **2** not clear; blurred: *This photograph is too fuzzy for me to identify the people in it. adjective,* **fuzz·i·er, fuzz·i·est.**

-fy, a suffix meaning: to make or become _____. *Simplify* means *to make* simple.

a hat	i it	oi oil	ch child	ə = { a in about
ā age	ī ice	ou out	ng long	e in taken
ä far	o hot	u cup	sh she	i in pencil
e let	ō open	ù put	th thin	o in lemon
ē equal	ô order	ü rule	ᵺ then	u in circus
ėr term			zh measure	

249

G g

G or **g** (jē), the seventh letter of the English alphabet. *noun, plural* **G's** or **g's.**

g or **g.,** gram or grams.

GA, Georgia (used with postal Zip Code).

Ga., Georgia.

gab·ble (gab′əl), to talk rapidly with little or no meaning: *The little boy gabbled to his toys. verb,* **gab·bles, gab·bled, gab·bling.**

ga·ble (gā′bəl), the triangular piece of wall between two sloping surfaces of a roof. *noun.*

GABLES

Ga·bon (gä bôn′), a country in west central Africa. *noun.*

gadg·et (gaj′it), a small tool or mechanical device designed to do a certain task: *I use a special gadget to loosen jar lids that are stuck. noun.*

gag (gag), **1** something put in a person's mouth to keep him or her from talking or crying out. **2** to stop up the mouth of with a gag: *The robbers tied the watchman's arms and gagged him.* **3** to strain in an effort to vomit: *I gagged on the bad-tasting medicine.* **4** a joke: *The comedian's gags made us laugh.* 1,4 *noun,* 2,3 *verb,* **gags, gagged, gag·ging.**

gai·e·ty (gā′ə tē), a being happy and full of fun; cheerful liveliness: *the gaiety of a holiday festival. noun.*

gai·ly (gā′lē), **1** in a happy way; merrily: *She was so excited by the good news that she danced gaily around the room.* **2** brightly: *They were gaily dressed in colorful costumes. adverb.*

gain (gān), **1** to come to have; get; obtain; win: *The farmer gained possession of more land. She gained recognition as an author.* **2** what one gains; increase, addition, or advantage: *a gain in weight.* **3** to get as an increase, addition, or advantage; profit: *The car gained speed. What will you gain by worrying?* 1,3 *verb,* 2 *noun.*

gain on, to come closer to; catch up with: *The second runner is gaining on the leader.*

gait (gāt), the kind of steps used in walking or running: *She walks with a springy gait. A gallop is one of the gaits of a horse. noun.*

gal., gallon or gallons.

ga·la (gā′lə), festive: *Thanksgiving is a gala day for our family. adjective.*

gal·ax·y (gal′ək sē), a group of billions of stars forming one system. The earth and sun are in the Milky Way galaxy. Many galaxies outside our own can be seen with a telescope. *noun, plural* **gal·ax·ies.**

Word History

galaxy *Galaxy* comes from a Greek word meaning "milk." The galaxy which includes the earth and its sun is often called the Milky Way, because it appears as a white band of light in the night sky.

gale (gāl), **1** a very strong wind: *Several small boats were sunk in the gale.* **2** a noisy outburst: *The joke caused gales of laughter. noun.*

gall[1] (gôl), **1** a bitter liquid made in the liver; bile. **2** anything very bitter. **3** too great boldness. *noun.*

gall[2] (gôl), to annoy; irritate: *The child was galled by being scolded so much. verb.*

gal·lant (gal′ənt), noble in spirit or in conduct; brave: *She was praised for her gallant action in saving the drowning child. adjective.*

gal·lant·ry (gal′ən trē), bravery; noble spirit or conduct: *The soldier was given a medal for his gallantry in the battle. noun.*

gal·le·on (gal′ē ən), a large, high ship of former times, usually with several decks. *noun.*

galleon

250

gal·ler·y (gal′ər ē), **1** a building or room used to show collections of pictures and statues. **2** the highest balcony of a theater. *noun, plural* **gal·ler·ies.**

gal·ley (gal′ē), **1** a long, narrow ship of former times having oars and sails. Galleys were often rowed by slaves or convicts. **2** the kitchen of a ship or airplane. *noun, plural* **gal·leys.**

galley (definition 1)

gal·lon (gal′ən), a unit for measuring liquids equal to 4 quarts. *noun.*

gal·lop (gal′əp), **1** the fastest gait of a horse or of many other four-footed animals. In a gallop, all four feet are off the ground at the same time in each leap. **2** to ride or go at a gallop: *The cowboys galloped after the steers. The wild horse galloped off.* **1** *noun,* **2** *verb.*

gal·lows (gal′ōz), a wooden frame made of a crossbar on two upright posts, used for hanging criminals by a rope. *noun, plural* **gal·lows.**

ga·losh·es (gə losh′iz), rubber or plastic boots worn over the shoes in wet or snowy weather. *noun plural.*

gam·ble (gam′bəl), **1** to play games of chance for money; bet: *Some people gamble on horse races.* **2** to risk; take a risk: *The firefighters gambled their lives to rescue the child from the burning building. She gambled in the stock market and made a fortune.* **3** a risky act or undertaking: *Putting money into a new business is often a gamble.* **1,2** *verb,* **gam·bles, gam·bled, gam·bling; 3** *noun.*

gam·bler (gam′blər), a person who gambles a great deal. *noun.*

game (gām), **1** a way of playing; something done for fun: *Tag is a game that we enjoy.* **2** a contest with certain rules, in which one person or side tries to win: *a football game, a game of checkers.* **3** a set of objects, such as dice, cards, round pieces of wood or plastic, and a board, used in playing certain kinds of games, such as checkers, backgammon, or the like. **4** a scheme; plan: *They tried to trick us, but we saw through their game.* **5** wild animals, birds, or fish hunted or caught for sport or for food. **6** having to do with wild animals, hunting, or fishing: *Game laws protect wildlife.*

7 brave; courageous: *The losing team put up a game fight.* **8** ready; eager: *They were game for any adventure.* **1-5** *noun,* **6-8** *adjective,* **gam·er, gam·est.**

gan·der (gan′dər), a male goose. *noun.*

gang (gang), **1** a group of people working or going around together: *A gang of workers repaired the road. A whole gang of us went swimming.* **2** a group engaged in wrongdoing: *Members of a gang were arrested for stealing cars.* **3 gang up on,** to get together with others to oppose or attack someone: *Some girls ganged up on her and pushed her down in the snow.* **1,2** *noun,* **3** *verb.*

gang·plank (gang′plangk′), a movable plank or ramp used in getting on and off a ship. *noun.*

gang·ster (gang′stər), a member of a gang of criminals. *noun.*

gang·way (gang′wā′), **1** a passageway, especially on a ship. **2** a gangplank. **3** Get out of the way! **1,2** *noun,* **3** *interjection.*

gap (gap), **1** a broken place; opening: *The cows got out of the field through a gap in the fence.* **2** an unfilled space; blank: *The story is not complete; there are several gaps in it.* **3** a pass through mountains. *noun.*

gape (gāp), **1** to open wide: *A deep hole in the earth gaped before us.* **2** to stare with the mouth open: *The crowd gaped at the tightrope walkers.* *verb,* **gapes, gaped, gap·ing.**

ga·rage (gə räzh′), **1** a place where motor vehicles are kept. **2** a shop for repairing motor vehicles. *noun.*

garage sale, a sale of used furniture, clothing, tools, or household goods, held in the seller's garage, yard, or basement.

garb (gärb), **1** the way one is dressed; clothing: *military garb, royal garb, splendid garb.* **2** to clothe: *The doctor was garbed in white.* **1** *noun,* **2** *verb.*

gar·bage (gär′bij), scraps of food to be thrown away from a kitchen, dining room, or store. *noun.*

gar·den (gärd′n), **1** a piece of ground used for growing vegetables, flowers, or fruits. **2** to take care of a garden: *I garden as a hobby.* **1** *noun,* **2** *verb.*

gar·den·er (gärd′nər), **1** a person hired to take care of a garden or lawn. **2** a person who makes a garden or works in a garden. *noun.*

gar·de·nia (gär dē′nyə), a sweet-smelling, white flower with smooth, waxlike petals. *noun.* [The *gardenia* was named for Dr. Alexander Garden. He was a Scottish botanist who lived from 1730 to 1791.]

gar·gle (gär′gəl), **1** to wash the throat or mouth with a liquid which is kept moving by the outgoing breath: *I gargled with hot salt water to relieve my*

G

sore throat. **2** a liquid used for gargling. 1 *verb,* **gar·gles, gar·gled, gar·gling;** 2 *noun.*

gar·goyle (gär′goil), a spout which sticks out from the gutter of a building and ends in a grotesque figure. It carries off rain water. *noun.*

gargoyle

gar·land (gär′lənd), **1** a wreath of flowers or leaves. **2** to decorate with garlands. 1 *noun,* 2 *verb.*

gar·lic (gär′lik), the bulb of a plant related to the onion, used in cooking and in salads. Its flavor is stronger than that of an onion. *noun.*

gar·ment (gär′mənt), any piece of clothing. *noun.*

gar·ner (gär′nər), to gather and store away: *Wheat is cut and garnered at harvest time. verb.*

gar·net (gär′nit), **1** a deep-red stone, used as a gem. **2** deep-red. 1 *noun,* 2 *adjective.*

gar·nish (gär′nish), **1** something laid on or around a dish as a decoration: *The turkey was served with a garnish of cranberries and parsley.* **2** to decorate food. 1 *noun, plural* **gar·nish·es;** 2 *verb.*

gar·ret (gar′it), the space in a house just below a sloping roof; attic. *noun.*

gar·ri·son (gar′ə sən), **1** the soldiers stationed in a fort or town to defend it. **2** a place that has a garrison. **3** to station soldiers in a fort or town to defend it. 1,2 *noun,* 3 *verb.*

gar·ter (gär′tər), a band or strap to hold up a stocking or sock. It is usually elastic. *noun.*

garter snake, a harmless snake, brown or green with long yellow stripes.

gas (gas), **1** a substance that is not a solid or a liquid. A gas has no shape or size of its own and can expand without limit. Air is a mixture of gases. **2** any mixture of gases that can be burned. Gas is used for cooking and heating. **3** a substance in the form of a gas that poisons, suffocates, or stuns. **4** to kill or injure by poisonous gas. **5** gasoline. 1-3,5 *noun, plural* **gas·es;** 4 *verb,* **gas·ses, gassed, gas·sing.**

gas·e·ous (gas′ē əs), in the form of or like gas: *Steam is water in a gaseous condition. adjective.*

gash (gash), **1** a long, deep cut or wound: *A piece of ice put a gash in his hand when he slipped off the sled.* **2** to make a long, deep cut or wound in: *I gashed my foot on a piece of broken glass.* 1 *noun, plural* **gash·es;** 2 *verb.*

gas mask, a tight covering that fits over the mouth and nose to prevent breathing poisonous gas or smoke.

gas·o·line (gas′ə lēn′ or gas′ə lēn′), a colorless liquid made from petroleum. It evaporates and burns very easily. Gasoline is used to run automobiles. *noun.*

gasp (gasp), **1** to try hard to get one's breath with open mouth. A person gasps when out of breath or surprised. **2** a trying hard to get one's breath with open mouth: *After the race she found it hard to talk between gasps for breath.* **3** to utter with gasps: *"Help! Help!" gasped the drowning man.* 1,3 *verb,* 2 *noun.*

gas station, filling station.

gate (gāt), a door in a wall or fence: *Someone left the gate open and the dog got out of the yard. noun.*

gate·way (gāt′wā′), **1** an opening in a wall or fence where a gate is. **2** a way to go in or out; way to get to something: *A good education can be a gateway to success. noun.*

gath·er (gaŦH′ər), **1** to bring or come together; collect: *He gathered his books and left for school. A crowd gathered to hear the speech.* **2** to pick: *He gathered a bouquet of flowers from the garden.* **3** to get or gain little by little: *The train gathered speed as it left the station.* **4** to put together in the mind; conclude: *I gather from the excitement that something important has happened.* **5** to pull together in folds: *The dressmaker gathered the skirt at the waist.* **6** one of the little folds between the stitches when cloth is gathered. 1-5 *verb,* 6 *noun.*

gath·er·ing (gaŦH′ər ing), an assembly; meeting: *We had a large family gathering at our house on Thanksgiving Day. noun.*

gaud·y (gô′dē), too bright to be in good taste; cheap and showy: *gaudy jewelry. adjective,* **gaud·i·er, gaud·i·est.**

gauge (gāj), **1** a standard measure or a scale of standard measurements. There are gauges of the thickness of wire and for the distance between the rails on railroads. **2** an instrument for measuring: *I used a gauge to find out if my bicycle tires needed more air.* **3** to measure accurately: *Instruments are used to gauge wind speed, rainfall, and air pressure.* **4** to estimate; judge: *It's hard to gauge the educational value of television.* 1,2 *noun,* 3,4 *verb,* **gaug·es, gauged, gaug·ing.**

gaunt (gônt), very thin and bony; with hollow eyes and a starved look: *Hunger had made him gaunt. adjective.*

gaunt·let (gônt′lit), **1** an iron glove which was part of a knight's armor. **2** a stout, heavy glove with a deep, flaring cuff. *noun.*

throw down the gauntlet, to give a challenge.

gauze (gôz), a very thin, light cloth, easily seen through. Gauze is often used for bandages. *noun.*

gave (gāv). See **give.** *She gave me some of her candy. verb.*

gav·el (gav′əl), a small wooden hammer used in a meeting or in court to signal for attention or order: *The chairman rapped on the table twice with his gavel. noun.*

gawk (gôk), to stare idly, rudely, or stupidly: *People driving by gawked at the accident but did not stop to help. verb.*

gay (gā), **1** happy and full of fun; merry: *The children were cheerful and gay on the day of the first snowfall.* **2** bright-colored: *a gay red and yellow scarf. adjective.*

gaze (gāz), **1** to look long and steadily: *For hours we sat gazing at the stars.* **2** a long, steady look. **1** *verb,* **gaz·es, gazed, gaz·ing; 2** *noun.*

ga·zelle (gə zel′), a small, graceful, deerlike animal of Africa and Asia. *noun, plural* **ga·zelles** or **ga·zelle.**

gazelle—about 2 feet (60 centimeters) high at the shoulder

ga·zette (gə zet′), a name used for certain newspapers: *We subscribe to the Greenwood Gazette. noun.*

gear (gir), **1** a wheel having teeth that fit into the teeth of another wheel, so that one wheel can turn the other. Gears pass motion from one part of a machine to another. They can also change the speed or direction of the motion. **2** the equipment needed for some purpose: *Fishing gear includes a line, a pole, and hooks.* **3** to make fit; adjust; adapt: *The classes were geared to the needs of the students.* **1,2** *noun,* **3** *verb.*

in gear, with the gears connected so that power can be passed from the engine to the wheels of a motor vehicle.

gears (definition 1)

gear·shift (gir′shift′), a device for changing from one set of gears to another in an automobile or other vehicle. *noun.*

gee (jē), an exclamation or mild oath, used to express surprise or enthusiasm: *Gee, it's almost time for dinner! interjection.*

geese (gēs), more than one goose. *noun plural.*

Gei·ger count·er (gī′gər koun′tər), a device which detects and measures radioactivity. [The *Geiger counter* was named for Hans Geiger, who lived from 1882 to 1947. He was a German scientist who helped to develop it.]

gel·a·tin (jel′ə tən), a substance like glue or jelly obtained by boiling the bones, hoofs, and other waste parts of animals. Gelatin is used in making glue and jellied desserts. *noun.*

gem (jem), **1** a precious stone, especially when cut or polished for ornament; jewel. Diamonds and rubies are gems. **2** a person or thing that is very beautiful or precious: *The gem of her collection was a rare Italian stamp. noun.*

gene (jēn), any one of many tiny parts joined together in the nucleus of a cell that control the characteristics that are inherited from parents. Genes control such things as the color of one's eyes, or the shape and color of flowers. *noun.*

gen·er·al (jen′ər əl), **1** of all; for all; from all: *A government takes care of the general welfare of its citizens.* **2** widespread; not limited to a few; for many; from many: *There was general concern in the city about the rising amount of crime.* **3** not detailed: *The teacher gave us only general instructions.* **4** not specialized: *The village had a general store that sold food, clothing, and hardware.* **5** a high officer in command of many soldiers in an army. **1-4** *adjective,* **5** *noun.*

in general, usually; commonly: *In general I don't like seafood, but this fish tastes good.*

gen·er·al·ize (jen′ər ə līz), to make into a general rule; conclude from particular facts: *If you know that cats, lions, leopards, pumas, and tigers eat meat, you can generalize that the cat family eats meat. verb,* **gen·er·al·iz·es, gen·er·al·ized, gen·er·al·iz·ing.**

gen·er·al·ly (jen′ər ə lē), **1** in most cases; usually: *They are generally on time.* **2** for the most part; widely: *It was once generally believed that the earth is flat.* **3** in a general way: *Generally speaking, we had a nice trip. adverb.*

gen·e·rate (jen′ə rāt′), to produce; cause to be: *The force of running water can be used to generate electricity. I couldn't generate any enthusiasm over their plan. verb,* **gen·e·rates, gen·e·rat·ed, gen·e·rat·ing.**

gen·e·ra·tion (jen′ə rā′shən), **1** the people born

in the same period. Your parents and their friends belong to one generation; you and your friends belong to the next generation. **2** about thirty years, or the time from the birth of one generation to the birth of the next generation. **3** one step in the descent of a family: *The picture showed four generations—great-grandmother, grandmother, mother, and baby.* **4** the act or process of producing: *Steam and water power are used for the generation of electricity. noun.*

gen·er·a·tor (jen′ə rā′tər), a machine for producing electricity. Generators use flowing water, steam, or other sources of energy to produce electricity. *noun.*

ge·ner·ic (jə ner′ik), not sold under a trademark or brand name: *generic drugs, generic canned goods. adjective.*

gen·e·ros·i·ty (jen′ə ros′ə tē), a being generous; unselfishness; willingness to share with others: *That wealthy family is known for its generosity. noun.*

gen·er·ous (jen′ər əs), **1** willing to share with others; unselfish: *Our teacher is always generous with his time.* **2** large; plentiful: *A quarter of a pie is a generous piece. adjective.*

gen·ial (jē′nyəl), smiling and pleasant; cheerful and friendly; kindly: *She was glad to see us again and gave us a genial welcome. adjective.*

ge·nie (jē′nē), (in old stories) a powerful spirit which can take human form and do magical things: *When Aladdin rubbed his lamp, the genie came and did what Aladdin asked. noun.*

gen·ius (jē′nyəs), **1** very great natural power of mind: *Important discoveries are usually made by men and women of genius.* **2** a person having such power: *Benjamin Franklin was a genius.* **3** a great natural ability: *Beethoven played the piano well, but he had a genius for composing music. noun, plural* **gen·ius·es.**

gen·tile or **Gen·tile** (jen′tīl), **1** a person who is not a Jew. **2** not Jewish. **1** *noun,* **2** *adjective.*

gen·til·i·ty (jen til′ə tē), good manners; refinement: *Her gentility was evident by the gracious way in which she greeted us. noun.*

gen·tle (jen′tl), **1** mild; not severe, rough, or violent: *A gentle rocking motion put the baby to sleep.* **2** soft; low: *the gentle sound of a purring cat.* **3** gradual; not at all extreme: *Our yard has a gentle slope down to the street.* **4** kindly; friendly: *a gentle disposition.* **5** easy to manage: *a gentle horse. adjective,* **gen·tler, gen·tlest.**

gen·tle·man (jen′tl mən), **1** a man of good family and social position: *He was a respected gentleman from an old, wealthy family.* **2** a man having good manners: *A gentleman would not push into line ahead of others.* **3** a polite term for any man: *"Gentlemen" is often used in speaking or writing to a group of men. noun, plural* **gen·tle·men.**

gen·tle·man·ly (jen′tl mən lē), like a gentleman; well-bred; polite. *adjective.*

gent·ly (jent′lē), **1** in a gentle way; tenderly; softly: *Handle the baby gently.* **2** gradually: *a gently sloping hillside. adverb.*

gen·u·ine (jen′yü ən), **1** real; true: *This wallet is genuine leather.* **2** sincere; honest: *We felt genuine regret when our neighbors moved away. adjective.*

ge·og·ra·pher (jē og′rə fər), a person who is an expert in geography. *noun.*

ge·o·graph·ic (jē′ə graf′ik), geographical. *adjective.*

ge·o·graph·i·cal (jē′ə graf′ə kəl), of geography; having something to do with geography. *adjective.*

ge·og·ra·phy (jē og′rə fē), the study of the earth's surface, climate, continents, countries, peoples, industries, and products. *noun.*

ge·o·log·ic (jē′ə loj′ik), geological: *geologic time. adjective.*

ge·o·log·i·cal (jē′ə loj′ə kəl), of geology; having something to do with geology: *a geological survey. adjective.*

ge·ol·o·gist (jē ol′ə jist), a person who is an expert in geology. *noun.*

ge·ol·o·gy (jē ol′ə jē), the science that deals with the composition and history of the earth, the moon, and similar heavenly bodies. The study of rocks is an important part of geology. *noun.*

ge·o·met·ric (jē′ə met′rik), made up of straight lines, circles, and other simple shapes; regular and evenly balanced. *adjective.*

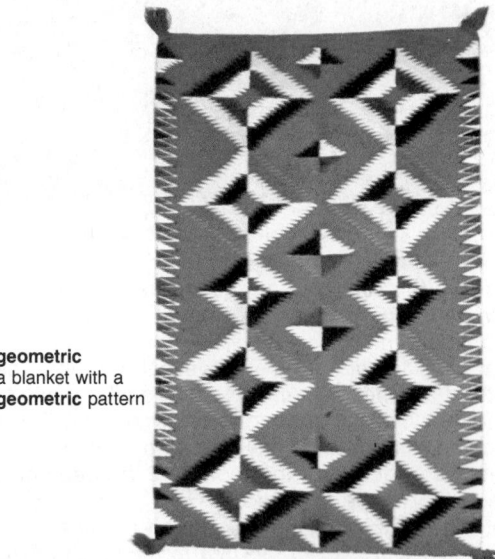

geometric
a blanket with a
geometric pattern

ge·om·e·try (jē om′ə trē), the branch of mathematics that measures and compares points, lines, angles, surfaces, and solids. *noun.*

Geor·gia (jôr′jə), **1** one of the southeastern states of the United States. *Abbreviation:* Ga. or GA *Capital:* Atlanta. **2** a country in southwestern Europe. *noun.*
[*Georgia,* the state, was named in 1732 for George II, king of England, who lived from 1683 to 1760.]

ge·o·ther·mal (jē′ō thėr′məl), having to do with or produced by the heat inside the earth: *Geothermal energy in the form of water from hot springs can be used to heat houses. adjective.*

ge·ra·ni·um (jə rā′nē əm), a plant with showy

geranium

a hat	i it	oi oil	ch child	a in about
ā age	ī ice	ou out	ng long	e in taken
ä far	o hot	u cup	sh she	ə = { i in pencil
e let	ō open	u̇ put	th thin	o in lemon
ē equal	ô order	ü rule	ᴛʜ then	u in circus
ėr term			zh measure	

flowers of red, pink, or white, often grown in pots for window plants. *noun.*

ger·bil (jer′bəl), an animal somewhat like a mouse with long hind legs. Gerbils are used for scientific experiments and are kept as pets. *noun.*

gerbil—about 8 inches (20 centimeters) long with the tail

germ (jėrm), **1** a simple living thing, too small to be seen without a microscope. Some germs cause disease. **2** the earliest form of a living thing; seed or bud. **3** the beginning of anything: *His tale gave me the germ of an idea for a book. noun.*

Ger·man (jer′mən), **1** of or having something to do with Germany, its people, or their language. **2** a person born or living in Germany. **3** the language of Germany. **1** *adjective,* **2,3** *noun.*

Word Source

German is also spoken in Austria, Switzerland, and other countries. Here are some words that have come into English from German:

accordion	hamburger	pretzel
dachshund	hamster	pumpernickel
delicatessen	kindergarten	sauerkraut
fife	noodle	waltz
frankfurter	poodle	wiener

German measles, a disease like measles but milder. It causes small red spots to break out on the skin.

German shepherd, a large, strong, intelligent dog often trained to work with soldiers and police or to guide blind persons.

Ger·ma·ny (jer′mə nē), a country in central Europe. From 1949 to 1990 Germany was divided into West Germany and East Germany. *noun.*

ger·mi·nate (jer′mə nāt), to start growing or developing; sprout: *Seeds germinate in the spring. verb,* **ger·mi·nates, ger·mi·nat·ed, ger·mi·nat·ing.**

ges·ture (jes′chər), **1** a movement of the hands, arms, or any part of the body, used instead of words or with words to help express an idea or feeling: *Speakers often make gestures with their hands to stress something they are saying.* **2** any action for effect or to impress others: *Her refusal was merely a gesture; she really wanted to go to the party with us.* **3** to make gestures; use gestures. **1,2** *noun,* **3** *verb,* **ges·tures, ges·tured, ges·tur·ing.**

get (get), **1** to come to have; obtain; receive: *I got a present.* **2** to reach; arrive: *I got home early last night.* **3** to catch; get hold of: *I got the cat by one leg.* **4** to cause to be or do: *Get the windows open.* **5** to become: *It is getting colder.* **6** to persuade; influence: *Try to get them to come, too.* **7** to hit; strike: *The ball got the batter on the arm.* **8** to understand: *The teacher explained the math problem, but I didn't get it. verb,* **gets, got, got** or **got·ten, get·ting.**

get away, 1 to go away: *Let's get away from here.* **2** to escape: *The prisoner got away.*

get away with, to take or do something and escape safely: *Don't let them get away with such lies.*

get in, 1 to go in: *I had hoped to get in without being seen.* **2** to put in: *They kept talking, and I couldn't get in a word.* **3** to arrive: *Our train should get in at 9 p.m.*

get off, 1 to come down from or out of: *We got off our horses.* **2** to take off: *Get your coat off.* **3** to escape punishment: *If you disobey again, you will not get off so easily.* **4** to start: *The horses in the race got off well.*

get on, 1 to go up on or into: *We got on a train.* **2** to put on: *Get on your boots; we have to go out in the snow.* **3** to advance: *to get on in years.* **4** to succeed: *How are you getting on in your new job?* **5** to agree: *The roommates get on with each other very well.*

get out, 1 to go out: *Let's get out of here!* **2** to become known: *The secret got out.*

get over, to recover from: *I finally got over my cold.*

get to, to be allowed to: *I got to stay up late last night.*

get together, 1 to come together; meet: *Let's get*

G

together next week. **2** to come to an agreement: *The jury was unable to get together.*

get up, 1 to arise: *She got up at six o'clock.* **2** to stand up: *I fell on the ice and couldn't get up.*

gey·ser (gī′zər), a spring that sends up fountains or jets of hot water or steam. *noun.*

Word History

geyser *Geyser* comes from an old word used in Iceland meaning "to gush."

geyser
a **geyser** in Yellowstone National Park

Gha·na (gä′nə), a country in western Africa. *noun.*

ghast·ly (gast′lē), **1** horrible: *The destruction caused by the forest fire was a ghastly sight.* **2** very pale; like a ghost: *The sick man looked ghastly.* **3** very bad: *a ghastly failure. adjective,* **ghast·li·er, ghast·li·est.**

ghet·to (get′ō), a part of a city where any racial group or nationality lives. *noun.*

ghost (gōst), the spirit of one who is dead appearing to the living: *The ghost of the murdered servant was said to haunt the house. noun.*

ghost·ly (gōst′lē), like a ghost; pale, dim, and shadowy: *A ghostly form walked across the stage. adjective,* **ghost·li·er, ghost·li·est.**

gi·ant (jī′ənt), **1** an imaginary being like a huge person. **2** a person of great size or very great power. **3** huge: *a giant potato.* **1,2** *noun,* **3** *adjective.*

gib·bon (gib′ən), a small ape of southeastern Asia that has very long arms. Gibbons live in trees. *noun.*

gibe (jīb), **1** to speak in a sneering way; jeer; scoff; sneer: *They gibed at my efforts to paint a picture.* **2** a jeer; taunt; sneer: *Their gibes hurt my feelings.* **1** *verb,* **gibes, gibed, gib·ing; 2** *noun.*

gid·dy (gid′ē), **1** dizzy; having a whirling in the head: *giddy from riding the merry-go-round.* **2** never serious; silly: *That giddy crowd thinks only of parties. adjective,* **gid·di·er, gid·di·est.**

gift (gift), **1** something given; present: *a birthday gift.* **2** a natural talent; special ability: *A great artist must have a gift for painting. noun.*

gift·ed (gif′tid), very able; having special ability: *a gifted musician. adjective.*

gi·gan·tic (jī gan′tik), like a giant; very large or powerful; huge: *An elephant is a gigantic animal. adjective.*

gig·gle (gig′əl), **1** to laugh in a silly or uncontrolled way. **2** a silly or uncontrolled laugh. **1** *verb,* **gig·gles, gig·gled, gig·gling; 2** *noun.*

Gi·la mon·ster (hē′lə mon′stər), a large, poisonous lizard with a thick tail and heavy body, covered with beadlike orange-and-black scales. It is found in the southwestern United States and northern Mexico.

Gila monster
about 18 inches (46 centimeters) long with the tail

gild (gild), to cover with a thin layer of gold. *verb,* **gilds, gild·ed** or **gilt, gild·ing.**

gill (gil), a part of the body of a fish, tadpole, crab, or other water animal by which the animal gets oxygen from water. *noun.*

gilt (gilt), **1** gilded. **2** material with which a thing is gilded: *The gilt is coming off from this frame.* **3** See **gild. 1** *adjective,* **2** *noun,* **3** *verb.*

gin[1] (jin), a strong alcoholic drink, made from grain and usually flavored with juniper berries. *noun.*

gin[2] (jin), a machine for separating cotton from its seeds. *noun.*

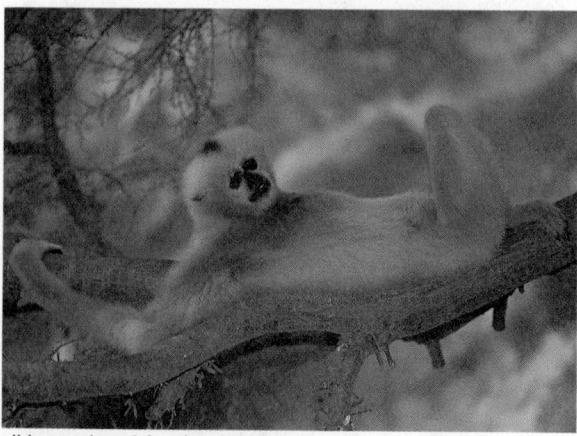

gibbon—about 3 feet (1 meter) tall

gin·ger (jin′jər), a spice made from the root of a tropical plant. The root is often preserved in syrup or candied. *noun.*

ginger ale, a bubbling drink flavored with ginger. It contains no alcohol.

gin·ger·bread (jin′jər bred′), a kind of cake flavored with ginger. Gingerbread is often made in fancy shapes. *noun.*

gin·ger·ly (jin′jər lē), with extreme care or caution: *to walk gingerly across the ice. adverb.*

gin·ger·snap (jin′jər snap′), a thin, crisp cookie flavored with ginger and sweetened with molasses. *noun.*

ging·ham (ging′əm), a cotton cloth made from colored threads. The patterns are usually in stripes, plaids, and checks. *noun.*
[*Gingham* comes from a Malay word meaning "striped."]

gip·sy (jip′sē), gypsy. *noun, plural* **gip·sies;** *adjective.*

gi·raffe (jə raf′), a large African animal that chews its cud and has hoofs, a very long neck and long legs, and a spotted skin. Giraffes are the tallest living animals. *noun.*

gird·er (gėr′dər), a main supporting beam. The weight of a floor is usually supported by girders. A tall building or big bridge often has steel girders for its frame. *noun.*

gir·dle (gėr′dl), **1** a tight-fitting undergarment covering the waist and hips, which shapes and supports the body. **2** a belt, sash, or cord, worn around the waist. **3** anything that surrounds: *a girdle of trees around a pond. noun.*

girl (gėrl), a female child from birth to about eighteen. *noun.*

girl·friend (gėrl′frend′), **1** a boy's sweetheart or steady female companion. **2** a female friend. *noun.*

girl·hood (gėrl′hud), the time of being a girl. *noun.*

girl·ish (gėr′lish), **1** of a girl. **2** like a girl. **3** like a girl's; suitable for a girl. *adjective.*

girl scout, a member of the Girl Scouts.

Girl Scouts, an organization for girls that seeks to develop character, citizenship, usefulness to others, and various skills.

girth (gėrth), **1** the measure around anything: *a man of large girth, the girth of a tree.* **2** a strap or band that keeps the saddle in place on a horse. *noun.*

give (giv), **1** to hand over as a present; make a gift of: *My parents gave me ice skates for my birthday.* **2** to hand over: *Give me that pencil.* **3** to pay: *She gave three dollars for the wagon.* **4** to let have; cause to have: *She gave us permission to go. Don't give the teacher any trouble.* **5** to cause by some action of the body: *Some boys give hard blows, even in play.* **6** to offer; present: *This newspaper gives a full story of the game.* **7** to put forth; utter: *He gave a cry of pain.* **8** to supply; produce: *Lamps give light.* **9** to yield to force: *The lock gave under hard pushing.* **10** a yielding to force.
1-9 *verb,* **gives, gave, giv·en, giv·ing;** 10 *noun.*

give away, 1 to give as a present: *She gave away her best toy.* **2** to present a bride to a bridegroom: *The bride was given away by her father.* **3** to cause to be known; reveal; betray: *The spy gave away secrets to the enemy.*

give in, to surrender; yield under pressure; admit defeat: *Some people will not give in even when they are proved wrong.*

give off, to send out; put forth: *This lamp gives off a very bright light.*

give out, 1 to send out; put forth: *The bomb fell, giving out a huge flash of fire.* **2** to distribute: *The supplies will be given out tomorrow.* **3** to make known: *Who has given out this information?* **4** to become used up or worn out: *My strength gave out after the long climb.*

give up, 1 to hand over; surrender: *When the troops saw that they were surrounded, they gave up.* **2** to stop having or doing: *We gave up the search when it got dark.* **3** to stop trying: *Don't give up so soon; try again and maybe you will succeed this time.*

giv·en (giv′ən), **1** stated: *You must finish the test in a given time.* **2** inclined; disposed: *given to boasting.* **3** See **give.** *That book was given to me.* 1,2 *adjective,* 3 *verb.*

giv·er (giv′ər), a person who gives. *noun.*

giz·zard (giz′ərd), a bird's second stomach, where the food from the first stomach is ground up. *noun.*

gla·cial (glā′shəl), icy; of ice; having much ice; having many glaciers: *During the glacial period, much of the Northern Hemisphere was covered with great ice sheets. adjective.*

gla·cier (glā′shər), a large mass of ice formed from the snow on high ground and moving very slowly down a mountain or along a valley. *noun.*

glacier—a **glacier** in Canada

glad | gleeful

glad (glad), **1** happy; pleased: *She is glad to see us.* **2** bringing joy; pleasant: *glad news.* **3** willing; ready: *I will be glad to go if you need me.* adjective, **glad·der, glad·dest.**

glad·den (glad/n), to make glad; become glad: *We were gladdened by the good news.* verb.

glade (glād), a little open space in a wood or forest. noun.

glad·i·a·tor (glad/ē ā/tər), a slave, captive, or paid fighter who fought at the public shows in the arenas in ancient Rome. noun.

glad·i·o·lus (glad/ē ō/ləs), a plant with spikes of large, handsome flowers in various colors. noun, plural **glad·i·o·li** (glad/ē ō/lī), **glad·i·o·lus·es.**

Word History

gladiolus *Gladiolus* comes from a Latin word meaning "sword." The leaves of the plant were thought to look like small swords.

glam·or (glam/ər), fascination; charm; attractiveness: *the glamor of circus life.* noun. Also spelled **glamour.**

glam·or·ous (glam/ər əs), fascinating; charming: *a glamorous job in a foreign city.* adjective.

glam·our (glam/ər). See **glamor.** noun.

glance (glans), **1** a quick look: *She gave the pictures only a glance.* **2** to look quickly: *I glanced out of the window.* **3** to hit and go off at a slant: *I dropped the cup and it glanced off the edge of the table.* 1 noun, 2,3 verb, **glanc·es, glanced, glanc·ing.**

gland (gland), an organ in the body which makes and gives out some substance. Glands make the liquid that keeps the mouth wet. A cow has glands which make milk. The liver, the kidneys, and the pancreas are glands. noun.

glare (gler *or* glar), **1** a strong, unpleasant light; light that shines so brightly that it hurts the eyes. **2** to shine strongly or unpleasantly; shine so brightly as to hurt the eyes: *There was no shade on the lamp, and the bulb glared so that I could not read.* **3** a fierce, angry stare. **4** to stare fiercely and with anger: *The teacher glared at him when he giggled.* 1,3 noun, 2,4 verb, **glares, glared, glar·ing.**

glar·ing (gler/ing *or* glar/ing), **1** shining so brightly that it hurts the eyes. **2** staring fiercely and angrily. **3** very easily seen: *The student made a glaring error in spelling.* adjective.

glass (glas), **1** a hard substance that breaks easily and can usually be seen through. Windows are made of glass. **2** something to drink from made of glass: *He filled the glass with water.* **3** an amount a glass can hold: *Drink a glass of water.* **4** a mirror: *Look at yourself in the glass.* **5 glasses,** a pair of glass or plastic lenses set in a frame, used to help poor vision. **6** made of glass: *a glass dish.* 1-5 noun, plural **glass·es;** 6 adjective.

glass·y (glas/ē), like glass; smooth; easily seen through: *With no wind, the small pond had a glassy surface.* adjective, **glass·i·er, glass·i·est.**

glaze (glāz), **1** to put glass in; cover with glass. Pieces of glass cut to the right size are used to glaze windows and picture frames. **2** a smooth, glassy surface or glossy coating: *the glaze on a china cup. A glaze of ice on the walk is dangerous.* **3** to cover with a shiny, smooth coating: *The pottery is glazed at the factory.* **4** to become shiny: *The sick man's eyes were glazed with fever.* 1,3,4 verb, **glaz·es, glazed, glaz·ing;** 2 noun.

gleam (glēm), **1** a flash or beam of light: *We saw the gleam of headlights through the rain.* **2** to send forth a gleam; shine: *A candle gleamed in the dark.* **3** a short appearance: *The rain brought a gleam of hope to the farmers during the drought.* 1,3 noun, 2 verb.

glean (glēn), **1** to gather stalks of grain left on the field by reapers. **2** to gather little by little: *The spy gleaned information by listening to the soldiers' talk.* verb.

glee (glē), lively joy; great delight: *The children laughed with glee at the clown's antics.* noun.

glee club, a group organized for singing songs.

glee·ful (glē/fəl), merry and gay; joyous. adjective.

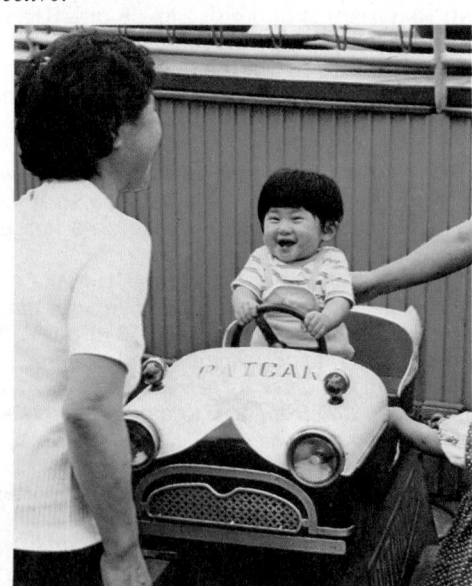

gleeful—He had a **gleeful** ride in the toy car.

258

glen (glen), a small, narrow valley. *noun.*

glide (glīd), **1** to move along smoothly, evenly, and easily: *Birds, ships, dancers, and skaters glide.* **2** a smooth, even, easy movement. **3** to come down slowly at a slant without using a motor: *The paper airplane glided to the floor.* 1,3 *verb,* **glides, glid·ed, glid·ing;** 2 *noun.*

glid·er (glī′dər), an airplane without a motor. Rising air currents keep a glider up in the air. *noun.*

glim·mer (glim′ər), **1** a faint, unsteady light. **2** to shine with a faint, unsteady light: *The candle glimmered and went out.* **3** a vague idea; dim notion; faint glimpse: *A few clouds gave a glimmer of hope that rain might come and end the drought.* 1,3 *noun,* 2 *verb.*

glimpse (glimps), **1** a very brief view; short look: *I caught a glimpse of the falls as our train went by.* **2** to catch a brief view of: *I glimpsed the falls as our train went by.* 1 *noun,* 2 *verb,* **glimps·es, glimpsed, glimps·ing.**

glint (glint), **1** a gleam; flash: *The glint in her eye showed that she was angry.* **2** to gleam; flash. 1 *noun,* 2 *verb.*

glis·ten (glis′n), **1** to shine; glitter; sparkle: *The stars glistened in the sky.* **2** a glitter; sparkle: *the glisten of snow.* 1 *verb,* 2 *noun.*

glit·ter (glit′ər), **1** to shine with a bright, sparkling light: *The jewels and new coins glittered.* **2** a bright, sparkling light: *The glitter of the harsh lights hurt my eyes.* **3** tiny, sparkling objects such as tinsel or spangles, used for decoration. 1 *verb,* 2,3 *noun.*

gloat (glōt), to gaze or think about intently and with satisfaction: *She gloated over her success. The miser gloated over his gold. verb.*

glob (glob), a shapeless mass; small lump: *The car spattered me with globs of mud. noun.*

glob·al (glō′bəl), **1** spread throughout the world: *the threat of global war.* **2** shaped like a globe: *a global map. adjective.*

globe (glōb), **1** anything round like a ball. **2** the earth; world. **3** a sphere with a map of the earth or the sky on it. *noun.*

gloom (glüm), **1** darkness; deep shadow; dim light. **2** dark thoughts and feelings; low spirits; sadness. *noun.*

gloom·i·ly (glü′mə lē), in a gloomy manner. *adverb.*

gloom·y (glü′mē), **1** dark; dim: *a gloomy winter day.* **2** in low spirits; sad; melancholy: *a gloomy mood.* **3** dismal; causing gloom; discouraging: *There were gloomy predictions of a major earthquake happening soon. adjective,* **gloom·i·er, gloom·i·est.**

glo·ri·fy (glôr′ə fī), **1** to give glory to; make glorious: *glorify a hero or a saint.* **2** to worship; praise: *hymns glorifying God. verb,* **glo·ri·fies, glo·ri·fied, glo·ri·fy·ing.**

glo·ri·ous (glôr′ē əs), **1** having or deserving glory. **2** giving glory: *Our team won a glorious victory.* **3** magnificent; splendid: *The children had a glorious time at the fair. adjective.*

glo·ry (glôr′ē), **1** great praise and honor; fame:

a hat	**i** it	**oi** oil	**ch** child	a in about
ā age	**ī** ice	**ou** out	**ng** long	e in taken
ä far	**o** hot	**u** cup	**sh** she	ə = { i in pencil
e let	**ō** open	**u̇** put	**th** thin	o in lemon
ē equal	**ô** order	**ü** rule	**ŦH** then	u in circus
ėr term			**zh** measure	

His heroic act won him glory. **2** to be proud; rejoice: *The teacher gloried in her class's achievements.* **3** brightness; splendor: *the glory of the royal palace.* **4** a condition of magnificence, splendor, or greatest prosperity: *The British empire reached its greatest glory in the 1800's, during the reign of Queen Victoria.* 1,3,4 *noun,* plural **glo·ries;** 2 *verb,* **glo·ries, glo·ried, glo·ry·ing.**

gloss (glôs), a smooth, shiny surface on anything: *Varnished furniture has a gloss. noun.*

glos·sar·y (glos′ər ē), a list of hard words with explanations: *Some schoolbooks have glossaries at the end. noun,* plural **glos·sar·ies.**

gloss·y (glô′sē), smooth and shiny: *She brushed the kitten's fur until it was glossy. adjective,* **gloss·i·er, gloss·i·est.**

glove (gluv), **1** a covering for the hand, usually with separate places for each of the four fingers and the thumb. **2** to cover with a glove. 1 *noun,* 2 *verb,* **gloves, gloved, glov·ing.**

glow (glō), **1** to shine because of heat; be red-hot or white-hot: *Embers still glowed in the fireplace after the fire had died down.* **2** the shine from something that is red-hot or white-hot: *the glow of molten steel.* **3** to give off light without heat: *Some clocks glow in the dark.* **4** a bright, warm color: *the glow of sunset.* **5** the warm feeling or color of the body: *the glow of health on her cheeks.* **6** to show a warm color; look warm: *His cheeks glowed as he jogged.* 1,3,6 *verb,* 2,4,5 *noun.*

glow·er (glou′ər), to stare angrily; scowl fiercely: *The fighters glowered at each other while they waited to start the match. verb.*

glow·worm (glō′wėrm′), any insect larva or insect which glows in the dark. Fireflies develop from some glowworms. *noun.*

glu·cose (glü′kōs), a kind of simple sugar that is found in the tissues of most living things. Glucose is an important source of food energy. *noun.*

glue (glü), **1** a substance used to stick things together. Glue is often made by boiling the hoofs, skins, and bones of animals in water. **2** any similar sticky substance. Glues are stronger than pastes. **3** to stick together with glue. **4** to fasten tightly: *Her hands were glued to the steering wheel as she drove down the dangerous mountain road.* 1,2 *noun,* 3,4 *verb,* **glues, glued, glu·ing.**

glum (glum), gloomy; dismal; sullen: *I felt very glum when my friend moved away. adjective,* **glum·mer, glum·mest.**

glut·ton (glut′n), a greedy eater; person who eats too much. *noun.*

gnarl (närl), a knot in wood; hard, rough lump: *Wood with gnarls is hard to cut. noun.*

G

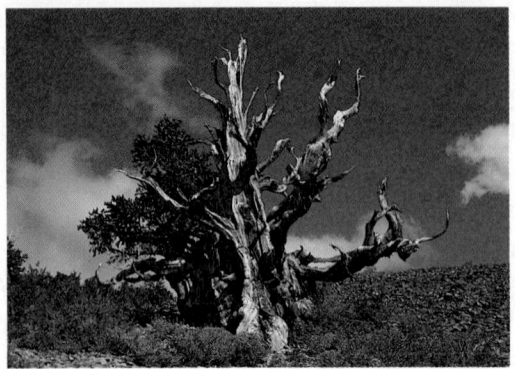

gnarled—a **gnarled** tree

gnarled (närld), rough and twisted; having knots: *The farmer's gnarled hands grasped the plow firmly. adjective.*

gnash (nash), to strike or grind the teeth together; grind together: *The angry animals gnashed their teeth. verb.*

gnat (nat), a small, two-winged fly somewhat like a mosquito. Most gnats make bites that itch. *noun.*

gnaw (nô), to bite at and wear away: *A mouse has gnawed right through the cover of this box. verb.*

gnome (nōm), a dwarf supposed to live in the earth and to guard treasures of precious metals and stones. *noun.*

go (gō), **1** to move along: *Cars go on the road.* **2** to move away; leave: *Don't go yet.* **3** to be in motion; act; work; run: *Make the washing machine go.* **4** to get to be; become: *to go mad.* **5** to be habitually; be: *to go hungry for a week.* **6** to proceed; advance: *to go to New York.* **7** to take part in the activity of: *to go skiing, to go swimming.* **8** to put oneself: *Don't go to any trouble for me.* **9** to extend; reach: *Does your memory go back that far?* **10** to pass: *Summer had gone. Vacation goes quickly.* **11** to be given: *First prize goes to you.* **12** to have its place; belong: *This book goes on the top shelf.* **13** to make a certain sound: *The cork went "pop!" verb*, **goes, went, gone, go·ing.**

go along, cooperate: *I'll go along with your plan.*

go by, 1 to pass: *We went by that store often.* **2** to be guided by; follow: *Go by what she says.* **3** to be known by: *He goes by the name of Smith.*

go in for, take part in; spend time and energy at: *Our whole family goes in for basketball.*

go off, 1 to leave; depart: *My sister has gone off to college.* **2** to be fired; explode: *The pistol went off unexpectedly.* **3** to start to ring; sound: *I was already awake when the alarm went off.*

go on, 1 to go ahead; continue: *After a pause he went on reading.* **2** to happen: *What goes on here?*

go out, 1 to go to a party or show: *We had a very good time when we went out Saturday night.* **2** to stop burning: *Don't let the candle go out.*

go up, 1 to ascend; rise: *The thermometer is going up.* **2** to increase: *The price of milk has gone up.*

go with, belong with; go well with: *This shade of blue goes with our furniture.*

let go, 1 allow to escape: *Let me go.* **2** give up one's hold: *I held the rope as long as I could, but I finally had to let go.*

goad (gōd), to drive or urge on; act as a spur to: *Hunger goaded her to steal food. verb.*

go·a·head (gō′ə hed′), permission to go ahead or begin: *The train engineer got the go-ahead from the signal tower. noun.*

goal (gōl), **1** the place where a race ends. **2** the place which players try to reach in certain games. **3** the points won by reaching this place. **4** something desired: *The goal of her ambition was to be a scientist. noun.*

goal·ie (gō′lē), a goalkeeper. *noun.*

goal·keep·er (gōl′kē′pər), a player who tries to keep the puck from crossing the goal in hockey. *noun.*

goat (gōt), an animal with horns, a beard, and hoofs that chews its cud. Goats are stronger, less timid, and more active than sheep. They are raised for their milk and their hides. *noun, plural* **goats** or **goat.**

get one's goat, to make a person angry or annoyed; tease a person.

goat·ee (gō tē′), a pointed beard on a man's chin. *noun.*

goatee

goat·skin (gōt′skin′), leather made from the skin of a goat. *noun.*

gob·ble¹ (gob′əl), to eat fast and greedily. *verb,* **gob·bles, gob·bled, gob·bling.**

gob·ble² (gob′əl), **1** the noise a turkey makes. **2** to make this noise or one like it. **1** *noun,* **2** *verb,* **gob·bles, gob·bled, gob·bling.**

gob·bler (gob′lər), a male turkey. *noun.*

gob·let (gob′lit), a drinking glass that stands high above its base on a stem, and has no handle. *noun.*

Word History

goblet *Goblet* comes from an old French word meaning "cup."

gob·lin (gob′lən), a mischievous spirit or elf in the form of an ugly-looking dwarf. *noun.*

god (god), **1** a being thought to have powers beyond those of human beings and considered worthy of worship. **2** a likeness or image; idol. **3** a person or thing greatly respected or thought of as very important: *Wealth and power are his gods.* *noun.*

God (god), an all-powerful being worshiped in most religions as the maker and ruler of the world. *noun.*

god·dess (god′is), a female god. *noun, plural* **god·dess·es.**

god·fa·ther (god′fä′ᴛʜər), a man who sponsors a child when it is baptized. The godfather promises to help the child to be a good Christian. *noun.*

god·ly (god′lē), obeying, loving, and fearing God; religious; pious. *adjective,* **god·li·er, god·li·est.**

god·moth·er (god′muᴛʜ′ər), a woman who sponsors a child when it is baptized. The godmother promises to help the child to be a good Christian. *noun.*

goes (gōz). See **go.** *He goes to school. verb.*

gog·gles (gog′əlz), large, close-fitting eyeglasses to protect the eyes from light or dust. *noun plural.*

go·ing (gō′ing), **1** a leaving: *His going was very sudden.* **2** moving; in action; working; running: *Set the clock going.* **3** the condition of the ground or road for walking or riding: *The going is bad through this muddy road.* **4** that goes; that can or will go: *That new business is a going concern.* **1,3** *noun,* **2,4** *adjective.*
  be going to, will; be about to: *Is it going to rain?*

gold (gōld), **1** a heavy, bright-yellow, precious metal that is a chemical element. Gold is used in making coins, watches, and rings. **2** made of this metal: *a gold watch.* **3** money in large sums; wealth; riches. **4** bright-yellow. **1,3** *noun,* **2,4** *adjective.*

gold·en (gōl′dən), **1** made of or containing gold: *The queen wore a golden crown.* **2** shining like gold; bright-yellow: *golden hair.* **3** very good; extremely favorable, valuable, or important: *a golden opportunity.* **4** very happy; flourishing: *a golden age. adjective.*

gold·en·rod (gōl′dən rod′), a plant with tall stalks of small yellow flowers. It blooms in the autumn. *noun.*

gold·finch (gōld′finch′), a small yellow songbird marked with black. *noun, plural* **gold·finch·es.**

gold·fish (gōld′fish′), a small fish, usually of a reddish or golden color, kept in garden pools or in glass bowls indoors. *noun, plural* **gold·fish** or **gold·fish·es.**

gold·smith (gōld′smith′), a person who makes articles of gold. *noun.*

golf (golf), **1** an outdoor game played by hitting a small, hard ball with one of a set of clubs. The player tries to drive the ball into a series of holes with as few strokes as possible. **2** to play this game. **1** *noun,* **2** *verb.*

gol·ly (gol′ē), an exclamation of wonder,

a hat	i it	oi oil	ch child	a in about
ā age	ī ice	ou out	ng long	e in taken
ä far	o hot	u cup	sh she	ə = i in pencil
e let	ō open	u̇ put	th thin	o in lemon
ē equal	ô order	ü rule	ᴛʜ then	u in circus
ėr term			zh measure	

pleasure, joy, or the like: *Golly, that's a huge tree! interjection.*

gon·do·la (gon′dl ə), **1** a long, narrow boat with a high peak at each end, used on the canals of Venice. **2** a car that hangs under a dirigible and holds the motors, passengers, and instruments. *noun.*
[*Gondola* was borrowed from an Italian word.]

gondola (definition 1)

gone (gôn), **1** moved away; left: *The students are gone on their vacation.* **2** dead: *Great-grandmother is gone now.* **3** used up; consumed: *Is all the candy gone?* **4** See **go.** *She has gone to the movies.* **1-3** *adjective,* **4** *verb.*

gong (gông), a piece of metal shaped like a bowl or a saucer which makes a loud noise when struck. A gong is a kind of bell. *noun.*

goldenrod

good (gůd), **1** having high quality; well done: *The teacher said my report was good.* **2** right; as it ought to be: *good health, good weather.* **3** behaving well; that does what is right: *a good boy.* **4** kind; friendly: *Say a good word for me.* **5** desirable: *a good book for children.* **6** reliable; dependable: *She showed good judgment.* **7** real; genuine: *It is not always easy to tell counterfeit money from good money.* **8** pleasant: *Have a good time.* **9** beneficial; useful: *drugs good for a fever.* **10** benefit: *What good will it do?* **11** satisfying: *a good meal.* **12** that which is good: *to find the good in people.* 1-9,11 *adjective,* **bet·ter, best;** 10,12 *noun.*

as good as, almost; practically: *The battle was as good as won.*

for good, forever; finally; permanently: *They have moved out for good.*

make good, 1 to make up for; pay for: *The boys made good the damage they had done.* **2** to succeed: *He made good in business.*

good-by (gůd′bī′), an expression of good wishes at parting: *He waved and called "Good-by!" as he drove off. We said good-by at the airport. interjection, noun, plural* **good-bys.**

[*Good-by* was shortened from the phrase *God be with you.*]

good-bye (gůd′bī′), good-by. *interjection, noun, plural* **good-byes.**

Good Friday, the Friday before Easter.

good-heart·ed (gůd′här′tid), kind and generous: *She is a good-hearted person, always ready to help out a neighbor. adjective.*

good-look·ing (gůd′lůk′ing), having a pleasing appearance; handsome. *adjective.*

good·ly (gůd′lē), **1** of good quality; excellent: *They own some goodly property.* **2** considerable; rather large: *a goodly quantity. adjective,* **good·li·er, good·li·est.**

good-na·tured (gůd′nā′chərd), pleasant; kindly; obliging; cheerful. *adjective.*

good·ness (gůd′nis), kindness; being good. *noun.*

goods (gůdz), **1** belongings; personal property: *When we moved we shipped our household goods in a van.* **2** a thing or things for sale; wares. *noun plural.*

good-sized (gůd′sīzd′), somewhat large: *He is a good-sized dog for his breed. adjective.*

good-tem·pered (gůd′tem′pərd), easy to get along with; cheerful; agreeable. *adjective.*

good·will (gůd′wil′), **1** kindly or friendly feeling. **2** the good reputation a business has with its customers. *noun.*

good·y (gůd′ē), **1** something very good to eat; a piece of candy or cake. **2** an exclamation of pleasure: *Oh, goody!* 1 *noun, plural* **good·ies;** 2 *interjection.*

goo·ey (gü′ē), sticky: *gooey candy. adjective,* **goo·i·er, goo·i·est.**

goof (güf), **1** to make a stupid mistake; blunder: *She really goofed when she mailed the letter without putting a stamp on it.* **2** a stupid mistake; blunder. 1 *verb,* 2 *noun.*

goof off, to waste time; avoid work: *They spent the afternoon goofing off.*

goof·y (gü′fē), silly; foolish: *He has such goofy ideas! adjective,* **goof·i·er, goof·i·est.**

goose (güs), **1** a tame or wild bird like a duck, but larger and with a longer neck. A goose has webbed feet. **2** a female goose. The male is called a gander. **3** the flesh of a goose used for food. **4** a silly person. *noun, plural* **geese.**

cook one's goose, to do damage to a person; ruin a person's plans or chances.

goose·ber·ry (güs′ber′ē), a small, sour berry somewhat like a currant but larger, that grows on a thorny bush. Gooseberries are used to make pies, tarts, or jam. *noun, plural* **goose·ber·ries.**

goose·bumps (güs′bumps′), gooseflesh. *noun plural.*

goose·flesh (güs′flesh′), a rough condition of the skin, like that of a plucked goose, caused by cold or fear. *noun.*

goose pimples, gooseflesh.

go·pher (gō′fər), a ratlike animal of North America with large cheek pouches. Gophers dig holes in the ground. *noun.*

gore[1] (gôr), blood that is spilled; thick blood: *The battlefield was covered with gore. noun.*

gore[2] (gôr), to wound with a horn or tusk: *The angry bull gored the farmer. verb,* **gores, gored, gor·ing.**

gorge (gôrj), **1** a deep, narrow valley, usually steep and rocky. **2** to eat greedily until full; stuff with food: *She gorged herself with cake at the party.* 1 *noun,* 2 *verb,* **gorg·es, gorged, gorg·ing.**

gor·geous (gôr′jəs), richly colored; very beautiful: *The peacock spread its gorgeous tail. adjective.*

go·ril·la (gə ril′ə), the largest and most powerful ape. It is found in the forests of central Africa. *noun.*

gorilla—up to 6 feet (2 meters) tall when standing

gor·y (gôr′ē), bloody. *adjective,* **gor·i·er, gor·i·est.**

gosh (gosh), an exclamation or mild oath: *Gosh, it's cold out today! interjection.*

gos·ling (goz′ling), a young goose. *noun.*

gos·pel (gos′pəl), **1** the teachings of Jesus and the Apostles. **2 Gospel,** any one of the first four books of the New Testament. They tell about the life and teachings of Jesus. **3** anything believed to be the absolute truth: *They took the doctor's words as gospel. noun.*
[*Gospel* comes from an earlier English word meaning "good news." This word was used to refer to the teachings of Jesus, thought of as good news for humanity.]

gos·sa·mer (gos′ə mər), very light, thin, and easily seen through. *adjective.*

gossamer—the **gossamer** wings of an insect

gos·sip (gos′ip), **1** idle talk, not always true, about other people and their private affairs: *I was angry when I heard the gossip that was being spread about me.* **2** to repeat what one knows or hears about other people and their private affairs: *The two of them were gossiping about someone they didn't like.* **3** a person who gossips a good deal: *He knows everyone's business and is the biggest gossip in town.* 1,3 *noun,* 2 *verb.*

got (got). See **get.** *We got the letter yesterday. We had got tired of waiting for it. verb.*

got·ten (got′n), got. See **get.** *It has gotten to be quite late. verb.*

gouge (gouj), **1** a chisel with a curved, hollow blade. Gouges are used for cutting round grooves or holes in wood. **2** to cut with a gouge or other sharp object; dig out: *I gouged my leg against the fence.* **3** a groove or hole made by gouging. 1,3 *noun,* 2 *verb,* **goug·es, gouged, goug·ing.**

gouge (definition 1)

gourds

gourd (gôrd), the fruit of a vine whose hard, dried shell is used for cups, bowls, and other utensils. *noun.*

gour·met (gu̇r′mā), a person who is expert in judging and choosing foods, wines, and the like. *noun.*

gov·ern (guv′ərn), **1** to rule; control; manage: *The election determined which party would govern the United States for four years.* **2** to determine or guide: *What reasons governed your decision? verb.*
[*Govern* comes from a Greek word meaning "to steer." From the idea of steering or directing the course of a ship developed the idea of ruling a people or nation.]

gov·ern·ess (guv′ər nis), a woman who teaches and trains children in their home. *noun, plural* **gov·ern·ess·es.**

gov·ern·ment (guv′ərn mənt), **1** the ruling of a country, state, district, or city: *Good government depends on informed citizens.* **2** a person or persons ruling a country, state, district, or city at any time: *The government of the United States consists of the President and the cabinet, the Congress, and the Supreme Court.* **3** a system of ruling: *The United States has a democratic form of government. noun.*

gov·er·nor (guv′ər nər), **1** an official elected as the head of a state of the United States. The governor of a state carries out the laws made by the state legislature. **2** an official appointed to rule a province or colony. *noun.*

gown (goun), **1** a woman's dress, especially a long fancy dress worn at parties. **2** a loose outer piece of clothing worn by graduating college students, judges, and others; robe. *noun.*

grab (grab), **1** to seize suddenly; snatch: *The dog grabbed the meat and ran.* **2** a snatching; sudden seizing: *I made a grab at the ball.* 1 *verb,* **grabs, grabbed, grab·bing;** 2 *noun.*

G

grace (grās), **1** beauty of form or movement: *The ballet dancer danced with much grace.* **2** a pleasing or agreeable quality: *They had all the social graces of a good host and hostess.* **3** a short prayer of thanks given before or after a meal. **4** to give grace or honor to: *The queen graced the ball with her presence.* 1-3 *noun,* 4 *verb,* **grac·es, graced, grac·ing.**

in one's good graces, favored or liked by: *I wonder if I am in the teacher's good graces.*

with good grace, pleasantly; willingly: *He obeyed the order with good grace.*

grace·ful (grās′fəl), **1** beautiful in form or movement: *a graceful dancer.* **2** pleasing; agreeable: *a graceful speech of thanks. adjective.*

gra·cious (grā′shəs), pleasant and kindly; courteous: *We were greeted in such a gracious manner that we immediately felt at ease. adjective.*

grack·le (grak′əl), a blackbird with shiny, black feathers. *noun.*

grackle—about 1 foot (30 centimeters) long

grade (grād), **1** a class in school: *the fifth grade.* **2** a degree in rank, quality, or value: *The best grade of milk is grade A.* **3** to sort; place according to class: *These apples are graded by size.* **4** a number or letter that shows how well one has done; mark: *My grade in English is B.* **5** to give a mark or grade to: *The teacher graded the papers.* **6** the slope of a road or railroad track: *a steep grade.* **7** to make more nearly level: *The road up that steep hill was graded.* 1,2,4,6 *noun,* 3,5,7 *verb,* **grades, grad·ed, grad·ing.**

grad·er (grā′dər), **1** a person or thing that grades. **2** a person who is in a certain grade at school: *a fifth grader. noun.*

grade school, an elementary school; grammar school.

grad·u·al (graj′ü əl), happening slowly by small steps or degrees; little by little: *This low hill has a gradual slope. adjective.*

grad·u·ate (graj′ü āt *for 1 and 3;* graj′ü it *for 2),* **1** to finish the course of a school or college and be given a diploma or paper saying so. **2** a person who has graduated and has a diploma. **3** to mark out in equal spaces for measuring: *Rulers are graduated in inches and centimeters.* 1,3 *verb,* **grad·u·ates, grad·u·at·ed, grad·u·at·ing;** 2 *noun.*

grad·u·a·tion (graj′ü ā′shən), **1** a graduating from a school or college. **2** the ceremony of graduating; graduating exercises. *noun.*

graft (graft), **1** to put a shoot or bud from one tree or plant into a slit in another tree or plant, so it will grow there as a part of it. **2** a shoot or bud used in grafting. A graft from a fine apple tree may be put on a worthless one to improve it. **3** to transfer a piece of skin or bone from one person or part of the body to another, so that it will grow there permanently. **4** a piece of skin or bone so transferred. 1,3 *verb,* 2,4 *noun.*

gra·ham (grā′əm), made from whole-wheat flour, including all the bran: *graham crackers. adjective.* [The word *graham* comes from Sylvester Graham, an American minister who lived from 1794 to 1851. He recommended the use of whole grains and vegetables in the diet.]

grain (grān), **1** the seed of wheat, oats, corn, and other cereal grasses. **2** one of the tiny bits of which sand, sugar, or salt is made up. **3** the smallest possible amount; tiniest bit: *There isn't a grain of truth in their story.* **4** the little lines and markings in wood or marble: *That mahogany table has a fine grain. noun.*

with a grain of salt, with a little doubt: *The story must be taken with a grain of salt.*

gram (gram), a unit of weight in the metric system. *noun.*

gram·mar (gram′ər), **1** the rules about the forms and uses of words in sentences. We study grammar to help us speak and write in a way that other people can understand. **2** the use of words according to these rules: *My English teacher's grammar is excellent. noun.*

grammar school, an elementary school.

gram·mat·i·cal (grə mat′ə kəl), of or according to the rules of grammar: *Our French teacher speaks grammatical English but has a French accent. "Between you and I" is a grammatical mistake; "between you and me" is correct. adjective.*

gran·ar·y (gran′ər ē *or* grā′nər ē), a place or building where grain is stored. *noun, plural* **gran·ar·ies.**

grand (grand), **1** large and of fine appearance: *The royal family lived in a grand palace.* **2** of very high or noble quality; dignified: *grand music, a grand old man.* **3** great; important; main: *I won a radio in the contest, but the grand prize was a new car.* **4** complete; including everything: *The grand total of all my purchases was $150.* **5** excellent; very good: *We had a grand time at the party. adjective.*

Grand Canyon, a very large and deep canyon of the Colorado River, in northern Arizona.

grand·child (grand′child′), a child of one's son or daughter. *noun, plural* **grand·chil·dren** (grand′chil′drən).

grand·dad (gran′dad′), a grandfather. *noun.*

grand·daugh·ter (grand′dô′tər), a daughter of one's son or daughter. *noun.*

gran·deur (gran′jər), greatness; majesty; nobility; splendor: *the grandeur of Niagara Falls. noun.*

grand·fa·ther (grand′fä′ŧHər), the father of one's father or mother. *noun.*

grandfather clock

a hat	i it	oi oil	ch child	a in about
ā age	ī ice	ou out	ng long	e in taken
ä far	o hot	u cup	sh she	ə = { i in pencil
e let	ō open	u̇ put	th thin	o in lemon
ē equal	ô order	ü rule	ᵺ then	u in circus
ėr term			zh measure	

grape·vine (grāp′vīn′), a vine that grapes grow on. *noun.*

graph (graf), **1** a line or diagram showing how one quantity depends on or changes with another. You could draw a graph to show how your weight has changed each year with your change in age. **2** to make a graph of. 1 *noun,* 2 *verb.*

graph (definition 1) This line **graph** shows the average growth in height of teenagers.

grandfather clock, a clock in a tall, wooden case, which stands on the floor.

grand jury, a jury of from 6 to 23 persons chosen to investigate accusations of crime and decide whether there is enough evidence for a trial in court.

grand·ma (grand′mä′), a grandmother. *noun.*

grand·moth·er (grand′muᵺ′ər), the mother of one's mother or father. *noun.*

grand·pa (grand′pä′), a grandfather. *noun.*

grand·par·ent (grand′per′ənt *or* grand′par′ənt), a grandfather or grandmother. *noun.*

grand·son (grand′sun′), a son of one's son or daughter. *noun.*

grand·stand (grand′stand′), the main seating place for people at an athletic field or parade. *noun.*

gran·ite (gran′it), a very hard gray or pink rock, much used for buildings and monuments. Granite is made of crystals of several different minerals and is formed when lava cools slowly underground. *noun.*

gran·ny (gran′ē), a grandmother. *noun, plural* **gran·nies.**

gra·no·la (grə nō′lə), a dry breakfast cereal of rolled oats, flavored with other things such as honey, chopped dried fruit, and nuts. *noun.*

grant (grant), **1** to allow; give what is asked: *to grant a request.* **2** to admit; accept without proof: *I grant that you are right so far.* **3** a gift, especially land or money given by the government: *The professor was given a research grant of $20,000.* 1,2 *verb,* 3 *noun.*

take for granted, to believe to be true; suppose: *We took for granted that the sailor could swim.*

grape (grāp), a small, round fruit, red, purple, or pale-green, that grows in bunches on a vine. Grapes are eaten raw or made into raisins, jelly, or wine. *noun.*

grape·fruit (grāp′früt′), the pale-yellow, juicy fruit of a tree grown in warm climates. Grapefruit are like oranges, but are larger and sourer. *noun, plural* **grape·fruit** *or* **grape·fruits.**

graph·ic (graf′ik), **1** lifelike; vivid: *Your graphic description of the English countryside made me feel as though I had been there myself.* **2** of or using pictures or diagrams: *graphic arts. adjective.*

graph·ics (graf′iks), pictures or diagrams made by a computer or video game. *noun plural.*

graph·ite (graf′īt), a soft, black form of carbon used for lead in pencils and for greasing machinery. *noun.*

[*Graphite* comes from a Greek word meaning "to write." Graphite was called this because it is used in pencils.]

grap·ple (grap′əl), to struggle; fight: *to grapple with a problem. The wrestlers grappled in the center of the ring. verb,* **grap·ples, grap·pled, grap·pling.**

grasp (grasp), **1** to seize and hold fast by closing the fingers around: *I grasped the sleeve of her coat as I fell.* **2** a seizing and holding tightly; clasp of the hand: *I almost lost my grasp on the rope.* **3** the power of seizing and holding; reach: *Success is within his grasp.* **4** to understand: *He grasped my meaning at once.* **5** an understanding: *She has a good grasp of arithmetic.* 1,4 *verb,* 2,3,5 *noun.*

grass (gras), **1** plants with green blades that cover fields, lawns, and pastures. Horses, cows, and sheep eat grass. **2** a plant that has jointed stems and long, narrow leaves. Wheat, corn, and sugar cane are grasses. **3** land covered with grass; lawn: *The children played on the grass.* noun, plural **grass·es.**

grass·hop·per (gras′hop′ər), an insect with wings and strong hind legs for jumping. *noun.*

grass·land (gras′land′), land with grass on it, used for pasture. *noun.*

grass·y (gras′ē), covered with grass. *adjective,* **grass·i·er, grass·i·est.**

grate[1] (grāt), **1** a framework of iron bars to hold burning fuel in a furnace or fireplace. **2** a framework of bars over a window or opening; grating. *noun.*

grate[2] (grāt), **1** to wear down or grind off in small pieces: *The cook grated the cheese before melting it.* **2** to make a harsh, jarring noise by rubbing: *The door grated on its old, rusty hinges.* **3** to have an annoying or unpleasant effect: *Their loud voices grate on my nerves.* verb, **grates, grat·ed, grat·ing.**

grate·ful (grāt′fəl), feeling kindly because of a favor received; thankful: *I am grateful for your help. adjective.*

grat·i·fi·ca·tion (grat′ə fə kā′shən), **1** a gratifying; satisfaction: *The gratification of a person's every wish is not always possible.* **2** something that pleases or satisfies: *Your faith in my ability is a gratification to me. noun.*

grat·i·fy (grat′ə fī), to please; to give pleasure or satisfaction to: *I was gratified to hear that you liked the scarf I knitted for you.* verb, **grat·i·fies, grat·i·fied, grat·i·fy·ing.**

gra·ting[1] (grā′ting), a grate; framework of parallel or crossed bars. Windows in a prison, bank, or ticket office often have gratings over them. *noun.*

gra·ting[2] (grā′ting), **1** irritating; unpleasant: *He had a grating habit of yawning noisily.* **2** harsh or jarring in sound: *a loud, grating voice. adjective.*

grat·i·tude (grat′ə tüd *or* grat′ə tyüd), a kindly feeling because of a favor received; desire to do a favor in return; thankfulness. *noun.*

grave[1] (grāv), **1** a hole dug in the ground where a dead body is to be buried. **2** any place of burial: *a watery grave. noun.*

grave[2] (grāv), **1** important; serious; critical: *a grave decision, a grave illness.* **2** solemn; dignified; sober: *a grave face. adjective,* **grav·er, grav·est.**

grav·el (grav′əl), pebbles and pieces of rock that are larger than grains of sand. Gravel is used for roads and paths. *noun.*

grave·yard (grāv′yärd′), a cemetery. *noun.*

grav·i·tate (grav′ə tāt′), to move or tend to move toward a body by the force of gravity: *The planets gravitate toward the sun.* verb, **grav·i·tates, grav·i·tat·ed, grav·i·tat·ing.**

grav·i·ta·tion (grav′ə tā′shən), the force or pull that makes all objects in the universe attract one another. Gravitation keeps the planets in their orbits around the sun. *noun.*

grav·i·ta·tion·al (grav′ə tā′shə nəl), of gravitation. *adjective.*

grav·i·ty (grav′ə tē), **1** the natural force that causes objects to move or tend to move toward the center of the earth. Gravity causes objects to have weight. **2** gravitation. **3** seriousness; importance: *The gravity of the situation was greatly increased by threats of war. noun.*

gra·vy (grā′vē), a sauce for meat, potatoes, or other food. It is made from the juice that comes out of meat during cooking. *noun, plural* **gra·vies.**

gray (grā), **1** a color that is a mixture of black and white. **2** having this color: *gray hair.* **3** dark; gloomy; dismal: *a gray, rainy day.* **1** *noun,* **2,3** *adjective.* Also spelled **grey.**

gray·ish (grā′ish), somewhat gray. *adjective.*

graze[1] (grāz), to feed on growing grass: *Cattle were grazing in the field.* verb, **graz·es, grazed, graz·ing.**

graze[2] (grāz), **1** to touch lightly in passing; rub lightly against: *The car grazed the garage door.* **2** to scrape the skin from: *She grazed her knee when she fell.* verb, **graz·es, grazed, graz·ing.**

grease (grēs *for 1 and 2;* grēs *or* grēz *for 3*), **1** soft, melted animal fat. **2** any thick, oily substance. **3** to put grease in or on: *to grease a cake pan. Please grease my car.* **1,2** *noun,* **3** *verb,* **greas·es, greased, greas·ing.**

greas·y (grē′sē *or* grē′zē), **1** having grease on it: *a greasy rag.* **2** containing much grease; oily: *Greasy food is hard to digest. adjective,* **greas·i·er, greas·i·est.**

great (grāt), **1** big; large: *a great forest, a great crowd.* **2** much; more than is usual: *great pain, great kindness.* **3** important; remarkable; famous: *a great singer, a great event, a great picture.* **4** very good; fine: *We had a great time at the party. adjective.*

Great Britain, England, Scotland, and Wales. Great Britain is the largest island of Europe.

Great Dane, a large, powerful, short-haired dog.

Great Dane
about 32 inches
(81 centimeters)
high at the shoulder

great-grand·child (grāt′grand′chīld′), a child of one's grandchild. *noun, plural* **great-grand·chil·dren** (grāt′grand′chil′dren).

great-grand·fa·ther (grāt′grand′fä′ᵺər), the father of one's grandparent. *noun.*

great-grand·moth·er (grāt′grand′muᵺ′ər), the mother of one's grandparent. *noun.*

great-grand·par·ent (grāt′grand′per′ənt *or* grāt′grand′par′ənt), a great-grandfather or a great-grandmother. *noun.*

Great Lakes, five very large lakes between the United States and Canada. The Great Lakes are named Ontario, Erie, Huron, Michigan, and Superior.

Great Lakes

a hat	i it	oi oil	ch child	⌈a in about
ā age	ī ice	ou out	ng long	e in taken
ä far	o hot	u cup	sh she	ə = ⟨ i in pencil
e let	ō open	u̇ put	th thin	o in lemon
ē equal	ô order	ü rule	ŦH then	⌊u in circus
ėr term			zh measure	

great·ly (grāt′lē), very much: *greatly feared. She greatly desired to be successful. adverb.*

great·ness (grāt′nis), **1** being great; bigness. **2** high place or power. **3** great mind or character. *noun.*

Great Plains, a region east of the Rocky Mountains in the United States and Canada. It is mostly pasture land.

Greece (grēs), a country in southeastern Europe. *noun.*

greed (grēd), a very strong desire to have a lot of something: *Their greed for money and success was never satisfied. noun.*

greed·i·ly (grē′dl ē), in a greedy manner. *adverb.*

greed·y (grē′dē), feeling a strong desire to have a lot of something: *The dictator was greedy for power and money. adjective,* **greed·i·er, greed·i·est.**

Greek (grēk), **1** of or having something to do with Greece, its people, or their language. **2** a person born or living in Greece. **3** the language of Greece. **1** *adjective,* **2,3** *noun.*

Word Source

Ancient <u>Greek</u> is the source of hundreds of English words, especially many of the terms we use in science. The following words came from Greek:

alphabet	dinosaur	metamorphosis
ameba	drama	meteorite
amphibian	electric	microscope
anthropology	elephant	octopus
astronaut	encyclopedia	panic
bacteria	galaxy	planet
Bible	govern	pope
church	gymnasium	rhinoceros
clinic	helicopter	skeleton
coma	hippopotamus	telephone
comet	lantern	thermometer
crater	licorice	truck
crocodile	marathon	xylophone
cyclone	marmalade	zoology
diagonal	melon	

green (grēn), **1** the color of most growing plants, grass, and the leaves of trees in summer. **2** having this color: *green paint.* **3** covered with growing plants, grass, or leaves: *green fields.* **4** not ripe; not fully grown: *Most green fruit is not good to eat.* **5** not trained; without experience: *Several of the players were green when the season started.* **6** ground covered with grass: *the village green.* **7 greens,** the leaves and stems of plants used for food: *beet greens.* **8** the very smooth area around the hole into which a player putts a golf ball. **1,6-8** *noun,* **2-5** *adjective.*

green·er·y (grē′nər ē), green plants, grass, or leaves. *noun.*

green·house (grēn′hous′), a building with a glass or plastic roof and sides, kept warm for growing plants; hothouse. *noun, plural* **green·hous·es** (grēn′hou′ziz).

green·ish (grē′nish), somewhat green. *adjective.*

green thumb, a remarkable ability to grow flowers and vegetables: *You certainly must have a green thumb to have such a beautiful garden.*

green·wood (grēn′wu̇d′), a forest in spring and summer when the trees are green with leaves. *noun.*

greet (grēt), **1** to speak or write to in a friendly, polite way; address in welcome; hail: *She greeted us with a friendly "Hello."* **2** to respond to: *His speech was greeted with cheers. verb.*

greet·ing (grē′ting), **1** the act or words of a person who greets somebody; welcome. **2 greetings,** friendly wishes on a special occasion. *noun.*

gre·nade (grə nād′), a small bomb which is thrown by hand or fired from a rifle. *noun.*

grew (grü). See **grow.** *It grew colder as the sun went down. verb.*

grey (grā). See **gray.** *noun, adjective.*

grey·hound (grā′hound′), a tall, slender dog with a long nose. Greyhounds can run very fast. *noun.*

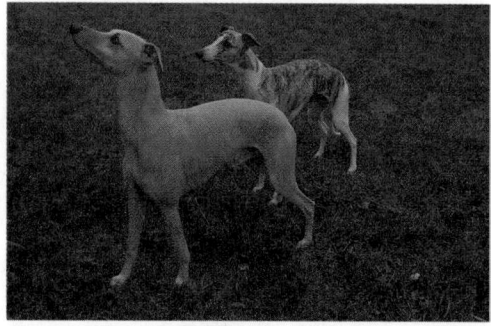
greyhound—about 28 inches (71 centimeters) at the shoulder

G

grid (grid), a pattern of evenly spaced lines running up and down and across. Grids are used on maps to locate places. *noun.*

grid·dle (grid′l), a heavy, flat metal pan or surface on which to cook pancakes, bacon, hamburgers, and similar foods. *noun.*

grid·i·ron (grid′ī′ərn), **1** a grill for broiling. **2** a football field. *noun.*

grief (grēf), great sadness caused by trouble or loss; deep sorrow. *noun.*

come to grief, to have trouble; fail.

griev·ance (grē′vəns), a real or imagined wrong; reason for being annoyed or angry: *He felt that the mechanics did a poor job and he reported his grievances to the owner of the garage. noun.*

grieve (grēv), to be very sad; make sad: *The children grieved over their kitten's death. The news of your illness grieved us. verb,* **grieves, grieved, griev·ing.**

griev·ous (grē′vəs), causing sadness; hard to bear: *My grandfather's death was a grievous loss to everyone in the family. adjective.*

grill (gril), **1** utensil with parallel bars for cooking directly over a fire. It is used to hold meat, fish, or fowl. **2** to cook on a grill; broil. **3** to question severely and persistently: *The detectives grilled several suspects concerning the crime.* **1** *noun,* **2,3** *verb.*

grille (gril), the metal or plastic piece that covers the opening in front of the radiator of an automobile. *noun.*

grim (grim), **1** stern; harsh; fierce: *My parents looked grim when they heard about the broken windows.* **2** not yielding; not relenting: *Though the runner was exhausted, she kept on with grim determination.* **3** horrible; frightful; ghastly: *As we walked past the cemetery, she made grim jokes about death and ghosts. adjective,* **grim·mer, grim·mest.**

gri·mace (grə mās′ *or* grim′is), **1** a twisting of the face: *a grimace caused by pain.* **2** to make faces:

grimace (definition 1)
a silly **grimace**

The clown grimaced at the children. **1** *noun,* **2** *verb,* **gri·mac·es, gri·maced, gri·mac·ing.**

grime (grīm), dirt rubbed deeply and firmly into a surface: *Soap and water removed only a little of the grime on the coal miner's hands. noun.*

grim·y (grī′mē), covered with grime; very dirty: *grimy hands. adjective,* **grim·i·er, grim·i·est.**

grin (grin), **1** to smile broadly: *She grinned and said, "Hello."* **2** a broad smile: *He gave me a friendly grin.* **1** *verb,* **grins, grinned, grin·ning; 2** *noun.*

grind (grīnd), **1** to crush into bits or powder: *That mill grinds corn into meal and wheat into flour.* **2** to sharpen, smooth, or wear by rubbing on something rough: *to grind an ax on a grindstone.* **3** to rub harshly together: *to grind one's teeth.* **4** long, hard work or study: *To some of the students, science was a grind.* **1-3** *verb,* **grinds, ground, grind·ing; 4** *noun.*

grind·stone (grīnd′stōn′), a flat, round stone set in a frame and turned by hand, foot, or a motor. It is used to sharpen tools, such as axes and knives, or to smooth and polish things. *noun.*

grip (grip), **1** a seizing and holding tight; tight grasp; firm hold: *The dog had a firm grip on the bone, and would not let go.* **2** to seize and hold tight; take a firm hold on: *The dog gripped the stick.* **3** a part to take hold of; handle. **4** firm control; power: *The country was in the grip of a severe drought.* **1,3,4** *noun,* **2** *verb,* **grips, gripped, grip·ping.**

gripe (grīp), **1** to complain: *He was always griping about something.* **2** a complaint. **1** *verb,* **gripes, griped, grip·ing; 2** *noun.*

gris·tle (gris′əl), a tough, elastic tissue found in meat; cartilage. *noun.*

grit (grit), **1** very fine bits of gravel or sand. **2** bravery; courage; endurance: *You showed a lot of grit when you stood up to that bully.* **3** to close tightly together; clench: *She gritted her teeth and plunged into the cold water.* **1,2** *noun,* **3** *verb,* **grits, grit·ted, grit·ting.**

grits (grits), coarsely ground grain, especially corn, with the outer covering removed. Grits are eaten boiled. *noun plural.*

grit·ty (grit′ē), of or containing grit; like grit; sandy. *adjective,* **grit·ti·er, grit·ti·est.**

griz·zled (griz′əld), grayish; gray: *a grizzled beard. adjective.*

griz·zly (griz′lē), a grizzly bear. *noun, plural* **griz·zlies.**

grizzly bear, a large, fierce, brownish-gray bear of western North America.

groan (grōn), **1** a sound made down in the throat that expresses grief, pain, or disapproval; deep, short moan: *When I tried to wake her, she rolled over and with a groan went back to sleep.* **2** to give a groan or groans: *The movers groaned as they lifted the piano.* **1** *noun,* **2** *verb.*

gro·cer (grō′sər), a person who sells food and household supplies. *noun.*

gro·cer·y (grō′sər ē), **1** a store that sells food and household supplies. **2 groceries,** articles of food

and household supplies sold by a grocer. *noun,*
plural **gro·cer·ies.**

grog·gy (grog′ē), **1** not steady; shaky; dazed: *A*
blow on the head made me groggy. **2** not
completely awake: *I had just awakened from a nap*
and still felt groggy. adjective, **grog·gi·er,**
grog·gi·est.

groom (grüm), **1** a person whose work is taking
care of horses. **2** to feed, rub down, brush, and
generally take care of horses. **3** to take care of
one's appearance; make neat and tidy: *He was*
always perfectly groomed. **4** a bridegroom.
1,4 *noun,* **2,3** *verb.*

groove (grüv), **1** a narrow channel or furrow,
especially one cut by a tool: *the grooves in a*
phonograph record. My desk has a groove for
pencils. **2** any similar channel; rut: *grooves in a dirt*
road. **3** to make a groove in: *The counter of the*
sink is grooved so that the water will run off.
1,2 *noun,* **3** *verb,* **grooves, grooved, groov·ing.**

groov·y (grü′vē), excellent; perfect; just right: *a*
groovy party. adjective, **groov·i·er, groov·i·est.**

grope (grōp), **1** to feel about with the hands: *He*
groped for a flashlight when the lights went out. **2** to
search blindly and uncertainly: *The detectives*
groped for some clue to the mysterious crime. **3** to
find by feeling about with the hands; feel one's
way slowly: *I groped my way across the dark*
room. verb, **gropes, groped, grop·ing.**

gross (grōs), **1** with nothing taken out; total;
whole; entire. Gross receipts are all the money
taken in before costs are deducted. **2** the total
amount. **3** twelve dozen; 144. **4** very easily seen;
glaring: *gross errors in adding.* **5** coarse; vulgar;
disgusting: *gross manners, gross language.*
1,4,5 *adjective,* **2,3** *noun, plural* **gross·es** for 2,
gross for 3.

gro·tesque (grō tesk′), odd or unnatural in
shape, appearance, or manner: *The book had*

<table>
<tr><td>a hat</td><td>i it</td><td>oi oil</td><td>ch child</td><td rowspan="6">a = {</td><td>a in about</td></tr>
<tr><td>ā age</td><td>ī ice</td><td>ou out</td><td>ng long</td><td>e in taken</td></tr>
<tr><td>ä far</td><td>o hot</td><td>u cup</td><td>sh she</td><td>i in pencil</td></tr>
<tr><td>e let</td><td>ō open</td><td>ú put</td><td>th thin</td><td>o in lemon</td></tr>
<tr><td>ē equal</td><td>ô order</td><td>ü rule</td><td>ᵺ then</td><td>u in circus</td></tr>
<tr><td>ėr term</td><td></td><td></td><td>zh measure</td><td></td></tr>
</table>

pictures of hideous dragons and other grotesque
monsters. *adjective.*

grouch (grouch), a grumbling and complaining
person. *noun, plural* **grouch·es.**

grouch·y (grou′chē), tending to grumble or
complain; surly; ill-tempered. *adjective,*
grouch·i·er, grouch·i·est.

ground[1] (ground), **1** the surface of the earth; soil:
A heavy blanket of snow covered the ground. **2** any
piece of land or region used for some purpose:
hunting grounds, a parade ground. **3 grounds,**
a the land, lawns, and gardens around a house or
school. **b** the small bits that sink to the bottom of
a drink such as coffee or tea; dregs; sediment.
4 in baseball, to hit a ball that rolls or bounces
along the ground. **5** to run aground; hit the bottom
or shore: *The boat grounded in shallow water.*
6 reason; foundation for what is said, thought, or
done: *What are your grounds for that statement?*
7 to fix firmly; establish: *This class is well*
grounded in arithmetic. His beliefs are grounded on
facts. **8** to connect an electric wire with the earth.
9 to keep a pilot or an aircraft from flying: *The*
pilot was grounded by injury. **10** to keep a child or
teenager from going out of the home for
entertainment, as punishment. **1-3,6** *noun,*
4,5,7-10 *verb.*

ground[2] (ground). See **grind.** *The miller ground*
the corn into meal. The wheat was ground to make
flour. verb.

ground·er (groun′dər), a baseball hit so as to
bounce or roll along the ground. *noun.*

ground·hog (ground′hôg′), a woodchuck.
Groundhogs grow fat in summer and sleep all
winter. **Groundhog Day,** February 2, is the day
when groundhogs are believed to come out of
their holes. If the sun is shining and the
groundhogs see their shadows, it is believed that
they go back in their holes and that winter lasts
for six more weeks. *noun.*

ground·wa·ter (ground′wô′tər), water that has
flowed into the ground and stayed there, usually
far below the surface. Groundwater supplies
springs and wells. *noun.*

group (grüp), **1** a number of persons or things
together: *A group of children were playing tag.* **2** a
number of persons or things belonging or classed
together: *Wheat, rye, and oats belong to the grain*
group. **3** to gather into a group or groups: *Group*
the numbers to form three columns. **1,2** *noun,*
3 *verb.*

group·ing (grü′ping), **1** the act or process of
putting persons or things into a group or groups.
2 a way of putting persons or things into a group
or groups. **3** a group. *noun.*

grotesque—There was a **grotesque** creature in the popular film.

269

G

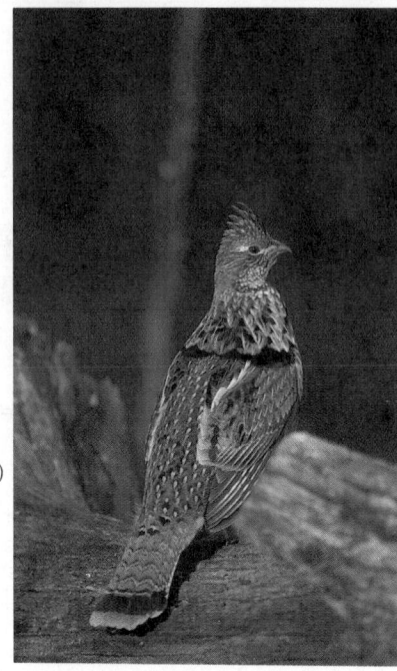

grouse
ruffed **grouse,**
17 inches
(43 centimeters)
long

grouse (grous), any of several birds that look like plump chickens with feathered legs. They are mostly brown, with some black or white feathers, and are hunted for food. *noun, plural* **grouse.**

grove (grōv), a group of trees standing together. An orange grove is an orchard of orange trees. *noun.*

grov·el (gruv′əl *or* grov′əl), to lie face downward; crawl at someone's feet; humble oneself: *The dog groveled before its owner when it was punished. verb.*

grow (grō), **1** to become bigger; increase: *Plants grow from seeds. Her business has grown fast.* **2** to live and become big: *Few trees grow in the desert.* **3** to plant and raise: *We grow cotton in the southern part of the United States.* **4** to become: *It grew cold. verb,* **grows, grew, grown, grow·ing.**
grow out of, to grow too large for; outgrow: *When I grew out of my jacket, I gave it to my little brother.*
grow up, to become full-grown; become an adult: *What will you be when you grow up?*

growl (groul), **1** to make a deep, low, angry sound: *The dog growled at the stranger.* **2** a sound like that made by a fierce dog; deep, warning snarl. **3** to grumble; complain: *The sailors growled about the poor food.* **4** to rumble: *Thunder growled in the distance.* **1,3,4** *verb,* **2** *noun.*

grown (grōn), **1** arrived at full growth. A grown person is an adult. **2** See **grow.** *The corn has grown very tall.* **1** *adjective,* **2** *verb.*

grown-up (grōn′up′), **1** arrived at full growth; adult: *a grown-up person.* **2** of, like, or suitable for adults: *grown-up manners.* **3** an adult: *The grown-ups helped the children decorate the room for the birthday party.* **1,2** *adjective,* **3** *noun.*

growth (grōth), **1** the process of growing; development. **2** a size, condition, or form produced by growing: *He will be a better athlete when he reaches full growth.* **3** what has grown or is growing: *A thick growth of bushes covered the ground. noun.*

grub (grub), **1** a soft, thick, wormlike larva of an insect, especially of a beetle. **2** to dig or dig up: *Pigs grub for roots.* **3** to work hard; toil. **4** food. **1,4** *noun,* **2,3** *verb,* **grubs, grubbed, grub·bing.**

grubs (definition 1)

grub·by (grub′ē), very dirty: *I put on grubby clothes to clean out the garage. adjective,* **grub·bi·er, grub·bi·est.**

grudge (gruj), **1** ill will; angry feeling against; dislike of long standing: *Our neighbors have had a grudge against us since we asked them to keep their dog out of our yard.* **2** to envy the possession of: *He grudged me my little prize even though he had won a better prize himself.* **3** to give or allow unwillingly: *My boss grudged me even a small raise in pay.* **1** *noun,* **2,3** *verb,* **grudg·es, grudged, grudg·ing.**
[*Grudge* comes from an old French word meaning "to grumble," or "to complain."]

gru·el (grü′əl), a nearly liquid food made by boiling oatmeal or other cereal in water or milk. *noun.*

gru·el·ing *or* **gru·el·ling** (grü′ə ling), very tiring; exhausting: *Mountain climbing can be grueling. adjective.*

grue·some (grü′səm), horrible; causing fear or horror: *a gruesome crime. adjective.*

gruff (gruf), **1** deep and harsh: *a gruff voice.* **2** rough; rude; unfriendly; bad-tempered: *a gruff manner. adjective.*

grum·ble (grum′bəl), **1** to complain in a bad-tempered way; mutter in discontent; find fault: *The students are always grumbling about the cafeteria's food.* **2** a mutter of discontent; bad-tempered complaint. **3** to make a low, heavy sound like far-off thunder. **1,3** *verb,* **grum·bles, grum·bled, grum·bling;** **2** *noun.*

grump·y (grum′pē), bad-tempered; grouchy: *I went to bed late last night and woke up this morning feeling grumpy. adjective,* **grump·i·er, grump·i·est.**

grunt (grunt), **1** the deep, hoarse sound that a hog makes. **2** a sound like this: *She lifted the heavy box with a grunt.* **3** to make this sound: *She grunted as she lifted the heavy box.* 1,2 *noun*, 3 *verb*.

guar·an·tee (gar′ən tē′), **1** a promise to pay or do something, especially to repair or replace goods if they are not as they should be: *We have a one-year guarantee on our new car.* **2** to promise to repair or replace something if it is not as it should be: *This company guarantees its clocks for a year.* **3** to promise to do something: *The store guaranteed to deliver my purchase by Friday.* **4** something that makes certain: *Failure to study is practically a guarantee of failure to learn.* 1,4 *noun*, 2,3 *verb*, **guar·an·tees, guar·an·teed, guar·an·tee·ing.**

guard (gärd), **1** to watch over; take care of; keep safe; defend: *The dog guarded the child day and night.* **2** to keep from escaping; check; hold back: *Guard the prisoners. Guard your tongue.* **3** a person or group that protects or watches. A soldier or group of soldiers protecting a person or place is a guard. **4** to take precautions: *Guard against cavities by brushing your teeth regularly.* **5** anything that gives protection; arrangement to give safety: *A helmet is a guard against head injuries.* **6** careful watch: *The shepherd kept guard over his sheep.* **7** a player at either side of the center in football. **8** either of two basketball players who usually play near the center of the court on offense. 1,2,4 *verb*, 3,5-8 *noun*.

off guard, not prepared to meet a sudden attack.

on guard, ready to defend or prevent; watchful: *A sentry should always be on guard.*

guard·i·an (gär′dē ən), **1** a person who takes care of another or of some special thing. **2** a person appointed by law to take care of the affairs of someone who is young or who cannot take care of his or her own affairs. *noun.*

Gua·te·ma·la (gwä′tə mä′lə), a country in Central America. *noun.*

guer·ril·la (gə ril′ə), **1** a member of a band of fighters who attack the enemy by sudden raids, ambushes, or the like. Guerrillas are not part of a regular army. **2** of or by guerrillas: *a guerrilla attack.* 1 *noun*, 2 *adjective*.

guess (ges), **1** to form an opinion when one does not know exactly: *Do you know this or are you just guessing?* **2** an opinion formed without really knowing: *My guess is that it will rain tomorrow.* **3** to get right by guessing: *Can you guess the answer to that riddle?* **4** to think; believe; suppose: *I guess I won't go with you after all.* 1,3,4 *verb*, 2 *noun*, *plural* **guess·es.**

guest (gest), **1** a person who is received and entertained at another's house or table; visitor. **2** a person who is staying at a hotel or motel. **3** a person invited to appear at a single performance of a television show, concert, or the like. *noun.*

guf·faw (gu fô′), **1** a burst of loud, coarse laughter: *The speaker's remarks were greeted with guffaws.* **2** to laugh loudly and coarsely: *The*

a hat	i it	oi oil	ch child	a in about
ā age	ī ice	ou out	ng long	e in taken
ä far	o hot	u cup	sh she	ə = i in pencil
e let	ō open	ů put	th thin	o in lemon
ē equal	ô order	ü rule	ŦH then	u in circus
ėr term			zh measure	

audience guffawed at the speaker's remarks. 1 *noun*, 2 *verb*.

guid·ance (gīd′ns), a guiding; direction; leadership: *Under her mother's guidance, she learned how to swim.* *noun.*

guide (gīd), **1** to show the way; lead; direct: *The scout guided us through the wilderness. The counselor guided him in the choice of a career.* **2** a person or thing that shows the way: *Tourists sometimes hire guides.* 1 *verb*, **guides, guid·ed, guid·ing;** 2 *noun.*

guided missile, a missile that is guided in flight to its target by radio signals from the ground or by automatic devices inside the missile.

guide word, a word put at the top of a page as a guide to the contents of the page. Guide words tell what are the first and last entries on the page. The guide words for this page are *grunt* and *guinea fowl.*

guild (gild), **1** a society for mutual aid or for some common purpose: *The author is a member of the Writers Guild.* **2** in the Middle Ages, a guild was a union of the people in one trade to keep standards high, and to look out for the interests of their trade. *noun.*

guile (gīl), crafty deceit; cunning; crafty behavior; sly tricks: *By guile the fox got the cheese from the crow.* *noun.*

guil·lo·tine (gil′ə tēn′), a machine for cutting off a person's head by a heavy blade that slides up and down in grooves made in two upright posts. *noun.*

[The *guillotine* was named for Joseph Guillotin, who lived from 1738 to 1814. He was a French doctor who suggested the use of this machine as a faster, more merciful way to execute criminals. It was first used in 1792 during the French Revolution.]

guilt (gilt), **1** the fact or condition of having done wrong; being guilty; being to blame: *The evidence proved their guilt.* **2** a feeling of having done wrong or being to blame: *Even though no one had seen him take the money, his guilt made him put it back.* *noun.*

guilt·y (gil′tē), **1** having done wrong; deserving to be blamed and punished: *The jury found her guilty of theft.* **2** knowing or showing that one has done wrong: *a guilty conscience, a guilty look.* *adjective*, **guilt·i·er, guilt·i·est.**

Guin·ea (gin′ē), a country in western Africa. *noun.*

guin·ea fowl (gin′ē foul′), a fowl somewhat like a pheasant, having dark-gray feathers with small, white spots. Guinea fowls are raised like chickens and used for food.

G

guinea pig
about 6 inches
(15 centimeters) long

guin·ea pig (gin′ē pig′), a small, fat animal with short ears and a short tail or no tail. Guinea pigs are kept as pets and used in scientific experiments.

guise (gīz), **1** a style of dress; garb: *The spy in the guise of a monk was not recognized by the enemy.* **2** appearance: *That theory is just an old idea in a new guise.* **3** pretense: *Under the guise of friendship they plotted treachery. noun.*

gui·tar (gə tär′), a musical instrument usually having six strings, played with the fingers or with a pick. *noun.*

gulch (gulch), a very deep, narrow valley with steep sides. *noun, plural* **gulch·es.**

gulf (gulf), **1** a large part of an ocean or sea with land around most of it: *The Gulf of Mexico is between Florida and Mexico.* **2** a wide separation: *The quarrel left a gulf between the old friends. noun.*

gull (gul), a graceful gray-and-white bird living on or near large bodies of water. A gull has long wings, webbed feet, and a thick, strong beak. *noun.*

gull—about 23 inches (58 centimeters) long

gul·li·ble (gul′ə bəl), easily deceived or cheated. *adjective.*

gul·ly (gul′ē), a ditch made by heavy rains or running water. *noun, plural* **gul·lies.**

gulp (gulp), **1** to swallow eagerly or greedily: *The hungry girl gulped down the bowl of soup.* **2** the act of swallowing: *He ate the cookie in one gulp.* **3** the amount swallowed at one time; mouthful: *She took a gulp of milk.* **4** to make a swallowing sound in the throat: *When I saw how far I had climbed up the tree, the thought of climbing back down made me gulp.* **1,4** *verb,* **2,3** *noun.*

gum[1] (gum), **1** the sticky juice of certain trees which is used to make candy and medicine and to make things stick together. **2** a tree that yields gum. **3** chewing gum. *noun.*

gum[2] (gum), the flesh around the teeth. *noun.*

gum·bo (gum′bō), a soup thickened with okra. *noun, plural* **gum·bos.**
[*Gumbo* comes from an African word, possibly a word meaning "okra."]

gum·drop (gum′drop′), a stiff, jellylike piece of candy. *noun.*

gun (gun), **1** weapon with a metal tube for shooting bullets or shells. Cannons, rifles, and pistols are guns. **2** anything resembling a gun in use or shape: *a spray gun.* **3** to shoot with a gun; hunt with a gun: *They went gunning for rabbits.* **4** to make something go faster; increase the speed of: *The truck driver gunned the engine to get up the hill.* **1,2** *noun,* **3,4** *verb,* **guns, gunned, gun·ning.**

gun·boat (gun′bōt′), a small warship that can be used in shallow water. *noun.*

gun·man (gun′mən), a person who uses a gun to rob or kill. *noun, plural* **gun·men.**

gun·ner (gun′ər), a member of the armed forces who handles and fires large guns. *noun.*

gun·pow·der (gun′pou′dər), a powder that explodes when touched with fire. Gunpowder is used in guns, blasting, and fireworks. *noun.*

gun·shot (gun′shot′), **1** a shot fired from a gun: *We heard gunshots.* **2** the distance that a gun will shoot: *The deer was within gunshot. noun.*

gun·wale (gun′l), the upper edge of a ship's or boat's side. *noun.*

gup·py (gup′ē), a very small fish of tropical fresh water, often kept in aquariums. The male is brightly colored. The female gives birth to live young instead of laying eggs. *noun, plural* **gup·pies.**
[*Guppy* was named for Robert Guppy. He was a British scientist of the West Indies, who sent the first samples of this fish to London in the 1800's.]

guppy—up to 2½ inches (6 centimeters) long

gur·gle (gėr′gəl), **1** to flow or run with a bubbling sound: *Water gurgles when it is poured out of a bottle or flows over stones.* **2** a bubbling sound. **3** to make a bubbling sound: *The baby gurgled happily.* **1,3** *verb,* **gur·gles, gur·gled, gur·gling; 2** *noun.*

gush (gush), **1** to rush out suddenly; pour out: *Oil gushed from the new well.* **2** a rush of water or other liquid from an enclosed space: *If you get a deep cut, there usually is a gush of blood.* **3** to talk in a silly way about one's interests or feelings. **1,3** *verb,* **2** *noun, plural* **gush·es.**

gush·er (gush′ər), an oil well that spouts a steady stream of oil without pumping. *noun.*

gust (gust), **1** a sudden, violent rush of wind: *A gush upset the small sailboat.* **2** an outburst of anger or other feeling: *gusts of laughter. noun.*

gut (gut), **1** the whole alimentary canal or one of its parts, such as the intestines or stomach. **2** a string made from the intestines of animals. Gut is used for violin strings and tennis rackets. *noun.*

gut·ter (gut′ər), **1** a channel or ditch along the side of a street or road to carry off water; low part of a street beside the sidewalk. **2** a channel or trough along the lower edge of a roof to carry off rain water. *noun.*

guy[1] (gī), a rope, chain, or wire attached to something to steady it. *noun.*

guy[2] (gī), a man or boy; fellow. *noun.*
[*Guy* was named for Guy Fawkes, who lived from 1570 to 1606. He was the leader of a plot to blow up the English Parliament in 1605. Images of him which were burned at annual celebrations of his capture were called guys. Later on, in the United States, the meaning "fellow" developed.]

Guy·an·a (gī an′ə), a country in northern South America. *noun.*

gym (jim), **1** gymnasium. **2** a class or course in which students are taught how to exercise and take care of the body; physical education. *noun.*

gym·na·si·um (jim nā′zē əm), a room or building fitted up for physical exercises or training and for indoor athletic sports. *noun.*
[*Gymnasium* comes from a Greek word meaning "naked." Greek athletes were naked during exercise and training.]

gym·nast (jim′nast), an expert in gymnastics. See picture. *noun.*

gym·nas·tics (jim nas′tiks), **1** exercises for developing the muscles, such as are done in a gymnasium. **2** a sport in which very difficult physical exercises are performed. **1** *noun plural,* **2** *noun singular.*

gyp (jip), to cheat; swindle: *He gypped me by selling me a watch that didn't run.* verb, **gyps, gypped, gyp·ping.**

gyp·sy (jip′sē), **1** Also, **Gypsy.** a person belonging to a wandering group of people who came from India long ago. **2** of the gypsies: *gypsy music.* **1** *noun, plural* **gyp·sies; 2** *adjective.* Also spelled **gipsy.**
[*Gypsy* was shortened from the name *Egyptian.* Gypsies were called this because they were supposed to have come from Egypt.]

gypsy moth, a brownish or white moth whose caterpillars damage trees by eating their leaves.

gy·rate (jī′rāt), to go in a circle or spiral; whirl; rotate: *A spinning top gyrates.* verb, **gy·rates, gy·rat·ed, gy·rat·ing.**

gyroscope

gy·ro·scope (jī′rə skōp), a wheel mounted inside a frame. When the wheel spins, it tends to resist any change in the direction in which its axle is pointed. Small gyroscopes are toy instruments. Large gyroscopes help to keep ships and aircraft steady on course. *noun.*

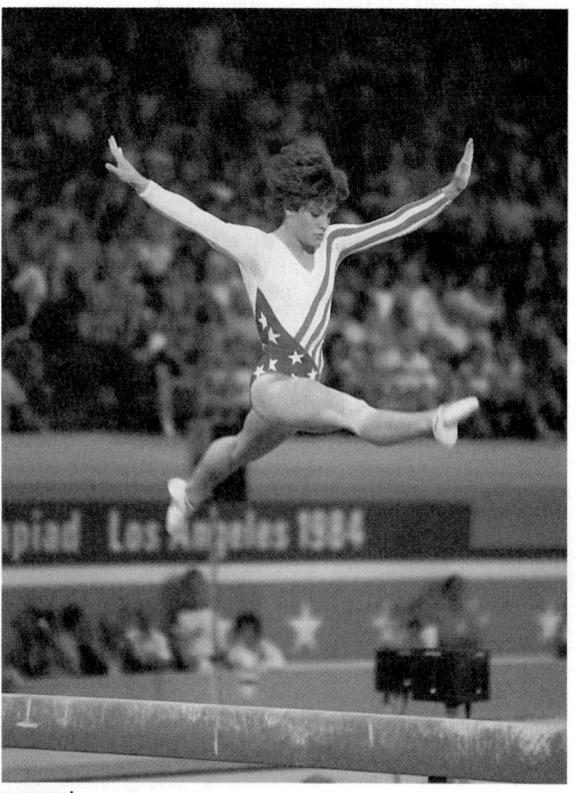

gymnast

G

H h

H or **h** (āch), the eighth letter of the English alphabet. *noun, plural* **H's** or **h's.**

ha (hä), **1** a cry of surprise, joy, or triumph: *"Ha! I've caught you!" cried the giant to Jack.* **2** the sound of a laugh: *"Ha! ha! ha!" laughed the boys. interjection.*

hab·it (hab′it), **1** custom; practice. Doing a thing over and over again makes it a habit. *Form the habit of brushing your teeth after every meal.* **2** the clothing worn by members of some religious orders. Monks and nuns often wear habits. *noun.*

hab·i·tat (hab′ə tat), a place where a living thing is naturally found: *The jungle is the habitat of monkeys. noun.*

hab·i·ta·tion (hab′ə tā′shən), **1** a place or building to live in. **2** a living in: *A barn is not fit for human habitation. noun.*

ha·bit·u·al (hə bich′ü əl), **1** done by habit: *a habitual smile. Habitual courtesy is always being polite to others.* **2** regular; steady: *A habitual reader reads a great deal.* **3** usual; customary: *The ice-cream man stood at his habitual corner. adjective.*

ha·ci·en·da (hä′sē en′də), a ranch or country house in Mexico or the southwestern United States. *noun.*

hack (hak), **1** to cut roughly: *She hacked the meat into jagged pieces.* **2** to give short, dry coughs. *verb.*

had (had). See **have.** *She had a party. A fine time was had by all who came. verb.*

had·dock (had′ək), a food fish of the northern Atlantic, somewhat like a cod, but smaller. *noun, plural* **had·dock** or **had·docks.**

had·n't (had′nt), had not.

hag (hag), **1** a very ugly old woman. **2** a witch. *noun.*

hag·gard (hag′ərd), looking worn from pain, fatigue, worry, or hunger; worn by care. *adjective.*

hai·ku (hī′kü), a poem of three lines and containing only 17 syllables. *noun, plural* **hai·ku.**

Word History

haiku *Haiku* comes from two Japanese words meaning "play" and "poem."

The falling flower
I saw drift back to the branch
Was a butterfly.

hail¹ (hāl), **1** small, roundish pieces of ice coming down from the clouds in a shower; frozen rain: *Hail fell with such violence that it broke windows.* **2** to fall in hail: *Sometimes it hails during a summer thunderstorm.* **3** a shower like hail: *A hail of bullets met the soldiers.* **4** to pour down in a shower like hail: *The angry crowd hailed insults at the speaker.* 1,3 *noun,* 2,4 *verb.*

hail² (hāl), **1** to greet; cheer; shout in welcome to: *The crowd hailed the winner.* **2** a shout of welcome; greeting; cheer. **3** greetings! welcome!: *Hail to the winner!* **4** to call out or signal to: *I hailed a taxi to take me to the airport.* 1,4 *verb,* 2 *noun,* 3 *interjection.*

hail from, to come from: *She hails from Boston.*

hail·stone (hāl′stōn′), a frozen drop of rain. Hailstones are usually very small, but sometimes they are as big as marbles. *noun.*

hair (her *or* har), **1** a fine threadlike growth from the skin of people and animals. **2** a mass of such growths: *I combed my hair.* **3** a fine growth from the outer layer of plants. *noun.*

hair·brush (her′brush′ *or* har′brush′), a stiff brush for smoothing the hair. *noun, plural* **hair·brush·es.**

hair·cut (her′kut′ *or* har′kut′), the act or manner of cutting the hair. *noun.*

hair·do (her′dü′ *or* har′dü′), a way of arranging the hair. *noun, plural* **hair·dos.**

hair·less (her′lis *or* har′lis), without hair. *adjective.*

haggard—Poverty, pain, and worry made the woman look **haggard.**

hair·y (her′ē *or* har′ē), covered with hair; having much hair: *hairy hands, a plant with hairy leaves. adjective,* **hair·i·er, hair·i·est.**

hale (hāl). **hale and hearty,** strong and well; healthy: *Grandpa is still hale and hearty at seventy. adjective.*

half (haf), **1** one of two equal parts: *A half of 4 is*

2. *Two halves make a whole.* **2** being one of two equal parts: *a half pound, a half hour.* **3** to a half of the full amount or degree: *a glass half full of milk.* **4** one of the two equal periods of play in certain games, such as football, basketball, or soccer. **5** partly; not completely: *I was only half awake when the phone rang. The potatoes were half cooked.* 1,4 *noun, plural* **halves**; 2 *adjective,* 3,5 *adverb.*

half past, (in stating the time of day) half an hour past the hour named: *Our school bus leaves at half past seven.*

not half bad, fairly good.

half·back (haf′bak′), a football player who runs with the ball, blocks for another runner, or tries to catch a pass. *noun.*

half brother, a brother related through one parent only.

half dollar, a coin of the United States and Canada, worth 50 cents.

half·heart·ed (haf′här′tid), lacking courage, interest, or enthusiasm: *I made a halfhearted attempt to finish my work before dinner. adjective.*

half-mast (haf′mast′), a position halfway or part way down from the top of a mast or staff. A flag is lowered to half-mast as a mark of respect for someone who has died or as a signal of distress. *noun.*

half-moon (haf′mün′), the moon when only half of its surface appears bright. *noun.*

half sister, a sister related through one parent only.

half·way (haf′wā′), **1** half the way: *The rope reached only halfway around the tree.* **2** partially; not completely: *a job that is halfway finished, a halfway satisfactory answer.* **3** midway: *Chicago was the halfway point in our trip from New York to Denver.* **4** not going far enough; incomplete: *Fires cannot be prevented by halfway measures.* 1,2 *adverb,* 3,4 *adjective.*

meet halfway, to do one's share to agree or be friendly with: *I'll meet you halfway and pay for the bat if you will buy the ball.*

hal·i·but (hal′ə bət), a very large flatfish, much used for food. Halibut sometimes weigh several hundred pounds. *noun, plural* **hal·i·but** or **hal·i·buts.**

[Halibut were commonly eaten on holy days, or religious festival days. For this reason, people in the Middle Ages in England used words meaning "holy" and "flatfish" to refer to this fish.]

Hal·i·fax (hal′ə faks), the capital of Nova Scotia, Canada. *noun.*

hall (hôl), **1** a way for going through a building: *A hall ran the length of the upper floor of the house.* **2** a passage or room at the entrance of a building: *Leave your umbrella in the hall.* **3** a large room for holding meetings, parties, or banquets: *No hall in town was large enough for the crowd gathered to hear the famous singer.* **4** a building for public business or meetings: *The mayor's office is in the town hall. noun.*

Hal·ley's com·et (hal′ēz kom′it), a comet

a hat	i it	oi oil	ch child	⎧ a in about
ā age	ī ice	ou out	ng long	⎪ e in taken
ä far	o hot	u cup	sh she	ə = ⎨ i in pencil
e let	ō open	u̇ put	th thin	⎪ o in lemon
ē equal	ô order	ü rule	ᴛʜ then	⎩ u in circus
ėr term			zh measure	

seen about every 76 years. It was seen in 1910 and in 1986.

[*Halley's* comet was named for Edmund Halley, who lived from 1656 to 1742. He was an English astronomer who first predicted the year that the comet would return to a point where it could be seen from Earth.]

hal·low (hal′ō), to make holy or sacred: *"Hallowed be Thy name." verb.*

Hal·low·een or **Hal·low·e'en** (hal′ō ēn′), the evening of October 31. *noun.*

hall·way (hôl′wā′), **1** a hall. **2** a passageway or room at the entrance of a building. *noun.*

ha·lo (hā′lō), **1** a ring of light around the sun, moon, or other shining body. **2** a golden circle or disk of light represented about the head of a saint or angel in pictures or statues. *noun, plural* **ha·los** or **ha·loes.**

halo (definition 2)

halt (hôlt), **1** to stop for a time: *The hikers halted and rested from their climb. The store halted deliveries during the strike.* **2** a stop for a time: *When there is a strike all work comes to a halt.* 1 *verb,* 2 *noun.*

hal·ter (hôl′tər), **1** a rope or strap for leading or tying an animal. **2** a blouse worn by women and girls which fastens behind the neck and across the back and leaves the arms and back bare. *noun.*

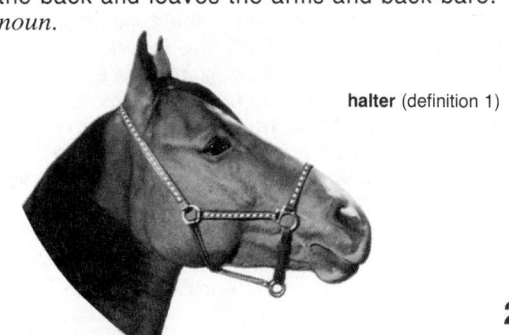
halter (definition 1)

H

halve (hav), **1** to divide into two equal parts; share equally: *He and I agreed to halve expenses on our trip.* **2** to reduce to half: *The new machine will halve the time and cost of doing the work by hand.* verb, **halves, halved, halv·ing.**

halves (havz), more than one half. Two halves make one whole. noun plural.

ham (ham), **1** meat from the upper part of a hog's hind leg, usually salted and smoked. **2** an amateur radio operator. noun.

ham·burg·er (ham′bèr′gər), **1** ground beef, usually shaped into round flat cakes and fried or broiled. **2** a sandwich made with hamburger, usually in a roll or bun. noun.
[*Hamburger* comes from a German word meaning "of Hamburg." Hamburg is a city in northern Germany.]

ham·let (ham′lit), a small village; little group of houses in the country. noun.

ham·mer (ham′ər), **1** a tool with a metal head and a handle, used to drive nails and to beat metal into shape. **2** something shaped or used like a hammer. The hammer of a gun explodes the charge. **3** to drive, hit, or work with a hammer: *I hammered a nail into the wall to hold up a picture.* **4** to beat into shape with a hammer: *The silver was hammered into bowls.* **5** to hit again and again: *The teacher hammered on the desk with a ruler to get the class to quiet down.* 1,2 noun, 3-5 verb.

ham·mer·head (ham′ər hed′), a shark whose wide head looks somewhat like a double-headed hammer. noun.

hammerhead—up to 15 feet (4½ meters) long

ham·mock (ham′ək), a hanging bed or couch made of canvas or a net of cord. noun.

ham·per[1] (ham′pər), to get in the way of; hold back; hinder: *Wet wood hampered our efforts to start the campfire.* verb.

ham·per[2] (ham′pər), a large basket with a cover: *a picnic hamper, a laundry hamper.* noun.

ham·ster (ham′stər), an animal somewhat like a mouse, but larger. Hamsters have a short tail and large cheek pouches. They are often kept as pets. noun.

hand (hand), **1** the end part of the arm, which takes and holds objects. Each hand has four fingers and a thumb. **2** a thing like a hand: *the hands of a clock or watch.* **3** a hired worker who uses his or her hands: *a factory hand.* **4** to give with the hand; pass: *Please hand me a spoon.* **5 hands,** possession; control: *This property is no longer in my hands.* **6** a part or share in doing something: *She had no hand in the matter.* **7** a side: *There was a small table at my left hand.* **8** a style of handwriting: *He writes in a clear hand.* **9** a skill; ability: *The artist's work showed a master's hand.*

10 a round of applause or clapping: *The crowd gave the winner a big hand.* **11** a promise of marriage: *He asked the king for his daughter's hand.* **12** the breadth of a hand; 4 inches: *This horse is 18 hands high.* **13** the cards held by a player in one round of a card game. **14** a single round in a card game. **15** of, for, by, or in the hand: *a hand mirror, hand weaving, a hand pump.* 1-3,5-14 noun, 4 verb, 15 adjective.

at hand, within reach; near: *When I type I always keep an eraser at hand.*

at second hand, from the knowledge or experience of another: *The story he heard at second hand proved to be untrue.*

by hand, by using the hands, not machinery: *Shoes were once made by hand, but today most of them are made by machine.*

hand down, to pass along: *Great-grandmother's ring is handed down to the oldest child in the family.*

hand in, to give; deliver: *Notebooks should be handed in at the end of class.*

hand out, to give out; distribute: *Who would like to help me hand out our new dictionaries?*

hand over, to give to another; deliver: *The passengers handed over their tickets to the conductor.*

have one's hands full, to be very busy; have all one can do: *The teacher has her hands full with such a large class.*

lend a hand, to help: *I asked my friend to lend me a hand with my homework.*

on hand, 1 within reach; near: *Try to be on hand when I need you.* **2** ready: *We have bandages on hand in case of an accident.*

on the other hand, from the opposite point of view: *On the other hand, it costs too much money.*

out of hand, out of control: *Don't let your temper get out of hand.*

hand·bag (hand′bag′), **1** a woman's small bag for money, keys, and cosmetics; purse. **2** a small bag to hold clothes and other things. noun.

hand·ball (hand′bôl′), **1** a game played by hitting a small, hard ball against a wall with the hand. **2** a ball used in this game. noun.

hand·bill (hand′bil′), a notice or advertisement, usually printed on one page, that is to be handed out to people: *We got information about the sale from a handbill.* noun.

hand·book (hand′bùk′), a small book of information or directions: *a handbook on birds, a handbook on automobile repairs.* noun.

hand·cuff (hand′kuf′), **1** one of two steel rings joined by a short chain and locked around the wrists of a prisoner. **2** to put handcuffs on. 1 noun, 2 verb.

hand·ful (hand′fùl′), **1** as much or as many as the hand can hold: *a handful of candy.* **2** a small number or quantity: *Only a handful of football fans sat watching the game.* noun, plural **hand·fuls.**

hand·i·cap (han′dē kap′), **1** something that puts a person at a disadvantage; something that hinders: *A sore throat was a handicap to the singer.*

2 to put at a disadvantage; hinder: *The swimmer was handicapped by a sore arm.* **3** a race, contest, or game in which better contestants are given special disadvantages and the rest are given special advantages, so that all have an equal chance to win. **4** the advantage or disadvantage given in such a race, contest, or game: *A runner with a handicap of 5 yards in a 100-yard dash must run either 95 yards or 105 yards.* 1,3,4 *noun,* 2 *verb,* **hand·i·caps, hand·i·capped, hand·i·cap·ping.**

hand·i·capped (han′dē kapt′), **1** having a physical or mental disability. **2 the handicapped,** people with physical or mental disabilities. 1 *adjective,* 2 *noun.*

hand·i·craft (han′dē kraft′), a trade or art requiring skill with the hands: *Weaving baskets from willow branches is a handicraft. noun.*

hand·i·work (han′dē werk′), the work done by a person's hands: *This workbench is my dad's handiwork. noun.*

hand·ker·chief (hang′kər chif), a soft, usually square piece of cloth used for wiping the nose, face, or hands. *noun.*

han·dle (han′dl), **1** the part of a thing made to be held or grasped by the hand. Spoons, pitchers, hammers, and pails have handles. **2** to touch, feel, or use with the hand: *I handled the old book carefully to avoid tearing the pages.* **3** to manage; direct: *The rider handled the horse well.* **4** to behave or act when handled: *This car handles easily.* **5** to treat; deal with: *The teacher handled discipline problems with ease.* **6** to deal in; trade in; buy and sell: *That store handles meat and groceries.* 1 *noun,* 2-6 *verb,* **han·dles, han·dled, han·dling.**

han·dle·bar (han′dl bär′). Often, **handlebars.** the curved bar on a bicycle or motorcycle that the rider holds and steers by. *noun.*

hand·made (hand′mād′), made by hand, not by machine: *handmade pottery. adjective.*

hand·out (hand′out′), a portion of food, clothing, or money handed out: *The beggar asked for a handout. noun.*

hand·rail (hand′rāl′), a railing used as a guard or support on a stairway or platform. *noun.*

hand·shake (hand′shāk′), the act of clasping and shaking each other's hands in friendship, agreement, or greeting. *noun.*

hand·some (han′səm), **1** good-looking; pleasing in appearance. We usually say that a man is handsome, but that a woman is pretty or beautiful. **2** fairly large; considerable: *A thousand dollars is a handsome sum of money.* **3** generous: *They gave the school a handsome gift of two hundred dollars. adjective,* **hand·som·er, hand·som·est.**

hand·spring (hand′spring′), a somersault made by springing onto the hands, flipping the body over backwards, and landing on the feet. *noun.*

hand·writ·ing (hand′rī′ting), **1** writing by hand; writing with pen or pencil: *The entire novel was in the author's own handwriting; none of it was typewritten.* **2** a manner or style of writing: *He*

a hat	i it	oi oil	ch child	a in about
ā age	ī ice	ou out	ng long	e in taken
ä far	o hot	u cup	sh she	ə = i in pencil
e let	ō open	u̇ put	th thin	o in lemon
ē equal	ô order	ü rule	ŦH then	u in circus
ėr term			zh measure	

recognized his mother's handwriting on the envelope. noun.

hand·y (han′dē), **1** easy to reach or use; saving work; useful: *There were handy shelves near the kitchen sink.* **2** skillful with the hands: *He is handy with tools. adjective,* **hand·i·er, hand·i·est.**

hang (hang), **1** to fasten or be fastened to something above: *Hang your cap on the hook. The swing hangs from a tree.* **2** to fasten or be fastened so as to leave swinging freely: *to hang a door on its hinges.* **3** to put to death by hanging with a rope around the neck. **4** to droop; bend down: *She hung her head in shame.* **5** to cover or decorate with things that are fastened to something above: *The walls were hung with pictures.* **6** to depend: *His future hangs on the court's decision.* **7** the way in which a thing hangs: *There's something wrong with the hang of this coat.* **8** the way of using or doing: *Riding a bicycle is easy after you get the hang of it.* **9** idea; meaning: *After studying an hour I finally got the hang of the lesson.* 1-6 *verb,* **hangs, hung** (or, usually, **hanged** for 3), **hang·ing;** 7-9 *noun.*

hang on, 1 to hold tight: *Hang on to my hand going down these steep stairs.* **2** to wait for a short time, especially when telephoning: *Please hang on while I check the calendar.*

hang up, 1 to put on a hook, hanger, peg, or the like: *Please hang up your clothes carefully.* **2** to end a telephone conversation by putting the receiver back in place: *I have to hang up now. Good-by.*

hang·ar (hang′ər), a storage building for aircraft. *noun.*

hang·er (hang′ər), a thing on which something else is hung: *a coat hanger. noun.*

hang·ing (hang′ing), **1** death by hanging with a rope around the neck. **2** a thing that hangs from a window, wall, or bed. Curtains and draperies are hangings. **3** fastened to something above: *a hanging basket of flowers.* 1,2 *noun,* 3 *adjective.*

hang·man (hang′mən), a person who puts condemned criminals to death by hanging them. *noun, plural* **hang·men.**

hang·nail (hang′nāl′), a bit of skin that hangs partly loose near a fingernail. *noun.*

hank (hangk), a coil or loop: *a hank of hair. noun.*

Ha·nuk·kah (hä′nə kə), a yearly Jewish festival that lasts eight days, mostly in December. It celebrates the recapture of the holy Jewish Temple many centuries ago. *noun.* [This festival, called the Feast of Dedication, comes directly from a Hebrew word meaning "dedication." The festival honors the memory of the dedication of the Temple again to the worship of God.]

H

hap·haz·ard (hap/haz/ərd), **1** not planned; random: *Haphazard answers are often wrong.* **2** by chance; at random: *Papers were scattered haphazard on the desk.* **1** *adjective,* **2** *adverb.*

hap·pen (hap/ən), **1** to take place; occur: *What happened at the party yesterday?* **2** to be or take place by chance: *Accidents will happen.* **3** to have the fortune; chance: *I happened to find my old diary yesterday.* **4** to be done: *Something has happened to this lock; the key won't turn. verb.*
happen on, 1 to meet: *The two friends happened on each other by chance.* **2** to find: *She happened on a dime while looking for her ball.*

hap·pen·ing (hap/ə ning), something that happens; event: *The evening newscast reviewed the happenings of the day. noun.*

hap·pi·ly (hap/ə lē), **1** in a happy manner; with pleasure, joy, and gladness: *They lived happily forever after.* **2** by luck; with good fortune: *Happily, I saved you from falling. adverb.*

hap·pi·ness (hap/ē nis), a being happy; gladness. *noun.*

hap·py (hap/ē), **1** feeling as you do when you are well and are having a good time; glad; pleased; contented: *She is happy in her work.* **2** showing that one is glad: *a happy smile, a happy look.* **3** lucky: *By a happy chance, I found the money I lost yesterday. adjective,* **hap·pi·er, hap·pi·est.**

hap·py-go-luck·y (hap/ē gō luk/ē), trusting to luck; carefree; easy going: *The happy-go-lucky student was not interested in getting high marks. adjective.*

har·ass (har/əs *or* hə ras/), **1** to trouble by repeated attacks: *Pirates harassed the villages along the coast.* **2** to disturb; worry: *The heat and the flies harassed us on the journey. verb.*

har·bor (här/bər), **1** a place of shelter for ships. **2** to give shelter to: *The dog's shaggy hair harbors fleas.* **3** to have and keep in the mind: *It's never good to harbor a grudge.* **1** *noun,* **2,3** *verb.*

hard (härd), **1** solid and firm to the touch; not soft: *a hard nut.* **2** firmly; solidly: *Don't hold my hand so hard.* **3** not yielding to influence; stern: *a hard master.* **4** needing much ability, effort, or time; difficult or troublesome: *a hard job, a hard lesson, a hard person to get along with.* **5** with difficulty: *The swimmer was breathing hard after he finished the race.* **6** acting with energy; industrious; energetic: *He is a hard worker and gets a lot done.* **7** with effort: *I worked hard on this project.* **8** with violence or vigor: *It is raining hard.* **9** violent or vigorous: *a hard storm.* **10** severe; causing much pain, trouble, or care: *We had a hard winter last year. When my parents were out of work, we had a hard time.* **11** severely; badly: *It will go hard with you if you are lying.* **12** containing mineral salts that keep soap from forming suds: *hard water.* **1,3,4,6,9,10,12** *adjective,* **2,5,7,8,11** *adverb.*
hard of hearing, somewhat deaf.

hard-boiled (härd/boild/), **1** boiled until hard: *hard-boiled eggs.* **2** not easily moved by the feelings; tough; rough. *adjective.*

hard coal, coal that burns with very little smoke or flame; anthracite.

hard·en (härd/n), to make or become hard: *When the candy cooled, it hardened. verb.*

hard·head·ed (härd/hed/id), **1** not easily excited or deceived; practical; clever. **2** stubborn; obstinate. *adjective.*

hard·heart·ed (härd/här/tid), without pity; cruel; unfeeling. *adjective.*

hard·ly (härd/lē), **1** only just; not quite; barely: *We hardly had time to eat breakfast. I am hardly strong enough to lift this heavy box.* **2** probably not: *They will hardly come in all this rain. adverb.*

hard·ship (härd/ship), something hard to bear; hard condition of living: *Hunger, cold, and sickness were among the hardships of pioneer life. noun.*

hard·ware (härd/wer/ *or* härd/war/), **1** articles made from metal. Locks, hinges, nails, screws, or knives are hardware. **2** a computer and any machine used with it, such as a disk drive or printer. *noun.*

hard·wood (härd/wud/), a hard, compact wood. Oak, cherry, maple, ebony, and mahogany are hardwoods. *noun.*

har·dy (här/dē), able to bear hard treatment; strong; robust: *Cold weather does not kill hardy plants. adjective,* **har·di·er, har·di·est.**

hare (her *or* har), an animal with long ears, a divided upper lip, a short tail, and long hind legs. A hare is very much like a rabbit, but larger. *noun, plural* **hares** *or* **hare.**

harm (härm), **1** something that causes pain or loss; injury; damage: *He slipped and fell down but suffered no harm.* **2** an evil; wrong: *It was an accident; she meant no harm.* **3** to damage; injure; hurt: *Do not pick or harm the flowers in the park.* **1,2** *noun,* **3** *verb.*

harm·ful (härm/fəl), causing harm; injurious; hurtful: *harmful germs. adjective.*

harm·less (härm/lis), causing no harm; not harmful: *It's only a harmless spider. adjective.*

har·mon·i·ca (här mon/ə kə), a small musical instrument with metal reeds. It is played by breathing in and out through a set of openings. *noun.*

har·mo·ni·ous (här mō/nē əs), **1** agreeing in feelings, ideas, or actions; getting on well together: *The children played together in a harmonious group.* **2** going well together: *A beautiful picture has harmonious colors.* **3** sweet-sounding; musical: *the harmonious sounds of a chorus. adjective.*

har·mo·nize (här/mə nīz), **1** to bring into harmony or agreement; make harmonious: *We harmonized the two plans by using parts of each one.* **2** to be in harmony or agreement: *The colors used in the room harmonized to give a pleasing effect.* **3** to add tones to a melody to make chords in music. **4** to sing or play in harmony: *We like to get together and harmonize before choir practice. verb,* **har·mo·niz·es, har·mo·nized, har·mo·niz·ing.**

har·mo·ny (här/mə nē), **1** an agreement in

harmony (definition 1)
They all lived together in perfect **harmony.**

a hat	i it	oi oil	ch child	⎰a in about
ā age	ī ice	ou out	ng long	e in taken
ä far	o hot	u cup	sh she	ə = ⎨ i in pencil
e let	ō open	u̇ put	th thin	o in lemon
ē equal	ô order	ü rule	ŦH then	⎱u in circus
ėr term			zh measure	

Har·ris·burg (har′is bėrg′), the capital of Pennsylvania. *noun.*

har·row (har′ō), **1** a heavy farm instrument with iron teeth or upright disks. Harrows are used to break up ground into fine pieces before planting seeds. **2** to pull a harrow over land: *As soon as we finish plowing and harrowing the field, we must sow the wheat.* **1** *noun,* **2** *verb.*

harrow (definition 1)
harpoon (definition 1)

feelings, ideas, or actions; getting on well together. **2** going well together: *In a beautiful landscape there is harmony of the different colors.* **3** the sounding together of musical tones in a chord. *noun, plural* **har·mo·nies.**

har·ness (här′nis), **1** the leather straps, bands, and other pieces used to hitch a horse or other animal to a carriage, wagon, or plow. **2** to put a harness on: *Harness the horse.* **3** to control and put to work or use: *Windmills can harness the power of the wind to pump water.* **1** *noun, plural* **har·ness·es; 2,3** *verb.*

harp (härp), a large stringed musical instrument. It is played by plucking the strings with the fingers. *noun.*

harp·ist (här′pist), a person who plays a harp. *noun.*

har·poon (här pün′), **1** a spear with a rope tied to it. It is used for catching whales and other sea animals. **2** to strike, catch, or kill with a harpoon. **1** *noun,* **2** *verb.*

harp·si·chord (härp′sə kôrd), a musical instrument with a keyboard like a piano. It has a tinkling sound from its strings being plucked by leather or quill points instead of being struck by hammers. *noun.*

harpsichord

harsh (härsh), **1** rough to the touch, taste, eye, or ear: *a harsh voice, a harsh climate.* **2** cruel; unfeeling; severe: *a harsh judge. adjective.*

Hart·ford (härt′fərd), the capital of Connecticut. *noun.*

har·vest (här′vist), **1** a reaping and gathering in of grain and other food crops. **2** to gather in and bring home for use: *to harvest wheat.* **3** one season's yield of any natural product; crop: *The clam harvest was small this year.* **1,3** *noun,* **2** *verb.*

har·vest·er (här′və stər), **1** a person who works in a harvest field; reaper. **2** a machine for harvesting crops, especially grain. *noun.*

H

harvest moon, the full moon at harvest time or about September 23.

has (haz). See **have.** *Who has my book? He has been sick. verb.*

hash (hash), **1** a mixture of cooked meat, potatoes, and other vegetables, chopped into small pieces and fried or baked. **2** a mess; jumble; muddle: *I made such a hash of the job that it had to be done over. noun.*

has·n't (haz'nt), has not.

haste (hāst), **1** a trying to be quick; hurry: *All my haste was of no use; I missed the bus anyway.* **2** quickness without thought or care; rashness: *Haste makes waste. noun.*

make haste, to hurry; be quick: *Make haste or you will miss your train.*

has·ten (hā'sn), to hurry; be quick or cause to be quick; speed: *Sunshine and rest hastened my recovery from illness. She hastened to explain that she had not meant to be rude. verb.*

hast·i·ly (hā'stl ē), **1** in a hurried way; quickly and not very carefully: *He glanced hastily at his watch.* **2** rashly: *A decision to change jobs should not be made hastily. adverb.*

hast·y (hā'stē), **1** quick; hurried: *He gave his watch a hasty glance and ran for the train.* **2** rash; not well thought out: *A hasty decision may cause unhappiness. adjective,* **hast·i·er, hast·i·est.**

hat (hat), a covering for the head when outdoors. A hat usually has a crown and a brim. *noun.*

hatch[1] (hach), **1** to bring forth young from an egg or eggs: *A hen hatches chickens.* **2** to come out from the egg: *Three of the chickens hatched today.* **3** to plan secretly; plot: *The spies hatched a scheme to steal government secrets. verb.*

hatch[2] (hach), **1** an opening in a ship's deck or in the floor or roof of a building. A ship's cargo is loaded through the hatch. The escape hatch in an airplane permits passengers to get out in an emergency. **2** a trap door covering such an opening. *noun, plural* **hatch·es.**

hatch·back (hach'bak'), an automobile that has a sloping back section that opens up as a door. *noun.*

hatch·er·y (hach'ər ē), a place for hatching eggs, especially of fish and chickens. *noun, plural* **hatch·er·ies.**

hatch·et (hach'it), a small ax with a handle about a foot long, for use with one hand. *noun.*

hate (hāt), **1** to dislike very much: *Cats usually hate dogs.* **2** a very strong dislike: *to feel hate toward one's enemies, to have a hate for war.* **1** *verb,* **hates, hat·ed, hat·ing;** **2** *noun.*

hate·ful (hāt'fəl), **1** causing hate: *hateful behavior.* **2** feeling hate; showing hate: *a hateful comment. adjective.*

ha·tred (hā'trid), a very strong dislike; hate. *noun.*

haugh·ty (hô'tē), too proud, and full of scorn for others: *haughty words. A haughty person is often unpopular. adjective,* **haugh·ti·er, haugh·ti·est.**

haul (hôl), **1** to pull or drag with force: *The logs were loaded on wagons and hauled to the mill by horses.* **2** to transport; carry: *Trucks, trains, and ships haul freight.* **3** the distance that a load is hauled: *Long hauls cost more than short ones.* **4** the amount won or taken at one time; catch: *The fishing boats made a good haul and came back fully loaded.* **1,2** *verb,* **3,4** *noun.*

haunch (hônch), **1** the part of the body around the hips: *The dog sat on its haunches.* **2** the leg and loin of an animal, used for food: *a haunch of venison. noun, plural* **haunch·es.**

haunt (hônt), **1** to go often to; visit frequently: *People say ghosts haunt that old house.* **2** a place visited often. **3** to be often with; come often to: *That song I heard this morning has haunted me all day. Memories of his youth haunted the old man.* **1,3** *verb,* **2** *noun.*

I HATE TO SEE THE OLD PLACE GO. IT'S ONE OF MY FAVORITE HAUNTS.

haunt·ed (hôn'tid), visited by ghosts: *They were afraid to go into the haunted house. adjective.*

have (hav), **1** to hold in one's hand; hold in one's keeping; hold in one's possession: *I have a stick in my hand. They have a big house and farm. A house has windows. She has no news of her brother.* **2** to be forced; be compelled: *All animals have to sleep. I will have to go now or I'll be late for work.* **3** to cause somebody to do something or something to be done: *Please have the store deliver the suit. She will have the car washed.* **4** to take; get: *Have a seat. You need to have a rest.* **5** to eat or drink: *Will you have a cup of tea? We always have breakfast in the kitchen.* **6** to go through; experience: *Have a good time at the party tonight.* **7** to allow; permit: *She won't have any noise while she is reading.* **8** to be ill with; suffer from: *I've had a headache all day.* **9** to hold in the mind: *have an idea.* **10** to be in a certain relation to: *She has three brothers.* **11** to give birth to: *She had a girl.* **12** to be the parent or parents of: *They have three children.* **13** *Have* is used with words like *asked, been, broken, done,* or *called* to express completed action. *They have eaten. She had gone before. I have called him. They will have left by Sunday* *afternoon. verb,* **has, had, hav·ing.**

have had it, to have put up with all that one can; have become fed up: *"I've had it!" she said. "I won't take the blame any longer.*

have on, to be wearing: *Do you have on a new coat?*

have to do with, to relate to; deal with: *Botany has to do with the study of plants.*

ha·ven (hā′vən), **1** a harbor, especially one for shelter from a storm. **2** a place of shelter and safety: *The warm cabin was a haven from the storm. noun.*

have·n't (hav′ənt), have not.

hav·oc (hav′ək), very great destruction or injury: *Tornadoes can create widespread havoc. noun.*

Ha·wai·i (hə wī′ē), a state of the United States in the northern Pacific, consisting of the Hawaiian Islands. *Abbreviation:* HI *Capital:* Honolulu. *noun.* [*Hawaii* comes from the Hawaiian name of the largest island in the group. According to legend, the original settlers of Hawaii named it for their homeland.]

Ha·wai·ian (hə wī′yən), **1** of or having something to do with Hawaii or its people. **2** a person born or living in Hawaii. **3** the original language of Hawaii. **1** *adjective,* **2,3** *noun.*

Hawaiian Islands, a group of islands in the northern Pacific.

hawk[1] (hôk), a bird of prey with a strong, hooked beak, and large curved claws. *noun.*

hawk[1]—about 2 feet (60 centimeters) long

hawk[2] (hôk), to carry about and offer for sale by shouting: *Peddlers hawked their wares in the street. verb.*

haw·thorn (hô′thôrn), a shrub or small tree with many thorns and clusters of fragrant white, red, or pink flowers and small, red berries. *noun.*

hay (hā), **1** grass, alfalfa, or clover cut and dried as food for cattle and horses. **2** to cut and dry grass, alfalfa, or clover for hay: *They are haying in the east field.* **1** *noun,* **2** *verb.*

hay fever, an allergy caused by the pollen of ragweed and other plants. Hay fever often causes sneezing, a runny nose, and itching nose and eyes.

hay·field (hā′fēld′), a field in which grass, alfalfa, or clover is grown for hay. *noun.*

hay·loft (hā′lôft′), a place in a stable or barn where hay is stored. *noun.*

hay·mow (hā′mou′), a place in a barn for storing hay. *noun.*

a hat	**i** it	**oi** oil	**ch** child	a in about
ā age	**ī** ice	**ou** out	**ng** long	e in taken
ä far	**o** hot	**u** cup	**sh** she	ə = i in pencil
e let	**ō** open	**u̇** put	**th** thin	o in lemon
ē equal	**ô** order	**ü** rule	**ŦH** then	u in circus
ėr term			**zh** measure	

hay·stack (hā′stak′), a large pile of hay outdoors. *noun.*

haz·ard (haz′ərd), **1** a risk; danger: *Mountain climbing is full of hazards.* **2** to take a chance with; risk: *I won't even hazard a guess.* **1** *noun,* **2** *verb.*

haz·ard·ous (haz′ər dəs), dangerous; risky. *adjective.*

hazardous—Building a skyscraper is **hazardous** work.

haze (hāz), a small amount of mist or smoke in the air: *A thin haze veiled the distant hills. noun.*

ha·zel (hā′zəl), **1** a shrub or small tree whose light-brown nuts are good to eat. **2** light-brown. **1** *noun,* **2** *adjective.*

ha·zy (hā′zē), **1** misty; smoky; dim: *a hazy sky.* **2** not distinct; obscure: *It was so long ago, I have only a hazy memory of what happened. adjective,* **ha·zi·er, ha·zi·est.**

H-bomb (āch′bom′), a hydrogen bomb. *noun.*

he (hē), **1** the boy, man, or male animal spoken about: *He works hard, but his work pays him well.* **2** a male: *Is your dog a he or a she?* **3** anyone: *He who hesitates is lost.* **1,3** *pronoun, plural* **they;** **2** *noun.*

head (hed), **1** the top part of the human body or the front part of most animal bodies where the eyes, ears, nose, mouth, and brain are. **2** the top part of anything: *the head of a pin, the head of a bed.* **3** the front part of anything: *the head of a line, the head of a comet.* **4** at the front or top: *the head group of a parade.* **5** to be at the front or the top of: *to head a parade.* **6** coming from in front: *a head wind.* **7** to move toward; face toward: *Our ship headed south.* **8** the chief person; leader: *A principal is the head of a school.* **9** chief; leading: *a head nurse.* **10** to be the head or chief of; lead: *Who will head the team?* **11** one or ones; an individual: *ten head of cattle.* **12** anything rounded like a head: *a head of cabbage.* **13** the striking or cutting part of a tool or implement: *You hit the nail with the head of a hammer.* **14** the mind; understanding; intelligence: *He has a good head for figures.* **15 heads,** the top side of a coin. 1-3,8,11-15 *noun, plural* **heads** for 1-3,8,12-15, **head** for 11; 4,6,9 *adjective,* 5,7,10 *verb.*

head off, to get in front of; check: *She tried to head off the runaway horse.*

out of one's head, crazy.

over one's head, too hard for one to understand: *Chemistry is way over my head.*

head·ache (hed′āk′), a pain in the head. *noun.*

head·band (hed′band′), a band worn around the head. *noun.*

head·dress (hed′dres′), a covering or decoration for the head: *On special occasions members of the tribe wore beautiful headdresses made of feathers and beads. noun, plural* **head·dress·es.**

head·first (hed′ferst′), **1** with the head first. **2** hastily; rashly. *adverb.*

head·gear (hed′gir′), a covering for the head; a hat, cap, helmet, or the like. *noun.*

head·ing (hed′ing), something written or printed at the top of a page or at the beginning of a chapter or letter. A name and address at the top of a letter is a heading. *noun.*

head·land (hed′lənd), a cape; point of land jutting out into water. *noun.*

head·light (hed′līt′), a bright light, usually one of a pair, at the front of a motor vehicle or railroad engine. *noun.*

head·line (hed′līn′), **1** the words printed in heavy type at the top of a newspaper article telling what it is about. **2** to list as the main attraction: *The circus headlined a famous animal trainer.* 1 *noun,* 2 *verb,* **head·lines, head·lined, head·lin·ing.**

head·long (hed′lông), **1** with the head first: *a headlong dive.* **2** in too great a rush; without stopping to think: *a headlong decision. adverb, adjective.*

head-on (hed′on′), with the head or front first: *a head-on collision. adjective, adverb.*

head·phone (hed′fōn′), an earphone held against one or both ears by a band over the head. *noun.*

head·quar·ters (hed′kwôr′tərz), **1** the place from which the chief or commanding officer of an army or police force sends out orders. **2** the main office; the center of operations or of authority: *The headquarters of the American Red Cross is in Washington. noun plural or singular.*

head·stand (hed′stand′), a balancing on the head, with the hands placed in front of the head for support. *noun.*

head start, an advantage or lead allowed to a person at the start of a race, a course of study, or the like.

head·stone (hed′stōn′), a stone, often carved, set at the head of a grave. *noun.*

head·strong (hed′strông′), rashly or foolishly determined to have one's own way; hard to control or manage: *a headstrong horse. adjective.*

head·wa·ters (hed′wô′tərz), the sources or upper parts of a river. *noun plural.*

head·way (hed′wā′), **1** motion forward: *The ship could make no headway against the strong wind and tide.* **2** progress with work or other activity: *Science has made much headway in fighting disease. noun.*

heal (hēl), to make or become well; return to health; cure: *The cut healed in a few days. verb.* [*Heal* comes from an old English word meaning "whole." The English word *health* comes from the same root. If someone is healed, or has good health, that person is whole, or sound.]

health (helth), **1** a being well or not sick; freedom from illness of any kind: *Food, sleep, and exercise are important to your health.* **2** the condition of the body or mind: *to be in excellent health. noun.*

health food, any food grown without chemicals or prepared without preservatives, chosen for its value as nourishment and believed to be good for one's health.

health·ful (helth′fəl), giving health; good for the health: *a healthful diet, healthful exercise. adjective.*

health·y (hel′thē), **1** having good health: *a healthy baby.* **2** giving health; good for the health: *healthy exercise. adjective,* **health·i·er, health·i·est.**

heap (hēp), **1** a pile of many things thrown or lying together: *a heap of stones.* **2** to form into a heap; gather in heaps: *I heaped the dirty clothes beside the washing machine.* **3** a large amount: *a heap of trouble.* **4** to give generously or in large amounts: *to heap praise on someone.* **5** to fill full or more than full: *to heap a plate with food.* 1,3 *noun,* 2,4,5 *verb.*

hear (hir), **1** to take in a sound or sounds through the ear: *We couldn't hear in the back row. I can hear my watch tick.* **2** to listen to: *You must hear what he has to say.* **3** to receive information: *Have you heard from your sister in Los Angeles? verb,* **hears, heard, hear·ing.**

headlong (definition 1)—The elephant ran **headlong** into a tree.

heard (hėrd). See **hear.** *I heard the noise. The sound was heard a mile away.* verb.

hear·ing (hir′ing), **1** the power to hear; sense by which sound is perceived: *The doctor tested my hearing.* **2** the act or process of perceiving sound, of listening, or of receiving information: *Hearing the good news made us happy.* **3** a chance to be heard: *The judge gave both sides a hearing.* **4** the distance that a sound can be heard: *I must stay within hearing of the telephone.* noun.

hearing aid, a small, electronic device which makes sounds louder, worn by people who cannot hear well.

hear·say (hir′sā′), common talk; gossip. noun.

heart (härt), **1** the part of the body that pumps the blood. **2** the part that feels, loves, hates, and desires: *a heavy heart, a kind heart. She knew in her heart that she was wrong.* **3** courage; enthusiasm: *The losing team still had plenty of heart.* **4** the middle; center: *in the heart of the forest.* **5** the main part; most important part: *the very heart of the matter.* **6** a figure shaped somewhat like this: ♥: *The valentine was covered with hearts.* **7** a playing card with one or more figures shaped like this. noun.

by heart, by memory: *I learned the poem by heart.*

cross one's heart, to make a sign of a cross over one's heart when swearing that something is true.

set one's heart on, to want something very badly.

take to heart, to think seriously about; be deeply affected by: *He took his piano teacher's advice to heart and practiced faithfully every day.*

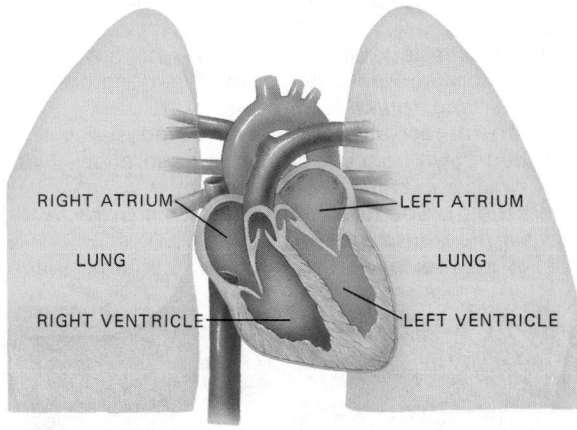

heart (definition 1)

heart·beat (härt′bēt′), a beat of the heart, which can be felt as a pulse at the wrist. noun.

heart·break (härt′brāk′), a crushing sorrow or grief. noun.

heart·bro·ken (härt′brō′kən), crushed by sorrow or grief. adjective.

heart·en (härt′n), to cheer; cheer up; encourage: *This good news will hearten you.* verb.

heart·felt (härt′felt′), sincere; genuine: *heartfelt sympathy.* adjective.

hearth (härth), **1** the stone or brick floor of a fireplace. **2** a fireside; home: *The soldiers longed to be at their own hearths.* noun.

heart·i·ly (här′tl ē), **1** with sincere feeling; warmly: *She welcomed her cousins heartily.* **2** with courage, spirit, or enthusiasm; vigorously: *to set to work heartily.* **3** with a good appetite: *to eat heartily.* **4** very; completely: *She is heartily tired of doing all the work herself.* adverb.

heart·i·ness (här′tē nis), **1** sincere feeling. **2** vigor. noun.

heart·less (härt′lis), without kindness or sympathy; unfeeling; cruel. adjective.

heart·y (här′tē), **1** warm and friendly; full of feeling; sincere: *We gave our old friends a hearty welcome.* **2** strong and well; vigorous: *Hearty pioneers moved westward.* **3** with plenty to eat; nourishing: *A hearty meal satisfied her appetite.* adjective, **heart·i·er, heart·i·est.**

heat (hēt), **1** the condition of being hot; hotness; warmth: *the heat of a fire.* **2** to make or become warm or hot: *The stove heats the room. The soup is heating slowly.* **3** hot weather: *the heat of summer.* **4** the hottest point; most violent stage; excitement: *In the heat of the argument we all lost our tempers.* **5** the form of energy that flows from a hotter object to a colder one and causes both objects to change temperature. **6** one trial in a race: *I won the first heat, but lost the final race.* 1,3-6 noun, 2 verb.

heat·er (hē′tər), a thing that gives heat or warmth, such as a stove, furnace, or radiator. noun.

heath (hēth), **1** open wasteland with heather or low bushes growing on it; moor. A heath has few or no trees. **2** a low bush growing on such land. Heather is one kind of heath. noun.

hea·then (hē′ᴛʜən), **1** a person who does not believe in the God of the Bible; person who is not a Christian, Jew, or Moslem. **2** people who are heathens. **3** of or having to do with heathens. 1,2 noun, plural **hea·thens** or **hea·then;** 3 adjective.

heath·er (heᴛʜ′ər), a low shrub which covers wastelands in Scotland and England. noun.

heat stroke, a sudden illness with fever and dry skin, caused by too much heat.

heave (hēv), **1** to lift with force or effort: *She heaved the heavy box onto the truck.* **2** to throw: *We heaved the old carpet out the back door.* **3** to give a sigh or groan with a deep, heavy breath. **4** to rise and fall alternately: *The waves heaved in the storm.* **5** a heaving; throw: *With a mighty heave my friends and I pushed the boat into the water.* 1-4 verb, **heaves, heaved, heav·ing;** 5 noun.

heav·en (hev′ən), **1** (in Christian and some other religious use) the place where God and the angels live. **2 Heaven,** God; Providence: *It was the will of Heaven.* **3** a place or condition of greatest happiness. **4 heavens, a** the sky: *Clouds floated lazily in the heavens.* **b** outer space: *Thousands of stars were shining in the heavens.* *noun.*

heav·en·ly (hev′ən lē), **1** of or in heaven: *heavenly angels.* **2** very beautiful or excellent; pleasing: *It was a heavenly day for a hike in the woods.* **3** of or in the heavens: *The sun, the moon, and the stars are heavenly bodies. adjective.*

heav·i·ly (hev′ə lē), in a heavy way or manner. *adverb.*

heav·i·ness (hev′ē nis), **1** a being heavy; great weight. **2** a sadness: *a heaviness in one's heart. noun.*

heav·y (hev′ē), **1** hard to lift or carry; of much weight: *The washing machine was a heavy load for the two of them to carry.* **2** of more than usual weight for its kind: *heavy silk.* **3** of great amount or force; greater than usual; large: *a heavy rain, a heavy vote.* **4** hard to bear or endure: *Their troubles became heavier.* **5** hard to digest: *heavy food.* **6** weighted down; laden: *air heavy with moisture, eyes heavy with sleep. adjective,* **heav·i·er, heav·i·est.**

He·brew (hē′brü), **1** a Jew; descendant of one of the desert tribes led by Moses that settled in Palestine. **2** Jewish. **3** the ancient language of the Jews, in which the Old Testament was written. Citizens of Israel speak a modern form of Hebrew. **1,3** *noun,* **2** *adjective.*

Word Source

Hebrew is one of the oldest languages still spoken today. The following words came into English from Hebrew:

amen	Jehovah	rabbi	Satan
Hanukkah	kosher	Sabbath	schwa

hec·tic (hek′tik), very exciting: *The children had a hectic time getting to school the morning after the big snowstorm. adjective.*

he'd (hēd), **1** he had. **2** he would.

hedge (hej), **1** a thick row of bushes or small trees planted as a fence. **2** to put a hedge around: *to hedge a garden.* **3** to avoid giving a direct answer; evade questions. **1** *noun,* **2,3** *verb,* **hedg·es, hedged, hedg·ing.**

hedge in, to hem in; surround on all sides: *The town was hedged in by mountains and a dense forest.*

hedge·hog (hej′hog′), **1** a small animal of Europe, Asia, and Africa, with spines on its back. When attacked, a hedgehog rolls up into a bristling ball. **2** a porcupine of North America. *noun.*

hedge·row (hej′rō′), a thick row of bushes or small trees forming a hedge. *noun.*

heed (hēd), **1** to give careful attention to; take notice of: *Now heed what I say.* **2** careful attention; notice: *Pay heed to her instructions.* **1** *verb,* **2** *noun.*

heed·less (hēd′lis), careless; thoughtless. *adjective.*

heel¹ (hēl), **1** the back part of the foot, below the ankle. **2** the part of a stocking or shoe that covers the heel. **3** the part of a shoe or boot that is under the heel or raises the heel: *The heels on these shoes are too high.* **4** anything shaped, used, or placed at an end like a heel, such as an end crust of bread, the rind of cheese, the rear end of a ship's keel, or the lower end of a mast. **5** a hateful person. **6** to follow closely, at one's heels: *The dog was trained to heel.* **1-5** *noun,* **6** *verb.*

heel² (hēl), to lean over to one side: *The sailboat heeled as it turned. verb.*

heft·y (hef′tē), **1** heavy: *It was too hefty a box to lift easily.* **2** big and strong: *The hefty wrestler threw his opponent to the floor. adjective,* **heft·i·er, heft·i·est.**

heif·er (hef′ər), a young cow that has not had a calf. *noun.*

height (hīt), **1** how tall a person is; how high anything is; how far up a thing goes: *the height of a mountain.* **2** a high point or place; hill: *We stood on a height above the river.* **3** the highest point; greatest degree: *Fast driving on icy roads is the height of folly. noun.*

height·en (hīt′n), **1** to make or become higher. **2** to make or become stronger or greater; increase: *The wind whistling in the trees outside heightened the suspense of the ghost story. verb.*

heir (er *or* ar), a person who has the right to somebody's property or title after the death of its owner. *noun.*

heir·ess (er′is *or* ar′is), **1** an heir who is a woman or girl. **2** a woman or girl inheriting great wealth. *noun, plural* **heir·ess·es.**

heir·loom (er′lüm′ *or* ar′lüm′), a possession handed down from generation to generation: *This old clock is a family heirloom. noun.*

held (held). See **hold¹**. *He held the kitten gently. The swing is held by strong ropes. verb.*

Hel·e·na (hel′ə nə), the capital of Montana. *noun.*

hedgehog (definition 1)—about 9 inches (23 centimeters) long

hel·i·cop·ter (hel′ə kop′tər), an aircraft without wings that is lifted from the ground and kept in the air by horizontal propellers. *noun.*

Word History

helicopter As a helicopter rises, its main set of whirling blades moves in a spiral path upward. The name of the aircraft comes from two Greek words meaning "spiral" and "wing." Although there is no actual wing, the whirling blades act as a wing.

hel·i·port (hel′ə pôrt′), an airport for helicopters. Heliports may be built on the tops of buildings. *noun.*

he·li·um (hē′lē əm), a very light gas that will not burn, much used in balloons and dirigibles. Helium is a chemical element. *noun.*

hell (hel), **1** (in Christian and some other religious use) the place where wicked persons are punished after death. **2** any very bad place or condition. *noun.*

he'll (hēl), **1** he will. **2** he shall.

hel·lo (he lō′ *or* hə lō′), **1** a call of greeting or surprise. We usually say "hello" when we call or answer a call on the telephone. *"Hello, Mother!" the boy said.* **2** a call or shout: *The girl gave a loud hello to let us know where she was.* **1** interjection, **2** noun, plural **hel·los.**

helm (helm), a handle or wheel by which a ship is steered. *noun.*

hel·met (hel′mit), a covering to protect the head. Knights wore helmets as part of their armor. Soldiers wear steel helmets; firefighters wear helmets made of leather or synthetic materials. *noun.*

help (help), **1** to give or do what is needed or useful: *My father helped me with my homework. Help me put my coat on.* **2** the act of helping; aid: *I need some help with my work. The dying woman was beyond help.* **3** a person or thing that helps: *A sewing machine is a help in making clothes. The storekeeper treats his help well.* **4** to make better: *This medicine will help your cough.* **5** a means of making better: *The medicine was a help.* **6** to avoid; keep from: *I can't help yawning.* 1,4,6 *verb,* 2,3,5 *noun.*

help oneself to, to take for or serve oneself: *Help yourself to the milk.*

help·er (hel′pər), a person or thing that helps. *noun.*

help·ful (help′fəl), giving help; useful. *adjective.*

help·ing (hel′ping), a portion of food served to a person at one time. *noun.*

helping verb, a verb used to make verb phrases. Some helping verbs are *am, be, can, do, have, may, must, shall,* and *will.* EXAMPLES: I *am* going; she *will* go; they *are* lost; *can* you help?

help·less (help′lis), not able to help or look after oneself: *a helpless baby. Though alone and helpless, he managed to keep himself afloat until help arrived. adjective.*

hem (hem), **1** a border or edge on a garment; edge made by folding over the cloth and sewing it down. **2** to fold over and sew down the edge of cloth: *to hem a skirt.* 1 *noun,* 2 *verb,* **hems, hemmed, hem·ming.**

hem in, hem around, or **hem about,** to close in or surround, and not let out.

hem·i·sphere (hem′ə sfir), **1** a half of a sphere or globe. **2** a half of the earth's surface. North and South America are in the Western Hemisphere; Europe, Asia, and Africa are in the Eastern Hemisphere. All the countries north of the equator are in the Northern Hemisphere; those south of the equator are in the Southern Hemisphere. *noun.*

hem·lock (hem′lok), **1** a poisonous plant with spotted stems, finely divided leaves, and small white flowers. **2** an evergreen tree with flat needles, small cones, and reddish bark. Bark from hemlocks is used in tanning. *noun.*

he·mo·glo·bin (hē′mə glō′bən), a substance in the red blood cells that carries oxygen from the lungs to the tissues of the body. Hemoglobin gives blood its red color. *noun.*

hemp (hemp), a tall plant of Asia whose tough fibers are made into heavy string, rope, and coarse cloth. *noun.*

hen (hen), **1** a full-grown female chicken. **2** the female of other birds. *noun.*

hence (hens), **1** therefore: *The king died, and hence his son became king.* **2** from now: *Football season begins three weeks hence. adverb.*

hence·forth (hens′fôrth′), from this time on. *adverb.*

hen·house (hen′hous′), a house for chickens. *noun, plural* **hen·hous·es** (hen′hou′ziz).

her (hėr), **1** *She* and *her* mean the girl or woman or female animal spoken about. *She is not here. Have you seen her? Find her.* **2** of her; belonging to her; done by her: *She has left her book. The cat won't let you touch her kittens. She has finished her work.* 1 *pronoun,* 2 *adjective.*

her·ald (her′əld), **1** in former times, a person who carried messages between rulers, and made public announcements. **2** to bring news of; announce: *The first robin heralded the coming of spring. The newspapers heralded the signing of a peace treaty.* 1 *noun,* 2 *verb.*

a hat	i it	oi oil	ch child	a in about
ā age	ī ice	ou out	ng long	e in taken
ä far	o hot	u cup	sh she	ə = { i in pencil
e let	ō open	ú put	th thin	o in lemon
ē equal	ô order	ü rule	ᴛH then	u in circus
ėr term			zh measure	

H

herb (érb *or* hèrb), a plant whose leaves and stems are used for medicine and seasoning. Sage, mint, and lavender are herbs. *noun.*

Her·cu·les (hér′kyə lēz′), a hero of Greek and Roman mythology famous for his great strength. *noun.*

herd (hèrd), **1** a group of animals of one kind, especially large animals, keeping, feeding, or moving together: *a herd of cows, a herd of horses, a herd of elephants.* **2** a large number of people. **3** to join together; flock together: *We all herded under an awning to get out of the rain.* **4** to form into a flock, herd, or group: *The farmer herded the cows over to the barn door.* **5** to tend or take care of cattle or sheep. **1,2** *noun,* **3-5** *verb.*

herds·man (hèrdz′mən), a person who tends a herd. *noun, plural* **herds·men.**

here (hir), **1** in this place; at this place: *We live here in the summer. We will stop here.* **2** to this place: *Bring the children here for their lesson.* **3** this place: *Where do we go from here?* **4** now; at this time: *Here the speaker paused.* **5** an answer showing that one is present when roll is called. **6** an exclamation used to call attention to a person or thing: *"Here! take away the dishes."* **1,2,4** *adverb,* **3** *noun,* **5,6** *interjection.*

here·af·ter (hir af′tər), **1** after this; after now; in the future. **2** the life or time after death. **1** *adverb,* **2** *noun.*

here·by (hir bī′), by this; by this means: *The license said, "You are hereby given the right to hunt and fish in Dover County."* *adverb.*

he·red·i·tar·y (hə red′ə ter′ē), **1** coming by inheritance: *"Prince" and "princess" are hereditary titles.* **2** holding a position by inheritance: *The queen of England is a hereditary ruler.* **3** passed on or caused by heredity: *Having brown eyes is hereditary.* *adjective.*

he·red·i·ty (hə red′ə tē), the passing of physical or mental characteristics from one generation of living things to the next. *noun.*

here's (hirz), here is.

her·e·sy (her′ə sē), **1** a belief different from the accepted belief of a church or some other group. **2** the holding of such a belief. *noun, plural* **her·e·sies.**

her·e·tic (her′ə tik), a person who holds a belief that is different from the accepted belief of a church or some other group. *noun.*

here·to·fore (hir′tə fôr′), before this time; until now. *adverb.*

her·it·age (her′ə tij), what is handed down from one generation to the next; inheritance: *The heritage of freedom is precious to Americans. noun.*

her·mit (hèr′mit), a person who goes away from others and lives alone. A hermit often lives a religious life. *noun.*

he·ro (hir′ō), **1** a person admired for bravery, great deeds, or noble qualities. **2** the most important male person in a story, play, or poem. *noun, plural* **her·oes.**

he·ro·ic (hi rō′ik), **1** like a hero; very brave; great; noble: *The lifeguard made a heroic rescue.* **2** of or

about heroes: *a heroic poem. adjective.*

her·o·in (her′ō ən), a poisonous, habit-forming drug. *noun.*

her·o·ine (her′ō ən), **1** a girl or woman admired for her bravery, great deeds, or noble qualities. **2** the most important female person in a story, play, or poem. *noun.*

her·o·ism (her′ō iz′əm), great bravery; daring courage. *noun.*

her·on (her′ən), a wading bird with a long neck, a long bill, and long legs. *noun.*

heron
about 4 feet
(1 meter) tall

her·ring (her′ing), a small food fish of the northern Atlantic Ocean. *noun, plural* **her·ring** or **her·rings.**

hers (hèrz), the one or ones belonging to her: *This money is hers. Your answers are wrong; hers are right. pronoun.*

her·self (hər self′), **1** *Herself* is used to make a statement stronger. *She herself did it. She herself brought the book.* **2** *Herself* is used instead of *she* or *her* in cases like: *She hurt herself. She did it by herself.* **3** her real or true self: *She is so tired that she's not herself. pronoun.*

he's (hēz), **1** he is. **2** he has.

hes·i·tant (hez′ə tənt), hesitating; doubtful; undecided: *I was hesitant about accepting the invitation. adjective.*

hes·i·tate (hez′ə tāt), **1** to hold back; feel doubtful; be undecided; show that one has not yet made up one's mind: *I hesitated about taking his side until I knew the whole story.* **2** to stop for an instant; pause: *She hesitated before asking the question. verb,* **hes·i·tates, hes·i·tat·ed, hes·i·tat·ing.**

hes·i·ta·tion (hez′ə tā′shən), the act of hesitating; doubt. *noun.*

hew (hyü), **1** to cut with an ax, sword, or the like: *I hewed down the tree.* **2** to cut into shape; form by cutting with an ax: *They hewed the logs into beams. verb,* **hews, hewed, hewed** or **hewn** (hyün), **hew·ing.**

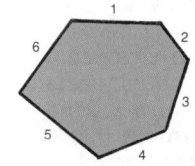

hexagons

a hat	i it	oi oil	ch child	a in about
ā age	ī ice	ou out	ng long	e in taken
ä far	o hot	u cup	sh she	ə = { i in pencil
e let	ō open	u̇ put	th thin	o in lemon
ē equal	ô order	ü rule	ŦH then	u in circus
ėr term			zh measure	

hex·a·gon (hek′sə gon), a figure having six angles and six sides. *noun.*

hey (hā), a sound made to attract attention, express surprise or other feeling, or ask a question: *"Hey! stop!" "Hey? what did you say?" interjection.*

hi (hī), a call of greeting; hello. *interjection.*

HI, Hawaii (used with postal Zip Code).

hi·ber·nate (hī′bər nāt), to spend the winter sleeping or resting, as woodchucks and some other wild animals do. *verb,* **hi·ber·nates, hi·ber·nat·ed, hi·ber·nat·ing.**

hi·ber·na·tion (hī′bər nā′shən), the act or state of hibernating. *noun.*

hic·cup (hik′up), **1** a sudden, uncontrollable intake of breath with a muffled clicking sound. **2 hiccups,** a condition of having one hiccup after another. **3** to have the hiccups. 1,2 *noun,* 3 *verb,* **hic·cups, hic·cupped, hic·cup·ping.**

hick·or·y (hik′ər ē), **1** a North American tree whose nuts are good to eat. **2** its tough, hard wood. *noun, plural* **hick·or·ies.**

hid (hid). See **hide**[1]. *The dog hid the bone. The money was hid in a safe place. verb.*

hid·den (hid′n), **1** put or kept out of sight; secret; not clear: *The story is about hidden treasure.* **2** See **hide**[1]. *The moon was hidden behind a dark cloud.* 1 *adjective,* 2 *verb.*

hide[1] (hīd), **1** to put out of sight; keep out of sight: *Hide it where no one else can find it.* **2** to shut off from sight; cover up: *Clouds hide the sun.* **3** to keep secret: *I tried to hide my disappointment. verb,* **hides, hid, hid·den** or **hid, hid·ing.**

hide[2] (hīd), an animal's skin. Leather is made from hide. *noun.*

hide-and-seek (hīd′n sēk′), a children's game in which one player tries to find the other players who have hidden. *noun.*

hide·a·way (hīd′ə wā′), a place for hiding or being alone: *No one could ever find our secret hideaway. noun.*

hid·e·ous (hid′ē əs), very ugly; frightful; horrible. *adjective.*

hideous
The actor was made up as a **hideous** mummy.

hide·out (hīd′out′), a place for hiding: *The spy had a hideout on the border. noun.*

hi·er·o·glyph·ic (hī′ər ə glif′ik), **1** a picture, character, or symbol standing for a word, idea, or sound. The ancient Egyptians used hieroglyphics instead of an alphabet like ours. **2 hieroglyphics,** writing that uses hieroglyphics. *noun.*

Word History

hieroglyphic *Hieroglyphic* is from a Greek word meaning "written in sacred pictures or symbols." The Greeks believed that only Egyptian priests could understand this special system of writing. Later on, language scholars came to understand what hieroglyphics meant.

A KINGLY
GIFT OF AN
OFFERING TABLE
TO
RA-HORUS
THE GREAT
GOD
LORD OF
HEAVEN

hieroglyphics
(definition 1)
Egyptian **hieroglyphics**

H

hi-fi (hī′fī′), a radio or phonograph that reproduces sound that is close to the quality of the original. *noun.*

high (hī), **1** tall: *a high building. The mountain is over 20,000 feet high.* **2** up above the ground: *a high leap, an airplane high in the air.* **3** up above others: *She is a high government official.* **4** greater, stronger, or better than usual; great: *a high wind, a high price.* **5** not low in pitch; sharp; shrill: *A soprano can sing high notes.* **6** at or to a high place, rank, amount, or pitch: *The price of gas has gone too high.* **7** a high point, level, or position: *Food prices reached a new high last month.* **8** an arrangement of gears to give the greatest speed. 1-5 *adjective,* 6 *adverb,* 7,8 *noun.*

high and dry, 1 up out of water: *The boat ran ashore, high and dry.* **2** alone; without help: *I was left high and dry to do all the work myself.*

high·chair (hī′cher′ *or* hī′char), a chair with a high seat and a tray, used for feeding babies. *noun.*

high jump, a contest to determine how high each contestant can jump over a raised crossbar.

high·land (hī′lənd), a country or region that is higher and hillier than the neighboring country. *noun.*

high·light (hī/līt/), the most interesting or outstanding part: *The highlight of our trip was a visit to the Grand Canyon.* noun.

high·ly (hī/lē), 1 in a high degree; very; very much: *highly amusing, highly recommended.* 2 very favorably: *He spoke highly of his best friend.* 3 at a high price: *highly paid.* adverb.

High·ness (hī/nis), a title of honor given to members of royal families: *The Prince of Wales is addressed as "Your Highness."* noun, plural **High·ness·es.**

high-rise (hī/rīz/), 1 having many stories; very tall: *a high-rise apartment building.* 2 a building having many stories. 1 adjective, 2 noun.

high school, a school attended after elementary school or junior high school.

high seas, the open ocean. The high seas are outside the authority of any country.

high spirits, cheerfulness; gaiety.

high-strung (hī/strung/), very sensitive; very nervous; easily excited: *We tried not to worry our uncle as he was very high-strung.* adjective.

high tide, the time when the ocean comes up highest on the shore. High tides occur twice daily.

high·way (hī/wā/), a main public road. noun.

high·way·man (hī/wā/mən), (in former times) a man who robbed travelers on the public road. noun, plural **high·way·men.**

hi·jack (hī/jak/), to rob or take by force. verb.

hike (hīk), 1 to take a long walk; tramp; march: *We hiked five miles today.* 2 a long walk; tramp or march: *It was a four-mile hike through the forest to the camp.* 1 verb, **hikes, hiked, hik·ing;** 2 noun.

hi·lar·i·ous (hə ler/ē əs *or* hə lar/ē əs), very merry; very funny; noisy and cheerful: *a hilarious party.* adjective.

hi·lar·i·ty (hə lar/ə tē), loud laughter; noisy cheerfulness. noun.

hill (hil), 1 a raised part of the earth's surface, not so big as a mountain. 2 a little heap or pile: *Ants and moles make hills.* noun.

hill·side (hil/sīd/), the side of a hill. noun.

hill·top (hil/top/), the top of a hill. noun.

hill·y (hil/ē), having many hills: *hilly country.* adjective, **hill·i·er, hill·i·est.**

hilt (hilt), the handle of a sword or dagger. noun.

him (him). *He* and *him* mean the boy or man or male animal spoken about. *Take him home. Give him a drink. Go to him.* pronoun.

Him·a·la·yas (him/ə lā/əz *or* hə mä/lyəz), a group of high mountains in southern Asia. Several of the highest mountains in the world are in the Himalayas. noun plural.

him·self (him self/), 1 *Himself* is used to make a statement stronger. *He himself did it. Did you see Roy himself?* 2 *Himself* is used instead of *he* or *him* in cases like: *He cut himself. He asked himself what he really wanted. He kept the toy for himself.* 3 his real or true self: *He feels like himself again.* pronoun.

hind (hīnd), back; rear: *a dog's hind legs.* adjective.

hin·der (hin/dər), to keep back; hold back; get in

the way of; make hard to do: *Deep mud hindered travel.* verb.

hin·drance (hin/drəns), 1 a person or thing that hinders; obstacle: *Noise was a hindrance to our studying.* 2 the act of hindering. noun.

Hin·du (hin/dü), 1 a person born or living in India. 2 having to do with the Hindus, their language, or their religion. 3 a person who believes in Hinduism. 1,3 noun, plural **Hin·dus;** 2 adjective.

Hin·du·ism (hin/dü iz/əm), the religion and social system of the Hindus. noun.

hinge (hinj), 1 a joint on which a door, gate, cover, or lid moves back and forth. 2 to furnish with hinges; attach by hinges: *The lid is hinged to the box.* 3 to depend: *The success of the picnic hinges on the kind of weather we will have.* 1 noun, 2,3 verb, **hing·es, hinged, hing·ing.**

hint (hint), 1 a slight sign; indirect suggestion: *A small black cloud gave a hint of a coming storm.* 2 to suggest slightly; show in an indirect way: *She hinted that she was tired by yawning several times.* 1 noun, 2 verb.

hip (hip), 1 the part that sticks out on each side of the body below a person's waist where the leg joins the body. 2 a similar part in animals, where the hind leg joins the body. noun.

hip·po (hip/ō), a hippopotamus. noun, plural **hip·pos.**

hip·po·pot·a·mus (hip/ə pot/ə məs), a huge, thick-skinned, almost hairless animal found in and near the rivers of Africa. Hippopotamuses feed on plants and can stay underwater for a long time. noun, plural **hip·po·pot·a·mus·es, hip·po·pot·a·mi** (hip/ə pot/ə mī).

Word History

hippopotamus *Hippopotamus* is from a Greek word meaning "river horse." The Greeks thought this huge animal was like a horse, but biologists have discovered it is more closely related to the pig.

hippopotamus—about 13 feet (4 meters) long

---

hire (hīr), 1 to pay for the use of a thing or the work or services of a person: *She hired a car and a driver. The storekeeper hired me to deliver groceries.* 2 payment for the use of a thing or the work or services of a person: *Are these boats for hire?* 1 verb, **hires, hired, hir·ing;** 2 noun.

his (hiz), 1 of him; belonging to him: *His name is Bill. This is his book.* 2 the one or ones belonging to him: *My books are new; his are old.* **1** *adjective,* **2** *pronoun.*

His·pan·ic (hi span′ik), **1** Spanish. **2** of or from South America. **3** a person of Spanish-speaking descent. 1,2 *adjective,* 3 *noun.*

hiss (his), **1** to make a sound like *ss*, or like a drop of water on a hot stove: *Air or steam rushing out of a small opening hisses. Geese and snakes hiss.* **2** a sound like *ss: Hisses were heard from many who disliked what the speaker was saying.* **3** to show disapproval of by hissing: *The audience hissed the dull play.* 1,3 *verb,* 2 *noun, plural* **hiss·es.**

his·to·ri·an (hi stôr′ē ən), a person who writes about history; expert in history. *noun.*

his·to·ric (hi stôr′ik), famous or important in history: *Plymouth Rock and Bunker Hill are historic spots. adjective.*

his·to·ri·cal (hi stôr′ə kəl), **1** of history; having something to do with history: *historical documents.* **2** based on history: *a historical novel.* **3** known to be real or true; in history, not in legend: *It is a historical fact that in 1920 women in the United States were granted the right to vote. adjective.*

his·tor·y (his′tər ē), a story or record of important past events that happened to a person or nation: *the history of the United States. noun, plural* **his·tor·ies.**

hit (hit), **1** to give a blow to; strike; knock: *I hit the ball with a bat. She hit her little brother.* **2** a blow; stroke: *I drove the stake into the ground with one hit.* **3** to come upon; meet with; find: *We hit the right road in the dark. We hit upon a plan for making money.* **4** to have a painful effect on; influence in a bad way: *They were hard hit by the failure of their business.* **5** a successful performance: *The new play is the hit of the season.* **6** a successful hitting of the baseball so that the batter gets at least to first base. 1,3,4 *verb,* **hits, hit, hit·ting;** 2,5,6 *noun.*

hit it off, to get along well together: *The two friends hit it off from the start.*

hitch (hich), **1** to fasten with a hook, ring, rope, or strap: *She hitched her horse to a post.* **2** a fastening; catch: *Our car has a hitch for pulling a trailer.* **3** a kind of knot used to fasten a rope to a post or to some other object for a short time. **4** to move or pull with a jerk: *He hitched his chair nearer to the fire.* **5** a short, sudden pull or jerk: *He gave his pants a hitch.* **6** something that delays or makes more difficult: *A hitch in their plans made them miss the train.* 1,4 *verb,* 2,3,5,6 *noun, plural* **hitch·es.**

hitch·hike (hich′hīk′), to travel by walking and getting free rides from passing automobiles or trucks. *verb,* **hitch·hikes, hitch·hiked, hitch·hik·ing.**

hith·er (hiꜰʜ′ər), here; to this place: *Come hither, child. adverb.*

hith·er·to (hiꜰʜ′ər tü′), up to this time; until now: *a fact hitherto unknown. adverb.*

hit·ter (hit′ər), a person or thing that hits. *noun.*

hive (hīv), **1** a house or box for bees to live in. **2** a large number of bees living together: *The whole*

hive was busy. **3** a busy place full of people or animals: *The kitchen was a hive of activity. noun.*

hives (hīvz), a condition in which the skin itches and shows raised patches of red. *noun.*

ho (hō), **1** an exclamation of surprise, joy, or scornful laughter. **2** an exclamation to get attention: *Ho! Listen to this! interjection.*

hoard (hôrd), **1** to save and store away: *The squirrel hoarded nuts for the winter. A miser hoards money.* **2** what is saved and stored away; things stored: *The squirrel kept its hoard of nuts in a tree.* 1 *verb,* 2 *noun.*

hoarse (hôrs), **1** sounding rough and deep: *the hoarse sound of the bullfrog.* **2** having a rough voice: *A bad cold can make you hoarse. adjective,* **hoars·er, hoars·est.**

hoax (hōks), a mischievous trick, especially a made-up story passed off as true: *The report of an attack on the earth from Mars was a hoax. noun, plural* **hoax·es.**

hob·ble (hob′əl), **1** to walk awkwardly; limp: *The hiker hobbled along with a sprained ankle.* **2** a

hitch (definition 3)

hive (definition 1)

H

limping walk. **3** to tie the legs of a horse together: *He hobbled his horse at night so that it would not wander away.* **4** a rope or strap used to hobble an animal. 1,3 *verb,* **hob·bles, hob·bled, hob·bling;** 2,4 *noun.*

hob·by (hob′ē), something a person likes to do as a pastime: *Our teacher's hobby is gardening.* *noun, plural* **hob·bies.**
[The earliest meaning of *hobby* was "a small horse" or "a pony." Later, the word was used to mean "a toy horse" or "a hobbyhorse." Still later, it came to mean "any favorite pastime."]

hob·by·horse (hob′ē hôrs′), a long stick with a horse's head, used as a toy horse by children. *noun.*

hob·gob·lin (hob′gob′lən), **1** a goblin; elf. **2** a ghost. *noun.*

ho·bo (hō′bō), a person who wanders about and lives by begging or doing odd jobs; tramp. *noun, plural* **ho·bos** *or* **ho·boes.**

hock·ey (hok′ē), a game played by two teams on ice or on a field. The players use curved sticks to drive a rubber disk or a ball into the other team's goal. *noun.*

hodge·podge (hoj′poj′), a disorderly mixture; mess; jumble. *noun.*

hoe (hō), **1** a tool with a thin blade set across the end of a long handle, used for loosening soil or cutting small weeds. **2** to loosen, dig, or cut with a hoe. 1 *noun,* 2 *verb,* **hoes, hoed, hoe·ing.**

hog (hog), **1** a full-grown pig, raised for food. **2** a selfish, greedy, or dirty person. **3** to take more than one's share of: *He accused his sister of hogging all the cookies.* 1,2 *noun,* 3 *verb,* **hogs, hogged, hog·ging.**

ho·gan (hō′gän′), a dwelling used by the Navaho Indians of North America. Hogans are built with logs and covered with earth. *noun.*

hogan

hog·gish (hog′ish), **1** like a hog; greedy; very selfish. **2** dirty; filthy. *adjective.*

hoist (hoist), **1** to raise on high; lift up, often with ropes and pulleys: *We hoisted the flag up the pole. The ship's crew began to hoist the sails.* **2** a push; boost: *She gave me a hoist up the wall.* **3** a device used for lifting heavy loads. 1 *verb,* 2,3 *noun.*

hold[1] (hōld), **1** to grasp and keep: *Please hold my hat. Hold my watch while I play this game.* **2** a grasp or grip: *Take a good hold of this rope.* **3** a

thing to hold by: *The face of the cliff had enough holds for a good climber.* **4** to keep in some place or position: *Hold the dish level. Hold the paper steady while you draw.* **5** to stay strong or secure; not break, loosen, or give way: *The dike held during the flood.* **6** to keep from acting; keep back: *Hold your breath.* **7** to keep from going away; detain: *Police held the burglary suspect for questioning.* **8** to keep in; contain: *How much water will this cup hold? This theater holds five hundred people.* **9** to have: *Shall we hold a meeting of the club? We hold some property in the city. She has held the office of mayor for four years. I hold a high opinion of them.* **10** to consider; think: *People once held that the world was flat.* 1,4-10 *verb,* **holds, held, hold·ing;** 2,3 *noun.*

hold on, 1 to keep one's hold: *Are you holding on to the railing?* **2** to keep on; continue: *The runner held on for nine miles before collapsing.* **3** stop! *Hold on! Wait until I get my coat.*

hold out, to continue; last: *The food will only hold out two days more.*

hold over, to keep or continue longer than the expected time: *The movie was so popular it was held over for another week.*

hold up, 1 to keep from falling; support: *The roof is held up by pillars.* **2** to show; display: *He held up the sign so we could all see it.* **3** to continue; last; endure: *If this wind holds up, we can go sailing.* **4** to stop; delay: *I don't want to hold you up if you're in a hurry.* **5** to stop by force and rob: *Bandits held up the stagecoach.*

hold[2] (hōld), the part inside of a ship or airplane where the cargo is carried. *noun.*

hold·er (hōl′dər), **2** a thing to hold something else with. Pads of cloth are used as holders for lifting hot dishes. *noun.*

hold·ing (hōl′ding), a piece of land or property: *The government has vast holdings in the West that are used as national parks. noun.*

hold·up (hōld′up′), **1** the act of stopping by force and robbing: *a bank holdup.* **2** a delay; stopping: *I was late because of a holdup in traffic. noun.*

hole (hōl), **1** an open place: *a hole in a stocking.* **2** a hollow place in something solid: *a hole in the road. Rabbits dig holes in the ground to live in.* **3** a small, round, hollow place on a golf course, into which a golf ball is hit. *noun.*

hol·i·day (hol′ə dā), a day when one does not work; a day for pleasure and enjoyment: *The Fourth of July is a holiday for everyone.*
[*Holiday* comes from earlier English words meaning "holy day" or "time of a religious festival."]

ho·li·ness (hō′lē nis), **1** a being holy or sacred. **2 Holiness,** a title used in speaking to or of the pope: *The pope is addressed as "Your Holiness" and spoken of as "His Holiness." noun.*

Hol·land (hol′ənd), a name used for the Netherlands, a country in western Europe. *noun.*

hol·ler (hol′ər), **1** to cry or shout loudly: *"Come quick," she hollered from the yard.* **2** a loud cry or shout: *She gave a holler.* 1 *verb,* 2 *noun.*

hol·low (hol′ō), **1** having nothing, or only air, inside; empty; with a hole inside; not solid: *A tube or pipe is hollow. Most rubber balls are hollow.* **2** shaped like a bowl or cup: *a hollow dish for soup.* **3** a hollow place; hole: *a hollow in the road.* **4** to bend or dig out to a hollow shape: *She hollowed a whistle out of the piece of wood.* **5** a low place between hills; valley: *Rip Van Winkle lived in Sleepy Hollow.* **6** as if coming from something hollow; deep and dull: *the hollow boom of a foghorn. The barrel gave out a hollow sound when I hit it.* **7** deep and sunken: *A starving person has hollow eyes and cheeks.* **8** not real or sincere; false: *I was not fooled by her hollow promises.* **1,2,6-8** *adjective,* **3,5** *noun,* **4** *verb.*

hol·ly (hol′ē), **1** an evergreen tree or shrub with shiny, sharp-pointed green leaves and bright-red berries. **2** its leaves and berries, often used as Christmas decorations. *noun, plural* **hol·lies.**

hol·ly·hock (hol′ē hok), a tall plant with clusters of large, showy flowers of various colors. *noun.*

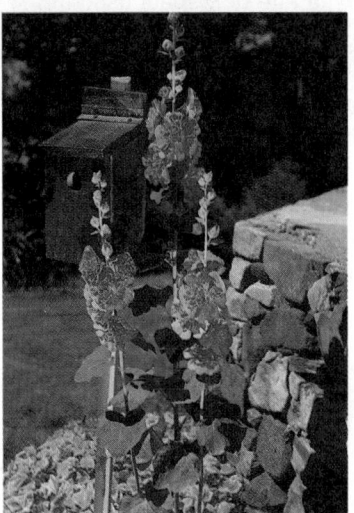

hollyhocks

hol·ster (hōl′stər), a leather case for a pistol, worn on a belt or under the shoulder. A holster for a rifle is attached to a saddle. *noun.*

ho·ly (hō′lē), **1** given or belonging to God; set apart for God's service; coming from God; sacred: *the Holy Bible, holy sacraments.* **2** like a saint; spiritually perfect; very good; pure in heart: *a holy man. adjective,* **ho·li·er, ho·li·est.**

hom·age (hom′ij), **1** respect; reverence; honor: *Everyone paid homage to the great leader.* **2** a pledge of loyalty and service by a vassal to a lord in the Middle Ages. *noun.*

home (hōm), **1** the place where a person or family lives; one's own house: *Her home is at 25 South Street.* **2** the place where a person was born or brought up; one's own town or country: *His home is Virginia.* **3** the place where a thing is specially common: *Alaska is the home of the fur seal.* **4** a place where people who are homeless, poor, old, sick, or blind may live: *a nursing home, a home for the aged.* **5** having to do with one's home;

domestic: *home cooking.* **6** (in sports) played in a team's hometown: *a home game.* **7** at or to one's home or country: *I want to go home.* **8** the goal in many games. **9** to the place aimed at: *The spear struck home. I drove the nail home.* **1-4,8** *noun,* **5,6** *adjective,* **7,9** *adverb.*

at home, at ease; comfortable: *Make yourself at home.*

home·land (hōm′land′), the country that is one's home; native land. *noun.*

home·less (hōm′lis), without a home: *a stray, homeless dog. adjective.*

home·like (hōm′līk′), like home; friendly; familiar; comfortable. *adjective.*

home·ly (hōm′lē), **1** ugly; plain; not good-looking: *a homely face.* **2** suited to home life; simple; everyday: *homely pleasures, homely food. adjective,* **home·li·er, home·li·est.**

home·made (hōm′mād′), made at home: *homemade bread. adjective.*

home·mak·er (hōm′mā′kər), a person who manages a home and its affairs. *noun.*

home plate, a flat, rubber slab beside which a baseball player stands to bat the ball. A player must touch the other three bases and then home plate in order to score a run.

hom·er (hō′mər), a home run in baseball. *noun.*

home·room (hōm′rüm′), a classroom where members of a class meet to do such things as answer roll call and hear announcements. *noun.*

home run, a hit in baseball which allows the batter to run around the bases and reach home plate to score a run.

home·sick (hōm′sik′), overcome by sadness because home is far away; ill with longing for home. *adjective.*

home·spun (hōm′spun′), **1** spun or made at home. **2** cloth made of yarn spun at home. **3** plain; simple: *homespun manners.* **1,3** *adjective,* **2** *noun.*

home·stead (hōm′sted′), **1** a house with its land and other buildings; farm with its buildings. **2** public land granted to a settler under certain conditions by the United States government. *noun.*

home·stead·er (hōm′sted′ər), **1** a person who has a homestead. **2** a settler granted a homestead by the United States government. *noun.*

home·town (hōm′toun′), the town or city where a person was born or brought up. *noun.*

home·ward (hōm′wərd), toward home: *We turned homeward. The ship is on its homeward course. adverb, adjective.*

home·wards (hōm′wərdz), homeward. *adverb.*

home·work (hōm′werk′), a lesson to be studied or prepared outside the classroom. *noun.*

a hat	**i** it	**oi** oil	**ch** child	
ā age	**ī** ice	**ou** out	**ng** long	a in about
ä far	**o** hot	**u** cup	**sh** she	ə = { e in taken
e let	**ō** open	**u̇** put	**th** thin	i in pencil
ē equal	**ô** order	**ü** rule	**ŦH** then	o in lemon
ėr term			**zh** measure	u in circus

H

hom·i·ny (hom′ə nē), kernels of corn that are hulled and used whole or coarsely ground. Hominy is often eaten boiled. *noun.*

ho·mog·e·nized milk (hə moj′ə nīzd milk′), milk in which the fat is spread evenly throughout and does not rise to the top in the form of cream.

hom·o·graph (hom′ə graf), a word having the same spelling as another word, but a different history and meaning. *Bass* (bas), meaning "a kind of fish," and *bass* (bās), meaning "a male singing voice," are homographs. *noun.*

hom·o·nym (hom′ə nim), a word having the same sound, or the same spelling, or both, as another word. Homonyms have different histories and meanings. *Mail,* meaning "letters," *mail,* meaning "armor," and *male,* meaning "masculine," are homonyms. *noun.*

hom·o·phone (hom′ə fōn), a word having the same sound as another, but a different history and meaning. *Ate* and *eight* are homophones. *noun.*

Hon·dur·as (hon dúr′əs), a country in Central America. *noun.*

hon·est (on′ist), **1** fair and upright; truthful; not lying, cheating, or stealing: *They are honest people.* **2** obtained by fair means; without lying, cheating, or stealing: *They made an honest profit. He lived an honest life.* **3** not hiding one's real nature; frank; open: *She is honest about her feelings. adjective.*

hon·es·ty (on′ə stē), honest behavior; honest nature; honest quality: *She shows honesty in all her business affairs. noun.*

hon·ey (hun′ē), **1** a thick, sweet, yellow liquid, good to eat, that bees make out of the drops they collect from flowers. **2** darling; dear: *"Is that you, honey?" she called. noun, plural* **hon·eys.**

hon·ey·bee (hun′ē bē′), a bee that makes honey. *noun.*

honeybees and **honeycomb** (definition 1)

hon·ey·comb (hun′ē kōm′), **1** a structure of wax made up of rows of six-sided cells. It is made by honeybees to store honey, pollen, and their eggs. **2** anything like this: *The village market was a honeycomb of tiny shops.* **3** to make or pierce with many holes or openings: *The old castle was honeycombed with passages.* **1,2** *noun,* **3** *verb.*

hon·ey·moon (hun′ē mün′), **1** a holiday spent together by a newly married couple. **2** to spend or have a honeymoon. **1** *noun,* **2** *verb.*

hon·ey·suck·le (hun′ē suk′əl), a climbing shrub with fragrant white, yellow, or red flowers. *noun.*

honk (hongk), **1** the cry of a wild goose. **2** a sound like the cry of a wild goose: *the honk of an automobile horn.* **3** to make such a sound: *We honked as we drove past our friends' house.* **1,2** *noun,* **3** *verb.*

Hon·o·lu·lu (hon′ə lü′lü), the capital of Hawaii. *noun.*

hon·or (on′ər), **1** credit for acting well; glory or fame; good name: *It was greatly to her honor to be given the scholarship.* **2 honors,** special mention given to a student by a school for having done work much above the average. **3** a source of credit; person or thing that reflects honor: *It is an honor to be chosen class president.* **4** a sense of what is right or proper; nobility of mind: *A person of honor always keeps a promise.* **5** great respect; high regard: *He was held in honor by all who knew him.* **6 Honor,** a title of respect used in speaking to a judge, mayor, governor, senator, or similar public official. **7** to show respect to: *We honor our country's dead soldiers every year on Memorial Day.* **1-6** *noun,* **7** *verb.*

hon·or·a·ble (on′ər ə bəl), **1** having or showing a sense of what is right and proper; honest; upright: *It is not honorable to lie or cheat.* **2** noble; worthy of honor: *Teaching is an honorable occupation. adjective.*

hon·or·ar·y (on′ə rer′ē), given or done as an honor: *The university awarded honorary degrees to three famous scientists. adjective.*

hood (húd), **1** a soft covering for the head and neck, either separate or as part of a coat: *My raincoat has a hood.* **2** anything like a hood in shape or use. **3** a metal covering over the engine of an automobile. *noun.*

hood·ed (húd′id), **1** having a hood: *I have a hooded jacket.* **2** shaped like a hood. *adjective.*

hood·lum (hüd′ləm), **1** a criminal or gangster. **2** a disorderly young person. *noun.*

hoof (húf), a hard, horny covering on the feet of horses, cattle, sheep, pigs, and some other animals. *noun, plural* **hoofs** or **hooves.**

hoof·beat (húf′bēt′), the sound made by an animal's hoof. *noun.*

hoofed (húft), having hoofs. *adjective.*

hook (húk), **1** a curved piece of metal, wood, or the like used to hold, catch, or fasten something: *Hang your coat on that hook.* **2** to take hold of, or fasten with, a hook: *The sharp corner of the desk hooked my sleeve. Will you hook my dress for me?* **3** to catch or take hold of with a hook. **4** a curved piece of wire, usually with a barb at the end, for catching fish. **5** to catch fish with a hook: *I hooked three trout.* **6** anything curved or bent like a hook: *His nose has a slight hook.* **7** to make into the shape of a hook: *I hooked my arm in hers and we started off.* **1,4,6** *noun,* **2,3,5,7** *verb.*

by hook or by crook, in any way at all; by fair means or foul.

hooked
A parrot has
a **hooked** beak.

a hat	i it	oi oil	ch child	⎧ a in about
ā age	ī ice	ou out	ng long	⎪ e in taken
ä far	o hot	u cup	sh she	ə = ⎨ i in pencil
e let	ō open	u̇ put	th thin	⎪ o in lemon
ē equal	ô order	ü rule	ᴛH then	⎩ u in circus
ėr term			zh measure	

hopper

hooked (hu̇kt), curved or bent like a hook. *adjective*.

hook·y (huk′ē). **play hooky,** to stay away from school without permission. *noun*.

hoop (hu̇p *or* hüp), **1** a ring or flat band in the form of a circle: *a hoop for holding embroidery, a basketball hoop*. **2** a large plastic ring used as a toy, especially for spinning around the body. **3** a circular frame formerly used to hold out a woman's skirt. *noun*.

hoo·ray (hu̇ rā′). See **hurrah**. *interjection, noun, verb*.

hoot (hüt), **1** the sound that an owl makes. **2** to make this sound or one like it. **3** a shout to show disapproval or scorn. **4** to shout disapproval of or scorn for: *The audience hooted the speaker's plan.* **1,3** *noun*, **2,4** *verb*.

hooves (hu̇vz), more than one hoof. *noun plural*.

hop¹ (hop), **1** to jump, or move by jumping, on one foot: *How far can you hop on your right foot?* **2** to jump, or move by jumping, with both or all feet at once: *Many birds hop. A kangaroo hops.* **3** to jump over: *to hop a ditch.* **4** a jump or leap: *He came up each step with a hop.* **1-3** *verb*, **hops, hopped, hop·ping;** **4** *noun*.

hop² (hop), **1** a vine having flower clusters that look like small, yellow pine cones. **2 hops,** the dried ripe flower clusters of the hop vine, used to flavor beer and other malt drinks. *noun*.

hope (hōp), **1** a feeling that what you desire will happen: *Her encouragement gave me hope.* **2** to wish and expect: *I hope to do well in school this year.* **3** a thing hoped for: *It is my hope that he succeeds.* **4** a cause of hope: *You are our only hope for winning the race.* **1,3,4** *noun*, **2** *verb*, **hopes, hoped, hop·ing.**

hope·ful (hōp′fəl), **1** feeling or showing hope; expecting to receive what one wants: *We were hopeful that the weather would improve.* **2** causing hope; giving hope; likely to succeed: *The news from my doctor was hopeful. adjective.*

hope·less (hōp′lis), **1** feeling no hope: *Our attempts to get help failed so often that we became hopeless.* **2** giving no hope: *a hopeless illness. adjective.*

Ho·pi (hō′pē), a member of a tribe of American Indians living in northern Arizona. *noun, plural* **Ho·pi** or **Ho·pis.**

hop·per (hop′ər), a container to hold something

and feed it into another part. A hopper is usually larger at the top than at the bottom. *noun*.

hop·scotch (hop′skoch′), a children's game in which the players hop over the lines of a figure drawn on the ground. *noun*.

horde (hôrd), a multitude; crowd; swarm: *Hordes of grasshoppers destroyed the crops. noun.* [An earlier meaning of this word was "a band of nomads of central Asia." The word came from a Turkish word meaning "a camp." Nomads did not have permanent homes, but lived wherever they set up their tents.]

ho·ri·zon (hə rī′zn), **1** the line where earth and sky seem to meet. You cannot see beyond the horizon. **2** the limit of one's thinking, experience, interest, or outlook: *Travel broadens one's horizons. noun.*

ho·ri·zon·tal (hôr′ə zon′tl), **1** parallel to the horizon; at right angles to a vertical line: *A ceiling is horizontal.* **2** flat; level: *The top of a table is a horizontal surface. adjective.*

hor·mone (hôr′mōn), a substance formed in certain glands, which enters the bloodstream and affects or controls the activity of some organ or tissue. *noun*.

horn (hôrn), **1** a hard, hollow growth on the heads of cattle, sheep, goats, and some other animals that is usually curved and pointed. **2** anything that sticks up on the head of an animal: *a snail's horns, an insect's horns.* **3** the substance or material of horns. A person's fingernails, the beaks of birds, the hoofs of horses, and tortoise shells are all made of horn. **4** a container made by hollowing out a horn. It was used to drink out of or to carry gunpowder in. **5** a musical instrument sounded by blowing into the smaller end. It was once made of horn, but now it is made of brass or other metal. **6** a device sounded as a warning signal: *an automobile horn.* **7** anything that sticks out like a horn or is shaped like a horn: *a saddle horn, the horn of a bay. noun.*

horned (hôrnd), having a horn, horns, or hornlike growths. *adjective*.

horned toad
about 4 inches
(10 centimeters) long

horned toad, a small lizard with a broad, flat body, short tail, and many hornlike spines.

hor·net (hôr′nit), a large wasp that can give a very painful sting. *noun.*

horn·y (hôr′nē), **1** made of horn or a substance like it. **2** hard like horn: *A farmer's hands are horny from work. adjective,* **horn·i·er, horn·i·est.**

ho·ro·scope (hôr′ə skōp), **1** a diagram used in telling fortunes by the planets and the stars. **2** a fortune told by using such a diagram. *noun.*

hor·ri·ble (hôr′ə bəl), **1** causing horror; frightful; shocking: *a horrible crime, a horrible disease.* **2** extremely unpleasant: *a horrible smell. adjective.*

hor·rid (hôr′id), **1** causing great fear; frightful: *There was a horrid car accident.* **2** very unpleasant: *What a horrid color! adjective.*

hor·ri·fy (hôr′ə fī), **1** to cause to feel horror: *The child was horrified by the large, snarling dog.* **2** to shock very much: *We were horrified by such rude behavior. verb,* **hor·ri·fies, hor·ri·fied, hor·ri·fy·ing.**

hor·ror (hôr′ər), **1** a shivering, shaking terror. **2** a very strong dislike: *I have a horror of guns.* **3** a thing that causes great fear: *For the soldier, war was a horror. noun.*

horse (hôrs), **1** a four-legged animal with hoofs, and a mane and tail of long, coarse hair. Horses have been used from very early times to pull loads and carry riders. **2** a supporting frame with legs: *Five boards laid on two horses made our picnic table.* **3** a padded piece of gymnasium equipment, supported by legs. It is used in jumping exercises and for gymnastics. **4 horse around,** to fool around; get into mischief. **1,2,3** *noun,* **4** *verb,* **hors·es, horsed, hors·ing. horse of a different color,** something different.

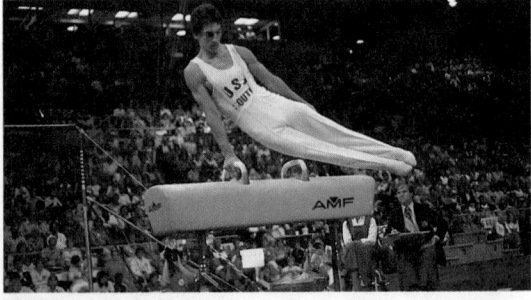

horse (definition 3)—a gymnast using a **horse**

horse·back (hôrs′bak′), **1** the back of a horse: *We went to the mountains on horseback.* **2** on the back of a horse: *to ride horseback.* **1** *noun,* **2** *adverb.*

horse·fly (hôrs′flī′), a large fly that bites animals, especially horses. *noun, plural* **horse·flies.**

horse·man (hôrs′mən), **1** a person who rides on horseback: *Three horsemen galloped down the road.* **2** a person who is skilled in riding or managing horses: *The horse show was put on by a group of horsemen. noun, plural* **horse·men.**

horse·play (hôrs′plā′), rough, boisterous fun: *Stop the horseplay before you break the furniture. noun.*

horse·pow·er (hôrs′pou′ər), a measure of the power of an engine. One horsepower is the power to lift 550 pounds one foot in one second. *noun.*

horse·rad·ish (hôrs′rad′ish), a plant with a white, hot-tasting root which is ground up and used as a relish with meat or other foods. *noun.*

horse·shoe (hôrs′shü′), a flat piece of metal shaped like a U, nailed to the bottom of a horse's hoof to protect it. *noun.*

horse·wom·an (hôrs′wùm′ən), **1** a woman who rides on horseback. **2** a woman who is skilled in riding or managing horses. *noun, plural* **horse·wom·en.**

hose (hōz), **1** a flexible tube of rubber or plastic for carrying a liquid or a gas. Hoses are used to water lawns and to fill tires with air. **2** stockings or socks. *noun, plural* **hos·es** for 1, **hose** for 2.

ho·sier·y (hō′zhər ē), stockings, socks, or the like: *The company made hosiery for men, women, and children. noun.*

hos·pi·ta·ble (hos′pi tə bəl *or* ho spit′ə bəl), giving or liking to give a welcome, food and shelter, and friendly treatment to guests or strangers: *a hospitable family, a hospitable reception. adjective.*

hos·pi·ta·bly (hos′pi tə blē *or* ho spit′ə blē), in a hospitable manner. *adverb.*

hos·pi·tal (hos′pi təl), a place for the care of the sick or injured. *noun.*
[Earlier meanings of *hospital* were "hostel" or "hotel," operated by a "host." *Hospital, hostel,* and *hotel* all come from a Latin word meaning "host[1]."]

hos·pi·tal·i·ty (hos′pə tal′ə tē), the generous treatment of guests or strangers. *noun.*

hos·pi·tal·ize (hos′pi tə līz), to put in a hospital for treatment: *She was hospitalized after the accident. verb,* **hos·pi·tal·iz·es, hos·pi·tal·ized, hos·pi·tal·iz·ing.**

host[1] (hōst), a person who receives another person as a guest: *Before we left the party, we thanked our hosts. noun.*

host[2] (hōst), a large number: *As it grew dark, a few stars appeared, then a host. noun.*

hos·tage (hos′tij), a person who is held as a prisoner until some demand is agreed to: *The convicts took guards as hostages until they were promised better living conditions. noun.*

hos·tel (hos′tl), a lodging place, especially a supervised lodging place for young people on bicycle or motorcycle trips or hikes; inn. *noun.*

host·ess (hō′stis), **1** a woman who receives another person as her guest. **2** a woman employed in a restaurant to welcome and serve people. *noun, plural* **host·ess·es.**

hos·tile (hos′tl), unfriendly; showing dislike or hatred: *She did hostile things such as telling lies about me. adjective.*

hos·til·i·ty (ho stil′ə tē), **1** unfriendliness; dislike or hatred: *They showed signs of hostility toward our plan.* **2 hostilities,** acts of war; warfare; fighting: *The peace treaty brought hostilities to an end. noun, plural* **hos·til·i·ties.**

hos·tler (os′lər *or* hos′lər), a person who takes care of horses at an inn or stable. *noun.*

hot (hot), **1** much warmer than the body: *That fire is hot.* **2** warmer than it usually is: *The weather is hot for April.* **3** feeling hot or warm: *That long run has made me hot.* **4** having a sharp, burning taste: *Pepper and mustard are hot.* **5** violent; fiery: *He has a hot temper.* **6** new; fresh: *I just got some hot news. The trail is still hot, so the police expect to catch the criminal.* **7** following closely: *We were in hot pursuit of the runaway horse. adjective,* **hot·ter, hot·test.**

hot cake, a pancake.

hot dog, 1 a sandwich made with a hot frankfurter enclosed in a bun. **2** a frankfurter.

ho·tel (hō tel′), a place where people traveling away from home can rent a room to sleep in. *noun.*

hot·house (hot′hous′), a building with a glass roof and sides, kept warm for growing plants; greenhouse. *noun, plural* **hot·hous·es** (hot′hou′ziz).

hot plate, a small, portable electric stove for cooking, with one or two burners.

hound (hound), **1** a dog of any of various breeds, most of which hunt by scent and have large, drooping ears and short hair. **2** any dog. **3** to urge on: *The children hounded their parents to buy a color TV.* 1,2 *noun,* 3 *verb.*

hour (our), **1** one of the 12 equal periods of time between noon and midnight, or between midnight and noon. 60 minutes make an hour. 24 hours make a day. **2** the time of day: *This clock strikes the hours and the half hours.* **3** the time for anything: *Our breakfast hour is at eight.* **4 hours,** time for work or study: *What are the hours in this office? Our school hours are 9 to 12 and 1 to 4. noun.*

hour·glass (our′glas′), a device for measuring time, made up of two glass bulbs connected by a narrow neck. It takes an hour for sand in the top bulb to pass through the neck to the bottom bulb. *noun, plural* **hour·glass·es.**

hour·ly (our′lē), **1** done, happening, or counted every hour: *There are hourly reports of the news and weather on this radio station.* **2** every hour: *Give two doses of the medicine hourly.* 1 *adjective,* 2 *adverb.*

a hat	i it	oi oil	ch child	⎧ a in about
ā age	ī ice	ou out	ng long	⎪ e in taken
ä far	o hot	u cup	sh she	ə = ⎨ i in pencil
e let	ō open	u̇ put	th thin	⎪ o in lemon
ē equal	ô order	ü rule	ŦH then	⎩ u in circus
ėr term			zh measure	

house (hous *for 1-4, 6-8;* houz *for 5*), **1** a building in which people live. **2** the people living in a house; household: *The noise woke up the whole house.* **3** a family with its ancestors and descendants, especially a noble family: *He was a prince of the house of David.* **4** a building for any purpose: *a tool house, a movie house.* **5** to take or put into a house; shelter: *Where can we house all these children?* **6** a place of business or a business firm: *a publishing house.* **7** an assembly for making laws. In the United States, the House of Representatives is the lower house of Congress; the Senate is the upper house. **8** an audience: *The singer sang to a large house.* 1-4, 6-8 *noun, plural* **hous·es** (hou′ziz); 5 *verb,* **hous·es, housed, hous·ing.**

house·boat (hous′bōt′), a boat that can be used as a place to live in. *noun.*

houseboat

house·fly (hous′flī′), a two-winged fly that lives around and in houses, feeding on food, garbage, and filth. *noun, plural* **house·flies.**

house·hold (hous′hōld), **1** all the people living in a house: *Everyone in our household helps with the chores.* **2** a home and its affairs: *They lived in a neat and orderly household.* **3** of a household; having to do with a household: *household expenses, household chores.* 1,2 *noun,* 3 *adjective.*

house·keep·er (hous′kē′pər), **1** a person who takes care of a household or who does housework. **2** a woman who is hired to manage or do housework in a home or hotel. *noun.*

hourglass
This hourglass was used on an English ship in the 1700s.

H

house·keep·ing (hous′kē′ping), the management of a home and its affairs; doing the housework. *noun.*

house·wife (hous′wīf′), a married woman who manages a home and its affairs for her family. *noun, plural* **house·wives** (hous′wīvz′).

house·work (hous′wėrk′), the work to be done in housekeeping, such as washing, ironing, cleaning, or cooking. *noun.*

hous·ing (hou′zing), houses or other places to live in: *The university built more housing for its students. noun.*

Hous·ton (hyü′stən), a city in Texas. *noun.*

hov·el (huv′əl), a house that is small, crude, and unpleasant to live in. *noun.*

hov·er (huv′ər), **1** to stay in or near one place in the air: *The two birds hovered over their nest.* **2** to stay in or near one place; wait nearby: *The dogs hovered around the kitchen door at mealtime.* **3** to be in an uncertain condition; waver: *The patient hovered between life and death. verb.*

how (hou), **1** in what way; by what means: *How can it be done? How did it happen? I wonder how you get there.* **2** to what degree or amount: *How tall is she? How hot is it? How long will it take you to do this?* **3** in what state or condition: *How is your health? Tell me how she is. How do I look?* **4** for what reason; why: *How is it you are late?* **1-4** *adverb,* **1,3** *conjunction.*

how come, why: *How come you didn't call me last night?*

how·dy (hou′dē), a call of greeting; hello: *The cowboy said, "Howdy, stranger!" interjection.*

how·ev·er (hou ev′ər), **1** nevertheless; yet; in spite of that: *We were very late for dinner; however, there was plenty left for us.* **2** to whatever degree or amount; no matter how: *I'll come however busy I am.* **3** in whatever way; by whatever means: *However did you get so dirty?* **1** *conjunction,* **2,3** *adverb.*

howl (houl), **1** to give a long, loud, mournful cry: *Our dog often howls at night. The winter winds howled around our cabin.* **2** a long, loud, mournful cry: *the howl of a wolf.* **3** to give a long, loud cry of pain or rage. **4** a loud cry of pain or rage. **5** a yell or shout: *We heard howls of laughter.* **6** to yell or shout: *It was so funny that we howled with laughter.* **1,3,6** *verb,* **2,4,5** *noun.*

hr., hour or hours.

hub (hub), **1** the central part of a wheel. **2** a center of interest, importance, or activity: *London is the hub of English life. noun.*

hub·bub (hub′ub), a loud, confused noise; uproar: *A fight caused a hubbub on the crowded playground. noun.*

huck·le·ber·ry (huk′əl ber′ē), a small berry that grows on a shrub. Huckleberries are like blueberries, but are darker in color. *noun, plural* **huck·le·ber·ries.**

hud·dle (hud′l), **1** to crowd close: *The sheep huddled together in a corner.* **2** to put close together: *She huddled all four boys into one bed.* **3** a grouping of football players to discuss the next play and to receive signals. **1,2** *verb,* **hud·dles, hud·dled, hud·dling; 3** *noun.*

hue (hyü), a color or a shade of color: *The room was painted in several hues of green. noun.*

huff (huf), **1** a fit of anger: *We had a heated argument, and she left in a huff.* **2** to puff; blow: *I huffed and puffed up the stairs with the heavy package.* **1** *noun,* **2** *verb.*

hug (hug), **1** to put the arms around and hold close: *The girl hugged her new puppy.* **2** a tight clasp with the arms: *She gave the puppy a hug.* **3** to keep close to: *The boat hugged the shore.* **1,3** *verb,* **hugs, hugged, hug·ging; 2** *noun.*

huge (hyüj), very big; unusually large or great: *A whale is a huge animal. He won a huge sum of money. adjective,* **hug·er, hug·est.**

hulk (hulk), a big, clumsy person or thing: *The wrestler was a hulk of a man who moved slowly and carefully. noun.*

hulk·ing (hul′king), big and clumsy: *He was a large, hulking boy. adjective.*

hull (hul), **1** the body or frame of a ship. Masts, sails, and rigging are not part of the hull. **2** the outer covering of a seed. **3** the small leaves around the stem of a strawberry and certain other fruits. **4** to remove the hull or hulls from: *to hull strawberries or dried beans.* **1-3** *noun,* **4** *verb.*

hum (hum), **1** to make a continuous, murmuring sound like that of a bee or of a spinning top: *The sewing machine hums busily.* **2** a continuous, murmuring sound: *the hum of bees, the hum of the city streets.* **3** to sing with closed lips, not sounding words: *She was humming a tune.* **4** to be busy and active: *Things really hummed at campaign headquarters just before the election.* **1,3,4** *verb,* **hums, hummed, hum·ming; 2** *noun.*

hu·man (hyü′mən), **1** of persons; that people have: *Kindness is a human trait. To know what will happen in the future is beyond human power.* **2** being a person or persons; having the form or qualities of people: *Men, women, and children are human beings. Those monkeys seem almost human.* **3** a person; human being: *Humans have large brains.* **1,2** *adjective,* **3** *noun.* [*Human* comes from a Latin word meaning "of man" or "of human beings."]

hu·mane (hyü mān′), kind; not cruel or brutal: *I believe in the humane treatment of animals. adjective.*

hu·man·i·ty (hyü man′ə tē), **1** people: *All humanity will be helped by advances in medical science.* **2** kindness: *Treat animals with humanity. noun.*

hum·ble (hum′bəl), **1** low in position or condition; not important; not grand: *He has a humble job with very low wages. They lived in a humble cottage of one room.* **2** modest; not proud: *a humble opinion, to be humble in spite of success.* **3** to make humble; make lower in position, condition, or pride: *The team that bragged they would win was humbled by a big defeat.* **1,2** *adjective,* **hum·bler, hum·blest; 3** *verb,* **hum·bles, hum·bled, hum·bling.**

hum·bly (hum′blē), in a humble manner. *adverb.*

hum·bug (hum′bug′), nonsense or pretense: *We thought his story about seeing a ghost was a lot of humbug. noun.*

hu·mid (hyü′mid), moist; damp: *We found that the air was very humid near the sea. adjective.*

hu·mid·i·ty (hyü mid′ə tē), the amount of moisture in the air: *People feel uncomfortable when the temperature and humidity are both high. noun.*

hu·mil·i·ate (hyü mil′ē āt), to lower the pride, dignity, or self-respect of: *They humiliated me by criticizing me in front of my friends. verb,* **hu·mil·i·ates, hu·mil·i·at·ed, hu·mil·i·at·ing.**

hu·mil·i·a·tion (hyü mil′ē ā′shən), a lowering of pride, dignity, or self-respect: *After bragging about my skiing, I suffered the humiliation of falling many times. noun.*

hu·mil·i·ty (hyü mil′ə tē), humbleness of mind; lack of pride; meekness. *noun.*

hum·ming·bird (hum′ing bėrd′), a very small, brightly colored American bird with a long, narrow bill and narrow wings that move so rapidly they make a humming sound in the air. *noun.*

hummingbird—about 4 inches (10 centimeters) long

hu·mor (hyü′mər), 1 a funny or amusing quality: *I see no humor in your tricks.* 2 the ability to see or show the funny or amusing side of things: *Her sense of humor enabled her to joke about her problems.* 3 a state of mind; mood; temper: *Is the teacher in a good humor this morning?* 4 to give in to the wishes of a person; agree with: *They humored the sick child by allowing her to have ice cream for breakfast.* 1-3 *noun,* 4 *verb.*
out of humor, cross; in a bad mood: *He gets out of humor if we tease him too much.*

hu·mor·ist (hyü′mər ist), a humorous talker; writer of jokes and funny stories. *noun.*

hu·mor·ous (hyü′mər əs), full of humor; funny; amusing: *We all laughed at the humorous story. adjective.*

hump (hump), 1 a rounded lump that sticks out: *Some camels have two humps on their backs.* 2 to raise or bend up into a lump: *The cat humped its back when it saw the dog.* 3 a mound. 1,3 *noun,* 2 *verb.*

hump·backed (hump′bakt′), hunchbacked. *adjective.*

a hat	i it	oi oil	ch child	a in about
ā age	ī ice	ou out	ng long	e in taken
ä far	o hot	u cup	sh she	ə = i in pencil
e let	ō open	ů put	th thin	o in lemon
ē equal	ô order	ü rule	₮H then	u in circus
ėr term			zh measure	

hu·mus (hyü′məs), a dark-brown part of the soil formed from decayed leaves and other vegetable matter. Humus contains valuable plant foods. *noun.*

hunch (hunch), 1 to draw, bend, or form into a hump: *He sat hunched up with his chin on his knees.* 2 a feeling or suspicion that you don't know the reason for: *I had a hunch it would rain, so I took my umbrella.* 1 *verb,* 2 *noun, plural* **hunch·es.**

hunch·back (hunch′bak′), a person having a backbone that curves outward, forming a hump on the back. *noun.*

hunch·backed (hunch′bakt′), having a hump on the back. *adjective.*

hun·dred (hun′drəd), ten times ten; 100. There are one hundred cents in a dollar. *noun, adjective.*

hun·dredth (hun′drədth), 1 next after the 99th. 2 one of 100 equal parts. *adjective, noun.*

hung (hung). See **hang.** *He hung up his cap. Your dress has hung here all day. verb.*

Hun·gar·i·an (hung ger′ē ən), 1 of Hungary, its people, or their language. 2 a person born or living in Hungary. 3 the language of Hungary. 1 *adjective,* 2,3 *noun.*

Hun·gar·y (hung′gər ē), a country in central Europe. *noun.*

hun·ger (hung′gər), 1 pains in the stomach caused by having had nothing to eat. 2 a desire or need for food: *I ate an apple to satisfy my hunger.* 3 a strong desire: *The bright boy had a hunger for knowledge.* 4 to have a strong desire: *The neglected child hungered for love and attention.* 1-3 *noun,* 4 *verb.*

hun·gri·ly (hung′grə lē), in a hungry manner: *They ate hungrily after their long hike. adverb.*

hun·gry (hung′grē), 1 feeling a desire or need for food: *I missed breakfast and was hungry all morning.* 2 showing hunger: *The stray cat had a hungry look.* 3 eager: *A person who longs to read and study is hungry for knowledge. adjective,* **hun·gri·er, hun·gri·est.**

hunk (hungk), a big lump or piece. *noun.*

hunt (hunt), 1 to go after wild birds or animals in order to kill them for food or for sport: *They went to the woods to hunt deer.* 2 the act of hunting: *I went on a duck hunt in the marsh.* 3 to search; seek; look: *hunt for a lost book.* 4 a search; attempt to find something: *The hunt for the lost child continued until she was found.* 1,3 *verb,* 2,4 *noun.*

hunt·er (hun′tər), 1 a person who hunts. 2 a horse or dog trained for hunting. *noun.*

hunts·man (hunts′mən), a hunter. *noun, plural* **hunts·men.**

hurdle (definition 2)—The **hurdles** is one event in track-and-field competition.

hur·dle (hėr′dl), **1** a barrier for people or horses to jump over in a race. **2 hurdles,** a race in which the runners jump over hurdles. **3** to jump over: *The horse hurdled both the fence and the ditch.* **4** something that stands in the way; difficulty or obstacle: *Getting my parents' consent was the last hurdle before I could join the football team.* **5** to overcome an obstacle or difficulty. 1,2,4 *noun,* 3,5 *verb,* **hur·dles, hur·dled, hur·dling.**

hurl (hėrl), to throw with much force; fling: *hurl a spear, hurl rocks. verb.*

Hur·on (hyur′ən), **Lake,** one of the five Great Lakes. *noun.*

hur·rah (hə rä′), **1** a shout of joy or approval: *Give a hurrah for the team!* **2** to shout hurrahs; cheer: *We hurrahed as the congresswoman rode by in the parade.* 1 *interjection, noun,* 2 *verb.* Also spelled **hooray.**

hur·ray (hə rā′), hurrah. *interjection, noun, verb.*

hur·ri·cane (hėr′ə kān), a storm with violent wind and, usually, very heavy rain. The wind in a hurricane blows at more than 75 miles (121 kilometers) per hour. *noun.*

hur·ried (hėr′ēd), done or made in a hurry; hasty: *a hurried escape, a hurried reply. adjective.*

hur·ry (hėr′ē), **1** to move or act more quickly than usual; rush: *She hurried to get to work on time. They hurried the sick child to the doctor.* **2** a hurried movement or action: *In his hurry he dropped the bag of groceries.* **3** eagerness to have quickly or do quickly: *She was in a hurry to meet her friends.* **4** to urge to greater speed or faster action: *Don't hurry the driver.* 1,4 *verb,* **hur·ries, hur·ried, hur·ry·ing;** 2,3 *noun.*

hurt (hėrt), **1** to cause pain or injury to: *The stone hurt my foot.* **2** a cut, bruise, or fracture; any wound or injury: *A scratch is not a serious hurt.* **3** to suffer pain: *My hand hurts.* **4** to have a bad effect on; do damage or harm to: *Large price increases can hurt sales. Did I hurt your feelings?* 1,3,4 *verb,* **hurts, hurt, hurt·ing;** 2 *noun.*

hurt·ful (hėrt′fəl), causing hurt, harm, or damage: *Telling lies about me was a mean and hurtful thing to do. adjective.*

hur·tle (hėr′tl), to move or rush violently: *The express train hurtled by. verb,* **hur·tles, hur·tled, hur·tling.**

hus·band (huz′bənd), a man who has a wife; married man. *noun.*
[*Husband* comes from an old Norse word meaning "one who dwells in a house" or "master of a house."]

hush (hush), **1** to stop making a noise; make or become silent or quiet: *The wind has hushed. Hush your dog.* **2** a stopping of noise; stillness: *In the hush after the storm, a bird began to sing.* **3** stop the noise! be silent! 1 *verb,* 2 *noun,* 3 *interjection.*

husk (husk), **1** the dry outer covering of certain seeds or fruits. An ear of corn has a husk. **2** to remove the husk from: *Husk the corn before cooking it.* 1 *noun,* 2 *verb.*

husk·i·ness (hus′kē nis), **1** a hoarseness or roughness of voice. **2** a being big and strong. *noun.*

husk·y[1] (hus′kē), **1** big and strong: *He was a husky young man who could lift heavy weights.* **2** sounding rough and deep; hoarse: *Her voice was husky because she had a cold. adjective,* **husk·i·er, husk·i·est.**

hus·ky[2] or **Hus·ky** (hus′kē), a strong, medium-sized dog used to pull sleds in arctic regions. A husky usually has a thick coat and a bushy tail. *noun, plural* **hus·kies** or **Hus·kies.**

hus·tle (hus′əl), **1** to move quickly; hurry: *I had to hustle to get the lawn mowed before it rained.* **2** to push or shove roughly: *Guards hustled the demonstrators away from the mayor's office.* **3** hurried movement: *The family prepared for the holidays with much hustle and bustle.* 1,2 *verb,* **hus·tles, hus·tled, hus·tling;** 3 *noun.*

hut (hut), a small, roughly made cabin: *The shepherd lived in a simple hut made of mud and straw. noun.*

hutch (huch), a box or pen for small animals. Rabbits are kept in hutches. *noun, plural* **hutch·es.**

hy·a·cinth (hī′ə sinth), a spring plant that grows from a bulb and has many small, fragrant flowers along its stem. *noun.*

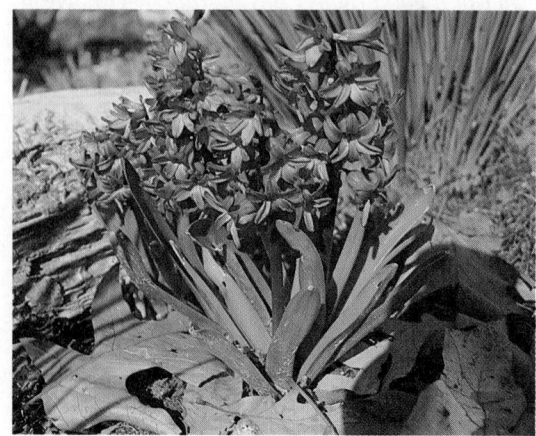

hyacinths

hy·brid (hī′brid), **1** the offspring of two living things of different kinds or species. The loganberry is a hybrid because it is a cross between a raspberry and a blackberry. **2** bred from two different kinds or species: *A mule is a hybrid animal produced from a female horse and a male donkey.* **1** *noun,* **2** *adjective.*

hy·drant (hī′drənt), a large water pipe that sticks up from the ground and has places where firefighters can connect hoses; fireplug. *noun.*

hy·dro·e·lec·tric (hī′drō i lek′trik), producing electricity by using the power of moving water: *Hydroelectric plants are sometimes located beside waterfalls. adjective.*

hy·dro·gen (hī′drə jən), a colorless gas that burns easily. Hydrogen is a chemical element that weighs less than any other known substance. It combines with oxygen to form water. *noun.*

hydrogen bomb, a bomb in which the combining of atoms of hydrogen produces an explosion of tremendous force; H-bomb. It is many times more powerful than the atomic bomb.

hy·e·na (hī ē′nə), a wild, wolflike animal of Africa and Asia which feeds on other animals at night. Hyenas are known for their terrifying yells. *noun.*

hyena—about 2 feet (60 centimeters) high at the shoulder

hy·giene (hī′jēn′), the rules and practices that help people keep well. Keeping one's body and surroundings clean is an important part of hygiene. *noun.*

hy·gien·ist (hī jē′nist), a person who helps a dentist by examining and cleaning patients' teeth and by taking X rays. *noun.*

hymn (him), a song of praise, especially in honor of God. *noun.*

hym·nal (him′nəl), a book of hymns. *noun.*

hy·phen (hī′fən), a mark (-) used to show that two or more words have been combined into a single term, as in *hide-and-seek.* A hyphen also shows that a word has been divided at the end of a line. *noun.*

a hat	i it	oi oil	ch child	a in about
ā age	ī ice	ou out	ng long	e in taken
ä far	o hot	u cup	sh she	ə = { i in pencil
e let	ō open	u̇ put	th thin	o in lemon
ē equal	ô order	ü rule	ᴛʜ then	u in circus
ėr term			zh measure	

hy·phen·ate (hī′fə nāt), to join words or divide a word by using a hyphen: *Hyphenate the word hurricane after the first r, or after the i, if it won't fit on one line. verb,* **hy·phen·ates, hy·phen·at·ed, hy·phen·at·ing.**

hyp·no·tism (hip′nə tiz′əm), a hypnotizing; putting into a sleeplike state. *noun.*

hyp·no·tist (hip′nə tist), a person who has the ability to hypnotize others. *noun.*

hyp·no·tize (hip′nə tīz), to put a person into a state similar to sleep, but more active. A hypnotized person tends to follow the spoken suggestions of the hypnotist and may feel no pain or other kinds of stimulation. *verb,* **hyp·no·tiz·es, hyp·no·tized, hyp·no·tiz·ing.**

hy·poc·ri·sy (hi pok′rə sē), a pretending to be what one is not, especially claiming to be very good or religious but not acting that way. *noun.*

hyp·o·crite (hip′ə krit), a person who pretends to be what he or she is not, especially someone who claims to be very good or religious but does not act that way. *noun.*

hy·po·der·mic (hī′pə dėr′mik), injected or used to inject under the skin: *The doctor used a hypodermic needle. adjective.*

hys·ter·i·a (hi stir′ē ə *or* hi ster′ē ə), excitement or emotion that is out of control: *When a fire broke out, fear of being trapped caused hysteria in the theater audience. noun.*

hys·ter·i·cal (hi ster′ə kəl), showing extreme lack of control; unnaturally excited: *The hysterical child was unable to stop crying. adjective.*

H

I i

I[1] or i (ī), the ninth letter of the English alphabet. *noun, plural* I's or i's.

I[2] (ī), the person who is speaking or writing: *John said, "I am ten years old." I like my dog, and he likes me.* pronoun, *plural* we.

IA, Iowa (used with postal Zip Code).

Ia., Iowa.

-ible, a suffix meaning able to be _____ed: A divis*ible* fraction means a fraction *able to be* divid*ed*.

ice (īs), 1 water made solid by cold; frozen water. 2 of ice; having something to do with ice: *an ice pack, ice cubes.* 3 to make cool with ice; put ice in or around: *We iced the fruit punch for the party.* 4 to turn to ice; freeze: *This lake ices over in winter.* 5 a frozen dessert, usually one made of sweetened fruit juice. 6 to cover cake with icing. 1,5 *noun,* 2 *adjective,* 3,4,6 *verb,* ic·es, iced, ic·ing.

Ice Age, a long period of time when much of the northern part of the earth was covered with glaciers. The Ice Age took place millions of years ago.

ice·berg (īs/bėrg/), a large mass of ice floating in the sea. A ship may be wrecked on an iceberg. *noun.*

Word History

iceberg *Iceberg* comes from a Dutch word meaning "ice mountain."

iceberg—The part of an iceberg under water is about eight times bigger than the part above water.

ice·boat (īs/bōt/), a triangular frame on runners, fitted with sails or an engine for sailing on ice. *noun.*

ice·bound (īs/bound/), held fast by ice; frozen in: *an icebound boat. adjective.*

ice·box (īs/boks/), 1 a refrigerator. 2 a box in which food is kept cool with ice. *noun, plural* ice·box·es.

ice·break·er (īs/brā/kər), a strong boat used to break a channel through ice. *noun.*

ice·cap (īs/kap/), a permanent covering of ice over an area, sloping down on all sides from a high center. *noun.*

ice cream, a smooth, frozen dessert made of various milk products sweetened and flavored.

Ice·land (īs/lənd), an island country in the northern Atlantic Ocean. *noun.*

ice skate, a shoe with a metal runner attached for skating on ice.

ice-skate (īs/skāt/), to skate on ice. *verb,* ice-skates, ice-skat·ed, ice-skat·ing.

i·ci·cle (ī/si kəl), a pointed, hanging stick of ice formed by the freezing of dripping water. *noun.*

i·ci·ly (ī/sə lē), very coldly. *adverb.*

ic·ing (ī/sing), a flavored mixture of sugar, butter or margarine, egg whites, and other things, used to cover cakes and other baked goods; frosting. *noun.*

i·cy (ī/sē), 1 like ice; very cold: *icy fingers.* 2 covered with ice; slippery: *The car skidded on the icy street.* 3 of ice: *an icy snowball.* 4 without warm feeling; cold and unfriendly: *She gave me an icy stare. adjective,* i·ci·er, i·ci·est.

I'd (īd), 1 I should. 2 I would. 3 I had.

ID, Idaho (used with postal Zip Code).

Id., Idaho.

I·da·ho (ī/də hō), one of the western states of the United States. *Abbreviation:* Id. or ID *Capital:* Boise. *noun.*

[*Idaho* may have come from an Apache name for the Comanche Indians.]

i·de·a (ī dē/ə), 1 a belief, plan, or picture in the mind: *Swimming is her idea of fun.* 2 a thought;

iceboat

icebreaker—an icebreaker in the Arctic Ocean

fancy; opinion: *I had no idea that the job would be so hard.* **3** the point or purpose: *The idea of a vacation is to get a rest. noun.*

i·de·al (ī dē′əl), **1** a perfect type; model to be imitated; what one would wish to be: *He is a person of high ideals. Her mother is her ideal.* **2** perfect; just as one would wish: *A warm, sunny day is ideal for a picnic.* **1** *noun,* **2** *adjective.*

i·den·ti·cal (ī den′tə kəl), **1** the same: *Both events happened on the identical day.* **2** exactly alike. *adjective.*

identical (definition 2)
The twins were wearing **identical** clothing.

i·den·ti·fi·ca·tion (ī den′tə fə kā′shən), **1** an identifying or a being identified. **2** something used to identify a person or thing: *She offered her driver's license as identification. noun.*

i·den·ti·fy (ī den′tə fī), **1** to recognize as being a particular person or thing; prove to be the same: *He identified the wallet as his by telling what it looked like and what was in it.* **2** to make the same; treat as the same: *A good king identifies his people's well-being with his own. verb,* **i·den·ti·fies, i·den·ti·fied, i·den·ti·fy·ing.**

i·den·ti·ty (ī den′tə tē), **1** individuality; who a person is; what a thing is: *The writer concealed his identity by signing his stories with a made-up name.* **2** an exact likeness: *The identity of the two crimes led the police to think that the same person committed them. noun, plural* **i·den·ti·ties.**

id·i·om (id′ē əm), a phrase or expression whose meaning cannot be understood from the ordinary meanings of the words in it. "Hold one's tongue" is an English idiom meaning "keep still." *noun.*

id·i·ot (id′ē ət), **1** a word once used to mean a person born with very little mental ability. Idiots never learn to read or count and can do only very simple tasks. **2** a very stupid or foolish person: *What an idiot I was to forget my keys! noun.*

id·i·ot·ic (id′ē ot′ik), very stupid or foolish. *adjective.*

i·dle (ī′dl), **1** doing nothing; not busy; not working: *the idle hours of a holiday. Give me some help; don't just stand there idle.* **2** lazy; not willing to do things: *Some idle students do very little schoolwork.* **3** useless; worthless: *to waste time in idle pleasure.* **4** without any good reason or cause: *Stop worrying about idle rumors.* **5** to do nothing; spend or waste time: *It's pleasant to idle away hours lying*

in a hammock. **6** to run slowly without transmitting power. A motor idles when it is out of gear and running slowly. **1-4** *adjective,* **i·dler, i·dlest;** **5,6** *verb,* **i·dles, i·dled, i·dling.**

i·dler (ī′dlər), a lazy person. *noun.*

i·dly (ī′dlē), in an idle manner; doing nothing: *He spent the afternoon idly on the beach. adverb.*

i·dol (ī′dl), **1** a thing, usually an image, that is worshiped as a god. **2** a person or thing that is loved very, very much: *The famous singer was an idol of the audience. noun.*

i·dol·ize (ī′dl īz), to love or admire very, very much: *Some baseball fans idolize their favorite players. verb,* **i·dol·iz·es, i·dol·ized, i·dol·iz·ing.**

if (if), **1** supposing that; on condition that; in case: *Come if you can. If it rains tomorrow, we shall stay at home.* **2** whether: *I wonder if he will go?* **3** although; even though: *It was a welcome if unexpected visit. conjunction.*

ig·loo (ig′lü), an Eskimo hut that is shaped like a dome, often built of blocks of hard snow. *noun, plural* **ig·loos.**

Word History

igloo *Igloo* comes from an Eskimo word meaning "house."

igloo—an **igloo** in northern Canada

ig·ne·ous (ig′nē əs), formed by the cooling and hardening of melted rock material. Lava and granite are igneous rocks. *adjective.*

ig·nite (ig nīt′), **1** to set on fire: *A spark from the campfire ignited the dry grass.* **2** to take fire; begin to burn: *Gasoline ignites easily. verb,* **ig·nites, ig·nit·ed, ig·nit·ing.**

ig·ni·tion (ig nish′ən), **1** a setting on fire. **2** a catching on fire. **3** in a gasoline engine, the switch

a hat	**i** it	**oi** oil	**ch** child	a in about
ā age	**ī** ice	**ou** out	**ng** long	e in taken
ä far	**o** hot	**u** cup	**sh** she	ə = { i in pencil
e let	**ō** open	**u̇** put	**th** thin	o in lemon
ē equal	**ô** order	**ü** rule	**ᴛʜ** then	u in circus
ėr term			**zh** measure	

301

and apparatus controlling the sparks that set the gasoline vapor on fire. *noun.*

ig·nor·ance (ig′nər əns), a lack of knowledge; being ignorant. *noun.*

ig·nor·ant (ig′nər ənt), knowing little or nothing. A person who has not had much chance to learn may be ignorant but not stupid. *People who live in the city are often ignorant of farm life. adjective.*

ig·nore (ig nôr′), to pay no attention to; disregard: *The driver ignored the traffic light and almost hit another car. verb,* **ig·nores, ig·nored, ig·nor·ing.**

i·gua·na (i gwä′nə), a large lizard with a row of spines along its back. It is found in tropical America. *noun.*

iguana—about 5 feet (1½ meters) long

il-, a prefix meaning "not." *Il*legal means *not* legal.

IL, Illinois (used with postal Zip Code).

ill (il), **1** sick; having some disease; not well: *ill with a fever.* **2** a sickness; disease: *All the ills she has had this year have left her very weak.* **3** bad; evil; harmful: *an ill wind, to do a person an ill turn.* **4** badly; harmfully: *Strength is ill used in harming people's property.* **5** an evil; harm: *Poverty and hunger are among the ills of our society.* **6** not good; imperfect: *ill manners, ill health.*
1,3,6 *adjective,* **worse, worst;** 2,5 *noun,* 4 *adverb.*

I'll (īl), **1** I shall. **2** I will.

Ill., Illinois.

il·le·gal (i lē′gəl), not lawful; against the law; forbidden by law. *adjective.*

il·leg·i·ble (i lej′ə bəl), not plain enough; very hard to read: *The ink had faded so that many words were illegible. adjective.*

Il·li·nois (il′ə noi′ *or* il′ə noiz′), one of the north central states of the United States. *Abbreviation:* Ill. or IL *Capital:* Springfield. *noun.*
[*Illinois* got its name from the way French explorers wrote the name of the Indians living in the area. The Indian name meant "men."]

il·lit·er·ate (i lit′ər it), **1** not knowing how to read and write: *People who have never gone to school are usually illiterate.* **2** a person who does not know how to read and write. **3** showing a lack of education: *illiterate writing.* 1,3 *adjective,* 2 *noun.*

ill-na·tured (il′nā′chərd), cross; disagreeable. *adjective.*

ill·ness (il′nis), a sickness; disease; an abnormal, unhealthy condition: *Scarlet fever is a serious illness. noun, plural* **ill·ness·es.**

il·log·i·cal (i loj′ə kəl), not logical or reasonable: *His illogical behavior makes it hard to guess what he will do next. adjective.*

ill-tem·pered (il′tem′pərd), having or showing a bad temper; cross. *adjective.*

ill-treat (il′trēt′), to treat cruelly; treat badly; do harm to; abuse. *verb.*

il·lu·mi·nate (i lü′mə nāt), **1** to light up; make bright: *Four large lamps illuminated the room.* **2** to make clear; explain: *Our teacher could illuminate almost any subject that we studied. verb,* **il·lu·mi·nates, il·lu·mi·nat·ed, il·lu·mi·nat·ing.**

il·lu·mi·na·tion (i lü′mə nā′shən), **1** a lighting up; making bright. **2** the amount of light; light. *noun.*

il·lu·sion (i lü′zhən), **1** something that appears to be different from what it actually is: *The long, straight highway gave the illusion of becoming narrower in the distance.* **2** a false idea or belief: *Many people have the illusion that wealth is the chief cause of happiness. noun.*

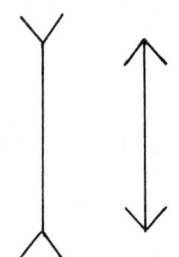

illusion (definition 1)
The line on the left appears longer than the line on the right, but that is an **illusion.** The lines are the same length.

il·lus·trate (il′ə strāt *or* i lus′trāt), **1** to make clear or explain by stories, examples, or comparisons: *The way that a pump works is used to illustrate how the heart sends blood around the body.* **2** to provide with pictures, diagrams, or maps that explain or decorate: *This book is well illustrated. verb,* **il·lus·trates, il·lus·trat·ed, il·lus·trat·ing.**

il·lus·tra·tion (il′ə strā′shən), **1** a picture, diagram, or map used to explain or decorate something. **2** a story, example, or comparison used to make clear or explain something: *The teacher cut an apple into four equal parts as an illustration of what one fourth means.* **3** the act or process of illustrating: *Her illustration of how to build a bookcase taught us a lot. noun.*

il·lus·tra·tive (i lus′trə tiv), illustrating; used to illustrate; helping to explain: *A good teacher uses many illustrative examples to explain ideas that are hard to understand. adjective.*

il·lus·tra·tor (il′ə strā′tər), an artist who makes pictures to be used as illustrations. *noun.*

il·lus·tri·ous (i lus′trē əs), very famous; great; outstanding: *Washington and Lincoln are illustrious Americans. adjective.*

ill will, dislike; spite; unkind or unfriendly feeling: *She bears ill will toward the people who cheated her.*

I'm (īm), I am.

im-, a prefix meaning "not." *Im*possible means *not* possible. *Im*patient means *not* patient.

im·age (im′ij), **1** a likeness or copy: *You will see your image in this mirror. She is almost the exact image of her mother.* **2** a statue; likeness made of stone, wood, or some other material: *The shelf was full of little images of all sorts of animals.* **3** a picture in the mind: *I can shut my eyes and see images of things and persons. noun.*

i·mag·i·na·ble (i maj′ə nə bəl), that can be imagined; possible: *We had the best time imaginable at the party. adjective.*

i·mag·i·nar·y (i maj′ə ner′ē), existing only in the imagination; not real: *The equator is an imaginary circle around the earth. adjective.*

i·mag·i·na·tion (i maj′ə nā′shən), **1** an imagining; power of forming pictures in the mind of things not present to the senses. A poet, artist, or inventor must have imagination to create new things or ideas or to combine old ones in new forms. **2** a creation of the mind; fancy: *Is it my imagination, or did I just see a mouse? noun.*

i·mag·i·na·tive (i maj′ə nə tiv), **1** showing imagination: *Fairy tales are imaginative.* **2** having a good imagination; able to imagine well: *The imaginative child made up stories about life on other planets.* **3** of imagination. *adjective.*

imaginative (definition 1)—I read an **imaginative** story about a boy no bigger than a mouse.

i·mag·ine (i maj′ən), to form a picture of in the mind; have an idea: *The girl likes to imagine herself a doctor. We can hardly imagine life without electricity. verb,* **i·mag·ines, i·mag·ined, i·mag·in·ing.**

im·be·cile (im′bə səl), **1** a word once used to mean a person born with very little mental ability. Imbeciles usually cannot learn to read but can do simple tasks. **2** very stupid; having little mental ability. **1** *noun,* **2** *adjective.*

im·i·tate (im′ə tāt), **1** to try to be like; follow the example of: *The little boy imitates his older brother.* **2** to copy; make or do something like: *A parrot imitates the sounds it hears.* **3** to act like: *He*

a hat	i it	oi oil	ch child	a in about
ā age	ī ice	ou out	ng long	e in taken
ä far	o hot	u cup	sh she	ə = { i in pencil
e let	ō open	u̇ put	th thin	o in lemon
ē equal	ô order	ü rule	₮н then	u in circus
ėr term			zh measure	

amused the class by imitating a duck, a monkey, and a bear.* **4** to be like; look like: *Wood is sometimes painted to imitate stone. verb,* **im·i·tates, im·i·tat·ed, im·i·tat·ing.**

im·i·ta·tion (im′ə tā′shən), **1** an imitating: *We learn many things by imitation.* **2** a copy or likeness: *Give as good an imitation as you can of a rooster crowing.* **3** not real: *You can buy imitation pearls in many jewelry stores.* **1,2** *noun,* **3** *adjective.*

im·mac·u·late (i mak′yə lit), without a spot or stain; absolutely clean: *The newly washed shirts were immaculate. adjective.*

im·ma·ture (im′ə chu̇r′, im′ə tu̇r′, or im′ə tyu̇r′), **1** not mature; not ripe; not full-grown. **2** acting in a childish way; not showing the good sense expected at one's age: *It is immature to expect to get your own way all the time. adjective.*

im·meas·ur·a·ble (i mezh′ər ə bəl), too big to be measured; very great: *the immeasurable ocean. adjective.*

im·me·di·ate (i mē′dē it), **1** coming at once; without delay: *Please send an immediate reply.* **2** closest; nearest: *Your immediate neighbors live next door.* **3** close; near: *I expect an answer today, tomorrow, or in the immediate future.* **4** having to do with the present: *What are your immediate plans? adjective.*

im·me·di·ate·ly (i mē′dē it lē), **1** at once; without delay: *I answered his letter immediately.* **2** next; with nothing between. *adverb.*

im·mense (i mens′), very big; huge; vast: *An ocean is an immense body of water. adjective.*

immense—People look tiny beside this **immense** machine.

im·mense·ly (i mens′lē), very greatly: *We enjoyed the party immensely. adverb.*

im·men·si·ty (i men′sə tē), very great size; boundless extent; vastness: *the ocean's immensity. noun, plural* **im·men·si·ties.**

im·merse (i mėrs′), **1** to dip or lower into a liquid until covered by it: *He immersed his aching feet in a bucket of hot water.* **2** to involve deeply; absorb: *The young pianist immersed herself in practice seven days a week.* verb, **im·mers·es, im·mersed, im·mers·ing.**

im·mi·grant (im′ə grənt), a person who comes into a foreign country or region to live: *Canada has many immigrants from Europe.* noun.

im·mi·grate (im′ə grāt), to come into a foreign country or region to live there. verb, **im·mi·grates, im·mi·grat·ed, im·mi·grat·ing.**

im·mi·gra·tion (im′ə grā′shən), entry into a foreign country or region to live: *There has been immigration to America from all the countries of Europe.* noun.

im·mi·nent (im′ə nənt), likely to happen soon; about to occur: *The black clouds, thunder, and lightning show that a storm is imminent.* adjective.

im·mor·al (i môr′əl), morally wrong; wicked: *Lying and stealing are immoral.* adjective.

im·mor·tal (i môr′tl), living forever; never dying: *A truly great artist gains immortal fame.* adjective.

im·mor·tal·i·ty (im′ôr tal′ə tē), **1** endless life; living forever. **2** fame that lasts forever. noun.

im·mov·a·ble (i mü′və bəl), too big or too heavy to be moved; firmly fixed: *immovable mountains.* adjective.

im·mune (i myün′), **1** protected from disease; having immunity: *Vaccination makes a person practically immune to polio. Some persons are immune to poison ivy.* **2** free; exempt: *Nobody is immune from criticism.* adjective.

im·mu·ni·ty (i myü′nə tē), **1** resistance to disease or poison: *One attack of measles usually gives a person immunity to that disease.* **2** freedom: *The law gives schools and churches immunity from taxation.* noun.

im·mu·nize (im′yə nīz), to protect from disease or poison; give immunity to: *Vaccination immunizes you against smallpox.* verb, **im·mu·niz·es, im·mu·nized, im·mu·niz·ing.**

imp (imp), **1** a young or small devil or demon. **2** a mischievous child. noun.

im·pact (im′pakt), **1** a striking of one thing against another; collision: *The impact of the heavy stone against the windowpane shattered the glass.* **2** a strong or dramatic effect: *Her speech had an impact on the audience.* noun.

im·pair (im per′ *or* im par′), to make worse; damage; harm; weaken: *Poor eating habits impaired his health.* verb.

im·pa·la (im pä′lə), a reddish-brown antelope found in Africa that is noted for long leaps. The male impala has long curved horns. noun.

im·part (im pärt′), **1** to give a share in; give: *to impart happiness to one's friends. The new furniture imparted an air of newness to the old house.* **2** to tell; communicate: *She imparted a love of learning to her students.* verb.

im·par·tial (im pär′shəl), fair; just; showing no more favor to one side than to the other: *A judge should be impartial.* adjective.

im·pass·a·ble (im pas′ə bəl), not able to be traveled over or across: *Snow and ice made the road impassable.* adjective.

im·pas·sioned (im pash′ənd), full of strong feeling; emotional: *She gave an impassioned speech in favor of equal rights for all people.* adjective.

im·pas·sive (im pas′iv), **1** without feeling or emotion; unmoved: *Her face was impassive when we told her the bad news.* **2** not feeling pain or injury; insensible: *The wounded man lay as impassive as if he were dead.* adjective.

im·pa·tience (im pā′shəns), **1** a lack of patience; being impatient. **2** uneasiness and eagerness; restlessness. noun.

im·pa·tient (im pā′shənt), **1** not patient; not willing to bear delay, opposition, pain, or bother: *He is impatient with his little brother.* **2** uneasy and eager; restless: *The horses are impatient to start in the race.* **3** showing lack of patience: *an impatient answer.* adjective.

im·peach (im pēch′), to accuse a public official of wrong conduct while in office. The charges are brought before a special kind of court, and the official is removed from office if found guilty. verb.

im·pede (im pēd′), to hinder; obstruct: *The deep snow impeded travel.* verb, **im·pedes, im·ped·ed, im·ped·ing.**

im·ped·i·ment (im ped′ə mənt), **1** a hindrance; obstacle. **2** a defect in speech: *Stuttering is a speech impediment.* noun.

im·pel (im pel′), to drive; force; cause: *The cold impelled her to go indoors.* verb, **im·pels, im·pelled, im·pel·ling.**

im·pen·e·tra·ble (im pen′ə trə bəl), not able to be entered, pierced, or passed: *The thorny branches made a thick, impenetrable hedge.* adjective.

im·per·a·tive (im per′ə tiv), not to be avoided; urgent; necessary: *It is imperative that this very sick child should stay in bed.* adjective.

im·per·cep·ti·ble (im′pər sep′tə bəl), that cannot be perceived or felt; very slight; gradual: *The road took an imperceptible rise over the low hill.* adjective.

im·per·fect (im pėr′fikt), not perfect; having some defect or fault: *A crack in the cup made it imperfect.* adjective.

impala—about 3 feet (1 meter) high at the shoulder

im·per·fec·tion (im′pər fek′shən), **1** a lack of perfection; imperfect condition or character. **2** a fault; defect. *noun.*

im·per·i·al (im pir′ē əl), **1** of or having something to do with an empire or its ruler: *the imperial palace.* **2** having to do with the rule or authority of one country over other countries and colonies: *England had imperial power over many other countries. adjective.*

im·per·il (im per′əl), to put in danger: *Children who play with matches imperil their lives. verb.*

im·per·i·ous (im pir′ē əs), haughty; arrogant; overbearing: *The nobles treated the common people in an imperious way, looking down on them and ordering them around. adjective.*

im·per·son·al (im pėr′sə nəl), referring to all or any persons, not to any special one: *The teacher's criticism of the class was impersonal. adjective.*

im·per·son·ate (im pėr′sə nāt), to pretend to be; mimic the voice, appearance, and manners of: *He was arrested for impersonating a police officer. verb,* **im·per·son·ates, im·per·son·at·ed, im·per·son·at·ing.**

im·per·ti·nence (im pėrt′n əns), **1** rudeness; disrespectful and impudent behavior. **2** an impertinent act or speech. *noun.*

im·per·ti·nent (im pėrt′n ənt), rude; disrespectful; impudent: *Talking back to older people is impertinent. adjective.*

im·pet·u·ous (im pech′ü əs), acting hastily, rashly, or with sudden feeling: *Children are more impetuous than adults. adjective.*

im·ple·ment (im′plə mənt), a useful piece of equipment; tool; instrument; utensil. Plows and threshing machines are farm implements. A broom, a pail, a shovel, and an ax are implements. *noun.*

im·plore (im plôr′), to beg a person to do something: *He implored his parents to let him go on the trip. verb,* **im·plores, im·plored, im·plor·ing.**

im·ply (im plī′), to mean a thing without saying it outright; express in an indirect way; suggest: *The teacher's smile implied that we were forgiven. verb,* **im·plies, im·plied, im·ply·ing.**

im·po·lite (im′pə līt′), not polite; having or showing bad manners; rude. *adjective.*

im·port (im pôrt′ *for 1;* im′pôrt *for 2-4*), **1** to bring in from a foreign country for sale or use: *The United States imports coffee from Brazil.* **2** an article brought into a country: *Rubber is a useful import.* **3** meaning: *Explain the import of your remark.* **4** importance: *matters of great import.* **1** *verb,* **2-4** *noun.*

im·por·tance (im pôrt′ns), being important; consequence; value: *Anybody can see the importance of good health. noun.*

im·por·tant (im pôrt′nt), meaning much; having value or influence: *important business, an important occasion. Our mayor is an important person in our town. adjective.*

im·por·ta·tion (im′pôr tā′shən), **1** a bringing in of merchandise from foreign countries. **2** something

a hat	i it	oi oil	ch child		a in about
ā age	ī ice	ou out	ng long		e in taken
ä far	o hot	u cup	sh she	ə =	i in pencil
e let	ō open	ů put	th thin		o in lemon
ē equal	ô order	ü rule	ᵺ then		u in circus
ėr term			zh measure		

brought in: *This piece of pottery is an importation from Mexico. noun.*

im·pose (im pōz′), to put a burden, punishment or tax on: *The judge imposed fines on each guilty person. verb,* **im·pos·es, im·posed, im·pos·ing. impose on** or **impose upon,** to take advantage of; use selfishly: *Do not let them impose on you.*

im·pos·ing (im pō′zing), impressive because of size, appearance, or dignity: *The Capitol at Washington, D.C., is an imposing building. adjective.*

im·pos·si·bil·i·ty (im pos′ə bil′ə tē), **1** a being impossible: *We all realize the impossibility of living long without food.* **2** something impossible: *Holding your breath for an hour is an impossibility. noun, plural* **im·pos·si·bil·i·ties.**

im·pos·si·ble (im pos′ə bəl), **1** not able to be or happen: *It is impossible for two and two to make six.* **2** not possible to use; not to be done: *They proposed an impossible plan.* **3** very hard to endure: *Spending the entire summer indoors would be impossible. adjective.*

im·pos·si·bly (im pos′ə blē), in an impossible manner. *adverb.*

im·pos·tor (im pos′tər), a person who pretends to be someone else in order to deceive or cheat others. *noun.*

im·prac·ti·ca·ble (im prak′tə kə bəl), not working well in practice: *impracticable suggestions. adjective.*

im·prac·ti·cal (im prak′tə kəl), not practical; not useful. *adjective.*

im·press (im pres′), **1** to have a strong effect on the mind or feelings of: *The movie about the pioneers impressed us with their courage.* **2** to fix in the mind: *I repeated the words to impress them in my memory. verb.*

im·pres·sion (im presh′ən), **1** an effect produced on a person: *The giraffe in the zoo made a great impression on the child.* **2** an idea; notion: *I have a vague impression that I left the front door unlocked.* **3** something made by pressure, such as a mark, stamp, or print: *A deer had left impressions of its hoofs in the soft dirt. noun.*

im·pres·sive (im pres′iv), able to impress the mind, feelings, or conscience: *The actors gave an impressive performance. adjective.*

im·print (im′print *for 1 and 2;* im print′ *for 3*), **1** a mark made by pressure; print: *Your foot made an imprint in the sand.* **2** an impression; mark: *Pain left its imprint on her face.* **3** to put by pressing: *He imprinted a kiss on his grandmother's cheek.* **1,2** *noun,* **3** *verb.*

im·pris·on (im priz′n), **1** to put in prison; keep in prison. **2** to confine closely; restrain. *verb.*

305

im·pris·on·ment (im priz′n mənt), **1** a putting or keeping in prison: *We read about the imprisonment of the convicted criminal.* **2** a being put or kept in prison: *His imprisonment lasted a year. noun.*

im·prob·a·ble (im prob′ə bəl), not probable; not likely to happen; not likely to be true: *They told an improbable story of seeing a ghost. adjective.*

im·prop·er (im prop′ər), **1** wrong; incorrect; not suitable: *That driver made an improper turn into a one-way street. A damp basement is an improper place to store books.* **2** showing bad judgment; not decent: *improper behavior. It is improper for you to read another person's diary. adjective.*

improper fraction, a fraction equal to or greater than 1. ⅗, ⅝, ⅞, 2¹⁄₁₂, and ⅚ are improper fractions.

im·prove (im prüv′), to make or become better: *Try to improve your spelling. His health is improving. verb,* **im·proves, im·proved, im·prov·ing.**

im·prove·ment (im prüv′mənt), **1** a making or becoming better: *Her schoolwork shows much improvement since last term.* **2** a change or addition that adds value: *The improvements in our house were costly.* **3** a person or thing that is better than a previous one; gain; advance: *Color television is an improvement over black-and-white television. noun.*

im·pro·vise (im′prə vīz), **1** to make up music or poetry on the spur of the moment; sing, recite, or speak without preparation: *She likes to improvise popular songs on the piano.* **2** to prepare or provide offhand: *The children improvised a tent out of blankets and poles. verb,* **im·pro·vis·es, im·pro·vised, im·pro·vis·ing.**

im·pru·dent (im prüd′nt), not wise or prudent; rash: *It is imprudent to rush into something without thinking of what may happen. adjective.*

im·pu·dence (im′pyə dəns), shameless boldness; very rude and disrespectful behavior. *noun.*

im·pu·dent (im′pyə dənt), shamelessly bold; very rude and disrespectful: *The impudent child made faces at us. adjective.*

im·pulse (im′puls), **1** a sudden, driving force or influence; thrust; push: *the impulse of hunger, the impulse of curiosity.* **2** a sudden inclination or tendency to act: *I had a strong impulse to call up one of the friends I met at camp. noun.*

im·pul·sive (im pul′siv), acting upon impulse; easily moved: *Impulsive people often buy things they don't need. adjective.*

im·pure (im pyùr′), **1** not pure; dirty: *The air in cities is often impure.* **2** mixed with something of lower value: *The salt we use is slightly impure.* **3** bad; corrupt: *impure talk. adjective.*

im·pur·i·ty (im pyùr′ə tē), **1** lack of purity; being impure. **2** an impure thing; thing that makes something else impure: *Filtering the water removed some of its impurities. noun, plural* **im·pur·i·ties.**

in (in), **1** within; not outside: *in the box. We live in the city.* **2** during: *It rained in the afternoon.* **3** at the

end of; after: *I'll be ready in an hour.* **4** into: *Go in the house.* **5** using; by means of: *She wrote in pencil. I paid in cash.* **6** from among; out of: *one in a hundred.* **7** because of; for: *The party is in honor of his birthday.* **8** to or at the position or condition of; affected by: *Is your brother in trouble?* **9** in or into some place; on the inside: *Come in. Lock the dog in.* **10** present, especially in one's home or office: *The doctor is not in today.* **1-8** *preposition,* **9,10** *adverb.*

ins and outs, 1 turns and twists: *She knows the ins and outs of the road because she has traveled it so often.* **2** different parts; details: *The manager knows the ins and outs of the business better than the owner.*

IN, Indiana (used with postal Zip Code).

in-, a prefix meaning: **1** not. *Incorrect means not correct.* **2** a lack of. *Injustice means a lack of justice.*

in., inch or inches.

in·a·bil·i·ty (in′ə bil′ə tē), a lack of ability, means, or power; being unable. *noun.*

in·ac·ces·si·ble (in′ək ses′ə bəl), **1** hard to get at; hard to reach or enter: *A house on top of a steep hill is inaccessible.* **2** not able to be reached or entered at all. *adjective.*

in·ac·cur·a·cy (in ak′yər ə sē), **1** a lack of accuracy: *Our arithmetic teacher showed us how to avoid inaccuracy when we subtract numbers.* **2** an error; mistake: *There are a few inaccuracies in your answers. noun, plural* **in·ac·cur·a·cies.**

in·ac·cur·ate (in ak′yər it), not accurate; not exact; containing mistakes. *adjective.*

in·ac·tive (in ak′tiv), not active; idle; sluggish: *Bears are inactive during the winter. adjective.*

in·ad·e·quate (in ad′ə kwit), not enough; not so much as is required; not adequate: *Inadequate food will cause weakness and sometimes headaches. adjective.*

in·ad·vis·a·ble (in′əd vī′zə bəl), unwise; not sensible; not advisable. *adjective.*

in·ap·pro·pri·ate (in′ə prō′prē it), not appropriate; not suitable; not fitting. *adjective.*

in·as·much as (in′əz much′ az′), because: *I stayed indoors today, inasmuch as it was raining.*

in·at·ten·tive (in′ə ten′tiv), not attentive; negligent; careless. *adjective.*

in·au·gu·rate (in ô′gyə rāt′), **1** to install in office with a ceremony: *A President of the United States is inaugurated every four years.* **2** to open for public use with a ceremony or celebration: *The new city hall was inaugurated with a parade and speeches. verb,* **in·au·gu·rates, in·au·gu·rat·ed, in·au·gu·rat·ing.**

in·au·gu·ra·tion (in ô′gyə rā′shən), **1** the act or ceremony of installing a person in office: *The inauguration of a President of the United States takes place on January 20.* **2** an opening for public use with a ceremony or celebration: *The inauguration of the new city hall began with a parade. noun.*

in·born (in′bôrn′), born in a person: *The artist had an inborn talent for drawing. adjective.*

Inca—These are the ruins of a mountain city built by the **Inca** hundreds of years ago.

In·ca (ing′kə), a member of an ancient people of South America. The Inca had a highly developed culture, and ruled a large empire in Peru and other parts of South America. This empire fell to the Spaniards in the 1500's. *noun, plural* **In·ca** *or* **In·cas.**

in·can·ta·tion (in′kan tā′shən), the use of a set of words spoken as a magic charm or to cast a magic spell. *noun.*

in·ca·pa·ble (in kā′pə bəl), having very little ability; not capable; not efficient: *An employer cannot afford to hire incapable workers. adjective.*

in·cense[1] (in′sens), a substance giving off a sweet smell when burned. *noun.*

in·cense[2] (in sens′), to make very angry: *Cruelty incenses kind people. verb,* **in·cens·es, in·censed, in·cens·ing.**

in·cen·tive (in sen′tiv), a thing that urges a person on; cause of action or effort; motive; stimulus: *The fun of playing the game was a greater incentive than the prize. noun.*

in·ces·sant (in ses′nt), never stopping; continual: *The incessant noise from the factory kept me awake all night. adjective.*

inch (inch), **1** a unit of length, 1/12 of a foot. An inch of rainfall is the amount of water that would cover a surface to the depth of one inch. **2** to move slowly or little by little: *The worm inched along.* **1** *noun, plural* **inch·es; 2** *verb.*

in·ci·dent (in′sə dənt), **1** a happening; event: *I saw a funny incident on the playground today.* **2** a less important happening that helps or adds to something else: *She told us all of the main facts of her trip and a few of the amusing incidents. noun.*

in·ci·den·tal (in′sə den′tl), **1** happening or likely to happen in connection with something else more important: *Certain discomforts are incidental to camping out.* **2** occurring by chance: *an incidental meeting of an old friend on the street.* **3** something incidental: *On our trip, we spent $58 for meals, room, and transportation and $5 for incidentals, such as candy, magazines, and stamps.* **1,2** *adjective,* **3** *noun.*

in·ci·den·tal·ly (in′sə den′tl ē), as an incident along with something else; by the way: *Incidentally, are you coming to the meeting tonight? adverb.*

in·cin·er·a·tor (in sin′ə rā′tər), a furnace or other device for burning trash and other things to ashes. *noun.*

in·ci·sor (in sī′zər), a tooth having a sharp edge for cutting; one of the front teeth. Human beings have eight incisors. *noun.*

in·cite (in sīt′), to urge on; stir up; rouse: *Their leaders incited the workers to strike. verb,* **in·cites, in·cit·ed, in·cit·ing.**

in·clem·ent (in klem′ənt), rough; stormy: *Inclement weather is common in winter. adjective.*

in·cli·na·tion (in′klə nā′shən), **1** a tendency: *He has an inclination to become overweight.* **2** a liking; preference: *an inclination for sports.* **3** a slope; slant: *That high roof has a sharp inclination. noun.*

in·cline (in klīn′ *for 1 and 3;* in′klīn *or* in klīn′ *for 2*), **1** to slope; slant: *The street inclines upward.* **2** a sloping surface; slope; slant. The side of a hill is an incline. **3** to lean; bend; bow: *She inclined her head toward the sound.* **1,3** *verb,* **in·clines, in·clined, in·clin·ing; 2** *noun.*

in·clined (in klīnd′), **1** favorable; willing; tending: *I am inclined to agree with you.* **2** sloping; slanting: *an inclined surface. adjective.*

inclined plane, a plank or other plane surface placed at an angle to the ground and used to move heavy weights to a higher level with little force.

inclined plane—An **inclined plane** makes it easier for a person in a wheelchair to enter a building.

in·close (in klōz′). See **enclose.** *verb,* **in·clos·es, in·closed, in·clos·ing.**

in·clo·sure (in klō′zhər). See **enclosure.** *noun.*

in·clude (in klüd′), **1** to contain: *Their farm includes 160 acres.* **2** to put in a total, a class, or the like; reckon in a count: *The price includes the land, house, and furniture. verb,* **in·cludes, in·clud·ed, in·clud·ing.**

in·clu·sion (in klü′zhən), an including; being included: *The inclusion of a tax on this item was incorrect. noun.*

in·clu·sive (in klü′siv), including; taking in; counting in: *"Read pages 10 to 20 inclusive" means "Begin with page 10 and read through to the very end of page 20."* *adjective.*

in·come (in′kum′), the money that comes in from property, business, or work: *A person's yearly income is all the money earned in a year.* *noun.*

income tax, a government tax on a person's income above a certain amount.

in·com·ing (in′kum′ing), coming in: *the incoming tide. adjective.*

in·com·par·a·ble (in kom′pər ə bəl), without an equal; matchless: *incomparable beauty. adjective.*

in·com·pe·tent (in kom′pə tənt), not able to do something; without ability or qualifications: *an incompetent mechanic. adjective.*

in·com·plete (in′kəm plēt′), not complete; lacking some part; unfinished. *adjective.*

in·com·pre·hen·si·ble (in′kom pri hen′sə bəl), impossible to understand. *adjective.*

in·con·sid·er·ate (in′kən sid′ər it), not thoughtful of others and their feelings; thoughtless. *adjective.*

in·con·sist·ent (in′kən sis′tənt), **1** not in agreement: *Your failure to arrive on time is inconsistent with your usual promptness.* **2** not keeping to the same rules or habits; changeable: *An inconsistent person says one thing today and the opposite tomorrow. adjective.*

in·con·spic·u·ous (in′kən spik′yü əs), not easily seen; not attracting very much attention: *They live in a small, inconspicuous gray house. adjective.*

in·con·ven·ience (in′kən vē′nyəns), **1** a cause of trouble; bother; lack of convenience or ease. **2** to cause trouble, difficulty, or bother to: *Will it inconvenience you to carry this package for me?* **1** *noun,* **2** *verb,* **in·con·ven·ienc·es, in·con·ven·ienced, in·con·ven·ienc·ing.**

in·con·ven·ient (in′kən vē′nyənt), troublesome; not convenient; causing bother, difficulty, or discomfort: *Shelves that are too high to reach easily are inconvenient. adjective.*

in·cor·po·rate (in kôr′pə rāt′), **1** to make something a part of something else; join or combine something with something else: *We will incorporate your suggestion in this new plan.* **2** to form into a corporation: *When the business became large, the owners incorporated it. verb,* **in·cor·po·rates, in·cor·po·rat·ed, in·cor·po·rat·ing.**

in·cor·rect (in′kə rekt′), **1** not correct; wrong; faulty: *The newspaper gave an incorrect account of the accident.* **2** not agreeing with an accepted standard of good behavior; not proper: *incorrect behavior. adjective.*

in·crease (in krēs′ for 1; in′krēs for 2 and 3), **1** to make or become greater, more numerous, or more powerful: *The driver increased the speed of the car.* **2** a gain in size or numbers; growth: *There has been a great increase in student enrollment during the past year.* **3** an amount added; result of increasing; addition: *There has been an increase of*

five cents in the gasoline tax. **1** *verb,* **in·creas·es, in·creased, in·creas·ing;** **2,3** *noun.*

in·creas·ing·ly (in krē′sing lē), more and more: *As we traveled south, the weather became increasingly warm. adverb.*

in·cred·i·ble (in kred′ə bəl), unbelievable; seeming too extraordinary to be possible; beyond belief. *adjective.*

in·cred·i·bly (in kred′ə blē), beyond belief; so as to be incredible: *an incredibly swift flight. adverb.*

in·cred·u·lous (in krej′ə ləs), not ready to believe; doubting: *Most people nowadays are incredulous of ghosts and witches. adjective.*

in·cu·bate (ing′kyə bāt), to sit on eggs in order to hatch them: *Birds incubate their eggs. verb,* **in·cu·bates, in·cu·bat·ed, in·cu·bat·ing.**

in·cu·ba·tor (ing′kyə bā′tər), **1** a box or chamber for hatching eggs by keeping them warm. **2** any similar device or machine. Very small babies and babies that are born too early are sometimes kept for a time in incubators. *noun.*

incubator (definition 2)

in·cur (in kėr′), to run or fall into something unpleasant; bring blame, punishment, or danger on oneself: *The explorers incurred great danger when they tried to cross the rapids. verb,* **in·curs, in·curred, in·cur·ring.**

in·cur·a·ble (in kyůr′ə bəl), not able to be cured: *an incurable invalid, an incurable disease. adjective.*

Ind., Indiana.

in·debt·ed (in det′id), owing money or gratitude; in debt: *We are indebted to science for many of our comforts.* adjective.

in·deed (in dēd′), **1** in fact; in truth; really; surely: *War is indeed terrible.* **2** an expression of surprise, doubt, or scorn: *Indeed! I never would have thought it.* **1** adverb, **2** interjection.

in·def·i·nite (in def′ə nit), **1** not clearly defined; not exact; vague: *"Maybe" is a very indefinite answer.* **2** not limited: *We have an indefinite time to finish this work.* adjective.

indefinite article, the article *a* or *an.* "A dog" or "an animal" means "any dog" or "any animal"; "the dog" means "a certain or particular dog."

in·del·i·ble (in del′ə bəl), not able to be erased or removed; permanent: *indelible ink. His experiences in India left an indelible impression on his memory.* adjective.

in·dent (in dent′), to begin a line farther from the left margin than the other lines: *The first line of a paragraph is usually indented.* verb.

in·de·pend·ence (in′di pen′dəns), a freedom from the control, support, influence, or help of others: *The American colonies won independence from England.* noun.

Independence Day, a holiday in honor of the adoption of the Declaration of Independence on July 4, 1776; Fourth of July.

in·de·pend·ent (in′di pen′dənt), **1** thinking or acting for oneself; not influenced by others: *an independent voter, an independent thinker.* **2** guiding, ruling, or governing oneself; not under another's rule: *The United States is an independent country.* **3** not depending on others for support: *Now that I have a good job, I can be completely independent.* **4** a person who votes without regard to party. **1-3** adjective, **4** noun.

in·de·scrib·a·ble (in′di skrī′bə bəl), not able to be described; beyond description: *a scene of indescribable beauty.* adjective.

in·dex (in′deks), **1** a list of what is in a book, telling on what pages to find each thing. An index is usually put at the end of the book and arranged in alphabetical order. **2** to provide with an index. **1** noun, plural **in·dex·es;** **2** verb.

index finger, the finger next to the thumb; forefinger.

In·di·a (in′dē ə), a country in southern Asia. noun.

In·di·an (in′dē ən), **1** one of the people who have lived in America from long before the time of the first European settlers; American Indian. **2** of or having something to do with American Indians. **3** of or having something to do with India or its people. **4** a person born or living in India. **1,4** noun, **2,3** adjective.

In·di·an·a (in′dē an′ə), one of the north central states of the United States. *Abbreviation:* Ind. or IN *Capital:* Indianapolis. noun.

[*Indiana* may have come from a modern Latin word meaning "American Indian."]

In·di·a·nap·o·lis (in′dē ə nap′ə lis), the capital of Indiana. noun.

a hat	i it	oi oil	ch child	a in about
ā age	ī ice	ou out	ng long	e in taken
ä far	o hot	u cup	sh she	ə = i in pencil
e let	ō open	ů put	th thin	o in lemon
ē equal	ô order	ü rule	ŦH then	u in circus
ėr term			zh measure	

Indian corn, corn.

Indian Ocean, an ocean south of Asia, east of Africa, and west of Australia.

Indian summer, a time of mild, dry, hazy weather in late autumn.

in·di·cate (in′də kāt), **1** to point out; point to; show; make known: *The arrow on a sign indicates the way to go. A dog indicates its feelings by growling, whining, barking, or wagging its tail.* **2** to be a sign of: *Fever indicates illness.* verb, **in·di·cates, in·di·cat·ed, in·di·cat·ing.**

in·di·ca·tion (in′də kā′shən), **1** the act of indicating: *We use different words for the indication of different meanings.* **2** a thing that indicates; sign: *There was no indication that the house was occupied.* noun.

in·di·ca·tor (in′də kā′tər), a pointer on a dial that shows the amount of heat, pressure, or speed. noun.

in·dif·fer·ence (in dif′ər əns), not caring; lack of interest or attention: *The child's indifference to food worried his parents.* noun.

in·dif·fer·ent (in dif′ər ənt), not caring one way or the other: *I was indifferent to their insults. I enjoyed the trip but she was indifferent.* adjective.

in·dif·fer·ent·ly (in dif′ər ənt lē), with indifference. adverb.

in·dig·e·nous (in dij′ə nəs), native; originating in the region or country where found: *Lions are indigenous to Africa.* adjective.

in·di·gest·i·ble (in′də jes′tə bəl), not able to be digested; hard to digest. adjective.

in·di·ges·tion (in′də jes′chən), difficulty in digesting food: *Eating too much and too fast may cause indigestion.* noun.

in·dig·nant (in dig′nənt), angry at something unworthy, unfair, or mean. adjective.

indignant
He was very **indignant** when I told him I didn't like his hair.

in·dig·na·tion (in′dig nā′shən), the feeling of being angry at something unworthy, unfair, or mean; anger mixed with scorn: *Cruelty to animals aroused his indignation.* noun.

in·dig·ni·ty (in dig′nə tē), an injury to one's dignity; insult: *He felt that his aunt's use of baby talk was an indignity.* noun, plural **in·dig·ni·ties.**

in·di·go (in′də gō), **1** a blue dye that can be obtained from various plants. It is now usually made artificially. **2** a plant from which indigo is obtained. **3** deep violet-blue. 1,2 noun, plural **in·di·gos** or **in·di·goes;** 3 adjective.

in·di·rect (in′də rekt′), **1** not going straight to the point: *She would not say yes or no, but gave an indirect answer to my question.* **2** not directly connected: *Happiness is an indirect result of doing one's work well.* **3** not direct; not straight: *We walk to town by a road that is indirect, but very pleasant.* adjective.

in·dis·creet (in′dis krēt′), not discreet; not wise and judicious. adjective.

indiscreet—It is **indiscreet** to tell your secrets.

in·dis·pen·sa·ble (in′dis pen′sə bəl), absolutely necessary: *Air is indispensable to life.* adjective.

in·dis·posed (in′dis pōzd′), **1** slightly ill: *I have been indisposed with a cold.* **2** unwilling. adjective.

in·dis·tinct (in′dis tingkt′), not clear to the eye, ear, or mind; confused; not distinct: *I have an indistinct memory of the accident.* adjective.

in·di·vid·u·al (in′də vij′ü əl), **1** a person: *He is the tallest individual in his family.* **2** a single object or living thing: *We saw a herd of giraffes containing 30 individuals.* **3** single; separate; for one only: *Benches are for several people; chairs are individual seats.* **4** belonging to or marking off one person or thing specially: *I can always identify her drawings because of their individual style.* 1,2 noun, 3,4 adjective.
[*Individual* comes from a Latin word meaning "not able to be divided" or "indivisible."]

in·di·vid·u·al·i·ty (in′də vij′ü al′ə tē), the sum of the qualities which make one object or living thing different from another: *Each human being begins in infancy to build an individuality of his or her own.* noun.

in·di·vid·u·al·ly (in′də vij′ü ə lē), **1** personally; one at a time; as individuals: *Sometimes our teacher helps us individually.* **2** each from the others: *People differ individually.* adverb.

in·di·vis·i·ble (in′də viz′ə bəl), not able to be divided: *"One nation under God, indivisible, with liberty and justice for all."* adjective.

in·do·lence (in′dl əns), laziness; dislike of work; idleness. noun.

in·do·lent (in′dl ənt), disliking work; lazy: *Indolent people usually do not exercise.* adjective.

in·dom·i·ta·ble (in dom′ə tə bəl), not able to be discouraged, beaten, or defeated: *The team's indomitable spirit was a help in winning a very close game.* adjective.

In·do·ne·sia (in′də nē′zhə), a country consisting of many islands off the coast of southeastern Asia. noun.

in·door (in′dôr′), done or used in a house or building: *indoor tennis.* adjective.

in·doors (in′dôrz′), in or into a house or building: *Go indoors.* adverb.

in·duce (in düs′ *or* in dyüs′), **1** to lead on; influence; persuade: *Advertisements induce people to buy.* **2** to cause; bring about: *The doctor says that this medicine will induce sleep.* verb, **in·duc·es, in·duced, in·duc·ing.**

in·duce·ment (in düs′mənt *or* in dyüs′mənt), something that influences or persuades: *A new bicycle for the winner was an inducement to try hard to win the contest.* noun.

in·duct (in dukt′), **1** to install in an official position: *He was inducted as governor.* **2** to take into the armed services. verb.

in·dulge (in dulj′), **1** to give way to one's pleasure; give oneself up to; allow oneself something desired: *A smoker indulges in tobacco.* **2** to give in to the wishes or whims of; humor: *We often indulge a sick person.* verb, **in·dulg·es, in·dulged, in·dulg·ing.**

in·dul·gence (in dul′jəns), **1** an indulging: *Friends often treat each other with indulgence.* **2** a thing indulged in: *Luxuries are indulgences.* **3** a favor; privilege: *Fond parents often allow their children special indulgences.* noun.

in·dul·gent (in dul′jənt), giving in to another's wishes or whims; too kind or agreeable: *Their indulgent parents gave them everything they wanted.* adjective.

in·dus·tri·al (in dus′trē əl), **1** of or produced by industry: *industrial products.* **2** having highly developed industries: *The United States and Great Britain are industrial nations.* **3** connected with or engaged in industry: *industrial workers, an industrial school.* adjective.

in·dus·tri·al·i·za·tion (in dus′trē ə lə zā′shən), the development of large industries in a country. noun.

in·dus·tri·al·ize (in dus′trē ə līz), to make industrial; develop large industries in a country. verb, **in·dus·tri·al·iz·es, in·dus·tri·al·ized, in·dus·tri·al·iz·ing.**

in·dus·tri·ous (in dus′trē əs), working hard and steadily: *An industrious student usually has good grades.* adjective.

in·dus·try (in′də strē), **1** any form of business, manufacture, or trade: *the automobile industry. Industries dealing with steel, copper, coal, and oil employ millions of people.* **2** all such business, manufacture, and trade taken as a whole:

Chicago is a center of industry. **3** hard work; steady effort: *She became a lawyer through much industry.* noun, plural **in·dus·tries.**

in·ed·i·ble (in ed/ə bəl), not fit to eat. *adjective.*

inedible—He tried to eat his shoe but found it **inedible.**

experienced; without practice; lacking the skill and wisdom gained from experience. *adjective.*

in·fal·li·ble (in fal/ə bəl), free from error; not able to be mistaken: *an infallible rule. adjective.*

in·fa·mous (in/fə məs), very wicked; so bad as to deserve public disgrace: *To betray your country is an infamous deed. adjective.*

in·fa·my (in/fə mē), **1** a very bad reputation; public disgrace: *Traitors are held in infamy.* **2** extreme wickedness. *noun, plural* **in·fa·mies.**

in·fan·cy (in/fən sē), **1** the time of being a baby; early childhood. **2** an early stage of anything: *Space travel is still in its infancy. noun.*

in·ef·fec·tive (in/ə fek/tiv), not producing the desired effect; of little use: *An ineffective medicine fails to cure a disease or relieve pain. adjective.*

in·ef·fi·cien·cy (in/ə fish/ən sē), the inability to get things done. *noun.*

in·ef·fi·cient (in/ə fish/ənt), **1** not able to produce a result without waste of time or energy; not efficient: *A machine that uses too much fuel is inefficient.* **2** not able to get things done; incapable: *The inefficient inspector examined only a few new refrigerators. adjective.*

in·e·qual·i·ty (in/i kwol/ə tē), a lack of equality; being unequal in amount, size, value, or rank: *There is a great inequality between the salaries of a bank president and a bank clerk. noun, plural* **in·e·qual·i·ties.**

in·ert (in ėrt/), lifeless; having no power to move or act: *A stone is an inert lump of matter. adjective.*

in·ev·i·ta·ble (in ev/ə tə bəl), not to be avoided; sure to happen; certain to come: *Death is an inevitable occurrence; it comes to everyone. adjective.*

in·ex·act (in/ig zakt/), not exact; with errors or mistakes; not just right. *adjective.*

in·ex·cus·a·ble (in/ik skyü/zə bəl), not able to be pardoned or excused: *an inexcusable insult, an inexcusable mistake. adjective.*

in·ex·haust·i·ble (in/ig zô/stə bəl), unable to be used up; very abundant: *The wealth of our country seems inexhaustible to many people abroad. adjective.*

in·ex·pen·sive (in/ik spen/siv), not expensive; cheap; low-priced. *adjective.*

in·ex·per·i·ence (in/ik spir/ē əns), a lack of experience; lack of practice; lack of skill or wisdom gained by experience. *noun.*

in·ex·per·i·enced (in/ik spir/ē ənst), not

infancy (definition 2)—air travel in its **infancy**

in·fant (in/fənt), **1** a baby; very young child. **2** of or for an infant: *an infant blanket, infant food.* **3** in an early stage; just beginning to develop: *an infant industry.* **1** *noun,* **2,3** *adjective.*

in·fan·tile (in/fən tīl), **1** of an infant or infants; having to do with infants: *Measles and chicken pox are infantile diseases.* **2** like an infant; childish: *She was upset by her friend's infantile show of temper. adjective.*

infantile paralysis, a disease that causes paralysis of various muscles; polio.

in·fan·try (in/fən trē), the soldiers trained, equipped, and organized to fight on foot. *noun.*

in·fect (in fekt/), **1** to cause disease in by bringing into contact with germs: *Dirt can infect an open cut. If you have a bad cold, you may infect the people around you.* **2** to influence by spreading from one to another: *The manager's good humor infected many who worked with her. verb.*

in·fec·tion (in fek/shən), **1** a causing of disease in people and other living things by bringing into contact with germs. **2** a disease caused in this manner, especially one that can spread from one person to another. *noun.*

in·fec·tious (in fek/shəs), **1** spread by infection: *Measles is an infectious disease.* **2** apt to spread from one to another: *He has a jolly, infectious laugh. adjective.*

in·fer (in fér′), to find out by reasoning; conclude: *I inferred from the smoke that something was burning. verb,* **in·fers, in·ferred, in·fer·ring.**

in·fer·ence (in′fər əns), that which is discovered by reasoning; conclusion: *What inference do you draw from smelling smoke? noun.*

in·fer·i·or (in fir′ē ər), **1** low in quality; below the average: *an inferior mind, an inferior grade of coffee.* **2** lower in quality; not so good; worse: *This cloth is inferior to real silk.* **3** lower in position or rank: *A lieutenant is inferior to a captain.* **4** a person who is lower in rank or station: *A good leader gets on well with inferiors.* **1-3** *adjective,* **4** *noun.*

in·fer·i·or·i·ty (in fir′ē ôr′ə tē), an inferior nature or condition; quality of being inferior. *noun.*

in·fer·nal (in fér′nl), **1** of the lower world; of hell. **2** fit to have come from hell: *The heartless conqueror showed infernal cruelty. adjective.*

in·fest (in fest′), to trouble or disturb frequently or in large numbers: *Mosquitoes infest swamps. The park was infested with tourists. verb.*

in·fi·del (in′fə dəl), **1** a person who does not believe in religion. **2** a person who does not accept a particular faith. During the Crusades, Moslems called Christians infidels. *noun.*

in·field (in′fēld′), **1** the part of a baseball field that is inside the lines connecting the bases; diamond. **2** the first, second, and third basemen and shortstop of a baseball team. *noun.*

in·field·er (in′fēl′dər), a baseball player who plays in the infield. *noun.*

in·fi·nite (in′fə nit), **1** without limits or bounds; endless: *the infinite reaches of outer space.* **2** very, very great: *Working a jigsaw puzzle sometimes takes infinite patience. adjective.*

in·fin·i·ty (in fin′ə tē), the condition of having no limits; endlessness: *the infinity of space. noun.*

in·firm (in férm′), weak; lacking strength or health: *The patient was old and infirm. adjective.*

in·fir·mi·ty (in fér′mə tē), **1** weakness; lack of strength or health. **2** sickness; illness: *the infirmities of age. noun, plural* **in·fir·mi·ties.**

in·flame (in flām′), **1** to excite; make more violent: *The stirring speech inflamed the crowd.* **2** to make unnaturally hot, red, sore, or swollen: *The thick smoke inflamed our eyes. verb,* **in·flames, in·flamed, in·flam·ing.**

in·flam·ma·ble (in flam′ə bəl), easily set on fire: *Paper is inflammable. adjective.*

in·flam·ma·tion (in′flə mā′shən), a diseased condition of some part of the body, marked by heat, redness, swelling, and pain: *A boil is an inflammation of the skin. noun.*

in·flate (in flāt′), **1** to force air or gas into a balloon, tire, or some other hollow thing, causing it to swell. **2** to swell or puff out: *After their victory the team was inflated with pride.* **3** to increase prices beyond the normal amount: *A poor harvest has inflated the price of grain. verb,* **in·flates, in·flat·ed, in·flat·ing.**

in·fla·tion (in flā′shən), **1** a swelling, especially with air or gas: *the inflation of a balloon.* **2** a sharp and sudden rise in the price of goods. *noun.*

in·flex·i·ble (in flek′sə bəl), **1** firm; unyielding: *Our teacher's decision was inflexible, and we could not talk her into changing it.* **2** stiff; rigid: *an inflexible rod. adjective.*

in·flict (in flikt′), **1** to give or cause a blow or wound: *A knife can inflict a bad wound.* **2** to force to endure suffering, punishment, or something unwelcome: *Only cruel people like to inflict pain. Our unpleasant neighbors inflicted themselves on us all afternoon. verb.*

in·flu·ence (in′flü əns), **1** the power of acting on others and having an effect without using force: *Use your influence to persuade your friends to join our club.* **2** a person or thing that has such power: *Her older sister has a good influence on her.* **3** to have such power or influence on: *The moon influences the tides. What we read influences our thinking.* **1,2** *noun,* **3** *verb,* **in·flu·enc·es, in·flu·enced, in·flu·enc·ing.**

in·flu·en·tial (in′flü en′shəl), **1** having influence: *Influential friends helped him to get a good job.* **2** using influence; producing results. *adjective.*

in·form (in fôrm′), **1** to tell; supply with knowledge, facts, or news: *Her letter informed us of when she expected to arrive.* **2** to tell something that will get another person or other people into trouble: *The criminal who was caught informed against the other robbers. verb.*

in·for·mal (in fôr′məl), not formal; without ceremony; casual: *an informal party. adjective.*

in·for·ma·tion (in′fər mā′shən), **1** knowledge given or received of some fact or event; news: *We have just received information of the astronauts' safe landing.* **2** things known; facts: *A dictionary contains much information about words. noun.*

in·fre·quent (in frē′kwənt), not frequent; occurring seldom or far apart; rare: *Her visits are infrequent, so we rarely see her. adjective.*

inflammable—The word **inflammable** has the same meaning as **flammable**.

in·fringe (in frinj′), to go beyond the proper or usual limits; trespass: *Do not infringe upon the rights of others.* verb, **in·fring·es, in·fringed, in·fring·ing.**

in·fur·i·ate (in fyůr′ē āt), to fill with wild, fierce anger; make furious; enrage: *Their insults infuriated us.* verb, **in·fur·i·ates, in·fur·i·at·ed, in·fur·i·at·ing.**

in·gen·ious (in jē′nyəs), **1** clever; skillful in making; good at inventing: *The ingenious girls made a trapdoor for their tree house.* **2** cleverly planned and made: *He made an ingenious bird feeder from an old tin can and some wire.* adjective.

in·ge·nu·i·ty (in′jə nü′ə tē *or* in′jə nyü′ə tē), skill in planning or inventing; cleverness. *noun.*

ingenuity—With **ingenuity** you can make a dragon puppet from an egg carton.

in·gen·u·ous (in jen′yü əs), frank and open; sincere: *He gave an ingenuous account of his acts, concealing nothing.* adjective.

in·got (ing′gət), a mass of gold, silver, or steel cast in a mold. *noun.*

MOLD

INGOT

in·gra·ti·ate (in grā′shē āt), to bring oneself into favor: *He tried to ingratiate himself with the teacher by cleaning the chalkboards.* verb, **in·gra·ti·ates, in·gra·ti·at·ed, in·gra·ti·at·ing.**

in·grat·i·tude (in grat′ə tüd *or* in grat′ə tyüd), a lack of thankfulness; being ungrateful. *noun.*

in·gre·di·ent (in grē′dē ənt), one of the parts of a mixture: *The ingredients of a cake usually include eggs, sugar, flour, and flavoring.* noun.

a hat	i it	oi oil	ch child	⌠a in about
ā age	ī ice	ou out	ng long	e in taken
ä far	o hot	u cup	sh she	ə = ⟨ i in pencil
e let	ō open	u̇ put	th thin	o in lemon
ē equal	ô order	ü rule	ᴛʜ then	⌡u in circus
ėr term			zh measure	

in·hab·it (in hab′it), to live in: *Fish inhabit the sea.* verb.

in·hab·it·ant (in hab′ə tənt), a person or animal that lives in a place: *Our town has ten thousand inhabitants.* noun.

in·hale (in hāl′), to breathe in; draw air, vapor, smoke, or odor into the lungs. verb, **in·hales, in·haled, in·hal·ing.**

in·her·ent (in hir′ənt), existing; belonging to a person or thing as a quality: *Her inherent curiosity about nature led her to study plants.* adjective.

in·her·it (in her′it), **1** to get or have something after the former owner dies; receive as an heir: *After Grandfather's death, Mother inherited all his property.* **2** to get from one's parents or ancestors. verb.

inherit (definition 2)
The girl **inherited** her hair color from her mother.

in·her·it·ance (in her′ə təns), anything inherited: *The house was his inheritance.* noun.

in·hos·pit·a·ble (in hos′pi tə bəl *or* in′ho spit′ə bəl), not hospitable; not making visitors comfortable: *Our inhospitable neighbor never offers visitors any refreshments.* adjective.

in·hu·man (in hyü′mən), without kindness, mercy, or tenderness; cruel; brutal: *He has an inhuman lack of concern for the suffering of others.* adjective.

in·iq·ui·ty (in ik′wə tē), **1** very great injustice; wickedness. **2** a wicked and unjust act: *Taking children from their parents and selling them was one of the iniquities of slavery.* noun, plural **in·iq·ui·ties.**

i·ni·tial (i nish′əl), **1** occurring at the beginning; first; earliest: *the initial letter of a word. His initial effort at skating was a failure.* **2** the first letter of a word: *The initials U.S. stand for United States.* **3** to mark or sign with initials: *Lee Ann Wong initialed the note L.A.W.* **1** adjective, **2** noun, **3** verb.

i·ni·ti·ate (i nish′ē āt), **1** to start; set going; begin: *This year we shall initiate a series of free concerts.*

2 to admit a person with ceremonies into a group or society: *The old members initiated the new members. verb,* **i·ni·ti·ates, i·ni·ti·at·ed, i·ni·ti·at·ing.**

i·ni·ti·a·tion (i nish′ē ā′shən), the ceremonies by which one is admitted to a group or society: *Everyone in the club attended the initiation of the new members. noun.*

i·ni·ti·a·tive (i nish′ē ə tiv), **1** an active part in starting any undertaking; lead: *She likes to take the initiative in planning class projects.* **2** the readiness and ability to start a thing: *A good leader must have initiative. noun.*

in·ject (in jekt′), **1** to force liquid into the body through a hollow needle: *The doctor injected penicillin into my arm.* **2** to throw in; insert: *While she and I were talking he injected a remark into the conversation. verb.*

in·jec·tion (in jek′shən), **1** the act or process of injecting: *Those drugs are given by injection as well as through the mouth.* **2** a liquid injected: *A drug is often given as an injection. noun.*

in·junc·tion (in jungk′shən), a command; order: *The driver obeyed the policeman's injunction to stop. noun.*

in·jure (in′jər), to do damage to; harm; hurt: *He was injured in an automobile accident. The misunderstanding injured their friendship. verb,* **in·jures, in·jured, in·jur·ing.**

in·jur·i·ous (in jùr′ē əs), causing injury; harmful: *Smoking is injurious to health. adjective.*

in·jur·y (in′jər ē), harm; hurt; damage: *She escaped from the train wreck without injury. noun, plural* **in·jur·ies.**

in·jus·tice (in jus′tis), **1** a lack of justice: *We were angry at the injustice of her decision to punish everyone after one person misbehaved.* **2** an unjust act: *It is an injustice to send an innocent person to jail. noun.*

ink (ingk), **1** a colored or black liquid used for writing or printing. **2** to put ink on; stain with ink. **1** *noun,* **2** *verb.*

in·kling (ing′kling), a hint; a slight suggestion; a vague notion: *Will you give me some inkling of what's going on? noun.*

ink·well (ingk′wel′), a container used to hold ink on a desk or table. *noun.*

ink·y (ing′kē), **1** like ink; dark; black. **2** covered or stained with ink. *adjective,* **ink·i·er, ink·i·est.**

in·laid (in′lād′), set in the surface as a decoration or design. *adjective.*

in·land (in′lənd), **1** away from the coast or the border; situated in the interior: *Illinois is an inland state.* **2** in or toward the interior: *He traveled inland from New York to Chicago.* **1** *adjective,* **2** *adverb.*

in-law (in′lô′), a person related by marriage. *noun.*

in·let (in′let), **1** a narrow strip of water running from a larger body of water into the land or between islands: *The fishing village was on a small inlet of the sea.* **2** an entrance. *noun.*

in·mate (in′māt), a person kept in a prison, asylum, or hospital. *noun.*

in·most (in′mōst), innermost. *adjective.*

inn (in), **1** a place where people can get meals and a room to sleep in. **2** a restaurant or tavern. *noun.*

in·ner (in′ər), **1** farther in; inside: *A closet is usually an inner room.* **2** more private; more secret: *He kept his inner thoughts to himself. adjective.*

inner ear, the part of the ear that is deepest inside the head. It contains the organs of balance and the organs that change sound into nerve messages that go to the brain.

in·ner·most (in′ər mōst), **1** farthest in; deepest within: *We went down to the innermost depths of the mine.* **2** most private; more secret: *He kept his innermost thoughts to himself. adjective.*

inner tube, a rubber tube that can be filled with air, placed inside some tires.

in·ning (in′ing), **1** a division of a baseball game during which each team has a turn at bat. **2** (in baseball) the turn that one team has to play and score before three outs are made. *noun.*

inn·keep·er (in′kē′pər), a person who owns, manages, or keeps an inn. *noun.*

in·no·cence (in′ə səns), **1** freedom from sin, wrong, or guilt: *The accused man proved his innocence of the crime.* **2** simplicity; lack of cunning: "*I hope you will buy me a present,*" *he said, with the innocence of a little child. noun.*

in·no·cent (in′ə sənt), **1** doing no wrong or evil; free from sin or wrong; not guilty: *In the United States a person is innocent until proved guilty.* **2** having a simple and trusting nature: *It was innocent of you to lend your bicycle to a stranger.* **3** doing no harm: *innocent amusements. adjective.*

in·no·va·tion (in′ə vā′shən), **1** a change made in the established way of doing things: *The new principal made many innovations.* **2** the act of making changes; bringing in new things or new ways of doing things: *Many people are opposed to innovation. noun.*

in·no·va·tive (in′ə vā′tiv), making changes; new and different. *adjective.*

in·nu·mer·a·ble (i nü′mər ə bəl *or* i nyü′mər ə bəl), too many to count; very, very many: *innumerable stars. adjective.*

inlaid
This wooden box has an **inlaid** design of ivory.

in·oc·u·late (in ok′yə lāt), to give to a person or animal a preparation made from killed or weakened germs. These cause a mild form of a certain disease, and the body builds up protection against the disease. *verb,* **in·oc·u·lates, in·oc·u·lat·ed, in·oc·u·lat·ing.**

in·oc·u·la·tion (in ok′yə lā′shən), the act or process of inoculating; the causing of a mild form of a disease to keep a person or animal from getting the regular disease. *noun.*

in·of·fen·sive (in′ə fen′siv), not offensive; harmless; not arousing objections: *"Please try to be more quiet" is an inoffensive way of telling people to stop their noise. adjective.*

in·put (in′pùt′), **1** any information that is put into a computer. **2** to put information into a computer. **1** *noun,* **2** *verb,* **in·puts, in·put, in·put·ting.**

in·quire (in kwīr′), to try to find out by questions; ask: *The detective went from house to house, inquiring if anyone had seen anything suspicious. verb,* **in·quires, in·quired, in·quir·ing.**

in·quir·y (in kwī′rē *or* in′kwər ē), **1** the act of inquiring; asking. **2** a search for truth, information, or knowledge: *His inquiry into the history of the town led him to many old books and newspapers.* **3** a question: *The guide answered all our inquiries. noun, plural* **in·quir·ies.**

in·quis·i·tive (in kwiz′ə tiv), curious; asking many questions: *Children are inquisitive because there are many things they wish to learn. adjective.*

in·road (in′rōd′), a raid; attack: *The costs of college made inroads upon her savings. noun.*

in·sane (in sān′), **1** not sane; crazy; mentally ill. **2** for insane people: *an insane asylum.* **3** extremely foolish: *People used to think that plans for flying machines were insane. adjective.*

in·san·i·ty (in san′ə tē), **1** the condition of being insane; madness; mental illness: *The lawyer claimed that the prisoner had murdered the guard during a fit of temporary insanity.* **2** extreme folly: *It is insanity to drive a car without any brakes. noun.*

in·sa·tia·ble (in sā′shə bəl), not able to be satisfied; very greedy: *The boy had an insatiable appetite for candy. adjective.*

in·scribe (in skrīb′), to write, engrave, or mark: *The ring was inscribed with her name. How shall we inscribe the watch? Please inscribe my initials on it. verb,* **in·scribes, in·scribed, in·scrib·ing.**

in·scrip·tion (in skrip′shən), something inscribed: *the inscription on a tombstone. noun.*

inscription

a hat	**i** it	**oi** oil	**ch** child		a in about
ā age	**ī** ice	**ou** out	**ng** long		e in taken
ä far	**o** hot	**u** cup	**sh** she	ə =	i in pencil
e let	**ō** open	**ù** put	**th** thin		o in lemon
ē equal	**ô** order	**ü** rule	**ŦH** then		u in circus
ėr term			**zh** measure		

in·sect (in′sekt), **1** any of a group of small animals without backbones, with bodies divided into three parts. Insects have three pairs of legs and one or two pairs of wings. Flies, mosquitoes, butterflies, and bees are insects. **2** any similar small animal, especially one without wings and with four pairs of legs. Spiders and centipedes are often called insects. *noun.*

Word History

insect *Insect* comes from a Latin word meaning "divided." An insect's body is divided into three sections.

HEAD   THORAX   WINGS

ABDOMEN

insect (definition 1)—a grasshopper

in·sec·ti·cide (in sek′tə sīd), a substance for killing insects. *noun.*

in·se·cure (in′si kyùr′), **1** not safe from danger, failure, or the like: *During an earthquake, people in high buildings are in an insecure position.* **2** likely to give way; not firm: *an insecure support, an insecure lock.* **3** not confident; fearful; timid: *He is so insecure that he has trouble making any decision. adjective.*

in·sen·si·ble (in sen′sə bəl), not sensitive; not able to feel or observe: *She appeared to be insensible to cold. adjective.*

in·sen·si·tive (in sen′sə tiv), not sensitive; without feeling: *an insensitive area of the skin. They were insensitive to the needs of others. adjective.*

in·sep·ar·a·ble (in sep′ər ə bəl), not able to be separated: *inseparable companions. adjective.*

in·sert (in sėrt′ *for 1;* in′sėrt′ *for 2*), **1** to put in; set in: *She inserted the key into the lock. He inserted a letter into the misspelled word.* **2** something put in or set in: *The book contained an insert of several pages of pictures.* **1** *verb,* **2** *noun.*

in·ser·tion (in sėr′shən), **1** the act of inserting: *The insertion of one word can change the meaning of a sentence.* **2** something inserted. *noun.*

in·side (in′sīd′ *for 1,2, and 5;* in′sīd′ *for 3 and 4*), **1** the part within; inner surface: *The inside of the box was lined with colored paper.* **2** on or by the inner side: *an inside seat, an inside pocket.* **3** in or into the inner part: *Please step inside. It is too nice a day to stay inside.* **4** in: *The nut is inside the shell.* **5** done or known by people on the inside of a group, a building, or the like: *The police thought that the theft was an inside job and suspected several employees.* **1** *noun,* **2,5** *adjective,* **3** *adverb,* **4** *preposition.*

inside out, 1 so that what should be inside is outside; with the inside showing: *He turned his pockets inside out.* **2** completely; thoroughly: *She learned her lessons inside out.*

in·sight (in′sīt′), wisdom and understanding in dealing with people or with facts: *We study science to gain insight into the world we live in. noun.*

in·sig·ni·a (in sig′nē ə), a medal, badge, or other distinguishing mark of a rank, an organization, or some honor: *The crown and scepter are insignia of royalty. noun, plural* **in·sig·ni·a** *or* **in·sig·ni·as.**

insignia—The eagle, shield, and anchor are **insignia** of the United States Navy.

in·sig·nif·i·cant (in′sig nif′ə kənt), **1** having little use or importance: *A tenth of a cent is an insignificant amount of money.* **2** having little meaning: *insignificant chatter. adjective.*

in·sin·cere (in′sin sir′), not sincere; deceitful: *He never intended to keep his insincere promises. adjective.*

in·sin·u·ate (in sin′yü āt), to hint; suggest in an indirect way: *To say "That worker can't do the job; it takes skill" is to insinuate that the worker is not skilled. verb,* **in·sin·u·ates, in·sin·u·at·ed, in·sin·u·at·ing.**

in·sist (in sist′), to keep firmly to some demand, some statement, or some opinion: *He insists that he had a right to use his brother's tools. She insists that we should all learn to ski. verb.*

in·sist·ence (in sis′təns), the act of insisting: *At the teacher's insistence the class became quiet. noun.*

in·sist·ent (in sis′tənt), **1** insisting; continuing to make a strong, firm demand or statement: *In spite of the rain she was insistent on going out.* **2** impossible to overlook or disregard: *Her insistent knocking on the door woke us up. adjective.*

in·so·lence (in′sə ləns), bold rudeness; insulting behavior or speech. *noun.*

in·so·lent (in′sə lənt), boldly rude; insulting: *They were insolent to walk away while you were talking to them. adjective.*

in·sol·u·ble (in sol′yə bəl), **1** not able to be dissolved: *Fat is insoluble in water.* **2** not able to be solved: *The detective finally gave up, declaring the mystery insoluble. adjective.*

in·som·ni·a (in som′nē ə), an inability to sleep; sleeplessness. *noun.*

in·spect (in spekt′), **1** to look over carefully; examine. **2** to examine formally or officially: *Government officials inspect factories and mines to make sure that they are safe for workers. verb.*

inspect (definition 1) After this engine is tested and **inspected** it will be used in a spacecraft.

in·spec·tion (in spek′shən), **1** an inspecting; examination: *An inspection of the roof showed no leaks.* **2** a formal or official examination: *The soldiers lined up for their daily inspection by their officers. noun.*

in·spec·tor (in spek′tər), **1** a person whose job is to inspect something: *The city building inspector told the landlord to fix the fire escape.* **2** a police officer ranking next below a superintendent. *noun.*

in·spi·ra·tion (in′spə rā′shən), **1** the influence of thought and strong feelings on actions, especially on good actions: *Some people get inspiration from sermons, some from nature.* **2** any influence that arouses effort or activity: *The teacher was an inspiration to his students.* **3** a sudden, brilliant idea. *noun.*

in·spire (in spīr′), **1** to fill with a thought or feeling: *A chance to try again inspired us with hope.* **2** to cause thought or feeling: *The leader's courage inspired confidence in others.* **3** to fill with excitement: *The speaker inspired the crowd.* **4** to arouse effort or activity in someone: *His teacher's criticism inspired him to study harder. verb,* **in·spires, in·spired, in·spir·ing.**
[*Inspire* comes from a Latin word meaning "to blow into" or "to breathe into."]

in·stall (in stôl′), **1** to place a person in office with ceremonies: *The new judge was installed without delay.* **2** to put in a place; settle: *The cat installed itself in a chair near the fireplace.* **3** to put in place for use: *The new owner of the house had a telephone installed. verb.*

in·stall·ment (in stôl′mənt), **1** a part of a sum of money that is to be paid at stated times: *The table* *cost $100; we paid in two monthly installments of $50 each.* **2** one of several parts issued at different times: *The serial story appeared in six installments.* *noun.*

in·stance (in′stəns), an example; case: *The pilot is an instance of a woman who carried out her childhood dreams of flying. noun.*

  for instance, as an example: *Her hobbies include, for instance, skating and stamp collecting.*

in·stant (in′stənt), **1** a particular moment: *Stop talking this instant!* **2** a moment of time: *He paused for an instant.* **3** without delay; immediate: *The medicine gave instant relief from pain.* **4** prepared beforehand and requiring little or no cooking, mixing, or additional ingredients: *instant coffee, instant pudding.* **1,2** *noun,* **3,4** *adjective.*

in·stan·ta·ne·ous (in′stən tā′nē əs), happening or done in an instant: *A flash of lightning is instantaneous. adjective.*

in·stant·ly (in′stənt lē), at once. *adverb.*

in·stead (in sted′), in another's place; as a substitute: *She stayed home, and her sister went riding instead. adverb.*

  instead of, rather than; in place of; as a substitute for: *Instead of studying, I watched television.*

in·step (in′step), **1** the upper part of the foot between the toes and the ankle. **2** the part of a shoe or stocking over this part of the foot. *noun.*

INSTEP

in·still (in stil′), to put into someone's mind little by little: *Reading good books instills a love for fine literature. verb.*

in·stinct (in′stingkt), **1** a way of acting that is born in an animal, not learned: *Ants do not learn to build nests but build them by instinct.* **2** a natural tendency or ability; talent: *Even as a child the artist had an instinct for drawing. noun.*

in·stinc·tive (in stingk′tiv), born in an animal, not learned: *The spinning of webs is instinctive in spiders. adjective.*

in·sti·tute (in′stə tüt *or* in′stə tyüt), **1** an organization for some special purpose. An art institute teaches or displays art. A technical school is often called an institute. **2** a building used by such an organization: *We spent the afternoon in the Art Institute.* **3** to set up; establish; begin: *After the accident the police instituted an inquiry into its causes.* **1,2** *noun,* **3** *verb,* **in·sti·tutes, in·sti·tut·ed, in·sti·tut·ing.**

in·sti·tu·tion (in′stə tü′shən *or* in′stə tyü′shən), **1** a club, society, or any organization established for some special purpose. A church, school, college, hospital, asylum, or prison is an institution. **2** a building used for the work of such an organization. **3** an established law or custom: *Marriage is an institution among most of the world's people. noun.*

in·struct (in strukt′), **1** to show how to do something; teach; train; educate: *We have one teacher who instructs us in reading, arithmetic, and science.* **2** to give directions or orders to; direct: *The owner of the house instructed the agent to sell it. verb.*

in·struc·tion (in struk′shən), **1** a teaching; training; education: *He devoted his life to the instruction of handicapped children.* **2 instructions,** directions or orders: *The teacher's instructions were clearly understood. noun.*

in·struc·tive (in struk′tiv), useful for instruction; giving information; instructing: *His confused directions were not very instructive. adjective.*

in·struc·tor (in struk′tər), a teacher. *noun.*

in·stru·ment (in′strə mənt), **1** a thing used to do something; tool; mechanical device: *A forceps and a drill are two instruments used by dentists.* **2** a device for producing musical sounds: *wind instruments, stringed instruments. A violin, cello, and piano were the instruments in the trio.* **3** a device for measuring, recording, or controlling. A thermometer is an instrument for measuring temperature. *noun.*

in·stru·men·tal (in′strə men′tl), **1** acting or serving as a means; useful; helpful: *A friend was instrumental in getting me a job.* **2** played on or written for musical instruments: *An orchestra provided instrumental music to accompany the singing. adjective.*

in·suf·fer·a·ble (in suf′ər ə bəl), unbearable: *insufferable rudeness. The heat of the desert at noon was insufferable. adjective.*

in·suf·fi·cient (in′sə fish′ənt), not enough; less than is needed: *The police had insufficient evidence to arrest the thief. adjective.*

in·su·late (in′sə lāt), to keep something from transferring electricity, heat, or sound by covering, lining, or surrounding it with a material that does not conduct electricity, heat, or sound: *Telephone wires are often insulated by a covering of rubber. verb,* **in·su·lates, in·su·lat·ed, in·su·lat·ing.**

in·su·la·tion (in′sə lā′shən), **1** an insulating or a being insulated: *The insulation of our house took several weeks to finish.* **2** a material used in insulating: *Rubber is a common insulation for electric wires. noun.*

a hat	i it	oi oil	ch child	a in about
ā age	ī ice	ou out	ng long	e in taken
ä far	o hot	u cup	sh she	ə = i in pencil
e let	ō open	u̇ put	th thin	o in lemon
ē equal	ô order	ü rule	ŦH then	u in circus
ėr term			zh measure	

insulator | intend

insulator—The **insulators** keep the electricity that goes through the wires from passing into the poles.

in·su·la·tor (in′sə lā′tər), something that insulates; something that prevents the passage of electricity, heat, or sound. *noun.*

in·su·lin (in′sə lən), a substance produced by the pancreas and necessary for the body to use sugar and starch. The lack of insulin is a cause of diabetes. *noun.*

in·sult (in sult′ *for 1;* in′sult *for 2*), **1** to say or do something very scornful, rude, or harsh to: *She insulted me by calling me a liar.* **2** a comment or action that is very scornful, rude, or harsh: *It is an insult to call someone stupid.* **1** *verb,* **2** *noun.*
[*Insult* comes from a Latin word meaning "to jump at." Later on, the meaning changed from the idea of a physical attack to an attack with words.]

in·sur·ance (in shúr′əns), **1** an insuring of property, person, or life. Fire insurance, burglary insurance, accident insurance, life insurance, and health insurance are some of the many kinds. **2** the business of insuring property, person, or life. **3** the amount of money for which property, person, or life is insured: *He has $10,000 life insurance, which his wife will receive if he dies first. noun.*

in·sure (in shúr′), **1** to agree to pay money if certain kinds of harm or loss happen to something or someone: *An insurance company will insure your house against fire.* **2** to make something or someone safe against loss or harm by paying money to an insurance company: *She insured her car against accident, theft, and fire.* **3** to make sure or safe; ensure: *Check your work to insure that it is accurate. verb,* **in·sures, in·sured, in·sur·ing.**

in·sur·gent (in sėr′jənt), **1** a person who rises in revolt; rebel: *The insurgents captured the town.* **2** rising in revolt: *The insurgent peasants burned the landowners' homes.* **1** *noun,* **2** *adjective.*

in·sur·rec·tion (in′sə rek′shən), a rising against established authority; revolt; rebellion. *noun.*

in·tact (in takt′), with nothing missing or broken; uninjured; whole. *adjective.*

in·take (in′tāk′), **1** the place where water, air, or gas enters a channel, pipe, or other narrow opening. **2** the act or process of taking in. **3** the amount or thing taken in: *The intake through the pipe was 5000 gallons a day. noun.*

in·te·grate (in′tə grāt), **1** to put or bring parts together into a whole: *The committee will try to integrate the different ideas into one uniform plan.*

2 to make schools, parks, and other public facilities available to people of all races on an equal basis: *to integrate a neighborhood. verb,* **in·te·grates, in·te·grat·ed, in·te·grat·ing.**

integrated circuit, an electrical circuit designed for a single function and built as a unit on or in a chip of silicon. An integrated circuit containing thousands of parts may be less than an inch across.

in·te·gra·tion (in′tə grā′shən), **1** an integrating: *She is responsible for the integration of the work of all the people involved with the project.* **2** the including of people of all races on an equal basis in schools, parks, neighborhoods, and the like. *noun.*

in·teg·ri·ty (in teg′rə tē), honesty; sincerity; uprightness: *I respect a person of integrity. noun.*

in·tel·lect (in′tə lekt), **1** the power of knowing; understanding; intelligence: *To learn arithmetic or spelling, you must use your intellect.* **2** a person of high mental ability: *He was one of the great intellects of his time. noun.*

in·tel·lec·tu·al (in′tə lek′chü əl), **1** needing or using intelligence; of the intellect: *Thinking is an intellectual process.* **2** a person who is well informed and intelligent. **1** *adjective,* **2** *noun.*

in·tel·li·gence (in tel′ə jəns), **1** the ability to learn and know; understanding; mind: *A dog has more intelligence than a worm. Intelligence tests are given in many schools.* **2** information, especially secret information about an enemy: *Spies supply our government with intelligence. noun.*

in·tel·li·gent (in tel′ə jənt), having or showing understanding; able to learn and know; quick at learning: *Elephants are intelligent animals. adjective.*

in·tel·li·gi·ble (in tel′ə jə bəl), able to be understood; clear. *adjective.*

in·tem·per·ance (in tem′pər əns), **1** a lack of moderation or self-control; excess: *His intemperance in eating caused him to become very fat.* **2** too much drinking of intoxicating liquor. *noun.*

in·tend (in tend′), to have in mind as a purpose; plan: *We intend to go home soon. They intend that their children will go to college.* **2** to mean for a

intact—Only one egg was still **intact** after I dropped the carton.

particular purpose, person, or use: *That gift was intended for you.* verb.

in·tense (in tens′), **1** very much; very great; very strong: *intense happiness, intense light. Intense heat melts iron. A bad burn causes intense pain.* **2** having or showing strong feeling. An intense person is one who feels things very deeply and is likely to be extreme in action. *adjective.*

in·ten·si·fy (in ten′sə fī), to make or become more intense: *The blowing snow intensified the danger of driving on the icy highway.* verb, **in·ten·si·fies, in·ten·si·fied, in·ten·si·fy·ing.**

in·ten·si·ty (in ten′sə tē), **1** the quality of being intense; great strength or force: *intensity of thought. When we left the shade of the porch, the intensity of the sunlight made us squint.* **2** the amount or degree of strength of electricity, heat, light, or sound per unit of area or volume. *noun, plural* **in·ten·si·ties.**

in·ten·sive (in ten′siv), deep and thorough: *New laws were passed following an intensive study of the causes of pollution.* *adjective.*

in·tent (in tent′), **1** a purpose; intention: *I'm sorry I hurt you; that wasn't my intent.* **2** a meaning: *What is the intent of that remark?* **3** very attentive; having the eyes or thoughts earnestly fixed on something; earnest: *A stare is an intent look.* **4** much interested; determined; having the attention fixed: *She is intent on finishing the job today.* **1,2** *noun,* **3,4** *adjective.*

intent (definition 3)
She is **intent** on painting the intricate design.

in·ten·tion (in ten′shən), a purpose; plan: *Our intention is to travel next summer.* noun.

in·ten·tion·al (in ten′shə nəl), done on purpose; meant; planned; intended: *The kick she gave me under the table was intentional; it was a signal to be quiet.* adjective.

in·ten·tion·al·ly (in ten′shə nə lē), with intention; on purpose. adverb.

in·ter·act (in′tər akt′), to act on each other: *The summer heat and my bad temper interacted, each making the other seem worse.* verb.

in·ter·cede (in′tər sēd′), to plead for another; ask a favor from one person for another: *He did not dare ask the teacher himself, so I interceded for him.* verb, **in·ter·cedes, in·ter·ced·ed, in·ter·ced·ing.**

in·ter·cept (in′tər sept′), to take, seize, or stop on the way from one place to another: *to intercept a letter, to intercept a messenger, to intercept a pass in a football game.* verb.

in·ter·change (in′tər chānj′ *for 1;* in′tər chānj′ *for 2 and 3*), **1** to put each of two or more persons or things in the place of the other; exchange: *If you interchange those two pictures, they'll look better.* **2** a putting each of two or more persons or things in the other's place; an exchange: *The word "team" may be turned into "meat" by the interchange of the first and last letters.* **3** the point at which a highway, especially an express highway, connects with another road without the streams of traffic interfering with each other. **1** *verb,* **in·ter·chang·es, in·ter·changed, in·ter·chang·ing; 2,3** *noun.*

interchange (definition 3)

in·ter·change·a·ble (in′tər chān′jə bəl), able to be put or used in each other's place; able to be switched: *interchangeable parts.* adjective.

in·ter·com (in′tər kom′), a system of microphones and loudspeakers by which people can talk to each other from different parts of a building, aircraft, ship, or tank. noun.

in·ter·est (in′tər ist), **1** a feeling of wanting to know, see, do, own, or share in: *He has an interest in collecting stamps.* **2** the power of arousing such a feeling: *A dull book lacks interest.* **3** anything for which a person has such a feeling. A business, activity, or pastime can be an interest. **4** to arouse such a feeling in; make curious and hold the attention of: *A good mystery interests most people.* **5** a share in property and actions: *She bought a half interest in the business.* **6** advantage; profit; benefit: *The parents look after the interests of the family.* **7** the money paid for the use of someone else's money. If you borrow money from a bank, you must pay interest on the loan. **1-3,5-7** *noun,* **4** *verb.*

in·ter·est·ed (in′tər ə stid), feeling or showing interest: *an interested spectator. adjective.*

in·ter·est·ing (in′tər ə sting), arousing interest; holding one's attention: *Stories about travel and adventure are interesting to most people. adjective.*

in·ter·fere (in′tər fir′), 1 to clash; come into opposition: *I will come Saturday if nothing interferes.* 2 to mix in the affairs of others; meddle: *That neighbor is always interfering in other people's affairs. Don't interfere with your sister when she's busy. verb,* **in·ter·feres, in·ter·fered, in·ter·fer·ing.**

in·ter·fer·ence (in′tər fir′əns), the act or fact of interfering: *Your interference spoiled our fun. noun.*

in·te·ri·or (in tir′ē ər), 1 the inside; inner surface or part: *The interior of the house was beautifully decorated.* 2 inner; on the inside: *The interior walls of the house were painted last year.* 3 the part of a region or country away from the coast or border: *There are deserts in the interior of Asia.* 4 away from the coast or border. *1,3 noun, 2,4 adjective.*

in·ter·jec·tion (in′tər jek′shən), 1 an exclamation regarded as a part of speech. *Oh! ah! alas!* and *hurrah!* are interjections. 2 a remark; exclamation. *noun.*

in·ter·lace (in′tər lās′), 1 to arrange threads, strips, or branches so that they go over and under each other: *Baskets are made by interlacing reeds or fibers.* 2 to cross each other over and under; mingle together: *The branches of the trees interlaced above the path. verb,* **in·ter·lac·es, in·ter·laced, in·ter·lac·ing.**

interlace
(definition 1)

in·ter·lock (in′tər lok′), to lock or join with one another: *The different pieces of a jigsaw puzzle interlock. verb.*

in·ter·lude (in′tər lüd), anything that is thought of as filling the time between two things: *There was an interlude of sunshine between two showers. noun.*

in·ter·me·di·ate (in′tər mē′dē it), 1 being or occurring between others; middle: *Classes are offered in beginning, intermediate, and advanced French. Gray is intermediate between black and white.* 2 something in between. *1 adjective, 2 noun.*

in·ter·mi·na·ble (in tėr′mə nə bəl), 1 never stopping; endless. 2 so long as to seem endless; very long and tiring. *adjective.*

in·ter·min·gle (in′tər ming′gəl), to mix together; mingle: *intermingle several styles of furniture in a room. verb,* **in·ter·min·gles, in·ter·min·gled, in·ter·min·gling.**

in·ter·mis·sion (in′tər mish′ən), the time between periods of activity; pause; interruption: *The band played from eight to twelve with a short intermission at ten. noun.*

in·ter·mit·tent (in′tər mit′nt), stopping and beginning again: *The pilot watched for an intermittent red light, flashing on and off every 15 seconds. adjective.*

in·tern (in′tėrn′), a doctor acting as an assistant and receiving training in a hospital. *noun.*

in·ter·nal (in tėr′nl), 1 inner; on the inside: *The accident caused internal injuries as well as cuts and bruises.* 2 having something to do with affairs within a country; domestic: *internal politics. Internal revenue is money from taxes on business and income in a country. adjective.*

in·ter·nal·ly (in tėr′nl ē), inside the body: *This ointment must not be taken internally. adverb.*

in·ter·na·tion·al (in′tər nash′ə nəl), having to do with two or more countries: *A treaty is an international agreement. adjective.*

in·ter·plan·e·tar·y (in′tər plan′ə ter′ē), situated or taking place between planets: *interplanetary distances, interplanetary travel. adjective.*

in·ter·pret (in tėr′prit), 1 to explain the meaning of: *to interpret a hard passage in a book, to interpret a dream.* 2 to bring out the meaning of: *The actress interpreted the part of the queen with great skill.* 3 to understand: *We interpret your silence as consent.* 4 to serve as an interpreter; translate. *verb.*

in·ter·pre·ta·tion (in tėr′prə tā′shən), 1 an interpreting; explanation: *People often give different interpretations to the same facts.* 2 a bringing out the meaning: *The musician's interpretation of the music was different from any I've heard before. noun.*

in·ter·pret·er (in tėr′prə tər), 1 a person who interprets. 2 a person whose business is translating from a foreign language: *Because my parents do not speak Spanish, their guide in Mexico had to act as their interpreter also. noun.*

in·ter·ro·gate (in ter′ə gāt), to ask questions of; examine by questions: *The lawyers interrogated the witness. verb,* **in·ter·ro·gates, in·ter·ro·gat·ed, in·ter·ro·gat·ing.**

in·ter·ro·ga·tion (in ter′ə gā′shən), a questioning: *Interrogation of the suspects took several hours. noun.*

in·ter·rog·a·tive (in′tə rog′ə tiv), 1 asking a question; having the form of a question: *an interrogative sentence, an interrogative tone of voice.* 2 a word used in asking a question. *Who, why,* and *what* are interrogatives. *1 adjective, 2 noun.*

in·ter·rupt (in′tə rupt′), to break in upon talk, work, rest, or a person speaking; hinder; stop: *A fire drill interrupted the lesson. verb.*

in·ter·rup·tion (in′tə rup′shən), an interrupting or a being interrupted; break; stop: *The rain continued without interruption all day. noun.*

in·ter·sect (in′tər sekt′), to cross each other; cross: *Streets usually intersect at right angles. verb.*

in·ter·sec·tion (in′tər sek′shən), a place where one thing crosses another: *My house is near the* *intersection of Main Street and Pine Avenue. noun.*

in·ter·sperse (in′tər spėrs′), to vary with something put here and there: *The grass is interspersed with beds of flowers. verb,* **in·ter·spers·es, in·ter·spersed, in·ter·spers·ing.**

in·ter·state (in′tər stāt′), between persons or organizations in different states; between states: *The federal government regulates interstate commerce. adjective.*

in·ter·twine (in′tər twīn′), to twine one with another: *The vines intertwined on the wall. verb,* **in·ter·twines, in·ter·twined, in·ter·twin·ing.**

in·ter·val (in′tər vəl), a time or space between things: *an interval of fifteen minutes for recess, an interval of quiet in a busy day. noun.*

at intervals, 1 now and then: *There was a drizzling rain falling at intervals.* **2** here and there: *Villages are located at intervals along the river.*

in·ter·vene (in′tər vēn′), **1** to come between; be between: *Six days intervene between Christmas and New Year's Day.* **2** to come in to help settle a dispute: *The President was asked to intervene in the coal strike. verb,* **in·ter·venes, in·ter·vened, in·ter·ven·ing.**

in·ter·ven·tion (in′tər ven′shən), **1** an intervening: *The strike was settled by the intervention of the President.* **2** interference, especially by one nation in the affairs of another. *noun.*

in·ter·view (in′tər vyü), **1** a meeting, generally of persons face to face, to talk over something special: *My parents had an interview with the teacher about my work.* **2** to visit and talk with: *Reporters from the newspaper interviewed the mayor.* **1** *noun,* **2** *verb.*

in·ter·view·er (in′tər vyü′ər), a person whose business is to visit and talk with other people, and to report the conversation in a newspaper or magazine, or on radio or television. *noun.*

in·ter·wo·ven (in′tər wō′vən), **1** woven together. **2** mixed together; mingled. *adjective.*

in·tes·tine (in tes′tən), **1** the part of the digestive system that extends below the stomach. Food from the stomach passes into the intestine where digestion is completed and water is absorbed. In adult human beings, the **small intestine** is about 20 feet (6 meters) long; the **large intestine** is about 5 feet (1.5 meters) long. **2 intestines,** the intestine. *noun.*

in·ti·ma·cy (in′tə mə sē), close acquaintance; closeness. *noun, plural* **in·ti·ma·cies.**

in·ti·mate[1] (in′tə mit), **1** very familiar; known very well; closely acquainted: *They have been intimate friends since childhood.* **2** a close friend. **3** far within; inmost: *a person's intimate thoughts.* **1,3** *adjective,* **2** *noun.*

in·ti·mate[2] (in′tə māt), **1** to hint; suggest: *Her smile intimated that she was pleased.* **2** to make known. *verb,* **in·ti·mates, in·ti·mat·ed, in·ti·mat·ing.**

in·tim·i·date (in tim′ə dāt), to frighten; make afraid; influence by fear: *to intimidate someone*

with threats. verb, **in·tim·i·dates, in·tim·i·dat·ed, in·tim·i·dat·ing.**

in·to (in′tü), **1** to the inside of; toward and inside: *Come into the house. We drove into the city. I will look into the matter.* **2** to the condition of; to the form of: *Divide the apple into three parts. Cold weather turns water into ice.* **3** against: *In the dark, she walked into the closet door. preposition.*

in·tol·er·a·ble (in tol′ər ə bəl), unbearable; too hard to be endured: *The pain of the toothache was intolerable. adjective.*

in·tol·er·ant (in tol′ər ənt), not tolerant; not willing to let others do and think as they choose. *adjective.*

in·tox·i·cate (in tok′sə kāt), **1** to make drunk: *Too much wine intoxicates people.* **2** to excite greatly: *The joy of victory intoxicated the team. verb,* **in·tox·i·cates, in·tox·i·cat·ed, in·tox·i·cat·ing.** [*Intoxicate* comes from a Latin word of the Middle Ages meaning "dipped in poison."]

in·tox·i·ca·tion (in tok′sə kā′shən), **1** an intoxicated condition; drunkenness. **2** great excitement. **3** (in medicine) poisoning. *noun.*

in·trep·id (in trep′id), fearless; very brave: *an intrepid mountain climber. adjective.*

in·tri·cate (in′trə kit), **1** with many twists and turns; perplexing; entangled; complicated: *An intricate knot is very hard to tie or untie.* **2** very hard to understand: *The directions for building the model plane were so intricate that I made several mistakes. adjective.*

intestine (definition 1)

in·trigue (in trēg′), **1** a crafty plot; secret scheme: *The king's younger brother took part in the intrigue to make himself king.* **2** to form and carry out plots; plan in a secret or underhand way: *He pretended to be loyal while he intrigued against the king.* **3** to excite the curiosity and

a hat	i it	oi oil	ch child	a in about
ā age	ī ice	ou out	ng long	e in taken
ä far	o hot	u cup	sh she	ə = { i in pencil
e let	ō open	ů put	th thin	o in lemon
ē equal	ô order	ü rule	ᴛʜ then	u in circus
ėr term			zh measure	

interest of: *The book's unusual title intrigued me.* 1 *noun,* 2,3 *verb,* **in·trigues, in·trigued, in·tri·guing.**

in·tro·duce (in/trə düs/ *or* in/trə dyüs/), **1** to bring in: *She introduced a story into the conversation.* **2** to put in; insert: *The doctor introduced a long tube into the sick man's throat so he could breathe.* **3** to bring into use, notice, or knowledge: *Television and space travel are introducing many new words into our language.* **4** to make known; bring into acquaintance with: *Mrs. Brown, may I introduce Mr. Smith? I introduced my visiting cousin to our city by showing her the sights.* **5** to begin: *He introduced his speech by telling a joke. verb,* **in·tro·duc·es, in·tro·duced, in·tro·duc·ing.**

in·tro·duc·tion (in/trə duk/shən), **1** an introducing: *The introduction of steel made tall buildings easier to build.* **2** a being introduced: *She was pleased by her introduction to so many new people.* **3** the beginning of a speech, a piece of music, or a book. **4** a thing made known; thing brought into use: *Television is a later introduction than radio. noun.*

in·tro·duc·tor·y (in/trə duk/tə rē), used to introduce; serving as an introduction; preliminary: *The speaker began her talk with a few introductory remarks about her subject. adjective.*

in·trude (in trüd/), to force oneself in; come unasked and unwanted: *Do not intrude upon the privacy of your neighbors. verb,* **in·trudes, in·trud·ed, in·trud·ing.**

in·trud·er (in trü/dər), one that intrudes. *noun.*

in·tru·sion (in trü/zhən), the act of intruding; coming unasked and unwanted: *Excuse my intrusion; I didn't know that you were busy. noun.*

in·un·date (in/un dāt), to overflow; flood: *Heavy rains caused the river to rise and inundate the valley. verb,* **in·un·dates, in·un·dat·ed, in·un·dat·ing.**

in·vade (in vād/), **1** to enter with force or as an enemy; attack: *Soldiers invaded the country to conquer it. Grasshoppers invaded the fields and ate the crops.* **2** to enter as if to take possession: *Tourists invaded the city.* **3** to interfere with; break in on; violate: *The law punishes people who invade the rights of others. verb,* **in·vades, in·vad·ed, in·vad·ing.**

in·vad·er (in vā/dər), a person or thing that invades. *noun.*

in·va·lid[1] (in/və lid), **1** a sick, weak person not able to get about and do things. **2** not well; weak and sick. **3** for the use of invalids: *an invalid chair.* **1** *noun,* 2,3 *adjective.*

in·val·id[2] (in val/id), not valid; without value: *Unless a check is signed, it is invalid. adjective.*

in·val·u·a·ble (in val/yü ə bəl), priceless; very precious; valuable beyond measure: *Good health is an invaluable blessing. adjective.*

in·var·i·a·ble (in ver/ē ə bəl *or* in var/ē ə bəl), always the same; not changing: *After dinner it was her invariable habit to take a walk. adjective.*

in·var·i·a·bly (in ver/ē ə blē *or* in var/ē ə blē), without change; without exception: *Spring invariably follows winter. adverb.*

in·va·sion (in vā/zhən), the act or fact of invading; entering by force or as an enemy; attack. *noun.*

in·vent (in vent/), **1** to make or think out something new: *Alexander Graham Bell invented the telephone.* **2** to make up: *Since they had no good reason for being late, they invented an excuse. verb.*

in·ven·tion (in ven/shən), **1** a making something new: *the invention of gunpowder.* **2** a thing invented: *Television is a modern invention.* **3** a made-up story; false statement: *That rumor is only an invention. noun.*

in·ven·tive (in ven/tiv), good at inventing: *An inventive person thinks up ways to save time, money, and work. adjective.*

in·ven·tor (in ven/tər), a person who invents. *noun.*

in·ven·to·ry (in/vən tôr/ē), **1** a complete and detailed list of articles. An inventory of property or goods tells how many there are of each article and what they are worth. **2** all the articles listed or to be listed; stock: *The store is having a sale to reduce its inventory.* **3** to make a detailed list of; enter in a list: *Some stores inventory their stock once a month.* 1,2 *noun, plural* **in·ven·to·ries;** 3 *verb,* **in·ven·to·ries, in·ven·to·ried, in·ven·to·ry·ing.**

in·vert (in vėrt/), **1** to turn upside down: *Remove the cake from the pan by inverting it onto a rack.* **2** to turn the other way; change to the opposite; reverse in position, direction, or order: *If you invert "I can," you have "Can I?" verb.*

in·ver·te·brate (in vėr/tə brit), **1** an animal

invertebrates (definition 1)

without a backbone. Worms and insects are invertebrates; fishes and mammals are vertebrates. **2** without a backbone: *an invertebrate animal.* **1** *noun,* **2** *adjective.*

in·vest (in vest′), **1** to use money to buy something which will produce a profit or an income or both: *If I had any money, I would invest it in land.* **2** to spend or put in time or energy: *Much time and energy have been invested in the cancer crusade. verb.*

in·ves·ti·gate (in ves′tə gāt), to search into; examine closely: *The detectives investigated the crime to find out who committed it. Scientists investigate nature to learn more about it. verb,* **in·ves·ti·gates, in·ves·ti·gat·ed, in·ves·ti·gat·ing.**

in·ves·ti·ga·tion (in ves′tə gā′shən), a careful search; detailed or careful examination: *An investigation of the accident by the police put the blame on the drivers of both cars. noun.*

in·ves·ti·ga·tor (in ves′tə gā′tər), a person who investigates. *noun.*

in·vest·ment (in vest′mənt), **1** an investing; laying out of money: *Getting an education is a wise investment of time and money.* **2** an amount of money invested: *His investments amount to thousands of dollars.* **3** something bought which is expected to yield money as interest or profit or both: *She has a good income from wise investments. noun.*

in·ves·tor (in ves′tər), a person who invests money. *noun.*

in·vig·o·rate (in vig′ə rāt′), to give vigor to; fill with life and energy: *Exercise invigorates the body. verb,* **in·vig·o·rates, in·vig·o·rat·ed, in·vig·o·rat·ing.**

in·vig·o·rat·ing (in vig′ə rā′ting), filling with life and energy; giving vigor to: *An invigorating breeze made our hike enjoyable. adjective.*

in·vin·ci·ble (in vin′sə bəl), not to be overcome; unconquerable: *After four victories in a row, our team seems invincible. adjective.*

in·vis·i·ble (in viz′ə bəl), not visible; not capable of being seen: *Thought is invisible. Germs are invisible to the naked eye. adjective.*

in·vi·ta·tion (in′və tā′shən), a polite request to come to some place or to do something. Formal invitations are written or printed. *The children received invitations to the party at the community center. noun.*

in·vite (in vīt′), **1** to ask someone politely to come to some place or to do something: *I invited some friends to a party.* **2** to make a polite request for: *She invited our opinion of her story.* **3** to give a chance for; tend to cause: *New Year's Day invites good resolutions. Carelessness invites trouble.* **4** to attract; tempt: *The cool water invited us to swim. verb,* **in·vites, in·vit·ed, in·vit·ing.**

in·vit·ing (in vī′ting), attractive; tempting: *The cool water of a mountain stream looks inviting after a long hike. adjective.*

in·vo·ca·tion (in′və kā′shən), a calling upon in prayer; appealing for help or protection: *A religious service often begins with an invocation to God. noun.*

in·vol·un·tar·y (in vol′ən ter′ē), **1** not voluntary; not done of one's own free will; unwilling: *Taking gym was involuntary on my part; the school requires it.* **2** not controlled by the will: *Breathing is mainly involuntary. adjective.*

in·volve (in volv′), **1** to have as a necessary part; take in; include: *Housework involves cooking, washing dishes, sweeping, and cleaning.* **2** to bring into difficulty or danger: *One foolish mistake can involve you in a good deal of trouble.* **3** to take up the attention of; occupy: *She was involved in working out a puzzle. verb,* **in·volves, in·volved, in·volv·ing.**

in·volved (in volvd′), complicated: *an involved sentence, an involved explanation. adjective.*

in·ward (in′wərd), **1** toward the inside: *a passage leading inward.* **2** on the inside; inner: *the inward surfaces of a hollow wall.* **3** into the mind or soul: *to turn one's thoughts inward.* **4** in the mind or soul: *an inward peace.* **1,3** *adverb,* **2,4** *adjective.*

in·ward·ly (in′wərd lē), **1** on the inside; within: *The patient was bleeding inwardly.* **2** in the mind or soul: *Inwardly he was somewhat bashful but he tried not to show it.* **3** not aloud or openly: *She chuckled inwardly to herself at the joke. adverb.*

i·o·dine (ī′ə dīn), **1** a substance used in medicine, in photography, and in making dyes. Iodine is a chemical element. **2** a brown liquid containing iodine, put on wounds to kill disease germs and prevent infection. *noun.*

IOU or **I.O.U.** (ī′ō′yü′), an informal written note that promises to pay a debt: *I gave my friend an IOU for two dollars. noun, plural* **IOU's** or **I.O.U.'s.**

I·o·wa (ī′ə wə), one of the midwestern states of the United States. *Abbreviation:* Ia. or IA *Capital:* Des Moines. *noun.*

[*Iowa* was named for an American Indian tribe, the Iowa. The name of the tribe came from a Dakota Indian word meaning "sleepy ones." Enemies of the Iowa Indians gave them this name to make fun of them.]

I·ran (i ran′ *or* i rän′), a country in southwestern Asia. *noun.*

I·raq (i rak′ *or* i räk′), a country in southwestern Asia. *noun.*

i·rate (ī′rāt *or* ī rāt′), angry; enraged. *adjective.*

ire (īr), anger; wrath. *noun.*

Ire·land (īr′lənd), **1** an island in the Atlantic Ocean, west of Great Britain. It is divided into the Republic of Ireland and Northern Ireland. **2 Republic of Ireland,** a country in southern and central Ireland. *noun.*

a hat	i it	oi oil	ch child	a in about
ā age	ī ice	ou out	ng long	e in taken
ä far	o hot	u cup	sh she	ə = i in pencil
e let	ō open	u̇ put	th thin	o in lemon
ē equal	ô order	ü rule	ŦH then	u in circus
ėr term			zh measure	

i·ris (ī′ris), **1** a plant with large, showy flowers, and leaves shaped like swords. **2** the colored part of the eye around the pupil. *noun, plural* **i·ris·es.**

I·rish (ī′rish), **1** of or having something to do with Ireland or its people. **2** the people of Ireland. **3** a language of Ireland. 1 *adjective,* 2 *noun plural,* 3 *noun singular.*

Irish setter, a hunting dog with long, silky, reddish-brown hair.

irk·some (ėrk′səm), tiresome; tedious: *Washing dishes all day would be an irksome task. adjective.*

i·ron (ī′ərn), **1** the commonest and most useful metal, from which tools and machinery are made. Steel is made from iron. Iron is a chemical element. **2** made of iron: *an iron fence.* **3** something made of iron: *a branding iron.* **4** like iron; hard; strong: *an iron will.* **5** an implement with a flat surface which is heated and used to press clothing. **6** to press with a heated iron. **7** a golf club with an iron or steel head. 1,3,5,7 *noun,* 2,4 *adjective,* 6 *verb.*

ironing board, a padded flat surface covered with a smooth cloth, on which clothes are ironed. Most ironing boards have folding legs.

i·ro·ny (ī′rə nē), **1** a way of speaking or writing in which the ordinary meaning of the words is the opposite of the thought in the speaker's mind: *The tallest person was called "Shorty" in irony.* **2** an event or outcome which is the opposite of what would naturally be expected: *By the irony of fate the farmers had rain when they needed sun, and sun when they needed rain. noun, plural* **i·ro·nies.**

Ir·o·quois (ir′ə kwoi), a member of a powerful confederacy of American Indian tribes. They lived mostly in what is now New York State. *noun, plural* **Ir·o·quois.**

ir·reg·u·lar (i reg′yə lər), **1** not regular; not according to rule; out of the usual order or natural way: *The doctor listened carefully to the irregular breathing of the feverish child.* **2** not even; not smooth; not straight: *New England has a very irregular coastline. adjective.*

ir·reg·u·lar·i·ty (i reg′yə lar′ə tē), **1** a lack of regularity; being irregular. **2** something irregular. *noun, plural* **ir·reg·u·lar·i·ties.**

ir·re·sist·i·ble (ir′i zis′tə bəl), not able to be resisted; too great to be withstood; overwhelming: *I had an irresistible desire for ice cream. adjective.*

ir·res·o·lute (i rez′ə lüt), not resolute; unable to make up one's mind; not sure of what one wants; hesitating: *Irresolute persons make poor leaders. adjective.*

ir·re·spon·si·ble (ir′i spon′sə bəl), untrustworthy; unreliable. *adjective.*

ir·rev·er·ent (i rev′ər ənt), not reverent; disrespectful. *adjective.*

ir·ri·gate (ir′ə gāt), to supply land with water by using ditches or by sprinkling: *After a desert is irrigated, crops will grow there. verb,* **ir·ri·gates, ir·ri·gat·ed, ir·ri·gat·ing.**

ir·ri·ga·tion (ir′ə gā′shən), a supplying land with water; irrigating: *Irrigation is needed to make crops grow in dry regions. noun.*

ir·ri·ta·ble (ir′ə tə bəl), **1** easily made angry; impatient: *When the rain spoiled her plans, she was irritable for the rest of the day.* **2** more sensitive than is natural or normal: *A baby's skin is often quite irritable. adjective.*

ir·ri·tant (ir′ə tənt), a thing that causes irritation: *Chlorine in swimming pools can be an irritant to the eyes. noun.*

ir·ri·tate (ir′ə tāt), **1** to arouse to impatience or anger; annoy; vex: *Their constant interruptions irritated me. Flies irritate horses.* **2** to make a part of the body more sensitive than is natural or normal: *Sunburn irritates the skin. verb,* **ir·ri·tates, ir·ri·tat·ed, ir·ri·tat·ing.**

ir·ri·ta·tion (ir′ə tā′shən), **1** an annoyance; vexation. **2** an irritating; being irritated: *Irritation of the nose can make you sneeze. noun.*

is (iz). *Is* is a form of **be.** *The earth is round. He is at school. It is going to rain. Flour is sold by the pound. verb.*

-ish, a suffix meaning: **1** somewhat _____: Sweet*ish* means *somewhat* sweet. **2** like a _____: Child*ish* means *like* a child. **3** like that of a _____: Girl*ish* means *like that of a* girl.

Is·lam (is′ləm), the religion based on the teachings of Mohammed as they appear in the Koran. *noun.*

is·land (ī′lənd), **1** a body of land surrounded by water: *Hawaii is made up of a group of islands.* **2** something that suggests a piece of land surrounded by water. Platforms in the middle of crowded streets are called **safety islands.** *noun.*

is·land·er (ī′lən dər), a person born or living on an island. *noun.*

isle (īl), **1** a small island. **2** an island. *noun.*

is·let (ī′lit), a little island. *noun.*

is·n't (iz′nt), is not.

i·so·late (ī′sə lāt), to set apart; separate from others: *People with contagious diseases should be isolated. verb,* **i·so·lates, i·so·lat·ed, i·so·lat·ing.**

i·so·la·tion (ī′sə lā′shən), **1** a setting apart. **2** a being set apart. *noun.*

i·sos·ce·les tri·an·gle (ī sos′ə lēz′ trī′ang′gəl), a triangle that has two sides equal.

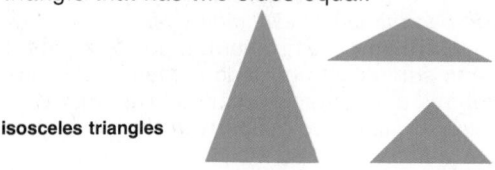

isosceles triangles

Is·ra·el (iz′rē əl), **1** a country in southwestern Asia, including the major part of Palestine. **2** an ancient Jewish kingdom in northern Palestine. *noun.*

Is·rae·li (iz rā′lē), **1** a person born or living in the country of Israel. **2** of or having to do with Israel or its people. 1 *noun, plural* **Is·rae·lis;** 2 *adjective.*

is·sue (ish′ü), **1** to send out; put forth: *This magazine is issued every week.* **2** something sent out: *That newsstand sells the latest issues of all the popular magazines and newspapers.* **3** a sending out; putting forth: *The government controls the issue of stamps.* **4** to come out; go out; proceed: *Smoke issues from the chimney.* **5** a point to be debated; problem: *The voters had four issues to settle.* 1,4 *verb,* **is·sues, is·sued, is·su·ing;** 2,3,5 *noun.*

-ist, a suffix meaning: **1** a person who does or makes a _____: Tour*ist* means *a person who makes a tour.* **2** a person who is an expert in _____: Botan*ist* means *a person who is an expert in* botany. **3** a person who plays a _____: Organ*ist* means *a person who plays an* organ. **4** a person who works with _____: Machin*ist* means *a person who works with* machines.

isth·mus (is′məs), a narrow strip of land, with water on both sides of it, connecting two larger bodies of land: *The Isthmus of Panama connects North America and South America. noun, plural* **isth·mus·es.**

isthmus

it (it), **1** the object, person, or living thing spoken about: *Here is your paper; read it. Look at it carefully. He said, "It is I. What is it you want?" It snows in winter. It is now my turn.* **2** in games, the player who must catch, find, or guess: *If I tag you, you're it.* 1 *pronoun, plural* **they;** 2 *noun.*

I·tal·ian (i tal′yən), **1** of or having something to do with Italy, its people, or their language. **2** a person born or living in Italy. **3** the language of Italy. 1 *adjective,* 2,3 *noun.*

Word Source

The Italian language developed from Latin. Although the words listed below have come into English from Italian, many can be traced back to Latin:

balcony	lasagna	pizza	soprano
baritone	macaroni	quarantine	spaghetti
concerto	oboe	salami	trombone
duet	opera	solo	umbrella
gondola	piano	sonata	zucchini
lagoon			

i·tal·ic (i tal′ik), **1** of or in type whose letters slant to the right. *These words are in italic type.* **2 italics,** type whose letters slant to the right. 1 *adjective,* 2 *noun plural.*
[*Italic* comes from a Latin word meaning "Italian" or "of Italy." Italic type was called this because it was introduced by an Italian printer from Venice in 1501.]

i·tal·i·cize (i tal′ə sīz), **1** to print in type in which

a hat	**i** it	**oi** oil	**ch** child	a in about
ā age	**ī** ice	**ou** out	**ng** long	e in taken
ä far	**o** hot	**u** cup	**sh** she	ə = i in pencil
e let	**ō** open	**ù** put	**th** thin	o in lemon
ē equal	**ô** order	**ü** rule	**ŦH** then	u in circus
ėr term			**zh** measure	

the letters slope to the right. Example: *This sentence is italicized.* **2** to underline written words with a single line. We italicize expressions which we wish to distinguish or emphasize. *verb,* **i·tal·i·ciz·es, i·tal·i·cized, i·tal·i·ciz·ing.**

It·a·ly (it′l ē), a country in southern Europe. *noun.*

itch (ich), **1** a prickling feeling in the skin that makes one want to scratch. **2** a disease causing this feeling. **3** to cause this feeling: *My mosquito bites itch.* **4** to feel this way in the skin: *My nose itches.* **5** a restless, uneasy feeling, longing, or desire for anything: *She had an itch to travel.* **6** to be restless with any desire: *I itched to find out their secret.* 1,2,5 *noun, plural* **itch·es;** 3,4,6 *verb.*

itch·y (ich′ē), **1** itching: *My nose was itchy all morning.* **2** restless; nervous: *I get itchy if I have to stay indoors all day. adjective,* **itch·i·er, itch·i·est.**

i·tem (ī′təm), **1** a separate thing or article: *The list had twelve items on it.* **2** a piece of news: *There were several interesting items in yesterday's newspaper. noun.*

i·tem·ize (ī′tə mīz), to give each item of; list by items: *The storekeeper itemized the bill to show the price of each article. verb,* **i·tem·iz·es, i·tem·ized, i·tem·iz·ing.**

it'll (it′l), **1** it will. **2** it shall.

its (its), of it; belonging to it: *The dog wagged its tail. adjective.*

it's (its), **1** it is. **2** it has.

it·self (it self′), **1** a form of *it* used to make a statement stronger: *The land itself is worth the money, without the house.* **2** a form used instead of *it, him,* or *her* in cases like: *The horse tripped and hurt itself. pronoun.*

-ity, a suffix meaning the state or condition of being _____: Timid*ity* means *the state of being* timid. The form *-ty* is often used instead of *-ity,* as in *safety.*

I've (īv), I have.

i·vo·ry (ī′vər ē), **1** a hard, white substance making up the tusks of elephants or walruses. Ivory is used for piano keys, knife handles, and ornaments. **2** a substance like ivory. **3** made of ivory. **4** of or like ivory. **5** creamy-white. 1,2 *noun, plural* **i·vor·ies;** 3,4,5 *adjective.*
[*Ivory* comes from an Egyptian word meaning both "elephant" and "ivory." Notice how closely these two ideas are related by looking at the word history for *elephant.*]

Ivory Coast, a country in western Africa.

i·vy (ī′vē), **1** a climbing plant with smooth, shiny evergreen leaves. **2** any of various other climbing plants, as poison ivy. *noun, plural* **i·vies.**

J j

J or **j** (jā), the tenth letter of the English alphabet. *noun, plural* **J's** or **j's.**

jab (jab), **1** to poke with something pointed; thrust forcefully: *He jabbed his fork into the potato.* **2** a poke with something pointed; a forceful thrust: *She gave him a jab with her elbow.* **1** *verb,* **jabs, jabbed, jab·bing; 2** *noun.*

jab·ber (jab′ər), **1** to talk very fast in a confused way; chatter. **2** a very fast, confused talk; chatter. **1** *verb,* **2** *noun.*

jack (jak), **1** a tool or machine for lifting or pushing up heavy weights a short distance: *He raised the car off the ground with a jack to change the flat tire.* **2 jack up,** to lift with a jack: *She jacked up the car to change the flat tire.* **3** a playing card with the picture of a servant or soldier on it. It is above a ten and below a queen. **4** a piece of metal tossed up and caught, used in the game of jacks. **5 jacks,** a child's game in which pieces of metal are tossed up and caught or picked up in various ways. Each player bounces the ball and picks up the jacks in between bounces. **1,3-5** *noun,* **2** *verb.*

jack·al (jak′əl), a wild animal of Africa and Asia somewhat like a dog and about as big as a fox. Jackals will often follow a lion or a leopard and eat what is left of the prey it kills. *noun.*

jackals—about 15 inches (38 centimeters) high at the shoulder

jack·et (jak′it), **1** a short coat. **2** an outer covering: *a book jacket. noun.*

jack·ham·mer (jak′ham′ər), a drilling tool run by compressed air. Jackhammers are used to break up pavements and other hard substances. *noun.*

jack-in-the-box (jak′in ᴛʜə boks′), a toy figure that springs up from a box when the lid is opened. *noun, plural* **jack-in-the-box·es.**

jack·knife (jak′nīf′), a large, strong pocketknife. A jackknife may have several blades of different sizes that fold into the handle. *noun, plural* **jack·knives** (jak′nīvz′).

jack-o'-lan·tern (jak′ə lan′tərn), a pumpkin hollowed out and cut to look like a face, used as a lantern at Halloween. *noun.*

jack·pot (jak′pot′), **1** the total amount bet in a game. **2** the big prize of a game. *noun.*
hit the jackpot, 1 to get the big prize. **2** to have a stroke of very good luck.

jack rabbit, a large hare of western North America, having very long legs and ears.

Jack·son (jak′sən), the capital of Mississippi. *noun.*

jade (jād), a hard stone used for jewelry and ornaments. Most jade is green. *noun.*

jad·ed (jā′did), worn out; tired; weary: *a jaded horse, a jaded look. adjective.*

jag·ged (jag′id), with sharp points sticking out: *We cut our bare feet on the jagged rocks. adjective.*

jag·uar (jag′wär), a large cat with spots, much like a leopard but more heavily built. Jaguars live in forests in tropical America. *noun.*

jaguar—about 7 feet (2 meters) long with the tail

jail (jāl), **1** a prison, especially one for persons awaiting trial or being punished for some small offense. **2** to put in jail; keep in jail: *The police arrested and jailed the suspected thief.* **1** *noun,* **2** *verb.*

jail·er or **jail·or** (jā′lər), the keeper of a jail. *noun.*

jam¹ (jam), **1** to press or squeeze tightly between two surfaces: *The ship was jammed between two rocks.* **2** to bruise or crush by squeezing: *I jammed my fingers in the door.* **3** to press or squeeze things or people tightly together: *A crowd jammed into the bus.* **4** a mass of people or things crowded together so that they cannot move freely: *She was delayed by the traffic jam.* **5** to fill or block up the way by crowding: *The river was jammed with logs.* **6** to stick or catch so that it cannot be worked: *The window has jammed; I cannot open it.* **7** to push hard or force: *I tried to jam one more book into the bookcase.* **8** a difficulty or tight spot: *I was in a jam.* **1-3,5-7** *verb,* **jams, jammed, jam·ming; 4,8** *noun.*

jam² (jam), fruit boiled with sugar until thick: *raspberry jam, plum jam. noun.*

Ja·mai·ca (jə mā′kə), an island country in the West Indies. *noun.*

jam·bo·ree (jam′bə rē′), **1** a large rally or gathering of Boy Scouts or Girl Scouts. **2** a noisy party. *noun.*

Jan., January.

jan·gle (jang′gəl), **1** to sound harshly; to cause to sound harshly: *I heard the jangle of pots and pans* *in the kitchen.* **2** a harsh sound: *the jangle of the telephone.* 1 *verb,* **jan·gles, jan·gled, jan·gling;** 2 *noun.*

jan·i·tor (jan′ə tər), a person hired to take care of a building or offices. Janitors do cleaning and make some repairs. *noun.*

Jan·u·ar·y (jan′yü er′ē), the first month of the year. It has 31 days. *noun.*
[*January* comes from Janus, the ancient Roman god of gates and doors and of beginnings and endings. He was shown with two faces, one looking forward and one looking backward. January is the time for looking back at the year just ended, and forward to the year beginning.]

Ja·pan (jə pan′), a country made up of several islands in the Pacific, along the eastern coast of Asia. *noun.*

Jap·a·nese (jap′ə nēz′), **1** of or having something to do with Japan, its people, or their language. **2** a person born or living in Japan. **3** the language of Japan. 1 *adjective,* 2,3 *noun, plural* **Jap·a·nese** for 2.

Word Source

Some Japanese words that have come into the English language are haiku, judo, karate, kimono, obi, soy sauce and tsunami.

jar¹ (jär), **1** a deep container with a wide mouth, usually made of glass: *We made pickles and put them up in jars.* **2** the amount that a jar can hold: *They ate a jar of peanut butter. noun.*
[The word *jar*¹ comes from an Arabic word meaning "an earthen vessel."]

jar² (jär), **1** to shake; rattle: *Your heavy footsteps jar my table.* **2** a shake; rattle: *I felt the jar of a slight earthquake.* **3** to have a harsh, unpleasant effect on: *The children's screams jarred my nerves.* 1,3 *verb,* **jars, jarred, jar·ring;** 2 *noun.*

jas·mine (jaz′mən), a shrub or vine with very fragrant yellow, white, or reddish flowers. *noun.*

jas·per (jas′pər), a colored quartz, usually red or brown. *noun.*

jaunt (jônt), a short journey, especially for pleasure: *We went on a one-day jaunt to the seashore and back. noun.*

jaun·ty (jôn′tē), easy and lively; carefree: *The happy boy walked with jaunty steps. adjective,* **jaun·ti·er, jaun·ti·est.**

jave·lin (jav′lən), a light spear thrown by hand. *noun.*

jaw (jô), **1** the lower part of the face. **2** the upper or lower bone or set of bones that together form the framework of the mouth. The lower jaw is movable. **3 jaws,** the parts in a tool or machine that bite or grasp. *noun.*

jay (jā), a noisy North American bird with a crest and blue feathers; blue jay. *noun.*

jay·walk (jā′wôk′), to walk across a street without paying attention to traffic rules. *verb.*

jay·walk·er (jā′wô′kər), a person who jaywalks. *noun.*

a hat	i it	oi oil	ch child	a in about
ā age	ī ice	ou out	ng long	e in taken
ä far	o hot	u cup	sh she	ə = i in pencil
e let	ō open	ủ put	th thin	o in lemon
ē equal	ô order	ü rule	ᴛʜ then	u in circus
ėr term			zh measure	

jazz (jaz), **1** a kind of music with a strong beat in which the accents fall at unusual places: *Jazz was first played in New Orleans.* **2** of or having to do with jazz: *a jazz band.* 1 *noun,* 2 *adjective.*
[*Jazz* was originally an American Negro word which came from a west African word.]

jeal·ous (jel′əs), **1** fearful that somebody you love may love someone else better, or may prefer someone else to you: *The child was jealous when anyone paid attention to the new baby.* **2** envious; full of envy: *He is jealous of his brother's good grades. adjective.*

jeal·ous·y (jel′ə sē), the state of feeling jealous; envy: *She could not hide her jealousy when her brother got a new bicycle. noun.*

jeans (jēnz), pants made of a strong cotton cloth. *noun plural.*
[*Jeans* comes from an earlier English word meaning "of Genoa," a city in Italy. The cloth from which jeans are made was called jean because it was first made in Genoa.]

jeep (jēp), a small but powerful motor vehicle often used in areas where there are rough roads or no roads. *noun.*
[*Jeep* probably comes from a fast way of pronouncing *G.P.,* the abbreviation for General Purpose Car. That was the name by which this type of vehicle was known in the United States Army during World War II.]

jeer (jir), **1** to make fun in a rude or unkind way; scoff: *Do not jeer at the mistakes or misfortunes of others.* **2** a mocking or insulting remark: *The mayor's speech asking for higher taxes was interrupted by jeers from the audience.* 1 *verb,* 2 *noun.*

Jef·fer·son Cit·y (jef′ər sən sit′ē), the capital of Missouri.

Je·ho·vah (ji hō′və), one of the names of God in the Old Testament. *noun.*

Jell-O (jel′ō), a trademark for a gelatin dessert that is usually fruit-flavored. *noun.*

jel·ly (jel′ē), **1** fruit juice boiled with sugar and then cooked until firm. **2** to become jelly; turn into jelly: *Some kinds of soup jelly when they are chilled.* 1 *noun, plural* **jel·lies;** 2 *verb,* **jel·lies, jel·lied, jel·ly·ing.**
[*Jelly* comes from a Latin word meaning "frozen" or "stiffened." Jelly was called this because it is liquid that has become stiff.]

jel·ly·bean (jel′ē bēn′), a small candy made of jellied sugar, usually shaped like a bean. *noun.*

jel·ly·fish (jel′ē fish′), a sea animal like a lump of jelly. Most jellyfish have long, trailing tentacles that can sometimes sting. *noun, plural* **jel·ly·fish** or **jel·ly·fish·es.**

jeop·ar·dy (jep′ər dē), danger; risk: *Many lives were in jeopardy during the forest fire.* noun.

jerk (jėrk), **1** a sudden, sharp pull, twist, or start: *The old car started with a jerk.* **2** a sudden movement of the muscles that one cannot control; twitch. **3** to pull or twist suddenly: *If the water is unexpectedly hot, you jerk your hand out.* **4** to move with a jerk: *The old wagon jerked along.* **5** a stupid or foolish person. 1,2,5 noun, 3,4 verb.

jerk·y[1] (jėr′kē), with sudden starts and stops; with jerks. adjective, **jerk·i·er, jerk·i·est.**

jerk·y[2] (jėr′kē), strips of dried meat, usually beef. noun.

jer·sey (jėr′zē), **1** a soft, knitted cloth used for clothing. **2** a shirt that is pulled on over the head, made of this cloth: *Our hockey team wears red jerseys.* noun, plural **jer·seys.**
[*Jersey* was named for the British island of *Jersey.* The cloth was called this because it had been made there for a long time.]

jest (jest), **1** a joke: *His jests weren't very funny.* **2** to joke: *I was just jesting, but they thought I meant what I said.* **3** to poke fun; make fun: *They jested at my idea until I proved it would work.* 1 noun, 2,3 verb.
in jest, in fun; not seriously: *Her words were spoken in jest.*

jest·er (jes′tər), a person who jests. In the Middle Ages, kings and queens often had jesters to amuse them with tricks, antics, and jokes. noun.

jester
The joker on a playing card is a **jester.**

Je·sus (jē′zəs), the founder of the Christian religion. noun.

jet[1] (jet), **1** a stream of water, steam, gas, or the like, sent with force, especially from a small opening: *A fountain sends up a jet of water.* **2** a spout or nozzle for sending out a jet. **3** to shoot forth in a jet or forceful stream; gush out: *Water jetted from the broken pipe.* **4** a jet plane. 1,2,4 noun, 3 verb, **jets, jet·ted, jet·ting.**

jet[2] (jet), **1** a hard, black kind of coal, glossy when polished, used for making beads, buttons, and ornaments. **2** deep, shining black: *jet hair.* 1 noun, 2 adjective.

jet engine, an engine which shoots out a jet of exhaust gases forcefully from the rear of the engine. The force of the jet drives the engine forward.

jet plane, an airplane that is driven by one or more jet engines.

jet-pro·pelled (jet′prə peld′), driven by a jet engine: *Many aircraft are jet-propelled.* adjective.

jet·ty (jet′ē), **1** a structure of stones or timbers projecting out from the shore to break the force of the current or waves; breakwater. **2** a landing place; pier. noun, plural **jet·ties.**

Jew (jü), **1** a person descended from the people led by Moses, who settled in Palestine and now live in Israel and many other countries. **2** a person whose religion is Judaism. noun.

jew·el (jü′əl), **1** a precious stone; gem. Jewels are used in the moving parts of some watches, as well as worn in pins and other ornaments. **2** a valuable ornament to be worn, often made of gold or silver and set with gems: *The queen wore the crown jewels at the ceremony.* **3** to set or decorate with jewels or with things like jewels. 1,2 noun, 3 verb.

jewel (definition 3)
The queen's gown was **jeweled** with pearls and priceless gems.

jew·el·er (jü′ə lər), a person who makes, sells, or repairs jewelry and watches. noun.

jew·el·ry (jü′əl rē), **1** jewels: *Mother keeps her jewelry in a small locked box.* **2** rings, bracelets, or other ornaments to be worn, usually set with imitation gems and made of silver- or gold-colored metal. noun.

Jew·ish (jü′ish), of the Jews or their religion: *the Jewish faith.* adjective.

jib (jib), a triangular sail in front of the most forward mast on a sailboat. noun.

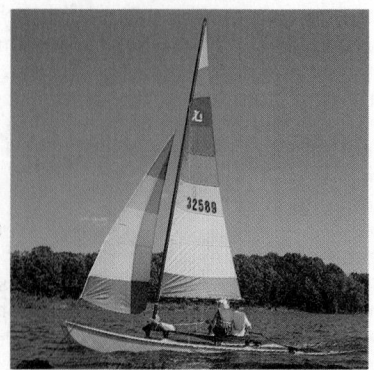

jib—The small sail at the front of the boat is the **jib.**

jif·fy (jif′ē), a moment; a very short time: *I was on my bike in a jiffy, pedaling down the drive.* *noun, plural* **jif·fies.**

jig (jig), **1** a lively dance. **2** the music for it. **3** to dance a jig. **1,2** *noun,* **3** *verb,* **jigs, jigged, jig·ging.**

jig·gle (jig′əl), **1** to shake or jerk slightly: *Don't jiggle the desk when I'm trying to write.* **2** a slight shake; light jerk. **1** *verb,* **jig·gles, jig·gled, jig·gling;** **2** *noun.*

jig·saw (jig′sô′), a narrow saw mounted in a frame and worked with an up-and-down motion, used to cut curves. *noun.*

jigsaw

jigsaw puzzle, a picture glued onto cardboard or wood and sawed into differently shaped pieces that can be fitted together again.

jin·gle (jing′gəl), **1** a sound like that of little bells, or of coins or keys striking together. **2** to make or cause to make such a sound: *He jingled the coins in his pocket.* **3** a verse or music that repeats similar sounds in a catchy way. "Higgledy, piggledy, my black hen" is a jingle. **1,3** *noun,* **2** *verb,* **jin·gles, jin·gled, jin·gling.**

jinx (jingks), a person or thing that brings bad luck. *noun, plural* **jinx·es.**

jit·ters (jit′ərz), extreme nervousness: *I had a case of jitters when I had to sing in public.* *noun plural.*

jit·ter·y (jit′ər ē), nervous: *I felt a little jittery before my first airplane ride.* *adjective.*

job (job), **1** a piece of work: *He had the job of painting the boat.* **2** work done for pay; employment: *Her sister is hunting for a job.* **3** anything a person has to do: *When you have guests, it's your job to entertain them.* *noun.*

jock·ey (jok′ē), a person who rides horses in races as a job. *noun, plural* **jock·eys.**

jog (jog), **1** to run slowly: *I jog several miles every day for exercise.* **2** a slow run: *We went for a jog in the park.* **3** to stir up your own or another person's memory: *He tied a string around his finger to jog his memory.* **4** to move up or down with a jerk or a

a hat	**i** it	**oi** oil	**ch** child		a in about
ā age	**ī** ice	**ou** out	**ng** long		e in taken
ä far	**o** hot	**u** cup	**sh** she	**ə** =	i in pencil
e let	**ō** open	**u̇** put	**th** thin		o in lemon
ē equal	**ô** order	**ü** rule	**ᵺ** then		u in circus
ėr term			**zh** measure		

shaking motion: *The rider jogged up and down on the horse's back.* **1,3,4** *verb,* **jogs, jogged, jog·ging;** **2** *noun.*

jog·ger (jog′ər), a person who jogs for exercise. *noun.*

jog·gle (jog′əl), to shake slightly. *verb,* **jog·gles, jog·gled, jog·gling.**

join (join), **1** to bring or put together; connect, fasten, or clasp together: *to join hands, to join an island to the mainland by a bridge.* **2** to unite with; come together with: *Join us as soon as you can. The stream joins the river just below the mill.* **3** to make or become one; combine; unite: *to join in marriage. The two clubs joined forces during the campaign.* **4** to take part with others: *to join in a song.* **5** to become a member of: *She joined a tennis club. My uncle has joined the army.* *verb.*

joint (joint), **1** the place at which two things or parts are joined together. A pocketknife has a joint to fold the blade inside the handle. **2** the place in an animal skeleton where two bones join. There is usually motion at a joint. **3** one of the parts of which a jointed thing is made up: *the middle joint of the finger.* **4** shared or done by two or more persons: *By our joint efforts we managed to push the car back on the road.* **5** sharing: *My sister and I are joint owners of this dog.* **1-3** *noun,* **4,5** *adjective.*

out of joint, moved out of place at the joint: *The fall put his shoulder out of joint.*

joint·ed (join′tid), having joints. *adjective.*

jointed—The legs of the crab are **jointed.**

joint·ly (joint′lē), together; as partners: *The two girls owned the boat jointly.* *adverb.*

joke (jōk), **1** something said or done to make somebody laugh; something funny: *Looking for the hat that was on my head was a good joke on me.* **2** to make jokes; say or do something as a joke: *As it got colder, we joked about the possibility of snow in July.* **3** a person or thing laughed at: *Some of the new clothing styles are a joke.* **1,3** *noun,* **2** *verb,* **jokes, joked, jok·ing.**

jok·er (jō′kər), **1** a person who jokes. **2** an extra playing card used in some games. *noun.*

jol·ly (jol′ē), **1** merry; very cheerful; full of fun: *She was a jolly person who laughed and joked a good deal.* **2** extremely; very: *a jolly good time.* **1** *adjective,* **jol·li·er, jol·li·est; 2** *adverb.*

jolt (jōlt), **1** to shake up; jar: *The wagon jolted us when it went over the rocks.* **2** a jerk; jar: *He put his brakes on suddenly, and the car stopped with a jolt.* **3** a sudden surprise or shock: *News of the plane crash gave them a jolt.* **4** to move in a jerky or jarring way: *The car jolted across the rough ground.* **1,4** *verb,* **2,3** *noun.*

jon·quil (jong′kwəl), a plant with yellow or white flowers that is much like a daffodil. Jonquils grow from bulbs. *noun.*

Jor·dan (jôrd′n), a country in southwestern Asia. *noun.*

jos·tle (jos′əl), to shove, push, or crowd against; elbow roughly: *We were jostled by the big crowd at the entrance to the circus.* *verb,* **jos·tles, jos·tled, jos·tling.**

jot (jot), to write briefly or in haste: *The waiter jotted down our order.* *verb,* **jots, jot·ted, jot·ting.**

jounce (jouns), to bounce; bump; jolt: *The old car jounced along the rough road.* *verb,* **jounc·es, jounced, jounc·ing.**

jour·nal (jėr′nl), **1** a daily record. A diary is a journal of what a person does, thinks, and feels. A ship's log is a journal of what happens on a ship. **2** a newspaper or magazine: *The family subscribed to a monthly farm journal.* **3** a book in which each item of business is written down: *The storekeeper kept a journal of his accounts.* *noun.*

jour·nal·ism (jėr′nl iz′əm), the work of gathering, writing, and presenting news in newspapers and magazines or on radio or television. *noun.*

jour·nal·ist (jėr′nl ist), a person whose job is in journalism. Reporters are journalists. *noun.*

jour·ney (jėr′nē), **1** a traveling from one place to another; trip: *a journey around the world.* **2** to travel; take a trip: *She journeyed to Europe last summer.* **1** *noun, plural* **jour·neys; 2** *verb.*
[*Journey* comes from a Latin word meaning "daily." Originally a journey was a trip that took a day to finish. Another English word from the same Latin word is *journal.* A journal is something that you write in every day.]

jour·ney·man (jėr′nē mən), a worker who knows a trade. *noun, plural* **jour·ney·men.**

joust (joust *or* just), **1** a combat between two knights on horseback, armed with lances and wearing armor. **2** to fight with lances on horseback. Knights used to joust with each other for sport. **1** *noun,* **2** *verb.*

jo·vi·al (jō′vē əl), good-hearted and full of fun; good-humored and merry: *Santa Claus is pictured as a jovial old fellow.* *adjective.*

jowl (joul), a fold of flesh hanging from or under the lower jaw. *noun.*

joy (joi), **1** happiness; glad feeling; glad behavior: *She jumped for joy when she saw the circus.* **2** something that causes gladness or happiness: *On a hot day, a cool swim is a joy.* *noun.*

joy·ful (joi′fəl), causing or showing joy; glad; happy: *joyful news, a joyful look. adjective.*

joy·ous (joi′əs), joyful; glad; happy: *The birth of their first child was a joyous occasion. adjective.*

joy ride, a ride in an automobile for pleasure, especially when the car is driven recklessly or without the owner's permission.

joy·stick (joi′stik′), an electronic device used to control video games and computer games. It is an upright rod that can be tilted forward and back, from side to side, or in other directions. *noun.*

jr. or **Jr.,** Junior.

ju·bi·lant (jü′bə lənt), showing joy; joyful: *She was jubilant when her team won the game. adjective.*

ju·bi·lee (jü′bə lē), an anniversary or other time of rejoicing or great joy. A 50th anniversary is called a golden jubilee. *noun.*

Ju·da·ism (jü′dē iz′əm), the religion of the Jews, based on the teachings of the Old Testament. *noun.*

judge (juj), **1** a public official appointed or elected to hear and decide cases in a court of law. **2** to act as a judge; hear and decide (cases) in a court of law. **3** a person chosen to settle a dispute or to decide who wins a race or contest. **4** to settle a dispute; decide who wins a race or contest. **5** a person who can decide how good a thing is: *a good judge of character, a judge of dogs in a dog show.* **6** to form an opinion of: *The librarian judged the merits of the new book.* **7** to criticize; blame: *You had little cause to judge him so harshly.* **1,3,5** *noun,* **2,4,6,7** *verb,* **judg·es, judged, judg·ing.**

judg·ment (juj′mənt), **1** an opinion; estimate: *In my judgment she is a better student than her sister.* **2** the power to judge well; good sense: *Since she has judgment in such matters, we will ask her.* **3** the act of judging, especially a decision made by a judge in a court of law: *The trial was over and the prisoner awaited the judgment of the court. noun.*

ju·di·cial (jü dish′əl), **1** of judges; having something to do with a court of law or the

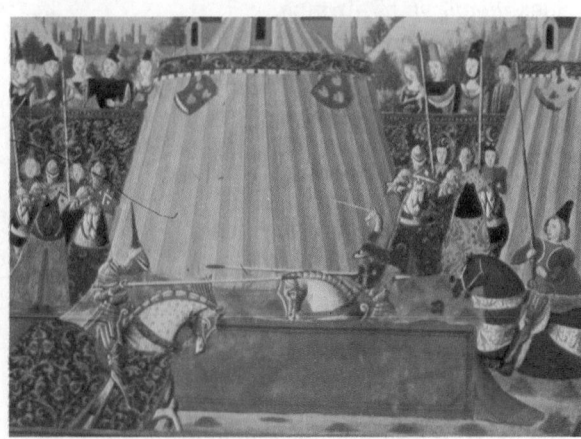

joust (definition 2)—knights **jousting**

administration of justice: *The judicial branch of the government enforces the laws.* **2** of or suited to a judge: *A judicial mind considers both sides fairly before making a decision. adjective.*

ju·di·cious (jü dish′əs), wise; sensible; having, using, or showing good judgment: *Judicious people save part of their income. adjective.*

ju·do (jü′dō), a way of fighting without weapons. In judo you use the strength and weight of your opponent to your advantage. *noun.*

[*Judo* comes from Japanese words meaning "soft" and "art." No hand weapons or armor are necessary in this means of defense.]

jug (jug), a container for holding liquids. A jug usually has a spout or a narrow neck and a handle. *noun.*

jug·gle (jug′əl), to keep several objects in the air at the same time by quickly tossing and catching them: *She can juggle three balls or plates. verb,* **jug·gles, jug·gled, jug·gling.**

jug·gler (jug′lər), a person who juggles. *noun.*

jug·u·lar (jug′yə lər), of the neck or throat. The **jugular veins** are in the neck. *adjective.*

juice (jüs), **1** the liquid part of fruits, vegetables, and meats: *lemon juice.* **2** a liquid in the body. The juices of the stomach help to digest food. *noun.*

juic·y (jü′sē), full of juice; having much juice: *a juicy orange. adjective,* **juic·i·er, juic·i·est.**

Ju·ly (ju lī′), the seventh month of the year. It has 31 days. *noun.*

[*July* was named in honor of the Roman leader Julius Caesar, who was born in this month.]

jum·ble (jum′bəl), **1** to mix or confuse: *She jumbled up everything in her drawer while hunting for her other blue sock.* **2** a muddle; mixed-up mess; state of confusion: *The broken radio was a jumble of wires and parts. verb,* **jum·bles, jum·bled, jum·bling;** 2 *noun.*

jum·bo (jum′bō), very big: *a jumbo jet. adjective.*

Word History

jumbo *Jumbo* comes from the name of Jumbo, a very large elephant exhibited by P. T. Barnum, an American showman. Originally this name may have come from a west African word meaning "elephant."

a hat	i it	oi oil	ch child	⎧ a in about
ā age	ī ice	ou out	ng long	⎪ e in taken
ä far	o hot	u cup	sh she	ə = ⎨ i in pencil
e let	ō open	ů put	th thin	⎪ o in lemon
ē equal	ô order	ü rule	ŦH then	⎩ u in circus
ėr term			zh measure	

jump (jump), **1** to spring from the ground; leap; bound: *How high can you jump? How far can you jump? Jump across the puddle.* **2** a spring from the ground; leap; bound: *The horse made a fine jump.* **3** to leap over: *to jump a stream. The speeding car jumped the curb and crashed.* **4** to cause to jump: *to jump a horse over a fence, to jump a child up and down.* **5** the distance jumped: *a ten-foot jump.* **6** to give a sudden movement or jerk: *We often jump when a sudden sight, noise, or touch startles us.* **7** a sudden, nervous movement or jerk: *He gave a jump at the noise of the gun.* **8** to rise suddenly: *The price of orange juice jumped when the orange crop was ruined.* **9** a sudden rise: *a jump in the cost of living.* 1,3,4,6,8 *verb,* 2,5,7,9 *noun.*

jump at, to accept eagerly and quickly: *I jumped at the chance to spend the summer on a ranch.*

jump·er[1] (jum′pər), a person or thing that jumps. *noun.*

jump·er[2] (jum′pər), a sleeveless dress to wear over a blouse. *noun.*

jump rope, 1 a children's game or a form of exercise which involves jumping over a rope as it is swung under the feet and over the head. **2** a rope with handles on each end used for this game or exercise.

jump·y (jum′pē), nervous; easily excited or frightened: *I felt jumpy after watching the scary TV show. adjective,* **jump·i·er, jump·i·est.**

junc·tion (jungk′shən), **1** a joining or being joined: *The junction of the two rivers results in a large flow of water downstream.* **2** a place of joining or meeting. A railroad junction is a place where railroad lines meet or cross. *noun.*

June (jün), the sixth month of the year. It has 30 days. *noun.*

[*June* was named for Juno, the Roman goddess who was queen of the gods.]

Ju·neau (jü′nō), the capital of Alaska. *noun.*

jun·gle (jung′gəl), wild land thickly overgrown with bushes, vines, and trees. Jungles are hot and humid regions with many kinds of plants and wild animals. *noun.*

jun·ior (jü′nyər), **1** the younger. The word *junior* is used of a son having the same name as his father. *Juan Roca, Junior, is the son of Juan Roca, Senior.* **2** a younger person: *She is her sister's junior by two years.* **3** of or for younger people: *They are playing in the junior chess tournament.* **4** of lower position; of less standing than some others: *a junior officer.* **5** a person of lower position, rank, or standing. **6** a student in the third year of high school or college. **7** of or having something to do with these students: *The junior* *class held a dance.* 1,3,4,7 *adjective*, 2,5,6 *noun*.

junior high school, a school consisting of grades 7, 8, and sometimes 9, attended after an elementary school of six grades. It is followed by high school.

ju·ni·per (jü′nə pər), an evergreen shrub or tree with tiny bluish cones that look like berries. *noun*.

junk¹ (jungk), trash; old paper, metal, and other rubbish. *noun*.

junk² (jungk), a Chinese sailing ship. *noun*.

junk²

junk food, food that contains calories but has little other value.

junk·yard (jungk′yärd′), a place where old, discarded things are collected and kept for sale. *noun*.

Ju·pi·ter (jü′pə tər), 1 the chief god of the ancient Romans. The Greeks called him Zeus. 2 the largest planet. It is the fifth in distance from the sun. *noun*.

jur·or (jùr′ər), a member of a jury. *noun*.

jur·y (jùr′ē), 1 a group of citizens selected to hear evidence in a case brought before a court of law. A jury must make its decision based on the evidence presented to it. 2 any group of persons chosen to give a judgment or to decide who is the winner: *The jury of teachers gave her poem the first prize. noun, plural* **jur·ies.**

just (just), 1 only; merely: *He went just because his friend was going.* 2 barely: *I just caught the train.* 3 quite; truly: *The weather is just glorious.* 4 exactly: *That is just a pound.* 5 nearly; almost exactly: *See the picture just above.* 6 a very little while ago: *He just left me.* 7 right; fair: *We felt that $100 was not a just price for our old car.* 8 good; righteous: *The man led a just life, and was*

admired by many. 1-6 *adverb*, 7,8 *adjective*.

jus·tice (jus′tis), 1 fairness; rightness; being just: *the justice of a claim. She never doubted the justice of her cause.* 2 a judge. The Supreme Court has nine justices. 3 judgment by law: *a court of justice. noun*.

jus·ti·fi·a·ble (jus′tə fī′ə bəl), able to be justified; proper: *Striking the person in self-defense was ruled a justifiable act. adjective*.

jus·ti·fi·ca·tion (jus′tə fə kā′shən), a fact or circumstance that justifies; good reason or excuse: *What is your justification for being so late? noun*.

jus·ti·fy (jus′tə fī), 1 to give a good reason for: *The fine quality of this cloth justifies its high cost.* 2 to show to be just or right: *Can you justify your act?* 3 to clear of blame or guilt: *The court ruled that he was justified in hitting the man in self-defense. verb,* **jus·ti·fies, jus·ti·fied, jus·ti·fy·ing.**

jut (jut), to stick out; project; stand out: *The pier jutted out from the shore into the water. verb,* **juts, jut·ted, jut·ting.**

jute (jüt), a strong fiber used for making coarse fabrics or rope. Jute is obtained from a tropical plant. *noun*.

ju·ve·nile (jü′və nəl *or* jü′və nīl), 1 of or for boys and girls: *juvenile books.* 2 a young person, especially someone under 18 years old. 1 *adjective*, 2 *noun*.

Jupiter (definition 2)
The sphere with bands of clouds and a large red spot is **Jupiter.** The other spheres are some of its moons.

K k

a hat	i it	oi oil	ch child	a in about
ā age	ī ice	ou out	ng long	e in taken
ä far	o hot	u cup	sh she	ə = i in pencil
e let	ō open	u̇ put	th thin	o in lemon
ē equal	ô order	ü rule	℉H then	u in circus
ėr term			zh measure	

K or **k** (kā), the 11th letter of the English alphabet. There are two k's in *kick*. *noun, plural* **K's** or **k's.**

ka·lei·do·scope (kə lī′də skōp), a tube containing bits of colored glass and two mirrors. As it is turned, it reflects continually changing patterns. *noun.*

Kam·pu·che·a (kam′pü chē′ə). See **Cambodia.** *noun.*

kan·ga·roo (kang′gə rü′), an Australian animal that has small front legs and very strong hind legs, which give it great leaping power. It uses its tail for balance. The female kangaroo has a pouch in front in which she carries her young. *noun, plural* **kan·ga·roos** or **kan·ga·roo.**

Kans., Kansas.

Kan·sas (kan′zəs), one of the midwestern states of the United States. *Abbreviation:* Kans. or KS *Capital:* Topeka. *noun.*
[*Kansas* was named for an American Indian tribe that once lived in the area. The name may have come from a native word of the Sioux Indians, meaning "people of the south wind."]

ka·o·lin (kā′ə lən), a fine white clay, used in making porcelain. *noun.*

kar·at (kar′ət), one 24th part gold. A gold ring of 18 karats is 18 parts pure gold and 6 parts other metals. Also spelled **carat.** *noun.*

ka·ra·te (kə rä′tē), a Japanese method of fighting without weapons by striking with the hands, elbows, knees, and feet at the opponent's body. Blows are aimed mostly at parts of the body which can easily be injured. *noun.*

Word History

karate *Karate* comes from Japanese words meaning "empty" and "hand." The idea is that karate requires no weapons in defending oneself.

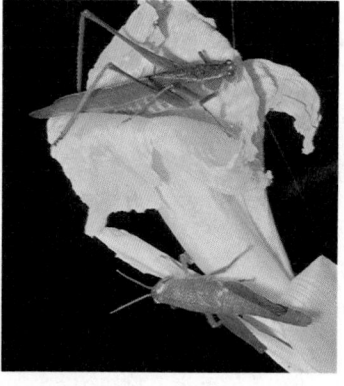

katydids
about 2 inches
(6 centimeters) long

ka·ty·did (kā′tē did′), a large green insect somewhat like a grasshopper. The male makes a shrill noise that sounds like its name by rubbing its front wings together. *noun.*

kay·ak (kī′ak), an Eskimo canoe made of skins stretched over a light frame of wood or bone with an opening in the middle for a person. *noun.*

kayak

Ka·zakh·stan (kə zäk′stän), a country in southwestern Asia. *noun.*

keel (kēl), the main timber or steel piece that extends the length of the bottom of a ship or boat. The whole ship is built up on the keel. *noun.*
keel over, 1 to upset; turn upside down: *The sailboat keeled over in the storm.* **2** to fall over suddenly: *He keeled over in a faint.*

keen (kēn), **1** sharp; shaped so as to cut well: *a keen blade.* **2** cutting; piercing; sharp: *a keen wind, a keen wit.* **3** able to do its work quickly and exactly: *a keen mind.* **4** full of enthusiasm; eager: *He is keen about sailing. adjective.*

keep (kēp), **1** to have for a long time or forever: *You may keep this book.* **2** to have and not let go: *Can you keep a secret?* **3** to have and take care of: *She keeps chickens on her farm.* **4** to take care of and protect; guard: *The bank keeps money for people.* **5** to hold back; prevent: *Keep the baby from crying.* **6** to stay or cause to stay in good condition: *A refrigerator keeps food fresh.* **7** to continue or cause to continue; to stay or cause to stay the same: *Keep along this road for two miles. Keep the fire burning.* **8** to be faithful to: *keep a promise.* **9** food and a place to sleep: *Part of her earnings pays for her keep.* **10** the strongest part of a castle or fort. 1-8 *verb*, **keeps, kept, keep·ing;** 9,10 *noun*.

for keeps, 1 for the winner to keep what he or she has won: *We were playing marbles for keeps.* **2** forever; permanently: *They have moved to Florida for keeps.*

keep on, to continue; go on: *The children kept on swimming in spite of the rain.*

keep up with, to go or move as fast as: *You walk so fast that I cannot keep up with you.*

keep·er (kē′pər), a person who watches, guards, or takes care of persons, animals, or things: *a keeper of a lighthouse, a zoo keeper. noun.*

keep·ing (kē′ping), **1** care; charge: *The two older children were left in their grandparents' keeping.* **2** agreement; harmony: *Don't trust him; his actions are not in keeping with his promises. noun.*

keep·sake (kēp′sāk′), a thing kept in memory of the giver: *Before my friend moved away, she gave me her picture as a keepsake. noun.*

keg (keg), a small barrel: *a keg of beer. noun.*

kelp (kelp), a large, tough, brown seaweed. *noun.*

ken·nel (ken′l), **1** a house for a dog. **2** Often, **kennels,** a place where dogs are bred or cared for. *noun.*

Ken·tuck·y (kən tuk′ē), one of the south central states of the United States. *Abbreviation:* Ky. or KY *Capital:* Frankfort.
[*Kentucky* may have come from a Cherokee Indian word meaning "meadow land."]

Ken·ya (ken′yə *or* kē′nyə), a country in eastern Africa. *noun.*

kept (kept). See **keep.** *He kept the book I gave him. The milk was kept cool. verb.*

ker·chief (kėr′chif), **1** a piece of cloth worn over the head or around the neck. **2** a handkerchief. *noun.*
[*Kerchief* is from old French words meaning "to cover the head."]

ker·nel (kėr′nl), **1** the softer part inside the hard shell of a nut or inside the stone of a fruit. **2** a grain or seed like that of wheat or corn. *noun.*

ker·o·sene (ker′ə sēn′), a thin oil made from petroleum. It is used as fuel in lamps, stoves, and some kinds of engines. *noun.*

ketch (kech), a small, strongly built sailing ship with two masts, and with its sails set lengthwise. *noun, plural* **ketch·es.**

ketch·up (kech′əp). See **catsup.** *noun.*

ket·tle (ket′l), **1** any metal container for boiling liquids or cooking fruit and vegetables. **2** a metal container with a handle and spout for heating water; teakettle. *noun.*

kettledrums

ket·tle·drum (ket′l drum′), a large brass or copper drum with a round bottom and a skin called parchment stretched over the top. *noun.*

key[1] (kē), **1** a small metal instrument for fastening and unfastening the lock of a door, a padlock, or any other thing. **2** anything shaped or used like it: *a roller-skate key.* **3** an answer to a puzzle or problem; guide to a solution: *the key to a crossword puzzle, the key to a mystery story.* **4** a sheet or book of answers: *a key to a test.* **5** a list or table that explains abbreviations or symbols, used in a dictionary or map. There is a pronunciation key in this dictionary. **6** controlling; very important: *the key industries of a nation.* **7** an important or essential person or thing: *A common interest in music is the key to their friendship.* **8** one of a set of parts pressed in playing a piano or other instruments, and in operating a typewriter or computer. **9** a scale or system of notes in music related to one another in a special way and based on a particular note: *a song written in the key of C.* **10** to regulate the pitch of; tune: *to key a musical instrument in preparation for a concert.* 1-5, 7-9 *noun, plural* **keys;** 6 *adjective*, 10 *verb.*

key up, to excite; make nervous: *The actors were keyed up on opening night.*

key[2] (kē), a low island or reef. There are keys south of Florida. *noun, plural* **keys.**

key·board (kē′bôrd′), the set of keys in a piano, organ, typewriter, or computer. *noun.*

key·hole (kē′hōl′), an opening in a lock through which a key is inserted. *noun.*

key·stone (kē′stōn′), **1** the middle stone at the top of an arch, holding the other stones or pieces in place. **2** the part on which other related parts depend. *noun.*

kg or **kg.,** kilogram or kilograms.

khak·i (kak′ē *or* kä′kē), **1** dull yellowish-brown. **2** a heavy cloth of this color, much used for soldiers' uniforms. **3 khakis,** a uniform made of this cloth: *Khakis will be worn in the parade.* 1 *adjective*, 2,3 *noun, plural* **khak·is.**

khan (kän), the ruler of a central Asian people

who conquered most of Asia during the 1200's. *noun.*

kick (kik), **1** to strike or strike out with the foot: *The horse kicked the boy.* **2** to move a thing by kicking: *to kick a ball along the ground, to kick off one's shoes, to kick up dust.* **3** a blow with the foot: *The horse's kick knocked me down.* **4** the backward spring of a gun when it is fired. **5** to spring back when fired; recoil: *This shotgun kicks.* **6** to complain; grumble; find fault: *My sister didn't kick when I ate her piece of cake.* **7** a thrill; excitement: *The children got a kick out of going to the circus.* 1,2,5,6 *verb,* 3,4,7 *noun.*

kick·ball (kik′bôl′), a game that is similar to baseball. The ball is rolled instead of thrown, and kicked instead of hit. *noun.*

kick·off (kik′ôf′), a kick that puts a football in play at the beginning of each half and after a score has been made. *noun.*

kick·stand (kik′stand′), a metal rod or other device attached to the frame or rear axle of a bicycle or motorcycle. It holds up a vehicle that is not being used. *noun.*

kid[1] (kid), **1** a young goat. **2** leather made from the skin of a young goat, used for gloves and shoes. **3** a child. **4** younger: *They are playing in the yard with my kid brother.* 1-3 *noun,* 4 *adjective.*

kid[2] (kid), to tease playfully; talk in a joking way: *Those two love to kid one another. verb,* **kids, kid·ded, kid·ding.**

kid·nap (kid′nap), to steal a child; carry off a person by force. *verb,* **kid·naps, kid·napped, kid·nap·ping,** or **kid·naped, kid·nap·ing.**

kid·ney (kid′nē), one of the pair of organs in the body that separate waste matter and water from the blood and pass them off through the bladder in liquid form. *noun, plural* **kid·neys.**

kidney

kidney bean, a large, red bean, shaped like a kidney and used as a vegetable.

kill (kil), **1** to put to death; cause the death of: *He was killed in an automobile accident.* **2** the act of killing. **3** an animal killed. **4** to put an end to; get rid of: *to kill odors, to kill faith.* **5** to use up time, especially in some idle or useless manner: *We killed an hour at the zoo.* 1,4,5 *verb,* 2,3 *noun.*

a hat	**i** it	**oi** oil	**ch** child	⎧ a in about
ā age	**ī** ice	**ou** out	**ng** long	⎪ e in taken
ä far	**o** hot	**u** cup	**sh** she	**ə** = ⎨ i in pencil
e let	**ō** open	**u̇** put	**th** thin	⎪ o in lemon
ē equal	**ô** order	**ü** rule	**ŦH** then	⎩ u in circus
ėr term			**zh** measure	

kill·deer (kil′dir′), a North American bird that has two black bands across its breast. It has a loud, shrill cry. *noun, plural* **kill·deers** or **kill·deer.**

killdeer—11 inches (28 centimeters) long

kill·er (kil′ər), a person, animal, or thing that kills. *noun.*

kill·joy (kil′joi′), a person who spoils other people's fun. *noun.*

kiln (kil *or* kiln), a furnace or oven for burning, baking, or drying something. Limestone is burned in a kiln to make lime. Bricks are baked in a kiln. *noun.*

ki·lo (kē′lō *or* kil′ō), **1** a kilogram. **2** a kilometer. *noun, plural* **ki·los.**

kil·o·gram (kil′ə gram′), the basic unit of weight in the metric system. It is equal to 1000 grams. *noun.*

ki·lom·e·ter (kə lom′ə tər *or* kil′ə mē′tər), a unit for measuring length or distance. It is equal to 1000 meters. *noun.*

kil·o·watt (kil′ə wot′), a unit for measuring electric power equal to 1000 watts. *noun.*

kilt (kilt), a pleated skirt, reaching to the knees, worn by men in parts of Scotland. *noun.*

kilt

335

kimono (definition 1)

ki·mo·no (kə mō′nə), **1** a loose outer garment held in place by a sash, worn by both men and women in Japan. **2** a woman's loose robe. *noun, plural* **ki·mo·nos.**

kin (kin), **1** a family or relatives: *All our kin came to the family reunion.* **2** family relationship: *What kin is she to you? noun.*

kind[1] (kīnd), **1** friendly; doing good rather than harm: *A kind person tries to help others. Sharing your lunch was a kind thing to do.* **2** gentle: *Be kind to animals. adjective.*

kind[2] (kīnd), **1** a sort; type: *I like many kinds of food. A kilt is a kind of skirt.* **2** a natural group: *The wolf hunted with others of its kind. noun.*

kind of, nearly; almost; somewhat: *The room was kind of dark.*

of a kind, of the same sort: *The cakes were all of a kind—chocolate.*

kin·der·gar·ten (kin′dər gärt′n), a school for children from about 4 to 6 years old that educates them by games, toys, and pleasant activities. *noun.*
[*Kindergarten* was borrowed from a German word meaning "children's garden."]

kind·heart·ed (kīnd′här′tid), having or showing a kind heart; kindly; sympathetic. *adjective.*

kin·dle (kin′dl), **1** to set on fire or catch fire; light: *I used a match to kindle the wood.* **2** to stir up; arouse: *The unfairness of the punishment kindled my anger. verb,* **kin·dles, kin·dled, kin·dling.**

kind·li·ness (kīnd′lē nis), **1** a kindly feeling or quality. **2** a kindly act. *noun, plural* **kind·li·ness·es.**

kin·dling (kind′ling), small pieces of wood for starting a fire. *noun.*

kind·ly (kīnd′lē), **1** kind; friendly: *kindly faces.* **2** in a kind or friendly way: *We thank you kindly for your help.* **3** please: *Kindly help me lift this box*

of books. **1** *adjective,* **kind·li·er, kind·li·est;** 2,3 *adverb.*

kind·ness (kīnd′nis), **1** a kind nature; being kind: *We admire his kindness.* **2** a kind act: *They showed me many kindnesses. noun, plural* **kind·ness·es.**

kin·dred (kin′drid), like; similar; related: *We are studying about dew, frost, and kindred facts of nature. adjective.*

king (king), **1** a man who rules a country and its people. **2** a person who has great power in industry, business, or sports; very important person. **3** something or someone best in its class: *The lion is often called the king of the beasts.* **4** a playing card with the picture of a king on it. It is above a queen and, usually, below an ace. **5** an important piece in the game of chess. A king can move one square in any direction. **6** a piece that has moved entirely across the board in checkers. It can move in any direction. *noun.*

king·dom (king′dəm), **1** a country that is governed by a king or a queen; land or territory ruled by one monarch. **2** the basic category used in classifying living things. Mice belong to the animal kingdom, maples to the vegetable kingdom, and mushrooms to the kingdom of fungi. *noun.*

king·fish·er (king′fish′ər), a bright-colored bird with a large head and a strong beak. Kingfishers eat fish and insects. *noun.*

kingfisher—14 inches (36 centimeters) long

king·ly (king′lē), **1** of or like a king; royal; noble: *kingly pride.* **2** fit for a king: *a kingly crown. adjective,* **king·li·er, king·li·est.**

king-size (king′sīz′), large or long for its kind: *a king-size package. adjective.*

kink (kingk), **1** a twist or curl in thread, rope, or hair. **2** to form a kink or kinks; make kinks in: *The rope kinked as she rolled it up.* **3** a pain or stiffness in a muscle; cramp: *a kink in the back, a kink in the leg.* 1,3 *noun,* 2 *verb.*

kin·ship (kin′ship), a being kin; family relationship: *His kinship with the owner of the factory helped him to get a job. noun.*

kins·man (kinz′mən), a male relative. Your brothers and uncles are your kinsmen. *noun, plural* **kins·men.**

kins·wo·man (kinz′wum′ən), a female relative. Your sisters and aunts are your kinswomen. *noun, plural* **kins·wom·en.**

kiss (kis), **1** to touch with the lips as a sign of love, greeting, or respect. **2** a touch with the lips as a sign of love, greeting, or respect. **3** a small piece of candy, usually of chocolate. 1 *verb,* 2,3 *noun,* *plural* **kiss·es.**

kit (kit), **1** the parts of anything to be put together by the buyer: *a model airplane kit.* **2** a person's equipment packed for traveling: *a soldier's kit.* **3** an outfit of tools or supplies: *a first-aid kit.* *noun.*

kitch·en (kich′ən), a room where food is cooked. *noun.*
[*Kitchen* comes from a Latin word meaning "to cook."]

kitch·en·ette (kich′ə net′), **1** a very small kitchen. **2** a part of a room fitted up as a kitchen. *noun.*

kite (kīt), **1** a light wooden frame covered with paper, cloth, or plastic. Kites are flown in the air on the end of a long string. **2** a hawk with long, pointed wings and often a long, forked tail. *noun.*

kit·ten (kit′n), a young cat. *noun.*

kit·ty (kit′ē), a pet name for a cat or kitten. *noun,* *plural* **kit·ties.**

Klee·nex (klē′neks), a trademark for a paper tissue used as a handkerchief. *noun.*

km or **km.,** kilometer or kilometers.

knack (nak), a special skill; power to do something easily: *That clown has the knack of making very funny faces. noun.*

knap·sack (nap′sak′), a cloth bag for clothes or equipment carried on the back. *noun.*

knave (nāv), a tricky or dishonest man; rascal. *noun.*

knead (nēd), **1** to press or mix together dough or clay into a soft mass. Kneading may be done with the hands or by machine. *The baker was kneading dough to make pastry.* **2** to press and squeeze with the hands; massage: *Kneading the muscles in a stiff shoulder helps to take away the stiffness. verb.*

knee (nē), **1** the joint between the thigh and the lower leg. **2** anything like a bent knee in shape or position. *noun.*

knee·cap (nē′kap′), the flat, movable bone at the front of the knee. *noun.*

kneel (nēl), to go down on one's knee or knees; rest on one's knees: *to kneel in prayer. I knelt down to pull a weed from the garden. verb,* **kneels,** **knelt** or **kneeled, kneel·ing.**

knell (nel), **1** the sound of a bell rung slowly after a death or at a funeral. **2** to ring slowly. **3** something regarded as a sign of death or as telling of a death: *Their refusal rang the knell of our hopes.* **4** to give a warning sound. 1,3 *noun,* 2,4 *verb.*

knelt (nelt). See **kneel.** *They knelt and prayed. verb.*

knew (nü *or* nyü). See **know.** *She knew the right answer. verb.*

knick·ers (nik′ərz), short, loose trousers gathered in at, or just below, the knee. *noun plural.*

knick·knack (nik′nak′), an ornament; trinket. *noun.*

a hat	i it	oi oil	ch child	(a in about
ā age	ī ice	ou out	ng long	e in taken
ä far	o hot	u cup	sh she	ə = { i in pencil
e let	ō open	ů put	th thin	o in lemon
ē equal	ô order	ü rule	ŦH then	(u in circus
ėr term			zh measure	

knife (nīf), **1** a thin, flat metal blade fastened in a handle so that it can be used to cut or spread. A table knife is stiff, with no joint; a pocketknife has a joint so that the sharp edge can be folded inside the handle. **2** a sharp blade forming part of a tool or machine: *The knives of a lawn mower cut grass.* **3** to cut or stab with a knife. 1,2 *noun, plural* **knives;** 3 *verb,* **knifes, knifed, knif·ing.**

knight (nīt), **1** (in the Middle Ages) a man raised to an honorable military rank and pledged to do good deeds. After serving as a page and squire, a man was made a knight by the king or a lord. **2** (in modern times) a man raised to an honorable rank because of great achievement or service. A man named John Smith becomes Sir John Smith, or Sir John, as a knight. **3** to raise to the rank of knight: *He was knighted by the queen.* **4** one of the pieces in the game of chess. 1,2,4 *noun,* 3 *verb.*

knight·hood (nīt′hůd), the rank of a knight. *noun.*

knit (nit), **1** to make cloth or an article of clothing by looping yarn or thread together with long needles, or by machinery which forms loops instead of weaving: *to knit a pair of socks.* **2** to join closely and firmly together: *The players were all knit into a team that played together smoothly.* **3** to grow together: *The doctor fixed his arm so that the broken bone would knit.* **4** to draw the brows together in wrinkles: *She knits her brows when she frowns. verb,* **knits, knit** or **knit·ted, knit·ting.**
[*Knit* comes from an older English word meaning "a knot." An earlier meaning of *knit* was "to tie in knots," or "to tie with knots."]

knives (nīvz), more than one knife. *noun plural.*

knob (nob), **1** a rounded lump: *Grandfather's cane has a large knob at the top.* **2** a handle, object, or part shaped like a rounded lump: *the knobs on a bureau drawer, the knob on the dial of a television set. noun.*

knob·by (nob′ē), **1** covered with knobs: *the knobby trunk of a tree.* **2** rounded like a knob: *the knobby, gold head of a cane. adjective,* **knob·bi·er, knob·bi·est.**

knock (nok), **1** to give a hard blow or blows to with the fist, knuckles, or anything hard; hit: *The ball knocked me on the head.* **2** a hit: *That knock on my head really hurt.* **3** to hit and cause to fall: *The speeding car knocked over a sign.* **4** to hit with a noise: *She knocked on the door.* **5** a hit with a noise: *I did not hear the knock on the door.* **6** to make a noise, especially a rattling or pounding noise: *The engine is knocking.* **7** the sound caused by loose parts or improper burning of fuel: *a knock in an engine.* 1,3,4,6 *verb,* 2,5,7 *noun.*

knock down, to take apart: *We knocked down*

K

the bookcases and packed them in the car.

knock out, to hit so hard as to make helpless or unconscious: *She was knocked out by the fall.*

knock·er (nok′ər), a hinged knob, ring, or the like, fastened on a door for use in knocking. A knocker is used as a signal that someone wishes to have the door opened. *noun.*

knock·out (nok′out′), a blow that makes an opponent helpless or unconscious: *The boxer won the fight by a knockout. noun.*

knoll (nōl), a small rounded hill; mound. *noun.*

knot (not), **1** a fastening made by tying or twining together pieces of one or more ropes, strings, or cords: *a square knot, a slip knot.* **2** to tie or twine together in a knot: *He knotted two ropes together.* **3** a tangle: *comb out the knots in one's hair.* **4** a group; cluster: *A knot of students stood talking outside the classroom.* **5** the hard mass formed in a tree where a branch grows out, which shows as a hard, round place in a board. **6** any hard mass or lump: *a knot in a muscle, a hand covered with knots.* **7** a unit of speed used on ships and aircraft, equal to 6076 feet per hour: *The ship's speed is 20 knots.* **1,3-7** *noun,* **2** *verb,* **knots, knot·ted, knot·ting.**

knot·hole (not′hōl′), a hole in a board formed by a knot falling out. *noun.*

knot·ty (not′ē), **1** full of knots: *knotty wood.* **2** difficult; puzzling: *a knotty problem. adjective,* **knot·ti·er, knot·ti·est.**

know (nō), **1** to have the facts of; be skilled in: *She knows arithmetic. The teacher really knew his subject.* **2** to have the facts and be sure that they are true: *We know that 2 and 2 are 4. She was there at the time; she will know.* **3** to have knowledge: *I know from experience how to bake a cake.* **4** to be acquainted with: *I know her very well, but I don't know her sister.* **5** to tell apart from others: *You will know his house by the red roof. verb,* **knows, knew, known, know·ing.**

know-how (nō′hou′), the ability to do something: *It takes a lot of know-how to operate such a complicated machine. noun.*

know·ing (nō′ing), suggesting clever or secret understanding: *a knowing look. adjective.*

know·ing·ly (nō′ing lē), on purpose; intentionally: *I would not knowingly hurt anyone. adverb.*

knowl·edge (nol′ij), **1** what one knows: *a gardener's knowledge of flowers.* **2** all that is known or can be learned: *Science is a part of knowledge.* **3** the fact of knowing: *The knowledge of our victory caused great joy.* **4** the act of knowing; familiarity with a thing, person, or subject: *a knowledge of the surrounding countryside. noun.*

known (nōn). **1** See **know.** *George Washington is known as the father of his country.* **2** familiar to all; generally recognized; well-known: *a known fact, a person of known ability.* **1** *verb,* **2** *adjective.*

knuck·le (nuk′əl), **1** a joint in a finger, especially one of the joints between a finger and the rest of the hand. **2 knuckle down,** to work hard: *to knuckle down to a job.* **3 knuckle under,** to yield; submit: *She would not knuckle under to their demands.* **1** *noun,* **2,3** *verb,* **knuck·les, knuck·led, knuck·ling.**

ko·a·la (kō ä′lə), a gray, furry animal of Australia that looks somewhat like a small bear and carries its young in a pouch. Koalas live in trees. *noun.*

koala—about 2 feet (60 centimeters) long

Ko·ran (kô ran′ or kô rän′), the sacred book of the Moslems. *noun.*

Ko·re·a (kô rē′ə), a former country on a peninsula in eastern Asia, now divided into North Korea and South Korea. *noun.*

ko·sher (kō′shər), right or clean according to Jewish law: *kosher meat. adjective.*
[*Kosher* comes from a Hebrew word meaning "proper" or "fit."]

Krem·lin (krem′lən), the citadel of Moscow. The chief offices of the Soviet government were in the Kremlin. *noun.*

KS, Kansas (used with postal Zip Code).

kum·quat (kum′kwot), a yellow or orange fruit that is somewhat like a small orange. It has a sour pulp, and is used in candy, jam, and preserves. *noun.*

Word History

kumquat *Kumquat* comes from Chinese words meaning "golden orange."

Ku·wait (kü wāt′), a country in southwestern Asia, on the peninsula of Arabia. *noun.*

KY, Kentucky (used with postal Zip Code).

Ky., Kentucky.

Kyr·gyz·stan (kir gēz′stän), a country in central Asia. *noun.*

L l

a hat	**i** it	**oi** oil	**ch** child		a in about
ā age	**ī** ice	**ou** out	**ng** long		e in taken
ä far	**o** hot	**u** cup	**sh** she	ə =	i in pencil
e let	**ō** open	**u̇** put	**th** thin		o in lemon
ē equal	**ô** order	**ü** rule	**ᴛʜ** then		u in circus
ėr term			**zh** measure		

L or l (el), the 12th letter of the English alphabet. *noun, plural* **L's** or **l's.**

l or **l.,** liter or liters.

L or **L.,** liter or liters.

LA, Louisiana (used with postal Zip Code).

La., Louisiana.

lab (lab), a laboratory. *noun.*

la·bel (lā′bəl), **1** a slip of paper or other material attached to anything and marked to show what or whose it is, or where it is to go: *I read the label on the box.* **2** to put or write a label on: *The bottle is labeled "Poison."* 1 *noun,* 2 *verb.*

la·bor (lā′bər), **1** work; toil: *The carpenter was well paid for his labor.* **2** workers as a group: *Labor favors safe working conditions.* **3** to do work; work hard; toil: *I labored all day at the factory.* **4** to move slowly and heavily: *The ship labored in the heavy seas. The old car labored as it climbed the steep hill.* 1,2 *noun,* 3,4 *verb.*

lab·o·ra·to·ry (lab′rə tôr′ē), a place with special equipment where scientific experiments and tests are done: *The drug was tested on animals in the laboratory. noun, plural* **lab·o·ra·to·ries.**

Labor Day, the first Monday in September. Labor Day is a legal holiday throughout the United States in honor of labor and laborers.

la·bored (lā′bərd), done with much effort; forced: *labored breathing. The student who was always late made up labored excuses. adjective.*

la·bor·er (lā′bər ər), **1** a person who does work that requires strength rather than skill and training. **2** a worker. *noun.*

la·bo·ri·ous (lə bôr′ē əs), needing or taking much effort; requiring hard work: *Climbing a mountain is laborious. adjective.*

labor union, a group of workers joined together to protect and promote their interests.

lace (lās), **1** an open weaving or net of fine thread in an ornamental pattern. **2** to trim with lace: *a velvet cloak laced with gold.* **3** a cord, string, or leather strip for pulling or holding together: *These shoes need new laces.* **4** to put laces through; pull

lace (definition 1)

or hold together with a lace or laces: *Lace up your shoes.* 1,3 *noun,* 2,4 *verb,* **lac·es, laced, lac·ing.**

lac·e·rate (las′ə rāt′), to tear roughly; mangle: *The bear's claws lacerated the hunter's arm. verb,* **lac·e·rates, lac·e·rat·ed, lac·e·rat·ing.**

lack (lak), **1** to have no; be without: *Some guinea pigs lack tails.* **2** a being without: *Lack of fire made him cold.* **3** to have not enough; need: *This book lacks excitement.* **4** a shortage; not having enough: *Lack of rest made them tired.* 1,3 *verb,* 2,4 *noun.*

lack·ing (lak′ing), **1** not having enough: *A weak person is lacking in strength.* **2** without; not having: *Lacking butter, we ate dry toast.* **3** absent; not here: *Water was lacking, so the crops began to dry up.* 1,3 *adjective,* 2 *preposition.*

lac·quer (lak′ər), **1** a varnish used to give a coating or a shiny appearance to metals, wood, or paper. **2** to coat with lacquer. 1 *noun,* 2 *verb.*

la·crosse (lə krôs′), a game played with a ball and loosely-strung rackets by two sides of ten players each. The players try to send the ball into a goal. *noun.*

lacrosse

lac·y (lā′sē), **1** of lace: *a lacy collar.* **2** like lace: *the lacy leaves of a fern. adjective,* **lac·i·er, lac·i·est.**

lad (lad), a boy; young man. *noun.*

lad·der (lad′ər), a set of rungs or steps fastened into two long pieces of wood, metal, or rope, for use in climbing up and down. *noun.*

lad·en (lād′n), loaded; burdened: *a ship laden with goods. The camels were laden with bundles of silk. adjective.*

la·dle (lā′dl), **1** a large, cup-shaped spoon with a long handle, for dipping out liquids. **2** to dip: *I ladled out the soup.* 1 *noun,* 2 *verb,* **la·dles, la·dled, la·dling.**

la·dy (lā′dē), **1** a woman of good family and social position: *a lady by birth.* **2** a woman having good

manners. **3** a polite term for any woman. "Ladies" is often used in speaking or writing to a group of women. **4 Lady,** a title used in writing or speaking about women of certain high ranks in Great Britain: *Lord and Lady Grey attended the Queen's reception. noun, plural* **la·dies.**
[*Lady* comes from an earlier English word originally meaning "one who kneads a loaf of bread" or "mistress of the house."]

la·dy·bird (lā/dē bėrd/), a ladybug. *noun.*

la·dy·bug (lā/dē bug/), a small, round, reddish beetle with black spots. It eats certain insects that are harmful to plants. *noun.*

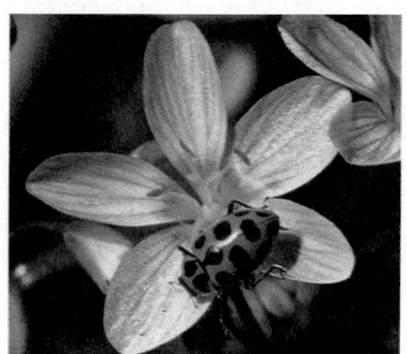

ladybug— about two times life-size

la·dy·in·wait·ing (lā/dē in wā/ting), a lady who accompanies or serves a queen or princess. *noun, plural* **la·dies·in·wait·ing.**

lag (lag), **1** to move too slowly; fall behind: *They lagged because they were tired.* **2** a falling behind: *There was a lag in forwarding mail to us after we moved.* **1** *verb,* **lags, lagged, lag·ging; 2** *noun.*

la·goon (lə gün/), a pond or small lake connected with a larger body of water. *noun.*

laid (lād). See **lay**[1]. *He laid down the heavy bundle. Those eggs were laid this morning. verb.*

lain (lān). See **lie**[2]. *The snow has lain on the ground a week. verb.*

lair (ler *or* lar), a den or resting place of a wild animal. *noun.*

lake (lāk), a body of water surrounded by land. A lake is larger than a pond and usually contains fresh water. *noun.*

lamb (lam), **1** a young sheep. **2** the meat from a lamb: *roast lamb.* **3** a young or dear person. *noun.*

lame (lām), **1** not able to walk properly; having a hurt leg or foot; crippled: *He limps because he has been lame since birth.* **2** stiff and sore: *My arm is lame from playing ball.* **3** to make lame; cripple: *The accident lamed her for life.* **4** poor; not very good: *Stopping to play is a lame excuse for being late to school.* **1,2,4** *adjective,* **lam·er, lam·est; 3** *verb,* **lames, lamed, lam·ing.**

la·ment (lə ment/), to mourn for; express sorrow for: *We lament the dead. verb.*

lamp (lamp), a thing that gives light. Oil lamps hold oil and a wick by which the oil is burned. A gas or electric light, especially when covered with a glass globe or other shade, is called a lamp. *noun.*

lance (lans), **1** a long wooden spear with a sharp iron or steel head: *The knights carried lances.* **2** to cut open with a surgeon's knife: *The dentist lanced the gum where a new tooth had difficulty in coming through.* **1** *noun,* **2** *verb,* **lanc·es, lanced, lanc·ing.**

land (land), **1** the solid part of the earth's surface: *After many weeks at sea, the sailors sighted land.* **2** to come to land; bring to land: *The ship landed at the pier.* **3** to come down from the air; come to rest: *The airplane landed in a field. The eagle landed on a rock.* **4** to go on shore from a ship or boat: *The passengers landed.* **5** the ground; soil: *This is good land for a garden.* **6** a country; region: *Switzerland is a mountainous land.* **7** to arrive: *The thief landed in jail.* **8** to catch; get: *land a job.* **1,5,6** *noun,* **2-4,7,8** *verb.*

land·form (land/fôrm/), the shape of the surface of the land. Mountains, hills, and plains are three kinds of landforms. *noun.*

land·ing (lan/ding), **1** a coming to land: *the landing of the Pilgrims at Plymouth. There are many millions of takeoffs and landings at the nation's airports each year.* **2** a place where persons or goods are landed from a ship or helicopter. A wharf, dock, or pier is a landing for boats. **3** a platform between flights of stairs. *noun.*

landing field, a field large enough and smooth enough for airplanes to land on and take off from.

land·la·dy (land/lā/dē), **1** a woman who owns buildings or land rented to others. **2** a woman who runs an inn or boardinghouse. *noun, plural* **land·la·dies.**

land·lord (land/lôrd/), **1** a person who owns buildings or land rented to others. **2** a person who runs an inn or boardinghouse. *noun.*

land·mark (land/märk/), **1** something familiar or easily seen, used as a guide: *The traveler did not lose her way in the forest because the rangers' high tower served as a landmark.* **2** any important fact or event; any happening that stands out above others: *The invention of the telephone was a landmark in the history of communication.* **3** a place that is important or interesting: *That building is a historical landmark. noun.*

land·own·er (land/ō/nər), a person who owns land. *noun.*

land·scape (land/skāp), **1** a view of scenery on land: *The two hills with the valley formed a beautiful landscape.* **2** a picture showing such a view. **3** to make land more pleasant to look at by arranging trees, shrubs, or flowers: *This park is landscaped.* **1,2** *noun,* **3** *verb,* **land·scapes, land·scaped, land·scap·ing.**

land·slide (land/slīd/), **1** a sliding down of a mass of soil or rock on a steep slope. **2** the mass that slides down. **3** an overwhelming number of votes for one political party or candidate: *She won the election by a landslide. noun.*

lane (lān), **1** a narrow road or street, often between grass, bushes, or fences. **2** any narrow way: *The bride and groom walked down a lane formed by two lines of wedding guests.* **3** a course or route used by cars, ships, or aircraft going in the same direction. **4** a long, narrow wooden floor used for bowling; alley. *noun.*

lan·guage (lang′gwij), **1** human speech, spoken or written: *Civilization would be impossible without language.* **2** the speech of one nation, tribe, or other large group of people: *the French language.* **3** a form, style, or kind of language: *bad language, poetic language, the language of chemistry.* **4** the expression of thoughts and feelings otherwise than by words: *sign language.* **5** a system of words, numbers, symbols, and abbreviations that stand for information and instructions in a computer. *noun.*
[*Language* comes from a Latin word that originally meant "tongue." The ancient Romans observed that the tongue was a very important organ for making speech sounds.]

lank (langk), **1** long and thin; slender; lean: *a lank teenager, lank grasses.* **2** straight and flat; not curly or wavy: *lank locks of hair. adjective.*

lank·y (lang′kē), awkwardly long and thin; tall and ungraceful: *He was a lanky teenager. adjective,* **lank·i·er, lank·i·est.**

Lan·sing (lan′sing), the capital of Michigan. *noun.*

lan·tern (lan′tərn), a case to protect a light from wind or rain. A lantern has sides of glass, paper, or some other material through which light can shine. *noun.*

Word History

lantern *Lantern* comes from a Greek word meaning "to shine."

La·os (lä′ōs *or* lā′os), a country in southeastern Asia. *noun.*

lap[1] (lap), the front part from the waist to the knees of a person sitting down, with the clothing that covers it: *I held the baby on my lap. noun.*

lap[2] (lap), **1** to lie together, one partly over or beside another: *The shingles lapped over each other.* **2** the part that laps over. **3** the entire length of something, as a track or a swimming pool: *I swam three laps before breakfast.* 1 *verb,* **laps, lapped, lap·ping;** 2,3 *noun.*

a hat	i it	oi oil	ch child	⎧ a in about
ā age	ī ice	ou out	ng long	⎪ e in taken
ä far	o hot	u cup	sh she	ə = ⎨ i in pencil
e let	ō open	u̇ put	th thin	⎪ o in lemon
ē equal	ô order	ü rule	ͭH then	⎩ u in circus
ėr term			zh measure	

lap[3] (lap), **1** to drink by lifting up with the tongue; lick: *Cats and dogs lap up water.* **2** to move or beat gently with a lapping sound; splash gently: *Little waves lapped against the boat.* **3** the act of lapping: *With one lap of the tongue the bear finished the honey.* **4** a sound of lapping: *The lap of waves against a boat put me to sleep.* 1,2 *verb,* **laps, lapped, lap·ping;** 3,4 *noun.*

la·pel (lə pel′), either of the two front parts of a coat folded back just below the collar. *noun.*

lapse (laps), **1** a slight mistake or error: *I had a lapse of memory and could not remember his name.* **2** a slipping by; passing away: *A minute is a short lapse of time.* **3** to slip by; pass away: *Our interest in the dull story soon lapsed.* **4** a slipping back; sinking down: *War is a lapse into savage ways.* **5** to slip back; sink down: *I tried to be tidy, but soon lapsed into my old sloppy ways.* 1,2,4 *noun,* 3,5 *verb,* **laps·es, lapsed, laps·ing.**

lar·ce·ny (lär′sə nē), theft. *noun, plural* **lar·ce·nies.**

larch (lärch), **1** a tree with small cones and needles that fall off in the autumn. **2** its strong, tough wood. *noun, plural* **larch·es.**

lard (lärd), the fat of pigs or hogs, melted down for use in cooking: *The cook uses lard in making pies. noun.*

lar·der (lär′dər), **1** a pantry; place where food is kept. **2** a stock of food: *The hunter's larder included flour, bacon, and deer meat. noun.*

large (lärj), of more than the usual size, amount, or number; big: *America is a large country. Ten thousand dollars is a large sum of money. Large crowds come to see our team play. adjective,* **larg·er, larg·est.**
at large, 1 free: *Is the escaped prisoner still at large?* **2** in general: *The people at large want peace.*

large intestine, the lower part of the intestine. It removes water from the waste material that has not been digested by the small intestine.

large·ly (lärj′lē), much; to a great extent: *A desert consists largely of sand. adverb.*

lar·i·at (lar′ē ət), a long rope with a loop at the end, used for catching horses and cattle; lasso. *noun.*
[*Lariat* comes from Spanish words meaning "the rope."]

lark[1] (lärk), **1** a small songbird of Europe, Asia, America, and northern Africa that sings while soaring in the air. The skylark is one kind of lark. **2** the meadowlark. *noun.*

lark[2] (lärk), something that is good fun; joke: *We went wading just for a lark. noun.*

lark·spur (lärk′spėr′), a plant with a tall stalk of thickly growing blue, pink, or white flowers. *noun.*

larva of a butterfly

lar·va (lär′və), the early wormlike form of an insect from the time it leaves the egg until it becomes a pupa. A caterpillar is the larva of a butterfly or moth. Maggots are the larvae of flies. The silkworm is a larva. *noun, plural* **lar·vae** (lär′vē).

lar·yn·gi·tis (lar′ən jī′tis), soreness and swelling of the part of the throat containing the vocal cords. Laryngitis usually causes a loss of voice for a time. *noun.*

lar·ynx (lar′ingks), the upper end of the windpipe, where the vocal cords are. *noun, plural* **la·ryn·ges** (lə rin′jēz), **lar·ynx·es.**

la·sa·gna (lə zä′nyə), a food made of chopped meat, cheese, and tomato sauce, baked with layers of wide noodles. *noun.*
[*Lasagna* was borrowed from an Italian word. It can be traced back to a Greek word meaning "a utensil" or "a cooking pot."]

la·ser (lā′zər), a device that makes a very narrow and very strong beam of light. Laser beams are used to cut or melt hard materials, remove diseased body tissues, and send television signals. *noun.*
[*Laser* comes from the words *light amplification by stimulated emission of radiation.* It was formed by using the first letter of these words except for *by* and *of.*]

laser—The doctor is using a **laser** to treat an eye problem.

lash[1] (lash), **1** the part of a whip that is not the handle: *The leather lash cut the side of the ox.* **2** a stroke or blow with a whip: *The ox was cut by a lash of the whip.* **3** to strike with a whip: *The driver of the team lashed her horses on.* **4** to beat back and forth: *The lion lashed its tail. The wind lashes the sails.* **5** to hit: *The wild horse lashed at the cowboy with its hoofs.* **6** one of the hairs on the edge of the eyelid; eyelash. 1,2,6 *noun, plural* **lash·es;** 3-5 *verb.*

lash[2] (lash), to tie or fasten with a rope: *We lashed logs together to make a raft. verb.*

lass (las), a girl; young woman. *noun, plural* **lass·es.**

las·sie (las′ē), a girl. *noun.*

las·so (las′ō), **1** a long rope with a loop at the end, used for catching horses and cattle; lariat. **2** to catch with a lasso. 1 *noun, plural* **las·sos** or **las·soes;** 2 *verb.*

last[1] (last), **1** coming after all others: *Z is the last letter; A is the first.* **2** after all others: *She came last in the line.* **3** latest: *When did you see him last? I saw him last week.* **4** most unlikely: *Fighting is the last thing I would do.* **5** that remains; that is left: *I ate the last apple.* **6** the end: *Be faithful to the last.* 1,3-5 *adjective,* 2,3 *adverb,* 6 *noun.*
at last, finally: *At last the baby fell asleep.*

last[2] (last), **1** to go on; continue in time: *The play lasted three hours. How long will our money last?* **2** to continue in good condition: *I hope these shoes last. verb.*

last·ing (las′ting), that lasts; that will last; that will last a long time: *The thrilling voyage had a lasting effect on me. adjective.*

latch (lach), **1** a catch for fastening a door, gate, or window, often one not needing a key. It consists of a movable piece of metal or wood that fits into a notch or opening. **2** to fasten with a latch: *Latch the door.* 1 *noun, plural* **latch·es;** 2 *verb.*

late (lāt), **1** after the usual or proper time: *We had a late supper because we came home late.* **2** near the end: *It was late in the evening.* **3** not long past; recent: *My parents bought a late model car. The late storm did much harm.* **4** recently dead: *The late Mary Lee was a good citizen.* 1-4 *adjective,* **lat·er** or **lat·ter, lat·est** or **last;** 1,2 *adverb,* **lat·er, lat·est** or **last.**
of late, lately; a short time ago; recently: *I haven't seen them of late.*

late·ly (lāt′lē), a little while ago; not long ago; of late: *He has not been looking well lately. adverb.*

la·tent (lāt′nt), present but not active; hidden: *The power of a grain of wheat to grow into a plant remains latent if it is not planted. adjective.*

lat·er·al (lat′ər əl), of the side; at the side; from the side; toward the side: *A lateral fin of a fish grows from its side. adjective.*

la·tex (lā′teks), a milky liquid found in some plants. It hardens in the air, and is used to make rubber and other products. *noun.*

lath (lath), a thin, narrow strip of wood, used with others like it to form a support for plaster or to make a lattice. *noun, plural* **laths** (laᴛнz).

lathe (lāᴛн), a machine for holding articles of wood or metal, and turning them rapidly against a cutting tool which shapes them. *noun.*

lath·er (laᴛн′ər), **1** the foam made from soap and

water. **2** to put lather on: *He lathers his face before shaving.* **3** to form a lather: *This soap lathers well.* **4** the foam formed in sweating: *the lather on a horse after a race.* 1,4 *noun,* 2,3 *verb.*

Lat·in (lat′n), **1** the language of the ancient Romans. **2** of Latin; in Latin: *Latin poetry.* **3** of the peoples (Italians, French, Spanish, and Portuguese) whose languages have come from Latin. 1 *noun,* 2,3 *adjective.*

Word Source

Latin was the language of ancient Rome. Here is a small sample of the hundreds of words that came into English from Latin:

author	human	motor	salute
aviation	individual	muscle	strict
binoculars	insect	notice	student
bus	insult	obey	stupid
cereal	jelly	offend	suspend
clock	journey	pen¹	tornado
companion	kitchen	pigeon	union
education	language	porpoise	vaccine
exaggerate	lava	pupil	vertebra
fool	liberty	reptile	video
fossil	locomotive	republic	virus
funnel	map	rotate	volcano
hospital	menu	salary	

Lat·in A·mer·i·ca (lat′n ə mer′ə kə), South America, Central America, Mexico, and most of the West Indies.

Lat·in-A·mer·i·can (lat′n ə mer′ə kən), of or having to do with Latin America. *adjective.*

La·ti·no (la tē′nō), a person born or living in Latin America. *noun, plural* **La·ti·nos.**

lat·i·tude (lat′ə tüd *or* lat′ə tyüd), **1** the distance north or south of the equator, measured in degrees. A degree of latitude is about 69 miles (111 kilometers). **2** room to act; freedom from narrow rules: *You are allowed much latitude in spending your allowance.* noun.

Word History

latitude *Latitude* comes from a Latin word meaning "wide." The earliest maps were flat, not round, and were wider than they were long. Lines of latitude were drawn across the width of the map. Look also at the word history of *longitude.*

latitude (definition 1)
circles of **latitude**

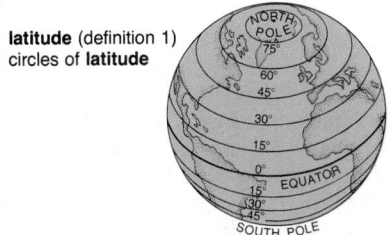

lat·ter (lat′ər), **1** the second of two: *Canada and the United States are in North America; the former lies north of the latter.* **2** more recent; later; toward

a hat	i it	oi oil	ch child	a in about
ā age	ī ice	ou out	ng long	e in taken
ä far	o hot	u cup	sh she	ə = i in pencil
e let	ō open	u̇ put	th thin	o in lemon
ē equal	ô order	ü rule	ŦH then	u in circus
ėr term			zh measure	

the end: *Friday comes in the latter part of the week. adjective.*

lat·tice (lat′is), wooden or metal strips crossed with open spaces between them. *noun.*

lattice—The space under the porch is enclosed with a **lattice.**

Lat·vi·a (lat′vē ə), a country in northern Europe. *noun.*

laud (lôd), to praise highly: *Our teacher lauded our efforts to raise money for the new library. verb.*

laugh (laf), **1** to make the sounds and movements that show one is happy or amused: *We all laughed at the clown's funny tricks.* **2** the sound made when a person laughs: *She gave a hearty laugh at the joke.* 1 *verb,* 2 *noun.*

laugh at, to make fun of: *They laughed at their friend for believing in ghosts.*

laugh·a·ble (laf′ə bəl), amusing; funny: *a laughable mistake. adjective.*

laugh·ter (laf′tər), the sound or action of laughing: *Laughter filled the room. noun.*

laugh track, recorded laughter played during a television or radio show to make it seem funnier.

launch¹ (lônch), **1** to cause to slide into the water; set afloat: *The new ship was launched from the supports on which it was built.* **2** to push out or put forth into the air: *The satellite was launched in a rocket.* **3** the act of launching a rocket, missile, aircraft, or ship: *The launch of the first space vehicle was a historic event.* **4** to start; set going; set out: *Friends launched us in business with a loan.* 1,2,4 *verb,* 3 *noun, plural* **launch·es.**

launch² (lônch), a small, open motorboat for pleasure trips. *noun, plural* **launch·es.**

launching pad, the surface or platform from which a rocket or missile is shot into the air.

laun·der (lôn′dər), to wash and iron clothes. *verb.*

Laun·dro·mat (lôn′drə mat), a trademark for a self-service laundry that has coin-operated washing machines and dryers. *noun.*

laun·dry (lôn′drē), **1** a room or building where clothes and linens are washed and ironed. **2** clothes and linens that have been washed or are to be washed. *noun, plural* **laun·dries.**

laurel (definition 1)
a branch of **laurel** with blossoms

lau·rel (lôr′əl), **1** a small evergreen tree with smooth, shiny leaves. **2** any tree or shrub like this. The mountain laurel has pale-pink clusters of flowers. **3 laurels, a** high honor; fame. **b** victory. *noun.*

la·va (lä′və), **1** the hot, melted rock flowing from a volcano. **2** the rock formed by the cooling of this melted rock. Some lavas are hard and glassy; others are light and porous. *noun.*

Word History

lava *Lava* comes from a Latin word meaning "to fall" or "to slide." Lava slides or falls down after it flows from a volcano.

lava
(definition 1)

lav·a·to·ry (lav′ə tôr′ē), **1** a bowl or basin to wash one's hands and face in. **2** a bathroom; toilet. *noun, plural* **lav·a·to·ries.**

lav·en·der (lav′ən dər), **1** pale-purple. **2** a small shrub with stalks of thickly growing fragrant, pale-purple flowers. Oil from lavender is used in perfumes, and its dried flowers and leaves are used to add scent to clothes, rooms, and the like. **1** *adjective,* **2** *noun.*

lav·ish (lav′ish), **1** very free in giving or spending; extravagant: *A very rich person can be lavish with money.* **2** very abundant; too abundant; more than is needed: *a lavish helping of ice cream.* **3** to give or spend very freely or too freely: *We lavished kindness on our sick friend.* **1,2** *adjective,* **3** *verb.*

law (lô), **1** a rule made by a country or state for all the people who live there: *Good citizens obey the laws. There is a law against spitting in trains.* **2** a system of rules formed to protect society: *English law is not like French law.* **3** the study of such a system of rules; profession of a lawyer: *This student is planning a career in law.* **4** any rule or principle: *Scientists study the laws of nature. noun.*

law·ful (lô′fəl), according to law; done as the law directs; allowed by law; rightful: *a lawful trial, lawful arrests. adjective.*

law·less (lô′lis), **1** paying no attention to the law; breaking the law: *A criminal leads a lawless life.* **2** having no laws: *In pioneer days much of the West was lawless. adjective.*

law·mak·er (lô′mā′kər), a person who helps make the laws of a country: *Senators are lawmakers. noun.*

law·mak·ing (lô′mā′king), **1** having the duty and power of making laws; legislative: *Congress is a lawmaking body.* **2** the making of laws; legislation. **1** *adjective,* **2** *noun.*

lawn (lôn), a piece of land covered with grass kept closely cut, especially near or around a house. *noun.*
[An earlier spelling of *lawn* was *laund.* This came from an old French word meaning "a wooded ground" or "a wasteland."]

lawn·mow·er (lôn′mō′ər), lawn mower. *noun.*

lawn mower, a machine with revolving blades for cutting the grass on a lawn.

law·suit (lô′süt′), a case in a court of law started by one person to claim something from another. *noun.*

law·yer (lô′yər), a person who knows the laws and gives advice about matters of law or acts for others in a court of law. *noun.*

lax (laks), **1** loose; slack; not firm: *The package was tied so loosely that the cord was lax.* **2** not strict; careless: *Don't become lax about the schedule you set for studying. adjective.*

lay[1] (lā), **1** to put down: *Lay your hat on the table.* **2** to beat down: *A storm laid the crops low. A shower has laid the dust.* **3** to place in a lying-down position: *Lay the baby down gently.* **4** to place or set: *Lay your hand on your heart. The British laid a tax on tea.* **5** to put: *Lay aside that book for me.*

The horse laid its ears back. **6** to put in place: *to lay bricks. They laid the carpet on the floor.* **7** to produce an egg or eggs: *Birds, fish, and reptiles lay eggs. All the hens were laying well. verb,* **lays, laid, lay·ing.**

lay aside, lay away, or **lay by,** to save: *I laid away a dollar a week toward buying a bicycle.*

lay in, to put aside for the future; provide: *The trapper laid in enough supplies for the winter.*

lay off, 1 to put out of work: *During the slack season many workers were laid off.* **2** to mark off: *The coach laid off the boundaries of the tennis court.* **3** to stop teasing or interfering with: *Lay off me! I'm trying to study.*

lay up, to cause to stay in bed because of illness: *I was laid up with a bad cold last week.*

lay² (lā). See **lie².** *I lay down for a rest. verb.*

lay·er (lā′ər), **1** a thickness of some material: *There are about six layers of paint on this wall. A layer cake is made of two or more layers.* **2** a person or thing that lays: *That hen is a champion layer. noun.*

lay·man (lā′mən), a person outside of any particular profession: *It is hard for most laymen to understand doctors' prescriptions. noun, plural* **lay·men.**

lay·off (lā′ôf′), a temporary period of not working: *There's been a layoff at the factory because sales are down. noun.*

la·zi·ly (lā′zə lē), in a lazy manner: *The cat stretched lazily in the sunlight. adverb.*

la·zi·ness (lā′zē nis), a dislike of work; unwillingness to work or be active. *noun.*

la·zy (lā′zē), **1** not willing to work or be active: *He lost his job because he was lazy.* **2** moving slowly; not very active: *A lazy stream winds through the meadows. adjective,* **la·zi·er, la·zi·est.**

lb., pound. *plural* **lb.** or **lbs.**

lead¹ (lēd), **1** to show the way by going along with or in front of: *She led the horses to water.* **2** to be first among; go first: *She leads the class in social studies. You may lead this time.* **3** to be a way or road: *Hard work leads to success.* **4** to pass or spend time in some special way: *He leads a quiet life in the country.* **5** to direct: *A general leads an army. She leads the community orchestra. I led the singing.* **6** the place of leader; place in front: *He always takes the lead when we plan to do anything.* **7** the main part in a play or other performance. **8** the amount that one is ahead: *He had a lead of 3 yards in the race.* **9** a guiding indication; clue: *The librarian gave me several good leads for finding the book I wanted.* 1-5 *verb,* **leads, led, lead·ing;** 6-9 *noun.*

lead² (led), **1** a heavy, easily melted, bluish-gray metal, used to make pipe. Lead is a chemical element. **2** made of lead: *a lead pipe.* **3** bullets: *a hail of lead.* **4** a long thin piece of graphite used in pencils. 1,3,4 *noun,* 2 *adjective.*

lead·en (led′n), **1** made of lead: *a leaden coffin.* **2** heavy; hard to lift or move: *leaden arms tired from working.* **3** bluish-gray: *Do you suppose those leaden clouds may mean snow? adjective.*

a hat	i it	oi oil	ch child	a in about
ā age	ī ice	ou out	ng long	e in taken
ä far	o hot	u cup	sh she	ə = { i in pencil
e let	ō open	u̇ put	th thin	o in lemon
ē equal	ô order	ü rule	ʈʜ then	u in circus
ėr term			zh measure	

lead·er (lē′dər), a person who leads, or is well fitted to lead: *a band leader. She is a born leader. noun.*

lead·er·ship (lē′dər ship), **1** a being a leader. **2** the ability to lead: *Leadership is an asset to an officer.* **3** direction: *Our group needs some leadership. noun.*

leaf (lēf), **1** one of the thin, flat, green parts of a tree or other plant that grow on the stem or grow up from the roots. **2** to put forth leaves: *The trees along the river leaf earlier than those on the hill.* **3** a thin sheet or piece: *a leaf of a book, gold leaf.* **4** to turn the pages: *to leaf through a book.* **5** a flat movable piece in the top of a table: *We put two extra leaves in the table for the party.* 1,3,5 *noun, plural* **leaves;** 2,4 *verb.*

turn over a new leaf, to start all over again; try to do or be better in the future: *I promised to turn over a new leaf and study harder.*

leaf·less (lēf′lis), having no leaves. *adjective.*

leaf·let (lēf′lit), **1** a small flat or folded sheet of paper with printing on it: *advertising leaflets.* **2** a small or young leaf. *noun.*

leaf·y (lē′fē), having many leaves; covered with leaves. *adjective,* **leaf·i·er, leaf·i·est.**

league¹ (lēg), **1** a union of persons, parties, or nations formed to help one another. **2** an association of sports clubs or teams: *a baseball league. noun.*

league² (lēg), an old unit for measuring length or distance, usually about 3 miles (5 kilometers). *noun.*

leak (lēk), **1** a hole or crack not meant to be there that lets something in or out: *a leak in the roof.* **2** to go in or out through a hole or crack, or in ways suggesting a hole or crack: *Water leaked into the basement. The news leaked out.* **3** to let something in or out which is meant to stay where it is: *My boat leaks and lets water in. That pipe leaks gas.* 1 *noun,* 2,3 *verb.*

leak·age (lē′kij), **1** a leaking; entrance or escape by a leak. **2** that which leaks in or out. **3** the amount of leaking: *a leakage of a pailful an hour. noun.*

leak·y (lē′kē), having a leak or leaks; leaking: *a leaky faucet. adjective,* **leak·i·er, leak·i·est.**

lean¹ (lēn), **1** to stand slanting, not upright; bend: *The small tree leans over in the wind.* **2** to rest the body against something sloping or slanting for support: *Lean against me.* **3** to set or put in a leaning position: *Lean the ladder against the wall.* **4** to depend: *to lean on a friend's advice.* **5** to be inclined; tend: *My parents lean toward the candidate running for reelection. verb.*

lean² (lēn), **1** not fat; thin: *a lean and hungry stray* dog. **2** meat having little fat. **3** producing little; scant: *a lean harvest, a lean year for business.* 1,3 *adjective,* 2 *noun.*

lean-to (lēn′tü′), **1** a small building attached to another building, with a roof that slopes downward. **2** a rough shelter built against a tree or post. It is usually open on one side. *noun, plural* **lean-tos.**

leap (lēp), **1** a jump or spring. **2** to jump: *The basketball player leaped high to block his opponent.* **3** to jump over: *She leaped the wall.* 1 *noun,* 2,3 *verb,* **leaps, leaped** or **leapt, leap·ing.**

leap·frog (lēp′frog′), a game in which one player leaps over another who is bending over. *noun.*

leapt (lept *or* lēpt), leaped. See **leap.** *verb.*

leap year, a year having 366 days. The extra day is February 29.

learn (lėrn), **1** to gain knowledge or skill: *Some people learn slowly.* **2** to memorize: *to learn a poem by heart.* **3** to find out; come to know: *He learned that ¼ + ¼ = ½.* **4** to find out about; gain knowledge of: *She is learning science and math.* **5** to become able by study or practice: *In school we learn to read.* *verb,* **learns, learned, learn·ing.**

learn·ed (lėr′nid), showing or requiring knowledge; scholarly: *a learned professor.* *adjective.*

learn·ing (lėr′ning), the possession of knowledge gained by study; scholarship: *men and women of great learning.* *noun.*

lease (lēs), **1** the right to use property for a certain length of time by paying rent for it. **2** a written statement saying for how long a certain property is rented and how much money shall be paid for it. **3** to rent: *We have leased an apartment for one year.* 1,2 *noun,* 3 *verb,* **leas·es, leased, leas·ing.**

leash (lēsh), **1** a strap or chain for holding an animal in check: *He led the dog on a leash.* **2** to hold in with a leash; control: *She leashed her anger and did not say a harsh word.* 1 *noun, plural* **leash·es;** 2 *verb.*

least (lēst), **1** less than any other; smallest: *Ten cents is a little money; five cents is less; one cent is least.* **2** the smallest amount; smallest thing: *The least you can do is to thank him.* **3** to the smallest extent or degree: *She liked that book least of all.* 1 *adjective,* 2 *noun,* 3 *adverb.*

at least, 1 at the lowest estimate; not less than: *You should brush your teeth at least once a day.* **2** at any rate; in any case: *Even if you don't want to go swimming, at least you can come with me.*

leath·er (leŦH′ər), **1** a material made from the skins of animals by removing the hair and then tanning them: *Shoes are made of leather.* **2** made of leather: *leather gloves.* 1 *noun,* 2 *adjective.*

leath·er·y (leŦH′ər ē), like leather; tough: *a leathery face. adjective.*

leave[1] (lēv), **1** to go away; go away from: *We leave tonight. They left the room.* **2** to stop living in, belonging to, or working at or for: *to leave the country, to leave one's job.* **3** to go without taking;

let stay behind: *to leave a book on the table.* **4** to let stay in a certain condition: *He left the good-by unsaid. I was left alone as before. The story left him unmoved.* **5** to give money or property to someone, often by a will, when one dies: *She left a large fortune to her children.* **6** to give or hand over to someone else to do: *I left the driving to my sister.* **7** to not attend to: *I shall leave my homework till tomorrow.* *verb,* **leaves, left, leav·ing.**

leave off, to stop: *Continue the story from where I left off.*

leave out, 1 to not say, do, or put in: *She left out two words when she read the sentence.* **2** to neglect; forget: *Since everyone was busy, he felt that he was left out.*

leave[2] (lēv), **1** consent; permission: *Have I your leave to go?* **2** permission to be absent from duty. A **leave of absence** is an official permission to stay away from one's work, school, or military duty. **3** the length of time for which one has leave of absence: *The soldier went home for a fifteen-day leave. noun.*

take leave of, to say good-by to: *She took leave of her family before she went back to college.*

leaves (lēvz), more than one leaf: *oak leaves.* *noun plural.*

Leb·a·non (leb′ə nən), a country in southwestern Asia, on the Mediterranean. *noun.*

lec·ture (lek′chər), **1** a planned speech or talk on a chosen subject given before an audience. **2** to give a lecture: *The professor lectured on American history.* **3** a scolding: *My parents give me a lecture when I come home late.* **4** to scold: *My parents lectured me when they found out I had lied.* 1,3 *noun,* 2,4 *verb,* **lec·tures, lec·tured, lec·tur·ing.**

lec·tur·er (lek′chər ər), a person who lectures. *noun.*

led (led). See **lead**[1]. *She led her younger brother across the street. We were led through the cave by a guide. verb.*

ledge (lej), **1** a narrow shelf: *a window ledge.* **2** a shelf or ridge of rock. *noun.*

lee (lē), **1** the side or part sheltered from the wind: *The wind was so fierce that we ran to the lee of the house.* **2** sheltered from the wind: *the lee side of a ship.* 1 *noun,* 2 *adjective.*

leech (lēch), a worm living in ponds and streams that sucks the blood of animals. *noun, plural* **leech·es.**

leech—up to 8 inches (20 centimeters) long

leek (lēk), a vegetable somewhat like a long, thick, green onion. *noun.*

leer (lir), **1** a sly, nasty look to the side; evil glance. **2** to give a sly, evil glance: *The prisoner leered at the witness during the trial.* **1** *noun,* **2** *verb.*

left[1] (left), **1** belonging to the side of the less-used hand (in most people); having something to do with the side of anything that is turned west when the main side is turned north: *I sprained my left ankle. A person has a right hand and a left hand.* **2** on this side when viewed from the front: *Take a left turn at the next light.* **3** on or to the left side: *Turn left.* **4** the left side or hand: *He sat at my left.* **1,2** *adjective,* **3** *adverb,* **4** *noun.*

left[2] (left). See **leave**[1]. *He left his hat in the hall. A book was left on the desk. She left at four o'clock.* *verb.*

left-hand (left′hand′), **1** on or to the left. **2** of, for, or with the left hand. *adjective.*

left-hand·ed (left′han′did), **1** using the left hand more easily and readily than the right. **2** done with the left hand. **3** made to be used with the left hand. *adjective.*

left·o·ver (left′ō′vər), **1** a thing that is left. Scraps of food from a meal are leftovers. **2** that is left; remaining: *I made some sandwiches with the leftover meat.* **1** *noun,* **2** *adjective.*

leg (leg), **1** one of the parts of the body on which people and animals stand and move about. **2** the part of a garment that covers a leg: *I fell and tore my pants' leg.* **3** anything shaped or used like a leg; any support that is much longer than it is wide: *a table leg.* **4** one of the parts or stages of any course: *the last leg of a trip. noun.*

pull one's leg, to fool, trick, or make fun of one: *He believed me, but I was only pulling his leg.*

leg·a·cy (leg′ə sē), **1** the money or other property left to a person by the will of someone who has died. **2** something that has been handed down from an ancestor. *noun, plural* **leg·a·cies.**

le·gal (lē′gəl), **1** of law: *legal knowledge.* **2** of lawyers: *legal advice.* **3** according to law; lawful: *Hunting is legal only during certain seasons.* *adjective.*

leg·end (lej′ənd), **1** a story coming down from the past, which many people have believed: *The stories about Robin Hood are legends, not history.* **2** such stories as a group: *Legend tells us that King Arthur was brave.* **3** the words accompanying a picture, diagram, or map: *The legend underneath the picture tells us that the city is Rome. noun.*

leg·end·ar·y (lej′ən der′ē), of a legend or legends. *adjective.*

leg·gings (leg′ingz), extra outer coverings of cloth or leather for the legs, for use out of doors. *noun plural.*

leg·i·ble (lej′ə bəl), easy to read; plain and clear: *Her handwriting is quite large and legible. adjective.*

le·gion (lē′jən), **1** a division in the ancient Roman army containing several thousand soldiers on foot and several hundred horsemen. **2** a large group of soldiers; army. *noun.*

leg·is·late (lej′ə slāt), to make laws: *Congress*

legislates for the United States. verb, **leg·is·lates, leg·is·lat·ed, leg·is·lat·ing.**

leg·is·la·tion (lej′ə slā′shən), **1** the making of laws: *Congress has the power of legislation.* **2** the laws made: *Important legislation is reported in today's newspaper. noun.*

leg·is·la·tive (lej′ə slā′tiv), **1** having to do with making laws: *legislative reforms.* **2** having the duty and power of making laws: *Congress is a legislative body.* **3** ordered by law; made to be as it is by law: *a legislative decree. adjective.*

leg·is·la·tor (lej′ə slā′tər), a person who makes laws; member of a group that makes laws. Senators and Representatives are legislators. *noun.*

leg·is·la·ture (lej′ə slā′chər), a group of persons that has the duty and power of making laws for a state or country. Each state of the United States has a legislature. *noun.*

le·git·i·mate (lə jit′ə mit), rightful; lawful; allowed: *Sickness is a legitimate reason for a child's absence from school. adjective.*

lei (lā), a wreath of flowers or leaves worn as an ornament around the neck or on the head. *noun, plural* **leis.**

lei
The woman is wearing a **lei** of leaves and yellow flowers.

legendary—The **legendary** Pied Piper rid the town of its rats.

lei·sure (lē′zhər), **1** the time free from required work in which you may rest, amuse yourself, and do the things you like to do: *She's been too busy to have much leisure.* **2** free; not busy: *leisure hours.* **1** *noun,* **2** *adjective.*

lei·sure·ly (lē′zhər lē), without hurry; taking plenty of time: *a leisurely person, to stroll leisurely through the park. adjective, adverb.*

lem·ming (lem′ing), a small animal that looks like a mouse, with a short tail and furry feet. Lemmings live in cold northern regions. *noun.*

lemming—about 6 inches (15 centimeters) long with the tail

lem·on (lem′ən), **1** the sour, light-yellow, juicy fruit of a tree grown in warm climates. The juice of lemons is much used for flavoring and for making lemonade. **2** clear light-yellow. **3** flavored with lemon. **4** something or someone that is worthless or unpleasant: *This car is a lemon.* **1,4** *noun,* **2,3** *adjective.*

lem·on·ade (lem′ə nād′), a drink made of lemon juice, sugar, and water. *noun.*

lend (lend), **1** to let another have or use for a time: *Will you lend me your bicycle for an hour?* **2** to make a loan or loans: *Banks lend money and charge interest.* **3** to give; give for a time; add: *The lovely old furniture lent charm to the room. The Red Cross lends aid in time of disaster. verb,* **lends, lent, lend·ing.**

length (lengkth *or* length), **1** how long a thing is; what a thing measures from end to end; longest way a thing can be measured: *the length of a room, eight inches in length.* **2** how long something lasts or goes on: *the length of a visit, the length of a book.* **3** distance: *The length of this race is one mile.* **4** a long stretch or extent: *It's been quite a length of time since our last meeting.* **5** something of a given length: *a length of rope. noun.*

at length, 1 at last: *At length, after many delays, the meeting started.* **2** with all the details; in full: *They told of their adventures at length.*

keep at arm's length, to discourage from becoming friendly: *Some people can keep others at arm's length without seeming aloof.*

length·en (lengk′thən *or* leng′thən), to make or become longer: *The tailor can lengthen those pants. verb.*

length·ways (lengkth′wāz′ *or* length′wāz′), lengthwise. *adverb, adjective.*

length·wise (lengkth′wīz′ *or* length′wīz′), in the direction of the length: *She cut the cloth lengthwise. adverb, adjective.*

length·y (lengk′thē *or* leng′thē), long; too long: *His directions were so lengthy that everybody lost interest. adjective,* **length·i·er, length·i·est.**

len·ient (lē′nyənt), mild; gentle; merciful: *a lenient judge, a lenient punishment. adjective.*

lens (lenz), **1** a curved piece of glass, or something like glass, that will bring closer together or send wider apart the rays of light passing through it. The lenses of a telescope make things look larger and nearer. **2** the part of the eye that focuses light rays upon the retina. *noun, plural* **lens·es.**

lent (lent). See **lend.** *I lent you my pencil.' He had lent me his knife. verb.*

Lent (lent), the forty weekdays before Easter, observed in many Christian churches as a time for fasting and repenting of sins. *noun.*

len·til (len′tl), a vegetable much like a bean. Lentils are cooked like peas and are often eaten in soup. *noun.*

leop·ard (lep′ərd), a large cat of Africa and Asia, having a dull-yellowish fur spotted with black. Some leopards are black and may be called panthers. *noun.*

leopard—about 8 feet (2½ meters) long with the tail

le·o·tard (lē′ə tärd), a tight-fitting one-piece garment, with or without sleeves. Dancers and gymnasts wear leotards. *noun.*
[*Leotard* was named for Jules Léotard, a French gymnast who lived during the 1800's.]

leotard
She is wearing a colorful **leotard.**

lep·er (lep′ər), a person who has leprosy. *noun.*

lep·re·chaun (lep′rə kôn), (in Irish legends) an elf resembling a little old man, believed to own hidden gold. *noun.*

lep·ro·sy (lep′rə sē), an infectious disease that causes lumps, spots, and open sores. Leprosy attacks the skin and nerves and weakens muscles. *noun.*

less (les), **1** smaller: *of less width, less importance.* **2** not so much; not so much of: *to have less rain, to eat less meat.* **3** a smaller amount or quantity: *could do no less, to weigh less than before, to refuse to take less than $5.* **4** to a smaller extent or degree; not so; not so well: *less bright, less important, less known, less talked of.* **5** with something taken away; without: *five less two.* **1,2** *adjective,* **3** *noun,* **4** *adverb,* **5** *preposition.*

-less, a suffix meaning: **1** without a _____; that has no _____: Home*less* means *without a* home. **2** that does not _____: A tire*less* worker means a worker *that does not* tire. **3** that cannot be _____ed: Count*less* stars means stars *that cannot be* count*ed.*

less·en (les′n), to make or become less: *The fever lessened during the night. verb.*

less·er (les′ər), **1** less; smaller: *Instead of the mile, she chose to run the lesser distance.* **2** the less important of two. *adjective.*

les·son (les′n), **1** something to be learned or taught; something that has been learned or taught: *Children study many different lessons in school.* **2** a unit of teaching or learning; what is to be studied or taught at one time: *Tomorrow we study the tenth lesson. noun.*

lest (lest), for fear that: *Be careful lest you fall from that tree. conjunction.*

let (let), **1** to allow; permit: *Let the dog have a bone. They let the visitor on board the ship.* **2** to rent; hire out: *That woman lets rooms to students.* **3** *Let* is used in giving suggestions and commands: *"Let's go fishing" means "I suggest that we go fishing." Let all members do their duty. verb,* **lets, let, let·ting.**

let down, 1 to lower: *We let the box down from the roof.* **2** to slow up: *As their interest in the work wore off, they began to let down.* **3** to disappoint: *Don't let us down today; we're counting on you to win.*

let in, to admit; permit to enter: *Let in some fresh air.*

let off, to permit to go free: *I was let off with a warning to do better in the future.*

let on, 1 to allow to be known; reveal one's knowledge of: *He didn't let on that he knew their secret.* **2** to make believe; pretend: *She let on that she didn't see me.*

let out, 1 to permit to go out: *They let me out of the hospital too soon.* **2** to make larger: *Let out the hem on this skirt.* **3** to dismiss or be dismissed: *Our school lets out at three o'clock.*

let up, to stop; pause: *They never let up in the fight.*

let·down (let′doun′), **1** a slowing up. **2** a

disappointment: *Losing the contest was a big letdown for him. noun.*

let's (lets), let us.

let·ter (let′ər), **1** a mark or sign that stands for any one of the sounds that make up words. There are 26 letters in our alphabet. **2** to mark with letters: *Please letter a new sign.* **3** a written or printed message: *He told me about his vacation in a letter.* **1,3** *noun,* **2** *verb.*

to the letter, very exactly; just as one has been told: *I carried out your orders to the letter.*

letter carrier, a person who collects and delivers mail.

let·ter·ing (let′ər ing), **1** letters drawn, painted, or stamped. **2** the act of making letters. *noun.*

let·ter·per·fect (let′ər pèr′fikt), knowing one's part or lesson perfectly: *I practiced my part in the play until I was letter-perfect. adjective.*

let·tuce (let′is), the large, crisp leaves of a garden plant, used in a salad. *noun.*

let·up (let′up′), a stop or pause: *There was no letup in the storm. noun.*

lev·ee (lev′ē), **1** a bank built to keep a river from overflowing: *There are levees in many places along the lower Mississippi River.* **2** a landing place for boats. *noun.*

level (definition 4)

lev·el (lev′əl), **1** flat; even; having the same height everywhere: *a level floor.* **2** of equal height or importance: *The table is level with the sill of the window.* **3** something that is level. **4** an instrument for showing whether a surface is level. **5** to make level; put on the same level: *The builder leveled the ground with a bulldozer.* **6** to raise and hold level for shooting; aim: *She leveled her rifle at the target.* **7** height: *The flood rose to a level of 60 feet.* **8** a stage of learning or achievement; position; rank: *She reads at a high level for her class.* **9** to be truthful or frank: *He wouldn't level with me.* **1,2** *adjective,* **3,4,7,8** *noun,* **5,6,9** *verb.*

lev·el·head·ed (lev′əl hed′id), having good

common sense; sensible: *Levelheaded people stay calm in an emergency. adjective.*

lev·er (lev′ər *or* lē′vər), **1** a bar or board used for lifting a weight at one end by pushing down at the other end. It must be supported at any point in between by a fixed part called a fulcrum. A lever is a simple machine. **2** a bar or handle used to operate a machine. *noun.*

lev·y (lev′ē), **1** to order to be paid: *The government levies taxes to pay its expenses.* **2** money collected by authority or force. 1 *verb,* **lev·ies, lev·ied, lev·y·ing;** 2 *noun, plural* **lev·ies.**

li·a·ble (lī′ə bəl), **1** likely; unpleasantly likely: *That glass is liable to break. You are liable to slip on ice.* **2** responsible; bound by law to pay: *The Postal Service is not liable for damage to a parcel unless it is insured. adjective.*

li·ar (lī′ər), a person who tells lies; person who says what is not true. *noun.*

lib·er·al (lib′ər əl), **1** generous: *A liberal giver gives much.* **2** plentiful; abundant: *There was a liberal supply of food at the party.* **3** tolerant; not narrow in one's ideas: *a liberal thinker.* **4** a person favorable to progress and reforms. 1-3 *adjective,* 4 *noun.*

lib·er·al·i·ty (lib′ə ral′ə tē), generosity; generous act or behavior. *noun, plural* **lib·er·al·i·ties.**

lib·er·ate (lib′ə rāt′), to set free: *In 1865 the United States liberated all slaves. verb,* **lib·er·ates, lib·er·at·ed, lib·er·at·ing.**

Li·ber·i·a (lī bir′ē ə), a country in western Africa. *noun.*

lib·er·ty (lib′ər tē), **1** freedom: *In 1865 the United States granted liberty to all slaves. The American colonies won their liberty.* **2** the right or power to

do as one pleases; power or opportunity to do something: *liberty of speech.* **3** permission granted to a sailor to go ashore. **4** too great freedom: *She took liberties with the facts to make the story more interesting. noun, plural* **lib·er·ties.**

at liberty, 1 free: *The escaped lion is still at liberty.* **2** allowed; permitted: *You are at liberty to make any choice you please.* **3** not busy: *The doctor will see us as soon as she is at liberty.*

[*Liberty* comes from a Latin word meaning "free." The English words *liberal, liberality,* and *liberate* all come from the same Latin root.]

li·brar·i·an (lī brer′ē ən), **1** a person in charge of a library. **2** a person trained for work in a library. *noun.*

li·brar·y (lī′brer′ē), **1** a collection of books, magazines, films, or recordings. Libraries may be public or private. **2** a room or building where such a collection is kept for public use and borrowing. *noun, plural* **li·brar·ies.**

Lib·y·a (lib′ē ə), a country in northern Africa. *noun.*

lice (līs), more than one louse. *noun plural.*

li·cense (lī′sns), **1** permission given by law to do something: *A license to drive an automobile is issued by the state.* **2** a paper, card, or plate showing such permission: *The policeman asked the reckless driver for his license.* **3** to permit by law: *A doctor is licensed to practice medicine.* **4** a being allowed to do something: *The farm family gave us license to fish in their brook.* 1,2,4 *noun,* 3 *verb,* **li·cens·es, li·censed, li·cens·ing.**

li·chen (lī′kən), a living thing that looks somewhat like moss. It grows in patches on rocks, trees, and other surfaces. Lichens are gray, yellow, brown, black, or greenish in color. *noun.*

lichen on a tree trunk

lick (lik), **1** to pass the tongue over: *to lick a stamp.* **2** to lap up with the tongue: *The cat licked the milk.* **3** a stroke of the tongue over something: *She gave the ice-cream cone a big lick.* **4** to pass about or play over like a tongue: *The flames were licking the roof of the burning house.* **5** a place where natural salt is found and where animals go to lick it up. **6** a blow: *I lost the fight, but I got in a few good licks.* **7** to beat or thrash. **8** to defeat in a fight; conquer. **9** a small quantity: *They didn't do a lick of work.* 1,2,4,7,8 *verb*, 3,5,6,9 *noun*.

lick·e·ty-split (lik′ə tē split′), at full speed; rapidly: *He ran lickety-split after the dog. adverb.*

lic·or·ice (lik′ər is *or* lik′ər ish), a black, sweet-tasting substance obtained from the dried root of a plant. Licorice is used in medicine and candy. *noun.*
[*Licorice* comes from two Greek words meaning "sweet" and "root."]

lid (lid), **1** a movable cover; top: *the lid of a box, a jar lid.* **2** an eyelid. *noun.*

lie[1] (lī), **1** something said that is not true; something that is not true said to deceive: *I went to school today; saying I didn't is a lie.* **2** to speak falsely; tell a lie: *He says that he has never lied, but I think he is lying when he says it.* 1 *noun*, 2 *verb*, **lies, lied, ly·ing.**

lie[2] (lī), **1** to have one's body in a flat position along the ground or other surface: *to lie on the grass, to lie in bed.* **2** to rest on a surface: *The book was lying on the table.* **3** to be kept or stay in a given state: *to lie idle, to lie hidden, to lie unused.* **4** to be; be placed: *a lake that lies to the south of us, a road that lies among trees, a ship lying offshore at anchor.* **5** to exist; be found to be: *The cure for ignorance lies in education. verb,* **lies, lay, lain, ly·ing.**

lieu·ten·ant (lü ten′ənt), **1** a person who acts in the place of someone higher in authority: *The scoutmaster used the two boys as his lieutenants.* **2** an army, air force, or marine officer ranking next below a captain. **3** an officer in the navy ranking much below a captain. In the navy the order is captain, commander, lieutenant commander, lieutenant, lieutenant junior grade, ensign. *noun.*

life (līf), **1** a being alive; living. People, animals, plants, bacteria, and all living things have life; rocks and metals do not. Life is shown by growing and reproducing. **2** the time of being alive: *During her life she was an outstanding doctor.* **3** a living being; person: *Five lives were lost.* **4** living things: *The desert island had almost no animal or vegetable life.* **5** a way of living: *a country life, a dull life.* **6** an account of a person's life: *Several lives of Lincoln have been written.* **7** spirit; vigor: *Put more life into your work.* **8** a period of being in power or able to operate: *The life of that government was very short. noun, plural* **lives.**

life belt, a life preserver in the form of a belt.

life·boat (līf′bōt′), a strong, open boat with oars, specially built for saving lives at sea. Lifeboats are usually carried aboard larger boats. *noun.*

life buoy, a cork or plastic ring, belt, or vest used as a life preserver; buoy.

life cycle, all the stages of development that a living thing passes through during its life.

life·guard (līf′gärd′), a person employed on a bathing beach or at a swimming pool to help in case of accident or danger to bathers. *noun.*

life jacket, a sleeveless jacket filled with a light

a hat	i it	oi oil	ch child		a in about
ā age	ī ice	ou out	ng long		e in taken
ä far	o hot	u cup	sh she	ə =	i in pencil
e let	ō open	u̇ put	th thin		o in lemon
ē equal	ô order	ü rule	ŦH then		u in circus
ėr term			zh measure		

material or with air, worn as a life preserver.

life·less (līf′lis), **1** without life: *a lifeless planet.* **2** dead: *The lifeless body floated ashore.* **3** dull: *a lifeless party. adjective.*

life·like (līf′līk′), like life; looking as if alive; like the real thing: *a lifelike portrait. adjective.*

life·long (līf′lông′), lasting all one's life: *a lifelong friendship. adjective.*

life preserver, a wide belt, ring, or vest made of plastic or cork, used to keep a person afloat in the water.

life·sav·ing (līf′sā′ving), **1** a saving of people's lives; keeping people from drowning. **2** designed or used to save people's lives. 1 *noun*, 2 *adjective.*

life-size (līf′sīz′), the same size as the living thing: *a life-size statue. adjective.*

life·time (līf′tīm′), the time of being alive; period during which a life lasts: *My grandparents have seen many changes in their lifetime. noun.*

lift (lift), **1** to raise; raise up higher; raise into the air; take up; pick up: *Please help me lift this heavy box.* **2** to rise and go; go away: *The fog lifted at dawn.* **3** to go up; be raised: *Mother's spirits lifted when she received the promotion.* **4** an elevating influence or result; a raising of the spirits: *Mother's promotion gave her a big lift.* **5** the act of lifting: *the lift of a helping hand.* **6** the distance through which a thing is lifted. **7** a helping hand: *Give me a lift with this job.* **8** a ride in a vehicle given to a traveler on foot; free ride: *Can you give me a lift home?* 1-3 *verb*, 4-8 *noun.*

lift·off (lift′ôf′), the firing or launching of a rocket. *noun.*

lig·a·ment (lig′ə mənt), a band of strong tissue that connects bones or holds organs of the body in place. *noun.*

light[1] (līt), **1** that by which we see: *The sun gives light to the earth.* **2** a thing that gives light. The sun, a lamp, or a lighthouse is called a light. **3** a supply of light: *A tall building cuts off our light.* **4** to cause to give light: *She lighted the lamp.* **5** to give light to; fill with light: *The room is lighted by six windows.* **6** bright; clear: *It was a moonlit night as light as day.* **7** brightness; clearness: *a strong or dim light.* **8** a bright part: *light and shade in a painting.* **9** to make bright or clear: *Her face was lighted by a smile.* **10** to become light: *The sky lights up at dawn.* **11** daytime: *The baker gets up before light.* **12** pale in color; approaching white: *light hair, light blue.* **13** to set fire to: *I lighted the candles.* **14** to take fire: *Matches light when you scratch them.* **15** knowledge; information: *We need more light on this subject.* **16** open view: *The reporter brought to light bribery in the city* *government.* **17** the aspect in which a thing is viewed: *The principal put the matter in the right light.* 1-3,7,8,11,15-17 *noun,* 4,5,9,10,13,14 *verb,* **lights, light·ed** or **lit, light·ing;** 6,12 *adjective.*

light[2] (līt), **1** easy to carry; not heavy: *a light load.* **2** having little weight for its size: *Feathers are light.* **3** having less than usual weight: *light summer clothing.* **4** less than usual in amount or force: *a light sleep, a light rain, a light meal.* **5** easy to bear or do: *light punishment, a light task.* **6** not looking heavy; graceful; delicate: *a light bridge, light carving.* **7** moving easily: *a light step.* **8** cheerfully careless; gay: *a light laugh.* **9** not serious enough: *a light mind, light of purpose.* **10** not important: *light losses.* **11** sandy: *a light soil. adjective.*

light[3] (līt), **1** to come down to the ground; alight: *She lighted from her horse.* **2** to come down from flight: *A bird lighted on the branch. verb,* **lights, light·ed** or **lit, light·ing.**

light out, to leave suddenly; go away quickly.

light·en[1] (līt′n), to brighten; become brighter: *The sky lightens before the dawn. Her face lightened. verb.*

light·en[2] (līt′n), **1** to reduce the load of; make or become lighter: *Your help lightened our work.* **2** to make or become more cheerful: *The good news lightened our hearts. verb.*

light·head·ed (līt′hed′id), dizzy; giddy; out of one's head: *The fever made me feel light-headed. adjective.*

light·heart·ed (līt′här′tid), without worry; carefree; cheerful; gay. *adjective.*

light·house (līt′hous′), a tower or framework with a bright light that shines far over the water. It is often located at a dangerous place to warn and guide ships. *noun, plural* **light·hous·es** (līt′hou′ziz).

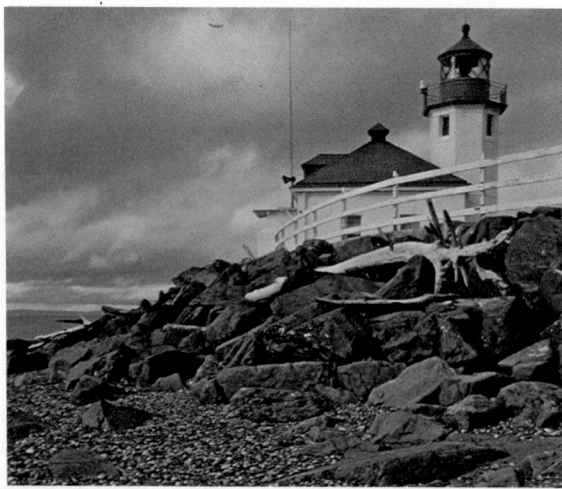
lighthouse

light·ning (līt′ning), a flash of electricity in the sky. The sound that it makes is thunder. *noun.*
lightning bug, a firefly.
lightning rod, a metal rod fixed on a building or ship to conduct lightning into the earth or water.

light-weight (līt′wāt′), not heavy; light in weight: *We packed the food in lightweight containers. adjective.*

light-year (līt′yir′), a unit of length used to measure distances in outer space. It is equal to the distance that light travels in one year, about six thousand billion (6,000,000,000,000) miles (ten thousand billion kilometers). *noun.*

lik·a·ble (līk′ə bəl), having qualities that win good will or friendship; pleasing; popular: *a very likable person. adjective.*

like[1] (līk), **1** much the same as; similar: *Our house is like theirs. I had a dollar and she had a like amount.* **2** such as one would expect of: *Isn't it just like them to be late?* **3** in the right condition for: *I feel like working.* **4** giving promise of: *It looks like rain.* **5** a person or thing like another; equal: *We shall not see his like again.* **6** in the same way as; as: *Snakes attract him like puppies attract most people.* 1-4 *preposition,* 1 *adjective,* 5 *noun,* 6 *conjunction.*

and the like, and other like things: *At the zoo we saw elephants, tigers, lions, and the like.*

like[2] (līk), **1** to be pleased with; be satisfied with: *Cats like milk.* **2** to have a kindly or friendly feeling for: *I like my friends and they like me.* **3** to wish or prefer; wish for: *I would like more time to finish this. Come whenever you like.* **4** **likes,** likings; preferences: *You know all my likes and dislikes.* 1-3 *verb,* **likes, liked, lik·ing;** 4 *noun.*

-like—bird**like**, pig**like**, elephant**like**, rabbit**like**, monkey**like**

-like, a suffix meaning: like; similar to: Daisy*like* means *like* a daisy.

like·li·hood (līk′lē húd), a strong chance; probability: *Is there any likelihood of rain today? noun.*

like·ly (līk′lē), **1** probable: *One likely result of this heavy rain is the rising of the river.* **2** probably: *I shall very likely be at home all day.* **3** to be expected: *It is likely to be hot in August.*

4 promising; suitable: *Is this a likely place to fish?*
1,3,4 *adjective,* **like·li·er, like·li·est;** 2 *adverb.*

lik·en (lī′kən), to compare; represent as like: *The young woman's voice was likened to that of a famous singer. verb.*

like·ness (līk′nis), 1 a resembling; being alike: *The boy's likeness to his father was striking.* 2 something that is like; picture: *This photograph is a good likeness of you.* 3 appearance; shape: *That cloud has the likeness of a dog. noun, plural* **like·ness·es.**

like·wise (līk′wīz′), 1 the same: *See what I do. Now you do likewise.* 2 also; moreover; too: *I must go home now, and you likewise. adverb.*

lik·ing (lī′king), preference; fondness; kindly feeling: *a liking for apples, a liking for children. noun.*

li·lac (lī′lək), 1 a shrub with clusters of tiny, fragrant, pale pinkish-purple or white flowers. 2 pale pinkish-purple. 1 *noun,* 2 *adjective.*
[*Lilac* comes from a Persian word meaning "bluish in color." The flowers of some varieties of lilac are bluish.]

lilt (lilt), 1 to sing or play a tune in a light, tripping manner. 2 a lively song or tune with a swing. 3 a lively, springing movement: *She walks with a lilt.* 1 *verb,* 2,3 *noun.*

lil·y (lil′ē), a plant with tall, slender stems and large, showy, bell-shaped flowers. The flowers are often divided into six parts. Lilies grow from bulbs. The white lily is a symbol of purity. *noun, plural* **lil·ies.**

lily of the valley, a plant having tiny, sweet-smelling, bell-shaped white flowers arranged up and down a single flower stem. *plural* **lilies of the valley.**

li·ma bean (lī′mə bēn′), a broad, flat, pale-green bean, used as a vegetable.
[The lima bean was first grown in tropical parts of South America and in Central America. It was named for *Lima,* the capital of Peru.]

limb (lim), 1 a leg, arm, or wing. 2 a large branch: *They sawed the dead limb off the tree. noun.*

lim·ber (lim′bər), 1 bending easily; flexible: *A piano player should have limber fingers. Willow is a limber wood.* 2 to make or become limber: *He is stiff when he begins to skate, but limbers up quickly.* 1 *adjective,* 2 *verb.*

lime[1] (līm), a white substance obtained by burning limestone, shells, or bones. Lime is used in making mortar and on fields to improve the soil. *noun.*

lime[2] (līm), the light-green, juicy fruit of a tree grown in warm climates. Limes are like lemons, but are smaller and sourer. The juice of limes is used for flavoring. *noun.*

lime·ade (līm′ād′), a drink made of lime juice, sugar, and water. *noun.*

lim·er·ick (lim′ər ik), a kind of humorous verse of five lines. *noun.*

lime·stone (līm′stōn′), a rock used for building and for making lime. Marble is a kind of limestone. *noun.*

a hat	i it	oi oil	ch child	(a in about
ā age	ī ice	ou out	ng long	e in taken
ä far	o hot	u cup	sh she	ə = { i in pencil
e let	ō open	ù put	th thin	o in lemon
ē equal	ô order	ü rule	ŦH then	(u in circus
ėr term			zh measure	

lim·it (lim′it), 1 the farthest point or edge; where something ends or must end: *the limit of one's vision. I have reached the limit of my patience.* 2 **limits,** boundary: *Keep within the limits of the school grounds.* 3 to set a limit to; restrict: *We must limit the expense to $10.* 1,2 *noun,* 3 *verb.*

lim·i·ta·tion (lim′ə tā′shən), a limiting; restriction: *There was no limitation on the amount of wood we could cut for the fireplace. noun.*

lim·it·ed (lim′ə tid), kept within limits; restricted: *limited space, a limited number of seats. adjective.*

limp[1] (limp), 1 a lame step or walk. 2 to walk with a limp: *After my fall, I limped for a few days.* 1 *noun,* 2 *verb.*

limp[2] (limp), not at all stiff; ready to bend or droop: *Spaghetti gets limp when cooked. adjective.*

Lin·coln (ling′kən), the capital of Nebraska. *noun.*

lin·den (lin′dən), a shade tree with heart-shaped leaves and clusters of small, sweet-smelling yellowish flowers. *noun.*

line[1] (līn), 1 a piece of rope, cord, or wire: *a telephone line.* 2 a cord for measuring or making level. A plumb line has a plumb at the end of a line and is used to find the depth of water or to see if a wall is vertical. 3 a long narrow mark: *Draw two lines here.* 4 anything that is like a long narrow mark: *the lines in your face.* 5 to mark with lines: *Please line your paper with a pencil and ruler.* 6 to cover with lines: *a face lined with age.* 7 a straight line: *The lower edges of the two pictures are about on a line.* 8 (in mathematics) the path traced by a moving point. It has length, but no thickness. 9 an edge or boundary: *the line between Texas and Mexico.* 10 a row of persons or things: *a line of chairs.* 11 to arrange in line: *Line your shoes along the edge of the shelf.* 12 to form a line along: *Cars lined the road for a mile.* 13 a row of words on a page or in a newspaper column: *a column of 40 lines.* 14 a short letter; note: *Drop me a line.* 15 a connected series of persons or things following one another in time: *trace back one's family line.* 16 a system of transportation: *a bus line, a subway line.* 17 a branch of business; kind of activity: *This is not my line.* 18 a kind or brand of goods: *This store carries the best line of shoes in town.* 19 **lines,** words that an actor speaks in a play: *to forget one's lines.* 20 in football: **a** the line of scrimmage. **b** the players along the line of scrimmage at the start of a play. 1-4,7-10,13-20 *noun,* 5,6,11,12 *verb,* **lines, lined, lin·ing.**
in line, in agreement: *His plan is in line with mine.*
line up, to form a line; form into a line: *Cars were lined up along the road for a mile.*

line² (līn), **1** to put a layer of paper, cloth, or felt inside a dress, hat, box, or bag. **2** to serve as a lining for: *This piece of silk would line your coat very nicely. verb,* **lines, lined, lin·ing.**

lin·e·age (lin′ē ij), **1** descent in a direct line from an ancestor. **2** a family; race. *noun.*

lin·e·ar (lin′ē ər), **1** made of lines; making use of lines: *linear designs.* **2** of length: *An inch is a linear measure. adjective.*

line graph, a graph in which points that stand for quantities are marked on a diagram and then connected by a series of short straight lines.

line graph
This **line graph** shows the temperature of a winter day for 12 hours.

line·man (līn′mən), **1** a person who sets up or repairs telephone or electric wires. **2** (in football) a player in the line; a center, guard, tackle, or end. *noun, plural* **line·men.**

lin·en (lin′ən), **1** cloth or thread made from flax **2** articles made of linen or some substitute. Tablecloths, napkins, sheets, towels, and shirts are all called linen. **3** made of linen. 1,2 *noun,* 3 *adjective.*

line of scrimmage, (in football) an imaginary line running across the field at any point where the ball is placed after a play has ended.

lin·er¹ (lī′nər), a ship or airplane belonging to a transportation system, *noun.*

lin·er² (lī′nər), a thing that lines or serves as a lining: *I put a fresh liner in the bottom of my desk drawer. noun.*

line segment, any part of a line. A line segment begins at one point on a line and ends at a second point.

line·up (līn′up′), **1** an arrangement of people or things in a line. A police lineup is an arrangement of a group of persons for identification. **2** (in sports) a list of the players taking part in a game. *noun.*

lin·ger (ling′gər), to stay on; go slowly, as if unwilling to leave: *She lingered after the others had left. verb.*

lin·go (ling′gō), language or talk that sounds strange or is not understood: *baseball lingo. noun, plural* **lin·goes.**

lin·ing (lī′ning), **1** a layer of material covering the inner surface of something: *the lining of a coat.* **2** See **line².** 1 *noun,* 2 *verb.*

link (lingk), **1** any ring or loop of a chain. **2** anything that joins or connects as a link does: *a cuff link. Fingerprints found at the scene of the crime formed a link in the chain of evidence against*

the burglary suspect. **3** to join as a link does; unite or connect: *Don't try to link me with this scheme.* 1,2 *noun,* 3 *verb.*

linking verb, a verb with little or no meaning of its own. It connects a noun or pronoun subject with a following adjective or noun. In "The trees are maples" and "He is a student," *are* and *is* are linking verbs.

links (lingks), a golf course. *noun plural.*

li·no·le·um (lə nō′lē əm), a floor covering made by putting a hard surface of ground cork mixed with linseed oil on a canvas back. *noun.*

lin·seed oil (lin′sēd′ oil′), a yellowish oil obtained by pressing the seed of flax. It is used in making paints and printing inks.

lint (lint), tiny bits of thread or fluff of any material. *noun.*

lin·tel (lin′tl), a horizontal beam or stone above a door or window to support the structure above it. *noun.*

li·on (lī′ən), a large cat of Africa and southern Asia that has a dull-yellowish coat. The male has a full, flowing mane of coarse hair. *noun.*

li·on·ess (lī′ə nis), a female lion. *noun, plural* **li·on·ess·es.**

lip (lip), **1** either one of the two fleshy, movable edges of the mouth. **2** the folding or bent-out edge of any opening: *the lip of a pitcher. noun.*

lip·stick (lip′stik′), a small stick of a waxlike substance, used for coloring the lips. *noun.*

liq·ue·fy (lik′wə fī), to make liquid; become liquid. *verb,* **liq·ue·fies, liq·ue·fied, liq·ue·fy·ing.**

liq·uid (lik′wid), **1** any substance that is not a solid or a gas; substance that flows freely like water. **2** in the form of a liquid; melted: *liquid soap, butter heated until it is liquid.* **3** clear and smooth-flowing in sound: *the liquid notes of a bird.* 1 *noun,* 2,3 *adjective.*

liq·uor (lik′ər), an alcoholic drink, such as brandy or whiskey. *noun.*

lisp (lisp), **1** to say the sounds of *th* as in *thin* and *then* instead of *s* or *z* in speaking: *A person who lisps might say, "Thing a thong" for "Sing a song."* **2** the act of saying a *th* sound for *s* and *z*: *I used to speak with a lisp.* 1 *verb,* 2 *noun.*

list¹ (list), **1** a series of names, numbers, words, or phrases: *a shopping list.* **2** to make a list of; enter in a list: *A dictionary lists words in alphabetical order.* 1 *noun,* 2 *verb.*

list² (list), **1** a tipping of a ship to one side; a tilt.

2 to tip to one side; tilt: *The sinking ship was listing so that water lapped its decks.* **1** *noun,* **2** *verb.*

lis·ten (lis′n), to try to hear; pay attention to in order to hear: *We listened for the sound of their car. I like to listen to music.* *verb.*

listen in, 1 to listen to others talking on a telephone: *I listened in on the extension to hear what they were saying.* **2** to listen to the radio: *Listen in next week for the names of the winners of the contest.*

list·less (list′lis), seeming too tired to care about anything; not interested in things; not caring to be active: *a dull and listless mood.* *adjective.*

lit¹ (lit), lighted. See **light¹.** *Have you lit the candles?* *verb.*

lit² (lit), lighted. See **light³.** *Two birds lit on my window sill.* *verb.*

li·ter (lē′tər), a unit of volume in the metric system, used for measuring liquids. *noun.*

lit·er·al (lit′ər əl), **1** following the exact words of the original: *The student made a literal translation into English of the letter written in Spanish.* **2** true to fact: *The reporter wrote a literal account of the fire.* *adjective.*

lit·er·al·ly (lit′ər ə lē), **1** word for word; without exaggeration; without imagination: *Write the story literally as it happened.* **2** actually: *The earthquake literally destroyed hundreds of homes.* *adverb.*

lit·er·ar·y (lit′ə rer′ē), having to do with literature. *adjective.*

lit·er·ate (lit′ər it), able to read and write. *adjective.*

lit·er·a·ture (lit′ər chür *or* lit′ər ə chər), **1** the writings of a period or of a country, especially those kept alive by their beauty of style or thought: *Shakespeare is a great name in English literature.* **2** all the books and articles on a subject: *the literature of stamp collecting.* *noun.*

lithe (līᴛʜ), bending easily; supple. *adjective.*

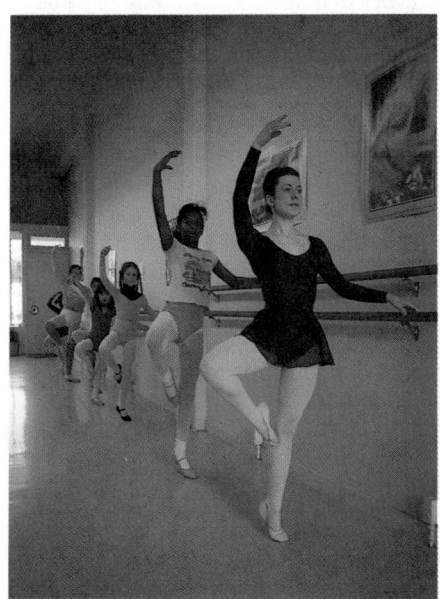

lithe—A ballet dancer must develop a **lithe** body.

a hat	i it	oi oil	ch child		a in about
ā age	ī ice	ou out	ng long		e in taken
ä far	o hot	u cup	sh she	ə =	i in pencil
e let	ō open	u̇ put	th thin		o in lemon
ē equal	ô order	ü rule	ᴛʜ then		u in circus
ėr term			zh measure		

Lith·u·a·ni·a (lith′ü ā′nē ə), a country in northern Europe. *noun.*

lit·mus pa·per (lit′məs pā′pər), paper treated with a blue dye. Blue litmus paper will turn red if put into an acid. Red litmus paper will turn blue if put into a base.

lit·ter (lit′ər), **1** little bits left about in disorder; things scattered about: *We picked up the litter.* **2** to scatter things about; leave odds and ends lying around; make untidy: *You have littered the room with your papers.* **3** the young animals produced at one time: *a litter of puppies.* **4** a stretcher for carrying a sick or wounded person. **5** a framework to be carried on men's shoulders, or by beasts of burden, with a couch usually enclosed by curtains. **1,3-5** *noun,* **2** *verb.*

litter (definition 5)

lit·ter·bug (lit′ər bug′), a person who throws trash on a road or sidewalk, or in a park. *noun.*

lit·tle (lit′l), **1** not big or large; small. A grain of sand or the head of a pin is little. **2** short; not long in time or in distance: *Wait a little while and I'll go a little way with you.* **3** not much: *A very sick child has little strength and can eat only a little food.* **4** a small amount: *I ate only a little.* **5** a short time or distance: *Move a little to the left. After a little you will feel better.* **6** to a small extent: *The teacher read from a book that was little known to us.* **1-3** *adjective,* **less** or **less·er, least,** or **lit·tler, lit·tlest; 4,5** *noun,* **6** *adverb* **less, least.**

little by little, by a small amount at a time; slowly; gradually.

Little League, a group of baseball teams organized for children from eight to twelve years of age.

Little Rock, the capital of Arkansas.

liv·a·ble (liv′ə bəl), fit to live in: *a livable house.* *adjective.*

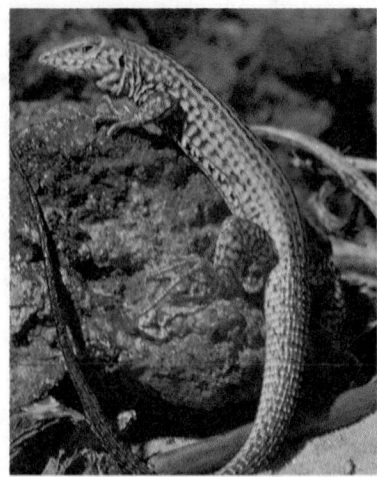

lizard—about 1 foot (30 centimeters) long

live¹ (liv), **1** to have life; be alive; exist: *All creatures have an equal right to live.* **2** to remain alive: *We could not live long without water.* **3** to keep up life: *Most people live by working.* **4** to dwell: *live in the country. Who lives in this house? verb,* **lives, lived, liv·ing.**

live² (līv), **1** having life; alive: *a live dog.* **2** burning or glowing: *live coals.* **3** carrying an electric current: *a live wire.* **4** loaded: *a live cartridge.* **5** not previously recorded on tape or film; broadcast during the actual performance: *a live television show. adjective.*

live·li·hood (līv′lē hủd), a means of living; support: *to write for a livelihood, to farm for a livelihood. noun.*

live·li·ness (līv′lē nis), vigor; activity; gaiety. *noun.*

live·long (liv′lông′), the whole length of; whole; entire: *We were busy the livelong day. adjective.*

live·ly (līv′lē), **1** full of life and spirit; active: *A good night's sleep made us all lively again.* **2** bright; vivid: *lively colors.* **3** cheerful; gay: *a lively conversation.* **4** in a lively manner. 1-3 *adjective,* **live·li·er, live·li·est;** 4 *adverb.*

liv·er (liv′ər), **1** the large, reddish-brown organ in people and animals that makes bile and helps the body absorb food. **2** the liver of an animal used as food. *noun.*

liv·er·y (liv′ər ē), **1** any uniform provided for servants, or adopted by a group or profession: *A nurse's livery is often white.* **2** a stable where horses are taken care of for pay or hired out. *noun, plural* **liv·er·ies.**

lives (līvz), more than one life. *noun plural.*

live·stock (līv′stok′), farm animals. Cows, horses, sheep, and pigs are livestock. *noun.*

liv·id (liv′id), **1** having a dull bluish or grayish color, as from a bruise. **2** very pale: *livid with rage. adjective.*

liv·ing (liv′ing), **1** having life; being alive: *a living plant.* **2** the condition of being alive: *The young people were filled with the joy of living.* **3** a means of keeping alive; livelihood: *She earns her living as a reporter.* **4** manner of life: *We enjoy country living.* **5** full of life; vigorous; strong; active: *a living faith.* **6** in actual existence; still in use; alive: *living languages.* **7** true to life; vivid: *a picture which is the living image of a person.* **8** of life; for living in: *the poor living conditions in the slums.* **9** sufficient to live on: *a living wage.* **10** See **live**¹. 1,5-9 *adjective,* 2-4 *noun,* 10 *verb.*

living room, a room for general family use.

liz·ard (liz′ərd), a reptile somewhat like a snake, but with four legs and a thicker body. *noun.*

lla·ma (lä′mə), a South American animal somewhat like a camel, but smaller and without a hump. Llamas have woolly hair and are used as beasts of burden. *noun, plural* **lla·mas** or **lla·ma.**

llamas—about 4 feet (1 meter) high at the shoulder

lo (lō), look! see! behold! *interjection.*

load (lōd), **1** what one is carrying; burden: *The cart has a load of hay. That's a load off my mind.* **2** the amount that usually is carried: *four loads of sand.* **3** to put in or put on whatever is to be carried: *to load a ship. He loaded the camera with film.* **4** one charge of powder and shot for a gun. **5** to put a charge in a gun: *The pioneer loaded his musket with powder and shot.* 1,2,4 *noun,* 3,5 *verb.*

loaf¹ (lōf), **1** bread baked as one piece. **2** anything like a loaf in shape. Meat loaf is meat chopped and mixed with other things and then baked. *noun, plural* **loaves.**

loaf² (lōf), to spend time idly; do nothing: *I can loaf all day Saturday. verb.*

loam (lōm), rich, fertile earth; earth in which decaying leaves and other plant matter are mixed with clay and sand. *noun.*

loan (lōn), **1** letting another have and use for a time; lending: *She asked for a loan of his pen.* **2** anything that is lent, especially money: *He asked his brother for a small loan.* **3** to make a loan; lend: *Her friend loaned her the money.* 1,2 *noun,* 3 *verb.*

loath (lōth), unwilling: *The little boy was loath to leave his father. adjective.*

loathe (lōᴛʜ), to feel strong dislike and disgust for; abhor; hate: *We loathe rotten food or a nasty smell. verb,* **loathes, loathed, loath·ing.**

loath·ing (lō′ᴛʜing), a strong dislike and disgust. *noun.*

loath·some (lōᴛH′səm), disgusting; making one feel sick: *Rotten meat has a loathsome odor.* *adjective.*

loaves (lōvz), more than one loaf. *noun plural.*

lob (lob), **1** a ball hit or thrown in a high arc. **2** to hit or throw a ball in a high arc. **1** *noun,* **2** *verb,* **lobs, lobbed, lob·bing.**

lob·by (lob′ē), **1** an entrance hall; passageway: *the lobby of a theater. A hotel lobby usually has chairs and couches to sit on.* **2** a person or persons that try to influence members of a lawmaking body. **3** to try to influence the members of a lawmaking body: *The conservation group lobbied to outlaw the use of certain traps by hunters.* **1,2** *noun, plural* **lob·bies; 3** *verb,* **lob·bies, lob·bied, lob·by·ing.**

lobe (lōb), a rounded part that sticks out or down. The lobe of the ear is the lower rounded end. *noun.*

lob·ster (lob′stər), a shellfish having five pairs of legs, with large claws on the front pair. Lobsters are used for food. Their shells turn a bright red when boiled. *noun.*

lobster—1 to 2 feet (30 to 60 centimeters) long with the claws

lo·cal (lō′kəl), **1** of a place; having something to do with a certain place or places: *the local doctor, local news.* **2** of just one part of the body: *a local application of sunburn ointment.* **3** making all, or almost all, stops: *a local train.* **4** a train, bus, subway, or the like, that makes all, or almost all, of the stops on its route. **1-3** *adjective,* **4** *noun.*

lo·cal·i·ty (lō kal′ə tē), place; region; one place and the places near it: *She knows many people in the locality of Boston. noun, plural* **lo·cal·i·ties.**

lo·cate (lō′kāt), **1** to establish in a place: *They have located their new store on Second Avenue.* **2** to establish oneself in a place: *Early settlers located where there was water.* **3** to find out the exact position of: *We followed the stream until we located its source.* **4** to state or show the position of: *Can you locate Africa on the globe? verb,* **lo·cates, lo·cat·ed, lo·cat·ing.**
be located, to lie or be situated: *The capital is located on a river.*

lo·ca·tion (lō kā′shən), **1** a locating or a being located: *The scouts argued about the location of the camp.* **2** position or place: *The camp was in a bad location as there was no water near it. noun.*

a hat	i it	oi oil	ch child	(a in about
ā age	ī ice	ou out	ng long	e in taken
ä far	o hot	u cup	sh she	ə = { i in pencil
e let	ō open	u̇ put	th thin	o in lemon
ē equal	ô order	ü rule	ᴛH then	(u in circus
ėr term			zh measure	

loch (lok), a Scottish word meaning: **1** a lake. **Loch Ness** is a very deep lake in northern Scotland, where some people believe a monster lives. **2** an arm of the sea partly shut in by land. Along the west coast of Scotland there are many lochs. *noun.*

lock[1] (lok), **1** a means of fastening doors, boxes, windows, and similar things, usually needing a key of special shape to open it: *Our front door has a lock.* **2** to fasten with a lock: *Lock and bar the door.* **3** to shut something in or out or up: *We lock up jewels in a safe.* **4** to hold fast: *The ship was locked in ice. The secret will be locked in my heart forever.* **5** to join, fit, jam, or link together: *The girls locked arms and walked down the street together.* **6** the part of a canal or dock in which the level of the water can be changed by letting water in or out, to raise or lower ships. **7** the part of a gun by means of which it is fired. **1,6,7** *noun,* **2-5** *verb.*

lock[1] (definition 6)

lock[2] (lok), **1** a curl of hair. **2 locks,** the hair of the head: *The child has curly locks. noun.*

lock·er (lok′ər), a chest, small closet, or cupboard that can be locked. *noun.*

lock·et (lok′it), a little ornamental case for holding a picture of someone or a lock of hair. A locket is usually worn around the neck on a chain or necklace. *noun.*

lock·jaw (lok′jô′), a form of tetanus in which the jaws become firmly closed. *noun.*

lock·smith (lok′smith′), a person who makes or repairs locks and keys. *noun.*

lo·co·mo·tion (lō′kə mō′shən), the act or power of moving from place to place. Walking, swimming, and flying are common forms of locomotion. *noun.*

lo·co·mo·tive (lō′kə mō′tiv), an engine that moves from place to place on its own power, used to pull railroad trains. *noun.*

lo·cust (lō′kəst), **1** a grasshopper that travels with others in great swarms, destroying the crops. **2** a tree with small, rounded leaflets and clusters of sweet-smelling white flowers. *noun.*

lode (lōd), a vein of metal ore: *The miners struck a rich lode of copper. noun.*

lode·stone (lōd′stōn′), a piece of iron ore that atracts iron and steel. *noun.*

lodge (loj), **1** to live in a place for a time: *We lodged in motels on our trip.* **2** to supply with a place to sleep or live in for a time: *Can you lodge us for the weekend?* **3** a place to live in; house, especially a small or temporary house: *My aunt and uncle rent a lodge in the mountains for the summer.* **4** to live in a rented room in another's house: *We are merely lodging at present.* **5** to get caught or stay in a place without falling or going farther: *My kite lodged in the branches of a big tree.* **6** to put before some authority: *We lodged a complaint with the police.* **7** a branch of a secret society. **8** a place where it meets. 1,2,4-6 *verb,* **lodg·es, lodged, lodg·ing;** 3,7,8 *noun.*

lodg·er (loj′ər), a person who lives in a rented room in another's house. *noun.*

lodg·ing (loj′ing), **1** a place where one is living only for a time: *a lodging for the night.* **2 lodgings,** a rented room or rooms in a house, not in a hotel. *noun.*

loft (lôft), **1** a space just below the roof in a cabin; attic. **2** the room under the roof of a barn: *This loft is full of hay.* **3** a balcony in a church or hall: *a choir loft.* **4** an upper floor of a business building or warehouse. *noun.*

loft·y (lôf′tē), **1** very high: *lofty mountains.* **2** proud; haughty: *He had a lofty contempt for others. adjective,* **loft·i·er, loft·i·est.**

log (lôg), **1** a length of wood just as it comes from the tree. **2** made of logs: *a log house.* **3** to cut down trees, cut them into logs, and get them out of the forest. **4** the daily record of a ship's voyage. **5** to enter in a ship's log. **6** a record of an airplane trip or the performance of an engine. **7** a float for measuring the speed of a ship. 1,4,6,7 *noun,* 2 *adjective,* 3,5 *verb,* **logs, logged, log·ging.**

lo·gan·ber·ry (lō′gən ber′ē), a large, purplish-red fruit, a cross between a raspberry and a blackberry. *noun, plural* **lo·gan·ber·ries.**
[*Loganberry* was formed by combining the name of James H. Logan, who lived from 1841 to 1928, with the word *berry.* He was an American judge who first grew this fruit in 1881.]

log·book (lôg′bùk′), a book in which a daily record of a ship's voyage is kept. *noun.*

log·ger (lôg′ər), a person whose work is logging. *noun.*

log·ging (lô′ging), the work of cutting down trees, sawing them into logs, and moving the logs out of the forest. *noun.*

log·ic (loj′ik), **1** reasoning; use of argument; a way of convincing or proving: *The logic of his argument made us believe that he was right.* **2** reason; sound sense: *There was much logic in what the speaker said. noun.*

log·i·cal (loj′ə kəl), **1** having something to do with logic: *logical reasoning.* **2** reasonable: *An upset stomach is a logical result of overeating.* **3** reasoning correctly: *a clear and logical mind. adjective.*

LO·GO (lō′gō), a simple language used to give instructions to computers. *noun.*
[*LOGO* comes from a Greek word meaning "word," "speech," or "reason." The English words *logic* and *logical* come from the same Greek root.]

loin (loin), **1** the part of the body of an animal or human being between the ribs and the hip. The loins are on both sides of the backbone and nearer to it than the flanks. **2** a piece of meat from this part of an animal: *a loin of pork. noun.*

loi·ter (loi′tər), **1** to linger idly; stop and play along the way: *She loitered along the street, looking into all the store windows.* **2** to spend time idly: *to loiter the hours away. verb.*

loll (lol), **1** to recline or lean in a lazy manner: *to loll on a sofa.* **2** to hang loosely or droop: *A dog's tongue lolls out in hot weather. verb.*

lol·li·pop (lol′ē pop), a piece of hard candy, usually on the end of a small stick. *noun.*

Lon·don (lun′dən), a city in England. London is the capital of the United Kingdom. *noun.*

lone (lōn), **1** without others; alone; single: *The lone traveler was glad to reach home.* **2** lonesome; lonely: *They lived a lone life after their children grew up and moved away. adjective.*

lone·li·ness (lōn′lē nis), a being lonely; solitude. *noun.*

lone·ly (lōn′lē), **1** feeling oneself alone and longing for company or friends: *He was lonely while his brother was away.* **2** without many people:

a lonely road. **3** alone: *a lonely tree. adjective.*
lone·li·er, lone·li·est.

lone·some (lōn′səm), **1** feeling lonely: *I was lonesome while you were away.* **2** making one feel lonely: *a lonesome journey. adjective.*

long[1] (lông), **1** measuring much from end to end: *An inch is short; a mile is long. A year is a long time. I read a long story.* **2** in length: *My table is three feet long.* **3** having a long, narrow shape: *a long board.* **4** a long time: *Summer will come before long.* **5** for a long time: *I can't stay long.* **6** for its whole length: *all summer long, all day long.* **7** A **long vowel** is a vowel like *a* in *late, e* in *be,* or *o* in *note.* 1-3,7 *adjective,* **long·er** (lông′gər), **long·est** (lông′gist); 4 *noun,* 5,6 *adverb.*

long[2] (lông), to wish very much; desire greatly: *I longed for my family. She longed to see her good friend. verb.*

long·hand (lông′hand′), ordinary writing, not shorthand or typewriting. *noun.*

long·horn (lông′hôrn′), one of a breed of cattle with very long horns, formerly common in the southwestern United States. *noun.*

long·ing (lông′ing), **1** a strong desire: *a longing for home.* **2** having or showing strong desire: *a child's longing look at a window full of toys.* 1 *noun,* 2 *adjective.*

lon·gi·tude (lon′jə tüd *or* lon′jə tyüd), distance east or west on the earth's surface, measured in degrees from a certain meridian. *noun.*

Word History

longitude *Longitude* comes from a Latin word meaning "long." The earliest maps were flat, not round. The length of a map is the distance from top to bottom. Lines of longitude were drawn in that direction. Look also at the word history of *latitude.*

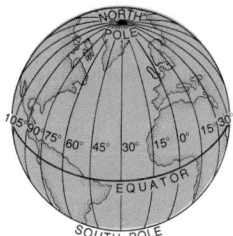

longitude
circles of **longitude**

---

lon·gi·tu·di·nal (lon′jə tüd′n əl *or* lon′jə tyüd′n əl), **1** of length; in length: *longitudinal measurements.* **2** running lengthwise: *The flag of the United States has longitudinal stripes. adjective.*

look (lük), **1** to see; try to see; turn the eyes: *Look at the pictures.* **2** to search: *I looked through the drawer to see if I could find my keys.* **3** a glance; seeing: *He took a quick look at the magazine.* **4** to face: *My bedroom looks upon the garden.* **5** to seem; appear: *She looks pale.* **6** appearance: *A deserted house has a desolate*

a hat	i it	oi oil	ch child	a in about
ā age	ī ice	ou out	ng long	e in taken
ä far	o hot	u cup	sh she	ə = i in pencil
e let	ō open	u̇ put	th thin	o in lemon
ē equal	ô order	ü rule	ᴛʜ then	u in circus
ėr term			zh measure	

longhorn—about 5 feet (1½ meters) high at the shoulder

look. **7 looks,** personal appearance: *a movie star's good looks.* 1,2,4,5 *verb,* 3,6,7 *noun.*

look after, to attend to; take care of: *Will you look after my bird while I'm away?*

look at, to pay attention to; examine: *You must look at all the facts.*

look down on, to despise: *The miser looked down on all beggars.*

look for, to expect: *We'll look for you tonight.*

look forward to, to expect with pleasure: *The children are looking forward to the picnic.*

look into, to examine; investigate: *The president of our club is looking into the problem.*

look on, to watch without taking part: *The teacher conducted the experiment while we looked on.*

look out, to be careful; watch out: *Look out for cars as you cross the street.*

look over, to examine; inspect: *I looked over my report for spelling errors.*

look up, 1 to find: *He looked up the unfamiliar word in a dictionary.* **2** to call on; visit: *Look me up when you come to town.* **3** to get better; improve: *Things are looking up for me since I got the new job.*

look up to, to respect: *The students looked up to their teacher.*

looking glass, a mirror.

look·out (lük′out′), **1** a sharp watch for someone to come or for something to happen: *Keep a good lookout for Mother.* **2** a place from which to watch. A crow's-nest is a lookout. **3** a person who has the duty of watching: *The lookout cried, "Land Ho!" noun.*

loom[1] (lüm), a machine for weaving cloth. *noun.*

loom[2] (lüm), to appear dimly or vaguely; appear as large or dangerous: *A large iceberg loomed through the thick gray fog. verb.*

loon—about 30 inches (75 centimeters) long

loon (lün), a large diving bird with webbed feet that eats fish. Loons have a loud, wild cry. *noun.*

loop (lüp), **1** the part of a curved string, ribbon, bent wire, or cord that crosses itself. **2** a thing, bend, course, or motion shaped like this. In writing, *b* and *g* and *h* and *l* have loops. *The road makes a wide loop around the lake.* **3** a fastening or ornament formed of cord bent and crossed. **4** to make a loop of. **5** to make loops in. **6** to fasten with a loop: *I looped the sail to the mast with a rope.* **7** to form a loop or loops. **8** a set of instructions that a computer carries out more than once. 1-3,8 *noun,* 4-7 *verb.*

loop·hole (lüp′hōl′), **1** a small opening in a wall for looking through, for letting in air, or for firing through at an enemy outside. **2** a means of escape: *The clever lawyer found a loophole in the law to save his client. noun.*

loose (lüs), **1** not fastened: *a loose thread.* **2** not tight: *loose clothing.* **3** not firmly set or fastened in: *a loose tooth.* **4** not bound together: *loose papers.* **5** free; not shut in or up: *The dog has been loose all night.* **6** not pressed close together: *loose earth, cloth with a loose weave.* **7** not strict, close, or exact: *a loose account of the accident.* **8** careless about morals or conduct: *a loose character.* **9** to set free; let go: *He loosed my arm from his grip.* **10** to make loose; untie; unfasten: *to loose a knot.* 1-8 *adjective,* **loos·er, loos·est;** 9,10 *verb,* **loos·es, loosed, loos·ing.**

loose-leaf (lüs′lēf′), having pages or sheets that can be taken out and replaced: *a loose-leaf notebook. adjective.*

loos·en (lü′sn), to make or become loose; untie; unfasten: *After our picnic we had to loosen our belts. verb.*

loot (lüt), **1** to rob; plunder: *The burglar looted the jewelry store.* **2** things taken by force; booty; spoils: *loot taken by soldiers from a captured town.* 1 *verb,* 2 *noun.*

lop (lop), **1** to cut; cut off. **2** to cut branches or twigs from. *verb,* **lops, lopped, lop·ping.**

lope (lōp), **1** to run with a long, easy stride: *The horse loped along the trail in an easy gallop.* **2** a long, easy stride. 1 *verb,* **lopes, loped, lop·ing;** 2 *noun.*

lop·sid·ed (lop′sī′did), larger or heavier on one side than the other; leaning to one side. *adjective.*

lord (lôrd), **1** an owner, ruler, or master; person who has the power. **2** to rule proudly or absolutely. **3 Lord, a** God. **b** Christ: *the year of our Lord.* **4** (in Great Britain) a man of any of certain high ranks. **5 Lord,** a title used in writing or speaking about men of certain high ranks in Great Britain: *Lord and Lady Grey attended the reception.* 1,3-5 *noun,* 2 *verb.*

lord it over, to boss: *She was the oldest and lorded it over the rest of us.*

[*Lord* comes from an earlier English word originally meaning "one who guards the loaf of bread" or "master of the house." In early times, the lord or master of the house was responsible for supplying food to the family and servants who lived and worked there.]

lord·ly (lôrd′lē), **1** like a lord; suitable for a lord; grand; magnificent. **2** haughty; insolent; scornful: *His lordly airs annoyed his country cousins. adjective,* **lord·li·er, lord·li·est.**

lore (lôr), **1** the facts and stories about a certain subject: *fairy lore, bird lore, Greek lore.* **2** learning; knowledge. *noun.*

Los An·ge·les (lôs an′jə ləs), a city in California.

lose (lüz), **1** to not have any longer; have taken away from one by accident, carelessness, parting, or death: *to lose a finger, to lose a friend, to lose one's life.* **2** to be unable to find: *to lose a book.* **3** to fail to keep: *to lose patience, to lose your temper.* **4** to miss; fail to get, catch, see, or hear: *to lose a train, to lose a few words of what was said.* **5** to fail to win; be defeated: *Our team lost.* **6** to waste; spend or let go by without any result: *to lose time waiting, to lose a chance.* **7** to cause to lose: *That one mistake lost me my job. verb,* **los·es, lost, los·ing.**

los·er (lü′zər), **1** a person or thing that loses or suffers loss: *Our team was the loser.* **2** a person or thing that loses consistently, or fails; failure: *a born loser. noun.*

loss (lôs), **1** a losing or having lost something: *The loss of health is serious, but the loss of a pencil is not.* **2** a person or thing lost: *Her house was a complete loss to the fire.* **3** the value of the thing lost: *The loss from the fire was $10,000.* **4** a defeat: *Our team had two losses and one tie out of ten games played. noun, plural* **loss·es.**

at a loss, puzzled; not sure: *The embarrassed child was at a loss as to how to act.*

lost (lôst), **1** See lose. *I lost my new pencil. My ruler is lost, too.* **2** no longer possessed or kept: *lost friendships.* **3** missing; no longer to be found: *lost books.* **4** not won: *a lost battle, a lost prize.* **5** hopeless: *a lost cause.* **6** not used to good purpose; wasted: *lost time.* 1 *verb,* 2-6 *adjective.*

lost in, so busy with something that one fails to notice anything else: *He was lost in a book and failed to hear us come in.*

lot (lot), **1** a number of persons or things considered as a group; collection: *This lot of oranges is better than the last.* **2** a plot of ground: *Her house is between two empty lots.* **3** a portion or part: *I divided the fruit into ten lots.* **4** one of a set of objects, such as bits of paper, wood, or the like, used to decide something by chance. **5** such a method of deciding: *It was settled by lot.* **6** a choice made in this way: *The lot fell to me.* **7** what one gets by lot; one's share or portion. **8** one's fate or fortune: *It was his lot later to become president.* **9** a lot or **lots,** a great deal; much: *I feel a lot better.* 1-8 *noun,* 9 *adverb.*

a lot of or **lots of,** a great many; much: *a lot of books, lots of money.*

lo·tion (lō′shən), a liquid containing medicine. Lotions are applied to the skin to relieve pain, to heal, to cleanse, or to benefit the skin. *noun.*

lot·ter·y (lot′ər ē), a scheme for distributing prizes by lot or chance. In a lottery a large number of tickets are sold, some of which draw prizes. *noun, plural* **lot·ter·ies.**

lo·tus (lō′təs), a kind of water lily having large, often floating leaves and showy flowers. *noun, plural* **lo·tus·es.**

lotus

loud (loud), **1** not quiet or soft; making a great sound: *a loud voice. The door slammed with a loud noise.* **2** noisy: *loud music.* **3** in a loud manner: *We called loud and long for our dog.* **4** showy in dress or manner: *loud clothes.* 1,2,4 *adjective,* 3 *adverb.*

loud·speak·er (loud′spē′kər), a device for making sounds louder, especially in a radio, phonograph, or public address system. *noun.*

Lou·i·si·an·a (lů ē′zē an′ə), one of the south central states of the United States. *Abbreviation:* La. or LA *Capital:* Baton Rouge. *noun.*

[*Louisiana* was named for Louis XIV, king of France. He lived from 1638 to 1715. The French explorer La Salle gave this name to all lands whose rivers drain into the Mississippi River.]

lounge (lounj), **1** to stand, sit, or lie at ease in a lazy way: *He lounged in an old chair.* **2** a

comfortable and informal room in which one can be at ease: *a theater lounge.* **3** a couch or sofa. 1 *verb,* **loung·es, lounged, loung·ing;** 2,3 *noun.*

louse (lous), a small, wingless insect that lives on the bodies of people and animals and sucks their blood. *noun, plural* **lice.**

louse
line shows actual length

lov·a·ble (luv′ə bəl), worthy of being loved; endearing: *She was a most lovable person, always kind and thoughtful. adjective.*

love (luv), **1** a fond, deep, tender feeling: *love for one's family, love for a sweetheart.* **2** to have such a feeling for: *I love my parents. I love my country.* **3** a person who is loved; sweetheart. **4** a strong liking: *a love of books.* **5** to like very much; take great pleasure in: *He loves music.* 1,3,4 *noun,* 2,5 *verb,* **loves, loved, lov·ing.**

love·li·ness (luv′lē nis), beauty; a delightful quality: *the loveliness of a warm spring day. noun.*

love·ly (luv′lē), **1** beautiful in appearance or character; lovable: *They are the loveliest children we know.* **2** very pleasing; delightful: *We had a lovely holiday. adjective,* **love·li·er, love·li·est.**

lov·er (luv′ər), **1** a person who is in love with another. **2** a person having a strong liking: *a lover of books. noun.*

lov·ing (luv′ing), feeling or showing love; affectionate; fond: *The orphan was adopted into a loving family. adjective.*

low (lō), **1** not high or tall: *low walls. This footstool is very low.* **2** in a low place; near the ground: *a low shelf, a low jump.* **3** below others; inferior: *a low grade of margarine, to rise from a low position as clerk to president of a company.* **4** small; less than usual: *a low price, low temperature, low speed.* **5** nearly used up: *Our supply of coal is very low.* **6** unfavorable; poor: *I have a low opinion of their work.* **7** not high in the musical scale: *a low note.* **8** not loud; soft: *a low whisper.* **9** at or to a low point, place, amount, or pitch: *The sun sank low. Supplies are running low.* **10** a low point, level, or position: *The low for tonight will be near freezing.* **11** an arrangement of gears to give the lowest speed and the greatest power: *She shifted into low before going up the steep hill.* 1-8 *adjective,* 9 *adverb,* 10,11 *noun.*

low·er (lō′ər), **1** to let down or haul down: *We lower the flag at night.* **2** to make or become less:

Lower the volume on the radio. Prices lowered somewhat during the winter. **3** not as high: *Prices were lower last year than this.* **1,2** *verb,* **3** *adjective, adverb.*

low·land (lō′lənd), land that is lower and flatter than the neighboring country. *noun.*

low·ly (lō′lē), **1** low in rank, position, or development: *a lowly clerk, a lowly job.* **2** humble; meek; modest in feeling, behavior, or condition: *He had a lowly opinion of himself. adjective,* **low·li·er, low·li·est.**

low spirits, sadness; depression: *The team suffered from low spirits after a series of defeats.*

low tide, the time when the ocean is lowest on the shore. Low tides occur twice daily.

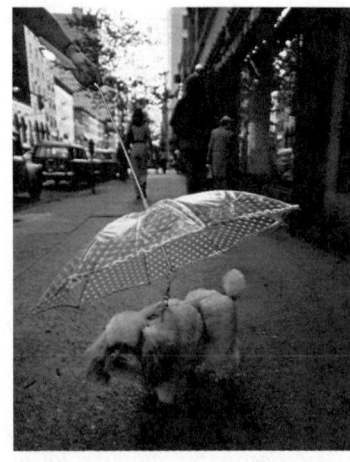
ludicrous
A dog with an umbrella is **ludicrous.**

low tide—The ship was stranded at **low tide.**

loy·al (loi′əl), true and faithful to someone or something: *Loyal friends don't desert you. She was a loyal citizen who defended her country. adjective.*

loy·al·ty (loi′əl tē), loyal feeling or behavior; faithfulness: *The knights pledged their loyalty to the king. noun, plural* **loy·al·ties.**

lu·bri·cant (lü′brə kənt), a slippery substance, such as oil or grease, for putting on parts of machines that move against one another, to make them smooth and slippery so that they will work easily. *noun.*

lu·bri·cate (lü′brə kāt), to make machinery smooth, slippery, and easy to work by putting on oil, grease, or the like. *verb,* **lu·bri·cates, lu·bri·cat·ed, lu·bri·cat·ing.**

lu·cid (lü′sid), **1** easy to follow or understand; clear: *A good explanation is lucid.* **2** sane: *An insane person sometimes has lucid intervals. adjective.*

luck (luk), **1** that which seems to happen or come to one by chance; fortune: *I won the game by luck, not by skill.* **2** good luck: *She gave me a penny for luck. noun.*

luck·i·ly (luk′ə lē), by good luck; fortunately: *Luckily I found my lost ring. adverb.*

luck·less (luk′lis), having or bringing bad luck; unlucky. *adjective.*

luck·y (luk′ē), having or bringing good luck: *This is a lucky day. adjective,* **luck·i·er, luck·i·est.**

lu·di·crous (lü′də krəs), absurd but amusing; ridiculous. *adjective.*

lug (lug), to pull along or carry with effort; drag: *We lugged the rug to the yard to clean it. verb,* **lugs, lugged, lug·ging.**

lug·gage (lug′ij), suitcases or handbags that a traveler carries on a trip. *noun.*

luke·warm (lük′wôrm′), **1** neither hot nor cold: *I like soup hot, not lukewarm.* **2** showing little enthusiasm; half-hearted: *a lukewarm greeting. adjective.*

lull (lul), **1** to soothe: *The soft music lulled me to sleep.* **2** to make or become calm or more nearly calm; quiet: *Their confidence lulled my fears.* **3** a period of calm or quiet: *a lull in a storm. I asked my question during a lull in the conversation.* **1,2** *verb,* **3** *noun.*

lubricate—Dorothy **lubricated** the Tin Man's rusty joints.

lul·la·by (lul′ə bī), a soft song that quiets a baby so that it falls asleep. *noun, plural* **lul·la·bies.**

lum·ber[1] (lum′bər), **1** timber that has been roughly cut into boards or planks, and prepared for use. **2** to cut and prepare lumber. **1** *noun,* **2** *verb.*

lum·ber[2] (lum′bər), to move along heavily and noisily; roll along with difficulty: *The old stagecoach lumbered down the road. verb.*

lum·ber·jack (lum′bər jak′), a person whose work is cutting down trees and getting out the logs. *noun.*

lum·ber·man (lum′bər mən), **1** a lumberjack. **2** a person whose work is buying and selling timber or lumber. *noun, plural* **lum·ber·men.**

lu·mi·nous (lü′mə nəs), **1** shining by its own light: *The sun and stars are luminous bodies.* **2** full of light; bright: *She painted luminous pictures of sunlit scenes. adjective.*

lump (lump), **1** a small, solid mass of no particular shape: *a lump of coal.* **2** a swelling; bump: *There is a lump on my head where I bumped it.* **3** to form into a lump or lumps: *The gravy lumped because we cooked it too fast.* **4** in lumps; in a lump: *lump sugar.* **5** to put together: *We will lump all our expenses.* **6** not in parts; whole: *I was given a lump sum of money for all my living expenses.* **1,2** *noun,* **3,5** *verb,* **4,6** *adjective.*

lump·y (lum′pē), full of lumps: *Mashed potatoes shouldn't be lumpy. adjective,* **lump·i·er, lump·i·est.**

lu·nar (lü′nər), of or like the moon: *a lunar eclipse, a lunar landscape. adjective.*

lunar month, the time between one new moon and the next, about 29½ days.

lu·na·tic (lü′nə tik), an insane person. *noun.*

lunch (lunch), **1** a light meal between breakfast and dinner: *We usually have lunch at noon.* **2** to eat lunch: *We lunched in the park.* **1** *noun, plural* **lunch·es;** **2** *verb.*

lunch·eon (lun′chən), a lunch, especially one for a group of people, for a special occasion: *a women's club luncheon. noun.*

lunch·room (lunch′rüm′), **1** a restaurant in which light meals are served. **2** a room in a school, factory, or office building, where light meals are served or lunches brought from home can be eaten. *noun.*

lunch·time (lunch′tīm′), the time at which lunch is served. *noun.*

lung (lung), either one of a pair of organs found in the chest of human beings and certain other animals that breathe air. Lungs give the blood the oxygen it needs, and take away carbon dioxide. *noun.*

lunge (lunj), **1** any sudden forward movement: *I made a lunge for the ball as it went by me.* **2** to move suddenly forward: *The dog lunged at the stranger.* **1** *noun,* **2** *verb,* **lung·es, lunged, lung·ing.**

lurch (lėrch), **1** a sudden leaning or roll to one side, like that of a ship, a car, or a staggering person: *The boat gave a lurch and upset.* **2** to make

a hat	i it	oi oil	ch child	(a in about
ā age	ī ice	ou out	ng long	e in taken
ä far	o hot	u cup	sh she	ə = { i in pencil
e let	ō open	u̇ put	th thin	o in lemon
ē equal	ô order	ü rule	ᴛʜ then	u in circus
ėr term			zh measure	

a lurch; stagger: *The injured animal lurched forward.* **1** *noun, plural* **lurch·es;** **2** *verb.*

lure (lu̇r), **1** the power of attracting or fascinating; charm; attraction: *Many people feel the lure of the sea.* **2** something that attracts or tempts: *Gold was the lure that attracted miners to California in 1849.* **3** to lead away or into something by arousing desire; attract; tempt: *Bees are lured by the scent of flowers.* **4** the bait, especially the artificial bait, used in fishing: *I used a shiny lure to catch the fish.* **1,2,4** *noun,* **3** *verb,* **lures, lured, lur·ing.**

lur·id (lu̇r′id), **1** lighted up with a red or fiery glare: *The sky was lurid with the flames of the burning city.* **2** terrible; sensational; startling: *The magazine had stories about murders and other lurid crimes. adjective.*

lurk (lėrk), to stay about without arousing attention; wait out of sight; be hidden: *A tiger was lurking in the jungle outside the village. verb.*

lus·cious (lush′əs), **1** delicious; richly sweet: *a luscious peach.* **2** very pleasing to taste, smell, hear, see, or feel: *a painting full of luscious colors. adjective.*

lush (lush), **1** tender and juicy; growing thick and green: *Lush grass grows along the river banks.* **2** having a thick growth; covered with growing things: *The hillside was lush with spring flowers. adjective.*

lus·ter (lus′tər), **1** a bright shine on the surface: *the luster of pearls.* **2** brightness: *the luster in the eyes of a happy child. noun.*

lust·i·ly (lus′tə lē), in a strong and healthy way; vigorously; heartily: *The baby cried lustily when hungry. adverb.*

lus·trous (lus′trəs), having luster; shining; glossy: *lustrous satin. adjective.*

lust·y (lus′tē), strong and healthy; full of energy: *a lusty athlete. adjective,* **lust·i·er, lust·i·est.**

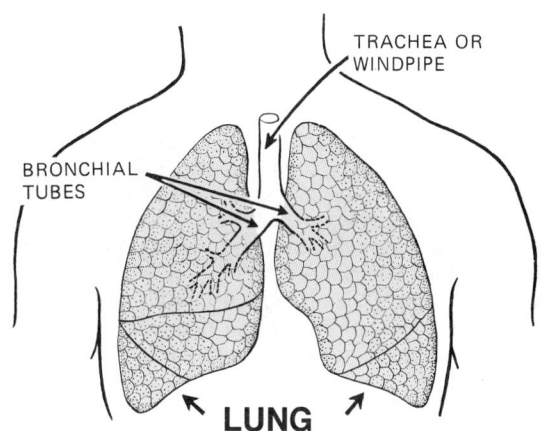

BRONCHIAL TUBES

TRACHEA OR WINDPIPE

LUNG

lute

lute (lüt), a stringed musical instrument of former times. It is like a large mandolin and is played by plucking the strings. *noun.*

Lux·em·bourg (luk′səm bėrg′), a country in western Europe. *noun.*

lux·ur·i·ant (lug zhŭr′ē ənt), **1** growing thick and green: *luxuriant jungle growth.* **2** producing abundantly: *rich, luxuriant soil.* **3** rich in ornament. *adjective.*

lux·ur·i·ous (lug zhŭr′ē əs), **1** giving luxury; very comfortable and beautiful: *a luxurious apartment with thick carpeting and expensive furniture.* **2** fond of luxury; tending toward luxury: *a luxurious taste for fine food. adjective.*

lux·ur·y (luk′shər ē), **1** the comforts and beauties of life beyond what are really necessary: *They were a wealthy family who could afford to live in luxury.* **2** a thing that one enjoys, usually something choice and costly: *They save some money for luxuries such as fine paintings.* **3** a thing pleasant but not necessary: *Candy is a luxury. noun, plural* **lux·ur·ies.**

-ly[1], a suffix meaning: in a _____way or manner: Cheerful*ly* means *in a* cheerful *way.* Soft*ly* means *in a* soft *manner.*

-ly[2], a suffix meaning: **1** like a _____: Ghost*ly* means *like a* ghost. **2** like that of a _____: Brother*ly* means *like that of a* brother. **3** of each or every _____; that happens or appears every _____: A month*ly* visit is a visit *that happens every* month. A dai*ly* newspaper is a newspaper *that appears every* day.

lye (lī), a strong solution used in making soap and in cleaning. *noun.*

ly·ing[1] (lī′ing), **1** a telling a lie; habit of telling lies: *Lying just got me into more trouble.* **2** See **lie**[1]. *I was not lying; I told the truth.* **1** *noun,* **2** *verb.*

ly·ing[2] (lī′ing). See **lie**[2]. *I was lying on the ground. verb.*

lymph (limf), a nearly colorless liquid in the tissues of the body, somewhat like blood without the red corpuscles. Lymph bathes and nourishes the tissues. *noun.*

lynch (linch), to put an accused person to death without a lawful trial: *An angry mob may lynch an innocent person. verb.*

lynx (lingks), a wildcat of the northern United States and Canada that has a short tail and rather long legs. *noun, plural* **lynx·es** or **lynx.**

lynx—about 3 feet (1 meter) long with the tail

lyre

lyre (līr), an ancient stringed musical instrument somewhat like a small harp. *noun.*

lyr·ic (lir′ik), **1** expressing strong personal emotion. A lyric poem is a short poem which gives the poet's own feelings about something. **2 lyrics,** the words for a song. **1** *adjective,* **2** *noun.*

lyr·i·cal (lir′ə kəl), expressing strong emotion in a beautiful manner, as in poetry; poetic: *She became almost lyrical when she described the scenery. adjective.*

M m

a hat	**i** it	**oi** oil	**ch** child	⌈ a in about
ā age	**ī** ice	**ou** out	**ng** long	| e in taken
ä far	**o** hot	**u** cup	**sh** she	ə = ⟨ i in pencil
e let	**ō** open	**u̇** put	**th** thin	| o in lemon
ē equal	**ô** order	**ü** rule	**ᴛʜ** then	⌊ u in circus
ėr term			**zh** measure	

M or **m** (em), the 13th letter of the English alphabet. *noun, plural* **M's** or **m's.**

m or **m.,** meter or meters.

ma (mä), mamma; mother. *noun.*

MA, Massachusetts (used with postal Zip Code).

ma'am (mam), madam: *Yes, ma'am. noun.*

mac·a·ro·ni (mak′ə rō′nē), a mixture of flour and water that has been dried, usually in the form of hollow tubes, to be cooked for food. *noun.*

mac·a·roon (mak′ə rün′), a very sweet cookie made of whites of eggs, sugar, and ground almonds or coconut. *noun.*

Mace (mās), trademark for a strong, irritating spray, used to keep an attacker away. *noun.*

Mac·e·do·ni·a (mas′ə dō′nē ə), a country in southeastern Europe. *noun.*

ma·chine (mə shēn′), **1** an arrangement of fixed and moving parts for doing work, each part having some special job to do: *Sewing machines and washing machines make housework easier.* **2** a device, such as a lever, which applies force or changes its direction, so more work can be done with less effort; simple machine. *noun.*

machine gun, a gun that can keep up a rapid fire of bullets.

ma·chin·er·y (mə shē′nər ē), **1** machines: *A factory contains much machinery.* **2** the parts or works of a machine: *The machinery of a typewriter should be kept clean. noun.*

machine shop, a workshop where people make or repair machines or parts of machines.

ma·chin·ist (mə shē′nist), a worker who shapes metal by using machines and power tools. *noun.*

mack·er·el (mak′ər əl), a saltwater fish of the North Atlantic, much used for food. *noun, plural* **mack·er·el** or **mack·er·els.**

mack·i·naw (mak′ə nô), **1** a kind of short coat made of heavy woolen cloth. **2** a kind of thick woolen blanket, often with bars of color, used in the northern and western United States and in Canada. *noun.*

mack·in·tosh (mak′ən tosh), a waterproof coat; raincoat. *noun, plural* **mack·in·tosh·es.**
[*Mackintosh* was named for Charles Macintosh, who lived from 1766 to 1843. He was the Scottish inventor of the process of waterproofing.]

ma·cron (mā′kron), a short, straight, horizontal line (-) placed over a vowel to show that it is pronounced in a certain way. EXAMPLES: came (kām), be (bē). *noun.*

mad (mad), **1** very angry: *The insult made me mad.* **2** out of one's mind; crazy; insane: *Her strange, sometimes violent behavior made me wonder if she were mad.* **3** much excited; wild: *The dog made*

mad efforts to catch up with the automobile. **4** foolish; unwise: *Trying to row across the ocean is a mad undertaking.* **5** blindly and unreasonably fond: *My friend is mad about swimming.* **6** having rabies. A mad dog often foams at the mouth and may bite people. *adjective,* **mad·der, mad·dest.**
like mad, furiously; very hard or fast: *I ran like mad to catch the train.*

Mad·a·gas·car (mad′ə gas′kər), an island country in the Indian Ocean, off the coast of Africa. *noun.*

mad·am (mad′əm), a polite title used in writing or speaking to any woman: *Yes, madam. noun.*

mad·ame (mad′əm *or* mä däm′), a French word meaning "Mrs." or "madam." *noun, plural* **mes·dames** (mā däm′).

mad·den (mad′n), to make very angry or excited; irritate greatly: *The crowd was maddened by the umpire's decision. verb.*

made (mād), **1** See **make.** *The cook made the cake. It was made of flour, milk, butter, eggs, and sugar.* **2** built; constructed; formed: *a strongly made swing.* **1** *verb,* **2** *adjective.*

mad·e·moi·selle (mad′ə mə zel′), a French word meaning "Miss." *noun.*

made-up (mād′up′), **1** not real; imaginary: *a made-up story.* **2** having on rouge, powder, or other cosmetics: *made-up lips. adjective.*

mad·house (mad′hous′), a place of uproar and confusion: *The arena was a madhouse after the team won the game. noun, plural* **mad·hous·es** (mad′hou′ziz).

Mad·i·son (mad′ə sən), the capital of Wisconsin. *noun.*

mad·man (mad′man′), an insane man; person who is crazy: *The explosion was probably the act of a madman. noun, plural* **mad·men.**

mad·ness (mad′nis), **1** a being crazy; loss of one's mind. **2** great rage; fury: *In his madness he kicked the fence post.* **3** a foolish act; folly: *It would be madness to try to sail a boat in this storm. noun.*

mag·a·zine (mag′ə zēn′), **1** a publication appearing regularly, containing stories and articles by various writers. Most magazines are published either weekly or monthly. **2** a room in a fort or warship for storing gunpowder and other substances that might explode. **3** a place for cartridges in a repeating rifle or revolver. *noun.*
[*Magazine* comes from an Arabic word meaning "storehouse." That was also the original meaning in English. Later on, the word came to have other meanings, all with the basic idea of things collected in one place.]

mag·got (mag′ət), the legless, wormlike larva of

a young fly that was just hatched from its egg. *noun.*

mag·ic (maj′ik), **1** the pretended art of making things happen by secret words, acts, or objects: *The fairy's magic changed the brothers into swans.* **2** the art of entertaining people by performing tricks that seem to be impossible: *The magician made scarfs appear and disappear by magic.* **3** done by magic or as if by magic: *A magic palace stood in place of their hut.* **1,2** *noun,* **3** *adjective.*

mag·i·cal (maj′ə kəl), done by magic or as if by magic: *The waving of the magician's wand produced a magical effect. adjective.*

ma·gi·cian (mə jish′ən), **1** a person who can use magic: *The wicked magician cast a spell over the princess.* **2** a person who entertains by magic tricks: *The magician pulled—not one, but three rabbits out of his hat! noun.*

Magic Marker, a trademark for a marking and drawing pen with a broad felt tip.

mag·is·trate (maj′ə strāt), **1** an officer of the government who has power to apply the law and put it in force. The President is the chief magistrate of the United States. **2** a judge. *noun.*

mag·ma (mag′mə), hot melted rock beneath the surface of the earth. *noun.*

mag·nate (mag′nāt), an important, powerful, or prominent person: *The shipping magnate owned many freighters. noun.*

mag·ne·sia (mag nē′zhə), a white, tasteless powder used in medicine. *noun.*

mag·ne·si·um (mag nē′zhē əm), a very lightweight, silver-white metal that burns with a dazzling white light. It is a chemical element, used for fireworks and with other metals to make strong, lightweight parts for automobiles and spacecraft. *noun.*

magnet (definition 1)

mag·net (mag′nit), **1** a stone or piece of iron or steel that attracts or draws to it bits of iron or steel. **2** anything that attracts: *On hot days the swimming pool was a magnet that attracted neighborhood children. noun.*

mag·net·ic (mag net′ik), **1** having to do with magnets or with the force in them: *A pocket compass has a magnetic needle.* **2** very attractive: *I like her because she has a magnetic personality. adjective.*

magnetic field, the space around a magnet or electric current in which magnetic force occurs.

magnetic pole, 1 one of the two places opposite each other on a magnet where its magnetic force is strongest. **2 Magnetic Pole,** one of the two places on the earth toward which a compass needle points: *The North Magnetic Pole is south of the geographic North Pole.*

Magnetic Pole
(definition 2)

magnetic tape, a plastic tape, coated with a magnetic substance, on which sounds, pictures, or information can be recorded.

mag·net·ism (mag′nə tiz′əm), **1** the kind of force that magnets have. **2** the power to attract or charm: *A person with magnetism has many friends and admirers. noun.*

mag·net·ize (mag′nə tīz), **1** to give magnetic force to: *You can magnetize a needle by rubbing it with a magnet.* **2** to attract or influence a person: *Her stirring speech magnetized the audience. verb.* **mag·net·iz·es, mag·net·ized, mag·net·iz·ing.**

magnet school, a school with special programs in certain subjects that are designed to attract students from all parts of a city or district.

mag·nif·i·cence (mag nif′ə səns), richness of material, color, and ornament; grand beauty; splendor: *We were dazzled by the magnificence of mountain scenery. noun.*

mag·nif·i·cent (mag nif′ə sənt), richly colored or decorated; grand; stately; splendid: *a magnificent palace, a magnificent view of the mountains. adjective.*

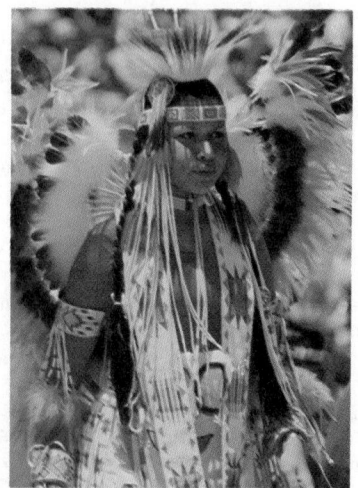

magnificent
She wore **magnificent** ceremonial attire.

mag·ni·fy (mag′nə fī), **1** to cause to look larger than the real size: *A microscope magnifies bacteria so that they can be seen and studied.* **2** to make too much of; go beyond the truth in telling: *Was the fish really that big, or are you magnifying its size?* *verb,* **mag·ni·fies, mag·ni·fied, mag·ni·fy·ing.**

magnifying glass, a lens or combination of lenses that causes things to look larger than they really are.

mag·ni·tude (mag′nə tüd *or* mag′nə tyüd), **1** greatness of size: *The magnitude of the destruction caused by the hurricane had to be seen to be believed.* **2** importance: *The war brought problems of very great magnitude to many nations.* *noun.*

mag·nol·ia (mag nō′lyə), a North American tree or shrub with large white, pink, or purplish flowers. There are several kinds. *noun.*
[*Magnolia* was named for Pierre Magnol, who lived from 1638 to 1715. He was a French botanist.]

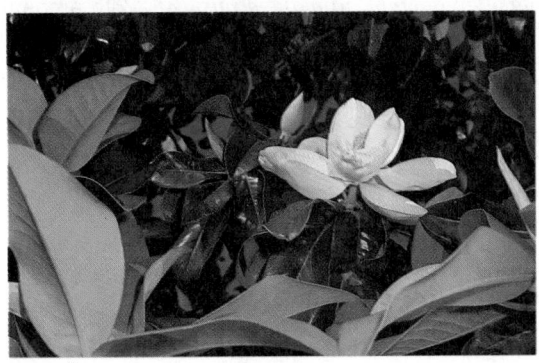

magnolia

mag·pie (mag′pī), a noisy, black-and-white bird with a long tail and short wings. *noun.*

ma·hog·a·ny (mə hog′ə nē), **1** a tree that grows in tropical America. **2** its dark reddish-brown wood. Because mahogany takes a very high polish, it is much used in making furniture. **3** dark reddish-brown. 1,2 *noun, plural* **ma·hog·a·nies;** 3 *adjective.*

maid (mād), **1** a girl or woman who has not married. **2** a woman servant. *noun.*

maid·en (mād′n), **1** a girl or young woman who has not married; maid. **2** never married: *a maiden aunt.* **3** first: *a ship's maiden voyage.* 1 *noun,* 2,3 *adjective.*

maid·en·hood (mād′n hůd), the condition or time of being a girl or young woman who has not married. *noun.*

maiden name, a woman's last name before marriage: *My maiden name is Smith, but my married name is Rogers.*

maid of honor, an unmarried woman who accompanies the bride and stands with her at a wedding.

mail[1] (māl), **1** letters, postcards, magazines, and packages to be sent by a postal service. **2** the system by which such mail is sent: *You can pay

a	hat	i	it	oi	oil	ch	child	⎧ a in about
ā	age	ī	ice	ou	out	ng	long	⎪ e in taken
ä	far	o	hot	u	cup	sh	she	ə = ⎨ i in pencil
e	let	ō	open	ů	put	th	thin	⎪ o in lemon
ē	equal	ô	order	ü	rule	ᴛʜ	then	⎩ u in circus
ėr	term					zh	measure	

most bills by mail. **3** all that comes by one post or delivery: *Has the mail come yet?* **4** to send by mail; put in a mailbox: *Should I mail that letter for you?* 1-3 *noun,* 4 *verb.*

mail[2] (māl), armor made of metal rings, small loops of chain linked together, or plates, for protecting the body against the enemy's arrows or spears. *noun.*

Suit of Mail, German about 1400
Courtesy of The Metropolitan Museum of Art

mail[2] used in the 1400s

mail·box (māl′boks′), **1** a public box from which mail is collected. **2** a private box at one's home or business to which mail is delivered. *noun, plural* **mail·box·es.**

mail carrier, a person who carries or delivers mail; postman.

mail·man (māl′man′), a mail carrier. *noun, plural* **mail·men.**

maim (mām), to cut off or make useless a part of the body, such as an arm, leg, finger, toe, or eye; injure seriously; cripple: *Two toes of his left foot were maimed by the power lawn mower.* *verb.*

main (mān), **1** most important; largest: *the main dish at dinner, the main street of a town.* **2** a large pipe which carries water, gas, sewage, or electricity to or from smaller branches: *When the water main broke, our street was flooded.* 1 *adjective,* 2 *noun.*

Maine (mān), one of the northeastern states of the United States. *Abbreviation:* Me. or ME *Capital:* Augusta. *noun.*
[*Maine* probably comes from the English phrase *the maine,* that is, the mainland. Explorers who found many islands off the coast may have used the term to refer to the mainland.]

main·land (mān′land′), the main part of a continent or country, apart from islands or small peninsulas along the shores: *A ferry carried people from the island to the mainland. noun.*

main·ly (mān′lē), for the most part; chiefly; mostly: *He is interested mainly in art. adverb.*

main·mast (mān′mast′ or mān′məst), the principal mast of a ship. *noun.*

main·sail (mān′sāl′ or mān′səl), the largest sail of a ship. *noun.*

main·spring (mān′spring′), the principal spring in a clock or watch that you wind. *noun.*

main·stay (mān′stā′), 1 a rope or wire supporting the mainmast. 2 a main support: *Loyal friends are a person's mainstay in time of trouble. noun.*

main·tain (mān tān′), 1 to keep; keep up; carry on: *One must maintain a footing in a tug-of-war.* 2 to provide for; support: *They could not maintain their family in comfort on such a small income.* 3 to uphold or defend: *The troops maintained their position under heavy fire.* 4 to keep in good repair: *The company employs people to maintain the machinery.* 5 to declare to be true: *He maintains that he was innocent. verb.*

main·te·nance (mān′tə nəns), 1 a maintaining: *Maintenance of quiet is necessary in a hospital.* 2 a being maintained; support: *A government collects taxes to pay for its maintenance.* 3 a keeping in good repair: *A state devotes much time to the maintenance of roads. noun.*

maize (māz), corn. *noun.*

ma·jes·tic (mə jes′tik), impressive; grand; dignified: *Majestic, snowcapped mountains towered above us. adjective.*

ma·jes·ti·cal·ly (mə jes′tik lē), grandly; in a majestic manner: *The wide river flowed majestically to the sea. adverb.*

maj·es·ty (maj′ə stē), 1 stately appearance; royal dignity; nobility: *the majesty of the royal court.* 2 **Majesty,** a title used in speaking to or of a king, queen, emperor, or the like: *Your Majesty, His Majesty, Her Majesty. noun, plural* **Maj·es·ties** for 2.

ma·jor (mā′jər), 1 more important; larger; greater: *The major part of a little baby's life is spent in sleeping.* 2 an army, air force, or marine officer ranking next above a captain. 1 *adjective,* 2 *noun.*

ma·jor·i·ty (mə jôr′ə tē), 1 the larger number; greater part; more than half: *A majority of the children chose red covers for the books they had made.* 2 the number by which the votes on one side are more than those on the other: *He had 18 votes, and she had 12; so he had a majority of 6. noun, plural* **ma·jor·i·ties.**

make (māk), 1 to bring into being; put together; build; form; shape: *to make a new dress, to make a fire, to make jelly.* 2 the way in which a thing is made; style; build; character: *Do you like the make of that coat?* 3 a kind; brand: *What make of car is this?* 4 to have the qualities needed for: *Wood makes a good fire.* 5 to cause; bring about: *to make trouble, to make a noise, to make peace.* 6 to force to: *We made him go home.* 7 to cause to be or become: *to make a room warm, to make a fool of oneself.* 8 to become; turn out to be: *He will make a good lawyer.* 9 to put into condition for use; arrange: *I make my own bed.* 10 to get; obtain; earn: *to make good marks, to make one's living.* 11 to do; perform: *to make a speech, to make an attempt, to make a mistake.* 12 to amount to; add up to; count as: *2 and 3 make 5.* 13 to think of as; figure to be: *I make the distance across the room 15 feet.* 14 to reach; arrive at: *Will the ship make harbor?* 15 to cause the success of: *One successful book made the young author.* 1,4-15 *verb,* **makes, made, mak·ing;** 2,3 *noun.*

make believe, to pretend: *The girl liked to make believe she was an airplane pilot.*

make fast, to attach firmly: *Make the boat fast.*

make off with, to steal; take without permission: *They made off with some apples.*

make out, 1 to write out: *She made out a shopping list.* 2 to show to be; try to prove: *They are trying to make me out to be selfish.* 3 to understand: *The boy had a hard time making out the problem.* 4 to see with difficulty: *I can barely make out what these letters are.* 5 to get along; manage: *We must try to make out with what we have.*

make up, 1 to put together: *to make up cloth into a shirt.* 2 to invent: *to make up a story.* 3 to give or do in place of: *I took a shortcut to make up for lost time.* 4 to become friends again after a quarrel: *We were always fighting and making up.* 5 to put rouge, powder, or other cosmetics on the face. 6 to compose; consist of; form: *Children made up the audience.* 7 to decide: *Make up your mind.*

make-be·lieve (māk′bi lēv′), 1 a pretending: *Elves live in the land of make-believe.* 2 pretended: *Some children have make-believe playmates.* 1 *noun,* 2 *adjective.*

mak·er (mā′kər), a person or thing that makes; manufacturer. *noun.*

make·shift (māk′shift′), something made to use for a time instead of the right thing: *When the electric lights went out, we used candles as a makeshift. noun.*

make·up (māk′up′), 1 the way in which a thing is made up or put together: *The makeup of the class includes children from different parts of the town.* 2 nature; disposition: *People of a nervous makeup are excitable.* 3 the cosmetics an actor

makeup (definition 3)
The actor carefully put on
his makeup.

The actor's makeup made
him look frightening.

a hat	i it	oi oil	ch child	a in about
ā age	ī ice	ou out	ng long	e in taken
ä far	o hot	u cup	sh she	ə = { i in pencil
e let	ō open	u̇ put	th thin	o in lemon
ē equal	ô order	ü rule	ŦH then	u in circus
ėr term			zh measure	

mall (môl), **1** a shopping center with stores built around a wide walk. **2** a wide public walk, especially one in a shopping center. *noun.*

mal·lard (mal′ərd), a wild duck of Europe, northern Asia, and North America. The male has a greenish-black head and a white band around its neck. *noun, plural* **mal·lards** or **mal·lard.**

uses in order to look the part. **4** lipstick, powder, rouge, etc., put on the face; cosmetics. *noun.*

mal·a·dy (mal′ə dē), **1** a sickness; illness; disease: *Cancer and malaria are serious maladies.* **2** any unwholesome condition: *Poverty and slums are social maladies. noun, plural* **mal·a·dies.**

ma·lar·i·a (mə ler′ē ə *or* mə lar′ē ə), a disease that causes chills, fever, and sweating. Malaria is transmitted by the bite of certain mosquitoes which have bitten infected persons. *noun.*

Ma·la·wi (mə lä′wē), a country in southeastern Africa. *noun.*

Ma·lay (mā′lā), the language spoken in Malaysia and nearby areas. *noun.*

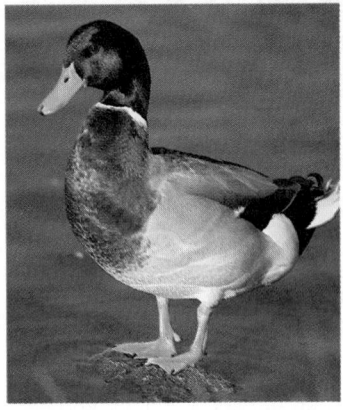

mallard
about 28 inches
(71 centimeters)
long

Word Source

Malay is the official language of Malaysia, and is also spoken on nearby islands. The following words came into English from Malay:

bamboo	cockatoo	orangutan
camphor	gingham	launch[2]
catsup	gong	paddy

Ma·lay·sia (mə lā′zhə), a country in southeastern Asia. *noun.*

male (māl), **1** a man or boy. **2** of or having to do with men or boys. **3** belonging to the sex that can fertilize eggs and be the father of young. Bucks, bulls, and roosters are male animals. **4** an animal belonging to this sex. 1,4 *noun,* 2,3 *adjective.*

Ma·li (mä′lē), a country in western Africa. *noun.*

mal·ice (mal′is), a wish to hurt or make suffer; spite: *Lincoln asked the people to act "with malice toward none, with charity for all." noun.*

ma·li·cious (mə lish′əs), wishing to hurt or make suffer; spiteful: *I think that story is nothing more than malicious gossip. adjective.*

ma·lign (mə līn′), **1** to speak evil of; slander: *You malign an honest person when you call that person a liar.* **2** evil; injurious: *Gambling often has a malign influence.* 1 *verb,* 2 *adjective.*

ma·lig·nant (mə lig′nənt), very harmful; able to cause death: *A cancer is a malignant growth. adjective.*

mal·le·a·ble (mal′ē ə bəl), able to be hammered or pressed into various shapes without being broken. Gold, silver, copper, and tin are malleable; they can be beaten into thin sheets. *adjective.*

mal·let (mal′it), a kind of hammer with a large head. Rubber mallets are used to pound out dents in metal. Wooden mallets with long handles are used to play croquet and polo. *noun.*

mal·nu·tri·tion (mal′nü trish′ən *or* mal′nyü trish′ən), a poorly nourished condition: *People suffer from malnutrition because of eating the wrong kinds of food as well as from lack of food. noun.*

malt (môlt), grain, usually barley, soaked in water until it sprouts and tastes sweet. Malt is used in making beer and ale. *noun.*

malt·ed milk (môl′tid milk′), a drink prepared by mixing a powder made of dried milk, malt, and wheat flour with milk, flavoring, and often ice cream.

mal·treat (mal trēt′), to treat roughly or cruelly; abuse: *There are laws against maltreating animals. verb.*

ma·ma or **mam·ma** (mä′mə), mother. *noun.*

mam·mal (mam′əl), one of a group of warm-blooded animals with a backbone and usually having hair. Mammals feed their young with milk from the mother's breasts. Human beings, cattle, dogs, cats, and whales are all mammals. *noun.*

M

mam·moth (mam′əth), **1** a large elephant with a hairy skin and long curved tusks. The last mammoth died thousands of years ago. **2** huge; gigantic: *Digging the Panama Canal was a mammoth undertaking.* **1** *noun,* **2** *adjective.* [Mammoths lived long ago in Europe and Northern Asia. The name for the animal comes from a Russian word.]

mammoth (definition 1)
about 10 feet (3 meters) high at the shoulder

man (man), **1** an adult male person. When a boy grows up, he becomes a man. **2** a human being; person: *No man can be certain of the future.* **3** the human race: *Man has existed for thousands of years.* **4** a male follower, servant, or employee: *Robin Hood and his merry men.* **5** a husband: *man and wife.* **6** one of the pieces that is moved about on a board in such games as chess and checkers. **7** to supply with a crew: *We can man ten ships.* **8** to serve or operate: *Man the guns.* **1-6** *noun, plural* **men;** **7,8** *verb,* **mans, manned, man·ning.** [*Man* comes from an earlier English word meaning "a human being." Look at the word history for *woman,* another word from the same root.]

man·age (man′ij), **1** to control; handle; direct: *Good riders manage their horses well. They hired someone to manage the business.* **2** to succeed in doing something: *I shall manage to keep warm with this blanket.* **3** to get along: *We managed on very little money. verb,* **man·ag·es, man·aged, man·ag·ing.**

man·age·ment (man′ij mənt), **1** control; handling; direction: *Bad management caused the bank's failure.* **2** the persons that manage a business or an institution: *The management of the store decided to increase the size of the parking lot. noun.*

man·ag·er (man′ə jər), a person who manages: *She is the manager of the department store. noun.*

man·dar·in (man′dər ən), **1** an official of high rank under the Chinese empire. **2** a small, sweet, spicy citrus fruit with a thin, orange-colored, very loose skin and sections that separate easily. *noun.*

man·date (man′dāt), **1** a command or official order. **2** a direction or authority given to a government by the votes of the people in an election: *The governor had a mandate to increase taxes. noun.*

mandolin

man·do·lin (man′də lin′), a musical instrument with a pear-shaped body and four to six pairs of metal strings. *noun.*

mane (mān), the long, heavy hair on the back of the neck of a horse, or around the head of a male lion. *noun.*

ma·neu·ver (mə nü′vər), **1** a planned movement of troops or warships: *Every year the army and navy held maneuvers for practice.* **2** a skillful plan or movement; clever trick: *When we refused to use his idea, he tried to force it on us by a series of maneuvers.* **3** to plan skillfully; use clever tricks; scheme: *Scheming people always maneuver to get what they want.* **4** to move or handle skillfully: *She maneuvered the car through the heavy traffic with ease.* **1,2** *noun,* **3,4** *verb.*

man·ga·nese (mang′gə nēz′), a hard, brittle, grayish-white metal. Manganese is a chemical element, often used mixed with other metals. *noun.*

man·ger (mān′jər), a box or trough in which hay or other food can be placed for horses or cows to eat. *noun.*

man·gle (mang′gəl), **1** to cut or tear roughly: *His hand was badly mangled when he caught it in some moving machinery.* **2** to do or play badly; ruin: *The child mangled the music because it was too difficult for her to play. verb,* **man·gles, man·gled, man·gling.**

man·go (mang′gō), the slightly sour, juicy, oval fruit of a tropical tree. Mangoes have a thick, yellowish-red rind, and are eaten ripe or are pickled when green. *noun, plural* **man·goes** or **man·gos.**

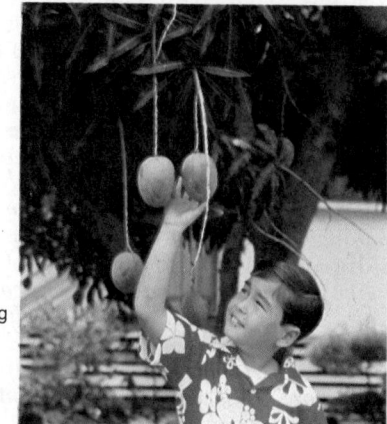
mango
The boy is picking a **mango.**

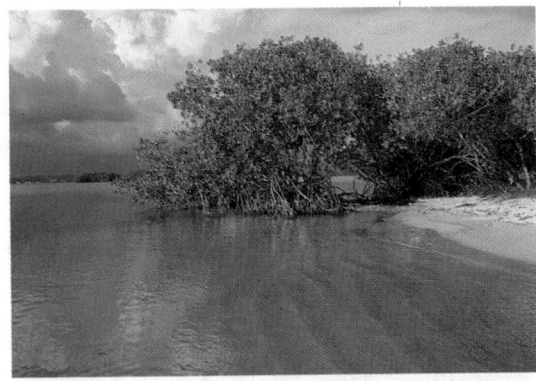

mangrove

a hat	**i** it	**oi** oil	**ch** child		a in about
ā age	**ī** ice	**ou** out	**ng** long		e in taken
ä far	**o** hot	**u** cup	**sh** she	**ə** =	i in pencil
e let	**ō** open	** u̇** put	**th** thin		o in lemon
ē equal	**ô** order	**ü** rule	**ŦH** then		u in circus
ėr term			**zh** measure		

man·grove (mang′grōv), a tropical tree or shrub having branches that send down many roots which look like trunks. Mangroves grow in swamps and along river banks. *noun.*

man·hole (man′hōl′), a hole in a street with a metal cover that can be taken off. Through a manhole, a worker can enter a sewer, or a chamber that contains electrical wiring, water mains, or telephone lines, in order to repair them. *noun.*

man·hood (man′hu̇d), **1** the condition or time of being a man: *The boy was about to enter manhood.* **2** the character or qualities of a man. *noun.*

ma·ni·a (mā′nē ə), **1** a mental illness during which a person becomes greatly excited, very active, and sometimes violent. **2** an unusual fondness; craze: *She has a mania for collecting shells. noun.*

ma·ni·ac (mā′nē ak), an insane person who is violent or destructive. *noun.*

man·i·cure (man′ə kyu̇r), **1** the trimming, cleaning, and sometimes the polishing of the fingernails. **2** to give the fingernails a manicure. 1 *noun,* 2 *verb,* **man·i·cures, man·i·cured, man·i·cur·ing.**

man·i·fes·ta·tion (man′ə fə stā′shən), a showing; act that shows or proves: *Entering the burning building was a manifestation of courage. noun.*

man·i·fold (man′ə fōld), **1** of many kinds; many and various: *manifold duties.* **2** having many parts or forms: *a manifold way to control prices. adjective.*

Ma·nil·a pa·per (mə nil′ə pā′pər), a strong, brown or brownish-yellow wrapping paper.

ma·nip·u·late (mə nip′yə lāt), **1** to handle or treat, especially with skill: *The driver of an automobile manipulates the steering wheel and pedals.* **2** to manage by clever use of influence, especially unfair influence: *He manipulated the class so that he was elected president instead of his more qualified opponent. verb,* **ma·nip·u·lates, ma·nip·u·lat·ed, ma·nip·u·lat·ing.**

Man·i·to·ba (man′ə tō′bə), a province in south central Canada. *Capital:* Winnipeg. *noun.*

man·kind (man′kīnd′ *for 1;* man′kīnd′ *for 2),*

1 the human race; all human beings: *Mankind has populated most areas of the earth.* **2** men as a group: *Mankind and womankind both like praise. noun.*

man·li·ness (man′lē nis), manly quality; manly behavior. *noun.*

man·ly (man′lē), having qualities that are by tradition admired in a man: *a manly show of strength and courage. adjective,* **man·li·er, man·li·est.**

man-made (man′mād′), made by people; not natural; artificial: *a man-made satellite. adjective.*

man·ner (man′ər), **1** a way of doing, being done, or happening: *The manner of their meeting makes a good story.* **2** a way of acting or behaving: *She has a kind manner.* **3 manners,** polite ways of behaving: *People with manners say "Please" and "Thank you." noun.*

man·ner·ly (man′ər lē), having or showing good manners; polite. *adjective.*

man-of-war (man′əv wôr′), a warship of a type used in former times. *noun, plural* **men-of-war.**

man·or (man′ər), **1** (in the Middle Ages) a large estate, part of which was set aside for the lord and the rest divided among the peasants. The peasants paid the lord rent in goods, services, or money. **2** a large estate. *noun.*

man·serv·ant (man′sėr′vənt), a male servant. *noun, plural* **men·serv·ants.**

man·sion (man′shən), a large house; stately residence. *noun.*

man·slaugh·ter (man′slô′tər), (in law) a killing that is accidental, or that is not planned: *The charge against the prisoner was changed from murder to manslaughter. noun.*

man·tel (man′tl), a shelf above a fireplace. *noun.*

man·tel·piece (man′tl pēs′), a mantel. *noun.*

man·tis (man′tis), an insect like a grasshopper, that holds its front legs doubled up as if praying; praying mantis. It eats other insects. *noun, plural* **man·tis·es.**

mantis
about 2½ inches
(6 centimeters)
long

man·tle (man′tl), **1** a loose cloak without sleeves. **2** anything that covers like a mantle: *The ground had a mantle of snow.* **3** the layer of the earth lying between its crust and its core. *noun.*

man·u·al (man′yü əl), **1** of the hands; done with the hands: *Performing surgery requires manual skill. Digging a trench with a shovel is manual labor.* **2** a small book that helps its readers to understand and use something; handbook: *A manual came with my pocket calculator.* **1** *adjective,* **2** *noun.*

man·u·fac·ture (man′yə fak′chər), **1** to make by hand or machine. A big factory manufactures goods in large quantities by using machines and dividing the work up among many people. **2** a making of articles by hand or by machine, especially in large quantities. **3** to make into something useful: *to manufacture steel into rails.* **4** to invent; make up: *Tardy students sometimes manufacture excuses.* **1,3,4** *verb,* **man·u·fac·tures, man·u·fac·tured, man·u·fac·tur·ing;** **2** *noun.*

man·u·fac·tur·er (man′yə fak′chər ər), a person or company whose business is manufacturing; owner of a factory. *noun.*

ma·nure (mə núr′ *or* mə nyúr′), animal waste, especially when put in or on the ground to make the soil rich for growing crops. *noun.*

man·u·script (man′yə skript), a handwritten or typewritten book or article. Manuscripts are sent to publishers to be made into printed books, magazine articles, and the like. *noun.*

man·y (men′ē), **1** consisting of a great number: *many years ago. There are many children in the city.* **2** a great number: *Do you know many of them?* **3** a large number of people or things: *There were many at the dance.* **1** *adjective,* **more, most;** **2,3** *noun, pronoun.*

how many, what number of: *How many days are there in March?*

map (map), **1** a drawing of the earth's surface or of part of it, showing countries, cities, rivers, seas, lakes, and mountains. **2** a drawing of the sky or of part of it, showing the positions of the stars and the planets. **3** to make a map of; show on a map: *Explorers mapped many areas of the earth.* **4** to plan; arrange in detail: *Each Monday we map out the week's work.* **1,2** *noun,* **3,4** *verb,* **maps, mapped, map·ping.**
[*Map* comes from a Latin word meaning "napkin" or "cloth." Early maps were drawn on cloth.]

ma·ple (mā′pəl), **1** a tree grown for shade, ornament, its wood, or its sap. There are many kinds of maples. They all have leaves with deep notches and winged seeds that grow in pairs. **2** its hard, light-colored wood. *noun.*

maple syrup, syrup made from the sap of one kind of maple.

mar (mär), to spoil the beauty of; damage; injure: *Weeds mar a garden. The nails in my shoes marred the floor. verb,* **mars, marred, mar·ring.**

Mar., March.

mar·a·thon (mar′ə thon), **1** a foot race of 26 miles, 385 yards (about 42 kilometers). **2** any long race or contest. *noun.*

marathon Our word *marathon* was named for Marathon, a plain in Greece. The news of a Greek military victory in 490 B.C. was carried by a runner all the way from Marathon to the city of Athens, about 25 miles away.

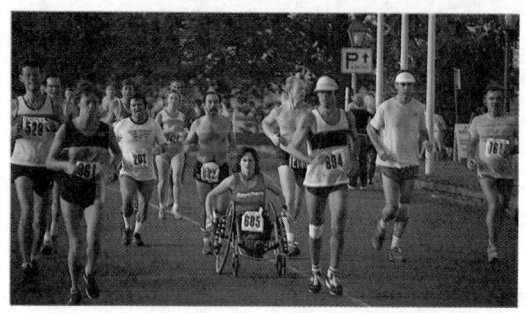

mar·ble (mär′bəl), **1** a hard limestone, white or colored, that can take a beautiful polish. Marble is much used for statues and in buildings. **2** made of marble: *a marble floor.* **3** a small, usually colored glass ball, used in children's games. **4 marbles,** a children's game played with these balls. Players take turns shooting a marble with a flick of the thumb to knock other marbles out of a ring. **1,3,4** *noun,* **2** *adjective.*

march (märch), **1** to walk as soldiers do, in time and with steps of the same length: *The members of the band marched in the parade to the beat of the drums.* **2** the act of marching: *The band began their march.* **3** music meant for marching: *She enjoys playing marches on the piano.* **4** to walk or go steadily: *He marched to the front of the room and began his speech.* **5** to cause to march or go: *The teacher marched the children out to the playground.* **6** to move forward; advance: *History marches on.* **7** progress: *History records the march of events.* **1,4-6** *verb,* **2,3,7** *noun, plural* **march·es.**

March (märch), the third month of the year. It has 31 days. *noun.*
[*March* comes from a Latin word meaning "of Mars," the Roman god of war.]

mare (mer *or* mar), a female horse, donkey, or zebra. *noun.*

mar·gar·ine (mär′jər ən *or* mär′jər ēn′), a substitute for butter, made from cottonseed oil, soybean oil, or the like; oleomargarine. *noun.*

mar·gin (mär′jən), **1** the blank space around a page, that has no writing or printing on it: *Do not write in the margin.* **2** edge; border: *the margin of the lake.* **3** an extra amount; amount beyond what is necessary; difference: *We allow a margin of 15 minutes in catching a train. noun.*

mar·i·gold (mar′ə gōld), a plant with yellow, orange, brownish, or red flowers. *noun.*

mar·i·jua·na (mar′ə wä′nə), the dried leaves and flowers of the hemp plant. Marijuana is a drug which is sometimes smoked for its effect. *noun.*

ma·ri·na (mə rē′nə), a dock where small boats can tie up. *noun.*

ma·rine (mə rēn′), **1** of the sea; found in the sea; produced by the sea: *Seals are marine animals.* **2** of shipping; of the navy; for use at sea: *marine law, marine power, marine supplies.* **3** Also, **Marine.** a person serving in the Marine Corps. **1,2** *adjective,* **3** *noun.*

Marine Corps, a branch of the armed forces of the United States with its own sea, air, and land units.

mar·i·ner (mar′ə nər), one who navigates a ship; sailor; seaman. *noun.*

mar·i·o·nette (mar′ē ə net′), a puppet moved by strings or wires, often on a little stage. *noun.*

marionette

mar·i·time (mar′ə tīm), **1** of the sea; having something to do with shipping and sailing: *Ships and sailors are governed by maritime law.* **2** on the sea; living on or near the sea: *Maritime people engage in boating and fishing.* *adjective.*

mark[1] (märk), **1** a trace or impression made by some object on another. A line, dot, stain, or scar is a mark. **2** a line or dot to show position: *This mark shows how far you jumped.* **3** the line where a race starts: *On the mark; get set; go.* **4** a sign or indication of: *Saying "Thank you" is a mark of good manners.* **5** a written or printed stroke or

sign: *punctuation marks. She took up her pen and made a few marks on the paper.* **6** a grade; letter or number to show how well one has done: *My mark in arithmetic was B.* **7** to give grades to; rate: *The teacher marked our examination papers.* **8** to make a mark on: *Be careful not to mark the table.* **9** to put in a pin or make a line to show where a place is: *Mark all the large cities on this map.* **10** to show clearly; be a sign or indication of: *A tall pine marks the beginning of the trail. A frown marked her displeasure.* **11** a target; something to be aimed at: *The empty can was an easy mark.* **12** to see; notice; give attention to: *Mark my words; her plan will not fail.* **1-6,11** *noun,* **7-10,12** *verb.*

make one's mark, to succeed; become well known: *That girl is a hard worker; she'll make her mark.*

mark off or **mark out,** to make lines to show the position of or to separate: *We marked out a tennis court. The hedge marks off our yard from our neighbor's yard.*

mark up, to damage; spoil the appearance of: *Don't mark up the desks.*

mark[2] (märk), a unit of money in East Germany and West Germany. *noun.*

marked (märkt), very noticeable; very plain: *There are marked differences between apples and oranges.* *adjective.*

mark·er (mär′kər), a kind of pen used to write or draw: *The children were busy drawing with their markers. noun.*

mar·ket (mär′kit), **1** an open space or covered building where food, cattle, or other things are shown for sale. **2** to sell: *The farmer cannot market all of his wheat.* **3** a store for the sale of food: *a meat market.* **4** to go shopping for food and other things: *We go marketing on Saturday morning.* **5** a particular area or group to which goods may be sold: *The United States is a large market for South American coffee.* **6** the demand for something; price offered: *The drought created a high market for corn.* **1,3,5,6** *noun,* **2,4** *verb.*

mar·ket·place (mär′kət plās′), a place where a market is held. *noun.*

mark·ing (mär′king), a mark or marks: *The bird had beautiful markings. noun.*

marks·man (märks′mən), a person who shoots well. *noun, plural* **marks·men.**

mar·ma·lade (mär′mə lād), a preserve similar to jam, made of oranges or of other fruit. The peel is usually sliced up and boiled with the fruit. *noun.* [*Marmalade* comes from two Greek words meaning "honey" and "apple."]

ma·roon[1] (mə rün′), very dark brownish-red. *adjective.*

M

ma·roon[2] (mə rün′), **1** to put a person ashore alone in a deserted place: *Pirates used to maroon people on desert islands.* **2** to leave in a lonely, helpless position: *During the storm we were marooned in a cabin miles from town.* verb.

mar·quis (mär′kwis or mär kē′), a nobleman ranking below a duke and above an earl or count. noun, plural **mar·quis·es, mar·quis** (mär kē′).

mar·quise (mär kēz′), **1** the wife or widow of a marquis. **2** a woman whose rank is equal to that of a marquis. noun.

mar·riage (mar′ij), **1** a living together as husband and wife; married life: *We wished the bride and groom a happy marriage.* **2** the ceremony of being married; wedding. noun.

mar·ried (mar′ēd), **1** living together as husband and wife: *a married couple.* **2** having a husband or wife: *a married man.* **3** of husband and wife: *Married life has many rewards.* adjective.

mar·row (mar′ō), the soft substance that fills the hollow central part of most bones. noun.

mar·ry (mar′ē), **1** to join as husband and wife: *The minister married them.* **2** to take as husband or wife: *He plans to marry her soon.* **3** to become married: *She married late in life.* verb, **mar·ries, mar·ried, mar·ry·ing.**

Mars (märz), **1** the Roman god of war. **2** the planet next beyond the earth. It is the fourth in distance from the sun. noun.

Mars (definition 2)
Mars appears red from the earth.

marsh (märsh), low land covered at times by water; soft, wet land; swamp. noun, plural **marsh·es.**

mar·shal (mär′shəl), **1** an officer of various kinds, especially a police officer. A United States marshal is an officer of a federal court whose duties are like those of a sheriff. **2** a person in charge of a parade or ceremony: *She is our parade marshal.* **3** to arrange in proper order: *She took great care in marshaling her facts for the debate.* **1,2** noun, **3** verb.

marsh·mal·low (märsh′mal′ō or märsh′mel′ō), a soft, white, spongy candy, covered with powdered sugar. noun.

marsh·y (mär′shē), soft and wet like a marsh: *a marshy field.* adjective, **marsh·i·er, marsh·i·est.**

mar·su·pi·al (mär sü′pē əl), a mammal that carries its young in a pouch. Kangaroos and opossums are marsupials. noun.

mart (märt), a market; center of trade: *New York and London are two great marts of the world.* noun.

mar·tial (mär′shəl), of war; suitable for war: *the martial arts.* adjective.

Mar·tian (mär′shən), **1** of the planet Mars: *The Martian atmosphere has little oxygen.* **2** a supposed inhabitant of the planet Mars. **1** adjective, **2** noun.

mar·tin (märt′n), a large swallow with a short beak and a forked tail. noun.

mar·tyr (mär′tər), **1** a person who is put to death or is made to suffer greatly because of his or her religion or other beliefs. Many of the early Christians were martyrs. **2** to put a person to death or torture because of his or her religion or other beliefs. **3** a person who suffers greatly. **1,3** noun, **2** verb.

mar·vel (mär′vəl), **1** something wonderful; astonishing thing: *The airplane is one of the marvels of science.* **2** to be filled with wonder; be astonished: *I marvel at your boldness. She marveled at the beautiful sunset.* **1** noun, **2** verb.

mar·vel·ous (mär′və ləs), **1** causing wonder; extraordinary: *The walk on the moon was a marvelous event.* **2** excellent; splendid; fine: *a marvelous time.* adjective.

Mar·y·land (mer′ə lənd), one of the southeastern states of the United States. *Abbreviation:* Md. or MD *Capital:* Annapolis. noun.
[Charles I, king of England, named *Maryland* in 1632 in honor of his queen, Henrietta Maria, who lived from 1609 to 1669.]

mas·cot (mas′kot), an animal, person, or thing supposed to bring good luck: *The children kept the stray dog as a mascot.* noun.

marsupial

mas·cu·line (mas′kyə lin), **1** of men or boys. **2** like a man; manly. *adjective.*

mash (mash), **1** to beat into a soft mass; crush to a uniform mass: *I'll mash the potatoes.* **2** a warm mixture of bran or meal and water for horses and other animals. 1 *verb,* 2 *noun, plural* **mash·es.**

mask (mask), **1** a covering to hide or protect the face: *The burglar wore a mask. The firefighter wore a gas mask.* **2** to cover the face with a mask: *I didn't recognize them because they were masked.* **3** a disguise: *Their dislike for each other was hidden under a mask of friendship.* **4** to hide or disguise: *A smile masked his disappointment.* 1,3 *noun,* 2,4 *verb.*

masking tape, a sticky tape used to hold things in place or to protect surfaces when painting.

ma·son (mā′sn), a person who builds with stone or brick. *noun.*

ma·son·ry (mā′sn rē), **1** a wall, foundation, or part of a building made of brick or stone. **2** the trade or skill of a mason. *noun.*

mas·que·rade (mas′kə rād′), **1** to disguise oneself; go about under false pretenses: *The king masqueraded as a beggar to find out if his people really liked him.* **2** a party or dance at which masks and fancy costumes are worn. 1 *verb,* **mas·que·rades, mas·que·rad·ed, mas·que·rad·ing;** 2 *noun.*

mass[1] (mas), **1** a lump: *a mass of dough.* **2** a large quantity together: *a mass of flowers.* **3** to gather together in quantity; form or collect into a mass: *Mass the peonies behind the roses. Many people massed in the square.* **4** the majority; greater part: *The great mass of the world's population wants to live in peace.* **5** of or by many people: *a mass protest.* **6** on a large scale: *By making mass purchases from factories, the department store was able to sell at low prices.* **7** bulk or size: *They were awed by the sheer mass of the iceberg.* **8** the quantity of matter anything contains. The mass of an object is always the same, whether on earth, on another planet, or in outer space. Its weight, which depends on the force of gravity, can vary. 1,2,4,7,8 *noun, plural* **mass·es;** 3 *verb,* 5,6 *adjective.*

Mass or **mass**[2] (mas), the main service of worship in the Roman Catholic Church and in some other churches. The Mass consists of many prayers and ceremonies. *noun, plural* **Mass·es** or **mass·es.**

Mass., Massachusetts.

Mas·sa·chu·setts (mas′ə chü′sits), one of the northeastern states of the United States. *Abbreviation:* Mass. or MA *Capital:* Boston. *noun.*
[*Massachusetts* got its name from Massachusetts Bay, which was named for an American Indian tribe, the Massachuset. This name probably meant "at the big hills," that is, the Blue Hills south of Boston.]

mas·sa·cre (mas′ə kər), **1** a savage killing of many people or animals. **2** to kill many people or animals needlessly or cruelly: *Big-game hunters massacred thousands of African wild animals.*

a hat	i it	oi oil	ch child	a in about
ā age	ī ice	ou out	ng long	e in taken
ä far	o hot	u cup	sh she	ə = i in pencil
e let	ō open	u̇ put	th thin	o in lemon
ē equal	ô order	ü rule	ᴛʜ then	u in circus
ėr term			zh measure	

1 *noun,* 2 *verb,* **mas·sa·cres, mas·sa·cred, mas·sa·cring.**

mas·sage (mə säzh′), **1** a rubbing and kneading the muscles and joints to increase the circulation of the blood: *A thorough massage feels good when you are tired.* **2** to give a massage to: *Let me massage your back for you.* 1 *noun,* 2 *verb,* **mas·sag·es, mas·saged, mas·sag·ing.**
[*Massage* comes from an Arabic word meaning "to touch" or "to stroke." Originally the idea in Arabic referred to simply touching various parts of the body.]

mas·sive (mas′iv), big and heavy; large and solid: *a massive wrestler. adjective.*

mast (mast), **1** a long pole of wood or steel set upright on a ship to support the sails and rigging. **2** any tall, upright pole: *the mast of a derrick. noun.*

mas·ter (mas′tər), **1** a person who has power or authority over others; owner, employer, or director: *The dog ran away from its master. The salesman asked to speak to the master of the house.* **2** a male teacher, especially in private schools: *The master taught his pupils how to read.* **3** a title of respect for a boy: *First prize goes to Master Henry Adams.* **4** an expert, such as a great artist or skilled workman. **5** very skilled: *She is a master painter.* **6** main; controlling: *a master plan, a master switch.* **7** to become the master of; conquer; control: *She learned to master her temper.* **8** to learn; become skillful at: *He has mastered riding his bicycle.* 1-4 *noun,* 5,6 *adjective,* 7,8 *verb.*

mas·ter·ful (mas′tər fəl), **1** fond of power or authority; domineering: *a masterful leader.* **2** expert; skillful; masterly: *The violinist gave a masterful performance. adjective.*

mas·ter·ly (mas′tər lē), expert; skillful: *a masterly painter, a masterly book. adjective.*

mas·ter·piece (mas′tər pēs′), **1** anything done or made with wonderful skill; perfect piece of art or workmanship. **2** a person's greatest piece of work. *noun.*

mas·ter·y (mas′tər ē), **1** power such as a master has; rule; control. **2** very great skill or knowledge: *The biologist showed a mastery of her field. noun.*

mast·head (mast′hed′), the top of a ship's mast. A crow's-nest near the masthead of the lower mast is used as a lookout. *noun.*

mas·to·don (mas′tə don), one of a group of extinct animals much like mammoths and present-day elephants. *noun.*

mat (mat), **1** a small rug of woven straw, rubber, or the like, used to protect a floor: *Wipe your feet on the mat. I stepped from the shower onto the bath mat.* **2** a piece of material to put under a dish,

M

vase, or lamp. A mat is put under a hot dish when it is brought to the table. **3** a thick pad covered with canvas or plastic that is spread on the floor for use in exercising, tumbling, wrestling, or relaxing. **4** anything growing thickly packed or tangled together: *a mat of weeds.* **5** to pack or tangle together like a mat: *The swimmer's wet hair was matted.* 1-4 *noun,* 5 *verb,* **mats, mat·ted, mat·ting.**

mat·a·dor (mat′ə dôr), the chief performer in a bullfight. The matador kills the bull with a sword. *noun.*

matador

match[1] (mach), a short, slender piece of wood or pasteboard tipped with a mixture that catches fire when rubbed on a rough or specially prepared surface. *noun, plural* **match·es.**

match[2] (mach), **1** an equal; person or thing equal to another or much like another: *A child is not a match for an adult.* **2** to be equal to in a contest: *No one could match the skill of the unknown archer.* **3** to be alike; go well together: *The rugs and the wallpaper match.* **4** to find the equal of or one exactly like: *Until I can match this wool, I won't be able to finish knitting the sweater.* **5** a game; contest: *a boxing match, a tennis match.* **6** to try one's skill or strength against; oppose: *She matched her skill against mine.* **7** a marriage: *In former times, parents often arranged matches for their children.* 1,5,7 *noun, plural* **match·es;** 2-4,6 *verb.*

match·less (mach′lis), so great or wonderful that it cannot be equaled: *Pioneer women had matchless courage. adjective.*

mate (māt), **1** one of a pair: *The eagle mourned its dead mate. Where is the mate to this glove?* **2** to join in a pair in order to produce young: *Birds mate in the spring.* **3** a husband or wife. **4** to marry. **5** an officer of a ship next below the captain. **6** a companion or fellow worker: *Hand me a hammer, mate.* 1,3,5,6 *noun,* 2,4 *verb,* **mates, mat·ed, mat·ing.**

ma·te·ri·al (mə tir′ē əl), **1** what a thing is made from or used for: *Wood and steel are building materials. We thought her childhood experiences were fine material for a novel.* **2** a fabric; cloth: *I chose a colorful material for the curtains.* **3** of matter or things; physical: *the material world.* **4** of

the body: *Food and shelter are material comforts.* 1,2 *noun,* 3,4 *adjective.*

ma·te·ri·al·ize (mə tir′ē ə līz), **1** to become an actual fact; be realized: *Our plans for the party did not materialize.* **2** to appear or cause to appear in material or bodily form: *A spirit materialized from the smoke of the magician's fire. verb,* **ma·te·ri·al·iz·es, ma·te·ri·al·ized, ma·te·ri·al·iz·ing.**

ma·ter·nal (mə tėr′nl), **1** of or like a mother; motherly: *maternal kindness.* **2** related on the mother's side of the family: *Everyone has two paternal grandparents and two maternal grandparents. adjective.*

math (math), mathematics. *noun.*

math·e·mat·i·cal (math′ə mat′ə kəl), **1** of mathematics; having something to do with mathematics: *Mathematical problems are not always easy.* **2** exact; accurate: *mathematical measurements. adjective.*

math·e·ma·ti·cian (math′ə mə tish′ən), a person who is an expert in mathematics. *noun.*

math·e·mat·ics (math′ə mat′iks), the science that deals with the measurement and relationships of quantities. Arithmetic is one part of mathematics. *noun.*

mat·i·nee (mat′n ā′), a dramatic or musical performance held in the afternoon. *noun.*

mat·ri·mo·ny (mat′rə mō′nē), the state of being married. *noun.*

ma·tron (mā′trən), **1** a wife or widow, especially an older married woman. **2** a woman who manages the household matters of a school, hospital, dormitory, or other institution. A police matron has charge of the women in a jail. *noun.*

mat·ter (mat′ər), **1** what things are made of; material; substance. Matter occupies space, has weight, and can exist as a solid, liquid, or gas. **2** an affair: *business matters, a matter of life and death.* **3** things written or printed: *reading matter.* **4** an amount; quantity: *a matter of two days, a matter of twenty miles.* **5** importance: *Let it go since it is of no matter.* **6** to be important: *Nothing seems to matter when you are very sick.* 1-5 *noun,* 6 *verb.*

as a matter of course, as something to be expected: *He accepted his daily chores as a matter of course.*

as a matter of fact, in truth; in reality; actually: *As a matter of fact I was not present yesterday.*

for that matter, so far as that is concerned: *For that matter, we did not know what we were doing.*

no matter, regardless of: *No matter how long it takes, I'm going to finish this project.*

What is the matter? What is the trouble? *What is the matter with the child?*

mat·ter-of-fact (mat′ər əv fakt′), sticking to facts; not imaginative or fanciful. *adjective.*

mat·tress (mat′ris), a covering of strong cloth stuffed with cotton, foam rubber, or some other material, and sometimes containing springs. It is used on a bed or as a bed. *noun, plural* **mat·tress·es.**

ma·ture (mə chůr′, mə tůr′, *or* mə tyůr′), **1** ripe;

full-grown: *Grain is harvested when it is mature.*
2 to ripen; come to full growth: *These apples are maturing fast.* **3** mentally or physically like an adult: *He is very mature for one so young.*
1,3 *adjective,* **2** *verb,* **ma·tures, ma·tured, ma·tur·ing.**

ma·tur·i·ty (mə chùr′ə tē, mə tùr′ə tē, *or* mə tyùr′ə tē), **1** a ripeness; full development: *The frost struck before the peaches could reach maturity.* **2** the condition of being mature: *He reached maturity at an early age. noun.*

maul (môl), **1** a very heavy hammer or mallet. **2** to beat and pull about; handle roughly: *The lion mauled its keeper badly.* **1** *noun,* **2** *verb.*

Mau·ri·ta·ni·a (môr′ə tā′nē ə), a country in western Africa. *noun.*

max·im (mak′səm), a rule of conduct; proverb: *"A stitch in time saves nine"* and *"Look before you leap"* are maxims. *noun.*

LOST TIME IS NEVER FOUND AGAIN.

maxim

max·i·mum (mak′sə məm), **1** the largest or highest amount; greatest possible amount: *Sixteen miles in a day was the maximum that any of our club walked last summer.* **2** largest; highest; greatest possible: *The maximum score on this test is 100.* **1** *noun,* **2** *adjective.*

may (mā), **1** to be permitted or allowed to: *May I have an apple? May I go now?* **2** to be possible that it will: *It may rain tomorrow. The train may be late.* **3** it is hoped that: *May you have a pleasant trip. verb, past tense* **might.**

May (mā), the fifth month of the year. It has 31 days. *noun.*
[*May* comes from a Latin word meaning "of Maia." Maia was a Roman goddess and wife of Vulcan, the Roman god of fire.]

may·be (mā′bē), possibly; perhaps: *Maybe you'll have better luck next time. adverb.*

may·on·naise (mā′ə nāz′), a salad dressing made of egg yolks, vegetable oil, vinegar or lemon juice, and seasoning, beaten together until thick. *noun.*

may·or (mā′ər), a person at the head of a city or town government. *noun.*

a hat	**i** it	**oi** oil	**ch** child	a in about
ā age	**ī** ice	**ou** out	**ng** long	e in taken
ä far	**o** hot	**u** cup	**sh** she	ə = i in pencil
e let	**ō** open	**ù** put	**th** thin	o in lemon
ē equal	**ô** order	**ü** rule	**ᴛʜ** then	u in circus
ėr term			**zh** measure	

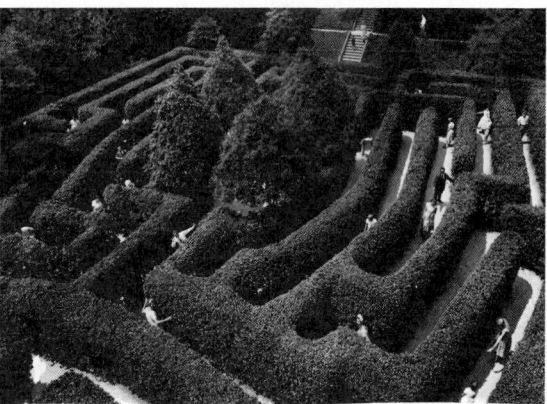

maze (definition 1)

maze (māz), **1** a network of paths through which it is hard to find one's way: *A guide led us through the maze of caves.* **2** a confusion; muddle: *I couldn't find what I wanted in the maze of papers on the desk. noun.*

MD, Maryland (used with postal Zip Code).

Md., Maryland.

M.D., Doctor of Medicine.

me (mē). *I* and *me* mean the person speaking. *She said, "Give the dog to me. I like it and it likes me." pronoun.*

ME, Maine (used with postal Zip Code).

Me., Maine.

mead·ow (med′ō), a piece of grassy land, especially one used for growing hay or as a pasture for grazing animals. *noun.*

meadowlark
about 10 inches
(25 centimeters) long

mead·ow·lark (med′ō lärk′), a bird of North America about as big as a robin, having a thick body, short tail, and a yellow breast marked with black. *noun.*

mea·ger (mē′gər), **1** poor; scanty: *a meager meal.* **2** thin; lean: *a meager face. adjective.*

M

meal[1] (mēl), **1** breakfast, lunch, dinner, or supper. **2** the food eaten or served at any one time: *We enjoyed each meal at the hotel. noun.*

meal[2] (mēl), grain ground up: *corn meal. noun.*

meal·time (mēl′tīm′), the usual time for eating a meal. *noun.*

meal·y (mē′lē), dry and easily crumbled: *mealy baked potatoes. adjective,* **meal·i·er, meal·i·est.**

mean[1] (mēn), **1** to have as its thought; intend to say: *Can you make out what this sentence means?* **2** to intend; have as a purpose; have in mind: *Do you think they mean to come? I mean to have the chops for dinner.* **3** to be important or valuable: *Good friends mean a lot to a person.* **4** to be a sign of; indicate: *Red means stop and green means go. verb,* **means, meant, mean·ing.**

mean[2] (mēn), **1** not noble; petty; unkind: *It is mean to spread gossip about your friends.* **2** of poor appearance; shabby: *The poor family lived in a mean hut.* **3** stingy; selfish: *A miser is mean about money.* **4** hard to manage; troublesome; bad-tempered: *a mean horse. adjective.*

mean[3] (mēn), **1** halfway between two extremes; average: *The mean number between 3 and 9 is 6.* **2 means, a** the method used to bring something about: *We won the game by fair means.* **b** wealth: *a man of means.* **1** *adjective,* **2** *noun.*

by all means, certainly; in any possible way; at any cost: *By all means stop in to see us.*

by means of, by the use of; through; with: *I found my dog by means of a notice in the paper.*

by no means, certainly not; in no way; not at all: *I shall by no means miss the chance to see her while she is in town.*

me·an·der (mē an′dər), **1** to follow a winding course: *A brook meanders through the meadow.* **2** to wander aimlessly: *We were meandering through the park.* **3** an aimless wandering. **1,2** *verb,* **3** *noun.*

mean·ing (mē′ning), that which is meant or intended: *The meaning of that sentence is clear. noun.*

meant (ment). See **mean**[1]. *He explained what he meant. That sign was meant as a warning. verb.*

mean·time (mēn′tīm′), the time between: *Dinner isn't ready yet; in the meantime, let's set the table. noun.*

mean·while (mēn′hwīl′), **1** in the time between: *I have to leave in an hour; meanwhile I'm going to rest.* **2** at the same time: *The children got lost in the woods; meanwhile, their parents were searching for them. adverb.*

mea·sles (mē′zəlz), **1** a disease most often of children that causes a bad cold, fever, and a breaking out of small red spots on the skin. Unless you are vaccinated against measles, you can catch the disease if you are around someone who has it. **2** a milder disease with similar breaking out; German measles. *noun singular or plural.*

meas·ure (mezh′ər), **1** to find the size or amount of anything; find how long, wide, deep, large, or much a thing is: *We measured the room and found it was 20 feet long and 15 feet wide. We measured the amount of water in the pail and found that it was two liters.* **2** to mark off or out, in inches, meters, pounds, liters, or some other unit: *Measure off 2 yards of this silk. Measure out a bushel of potatoes.* **3** to be of a certain size or amount: *Buy some paper that measures 20 by 25 centimeters.* **4** a size or amount: *His waist measure is 30 inches.* **5** something with which to measure. A yardstick, a meterstick, and a cup are common measures. **6** a unit or standard of measure, such as an inch, a kilometer, an acre, a liter, a gallon, a pound, or a gram. **7** any standard of comparison, estimation, or judgment: *Academic achievement is not the only measure of one's success in school.* **8** a system of measurement: *liquid measure, dry measure, square measure.* **9** a quantity, degree, or proportion: *Carelessness is in large measure responsible for many accidents.* **10** a bar of music. **11** an action meant as means to an end: *What measures shall we take to solve this problem?* **12** a proposed law; a law: *This measure has passed the Senate.* **1-3** *verb,* **meas·ures, meas·ured, meas·ur·ing;** **4-12** *noun.*

measure up to, to meet the standard of: *The movie did not measure up to my expectations.*

measure (definition 10)

meas·ure·ment (mezh′ər mənt), **1** a measuring; finding the size, quantity, or amount: *The measurement of length by a yardstick is easy.* **2** a size, quantity, or amount found by measuring: *The measurements of the room are 10 by 15 feet.* **3** a system of measuring or of measures: *Metric measurement is used in most countries. noun.*

meat (mēt), **1** animal flesh used for food. Fish and poultry are not usually called meat. **2** food of any kind: *meat and drink.* **3** the part of anything that can be eaten: *The meat of the walnut is tasty.* **4** the essential part or parts: *the meat of an argument, the meat of a book. noun.*

me·chan·ic (mə kan′ik), a person skilled at working with tools, especially someone who repairs machines: *an automobile mechanic. noun.*

me·chan·i·cal (mə kan′ə kəl), **1** having something to do with machinery: *She is good at solving mechanical problems.* **2** made or worked by machinery: *a mechanical doll.* **3** without expression: *The performance was very mechanical. adjective.*

me·chan·ics (mə kan′iks), **1** the branch of physics dealing with the action of forces on solids, liquids, and gases at rest or in motion. **2** knowledge dealing with machinery. *noun.*

mech·a·nism (mek′ə niz′əm), a machine or its working parts: *the mechanism of a watch. noun.*

mech·a·nize (mek′ə nīz), to do by machinery, rather than by hand: *Much housework can be mechanized. verb,* **mech·a·niz·es, mech·a·nized, mech·a·niz·ing.**

med·al (med′l), a piece of metal like a coin, with a figure or inscription stamped on it: *She received the gold medal for winning the race. noun.*

medal
a **medal** won in the Olympic games

me·dal·lion (mə dal′yən), **1** a large medal. **2** a design or ornament shaped like a medal. A design on a book or a pattern in lace may be called a medallion. *noun.*

med·dle (med′l), to busy oneself with or in other people's things or affairs without being asked or needed: *Don't meddle with my books or my toys. That busybody has been meddling in my business. verb,* **med·dles, med·dled, med·dling.**

med·dler (med′lər), a person who interferes or meddles. *noun.*

med·dle·some (med′l səm), meddling; interfering; likely to meddle in other people's affairs. *adjective.*

me·di·a (mē′dē ə), more than one medium. See definitions 3-5 of **medium.** *noun plural.*

me·di·ate (mē′dē āt), to come in to help settle a dispute; act in order to bring about an agreement between persons or sides: *to mediate in a quarrel, to mediate between a company and its striking employees. verb,* **me·di·ates, me·di·at·ed, me·di·at·ing.**

med·i·cal (med′ə kəl), having to do with healing or with the science and art of medicine: *medical advice, medical schools, medical supplies. adjective.*

me·dic·i·nal (mə dis′n əl), having value as medicine; healing; helping; relieving. *adjective.*

med·i·cine (med′ə sən), **1** a substance, such as a drug, used to treat, prevent, or cure disease: *While I was sick I had to take my medicine three times a day.* **2** the science of treating, preventing, or curing disease and improving health: *You must study medicine for several years before you can become a doctor. noun.*

medicine man, a person considered by American Indians to have close contact with the world of spirits and to have the power to cure sickness.

me·di·e·val (mē′dē ē′vəl), of or belonging to the Middle Ages (the years from about A.D. 500 to about 1450). *adjective.*

me·di·o·cre (mē′dē ō′kər), of average or lower than average quality; ordinary; neither good nor bad: *He is a mediocre student. adjective.*
[*Mediocre* comes from two Latin words meaning "middle" and "jagged mountain." The root idea was that climbing halfway up a mountain was an average thing to do. Later the meaning changed to include ordinary or average success in anything done.]

med·i·tate (med′ə tāt), to think quietly; reflect, especially about serious things. *verb,* **med·i·tates, med·i·tat·ed, med·i·tat·ing.**

med·i·ta·tion (med′ə tā′shən), any quiet thought, especially about serious things. *noun.*

Med·i·ter·ra·ne·an Sea (med′ə tə rā′nē ən sē′), a large sea bordered by Europe, Asia, and Africa.

me·di·um (mē′dē əm), **1** having a middle position, quality, or condition: *Eggs can be cooked hard, soft, or medium. He is of medium height.* **2** that which is in the middle; neither one extreme nor the other; middle condition: *a happy medium between city and country life.* **3** a substance or agent through which anything acts; means: *Money is a medium of exchange. Copper wire is a medium for conducting electricity.* **4** Usually, **media.** a means of communication, especially to large numbers of people: *Newspapers and television are important advertising media. Television is a completely different medium from the stage.* **5** a substance in which something can live; environment: *Water is the only medium in which fish can live.* **1** *adjective,* **2-5** *noun, plural* **me·di·ums** or **me·di·a** for 3-5.

med·ley (med′lē), a piece of music made up of parts from other pieces. *noun, plural* **med·leys.**

meek (mēk), giving up too easily; not strong enough to resist; too shy or humble: *Don't be meek about asking for the job. adjective.*

meet (mēt), **1** to come face to face with something or someone coming from the other direction: *Our car met another car on a narrow road.* **2** to come together; join: *Two roads met near the bridge.* **3** to keep an appointment with: *Meet me at one o'clock.* **4** to be introduced to: *Have you met my sister?* **5** to fulfill; satisfy; pay: *He did not have enough money to meet his bills.* **6** a gathering for athletic competition: *Everyone has gone to the track meet.* **1-5** *verb,* **meets, met, meet·ing; 6** *noun.*

meet with, 1 to find by chance; encounter: *We*

met with bad weather. **2** to have; get: *The plan met with approval.*

meet·ing (mē′ting), **1** a coming together: *The meeting of the two streams produces a large river.* **2** a gathering or assembly of persons for worship: *a Quaker meeting, a prayer meeting.* **3** any gathering or assembly: *Our club held a meeting.* *noun.*

meg·a·phone (meg′ə fōn), a device shaped like a funnel and used to increase the sound of the voice: *The cheerleader yelled through a megaphone. noun.*

Word History

megaphone With a megaphone one can make the voice very loud, or be heard over a great distance. *Megaphone* comes from two Greek words meaning "great" and "sound."

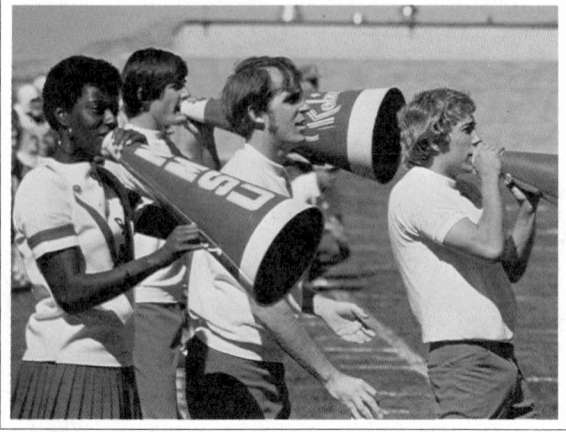

mel·an·chol·y (mel′ən kol′ē), **1** sadness; low spirits; tendency to be sad. **2** sad; gloomy. **3** causing sadness: *a melancholy scene.* **1** *noun*, **2,3** *adjective.*

mel·low (mel′ō), **1** ripe, soft, and with a good flavor; sweet and juicy: *a mellow apple.* **2** soft and rich: *a violin with a mellow tone, velvet with a mellow color.* **3** softened and made wise by age and experience: *He has grown mellow as he has aged. adjective.*

me·lod·ic (mə lod′ik), **1** having to do with melody. **2** melodious. *adjective.*

me·lo·di·ous (mə lō′dē əs), **1** sweet-sounding; pleasing to the ear; musical: *a melodious voice.* **2** producing melody: *melodious birds. adjective.*

mel·o·dy (mel′ə dē), **1** a succession of single tones in music; tune. Music has melody, harmony, and rhythm. **2** the main tune in a piece of music: *He sang the melody to a piano accompaniment. noun, plural* **mel·o·dies.**

mel·on (mel′ən), a large, sweet, juicy fruit with a hard rind. Melons grow on vines. Cantaloupes and watermelons are kinds of melons. *noun.*
[*Melon* comes from two Greek words meaning "apple" and "gourd" or "ripe fruit." Melons were thought to look like apples.]

melt (melt), **1** to turn from a solid into a liquid by heating. Ice becomes water when it melts. **2** to dissolve: *Sugar melts in water.* **3** to disappear gradually: *The clouds melted away, and the sun came out.* **4** to change very gradually: *In the rainbow, the green melts into blue, the blue into violet.* **5** to make or become gentle; soften: *Their kindness melted her heart. verb.*

melt·down (melt′doun′), an accident in a nuclear reactor, involving the failure of cooling systems and an increase of heat in the nuclear fuel until the fuel melts through its container and gets out. *noun.*

mem·ber (mem′bər), **1** a person, animal, or thing belonging to a group: *Every member of the family was home for the holidays. The club has one hundred members.* **2** a part of a plant, animal, or human body, especially a leg, arm, or wing. *noun.*

mem·ber·ship (mem′bər ship), **1** the fact of being a member: *Do you enjoy your membership in the Boy Scouts?* **2** the members: *All of the club's membership was present. noun.*

mem·brane (mem′brān), **1** a thin, soft layer or sheet of living tissue, that lines or covers a living thing or some part of a living thing. **2** a similar layer of vegetable tissue. *noun.*

me·men·to (mə men′tō), something serving as a reminder of what is past; souvenir: *These post cards are mementos of our trip. noun, plural* **me·men·tos** or **me·men·toes.**

mem·o (mem′ō), a memorandum. *noun, plural* **mem·os.**

mem·or·a·ble (mem′ər ə bəl), worth remembering; not to be forgotten; notable: *Graduation from school is a memorable occasion. adjective.*

"At the Front," George C. Lambdin.
Courtesy of The Detroit Institute of Art

melancholy (definition 2)—The soldier became **melancholy** at the thought of being so far from home.

mem·o·ran·dum (mem′ə ran′dəm), **1** a short written statement for future use; note to aid one's memory: *Make a memorandum of what we will need to take on the trip.* **2** an informal letter, note, or report: *I sent him a memorandum suggesting a meeting tomorrow. noun.*

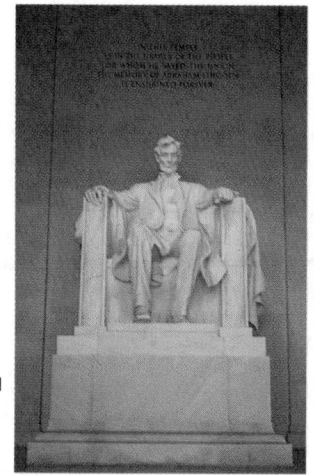

memorial
The Lincoln **Memorial** in Washington D.C.

a hat	i it	oi oil	ch child	⎧ a in about
ā age	ī ice	ou out	ng long	⎪ e in taken
ä far	o hot	u cup	sh she	ə = ⎨ i in pencil
e let	ō open	u̇ put	th thin	⎪ o in lemon
ē equal	ô order	ü rule	₮H then	⎩ u in circus
ėr term			zh measure	

servant; low: *Cinderella had to do menial tasks.* *adjective.*

me·no·rah (mə nôr′ə), a candlestick with eight branches used during the Jewish festival of Hanukkah. *noun.*

menorah

me·mo·ri·al (mə môr′ē əl), something that is a reminder of some event or person, such as a statue, an arch or column, a book, or a holiday. *noun.*

Memorial Day, a holiday for remembering and honoring members of the United States armed services who have died. In most states, it is usually celebrated on the last Monday in May.

mem·o·rize (mem′ə rīz′), to commit to memory; learn by heart: *We have all memorized the alphabet.* *verb,* **mem·o·riz·es, mem·o·rized, mem·o·riz·ing.**

mem·or·y (mem′ər ē), **1** the ability to remember or keep in the mind: *She has a good memory, so she will recall when that happened.* **2** a person, thing, or event that is remembered: *I was so young when we moved that our old house is only a vague memory.* **3** all that a person remembers: *This is the hottest summer within my memory.* **4** the part of a computer in which information and instructions are stored; storage. *noun, plural* **mem·or·ies.**

in memory of, to help in remembering; as a reminder of: *I send you this card in memory of our happy summer together.*

men (men), **1** more than one man. **2** human beings; persons in general: *"All men are created equal."* *noun plural.*

men·ace (men′is), **1** a threat: *The forest fire was a menace to the nearby cabins.* **2** to threaten: *Floods menaced the valley towns with destruction.* **1** *noun,* **2** *verb,* **men·ac·es, men·aced, men·ac·ing.**

me·nag·er·ie (mə naj′ər ē), a collection of wild animals kept in cages for exhibition. *noun.*

mend (mend), **1** to put in good condition again; repair: *to mend a broken doll, to mend clothing.* **2** a place that has been mended: *The mend in your shirt scarcely shows.* **3** to get better from an illness or injury; get back one's health: *My sprained ankle has mended.* **1,3** *verb,* **2** *noun.*

on the mend, getting better: *My health is on the mend.*

me·ni·al (mē′nē əl), belonging to or suited to a

-ment, a suffix meaning: **1** the act of _____ing: Enjoy*ment* means *the act of* enjoy*ing.* **2** the condition of being _____ed: Amaze*ment* means *the condition of being* amaze*d.* **3** the product or result of _____ing: Measure*ment* means *the result of* measur*ing.* **4** a thing that _____s: Induce*ment* means *a thing that* induce*s.*

men·tal (men′tl), **1** of the mind; by the mind; for the mind: *mental illness, mental arithmetic.* **2** having an illness of the mind; for people having an illness of the mind: *a mental patient, a mental hospital.* *adjective.*

men·tal·ly (men′tl ē), with the mind; in the mind: *Grandmother is still strong physically and mentally.* *adverb.*

men·tion (men′shən), **1** to speak about: *I mentioned your idea to the group that is planning the picnic.* **2** a short statement: *A mention of the game appeared in the newspaper.* **1** *verb,* **2** *noun.*

men·u (men′yü), **1** a list of the food for sale in a restaurant or other place where people go to eat. **2** a list of things to choose from, shown by a computer to the user: *You can play any game on the menu. noun.*

[*Menu* comes from a Latin word meaning "made small." The idea here is that a menu is a listing of all the small details of a meal, or a list of all the meals that a customer can choose from.]

me·ow (mē ou′), **1** a sound made by a cat or kitten. **2** to make this sound. **1** *noun,* **2** *verb.*

mer·ce·nar·y (mėr′sə ner′ē), **1** working for

M

money only; acting with money as the motive. **2** a soldier serving for pay in a foreign army. 1 *adjective*, 2 *noun*, *plural* **mer·ce·nar·ies.**

mer·chan·dise (mėr′chən dīz), goods for sale; articles bought and sold: *Most drugstores sell books, games, pencils, and other sorts of merchandise as well as medicines. noun.*

mer·chant (mėr′chənt), **1** a person who buys and sells goods for a living: *Some merchants do most of their business with foreign countries.* **2** a storekeeper. **3** trading; having something to do with trade: *merchant ships.* 1,2 *noun*, 3 *adjective.*

merchant marine, the ships used in trade.

mer·ci·ful (mėr′si fəl), having mercy; showing or feeling mercy; full of mercy. *adjective.*

mer·ci·less (mėr′si lis), without pity; having no mercy; showing no mercy: *merciless cruelty. adjective.*

mer·cur·y (mėr′kyər ē), a heavy, silver-white metal that is liquid at ordinary temperatures. Mercury is a chemical element. It is used in thermometers. *noun.*
[The metal was named for the Roman god Mercury, apparently because of the metal's tendency to flow quickly because it is heavy. Mercury was the swift messenger of the gods.]

Mer·cur·y (mėr′kyər ē), **1** in Roman myths, the god who served as messenger for the other gods. **2** the planet closest to the sun. *noun.*

mer·cy (mėr′sē), **1** more kindness than justice requires; kindness beyond what can be claimed or expected: *The judge showed mercy to the young offender.* **2** something to be thankful for; a blessing: *It's a mercy you weren't hurt in the accident. noun, plural* **mer·cies.**
at the mercy of, in the power of: *We were at the mercy of the storm.*

mere (mir), nothing else than; only: *The mere sight of a dog makes me afraid. The cut was the merest scratch. adjective, superlative* **mer·est.**

mere·ly (mir′lē), simply; only; and nothing more; and that is all: *I am merely a member of the club, not one of the officers. adverb.*

merge (mėrj), to join into one; combine; unite: *The big company merged various small businesses. verb,* **merg·es, merged, merg·ing.**

me·rid·i·an (mə rid′ē ən), **1** any imaginary circle that goes around the earth and passes through the North and South Poles. **2** one half of such a circle, running from the North to the South Pole. All the places on one meridian have the same longitude. *noun.*

mer·it (mer′it), **1** goodness; worth; value; that which deserves reward or praise: *You will be marked according to the merit of your work.* **2** to deserve: *Your excellent work merits praise.* **3 merits,** the real facts or qualities, whether good or bad: *I approve of your plan on its merits, not just because you are my friend.* 1,3 *noun*, 2 *verb.*

mer·maid (mėr′mād′), (in stories) a creature of the sea, with the head and body of a woman and the tail of a fish. *noun.*

mer·ri·ly (mer′ə lē), in a merry manner; laughingly and gaily. *adverb.*

mer·ri·ment (mer′ē mənt), laughter and gaiety; fun; mirth; merry enjoyment. *noun.*

mer·ry (mer′ē), **1** full of fun; loving fun; cheerful and gay: *a merry laugh.* **2** causing joy and happiness: *a merry holiday. adjective,* **mer·ri·er, mer·ri·est.**

mer·ry-go-round (mer′ē gō round′), a set of animal figures and seats on a platform that goes round and round by machinery. People ride on them for fun. *noun.*

mer·ry·mak·ing (mer′ē mā′king), **1** laughter and gaiety; fun. **2** a gay festival; merry entertainment. *noun.*

me·sa (mā′sə), a high, steep hill that has a flat top and stands alone. A mesa is usually larger and steeper than a butte. *noun.*

Word History

mesa *Mesa* comes from a Latin word meaning "table." A mesa was called this because its flat top looked like the top of a table.

mes·dames (mā däm′), the plural of **madame.** *noun.*

mesh (mesh), **1** a net; network: *Some insects are so small that they can pass through the mesh of a window screen.* **2** to fit together; connect. Gears are made so that the teeth of one can mesh with the teeth of another. 1 *noun, plural* **mesh·es;** 2 *verb.*

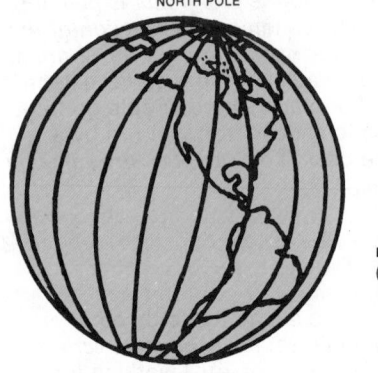

NORTH POLE

meridians
(definition 2)

SOUTH POLE

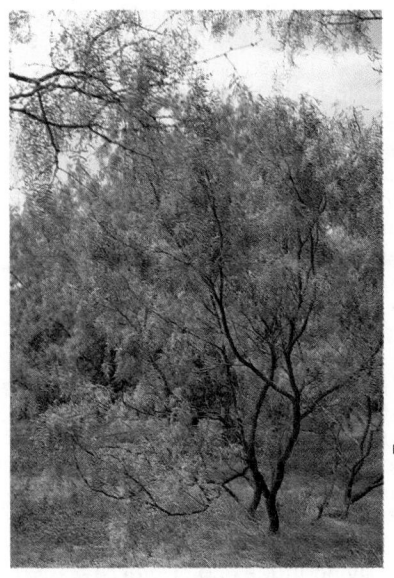

mesquite

a hat	**i** it	**oi** oil	**ch** child		a in about
ā age	**ī** ice	**ou** out	**ng** long		e in taken
ä far	**o** hot	**u** cup	**sh** she	**ə** =	i in pencil
e let	**ō** open	**u̇** put	**th** thin		o in lemon
ē equal	**ô** order	**ü** rule	**ŦH** then		u in circus
ėr term			**zh** measure		

me·squite (me skēt′), a tree or shrub common in the southwestern United States and Mexico. Mesquite often grows in dense clumps or thickets and bears pods that are used as food for cattle. *noun.*
[*Mesquite* comes from the American Indian name for the plant.]

mess (mes), **1** a dirty or untidy mass or group of things; dirty or untidy condition: *Please clean up the mess in your room.* **2** to make dirty or untidy: *She messed up her book by scribbling in it.* **3** to make a failure of; spoil: *He messed up his chances of winning the race.* **4** an unpleasant or unsuccessful affair or state of affairs: *I made a mess of the test.* **5** a group of people who take meals together regularly, especially such a group in the army or navy. 1,4,5 *noun, plural* **mess·es;** 2,3 *verb.*
mess about or **mess around,** to busy oneself without seeming to accomplish anything: *On my vacation I read and messed about with my flowers.*
mess around with or **mess with,** to fool with; get involved with: *Don't mess with the dog; it bites.*
mes·sage (mes′ij), **1** the words sent or delivered by one person or group to another: *a telephone message, the President's message to Congress. noun.*
mes·sen·ger (mes′n jər), a person who carries a message or goes on an errand. *noun.*
mes·sieurs (mes′ərz *or* mā syü′), the plural of **monsieur.** *noun.*
mess·y (mes′ē), in a mess; like a mess; untidy: *The attic was so messy, it took two days to clean it. adjective,* **mess·i·er, mess·i·est.**
met (met). See **meet.** *My father met us this morning at ten o'clock. We were met at the gate by our three dogs. verb.*
me·tab·o·lism (mə tab′ə liz′əm), the processes by which all living things turn food into energy and living tissue. Growth and action depend on metabolism. *noun.*

met·al (met′l), **1** a substance such as iron, gold, silver, steel, or aluminum. Metals are usually shiny, and they conduct heat and electricity well. Metals can be melted, and they can be hammered into thin sheets. **2** made of a metal, or a mixture of metals. 1 *noun,* 2 *adjective.*
me·tal·lic (mə tal′ik), **1** of or containing metal: *a metallic substance.* **2** like metal: *This drapery fabric has a metallic gleam. adjective.*
met·a·mor·phic (met′ə môr′fik), changed by heat and pressure. Slate is a metamorphic rock that is formed from shale, a sedimentary rock. *adjective.*
met·a·mor·pho·sis (met′ə môr′fə sis), a change of form. Tadpoles become frogs by metamorphosis; they lose their tails and grow legs. *noun, plural* **met·a·mor·pho·ses** (met′ə môr′fə sēz′).

Word History

metamorphosis *Metamorphosis* comes from two Greek words meaning "after" and "form." The adult form of an organism is reached after it undergoes changes in form.

| 1 | 2 | 3 | 4 |

metamorphosis of a butterfly
1 caterpillar before change **2** it sheds skin, exposing chrysalis
3 chrysalis entirely exposed **4** adult emerges from chrysalis

met·a·phor (met′ə fôr), a spoken or written expression in which something is described by comparing it to something else, without using the words *like* or *as.* "A heart of stone" is a metaphor. "A heart like stone" is not a metaphor. *noun.*
mete (mēt), to give to each person a proper share or what is due that person; distribute: *to mete out praise, to mete out punishment. verb,* **metes, met·ed, met·ing.**
me·te·or (mē′tē ər), a mass of stone or metal that comes toward the earth from outer space with enormous speed; shooting star. Meteors become so hot from rushing through the air that they glow and often burn up. *noun.*
me·te·or·ic (mē′tē ôr′ik), **1** of meteors: *meteoric dust, a meteoric shower.* **2** swift; brilliant and soon ended: *The singer had a meteoric rise to fame. adjective.*

M

me·te·or·ite (mē′tē ə rīt′), a mass of stone or metal that has reached the earth from outer space. *noun.*

Word History

meteorite A *meteorite* is a *meteor* that has struck the surface of the earth. Both words come from a Greek word meaning "thing in the air." A meteor is called this because of its visible, glowing appearance in the sky. The ending *-ite* of *meteorite* means "a rocky substance."

me·te·or·ol·o·gist (mē′tē ə rol′ə jist), an expert in meteorology. *noun.*

me·te·or·ol·o·gy (mē′tē ə rol′ə jē), the science that deals with weather and the atmosphere. Meteorology includes the study of atmospheric conditions such as wind, moisture, and temperature. Weather forecasts are also part of meteorology. *noun.*

me·ter[1] (mē′tər), 1 any kind of poetic rhythm; the arrangement of beats or accents in a line of poetry: *The meter of "Jack and Jill went up the hill" is not the meter of "One, two, buckle my shoe."* 2 the arrangement of beats in music. *noun.*

me·ter[2] (mē′tər), the basic unit of length in the metric system. *noun.*

me·ter[3] (mē′tər), something that measures, or measures and records: *a gas meter, a water meter.* *noun.*

me·ter·stick (mē′tər stik′), a stick one meter long, used for measuring. *noun.*

meth·od (meth′əd), 1 a way of doing something: *a method of teaching music. Roasting is one method of cooking meat.* 2 an order or system in getting things done or in thinking: *If you used more method, you wouldn't waste so much time. noun.*

me·thod·i·cal (mə thod′ə kəl), 1 done according to a method; orderly: *a methodical check of one's work.* 2 acting according to a method: *A scientist is usually a methodical person. adjective.*

met·ric (met′rik), of the metric system: *metric measurements, metric weights. adjective.*

metric system, a system of measurement which counts by tens. Its basic unit of length is the meter, and its basic unit of weight is the kilogram. A common unit of capacity in the metric system is the liter.

metric ton, a unit of weight in the metric system, equal to 1000 kilograms.

met·ro·nome (met′rə nōm), a clocklike device that can be adjusted to tick at different speeds. People practicing music sometimes use a metronome to help them keep time. *noun.*

me·trop·o·lis (mə trop′ə lis), 1 a large city; important center: *Chicago is a busy metropolis.* 2 the most important city of a country or region: *New York is the metropolis of the United States. noun, plural* **me·trop·o·lis·es.**

met·ro·pol·i·tan (met′rə pol′ə tən), of a large city; belonging to large cities: *metropolitan newspapers.* A **metropolitan area** is the area or region including a large city and its suburbs. *adjective.*

met·tle (met′l), disposition; spirit; courage. *noun.* **on one's mettle,** ready to do one's best.

mew (myü), 1 the sound made by a cat or kitten. 2 to make this sound: *Our kitten mews when it gets hungry.* 1 *noun,* 2 *verb.*

Mex·i·can (mek′sə kən), 1 of or having something to do with Mexico or its people. 2 a person born or living in Mexico. 1 *adjective,* 2 *noun.*

Mexican Spanish, the Spanish language as it is spoken in Mexico.

Mex·i·co (mek′sə kō), 1 a country in North America, just south of the United States. 2 **Gulf of Mexico,** a gulf of the Atlantic Ocean between the southeastern United States and Mexico. *noun.*

Mexico City, the capital of Mexico.

mg or **mg.,** milligram or milligrams.

MI, Michigan (used with postal Zip Code).

mi., mile or miles.

mi·ca (mī′kə), a mineral that divides into thin, partly transparent layers. Mica is used as an insulator, especially in small electrical appliances such as toasters. *noun.*

mice (mīs), more than one mouse. *noun plural.*

Mich., Michigan.

Mich·i·gan (mish′ə gən), 1 one of the north central states of the United States. *Abbreviation:* Mich. or MI *Capital:* Lansing. 2 **Lake Michigan,** one of the five Great Lakes. *noun.*

[The state of *Michigan* got its name from Lake Michigan. This name came from an American Indian word meaning "the big lake."]

mi·crobe (mī′krōb), any living thing so small that it can be seen only with a microscope; germ. Some microbes cause diseases. *noun.*

mi·cro·com·pu·ter (mī′krō kəm pyü′tər), a small computer, able to carry out only one activity at a time. Most home computers and classroom computers are microcomputers. *noun.*

mi·cro·film (mī′krō film′), 1 a kind of film used to make very small photographs of pages from a book or newspaper, or of other records, to store them in a very small space. 2 to photograph on microfilm: *The spy microfilmed the plans.* 1 *noun,* 2 *verb.*

mi·cro·phone (mī′krə fōn), an instrument for magnifying small sounds or for transmitting sounds. Microphones change sound waves into an electric current. Radio and television stations use microphones for broadcasting. *noun.*

mi·cro·proc·es·sor (mī′krō pros′əs ər), the basic working part of a microcomputer, built as a tiny integrated circuit. Microprocessors are used to control the operation of cars, video games, microwave ovens, and other machines as well as in computers. *noun.*

mi·cro·scope (mī′krə skōp), an instrument with a lens or combination of lenses for making small things look larger. Bacteria, blood cells, and other objects not visible to the naked eye are clearly visible through a microscope. *noun.*

Word History

microscope *Microscope* comes from two Greek words meaning "small" and "look at."

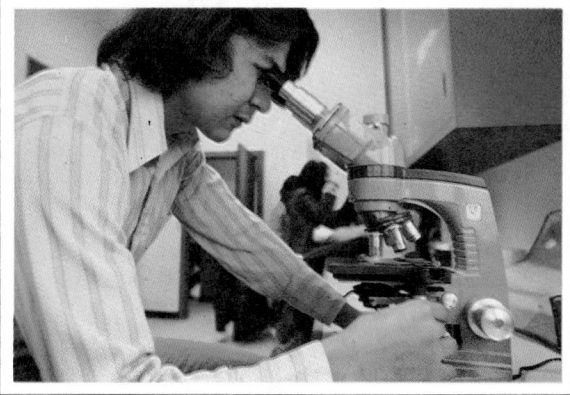

mi·cro·scop·ic (mī′krə skop′ik), not able to be seen without using a microscope; tiny: *microscopic germs. adjective.*

mi·cro·wave ov·en (mī′krō wāv′ uv′ən), an oven in which food is cooked by the heat produced by a certain kind of radio wave. These waves go into the food and cook it quickly.

mid (mid), middle. *adjective.*

mid·air (mid′er′ *or* mid′ar′), the middle of the air; the air above the ground: *The acrobat made a somersault in midair. noun.*

mid·day (mid′dā′), the middle of the day; noon. *noun.*

mid·dle (mid′l), **1** the point or part that is the same distance from each end or side; center: *the middle of the road.* **2** halfway between; in the center; at the same distance from either end or side: *the middle house in the row.* **3** in between; medium: *a man of middle size.* 1 *noun,* 2,3 *adjective.*

mid·dle-aged (mid′l ājd′), neither young nor old; from about 40 to about 65 years of age. *adjective.*

Middle Ages, the period in European history between ancient and modern times, from about A.D. 500 to about 1450.

middle class, the class of people between the very wealthy class and the class of unskilled

laborers and unemployed people. The middle class includes business and professional people, office workers, and many skilled workers.

middle ear, a hollow space between the eardrum and the inner ear. In human beings it contains three small bones which pass on sound waves from the eardrum to the inner ear.

Middle East, a region from the eastern Mediterranean to Iran. Egypt, Israel, Turkey, and Iraq are in the Middle East.

middle school, a school between elementary school and high school, usually including grades 5 through 9.

Middle West, the part of the United States west of the Appalachian Mountains, east of the Rocky Mountains, and north of the Ohio River and the southern boundaries of Missouri and Kansas; Midwest.

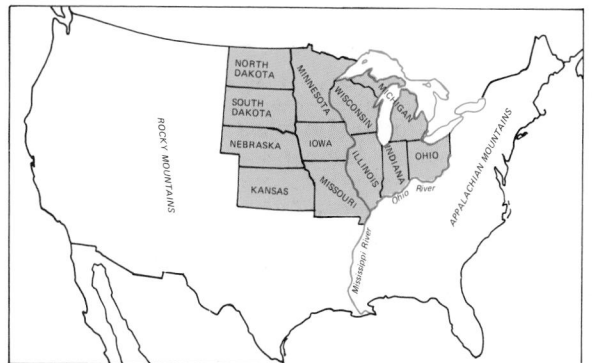

Middle West

midge (mij), a small, two-winged fly; gnat. *noun.*

midg·et (mij′it), a person very much smaller than normal but shaped the same as other people; tiny person. *noun.*

mid·land (mid′lənd), **1** the middle part of a country; the interior. **2** in or of the middle part of a country. 1 *noun,* 2 *adjective.*

mid·night (mid′nīt′), twelve o'clock at night; the middle of the night. *noun.*

midst[1] (midst), **1** the middle point or part; middle: *I had to leave school in the midst of the afternoon.* **2** the position or condition of being surrounded, especially by a number of people: *There is a stranger in our midst. noun.*

midst[2] or **'midst** (midst), amidst. *preposition.*

mid·stream (mid′strēm′), the middle of a stream. *noun.*

mid·sum·mer (mid′sum′ər), **1** the middle of summer. **2** the time around June 21. **3** in the middle of summer. 1,2 *noun,* 3 *adjective.*

a hat	i it	oi oil	ch child	⎧ a in about
ā age	ī ice	ou out	ng long	e in taken
ä far	o hot	u cup	sh she	ə = ⎨ i in pencil
e let	ō open	u̇ put	th thin	o in lemon
ē equal	ô order	ü rule	ŦH then	⎩ u in circus
ėr term			zh measure	

mid·way (mid′wā′), **1** halfway; in the middle: *midway between these trees and the lake, a midway position.* **2** a place for games, rides, and other amusements at a fair. **1** *adverb, adjective,* **2** *noun.*

Mid·west (mid′west′), the Middle West. *noun.*

Mid·west·ern (mid′wes′tərn), of the Middle West. *adjective.*

mid·win·ter (mid′win′tər), **1** the middle of winter. **2** the time around December 21. **3** in the middle of winter. **1,2** *noun,* **3** *adjective.*

mien (mēn), the manner of holding the head and body; way of acting and looking: *She has the mien of an athlete. noun.*

might¹ (mīt). See **may.** *Mother said that we might play in the barn. He might have done it when you were not looking. verb.*

might² (mīt), great power; strength: *Work with all your might. noun.*

might·i·ly (mī′tə lē), **1** in a mighty manner; powerfully; vigorously: *We freed the car from the snowbank by pushing mightily.* **2** very much; greatly: *We were mightily pleased at winning. adverb.*

might·y (mī′tē), **1** showing strength or power; powerful; strong: *a mighty ruler, mighty force.* **2** very great: *a mighty famine.* **3** very: *a mighty long time.* **1,2** *adjective,* **might·i·er, might·i·est;** **3** *adverb.*

mi·grant (mī′grənt), **1** migrating; roving: *a migrant worker.* **2** a person or animal that migrates. **1** *adjective,* **2** *noun.*

mi·grate (mī′grāt), **1** to move from one place to settle in another: *Many pioneers from New England migrated to other parts of the United States.* **2** to go from one region to another with the change in the seasons: *Most birds migrate to warmer countries in the winter. verb,* **mi·grates, mi·grat·ed, mi·grat·ing.**

mi·gra·tion (mī grā′shən), a moving from one place to another: *Some kinds of birds travel thousands of miles on their migrations. noun.*

mike (mīk), a microphone. *noun.*

mild (mīld), **1** gentle; kind: *He has a mild disposition.* **2** not harsh or severe; warm; calm; temperate: *a mild climate, a mild winter.* **3** soft or sweet to the senses; not sharp, sour, bitter, or strong in taste: *mild cheese, a mild cigar. adjective.*

mil·dew (mil′dü *or* mil′dyü), **1** a kind of fungus that appears on plants or on paper, clothes, or leather during damp weather: *Mildew killed the rosebuds in our garden.* **2** to become covered with mildew: *A pile of damp clothes in the closet mildewed.* **1** *noun,* **2** *verb.*

mile (mīl), **1** a unit for measuring length or distance. It is equal to 5280 feet. **2 nautical mile,** a unit for measuring length or distance. It is equal to about 6076 feet. *noun.*

mile·age (mī′lij), the miles traveled: *Our car's mileage last year was 10,000 miles. noun.*

mile·stone (mīl′stōn′), **1** a stone set up on a road to show the distance in miles to a certain place. **2** an important event: *The invention of printing was a milestone in progress. noun.*

mil·i·tant (mil′ə tənt), **1** fighting; warlike: *a militant group. She has a militant attitude.* **2** a warlike person. **1** *adjective,* **2** *noun.*

mil·i·tar·y (mil′ə ter′ē), **1** of armed forces or war: *military government, military heroism.* **2** done by soldiers: *military maneuvers.* **3 the military,** the armed forces: *an officer of the military.* **1,2** *adjective,* **3** *noun.*

mi·li·tia (mə lish′ə), an army of citizens who are not regular soldiers but who are trained for war or any other emergency. Every state of the United States has a militia called the National Guard. *noun.*

milk (milk), **1** the white liquid from cows, which we drink and use in cooking. **2** a similar liquid produced by the adult females of many other animals as food for their young ones. **3** the white juice of a plant, tree, or nut: *coconut milk.* **4** to draw milk from an animal such as a cow or goat. **1-3** *noun,* **4** *verb.*

milk·man (milk′man′), a person who sells or delivers milk. *noun, plural* **milk·men.**

milk shake, a drink prepared by shaking or beating together milk, flavoring, and ice cream.

milk·weed (milk′wēd′), a plant with white juice that looks like milk and seed pods containing long, silky hairs. *noun.*

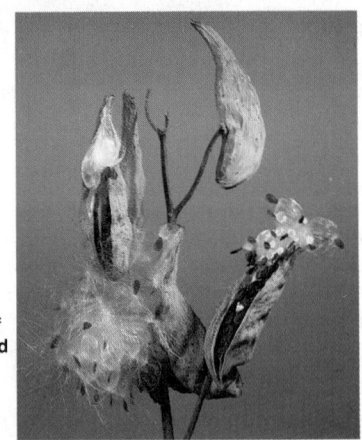

milkweed
seed pods of
the **milkweed**

milk·y (mil′kē), **1** like milk; white as milk. **2** of milk; containing milk. *adjective,* **milk·i·er, milk·i·est.**

Milky Way, a broad band of faint light that stretches across the sky at night. The Milky Way is the galaxy in which the earth and the sun are located. It is made up of countless stars, most of which are too far away to be seen separately without a telescope.

mill (mil), **1** a building containing a machine for grinding grain into flour or meal. **2** any machine for crushing or grinding: *a coffee mill.* **3** to grind very fine. **4** a building where manufacturing is done: *Cotton cloth is made in a cotton mill.* **5** to move about in a confused way: *The frightened cattle began to mill around.* **1,2,4** *noun,* **3,5** *verb.*

mill·er (mil′ər), a person who owns or runs a mill, especially a flour mill. *noun.*

mil·let (mil′it), the very small grain of a kind of cereal grass, grown for food or hay. *noun.*

mil·li·gram (mil′ə gram), a unit of weight equal to 1/1000 of a gram. *noun.*

mil·li·li·ter (mil′ə lē′tər), a unit of capacity equal to 1/1000 of a liter. *noun.*

mil·li·me·ter (mil′ə mē′tər), a unit of length equal to 1/1000 of a meter. *noun.*

mil·lion (mil′yən), one thousand thousand; 1,000,000. *noun, adjective.*

mil·lion·aire (mil′yə ner′ *or* mil′yə nar′), a person who has a million or more dollars. *noun.*

mil·lionth (mil′yənth), **1** next after the 999,999th. **2** one of a million equal parts. *adjective, noun.*

mill·stone (mil′stōn′), **1** either of a pair of round flat stones for grinding corn, wheat, or other grain. **2** a heavy burden. *noun.*

mill wheel, a wheel that is turned by water and supplies power for a mill.

mill wheel

mime (definition 1)
The **mime** gave a performance on the sidewalk.

mime (mīm), **1** an actor, especially in a pantomime. **2** to act without using words; act in a pantomime: *The actor mimed with great talent and power.* **1** *noun,* **2** *verb,* **mimes, mimed, mim·ing.**

mim·e·o·graph (mim′ē ə graf), **1** a machine for making copies of written or typewritten material by means of stencils. **2** to make copies with such a machine. **1** *noun,* **2** *verb.*

a hat	i it	oi oil	ch child	⎧a in about
ā age	ī ice	ou out	ng long	⎪e in taken
ä far	o hot	u cup	sh she	ə =⎨i in pencil
e let	ō open	ù put	th thin	⎪o in lemon
ē equal	ô order	ü rule	ŦH then	⎩u in circus
ėr term			zh measure	

mimic (definition 4)—This insect **mimics** a twig.

mim·ic (mim′ik), **1** to make fun of by imitating: *The children mimicked the babysitter's English accent.* **2** a person or thing that imitates. **3** to copy closely; imitate: *A parrot can mimic voices.* **4** resemble closely in form or color. **1,3,4** *verb,* **mim·ics, mim·icked, mim·ick·ing; 2** *noun.*

min., minute or minutes.

min·a·ret (min′ə ret′), a slender, high tower attached to a Moslem mosque with one or more projecting balconies. From these balconies the people are called to prayer. *noun.*

Word History

minaret *Minaret* comes from an Arabic word meaning originally "lighthouse" or "candlestick." A minaret was called this because of its tall, slender shape.

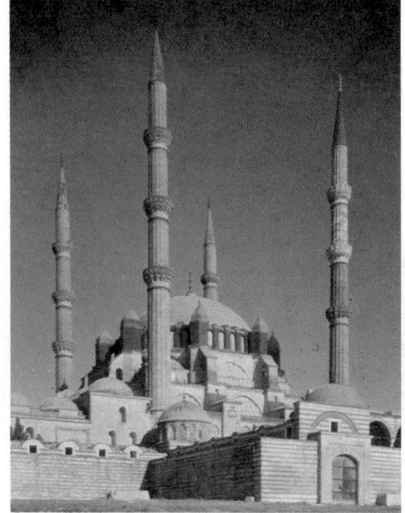

minaret
mosque with four **minarets**

M

mince (mins), **1** to chop up into very small pieces. **2** mincemeat. 1 *verb*, **minc·es, minced, minc·ing;** 2 *noun*.

mince·meat (mins′mēt′), a mixture of chopped apples, suet, raisins, currants, spices, and sometimes meat. Mincemeat is used as a pie filling. *noun*.

mind (mīnd), **1** the part of a person that knows and thinks and feels and wishes and chooses. **2** intelligence; mental ability; intellect: *She has a good mind.* **3** a person who has intelligence. **4** reason; sanity: *He must have been out of his mind to do that.* **5** what one thinks or feels; opinion; view: *I used to like that TV program, but I changed my mind.* **6** attention; mental effort: *Keep your mind on your work.* **7** memory: *Keep the rules in mind.* **8** to notice; observe: *Now mind, these are not my ideas.* **9** to be careful concerning: *Mind the step.* **10** to take care: *Mind that you come on time.* **11** to look after; take care of; attend to: *Please mind the baby. Why don't you mind your own business?* **12** to obey: *Mind your father and mother.* **13** to feel bad about; object to: *Some people don't mind cold weather.* 1-7 *noun*, 8-13 *verb*.

have a mind to, to intend to; think of doing: *I have a mind to go swimming.*

keep in mind, to give one's attention to; remember: *I hope you will keep my suggestions in mind.*

make up one's mind, to decide: *I made up my mind to study harder and get better grades.*

never mind, it doesn't matter; don't worry: *Never mind, we'll be able to go tomorrow instead of today.*

on one's mind, in one's mind; in one's thoughts: *With all this work I must do, I've got a lot on my mind.*

put in mind, to remind: *Your joke puts me in mind of a joke I heard yesterday.*

set one's mind on, to want very much: *I set my mind on owning a horse.*

to one's mind, to one's way of thinking; in one's opinion: *To my mind, this plan has a few flaws.*

mind·ful (mīnd′fəl), taking thought; careful: *We had to be mindful of every step we took on the slippery sidewalk. adjective.*

mine[1] (mīn), the one or ones belonging to me: *This book is mine. pronoun.*

mine[2] (mīn), **1** a large hole or space dug in the earth to get out ores, precious stones, coal, salt, or anything valuable: *a coal mine, a gold mine.* **2** to dig into the earth to take out ores, coal, or other valuable things: *When gold was discovered in California, people rushed there to mine.* **3** to get from a mine: *to mine coal, to mine gold.* **4** a rich or plentiful source: *The book proved to be a mine of information about radio.* **5** a small bomb placed in or under water, or buried just beneath the ground, to explode and destroy enemy shipping, troops, or equipment. **6** to lay mines under: *The enemy secretly mined the mouth of the harbor, and many ships were destroyed.* 1,4,5 *noun*, 2,3,6 *verb*, **mines, mined, min·ing.**

min·er (mī′nər), a person who works in a mine. *noun.*

min·er·al (min′ər əl), **1** a substance obtained by mining or digging in the earth. Coal, gold, and mica are minerals. **2** any substance that is not a plant, an animal, or another living thing. Sand is a mineral. **3** containing minerals: *mineral water.* 1,2 *noun*, 3 *adjective.*

min·er·al·o·gy (min′ə rol′ə jē), the science of minerals. *noun.*

min·gle (ming′gəl), **1** to mix: *Two rivers that join mingle their waters.* **2** to associate: *I tried to mingle with everyone at the party. verb,* **min·gles, min·gled, min·gling.**

min·i (min′ē), small or short for its kind: *Our weekend in New York was a mini vacation. adjective.*

min·i·a·ture (min′ē ə chùr), **1** anything copied on a small scale: *In the museum there is a miniature of the ship "Mayflower."* **2** done or made on a very small scale; tiny: *miniature cars, miniature furniture for a doll's house.* **3** a very small painting, usually a portrait. 1,3 *noun*, 2 *adjective.*

min·i·bike (min′ē bīk′), a small motorcycle. *noun.*

min·i·mum (min′ə məm), **1** the least possible amount; lowest amount: *Each of the children had to drink some milk at breakfast; half a glass was the minimum.* **2** least possible; lowest: *Eighteen is the minimum age for voting in the United States.* 1 *noun*, 2 *adjective.*

min·ing (mī′ning), **1** the work or business of taking ores, coal, or other minerals from mines. **2** the laying of explosive mines underground or underwater. *noun.*

min·is·ter (min′ə stər), **1** a member of the clergy serving a church; spiritual guide; pastor. **2** to be of service or aid; be helpful: *He ministered to the needs of his sick friend.* **3** a person who is given charge of a department of the government: *the Minister of Finance.* 1,3 *noun*, 2 *verb.*

[*Minister* comes from a Latin word meaning "servant." The original meaning was later changed to include the idea of one who helps, supports, or assists.]

min·is·try (min′ə strē), **1** the office, duties, or time of service of a minister. **2** the clergy; the ministers of a denomination. **3** the ministers of a government, in certain countries. Ministers of a government in these countries are often the same as cabinet members in the United States. *noun, plural* **min·is·tries.**

mink (mingk), **1** an animal like a weasel that lives in water part of the time. **2** its valuable brown fur. *noun.*

mink
about 2 feet
(60 centimeters)
long with the tail

Minn., Minnesota.

Min·ne·so·ta (min′ə sō′tə), one of the midwestern states of the United States. *Abbreviation:* Minn. or MN *Capital:* St. Paul. *noun.*
[*Minnesota* was named for the Minnesota River. This name came from American Indian words meaning "sky-colored water."]

min·now (min′ō), **1** a very small freshwater fish. **2** any fish when it is very small. *noun.*

mi·nor (mī′nər), **1** smaller; lesser; less important: *Correct the important errors in your paper before you bother with the minor ones.* **2** a person under 18 or 21 years, the legal age of responsibility. **1** *adjective,* **2** *noun.*

mi·nor·i·ty (mə nôr′ə tē), **1** the smaller number or part; less than half: *A minority of the children wanted a party, but the majority chose a picnic.* **2** a group within a country, state, or other area that is different from the larger part of the population in some way, such as race or religion. *noun, plural* **mi·nor·i·ties.**

min·strel (min′strəl), a singer or musician in the Middle Ages who entertained in the household of a noble or went about singing or reciting poems. *noun.*

mint[1] (mint), **1** a sweet-smelling plant used for flavoring. Peppermint and spearmint are kinds of mint. **2** a piece of candy flavored with mint. *noun.*

mint[2] (mint), **1** a place where money is coined by public authority. **2** to coin money: *The government has not minted many silver dollars lately.* **3** a large amount: *That furniture must have cost a mint.* **4** as good as new; spotless: *That car is still in mint condition, although it is two years old.* **1,3** *noun,* **2** *verb,* **4** *adjective.*

min·u·end (min′yü end), a number from which another is to be subtracted: *In 100 − 23 = 77, the minuend is 100.* *noun.*

min·u·et (min′yü et′), **1** a slow dance fashionable in the 1600's and 1700's. **2** the music for it. *noun.*

mi·nus (mī′nəs), **1** less; decreased by: *12 minus 3 leaves 9.* **2** lacking: *a book minus its cover.* **3** less than: *A mark of B minus is not so high as a mark of B.* **4** the sign (−) meaning that the quantity following it is to be subtracted. **5** less than zero: *Yesterday the temperature was minus ten degrees.* **1,2** *preposition,* **3,5** *adjective,* **4** *noun, plural* **mi·nus·es.**

min·ute[1] (min′it), **1** one of the 60 equal periods of time that make up an hour; 60 seconds. **2** a short time; an instant: *I'll be there in a minute.* **3** an exact point of time: *The minute you see them, call me.* **4** one sixtieth of a degree. 10°10′ means ten degrees and ten minutes. **5 minutes,** an official written account of what happened at a meeting. *noun.*

mi·nute[2] (mī nüt′ *or* mī nyüt′), **1** very small; tiny: *Even a minute speck of dust makes him cough.* **2** going into small details: *They gave me minute instructions. adjective.*

min·ute hand (min′it hand′), the hand on a clock or watch that indicates minutes. It moves around the whole dial once in an hour.

min·ute·man (min′it man′), a member of the American militia just before and during the Revolutionary War. The minutemen kept themselves ready for military service at a minute's notice. *noun, plural* **min·ute·men.**

mir·a·cle (mir′ə kəl), **1** a wonderful happening that is beyond the known laws of nature: *It would be a miracle if the sun should stand still in the heavens for an hour.* **2** something marvelous; wonder: *It was a miracle you weren't hurt in that accident.* **3** a remarkable example: *The teacher was a miracle of patience to put up with the children's racket. noun.*

mi·rac·u·lous (mə rak′yə ləs), **1** going against the known laws of nature: *The miraculous fountain of youth was supposed to make old people young again.* **2** wonderful; marvelous: *The famous actor gave a miraculous performance. adjective.*

mi·rage (mə räzh′), an illusion, usually in the desert, at sea, or on a paved road, in which some distant scene appears to be much closer than it actually is. *noun.*

mire (mīr), **1** soft, deep mud; slush. **2** to get stuck in mire: *He mired his car and had to go for help.* **1** *noun,* **2** *verb,* **mires, mired, mir·ing.**

mir·ror (mir′ər), **1** a glass in which you can see yourself; looking glass; surface that reflects light. **2** to reflect as a mirror does: *The still water mirrored the trees along the bank.* **3** whatever reflects or gives a true description: *This book is a mirror of the life of the pioneers.* **1,3** *noun,* **2** *verb.*

mirth (mėrth), merry fun; laughter: *The people at the party were full of mirth. noun.*

mirth·ful (mėrth′fəl), merry; jolly. *adjective.*

mis-, a prefix meaning: **1** bad or wrong: *Misbehavior* means *bad* behavior. The *misuse of a word means the *wrong* use of a word. **2** badly or wrongly: *Misbehave* means to behave *badly.* To *miscount* means to count *wrongly.*

mis·be·have (mis′bi hāv′), to behave badly: *Some of the children misbehaved at the picnic. verb,* **mis·be·haves, mis·be·haved, mis·be·hav·ing.**

mis·be·hav·ior (mis′bi hā′vyər), bad behavior. *noun.*

mis·cel·la·ne·ous (mis′ə lā′nē əs), not all of one kind or nature: *He had a miscellaneous collection of stones, butterflies, stamps, and many other things. adjective.*

mis·chief (mis′chif), **1** conduct that causes harm or trouble, often without meaning it: *Playing with matches is mischief that may cause a fire.* **2** harm; injury, usually done by some person: *Spreading* *gossip can do a lot of mischief.* **3** a person who does harm, often just in fun: *Where have you hidden my glasses, you little mischief?* **4** merry teasing: *Her eyes were full of mischief.* noun.

mis·chie·vous (mis′chə vəs), **1** full of mischief; naughty: *The mischievous child poured honey all over the kitchen.* **2** harmful: *He broke up their friendship by telling mischievous lies.* **3** full of playful tricks and teasing fun: *My friends were feeling mischievous and hid my glasses as a joke.* adjective.

mis·con·duct (mis kon′dukt), bad behavior: *The children were punished for their misconduct.* noun.

mis·count (mis kount′ for 1; mis′kount′ for 2), **1** to count wrongly or incorrectly: *I miscounted the number of dollars in my wallet.* **2** a wrong or incorrect count. **1** verb, **2** noun.

mis·deed (mis dēd′), a bad act; wicked deed. noun.

mis·di·rect (mis′də rekt′), to direct wrongly; give wrong directions to. verb.

mi·ser (mī′zər), a person who loves money for its own sake; one who lives poorly in order to save money and keep it. noun.

mis·er·a·ble (miz′ər ə bəl), **1** very unhappy: *The sick child was often miserable.* **2** causing trouble or unhappiness: *I have a miserable cold.* **3** poor; mean; wretched: *The run-down old house stood in miserable surroundings.* adjective.

mis·er·y (miz′ər ē), great distress or suffering caused by being unhappy, poor, or in pain: *Think of the misery of having no home or friends.* noun, plural **mis·er·ies.**

mis·fit (mis′fit′), a person who does not fit in a job or a group. noun.

mis·for·tune (mis fôr′chən), **1** bad luck: *She had the misfortune to break her arm.* **2** a piece of bad luck; unlucky accident or happening: *The flood was a great misfortune for the people whose homes were damaged.* noun.

mis·giv·ing (mis giv′ing), a feeling of doubt or worry: *We started off through the storm with some misgivings.* noun.

mis·guid·ed (mis gī′did), led into mistakes or wrongdoing; misled: *The misguided student let others copy his homework.* adjective.

mis·hap (mis′hap), an unlucky accident: *He had a terrible mishap while riding his bicycle.* noun.

mishap

mis·judge (mis juj′), **1** to judge wrongly: *The archer misjudged the distance to the target, and his arrow fell short.* **2** to judge unjustly: *The teacher was sorry that she had misjudged the girl's honesty.* verb, **mis·judg·es, mis·judged, mis·judg·ing.**

mis·laid (mis lād′). See **mislay.** *She mislaid her books. I have mislaid my pen.* verb.

mis·lay (mis lā′), to put in a place and then forget where it is: *I am always mislaying my gloves.* verb, **mis·lays, mis·laid, mis·lay·ing.**

mis·lead (mis lēd′), **1** to cause to go in the wrong direction: *Our guide misled us, and we got lost.* **2** to lead to think what is not so; deceive: *Some advertisements are so exaggerated that they mislead people.* verb, **mis·leads, mis·led, mis·lead·ing.**

mis·lead·ing (mis lē′ding), causing mistakes or wrong conclusions; deceiving: *The detectives found that the false clue was misleading.* adjective.

mis·led (mis led′). See **mislead.** *We were misled by the false claims.* verb.

mis·man·age (mis man′ij), to manage badly: *If you mismanage the business, you will lose money.* verb, **mis·man·ag·es, mis·man·aged, mis·man·ag·ing.**

mis·man·age·ment (mis man′ij mənt), bad management. noun.

mis·place (mis plās′), **1** to put in a place and then forget where it is: *I misplaced my glasses.* **2** to put in the wrong place or position: *That street light is misplaced; it should be near the corner.* verb, **mis·plac·es, mis·placed, mis·plac·ing.**

mis·print (mis′print′ for 1; mis print′ for 2), **1** a mistake in printing. **2** to print wrongly: *They misprinted a word on page 3.* **1** noun, **2** verb.

mis·pro·nounce (mis′prə nouns′), to pronounce incorrectly: *Many people mispronounce the word "mischievous."* verb, **mis·pro·nounc·es, mis·pro·nounced, mis·pro·nounc·ing.**

mis·read (mis rēd′), **1** to read incorrectly: *I misread the sign and missed the turn.* **2** to misunderstand; interpret incorrectly: *You misread my joke if you think it was meant as an insult.* verb, **mis·reads, mis·read** (mis red′), **mis·read·ing.**

mis·rule (mis rül′), **1** bad or unwise government: *After years of misrule, the country was ready for a new leader.* **2** to govern badly: *The king misruled his people.* **1** noun, **2** verb, **mis·rules, mis·ruled, mis·rul·ing.**

miss (mis), **1** to fail to hit: *I swung at the ball and missed.* **2** a failure to hit or reach: *I had two misses and four hits at target practice.* **3** to fail to find, get, or meet: *I set out to meet my father, but in the dark I missed him.* **4** to let slip by; not seize: *I missed the chance of a ride to town.* **5** to fail to catch: *We were caught in traffic and missed the plane.* **6** to leave out: *to miss a word in reading.* **7** to fail to do or answer correctly: *I missed three words in today's spelling lesson.* **8** to fail to see, hear, or understand: *She missed the point of my remark.* **9** to fail to keep, do, or be present at: *I missed my music lesson today.* **10** to notice the absence of; feel keenly the absence of: *I missed you while you were away.* **1,3-10** verb, **2** noun, plural **miss·es.**

Miss (mis), **1** a title put in front of a girl's or unmarried woman's name: *Miss Brown, the Misses Brown, the Miss Browns.* **2 miss,** a girl or young unmarried woman. *noun, plural* **Miss·es.**

Miss., Mississippi.

mis·shap·en (mis shā′pən), badly shaped; deformed. *adjective.*

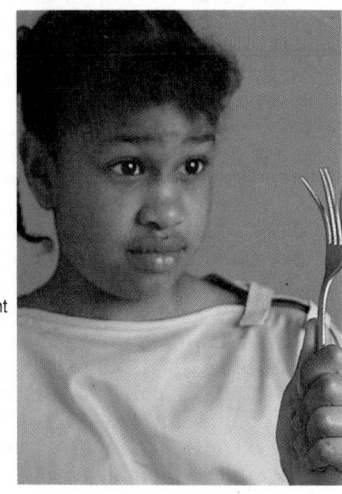

misshapen
The fork was bent and **misshapen.**

mis·sile (mis′əl), **1** an object that is thrown, hurled, or shot, such as a stone, a bullet, an arrow, or a lance. **2** a rocket that carries a bomb to a target. Missiles can be launched from land, air, or sea. *noun.*

miss·ing (mis′ing), **1** lacking or wanting: *It was a good cake but something was missing.* **2** lost; gone; out of its usual place: *The missing ring was found under the dresser. One of the books was missing.* **3** absent: *Four children were missing from class today. adjective.*

mis·sion (mish′ən), **1** a sending or being sent on some special work; errand: *He was sent on a mission to a foreign government.* **2** the persons sent out on some special business: *She was one of a mission sent by our government to France.* **3** a center or headquarters for religious or social work: *The church set up a mission in a run-down area to help people in need.* **4** one's business or purpose in life; one's calling: *It seemed to be her mission to help improve living conditions in the city. noun.*

mis·sion·ar·y (mish′ə ner′ē), a person who carries on the work of a religious mission, often in a foreign country: *Missionaries helped start churches, schools, and hospitals in many places. noun, plural* **mis·sion·ar·ies.**

Mis·sis·sip·pi (mis′ə sip′ē), **1** a large river in the central United States. **2** one of the south central states of the United States. *Abbreviation:* Miss. or MS *Capital:* Jackson. *noun.*

[The state of *Mississippi* got its name from the Mississippi River. This name came from an American Indian word meaning "the big river."]

Mis·sour·i (mə zùr′ē *or* mə zùr′ə), **1** a large river in the northern United States. **2** one of the

a hat	**i** it	**oi** oil	**ch** child	a in about
ā age	**ī** ice	**ou** out	**ng** long	e in taken
ä far	**o** hot	**u** cup	**sh** she	ə = { i in pencil
e let	**ō** open	**ù** put	**th** thin	o in lemon
ē equal	**ô** order	**ü** rule	**ŦH** then	u in circus
ėr term			**zh** measure	

midwestern states of the United States. *Abbreviation:* Mo. or MO *Capital:* Jefferson City. *noun.*

[The state of *Missouri* got its name from the Missouri River. The river was named for an American Indian tribe, the Missouri, who lived near the mouth of the river. The name probably meant "people of the big canoes."]

mis·spell (mis spel′), to spell incorrectly. *verb,* **mis·spells, mis·spelled** or **mis·spelt** (mis spelt′), **mis·spell·ing.**

mis·spent (mis spent′), spent foolishly or wrongly; wasted: *a misspent fortune, a misspent life. adjective.*

mist (mist), **1** a cloud of very fine drops of water in the air; fog. **2** a cloud of very fine drops of any liquid in the air: *A mist of perfume spread over the room.* **3** to come down in mist; rain in very fine drops: *It is misting.* **4** anything that dims or blurs: *She did not cry, but a mist came over her eyes. A mist of prejudice spoiled his judgment.* **5** to cover or become covered with a mist; make or become dim: *Tears misted his eyes.* 1,2,4 *noun,* 3,5 *verb.*

mis·take (mə stāk′), **1** an error; blunder; misunderstanding of a thing's meaning: *I used your towel by mistake.* **2** to misunderstand what is seen or heard; take in a wrong sense: *We mistook her polite words for friendliness.* **3** to take wrongly; take to be some other person or thing: *I mistook him for his brother.* 1 *noun,* 2,3 *verb,* **mis·takes, mis·took, mis·tak·en, mis·tak·ing.**

mis·tak·en (mə stā′kən), **1** wrong in opinion; having made a mistake: *I saw I was mistaken and admitted my error.* **2** wrong; wrongly judged; misplaced: *It was a mistaken kindness to give that boy more candy; it will make him sick.* **3** See **mistake.** *They have mistaken me for someone else.* 1,2 *adjective,* 3 *verb.*

mis·tak·en·ly (mə stā′kən lē), by mistake; wrongly. *adverb.*

Mis·ter (mis′tər), **1** Mr., a title put before a man's name or the name of his office: *Mr. Stein, Mr. President.* **2** sir: *Mister, can you help me? noun.*

mis·tle·toe (mis′əl tō), a plant with white berries, that grows as a parasite on trees. It is used as a Christmas decoration. *noun.*

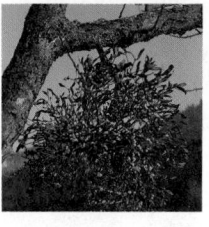

mistletoe

mis·took (mis tùk′). See **mistake**. *I mistook you for your sister yesterday.* verb.

mis·treat (mis trēt′), to treat badly: *It is cruel to mistreat animals.* verb.

mis·tress (mis′tris), **1** a woman who is at the head of a household. **2** a woman who owns or controls something: *The kitten greeted its mistress with loud meows.* noun, plural **mis·tress·es.**

mis·trust (mis trust′), **1** to feel no confidence in; doubt: *I mistrusted my ability to learn to swim.* **2** a lack of trust or confidence; suspicion: *He looked with mistrust at the stranger.* 1 verb, 2 noun.

mist·y (mis′tē), **1** covered with mist: *misty hills.* **2** not clearly seen; vague; indistinct: *We had only a misty view of the skyline.* adjective, **mist·i·er, mist·i·est.**

misty (definition 1)—It was a **misty** day.

mis·un·der·stand (mis′un′dər stand′), **1** to understand wrongly: *I completely misunderstood the meaning of the poem.* **2** to take in a wrong way; give the wrong meaning to: *We tried to help, but they misunderstood our intentions.* verb, **mis·un·der·stands, mis·un·der·stood, mis·un·der·stand·ing.**

mis·un·der·stand·ing (mis′un′dər stan′ding), **1** a wrong understanding; failure to understand; mistake as to meaning. **2** a disagreement: *After their misunderstanding they scarcely spoke to each other.* noun.

mis·un·der·stood (mis′un′dər stùd′). See **misunderstand.** *She misunderstood what the teacher said and so did the wrong homework.* verb.

mis·use (mis yüz′ for 1 and 2; mis yüs′ for 3), **1** to use for the wrong purpose: *He misuses his knife at the table by lifting food with it.* **2** to treat badly: *The children misused their dog by trying to ride on its back.* **3** a wrong use: *I notice a misuse of the word "who" in your letter.* 1,2 verb, **mis·us·es, mis·used, mis·us·ing;** 3 noun.

mite¹ (mīt), a tiny animal that is related to the

mite¹
The dot shows
its actual size.

spider and has eight legs. It lives in foods, on plants, or on other animals. noun.

mite² (mīt), anything very small; little bit: *I can't eat even a mite of supper.* noun.

mitt (mit), **1** a glove with a big pad over the palm and fingers, used by baseball players: *a catcher's mitt.* **2** a mitten. noun.

mit·ten (mit′n), a kind of winter glove, covering the four fingers together and the thumb separately. noun.

mix (miks), **1** to put together; combine and stir well: *We mixed butter, sugar, milk, flour, eggs, and flavoring for a cake.* **2** to prepare by putting different things together: *She mixed pancakes for breakfast.* **3** to join: *They mixed business and pleasure at lunch.* **4** to be mixed; blend: *Oil and water will not mix.* **5** to get along together; make friends easily: *She likes people and mixes well in almost any group.* **6** a mixture: *A strange mix of people attended the opening of the play.* **7** a preparation that is already mixed: *I used a mix to make the crust of this pie.* 1-5 verb, **mix·es, mixed, mix·ing;** 6,7 noun, plural **mix·es.**

mix up, 1 to confuse: *I was so mixed up that I did very badly on the test.* **2** to involve; concern: *They were mixed up in a dishonest scheme to cheat people.*

mixed (mikst), **1** formed of different kinds: *He bought a pound of mixed nuts. She had mixed emotions about moving.* **2** of or for both men and women: *We belong to a mixed chorus.* adjective.

mixed number, a whole number and a fraction, such as 3⅝ and 28¾.

mix·er (mik′sər), a machine that mixes: *We used our electric mixer to stir the cake batter.* noun.

mix·ture (miks′chər), **1** a mixing: *The mixture of the paints took almost ten minutes.* **2** a mixed condition: *At the end of the movie I felt a mixture of relief and disappointment.* **3** something that has been mixed: *Orange is a mixture of yellow and red.* noun.

mix-up (miks′up′), confusion; mess: *Our books arrived late because of a mix-up in the orders.* noun.

ml or **ml.,** milliliter or milliliters.

mL or **mL.,** milliliter or milliliters.

mm or **mm.,** millimeter or millimeters.

MN, Minnesota (used with postal Zip Code).

MO, Missouri (used with postal Zip Code).

mo., month or months.

Mo., Missouri.

moan (mōn), **1** a long, low sound of suffering. **2** any similar sound: *the moan of the winter wind.* **3** to make moans: *The sick man moaned in his sleep.* **4** to complain; grieve: *They were always moaning about their bad luck.* 1,2 noun, 3,4 verb.

moat (mōt), **1** a deep, wide ditch, usually filled with water, dug around a castle or town. A moat was used as a protection against enemies in the Middle Ages. **2** a similar ditch used to separate animals in zoos. noun.

mob (mob), **1** a lawless crowd, easily moved to act without thinking. **2** a large number of people;

a hat	**i** it	**oi** oil	**ch** child	a in about
ā age	**ī** ice	**ou** out	**ng** long	e in taken
ä far	**o** hot	**u** cup	**sh** she	ə = { i in pencil
e let	**ō** open	**u̇** put	**th** thin	o in lemon
ē equal	**ô** order	**ü** rule	**ŦH** then	u in circus
ėr term			**zh** measure	

crowd. **3** to crowd around, especially in curiosity or anger: *The eager children mobbed the ice-cream truck the moment it appeared.* 1,2 *noun,* 3 *verb,* **mobs, mobbed, mob·bing.**

mo·bile (mō′bəl *for 1 and 2;* mō′bēl *for 3*), **1** movable; easy to move: *Several mobile classrooms were brought to the crowded school.* **2** moving or changing easily: *A mobile mind is one that is easily moved by ideas or feelings.* **3** a decoration hanging from fine wires or threads and balanced to move in a slight breeze. 1,2 *adjective,* 3 *noun.*

moc·ca·sin (mok′ə sən), **1** a soft leather shoe without a heel. Moccasins were first made by North American Indians out of deerskin. **2** a poisonous American snake; water moccasin. *noun.*

mock (mok), **1** to laugh at; make fun of: *Rude people in the audience mocked the new play.* **2** to make fun of by copying or imitating: *My friends mocked the way I hobbled around on my sore foot.* **3** to imitate; copy: *Catbirds mock the songs of other birds.* **4** not real; imitation: *The troops took part in a mock battle.* 1-3 *verb,* 4 *adjective.*

mock·er·y (mok′ər ē), **1** a making fun; ridicule: *Their mockery of my new clothes hurt my feelings.* **2** a bad copy or imitation: *Their pretended sorrow was but a mockery of real grief. noun, plural* **mock·er·ies.**

mock·ing·bird (mok′ing bėrd′), a grayish songbird that imitates the calls of other birds. *noun.*

mockingbird—about 11 inches (28 centimeters) long

mode[1] (mōd), the way or manner in which a thing is done; method: *Riding a donkey is a slow mode of travel. noun.*

mode[2] (mōd), the style, fashion, or custom that is current; way most people are behaving, talking, or dressing: *Blue jeans have been the mode for many students the past few years. noun.*

mod·el (mod′l), **1** a small copy of something: *A globe is a model of the earth. His hobby is making models of sailing ships.* **2** a figure in clay or wax that is to be copied in marble, bronze, or other material: *The sculptor was working on a clay model for a statue.* **3** to make, shape, or fashion; design or plan: *In art class I modeled a kitten in clay.* **4** the way in which a thing is made; style: *Our television set is a new model.* **5** a thing or person to be

copied or imitated: *Your mother is a fine person; make her your model.* **6** to follow as a pattern or example: *Model yourself on your father.* **7** just right or perfect, especially in conduct: *They tried very hard to be model parents.* **8** serving as a pattern or example: *We visited a model farm recently.* **9** a person who poses for artists and photographers. **10** a person employed by a clothing store to wear clothes that are for sale, so that customers can see how they look. **11** to be a model: *Would you like to model for a department store?* 1,2,4,5,9,10 *noun,* 3,6,11 *verb,* 7,8 *adjective.*

mo·dem (mō′dem), an electronic device that enables a computer to send or receive information or instructions by telephone lines. *noun.*

mod·er·ate (mod′ər it *for 1;* mod′ə rāt′ *for 2*), **1** kept or keeping within proper bounds; not extreme: *The bus traveled at moderate speed.* **2** to make or become less extreme or violent: *The wind is moderating.* 1 *adjective,* 2 *verb,* **mod·er·ates, mod·er·at·ed, mod·er·at·ing.**

mod·e·ra·tion (mod′ə rā′shən), **1** the act of moderating or of moving away from an extreme: *We all welcomed the moderation of the uncomfortably hot weather.* **2** a reasonable amount or degree: *It is all right to eat candy in moderation. noun.*

mod·ern (mod′ərn), **1** of the present time; of times not long past: *Color television is a modern invention.* **2** up-to-date; not old-fashioned: *They are young and have modern ideas. adjective.*

mod·ern·ize (mod′ər nīz), to make or become modern; bring up to present ways or standards: *We plan to modernize our kitchen. verb,* **mod·ern·iz·es, mod·ern·ized, mod·ern·iz·ing.**

mod·est (mod′ist), **1** not thinking too highly of oneself; not vain; humble: *In spite of many honors, the scientist remained a modest person.* **2** shy; not bold; held back by a sense of what is fit and proper: *The modest child did not speak to the guests, but sat quietly next to his mother.* **3** not displaying or calling attention to one's body. *adjective.*

mod·est·y (mod′ə stē), **1** a not thinking too highly of oneself; being humble. **2** a being shy or bashful. **3** a not displaying or calling attention to one's body. *noun.*

mod·i·fi·ca·tion (mod′ə fə kā′shən), **1** a partial alteration or change: *With these modifications your composition will do for the school paper.* **2** a making less severe or strong; toning down: *A modification of the workers' demands helped settle the long strike.* **3** a changed form; variety: *This new car is a modification of last year's model. noun.*

M

mod·i·fy (mod′ə fī), **1** to change somewhat: *They have modified the design of that automobile.* **2** to make less; tone down; make less severe or strong: *The workers modified their demands.* **3** to limit the meaning of: *In "red rose," red modifies rose. verb,* **mod·i·fies, mod·i·fied, mod·i·fy·ing.**

mod·ule (moj′ůl), a unit or system complete in itself which is part of a larger system and is designed for a particular use: *The astronauts landed on the moon in the spacecraft's lunar module. noun.*

Mo·ham·med (mō ham′id), the founder of Islam, the religion of the Moslems. *noun.*

Mo·hawk (mō′hôk), a member of an Iroquois tribe of American Indians formerly living in central New York State. *noun, plural* **Mo·hawks** or **Mo·hawk.**

moist (moist), slightly wet; damp: *Apply the polish with a moist cloth. adjective.*

mois·ten (mois′n), to make moist; become moist: *His eyes moistened with tears. verb.*

mois·ture (mois′chər), a slight wetness; water or other liquid spread in very small drops in the air or on a surface. Dew is moisture that collects at night on the grass. *noun.*

mo·lar (mō′lər), a tooth with a broad surface for grinding; one of the back teeth. Adult human beings have twelve molars. *noun.*

mo·las·ses (mə las′iz), a sweet, brown syrup. Molasses is obtained in the process of making sugar from sugarcane. *noun.*
[*Molasses* comes from a Latin word meaning "honey." The syrup looks and flows like honey.]

mold[1] (mōld), **1** a hollow shape in which anything is formed or cast, such as the mold into which melted metal is poured to harden into shape, or the mold in which jelly is left to stiffen. **2** the shape or form which is given by a mold: *The molds of ice cream were turkeys and pumpkins.* **3** to make or form into shape: *We molded the dough into loaves to be baked.* **1,2** *noun,* **3** *verb.*

mold[2] (mōld), **1** a woolly or furry growth, often greenish in color, that appears on food and other animal or vegetable substances when they are left too long in a warm, moist place. Mold is a fungus. **2** to become covered with mold: *This food will mold unless you refrigerate it.* **1** *noun,* **2** *verb.*

mold·er (mōl′dər), to crumble away; break up gradually into dust. *verb.*

mold·ing (mōl′ding), a strip, usually of wood, around the upper or lower walls of a room, or around doorways or window frames. *noun.*

Mol·do·va (môl dō′və), a country in eastern Europe. *noun.*

mold·y (mōl′dē), **1** covered with mold: *There was moldy cheese in the refrigerator.* **2** musty; stale: *a moldy smell. adjective,* **mold·i·er, mold·i·est.**

mole[1] (mōl), a spot on the skin, usually brown. *noun.*

mole[2] (mōl), a small animal that lives underground most of the time. Moles have velvety fur and very small eyes that cannot see well. *noun.*

mol·e·cule (mol′ə kyůl), **1** the smallest particle into which a substance can be divided without chemical change. **2** a very small particle. *noun.*

mo·lest (mə lest′), to meddle with and injure; interfere with and trouble; disturb: *It is cruel to molest animals. verb.*

mol·lusk (mol′əsk), an animal with a soft body, usually protected with a shell. Snails, oysters, clams, octopuses, and squids are mollusks. *noun.*

mollusks

molt (mōlt), to shed the feathers, skin, hair, or shell before a new growth. Birds, snakes, and insects molt. *verb.*

mol·ten (mōlt′n), melted: *Molten rock is called lava. adjective.*

mom (mom), mother. *noun.*

mo·ment (mō′mənt), **1** a very short space of time; instant: *I'll be with you in a moment.* **2** a particular point of time: *I started the very moment I got your message. noun.*

mo·men·tar·i·ly (mō′mən ter′ə lē), **1** for a moment: *She hesitated momentarily.* **2** at every moment; from moment to moment: *The danger was increasing momentarily.* **3** at any moment: *We were expecting our visitors momentarily. adverb.*

mo·men·tar·y (mō′mən ter′ē), lasting only a moment: *There was a momentary hesitation before she spoke. adjective.*

mo·men·tous (mō men′təs), very important: *Choosing between peace and war is a momentous decision. adjective.*

mo·men·tum (mō men′təm), the force with which an object moves: *A falling object gains momentum as it falls. The momentum of the racing cars carried them far beyond the finish line. noun.*

mom·ma (mom′ə), mama; mother. *noun.*

mom·my (mom′ē), mother. *noun, plural* **mom·mies.**

Mon., Monday.

mon·arch (mon′ərk), **1** a king, queen, emperor,

or other ruler. **2** a large, orange-and-black butterfly. *noun.*

mon·ar·chy (mon′ər kē), **1** a government by a monarch. **2** a nation governed by a monarch. *noun, plural* **mon·ar·chies.**

mon·as·ter·y (mon′ə ster′ē), a building where monks live and work together. *noun, plural* **mon·as·ter·ies.**

Mon·day (mun′dē), the second day of the week; the day after Sunday. *noun.*
[*Monday* comes from an earlier English word meaning "the moon's day." It was called this because it follows Sunday, that is, the sun's day.]

mo·ner·an (mə nir′ən), any living thing that lacks a nucleus. Bacteria and some algae are classed as monerans. *noun.*

mon·ey (mun′ē), **1** coins of gold, silver, copper, or other metals, or paper money issued by a government. **2** anything of value used for buying and selling. A bank check or a piece of gold or silver is money. **3** wealth: *He is a man of money. noun.*

make money, 1 to get money: *She made money in the stock market.* **2** to become rich: *My ambition is to make money and retire young.*

Mon·go·li·an Peo·ple's Re·pub·lic (mong gō′lē ən pē′pəlz ri pub′lik), a country in central Asia.

mon·goose (mong′güs), a slender animal of Africa and Asia. It is noted for its ability to kill poisonous snakes. *noun, plural* **mon·goos·es.**

mongooses
about 2 feet
(60 centimeters)
long with the tail

mon·grel (mung′grəl *or* mong′grəl), an animal or plant of mixed breed, especially a dog. *noun.*

mon·i·tor (mon′ə tər), **1** a pupil in school with special duties, such as helping to keep order and taking attendance. **2** a receiver or other device that is used to check or control something: *Most banks have TV monitors to observe customers and prevent holdups.* **3** to check or control something by a receiver or other device: *Police monitor traffic by using cars equipped with radar.* **4** a screen on which a computer shows information or instructions. A television set may be used as a monitor with some computers. **1,2,4** *noun,* **3** *verb.*

monk (mungk), a man who gives up everything else for religion and enters a monastery to live. *noun.*

a hat	**i** it	**oi** oil	**ch** child	a in about
ā age	**ī** ice	**ou** out	**ng** long	e in taken
ä far	**o** hot	**u** cup	**sh** she	i in pencil
e let	**ō** open	**u̇** put	**th** thin	o in lemon
ē equal	**ô** order	**ü** rule	**ᴛʜ** then	u in circus
ėr term			**zh** measure	

ə =

mon·key (mung′kē), **1** an animal of the group most like human beings. Monkeys are very intelligent animals. **2** one of the smaller animals in this group, not a chimpanzee, gorilla, or other large ape. It usually has a long tail. **3** a person, especially a child, who is full of mischief. **4** to play; fool; trifle: *Don't monkey with the television.* **1-3** *noun, plural* **mon·keys; 4** *verb.*

make a monkey out of, to make a fool of.

monkey wrench, a wrench with a movable jaw that can be adjusted to fit different sizes of nuts.

mon·o·cle (mon′ə kəl), an eyeglass for one eye. *noun.*

monocle

mon·o·cot (mon′ə kot), a flowering plant with seeds that have one seed leaf. Monocots have petals in groups of three. Daffodils, bananas, oats, and palm trees are monocots. *noun.*

mon·o·gram (mon′ə gram), a person's initials combined in one design. Monograms are used on note paper, table linen, clothing, and jewelry. *noun.*

mon·o·logue (mon′l ôg), **1** a long speech by one person in a group. **2** an entertainment by a single speaker. **3** a play for a single actor. **4** a part of a play in which a single actor speaks alone. *noun.*

mon·o·plane (mon′ə plān), an airplane with only one pair of wings. Most modern airplanes are monoplanes. *noun.*

mo·nop·o·lize (mə nop′ə līz), **1** to have or get complete possession or control of: *One company in the country monopolized the production of copper wire.* **2** to occupy wholly; keep entirely to oneself: *Don't monopolize your teacher's time. verb,* **mo·nop·o·liz·es, mo·nop·o·lized, mo·nop·o·liz·ing.**

mo·nop·o·ly (mə nop′ə lē), **1** the complete control of a product or service: *The electric company has a monopoly on providing electrical service in the area it serves.* **2** a person or company with such complete control. **3** the complete possession or control of something: *a monopoly on another person's time. noun, plural* **mo·nop·o·lies.**

mon·o·rail (mon′ə rāl), **1** a single rail serving as a complete track for the vehicles that run on it. **2** a railway in which cars run on a single rail, either balanced on it or suspended from it. *noun.*

monorail (definition 2)

mon·o·syl·la·ble (mon′ə sil′ə bəl), a word of one syllable. *Yes* and *no* are monosyllables. *noun.*

mon·o·tone (mon′ə tōn), a sameness of tone or of color: *Don't read in a monotone; use expression.* *noun.*

mo·not·o·nous (mə not′n əs), **1** continuing in the same tone: *She spoke in a monotonous voice.* **2** not varying; without change: *monotonous food.* **3** tiring or boring because of its sameness: *Sorting mail is monotonous work. adjective.*

mo·not·o·ny (mə not′n ē), **1** sameness of tone or pitch: *The monotony of the man's voice was irritating.* **2** a lack of variety; tiring or boring sameness: *the monotony of the desert. noun.*

mon·sieur (mə syėr′), a French word meaning "Mr." or "sir." *noun, plural* **mes·sieurs** (mes′ərz *or* mā syü′).

mon·soon (mon sün′), **1** a seasonal wind of the Indian Ocean and southern Asia. It blows from the southwest from April to October and from the northeast during the rest of the year. **2** a season during which this wind blows from the southwest, usually accompanied by heavy rains. *noun.*

mon·ster (mon′stər), **1** any animal or plant that is very unlike those usually found in nature. A cow with two heads is a monster. **2** an imaginary creature of strange or horrible appearance, such as a dragon. **3** a huge creature or thing. **4** a person too wicked to be considered human: *a horrible crime committed by a monster of cruelty. noun.*

mon·stros·i·ty (mon stros′ə tē), **1** a monster. A cow with two heads is a monstrosity. **2** something that is huge, ugly, shocking, or horrible: *That new building is a monstrosity. noun, plural* **mon·stros·i·ties.**

mon·strous (mon′strəs), **1** huge; enormous: *A monstrous wave sank the tiny fishing vessel.* **2** wrongly formed or shaped; like a monster: *A calf born with two heads is a monstrous creature.* **3** shocking; horrible; dreadful: *Murder is a monstrous crime. adjective.*

Mont., Montana.

Mon·tan·a (mon tan′ə), one of the western states of the United States. *Abbreviation:* Mont. or MT *Capital:* Helena. *noun.*
[*Montana* comes from a Spanish word meaning "region having many mountains."]

Mont·gom·er·y (mont gum′ər ē), the capital of Alabama. *noun.*

month (munth), one of the twelve periods of time into which a year is divided. April, June, September, and November have 30 days; February has 28 days except in leap years; all the other months have 31 days. *noun.*

month·ly (munth′lē), **1** of a month; for a month; lasting a month: *a monthly supply, a monthly salary.* **2** done, happening, or paid once a month: *a monthly meeting, a monthly examination.* **3** once a month; every month: *Some magazines come monthly.* **4** a magazine published once a month. **1,2** *adjective,* **3** *adverb,* **4** *noun, plural* **month·lies.**

Mont·pel·ier (mont pē′lyər), the capital of Vermont. *noun.*

Mont·re·al (mon′trē ôl′), a city in Canada. *noun.*

mon·u·ment (mon′yə mənt), **1** something set up to honor a person or an event; anything that keeps alive the memory of a person or an event. A monument may be a building, pillar, arch, statue, tomb, or stone. **2** a permanent or prominent instance: *The Hoover Dam is a monument of engineering. noun.*

mon·u·men·tal (mon′yə men′tl), **1** of a monument: *monumental decorations.* **2** serving as a monument: *a monumental chapel.* **3** like a monument: *a monumental mountain peak.* **4** weighty and lasting; important: *The Constitution of the United States is a monumental document.* **5** very great: *monumental ignorance. adjective.*

moo (mü), **1** the sound made by a cow. **2** to make this sound. **1** *noun, plural* **moos; 2** *verb.*

mood (müd), a state of mind or feeling: *I am in the mood to play now; I don't want to study. noun.*

mood·y (mü′dē), **1** likely to have changes of mood: *Some people have a moody disposition.* **2** often having gloomy moods: *She has been moody ever since she lost her job.* **3** sunk in sadness; gloomy; sullen: *He sat in moody silence. adjective,* **mood·i·er, mood·i·est.**

moon (mün), **1** a heavenly body that revolves around the earth once in about 29½ days. The moon shines in the sky at night and looks bright because it reflects the sun's light. **2** the American Indian month of about 29½ days. **3** a satellite of any planet: *the moons of Jupiter. noun.*

moon·beam (mün′bēm′), a ray of moonlight. *noun.*

moon·light (mün′līt′), **1** the light of the moon. **2** having the light of the moon: *a moonlight night.* **3** while the moon is shining; by night: *We went out to the pool to take a moonlight swim.* **1** *noun,* **2,3** *adjective.*

moon·lit (mün′lit′), lighted by the moon: *We could see the coyotes on the moonlit hill. adjective.*

moor[1] (mùr), to put or keep a ship in place by means of ropes or chains fastened to the shore or to anchors: *We moored the boat to the dock. verb.*

moor[2] (mùr), an open wasteland, usually covered with heather: *Sheep are raised on the moors of Scotland. noun.*

Moor (mùr), a person born or living in northwestern Africa. The Moors are Moslems who speak Arabic. In the A.D. 700's the Moors invaded and conquered Spain. They were driven out in 1492. *noun.*

moose (müs), an animal somewhat like a large deer, living in Canada and the northern part of the United States. The male has a large head and broad antlers. *noun, plural* **moose.**

Word History

moose *Moose* comes from a North American Indian word meaning "he strips off the bark." The moose was called this because it strips off and eats the bark of trees.

moose—about 6 feet (2 meters) high at the shoulder

mop (mop), **1** a bundle of coarse yarn or cloth, or a sponge, fastened at the end of a stick and used for cleaning floors, dishes, and other things. **2** to wash or wipe up; clean with a mop: *mop the floor.* **3** to wipe tears or sweat from: *She mopped her brow with a handkerchief.* **4** a thick head of hair like a mop. 1,4 *noun,* 2,3 *verb,* **mops, mopped, mop·ping.**

mope (mōp), to be dull, silent, and sad: *He has been moping indoors all afternoon. verb,* **mopes, moped, mop·ing.**

mo·ral (môr′əl), **1** good in character or conduct; virtuous according to civilized standards of right and wrong; right; just: *a moral act, a moral person.* **2 morals,** character or behavior in matters of right and wrong: *a person of excellent morals.* **3** having to do with character or with the difference between right and wrong: *Whether to keep a large sum of money you have found or to turn it over to the police is a moral question.* **4** the lesson, inner meaning, or teaching of a fable, a story, or an event: *The moral of the story was "Look before you leap."* **5** teaching a good lesson; having a good influence: *moral essays, a moral book.* 1,3,5 *adjective,* 2,4 *noun.*

mo·rale (mə ral′), moral or mental condition in regard to courage, confidence, or enthusiasm: *The morale of the team was low after its defeat. noun.*

a hat	i it	oi oil	ch child	a in about
ā age	ī ice	ou out	ng long	e in taken
ä far	o hot	u cup	sh she	ə = { i in pencil
e let	ō open	u̇ put	th thin	o in lemon
ē equal	ô order	ü rule	ŦH then	u in circus
ėr term			zh measure	

mo·ral·i·ty (mə ral′ə tē), **1** the right or wrong of an action: *They spent the evening arguing about the morality of war.* **2** doing right; virtue: *They have high standards of morality. noun.*

mo·ral·ly (môr′ə lē), **1** in a moral manner: *to behave morally.* **2** from a moral point of view: *What they did was morally wrong. adverb.*

mo·rass (mə ras′), a piece of low, soft, wet ground; swamp. *noun, plural* **mo·rass·es.**

mo·ray (môr′ā), a fierce, often brightly colored eel found in warm seas. *noun.*

moray—up to 6 feet (2 meters) long

mor·bid (môr′bid), unhealthy; not wholesome: *morbid ideas, a morbid book. adjective.*

more (môr), **1** greater in amount, degree, or number: *more humid, more people. A foot is more than an inch.* **2** a greater or additional amount, degree, or number: *Tell me more about your camping trip. Seven people will not be enough for a softball team; we will need more.* **3** in a higher degree; to a greater extent: *A burn hurts more than a scratch does.* **4** in addition; farther: *Take one step more.* **5** further; additional: *This plant needs more sun.* **6** *More* helps to make the comparative form of most adverbs, and of most adjectives longer than one syllable: *more easily, more truly, more careful.* "More common" means "commoner." 1,5 *adjective, comparative of* **much** *and* **many;** 2 *noun,* 3,4,6 *adverb, comparative of* **much.**

more or less, 1 somewhat: *Most people are more or less selfish.* **2** about; approximately: *The distance is fifty miles, more or less.*

more·o·ver (môr ō′vər), also; besides: *I don't want to go skating and, moreover, the ice is too thin. adverb.*

morn (môrn), the morning. *noun.*

morn·ing (môr′ning), the early part of the day, ending at noon. *noun.*

morn·ing-glo·ry (môr′ning glôr′ē), a climbing vine that has heart-shaped leaves and funnel-shaped blue, lavender, pink, or white flowers. Its flowers open early in the morning but

M

close later in the sunlight. *noun, plural*
morn·ing·glo·ries.

Mo·roc·co (mə rok′ō), a country in northern
Africa. *noun.*

mo·ron (môr′on), **1** a person born with little
mental ability. Morons can usually learn to read
and to work at simple jobs. **2** a very stupid or
foolish person. *noun.*

mo·rose (mə rōs′), gloomy; sullen: *Many days of
rain made me feel morose. adjective.*

mor·row (môr′ō), **1** the following day or time.
2 "Good morrow" is an old way of saying "Good
morning." *noun.*

Morse code (môrs′ kōd′), a system by which
letters, numbers, and other signs are expressed
by dots, dashes, and spaces or by long and short
sounds or flashes of light. Morse code is now
used mainly for signaling.

mor·sel (môr′səl), a small piece or amount,
especially of food: *I was so hungry I ate every
morsel on my plate. noun.*

mor·tal (môr′tl), **1** sure to die sometime: *all
mortal creatures.* **2** a human being: *No mortal
could have survived the fire.* **3** causing death: *a
mortal wound, a mortal illness.* **4** to the death: *a
mortal enemy, a mortal battle.* **5** very great;
extreme: *mortal terror.* **6** causing death of the
soul, according to the Roman Catholic Church:
Murder is a mortal sin. **1,3-6** *adjective,* **2** *noun.*

mor·tal·ly (môr′tl ē), **1** so as to cause death:
The soldier fell mortally wounded. **2** very greatly;
bitterly: *She was mortally offended by your remark.
adverb.*

mor·tar (môr′tər), a mixture of lime, cement,
sand, and water for holding bricks or stones
together. *noun.*

mort·gage (môr′gij), a claim on property, given
to a person, bank, or firm that has loaned money
in case the money is not repaid when due. *noun.*

mo·sa·ic (mō zā′ik), a picture or design made by
fitting together small pieces of stone, glass, tile,
or wood of different colors. Mosaics are used in
the floors, walls, or ceilings of some fine
buildings. *noun.*

mosaic

Mos·cow (mos′kou), the capital of Russia and
formerly of the Soviet Union. *noun.*

Mos·lem (moz′ləm), **1** a follower of Mohammed;
believer in the religion founded by him. **2** of
Mohammed or the religion founded by him.
1 *noun, plural* **Mos·lems** *or* **Mos·lem;** **2** *adjective.*
Also spelled **Muslim.**

mosque (mosk), a Moslem place of worship.
noun.

mosque

mo·squi·to (mə skē′tō), a small, slender insect
with two wings. The female bites and sucks blood
from people and animals, causing itching. There
are many kinds of mosquitoes; one kind transmits
malaria; another transmits yellow fever. *noun,
plural* **mo·squi·toes** *or* **mo·squi·tos.**

moss (môs), the very small, soft, green plants that
grow close together like a carpet on the ground,
on rocks, or on trees. *noun, plural* **moss·es.**

moss·y (mô′sē), **1** covered with moss: *a mossy
bank.* **2** like moss: *mossy green. adjective,*
moss·i·er, moss·i·est.

most (mōst), **1** greatest in amount, degree, or
number: *The winner gets the most money.* **2** the
greatest amount, degree, or number: *We did most
of the work around the house. Who gave the most?*
3 in the highest degree; to the greatest extent:
This tooth hurts most. They were most kind to me.
4 almost all: *Most people like ice cream.* **5** *Most*
helps to make the superlative form of almost all
adverbs, and of almost all adjectives longer than
one syllable: *most easily, most truly, most careful.*
"Most common" means "commonest." **1,4**
adjective, superlative of **much** *and* **many;** **2** *noun,*
3,5 *adverb, superlative of* **much.**

at most *or* **at the most,** not more than: *Within an
hour at most I will tell you.*

for the most part, mainly; usually: *The attempts
were for the most part unsuccessful.*

most·ly (mōst′lē), almost all; for the most part;
mainly; chiefly: *The work is mostly done. adverb.*

mo·tel (mō tel′), a roadside hotel or a group of
furnished cottages or cabins providing overnight
lodging for motorists. *noun.*
[*Motel* was formed by joining parts of the words
motor and *hotel.*]

moth (môth), a winged insect very much like a
butterfly, but flying mostly at night. One kind lays
eggs in cloth and fur, and its larvae eat holes in
the material. Some larvae, such as the silkworm,

moth—This kind of **moth** has a wingspread of 5 inches (13 centimeters).

a hat	i it	oi oil	ch child		a in about
ā age	ī ice	ou out	ng long		e in taken
ä far	o hot	u cup	sh she	ə =	i in pencil
e let	ō open	u̇ put	th thin		o in lemon
ē equal	ô order	ü rule	ᴛʜ then		u in circus
ėr term			zh measure		

are useful to people. *noun, plural* **moths** (môᴛʜz *or* môths).

moth·ball (môth′bôl′), a small ball of camphor or other strong-smelling substance, used to keep moths away from wool, silk, fur, and other types of clothing. *noun.*

moth·er (muᴛʜ′ər), **1** a female parent. **2** to take care of: *She mothers her baby sister.* **3** the cause or source of anything: *Necessity is the mother of invention.* **4** the head of a large community of religious women. **5** native: *one's mother country. English is our mother tongue.* 1,3,4 *noun,* 2 *verb,* 5 *adjective.*

moth·er·hood (muᴛʜ′ər hu̇d), the condition of being a mother. *noun.*

moth·er-in-law (muᴛʜ′ər in lô′), the mother of one's husband or wife. *noun, plural* **moth·ers-in-law.**

moth·er·less (muᴛʜ′ər lis), having no mother: *a motherless child. adjective.*

moth·er·ly (muᴛʜ′ər lē), of or like a mother; kindly: *a motherly person, a motherly smile. adjective.*

moth·er-of-pearl (muᴛʜ′ər əv pėrl′), the hard, smooth, shiny lining of the shell of the pearl oyster and certain other shells. It changes colors when moved or turned in the light. It is used to make buttons and ornaments. *noun.*

mo·tion (mō′shən), **1** movement; moving; change of position or place. Anything is in motion which is not at rest. *Can you feel the motion of the ship?* **2** to make a movement, as of the hand or head, to show one's meaning: *She motioned to show us the way.* **3** to show a person what to do by such a movement: *He motioned me out.* **4** a formal suggestion made in a meeting, to be voted on: *I made a motion to adjourn.* 1,4 *noun,* 2,3 *verb.*

mo·tion·less (mō′shən lis), not moving. *adjective.*

motion picture, a series of pictures shown on a screen in such rapid succession that the viewer gets the impression that the persons and things pictured are moving; moving picture; movie.

mo·tive (mō′tiv), a thought or feeling that makes one act; reason for doing something: *My motive in going was a wish to travel. noun.*

mot·ley (mot′lē), **1** made up of different things: *In the drawer I found a motley collection of butterflies, shells, and stamps.* **2** of different colors like a clown's suit. **3** a suit of more than one color worn by clowns: *At the party he wore motley.* 1,2 *adjective,* 3 *noun.*

mo·tor (mō′tər), **1** an engine that makes a machine go: *an electric motor.* **2** run by a motor: *a motor vehicle.* **3** having to do with or by means of automobiles: *a motor tour.* **4** to travel by automobile: *We motored to Colorado during vacation.* **5** causing or having to do with motion. Motor nerves arouse muscles to action. 1 *noun,* 2,3,5 *adjective,* 4 *verb.*

[*Motor* comes from a Latin word meaning "to move." Other English words from the same Latin root include *motion* and *motive.*]

mo·tor·boat (mō′tər bōt′), a boat that is propelled by a motor. *noun.*

mo·tor·cy·cle (mō′tər sī′kəl), a motor vehicle with two wheels, which looks like a bicycle but is heavier and larger. *noun.*

mo·tor·ist (mō′tər ist), a person who drives or travels in an automobile. *noun.*

motor vehicle, any vehicle run by a motor, which travels on wheels on roads and highways. Cars, trucks, buses, and motorcycles are motor vehicles.

mot·tled (mot′ld), spotted or streaked with different colors. *adjective.*

mot·to (mot′ō), **1** a brief sentence adopted as a rule of conduct: *"Think before you speak" is a good motto.* **2** a sentence, word, or phrase written or engraved on some object. *noun, plural* **mot·toes** *or* **mot·tos.**

mound (mound), **1** a bank or heap of earth, stones, or other material: *a mound of hay.* **2** the slightly elevated ground from which a baseball pitcher pitches. *noun.*

mount[1] (mount), **1** to go up: *to mount a hill, to mount a ladder.* **2** to get up on: *to mount a horse, to mount a platform.* **3** to get on a horse: *The riders mounted quickly.* **4** a horse for riding: *The riding instructor had an excellent mount.* **5** to rise; increase; rise in amount: *The cost of living mounts steadily.* **6** to put in proper position or order for use: *to mount specimens on slides.* **7** to fix in a setting, backing, or support: *to mount a picture on cardboard.* **8** a setting; backing; support: *the mount for a picture.* 1-3, 5-7 *verb,* 4,8 *noun.*

mount[2] (mount), a mountain; high hill. *Mount* is often used before the names of mountains, as in *Mount Everest. noun.*

moun·tain (moun′tən), **1** a very high hill. **2** of or having something to do with mountains: *mountain* air, *mountain plants.* **3** a very large heap or pile of anything: *a mountain of rubbish. She overcame a mountain of difficulties.* **1,3** *noun,* **2** *adjective.*

moun·tain·eer (moun′tə nir′), a person skilled in mountain climbing. *noun.*

mountain goat, a white, goatlike antelope of the Rocky Mountains.

mountain goat—3 feet (1 meter) high at the shoulder

mountain lion, a large cat with brownish-yellow fur, that lives in parts of North and South America; puma.

moun·tain·ous (moun′tə nəs), **1** covered with mountain ranges: *mountainous country.* **2** huge: *a mountainous wave. adjective.*

mountain range, a row of mountains; large group of mountains.

moun·tain·side (moun′tən sīd′), the slope of a mountain below the top. *noun.*

moun·tain·top (moun′tən top′), the top or summit of a mountain. *noun.*

mount·ed (moun′tid), serving on horseback: *Chicago and New York City have mounted police. adjective.*

mourn (môrn), **1** to grieve: *People mourned over the death of their neighbors in the tornado.* **2** to feel or show sorrow over: *They mourned their lost dog. verb.*

mourn·ful (môrn′fəl), full of grief; sad; sorrowful: *a mournful voice. adjective.*

mourn·ing (môr′ning), **1** an outward sign of sorrow for a person's death, such as the wearing of black clothing or the flying of flags at half-mast. **2** the clothes or decorations that show sorrow for death. *noun.*

mouse (mous), a small, gnawing animal with soft fur, a pointed snout, and a long, thin tail. Some kinds of mice are commonly found in houses. Others live in fields and meadows. *noun, plural* **mice.**

mous·tache (mus′tash). See **mustache.** *noun.*

mouth (mouth), **1** the opening through which a person or animal takes in food; space containing the tongue and teeth. **2** an opening suggesting a mouth: *the mouth of a cave, the mouth of a bottle.* **3** the part of a river or the like where its waters flow into some other body of water. *noun, plural* **mouths** (mouᵗ Hz).

mouth·ful (mouth′fül), as much as the mouth can easily hold: *He took a mouthful of ice cream. noun, plural* **mouth·fuls.**

mouth organ, a harmonica.

mouth·piece (mouth′pēs′), the part of a musical instrument, telephone, or pipe that is placed in, against, or near a person's mouth. *noun.*

mov·a·ble (mü′və bəl), **1** able to be moved, or to be carried from place to place: *movable furniture. Our fingers are movable.* **2** changing from one date to another in different years: *Thanksgiving is a movable holiday. adjective.* Also spelled **moveable.**

move (müv), **1** to change the place or position of: *Do not move your hand. Move your chair to the table.* **2** to change place or position: *The child moved in his sleep.* **3** to change one's place of living: *We move to the country next week.* **4** to put or keep in motion; shake; stir: *The wind moves the leaves.* **5** to make progress; go: *The train moved slowly.* **6** an act of moving; movement: *an impatient move of the head.* **7** an action taken to bring about some result: *Our next move was to earn some money.* **8** to cause to do something: *What moved you to get up so early this morning?* **9** to arouse to laughter or some feeling: *The sad story moved us to tears.* **10** (in games) to change to a different square according to rules: *move a pawn in chess.* **11** the moving of a piece in chess and other games: *That was a good move.* **12** a player's turn to move in a game: *It is your move now.* **13** (in a meeting) to bring forward or propose: *Madam Chairman, I move that the report of the treasurer be adopted.* **1-5,8-10,13** *verb,* **moves, moved, mov·ing;** **6,7,11,12** *noun.*

move in, to move oneself, one's family, or one's belongings into a new place to live: *The new couple is moving in next week.*

move out, to move oneself, one's family, or one's belongings out of the place where one has lived: *We have to move out by the end of the month.*

on the move, moving about: *She is interested in many activities and is always on the move.*

move·a·ble (mü′və bəl). See **movable.** *adjective.*

move·ment (müv′mənt), **1** a moving: *We run by movements of the legs.* **2** the moving parts of a machine; special group of connected parts that move together. The movement of a watch consists of many little wheels. **3** the efforts and results of a group of people working together to reach a

movement (definition 2)

common goal: *The civil rights movement was responsible for many new laws.* noun.

mov·er (mü′vər), a person or company whose business is moving furniture from one house or place to another. *noun.*

mov·ie (mü′vē), **1** a motion picture: *I enjoyed that movie.* **2 the movies,** a showing of motion pictures: *We went to the movies last night. noun.*

mov·ing (mü′ving), **1** changing or able to change place or position: *a moving car.* **2** causing action: *He was the moving spirit in planning for the party.* **3** arousing pity or tender feeling; stirring the emotions: *a moving story.* **4** See **move.** 1-3 *adjective,* 4 *verb.*

moving picture, a motion picture.

mow[1] (mō), **1** to cut down grass or grain with a machine or a scythe: *to mow grass. I was mowing yesterday.* **2** to cut down the grass or grain from: *to mow a field. verb,* **mows, mowed** or **mown, mow·ing.**

mow[2] (mou), **1** a place in the barn where hay or grain is piled or stored. **2** a pile or stack of hay or grain in a barn. *noun.*

mow·er (mō′ər), a person or thing that mows: *a lawn mower. noun.*

mown (mōn), mowed. See **mow**[1]. *New-mown hay is hay that has just been cut. verb.*

Mo·zam·bique (mō′zam bēk′), a country in southeastern Africa. *noun.*

Mr. or **Mr** (mis′tər), a title put in front of a man's name or the name of his position: *Mr. Stern, Mr. Speaker.*

Mrs. or **Mrs** (mis′iz), a title put in front of a married woman's name: *Mrs. Jackson.*

MS, Mississippi (used with postal Zip Code).

Ms. or **Ms** (miz), a title put in front of a woman's name: *Ms. Karen Hansen. plural* **Mses.**

MT, Montana (used with postal Zip Code).

Mt., mount or mountain: *Mt. Whitney. plural* **Mts.**

much (much), **1** in great amount or degree: *much rain, much pleasure, not much money.* **2** a great amount: *I did not hear much of the talk. Too much of this cake will make you sick.* **3** to a high degree; greatly: *I was much pleased with the toy.* **4** nearly; about: *This is much the same as the others.* 1 *adjective,* **more, most;** 2 *noun,* 3,4 *adverb,* **more, most.**

how much, 1 what price: *How much is that shirt?* **2** what amount: *How much of this can you eat?* **3** what amount of: *How much ice cream did you eat?*

not much of a, not a very good: *Fifty dollars a week is not much of a wage.*

too much for, more than a match for: *My arguments were too much for them, and they admitted I was right.*

mu·ci·lage (myü′sə lij), a sticky, gummy substance used to make things stick together. *noun.*

muck (muk), dirt; filth. *noun.*

mu·cous mem·brane (myü′kəs mem′brān), the lining of the nose, throat, and other passages and cavities of the body that are open to the air.

mu·cus (myü′kəs), a slimy substance that moistens and protects the linings of the body. A cold in the head causes mucus to flow freely. *noun.*

mud (mud), earth so wet that it is soft and sticky: *mud on the ground after rain. noun.*

mud·dle (mud′l), **1** to mix up; get things into a mess: *Somebody really muddled that job.* **2** to think or act in a confused, blundering way: *to muddle over a problem, to muddle through a difficulty.* **3** a mess; disorder; confusion: *After the party the room was in a muddle.* 1,2 *verb,* **mud·dles, mud·dled, mud·dling;** 3 *noun.*

mud·dy (mud′ē), **1** of or like mud: *muddy footprints on the floor.* **2** having much mud; covered with mud: *a muddy road.* **3** clouded with mud; dull; not pure: *muddy water, a muddy color.* **4** confused; not clear: *muddy thinking.* **5** to make or become muddy: *His boots muddied the floor when he came into the kitchen.* 1-4 *adjective,* **mud·di·er, mud·di·est;** 5 *verb,* **mud·dies, mud·died, mud·dy·ing.**

muff (muf), **1** a covering of fur or other material for keeping both hands warm. One hand is put in at each end. **2** to handle awkwardly: *He muffed his chance to get the job.* 1 *noun,* 2 *verb.*

muff (definition 1) The older child is holding a **muff.**

muf·fin (muf′ən), a small, round cake made of wheat flour, cornmeal, or the like. Muffins are usually served hot and eaten with butter. *noun.*

muf·fle (muf′əl), **1** to wrap or cover up in order to keep warm and dry: *I muffled my throat in a warm scarf.* **2** to dull or deaden a sound: *The wind muffled our voices. verb,* **muf·fles, muf·fled, muf·fling.**

muf·fler (muf′lər), **1** a wrap or scarf worn around the neck for warmth. **2** anything used to deaden sound. An automobile muffler attached to the exhaust pipe deadens the sound of the engine's exhaust. *noun.*

M

mug (mug), **1** a heavy china or metal drinking cup with a handle. **2** the amount a mug holds: *drink a mug of milk.* **3** to attack a person from behind, usually to rob. **4** to exaggerate one's facial expressions, as in acting; make funny faces or smiles. 1,2 *noun,* 3,4 *verb,* **mugs, mugged, mug·ging.**

mug·gy (mug′ē), warm and humid: *The weather was muggy. adjective,* **mug·gi·er, mug·gi·est.**

mul·ber·ry (mul′ber′ē), **1** a tree with small, berrylike fruit that can be eaten. The leaves of one kind of mulberry are used for feeding silkworms. **2** its sweet, usually dark purple fruit. **3** dark purplish-red. 1,2 *noun, plural* **mul·ber·ries;** 3 *adjective.*

mulch (mulch), **1** a loose material, such as straw, leaves, or sawdust, spread on the ground around trees or plants. Mulch is used to protect the roots from cold or heat, to prevent evaporation of moisture from the soil, or to keep the fruit clean. As mulch decays it makes the soil richer. **2** to cover with straw or leaves. 1 *noun, plural* **mulches;** 2 *verb.*

mule (myül), **1** an animal which is the offspring of a male donkey and a female horse. It has the form and size of a horse, but the large ears, small hoofs, and tufted tail of a donkey. **2** a stubborn person. *noun.*

mul·ish (myü′lish), like a mule; stubborn; obstinate. *adjective.*

mul·let (mul′it), a fish that lives close to the shore in warm waters and is good to eat. There are red mullet and gray mullet. *noun, plural* **mul·let** or **mul·lets.**

mul·ti·ple (mul′tə pəl), **1** of, having, or involving many parts, elements, or relations: *a person of multiple interests.* **2** a number that can be divided by another number a certain number of times without a remainder: *12 is a multiple of 3.* 1 *adjective,* 2 *noun.*

mul·ti·pli·cand (mul′tə plə kand′), a number to be multiplied by another: *In 497 multiplied by 5, the multiplicand is 497. noun.*

mul·ti·pli·ca·tion (mul′tə plə kā′shən), the operation of multiplying one number by another: *12 times 3 = 36 is a simple multiplication. noun.*

mul·ti·pli·er (mul′tə plī′ər), a number by which another number is to be multiplied: *In 83 multiplied by 5, 5 is the multiplier. noun.*

mul·ti·ply (mul′tə plī), **1** to add a number a given number of times: *To multiply 6 by 3 means to add 6 three times, making 18.* **2** to increase in number: *As we climbed up the mountain the dangers and difficulties multiplied. verb,* **mul·ti·plies, mul·ti·plied, mul·ti·ply·ing.**

mul·ti·tude (mul′tə tüd *or* mul′tə tyüd), a great many; crowd: *a multitude of difficulties, a multitude of enemies. noun.*

mum (mum), silent; saying nothing: *Keep mum about this; tell no one. adjective.*

mum·ble (mum′bəl), **1** to speak unclearly, as a person does when the lips are partly closed: *She mumbled something about not being able to come to the party.* **2** a mumbling; speech that is unclear: *There was a mumble of protest from the team against the umpire's decision.* 1 *verb,* **mum·bles, mum·bled, mum·bling;** 2 *noun.*

mum·my (mum′ē), a dead body preserved from decay. Egyptian mummies have lasted more than 3000 years. *noun, plural* **mum·mies.**

mummy
an Egyptian **mummy**

mumps (mumps), a disease most often of children that causes swelling of the neck and face and makes it hard to swallow. Unless you are vaccinated against mumps, you can catch the disease if you are around someone who has it. *noun.*

munch (munch), to chew steadily and vigorously; chew noisily: *The horse munched its oats. verb.*

mu·nic·i·pal (myü nis′ə pəl), of or having something to do with the affairs of a city or town: *The state police assisted the municipal police. adjective.*

mu·ni·tion (myü nish′ən). **munitions,** material used in war. Munitions are military supplies such as guns, ammunition, or bombs. *noun.*

mur·al (myůr′əl), a picture painted on a wall. *noun.*

mural—The building was decorated with **murals.**

mur·der (mėr′dər), **1** the unlawful killing of a human being when it is planned beforehand. **2** to kill a human being intentionally. **3** to do something very badly; spoil or ruin: *The singer really murdered that song.* 1 *noun,* 2,3 *verb.*

mur·der·er (mėr′dər ər), a person who murders somebody. *noun.*

mur·der·ous (mėr′dər əs), **1** able to kill: *The villain aimed a murderous blow at the hero's back.* **2** ready to murder: *a murderous villain.* **3** causing murder: *a murderous hate. adjective.*

murk·y (mėr′kē), dark; gloomy: *a murky prison, a murky day. adjective,* **murk·i·er, murk·i·est.**

mur·mur (mėr′mər), **1** a soft, unclear sound that rises and falls a little and goes on without breaks: *the murmur of a stream.* **2** to make such a soft, unclear sound: *The brook murmured on its way down the mountain.* **3** to speak too softly to be clearly heard or plainly understood: *The shy boy murmured his thanks.* **1** *noun,* **2,3** *verb.*

mus·cle (mus′əl), **1** the tissue in the bodies of people and animals that can be tightened or loosened to make the body move. **2** a special bundle of such tissue which moves some particular bone or part: *You can feel the muscles in your arm.* **3** strength: *He didn't have enough muscle to budge the refrigerator. noun.*
[*Muscle* comes from a Latin word meaning "a little mouse." It was called this because the shape and rippling movements of some muscles, as in the arm, suggest the shape and movements of a little mouse.]

mus·cu·lar (mus′kyə lər), **1** of the muscles; influencing the muscles: *a muscular strain.* **2** having well-developed muscles; strong: *a muscular arm. adjective.*

muse (myüz), to think in a dreamy way; think: *She spent the whole afternoon in musing. verb,* **mus·es, mused, mus·ing.**

mu·se·um (myü zē′əm), a building or rooms in which a collection of objects illustrating science, ancient life, art, or other subjects is kept and displayed. *noun.*

mush (mush), **1** cornmeal boiled in water or milk. **2** a soft, thick mass: *After the heavy rain the old dirt road turned to mush. noun.*

mush·room (mush′rüm), **1** a small fungus shaped like an umbrella, that grows very fast. Some mushrooms are good to eat; some are poisonous. **2** of or like a mushroom: *a mushroom cloud.* **3** to grow rapidly: *Her business mushroomed when she opened the new store.* **1** *noun,* **2** *adjective,* **3** *verb.*

mu·sic (myü′zik), **1** the art of making sounds that are beautiful, and putting them together into beautiful arrangements. **2** beautiful, pleasing, or interesting arrangements of sounds. **3** written or printed signs for tones: *Can you read music?* **4** any pleasant sound: *the music of a bubbling brook. noun.*
set to music, to provide with music: *My piano teacher set my poem to music so I could sing it at the school concert.*

mu·si·cal (myü′zə kəl), **1** of or producing music: *a musical instrument, a musical composer.* **2** sounding beautiful or pleasing; like music: *a musical voice.* **3** set to music or accompanied by music: *a musical performance.* **4** fond of or skilled in music: *a musical family.* **5** a play or motion picture with songs, choruses, and dances. **1-4** *adjective,* **5** *noun.*

mu·si·cal·ly (myü′zik lē), **1** in a musical manner: *The bells rang musically.* **2** in music: *She is well educated musically. adverb.*

music box, a box or case containing a device that produces music mechanically.

mu·si·cian (myü zish′ən), a person skilled in music, especially one who sings, plays, writes, or conducts music as a profession or business: *An orchestra is composed of many musicians. noun.*

mus·ket (mus′kit), a kind of old gun with a long barrel. Soldiers used muskets before rifles were invented. *noun.*

mus·ket·eer (mus′kə tir′), a soldier armed with a musket. *noun.*

musk·mel·on (musk′mel′ən), a small, juicy melon with orange pulp and a hard rind. The cantaloupe is a muskmelon. *noun.*

musk ox, an animal of Greenland and northern North America that chews its cud and has hoofs and a shaggy coat. It looks like a sheep in some ways and like an ox in others.

musk ox—up to 5 feet (1½ meters) high at the shoulder

muskrat (definition 1) about 22 inches (56 centimeters) long with the tail

musk·rat (musk′rat′), **1** a water animal of North America somewhat like a rat, but larger. **2** its dark-brown fur. Muskrat is valuable for making coats. *noun, plural* **musk·rats** *or* **musk·rat.**

Mus·lim (muz′ləm), Moslem. *noun, adjective.*

a hat	i it	oi oil	ch child	a in about
ā age	ī ice	ou out	ng long	e in taken
ä far	o hot	u cup	sh she	ə = { i in pencil
e let	ō open	u̇ put	th thin	o in lemon
ē equal	ô order	ü rule	ᴛʜ then	u in circus
ėr term			zh measure	

mus·lin (muz′lən), a closely woven cotton cloth, used especially for sheets. *noun.*

muss (mus), 1 to put into disorder; rumple: *The children's clothes were mussed.* 2 a disorder; mess: *Straighten up your room; it's in a dreadful muss.* 1 *verb,* 2 *noun.*

mus·sel (mus′əl), a water animal that has two hinged parts to its shell. Mussels look like clams and are found in both fresh and salt water. *noun.*

must (must), 1 to have to; be forced to: *You must eat to live.* 2 ought to; should: *I must keep my promise. You must read this story.* 3 to be certain to be or do: *You must be joking. I must seem very rude. verb, past tense* **must.**

mus·tache (mus′tash), the hair growing on a man's upper lip. *noun.* Also spelled **moustache.**

mus·tang (mus′tang), a small wild or half-wild horse of the North American plains. *noun.*

[*Mustang* comes from a Mexican Spanish word meaning "not tamed."]

mus·tard (mus′tərd), a yellow powder or paste with a sharp, hot taste, made from the seeds of a plant. Mustard is used as a seasoning. *noun.*

mus·ter (mus′tər), 1 to assemble; gather together; collect: *The guards were mustered for roll call.* 2 to stir to action; rouse: *to muster up courage. verb.*

must·n't (mus′nt), must not: *The owner of this property says we mustn't skate here.*

mus·ty (mus′tē), having a smell or taste suggesting mold or damp; moldy: *a musty room, musty crackers. adjective,* **mus·ti·er, mus·ti·est.**

mute (myüt), 1 silent; not making any sound: *The child stood mute with embarrassment.* 2 dumb; unable to speak. 3 a person who cannot speak. 4 a clip or pad put on a musical instrument to soften the sound. 5 to put such a device on a musical instrument: *She muted the strings of her violin.* 1,2 *adjective,* 3,4 *noun,* 5 *verb,* **mutes, mut·ed, mut·ing.**

mu·ti·late (myü′tl āt), 1 to cut off or tear off a limb or other important part of; injure badly by cutting or tearing off some part: *Several passengers were mutilated in the train wreck.* 2 to destroy or ruin some part of: *The book was badly mutilated by someone who had torn out some pages. verb,* **mu·ti·lates, mu·ti·lat·ed, mu·ti·lat·ing.**

mu·ti·ny (myüt′n ē), 1 an open rebelling against lawful authority, especially by sailors or soldiers against their officers. 2 to take part in a mutiny; rebel. 1 *noun, plural* **mu·ti·nies;** 2 *verb,* **mu·ti·nies, mu·ti·nied, mu·ti·ny·ing.**

mutt (mut), a dog, especially a mongrel. *noun.*

mut·ter (mut′ər), 1 to speak or utter words unclearly, with lips partly closed; mumble: *He muttered some rude remarks.* 2 to complain; grumble: *The shoppers muttered about the high price of meat.* 3 speech or sound that is unclear; mumble: *We heard a mutter of discontent.* 1,2 *verb,* 3 *noun.*

mut·ton (mut′n), the meat from a sheep: *We had roast mutton for dinner. noun.*

mu·tu·al (myü′chü əl), 1 done, said, or felt by each toward the other; given and received: *mutual promises, mutual dislike. A family has mutual affection when each person likes the others and is liked by them.* 2 each to the other: *mutual enemies.* 3 belonging to each of several: *We are happy to have him as our mutual friend. adjective.*

mu·tu·al·ly (myü′chü ə lē), each toward the other: *Those three girls have been mutually friendly for years. adverb.*

muz·zle (muz′əl), 1 the part of an animal's head that extends forward and contains the nose, mouth, and jaws. Dogs and horses have muzzles. 2 a cover or cage of straps or wires to put over an animal's head to keep it from biting or eating. 3 to put such a muzzle on: *to muzzle a dog.* 4 to force a person to keep silent about something: *Fear that he might betray his friends muzzled him.* 5 the open front end of a gun or pistol. 1,2,5 *noun,* 3,4 *verb,* **muz·zles, muz·zled, muz·zling.**

my (mī), of me; belonging to me: *I learned my lesson. My house is around the corner. adjective.*

My·an·mar (mī än′mär), a country in southeastern Asia. Its former name was Burma. *noun.*

myr·i·ad (mir′ē əd), a very great number: *There are myriads of stars. noun.*

myr·tle (mėr′tl), 1 an evergreen shrub of the southern part of Europe, with shiny leaves and fragrant white flowers. 2 a low, creeping evergreen vine found in Canada and the United States, with blue flowers. *noun.*

my·self (mī self′), 1 *Myself* is used with *I* or *me* to make a statement stronger. *I did it myself.* 2 *Myself* is used instead of *I* or *me* in cases like: *I can cook for myself. I hurt myself.* 3 my real self: *I am not myself today. pronoun.*

mys·te·ri·ous (mi stir′ē əs), 1 hard to explain or understand; full of mystery: *The mysterious, haunting call echoed across the lake.* 2 suggesting mystery: *a mysterious look. adjective.*

mys·ter·y (mis′tər ē), 1 a secret; something that is hidden or unknown: *Astronomers search out the mysteries of the universe.* 2 something that is not explained or understood: *the mystery of the migration of birds.* 3 a novel or other story about a mysterious event or events which are not explained until the end, so as to keep the reader in suspense. *noun, plural* **mys·ter·ies.**

mys·ti·fy (mis′tə fī), to confuse completely; puzzle: *The magician's tricks mystified us. verb,* **mys·ti·fies, mys·ti·fied, mys·ti·fy·ing.**

myth (mith), 1 a legend or story, usually one that attempts to account for something in nature: *The story of Proserpina is a famous myth that explains summer and winter.* 2 a made-up person or thing: *Her trip to Europe was a myth invented to impress the other girls. noun.*

myth·i·cal (mith′ə kəl), 1 of a myth; like a myth; in myths: *mythical monsters, mythical places.* 2 imaginary; not real; made-up: *Their wealth is merely mythical. adjective.*

my·thol·o·gy (mi thol′ə jē), myths: *Greek mythology. noun, plural* **my·thol·o·gies.**

N n

a hat	i it	oi oil	ch child	(a in about
ā age	ī ice	ou out	ng long	e in taken
ä far	o hot	u cup	sh she	ə = { i in pencil
e let	ō open	ů put	th thin	o in lemon
ē equal	ô order	ü rule	ŦH then	(u in circus
ėr term			zh measure	

N or **n** (en), the 14th letter of the English alphabet. *noun, plural* **N's** or **n's.**

N or **N.**, **1** north. **2** northern.

nag¹ (nag), to scold; annoy; find fault with all the time: *I will clean up my room if you will stop nagging me. When he was sick he nagged at everybody. verb,* **nags, nagged, nag·ging.**

nag² (nag), **1** a horse. **2** an old or inferior horse. *noun.*

nail (nāl), **1** a slender piece of metal having a point at one end and usually a flat or rounded head at the other end. Nails are hammered into or through pieces of wood to hold them together. **2** to fasten with a nail or nails: *I nailed the poster to the wall.* **3** to catch; seize: *The police were able to nail the thief.* **4** the hard layer of horn at the end of a finger or toe. 1,4 *noun,* 2,3 *verb.*

hit the nail on the head, to guess or understand correctly; say or do something just right.

na·ked (nā′kid), **1** bare; with no clothes on: *When you are barefoot you have naked feet.* **2** not covered: *naked fields.* **3** without the addition of anything else; plain: *The naked truth sometimes hurts. You cannot see bacteria with the naked eye; you need a microscope. adjective.*

name (nām), **1** the word or words by which a person, animal, place, or thing is spoken of or to: *Our cat's name is Mitten. "The Corn State" is a name for Iowa.* **2** to give a name to: *to name a newborn baby.* **3** to call by name; mention by name: *Three persons were named in the report.* **4** to give the right name for: *Can you name these flowers?* **5** reputation: *She made a name for herself as a writer.* **6** to nominate; appoint: *He was named captain of the team.* **7** to choose; settle on: *The class named the day for its party.* 1,5 *noun,* 2-4,6,7 *verb,* **names, named, nam·ing.**

call names, to call bad names; swear at; curse: *You can call me names, but I won't change my mind.*

in the name of, 1 for the sake of: *In the name of decency, you should offer to pay for the window you broke.* **2** acting for: *I ordered the supplies in the name of my boss.*

name·less (nām′lis), **1** having no name: *We fed the nameless kitten.* **2** not marked with a name: *a nameless grave.* **3** not named; unknown: *a book by a nameless writer. adjective.*

name·ly (nām′lē), that is to say: *We visited two cities—namely, New York and Chicago. adverb.*

name·sake (nām′sāk′), one having the same name as another, especially one named after another: *My sister, Florence, is the namesake of Florence Nightingale. noun.*

nap¹ (nap), **1** a short sleep: *The baby takes a nap after lunch.* **2** to take a short sleep: *Grandfather naps in his armchair.* 1 *noun,* 2 *verb,* **naps, napped, nap·ping.**

nap² (nap), the soft, short, woolly threads or hairs on the surface of cloth: *the nap on velvet. noun.*

nape (nāp), the back of the neck. *noun.*

nape
The cat carried the kitten by the **nape** of the neck.

naph·tha (naf′thə *or* nap′thə), a liquid made from petroleum or coal tar used as fuel and to take spots from clothing. *noun.*

nap·kin (nap′kin), a piece of cloth or paper used at meals for protecting the clothing or for wiping the lips or fingers. *noun.*

nar·cis·sus (när sis′əs), a spring plant with yellow or white flowers and long, thin leaves. It grows from a bulb. Jonquils and daffodils are narcissuses. *noun, plural* **nar·cis·sus·es** or **nar·cis·sus.**

narcissus

N

nar·cot·ic (när kot′ik), any drug that causes sleep and dulls pain. Opium is a narcotic. *noun.*

nar·rate (nar′āt), to tell the story of: *I narrated the story while my friend acted it out. verb,* **nar·rates, nar·rat·ed, nar·rat·ing.**

nar·ra·tion (na rā′shən), 1 the act of telling: *Her narration of the story was excellent.* 2 a narrative; story. *noun.*

nar·ra·tive (nar′ə tiv), 1 a story; tale: *Her trip through Asia made an interesting narrative.* 2 telling a story: *"Hiawatha" is a narrative poem.* 1 *noun,* 2 *adjective.*

nar·ra·tor (nar′ā tər), a person who tells a story. *noun.*

nar·row (nar′ō), 1 not wide; having little width; less wide than usual for its kind: *A path a foot wide is narrow.* 2 **narrows,** the narrow part of a river, strait, sound, valley, or pass. 3 limited; small: *He had only a narrow circle of friends.* 4 to become smaller in width or extent; make or become narrow: *The road narrows here.* 5 close; with a small margin: *a narrow escape.* 6 not ready to listen to new ideas and judge them fairly; prejudiced: *A person with a narrow mind is often afraid of new ideas.* 1,3,5,6 *adjective,* 2 *noun,* 4 *verb.*

na·sal (nā′zəl), of, in, or from the nose: *nasal bones, a nasal discharge. adjective.*

Nash·ville (nash′vil), the capital of Tennessee. *noun.*

na·stur·tium (nə stèr′shəm), a plant with yellow, orange, or red flowers, and rather sharp-tasting seeds and leaves. *noun.*

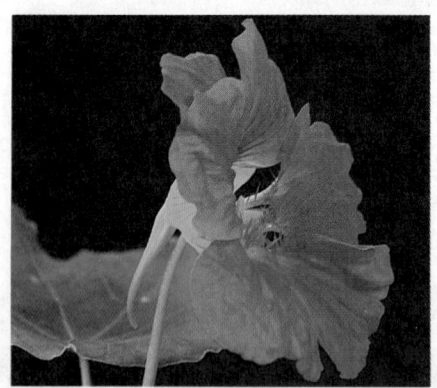

nasturtium

nas·ty (nas′tē), 1 mean; cruel; hateful: *Several nasty people threw rocks at the birds on the lake.* 2 very unpleasant: *The nasty weather ruined our plans for a picnic.* 3 dirty; filthy: *Dead fish and garbage littered the surface of the nasty creek.* 4 rather serious; bad: *a nasty cut on the hand. adjective,* **nas·ti·er, nas·ti·est.**

na·tion (nā′shən), 1 a country; group of people occupying the same region, united under the same government, and usually speaking the same language: *The United States and France are nations.* 2 a people, race, or tribe; those having the same descent, language, and history: *the Scottish nation. noun.*

na·tion·al (nash′ə nəl), of a nation; belonging to a whole nation: *national laws. adjective.*

na·tion·al·ism (nash′ə nə liz′əm), patriotic feelings or efforts. *noun.*

na·tion·al·i·ty (nash′ə nal′ə tē), 1 a nation: *Several nationalities are represented in the line of ancestors of most Americans.* 2 the condition of belonging to a nation. Citizens of the same country have the same nationality. *noun, plural* **na·tion·al·i·ties.**

na·tion·al·ly (nash′ə nə lē), throughout the nation: *The President's speech was broadcast nationally. adverb.*

national park, land kept by the national government for people to enjoy because of its beautiful scenery or historical interest.

na·tion·wide (nā′shən wīd′), extending throughout the nation: *a nationwide election. adjective.*

na·tive (nā′tiv), 1 a person born in a certain place or country. The natives are the people living in a place, not visitors or foreigners. 2 born in a certain place or country: *People born in New York are native sons and daughters of New York.* 3 belonging to one because of one's birth: *The United States is my native land.* 4 belonging to one because of one's nation or ancestors: *French is his native language.* 5 natural; born in a person: *native ability.* 6 one of the people originally living in a place or country and found there by explorers or settlers. 7 of these people: *native customs, native tribes.* 8 a living thing that originated in a place: *The lion is a native of Africa.* 9 originating, grown, or produced in a certain place: *Tobacco is native to America.* 1,6,8 *noun,* 2-5,7,9 *adjective.*

Native American, one of the people who have lived in America from long before the time of the first European settlers; American Indian.

na·tiv·i·ty (nə tiv′ə tē), 1 birth. 2 **the Nativity,** the birth of Christ. *noun, plural* **na·tiv·i·ties.**

nat·u·ral (nach′ər əl), 1 produced by nature; coming in the ordinary course of events: *natural feelings and actions, a natural death.* 2 not artificial; not made by human beings: *Coal and oil are natural products.* 3 belonging to the nature one is born with: *It is natural for ducks to swim.* 4 like nature; true to life: *The picture looked natural.* 5 (in music) not changed in pitch by a sharp or a flat. 6 a person who is especially suited for something because of inborn talent or ability: *He is a natural on the saxophone.* 1-5 *adjective,* 6 *noun.*

natural gas, a gas formed naturally in the earth. Natural gas is used for cooking and heating.

nat·u·ral·ist (nach′ər ə list), a person who makes a study of animals, plants, or other living things. *noun.*

nat·u·ral·ize (nach′ər ə līz), to admit a foreigner to citizenship. After living in the United States for a certain number of years, an immigrant can be naturalized if he or she passes a test. *verb,* **nat·u·ral·iz·es, nat·u·ral·ized, nat·u·ral·iz·ing.**

nat·u·ral·ly (nach′ər ə lē), 1 in a natural way: *Speak naturally; don't try to imitate someone else.*

2 by nature: *She was a naturally athletic child.* **3** as might be expected; of course: *She offered me some candy; naturally, I took it. adverb.*

natural resources, materials supplied by nature that are useful or necessary for life. Minerals and forests are natural resources.

natural science, any science dealing with the facts of nature or the physical world. Biology, geology, physics, and chemistry are natural sciences.

na·ture (nā′chər), **1** the world; all things except those made by human beings: *the wonders of nature.* **2** the basic characteristic born in a person or animal and always present; quality; character: *It is the nature of birds to fly. It is against his nature to be unkind.* **3** life without artificial things: *Wild animals live in a state of nature.* **4** sort; kind: *books of a scientific nature. noun.*

naught (nôt), **1** nothing: *All my studying came to naught; I failed the test.* **2** zero; 0. *noun.*

naugh·ti·ness (nô′tē nis), bad behavior; disobedience; mischief. *noun.*

naugh·ty (nô′tē), bad; not behaving well: *The naughty child hit the baby. adjective,* **naugh·ti·er, naugh·ti·est.**

nau·se·a (nô′zē ə *or* nô′shə), the feeling that one is about to vomit. *noun.*
[*Nausea* comes from a Greek word meaning "a ship." The original Greek meaning for the illness was "being seasick from the rolling motion of a ship."]

nau·se·ate (nô′zē āt *or* nô′shē āt), to make or become sick; feel about to vomit. *verb,* **nau·se·ates, nau·se·at·ed, nau·se·at·ing.**

nau·ti·cal (nô′tə kəl), having something to do with ships, sailors, or navigation. *adjective.*

Nav·a·ho (nav′ə hō). See **Navajo.** *noun, plural* **Nav·a·ho, Nav·a·hos,** *or* **Nav·a·hoes.**

Nav·a·jo (nav′ə hō), a member of a tribe of American Indians living mainly in New Mexico, Arizona, and Utah. *noun, plural* **Nav·a·jo, Nav·a·jos,** *or* **Nav·a·joes.**

na·val (nā′vəl), **1** of or for warships or the navy: *naval supplies, a naval officer.* **2** having a navy: *Spain was once a great naval power. adjective.*

na·vel (nā′vəl), the scar in the middle of the stomach. It is what remains after cutting the cord that connects a newborn infant to its mother's body. *noun.*

nav·i·ga·ble (nav′ə gə bəl), able to be traveled on by ships: *The Mississippi is a navigable river. adjective.*

nav·i·gate (nav′ə gāt), **1** to sail, manage, or steer a ship, aircraft, or rocket: *She navigated the sailboat through the choppy waters.* **2** to sail on or over a sea or river: *The steamboat captain navigated the Mississippi for twenty years. verb,* **nav·i·gates, nav·i·gat·ed, nav·i·gat·ing.**

nav·i·ga·tion (nav′ə gā′shən), **1** a navigating: *Navigation was difficult during the storm.* **2** the art or science of figuring out the position and course of a ship, aircraft, or rocket. *noun.*

nav·i·ga·tor (nav′ə gā′tər), **1** a person who has

a hat	i it	oi oil	ch child	(a in about
ā age	ī ice	ou out	ng long	e in taken
ä far	o hot	u cup	sh she	ə = i in pencil
e let	ō open	u̇ put	th thin	o in lemon
ē equal	ô order	ü rule	ᴛʜ then	u in circus
ėr term			zh measure	

charge of the navigating of a ship or aircraft; person who is skilled in navigating. **2** an explorer of the seas: *Columbus was a great navigator. noun.*

na·vy (nā′vē), **1** a large, organized group of officers and sailors trained and equipped for war, and the ships of war on which they serve. **2** a dark blue; navy blue. **3** having this color: *a navy sweater.* **1,2** *noun, plural* **na·vies; 3** *adjective.*

navy blue, a dark blue.

nay (nā), **1** no. **2** not only that, but also: *We are willing—nay, eager—to go.* **3** vote or voter against something: *The yeas outnumber the nays, so the plan is approved.* **1,2** *adverb,* **3** *noun.*

NC, North Carolina (used with postal Zip Code).

N.C., North Carolina.

ND, North Dakota (used with postal Zip Code).

N.Dak., North Dakota.

NE or **N.E., 1** northeast. **2** northeastern.

NE, Nebraska (used with postal Zip Code).

near (nir), **1** close; not far; to or at a short distance: *They searched far and near. The holiday season is drawing near.* **2** close by; not distant: *The post office is quite near.* **3** close to: *Our house is near the river.* **4** to approach; come or draw close to: *The train slowed as it neared the station.* **5** close in feeling or relationship: *near and dear friends, a near relative.* **6** almost; nearly: *The war lasted near a year.* **7** short; direct: *Take the nearest route.* **8** by a close margin; narrow: *We had a near escape.* **1,6** *adverb,* **2,5,7,8** *adjective,* **3** *preposition,* **4** *verb.*

near at hand, 1 within easy reach: *The telephone was near at hand in case of emergency.* **2** not far in the future: *Summer is near at hand.*

near·by (nir′bī′), near; close at hand: *a nearby house. They went nearby to visit friends. adjective, adverb.*

near·ly (nir′lē), **1** almost: *It is nearly bedtime.* **2** closely: *It will cost more than we can afford, as nearly as I can figure it. adverb.*

near·sight·ed (nir′sī′tid), not able to see far; seeing things clearly at a short distance only. Nearsighted people often wear glasses. *adjective.*

neat (nēt), **1** clean and in order: *a neat desk, a neat room, a neat suit.* **2** able and willing to keep things in order: *a neat child.* **3** skillful; clever: *a neat trick.* **4** wonderful; fine: *It was a neat party. adjective.*

Nebr., Nebraska.

Ne·bras·ka (nə bras′kə), one of the midwestern states of the United States. *Abbreviation:* Nebr. or NE *Capital:* Lincoln.
[*Nebraska* comes from American Indian words meaning "flat river." This was originally the Indian name for the Platte River, which flows through the state.]

N

nec·es·sar·i·ly (nes′ə ser′ə lē), **1** because of necessity: *Leaves are not necessarily green.* **2** as a necessary result: *War necessarily causes misery and waste. adverb.*

nec·es·sar·y (nes′ə ser′ē), **1** needed; having to be done: *The repairs to the car were necessary.* **2** that must be: *Death is a necessary end. adjective.*

ne·ces·si·tate (nə ses′ə tāt), to make necessary: *Her injured leg necessitated an operation. verb,* **ne·ces·si·tates, ne·ces·si·tat·ed, ne·ces·si·tat·ing.**

ne·ces·si·ty (nə ses′ə tē), **1** a need; something that has to be: *He understood the necessity of eating the proper foods.* **2** a thing which cannot be done without; necessary thing: *Food and water are necessities.* **3** the state of being in need; poverty: *This poor family is in great necessity. noun, plural* **ne·ces·si·ties.**

neck (nek), **1** the part of the body that connects the head with the shoulders. **2** the part of a garment that fits the neck: *the neck of a shirt.* **3** any narrow part like a neck: *She held the bottle by the neck. noun.*

neck and neck, equal or even in a race or contest.

neck·er·chief (nek′ər chif), a cloth worn around the neck. *noun.*

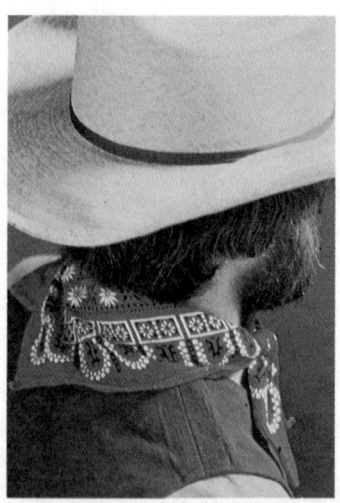

neckerchief

neck·lace (nek′lis), a string of jewels, gold, silver, or beads worn around the neck as an ornament. *noun.*

neck·tie (nek′tī′), a narrow length of cloth worn around the neck, under the collar of a shirt, and tied in front. *noun.*

nec·tar (nek′tər), a sweet liquid found in many flowers. Bees gather nectar and make it into honey. *noun.*

nec·ta·rine (nek′tə rēn′), a kind of peach having no down on its skin. *noun.*

need (nēd), **1** to be in want of; ought to have; be unable to do without: *I need a new hat. Plants need water.* **2** a thing wanted or lacking; that for which a want is felt: *In the jungle their need was fresh water.* **3** a want; lack: *Your handwriting shows a*

need of practice. **4** a time of need; condition of need: *When I lacked money, my uncle was a friend in need.* **5** a lack of money; being poor: *This family's need was so great the children did not have shoes.* **6** must; should; have to; ought to: *He need not go. Need she go?* **7** something that has to be: *There is no need to hurry.* 1,6 *verb,* 2-5,7 *noun.*

need·ful (nēd′fəl), needed; necessary: *a needful change. adjective.*

nee·dle (nē′dl), **1** a very slender tool, sharp at one end, and with a hole or eye to pass a thread through, used in sewing. **2** a slender rod used in knitting. **3** a rod with a hook at one end used in crocheting. **4** a thin steel pointer on a compass or on electrical machinery. **5** a very slender steel tube with a sharp point at one end. It is used for injecting liquid below the skin. *The doctor stuck the needle into my arm.* **6** the small, pointed piece of metal, sapphire, or diamond in a phonograph which picks up and transmits the vibrations from the record. **7** the needle-shaped leaf of a fir tree or pine tree. **8** an object resembling a needle in sharpness: *needles of broken glass.* **9** to annoy or provoke with repeated teasing or mocking: *They kept needling me about my new glasses.* 1-8 *noun,* 9 *verb,* **nee·dles, nee·dled, nee·dling.**

need·less (nēd′lis), not needed; unnecessary: *It is silly to take a needless risk. adjective.*

nee·dle·work (nē′dl wėrk′), work done with a needle; sewing; embroidery. *noun.*

need·n't (nēd′nt), need not.

need·y (nē′dē), very poor; not having enough to live on: *a needy family. adjective,* **need·i·er, need·i·est.**

ne'er (ner), never. *adverb.*

neg·a·tive (neg′ə tiv), **1** saying no: *A shake of the head is negative.* **2** a word or statement that says no or denies: *"I won't" is a negative.* **3** not positive: *Negative suggestions are not helpful.* **4** minus; counting down from zero: *Three below zero is a negative quantity.* **5** of the kind of electricity that electrons have. Negative electricity travels along wires and is used for power. **6** a photographic image in which the lights and shadows are reversed. Prints are made from it. **7** showing the absence of a particular disease, condition, or germ. 1,3-5,7 *adjective,* 2,6 *noun.*

negative (definition 6)

neglect (definition 3)
The house showed years of **neglect**.

a hat	**i** it	**oi** oil	**ch** child	a in about
ā age	**ī** ice	**ou** out	**ng** long	e in taken
ä far	**o** hot	**u** cup	**sh** she ə =	i in pencil
e let	**ō** open	**u̇** put	**th** thin	o in lemon
ē equal	**ô** order	**ü** rule	**ᴛʜ** then	u in circus
ėr term			**zh** measure	

ne·glect (ni glekt′), **1** to give too little care or attention to: *Don't neglect your health.* **2** to omit; fail: *She neglected to tell us what happened.* **3** a lack of care or attention: *The car has been ruined by years of neglect.* **4** a being neglected: *The children suffered from neglect when their mother was ill.* 1,2 *verb,* 3,4 *noun.*

neg·li·gence (neg′lə jəns), a neglect; lack of proper care or attention: *Negligence was the cause of the accident. noun.*

neg·li·gent (neg′lə jənt), showing neglect; careless: *The negligent driver caused the accident. adjective.*

ne·go·ti·ate (ni gō′shē āt), **1** to talk over and arrange terms: *Both countries are negotiating for an end to the war.* **2** to arrange for: *They finally negotiated a peace treaty. verb,* **ne·go·ti·ates, ne·go·ti·at·ed, ne·go·ti·at·ing.**

ne·go·ti·a·tion (ni gō′shē ā′shən), a talking over and arranging terms; arrangement: *Both sides waited anxiously as the negotiations for peace went on for months. noun.*

Ne·gro (nē′grō), **1** a member of one of the large groups into which the human race is divided. Negroes originally lived in central and southern Africa, but now live in many other parts of the world. **2** of or having to do with this large group of people. 1 *noun, plural* **Ne·groes;** 2 *adjective.*

neigh (nā), **1** a sound that a horse makes. **2** to make such a sound. 1 *noun,* 2 *verb.*

neigh·bor (nā′bər), **1** someone who lives in the next house or nearby. **2** a person or thing that is near or next to another: *The big tree brought down several of its smaller neighbors as it fell.* **3** to live or be near to: *Canada neighbors the United States.* **4** a fellow human being. 1,2,4 *noun,* 3 *verb.*

neigh·bor·hood (nā′bər hud), **1** the region near some place or thing: *She lives in the neighborhood of the mill.* **2** a place; district: *Is North Street in a good neighborhood?* **3** people living near one another; people of a place: *The whole neighborhood came to the big party.* **4** of a neighborhood: *I like to read the school sports page in our neighborhood newspaper.* 1-3 *noun,* 4 *adjective.*

in the neighborhood of, somewhere near; about: *Her new car cost in the neighborhood of $8000.*

neigh·bor·ing (nā′bər ing), living or being near; bordering; near: *While we were boating on the lake, we heard the bird calls from the neighboring woods. adjective.*

neigh·bor·ly (nā′bər lē), kindly; friendly: *It was very neighborly of them to help us move in. adjective.*

nei·ther (nē′ᴛʜər *or* nī′ᴛʜər), **1** not either: *Neither you nor I will go. Neither statement is true. Neither of the statements is true.* **2** nor yet; nor: *They didn't go; neither did we.* 1,2 *conjunction,* 1 *adjective,* 1 *pronoun.*

ne·on (nē′on), a colorless, odorless gas, forming a very small part of the air. Neon is a chemical element, and glows when electricity is passed through it. Tubes containing neon are used in electric signs. *noun.*
[*Neon* comes from a Greek word meaning "new."]

neon

Ne·pal (nə pôl′), a country in south central Asia. *noun.*

neph·ew (nef′yü), a son of one's brother or sister; son of one's brother-in-law or sister-′ *noun.*

Nep·tune (nep′tün *or* nep′tyün), **1** th′ god of the sea. **2** the fourth largest p′ from the earth that it cannot be se telescope. *noun.*

nerve (nėrv), **1** a fiber or bun′ connects the brain or spinal c′ parts of the body. Nerves carry ′

N

nerve (definition 2)
It takes great **nerve** to hang by one hand from an airplane.

from the brain. **2** mental strength; courage. **3** rude boldness: *They had a lot of nerve to say that we were talking too loud. noun.*

get on one's nerves, to bother one greatly.

nerv·ous (nėr′vəs), **1** of the nerves: *a nervous disorder, nervous energy.* **2** easily excited or upset: *A person who has been overworking is likely to become nervous.* **3** restless or uneasy; timid: *Are you nervous about staying alone at night? adjective.*

nervous system, a system of nerve fibers, nerve cells, and other nerve tissue in a person or animal. Your nervous system includes the brain and spinal cord, and controls all your body activities.

-ness, a suffix meaning: a being _____: *Carefulness* means *a being* careful.

nest (nest), **1** a structure shaped something like a bowl, built by birds out of twigs, leaves, or straw, as a place in which to lay their eggs and protect their young ones: *a robin's nest.* **2** a structure or place used by insects, fishes, turtles, rabbits, or the like, for a similar purpose: *a squirrel's nest, a wasp's nest.* **3** the birds or animals living in a nest: *We found a nest of rabbits in our backyard.* **4** a warm, cozy place; place to sleep: *The little boy made a cozy nest among the sofa cushions and cuddled down in it.* **5** to make and use a nest: *The bluebirds are nesting here now.* 1-4 *noun,* 5 *verb.*

nes·tle (nes′əl), **1** to settle oneself comfortably or cozily: *She nestled down into the big chair.* **2** to be sheltered: *The little house nestled among the trees.* **3** to press close for comfort or in affection: *to nestle up to one's mother or father, to nestle a baby in one's arms. verb,* **nes·tles, nes·tled, nes·tling.**

net¹ (net), **1** an open fabric made of string, cord, or thread, knotted together in such a way as to leave holes regularly arranged. A fish net is used for catching fish. A mosquito net keeps off mosquitoes. A hair net holds the hair in place. A tennis net is used in the game of tennis. **2** anything like a net; a set of threads, strands, or strips that cross each other. **3** a trap or snare: *The suspects were caught in the net of their own ...* **4** to catch in a net. 1-3 *noun,* 4 *verb,* **nets, ...ted, net·ting.**

... (net), **1** remaining after deductions; free from

deductions. A net gain or profit is the actual gain after all working expenses have been paid. The net weight of a glass jar of candy is the weight of the candy itself. The net price of something is the actual price paid, after all deductions are made. **2** to gain: *The sale netted me a good profit.* 1 *adjective,* 2 *verb,* **nets, net·ted, net·ting.**

Neth·er·lands (neŦH′ər ləndz), **the,** a country in northwestern Europe. *noun.*

net·tle (net′l), **1** a kind of plant having sharp leaf hairs that sting the skin when touched. **2** to

nettle
(definition 1)

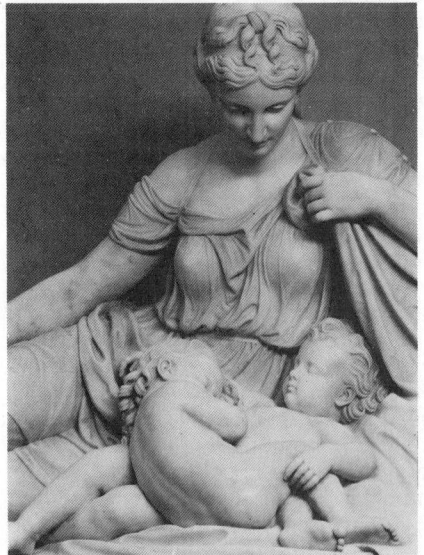

nestle (definition 3)
The children **nestled** against their mother.

net¹ (definition 4)—The children **netted** a fish.

irritate; make angry; provoke; vex: *Their refusal to help nettled me.* 1 *noun,* 2 *verb,* **net·tles, net·tled, net·tling.**

net·work (net′wėrk′), **1** any system of lines that cross: *a network of vines, a network of railroads.* **2** a group of radio or television stations that work together, so that what is broadcast by one may be broadcast by all. *noun.*

neu·tral (nü′trəl *or* nyü′trəl), **1** on neither side in a quarrel or war: *Switzerland was neutral during World War II.* **2** having little or no color: *White and gray are neutral colors.* **3** (in chemistry) neither an acid nor a base. **4** the position of gears when they do not transmit motion from the engine to the wheels or other working parts. 1-3 *adjective,* 4 *noun.*

neu·tral·ize (nü′trə līz *or* nyü′trə līz), **1** to make neutral; keep war out of: *The city was neutralized so that peace talks could be held there.* **2** to make of no effect; cancel the effect of; make up for the effect of: *I neutralized the bright colors in my room by using a tan rug.* *verb,* **neu·tral·iz·es, neu·tral·ized, neu·tral·iz·ing.**

neu·tron (nü′tron *or* nyü′tron), a tiny particle that is neither positive nor negative electrically. Neutrons occur in the nucleus of all atoms except hydrogen. *noun.*

Nev., Nevada.

Ne·vad·a (nə vad′ə *or* nə vä′də), one of the western states of the United States. *Abbreviation:* Nev. or NV *Capital:* Carson City. *noun.*
[A range of mountains in eastern California and western Nevada is named *Sierra Nevada,* Spanish words for "snow-covered mountain range." The name of the state comes from the word meaning "snow-covered."]

nev·er (nev′ər), **1** not ever; at no time: *She has never been to New York.* **2** not at all: *He will be never the wiser.* *adverb.*

nev·er·more (nev′ər môr′), never again. *adverb.*

nev·er·the·less (nev′ər ᴛʜə les′), however; none the less; for all that; in spite of it: *She was very tired; nevertheless she kept on working.* *adverb.*

new (nü *or* nyü), **1** never having been before; just recently made, known, felt, or discovered: *She invented a new machine. That's a new idea.* **2** lately grown, come, or made; not old: *a new bud.* **3** not used before; not worn or used up: *We bought some new furniture.* **4** beginning again: *Sunrise marks a new day.* **5** not familiar; not yet used: *a new country to me, new to the work.* **6** later; modern; recent: *the new dances.* **7** just come; having recently arrived in a new place or position: *We have a new teacher. She is a new arrival in town.* **8** newly; recently or lately; freshly: *new-fallen snow.* 1-7 *adjective,* 8 *adverb.*

new·born (nü′bôrn′ *or* nyü′bôrn′), **1** recently or only just born: *a newborn baby.* **2** ready to start a new life; born again: *They continued their search with newborn hope.* *adjective.*

New Bruns·wick (nü′ brunz′wik *or* nyü′ brunz′wik), a province in southeastern Canada. *Capital:* Fredericton.

a hat	**i** it	**oi** oil	**ch** child	a in about
ā age	**ī** ice	**ou** out	**ng** long	e in taken
ä far	**o** hot	**u** cup	**sh** she	**ə** = i in pencil
e let	**ō** open	**u̇** put	**th** thin	o in lemon
ē equal	**ô** order	**ü** rule	**ᴛʜ** then	u in circus
ėr term			**zh** measure	

new·com·er (nü′kum′ər *or* nyü′kum′ər), a person who has just come or who came recently. *noun.*

New England, the northeastern part of the United States. Maine, New Hampshire, Vermont, Massachusetts, Rhode Island, and Connecticut are the New England states.

new·fan·gled (nü′fang′gəld *or* nyü′fang′gəld), lately come into fashion; of a new kind. *adjective.*

New·found·land (nü′fənd lənd *or* nü found′lənd; nyü′fənd lənd *or* nyü found′lənd), a province in eastern Canada. *Capital:* St. John's. *noun.*

New Hamp·shire (nü′ hamp′shər *or* nyü′ hamp′shər), one of the northeastern states of the United States. *Abbreviation:* N.H. or NH *Capital:* Concord.
[*New Hampshire* was named in 1629 for Hampshire, a county in England.]

New Jer·sey (nü′ jėr′zē *or* nyü′ jėr′zē), one of the northeastern states of the United States. *Abbreviation:* N.J. or NJ *Capital:* Trenton.
[*New Jersey* was named in 1664 for the British island of Jersey.]

new·ly (nü′lē *or* nyü′lē), lately; recently: *newly discovered, newly painted walls.* *adverb.*

New Mexico, one of the southwestern states of the United States. *Abbreviation:* N.Mex. or NM *Capital:* Santa Fe.
[*New Mexico* is a translation of the Spanish name *Nuevo México.* A Spanish explorer first gave this name to the area in 1562 to suggest that it would be as rich as the country of Mexico.]

N

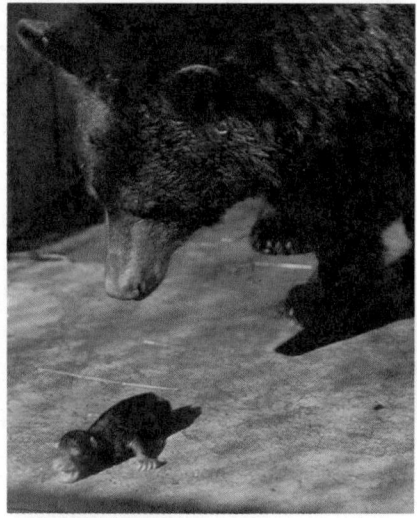

newborn (definition 1)
The bear watched over her **newborn** cub.

new moon, the moon when seen as a thin crescent with the hollow side on the left or when it appears almost invisible.

news (nüz *or* nyüz), **1** something told as having just happened; information about something which has just happened or will soon happen: *The news that our teacher was leaving made us sad.* **2** a report of a current happening or happenings in a newspaper or on television or radio. *noun.*

news·boy (nüz′boi′ *or* nyüz′boi′), a person who sells or delivers newspapers. *noun.*

news·cast (nüz′kast′ *or* nyüz′kast′), a television or radio program devoted to current events and news bulletins. *noun.*

news·pa·per (nüz′pā′pər *or* nyüz′pā′pər), sheets of paper printed every day or week, telling the news, carrying advertisements, and having stories, pictures, articles, and useful information. *noun.*

news·reel (nüz′rēl′ *or* nyüz′rēl′), a motion picture showing current events. *noun.*

news·stand (nüz′stand′ *or* nyüz′stand′), a place where newspapers and magazines are sold. *noun.*

news·y (nü′zē *or* nyü′zē), full of news: *She wrote a newsy letter to the folks back home. adjective,* **news·i·er, news·i·est.**

newt (nüt *or* nyüt), a small salamander that lives in water part of the time. *noun.*

newt—about 4 inches (10 centimeters) long

New Testament, the part of the Bible which contains the life and teachings of Jesus recorded by His followers, together with their own experiences and teachings.

New World, North America and South America.

New Year *or* **New Year's,** January 1; the first day or days of the year.

New Year's Day, January 1.

New York (nü′ yôrk′ *or* nyü′ yôrk′), **1** one of the northeastern states of the United States. *Abbreviation:* N.Y. *or* NY *Capital:* Albany. **2** a city in this state. New York is the largest city in the United States.
[The state of *New York* was named in 1664 in honor of the Duke of York, who lived from 1633 to 1701, by his brother Charles II, king of England.]

New Zea·land (nü′ zē′lənd *or* nyü′ zē′lənd), an island country in the southern Pacific Ocean.

next (nekst), **1** nearest: *The telephone is in the next room.* **2** following at once: *the next train. The next day after Sunday is Monday.* **3** the first time after this: *When you next come, bring it.* **4** in the place or time or position that is nearest: *I am going to do my arithmetic problems next. His name comes next.* **5** nearest to: *We live in the house next the church.* **1,2** *adjective,* **3,4** *adverb,* **5** *preposition.*

next door, in or at the next house or apartment: *He lives next door.*

next-door (nekst′dôr′), in or at the next house: *my next-door neighbor. adjective.*

NH, New Hampshire (used with postal Zip Code).

N.H., New Hampshire.

nib·ble (nib′əl), **1** to eat away with quick small bites, as a rabbit or a mouse does. **2** to bite gently or lightly: *A fish nibbles at the bait.* **3** a nibbling; small bite. **1,2** *verb,* **nib·bles, nib·bled, nib·bling;** **3** *noun.*

Nic·a·ra·gua (nik′ə rä′gwə), a country in Central America. *noun.*

nice (nīs), **1** pleasing; agreeable; satisfactory: *a nice day, a nice ride, a nice child.* **2** thoughtful and kind: *They were nice to me.* **3** showing care or skill; very fine: *a nice piece of writing, a nice shot, a nice try. adjective,* **nic·er, nic·est.**
[Earlier meanings of *nice* were "foolish" and "shy." It comes from a Latin word meaning "not knowing" or "knowing little."]

niche (nich), **1** a recess or hollow in a wall for a statue or vase. **2** a suitable place or position; place for which a person is suited: *I found my niche in the drama club. noun.*

niche
(definition 1)

nick (nik), **1** a place where a small bit has been cut or broken out: *She cut nicks in a stick to keep score.* **2** to make a nick or nicks in. **1** *noun,* **2** *verb.*
in the nick of time, just at the right moment: *We reached home in the nick of time; a minute later there was a downpour.*

nick·el (nik′əl), **1** a hard, silvery-white metal that is used to plate other metals and is mixed with other metals to make alloys. Nickel is a chemical element. **2** a coin of the United States and Canada equal to 5 cents. Twenty nickels make one dollar. *noun.*

nick·er (nik′ər), **1** to neigh: *The horse nickered when it saw my armful of hay.* **2** a neigh: *When I heard a nicker, I knew there must be a horse nearby.* **1** *verb,* **2** *noun.*

nick·name (nik′nām′), **1** a name added to a person's real name, or used instead of it: *"Ed" is a nickname for "Edward."* **2** to give a nickname to: *They nicknamed the redheaded girl Rusty.* **1** *noun,* **2** *verb,* **nick·names, nick·named, nick·nam·ing.**

nic·o·tine (nik′ə tēn′), a poison contained in the leaves, roots, and seeds of tobacco. *noun.*
[*Nicotine* was formed from the name of Jacques Nicot, who lived from 1530 to 1600. He was a French official in Portugal who introduced tobacco into France in 1560.]

niece (nēs), a daughter of one's brother or sister; daughter of one's brother-in-law or sister-in-law. *noun.*

nif·ty (nif′tē), wonderful; fine, especially in a clever way: *What a nifty radio.* *adjective,* **nif·ti·er, nif·ti·est.**

Ni·ger (nī′jər), a country in western Africa. *noun.*

Ni·ger·i·a (nī jir′ē ə), a country in western Africa. *noun.*

nigh (nī), **1** near. **2** nearly. **1,2** *adverb,* **1** *adjective,* **1** *preposition.*

night (nīt), **1** the time between evening and morning; time from sunset to sunrise, especially when it is dark. **2** evening: *What night is the play? The fireworks will begin as soon as it is night.* *noun.*

night crawl·er (nīt′ krôl′ər), a large earthworm that comes to the surface of the ground at night.

night·fall (nīt′fôl′), the coming of night. *noun.*

night·gown (nīt′goun′), a long, loose garment worn by a woman or child in bed. *noun.*

night·in·gale (nīt′n gāl), a small, reddish-brown bird of Europe. The nightingale sings sweetly at night as well as in the daytime. *noun.*

nightingales
about 7 inches
(18 centimeters)
long

night·ly (nīt′lē), **1** happening every night or at night: *the nightly news on TV. A raccoon was a nightly visitor to our garbage can.* **2** every night or at night: *Performances are given nightly except on Sunday. Many animals come out only nightly.* **1** *adjective,* **2** *adverb.*

night·mare (nīt′mer′ or nīt′mar′), **1** a terrible dream: *I had a nightmare about falling off a high building.* **2** a terrible experience: *The hurricane was a nightmare.* *noun.*

night·time (nīt′tīm′), the time between evening and morning. *noun.*

Nile (nīl), a river in Africa. The Nile is the longest river in the world. *noun.*

nim·ble (nim′bəl), quick-moving; active and sure-footed; light and quick: *The nimble goat leaped from ledge to ledge on the mountainside.* *adjective,* **nim·bler, nim·blest.**

nim·bly (nim′blē), quickly and lightly: *Her fingers flew nimbly over the piano keys.* *adverb.*

nine (nīn), **1** one more than eight; 9. Six and three make nine. **2** a set of nine persons or things: *a baseball nine.* **1,2** *noun,* **1** *adjective.*

nine·teen (nīn′tēn′), nine more than ten; 19. *noun, adjective.*

nine·teenth (nīn′tēnth′), **1** next after the 18th. **2** one of 19 equal parts. **1** *adjective,* **1,2** *noun.*

nine·ti·eth (nīn′tē ith′), **1** next after the 89th. **2** one of 90 equal parts. **1** *adjective,* **1,2** *noun.*

nine·ty (nīn′tē), nine times ten; 90. *noun, plural* **nine·ties;** *adjective.*

ninth (ninth), **1** next after the eighth. **2** one of nine equal parts. **1** *adjective,* **1,2** *noun.*

nip[1] (nip), **1** to squeeze tight and quickly; pinch; bite: *The crab nipped my toe.* **2** a tight squeeze; pinch; sudden bite. **3** to take off by biting, pinching, or snipping: *to nip twigs from a bush.* **4** to hurt at the tips; spoil; injure: *Some of our tomato plants were nipped by frost.* **5** to have a sharp, biting effect on: *A cold wind nipped our ears.* **6** a sharp cold; chill: *There is a nip in the air this frosty morning.* **1,3-5** *verb,* **nips, nipped, nip·ping;** **2,6** *noun.*

nip[2] (nip), a small drink. *noun.*

nip·ple (nip′əl), **1** a roundish tip on the front of the breast, slightly darker than the surrounding skin. Infants and baby animals suck milk from the female nipple. **2** the rubber cap of a baby's bottle, through which the baby gets milk and other liquids. *noun.*

ni·tro·gen (nī′trə jən), a gas without color, taste, or odor which forms about four fifths of the air. Nitrogen is a chemical element. All living things need nitrogen. *noun.*

nit·wit (nit′wit′), a very stupid person. *noun.*

N

NJ, New Jersey (used with postal Zip Code).

N.J., New Jersey.

NM, New Mexico (used with postal Zip Code).

N.Mex., New Mexico.

no (nō), **1** a word used to say that you can't or won't, or that something is wrong: *Will you come? No. Can a cow fly? No.* **2** not any: *Dogs have no wings.* **3** not at all: *He is no better.* **4** a vote against; person voting against: *The noes won.* 1,3 *adverb,* 2 *adjective,* 4 *noun, plural* **noes.**

no., number.

no·bil·i·ty (nō bil′ə tē), **1** people of noble rank, title, or birth. Counts, countesses, dukes, and earls belong to the nobility. **2** noble character: *the nobility of a great deed, the nobility of a grand cathedral. noun.*

no·ble (nō′bəl), **1** high and great by birth, rank, or title: *a noble family.* **2** a person high and great by birth, rank, or title: *Nobles who opposed the king plotted against him.* **3** high and great in character; showing greatness of mind; good: *a noble person, a noble deed.* **4** excellent; fine; splendid; magnificent: *Niagara Falls is a noble sight.* 1,3,4 *adjective,* **no·bler, no·blest;** 2 *noun.*

no·ble·man (nō′bəl mən), a man of noble rank, title, or birth. *noun, plural* **no·ble·men.**

no·ble·wom·an (nō′bəl wúm′ən), a woman of noble rank, title, or birth. *noun, plural* **no·ble·wom·en.**

no·bly (nō′blē), in a noble manner; in a splendid way; as a noble person would do: *The climbers struggled nobly to reach the top of the mountain. adverb.*

no·bod·y (nō′bod′ē), **1** no one; no person: *Nobody would help me.* **2** a person of no importance: *I was ignored and made to feel like a nobody.* 1 *pronoun,* 2 *noun, plural* **no·bod·ies.**

noc·tur·nal (nok tėr′nl), **1** of the night: *Stars are a nocturnal sight.* **2** in the night: *a nocturnal visitor.* **3** active in the night: *The owl is a nocturnal bird. adjective.*

nod (nod), **1** to bow the head slightly and raise it again quickly. **2** to say yes by nodding: *Father quietly nodded his consent.* **3** a nodding of the head: *She gave us a nod as she passed.* **4** to let the head fall forward and bob about when sleepy or falling asleep. 1,2,4 *verb,* **nods, nod·ded, nod·ding;** 3 *noun.*

node (nōd), **1** a knot, knob, or swelling. **2** a joint on a stem where leaves grow out. *noun.*

Word History

node *Node* comes from a Latin word meaning "knot."

No·el (nō el′), **1** Christmas. **2** noel, a Christmas song. *noun, plural* **no·els** for 2.

[*Noel* comes from a French word meaning "Christmas." In French, the word is spelled *Noël.* As a first name for either boys or girls, this name was often given to children born on Christmas Day.]

no-good (nō′gùd′), not good for anything; worthless: *Let's throw out those no-good toys. adjective.*

noise (noiz), **1** a sound that is not musical or pleasant: *The noise kept me awake.* **2** any sound: *the noise of rain on the roof.* **3** a din of voices and movements; loud shouting: *They made so much noise that they were asked to leave the theater. noun.*

noise·less (noiz′lis), making no noise; making little noise: *a noiseless typewriter. adjective.*

nois·i·ly (noi′zə lē), in a noisy manner. *adverb.*

nois·y (noi′zē), **1** making much noise: *a noisy crowd, a noisy machine.* **2** full of noise: *a noisy street, a noisy house, the noisy city. adjective,* **nois·i·er, nois·i·est.**

no·mad (nō′mad), a member of a tribe which moves from place to place to have food or pasture for its cattle: *Many Arabs are nomads. noun.*

nomad—The **nomads** camped near the ruins for a few days.

no·mad·ic (nō mad′ik), of nomads or their life; wandering: *Nomadic people often live in tents. adjective.*

nom·i·nate (nom′ə nāt), **1** to name as candidate for an office: *He was nominated for President, but he was never elected.* **2** to appoint to an office: *In 1933 Roosevelt nominated the first woman cabinet member in United States history. verb,* **nom·i·nates, nom·i·nat·ed, nom·i·nat·ing.**

nom·i·na·tion (nom′ə nā′shən), **1** a naming as candidate for office: *The nominations for president of the club were written on the blackboard.* **2** a selection for office; appointment to office: *Her nomination as Ambassador to France was approved by the Senate.* **3** a being nominated: *Her friends were pleased by her nomination. noun.*

nom·i·nee (nom′ə nē′), a person nominated to or for an office. *noun.*

non-, a prefix meaning: **1** not; not a: *Non*breakable means *not* breakable. *Non*member means *not a* member. **2** the opposite of; lack of: *Non*agreement means *the opposite of* or *lack of* agreement.

non·cha·lant (non′shə länt′), without enthusiasm; coolly unconcerned; indifferent: *She remained quite nonchalant during all the excitement. adjective.*

non·con·duc·tor (non′kən duk′tər), a substance which does not readily conduct heat, electricity, or sound. Rubber is a nonconductor of electricity. *noun.*

non·de·script (non′də skript), not easily described; not of any one particular kind: *We drove past a block of nondescript houses. adjective.*

none (nun), **1** not any: *We have none of that paper left.* **2** no one; not one: *None of these is a special case.* **3** no persons: *None have arrived.* **4** not at all: *Our supply is none too great.* 1-3 *pronoun,* 4 *adverb.*

non·fic·tion (non fik′shən), writing that is not fiction. Nonfiction deals with real people and events rather than imaginary ones. *noun.*

non·sense (non′sens), words, ideas, or acts without meaning; foolish talk or doings; plan or suggestion that is foolish: *That tale about the ghost that haunts the old mansion is nonsense. noun.*

non·stop (non′stop′), without stopping: *We took a nonstop flight from Chicago to Paris. He flew nonstop from New York to Los Angeles. adjective, adverb.*

non·vi·o·lent (non vī′ə lənt), not violent; against violence: *I only watch nonviolent movies. adjective.*

noo·dle (nü′dl), a mixture of flour, water, and eggs, dried into hard flat strips. *noun.*

nook (nůk), **1** a cozy little corner: *The cat liked to sleep in a nook by the furnace.* **2** a hidden spot; sheltered place: *There is a wonderful nook in the woods behind our house. noun.*

noon (nün), 12 o'clock in the daytime; the middle of the day. *noun.*

noon·day (nün′dā′), noon. *noun.*

no one, no person; nobody.

noon·time (nün′tīm′), noon. *noun.*

noose (nüs), a loop at the end of a rope with a knot through which the rope can slip to tighten the loop. Nooses are used in lassos. *noun.*

nor (nôr), and no; and not: *We had neither food nor water with us. I have not gone there, nor will I ever go. conjunction.*

nor·mal (nôr′məl), **1** usual; most commonly occurring: *The normal temperature of the human body is 98.6 degrees.* **2** the usual state or level: *After the heavy rains, the river was 10 feet above normal.* **3** being healthy in body or mind: *Your tonsils look normal. It is not normal to feel sad all the time.* 1,3 *adjective,* 2 *noun.*

Norse (nôrs), **1** of ancient Scandinavia, its people, or their language. **2** the people of ancient Scandinavia. **3** the language of these people. 1 *adjective,* 2 *noun plural,* 3 *noun singular.*

north (nôrth), **1** the direction to which a compass needle points; direction to the right as one faces the setting sun. **2** toward the north; farther toward

the north: *Drive north for the next mile.* **3** coming from the north: *a north wind.* **4** in the north: *the north window of a house.* **5** the part of any country toward the north. **6 the North,** the northern part of the United States; the states north of Maryland, the Ohio River, and Missouri. 1,5,6 *noun,* 2-4 *adjective,* 2 *adverb.*

north of, farther north than: *The United States is north of Mexico.*

North America, a continent northwest of South America and west of the Atlantic Ocean. It is the third largest continent; only Asia and Africa are larger. The United States, Canada, and Mexico are countries in North America.

North American, 1 of North America; having something to do with North America or its people; from North America. **2** a person born or living in North America.

North Car·o·li·na (nôrth′ kar′ə lī′nə), one of the southeastern states of the United States. *Abbreviation:* N.C. or NC *Capital:* Raleigh. [North Carolina was named in honor of Charles I, king of England, who lived from 1600 to 1649. His name in Latin is Carolus.]

North Da·ko·ta (nôrth′ də kō′tə), one of the midwestern states of the United States. *Abbreviation:* N.Dak. or ND *Capital:* Bismarck. [North Dakota got its name from an American Indian tribe, the Dakota, meaning "allies" or "friends."]

north·east (nôrth′ēst′), **1** halfway between north and east. **2** a northeast direction. **3** a place that is in the northeast part or direction. **4** toward the northeast: *At this point the road turns northeast.* **5** coming from the northeast: *a northeast wind.* **6** in the northeast: *the northeast district.* 1,5,6 *adjective,* 2,3 *noun,* 4 *adverb.*

north·east·ern (nôrth′ē′stərn), **1** toward the northeast. **2** from the northeast. **3** of the northeast. *adjective.*

north·er·ly (nôr′ŦHər lē), **1** toward the north: *The windows face northerly.* **2** from the north: *a northerly wind. adjective, adverb.*

north·ern (nôr′ŦHərn), **1** toward the north: *the northern side of a building.* **2** coming from the north: *a northern breeze.* **3** of or in the north: *They have traveled in northern countries.* **4 Northern,** of or in the northern part of the United States: *Boston is a Northern city. adjective.*

north·ern·er (nôr′ŦHər nər), **1** a person born or living in the north. **2 Northerner,** a person born or living in the northern part of the United States. *noun.*

Northern Ireland, the northern part of Ireland. It is associated with Great Britain.

northern lights
The **northern lights** appear most often at night in the far north.

northern lights, the streamers and bands of light appearing in the sky in northern regions.

north·ern·most (nôr′ŦHərn mōst), farthest north. *adjective.*

North Korea, a country in eastern Asia.

North Pole, the northern end of the earth's axis.

North Star, a bright star almost directly above the North Pole.

north·ward (nôrth′wərd), toward the north; north: *I walked northward. The orchard is on the northward slope of the hill. adjective, adverb.*

north·wards (nôrth′wərdz), northward. *adverb.*

north·west (nôrth′west′), 1 halfway between north and west. 2 a northwest direction. 3 a place that is in the northwest part or direction. 4 toward the northwest: *The road from Chicago to Minneapolis runs northwest.* 5 coming from the northwest: *a northwest wind.* 6 in the northwest: *the northwest district.* 1,5,6 *adjective,* 2,3 *noun,* 4 *adverb.*

north·west·ern (nôrth′wes′tərn), 1 toward the northwest. 2 from the northwest. 3 of the northwest. *adjective.*

Northwest Territories, a division of northern Canada, east of the Yukon Territory.

Nor·way (nôr′wā), a country in northern Europe. *noun.*

Nor·we·gian (nôr wē′jən), 1 of Norway, its people, or their language. 2 a person born or living in Norway. 3 the language of Norway. 1 *adjective,* 2,3 *noun.*

nose (nōz), 1 the part of the face or head just above the mouth. The nose has openings for breathing and smelling. 2 the sense of smell: *That dog has a good nose for hunting.* 3 to smell; investigate or discover by smell: *The hounds nosed out the scent of the fox.* 4 to touch, rub, or push with the nose: *The cat nosed its kittens.* 5 a part that stands out, especially at the front of anything: *the nose of an airplane.* 1,2,5 *noun,* 3,4 *verb,* **nos·es, nosed, nos·ing.**

under one's nose, in plain sight: *I lost my pencil, but found it again right under my nose.*

nose·bleed (nōz′blēd′), a flow of blood from the nose. *noun.*

nose cone, the cone-shaped front section of a missile or rocket, made to carry a bomb to a target or to carry instruments or passengers into space.

nose dive, 1 a swift plunge downward by an airplane. 2 a sudden, sharp drop: *The thermometer took a nose dive the first day of winter.*

nose-dive (nōz′dīv′), to take a nose dive. *verb,* **nose-dives, nose-dived, nose-div·ing.**

nos·ey (nō′zē). See **nosy.** *adjective,* **nos·i·er, nos·i·est.**

nos·tril (nos′trəl), either of the two openings in the nose. Air is breathed into the lungs, and smells come into the sensitive parts of the nose, through the nostrils. *noun.*

nos·y (nō′zē), prying, inquisitive, or overly curious about other people's business: *Our nosy neighbors were always asking questions about our family. adjective,* **nos·i·er, nos·i·est.** Also spelled **nosey.**

not (not), a word that says no: *Cold is not hot. Six and two do not make ten. adverb.*

no·ta·ble (nō′tə bəl), 1 worth noticing; remarkable; important: *Last week's eruption of the volcano was a notable event.* 2 a person who is notable: *Many notables came to the reception at the White House.* 1 *adjective,* 2 *noun.*

no·ta·bly (nō′tə blē), in a notable manner; to a notable degree: *Many countries are notably lacking in fertile soil and minerals. adverb.*

no·ta·tion (nō tā′shən), 1 a set of signs or symbols that represent numbers or other things. Mathematics and music each have special systems of notation. 2 a note to help the memory: *I made a notation in the margin of the book. noun.*

notch (noch), 1 a nick or cut shaped like a V, made in an edge or on a curving surface: *People used to cut notches on a stick to keep count of numbers.* 2 to make a notch or notches in. 1 *noun, plural* **notch·es;** 2 *verb.*

note (nōt), 1 a short sentence, phrase, or single word, written down to remind one of what was in a book, a speech, or an agreement: *Sometimes our teacher has us take notes on what we read. I must make a note of that.* 2 to write down as a thing to be remembered: *Our class notes the weather daily on a chart.* 3 a comment, remark, or piece of information added concerning a word or a passage in a book, often to help pupils in studying the book: *A footnote is a note at the bottom of the page about something on the page.* 4 a very short letter: *a note of thanks.* 5 greatness; fame: *a person of note.* 6 to observe; notice; give attention to: *Now note what I do next.* 7 (in music) the written sign to show the pitch and the length of a

notes (definition 7)

sound. **8** a single musical sound: *Sing this note for me.* **9** any one of the keys of a piano: *to strike the wrong note.* **10** a special tone or way of expression: *There was a note of determination in her voice.* 1,3-5,7-10 *noun,* 2,6 *verb,* **notes, not·ed, not·ing.**

take note of, to give attention to; observe: *No one took any note of my leaving.*

note·book (nōt′bůk′), a book in which to write notes of things to be learned or remembered. *noun.*

not·ed (nō′tid), well-known; specially noticed; famous: *Samson was noted for strength. adjective.*

note·wor·thy (nōt′wėr′THē), worthy of notice; remarkable: *a noteworthy achievement. adjective.*

a hat	i it	oi oil	ch child	a in about
ā age	ī ice	ou out	ng long	e in taken
ä far	o hot	u cup	sh she	ə = i in pencil
e let	ō open	ů put	th thin	o in lemon
ē equal	ô order	ü rule	₮H then	u in circus
ėr term			zh measure	

noteworthy—The completion of the first transcontinental railroad was a **noteworthy** event.

noth·ing (nuth′ing), **1** not anything: *Nothing arrived by mail.* **2** a thing or person of no value or importance: *Don't worry, it's nothing.* **3** zero. **4** not at all: *She looks nothing like her sister.* 1 *pronoun,* 2,3 *noun,* 4 *adverb.*

no·tice (nō′tis), **1** attention; observation: *A sudden movement caught his notice.* **2** to see; give attention to; observe: *I noticed a hole in my sock.* **3** information; warning: *The whistle blew to give notice that the boat was about to leave.* **4** a written or printed announcement or sign: *There is a notice in the newspaper about their wedding. We posted notices about our garage sale.* **5** a telling that one is leaving or must leave rented quarters or a job at a given time: *I gave two weeks' notice when I quit my job.* 1,3-5 *noun,* 2 *verb,* **no·tic·es, no·ticed, no·tic·ing.**

[The word *notice* comes from a Latin word meaning "come to know." Other English words from the same Latin root include *notion* and *notorious.*]

take notice of, to give attention to; observe: *Take no notice of them.*

no·tice·a·ble (nō′ti sə bəl), **1** easily seen or noticed: *Our kitten is very noticeable because its fur is yellow.* **2** worth noticing: *The class has made a noticeable improvement in spelling since the last test. adjective.*

no·ti·fi·ca·tion (nō′tə fə kā′shən), a notice: *She received a notification of the meeting. noun.*

no·ti·fy (nō′tə fī), to let know; give notice to; announce to; inform: *Our teacher notified us that there would be a test on Monday.* verb, **no·ti·fies, no·ti·fied, no·ti·fy·ing.**

no·tion (nō′shən), **1** an idea; understanding: *I have no notion of what you mean.* **2** an opinion; view; belief: *People have different notions about how children should be raised.* **3** intention: *He has no notion of risking his money.* **4** a desire or thought that suddenly occurs to one: *I had a notion to take a short vacation, but changed my mind.* **5** a foolish idea or opinion: *Grow oranges in Alaska? What a notion!* **6 notions,** small useful articles, such as pins, needles, thread, or tape. *noun.*

no·to·ri·ous (nō tôr′ē əs), well-known or commonly known, especially because of something bad: *Our neighbors are notorious for giving noisy parties. adjective.*

notorious
Jesse James was a **notorious** outlaw.

not·with·stand·ing (not′wiTH stan′ding *or* not′with stan′ding), **1** in spite of: *I bought it notwithstanding the high price.* **2** nevertheless: *It is raining; but I shall go, notwithstanding.* 1 *preposition,* 2 *adverb.*

noun (noun), a word used as the name of a person, place, thing, quality, or event. Words like *Lisa, table, kindness, skill,* and *party* are nouns. *noun.*

nour·ish (nėr′ish), **1** to make grow, or keep alive and well, with food; feed: *Milk nourishes a baby.* **2** to support; encourage: *Getting a letter published in the newspaper nourished her hopes of being a writer. verb.*

nour·ish·ment (nėr′ish mənt), food: *They were thin and pale from lack of proper nourishment. noun.*

Nov., November.

Nova Sco·tia (nō′və skō′shə), a province in southeastern Canada. *Capital:* Halifax.

nov·el (nov′əl), **1** of a new kind or nature; strange; new. **2** a made-up story with characters and a plot, long enough to fill one or more volumes. Novels are usually about people, scenes, and happenings such as might be met in real life. **1** *adjective,* **2** *noun.*

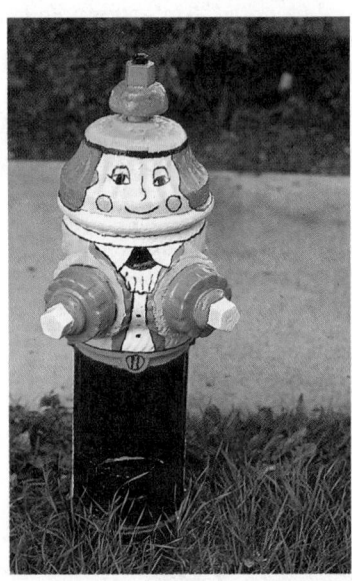

novel (definition 1)
This is a **novel** way to paint a fire hydrant.

nov·el·ist (nov′ə list), a person who writes novels. *noun.*

nov·el·ty (nov′əl tē), **1** newness: *After the novelty of the game wore off, we didn't want to play it any more.* **2** a new or unusual thing: *Staying up late was a novelty to the children.* **3 novelties,** small, unusual articles, such as toys or cheap jewelry. *noun, plural* **nov·el·ties.**

No·vem·ber (nō vem′bər), the 11th month of the year. It has 30 days. *noun.*
[*November* came from a Latin word meaning "nine." In the ancient Roman calendar, November was the ninth month of the year, which began in March.]

nov·ice (nov′is), **1** a beginner; one who is new to something: *Novices are likely to make some mistakes.* **2** a person who is not yet a monk or nun, but is in a period of trial and preparation. *noun.*

now (nou), **1** at this time: *He is here now. Most people do not believe in ghosts now.* **2** by this time: *She must have reached the city now.* **3** this time: *by now, until now, from now on.* **4** at once: *Do it now!* **5** since; now that: *Now I am older, I have* changed my mind. *Now you mention it, I do remember.* **6** as things are; as it is: *Now I can never believe you again.* **7** then; next: *Now you see it; now you don't.* **8** a little while ago: *I just now saw him.* **9** *Now* is used in many sentences where it makes very little difference in the meaning: *Now what do you mean? Oh, come now! Now you knew that was wrong.* **1,2,4,6-9** *adverb,* **3** *noun,* **5** *conjunction.*

now and then or **now and again,** from time to time; once in a while: *I see him now and then, but not often.*

now·a·days (nou′ə dāz′), at the present day; in these times: *Nowadays people travel in automobiles rather than carriages. adverb.*

no·where (nō′hwer *or* nō′hwär), **1** in no place; at no place; to no place. **2** a place that is not well-known or is far from everything else: *Our car broke down in the middle of nowhere.* **1** *adverb,* **2** *noun.*

noz·zle (noz′əl), a tip put on a hose or pipe forming an outlet: *He adjusted the nozzle so that the water came out in a fine spray. noun.*

nub (nub), **1** a part sticking out; knob. **2** the point or main idea of anything: *Now we've reached the nub of the problem. noun.*

nu·cle·ar (nü′klē ər *or* nyü′klē ər), **1** having to do with a nucleus, especially the nucleus of an atom: *Neutrons and protons are nuclear particles.* **2** of or having to do with atoms, atomic energy, or atomic weapons; atomic: *a nuclear reactor, the nuclear age. adjective.*

nuclear energy, the energy that exists inside the nucleus of an atom; atomic energy. Nuclear energy can be released by splitting or combining the centers of some kinds of atoms.

nu·cle·us (nü′klē əs *or* nyü′klē əs), **1** a central part or thing around which other parts or things are collected: *An encyclopedia, several magazines, and several dozen children's story books formed the nucleus of the classroom library.* **2** the central part of an atom, consisting of protons and neutrons. The nucleus forms a core around which electrons orbit. **3** a special part found in most living cells which controls their growth and their division to form new cells. *noun, plural* **nu·cle·i** (nü′klē ī *or* nyü′klē ī), **nu·cle·us·es.**

nucleus (definition 3)
the **nucleus** of a cell that is going to divide

nude (nüd *or* nyüd), with no clothes on; naked. *adjective.*

nudge (nuj), **1** to push slightly to attract attention: *She nudged me with her elbow when it was my turn to play.* **2** a slight push. 1 *verb,* **nudg·es, nudged, nudg·ing;** 2 *noun.*

nug·get (nug′it), a lump; valuable lump. *noun.*

nugget—a **nugget** of gold

nui·sance (nü′sns *or* nyü′sns), a thing or person that annoys, troubles, offends, or is disagreeable: *Flies are a nuisance. noun.*

numb (num), **1** having lost the power of feeling or moving: *My fingers are numb with cold.* **2** to make numb: *The dentist gave me a shot to numb my jaw.* **3** to dull the feelings of: *The news of her death numbed them with grief.* 1 *adjective,* 2,3 *verb.*

num·ber (num′bər), **1** the count or sum of a group of things or persons; amount: *The number of students in our class is twenty.* **2** a word that tells exactly how many. Two, thirteen, twenty-one, and one hundred are such numbers. **3** a word that tells rank or place in a series. Second and thirteenth are such numbers. **4** a figure or mark that stands for a number; numeral. 2, 7, and 9 are numbers. **5** to give a number to: *The pages of this book are numbered.* **6** to be or amount to a given number: *The states in the Union number 50. This city numbers a million people.* **7** a quantity, especially a rather large quantity: *We saw a number of birds.* **8 numbers,** arithmetic: *She is very clever at numbers.* **9** one of a numbered series, often a particular numeral identifying a person or thing: *a telephone number, a house number.* **10** a single part of a program: *The program consisted of four musical numbers.* **11** to limit; fix the number of: *Our old dog's days are numbered.* **12** (in grammar) a word form or ending which shows whether one or more is meant. *Boy, ox,* and *this* are in the singular number; *boys, oxen,* and *these* are in the plural number. 1-4,7-10,12 *noun,* 5,6,11 *verb.*
without number, too many to be counted: *stars without number.*

num·ber·less (num′bər lis), very numerous; too

a hat	**i** it	**oi** oil	**ch** child	a in about
ā age	**ī** ice	**ou** out	**ng** long	e in taken
ä far	**o** hot	**u** cup	**sh** she	ə = { i in pencil
e let	**ō** open	**u̇** put	**th** thin	o in lemon
ē equal	**ô** order	**ü** rule	**ᴛʜ** then	u in circus
ėr term			**zh** measure	

many to count: *There are numberless fish in the sea. adjective.*

number line, a line divided into equal segments by points marked with numbers in order.

nu·mer·al (nü′mər əl *or* nyü′mər əl), a figure or group of figures standing for a number. 7, 25, 463, III, and XIX are numerals. *noun.*

nu·me·ra·tor (nü′mə rā′tər *or* nyü′mə rā′tər), the number above or to the left of the line in a fraction, which shows how many equal parts of the whole make up the fraction: *In ⅜, 3 is the numerator and 8 is the denominator. noun.*

nu·mer·i·cal (nü mer′ə kəl *or* nyü mer′ə kəl), having something to do with numbers; in numbers; by numbers: *numerical order. adjective.*

nu·mer·ous (nü′mər əs *or* nyü′mər əs), very many: *The child asked numerous questions. adjective.*

nun (nun), a woman who gives up many things and lives a life devoted to religion. Nuns often live together in groups that teach, care for the poor and sick, and perform many other duties. *noun.*

nup·tial (nup′shəl), **1** of marriage or weddings. **2 nuptials,** a wedding or the wedding ceremony. 1 *adjective,* 2 *noun.*

nurse (nėrs), **1** a person who is trained to take care of the sick, the injured, or the old. Nurses often work with doctors in hospitals, assisting them and carrying out their instructions. **2** to be or act as a nurse for sick people; wait on or try to cure the sick: *They nursed their children through the flu.* **3** to cure or try to cure by care: *She nursed a bad cold by going to bed.* **4** a woman who cares for and brings up the young children or babies of other persons. **5** to nourish; make grow; protect: *to nurse a hatred in the heart, to nurse a plant.* **6** to treat with special care: *He nursed his sore arm by using it very little.* **7** to give milk to a baby at the breast. **8** to suck milk from the breast of a mother. 1,4 *noun,* 2,3,5-8 *verb,* **nurs·es, nursed, nurs·ing.**

nurse·maid (nėrs′mād′), a girl or woman employed to care for children. *noun.*

nurs·er·y (nėr′sər ē), **1** a room set apart for the use and care of babies. **2** a place where babies and small children are cared for during the day: *a day nursery.* **3** a piece of ground or place where young plants are raised for transplanting or sale. *noun, plural* **nurs·er·ies.**

nursery school, a school for children not old enough to go to kindergarten.

nursing home, a place for the care of old people or anyone who needs nursing care over a long period of time.

nur·ture (nėr′chər), **1** to rear; bring up; care for;

N

train: *They nurtured the child as if she were their own.* **2** a rearing; bringing up; training; education: *The two sisters had received very different nurture, one at home and the other at a convent.* **3** to nourish; feed: *to nurture resentment.* **4** nourishment; food. 1,3 *verb*, **nur·tured, nur·tur·ing;** 2,4 *noun.*

nut (nut), **1** a dry fruit or seed with a hard woody or leathery shell and a kernel inside which is often good to eat. **2** the kernel of a nut: *The recipe called for chopped nuts.* **3** a small piece of metal or plastic with a hole in the center containing a screw thread. It screws onto a bolt to hold the bolt in place. **4** a foolish, odd, or crazy person. *noun.*

nut·crack·er (nut′krak′ər), a device for cracking the shells of nuts. *noun.*

nut·meg (nut′meg), a hard, spicy seed about as big as a marble, obtained from the fruit of a tropical tree. The seed is grated and used for flavoring food. *noun.*

nu·tri·ent (nü′trē ənt *or* nyü′trē ənt), any substance that is required by living things for energy, growth, and repair of tissues: *Eating a variety of foods helps us to get all of the nutrients we need to be healthy. noun.*

nu·tri·tion (nü trish′ən *or* nyü trish′ən), **1** food; nourishment: *A balanced diet provides nutrition for your body.* **2** the series of processes by which food is used by living things for growth and energy. *noun.*

nu·tri·tious (nü trish′əs *or* nyü trish′əs), nourishing; valuable as food: *Eggs are nutritious. adjective.*

nuts (nuts), crazy: *He's nuts to try a dangerous stunt like that. adjective.*

nut·ty (nut′ē), **1** like nuts; tasting like nuts: *This cereal has a nutty flavor.* **2** odd or silly: *We did nutty things like jumping in a pool with our clothes on. adjective,* **nut·ti·er, nut·ti·est.**

nuz·zle (nuz′əl), to rub with the nose; press the nose against. *verb,* **nuz·zles, nuz·zled, nuz·zling.**

NV, Nevada (used with postal Zip Code).

NW or **N.W., 1** northwest. **2** northwestern.

NY, New York (used with postal Zip Code).

N.Y., New York.

ny·lon (nī′lon), a synthetic substance that is very strong and somewhat elastic, and that wears well. Nylon can be made into cloth or plastic. Clothing, tents, stockings, and brushes are made of nylon. *noun.*

nymph
(definition 2)
the **nymph**
of a
grasshopper

nymph (nimf), **1** a Greek or Roman goddess of nature, usually in the form of a beautiful and graceful young woman. Nymphs were thought to live in seas, rivers, fountains, hills, woods, or trees. **2** an insect in a stage of development in which it looks like the adult, but is smaller and has no wings. *noun.*

nuzzle—His horse **nuzzled** him.

O o

O or **o** (ō), the 15th letter of the English alphabet. *noun, plural* **O's** or **o's.**

O., Ohio.

oaf (ōf), **1** a very stupid person. **2** a clumsy person. *noun.*

oak (ōk), **1** a tree or shrub having nuts which are called acorns. There are many kinds of oaks, found in most parts of the world. **2** its hard, strong wood, used in building, especially for floors. *noun.*

oar (ôr), **1** a long pole with a broad, flat end, used in rowing. Sometimes an oar is used to steer a boat. **2** a person who rows: *He is the best oar in the crew. noun.*

o·a·sis (ō ā′sis), a place in the desert where there is water and where trees and plants can grow. *noun. plural* **o·a·ses** (ō ā′sēz′).

oath (ōth), **1** a statement that something is true or a solemn promise, which God or some holy person or thing is called on to witness: *I gave an oath that I would tell the truth.* **2** a curse; word used in swearing: *The pirate cursed us with fearful oaths. noun, plural* **oaths** (ōᴛнz *or* ōths).

oat·meal (ōt′mēl′), **1** oats partially ground up and flattened into small flakes. **2** a cooked cereal made from this: *We often have oatmeal with cream and sugar for breakfast. noun.*

oats (ōts), the grain of a kind of cereal grass, or the plant that it grows on. The grain is used to make oatmeal and as a food for horses and other farm animals. *noun singular or plural.*

o·be·di·ence (ō bē′dē əns), a doing what one is told to do; submitting to authority or law: *They were strict parents who demanded complete obedience from their children. noun.*

o·be·di·ent (ō bē′dē ənt), doing what one is told to do; willing to obey: *The obedient dog came at its owner's whistle. adjective.*

ob·e·lisk (ob′ə lisk), a tapering, four-sided shaft of stone with a top shaped like a pyramid. *noun.*

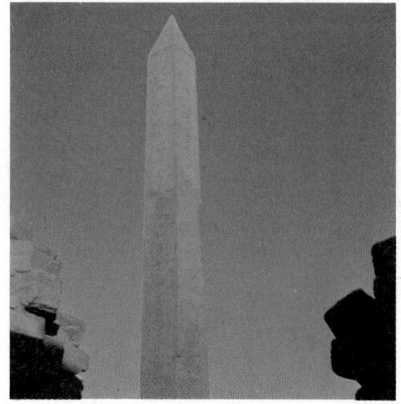

obelisk

o·bey (ō bā′), **1** to do what one is told to do; follow orders: *The dog obeyed its owner and went home.* **2** to act in agreement with; carry out: *A good citizen obeys the laws. verb.*
[*Obey* comes from two Latin words meaning "listen to."]

o·bi (ō′bē), a long, broad sash worn by Japanese around the waist of a kimono. *noun, plural* **o·bis.**

OBI

ob·ject (ob′jikt *for 1-4;* əb jekt′ *for 5 and 6*), **1** something that can be seen or touched; thing: *What is that object by the fence?* **2** a person or thing toward which feeling, thought, or action is directed: *The rare disease became an object of study.* **3** a thing intended; purpose; end; goal: *My object in coming here was to help you.* **4** a word or group of words which receives the action of a verb, or which follows a preposition. In "He threw the ball to his sister," *ball* is the object of the verb *threw,* and *sister* is the object of the preposition *to.* **5** to be opposed; feel dislike: *Many people object to loud noise.* **6** to give as a reason against something: *I objected that it was too cold for camping.* 1-4 *noun,* 5,6 *verb.*

ob·jec·tion (əb jek′shən), **1** something said in objecting; reason or argument against something: *One of the objections to the new plan was that it would cost too much.* **2** a feeling of disapproval or dislike: *an energetic person with no objection to hard work. noun.*

ob·jec·tion·a·ble (əb jek′shə nə bəl), unpleasant: *an objectionable odor. adjective.*

ob·jec·tive (əb jek′tiv), **1** something aimed at; purpose; goal: *My objective this summer will be learning to play tennis better.* **2** true to the facts; not influenced by personal thoughts or feelings: *The witness gave an objective report of the accident.* 1 *noun,* 2 *adjective.*

ob·li·gate (ob′lə gāt), to bind by law or a sense of duty: *A witness in court is obligated to tell the truth. verb,* **ob·li·gates, ob·li·gat·ed, ob·li·gat·ing.**

ob·li·ga·tion (ob′lə gā′shən), a duty under the law or from personal feeling: *We have an obligation to help our friends when they need help. The person who caused the damage is under an obligation to pay for it. noun.*

o·blige (ə blīj′), 1 to require; compel; force: *I am obliged to leave early to catch my train.* 2 to make someone grateful by doing a favor: *We are very much obliged for your offer to help.* 3 to do a favor for: *Kindly oblige me by closing the door. verb,* **o·blig·es, o·bliged, o·blig·ing.**

o·blig·ing (ə blī′jing), willing to do favors; helpful: *Her obliging nature wins friends. adjective.*

o·blique (ə blēk′), slanting; not straight up and down; not straight across. *adjective.*

o·blit·e·rate (ə blit′ə rāt′), to blot out; remove all traces of; destroy: *The heavy rain obliterated all of the footprints. verb,* **o·blit·e·rates, o·blit·er·at·ed, o·blit·er·at·ing.**

o·bliv·i·on (ə bliv′ē ən), the condition of being entirely forgotten: *Many ancient cities have long since passed into oblivion. noun.*

o·bliv·i·ous (ə bliv′ē əs), forgetful; not mindful: *The book was so interesting that I was oblivious of my surroundings. adjective.*

ob·long (ob′lông), longer than broad: *an oblong loaf of bread. adjective.*

ob·nox·ious (əb nok′shəs), offensive; very disagreeable; hateful: *Their constant rudeness and bad manners made them obnoxious to me. adjective.*

o·boe (ō′bō), a wooden wind instrument in which the thin, high tone is produced by a double reed mouthpiece. *noun.*

oboe

ob·scene (əb sēn′), offending modesty or decency: *obscene language. adjective.*

ob·scure (əb skyúr′), 1 not clearly expressed; hard to understand: *an obscure passage in a book.* 2 not well known; attracting no notice: *an obscure little village, an obscure poet.* 3 hidden; not easily discovered: *an obscure path.* 4 not distinct; not clear: *an obscure shape, obscure sounds.* 5 to dim; darken; hide from view: *Clouds obscure the sun.* 1-4 *adjective,* 5 *verb,* **ob·scures, ob·scured, ob·scur·ing.**

ob·scur·i·ty (əb skyúr′ə tē), 1 a lack of clearness; difficulty in being understood: *The obscurity of the book caused an argument over its meaning.* 2 the condition of being unknown: *Abraham Lincoln rose from obscurity to fame. noun, plural* **ob·scur·i·ties.**

ob·serv·ance (əb zėr′vəns), the act of observing or keeping laws or customs: *Observance of the traffic laws is the sign of a good driver. noun.*

ob·serv·ant (əb zėr′vənt), quick to notice; watchful: *If you are observant in the fields and woods, you will find many flowers that others fail to notice. adjective.*

ob·ser·va·tion (ob′zėr vā′shən), 1 the act, habit, or power of seeing and noting: *By trained observation a doctor can tell much about the condition of a patient.* 2 the fact of being seen; notice; being seen: *The spy avoided observation.* 3 something seen and noted: *During science experiments she kept careful records of her observations.* 4 a remark: *"Haste makes waste," was Father's observation when I spilled the milk. noun.*

ob·serv·a·to·ry (əb zėr′və tôr′ē), a place or building equipped with telescopes and other instruments for observing the stars and other heavenly bodies. *noun, plural* **ob·serv·a·to·ries.**

ob·serve (əb zėrv′), 1 to see and note; notice: *Did you observe anything strange in her behavior?* 2 to examine closely; study: *An astronomer observes the stars.* 3 to remark; comment: *"Bad weather ahead," she observed.* 4 to keep; follow in practice: *The teacher asked us to observe the rule about not walking on the grass.* 5 to show regard for; celebrate: *to observe the Sabbath. verb,* **ob·serves, ob·served, ob·serv·ing.**

ob·serv·er (əb zėr′vər), a person who observes. *noun.*

obsidian

ob·sid·i·an (ob sid′ē ən), a hard, dark, glassy rock that is formed when lava cools. *noun.*

ob·so·lete (ob′sə lēt), 1 no longer in use. 2 out of date: *We still use this machine though it is obsolete. adjective.*

obsolete (definition 1)
Automobiles made horse-drawn buggies **obsolete.**

ob·sta·cle (ob′stə kəl), something that stands in the way or stops progress; hindrance: *A tree fallen across the road was an obstacle to our car.* *noun.*

ob·sti·nate (ob′stə nit), stubborn; not giving in. *adjective.*

ob·struct (əb strukt′), **1** to block up; make hard to pass through: *Fallen trees obstruct the road.* **2** to be in the way of; hinder: *A shortage of materials obstructed the work of the factory.* *verb.*

ob·struc·tion (əb struk′shən), **1** a thing that obstructs; something in the way; obstacle: *The old path was blocked by such obstructions as boulders and fallen trees.* **2** a blocking; hindering: *The obstruction of justice is a crime.* *noun.*

ob·tain (əb tān′), to get through effort; come to have: *to obtain a job one applies for, to obtain knowledge through study.* *verb.*

ob·tain·a·ble (əb tā′nə bəl), able to be gotten: *Rapid shipping makes fresh fruits and vegetables obtainable almost everywhere.* *adjective.*

ob·tuse (əb tüs′ *or* əb tyüs′), **1** not sharp; blunt. **2** slow in understanding; stupid: *They were too obtuse to take the hint.* *adjective.*

obtuse angle, an angle greater than a right angle.

RIGHT ANGLE   OBTUSE ANGLE

ob·vi·ous (ob′vē əs), easily seen or understood; not to be doubted; plain: *It is obvious that two and two make four.* *adjective.*

oc·ca·sion (ə kā′zhən), **1** a particular time: *We have met them on several occasions.* **2** a special event: *The jewels were worn only on great occasions, such as a royal wedding or a coronation.* **3** a good chance; opportunity: *The trip we took together gave us an occasion to get better acquainted.* *noun.*

oc·ca·sion·al (ə kā′zhə nəl), happening or coming now and then, or once in a while: *We had fine weather all through July except for an occasional thunderstorm.* *adjective.*

oc·ca·sion·al·ly (ə kā′zhə nə lē), now and then; once in a while; at times. *adverb.*

oc·cu·pant (ok′yə pənt), a person who occupies: *The occupant of the shack stepped out as I approached.* *noun.*

oc·cu·pa·tion (ok′yə pā′shən), **1** the work a person does regularly or to earn a living; business; employment; trade: *Caring for the sick is a nurse's occupation.* **2** a possession; occupying; being occupied: *the occupation of a town by the enemy, the occupation of a house by a family.* *noun.*

oc·cu·py (ok′yə pī), **1** to take up; fill: *The building occupies an entire block. The lessons occupy the morning.* **2** to keep busy; engage; employ:

a	hat	i	it	oi	oil	ch	child		a in about
ā	age	ī	ice	ou	out	ng	long		e in taken
ä	far	o	hot	u	cup	sh	she	ə =	i in pencil
e	let	ō	open	ù	put	th	thin		o in lemon
ē	equal	ô	order	ü	rule	ᵀʜ	then		u in circus
ėr	term					zh	measure		

Composing music occupied her attention. **3** to take possession of: *The enemy occupied our fort.* **4** to hold; have in use: *A judge occupies an important position.* **5** to live in: *Two families occupy the house next door.* *verb,* **oc·cu·pies, oc·cu·pied, oc·cu·py·ing.**

oc·cur (ə kėr′), **1** to happen; take place: *Storms often occur in winter.* **2** to be found; exist: *"E" occurs in print more often than any other letter.* **3** to come to mind; suggest itself: *Has it occurred to you to close the windows? verb,* **oc·curs, oc·curred, oc·cur·ring.**

oc·cur·rence (ə kėr′əns), **1** an occurring: *The occurrence of storms delayed our trip.* **2** a happening; event: *Her visit was an unexpected occurrence.* *noun.*

o·cean (ō′shən), **1** the great body of salt water that covers almost three fourths of the earth's surface; the sea. **2** any of its four main divisions—the Atlantic, Pacific, Indian, and Arctic oceans. The waters around Antarctica are considered by some to form a separate ocean. *noun.*

o·cean·og·ra·phy (ō′shə nog′rə fē), the science that deals with the oceans and seas and with the living things in them. *noun.*

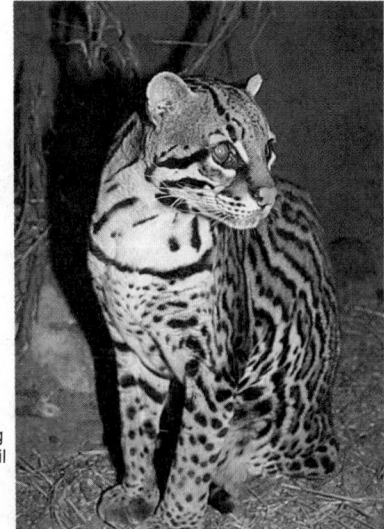

ocelot
about 3 feet
(1 meter) long
without the tail

oc·e·lot (os′ə lot *or* ō′sə lot), a large cat with spots, somewhat like a leopard but much smaller. It is found from Texas through Mexico and into parts of South America. *noun.*

o'clock (ə klok′), by the clock; according to the clock: *We have dinner at six o'clock. adverb.*

Oct., October.

oc·ta·gon (ok′tə gon), a figure having eight angles and eight sides. *noun.*

oc·tave (ok′tiv), **1** the interval between a musical tone and another tone having twice (or half) as many vibrations per second. From one tone called C to the next tone called C is an octave. **2** the eighth tone above (or below) a given tone, having twice (or half) as many vibrations per second. **3** the series of tones or of keys of an instrument filling the interval between a tone and its octave. *noun.*

octave
(definition 1)

Oc·to·ber (ok tō′bər), the tenth month of the year. It has 31 days. *noun.*
[*October* came from a Latin word meaning "eight." In the ancient Roman calendar, October was the eighth month of the year, which began in March.]

oc·to·pus (ok′tə pəs), a sea animal having a soft body and eight arms with suckers on them. It is a mollusk without a shell. *noun, plural* **oc·to·pus·es.**

Word History

octopus *Octopus* comes from a Greek word meaning "having eight feet." We define the octopus as having eight arms. In earlier times these arms were thought of as looking like legs with feet.

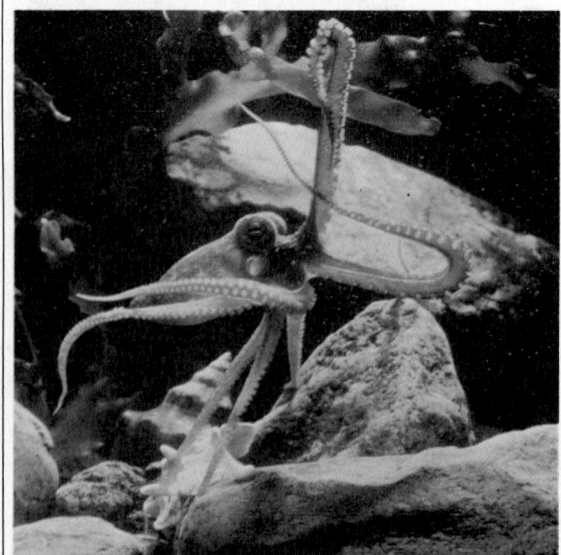

octopus
from 6 inches (15 centimeters) to 20 feet (6 meters) across

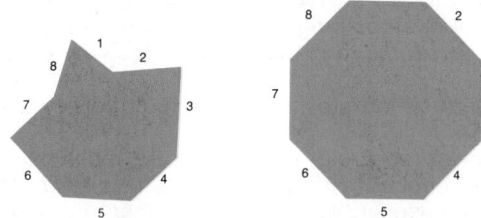

octagon—two kinds of **octagons**

odd (od), **1** strange; peculiar; unusual: *What an odd house; it has no windows.* **2** leaving a remainder of 1 when divided by 2: *Three, five, and seven are odd numbers.* **3** being one of a pair or set of which the rest is missing: *Every time she does her laundry, she ends up with at least one odd sock.* **4** extra; occasional: *He could not find regular work and had to take odd jobs. adjective.*

odd·i·ty (od′ə tē), a strange, unusual, or peculiar person or thing. *noun, plural* **odd·i·ties.**

odd·ly (od′lē), in a strange or unusual manner: *an oddly shaped cup. adverb.*

odds (odz), a difference in favor of one and against another; advantage. In betting, odds of 3 to 1 mean that 3 will be paid if the bet is lost for every 1 that will be received if the bet is won. *The odds are in our favor and we should win. noun plural.*

at odds, quarreling; disagreeing: *The two brothers were often at odds.*

odds and ends, stray bits left over; remnants: *I went about the house picking up the odds and ends.*

o·di·ous (ō′dē əs), very displeasing; hateful; offensive: *an odious smell, odious lies. adjective.*

o·dor (ō′dər), a smell: *the odor of roses, the odor of garbage. noun.*

o·dor·less (ō′dər lis), without any odor: *Pure water is odorless. adjective.*

od·ys·sey or **Od·ys·sey** (od′ə sē), a long series of wanderings and adventures: *Her odyssey in sports competitions took her all the way to the Olympic games. noun, plural* **od·ys·seys** or **Od·ys·seys.**

o'er (ôr), over. *adverb, preposition.*

of (ov, uv, *or* əv), **1** belonging to: *the children of the family, a friend of my childhood, the news of the day, the driver of the car, the cause of the quarrel.* **2** made from: *a house of bricks, castles of sand.* **3** that has; with: *a house of six rooms.* **4** that is; named: *the city of Chicago.* **5** away from; from: *north of Boston.* **6** about; concerning; having to do with: *to think well of someone, to be fifteen years of age.* **7** out of; owing to: *to expect much of a new medicine. She came of a noble family.* **8** among: *Many of my classmates were at the party.* **9** before: *The time is twenty of seven. preposition.*

off (ôf), **1** from the usual position or condition: *I took off my hat.* **2** from; away from; far from: *He pushed me off my seat. We are miles off the main road.* **3** away; at a distance; to a distance: *to go off on a journey. Christmas is only five weeks off.* **4** subtracted from: *25 dollars off the regular price.*

5 near to; by: *They live right off the bus route.* **6** so as to stop or lessen: *Turn the water off. The game was called off.* **7** no longer planned; canceled: *The game is off.* **8** not on; not connected; loose: *The electricity is off. A button is off his coat.* **9** without work: *an afternoon off. She likes to read during off hours.* **10** wholly; in full: *She cleared off her desk.* **11** in error; wrong: *Your answer is way off.* 1,3,6,9,10 *adverb*, 2,4,5,8 *preposition*, 7-9,11 *adjective*.

be off, to go away; leave quickly: *I'm off now for the party.*

off and on, now and then: *He has lived in Europe off and on for ten years.*

of·fend (ə fend′), to pain; displease; hurt the feelings of; make angry: *My friend was offended by my laughter. verb.*

[*Offend* comes from two Latin words meaning "strike against." As time passed, the meaning changed from "to attack physically" to "to hurt the feelings of." Other English words from the same source are *offense* and *offensive*.]

of·fend·er (ə fen′dər), a person who does wrong or breaks a law: *No smoking here; offenders will be fined $50. noun.*

of·fense (ə fens′ for 1 and 2; ô′fens for 3), **1** a breaking of the law; crime; sin: *The punishment for that offense is two years in prison. Lying and cruelty are offenses.* **2** an offending; hurting someone's feelings: *No offense was meant.* **3** an attacking team or force: *Our football team has a good offense. noun.*

give offense, to offend: *I did not mean to give offense to you.*

take offense, to be offended: *I did not take offense at the coach's criticism of my playing.*

of·fen·sive (ə fen′siv), **1** giving offense; irritating; annoying: *"Shut up" is an offensive remark.* **2** unpleasant; disagreeable; disgusting: *The bad eggs had an offensive odor.* **3** used for attack; having something to do with attack: *offensive weapons, an offensive war for conquest.* **4** a position or attitude of attack: *The army took the offensive.* **5** an attack: *Our planes bombed the enemy lines on the night before the offensive.* 1-3 *adjective,* 4,5 *noun.*

of·fer (ô′fər), **1** to hold out to be taken or refused; present: *to offer one's hand. She offered us her help.* **2** to be willing if another approves: *They offered to help.* **3** to propose; suggest: *to offer a price. She offered a few ideas to improve the plan.* **4** to try; attempt: *The thieves offered no resistance to the police.* **5** the act of offering: *an offer of money, an offer to sing.* **6** a thing that is offered: *an offer of $70,000 for a house.* 1-4 *verb,* 5,6 *noun.*

of·fer·ing (ô′fər ing), **1** something given as an act of worship. **2** a contribution; gift. *noun.*

off·hand (ôf′hand′ for 1; ôf′hand′ for 2 and 3), **1** at once; without previous thought or preparation: *The carpenter could not tell offhand the cost of his work.* **2** done or made without previous thought or preparation: *Her offhand opinion turned out to be* quite accurate. **3** casual; informal: *They played in an offhand way, without even keeping score.* 1 *adverb,* 2,3 *adjective.*

of·fice (ô′fis), **1** a place in which the work of a business or profession is done; room or rooms in which to work: *The doctor's office is on the second floor.* **2** the staff or persons carrying on work in such a place: *Half the office is on vacation.* **3** a position, especially a public position: *to accept or resign an office. The President holds the highest public office in the United States. noun.*

of·fi·cer (ô′fə sər), **1** a person who commands others in the armed forces. Majors, generals, captains, and admirals are officers. **2** a person who holds a public, government, or other office: *a police officer, an officer of a company. noun.*

of·fi·cial (ə fish′əl), **1** a person who holds an office; officer: *The mayor is a public official.* **2** of a position of authority: *an official uniform, official business.* **3** having authority: *An official record is kept of the proceedings of Congress.* 1 *noun,* 2,3 *adjective.*

JACK ATE LEAN MEAT, HIS WIFE ATE FAT, THEY **OFFSET** EACH OTHER DINING LIKE THAT.

off·set (ôf′set′), to make up for: *Her speed offset the strength of her opponent, and she won the tennis match. verb,* **off·sets, off·set, off·set·ting.**

off·shoot (ôf′shüt′), a shoot from a main stem; branch: *an offshoot of a plant. noun.*

a hat	i it	oi oil	ch child	(a in about
ā age	ī ice	ou out	ng long		e in taken
ä far	o hot	u cup	sh she	ə = { i in pencil
e let	ō open	u̇ put	th thin		o in lemon
ē equal	ô order	ü rule	₮H then	(u in circus
ėr term			zh measure	

off·shore (ôf′shôr′), off or away from the shore: *The wind was blowing offshore. We saw offshore oil wells along the coast.* adjective, adverb.

off·spring (ôf′spring′), the young of a person, animal, plant, or other living thing; descendant: *All their offspring had red hair.* noun, plural **off·spring.**

off·stage (ôf′stāj′), away from the part of the stage that the audience can see: *to describe events that took place offstage.* adjective, adverb.

oft (ôft), often. adverb.

of·ten (ô′fən), many times; frequently: *We often go to the seashore for a vacation. We see our neighbors often.* adverb.

o·gre (ō′gər), (in fairy tales) a giant or monster that was believed to eat people. noun.

ogre

oh or **Oh** (ō), a word used to express surprise, joy, pain, and other feelings: *Oh, dear me!* interjection.

OH, Ohio (used with postal Zip Code).

O·hi·o (ō hī′ō), one of the north central states of the United States. *Abbreviation:* O. or OH *Capital:* Columbus. noun.
[*Ohio* got its name from the Ohio River. It may have come from an Iroquois Indian word meaning ''fine'' or ''beautiful.'']

oil (oil), **1** any of several kinds of thick, fatty or greasy liquids that are lighter than water, burn easily, and will not mix or dissolve in water but will dissolve in alcohol. Mineral oils, such as kerosene, are used for fuel; animal and vegetable oils, such as olive oil, are used in cooking. **2** a dark-colored liquid found in the earth; petroleum. **3** to put oil on or in: *to oil the squeaky hinges of a door.* **4** any paint made by grinding coloring matter in oil. **5** an oil painting. 1,2,4,5 *noun,* 3 *verb.*

oil painting, a picture painted with colors made by mixing pigment with oil.

oil well, a well drilled to get oil.

oil·y (oi′lē), **1** of oil: *an oily smell.* **2** containing oil: *oily salad dressing.* **3** covered or soaked with oil: *oily rags.* **4** like oil; smooth; slippery: *an oily liquid.* adjective, **oil·i·er, oil·i·est.**

oint·ment (oint′mənt), any greasy substance used on the skin to heal it or to make it soft. Ointments often contain medicine. noun.

OK or **O.K.** (ō′kā′), **1** all right: *The new schedule was OK. ''OK, OK!''* he yelled. **2** to say that something is all right; approve: *My teacher has to OK my class schedule.* **3** an approval: *She gave the plan her OK.* 1 *adjective, adverb, interjection,* 2 *verb,* **OK's, OK'd, OK'ing** or **O.K.'s, O.K.'d, O.K.'ing;** 3 *noun, plural* **OK's** or **O.K.'s.** Also spelled **okay.**

OK, Oklahoma (used with postal Zip Code).

o·kay (ō′kā′). See **OK.** adjective, adverb, interjection, verb, noun.

Okla., Oklahoma.

O·kla·ho·ma (ō′klə hō′mə), one of the southwestern states of the United States. *Abbreviation:* Okla. or OK *Capital:* Oklahoma City. noun.
[*Oklahoma* came from Choctaw Indian words meaning ''red people.'']

Oklahoma City, the capital of Oklahoma.

o·kra (ō′krə), the sticky pods of a plant, used as a vegetable and in soups. noun.
[*Okra* comes from a west African name for the okra plant.]

okra

old (ōld), **1** not young; aged; having lived for a long time: *old people, an old oak tree.* **2** of age; in age: *The baby is ten months old.* **3** not new or recent; dating far back; ancient: *an old debt, an old castle.* **4** much worn by age or use: *an old coat.* **5** of long standing; over a long period of time: *We are old friends.* **6** former: *An old pupil came back to visit our teacher.* **7** the time of long ago; the past: *the knights of old.* 1-6 *adjective,* **old·er, old·est** or **eld·er, eld·est;** 7 *noun.*

old age, the years of life from about 65 on.

old·en (ōl′dən), old; of old; ancient: *In olden times very few people lived to old age.* adjective.

old-fash·ioned (ōld′fash′ənd), **1** out-of-date; of an old style: *old-fashioned clothing.* **2** keeping to old ways or ideas: *My grandparents are quite old-fashioned.* adjective.

Old Testament, the earlier part of the Bible, which contains the religious and social laws of the

Jews, a record of their history, important works of their literature, and writings of their prophets.

old-time (ōld′tīm′), of former times; like old times: *old-time automobiles. adjective.*

old-tim·er (ōld′tī′mər), a person who has lived a long time or been a member of a group for a long time: *The neighborhood old-timers remember when the streets were not paved. noun.*

Old World, Europe, Asia, and Africa.

o·le·o·mar·gar·ine (ō′lē ō mär′jər ən), a substitute for butter made from vegetable oils; margarine. *noun.*

ol·ive (ol′iv), **1** the small oval fruit of an evergreen tree that grows in warm regions. Olives have a hard stone and a bitter pulp. They are eaten green or ripe, as a relish, and are used to make olive oil. **2** yellowish-green; yellowish-brown. **1** *noun,* **2** *adjective.*

olives (definition 1)

olive oil, oil pressed from olives, used in cooking.

O·lym·pi·a (ō lim′pē ə), the capital of Washington. *noun.*

O·lym·pic (ō lim′pik), **1** of the Olympic games: *an Olympic athlete.* **2 Olympics,** the Olympic games. **1** *adjective,* **2** *noun plural.*

Olympic games, athletic contests held every four years in a different country. Athletes from many nations compete in them.

[The modern *Olympic games* take their name from contests in athletics, poetry, and music, held every four years by the ancient Greeks. *Olympic* comes from Olympia, the Greek name of the plain where the contests were held.]

ome·let or **ome·lette** (om′lit), eggs beaten with milk or water, fried or baked, and then folded over, often around a filling. *noun.*

o·men (ō′mən), a sign of what is to happen; object or event that is believed to mean good or bad fortune: *Spilling salt is said to be an omen of bad luck. noun.*

om·i·nous (om′ə nəs), unfavorable; threatening. *adjective.*

o·mis·sion (ō mish′ən), anything omitted: *His song was the only omission from the program. noun.*

o·mit (ō mit′), to leave out: *Many of my spelling mistakes are caused by omitting letters. verb,* **o·mits, o·mit·ted, o·mit·ting.**

a hat	**i** it	**oi** oil	**ch** child	⎧ a in about
ā age	**ī** ice	**ou** out	**ng** long	⎪ e in taken
ä far	**o** hot	**u** cup	**sh** she	ə = ⎨ i in pencil
e let	**ō** open	**ů** put	**th** thin	⎪ o in lemon
ē equal	**ô** order	**ü** rule	**ᴛʜ** then	⎩ u in circus
ėr term			**zh** measure	

on (ôn), **1** above and supported by: *This book is on the table.* **2** touching so as to cover or be around: *I put the ring on my finger.* **3** close to: *a house on the shore.* **4** in the direction of; toward: *The protesters marched on the Capitol.* **5** against; upon: *The picture is on the wall.* **6** farther: *March on.* **7** by means of; by the use of: *I just talked to her on the phone.* **8** in the condition of: *on duty.* **9** in or into a condition, process, position, or action: *Turn the gas on.* **10** taking place: *The race is on.* **11** in use; operating: *The radio is on.* **12** at the time of; during: *They greeted us on our arrival.* **13** from a time; forward: *later on, from that day on.* **14** concerning: *a book on animals.* **15** for the purpose of: *He went on an errand.* **16** among: *I am not on the committee considering new members for our club.* **1-5,7,8,12,14-16** *preposition,* **6,9,13** *adverb,* **10,11** *adjective.*

and so on, and more of the same: *Fruits such as oranges, lemons, grapefruit, and so on contain a vitamin that we need daily.*

on and on, without stopping: *We talked on and on through the whole afternoon.*

once (wuns), **1** one time: *Read it once more.* **2** a single occasion: *Once is enough.* **3** at some one time in the past; formerly: *That small town was once the capital of the state.* **4** when; if ever: *Most people like to swim, once they have learned how.* **1,3** *adverb,* **2** *noun,* **4** *conjunction.*

at once, 1 immediately: *You must come at once.* **2** at the same time: *All three children spoke at once.*

once in a while, now and then; not very often:

ominous
The sky looked very **ominous** just before the storm broke.

We see our cousins once in a while.

once upon a time, long ago: *Once upon a time there were dinosaurs.*

on·com·ing (ôn′kum′ing), approaching or advancing: *oncoming traffic. adjective.*

one (wun), **1** the number 1. **2** a single: *one person, one apple.* **3** a single person or thing: *I like the ones in that box.* **4** some: *One day you will be sorry.* **5** some person or thing: *Two of you may go, but one must stay.* **6** any person, standing for people in general: *One does not like to be left out.* 1,3 *noun,* 2,4 *adjective,* 5,6 *pronoun.*

at one, in agreement: *The two judges were at one about the winner.*

one by one, one after another: *They came out the door one by one.*

one another, each other: *They looked at one another.*

one-celled (wun′seld′), having only one cell: *Bacteria are one-celled living things. adjective.*

one·self (wun self′), one's own self: *At the age of seven one ought to dress oneself. pronoun.*

one-sid·ed (wun′sī′did), unfair; partial; seeing only one side of a question: *The umpire seemed one-sided in his decisions, always favoring the home team. adjective.*

one-way (wun′wā′), moving or allowing movement in only one direction: *a one-way street, a one-way ticket. adjective.*

on·ion (un′yən), the bulb of a garden plant, eaten raw or used in cooking. Onions have a sharp, strong smell and taste. *noun.*

on·look·er (ôn′lük′ər), a spectator; person who watches without taking part: *Only a few children were actually playing; the rest were onlookers. noun.*

on·ly (ōn′lē), **1** by itself or themselves; and no more: *Water is her only drink. These are the only roads along the shore.* **2** just; merely: *She sold only two.* **3** and no one else; and nothing more; and that is all: *Only he remained. I did it only through friendship.* **4** except that; but: *He would have started, only it rained.* **5** best; finest: *He is the only writer for my taste.* 1,5 *adjective,* 2,3 *adverb,* 4 *conjunction.*

if only, I wish: *If only the sun would shine!*

only too, very: *She was only too glad to help us.*

on·rush (ôn′rush′), a very strong or forceful forward rush: *He was knocked down by the onrush of water. noun.*

on·set (ôn′set′), **1** the beginning: *The onset of this disease is gradual.* **2** an attack: *The onset of the enemy took us by surprise. noun.*

on·slaught (ôn′slôt′), a vigorous attack: *The pirates made an onslaught on the ship. noun.*

on·stage (ôn′stāj′), on the part of the stage that the audience can see: *The actor's first onstage appearance was greeted with applause from the audience. adjective, adverb.*

On·tar·i·o (on ter′ē ō), **1** a province in Canada, north of the Great Lakes. *Capital:* Toronto. **2 Lake Ontario,** one of the five Great Lakes. *noun.*

on·to (ôn′tü), on to; to a position on: *to throw a ball onto the roof, to get onto a horse, a boat driven onto the rocks. preposition.*

on·ward (ôn′wərd), on; further on; toward the front; forward: *The crowd around the store window began to move onward. An onward movement began. adverb, adjective.*

on·wards (ôn′wərdz), onward. *adverb.*

ooze[1] (üz), to pass out slowly; leak out little by little: *Blood still oozed from the cut. His courage oozed away as he waited. verb,* **ooz·es, oozed, ooz·ing.**

ooze[2] (üz), a soft mud or slime, especially at the bottom of a pond or river or of the ocean. *noun.*

o·pal (ō′pəl), a gem that shows beautiful changes of color. Opals are often milky white with streaks of different colors. *noun.*

opal

o·paque (ō pāk′), **1** not letting light through; not transparent: *A brick wall is opaque.* **2** not shining; dark; dull: *The car's finish had become opaque. adjective.*

o·pen (ō′pən), **1** not shut; not closed; letting anyone or anything in or out: *She climbed in through the open window.* **2** not closed up, fastened, or tied: *an open box. The drawer was open. Your dress is open in the back.* **3** not closed in: *the open sea, an open field, an open car.* **4** ready for customers to enter: *The bank is open from 9 to 3 on Tuesdays.* **5** the open, a an open or clear space; open country; open air. **b** public view or knowledge: *The secret is now out in the open.* **6** unfilled; not taken: *a position still open.* **7** able to be entered, used, shared, or attended by all, or by those mentioned: *The meeting is open to the public. The race is open to ten-year-old girls.* **8** not covered or protected; exposed: *an open fire, an open jar.* **9** not hidden or secret: *open war, an open disregard of rules.* **10** ready to listen to new ideas and judge them fairly; not prejudiced: *She has an open mind.* **11** frank and sincere: *an open heart. Please be open with me.* **12** to make or become open: *Open the window. The door opened.* **13** to have an opening or passage: *This door opens into the dining room.* **14** to spread out or unfold: *to open a book, to open a letter.* **15** to start or set up; establish: *He opened a new store.* **16** to begin: *to open a debate. School opens in September.* 1-4,6-11 *adjective,* 5 *noun,* 12-16 *verb.*

open to, ready to take; willing to consider: *open to suggestions.*

open up, to make or become open; open a way to: *The pioneers who opened up the American West included men, women, and children.*

open air, the outdoors: *Children like to play in the open air.*

o·pen·er (ō′pə nər), **1** something that is used to open closed containers: *Where is the can opener?* **2** the first game of a scheduled series: *Our team won the opener. noun.*

o·pen·heart·ed (ō′pən här′tid), free in expressing one's real thoughts, opinions, and feelings; frank. *adjective.*

o·pen·ing (ō′pə ning), **1** a hole; gap; an open or clear space: *an opening in a wall, an opening in the forest.* **2** the first part; the beginning: *The opening of the story took place in New York.* **3** first; beginning: *the opening words of her speech.* **4** a formal beginning: *The opening of the art exhibit will be at three o'clock.* **5** a job that is open or vacant: *an opening for a teller in a bank.* **6** a favorable chance or opportunity: *I kept waiting for an opening to ask for a new bike.* 1,2,4-6 *noun,* 3 *adjective.*

o·pen·ly (ō′pən lē), without secrecy; frankly: *I discussed my problem openly. adverb.*

op·er·a (op′ər ə), a play that is mostly sung, with costumes, scenery, acting, and music to go with the singing. *noun.*

op·e·rate (op′ə rāt′), **1** to be at work; run: *The machinery operates night and day.* **2** to keep at work; manage: *to operate an elevator. The company operates three factories.* **3** to produce a desired effect: *The medicine operated quickly.* **4** to perform surgery: *The doctor operated on the injured man, removing his damaged lung. verb,* **op·e·rates, op·e·rat·ed, op·e·rat·ing.**

op·e·ra·tion (op′ə rā′shən), **1** a keeping at work or in motion; working: *The operation of an airline needs many people.* **2** the way a thing works: *The operation of this machine is simple.* **3** a treatment of diseases and injuries involving surgery: *Taking out an inflamed appendix is a common operation.* **4** a movement of soldiers, ships, or supplies: *Military and naval operations were carried on in secret. noun.*

in operation, in action or in use: *The motor is now in operation.*

op·e·ra·tor (op′ə rā′tər), a person who operates a machine or other device: *a telephone operator, a computer operator. noun.*

op·e·ret·ta (op′ə ret′ə), a short, amusing opera with some spoken parts. *noun.*

o·pin·ion (ə pin′yən), **1** what one thinks; belief not based on actual knowledge or proof; judgment: *In my opinion, their plan will never succeed.* **2** a judgment of worth; impression: *I have a good opinion of her.* **3** a formal judgment by an expert; professional advice: *He wanted the doctor's opinion about the cause of his headache. noun.*

o·pi·um (ō′pē əm), a powerful drug that causes sleep and eases pain. Opium is made from a kind of poppy. *noun.*

o·pos·sum (ə pos′əm), a small animal that lives in trees and carries its young in a pouch. When it is caught, it becomes limp and appears to be dead. The opossum is common in the southern part of the United States. An opossum is often

opossum
about 2½ feet
(76 centimeters)
long with the tail

called a possum. *noun, plural* **o·pos·sums** or **o·pos·sum.**

op·po·nent (ə pō′nənt), a person who is on the other side in a fight, game, or discussion; person fighting, struggling, or speaking against another: *She defeated her opponent in the election. noun.* [*Opponent* comes from two Latin words meaning "place against."]

op·por·tu·ni·ty (op′ər tü′nə tē *or* op′ər tyü′nə tē), a good chance; favorable time; convenient occasion: *I had an opportunity to earn some money baby-sitting. I have had no opportunity to give him your message. noun, plural* **op·por·tu·ni·ties.**

op·pose (ə pōz′), **1** to be against; be in the way of; act, fight, or struggle against; try to hinder; resist: *Many people opposed building a new highway because of the cost.* **2** to put in contrast: *Night is opposed to day. Love is opposed to hate. verb,* **op·pos·es, op·posed, op·pos·ing.**

op·po·site (op′ə zit), **1** placed against; as different in direction as can be; face to face; back to back: *The house straight across the street is opposite to ours.* **2** as different as can be; just contrary: *Sour is opposite to sweet.* **3** a thing or person as different as can be: *Night is the opposite of day. A saint is the opposite of a sinner.* 1,2 *adjective,* 3 *noun.*

op·po·si·tion (op′ə zish′ən), **1** an action against; resistance: *There was some opposition to the workers' request for higher wages.* **2** contrast: *His views are in opposition to mine.* **3** a political party opposed to the party which is in power. *noun.*

op·press (ə pres′), **1** to govern harshly; keep down unjustly or by cruelty: *The people were oppressed by the invaders.* **2** to weigh down; lie heavily on; burden: *A sense of trouble ahead oppressed her spirits. verb.*

op·pres·sion (ə presh′ən), cruel or unjust treatment: *The oppression of the people by the invaders caused much suffering. noun.*

op·pres·sive (ə pres′iv), **1** hard to bear; burdensome: *The great heat was oppressive.* **2** harsh; severe; unjust: *Oppressive measures were taken to crush the rebellion. adjective.*

op·tic (op′tik), of the eye; of the sense of sight. The **optic nerve** goes from the eye to the brain. *adjective.*

op·ti·cal (op′tə kəl), **1** of the eye or the sense of sight; visual: *an optical illusion. Being nearsighted is an optical defect.* **2** made to assist sight: *Telescopes and microscopes are optical instruments. adjective.*

op·ti·cian (op tish′ən), a maker or seller of eyeglasses and other instruments that assist sight. *noun.*

op·ti·mism (op′tə miz′əm), **1** the tendency to look on the bright side of things: *Her optimism always lifts my spirits.* **2** the belief that everything will turn out for the best: *I questioned his optimism about our school's financial situation. noun.*

op·ti·mis·tic (op′tə mis′tik), **1** inclined to look on the bright side of things: *She is an optimistic person.* **2** hoping for the best: *I am optimistic about the chance of good weather for the trip tomorrow. adjective.*

op·tion·al (op′shə nəl), left to one's choice; not required: *Attendance at the school picnic is optional. adjective.*

op·tom·e·trist (op tom′ə trist), a person skilled in examining the eyes and prescribing eyeglasses. An optometrist is not a doctor but is legally allowed to do such work. *noun.*

or (ôr), **1** The word *or* is used to suggest a choice. It connects words, and sometimes groups of words, of equal importance in a sentence. *You can go or stay. Is it sweet or sour?* **2** *Or* may state the only choice left: *Either eat this or go hungry.* **3** *Or* may state what will happen if the first does not happen: *Hurry, or you will be late.* **4** *Or* may explain what goes before or that two things are the same: *an igloo or Eskimo snow house. We had orchestra, or main floor, seats. conjunction.*

-or, a suffix meaning a person or thing that _____s: *Actor* means *a person that* acts. *Generator* means *a thing that* generates.

OR, Oregon (used with postal Zip Code).

o·ral (ôr′əl), **1** spoken; using speech: *An oral agreement is not enough; we must have a written promise.* **2** of the mouth: *The oral opening in an earthworm is small. adjective.*

o·ral·ly (ôr′ə lē), **1** by spoken words. **2** by the mouth. *adverb.*

o·range (ôr′inj), **1** the round, reddish-yellow, juicy fruit of a tree grown in warm climates. Oranges are good to eat. **2** reddish-yellow. **1** *noun,* **2** *adjective.*

[Oranges were first grown in northern India. The name of the fruit comes from a Persian word.]

o·range·ade (ôr′inj ād′), a drink made of orange juice, sugar, and water. *noun.*

o·rang·ou·tang (ə rang′ə tang′), orangutan. *noun.*

o·rang·u·tan (ə rang′ə tan′), a large ape of the forests of islands off southeast Asia, having very long arms and long, reddish-brown hair. *noun.*

Word History

orangutan *Orangutan* comes from Malay words meaning "man of the woods."

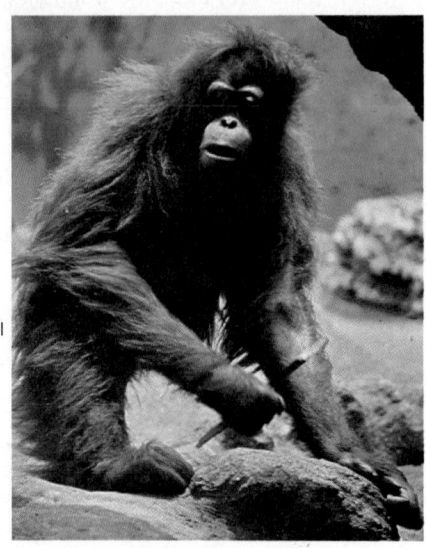

orangutan
about 4½ feet
(1½ meters) tall

---

o·ra·tion (ô rā′shən), a formal public speech delivered on a special occasion. *noun.*

o·ra·tor (ôr′ə tər), **1** a person who makes an oration. **2** a person who can speak very well in public. *noun.*

o·ra·to·ry (ôr′ə tôr′ē), **1** skill in public speaking; fine speaking. **2** the art of public speaking. *noun.*

orb (ôrb), **1** a sphere; globe. **2** a sun, moon, planet, or star. *noun.*

or·bit (ôr′bit), **1** the path of the earth or any one of the planets about the sun. **2** the path of any heavenly body about another heavenly body. **3** the path of an artificial satellite around the earth. **4** to travel around the earth or some other heavenly body in an orbit: *Some artificial satellites can orbit the earth in less than an hour.* **1-3** *noun,* **4** *verb.*

or·chard (ôr′chərd), **1** a piece of ground on which fruit trees are grown. **2** the trees in an orchard: *The orchard should bear a good crop this year. noun.*

or·ches·tra (ôr′kə strə), **1** the musicians playing at a concert, an opera, or a play. **2** the violins, cellos, horns, and other instruments played together by the musicians in an orchestra. **3** the part of a theater just in front of the stage, where the musicians sit to play. **4** the main floor of a theater, especially the part near the front: *Buy two seats in the orchestra. noun.*

or·ches·tral (ôr kes′trəl), of an orchestra; composed for or performed by an orchestra. *adjective.*

a hat	i it	oi oil	ch child	a in about
ā age	ī ice	ou out	ng long	e in taken
ä far	o hot	u cup	sh she	ə = i in pencil
e let	ō open	u̇ put	th thin	o in lemon
ē equal	ô order	ü rule	ŦH then	u in circus
ėr term			zh measure	

orchid (definition 1)

or·chid (ôr′kid), **1** a plant with flowers that often have unusual shapes and colors. **2** light-purple. **1** *noun*, **2** *adjective*.

or·dain (ôr dān′), **1** to order; decide; pass as a law: *The law ordains that all citizens shall have equal rights.* **2** to appoint officially as a minister, priest, or rabbi in a formal ceremony. *verb.*

or·deal (ôr dēl′), a severe test or experience: *I dreaded the ordeal of going to the dentist. noun.*

or·der (ôr′dər), **1** the way one thing follows another: *in order of size, in alphabetical order, to copy them in order.* **2** the condition in which every part or piece is in its right place: *After the movers left, we placed the furniture in order throughout the house.* **3** the state or condition of things in which the law is obeyed and there is no trouble: *to keep order. Order was established after the riot.* **4** a command; telling what to do: *Our parents expect us to obey their orders.* **5** to tell what to do; give an order to; command; bid: *The teacher ordered the class to sit down.* **6** to ask for; give someone an order for: *I ordered fish for dinner. We ordered eggs and milk from the corner grocery.* **7** a spoken or written request for goods: *I gave the grocer an order for two dozen eggs and four loaves of bread.* **8** the goods so requested: *When will you be able to deliver our order?* **9** a society of monks, friars, or nuns: *the order of Saint Francis.* **1-4,7-9** *noun*, **5,6** *verb.*

by order, according to an order given by the proper person: *The bank was closed by order of the governor.*

in order to, as a means to; with a view to; for the purpose of: *She worked hard in order to win the prize.*

out of order, 1 in the wrong arrangement or condition: *He listed the states alphabetically, but California was out of order.* **2** not working right: *My watch is out of order.*

ordered pair, (in mathematics) any two numbers written in a special order with one first and the other second. (2,5) is an ordered pair.

or·der·ly (ôr′dər lē), **1** in order; with regular arrangement, method, or system: *an orderly arrangement of dishes on shelves, an orderly mind.* **2** keeping order; well-behaved or regulated: *an orderly class.* **3** a soldier who attends a superior officer to carry orders. **4** a hospital attendant who keeps things clean and in order. **1,2** *adjective*, **3,4** *noun, plural* **or·der·lies.**

or·di·nance (ôrd′n əns), a rule or law made by authority; decree: *Some cities have ordinances forbidding the use of soft coal. noun.*

or·di·nar·i·ly (ôrd′n er′ə lē), usually; commonly; normally: *We ordinarily go to the movies on Saturday. adverb.*

or·di·nar·y (ôrd′n er′ē), **1** usual; regular; normal: *My ordinary lunch is soup, a sandwich, and milk.* **2** not special; common; everyday; average: *Our neighbors are ordinary people. adjective.*

out of the ordinary, unusual; not regular: *Such a long delay is out of the ordinary.*

ore (ôr), a mineral or rock containing enough of a metal or metals to make mining it profitable: *Gold ore was discovered in California in 1848. noun.*

Oreg., Oregon.

o·reg·a·no (ə reg′ə nō), a sweet-smelling herb whose leaves are used for seasoning food. *noun.*

O·re·gon (ôr′ə gon *or* ôr′ə gən), one of the Pacific states of the United States. *Abbreviation:* Oreg. *or* OR *Capital:* Salem. *noun.*
[*Oregon* probably got its name from the Oregon River, a name once given to the Columbia River.]

or·gan (ôr′gən), **1** a musical instrument that has pipes of different lengths and often several sets of keys. The tones are produced by air being blown through the pipes by a bellows. **2** a similar instrument with one or more sets of keys but without pipes. The tones are produced by electrical devices. **3** any part of an animal or plant that is made up of different kinds of tissues organized to carry out a particular function. The eyes, ears, stomach, heart, and lungs are organs of the body. Stamens and pistils are organs of flowers. *noun.*

or·gan·ic (ôr gan′ik), **1** of, having to do with, or gotten from living things. Decaying grass and animal manure are organic fertilizers. **2** grown by using decaying things that were alive instead of artificial fertilizers: *organic foods. adjective.*

or·gan·ism (ôr′gə niz′əm), a living body; an individual animal, plant, or other living thing. *noun.*

or·gan·ist (ôr′gə nist), a person who plays an organ. *noun.*

or·gan·i·za·tion (ôr′gə nə zā′shən), **1** a group of persons united for some purpose. Churches, clubs, and political parties are organizations. **2** a grouping and arranging parts to form a whole; organizing: *The organization of a big picnic takes time and thought.* **3** the way in which a thing's parts are arranged to work together: *The organization of the human body is very complicated. noun.*

or·gan·ize (ôr′gə nīz), **1** to put into working order; get together and arrange: *Let's organize a volleyball team.* **2** to combine in a company, labor union, or political party: *to organize the miners.* *verb,* **or·gan·iz·es, or·gan·ized, or·gan·iz·ing.**

o·ri·ent (ôr′ē ənt *for 1 and 2;* ôr′ē ent *for 3 and 4*), **1** the east. **2 the Orient,** the East; eastern countries. China and Japan are important nations of the Orient. **3** to place so that it faces in any indicated direction: *The building is oriented north and south.* **4** to adjust to a new situation; bring into the right relationship to surroundings: *I had to orient myself on coming to a new city. The college has a program to orient freshman students.* **1,2** *noun,* **3,4** *verb.*
[*Orient* comes from a Latin word meaning "the place of the rising sun" or "the East." For the Romans, countries in the Orient lay to the east, toward the rising sun. In the United States, we think of the Orient as lying to the west, across the Pacific.]

O·ri·en·tal (ôr′ē en′tl), **1** Eastern; of the Orient: *Oriental customs.* **2** a person born or living in the East, especially the Far East. The Chinese and Japanese are Orientals. **3** a person whose ancestors came from the Far East. **1** *adjective,* **2,3** *noun.*

o·ri·gin (ôr′ə jin), **1** a beginning; starting point; thing from which anything comes: *the origin of the quarrel, the origin of a disease.* **2** parentage; birth: *She is of Mexican origin.* *noun.*

o·rig·i·nal (ə rij′ə nəl), **1** first; earliest: *The Dutch were the original settlers of New York. The hat has been marked down from its original price.* **2** not copied or imitated; new; fresh: *She wrote an original poem.* **3** inventive; able to do, make, or think something new: *Edison had an original mind.* **4** a thing from which another is copied, imitated, or translated: *The original of this picture is in Rome.* **1-3** *adjective,* **4** *noun.*

o·rig·i·nal·i·ty (ə rij′ə nal′ə tē), **1** the ability to do, make, or think up something new: *She is an artist with great originality.* **2** newness; freshness: *I was impressed by the play's originality.* *noun.*

o·rig·i·nal·ly (ə rij′ə nə lē), **1** by origin: *He is originally from Canada.* **2** at first; in the first place: *This house was originally quite small.* **3** in an original manner: *We want this room decorated originally.* *adverb.*

o·rig·i·nate (ə rij′ə nāt), **1** to cause to be; invent: *to originate a new style of painting.* **2** to come into being; begin; arise: *Where did that story originate?* *verb,* **o·rig·i·nates, o·rig·i·nat·ed, o·rig·i·nat·ing.**

o·ri·ole (ôr′ē ōl), an American songbird having yellow-and-black or orange-and-black feathers. *noun.*

or·na·ment (ôr′nə mənt *for 1;* ôr′nə ment *for 2*), **1** something pretty; something to add beauty: *Lace, jewels, vases, and statues are ornaments.* **2** to add beauty to; make more pleasing or attractive; decorate: *The dress was ornamented with beads.* **1** *noun,* **2** *verb.*

or·na·men·tal (ôr′nə men′tl), for ornament; decorative: *There were ornamental tiles around the fireplace. adjective.*

or·nate (ôr nāt′), having much decoration; very ornamented. *adjective.*

ornate
The dancer wore an **ornate** costume.

or·ner·y (ôr′nər ē), very mean; bad-tempered: *an ornery person. adjective,* **or·ner·i·er, or·ner·i·est.**

or·phan (ôr′fən), **1** a child whose parents are dead. **2** to make an orphan of: *The war orphaned the child.* **1** *noun,* **2** *verb.*

or·phan·age (ôr′fə nij), a home for orphans. *noun.*

or·tho·don·tist (ôr′thə don′tist), a dentist whose work is straightening teeth. *noun.*

or·tho·dox (ôr′thə doks), **1** generally accepted; approved by convention; customary: *orthodox ideas about bringing up children.* **2** having generally accepted views or opinions, especially in religion. *adjective.*

os·ten·ta·tious (os′ten tā′shəs), done for display; intended to attract notice: *She wore ostentatious jewels fit for a queen. adjective.*

oriole—8 inches (20 centimeters) long

os·trich (ôs′trich), a large bird of Africa that can run fast but cannot fly. Ostriches have two toes and are the largest of existing birds. They have large feathers or plumes which were used for

ostrich
up to 8 feet
(2½ meters)
tall

a hat	i it	oi oil	ch child	⎧ a in about
ā age	ī ice	ou out	ng long	e in taken
ä far	o hot	u cup	sh she	ə = ⎨ i in pencil
e let	ō open	u̇ put	th thin	o in lemon
ē equal	ô order	ü rule	ᴛʜ then	u in circus
ėr term			zh measure	⎩

decorating hats and fans. *noun, plural*
os·trich·es.

oth·er (uᴛʜ′ər), **1** remaining: *I am home, but the other members of the family are away.* **2** additional or further: *I have no other place to go.* **3** not the same as one or more already mentioned: *Come some other day.* **4** different: *Do you have a color other than red?* **5** the other one; not the same ones: *Each praises the other.* **6** another person or thing: *There are others to consider.* **7** in any different way; otherwise: *I could not do other than I did.* 1-4 *adjective,* 5,6 *pronoun,* 7 *adverb.*
every other, every second; alternate: *We have spelling every other day.*
the other day or **the other night,** recently.

oth·er·wise (uᴛʜ′ər wīz′), **1** in a different way; differently: *I could not act otherwise.* **2** different: *It might have been otherwise.* **3** in other ways: *It is windy, but otherwise a nice day.* **4** or else; if not: *Come at once; otherwise you will be too late.* 1,3 *adverb,* 2 *adjective,* 4 *conjunction.*

ot·ter (ot′ər), **1** an animal with thick, glossy, brown fur and webbed toes with claws. Otters live near water and are good swimmers. **2** its short, thick, glossy, brown fur. *noun, plural* **ot·ters** or **ot·ter.**

otter (definition 1)—up to 4 feet (1 meter) long with the tail

ouch (ouch), an exclamation expressing sudden pain. *interjection.*

ought (ôt), **1** to have a duty; be obliged: *You ought to obey your parents.* **2** to be right or

suitable: *Cruelty ought not to be allowed.* **3** to be wise: *I ought to go before it rains.* **4** to be expected: *At your age you ought to know better.* **5** to be very likely: *It ought to be a fine day tomorrow. verb.*

ounce (ouns), **1** a unit of weight equal to 1/16 of a pound. **2** a unit for measuring liquids; fluid ounce. 16 ounces = 1 pint. **3** a little bit; very small amount: *An ounce of prevention is worth a pound of cure. noun.*

our (our), of us; belonging to us: *Our classes were interesting. We need our coats now. adjective.*

ours (ourz), the one or ones belonging to us: *This garden is ours. Ours is a large house. pronoun.*

our·selves (our selvz′), **1** *Ourselves* is used to make a statement stronger. *We ourselves will do the work.* **2** *Ourselves* is used instead of *we* or *us* in cases like: *We cook for ourselves. We help ourselves.* **3** our real or true selves: *We were not ourselves after the accident. pronoun plural.*

-ous, a suffix meaning full of _____: *Joyous* means *full of* joy.

oust (oust), to force out; drive out: *The sparrows have ousted the bluebirds from their nest. verb.*

out (out), **1** away; forth: *The water will rush out. Spread the rug out.* **2** not in or at a usual place, as one's home or place of work: *My mother is out just now.* **3** (in baseball) no longer at bat or on base: *The outfielder caught the fly and the batter was out.* **4** (in baseball) a being out or putting out: *A team's turn at bat lasts until three outs are made.* **5** not in use, action, control, or fashion: *The fire is out. The election results show that our present mayor is out. That style is out this year.* **6** through to the outside: *She went out the door.* **7** into the open; made public; made known; into being; so as to be seen: *The secret is out now. The new book will be out next month. Many flowers were coming out.* **8** to or at an end: *Let them fight it out.* **9** aloud; plainly: *Speak out so that all can hear.* **10** completely: *to fit out a boat, to clean out a closet.* **11** to others: *to let out rooms. Give out the books.* **12** from a number; from among others: *Pick out an apple for me. She picked out a new coat.* **13** not possible; not to be considered: *I have no money, so going to the movies is out.* 1,2,7-12 *adverb,* 3,5,13 *adjective,* 4 *noun,* 6 *preposition.*
out of, 1 from within: *He came out of the house.* **2** not within: *He is out of town.* **3** away from; beyond: *The airplane was soon out of sight. This style went out of fashion.* **4** without: *I am out of work. We are out of coffee.* **5** from: *My dress is made out of silk.* **6** from among: *three out of four people. We picked our puppy out of that litter.* **7** because of: *I went only out of curiosity.*

O

out-and-out (out′n out′), thorough; complete: *an out-and-out defeat. adjective.*

out·board mo·tor (out′bôrd′ mō′tər), a small motor attached to the stern of a boat or canoe.

out·break (out′brāk′), **1** a breaking out: *an outbreak of flu, outbreaks of anger.* **2** a riot; public disturbance: *The outbreak ended when the police arrived. noun.*

out·build·ing (out′bil′ding), a shed or building built against or near a main building: *Barns are outbuildings on a farm. noun.*

out·burst (out′bėrst′), a bursting forth: *an outburst of laughter, an outburst of anger. noun.*

out·cast (out′kast′), a person who is driven away from home and friends: *The criminal was an outcast. noun.*

out·come (out′kum′), a result; consequence: *the outcome of a race. noun.*

out·cry (out′krī′), **1** a crying out; sudden cry or scream. **2** a strong expression of disapproval; protest: *The raising of taxes caused a public outcry. noun, plural* **out·cries.**

out·dat·ed (out dā′tid), out-of-date; old-fashioned: *a person with outdated ideas. adjective.*

out·did (out did′). See **outdo.** *She outdid all the other diving contestants. verb.*

out·dis·tance (out dis′təns), to leave behind: *The winner outdistanced all the other runners in the race. verb,* **out·dis·tanc·es, out·dis·tanced, out·dis·tanc·ing.**

out·do (out dü′), to do more or better than; surpass: *She's such a good tennis player that I know I won't be able to outdo her. verb,* **out·does, out·did, out·done, out·do·ing.**

out·done (out dun′). See **outdo.** *He has outdone his previous record for the race. verb.*

out·door (out′dôr′), done, used, or living outdoors: *Tag is an outdoor game. adjective.*

out·doors (out′dôrz′), **1** out in the open air; not indoors or in the house: *Let's go outdoors to play.* **2** the world outside of houses; the open air: *We must protect the wildlife of the great outdoors.* **1** *adverb,* **2** *noun.*

out·er (ou′tər), farther out; on the outside: *Shingles are used as an outer covering for many roofs. adjective.*

out·er·most (ou′tər mōst), farthest out: *They sailed off to the outermost island. adjective.*

outer space, the space beyond the earth's atmosphere: *The moon is in outer space.*

out·field (out′fēld′), **1** the part of the baseball field beyond the diamond or infield. **2** the three players in the outfield. *noun.*

out·field·er (out′fēl′dər), a baseball player who plays in the outfield. *noun.*

out·fit (out′fit), **1** all the articles necessary for any undertaking or purpose: *the outfit for a camping trip.* **2** a set of clothes that match or go well together: *That jacket and dress make a lovely outfit.* **3** to furnish with everything necessary for any purpose; equip: *She outfitted herself for camp.* **4** a group working together, such as a group of soldiers: *His father and mine were in the same outfit during the war.* **1,2,4** *noun,* **3** *verb,* **out·fits, out·fit·ted, out·fit·ting.**

out·go·ing (out′gō′ing), **1** outward bound; departing: *outgoing steamships.* **2** friendly and helpful to others: *An outgoing person can usually make friends. adjective.*

out·grew (out grü′). See **outgrow.** *He used to stutter, but he outgrew it. verb.*

out·grow (out grō′), **1** to grow too large for: *to outgrow one's clothes.* **2** to grow beyond or away from; get rid of by growing older: *to outgrow early friends, to outgrow a babyish habit.* **3** to grow faster or taller than: *By the time he was ten, he had outgrown his older brother. verb,* **out·grows, out·grew, out·grown, out·grow·ing.**

out·grown (out grōn′). See **outgrow.** *My last year's clothes are now outgrown. verb.*

out·growth (out′grōth′), a natural development, product, or result: *This big store is an outgrowth of a little shop. noun.*

out·ing (ou′ting), a short pleasure trip; walk or drive; holiday spent outdoors away from home: *On Sunday the family went on an outing to the beach. noun.*

out·land·ish (out lan′dish), not familiar; strange or ridiculous; odd: *The singer wore an outlandish purple wig. adjective.*

out·last (out last′), to last longer than. *verb.*

out·law (out′lô′), **1** a lawless person; criminal. **2** to make or declare unlawful: *A group of nations agreed to outlaw war.* **1** *noun,* **2** *verb.*

out·lay (out′lā′), **1** an expense; laying out money; spending: *a large outlay for clothing.* **2** the amount spent: *an outlay of eleven dollars. noun.*

out·let (out′let), **1** a means or place of letting out or getting out; a way out; opening; exit: *the outlet of a lake, an outlet for one's energies.* **2** a place in a wall for inserting an electric plug. *noun.*

out·line (out′līn′), **1** a line that shows the shape of an object: *The outline of Italy suggests a boot. We saw the outlines of the mountains against the evening sky.* **2** a drawing or style of drawing that gives only outer lines: *Make an outline of the scene before you paint it.* **3** to draw the outer line of anything: *Outline a map of America.* **4** a brief plan; rough draft: *Make an outline before trying to write a composition. The teacher gave a brief outline of the work planned for the term.* **5** to give a plan of; sketch: *She outlined their trip abroad.* **1,2,4** *noun,* **3,5** *verb,* **out·lines, out·lined, out·lin·ing.**

out·live (out liv′), to live longer than; last longer than; survive; outlast: *She outlived her older sister. The idea was good once, but it has outlived its usefulness. verb,* **out·lives, out·lived, out·liv·ing.**

out·look (out′lůk′), **1** what one sees on looking out; view: *The room has a pleasant outlook.* **2** what seems likely to happen; prospect: *The outlook for our picnic is bad, for it looks as if it's going to rain.* **3** a way of thinking about things; attitude of mind; point of view: *a gloomy outlook on life. noun.*

out·ly·ing (out′lī′ing), lying outside the

boundary; far from the center; remote: *We live in an outlying suburb of the city.* adjective.

out·mod·ed (out mō′did), out-of-date: *I had no interest in their outmoded ideas.* adjective.

out·num·ber (out num′bər), to be more than; exceed in number: *They outnumbered us three to one.* verb.

out-of-date (out′əv dāt′), old-fashioned; not in present use: *A horse and buggy is an out-of-date means of traveling.* adjective.

out-of-door (out′əv dôr′), outdoor. adjective.

out-of-doors (out′əv dôrz′), 1 outdoor. 2 outdoors. 1 adjective, 2 noun, adverb.

out·post (out′pōst′), 1 a guard, or small number of soldiers, placed at some distance from an army or camp, to prevent surprise. 2 the place where they are stationed. noun.

out·put (out′pùt′), 1 an amount produced; product or yield: *the daily output of automobiles.* 2 a putting forth: *It will take a great output of energy for us to do such a difficult job well.* 3 any information that is produced by a computer. 4 to produce information: *Can you have the computer output these answers as a graph?* 1-3 noun, 4 verb, **out·puts, out·put, out·put·ting.**

out·rage (out′rāj), 1 an act showing no regard for the rights or feelings of others; very offensive act; shameful act of violence; offense; insult: *Setting the house on fire was an outrage.* 2 to offend greatly; insult; do violence to: *The British government outraged the colonists by taxing them unfairly.* 1 noun, 2 verb, **out·rag·es, out·raged, out·rag·ing.**

out·ra·geous (out rā′jəs), shocking; very bad or insulting: *outrageous language.* adjective.

out·ran (out ran′). See **outrun**. *He outran me easily.* verb.

out·rig·ger (out′rig′ər), a framework ending in a float, extending outward from the side of a light boat or canoe to keep it from turning over. noun.

outrigger

out·right (out′rīt′), 1 altogether; entirely; not gradually: *We paid for our car outright.* 2 openly; without restraint: *We laughed outright.* 3 complete; total; absolute: *an outright criminal, an outright refusal.* 1,2 adverb, 3 adjective.

out·run (out run′), to run faster than: *She can outrun her older sister.* verb, **out·runs, out·ran, out·run, out·run·ning.**

a hat	i it	oi oil	ch child	⎧ a in about
ā age	ī ice	ou out	ng long	⎪ e in taken
ä far	o hot	u cup	sh she	ə = ⎨ i in pencil
e let	ō open	ù put	th thin	⎪ o in lemon
ē equal	ô order	ü rule	ᴛʜ then	⎩ u in circus
ėr term			zh measure	

out·side (out′sīd′), 1 the side or surface that is out; outer part: *to polish the outside of a car, the outside of a house.* 2 on the outside; of or nearer the outside; outer: *The outside covering of a nut is called the hull.* 3 on or to the outside; outdoors: *Run outside and play.* 4 out of; beyond the limits of: *Stay outside the house. That is outside my plans.* 5 barely possible; very slight: *There is an outside chance that our team might win.* 6 not belonging to a certain group; from another place: *We may need some outside help on this project.* 1 noun, 2,5,6 adjective, 3 adverb, 4 preposition.

at the outside, at the utmost limit: *I can do it in a week, at the outside.*

out·sid·er (out′sī′dər), a person not belonging to a particular group, set, company, party, or district. noun.

out·skirts (out′skėrts′), the outer parts or edges of a town or district; outlying parts: *They have a farm on the outskirts of town.* noun plural.

out·smart (out smärt′), to be more clever than; get the better of: *I outsmarted everyone and won the game.* verb.

out·spo·ken (out′spō′kən), frank; not reserved: *Your own family is likely to be outspoken in its remarks about you.* adjective.

out·spread (out′spred′ for 1; out spred′ for 2), 1 spread out; extended: *an eagle with outspread wings.* 2 to spread out; extend. 1 adjective, 2 verb, **out·spreads, out·spread, out·spread·ing.**

out·stand·ing (out stan′ding), 1 standing out from others; well-known; important: *an outstanding student.* 2 unpaid: *outstanding debts.* adjective.

out·stretched (out′strecht′), stretched out; extended: *He welcomed his old friend with outstretched arms.* adjective.

out·ward (out′wərd), 1 going toward the outside; turned toward the outside: *an outward motion. She gave one outward glance.* 2 on or toward the outside: *The coat was turned with the lining outward.* 3 able to be seen; plain to see; on the surface: *Her outward behavior was calm and quiet.* 1,3 adjective, 2 adverb.

out·ward·ly (out′wərd lē), 1 on the outside or outer surface. 2 in appearance: *Though scared, the boy remained outwardly calm.* adverb.

out·wards (out′wərdz), outward. adverb.

out·weigh (out wā′), 1 to weigh more than: *He outweighs me by ten pounds.* 2 to exceed in value, importance, or influence: *The advantages of the plan outweigh its disadvantages.* verb.

out·wit (out wit′), to get the better of; be too clever for: *She usually outwits me and wins at checkers.* verb, **out·wits, out·wit·ted, out·wit·ting.**

O

out·worn (out′wôrn′), **1** worn out: *outworn clothes.* **2** out-of-date; outgrown: *outworn ideas. adjective.*

o·val (ō′vəl), **1** shaped like an egg. **2** shaped like an ellipse. **3** something having an oval shape. **1,2** *adjective,* **3** *noun.*

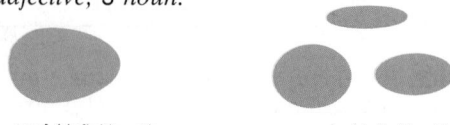

oval (definition 1)   **ovals** (definition 2)

o·var·y (ō′vər ē), **1** the part of a female animal in which eggs are produced. **2** the part of a plant enclosing the young seeds. *noun, plural* **o·var·ies.**

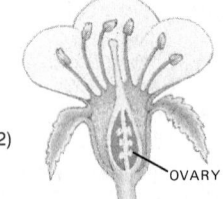

ovary (definition 2)

OVARY

ov·en (uv′ən), **1** an enclosed space usually in a stove, for baking, roasting, and sometimes broiling food. **2** a small furnace for heating or drying pottery. *noun.*

o·ver (ō′vər), **1** above: *the sky over our heads. We have a captain over us.* **2** above and to the other side of; across: *to leap over a wall. Can you climb over that hill?* **3** across a space or distance: *Come over to my house.* **4** down; out and down from an edge or from an upright position: *If you go too near the edge, you may fall over.* **5** out and down from; down from the edge of: *The ball rolled over the side of the porch.* **6** so as to cover the surface: *The river has frozen over.* **7** about or upon, so as to cover: *Spread the canvas over the new cement.* **8** at all or various places on; on: *A smile came over her face. Farms were scattered over the valley.* **9** here and there on or in; round about; all through: *to travel over the United States. I went over my notes before the test.* **10** from beginning to end; at some length: *to read a newspaper over.* **11** again: *I had to write my paper over.* **12** during: *We were out of town over the weekend.* **13** at an end: *The play is over.* **14** about; concerning: *He is troubled over his health. I was upset over our argument.* **15** more than; beyond: *It cost over ten dollars.* **16** too; more; besides: *I ate two apples and had one left over.* **17** so that the other side is up or showing; upside down: *Turn over a page.* **18** more than: *Over fifty persons came to the party.* **19** in a place for a period of time: *We stayed over in New York City until Monday.* **20** at one's home: *Can they sleep over?* **1,2,5,7-9,12,14,15** *preposition,* **1,3,4,6,10,11,16-20** *adverb,* **13** *adjective.*

over again, once more: *Let's do that over again.*

over and over, again and again: *Practice the song over and over until you do it right.*

over-, a prefix meaning: **1** above: *Overhead* means *above* the head. **2** across: *Overseas* means *across* the seas. **3** too; too much; too long: *Overdo* means to do *too much.* **4** above normal; extra: *Overtime* means *extra* time.

o·ver·all (ō′vər ôl′ for 1 and 2; ō′vər ôl′ for 3), **1** from one end to the other: *I asked the clerk to give me an overall measurement of the rug.* **2** including everything: *The carpenter gave us an overall estimate of the cost of repairing the garage.* **3** generally; considering everything: *Overall, it was a very exciting motion picture.* **1,2** *adjective,* **3** *adverb.*

o·ver·alls (ō′vər ôlz′), loose trousers with a piece covering the chest. Overalls are usually worn over clothes to keep them clean. *noun plural.*

o·ver·ate (ō′vər āt′). See **overeat.** *I have a stomach ache because I overate. verb.*

o·ver·bear·ing (ō′vər ber′ing or ō′vər bar′ing), inclined to dictate; forcing others to one's own will; masterful; domineering: *We found it hard to like our overbearing new neighbors. adjective.*

o·ver·board (ō′vər bôrd′), from a ship or boat into the water: *to fall overboard. adverb.*

o·ver·bur·den (ō′vər bėrd′n), to overload; load with too great a burden: *I felt overburdened by so much homework. verb.*

o·ver·came (ō′vər kām′). See **overcome.** *I finally overcame my fear. verb.*

o·ver·cast (ō′vər kast′), cloudy; dark; gloomy: *The sky was overcast before the storm. adjective.*

o·ver·charge (ō′vər chärj′), to charge too high a price: *The grocer overcharged you for the eggs. verb,* **o·ver·charg·es, o·ver·charged, o·ver·charg·ing.**

o·ver·coat (ō′vər kōt′), a heavy coat worn over the regular clothing for warmth in cold weather. *noun.*

o·ver·come (ō′vər kum′), **1** to get the better of; win the victory over; conquer; defeat: *to overcome an enemy, to overcome difficulties, to overcome a fault.* **2** to make weak or helpless: *The child was overcome by weariness and fell asleep. verb,* **o·ver·comes, o·ver·came, o·ver·come, o·ver·com·ing.**

o·ver·crowd (ō′vər kroud′), to crowd too much; put in too much or too many: *The bus was overcrowded. verb.*

o·ver·did (ō′vər did′). See **overdo.** *She overdid her exercises and became very tired. verb.*

o·ver·do (ō′vər dü′), **1** to do too much: *When getting over an illness you mustn't overdo.* **2** to cook too much: *The vegetables were overdone. verb,* **o·ver·does, o·ver·did, o·ver·done, o·ver·do·ing.**

o·ver·done (ō′vər dun′). See **overdo.** *verb.*

o·ver·dose (ō′vər dōs′), too big a dose: *You must be careful not to take an overdose of medicine. noun.*

o·ver·dress (ō′vər dres′), to wear clothes that are too fancy or formal: *My sister hopes that she didn't overdress for the party. verb.*

o·ver·due (ō′vər dü′ or ō′vər dyü′), more than

due; due some time ago but not yet arrived or paid: *The train is overdue. This bill is overdue.* *adjective.*

o·ver·eat (ō′vər ēt′), to eat too much. *verb,* **o·ver·eats, o·ver·ate, o·ver·eat·en, o·ver·eat·ing.**

o·ver·eat·en (ō′vər ēt′n). See **overeat.** *Nearly everyone has overeaten at the picnic. verb.*

o·ver·flow (ō′vər flō′ for 1-5; ō′vər flō′ for 6), **1** to flow over or beyond the limits: *Rivers often overflow in the spring.* **2** to cover; flood: *The river overflowed my garden.* **3** to have the contents flowing over: *My cup is overflowing.* **4** to flow over the top of: *Stop! The milk is overflowing the cup.* **5** to extend out beyond; be too many for: *The crowd overflowed the small room and filled the hall.* **6** an overflowing; excess: *The overflow from the glass ran onto the table.* 1-5 *verb,* **o·ver·flows, o·ver·flowed, o·ver·flown** (ō′vər flōn′), **o·ver·flow·ing;** 6 *noun.*

o·ver·grew (ō′vər grü′). See **overgrow.** *Vines overgrew the wall. verb.*

o·ver·grow (ō′vər grō′), **1** to grow over: *The wall is overgrown with vines.* **2** to grow too fast; become too big. *verb,* **o·ver·grows, o·ver·grew, o·ver·grown, o·ver·grow·ing.**

o·ver·grown (ō′vər grōn′), **1** grown too big or too fast: *an overgrown child.* **2** See **overgrow.** *The vines have overgrown the wall.* 1 *adjective,* 2 *verb.*

o·ver·hand (ō′vər hand′), with the hand raised above the shoulder: *an overhand throw, to pitch overhand. adjective, adverb.*

overhand

o·ver·hang (ō′vər hang′), to hang over; stick out over: *Trees overhang the street to form an arch of branches. verb,* **o·ver·hangs, o·ver·hung, o·ver·hang·ing.**

o·ver·haul (ō′vər hôl′ for 1 and 2; ō′vər hôl′ for 3), **1** to examine completely so as to make repairs or changes that are needed: *Once a year we overhaul our boat.* **2** to gain upon; overtake: *An automobile can overhaul any horse.* **3** an overhauling: *We give our boat an annual overhaul.* 1,2 *verb,* 3 *noun.*

o·ver·head (ō′vər hed′ for 1; ō′vər hed′ for 2 and 3), **1** over the head; on high; above: *the stars overhead.* **2** placed above; placed high up: *overhead wires.* **3** the general expenses of running a business, such as rent, lighting, heating, taxes, and repairs. 1 *adverb,* 2 *adjective,* 3 *noun.*

o·ver·hear (ō′vər hir′), to hear when one is not

meant to hear: *They spoke so loud that I could not help overhearing what they said. verb,* **o·ver·hears, o·ver·heard, o·ver·hear·ing.**

o·ver·heard (ō′vər hèrd′). See **overhear.** *I overheard what you told them. verb.*

o·ver·heat (ō′vər hēt′), to make or become too hot, especially beyond the point of safety or comfort: *My car overheated when we drove through the mountains. verb.*

o·ver·hung (ō′vər hung′ for 1; ō′vər hung′ for 2), **1** hung from above: *an overhung door.* **2** See **overhang.** *A big awning overhung the sidewalk.* 1 *adjective,* 2 *verb.*

o·ver·joyed (ō′vər joid′), very joyful; filled with joy; delighted. *adjective.*

o·ver·laid (ō′vər lād′). See **overlay.** *The workmen overlaid the dome with gold. verb.*

o·ver·land (ō′vər land′), on land; by land: *to travel overland from Maine to Texas, an overland route. adverb, adjective.*

o·ver·lap (ō′vər lap′), to lap over; partly cover and extend beyond: *Shingles are laid to overlap each other. verb,* **o·ver·laps, o·ver·lapped, o·ver·lap·ping.**

o·ver·lay (ō′vər lā′ for 1; ō′vər lā′ for 2), **1** to lay or place one thing over or upon another. **2** something laid over something else; covering; ornamental layer: *an overlay of gold on a statue.* 1 *verb,* **o·ver·lays, o·ver·laid, o·ver·lay·ing;** 2 *noun.*

o·ver·load (ō′vər lōd′ for 1; ō′vər lōd′ for 2), **1** to load too heavily: *to overload a boat.* **2** too great a load: *The overload of electric current blew the fuse.* 1 *verb,* 2 *noun.*

o·ver·look (ō′vər lùk′), **1** to fail to see: *Here are some letters which you overlooked.* **2** to pay no attention to; excuse: *I will overlook your bad behavior this time.* **3** to have a view of from above; be higher than: *This high window overlooks half the city. verb.*

o·ver·lord (ō′vər lôrd′), a person who is lord over another lord or other lords: *The duke was the overlord of the barons and knights. noun.*

o·ver·ly (ō′vər lē), too; too much; excessively: *Our city is overly populated. adverb.*

o·ver·night (ō′vər nīt′ for 1 and 4; ō′vər nīt′ for 2 and 3), **1** during the night: *to stay overnight with friends.* **2** done or occurring during the night: *an overnight stop.* **3** for the night: *An overnight bag contains articles needed for one night's stay.* **4** immediately; at once; in a very short time: *Change will not come overnight.* 1,4 *adverb,* 2,3 *adjective.*

o·ver·pass (ō′vər pas′), a bridge over a road, railroad, or canal. *noun, plural* **o·ver·pass·es.**

a hat	i it	oi oil	ch child	⎧ a in about
ā age	ī ice	ou out	ng long	e in taken
ä far	o hot	u cup	sh she	ə = ⎨ i in pencil
e let	ō open	ù put	th thin	o in lemon
ē equal	ô order	ü rule	ŦH then	⎩ u in circus
ėr term			zh measure	

437

o·ver·pow·er (ō′vər pou′ər), **1** to conquer; overcome; overwhelm: *to overpower an enemy. Several people were overpowered by the heat.* **2** to be much greater or stronger than: *I tried to remain calm, but my anger overpowered every other feeling. verb.*

o·ver·ran (ō′vər ran′). See **overrun.** *verb.*

o·ver·rate (ō′vər rāt′), to rate or estimate too highly: *I overrated my strength and had to ask for help. verb,* **o·ver·rates, o·ver·rat·ed, o·ver·rat·ing.**

o·ver·rule (ō′vər rül′), to rule or decide against an argument, objection, or the like; set aside: *The president overruled my plan. verb,* **o·ver·rules, o·ver·ruled, o·ver·rul·ing.**

o·ver·run (ō′vər run′), **1** to spread over and spoil or harm in some way: *Weeds had overrun the old garden. Enemy troops overran the fort.* **2** to spread over: *Vines overran the wall.* **3** to run or go beyond; exceed: *The speaker overran the time set for her. verb,* **o·ver·runs, o·ver·ran, o·ver·run, o·ver·run·ning.**

o·ver·saw (ō′vər sô′). See **oversee.** *verb.*

o·ver·seas (ō′vər sēz′ *for 1;* ō′vər sēz′ *for 2 and 3*), **1** across the sea; beyond the sea; abroad: *to travel overseas.* **2** done, used, or serving overseas: *overseas military service.* **3** of countries across the sea; foreign: *overseas trade.* **1** *adverb,* **2,3** *adjective.*

o·ver·see (ō′vər sē′), to look after and direct work or workers; manage; supervise: *to oversee a factory. verb,* **o·ver·sees, o·ver·saw, o·ver·seen, o·ver·see·ing.**

o·ver·seen (ō′vər sēn′). See **oversee.** *verb.*

o·ver·se·er (ō′vər sē′ər), a person who oversees others or their work. *noun.*

o·ver·shad·ow (ō′vər shad′ō), **1** to be more important than: *Preparations for the school play soon overshadowed other student activities.* **2** to cast a shadow over: *Storm clouds suddenly overshadowed the valley. verb.*

o·ver·shoe (ō′vər shü′), a waterproof shoe or boot, often made of rubber, worn over another shoe to keep the foot dry and warm. *noun.*

o·ver·shoot (ō′vər shüt′), **1** to shoot over: *to overshoot a target.* **2** to go beyond or past: *The airplane overshot the runway. verb,* **o·ver·shoots, o·ver·shot, o·ver·shoot·ing.**

o·ver·shot (ō′vər shot′). See **overshoot.** *verb.*

o·ver·sight (ō′vər sīt′), a failure to notice or think of something: *Through an oversight, the kitten got no supper last night. noun.*

o·ver·sized (ō′vər sīzd′), too big; larger than the usual or proper size: *This oversized book is hard to carry. adjective.*

o·ver·sleep (ō′vər slēp′), to sleep beyond a certain hour; sleep too long. *verb,* **o·ver·sleeps, o·ver·slept, o·ver·sleep·ing.**

o·ver·slept (ō′vər slept′). See **oversleep.** *I overslept and missed the bus. verb.*

o·ver·spread (ō′vər spred′), to spread over: *Ivy overspread the cottage. verb,* **o·ver·spreads, o·ver·spread, o·ver·spread·ing.**

o·ver·stay (ō′vər stā′), to stay beyond the time of: *Don't overstay your welcome. verb.*

o·ver·step (ō′vər step′), to go beyond; exceed: *I'm afraid I've overstepped the rules. verb,* **o·ver·steps, o·ver·stepped, o·ver·step·ping.**

o·ver·take (ō′vər tāk′), **1** to catch up with: *The blue car overtook ours.* **2** to come upon suddenly: *A storm had overtaken the children. verb,* **o·ver·takes, o·ver·took, o·ver·tak·en, o·ver·tak·ing.**

o·ver·tak·en (ō′vər tā′kən). See **overtake.** *verb.*

o·ver·threw (ō′vər thrü′). See **overthrow.** *verb.*

o·ver·throw (ō′vər thrō′ *for 1;* ō′vər thrō′ *for 2*), **1** to take away the power of; defeat: *The people overthrew the government.* **2** to defeat; upset: *the overthrow of the government.* **1** *verb,* **o·ver·throws, o·ver·threw, o·ver·thrown, o·ver·throw·ing; 2** *noun.*

o·ver·thrown (ō′vər thrōn′). See **overthrow.** *The government was overthrown. verb.*

o·ver·time (ō′vər tīm′), **1** extra time; time beyond the regular hours: *I was paid for the overtime I worked.* **2** beyond the regular hours: *They worked overtime.* **1** *noun,* **2** *adverb.*

o·ver·tone (ō′vər tōn′), a fainter and higher musical tone heard along with the main tone. *noun.*

o·ver·took (ō′vər tůk′). See **overtake.** *verb.*

o·ver·ture (ō′vər chər), **1** an offer; proposal: *The enemy is making overtures for peace.* **2** a musical composition played by the orchestra as an introduction to an opera or other long musical composition. *noun.*

o·ver·turn (ō′vər tern′), **1** to turn upside down; upset: *The boat overturned.* **2** to make fall down; overthrow; defeat; destroy the power of: *The rebels overturned the government. verb.*

o·ver·weight (ō′vər wāt′), having too much weight: *I am a little overweight for my height. adjective.*

o·ver·whelm (ō′vər hwelm′), to crush; overcome completely. *verb.*

overwhelm
He was **overwhelmed** by the fury of her attack.

o·ver·work (ō′vər werk′ *for 1*; ō′vər werk′ *for 2*), **1** too much or too hard work: *exhausted from overwork.* **2** to work too hard or too long: *Don't overwork in this hot weather.* 1 *noun,* 2 *verb.*

owe (ō), **1** to have to pay; be in debt to: *I owe the grocer a dollar.* **2** to be in debt: *I still owe for my share of the expenses.* **3** to have to give: *I really think you owe me an apology for what you just said.* **4** to be obliged or indebted for: *We owe a great deal to our parents. verb,* **owes, owed, ow·ing.**

ow·ing (ō′ing), due; owed: *to pay what is owing. adjective.*

owing to, on account of; because of: *Owing to the bad weather, we canceled our trip.*

owl (oul), a bird with a big head, big eyes, and a short, hooked beak. Owls hunt mice and small birds at night. Some kinds have tufts of feathers on their heads called "horns" or "ears." You can tell an owl by the hoot it makes. *noun.*

owl·et (ou′lit), **1** a young owl. **2** a small owl. *noun.*

own (ōn), **1** to have; possess: *I own many books.* **2** of oneself; belonging to oneself or itself: *This is my own book.* **3** to admit; confess: *I own you are right. I own to being afraid.* 1,3 *verb,* 2 *adjective.*

of one's own, belonging to oneself: *You have a good mind of your own.*

on one's own, not ruled or directed by someone else: *As a young man, he traveled about the world on his own.*

own up, to confess fully: *to own up to a crime.*

own·er (ō′nər), the one who owns: *Who is the owner of this dog? noun.*

own·er·ship (ō′nər ship), the state of being an owner; the possessing of something; right of possession: *She claimed ownership of the abandoned car. noun.*

ox (oks), the full-grown male of cattle that cannot father young and is used to pull loads or for beef. *noun, plural* **ox·en.**

ox·cart (oks′kärt′), a cart drawn by oxen. *noun.*

oxcart

a hat	**i** it	**oi** oil	**ch** child	⎧ a in about
ā age	**ī** ice	**ou** out	**ng** long	e in taken
ä far	**o** hot	**u** cup	**sh** she	ə = ⎨ i in pencil
e let	**ō** open	**u̇** put	**th** thin	o in lemon
ē equal	**ô** order	**ü** rule	**ᴛʜ** then	⎩ u in circus
ėr term			**zh** measure	

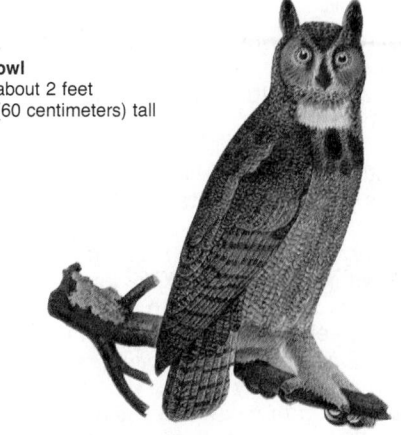

owl
about 2 feet
(60 centimeters) tall

ox·en (ok′sən), more than one ox. *noun plural.*
ox·ford (ok′sfərd), a kind of low shoe. *noun.*
[The shoe was named for Oxford, a city in England.]

oxfords

ox·i·dize (ok′sə dīz), to combine with oxygen. When a substance burns or rusts, it oxidizes. *verb,* **ox·i·diz·es, ox·i·dized, ox·i·diz·ing.**

ox·y·gen (ok′sə jən), a gas without color, taste, or odor that forms about one fifth of the air and about one third of water. Oxygen is a chemical element. Animals and plants cannot live without oxygen. Fire will not burn without oxygen. *noun.*

oys·ter (oi′stər), a shellfish with a rough, irregular shell in two halves. Oysters are much used as food. They are found in shallow water along seacoasts. Some kinds produce pearls inside them. *noun.*

oz., ounce. *plural* **oz.** or **ozs.**

o·zone (ō′zōn), a form of oxygen with a sharp smell, produced by electricity and present in the air especially after a thunderstorm. Ozone is a poisonous gas often found in smog. *noun.*

O

P p

P or **p** (pē), the 16th letter of the English alphabet. *noun, plural* **P's** or **p's.**

mind one's P's and Q's, to be careful about what one says or does.

p., page.

pa (pä), papa; father; daddy. *noun.*

PA, Pennsylvania (used with postal Zip Code).

Pa., Pennsylvania.

pace (pās), **1** a step: *He took three paces into the room.* **2** to walk with regular steps: *The tiger paced back and forth in its cage.* **3** the length of a step in walking; about 2½ feet or three quarters of a meter: *There were perhaps ten paces between me and the bear.* **4** to measure by paces: *We paced off the distance and found it to be 69 paces.* **5** a way of stepping. The walk, trot, and gallop are some of the paces of the horse. **6** a rate; speed: *to walk at a fast pace.* 1,3,5,6 *noun,* 2,4 *verb,* **pac·es, paced, pac·ing.**

keep pace with, to keep up with; go as fast as: *They walked so fast I couldn't keep pace with them.*

set the pace, 1 to set a rate of speed for others to keep up with. **2** to be an example or model for others to follow.

pa·cif·ic (pə sif′ik), peaceful: *pacific weather. The Quakers are a pacific people. adjective.*

Pa·cif·ic (pə sif′ik), **1** an ocean west of North and South America. It extends to Asia and Australia. **2** of, on, or near the Pacific Ocean: *The Pacific coast of the United States has beautiful scenery.* 1 *noun,* 2 *adjective.*

pac·i·fy (pas′ə fī), **1** to make calm; quiet down; give peace to: *Can't you pacify that screaming baby? We tried to pacify our angry neighbor.* **2** to bring under control; control by force: *Soldiers were sent to pacify the country. verb,* **pac·i·fies, pac·i·fied, pac·i·fy·ing.**

pack (pak), **1** a bundle of things wrapped up or tied together for carrying: *The hikers carried packs on their backs.* **2** to put together in a bundle, box, bale, or other container: *Pack your books in this box.* **3** to fill with things; put one's things into: *Pack your trunk.* **4** to press or crowd closely together: *A hundred people were packed into one small room.* **5** to fill a space with all that it will hold: *A large audience packed the small theater.* **6** a set; lot; a number together: *a pack of thieves, a pack of nonsense, a pack of lies.* **7** a number of animals of the same kind hunting together: *Wolves hunt in packs; tigers hunt alone.* **8** a complete set of playing cards, usually 52. 1,6-8 *noun,* 2-5 *verb.*

pack·age (pak′ij), **1** a bundle of things packed or wrapped together; box with things packed in it;

parcel. **2** to put in a package or wrapper: *packaged foods. Grocery stores package some fruits and vegetables.* 1 *noun,* 2 *verb,* **pack·ag·es, pack·aged, pack·ag·ing.**

pack animal, an animal used for carrying loads or packs.

pack animals

pack·et (pak′it), a small package; parcel: *a packet of letters. noun.*

pact (pakt), an agreement: *The three nations signed a peace pact. noun.*

pad[1] (pad), **1** a soft mass used for comfort, protection, or stuffing; cushion: *The baby's carriage has a pad.* **2** to fill with something soft; stuff: *to pad a chair.* **3** a cushionlike part on the bottom side of the feet of dogs, foxes, and some other animals. **4** a number of sheets of paper fastened tightly together; tablet. **5** a cloth soaked with ink to use with a rubber stamp. **6** a launching pad. 1,3-6 *noun,* 2 *verb,* **pads, pad·ded, pad·ding.**

pad[2] (pad), to walk or trot softly: *I padded across the rug barefoot. verb,* **pads, pad·ded, pad·ding.**

pad·ding (pad′ing), any material used to pad with, such as cotton or foam rubber. *noun.*

pad·dle[1] (pad′l), **1** a short oar with a broad blade at one end or both ends, usually held with both hands in rowing a boat or canoe. **2** to move a boat or a canoe with a paddle or paddles. **3** a broad piece of wood with a handle at one end, used for stirring, for mixing, for beating clothes, and in other ways. **4** a paddle-shaped wooden implement with a short handle, used to hit the ball in Ping-Pong. **5** to beat with a paddle; spank. **6** an electronic device used to control video games and computer games. It is a flat handle containing a wheel and a button. 1,3,4,6 *noun,* 2,5 *verb,* **pad·dles, pad·dled, pad·dling.**

pad·dle[2] (pad′l), to move the hands or feet about in water: *Children love to paddle at the beach. verb,* **pad·dles, pad·dled, pad·dling.**

paddle wheel

a hat	i it	oi oil	ch child	(a in about
ā age	ī ice	ou out	ng long	e in taken
ä far	o hot	u cup	sh she	ə = i in pencil
e let	ō open	u̇ put	th thin	o in lemon
ē equal	ô order	ü rule	ᴛʜ then	u in circus
ėr term			zh measure	

paddle wheel, a wheel with large flat boards fixed around it. They move a ship through the water.

pad·dock (pad′ək), **1** a small, enclosed field near a stable or house, used for exercising animals or as a pasture. **2** a pen for horses at a racetrack. *noun.*

pad·dy (pad′ē), a flooded area with raised banks around its sides, for growing rice. *noun, plural* **pad·dies.**

Word History

paddy *Paddy* comes from a Malay word meaning "rice."

pad·lock (pad′lok′), **1** a lock that can be put on and removed. It hangs by a curved bar, hinged at one end and snapped shut at the other. **2** to fasten with a padlock. **1** *noun,* **2** *verb.*

pa·dre (pä′drā), father. It is used as a name for a priest, especially in regions where Spanish, Portuguese, or Italian is spoken. *noun.*

pa·gan (pā′gən), **1** a person who is not a Christian, Jew, or Moslem; one who worships many gods or no god; heathen. The ancient Greeks and Romans were pagans. **2** having something to do with pagans; heathen: *pagan customs.* **1** *noun,* **2** *adjective.*

page[1] (pāj), **1** one side of a sheet or piece of paper: *a page in this book.* **2** a happening or time considered as part of history: *The settling of the West is an exciting page in our history. noun.*

page[2] (pāj), **1** a person who runs errands or delivers messages. Pages at hotels usually wear uniforms. **2** to try to find a person in a public place by having his or her name called out. **3** a youth who waits on a person of high position. **4** a youth who was preparing to be a knight. **1,3,4** *noun,* **2** *verb,* **pag·es, paged, pag·ing.**

pag·eant (paj′ənt), **1** an elaborate spectacle; procession in costume; pomp; display: *The coronation of a new ruler is always a splendid pageant.* **2** a public entertainment that represents scenes from history, legend, or the like: *Our school gave a pageant of the coming of the Pilgrims to America. noun.*

pa·go·da (pə gō′də), a temple having many stories, with a roof curving upward from each story. There are pagodas in India, Japan, and China. *noun.*

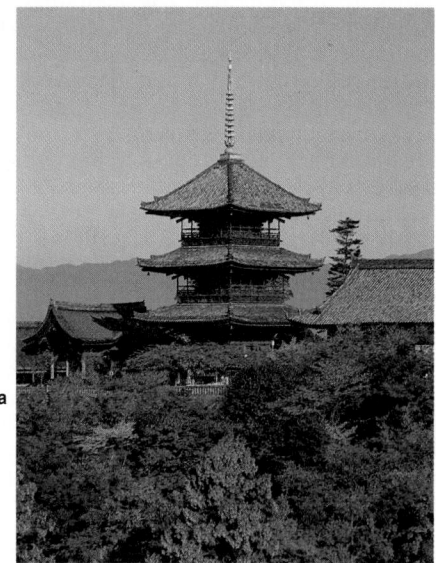

pagoda

paid (pād). See **pay.** *I have paid my bills. These bills are all paid. verb.*

pail (pāl), **1** a round container for carrying liquids, sand, or the like; bucket. **2** the amount a pail holds. *noun.*

pail·ful (pāl′fu̇l), the amount that fills a pail. *noun, plural* **pail·fuls.**

pain (pān), **1** a feeling of being hurt; suffering: *A cut gives pain. A toothache is a pain. The death of one we love causes us pain.* **2** to cause to suffer; give pain: *Does your tooth pain you?* **1** *noun,* **2** *verb.*

take pains, to be careful: *I took pains to write neatly.*

pain·ful (pān′fəl), hurting; causing pain; unpleasant: *They both suffered painful injuries. It*

P

was my painful duty to tell them they had failed the test. adjective.

pain·less (pān′lis), without pain; causing no pain. *adjective.*

pains·tak·ing (pānz′tā′king), very careful: *The carpenter trimmed the edges of the boards with painstaking care. adjective.*

paint (pānt), **1** a solid coloring matter mixed with a liquid, that can be put on a surface to make a layer or film of white, black, or colored matter. **2** to cover or decorate with paint: *to paint a house.* **3** to represent an object in colors: *The artist painted fairies and angels.* **4** to picture vividly in words. **1** *noun,* **2-4** *verb.*

paint·brush (pānt′brush′), a brush for putting on paint. *noun, plural* **paint·brush·es.**

paint·er (pān′tər), **1** a person who paints pictures; artist. **2** a person who paints houses or woodwork. *noun.*

paint·ing (pān′ting), **1** a picture; something painted. **2** the act of one who paints. *noun.*

pair (per *or* par), **1** a set of two; two that go together: *a pair of shoes, a pair of horses.* **2** to arrange or be arranged in pairs: *My socks are neatly paired in a drawer.* **3** a single thing consisting of two parts that cannot be used separately: *a pair of scissors, a pair of trousers.* **4** two animals that are mated. **5** to join in a pair; mate: *Some animals pair for life.* **1,3,4** *noun,* *plural* **pairs** *or* **pair;** **2,5** *verb.*

pair off, to arrange in pairs; form into pairs.

Pai·ute (pī yüt′), **1** a member of a tribe of American Indians living in Utah. **2** the language of this tribe. *noun, plural* **Pai·ute** *or* **Pai·utes** for 1.

pa·ja·mas (pə jä′məz *or* pə jam′əz), clothes to sleep or lounge in, consisting of a shirt and loose trousers. *noun plural.*

[The word *pajamas* comes from a word from a language of India, meaning "leg clothing." Originally the word referred to loose trousers worn by people in India. Later on, the word was used to mean a two-piece outfit to sleep in.]

Pak·i·stan (pak′ə stan), a country in southern Asia. *noun.*

pal (pal), **1** a close friend; playmate. **2** to be on very friendly terms: *We palled around together for years.* **1** *noun,* **2** *verb,* **pals, palled, pal·ling.**

pal·ace (pal′is), **1** a very large house, especially the official home of a king or queen. **2** a very fine house or building. *noun.*

pal·ate (pal′it), the roof of the mouth. The bony part in front is the hard palate, and the fleshy part in back is the soft palate. *noun.*

pale (pāl), **1** without much color; whitish: *When you have been ill, your face is sometimes pale.* **2** not bright; dim: *a pale blue. The bright stars are surrounded by hundreds of pale ones.* **3** to turn pale: *Their faces paled at the bad news.* **1,2** *adjective,* **pal·er, pal·est;** **3** *verb,* **pales, paled, pal·ing.**

pale·face (pāl′fās′), a white person. The American Indians are said to have called white people palefaces. *noun.*

pa·le·on·tol·o·gist (pā′lē on tol′ə jist), a person who is an expert in the science of prehistoric forms of life. Paleontologists study fossil plants and animals. *noun.*

Pal·es·tine (pal′ə stīn), a region in southwestern Asia on the Mediterranean Sea. In olden times the Jews came there from Egypt. Jesus was born in Palestine. It is now divided chiefly between Israel and Jordan. *noun.*

pal·ette (pal′it), a thin board, usually oval or oblong, with a thumb hole at one end, used by artists to lay and mix colors on. *noun.*

pal·in·drome (pal′in drōm), a word, verse, sentence, or number which reads the same backward or forward. *Madam* and *radar* are palindromes; "Madam, I'm Adam" is a palindrome; 9449 is a palindrome. *noun.*

pal·i·sade (pal′ə sād′), **1** a fence of long, strong, wooden stakes pointed at the top end and set firmly in the ground to enclose or defend. **2 palisades,** a line of high, steep cliffs. *noun.*

pall[1] (pôl), a dark, gloomy covering: *A thick pall of smoke shut out the sun from the city. noun.*

pall[2] (pôl), to become distasteful or very tiresome because there has been too much of it: *Even the most tasty food palls if it is served every day. verb.*

pal·let (pal′it), a bed of straw; poor bed. *noun.*

pal·lid (pal′id), lacking color; pale: *Illness may cause a pallid complexion. adjective.*

pal·lor (pal′ər), a lack of color from fear, illness, or death; paleness. *noun.*

palm[1] (päm), **1** the inside of the hand between the wrist and the fingers. **2** to conceal in the hand: *The magician palmed the nickel.* **1** *noun,* **2** *verb.*

palm off, to pass off or get accepted by tricks, fraud, or false representation.

palm[2] (päm), any of many kinds of trees growing in warm climates. Most palms have tall trunks, no branches, and many large leaves at the top. *noun.*

pal·met·to (pal met′ō), a kind of palm with fan-shaped leaves, abundant on the southeastern coast of the United States. *noun, plural* **pal·met·tos** *or* **pal·met·toes.**

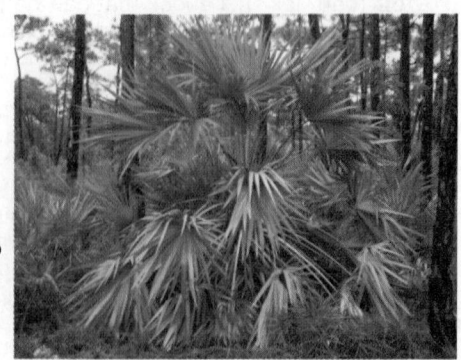

palmetto

Palm Sunday, the Sunday before Easter.

pal·o·mi·no (pal′ə mē′nō), a golden-tan horse whose mane and tail are usually lighter colored. *noun, plural* **pal·o·mi·nos.**

My love of horses is so great, my heart begins to PALPITATE!

a hat	i it	oi oil	ch child	a in about
ā age	ī ice	ou out	ng long	e in taken
ä far	o hot	u cup	sh she	ə = i in pencil
e let	ō open	u̇ put	th thin	o in lemon
ē equal	ô order	ü rule	ᵺ then	u in circus
ėr term			zh measure	

pal·pi·tate (pal′pə tāt), to beat very rapidly: *Your heart palpitates when you are excited. verb,* **pal·pi·tates, pal·pi·tat·ed, pal·pi·tat·ing.**

pal·sy (pôl′zē), paralysis, most often a form of paralysis that comes late in life and causes trembling and muscular weakness. *noun.*

pal·try (pôl′trē), almost worthless; trifling; petty: *I sold my old, rusted bicycle for a paltry sum of money. adjective,* **pal·tri·er, pal·tri·est.**

pam·pas (pam′pəz), the vast grassy plains of South America, with no trees. *noun plural.*

pam·per (pam′pər), to indulge too much; allow too many privileges: *to pamper a child, to pamper a sick person, to pamper one's appetite. verb.*

pam·phlet (pam′flit), a booklet in paper covers. *noun.*

pan (pan), **1** a dish for cooking and other household uses, usually broad, shallow, and with no cover: *pots and pans.* **2** anything like this. Gold and other metals are sometimes obtained by washing ore in pans. The dishes on a pair of scales are called pans. **3** to wash gravel or sand in a pan to separate the gold. 1,2 *noun,* 3 *verb,* **pans, panned, pan·ning.**

pan out, to turn out or work out: *Their latest scheme panned out well.*

Pan·a·ma (pan′ə mä), **1** an isthmus or narrow neck of land that connects North and South America. **2** a country in Central America on the Isthmus of Panama. *noun.*

Panama Canal, a canal cut across the Isthmus of Panama to connect the Atlantic and Pacific oceans.

pan·cake (pan′kāk′), a thin, flat cake made of batter and fried in a pan or on a griddle. *noun.*

pan·cre·as (pan′krē əs), a gland near the stomach. It produces insulin and helps the body to digest food. *noun, plural* **pan·cre·as·es.**

pan·da (pan′də), **1** a bearlike animal of Tibet and parts of China, mostly white with black legs, often called the **giant panda.** **2** a reddish-brown animal somewhat like a raccoon, that lives in the mountains of India. *noun.*

pane (pān), a single sheet of glass or plastic in a division of a window, a door, or a sash: *Big hailstones and sudden gusts of wind broke several panes of glass. noun.*
[*Pane* comes from a Latin word meaning "cloth." Early panes were strips of cloth, oiled paper, and so forth.]

pan·el (pan′l), **1** a strip or surface that is different in some way from what is around it. A panel is often sunk below or raised above the rest, and used for a decoration. Panels may be in a door or other woodwork, on large pieces of furniture, or made as parts of a dress. **2** a flat piece or section of material used in construction or as decoration: *plywood panels.* **3** to arrange in panels; furnish or decorate with panels: *The walls of the dining room were paneled with oak.* **4** a list of persons called as jurors; members of a jury. **5** a group formed for discussion: *A panel of experts gave its opinion on ways to solve the problem.* **6** the board containing the instruments, controls, or indicators used in operating an automobile, aircraft, computer, or other mechanism. 1,2,4-6 *noun,* 3 *verb.*

pan·el·ing (pan′l ing), **1** wood or other material for panels. **2** panels applied as decoration. *noun.*

pang (pang), **1** a sudden, short, sharp pain: *the pangs of a toothache.* **2** a sudden feeling: *A pang of pity moved my heart. noun.*

pan·ic (pan′ik), **1** sudden uncontrollable fear that causes a person or group to lose self-control; unreasoning fear: *When the theater caught fire, there was a panic.* **2** to be affected with panic: *The audience panicked when the fire broke out.* 1 *noun,* 2 *verb,* **pan·ics, pan·icked, pan·ick·ing.**
[*Panic* comes from a Greek word meaning "of Pan." Pan was a Greek god whose appearance was thought to cause terror among people who saw him.]

Courtesy of The Smithsonian Institution

panda (definition 1)—about 5 feet (1½ meters) long

pan·ick·y (pan′ə kē), **1** caused by panic: *panicky haste.* **2** feeling panic; liable to panic: *When fire broke out in the theater, the audience became panicky. adjective.*

pan·ic-strick·en (pan′ik strik′ən), frightened out of one's wits. *adjective.*

pan·o·ram·a (pan′ə ram′ə), a wide, unbroken view of a surrounding region: *a panorama of beach and sea. noun.*

pan·sy (pan′zē), a flower somewhat like a violet but much larger and having flat petals usually of several colors. *noun, plural* **pan·sies.**
[*Pansy* comes from an old French word meaning "thought." The flower was called this because it was considered the symbol of thought or remembrance.]

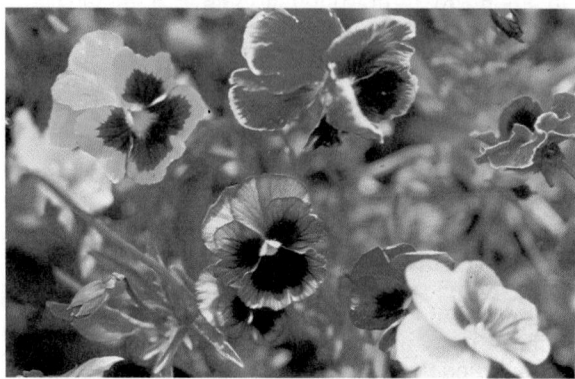
pansies

pant (pant), **1** to breathe hard and quickly: *He is panting from playing tennis.* **2** a short, quick breath. **1** *verb,* **2** *noun.*

pan·ther (pan′thər), **1** a leopard, most often a black leopard. **2** a puma. **3** a jaguar. *noun, plural* **pan·thers** or **pan·ther.**

pan·ties (pan′tēz), a kind of underwear with short legs worn by women or children. *noun plural.*

pan·to·mime (pan′tə mīm), **1** a play without words in which the actors express themselves by gestures. **2** gestures without words. **3** to express by gestures: *They pantomimed being hungry by pointing to their mouths and their stomachs.* **1,2** *noun,* **3** *verb,* **pan·to·mimes, pan·to·mimed, pan·to·mim·ing.**

pan·try (pan′trē), a small room in which food, dishes, silverware, or table linen is kept. *noun, plural* **pan·tries.**
[*Pantry* comes from a Latin word meaning "bread." Originally the word meant a room where bread was kept.]

pants (pants), a two-legged outer garment reaching from the waist to the ankles or sometimes to the knees; trousers. *noun plural.*

pant·suit (pant′süt′), a woman's or girl's suit consisting of a jacket and trousers. *noun.*

pa·pa (pä′pə), father; daddy. *noun.*

pa·pal (pā′pəl), of or having to do with the pope: *a papal letter. adjective.*

papaya

pa·pa·ya (pə pä′yə), the fruit of a palmlike tropical American tree. Papayas look somewhat like melons, have yellowish pulp, and are good to eat. *noun.*

pa·per (pā′pər), **1** a material used for writing, printing, drawing, wrapping packages, and covering walls. Paper is made in thin sheets from wood pulp, rags, and straw. **2** a piece or sheet of paper. **3** a piece or sheet of paper with writing or printing on it; document: *Important papers were stolen.* **4 papers,** documents telling who or what one is. **5** a newspaper. **6** an article; essay: *The professor read a paper on the teaching of English.* **7** made of paper: *paper dolls.* **8** like paper; thin: *almonds with paper shells.* **9** wallpaper. **10** to cover with wallpaper: *to paper a room.* **1-6,9** *noun,* **7,8** *adjective,* **10** *verb.*

pa·per·back (pā′pər bak′), a book with a paper binding or cover. *noun.*

pa·per·boy (pā′pər boi′), a person who delivers or sells newspapers; newsboy. *noun.*

paper clip, a flat, bent piece of wire forming a clip for holding papers together.

paper money, money made of paper, not metal. A dollar bill is paper money.

pa·pier-mâ·ché (pā′pər mə shā′), a paper pulp mixed with some stiffener and molded into various shapes when moist. It becomes hard and strong when dry. *noun.*

pa·poose (pa püs′), a North American Indian baby. The use of this word is often considered offensive. *noun.*

pa·pri·ka (pa prē′kə *or* pap′rə kə), a red spice used to season food. It is made from sweet red peppers, ground up fine. *noun.*
[*Paprika* was borrowed directly from a Hungarian word. It can be traced back to a Greek word meaning "pepper."]

pa·py·rus (pə pī′rəs), a tall water plant from which the ancient Egyptians, Greeks, and Romans made a kind of paper to write on. *noun.*

par (pär), **1** equality; equal level: *She is quite on a par with her brother in intelligence.* **2** an average or normal amount, degree, or condition: *A sick person feels below par. noun.*

par·a·ble (par′ə bəl), a brief story used to teach some truth or moral lesson. *noun.*

par·a·chute (par/ə shüt), **1** a device shaped something like an umbrella, made of nylon or silk, used in jumping safely from an aircraft. **2** to come down by parachute: *The pilot of the burning plane parachuted safely to the ground.* 1 *noun*, 2 *verb*, **par·a·chutes, par·a·chut·ed, par·a·chut·ing.**

pa·rade (pə rād/), **1** a march for display; procession: *The circus had a parade.* **2** to march in a procession; walk proudly as if in a parade. **3** to make a great show of: *to parade one's wealth.* 1 *noun*, 2,3 *verb*, **pa·rades, pa·rad·ed, pa·rad·ing.**

par·a·dise (par/ə dīs), **1** heaven. **2** a place or condition of great happiness: *The summer camp was a paradise for her. noun.*

par·a·dox (par/ə doks), a statement that may be true but seems to say two opposite things: *"More haste, less speed"* and *"The child is father to the man"* are paradoxes. *noun*, plural **par·a·dox·es.**

par·af·fin (par/ə fin), a white, tasteless substance like wax, used for making candles and for sealing jars of jelly or jam. *noun.*

par·a·graph (par/ə graf), **1** a group of sentences that are about the same idea. Paragraphs begin on a new line and are usually indented. **2** to divide into paragraphs. 1 *noun*, 2 *verb*.

Par·a·guay (par/ə gwā or par/ə gwī), a country in central South America. *noun.*

par·a·keet (par/ə kēt), a small parrot with a slender body and a long tail. *noun.*

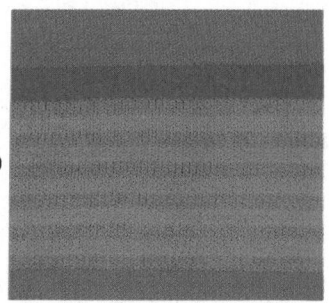

parallel (definition 1)
parallel stripes

par·al·lel (par/ə lel), **1** at or being the same distance apart everywhere, like the two rails of a railroad track. **2** to be at the same distance from throughout the length: *The street parallels the railroad.* **3** a parallel line or surface. **4** The imaginary parallel circles around the earth, marking degrees of latitude, are called parallels. **5** a comparison to show likeness: *to draw a parallel between this winter and last winter.* **6** to be or find a case which is similar or parallel to: *Can you parallel that for friendliness?* **7** similar; corresponding: *parallel customs in different countries.* 1,7 *adjective*, 2,6 *verb*, 3-5 *noun*.

par·al·lel·o·gram (par/ə lel/ə gram), a figure with four sides whose opposite sides are parallel and equal. *noun.*

parallelograms

a hat	i it	oi oil	ch child		a in about
ā age	ī ice	ou out	ng long		e in taken
ä far	o hot	u cup	sh she	ə =	i in pencil
e let	ō open	u̇ put	th thin		o in lemon
ē equal	ô order	ü rule	ᵺ then		u in circus
ėr term			zh measure		

pa·ral·y·sis (pə ral/ə sis), **1** a lessening or loss of the power of motion or feeling in any part of the body: *Polio sometimes causes a paralysis of the legs.* **2** a condition of helpless lack of activity; crippling: *The war caused a paralysis of trade. noun.*

par·a·lyze (par/ə līz), **1** to cause a lessening or loss of the power of motion or feeling in any part of the body: *The patient's left arm was paralyzed.* **2** to make powerless or helpless; stun: *Fear paralyzed my mind. verb*, **par·a·lyz·es, par·a·lyzed, par·a·lyz·ing.**

par·a·me·ci·um (par/ə mē/sē əm), a very small one-celled living thing shaped like a slender slipper. Paramecia live in fresh water. They are not animals or plants but another kind of life, called protists. *noun*, plural **par·a·me·ci·a** (par/ə mē/sē ə).

paramecium

par·a·med·ic (par/ə med/ik), a person who is trained to assist a physician, especially one who gives medical treatment at the scene of an emergency. *noun.*

par·a·mount (par/ə mount), above others; chief in importance; supreme: *Truth is of paramount importance. adjective.*

par·a·pet (par/ə pet), a low wall or mound of stone or earth to protect soldiers. *noun.*

par·a·site (par/ə sīt), a living thing that spends its life on or in another from which it gets its food, often harming the other in the process. Lice and tapeworms are parasites on animals. Mistletoe is a parasite on oak trees. *noun.*

parasites—Wasp larvae feed on a tomato hornworm.

P

par·a·sol (par′ə sôl), a light umbrella used as a protection from the sun. *noun.*

par·a·troop·er (par′ə trü′pər), a soldier trained to use a parachute for descent from an aircraft into a battle area. *noun.*

par·cel (pär′səl), **1** a bundle of things wrapped or packed together; package: *I had my arms filled with parcels.* **2** a piece: *a parcel of land. noun.*
  parcel out, to divide into portions or distribute in portions: *The two big nations parceled out the little country between them.*

parcel post, the branch of the Postal Service which carries parcels.

parch (pärch), **1** to dry by heating; roast slightly: *Corn is sometimes parched.* **2** to make or become hot and dry or thirsty: *I am parched with the heat. verb.*

parch·ment (pärch′mənt), **1** the skin of sheep or goats, prepared for use as a writing material. **2** paper that looks like parchment. *noun.*

par·don (pärd′n), **1** forgiveness: *I beg your pardon, but I didn't hear you.* **2** to set free from punishment: *The governor pardoned the prisoner.* **3** a setting free from punishment: *The pardon freed an innocent person.* **1,3** *noun,* **2** *verb.*

pare (per *or* par), **1** to cut, trim, or shave off the outer part of; peel: *to pare an apple.* **2** to cut away little by little: *to pare down expenses. verb,* **pares, pared, par·ing.**

par·ent (per′ənt *or* par′ənt), **1** a father or mother. **2** any living thing that produces offspring. *noun.*

par·ent·age (per′ən tij *or* par′ən tij), descent from parents; family line; ancestors. *noun.*

pa·ren·tal (pə ren′tl), of or having something to do with a parent or parents: *The teenager resented parental advice. adjective.*

pa·ren·the·ses (pə ren′thə sēz′), more than one parenthesis. The pronunciations in this dictionary are enclosed in parentheses. *noun plural.*

pa·ren·the·sis (pə ren′thə sis), either or both of two curved lines ( ) used to set off a word, phrase, or sentence inserted within a sentence to explain or qualify something. *noun, plural* **pa·ren·the·ses.**

Par·is (par′is), the capital of France. *noun.*

par·ish (par′ish), **1** a district that has its own church and clergyman. **2** the people of a parish. **3** (in Louisiana) a county. *noun, plural* **par·ish·es.**

park (pärk), **1** land set apart for the pleasure of the public: *Many cities have beautiful parks.* **2** land set apart for wild animals. **3** to leave a car or other vehicle for a time in a certain place: *Park your car here.* **1,2** *noun,* **3** *verb.*

par·ka (pär′kə), a jacket with a hood. *noun.*
[Another meaning of *parka* is "a fur jacket with a hood, worn in Alaska and the northeastern part of Asia." The word was introduced to Alaska from Russia and Siberia, where it meant "an animal's skin" or "a pelt."]

park·way (pärk′wā′), a broad road with spaces planted with grass, trees, or flowers. *noun.*

par·ley (pär′lē), **1** a conference or informal talk to discuss terms or matters in dispute: *The general held a parley with the enemy.* **2** to discuss matters, especially with an enemy. **1** *noun, plural* **par·leys; 2** *verb.*

par·lia·ment (pär′lə mənt), a council or congress that is the highest lawmaking body in some countries, including Canada and Great Britain. *noun.*

par·lor (pär′lər), **1** a room for receiving or entertaining guests; sitting room. **2** a room or group or rooms used for business purposes; shop: *a beauty parlor, an ice-cream parlor. noun.*

pa·ro·chi·al (pə rō′kē əl), of or in a parish: *a parochial school. adjective.*

pa·role (pə rōl′), **1** the release of a prisoner from jail before the full term is served. **2** to grant an early release from jail before the full term is served: *The prisoner was paroled after serving two years of a three-year sentence.* **1** *noun,* **2** *verb,* **pa·roles, pa·roled, pa·rol·ing.**

par·rot (par′ət), **1** a bird with a stout, hooked bill and often with bright-colored feathers. Some parrots can imitate sounds and repeat words and sentences. **2** to repeat without understanding: *The pupils parroted the difficult, unfamiliar words.* **1** *noun,* **2** *verb.*

parrot (definition 1) about 1 foot (30 centimeters) tall

par·ry (par′ē), **1** to block; turn aside a thrust, weapon, or question: *He parried the sword with his dagger. She parried our question by asking us one.* **2** the act of blocking. **1** *verb,* **par·ries, par·ried, par·ry·ing; 2** *noun, plural* **par·ries.**

par·sley (pär′slē), a garden plant with finely divided, fragrant leaves. Parsley is used to flavor food and to trim platters of meat or fish. *noun.*

par·snip (pär′snip), the long, tapering, whitish root of a garden plant. Parsnips are eaten as a vegetable. *noun.*

par·son (pär′sən), **1** a minister in charge of a parish. **2** any clergyman; minister. *noun.*

par·son·age (pär′sə nij), a house provided for a minister by a church. *noun.*

part (pärt), **1** something less than the whole; not all: *He ate part of an apple.* **2** each of several equal quantities into which a whole may be divided; fraction: *A dime is a tenth part of a dollar.* **3** a thing that helps to make up a whole: *A radio has many parts.* **4** a share: *I had no part in the mischief.* **5** a side in a dispute or contest: *She always takes her sister's part.* **6** a character in a play or motion picture; role: *He played the part of Hamlet.* **7** to divide into two or more pieces. **8** to force apart; divide: *Several mounted police parted the crowd.* **9** to go apart; separate: *The friends parted in anger.* **10** a dividing line left in combing one's hair. **11** one of the voices or instruments in music. The four parts in singing are soprano, alto, tenor, and bass. **12** music for it. **13** less than the whole; partial: *a part payment on a car.* **14** partly; in some measure or degree: *part Irish.* 1-6,10-12 *noun*, 7-9 *verb*, 13 *adjective*, 14 *adverb*.

for the most part, mostly: *Our plan was for the most part successful.*

part with, to give up; let go: *I hated to part with my savings.*

take part, to take or have a share: *She took no part in the discussion.*

par·take (pär tāk′), **1** to eat or drink some: *Will you partake of our lunch?* **2** to take or have a share: *They plan to partake in the celebration.* *verb,* **par·takes, par·took, par·tak·en, par·tak·ing.**

par·tak·en (pär tā′kən). See **partake.** *verb.*

par·tial (pär′shəl), **1** not complete; not total: *My parents made a partial payment on our new car.* **2** inclined to favor one side more than another; favoring unfairly: *Parents should not be partial to any one of their children.* **3** having a liking for; favorably inclined: *I am partial to sports. adjective.*

par·tial·ly (pär′shə lē), in part; not generally or totally; partly. *adverb.*

par·tic·i·pant (pär tis′ə pənt), a person who shares or participates. *noun.*

par·tic·i·pate (pär tis′ə pāt), to have a share; take part: *The teacher participated in the children's games. verb,* **par·tic·i·pates, par·tic·i·pat·ed, par·tic·i·pat·ing.**

par·tic·i·pa·tion (pär tis′ə pā′shən), a participating; taking part: *Participation in gym class is required of all students. noun.*

par·ti·ci·ple (pär′tə sip′əl), a form of a verb which may also be used as an adjective. In the sentence *The girl writing at the blackboard is Sue, writing* is a present participle. In the sentence *The police found the stolen silver, stolen* is a past participle. *noun.*

par·ti·cle (pär′tə kəl), a very little bit: *I got a particle of dust in my eye. noun.*

par·tic·u·lar (pər tik′yə lər), **1** apart from others; considered separately; single: *That particular chair is already sold.* **2** belonging to some one person, thing, group, or occasion: *His particular task is to care for the dog.* **3** different from others; unusual; special: *This vacation was of particular importance to her, for she was going to Brazil. He is a particular friend of mine.* **4** hard to please; wanting everything to be just right; very careful: *They are very particular; nothing but the best will do.* **5** an individual part; item; point: *All the*

particulars of the accident are now known. 1-4 *adjective,* 5 *noun.*

in particular, especially: *We strolled around, not going anywhere in particular.*

par·tic·u·lar·ly (pər tik′yə lər lē), in a high degree; especially: *The teacher praised her particularly. I am particularly fond of him. She mentioned that point particularly. adverb.*

part·ing (pär′ting), **1** a departure; going away; taking leave: *The friends were sad at parting.* **2** given, taken, or done at parting: *a parting request, a parting shot.* 1 *noun,* 2 *adjective.*

par·ti·san (pär′tə zən), a strong supporter of a person, party, or cause; one whose support is based on feeling rather than on reasoning. *noun.*

par·ti·tion (pär tish′ən), **1** a division into parts: *the partition of a person's wealth when he or she dies.* **2** to divide into parts: *to partition a territory into three states, to partition a house into rooms.* **3** a wall between rooms. 1,3 *noun,* 2 *verb.*

part·ly (pärt′lē), in part; in some measure or degree: *They are partly to blame. adverb.*

part·ner (pärt′nər), **1** a member of a company or firm who shares the risks and profits of the business. **2** a wife or husband. **3** a companion in a dance. **4** a player on the same team or side in a game. *noun.*

part·ner·ship (pärt′nər ship), a being a partner; association; joint interest: *a business partnership, the partnership of marriage. noun.*

part of speech, any of the groups into which words are divided according to their use in sentences. The parts of speech are the noun, pronoun, adjective, verb, adverb, preposition, conjunction, and interjection.

par·took (pär tùk′). See **partake.** *He partook of food and drink. verb.*

par·tridge (pär′trij), (in the United States) a ruffed grouse or a quail. *noun, plural* **par·tridg·es** or **par·tridge.**

part-time (pärt′tīm′), for part of the usual time: *A part-time job helped her finish college. adjective.*

part·way (pärt′wā′), not completely; only to a partial degree: *The bridge was only partway finished by the end of last year. adverb.*

par·ty (pär′tē), **1** a group of people having a good time together: *She invited her friends to a party.* **2** a group of people doing something together: *a dinner party, a scouting party of three soldiers.* **3** a group of people organized to gain political influence and control: *the Democratic Party.* **4** of or having something to do with a party of people: *They have strong party loyalties.* **5** one who takes part in, aids, or knows about: *He was a party to our secret.* **6** a person: *The party you are*

a hat	i it	oi oil	ch child	a in about
ā age	ī ice	ou out	ng long	e in taken
ä far	o hot	u cup	sh she	ə = i in pencil
e let	ō open	ù put	th thin	o in lemon
ē equal	ô order	ü rule	ŦH then	u in circus
ėr term			zh measure	

telephoning is out. 1-3,5,6 *noun, plural* **par·ties;** 4 *adjective.*

pass (pas), **1** to go by; move past: *The parade passed. We passed a truck. They pass our house every day.* **2** to move on: *The days pass quickly. The salesman passed from house to house.* **3** to go from person to person: *The property passed from father to daughter.* **4** to hand around; hand from one to another: *Please pass the butter.* **5** to throw the ball to another player in such games as basketball and football. **6** a throw of the ball to another player in such games as basketball and football. **7** to approve or be approved: *Congress passed the new tax bill. The bill passed by only three votes.* **8** to be successful in an examination: *She passed Spanish.* **9** to come to an end; die: *King Arthur passed in peace.* **10** to use or spend: *We passed the days happily.* **11** to be taken: *That cloth could pass for real silk.* **12** to go without notice: *They were rude, but I let it pass.* **13** a written permission: *No one can get in the fort without a pass.* **14** a free ticket: *a pass to the circus.* **15** a narrow road, path, or opening: *A pass crosses the mountains.* 1-5,7-12 *verb,* **pass·es, passed, pass·ing;** 6,13-15 *noun, plural* **pass·es.**

pass away, to come to an end; die.

pass off, to use trickery or dishonesty to get something accepted as something else: *The criminal was caught passing off counterfeit money to stores.*

pass out, 1 to give out; distribute: *Please pass out this test to the members of the class.* **2** to faint; lose consciousness: *We carried him home after he passed out.*

pass up, to do without; give up; refuse: *I'll pass up the extra piece of pie.*

pass·a·ble (pas′ə bəl), **1** fairly good; moderate: *She has a passable knowledge of French.* **2** able to be traveled over or crossed: *The flooded road was barely passable. adjective.*

pas·sage (pas′ij), **1** a hall or way through a building; passageway. **2** a passing or moving along: *Our tastes can change with the passage of time.* **3** a short part of a piece of writing or music: *The author read a passage from his latest book.* **4** a going across; voyage: *We had a stormy passage across the Atlantic.* **5** a making into law by a favoring vote of a legislature: *The senator favored the passage of the tax bill. noun.*

pas·sage·way (pas′ij wā′), a way along which one can pass; passage. *noun.*

pas·sen·ger (pas′n jər), a traveler in an aircraft, bus, ship, train, or car: *The bus carried 30 passengers. noun.*

passenger pigeon, a wild pigeon of North America, now extinct, that flew far in very large flocks.

pass·er·by (pas′ər bī′), one that passes by: *A passer-by saw the accident. noun, plural* **pass·ers·by.**

pass·ing (pas′ing), **1** going by; moving past: *We waved at the people in the passing train.* **2** a going by; departure: *The passing of summer meant that* the school vacation was over. **3** done or given in passing; hurried; hasty: *She gave the book only a passing glance.* **4** short; brief; not lasting long: *He made a passing mention of his last visit to us.* **5** allowing one to pass an examination or test: *Any mark above 75 will be a passing mark.* **6** death; ending: *We all heard the news of the former president's passing.* 1,3-5 *adjective,* 2,6 *noun.*

in passing, by the way; incidentally: *In passing, I'd like to compliment you on your excellent work.*

pas·sion (pash′ən), **1** a very strong feeling: *Hate and fear are passions.* **2** a rage; violent anger: *He flew into a passion.* **3** love between a man and a woman. **4** a very strong liking: *She has a passion for music.* **5** a thing for which a strong liking is felt: *Music is her passion. noun.*

pas·sion·ate (pash′ə nit), **1** having or showing strong feelings: *She is a passionate believer in equal rights for all.* **2** easily moved by anger: *He is a passionate man who often loses his temper.* **3** resulting from strong feeling: *He made a passionate speech against death sentences. adjective.*

pas·sive (pas′iv), **1** not acting in return; being acted on without itself acting: *a passive mind, a passive disposition.* **2** not resisting; yielding or submitting to the will of another: *The children gave passive obedience to their strict parents. adjective.*

Pass·o·ver (pas′ō′vər), an annual Jewish holiday in memory of the escape of the Hebrews from Egypt, where they had been slaves. It comes in March or April and lasts eight days. *noun.*

pass·port (pas′pôrt), a paper or book giving one official permission to travel in a foreign country, under the protection of one's own government. *noun.*

pass·word (pas′werd′), a secret word that allows a person speaking it to pass a guard. *noun.*

past (past), **1** gone by; ended: *Summer is past. Our troubles are past.* **2** just gone by: *The past year was full of trouble.* **3** the time gone by; time before; what has happened: *Life began far back in the past. History is a study of the past.* **4** one's past

passenger pigeons
about 16 inches
(41 centimeters) long

life or history: *a nation with a glorious past. I cannot change my past.* **5** beyond: *It is half past two. The children ran past the house.* **6** passing by; by: *The bus goes past once an hour.* **7** having formerly served in an office or position: *She is a past president of the club.* **8** expressing something that happened or existed in time gone by: *The past tense of the verb "laugh" is "laughed."* 1,2,7,8 *adjective,* 3,4 *noun,* 5 *preposition,* 6 *adverb.*

pas·ta (pä′stə), any of several kinds of food, such as macaroni, spaghetti, or noodles. Pasta is made of flour, water, and sometimes milk or eggs. It is shaped into various forms and dried. *noun.*

pasta

paste (pāst), **1** a mixture used to stick things together. It is often made of flour and water boiled together. **2** to stick with paste. **3** food prepared from tomatoes, ground nuts, meat, or fish cooked down to a soft, thick mass: *We used tomato paste in the sauce.* 1,3 *noun,* 2 *verb,* **pastes, past·ed, past·ing.**

paste·board (pāst′bôrd′), a stiff material made of sheets of paper pasted together or of paper pulp pressed and dried. *noun.*

pas·tel (pa stel′), **1** a kind of chalklike crayon used in drawing. **2** a drawing made with such crayons. **3** soft and pale: *The room was painted pastel blue.* 1,2 *noun,* 3 *adjective.*

pas·teur·ize (pas′chə rīz′), to heat milk or other liquids hot enough and long enough to kill certain harmful germs. *verb,* **pas·teur·iz·es, pas·teur·ized, pas·teur·iz·ing.**

[*Pasteurize* was formed from the name of Louis Pasteur, who lived from 1822 to 1895. He was a French scientist who invented this way of keeping milk from spoiling.]

pas·time (pas′tīm′), a pleasant way of passing time; amusement; recreation. Games and sports are pastimes. *noun.*

pas·tor (pas′tər), a minister in charge of a church; spiritual guide. *noun.*

pas·tor·al (pas′tər əl), of shepherds or country life: *The pastoral tribes of the mountains graze their sheep on the hillside. adjective.*

pas·try (pā′strē), **1** pies, tarts, or other baked food made with dough rich in butter or other shortening. **2** the dough for such food. *noun,* plural **pas·tries.**

pas·ture (pas′chər), **1** a grassy field or hillside;

a hat	i it	oi oil	ch child	⎧ a in about
ā age	ī ice	ou out	ng long	⎪ e in taken
ä far	o hot	u cup	sh she	ə = ⎨ i in pencil
e let	ō open	u̇ put	th thin	⎪ o in lemon
ē equal	ô order	ü rule	ŦH then	⎩ u in circus
ėr term			zh measure	

grassy land on which cattle, sheep, or horses can feed. **2** grass and other growing plants: *These lands supply good pasture.* **3** to put cattle, sheep, or horses out to pasture: *The farmer pastured his cattle near the stream.* **4** to feed on growing grass. 1,2 *noun,* 3,4 *verb,* **pas·tures, pas·tured, pas·tur·ing.**

past·y (pā′stē), **1** like paste: *This pasty rice tastes awful.* **2** pale: *Her face was pasty and she looked sick. adjective,* **past·i·er, past·i·est.**

pat (pat), **1** to strike or tap lightly with something flat: *He patted the dough into a flat cake.* **2** to tap with the hand as a sign of sympathy, approval, or affection: *She stooped to pat the dog.* **3** a light stroke or tap with the hand or with something flat. **4** a small mass, especially of butter. **5** apt; suitable; to the point: *The teacher gave a pat reply to the questions.* 1,2 *verb,* **pats, pat·ted, pat·ting;** 3,4 *noun,* 5 *adjective.*

patch (pach), **1** a piece put on to mend a hole or a tear, or as a decoration. **2** a cloth bandage or pad put over a wound, a sore, or a hurt eye to protect it. **3** to put patches on; mend; protect with a patch or patches: *I patched the hole in the knee of my jeans.* **4** to piece together; make or repair hastily: *He tried to patch the faucet so the leak would stop.* **5** a small, uneven spot that is different from what surrounds it: *There were several brown patches on the lawn.* **6** a piece of ground: *We have a strawberry patch in our garden.* 1,2,5,6 *noun,* plural **patch·es;** 3,4 *verb.*

patch up, 1 to put an end to; settle: *patch up a quarrel.* **2** to make right hastily or for a time: *patch up a leaking faucet.*

patch·work (pach′wėrk′), **1** pieces of cloth of various colors or shapes sewed together. **2** made of such pieces of cloth. 1 *noun,* 2 *adjective.*

patchwork (definition 1)—**patchwork** for a quilt

P

pat·ent (pat′nt), **1** a government document which grants a person or company sole rights to make, use, or sell a new invention for a certain number of years. **2** given or protected by a patent. **3** to get a patent for: *She patented her new invention.* **1** *noun,* **2** *adjective,* **3** *verb.*

patent leather, leather with a very glossy, smooth surface, usually black. Some shoes are made of patent leather.

pa·ter·nal (pə ter′nl), **1** of or like a father; fatherly: *Their uncle has taken a paternal interest in their welfare since their father died.* **2** related on the father's side of the family: *Everyone has two paternal grandparents and two maternal grandparents.* *adjective.*

path (path), **1** a way made by people or animals walking. It is usually too narrow for automobiles or wagons. **2** the line along which a person or thing moves; route; track: *The moon has a regular path through the sky.* *noun, plural* **paths** (paᴛʜz or paths).

pa·thet·ic (pə thet′ik), pitiful; arousing pity: *The starving people were pathetic.* *adjective.*

path·way (path′wā′), a path. *noun.*

pa·tience (pā′shəns), a willingness to put up with waiting, pain or trouble; a calm bearing of anything that annoys or hurts: *He showed great patience with the quarreling children.* *noun.*

pa·tient (pā′shənt), **1** having patience; showing patience: *The teacher was patient with the class.* **2** a person who is being treated by a doctor. **1** *adjective,* **2** *noun.*

pat·i·o (pat′ē ō), **1** an inner court or yard open to the sky. Patios are found especially in houses built in Spanish or Spanish-American style. **2** a terrace for outdoor eating or lounging. *noun, plural* **pat·i·os.**

pa·tri·arch (pā′trē ärk), **1** the father and ruler of a family or tribe. In the Bible, Abraham, Isaac, and Jacob were patriarchs. **2** a highly respected elderly man. *noun.*

pa·tri·ot (pā′trē ət), a person who loves his or her country and gives it loyal support. *noun.*

pa·tri·ot·ic (pā′trē ot′ik), having or showing love and loyal support of one's country: *It is patriotic to fly the American flag on the Fourth of July.* *adjective.*

pa·tri·ot·ism (pā′trē ə tiz′əm), love and loyal support of one's country. *noun.*

pa·trol (pə trōl′), **1** to go around in an area watching and guarding in order to protect life and property: *The police patrolled once every hour.* **2** a going of the rounds to watch or guard. **3** persons who patrol: *The patrol was changed at midnight.* **4** a group of soldiers, ships, or airplanes, sent out to find out all they can about the enemy. **1** *verb,* **pa·trols, pa·trolled, pa·trol·ling;** **2-4** *noun.*

pa·tron (pā′trən), **1** a regular customer; person who shops at a store or goes to a hotel or restaurant regularly. **2** a person who gives approval and support to some person, art, cause, or undertaking: *She is a well-known patron of art and has helped several young painters.*

3 guarding; protecting: *a patron saint.* **1,2** *noun,* **3** *adjective.*

pa·tron·age (pā′trə nij or pat′rə nij), **1** regular business given to a store, hotel, or restaurant by customers. **2** favor, encouragement, or support given by a patron. **3** the power to give jobs or favors: *the patronage of a governor, mayor, or member of Congress.* *noun.*

pa·tron·ize (pā′trə nīz or pat′rə nīz), **1** to be a regular customer of; give regular business to: *We patronize our neighborhood stores.* **2** to act as a patron toward; support or protect: *We patronize the ballet.* *verb,* **pa·tron·iz·es, pa·tron·ized, pa·tron·iz·ing.**

pat·sy (pat′sē), an easy victim; the person who is blamed: *If the plan doesn't work out, don't let them make you the patsy.* *noun, plural* **pat·sies.**

pat·ter (pat′ər), **1** to make rapid taps: *The rain pattered on the windowpane.* **2** to move with a rapid tapping sound: *Bare feet pattered along the hard floor.* **3** a series of quick taps or the sound they make: *the patter of raindrops.* **1,2** *verb,* **3** *noun.*

pat·tern (pat′ərn), **1** an arrangement of forms and colors; design: *The wallpaper had a striped pattern.* **2** a model or guide for something to be made: *I used a paper pattern in cutting the cloth for my coat.* **3** a fine example; model to be followed: *He was a pattern of generosity.* **4** to make according to a pattern: *Pattern yourself after her.* **5** a way of doing things that is repeated in the same order or manner: *The migration patterns of birds are studied by many scientists.* **1-3,5** *noun,* **4** *verb.*

pat·ty (pat′ē), a small, round, flat piece of food: *a hamburger patty, a peppermint patty.* *noun, plural* **pat·ties.**

pau·per (pô′pər), a very poor person; person supported by charity. *noun.*

pause (pôz), **1** to stop for a time; wait: *I paused for a moment to look in a store window.* **2** a brief stop or rest: *After a pause for lunch we returned to work.* **1** *verb,* **paus·es, paused, paus·ing;** **2** *noun.*

pave (pāv), **1** to cover a street, sidewalk, or driveway with a pavement: *The driveway leading to the garage was paved with concrete.* **2** to prepare; make smooth or easy: *The invention paved the way for new discoveries.* *verb,* **paves, paved, pav·ing.**

pave·ment (pāv′mənt), **1** a covering or surface for streets, sidewalks, or driveways, made of asphalt, concrete, gravel, or stones. **2** a paved road. *noun.*

pa·vil·ion (pə vil′yən), **1** a light building, usually one somewhat open, used for shelter or pleasure: *The swimmers took shelter from the sudden storm in the beach pavilion.* **2** a large tent with a floor raised on posts. **3** one of a group of buildings forming a hospital. **4** any building that houses an exhibition at a fair. *noun.*

pav·ing (pā′ving), **1** material for pavement. **2** a pavement. *noun.*

paw (pô), **1** the foot of a four-footed animal having

claws. Cats and dogs have paws. **2** to strike or scrape with the paws or feet: *The cat pawed the mouse it had caught. The horse pawed the ground, eager to be going again.* **3** to handle awkwardly or roughly: *Stop pawing the tomatoes, or you'll bruise them.* **1** *noun,* **2,3** *verb.*

pawn[1] (pôn), **1** to leave something with another person as security that borrowed money will be returned; pledge: *I pawned my watch to buy food until I could get work.* **2** something left as security. **1** *verb,* **2** *noun.*

pawn[2] (pôn), **1** the least important piece in the game of chess. Pawns are often given up to gain some advantage. **2** an unimportant person or thing used by somebody to gain some advantage. *noun.*

pawn·bro·ker (pôn′brō′kər), a person who lends money in return for something of value that is left as a pledge that the money will be paid back. *noun.*

Paw·nee (pô nē′), a member of a tribe of American Indians that once lived in Nebraska and Kansas, and now lives in Oklahoma. *noun, plural* **Paw·nee** or **Paw·nees.**

pay (pā), **1** to give money to for things or work: *Pay the doctor.* **2** the money given for things or work: *He gets his pay every Friday.* **3** to give money for: *Pay your fare. Pay your debts.* **4** to give what is due: *She owes it and must pay.* **5** to return for favors or hurts; reward or punish: *He paid them for their insults by causing them trouble.* **6** to give; offer: *to pay attention, to pay a compliment.* **7** to give a profit; be worthwhile: *It pays to be polite.* **1,3-7** *verb,* **pays, paid, pay·ing;** **2** *noun.*

pay back, 1 to return borrowed money: *She paid back the money she borrowed.* **2** to give the same treatment as received: *I hope to be able to pay back their help.*

pay off, 1 to give all the money that is owed; pay in full: *He used the money to pay off his loan.* **2** to have a good result: *Years of practice paid off, and she is now a successful violinist.*

pay·ment (pā′mənt), **1** a paying: *The payment of these bills is very important.* **2** the amount paid: *We have a monthly payment of $150 on our car.* **3** something paid; pay: *The pleasure of helping you is payment enough. noun.*

pay·roll (pā′rōl′), **1** a list of persons to be paid and the amount that each one is to receive: *Her store has ten people on the payroll.* **2** the total amount to be paid to them: *As the company grew, the payroll got larger. noun.*

pea (pē), one of the round seeds, eaten as a vegetable, that are inside the long, green pod of a garden plant. *noun.*

peace (pēs), **1** freedom from quarreling or disagreement; condition of quiet, order, and security: *It is nice to have peace in one's home.* **2** freedom from war: *He works for world peace.* **3** an agreement between enemies to end war: *The leaders of the warring countries signed the peace.* **4** a quiet condition; calm; stillness: *peace of mind. We enjoy the peace of the country. noun.*

a hat	i it	oi oil	ch child		a in about
ā age	ī ice	ou out	ng long		e in taken
ä far	o hot	u cup	sh she	ə =	i in pencil
e let	ō open	u̇ put	th thin		o in lemon
ē equal	ô order	ü rule	ꜩH then		u in circus
ėr term			zh measure		

peace·a·ble (pē′sə bəl), peaceful. *adjective.*

peace·ful (pēs′fəl), **1** quiet; calm; full of peace: *It was peaceful in the mountains.* **2** liking peace; keeping peace: *peaceful neighbors. adjective.*

peace pipe, a pipe smoked by North American Indians as a token or pledge of peace.

peace pipe

peach (pēch), **1** a juicy, nearly round, yellowish-pink fruit having a downy skin and a rough stone inside. Peaches grow on trees and are good to eat. **2** yellowish-pink. **1** *noun, plural* **peach·es;** **2** *adjective.*

pea·cock (pē′kok′), a large bird with beautiful green, blue, and gold feathers. The tail feathers of the male have spots like eyes on them and can be spread out and held upright like a fan. *noun, plural* **pea·cocks** or **pea·cock.**

pea·hen (pē′hen′), a female peacock. *noun.*

peak (pēk), **1** the pointed top of a mountain or hill: *We saw the snowy peaks in the distance.* **2** a mountain that stands alone: *Pikes Peak.* **3** any pointed end or top: *the peak of a roof.* **4** the highest point: *That famous scientist has reached the peak of his profession.* **5** the front part or the brim of a cap, that stands out. *noun.*

peal (pēl), **1** a loud, long sound: *I heard a peal of thunder and realized the storm was near.* **2** the loud ringing of bells. **3** to sound out in a long, loud sound or ring: *The bells pealed forth their message of joy.* **1,2** *noun,* **3** *verb.*

pea·nut (pē′nut′), the nutlike seed of a plant. Peanuts are contained in pods that ripen underground. They are roasted and used as food or pressed to get an oil for cooking. *noun.*

peanut brittle, a hard, easily broken candy that contains peanuts.

peanut butter, a food made of peanuts ground until soft and smooth. It is spread on bread or crackers.

pear (per *or* par), a sweet, juicy, yellowish fruit rounded at one end and smaller toward the stem end. Pears grow on trees and are good to eat. *noun.*

pearl (pėrl), **1** a white or nearly white gem that

pearl (definition 2)—The insect was covered with **pearls** of dew.

has a soft shine like satin. Pearls are found inside the shell of a kind of oyster, or in other similar shellfish. **2** a thing that looks like a pearl. **3** very pale, clear, bluish-gray. 1,2 *noun,* 3 *adjective.*

pearl·y (pėr′lē), like a pearl in color or luster: *She had pearly white teeth. adjective,* **pearl·i·er, pearl·i·est.**

peas·ant (pez′nt), **1** a farmer of the working class in Europe. **2** of peasants: *peasant labor.* 1 *noun,* 2 *adjective.*

peas·ant·ry (pez′n trē), peasants. *noun.*

peat (pēt), a kind of turf, used as fuel after being dried. Peat is made of partly rotted moss and plants. *noun.*

peb·ble (peb′əl), a small stone, usually worn smooth and round by being rolled about by water. *noun.*

peb·bly (peb′lē), having many pebbles; covered with pebbles: *The pebbly beach hurt our bare feet. adjective,* **peb·bli·er, peb·bli·est.**

pe·can (pi kän′ *or* pi kan′), a nut that grows on a tree of the southern United States and is shaped like an olive and has a smooth shell. Pecans are good to eat. *noun.*

pecan

pec·car·y (pek′ər ē), a wild animal with hoofs that is somewhat like a pig. It is found in South America and as far north as Texas. *noun, plural* **pec·car·ies** or **pec·car·y.**

peck[1] (pek), **1** to strike at and pick up with the beak: *The hen pecked corn.* **2** a stroke made with the beak: *The canary gave me a peck.* **3** to make by striking with the beak: *The woodpecker pecked*

holes in the trees. **4** a hole or mark made by pecking. **5** to make a pecking motion. **6** a stiff, unwilling kiss. 1,3,5 *verb,* 2,4,6 *noun.*

peck at, to eat only a little, bit by bit: *Because he is not feeling well, he just pecks at his food.*

peck[2] (pek), **1** a unit of measure for grain, fruit, vegetables, and other dry things, equal to 8 quarts or one fourth of a bushel: *a peck of potatoes.* **2** a great deal: *They have had a peck of trouble this year. noun.*

pe·cul·iar (pi kyü′lyər), **1** strange; odd; unusual: *It was peculiar that the fish market had no fish last Friday.* **2** special; belonging to one person or thing and not to another: *This type of pottery was peculiar to the ancient Egyptians. adjective.*

pe·cu·li·ar·i·ty (pi kyü′lē ar′ə tē), **1** a being peculiar; strange or unusual quality: *We noticed the peculiarity of her manner at once.* **2** some little thing that is strange or odd: *One of his peculiarities is that his eyes are not the same color. noun, plural* **pe·cu·li·ar·i·ties.**

ped·al (ped′l), **1** a lever worked by the foot; the part on which the foot is placed to move any kind of machinery. Organs have pedals for changing the tone. The two pedals of a bicycle, pushed down one after the other, make it go. **2** to work or use the pedals of; move by pedals: *I pedaled my bicycle slowly up the hill.* 1 *noun,* 2 *verb.*

ped·dle (ped′l), to carry from place to place and sell: *The salesman peddled brushes from house to house. verb,* **ped·dles, ped·dled, ped·dling.**

ped·dler (ped′lər), a person who travels about selling things carried in a pack or in a truck, wagon, or cart. *noun.*

ped·es·tal (ped′i stəl), **1** a base on which a column or a statue stands. **2** a base of a tall vase or lamp. *noun.*

pe·des·tri·an (pə des′trē ən), **1** a person who goes on foot; walker: *Pedestrians have to watch for automobiles turning corners.* **2** going on foot; walking. 1 *noun,* 2 *adjective.*

pe·di·a·tri·cian (pē′dē ə trish′ən), a doctor who specializes in children's diseases and the care of babies and children. *noun.*

ped·i·gree (ped′ə grē′), a list of ancestors of a person or animal; family tree. *noun.*

peek (pēk), **1** to look quickly and slyly; peep: *You must not peek while you are counting in*

peccary—about 3 feet (1 meter) long

hide-and-seek. **2** a quick, sly look: *I took a peek into the oven to see what we were having for dinner.* 1 *verb,* 2 *noun.*

peel (pēl), **1** the outer covering of fruit or vegetables; rind. **2** to strip the skin, rind, or bark from: *He peeled the orange.* **3** to strip: *I peeled the tape off my hand.* **4** to come off: *The paint on the shed is peeling.* 1 *noun,* 2-4 *verb.*

peep[1] (pēp), **1** to look quickly or secretly, often from a hiding place: *The child peeped through the curtains at the guests.* **2** a quick or secret look: *When no one was around, he took a peep at his birthday presents.* **3** to look out, as if peeping; come partly out: *Violets peeped among the leaves.* **4** the first looking or coming out: *She got up at the peep of day.* 1,3 *verb,* 2,4 *noun.*

peep[2] (pēp), **1** a cry of a young bird or chicken; sound like a chirp or a squeak. **2** to make such a sound; chirp: *We could hear the birds peeping in their nest.* 1 *noun,* 2 *verb.*

peer[1] (pir), **1** a person of the same rank, ability, or qualities as another; equal: *She is so fine a writer that it would be hard to find her peer.* **2** a person of British nobility such as a duke or baron. *noun.*

peer[2] (pir), **1** to look closely to see clearly, as a near-sighted person does. **2** to come out slightly; peep out: *The sun was peering from behind a cloud.* *verb.*

peer[2] (definition 1)
She **peered** at the goldfish.

peer·less (pir′lis), without an equal; matchless: *His peerless performance won him a prize.* *adjective.*

pee·vish (pē′vish), cross; fretful; complaining: *A peevish child is unhappy and makes others unhappy.* *adjective.*

peg (peg), **1** a pin or small bolt of wood or metal used to fasten parts together, to hang things on, to stop a hole, to make fast a rope or string on, or to mark the score in a game. **2** to fasten or hold with pegs: *We must peg down our tent.* **3** to work hard: *He pegged away at his studies so that he would get high marks.* 1 *noun,* 2,3 *verb,* **pegs, pegged, peg·ging.**

take down a peg, to humble; lower the pride of: *Three losses in a row took the team down a peg.*

Pe·king (pē′king′), the capital of China. *noun.*

Pe·king·ese (pē′kə nēz′), a small dog with long hair and a broad, flat face. *noun, plural* **Pe·king·ese.**

pelican—about 4 feet (1 meter) long. **Pelicans** bring food up from their stomachs to their pouches for their young to eat.

pel·i·can (pel′ə kən), a very large, fish-eating water bird with a huge bill and a pouch on the bottom side of the bill for scooping up fish. *noun.*

pel·let (pel′it), a little ball of mud, paper, hail, snow, food, or medicine; pill. *noun.*

pell-mell (pel′mel′), **1** in a rushing, tumbling mass or crowd: *The children dashed pell-mell down the beach and into the waves.* **2** in great haste: *He ran pell-mell down the street.* *adverb.*

pelt[1] (pelt), **1** to throw things at; attack; assail: *We pelted each other with snowballs.* **2** to beat heavily: *The rain came pelting down.* *verb.*

pelt[2] (pelt), the skin of a sheep, goat, or small fur-bearing animal, before it is tanned. *noun.*

pen[1] (pen), **1** an instrument used in writing with ink. **2** to write: *I penned a brief note.* 1 *noun,* 2 *verb,* **pens, penned, pen·ning.**

[*Pen*[1] comes from a Latin word meaning "feather." The first pens were made from feathers or quills. The lower end of a feather, the part attached to a bird's skin, was cut to a point and then split. When dipped into ink, this sharpened quill could be used for writing.]

Pekingese—11 inches (28 centimeters) high at the shoulder

P

453

pen² (pen), **1** a small, closed yard for cows, sheep, pigs, chickens, or other farm animals. **2** to shut in a pen. **3** to shut in; confine closely: *The fox was penned in a corner with no way of escape.* **1** *noun,* **2,3** *verb,* **pens, penned, pen·ning.**

pe·nal·ize (pē′nl īz), **1** to declare punishable by law or by rule; set a penalty for: *Speeding on city streets is penalized. Fouls are penalized in many games.* **2** to inflict a penalty on; punish: *Our football team was penalized five yards. verb,* **pe·nal·iz·es, pe·nal·ized, pe·nal·iz·ing.**

pen·al·ty (pen′l tē), **1** a punishment: *The penalty for speeding is usually a fine.* **2** a disadvantage placed on a side or player for breaking the rules of some game or contest. *noun, plural* **pen·al·ties.**

pen·ance (pen′əns), **1** a punishment borne to show sorrow for sin, to make up for a wrong done, and to obtain pardon for sin. **2** any act done to show that one is sorry or repents: *They did penance for cheating by staying after school. noun.*

pence (pens), more than one British penny. *noun plural.*

pen·cil (pen′səl), **1** a pointed tool to write or draw with. It is made of a thin rod of graphite enclosed by wood or by a metal tube. **2** to mark or write with a pencil. **1** *noun,* **2** *verb.*

pend·ant (pen′dənt), a hanging ornament, such as a locket. *noun.*

pend·ing (pen′ding), **1** waiting to be decided or settled: *while the agreement was pending.* **2** while waiting for; until: *Pending your return, we'll get everything ready.* **3** during: *pending the investigation.* **1** *adjective,* **2,3** *preposition.*

pendulum

pen·du·lum (pen′jə ləm), a weight hung from a fixed point so that it is free to swing to and fro. The movement of the works of a tall clock is often timed by a pendulum. *noun.*

pen·e·trate (pen′ə trāt), **1** to get into or through: *A bullet can penetrate this wall, or two inches into that wall.* **2** to pierce through; make a way: *Our eyes could not penetrate the darkness. Even where the trees were thickest, the sunshine penetrated.* **3** to see into; understand: *I could not penetrate the*

mystery. verb, **pen·e·trates, pen·e·trat·ed, pen·e·trat·ing.**

pen·e·tra·tion (pen′ə trā′shən), the act or power of penetrating. *noun.*

pen·guin (pen′gwin), a sea bird with flippers for diving and swimming in place of wings for flying. Penguins live in Antarctica and other cold areas of the Southern Hemisphere. *noun.*

penguins
about 3 feet (1 meter) tall

pen·i·cil·lin (pen′ə sil′ən), a very powerful drug used to kill the bacteria that cause certain diseases. It is made from a fungus mold. *noun.*

pe·nin·su·la (pə nin′sə lə), a piece of land almost surrounded by water, or extending far out into the water. Florida is a peninsula. *noun.*
[*Peninsula* comes from two Latin words meaning "almost" and "island."]

pen·i·tence (pen′ə təns), a feeling of sorrow for doing wrong; repentance. *noun.*

pen·i·tent (pen′ə tənt), sorry for doing wrong; repenting: *The penitent student promised never to cheat again. adjective.*

pen·i·ten·tiar·y (pen′ə ten′shər ē), a prison for criminals. *noun, plural* **pen·i·ten·tiar·ies.**

pen·knife (pen′nīf′), a small pocketknife. *noun, plural* **pen·knives** (pen′nīvz′).

pen·man·ship (pen′mən ship), handwriting; writing with pen or pencil. *noun.*

pen name, a name used by a writer instead of his or her real name.

pen·nant (pen′ənt), a flag, usually long and narrow, used on ships, in signaling, or as a school banner. In some sports, the best team wins a pennant. *noun.*

pen·ni·less (pen′ē lis), without a cent of money; very poor: *I've lost all my money and now I'm penniless. adjective.*

Penn·syl·van·ia (pen′səl vā′nyə), one of the northeastern states of the United States. *Abbreviation:* Pa. or PA *Capital:* Harrisburg. *noun.*
[*Pennsylvania,* meaning "Penn's woods," was formed by combining the name Penn with a Latin word meaning "woods." It was named by King Charles II of England in 1681 in honor of the father of the colony's founder, William Penn.]

pen·ny (pen′ē), **1** a cent; coin of the United States and Canada. One hundred pennies make one dollar. **2** a British coin. One hundred pennies make one pound. **3** a former British coin equal to one twelfth of a shilling. Until 1971, 240 pennies made one pound. *noun, plural* **pen·nies** or (for definitions 2 and 3) **pence.**
  a pretty penny, a large sum of money.
pen pal, a person with whom one exchanges letters regularly. Pen pals often live in different countries and have never met.
pen·sion (pen′shən), **1** a regular payment to a person which is not wages. A pension is paid by an employer to a person who is retired or disabled. **2** to give a pension to: *The company pensioned several employees who were sixty-five years old.* **1** *noun,* **2** *verb.*
pen·sive (pen′siv), thoughtful in a serious or sad way: *She was in a pensive mood, and sat staring out the window. adjective.*
pen·ta·gon (pen′tə gon), a figure having five angles and five sides. *noun.*

pentagon

pentagon
The **Pentagon** in Washington, D.C., is a building with five sides.

pent·house (pent′hous′), an apartment or other dwelling located on the top of a building. *noun, plural* **pent·hous·es** (pent′hou′ziz).
pe·o·ny (pē′ə nē), a garden plant with large, showy red, pink, or white flowers. *noun, plural* **pe·o·nies.**
peo·ple (pē′pəl), **1** men, women, and children; persons: *There were ten people present.* **2** a race; nation: *Asian peoples, the American people.* **3** persons in general; the public: *A democracy is a government of the people.* **4** the persons of a place, class, or group: *City people live in a noisier environment than country people do.* **5** one's family; relatives: *He spends his holidays with his people.* **6** to fill with people: *Many nations helped people*

America. 1-5 *noun, plural* **peo·ple** or (for definition 2) **peo·ples;** 6 *verb,* **peo·ples, peo·pled, peo·pling.**
pep (pep), **1** spirit; energy; vim. **2 pep up,** to fill or inspire with energy; put new life into: *A brisk walk after dinner will pep you up.* **1** *noun,* **2** *verb,* **peps, pepped, pep·ping.**
pep·per (pep′ər), **1** a seasoning with a hot taste, used for soups, meats, or vegetables. Pepper is made by grinding the berries of a vine grown in parts of Asia. **2** a hollow green or red vegetable that is eaten raw, cooked, or pickled. **3** to season with pepper; sprinkle with pepper. **4** to hit with small objects sent thick and fast: *We peppered them with snowballs.* **1,2** *noun,* **3,4** *verb.*
pep·per·mint (pep′ər mint), **1** a kind of mint grown for its oil which is used in medicine and candy. **2** a candy flavored with peppermint oil. *noun.*
per (pər *or* pėr), for each: *a pint of milk per child, ten cents per pound. preposition.*
per cap·i·ta (pər kap′ə tə), for each person: *$100 divided by five people is $20 per capita.*
per·ceive (pər sēv′), **1** to be aware of through the senses; see, hear, taste, smell, or feel: *Many animals do not perceive colors as we do.* **2** to take in with the mind; understand; observe: *I soon perceived that I couldn't make him change his mind. verb,* **per·ceives, per·ceived, per·ceiv·ing.**
per·cent (pər sent′), parts in each hundred; hundredths. The symbol for percent is %. *Five percent of 100 is 5. noun.*
per cent. See **percent.**
per·cent·age (pər sen′tij), **1** a rate or proportion of each hundred; part of each hundred: *What percentage of children were absent?* **2** a part; proportion: *A large percentage of schoolbooks now have pictures. noun.*
per·cep·ti·ble (pər sep′tə bəl), able to be perceived: *The other ship was barely perceptible in the fog. adjective.*
per·cep·ti·bly (pər sep′tə blē), in a perceptible way or amount; noticeably. *adverb.*
per·cep·tion (pər sep′shən), **1** the act of being aware of something: *My perception of time became confused when I flew from New York to Hawaii.* **2** an understanding: *She had a clear perception of the problem, and soon solved it. noun.*
perch[1] (pėrch), **1** a bar, branch, or anything else on which a bird can come to rest. **2** to come to rest; settle; sit: *A robin perched on the branch.* **3** a rather high seat or position. **4** to sit rather high: *He perched on a stool.* **5** to place high up: *a village perched on a high hill.* **1,3** *noun, plural* **perch·es; 2,4,5** *verb.*

perch² (pėrch), **1** a small freshwater fish, used for food. **2** a similar saltwater fish. *noun, plural* **perch** or **perch·es.**

per·chance (pər chans′), perhaps. *adverb.*

per·co·late (pėr′kə lāt), to drip or drain through small holes or spaces: *Let the coffee percolate for seven minutes. verb,* **per·co·lates, per·co·lat·ed, per·co·lat·ing.**

per·cus·sion (pər kush′ən), **1** the striking of one thing against another with force; blow. **2** the shock made by the striking of one thing against another with force. *noun.*

percussion instrument, a musical instrument played by striking it, such as a drum, cymbal, or piano.

pe·ren·ni·al (pə ren′ē əl), **1** lasting for a very long time: *the perennial beauty of the hills.* **2** living more than two years: *perennial garden plants.* **3** a perennial plant. Roses are perennials. 1,2 *adjective,* 3 *noun.*

per·fect (pėr′fikt *for 1,3-5, and 7;* pər fekt′ *for 2 and 6*), **1** having no faults; not spoiled at any point: *a perfect spelling paper, a perfect apple, a perfect life.* **2** to remove all faults from; make perfect; add the finishing touches to: *to perfect an invention. The artist was perfecting his picture.* **3** completely skilled; expert: *a perfect golfer.* **4** having all its parts there; complete: *The set was perfect; nothing was missing or broken.* **5** exact: *a perfect copy, a perfect circle.* **6** to carry through; complete: *to perfect a plan.* **7** entire; complete: *She was a perfect stranger to us.* 1,3-5,7 *adjective,* 2,6 *verb.*

per·fec·tion (pər fek′shən), **1** a perfect or faultless condition; highest excellence: *Her goal was to achieve perfection in her work.* **2** a making complete or perfect: *Perfection of our plans will take another week. noun.*

to perfection, perfectly: *The orchestra played the difficult piece to perfection.*

per·fect·ly (pėr′fikt lē), **1** in a perfect manner: *He played the piano piece perfectly.* **2** completely; fully: *The meaning is perfectly clear. adverb.*

per·fo·rate (pėr′fə rāt′), **1** to make a hole or holes through: *The target was perforated by bullets.* **2** to make a row or rows of holes through: *Sheets of postage stamps are perforated. verb,* **per·fo·rates, per·fo·rat·ed, per·fo·rat·ing.**

per·form (pər fôrm′), **1** to do; carry out: *Perform your duties well. The surgeon performed an operation.* **2** to act, play, sing, or do tricks in public: *We went to the circus to see the animals perform. verb.*

per·form·ance (pər fôr′məns), **1** a carrying out; doing: *The firefighter was injured in the performance of his duties.* **2** a thing performed; act; deed: *The child's kicks and screams made a disgraceful performance.* **3** the giving of a play, circus, or other show: *The evening performance is at 8 o'clock. noun.*

per·form·er (pər fôr′mər), a person who performs, especially one who performs to entertain others. Singers, dancers, and magicians are performers. *noun.*

percussion instruments

per·fume (pėr′fyüm *for 1 and 2;* pər fyüm′ *for 3*), **1** a liquid having a sweet smell: *She wore a perfume that smelled like apple blossoms.* **2** a sweet smell: *the perfume of the flowers.* **3** to fill with sweet odor: *Flowers perfumed the air.* 1,2 *noun,* 3 *verb,* **per·fumes, per·fumed, per·fum·ing.**

per·haps (pər haps′), it may be; possibly: *Perhaps a letter will come to you today. adverb.*

per·il (per′əl), the chance of harm; danger: *This bridge is not safe; cross it at your peril. noun.*

456

per·il·ous (per′ə ləs), dangerous: *They survived a perilous crossing of the ocean in a tiny boat.* adjective.

pe·rim·e·ter (pə rim′ə tər), the distance around an area or around a figure such as a square, triangle, or oval. noun.

per·i·od (pir′ē əd), **1** a portion of time: *She visited us for a short period.* **2** a certain series of years: *the period of World War II.* **3** a portion of a game during which there is actual play. **5** one of the portions of time into which a school day is divided. **5** the dot (.) marking the end of most sentences or showing an abbreviation, as in Mr. or Dec. noun.

per·i·od·ic (pir′ē od′ik), **1** occurring, appearing, or done again and again at regular times: *The coming of the new moon is a periodic event.* **2** happening every now and then: *Our school has periodic fire drills.* adjective.

per·i·od·i·cal (pir′ē od′ə kəl), a magazine that is published at regular times, less often than daily: *This periodical comes out monthly.* noun.

per·i·od·i·cal·ly (pir′ē od′ik lē), **1** at regular times. **2** every now and then. adverb.

per·i·scope (per′ə skōp), an instrument that allows those in a submarine to see a view of the surface. It is a tube with an arrangement of prisms or mirrors that reflect light rays down the tube. noun.

per·ish (per′ish), to be destroyed; die: *They perished in the fire. Flowers perish when frost comes.* verb.

per·ish·a·ble (per′i shə bəl), likely to spoil or decay: *Bananas are perishable.* adjective.

perk (pėrk), to raise quickly: *The dog perked its ears when it heard its owner.* verb.

perk up, to brighten up; become more cheerful and lively: *Perk up; things will get better.*

per·ma·nence (pėr′mə nəns), a being permanent; lasting quality or condition: *The study compared the permanence of different kinds of building materials.* noun.

per·ma·nent (pėr′mə nənt), lasting; intended to last; not for a short time only: *a permanent filling in a tooth. After doing odd jobs for a week, I got a permanent position as a clerk in a store.* adjective.

per·me·ate (pėr′mē āt), to spread through the whole of; pass through; soak through: *The smoke permeated the house. Water will easily permeate cotton.* verb, **per·me·ates, per·me·at·ed, per·me·at·ing.**

per·mis·sion (pər mish′ən), consent; leave: *She asked the teacher's permission to leave early.* noun.

per·mit (pər mit′ *for 1;* pėr′mit *for 2*), **1** to let; allow: *My parents will not permit me to stay up late. The law does not permit smoking in this store.* **2** a license or written order giving permission to do something: *Have you a permit to fish in this lake?* **1** verb, **per·mits, per·mit·ted, per·mit·ting; 2** noun.

per·pen·dic·u·lar (pėr′pən dik′yə lər), **1** straight up and down; vertical: *a perpendicular cliff.* **2** at right angles. One line is perpendicular to another when it makes a square corner with another. The floor of a room is perpendicular to the side walls and parallel to the ceiling. adjective.

per·pe·trate (pėr′pə trāt), to do or commit a crime, fraud, trick, or anything bad or foolish: *They were arrested for perpetrating a robbery.* verb, **per·pe·trates, per·pe·trat·ed, per·pe·trat·ing.**

per·pet·u·al (pər pech′ü əl), **1** eternal; lasting forever: *the perpetual hills.* **2** continuous; never stopping: *The waters of the river go over the falls with a perpetual roar.* adjective.

per·pet·u·al·ly (pər pech′ü ə lē), forever. adverb.

per·pet·u·ate (pər pech′ü āt), to make lasting; keep from being forgotten: *A statue helps perpetuate the memory of a well-known person.* verb, **per·pet·u·ates, per·pet·u·at·ed, per·pet·u·at·ing.**

per·plex (pər pleks′), to trouble with doubt; puzzle; confuse. verb.

perplex—The difficult jigsaw puzzle **perplexed** them.

per·plex·i·ty (pər plek′sə tē), confusion; being puzzled; not knowing what to do or how to act: *My perplexity was so great that I asked everyone for advice.* noun.

per·se·cute (pėr′sə kyüt), to treat badly, especially because of one's beliefs: *The Pilgrims came to America from England, because they were persecuted for their religious beliefs.* verb, **per·se·cutes, per·se·cut·ed, per·se·cut·ing.**

per·se·cu·tion (pėr′sə kyü′shən), a persecuting or a being persecuted: *The Christians' persecution by the ancient Romans forced many of them into hiding.* noun.

per·se·ver·ance (pėr′sə vir′əns), a sticking to a purpose or an aim; never giving up what one has set out to do: *By perseverance she finally learned to swim.* noun.

a hat	i it	oi oil	ch child	(a in about
ā age	ī ice	ou out	ng long	e in taken
ä far	o hot	u cup	sh she	ə = { i in pencil
e let	ō open	ů put	th thin	o in lemon
ē equal	ô order	ü rule	ᴛʜ then	(u in circus
ėr term			zh measure	

457

per·se·vere (pėr′sə vir′), to continue steadily in doing something hard; persist. To try, try, try again is to persevere. *verb,* **per·se·veres, per·se·vered, per·se·ver·ing.**

Per·sian (pėr′zhən), the language spoken in Iran. *noun.*

Persian Gulf War, a United Nations military operation led by United States forces against Iraq in 1991. It forced Iraq to retreat from its 1990 invasion of Kuwait. Also called **Desert Storm.**

per·sim·mon (pər sim′ən), the yellowish-orange, plumlike fruit of a North American tree. Persimmons are very bitter when green, but sweet and good to eat when very ripe. *noun.*

per·sist (pər sist′), **1** to refuse to stop or be changed: *Though we've asked her not to, she persists in reading at the dinner table.* **2** to last; stay; endure: *On some very high mountains snow persists throughout the year. verb.*

per·sist·ence (pər sis′təns), **1** a refusing to stop or be changed: *the persistence of a fly buzzing around my head.* **2** a continuing existence: *the stubborn persistence of a cough. noun.*

per·sist·ent (pər sis′tənt), **1** refusing to stop or give up: *The child was persistent in her demands for cookies and candy.* **2** lasting; going on; continuing: *a persistent headache that lasted for three days. adjective.*

per·son (pėr′sən), **1** a man, woman, or child; human being: *Any person who wishes may come to the fair.* **2** the human body: *The person of the king was well guarded. noun.*

in person, with or by one's own action or presence; personally: *Come in person; do not write or phone.*

per·son·al (pėr′sə nəl), **1** belonging to a person; private: *a personal letter.* **2** done in person; directly by oneself, not through others or by letter or telephone: *The author made personal appearances at several bookstores to autograph her books.* **3** of the body: *personal cleanliness.* **4** about or against a person or persons: *personal remarks. adjective.*

per·son·al·i·ty (pėr′sə nal′ə tē), **1** the personal or individual quality that makes one person be different or act differently from another: *She has a warm, friendly personality that makes her popular with other students.* **2** a well-known person: *I collect autographs of famous personalities in the entertainment world. noun, plural* **per·son·al·i·ties.**

per·son·al·ly (pėr′sə nə lē), **1** in person; not by the aid of others: *The owner of this store deals personally with customers.* **2** as far as oneself is concerned: *Personally, I like apples better than oranges.* **3** as a person: *I don't know her personally, but I've been told she is a talented writer.* **4** as being meant for oneself: *Don't take what I said personally; I didn't mean to insult you. adverb.*

per·son·i·fi·ca·tion (pər son′ə fə kā′shən), a figure of speech in which a thing or quality is spoken of as if it is alive, as in "The rusty hinges complained noisily." *noun.*

per·son·nel (pėr′sə nel′), the people employed in any work, business, or service: *The factory did not have enough personnel to complete the large order on time. noun.*

per·spec·tive (pər spek′tiv), **1** the art of picturing objects on a flat surface so as to give the appearance of distance. **2** the effect of distance on the appearance of objects. **3** the effect of distance of events upon the mind: *Many happenings of last year seem less important when viewed in perspective. noun.*

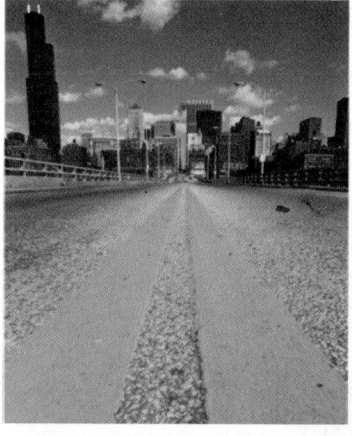

perspective (definition 2) The yellow lines on the street seem to meet at the horizon because of **perspective.**

per·spi·ra·tion (pėr′spə rā′shən), **1** sweat: *a forehead damp with perspiration.* **2** a sweating: *Perspiration helps the body to cool itself. noun.*

per·spire (pər spīr′), to sweat: *The room was so hot I began to perspire. verb,* **per·spires, per·spired, per·spir·ing.**

per·suade (pər swād′), to win over to do or believe; make willing or sure by urging or arguing: *I knew I should study, but he persuaded me to go to the movies. verb,* **per·suades, per·suad·ed, per·suad·ing.**

per·sua·sion (pər swā′zhən), **1** a persuading: *All our attempts at persuasion were useless; she would not go.* **2** the power of persuading: *He is a poor salesman because he lacks persuasion. noun.*

per·sua·sive (pər swā′siv), able or likely to persuade: *Your persuasive argument convinced me. adjective.*

pert (pėrt), not serious or respectful; too free in speech or action: *Her pert reply annoyed us. adjective.*

per·tain (pər tān′), to have to do with; be related; refer: *My question pertains to yesterday's homework. verb.*

per·ti·nent (pèrt′n ənt), having something to do with what is being considered; relating to the matter in hand; to the point: *If your question is pertinent, I will answer it. adjective.*

per·turb (pər tèrb′), to disturb greatly; make uneasy or troubled: *My parents were perturbed by my grades. verb.*

Pe·ru (pə rü′), a country in western South America. *noun.*

pe·ruse (pə rüz′), **1** to read thoroughly and carefully. **2** to read. *verb,* **pe·rus·es, pe·rused, pe·rus·ing.**

per·vade (pər vād′), to go or spread throughout; be throughout: *The odor of pines pervades the air. verb,* **per·vades, per·vad·ed, per·vad·ing.**

per·verse (pər vèrs′), **1** contrary and willful; stubborn: *The perverse child did just what we said not to do.* **2** wicked. *adjective.*

pes·ky (pes′kē), troublesome; annoying: *A pesky mosquito kept flying around my head. adjective,* **pes·ki·er, pes·ki·est.**

pe·so (pā′sō), the unit of money in various countries of Latin America and in the Philippines. *noun, plural* **pe·sos.**

pes·si·mis·tic (pes′ə mis′tik), **1** having a tendency to look on the dark side of things or to see all the difficulties and disadvantages: *a pessimistic person.* **2** expecting the worst: *I was pessimistic about passing the test because I hadn't studied. adjective.*

pest (pest), **1** an insect, animal, or the like that is harmful or destructive: *garden pests.* **2** a thing or person that is annoying; nuisance: *Don't be such a pest! noun.*

pes·ter (pes′tər), to annoy; trouble: *Flies pester us. Don't pester me with foolish questions. verb.*

pes·ti·cide (pes′tə sīd), a substance used to kill pests. Farmers often use pesticides to kill insects that might destroy their crops. *noun.*

pes·ti·lence (pes′tl əns), a disease that spreads rapidly, causing many deaths. Smallpox, yellow

fever, and the plague are pestilences that killed many people in former times. *noun.*

pet (pet), **1** an animal kept as a companion and treated with affection. **2** treated as a pet: *a pet rabbit.* **3** to stroke or pat; touch lovingly and gently: *Her dog was jealous while she was petting the kitten.* **4** a darling or favorite: *He is the teacher's pet.* **1,4** *noun,* **2** *adjective,* **3** *verb,* **pets, pet·ted, pet·ting.**

pet·al (pet′l), one of the parts of a flower that are usually colored. A rose has many petals. *noun.*

pe·tite (pə tēt′), little; of small size: *It surprised me that such a petite young woman was so strong. adjective.*

pe·ti·tion (pə tish′ən), **1** a written request to someone in authority for some right or privilege, often signed by many people: *The home owners on our street signed a petition asking the city council for a new sidewalk.* **2** to make such a request to: *Several classes petitioned the principal to improve the lunches in the school cafeteria.* **1** *noun,* **2** *verb.*

pet·ri·fy (pet′rə fī), **1** to turn into stone or a substance like stone: *Ancient tree trunks that have petrified can be seen in Arizona.* **2** to paralyze with fear, horror, or surprise: *I was petrified when lightning struck our house. verb,* **pet·ri·fies, pet·ri·fied, pet·ri·fy·ing.**

pe·tro·le·um (pə trō′lē əm), an oily, dark-colored liquid that is found in the earth. Gasoline, kerosene, and many other products are made from petroleum. *noun.*

[*Petroleum* comes from a Greek word meaning "rock" and a Latin word meaning "oil." Petroleum lies deep below the earth's surface. Wells are drilled through earth and rock to reach it.]

pet·ti·coat (pet′ē kōt), a skirt worn beneath a dress or outer skirt by women and girls. *noun.*

pet·ty (pet′ē), **1** small; having little importance or value: *Don't let petty disturbances upset you.* **2** mean: *A gossip has a petty mind. adjective,* **pet·ti·er, pet·ti·est.**

pet·u·lant (pech′ə lənt), likely to have little fits of bad temper; irritable over trifles; peevish. *adjective.*

pe·tun·ia (pə tü′nyə *or* pə tyü′nyə), a common garden plant that has white, pink, and purple flowers shaped like funnels. *noun.*

pew (pyü), a bench in church for people to sit on, fastened to the floor and with a back. *noun.*

pe·wee (pē′wē), a small American bird with an olive-colored or gray back. Its call sounds somewhat like its name. *noun.*

pew·ter (pyü′tər), **1** a metal made by combining tin with lead, copper, or other metals. Pewter is

pewter (definition 2)

used to make dishes and other utensils. **2** made of pewter: *a pewter mug.* **1** *noun,* **2** *adjective.*

phan·tom (fan′təm), **1** a vague, dim, or shadowy appearance; ghost. **2** like a ghost; unreal: *a phantom ship.* **1** *noun,* **2** *adjective.*

phar·aoh (fer′ō), the title given to the kings of ancient Egypt. *noun.*

phar·ma·cist (fär′mə sist), a druggist. *noun.*

phar·ma·cy (fär′mə sē), a store where drugs and other medicines are sold; drugstore. *noun,* *plural* **phar·ma·cies.**

phase (fāz), **1** one of the changing states or stages of development of a person or thing: *At present his voice is changing; that is a phase all boys go through.* **2** one side, part, or view of something: *What phase of arithmetic are you studying now?* **3** the shape of the lighted part of the moon or a planet at a given time. *noun.*

phase (definition 3)—phases of the moon

pheas·ant (fez′nt), a bird with a long tail and brightly colored feathers that is hunted and used for food. Wild pheasants live in many parts of Europe and America. *noun, plural* **pheas·ants** or **pheas·ant.**

phe·nom·e·na (fə nom′ə nə), more than one phenomenon. *noun, plural.*

phe·nom·e·nal (fə nom′ə nəl), extraordinary: *a phenomenal memory. adjective.*

phe·nom·e·non (fə nom′ə non), **1** a fact, event, or circumstance that can be observed: *Lightning is an electrical phenomenon. Fever and inflammation are phenomena of disease.* **2** something or someone extraordinary or remarkable: *The fond parents think their child is a phenomenon. noun, plural* **phe·nom·e·na** or (for definition 2) **phe·nom·e·nons.**

Phil·a·del·phi·a (fil′ə del′fē ə), a city in Pennsylvania. *noun.*

phil·an·throp·ic (fil′ən throp′ik), charitable; benevolent; kindly. *adjective.*

phi·lan·thro·pist (fə lan′thrə pist), a person who helps people, often by giving large sums of money to worthy causes. *noun.*

Phil·ip·pine (fil′ə pēn′), of or having something

to do with the Philippines or their people. *adjective.*

Phil·ip·pines (fil′ə pēnz′), a country made up of over 7000 islands in the Pacific Ocean southeast of Asia. The United States governed the Philippines before they gained independence in 1946. *noun plural.*

phi·los·o·pher (fə los′ə fər), **1** a person who studies philosophy a great deal. **2** an author or founder of a system of philosophy. **3** a person who is calm and reasonable under hard conditions, accepting life and making the best of it. *noun.*

phil·o·soph·ic (fil′ə sof′ik), philosophical. *adjective.*

phil·o·soph·i·cal (fil′ə sof′ə kəl), **1** of philosophy: *a philosophical discussion.* **2** wise, calm, and reasonable: *I tried to be philosophical about my disappointments. adjective.*

phi·los·o·phy (fə los′ə fē), **1** the study which attempts to discover and understand the basic nature of knowledge and reality. **2** a system for guiding one's own life: *the philosophy of a Puritan. noun, plural* **phi·los·o·phies.**

phlegm (flem), the thick mucus that appears in the nose and throat during a cold. *noun.*

phlox (floks), a common garden plant that has showy flower clusters of various colors. *noun, plural* **phlox·es.**

phoe·be (fē′bē), a small North American bird with a grayish-brown back, a yellowish-white breast, and a low crest on the head. It catches and eats insects as it flies. *noun.*

Phoe·nix (fē′niks), the capital of Arizona. *noun.*

phone (fōn), telephone. *noun, verb,* **phones, phoned, phon·ing.**

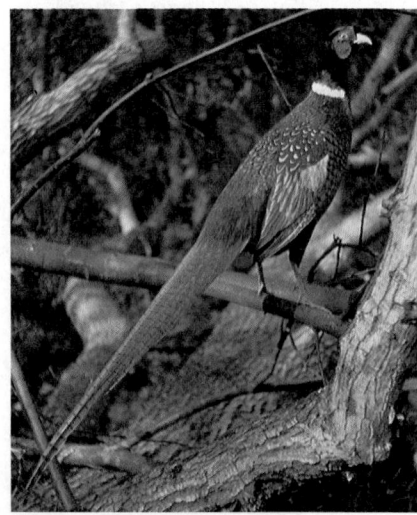

pheasant
about 3½ feet (1 meter) long with the tail

pho·net·ic (fə net′ik), representing sounds made with the voice. Phonetic symbols are marks used to show pronunciation. We use ō as the phonetic symbol for the sound of *o* in *photo. adjective.*

pho·no·graph (fō′nə graf), an instrument that

reproduces sounds from records; record player. As a record turns, the grooves on its surface cause the phonograph needle to vibrate. These vibrations are changed into electricity which causes a loudspeaker to produce sound. *noun.*

pho·ny (fō′nē), **1** not genuine; fake: *The jeweler told her that the diamond was phony.* **2** a fake; pretender: *The doctor turned out to be a phony who had no medical training.* **1** *adjective,* **pho·ni·er, pho·ni·est; 2** *noun, plural* **pho·nies.**

phos·phor·us (fos′fər əs), a yellow or white waxy substance that burns slowly at ordinary temperatures and glows in the dark. Phosphorus is a chemical element. *noun.*

pho·to (fō′tō), a photograph. *noun, plural* **pho·tos.**

pho·to·graph (fō′tə graf), **1** a picture made with a camera. A photograph is made by the action of the light rays from the thing pictured passing through the lens of the camera onto the film. **2** to take a photograph of. **1** *noun,* **2** *verb.*

pho·tog·ra·pher (fə tog′rə fər), **1** a person who takes photographs. **2** a person whose business is taking photographs. *noun.*

pho·to·graph·ic (fō′tə graf′ik), used in or produced by photography: *photographic supplies, a photographic record of a trip. adjective.*

pho·tog·ra·phy (fə tog′rə fē), the taking of photographs: *My photography is improving. noun.*

pho·to·syn·the·sis (fō′tō sin′thə sis), the process by which green plants use the energy of light to make their own food from carbon dioxide and water. *noun.*

phrase (frāz), **1** two or more words that have a meaning but do not contain a subject and verb, and do not form a complete sentence. *At school, in the house,* and *hoping to see you soon* are phrases. **2** an expression often used: *"Call up" is the common phrase for "make a telephone call to."* **3** to express in a particular way: *I tried to phrase my excuse politely.* **1,2** *noun,* **3** *verb,* **phras·es, phrased, phras·ing.**

phys·i·cal (fiz′ə kəl), **1** of the body: *physical exercise, physical strength.* **2** a medical examination by a doctor: *I had to have a physical before I could go to summer camp.* **3** of matter; material: *The tide is a physical force.* **4** according to the laws of nature: *It is a physical impossibility for the sun to rise in the west.* **5** dealing with the natural features of the earth. **Physical geography** teaches about the earth's formation, climate, clouds, and tides. **1,3-5,** *adjective,* **2** *noun.*

physical change, a change in which the shape or form of a substance becomes different but the nature of the substance stays the same. A change from a liquid to a solid, as when water freezes into ice, is a physical change.

phys·i·cal·ly (fiz′ik lē), in a physical manner; in physical respects; as regards the body: *She was in fine condition both physically and mentally. adverb.*

phy·si·cian (fə zish′ən), a doctor of medicine. *noun.*

a hat	i it	oi oil	ch child	⎧ a in about
ā age	ī ice	ou out	ng long	⎪ e in taken
ä far	o hot	u cup	sh she	ə = ⎨ i in pencil
e let	ō open	u̇ put	th thin	⎪ o in lemon
ē equal	ô order	ü rule	ᵹH then	⎩ u in circus
ėr term			zh measure	

phys·i·cist (fiz′ə sist), a person who is an expert in physics. *noun.*

phys·ics (fiz′iks), the science that deals with matter and energy and their relationships to each other. Physics includes the study of mechanics, heat, light, sound, electricity, magnetism, and atomic energy. *noun.*

phys·i·ol·o·gy (fiz′ē ol′ə jē), the science dealing with the normal working of living things or their parts: *animal physiology, human physiology. noun.*

phy·sique (fə zēk′), body; bodily structure: *The swimmer had a strong physique. noun.*

pi (pī), the Greek letter π, used as the symbol for the ratio of the circumference of any circle to its diameter. π is equal to about 3.1416. *noun.*

pi·an·ist (pē an′ist *or* pē′ə nist), a person who plays the piano. *noun.*

pi·an·o (pē an′ō), a musical instrument whose tones come from many wires called strings. When you strike the keys, small hammers hit the strings and produce sounds. *noun, plural* **pi·an·os.**
[*Piano* was shortened from *pianoforte*, which came from three Italian words meaning "soft and loud." The piano was called this because of the many different tones that can be played on it.]

pi·az·za (pē az′ə *for 1;* pē ät′sə *or* pē az′ə *for 2*), **1** a large porch along one or more sides of a house. **2** an open public square in Italian towns. *noun.*

pic·co·lo (pik′ə lō), a musical instrument that looks like a small flute but sounds an octave higher. *noun, plural* **pic·co·los.**

piccolo

pick[1] (pik), **1** to choose; select: *I picked a blue shirt to wear with my jeans.* **2** a choice or selection: *This red rose is my pick.* **3** the best part: *We got a high price for the pick of our peaches.* **4** to pull away with the fingers; gather: *We pick fruit.* **5** to use something pointed to remove things from: *to pick one's teeth, to pick a bone.* **6** to open with a pointed instrument or wire: *The burglar picked the lock on the garage.* **7** to steal the contents of: *Someone picked my pocket.* **8** to pluck the strings of a musical instrument: *I picked the strings of the banjo.* **9** a thing held in the fingers and used to pluck the strings of a musical instrument. **10** to seek and find: *Don't pick a quarrel with them.* 1,4-8,10 *verb,* 2,3,9 *noun.*

pick at, 1 to pull on with the fingers: *She picked at the scab on her finger.* **2** to eat a bit at a time: *The bird picks at the bread. Don't pick at your food.*

pick on, 1 to find fault with: *The teacher picked on him for always being late.* **2** to annoy; tease: *My older brother and sister are always picking on me.*

pick out, 1 to choose; select: *Pick out a coat you like.* **2** to tell a person or thing apart from its surroundings; recognize: *Can you pick me out in this group picture?*

pick up, 1 to take up; lift: *She picked up a hammer.* **2** to get by chance: *I picked up a bargain at the sale.* **3** to learn without being taught: *He picks up games easily.* **4** to take into a vehicle or ship; give a ride to: *The bus stopped at the corner to pick up passengers.* **5** to get and take along with you: *I picked up a pizza on my way home.* **6** to increase the speed; go or make go faster: *The bus picked up speed on its way down the mountain.* **7** to succeed in seeing or hearing: *She picked up a radio broadcast from Paris.* **8** to tidy up; put in order: *to pick up a room.*

pick[2] (pik), **1** a pickax. **2** a sharp-pointed tool. Ice is broken into pieces with a pick. *noun.*

pick·ax or **pick·axe** (pik′aks′), a tool with a heavy metal bar, pointed at one or both ends, attached through the center to a wooden handle. It is used for breaking up dirt or rocks. *noun, plural* **pick·ax·es.**

pick·er·el (pik′ər əl), a freshwater fish that is smaller than the pike and has a long, pointed head. It is used for food. *noun, plural* **pick·er·el** or **pick·er·els.**

pick·et (pik′it), **1** a pointed stake or peg placed upright to make a fence or driven into the ground to tie a horse to. **2** a person stationed by a labor union near a factory or store where there is a strike. Pickets try to prevent employees from working or customers from buying. **3** a person who demonstrates to support a cause or to protest something. **4** to walk about or stand near as a picket: *to picket a factory during a strike.* 1-3 *noun,* 4 *verb.*

pick·le (pik′əl), **1** salt water, vinegar, or other liquid in which meat and vegetables can be preserved. **2** a cucumber preserved in pickle. **3** any other vegetable preserved in pickle. **4** to preserve in pickle: *to pickle beets.* **5** trouble; difficulty: *I got in a bad pickle today.* 1-3,5 *noun,* 4 *verb,* **pick·les, pick·led, pick·ling.**

pick·pock·et (pik′pok′it), a person who steals from people's pockets or purses. *noun.*

pick·up (pik′up′), **1** a picking up: *the daily pickup of mail.* **2** the ability to go faster quickly; increase in speed; acceleration: *Although our car is ten years old, it still has good pickup.* **3** a pickup truck. *noun.*

pickup truck, a small, light truck with an open back, used for light hauling.

pic·nic (pik′nik), **1** a pleasure trip or party, with a meal in the open air: *We had a picnic at the beach.* **2** to go on such a trip: *Our family often picnics at the beach.* **3** to eat in picnic style: *We picnicked in the backyard.* 1 *noun,* 2,3 *verb,* **pic·nics, pic·nicked, pic·nick·ing.**

pic·nick·er (pik′ni kər), a person who picnics. *noun.*

pic·to·graph (pik′tə graf), **1** a picture used as a sign or symbol: *The symbols used in written Chinese developed from pictographs.* **2** a chart or diagram showing facts or information by using such pictures. *noun.*

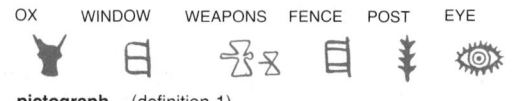

OX   WINDOW   WEAPONS FENCE POST   EYE

pictograph—(definition 1)

pic·to·ri·al (pik tôr′ē əl), **1** having something to do with pictures; expressed in pictures. **2** illustrated by pictures: *a pictorial history, a pictorial magazine. adjective.*

pic·ture (pik′chər), **1** a drawing, painting, portrait, or photograph; printed copy of any of these: *The book contains a good picture of a tiger.* **2** to draw or paint; make into a picture: *The artist pictured life in the old West.* **3** a likeness; image: *He is the picture of his father.* **4** to form a picture of in the mind; imagine: *It is hard to picture life a hundred years ago.* **5** a vivid description: *The speaker gave us a good picture of life in the old West.* **6** to show by words; describe vividly: *The speaker pictured the suffering of the poor.* **7** a motion picture. **8** an image on a television set. 1,3,5,7,8 *noun,* 2,4,6 *verb,* **pic·tures, pic·tured, pic·tur·ing.**

pic·tur·esque (pik′chə resk′), **1** quaint or interesting enough to be used as the subject of a picture: *a picturesque old mill.* **2** making a picture for the mind; vivid: *picturesque language. adjective.*

picture tube, a glass tube, narrow at one end and widening at the other end to form a screen on which television pictures or computer information appear.

pie (pī), fruit, meat, or the like, enclosed in pastry and baked: *apple pie, chicken pie. noun.*

piece (pēs), **1** one of the parts into which a thing is divided or broken; bit: *The cup broke in pieces.* **2** a portion; limited part; small quantity: *a piece of land containing two acres, a piece of bread.* **3** a single thing of a set or class: *This set of china has*

144 pieces. **4** a single composition in an art: *a piece of poetry, a piece of music.* **5** a coin: *A nickel is a five-cent piece.* **6** an example; instance: *That silly story is a piece of nonsense.* **7** to make or repair by adding or joining pieces: *to piece a quilt.* **8** to join the pieces of: *After listening to three witnesses, we were able to piece together the story.* 1-6 *noun,* 7,8 *verb,* **piec·es, pieced, piec·ing.**

piece of one's mind, a scolding: *She gave them a piece of her mind for coming late again.*

piece of eight, an old Spanish peso, used by the Spanish in Spain and America.

pied (pīd), having patches of two or more colors; many-colored. *adjective.*

pier (pir), **1** a structure built out over the water, and used as a walk or a landing place. **2** one of the solid supports on which the arches of a bridge rest; pillar. *noun.*

pier (definition 1)

pierce (pirs), **1** to go into; go through: *A tunnel pierces the mountain.* **2** to make a hole in; bore into or through: *A nail pierced the tire of our car.* **3** to force a way through or into: *The cold wind pierced our clothes. A sharp cry pierced the air.* verb, **pierc·es, pierced, pierc·ing.**

Pierre (pir), the capital of South Dakota. *noun.*

pi·e·ty (pī′ə tē), **1** a being pious; reverence for God; religious character or conduct; holiness; goodness. **2** a pious act, remark, or belief. *noun,* plural **pi·e·ties.**

pig (pig), **1** an animal with a stout, heavy body, hoofs, and a broad snout. It is raised for its meat. **2** a person who is greedy, dirty, dull, sullen, or stubborn. *noun.*

pig·eon (pij′ən), a bird with a plump body and short tail and legs; dove. *noun.*
[*Pigeon* comes from a Latin word meaning "to cheep."]

pig·eon-toed (pij′ən tōd′), having the toes or feet turned inward. *adjective.*

pig·gy·back (pig′ē bak′), on the back: *a piggyback ride. Flatcars often take trucks piggyback from one place to another. adjective, adverb.*

pig-head·ed (pig′hed′id), stubborn; refusing to change one's opinion or action: *Some people can be very pig-headed. adjective.*

pig·let (pig′lit), a little pig. *noun.*

pig·ment (pig′mənt), a coloring matter. Paint and dyes are made by mixing pigments with liquid. The color of a person's hair, skin, and eyes is due to pigment in the cells of the body. *noun.*

pig·pen (pig′pen′), **1** a pen where pigs are kept. **2** a filthy place. *noun.*

pig·sty (pig′stī), a pigpen. *noun,* plural **pig·sties.**

pig·tail (pig′tāl′), a braid of hair hanging from the back of the head. *noun.*

pike (pīk), a large freshwater fish with a long, pointed head. *noun,* plural **pike** or **pikes.**

pile[1] (pīl), **1** many things lying one upon another in a more or less orderly way: *a pile of wood.* **2** a mass like a hill or mound: *a pile of dirt.* **3** to make into a pile; heap up; stack: *The campers piled the extra wood in a corner.* **4** to gather or rise in piles: *Snow piled against the fences.* **5** a large amount: *I have a pile of work to do.* **6** to cover with large amounts: *to pile a plate with food.* **7** to go in a confused, rushing crowd or group: *We piled out of the bus into the schoolyard. They all piled into the car.* 1,2,5 *noun,* 3,4,6,7 *verb,* **piles, piled, pil·ing.**

pile[2] (pīl), a heavy beam driven upright into the ground or the bed of a river to help support a bridge, wharf, or building. *noun.*

pile[3] (pīl), a soft, thick nap on velvet, plush, and many carpets: *The pile of that rug is almost half an inch long. noun.*

pil·fer (pil′fər), to steal in small quantities: *The hungry hikers pilfered apples from an orchard.* verb.

pil·grim (pil′grəm), **1** a person who goes on a journey to a sacred or holy place as an act of religious devotion. In the Middle Ages, many people used to go as pilgrims to Jerusalem and to holy places in Europe. **2** a traveler; wanderer. **3 Pilgrim,** one of the English settlers who founded Plymouth, Massachusetts, in 1620. *noun.*

pil·grim·age (pil′grə mij), **1** a pilgrim's journey; journey to some sacred place. **2** a long journey. *noun.*

pill (pil), medicine made up into a tiny ball to be swallowed whole. *noun.*

pil·lage (pil′ij), **1** to plunder; rob with violence: *Pirates pillaged the towns along the coast.* **2** plunder; robbery. 1 *verb,* **pil·lag·es, pil·laged, pil·lag·ing;** 2 *noun.*

pil·lar (pil′ər), **1** a slender upright support; column. Pillars are usually made of stone, wood, or metal and used as supports or ornaments for a building. Sometimes a pillar stands alone as a monument. **2** anything slender and upright like a pillar: *Pillars of smoke rose from the burning building. noun.*

P

pillory (definition 1)

pincers (definition 2)—**pincers** of a crab

pil·lor·y (pil′ər ē), **1** a frame of wood with holes through which a person's head and hands were put. The pillory was formerly used as a punishment, being set up in a public place where the crowd could make fun of the offender. **2** to put in the pillory. 1 *noun, plural* **pil·lor·ies;** 2 *verb,* **pil·lor·ies, pil·lor·ied, pil·lor·y·ing.**

pil·low (pil′ō), a bag or case filled with feathers, down, or other soft material, usually used to support the head when resting or sleeping. *noun.*

pil·low·case (pil′ō kās′), a cloth cover for a pillow. *noun.*

pi·lot (pī′lət), **1** a person who operates the controls of an aircraft or spacecraft in flight. **2** a person who steers a ship or boat. **3** a person whose business is to steer ships in or out of a harbor or through dangerous waters. A ship takes on a pilot before coming into a harbor. **4** to act as a pilot of; steer: *to pilot an airplane.* 1-3 *noun,* 4 *verb.*

pi·men·to (pə men′tō). See **pimiento.** *noun, plural* **pi·men·tos.**

pi·mien·to (pə men′tō *or* pi myen′tō), a kind of sweet pepper, used as a vegetable, relish, and stuffing for green olives. *noun, plural* **pi·mien·tos.**

pim·ple (pim′pəl), a small, sore, red swelling of the skin. *noun.*

pin (pin), **1** a short slender piece of wire with a point at one end and a head at the other, for fastening things together. **2** a badge or an ornament with a pin or clasp to fasten it to the clothing: *She wore her class pin.* **3** a peg made of wood, metal, or plastic, used to fasten things together, hold something, or hang things on. **4** any of various fastenings, such as a clothespin or a safety pin. **5** to fasten with a pin or pins; put a pin through: *I pinned a notice on the bulletin board.* **6** to hold fast in one position: *When the tree fell, its branches pinned the lumberjack's leg to the ground.* **7** a bottle-shaped piece of wood used in the game of bowling. 1-4,7 *noun,* 5,6 *verb,* **pins, pinned, pin·ning.**

on pins and needles, very worried or uneasy: *I was on pins and needles until I found out I passed the test.*

pi·ña·ta (pē nyä′tə), a pot filled with candy, fruit, and small toys, hung at Christmas time in Mexico and other Latin-American countries. Blindfolded children swing sticks in order to break the pot to get what is inside. *noun, plural* **pi·ña·tas.**

[*Piñata* was borrowed from a Spanish word.]

pin·cers (pin′sərz), **1** a tool for gripping and holding tight, made like scissors but with jaws instead of blades. **2** the large claw with which crabs, lobsters, and crayfish pinch or nip; pair of claws. *noun plural or singular.*

pinch (pinch), **1** to squeeze with thumb and forefinger: *I pinched the baby's cheek playfully.* **2** an act of pinching: *I gave the baby's cheek a playful pinch.* **3** to press so as to hurt; squeeze: *These new shoes pinch my feet.* **4** a sharp pressure that hurts; a squeeze: *the pinch of tight shoes.* **5** a sharp discomfort or distress: *the pinch of hunger.* **6** to cause to shrink or become thin: *a face pinched by hunger.* **7** a time of special need; emergency: *I will help you in a pinch.* **8** as much as can be taken up with the tips of finger and thumb; very small amount: *a pinch of salt.* **9** to be stingy; be stingy with: *The miser even pinched pennies.* 1,3,6,9 *verb,* 2,4,5,7,8 *noun, plural* **pinch·es.**

pinch-hit (pinch′hit′), **1** (in baseball) to bat for another player, especially when a hit is badly needed. **2** to take another's place in an emergency: *I had to pinch-hit for my brother when he was sick and couldn't deliver the papers.* *verb,* **pinch-hits, pinch-hit, pinch-hit·ting.**

pinch hitter, a person who pinch-hits for another.

pin·cush·ion (pin′kush′ən), a small cushion to stick pins in until they are needed. *noun.*

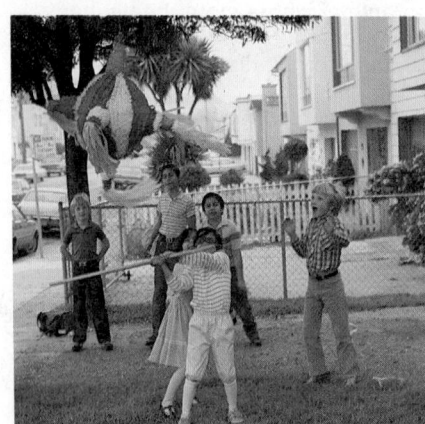

piñata

pine[1] (pīn), **1** a tree that bears cones and has evergreen leaves shaped like needles. Many pines are of value for lumber, tar, and turpentine. **2** the wood of the pine. *noun.*

pine[2] (pīn), to long eagerly; yearn: *The homesick children were pining for their parents. verb,* **pines, pined, pin·ing.**

pine·ap·ple (pī′nap′əl), the large, juicy fruit of a tropical plant with slender, stiff leaves. Pineapples look something like big pine cones and are good to eat. *noun.*

ping (ping), **1** a sound like that of a rifle bullet whistling through the air or striking an object. **2** to make such a sound. **1** *noun,* **2** *verb.*

Ping-Pong (ping′pong′), a trademark for a game played on a large table marked somewhat like a tennis court, using small wooden paddles and a light, hollow, plastic ball; table tennis. *noun.*

pin·ion (pin′yən), to bind; bind the arms of: *The bank robbers pinioned the guard's arms. verb.*

pink (pingk), **1** a color that is a mixture of red and white; light or pale red. **2** having this color. **3** the highest degree or condition: *Exercise helps keep a person in the pink of health.* **4** a garden plant with spicy-smelling flowers of various colors, mostly white, pink, and red. A carnation is one kind of pink. **1,3,4** *noun,* **2** *adjective.*

pink·eye (pingk′ī′), a disease that causes soreness of the thin lining that forms the inner surface of the eyelids and the front part of the eyeball. You can catch pinkeye from someone who has it. *noun.*

pink·ish (ping′kish), somewhat pink. *adjective.*

pin·na·cle (pin′ə kəl), **1** a high peak or point of rock, ice, a mountain, or a building: *a snow-covered pinnacle of the Alps.* **2** the highest point: *at the pinnacle of her fame. noun.*

piñ·on (pin′yən or pē′nyōn), a kind of low pine tree, especially of the Rocky Mountains, that produces large, nutlike seeds which are good to eat. *noun, plural* **piñ·ons.**

pin·point (pin′point′), **1** the point of a pin. **2** something very small or sharp: *A pinpoint of light sparkled against the deep blue sky.* **3** to aim at or locate exactly: *The pilot was trying to pinpoint a field for landing.* **1,2** *noun,* **3** *verb.*

pint (pīnt), a unit for measuring liquids equal to half a quart or 16 fluid ounces. *noun.*

pin·to (pin′tō), **1** spotted in two or more colors: *a pinto pony.* **2** a spotted, white and black or white and brown horse. **1** *adjective,* **2** *noun, plural* **pin·tos.**

pi·o·neer (pī′ə nir′), **1** a person who settles in a part of a country, preparing it for others. **2** a person who goes first, or does something first, and so prepares a way for others: *a pioneer in medical science.* **3** to prepare or open up for others; take the lead: *Astronauts are pioneering the exploration of outer space.* **1,2** *noun,* **3** *verb.*

pi·ous (pī′əs), religious; having or showing deep respect for God: *She is a pious woman who goes to church every morning. adjective.*

pipe (pīp), **1** a tube through which a liquid or gas flows. **2** to carry by means of a pipe or pipes: *Water is piped from the lake into the reservoir.* **3** to supply with pipes: *Our street is being piped for gas.* **4** a tube of clay, wood, or other material, with a bowl at one end, for smoking. **5** a musical instrument with a single tube into which the player blows. **6** to play music on a pipe: *The shepherd piped a strange melody.* **7** any one of the tubes in an organ. **8** to make a shrill noise; speak or sing in a shrill voice: *The child piped, "I'm hungry!"* **9** a shrill sound, voice, or song: *the pipe of the lark.* **1,4,5,7,9** *noun,* **2,3,6,8** *verb,* **pipes, piped, pip·ing.**

pipe·line (pīp′līn′), a line of pipes for carrying oil or gas, usually over a considerable distance. *noun.*

pip·er (pī′pər), a person who plays on a pipe or bagpipe. *noun.*

pip·ing (pī′ping). **piping hot,** so hot as to hiss; very hot; boiling: *The tea is piping hot. adjective.*

pique (pēk), **1** a feeling of anger at being slighted; wounded pride: *In a pique, he left the party.* **2** to wound the pride of: *It piqued her that we had a secret she did not share.* **3** to arouse; stir up: *Our curiosity was piqued by the locked trunk.* **1** *noun,* **2,3** *verb,* **piques, piqued, pi·quing.**

pi·ra·cy (pī′rə sē), robbery on the sea. *noun.*

pi·rate (pī′rit), a person who attacks and robs ships; robber on the sea. *noun.*

pis·ta·chi·o (pi stash′ē ō or pi stä′shē ō), a small, greenish nut having the flavor of almonds. *noun, plural* **pis·ta·chi·os.**

pis·til (pis′tl), the part of a flower that produces seeds. *noun.*

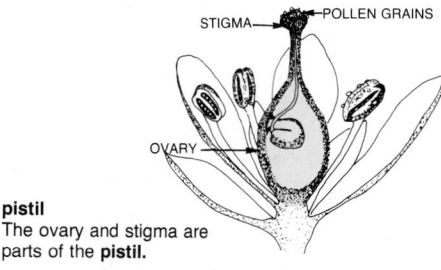

pistil
The ovary and stigma are parts of the **pistil.**

pis·tol (pis′tl), a small, short gun held and fired with one hand. *noun.*

[*Pistol* comes from a word from Czechoslovakia, meaning "pipe." A pistol barrel is like a small metal pipe.]

pis·ton (pis′tən), a short cylinder, or a flat, round piece of wood or metal, fitting closely inside a tube or hollow cylinder. It moves rapidly back and

piston—The drawing shows how an automobile **piston** (shown in blue) moves inside a cylinder. A spark causes the gasoline vapor to explode and drive the **piston**.

forth, powered by the force of exploding gasoline vapor or steam. Pistons are used in pumps, engines, and compressors. *noun.*

pit[1] (pit), **1** a hole or cavity in the ground. A mine or the shaft of a mine is a pit. **2** a little hollow place or scar, such as is left by smallpox. **3** to mark with small pits or scars: *The smallpox victim's face was deeply pitted.* **4** to set to fight or compete; match: *She was pitted against her friend in the last round of the tennis match.* 1,2 *noun,* 3,4 *verb,* **pits, pit·ted, pit·ting.**

pit[2] (pit), **1** the hard seed of a cherry, peach, plum, date, or similar fruit; stone. **2** to remove the pits from fruit: *I pitted cherries to make a cherry pie.* 1 *noun,* 2 *verb,* **pits, pit·ted, pit·ting.**

pitch[1] (pich), **1** to throw; fling; hurl; toss: *They were pitching horseshoes.* **2** (in baseball) to throw a ball to the player batting. **3** the act of pitching; a throw or toss: *The first pitch was a strike.* **4** to fix firmly in the ground; set up: *to pitch a tent.* **5** to fall or plunge forward: *I lost my balance and pitched down the stairs.* **6** to plunge with the bow rising and then falling: *The ship pitched about in the storm.* **7** degree of highness or lowness of a sound. **8** a talk, argument, plan, or offer used to persuade, as in selling: *The clerk had developed a strong sales pitch.* **9** the amount of slope: *Some roads in the Rocky Mountains have a very steep pitch.* 1,2,4-6 *verb,* 3,7-9 *noun,* plural **pitch·es.**
pitch in, to work hard: *All of us pitched in, and the job was soon finished.*

pitch[2] (pich), a black, sticky substance made from tar or turpentine, used to cover the seams of wooden ships, to cover roofs, or to make pavements. *noun,* plural **pitch·es.**

pitch·er[1] (pich′ər), **1** a container made of china, glass, or silver, with a lip at one side and a handle at the other. Pitchers are used for holding and pouring out water, milk, and other liquids. **2** the amount that a pitcher holds: *He drank a pitcher of milk. noun.*

pitch·er[2] (pich′ər), a player on a baseball team who throws a ball to the batter to hit. *noun.*

pitch·fork (pich′fôrk′), a large fork with a long handle for lifting and throwing hay. *noun.*

pit·e·ous (pit′ē əs), to be pitied; deserving pity: *A starving person is a piteous sight. adjective.*

pit·fall (pit′fôl′), any trap or hidden danger. *noun.*

pith (pith), **1** the central spongy tissue in the stems of certain plants. **2** anything like this tissue: *the pith of an orange. noun.*

pit·i·a·ble (pit′ē ə bəl), **1** to be pitied; deserving pity. **2** deserving contempt; mean; to be scorned: *Their half-hearted attempts to help with the work were pitiable. adjective.*

pit·i·ful (pit′i fəl), **1** to be pitied; piteous; deserving pity: *The rabbit caught in the trap was a pitiful sight.* **2** deserving contempt: *a pitiful excuse. adjective.*

pit·i·less (pit′ē lis), without pity or mercy. *adjective.*

pit·y (pit′ē), **1** sympathy; sorrow for another's suffering or distress; feeling for the sorrows of others: *We felt pity for the lost, hungry puppy.* **2** to feel pity for: *I pitied the homeless puppy.* **3** a cause for pity or regret; thing to be sorry for: *It is a pity to be kept in the house in fine weather.* 1,3 *noun,* 2 *verb,* **pit·ies, pit·ied, pit·y·ing.**
have pity on or **take pity on,** to show pity for: *Have pity on the poor beggar.*

piv·ot (piv′ət), **1** a shaft, pin, or point on which something turns. The pin of a hinge is a pivot. **2** to turn on a pivot or as if on a pivot: *to pivot on one's heel.* **3** a turn on a pivot or as if on a pivot: *With a quick pivot he threw the ball to his teammate.* 1,3 *noun,* 2 *verb.*

pix·y or **pix·ie** (pik′sē), a fairy or an elf. *noun,* plural **pix·ies.**

piz·za (pēt′sə), a spicy Italian dish made by baking a large flat layer of bread dough covered with cheese, tomato sauce, herbs, and other things. *noun.*

pl., plural.

plac·ard (plak′ärd), a notice to be posted in a public place; poster. *noun.*

place (plās), **1** the part of space occupied by a person or thing: *This should be a nice, quiet place to rest.* **2** a city, town, village, district, island, or the like: *What place do you come from?* **3** a building or spot used for some particular purpose: *A store or office is a place of business.* **4** a house; dwelling: *They have a beautiful place in the country.* **5** a part or spot in a body or surface: *a sore place on one's foot, to mark one's place in a book.* **6** the right position; usual position: *There is a time and place for everything. Each book is in its place on the shelf.* **7** a rank; position; way of life: *She won first place in the contest. They have a high place in society.* **8** the position of a figure in a number: *In the number 365, the figure 3 is in the hundreds place.* **9** a space or seat for a person: *We took our places at the table.* **10** to put in a particular spot, position, or condition: *Place the books on the table. The orphan was placed in a home. We placed an order for hats with this store. The people placed confidence in their leader.* **11** to identify by remembering the place, time, or situation in which a person or thing was known before: *I know that person's face, but I can't place her.* **12** to finish in a certain position in a race or competition: *I placed third in the swimming meet.*

13 duty; business: *It is not my place to find fault.* 1-9,13 *noun,* 10-12 *verb,* **plac·es, placed, plac·ing.**

in place of, instead of: *Use water in place of milk in that recipe.*

take place, to happen; occur: *Where did the accident take place?*

place value, the value which a figure has because of its place in a number. In 438, the place values of the figures are 4 × 100, 3 × 10, and 8 × 1.

plac·id (plas′id), pleasantly calm or peaceful; quiet: *a placid temper. adjective.*

placid—We saw clouds reflected in the **placid** water.

plague (plāg), **1** a very dangerous disease that spreads rapidly from person to person and often causes death. **2** a thing or person that torments, annoys, troubles, offends, or is disagreeable: *Weeds are a plague to a gardener.* **3** to bother; annoy; trouble: *The people were plagued with high taxes.* 1,2 *noun,* 3 *verb,* **plagues, plagued, pla·guing.**

plaid (plad), **1** any cloth with a pattern of checks and crisscross stripes of different widths and colors. **2** a pattern of this kind. **3** having a pattern of checks or stripes: *a plaid dress.* 1,2 *noun,* 3 *adjective.*

plaid (definition 1)

plain (plān), **1** clear; easy to understand; easily seen or heard: *The meaning is plain.* **2** clearly; in a plain manner: *He could speak plain at an early age.* **3** without ornament or decoration; simple: *a plain coat.* **4** all of one color: *a plain blue shirt.* **5** not rich or highly seasoned: *plain food.* **6** common; ordinary; simple in manner: *They were plain, hard-working people.* **7** not pretty or handsome; homely: *a plain face.* **8** frank; honest; sincere: *plain speech.* **9** a flat stretch of land: *Cattle wandered over the western plains.* 1,3-8 *adjective,* 2 *adverb,* 9 *noun.*

a hat	i it	oi oil	ch child	⎧ a in about
ā age	ī ice	ou out	ng long	⎪ e in taken
ä far	o hot	u cup	sh she	ə = ⎨ i in pencil
e let	ō open	u̇ put	th thin	⎪ o in lemon
ē equal	ô order	ü rule	ŦH then	⎩ u in circus
ėr term			zh measure	

Plains Indian, a member of any of the American Indian tribes that lived in the Great Plains.

plain-spo·ken (plān′spō′kən), plain or frank in speech: *a plain-spoken man, a plain-spoken criticism. adjective.*

plain·tive (plān′tiv), mournful; sad: *a plaintive song. adjective.*

plan (plan), **1** a way of making or doing something that has been worked out beforehand: *Our summer plans were upset by mother's illness.* **2** to think out beforehand how something is to be made or done; design or scheme: *Have you planned your trip?* **3** to have in mind as a purpose; intend: *I plan to go to New York next week.* **4** a drawing or diagram to show how a garden, a floor of a house, a park, or the like, is arranged. **5** to make a drawing or diagram of: *The architect is planning a new garage for us.* 1,4 *noun,* 2,3,5 *verb,* **plans, planned, plan·ning.**

plane[1] (plān), **1** any flat or level surface: *a plane of smooth rock, the plane of a table.* **2** flat; level: *a perfectly plane surface.* **3** a level; grade: *Try to keep your work on a high plane.* **4** an airplane. 1,3,4 *noun,* 2 *adjective.*

plane[2] (plān), **1** a tool with a blade for smoothing wood. **2** to smooth wood with a plane: *The carpenter planed the boards.* 1 *noun,* 2 *verb,* **planes, planed, plan·ing.**

plan·et (plan′it), one of the heavenly bodies that move around the sun. Mercury, Venus, the earth, Mars, Jupiter, Saturn, Uranus, Neptune, and Pluto are planets. *noun.*

[*Planet* comes from a Greek word meaning "wandering." People of ancient times thought of the planets as stars that moved about while the other stars stayed in one place.]

plan·e·tar·i·um (plan′ə ter′ē əm *or* plan′ə tar′ē əm), a building with special equipment for showing the movements of the sun,

planetarium

moon, planets, and stars. These movements are shown by projecting lights on the inside of a dome. *noun.*

plan·e·tar·y (plan′ə ter′ē), of a planet; having something to do with planets. *adjective.*

plank (plangk), a long, flat piece of sawed timber thicker than a board. *noun.*

plank·ton (plangk′tən), the small living things that float or drift in water, especially at or near the surface. Plankton provides food for many fish. *noun.*

plant (plant), **1** any living thing that can make its own food from sunlight, air, and water. Plants cannot move about by themselves. Trees, bushes, vines, grass, vegetables, and seaweed are all plants. **2** to put in the ground to grow: *She planted sunflower seeds in the backyard.* **3** to set firmly; put; place: *The climbers planted a flag on the top of the mountain. I planted my feet far apart.* **4** to put ideas, feelings, or beliefs in: *Parents try to plant ideas of honesty and kindness in their children.* **5** a building, machinery, and tools used in manufacturing some article or in producing something. 1,5 *noun,* 2-4 *verb.*

plan·tain (plan′tən), a kind of banana, but longer and starchier, eaten cooked. *noun.*

plan·ta·tion (plan tā′shən), a large farm or estate on which cotton, tobacco, sugar cane, or rubber trees are grown. The work on a plantation is done by laborers who live there. *noun.*

plant·er (plan′tər), **1** a person who owns or runs a plantation: *a cotton planter.* **2** a machine for planting: *a corn planter.* **3** a box, stand, or other container, usually decorative, for plants. *noun.*

plaque (plak), **1** an ornamental tablet of metal, porcelain, or the like, often with writing carved on it. **2** a thin film containing germs, which forms on the teeth. Plaque can cause tooth decay. *noun.*

plas·ma (plaz′mə), the clear, almost colorless, liquid part of blood, in which the corpuscles or blood cells float. *noun.*

plas·ter (plas′tər), **1** a soft mixture of lime, sand, and water that hardens as it dries. Plaster is used for covering walls or ceilings. **2** to cover a wall or ceiling with plaster. **3** to spread with anything thickly: *His shoes were plastered with mud.* 1 *noun,* 2,3 *verb.*

plaster of Paris, a mixture of a white powder and water, which hardens quickly. It is used for making molds, casts, and cheap statues.

plas·tic (plas′tik), **1** any of various artificial substances that can be shaped or molded when hot and become hard when cooled. Some plastics are very strong and tough. Vinyl and nylon are plastics. **2** made of a plastic: *a plastic bottle, a plastic dish.* **3** easily molded or shaped: *Clay, wax, and plaster are plastic substances.* 1 *noun,* 2,3 *adjective.*

plate (plāt), **1** a dish, usually round, that is almost flat. Our food is served on plates. **2** something having a similar shape: *A plate is passed in our church to receive the collection.* **3** the food served on a dish or to one person at a meal: *a plate of*

stew. *The fund-raising dinner cost $50 a plate.* **4** to cover with a thin layer of silver, gold, or some other metal: *The spoon was plated with silver.* **5** a thin, flat sheet or piece of metal or other material: *a plate of glass. The warship was covered with steel plates.* **6** a thin, flat piece of metal or plastic on which something is stamped or engraved: *a license plate.* **7** one of the large drifting sections which make up the earth's surface. **8 the plate,** (in baseball) the home base. 1-3,5-8 *noun,* 4 *verb,* **plates, plat·ed, plat·ing.**

pla·teau (pla tō′), a plain in the mountains or high above sea level; large, high plain. *noun,* plural **pla·teaus, pla·teaux** (pla tōz′).

Word History

plateau A plateau is a flat area of land. Its name comes from an older French word meaning "flat." Another English word from the same source is *plate.*

---

plat·form (plat′fôrm), **1** a raised level surface: *There is a platform beside the track at the railroad station. The hall has a platform for speakers.* **2** a plan of action or statement of beliefs of a group: *The platform of the new political party demands lower taxes. noun.*

plat·i·num (plat′n əm), a heavy, precious metal that looks like silver. Platinum does not tarnish or melt easily. It is used for making chemical and industrial equipment and in jewelry. Platinum is a chemical element. *noun.*

pla·toon (plə tün′), the part of an army commanded by a lieutenant. Two or more squads make a platoon. *noun.*

plat·ter (plat′ər), a large, shallow dish for holding or serving food, especially meat and fish. *noun.*

plau·si·ble (plô′zə bəl), appearing true, reasonable, or fair: *She gave a plausible excuse for being late. adjective.*

play (plā), **1** fun; sport; something done to amuse oneself: *The children are happy at play.* **2** to have fun; do something in sport; perform: *The kitten plays with its tail. He played a joke on his sister.* **3** to take part in a game: *Children play tag and ball.* **4** to take part in a game against: *Our team played the sixth-grade team.* **5** a turn, move, or act in a game: *It is your play next. She made a good play at checkers.* **6** to put into action in a game: *Play your card.* **7** a story written for or acted on the stage: *"Romeo and Juliet" is a famous play.* **8** the performance of such a story on television, radio, the stage, or in a motion picture. **9** to act a part; act the part of: *The famous actress played Juliet.* **10** to act; act as, like, or in a certain way:

to play sick, to play the fool, to play fair. **11** action: *fair play, foul play. He brought all his strength into play to move the rock.* **12** to make believe; pretend in fun: *Let's play the hammock is a boat.* **13** to make music; produce music on an instrument: *I wish I could play well enough to be in the school orchestra.* **14** to perform on a musical instrument: *to play the piano.* **15** to cause to produce recorded or broadcast sound: *to play a record, to play the radio.* **16** freedom for action or motion: *We gave our imagination full play in telling what we could do with a million dollars.* **17** to cause to act or move; direct; aim: *to play a hose on a burning building.* **18** to act carelessly; do foolish things: *Don't play with matches.* 1,5,7,8,11,16 *noun,* 2-4,6,9,10,12-15,17,18 *verb.*

play·er (plā′ər), **1** a person who plays: *a baseball player, a card player, a flute player.* **2** a thing or device that plays: *A phonograph is a record player. noun.*

play·ful (plā′fəl), **1** full of fun; fond of playing: *a playful puppy.* **2** joking; not serious: *a playful remark. adjective.*

play·ground (plā′ground′), a place for outdoor play. *noun.*

play·house (plā′hous′), **1** a small house for a child to play in. **2** a theater. *noun, plural* **play·hous·es** (plā′hou′ziz).

playing card, one of a set of cards to play games with.

play·mate (plā′māt′), a person who plays with another. *noun.*

play·off or **play-off** (plā′ôf′), **1** a game or a series of games played after the regular season to decide a championship. **2** an extra game or round played to settle a tie. *noun.*

play·pen (plā′pen′), a small folding enclosure for a baby or young child to play in. *noun.*

play·room (plā′rüm′), a room for children to play in. *noun.*

play·thing (plā′thing′), a thing to play with; toy. *noun.*

play·wright (plā′rīt′), a writer of plays; dramatist. *noun.*

plaz·a (plaz′ə), a public square in a city or town. *noun.*

plea (plē), **1** a request; asking: *The homeless people made a plea for help.* **2** an excuse; defense: *The plea of the man who drove past the red light was that he did not see it. noun.*

plead (plēd), **1** to ask earnestly; make an earnest appeal: *When the rent was due, the poor family pleaded for more time.* **2** to offer as an excuse: *The woman who stole pleaded poverty.* **3** to speak for or against in a court of law: *He had a good lawyer to plead his case.* **4** to answer to a charge in a court of law: *An accused person has the choice of pleading guilty or not guilty. verb,* **pleads, plead·ed** or **pled, plead·ing.**

pleas·ant (plez′nt), **1** that pleases; giving pleasure: *a pleasant swim on a hot day.* **2** friendly; easy to get along with: *She is a pleasant person.* **3** fair; not stormy: *a pleasant day. adjective.*

a hat	**i** it	**oi** oil	**ch** child	a in about
ā age	**ī** ice	**ou** out	**ng** long	e in taken
ä far	**o** hot	**u** cup	**sh** she	ə = i in pencil
e let	**ō** open	**ù** put	**th** thin	o in lemon
ē equal	**ô** order	**ü** rule	**ҭн** then	u in circus
ėr term			**zh** measure	

please (plēz), **1** to be agreeable or be agreeable to; give pleasure: *Toys please children. Such a fine meal cannot fail to please.* **2** to wish; think fit: *Do what you please.* **3** to be so kind as to; be good or nice enough to. *Please* is used with requests and commands as a means of being polite. *Would you please go to the store for some milk? Please come here. verb,* **pleas·es, pleased, pleas·ing.**

pleas·ing (plē′zing), giving pleasure; pleasant: *a very pleasing young man, a pleasing smile. adjective.*

pleas·ur·a·ble (plezh′ər ə bəl), pleasant; agreeable. *adjective.*

pleas·ure (plezh′ər), **1** a feeling of being pleased; delight; joy: *His pleasure in the gift was obvious.* **2** something that pleases; cause of joy or delight: *It would be a pleasure to see you again. noun.*

pleat (plēt), **1** a flat, usually narrow, fold made in cloth by doubling it on itself: *My new skirt has many pleats.* **2** to fold or arrange in pleats: *to pleat a skirt.* 1 *noun,* 2 *verb.*

pled (pled). See **plead.** *The lawyer pled her case. verb.*

pledge (plej), **1** an earnest promise: *They signed a pledge to give money to charity.* **2** to promise earnestly: *We pledge allegiance to the flag.* **3** something given to another as a guarantee of good faith or of a future action; security: *She left the jewelry as a pledge for the loan.* **4** to give as security. 1,3 *noun,* 2,4 *verb,* **pledg·es, pledged, pledg·ing.**

plen·te·ous (plen′tē əs), plentiful. *adjective.*

plen·ti·ful (plen′ti fəl), more than enough; ample; abundant: *We had a plentiful supply of food. adjective.*

plen·ty (plen′tē), a full supply; all that one needs; a large enough number or amount: *You have plenty of time to catch the train. noun.*

pli·a·ble (plī′ə bəl), easily bent; flexible; supple: *Willow twigs are pliable. adjective.*

pli·ant (plī′ənt), bending easily; pliable: *pliant leather. adjective.*

pli·ers (plī′ərz), a tool with pincers for holding small objects firmly, or for bending or cutting wire. *noun plural or singular.*

pliers

plight[1] (plīt), a condition or situation, usually bad: *He was in a sad plight when he became ill and had no money. noun.*

plight[2] (plīt), to pledge; promise earnestly: *to plight one's loyalty. verb.*

plod (plod), **1** to walk heavily; trudge: *The old man plods wearily along the road.* **2** to proceed in a slow or dull way; work patiently with effort: *He plods away at his lessons until he learns them. verb,* **plods, plod·ded, plod·ding.**

plop (plop), **1** a sound like that of a flat object striking water without a splash. **2** to make such a sound. **3** to fall or cause to fall: *She plopped her books down on the table.* **1** *noun,* **2,3** *verb,* **plops, plopped, plop·ping.**

plot (plot), **1** a secret plan, especially to do something wrong: *They formed a plot to rob the bank.* **2** to plan; plan secretly with others to do something wrong: *The rebels plotted against the government.* **3** the main story of a play, novel, or poem: *Some people like plots filled with action and adventure.* **4** a small piece of ground: *a garden plot.* **5** to make a map or diagram of: *The pilot plotted the plane's course.* **1,3,4** *noun,* **2,5** *verb,* **plots, plot·ted, plot·ting.**

plough (plou). See **plow**. *noun, verb.*

plov·er (pluv′ər *or* plō′vər), a bird with a short tail, a short bill, and long, pointed wings. *noun.*

plover—about 10 inches (25 centimeters) long

plow (plou), **1** a big, heavy farm instrument for cutting the soil and turning it over. **2** to turn up the soil with a plow: *to plow a field.* **3** a snowplow. **4** to use a plow. **5** to move through anything as a plow does; advance slowly and with effort: *The ship plowed through the waves.* **1,3** *noun,* **2,4,5** *verb.* Also spelled **plough.**

plow·share (plou′sher′ *or* plou′shar′), the blade of a plow; part of a plow that cuts the soil. *noun.*

pluck (pluk), **1** to pick; pull off: *He plucked flowers in the garden.* **2** to pull; pull at; tug; jerk: *She plucked at the loose threads of her coat.* **3** the act of picking or pulling. **4** to pull on the strings of a musical instrument; play by picking at the strings: *She was plucking the banjo softly.* **5** to pull the feathers out of: *to pluck a chicken before cooking it.* **1,2,4,5** *verb,* **3** *noun.*

plug (plug), **1** a piece of wood or other substance used to stop up a hole. **2** to stop up or fill with a plug: *They plugged the hole with cement.* **3** a device at the end of a wire to make an electrical connection by fitting into a socket. **4** to work steadily; plod: *We plugged away at our typewriters.* **1,3** *noun,* **2,4** *verb,* **plugs, plugged, plug·ging.**
plug in, to make an electrical connection by inserting a plug: *Plug in the television set.*

plum (plum), **1** a round, juicy fruit with smooth skin and a stone inside. Plums are red, green, purple, or yellow. They grow on trees and are good to eat. **2** something good: *This new job is a fine plum for her.* **3** dark bluish-purple. **1,2** *noun,* **3** *adjective.*

plum·age (plü′mij), the feathers of a bird. *noun.*

plumage
The rooster had bright **plumage.**

plumb (plum), **1** a small weight. A plumb is hung on the end of a line used to measure the depth of water or to see if a wall is vertical. **2** to test or measure by a plumb line: *Our line was not long enough to plumb the depths of the lake.* **1** *noun,* **2** *verb.*

plumb·er (plum′ər), a person whose work is putting in and repairing water pipes, sinks, bathtubs, and the like in buildings: *When the water pipe froze, we sent for a plumber. noun.*

plumb·ing (plum′ing), **1** the work or trade of a plumber. **2** the water pipes, sinks, bathtubs, and the like in a building: *bathroom plumbing. noun.*

a hat	i it	oi oil	ch child		a in about
ā age	ī ice	ou out	ng long		e in taken
ä far	o hot	u cup	sh she	ə =	i in pencil
e let	ō open	u̇ put	th thin		o in lemon
ē equal	ô order	ü rule	ŦH then		u in circus
ėr term			zh measure		

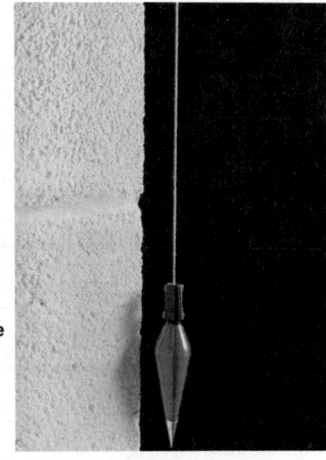

plumb line

plumb line, a line with a plumb at the end, used to find the depth of water or to see if a wall is vertical.

plume (plüm), **1** a large, long feather; feather. **2** a feather, bunch of feathers, or tuft of hair worn as an ornament on a hat or helmet. *noun.*

plum·met (plum′it), to drop suddenly; plunge: *The wounded bird plummeted to the ground. verb.*

plump[1] (plump), pleasantly round and full: *plump cheeks, a plump figure. adjective.*

plump[2] (plump), **1** to fall or drop heavily or suddenly: *All out of breath, she plumped down on a chair.* **2** heavily or suddenly: *He ran plump into me.* **1** *verb,* **2** *adverb.*

plun·der (plun′dər), **1** to rob by force; rob: *The pirates entered the harbor and began to plunder the town.* **2** things stolen; booty; loot: *They carried off the plunder in their ships.* **1** *verb,* **2** *noun.*

plunge (plunj), **1** to throw or thrust with force into a liquid or into a place: *Plunge your hand into the water.* **2** to throw oneself into water, danger, or a fight: *She plunged into the lake to save the drowning swimmer.* **3** to fall or move suddenly downward: *The plane plunged toward earth.* **4** a jump or thrust; dive: *The diver plunged from the cliff into the sea.* **1-3** *verb,* **plung·es, plunged, plung·ing;** **4** *noun.*

plunk (plungk), **1** to make a sudden twanging sound like the plucking of a stringed musical instrument; twang: *Raindrops plunked into the puddles near the back door.* **2** to throw, put, drop, or fall heavily or suddenly: *I plunked a quarter down on the counter. verb.*

plur·al (plur′əl), **1** more than one in number. *Cat* is singular; *cats* is plural. **2** a form of a word to show that it means more than one. *Books* is the plural of *book; men* is the plural of *man; we* is the plural of *I; these* is the plural of *this.* **1** *adjective,* **2** *noun.*

plus (plus), **1** added to: *3 plus 2 equals 5.* **2** and also: *The work of an engineer requires intelligence plus experience.* **3** and more: *Her mark was B plus.* **4** the sign (+) meaning that the quantity following it is to be added. **1,2** *preposition,* **3** *adjective,* **4** *noun, plural* **plus·es** or **plus·ses.**

plush (plush), a fabric like velvet but thicker and softer. *noun.*

Plu·to (plü′tō), **1** the Greek and Roman god of the region of the dead. **2** the smallest planet and the one farthest from the sun. *noun.*

plu·to·ni·um (plü tō′nē əm), a radioactive metal produced artificially from uranium. Plutonium is a chemical element. It is used as a source of atomic energy. *noun.*

ply[1] (plī), to urge again and again: *She plied me with questions to make me tell her what was in the package. verb,* **plies, plied, ply·ing.**

ply[2] (plī), a thickness, fold, or twist: *Three-ply rope is made up of three twists. noun, plural* **plies.**

ply·wood (plī′wu̇d′), a board or boards made of several thin layers of wood glued together. *noun.*

p.m. or **P.M.,** the time from noon to midnight: *School ends at 3 p.m.*
[The abbreviations *p.m.* and *P.M.* stand for the Latin words *post meridiem,* meaning "after noon."]

pneu·mo·ni·a (nü mō′nyə or nyü mō′nyə), a serious disease that can cause swelling of the lungs, high fever, and difficulty in breathing. Pneumonia often follows a bad cold or other disease. *noun.*

P.O. or **p.o.,** post office.

poach[1] (pōch), to trespass on another's land, especially to hunt or fish. *verb.*

poach[2] (pōch), to cook an egg by breaking it into boiling water. *verb.*
[When an egg is poached, the white hardens around the yolk, enclosing it as if in a pocket or bag. *Poach*[2] comes from an older French word meaning "pocket" or "bag." *Pouch* is another English word from the same source.]

pock (pok), a pimple, mark, or pit left on the skin by smallpox and certain other diseases. *noun.*

pock·et (pok′it), **1** a small bag sewed into clothing for carrying money or other small articles. **2** to put in one's pocket. **3** meant to be carried in a pocket: *a pocket handkerchief.* **4** small enough to go in a pocket: *a pocket camera.* **5** an air pocket. **1,5** *noun,* **2** *verb,* **3,4** *adjective.*

pock·et·book (pok′it bu̇k′), **1** a woman's purse. **2** a wallet; billfold. *noun.*

pock·et·ful (pok′it fu̇l), as much as a pocket will hold. *noun, plural* **pock·et·fuls.**

pock·et·knife (pok′it nīf′), a small knife with one or more blades that fold into the handle. *noun, plural* **pock·et·knives** (pok′it nīvz′).

pod (pod), a shell or case in which plants like beans and peas grow their seeds. Pods split open when they are ripe. *noun.*

po·em (pō′əm), a piece of writing that expresses the writer's imagination, usually about some inner

P

feeling. A poem is often arranged in patterns of lines, rhyme, rhythm, or accent. *noun.*

po·et (pō′it), a person who writes poems. *noun.*

po·et·ic (pō et′ik), of or like poems or poets: *She told the story in poetic language. adjective.*

po·et·ry (pō′i trē), **1** poems: *Have you read much poetry?* **2** the art of writing poems: *Shakespeare was a master of English poetry. noun.*

poin·set·ti·a (poin set′ē ə), a plant with large scarlet leaves that look like flower petals. Poinsettias are much used as Christmas decorations. *noun.*
[*Poinsettia* was named for Joel Poinsett, who lived from 1779 to 1851. He was an American official in Mexico who introduced the plant in the United States.]

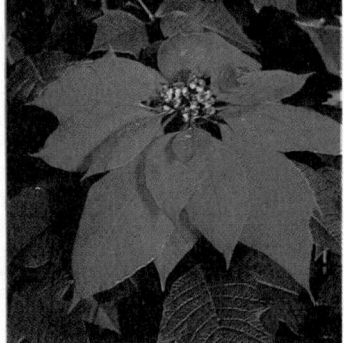

poinsettia

point (point), **1** a sharp end: *the point of a needle.* **2** a period in writing; a decimal point in numbers. **3** (in mathematics) something that has position without length or width. Two lines meet or cross at a point. **4** a place; spot: *Stop at this point.* **5** a degree; stage: *the freezing point, the boiling point.* **6** an item; small part: *The speaker replied to the argument point by point.* **7** a special quality or feature: *Courage and endurance were her good points.* **8** the main idea or purpose: *I did not get the point of the joke.* **9** to aim: *The archer pointed the arrow at the target.* **10** to show position or direction with the finger: *He pointed the way to the village over the hills.* **11** a direction. North, northeast, south, and southwest are some of the 32 points of a compass. **12** a piece of land with a sharp end sticking out into the water; cape. **13** a unit of scoring: *We won the game by three points.* 1-8,11-13 *noun,* 9,10 *verb.*

beside the point, having nothing to do with the subject; not appropriate: *Her remark was careless and beside the point.*

make a point of, to insist on: *I made a point of arriving on time.*

on the point of, just about to do: *She was on the point of going out when a neighbor came in.*

point out, to show or call attention to; indicate: *Please point out my mistakes.*

to the point, appropriate to the subject; apt: *His speech was brief and to the point.*

point·ed (poin′tid), **1** having a point or points: *a pointed roof.* **2** sharp; piercing: *a pointed wit.* **3** directed; aimed: *a pointed remark. adjective.*

point·er (poin′tər), **1** a person or thing that points. **2** a long, tapering stick used in pointing things out on a map or chalkboard. **3** the hand of a clock, gauge, or instrument. **4** a short-haired hunting dog. A pointer is trained to show where game is by standing still with its head and body pointing toward it. **5** a hint; suggestion: *She gave him some pointers on improving his tennis. noun.*

point·less (point′lis), without meaning or purpose: *a pointless question. adjective.*

point of view, an attitude of mind: *Farmers and campers have different points of view toward rain.*

poise (poiz), **1** to balance: *The athlete poised the weight in the air before throwing it.* **2** a state of balance: *He stood with perfect poise on the swaying branch.* **3** calm; self-confidence: *She has such poise that she is never embarrassed.* 1 *verb,* **pois·es, poised, pois·ing;** 2,3 *noun.*

poi·son (poi′zn), **1** any substance that is very dangerous to life or health when it is breathed or swallowed. Arsenic and lead are poisons. **2** to kill or harm by poison. **3** to put poison in or on: *to poison food, to poison arrows.* **4** to have a very harmful effect on: *Jealousy poisoned their friendship.* 1 *noun,* 2-4 *verb.*

poison ivy, a climbing plant that looks like ivy, which can cause a painful rash on the skin if the plant is touched.

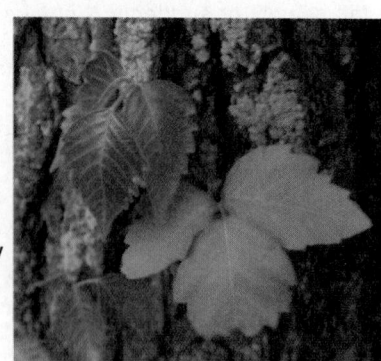

poison ivy

poi·son·ous (poi′zn əs), containing poison; very harmful to life or health: *The rattlesnake's bite is poisonous. adjective.*

poke (pōk), **1** to push against with something pointed; jab: *to poke the ashes of a fire. He poked me in the ribs with his elbow.* **2** to thrust; push: *The dog poked its head out of the car window.* **3** a poking; thrust; push. **4** to go in a lazy way; loiter: *She felt tired and just poked around the house all day.* 1,2,4 *verb,* **pokes, poked, pok·ing;** 3 *noun.*

pok·er[1] (pō′kər), a metal rod for stirring a fire. *noun.*

po·ker[2] (pō′kər), a card game in which the players bet on the value of the cards that they hold in their hands. *noun.*

pok·y or **pok·ey** (pō′kē), slow; dull: *wallking along in a slow, poky way. adjective,* **pok·i·er, pok·i·est.**

Po·land (pō′lənd), a country in central Europe. *noun.*

po·lar (pō′lər), of or near the North or South Pole: *It is very cold in the polar regions. adjective.*

polar bear, a large white bear of the arctic regions.

polar bear—about 4 feet (1 meter) high at the shoulder and about 8 feet (2½ meters) long

pole[1] (pōl), a long, slender, usually round piece of wood or the like: *a telephone pole, a totem pole. noun.*

pole[2] (pōl), **1** either end of the earth's axis. The North Pole and the South Pole are opposite each other. **2** either end of a battery or magnet. The magnetic or electrical force at one pole is opposite to the force at the other pole. *noun.*

pole·cat (pōl′kat′), **1** a small, dark-brown European animal somewhat like a weasel. It has a very strong, unpleasant smell. **2** a skunk. *noun.*

pole·star (pōl′stär′), the North Star, a star that is almost directly above the North Pole, and was formerly much used as a guide by sailors. *noun.*

pole vault, an athletic contest in which people try to jump over a high crossbar by using a long pole.

po·lice (pə lēs′), **1** persons whose duty is keeping order and arresting people who break the law. **2** to keep in order: *to police the streets.* 1 *noun,* 2 *verb,* **po·lic·es, po·liced, po·lic·ing.**

a hat	**i** it	**oi** oil	**ch** child		a in about
ā age	**ī** ice	**ou** out	**ng** long		e in taken
ä far	**o** hot	**u** cup	**sh** she	ə =	i in pencil
e let	**ō** open	**ů** put	**th** thin		o in lemon
ē equal	**ô** order	**ü** rule	**ŦH** then		u in circus
ėr term			**zh** measure		

po·lice·man (pə lēs′mən), a member of the police. *noun, plural* **po·lice·men.**

po·lice·wom·an (pə lēs′wům′ən), a woman who is a member of the police. *noun, plural* **po·lice·wom·en.**

pol·i·cy[1] (pol′ə sē), a plan of action; way of management: *government policies. It is a poor policy to promise more than you can do. noun, plural* **pol·i·cies.**

pol·i·cy[2] (pol′ə sē), a written agreement about insurance: *An insurance policy should make clear when money will be paid, and how much. noun, plural* **pol·i·cies.**

po·li·o (pō′lē ō), a disease most often of children that causes fever, paralysis of various muscles, and sometimes death; infantile paralysis; poliomyelitis. Unless you are vaccinated against polio, you can catch the disease if you are around someone who has it. *noun.*

po·li·o·my·e·li·tis (pō′lē ō mī′ə lī′tis), polio. *noun.*

pol·ish (pol′ish), **1** to make or become smooth and shiny: *to polish shoes. The silverware polished beautifully.* **2** a substance used to give smoothness or shine: *silver polish.* **3** smoothness; shiny condition: *The polish of the furniture reflected our faces like a mirror.* 1,2 *verb,* 2,3 *noun, plural* **pol·ish·es.**

Pol·ish (pō′lish), **1** of or having something to do with Poland, its people, or their language. **2** the language of Poland. 1 *adjective,* 2 *noun.*

po·lite (pə līt′), behaving properly; having or showing good manners: *The polite girl gave the old man her seat on the bus. adjective,* **po·lit·er, po·lit·est.**

po·lit·i·cal (pə lit′ə kəl), **1** having something to do with government: *Treason is a political offense.* **2** of politicians or their methods: *a political party, political meetings. adjective.*

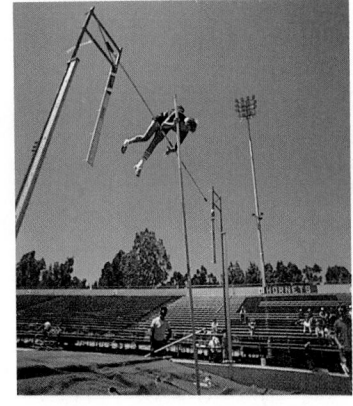

pole vault

P

pol·i·ti·cian (pol′ə tish′ən), a person whose occupation or chief activity is government: *Politicians are busy near election time.* noun.

pol·i·tics (pol′ə tiks), **1** the work of government; management of public business: *The senator was engaged in politics for many years.* **2** political principles or opinions: *Her politics are very liberal.* noun singular or plural.

pol·ka (pōl′kə *or* pō′kə), **1** a kind of lively dance. **2** the music for it. noun.

pol·ka dot (pō′kə dot′), a dot or round spot repeated to form a pattern on cloth.

poll (pōl), **1** a voting; collection of votes: *The class had a poll to decide where it would have its picnic.* **2 polls,** a place where votes are cast and counted: *The polls will be open all day.* **3** to receive at an election: *The mayor polled a record vote.* **4** a survey of public opinion about a particular subject. **5** to ask for opinions from; question: *The principal polled the students to learn how many liked the food in the cafeteria.* 1,2,4 *noun,* 3,5 *verb.*

pol·len (pol′ən), a fine, yellowish powder released from the anthers of flowers. Grains of pollen carried to the pistils of flowers fertilize them. noun.

pol·li·nate (pol′ə nāt), to carry pollen to; shed pollen on. Many flowers are pollinated by bees. *verb.* **pol·li·nates, pol·li·nat·ed, pol·li·nat·ing.**

pol·li·na·tion (pol′ə nā′shən), a carrying of pollen to; a shedding of pollen on: *Bees carry out the pollination of many flowers.* noun.

pol·li·wog (pol′ē wog), a tadpole. noun.

pol·lu·tant (pə lüt′nt), something that pollutes: *The water from a factory may be a pollutant of the stream it flows into.* noun.

pol·lute (pə lüt′), to make dirty or impure: *The water at the bathing beach was polluted by refuse from the factory.* verb, **pol·lutes, pol·lut·ed, pol·lut·ing.**

pol·lu·tion (pə lü′shən), **1** the dirtying of any part of an environment, especially with waste material: *Exhaust from automobiles causes air pollution.* **2** anything that dirties an environment, especially waste material: *Pollution in the lake killed many fish.* noun.

po·lo (pō′lō), a game like hockey, played on horseback with long-handled mallets and a wooden ball. noun.

pol·y·gon (pol′ē gon), a figure with three or more straight sides and angles. noun.

Word History

polygon *Polygon* comes from two Greek words meaning "many" and "angle."

polyps

pol·yp (pol′ip), a rather simple form of water animal consisting largely of a stomach with fingerlike tentacles around the edge to gather in food. Polyps often grow in colonies, with their bases connected. Coral is made by polyps. noun.

pome·gran·ate (pom′gran′it *or* pom′ə gran it), the reddish-yellow fruit of a small tree. Pomegranates have thick skin, red pulp, and many seeds. The pulp has a pleasant, slightly sour taste. noun.

pom·mel (pum′əl *or* pom′əl), the part of a saddle that sticks up at the front. noun.

POMMEL

pomp (pomp), a stately or showy display; magnificence: *The new ruler was crowned with great pomp.* noun.

pom·pon (pom′pon), an ornamental ball of feathers, silk, wool, or the like, worn on a hat or on shoes. noun.

pomp·ous (pom′pəs), fond of display; acting too proudly; trying to seem magnificent: *The leader of the band bowed in a pompous manner.* adjective.

pon·cho (pon′chō), a large piece of cloth or other material, often waterproof, with a slit in the middle for the head to go through. Ponchos are worn in South America as cloaks. Waterproof ponchos are

poncho
He is wearing a striped **poncho.**

a hat	**i** it	**oi** oil	**ch** child	⎧ a in about
ā age	**ī** ice	**ou** out	**ng** long	⎪ e in taken
ä far	**o** hot	**u** cup	**sh** she	**ə** = ⎨ i in pencil
e let	**ō** open	**u̇** put	**th** thin	⎪ o in lemon
ē equal	**ô** order	**ü** rule	**ŦH** then	⎩ u in circus
ėr term			**zh** measure	

pooh (pü), an exclamation expressing disrespect or disapproval: *Pooh! You don't frighten me.* *interjection.*

pool[1] (pül), **1** a tank of water to swim in: *a swimming pool.* **2** a small pond; small body of still water: *a forest pool.* **3** a puddle: *a pool of grease under a car. noun.*

pool[2] (pül), **1** a game played with 16 hard balls on a special table with six pockets. A long stick called a cue is used to hit the balls into the pockets. **2** to put things or money together for common advantage: *We plan to pool our savings to buy a boat.* **3** a system or arrangement in which money, vehicles, or other things are put together by different people, so that they all may benefit: *a car pool.* **1,3** *noun,* **2** *verb.*

pontoons

used in the armed forces and by hikers and campers. *noun, plural* **pon·chos.**

pond (pond), a body of still water, smaller than a lake: *a duck pond. noun.*

pon·der (pon′dər), to think over; consider carefully: *to ponder a problem. verb.*

pon·der·ous (pon′dər əs), **1** very heavy. **2** heavy and clumsy: *A hipppopotamus is ponderous.* **3** dull; tiresome: *The speaker talked in a ponderous way.* *adjective.*

pon·toon (pon tün′), either of two boat-shaped parts of an airplane, used for landing on or taking off from water. *noun.*

po·ny (pō′nē), a kind of small horse. Ponies are usually less than 5 feet (a meter and a half) tall at the shoulder. *noun, plural* **po·nies.**

pony express, a system of carrying letters and small packages in the western United States in 1860 and 1861 by riders on fast ponies or horses.

poo·dle (pü′dl), an intelligent pet dog with thick, curly hair. *noun.*

Word History

poodle *Poodle* comes from a German word meaning "puddle dog." The breed was called this because it is fond of water.

poodle—about 17 inches (43 centimeters) high at the shoulder

poor (pu̇r), **1** having a few things or nothing: *The children were so poor that they had no shoes.* **2** **the poor,** those who have little or nothing. **3** not good in quality; lacking something needed: *poor soil, a poor crop, a poor cook, a poor story.* **4** needing pity; unfortunate: *This poor child is hurt.* **1,3,4** *adjective,* **2** *noun.*

poor·ly (pu̇r′lē), in a poor manner; not enough; badly: *A desert is poorly supplied with water. The student did poorly on the test. adverb.*

pop[1] (pop), **1** to make a short, quick, explosive sound: *The firecrackers popped in bunches.* **2** a short, quick, explosive sound: *The bottle opened with a pop.* **3** to burst open; cause to burst open: *The balloon popped. We popped some popcorn.* **4** to move, go, or come suddenly or unexpectedly: *Our neighbor popped in for a short call.* **5** to thrust or put suddenly: *She popped her head out through the window.* **6** a bubbling soft drink: *strawberry pop.* **1,3-5** *verb,* **pops, popped, pop·ping;** **2,6** *noun.*

pop[2] (pop), papa; father. *noun.*

pop·corn (pop′kôrn′), **1** a kind of corn, the

kernels of which burst open and puff out when heated. **2** the white, puffed-out kernels. *noun.*

pope or **Pope** (pōp), the head of the Roman Catholic Church.

[*Pope* comes from a Greek word meaning "father."]

pop·lar (pop′lər), **1** a tree that grows rapidly and produces light, soft wood. The cottonwood is one kind of poplar. **2** its wood. *noun.*

pop·py (pop′ē), a plant with delicate, showy red, yellow, or white flowers. Opium is made from one kind of poppy. *noun, plural* **pop·pies.**

Pop·si·cle (pop′sə kəl), a trademark for flavored, sweetened ice that is molded onto a stick. *noun.*

pop·u·lace (pop′yə lis), the common people. *noun.*

pop·u·lar (pop′yə lər), **1** liked by most people: *a popular song.* **2** liked by acquaintances or associates: *His good nature makes him the most popular boy in the school.* **3** of the people; by the people; representing the people: *a popular election. The United States has a popular government.* **4** widespread among many people; common: *It is a popular belief that black cats bring bad luck. adjective.*

pop·u·lar·i·ty (pop′yə lar′ə tē), the fact or condition of being liked by most people. *noun.*

pop·u·late (pop′yə lāt), **1** to live in; inhabit: *a densely populated city.* **2** to furnish with inhabitants: *Europe helped populate America. verb.* **pop·u·lates, pop·u·lat·ed, pop·u·lat·ing.**

pop·u·la·tion (pop′yə lā′shən), **1** the people of a city, country, or district. **2** the number of people living in a place. **3** all the living things of one kind that live in a single place: *Pollution has harmed the river's trout population. noun.*

pop·u·lous (pop′yə ləs), full of people; having many people per square mile: *California is the most populous state of the United States. adjective.*

porcelain—figures made of **porcelain**

por·ce·lain (pôr′sə lin), a very fine earthenware; china. Porcelain may be so thin that light shines through it. *noun.*

porch (pôrch), a structure along the outside of a house, with a roof but with no walls or with walls having many windows: *House has a big front porch. noun, plural* **porch·es.**

por·cu·pine (pôr′kyə pīn), an animal covered with spines called quills. *noun.*

Word History

porcupine *Porcupine* comes from two Latin words meaning "pig" and "thorn." The porcupine was called this because it looked like a small pig covered with sharp spines.

porcupine—about 2½ feet (76 centimeters) long with the tail

pore¹ (pôr), to look at or study long and steadily: *I pored over the book trying to find the answer. verb,* **pores, pored, por·ing.**

pore² (pôr), a very small opening. Sweat comes through the pores in the skin. *noun.*

pork (pôrk), the meat of a pig used for food. *noun.*

po·rous (pôr′əs), full of pores through which liquids or gases can pass: *Cloth is porous. Aluminum is not porous. adjective.*

por·poise (pôr′pəs), a sea animal with a blunt, rounded snout. It looks like a small whale. *noun, plural* **por·pois·es** or **por·poise.**

Word History

porpoise *Porpoise* comes from two Latin words meaning "pig" and "fish." The porpoise has a rounded snout like a pig's.

porpoise—about 6 feet (2 meters) long

por·ridge (pôr′ij), a food made of oatmeal or other grain boiled in water or milk until it thickens. *noun.*

port¹ (pôrt), **1** a harbor; place where ships and boats can be sheltered from storms. **2** a place where ships and boats can load and unload; city or town by a harbor: *New York City is an important port. noun.*

port² (pôrt), the side of a ship, boat, or aircraft to the left of a person facing the front. *noun.*

port³ (pôrt), a strong, sweet, dark-red wine. *noun.*

por·ta·ble (pôr′tə bəl), capable of being carried or moved; easily carried: *a portable typewriter. adjective.*

por·tage (pôr′tij), a carrying of boats or provisions overland from one river or lake to another. *noun.*

por·tal (pôr′tl), a door, gate, or entrance, usually an impressive one. *noun.*

por·tend (pôr tend′), to indicate beforehand; give warning of: *Black clouds portend a storm. verb.*

por·tent (pôr′tent), a warning of coming evil; sign; omen: *The black clouds were a portent of bad weather. noun.*

por·ter (pôr′tər), **1** a person employed to carry burdens or baggage: *Give your bags to the porter.* **2** an attendant in a sleeping car of a railway train. *noun.*

port·hole (pôrt′hōl′), an opening in a ship's side to let in light and air. *noun.*

por·ti·co (pôr′tə kō), a roof supported by columns, forming a porch or a covered walk. *noun, plural* **por·ti·coes** or **por·ti·cos.**

portico

por·tion (pôr′shən), **1** a part or share: *A portion of each school day is devoted to arithmetic.* **2** an amount of food served to a person at one time: *I can't eat such a large portion.* **3** to divide into parts or shares: *The money was portioned out among the children.* **1,2** *noun,* **3** *verb.*

port·ly (pôrt′lē), fat or large in a dignified or stately way. *adjective,* **port·li·er, port·li·est.**

por·trait (pôr′trit *or* pôr′trāt), a picture of a person, especially of the face. *noun.*

por·tray (pôr trā′), **1** to make a likeness of in a drawing or painting; make a picture of: *to portray a historical scene.* **2** to picture in words; describe: *The book "Black Beauty" portrays the life of a horse.* **3** to act the part of in a play or motion picture: *The actor portrayed a doctor. verb.*

Por·tu·gal (pôr′chə gəl), a country in southwestern Europe. *noun.*

a hat	i it	oi oil	ch child	
ā age	ī ice	ou out	ng long	a in about
ä far	o hot	u cup	sh she	e in taken
e let	ō open	u̇ put	th thin	ə = i in pencil
ē equal	ô order	ü rule	ᴛʜ then	o in lemon
ėr term			zh measure	u in circus

Por·tu·guese (pôr′chə gēz′), **1** of Portugal, its people, or their language. **2** a person born or living in Portugal. **3** the language of Portugal. **1** *adjective,* **2,3** *noun, plural* **Por·tu·guese** for 2.

Word Source

Portuguese is also the chief language of Brazil. The following words came into English from Portuguese:

cobra	dodo	jaguar	mango	teak
coco	flamingo	junk	pagoda	zebra

pose (pōz), **1** a position of the body; way of holding the body: *a natural pose, a pose taken in exercising.* **2** to hold the body in one position: *She posed an hour for her portrait.* **3** an attitude assumed for effect; pretense: *Her interest in people is real; it isn't just a pose.* **4** to pretend something for effect: *They posed as a rich couple although they had little money.* **1,3** *noun,* **2,4** *verb,* **pos·es, posed, pos·ing.**

po·si·tion (pə zish′ən), **1** the place where a thing or person is: *The flowers grew in a sheltered position behind the house.* **2** a way of being placed: *Put the baby in a comfortable position.* **3** a job: *He has a position in a bank.* **4** a rank; standing, especially high standing: *She was raised to the position of manager.* **5** a way of thinking; set of opinions: *What is your position on this question? noun.*

portrait of Pocahontas

pos·i·tive (poz′ə tiv), **1** permitting no question; without doubt; sure: *We have positive evidence that the earth moves around the sun.* **2** definite; emphatic: *"No. I will not," was his positive refusal.* **3** able to do or add something; practical: *Don't just make a negative criticism; give us some positive help.* **4** showing agreement or approval: *a positive*

P

answer to a question. **5** of the kind of electricity that protons have. **6** greater than zero: *Five above zero is a positive quantity. adjective.*

pos·i·tive·ly (poz′ə tiv lē), **1** in a positive way: *The audience reacted positively to our play.* **2** to a great extreme; absolutely: *I was positively furious at them for being so rude. adverb.*

pos·se (pos′ē), a group of citizens called together by a sheriff to help maintain law and order: *The posse chased the bandits across the prairie. noun.*

pos·sess (pə zes′), **1** to own; have: *My aunt possessed great intelligence and determination.* **2** to control; influence strongly: *She was possessed by the desire to be rich. verb.*

pos·ses·sion (pə zesh′ən), **1** a possessing; having; ownership: *The books you lost are in my possession.* **2** a thing possessed; property: *Please move your possessions from my room.* **3** a territory under the rule of a country: *Guam is a possession of the United States. noun.*

pos·ses·sive (pə zes′iv), **1** showing possession. *My, your, his,* and *our* are possessive adjectives because they indicate who possesses or owns. **2** word showing possession. In "your book," *your* is a possessive. **3** selfish with one's belongings: *She is very possessive of her books and will not lend them.* **1,3** *adjective,* **2** *noun.*

pos·ses·sor (pə zes′ər), a person who possesses; owner; holder. *noun.*

pos·si·bil·i·ty (pos′ə bil′ə tē), **1** a being possible: *There is a possibility that the train may be late.* **2** a possible thing, person, or event: *A whole week of rain is a possibility. noun, plural* **pos·si·bil·i·ties.**

pos·si·ble (pos′ə bəl), **1** capable of being done or happening: *It is possible to cure tuberculosis. Space travel is now possible.* **2** not known to be true, but perhaps true: *It is possible that they left without us.* **3** able to be done or chosen properly: *the only possible action, the only possible candidate. adjective.*

pos·si·bly (pos′ə blē), **1** no matter what happens: *I cannot possibly go.* **2** perhaps: *Possibly you are right. adverb.*

pos·sum (pos′əm), an opossum. *noun, plural* **pos·sums** or **pos·sum.**

post¹ (pōst), **1** a piece of timber, metal, or other solid substance firmly set up, usually to support something else: *the posts of a door, a hitching post.* **2** to fasten a notice up in a place where it can easily be seen: *The list of winners will be posted soon.* **1** *noun,* **2** *verb.*

post² (pōst), **1** a place where a soldier, police officer, guard, or the like is stationed. **2** a military base where soldiers are stationed; fort. **3** to station at a post: *They posted guards at the door.* **4** a job or position: *the post of secretary, a diplomatic post.* **5** a trading station, especially in unsettled country; trading post. **1,2,4,5** *noun,* **3** *verb.*

post³ (pōst), **1** a system for carrying letters, papers, or packages; the mail: *I shall send the package by post.* **2** a single delivery of mail: *This morning's post has come.* **3** to send by mail; put into the mailbox; mail: *to post a letter.* **4** to supply with up-to-date information; inform: *Keep me posted about your new job.* **1,2** *noun,* **3,4** *verb.*

post·age (pō′stij), the amount paid on anything sent by mail. *noun.*

postage stamp, an official stamp placed on mail to show that postage has been paid.

post·al (pō′stəl), having to do with mail and post offices: *postal regulations, a postal clerk. adjective.*

postal card, a post card.

Postal Service, the service that takes charge of mail for the government.

post card, a small card for sending a message by mail. Some post cards have pictures on one side.

post·er (pō′stər), a large printed sheet or notice put up on a wall. *noun.*

pos·ter·i·ty (po ster′ə tē), **1** the generations of the future: *Posterity may travel to distant planets.* **2** anyone's children, and their children, and their children, and so on and on. *noun.*

post·man (pōst′mən), a person who carries and delivers mail for the government. *noun, plural* **post·men.**

post·mark (pōst′märk′), **1** an official mark stamped on mail to cancel the postage stamp and record the place and date of mailing. **2** to stamp with a postmark. **1** *noun,* **2** *verb.*

post·mas·ter (pōst′mas′tər), a person in charge of a post office. *noun.*

post office, a place where mail is handled and postage stamps are sold.

post·paid (pōst′pād′), with the postage paid for. *adjective.*

post·pone (pōst pōn′), to put off till later; put off to a later time; delay: *The ball game was postponed because of rain. verb,* **post·pones, post·poned, post·pon·ing.**

post·script (pōst′skript), an addition to a letter, written below the writer's name. *noun.*

pos·ture (pos′chər), **1** a position of the body; way of holding the body: *Good posture is important to health.* **2** to take a position: *The dancer postured before the mirror, bending and twisting her body.* **1** *noun,* **2** *verb,* **pos·tures, pos·tured, pos·tur·ing.**

post·war (pōst′wôr′), after the war. *adjective.*

po·sy (pō′zē), **1** a flower. **2** a bunch of flowers; bouquet. *noun, plural* **po·sies.**

pot (pot), **1** a kind of round container. There are many different kinds and shapes of pots. They are made of metal, earthenware, and other substances. A pot may hold food or drink or contain earth for flowers to grow in. **2** the amount a pot will hold: *a small pot of beans.* **3** to put into a pot: *I potted the young tomato plants.* **1,2** *noun,* **3** *verb,* **pots, pot·ted, pot·ting.**

po·tas·si·um (pə tas′ē əm), a soft, silver-white metal. Potassium is necessary for the growth of plants, and is used in making soap and fertilizers. It is a chemical element. *noun.*

po·ta·to (pə tā′tō), **1** a round or oval, hard, starchy vegetable with a thin skin. It is one of the most widely used vegetables in Europe and America. Potatoes grow underground. **2** a sweet potato. *noun, plural* **po·ta·toes.**

potato chip, a thin slice of potato fried in deep fat.

po·tent (pōt′nt), powerful; having great power; strong: *a potent remedy for a disease. adjective.*

po·ten·tate (pōt′n tāt), **1** a person having great power. **2** a ruler. Kings, queens, and emperors are potentates. *noun.*

po·ten·tial (pə ten′shəl), possible as opposed to actual; capable of coming into being or action: *There is a potential danger of being bitten when playing with a strange dog. adjective.*

pot·hold·er (pot′hōl′dər), a thick pad of cloth or other material for handling hot pots and lids. *noun.*

po·tion (pō′shən), a drink, especially one used as a medicine or poison, or in magic. *noun.*

pot·pie (pot′pī′), meat, or poultry, and vegetables baked in a pie. *noun.*

pot·shot (pot′shot′), **1** a shot fired without careful aim at a close target. **2** criticism, usually made in a careless way. *noun.*

pot·ter[1] (pot′ər), a person who makes pots, dishes, or vases out of clay. *noun.*

potter[1]

pot·ter[2] (pot′ər), to keep busy in a rather useless way; putter: *I like to potter in the garden on weekends. verb.*

pot·ter·y (pot′ər ē), pots, dishes, or vases made from clay and hardened by heat. *noun.*

pouch (pouch), **1** a bag or sack: *a tobacco pouch.* **2** a natural part of some animals that is like a bag or pocket. A kangaroo has a pouch for carrying its young. A chipmunk has cheek pouches for carrying food. *noun, plural* **pouch·es.**

poul·try (pōl′trē), birds, such as chickens, turkeys, geese, or ducks, raised for their meat or eggs. *noun.*

a hat	**i** it	**oi** oil	**ch** child		a in about
ā age	**ī** ice	**ou** out	**ng** long		e in taken
ä far	**o** hot	**u** cup	**sh** she	**ə** =	i in pencil
e let	**ō** open	**u̇** put	**th** thin		o in lemon
ē equal	**ô** order	**ü** rule	**ŦH** then		u in circus
ėr term			**zh** measure		

pounce (pouns), **1** to jump suddenly and seize: *The cat pounced upon the mouse.* **2** a sudden swoop. **1** *verb,* **pounc·es, pounced, pounc·ing;** **2** *noun.*

[*Pounce* comes from an earlier English word meaning "talon" or "claw." To pounce originally meant "to seize with the talons."]

pound[1] (pound), **1** a unit of weight equal to 16 ounces. **2** a unit of money in Great Britain equal to 100 pence. £1.00 means one pound. *noun, plural* **pounds** or **pound.**

pound[2] (pound), **1** to hit hard again and again; hit heavily: *She pounded the door with her fist.* **2** to beat hard; throb: *After running fast you can feel your heart pound.* **3** to make into a powder or pulp by pounding: *They pounded the grains of corn into meal. verb.*

pound[3] (pound), an enclosed place in which to keep stray animals: *I found my lost dog at the pound. noun.*

pour (pôr), **1** to flow or cause to flow in a steady stream: *I poured the milk from the bottle into the cups. The crowd poured out of the theater.* **2** to rain heavily. *verb.*

pout (pout), **1** to show unhappiness by pushing out the lips, sulking, or looking angry: *The child was pouting because he couldn't have the new toy.* **2** a pushing out of the lips, sulking, or looking angry when unhappy. **1** *verb,* **2** *noun.*

pout (definition 1)
She often **pouts** when she can't get what she wants.

pov·er·ty (pov′ər tē), **1** the condition of being poor: *Their tattered clothing and broken furniture indicated their poverty.* **2** poor quality: *The poverty of the soil makes the crops small. noun.*

pow·der (pou′dər), **1** a solid reduced to dust by pounding, crushing, or grinding. **2** to make into powder; become powder: *The soil powdered in the heat.* **3** some special kind of powder: *face powder, bath powder.* **4** to sprinkle or cover with powder: *She powdered her face. Snow powdered the trees.* **5** gunpowder: *Soldiers used to carry their powder in a powder horn.* 1,3,5 *noun,* 2,4 *verb.*

powder horn, a flask made of the horn of an animal, used to carry gunpowder.

powder horn—a man pouring gunpowder from a **powder horn** into a rifle during the Revolutionary War

pow·der·y (pou′dər ē), **1** like powder; in the form of powder: *powdery snow.* **2** sprinkled or covered with powder. *adjective.*

pow·er (pou′ər), **1** strength; might; force: *Penicillin is a medicine of great power.* **2** the ability to do or act: *I will give you all the help in my power.* **3** authority; right; control; influence: *Congress has power to declare war.* **4** a person or thing that has authority or influence; important nation: *Five powers held a peace conference.* **5** energy or force that can do work: *Running water can produce electric power.* **6** to provide with power or energy: *a boat powered by an outboard motor.* **7** operated by a motor; equipped with its own motor: *a power drill.* 1-5 *noun,* 6 *verb,* 7 *adjective.*
in power, having control or authority.

pow·er·ful (pou′ər fəl), having great power or force; mighty; strong: *a powerful person, a powerful medicine, a powerful argument, a powerful nation. adjective.*

pow·er·house (pou′ər hous′), a building containing boilers, engines, or generators for producing electric power. *noun, plural* **pow·er·hous·es** (pou′ər hou′ziz).

pow·er·less (pou′ər lis), without power; helpless: *The mouse was powerless in the cat's claws. adjective.*

pow·wow (pou′wou′), **1** a ceremony of the North American Indians, usually accompanied by magic, feasting, and dancing, performed for the cure of disease, success in hunting, or for other purposes. **2** a council or conference of or with North American Indians. **3** any conference or meeting. **4** to hold a powwow; confer. 1-3 *noun,* 4 *verb.*

pp., pages.

PR, Puerto Rico (used with postal Zip Code).

pr., pair.

P.R., Puerto Rico.

prac·ti·ca·ble (prak′tə kə bəl), **1** able to be done;

capable of being put into practice: *a practicable idea.* **2** able to be used: *a practicable road. adjective.*

prac·ti·cal (prak′tə kəl), **1** having something to do with action or practice rather than thought or theory: *Earning a living is a practical matter.* **2** fit for actual practice: *a practical plan.* **3** useful: *An outdoor swimming pool is more practical in Florida than in Minnesota.* **4** having good sense: *A practical person does not spend time and money foolishly. adjective.*

practical joke, a trick or prank played on someone.

prac·ti·cal·ly (prak′tik lē), **1** really; so far as what the results will be; in effect: *She is only a clerk, but she is in the store so much that she practically runs the business.* **2** almost; nearly: *Our house is around the corner, so we are practically home.* **3** in a practical way; in a useful way: *You must stop wishing and start thinking practically. adverb.*

prac·tice (prak′tis), **1** an action done many times over for skill: *Practice makes perfect.* **2** a skill gained by experience or exercise: *He was out of practice at batting.* **3** to do some act again and again to learn to do it well: *She practiced pitching the ball. I practice on the piano every day.* **4** to do usually; make a custom of: *Practice what you preach.* **5** the usual way; custom: *It is the practice at the factory to blow a whistle at noon.* **6** to work at or follow as a profession, art, or occupation: *to practice medicine.* **7** a working at or following a profession: *She is engaged in the practice of law.* **8** the business of a doctor or a lawyer: *The old doctor sold his practice to a younger doctor.* **9** action; actual performance: *The young teacher was about to put his ideas about education into practice.* 1,2,5,7-9 *noun,* 3,4,6 *verb,* **prac·tic·es, prac·ticed, prac·tic·ing.**

prac·ticed (prak′tist), skilled; expert; experienced: *Years of study have made him a practiced musician. adjective.*

prair·ie (prer′ē), a large area of level or rolling land with grass but few or no trees. *noun.*

prairie dog, an animal with small round ears and short legs. It is like a woodchuck but smaller. Prairie dogs dig tunnels and have a shrill bark like a dog.

prairie dogs—about 15 inches (38 centimeters) long with the tail

a hat	i it	oi oil	ch child	⎧ a in about
ā age	ī ice	ou out	ng long	e in taken
ä far	o hot	u cup	sh she	ə = ⎨ i in pencil
e let	ō open	u̇ put	th thin	o in lemon
ē equal	ô order	ü rule	ᴛʜ then	u in circus
ėr term			zh measure	⎩

prairie schooner

prairie schooner, a large covered wagon used in crossing the plains of North America before the railroads were built.

praise (prāz), **1** a saying that a thing or person is good; words that tell the worth or value of a thing or person: *Everyone heaped praise upon the winning team.* **2** to speak well of: *The coach praised the team for its fine playing.* **3** to worship in words or song: *to praise God.* **1** *noun,* **2,3** *verb,* **prais·es, praised, prais·ing.**

praise·wor·thy (prāz′wėr′ᴛʜē), worthy of praise; deserving approval. *adjective.*

prance (prans), **1** to spring about on the hind legs: *Horses prance when they feel lively.* **2** to move gaily or proudly: *The children pranced about in their new Halloween costumes. verb,* **pranc·es, pranced, pranc·ing.**

prank (prangk), a playful trick; piece of mischief: *On April Fools' Day people play pranks on each other. noun.*

prat·tle (prat′l), **1** to talk freely and carelessly, as some children do. **2** to talk in a foolish way; babble. *verb,* **prat·tles, prat·tled, prat·tling.**

pray (prā), **1** to ask from God; speak to God in worship: *They prayed for God's help.* **2** to ask earnestly for: *I pray your forgiveness.* **3** please: *Pray come with me. verb.*

prayer (prer *or* prar), **1** the act of praying: *We knelt in prayer.* **2** the thing prayed for: *Our prayers were granted.* **3** a form of words to be used in praying: *the Lord's Prayer. noun.*

praying mantis, a mantis.

pre-, a prefix meaning: **1** before: *Prewar preparations mean preparations made before a war.* **2** beforehand; in advance: To *preview means to view beforehand. Prepay means to pay in advance.*

preach (prēch), **1** to speak on a religious subject; deliver a sermon: *Our minister preaches on Sunday morning.* **2** to urge; advise; recommend strongly: *The coach was always preaching about exercise and fresh air. verb.*

preach·er (prē′chər), a person who preaches; minister. *noun.*

pre·car·i·ous (pri ker′ē əs *or* pri kar′ē əs), uncertain; not safe; not secure; dangerous: *A racing-car driver leads a precarious life. Her hold on the branch was precarious. adjective.*

pre·cau·tion (pri kô′shən), care taken in advance: *Locking doors is a precaution against thieves. noun.*

pre·cede (prē sēd′), to go before; come before: *The letter A precedes B in the alphabet. The band preceded the floats in the parade. verb,* **pre·cedes, pre·ced·ed, pre·ced·ing.**

prec·e·dent (pres′ə dənt), an action that may serve as an example or reason for later action: *A decision of a court often serves as a precedent in other courts. noun.*

pre·ced·ing (prē sē′ding), going before; coming before; previous: *Turn back and look on the preceding page for the answer. adjective.*

pre·cept (prē′sept), a rule or direction: *"If at first you don't succeed, try, try again" is a familiar precept. noun.*

pre·cinct (prē′singkt), a part or district of a city: *a police precinct. There are over 300 election precincts in that city. noun.*

pre·cious (presh′əs), **1** having great value. Gold and silver are often called the precious metals. Diamonds and rubies are precious stones. **2** much loved; dear: *a precious child. adjective.*

prec·i·pice (pres′ə pis), a very steep cliff or slope. *noun.*
[*Precipice* comes from a Latin word meaning "a headlong fall." Carelessness around a precipice could result in a headlong fall.]

pre·cip·i·tate (pri sip′ə tāt), **1** to hasten the beginning of; bring about suddenly: *The nobles' harsh treatment of the peasants precipitated the uprising.* **2** to condense water vapor from the air in the form of rain, dew, or snow. *verb,* **pre·cip·i·tates, pre·cip·i·tat·ed, pre·cip·i·tat·ing.**

pre·cip·i·ta·tion (pri sip′ə tā′shən), **1** a sudden bringing on: *the precipitation of a quarrel.* **2** the water that falls to the earth in the form of rain, snow, sleet, or hail: *The forecast is for some precipitation this afternoon. noun.*

pre·cise (pri sīs′), **1** exact; accurate; definite: *The directions they gave us were so precise that we found our way easily. The precise sum was 34 cents.* **2** very careful: *precise handwriting.* **3** strict: *We had precise orders to come home by nine o'clock. adjective.*

pre·ci·sion (pri sizh′ən), accuracy; being exact: *the precision of a machine, to speak with precision. noun.*

pre·clude (pri klüd′), to shut out; make impossible; prevent: *We were disappointed when the heavy thunderstorm precluded our having a picnic at the beach. verb,* **pre·cludes, pre·clud·ed, pre·clud·ing.**

P

precocious—The **precocious** little girl could use many difficult words.

pre·co·cious (pri kō′shəs), developed earlier than usual. *adjective.*
[*Precocious* comes from a Latin word meaning "to ripen early." In Latin this word referred to plants and fruit. In English it is used to describe people.]

pred·a·tor (pred′ə tər), an animal that lives by killing and eating other animals. *noun.*

predatory
Snakes are **predatory;** some snakes prey on birds' eggs.

pred·a·to·ry (pred′ə tôr′ē), preying upon other animals. Lions are predatory animals; hawks are predatory birds. *adjective.*

pred·e·ces·sor (pred′ə ses′ər), a person holding a position or office before another person. *noun.*

pre·dic·a·ment (pri dik′ə mənt), an unpleasant, difficult, or bad situation: *She was in a predicament when she missed the last train home. noun.*

pred·i·cate (pred′ə kit), the word or words in a sentence that tell what is said about the subject. In "Dogs bark," "The dogs dug holes," and "The dogs are beagles," *bark, dug holes,* and *are beagles* are all predicates. *noun.*

pre·dict (pri dikt′), to tell beforehand; prophesy: *The Weather Service predicts rain for tomorrow. verb.*

pre·dic·tion (pri dik′shən), a thing predicted; prophecy: *The official predictions about the weather often come true. noun.*

pre·dom·i·nant (pri dom′ə nənt), **1** having more power, authority, or influence than others; superior: *The United States has become the predominant nation in the Western Hemisphere today.* **2** most extensive; most noticeable: *Green was the predominant color in the forest. adjective.*

pre·dom·i·nate (pri dom′ə nāt), to be greater in power, strength, influence, or numbers: *Sunny days predominate over rainy days in desert regions.* verb, **pre·dom·i·nates, pre·dom·i·nat·ed, pre·dom·i·nat·ing.**

preen (prēn), **1** to smooth or arrange the feathers with the beak. **2** to dress or groom oneself carefully. *verb.*

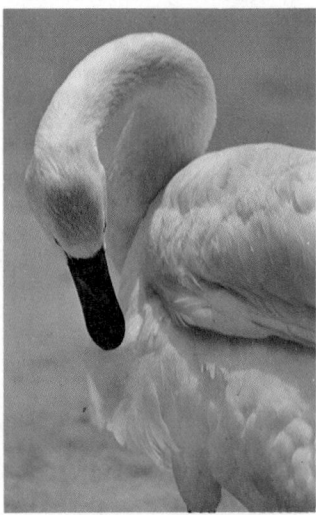

preen (definition 1)
The swan **preened** itself.

pref·ace (pref′is), an introduction to a book, writing, or speech: *Does your history book have a preface written by the author? noun.*

pre·fer (pri fėr′), **1** to like better: *I will come later, if you prefer. She prefers swimming to fishing.* **2** to put forward; present: *The policeman preferred charges of speeding against the driver.* verb, **pre·fers, pre·ferred, pre·fer·ring.**

pref·er·a·ble (pref′ər ə bəl), more desirable; to be preferred. *adjective.*

pref·er·a·bly (pref′ər ə blē), by choice: *She needs an assistant, preferably a college graduate. adverb.*

pref·er·ence (pref′ər əns), **1** the act or attitude of liking better: *My preference is for beef rather than lamb.* **2** a thing preferred; first choice: *My preference in reading is a mystery story. noun.*

pre·fix (prē′fiks), a syllable, syllables, or word put at the beginning of a word to change its meaning or make another word, as *pre-* in *prepaid, under-* in *underline, dis-* in *disappear, un-* in *unlike,* and *re-* in *reopen. noun, plural*

a hat	i it	oi oil	ch child	⎧ a in about
ā age	ī ice	ou out	ng long	e in taken
ä far	o hot	u cup	sh she	ə = ⎨ i in pencil
e let	ō open	ù put	th thin	o in lemon
ē equal	ô order	ü rule	ŦH then	⎩ u in circus
ėr term			zh measure	

Word History

prefix *Prefix* comes from a Latin word meaning "to fasten in front."

overpay
impolite
incorrect
misplace
nonfiction

preg·nant (preg′nənt), soon to have a baby; with one or more babies growing inside the body. *adjective.*

pre·heat (prē hēt′), to heat before using: *Be sure to preheat the oven before putting in the pie. verb.*

pre·his·to·ric (prē′hi stôr′ik), of or belonging to times before histories were written: *Prehistoric peoples used stone tools. adjective.*

prehistoric—the skeleton of a **prehistoric** animal

prej·u·dice (prej′ə dis), 1 an opinion formed without taking time and care to judge fairly: *Their dislike of foreigners is simply prejudice.* 2 to cause a prejudice in; fill with prejudice: *One unfortunate experience prejudiced them against all lawyers.* 1 *noun,* 2 *verb,* **prej·u·dic·es, prej·u·diced, prej·u·dic·ing.**

pre·lim·i·nar·y (pri lim′ə ner′ē), 1 coming before the main business; leading to something more important: *After some preliminary announcements, the main speaker was introduced.* 2 a preliminary step; something preparatory: *An examination is a preliminary to entering that school.* 1 *adjective,* 2 *noun, plural* **pre·lim·i·nar·ies.**

prel·ude (prel′yüd), anything serving as an introduction; something leading up to: *The rain was a prelude to the terrible storm. noun.*

pre·ma·ture (prē′mə chùr′, prē′mə tùr′ *or* prē′mə tyùr′), before the proper time; too soon: *Their arrival an hour before the party began was premature. adjective.*

pre·med·i·tate (prē med′ə tāt), to plan beforehand: *The murder was premeditated. verb,* **pre·med·i·tates, pre·med·i·tat·ed, pre·med·i·tat·ing.**

pre·mier (pri mir′), a prime minister; chief officer. *noun.*

prem·is·es (prem′ə səz), a house or building with its grounds. *noun plural.*

pre·mi·um (prē′mē əm), 1 a reward; prize: *Some magazines give premiums for obtaining new subscriptions.* 2 the money paid for insurance: *I pay premiums on my life insurance four times a year. noun.*

pre·oc·cu·pied (prē ok′yə pīd), having one's attention focused on something; lost in thought: *She was too preoccupied to hear the doorbell. adjective.*

pre·paid (prē pād′). See **prepay.** *Send this shipment prepaid. verb.*

prep·a·ra·tion (prep′ə rā′shən), 1 a preparing; making ready: *I sharpened the knife in preparation for carving the meat.* 2 a thing done to get ready: *He made thorough preparations for his trip by carefully planning which way to go.* 3 a specially made medicine or food or mixture of any kind: *There is a new preparation for removing rust. noun.*

pre·pare (pri per′ *or* pri par′), to make ready; get ready: *to prepare lessons, to prepare dinner. verb,* **pre·pares, pre·pared, pre·par·ing.**

pre·pay (prē pā′), to pay for in advance: *to prepay a bill. verb,* **pre·pays, pre·paid, pre·pay·ing.**

prep·o·si·tion (prep′ə zish′ən), a word that shows certain relations between other words. *With, for, by,* and *in* are prepositions in the sentence "Someone *with* flowers *for* sale walked *by* our house *in* the morning." *noun.*

pre·pos·ter·ous (pri pos′tər əs), against nature, reason, or common sense; absurd; senseless; foolish: *It would be preposterous to shovel snow with a teaspoon. That the moon is made of green cheese is a preposterous notion. adjective.*

pre·school (prē′skül′), 1 before the age of going to regular school: *This toy is good for preschool children.* 2 a school for children below the age of five: *My three-year-old sister is in preschool.* 1 *adjective,* 2 *noun.*

pre·scribe (pri skrīb′), to order as medicine or

P

treatment: *The doctor prescribed penicillin. verb.*
pre·scribes, pre·scribed, pre·scrib·ing.
pre·scrip·tion (pri skrip/shən), a written
direction or order for preparing and using a
medicine: *The doctor wrote a prescription for my
cough. noun.*
pres·ence (prez/ns), **1** a being present in a
place: *I just learned of their presence in the city.*
2 the place where a person is: *The messenger was
admitted to the king's presence.* **3** something
present, especially a ghost or spirit. *noun.*
in the presence of, in the sight or company of: *I
signed my name in the presence of two witnesses.*
presence of mind, the ability to think calmly
and quickly when taken by surprise: *When her
friend began to faint, she had the presence of mind
to stop his fall.*
pres·ent[1] (prez/nt), **1** being in the place or thing
in question; at hand; not absent: *Every member of
the class was present. Oxygen is present in the air.*
2 at this time; being or occurring now: *the present
ruler, present prices.* **3** now; this time; the time
being: *That is enough for the present. I am
comfortable at present.* **4** expressing something
happening or existing now: *the present tense of a
verb.* **1,2,4** *adjective,* **3** *noun.*
pre·sent[2] (pri zent/ for 1 and 3-7; prez/nt for 2),
1 to give: *They presented flowers to their teacher.*
2 a gift; something given: *a birthday present.* **3** to
introduce; make acquainted; bring a person
before somebody: *He was presented at court. Ms.
Smith, may I present Mr. Brown?* **4** to show;
display; exhibit: *The new library presents a fine
appearance.* **5** to bring before the public: *Our class
presented a play.* **6** to offer; set forth in words: *The
speaker presented arguments for her side.* **7** to hand
in; send in: *The plumber presented his bill.*
1,3-7 *verb,* **2** *noun.*
present with, to give to: *Our class presented the
school with a picture.*
pre·sent·a·ble (pri zen/tə bəl), fit to be seen;
suitable in appearance: *The house looked
presentable for company. adjective.*
pres·en·ta·tion (prez/n tā/shən), **1** the act of
giving; delivering: *the presentation of a gift.* **2** the
gift that is presented. **3** an offering to be
considered: *the presentation of a plan.* **4** an offering
to be seen; exhibition; showing: *the presentation of
a play or motion picture.* **5** a formal introduction:
the presentation of a lady to the queen. noun.
pres·ent·ly (prez/nt lē), **1** before long; soon: *I
will do the dishes presently.* **2** at the present time;
now: *She is presently in fourth grade. adverb.*
pres·er·va·tion (prez/ər vā/shən), **1** a
preserving; keeping safe: *Doctors work for the
preservation of our health.* **2** a being preserved;
being kept safe: *Egyptian mummies have been in a
state of preservation for thousands of years. noun.*
pre·serv·a·tive (pri zėr/və tiv), any substance
that will prevent decay or injury: *Paint is a
preservative for wood surfaces. Salt is a preservative
for meat. noun.*
pre·serve (pri zėrv/), **1** to keep from harm or

change; keep safe; protect: *Good nutrition helps
to preserve one's health.* **2** to keep up; maintain:
You must preserve your calm. **3** to keep from
spoiling: *Ice helps to preserve food.* **4** to prepare
food to keep it from spoiling. Boiling with sugar,
salting, smoking, and pickling are different ways
of preserving food. **5 preserves,** fruit cooked with
sugar and sealed from the air: *Try our homemade
plum preserves.* **6** a place where wild animals, fish,
or trees and plants are protected: *People are not
allowed to hunt in that preserve.* **1-4** *verb,*
pre·serves, pre·served, pre·serv·ing; 5,6 *noun.*
pre·serv·er (pri zėr/vər), a person or thing that
saves and protects from danger. Life preservers
help to save people from drowning. *noun.*
pre·side (pri zīd/), to hold the place of authority;
have charge of a meeting: *Our principal will
preside at our election of school officers. verb,*
pre·sides, pre·sid·ed, pre·sid·ing.
pres·i·den·cy (prez/ə dən sē), **1** the office of
president: *She was elected to the presidency of the
Junior Club.* **2** Often, **Presidency.** the office of
the highest executive officer of a republic. **3** the
time during which a president is in office: *The
United States entered World War II in the
presidency of Franklin D. Roosevelt. noun, plural*
pres·i·den·cies.
pres·i·dent (prez/ə dənt), **1** the chief officer of a
company, college, society, or club. **2 President,**
the highest officer of a modern republic. *noun.*
pres·i·dent-e·lect (prez/ə dənt i lekt/), a
president who has been elected but not yet
inaugurated. *noun.*
pres·i·den·tial (prez/ə den/shəl), having
something to do with a president or presidency: *a
presidential election, a presidential candidate.
adjective.*
press (pres), **1** to use force or weight against;
push with steady force: *Press the button to ring the
bell.* **2** to squeeze; squeeze out: *Press all the juice
from the oranges.* **3** to make smooth; flatten: *to
press clothes with an iron.* **4** to clasp; hug: *I
pressed the puppy to me.* **5** a pressing; pressure;
push: *The press of many duties keeps the principal
very busy.* **6** a machine for pressing: *an ironing
press.* **7** a printing press. **8** newspapers,
magazines, radio, and television, and the people
who report for them: *The mayor's speech was
reported by the press.* **9** to keep on pushing one's
way; push ahead with eagerness or haste: *We
pressed on in spite of the strong wind.* **10** to urge;
keep asking somebody earnestly: *We pressed our
guests to stay until the snow stopped.* **1-4,9,10** *verb,*
5-8 *noun, plural* **press·es.**
press·ing (pres/ing), needing immediate action
or attention; urgent: *A person with a broken leg is
in pressing need of a doctor's help. She left town
quickly on some pressing business. adjective.*
pres·sure (presh/ər), **1** the continued action of a
weight or force: *The small box was flattened by the
pressure of the heavy book on it.* **2** the force per
unit of area: *There is a pressure of 20 pounds to
the square inch on this tire.* **3** stress; strain: *I don't*

work well under pressure. **4** a forceful influence: *I was under pressure from the others to change my mind.* **5** to force or urge by exerting pressure: *The car dealer tried to pressure my parents into buying a car.* 1-4 *noun,* 5 *verb,* **pres·sures, pres·sured, pres·sur·ing.**

pres·tige (pre stēzh′), reputation, influence, or distinction, based on what is known about one's abilities, achievements, or associations: *Her prestige rose when her classmates learned that she knew how to ski. noun.*

pres·to (pres′tō), an exclamation used to express quick or sudden action: *Then—presto—the rabbit disappeared. interjection.*

pre·sum·a·bly (pri zü′mə blē), probably: *Presumably, they will arrive by noon. adverb.*

pre·sume (pri züm′), to suppose; take for granted without proving: *You'll play out of doors, I presume, if there is sunshine.* verb, **pre·sumes, pre·sumed, pre·sum·ing.**

pre·sump·tion (pri zump′shən), a thing taken for granted: *Since she left the house last, the presumption was that she locked the door. noun.*

pre·sump·tu·ous (pri zump′chü əs), too bold; daring too much. *adjective.*

pre·tend (pri tend′), **1** to make believe: *Let's pretend that we are grown-ups.* **2** to claim falsely: *I pretended to like the meal so that my host would be pleased.* **3** to claim: *I don't pretend to be a musician.* **4** imaginary; make-believe: *The child had a pretend horse.* 1-3 *verb,* 4 *adjective.*

pre·tense (prē′tens), **1** make-believe; pretending: *My anger was all pretense.* **2** a false appearance: *Under pretense of dropping a pencil, the student looked at a classmate's test.* **3** a false claim: *They made a pretense of knowing our secret.* **4** a showing off: *a person who is quiet and free from pretense. noun.*

pre·ten·sion (pri ten′shən), **1** a claim: *The young prince has pretensions to the throne.* **2** a doing things for show or to make a fine appearance; showy display: *We were annoyed by the pretensions of our wealthy neighbor. noun.*

pre·ten·tious (pri ten′shəs), **1** making claims to excellence or importance: *a pretentious person.* **2** doing things for show or to make a fine appearance: *a pretentious style of entertaining guests. adjective.*

pre·text (prē′tekst), a false reason concealing the real reason; misleading excuse; pretense: *She did not go, on the pretext of being too busy. noun.*

pret·ti·ly (prit′ə lē), in a pretty manner. *adverb.*

pret·ti·ness (prit′ē nis), a pleasing appearance. *noun.*

pret·ty (prit′ē), **1** pleasing; attractive: *a pretty face, a pretty dress, a pretty tune.* **2** fairly; rather: *It is pretty late.* 1 *adjective,* **pret·ti·er, pret·ti·est;** 2 *adverb.*

pret·zel (pret′səl), a crisp cracker, usually in the form of a knot or stick, salted on the outside. *noun.*

pre·vail (pri vāl′), **1** to exist in many places; be in general use: *Making resolutions on New Year's*

a hat	i it	oi oil	ch child	⎧ a in about
ā age	ī ice	ou out	ng long	⎪ e in taken
ä far	o hot	u cup	sh she	ə = ⎨ i in pencil
e let	ō open	u̇ put	th thin	⎪ o in lemon
ē equal	ô order	ü rule	ᴛʜ then	⎩ u in circus
ėr term			zh measure	

Day is a custom that still prevails. **2** to be the stronger; win the victory; succeed: *to prevail against an enemy. Reason prevailed over emotion. verb.*

pre·vail·ing (pri vā′ling), in general use; common: *The prevailing summer winds here are from the west. adjective.*

prev·a·lence (prev′ə ləns), widespread occurrence; general use: *the prevalence of complaints about the weather. noun.*

prev·a·lent (prev′ə lənt), widespread; in general use; common: *Colds are prevalent in the winter. adjective.*

pre·vent (pri vent′), **1** to keep from; hinder: *Illness prevented me from doing my work.* **2** to keep from happening: *Vaccination prevents smallpox. verb.*

pre·vent·a·ble (pri ven′tə bəl), able to be prevented: *The accident was preventable. adjective.*

pre·ven·tion (pri ven′shən), a preventing; hindering: *the prevention of fire. noun.*

pre·ven·tive (pri ven′tiv), able to prevent or hinder: *Preventive measures were taken to stop the spread of the disease. adjective.*

pre·view (prē′vyü′), **1** an advance view, inspection, or survey: *a preview of things to come.* **2** to view beforehand. **3** an advance showing of a performance or scenes from a motion picture, play, or television program. 1,3 *noun,* 2 *verb.*

pre·vi·ous (prē′vē əs), coming or being before; earlier: *He did better in the previous lesson. adjective.*
[*Previous* comes from a Latin word meaning "leading the way" or "going before."]

pre·vi·ous·ly (prē′vē əs lē), at a previous time; before: *We had met previously. adverb.*

prey (prā), **1** an animal hunted or seized for food: *Mice and birds are the prey of cats.* **2** the habit of hunting and killing other animals for food: *Hawks are birds of prey.* noun, *plural* **prey.**

prey on or **prey upon,** **1** to hunt or kill for food: *Cats prey upon mice.* **2** to do harm; be a strain upon: *Worry about debts preyed on her mind.*

price (prīs), **1** the amount for which a thing is sold or can be bought; cost to the buyer: *The price of this hat is $10.* **2** to put a price on; set the price of: *The hat was priced at $10.* **3** to ask the price of; find out the price of: *Mother is pricing cars.* **4** a reward offered for the capture of a person alive or dead: *Every member of the gang has a price on his head.* **5** what must be given or done to obtain a thing; amount paid for any result: *The Pilgrims paid a heavy price for staying in America; half of them died during the first winter.* 1,4,5 *noun,* 2,3 *verb,* **pric·es, priced, pric·ing.**

P

price·less (prīs′lis), very, very valuable: *Many museums have collections of priceless works of art.* adjective.

prick (prik), **1** a little hole or mark made by a sharp point. **2** to make a little hole or mark on with a sharp point: *I pricked my finger on a thorn.* **3** a pain like that made by a sharp point. **4** to point upwards; raise: *The dog pricked up its ears at the noise.* 1,3 *noun,* 2,4 *verb.*

prick·le (prik′əl), **1** a small, sharp point; thorn. **2** to feel a prickly or smarting sensation: *My skin prickled as I listened to the scary story.* 1 *noun,* 2 *verb,* **prick·les, prick·led, prick·ling.**

prick·ly (prik′lē), **1** having many sharp points or thorns: *a prickly rosebush, a prickly porcupine.* **2** sharp and stinging; smarting: *Heat sometimes causes a prickly rash on the skin.* adjective, **prick·li·er, prick·li·est.**

prickly pear, the pear-shaped fruit of a kind of cactus. Prickly pears are good to eat.

prickly pears

pride (prīd), **1** a high opinion of one's own worth or possessions: *Pride in our city should make us help to keep it clean.* **2** the pleasure or satisfaction in something concerned with oneself: *I take pride in a hard job well done.* **3** something that one is proud of: *Their children are their great pride.* **4** too high an opinion of oneself: *Pride goes before a fall.* **5** **pride oneself on,** to be proud of: *I pride myself on being punctual.* 1-4 *noun,* 5 *verb,* **prides, prid·ed, prid·ing.**

pried (prīd). See **pry.** *verb.*

priest (prēst), a clergyman or minister of a Christian church. *noun.*

priest·ly (prēst′lē), **1** of or having something to do with a priest: *priestly robes.* **2** like a priest; suitable for a priest: *a priestly desire to help those in need.* adjective.

prim (prim), very proper and correct in speaking and dressing. adjective, **prim·mer, prim·mest.**

pri·mar·i·ly (prī mer′ə lē *or* prī′mer′ə lē), **1** above all; chiefly; principally: *That student is primarily interested in science.* **2** at first; originally. adverb.

pri·mar·y (prī′mer′ē), **1** first in time; first in order; original: *The primary causes of the war go back many years.* **2** chief; first in importance: *The primary reason for eating a balanced diet is good*

health. **3** an election in which members of a political party choose candidates for office. Primaries are held before the regular election. 1,2 *adjective,* 3 *noun, plural* **pri·mar·ies.**

primary accent, 1 the strongest accent in the pronunciation of a word. **2** a mark (′) used to show this.

primary color, any of a group of colors which, when mixed together, can produce all other colors. Red, yellow, and blue are primary colors.

primary school, the first three or four grades of elementary school.

pri·mate (prī′māt), one of a group of mammals that have very advanced brains, and hands with thumbs that can be used to hold on to things. Primates are the most highly developed mammals. Apes, monkeys, and human beings are primates. *noun.*

prime[1] (prīm), **1** first in rank; chief: *The town's prime need is a new school.* **2** first in quality; first-rate; excellent: *prime ribs of beef.* adjective.

prime[2] (prīm), the best part; best time; best condition: *A person of forty is in the prime of life.* *noun.*

prime[3] (prīm), to prepare by putting something in or on. New wood is primed with a special first coat of paint so that the final coat will not soak in. *verb,* **primes, primed, prim·ing.**

prime meridian, the meridian from which the longitude east and west is measured. It passes through Greenwich, England, and its longitude is 0 degrees.

prime minister, the chief official in certain governments. Canada and Great Britain have prime ministers.

prime number, a number that can be divided without a remainder only by itself and 1. 2, 3, 5, 7, and 11 are prime numbers.

prim·er (prim′ər), **1** a first book in reading. **2** a first book; beginner's book: *a primer in arithmetic.* *noun.*

pri·me·val (prī mē′vəl), **1** of or having something to do with the earliest age of the earth: *In its primeval state the earth was without any forms of life.* **2** ancient: *primeval forests untouched by the ax.* adjective.

prim·i·tive (prim′ə tiv), **1** of early times; of long ago: *Primitive people often lived in caves.* **2** very simple; such as people had early in human history: *A primitive way of making fire is by rubbing two sticks together.* adjective.

prim·rose (prim′rōz′), **1** a plant having showy, bell-shaped or funnel-shaped flowers of various colors. There are many kinds of primroses. The common one of Europe has pale-yellow flowers. **2** pale-yellow. 1 *noun,* 2 *adjective.*

prince (prins), **1** a son of a king or queen; son of a king's or queen's son. **2** the greatest or best of a group; chief: *a merchant prince.* *noun.*

Prince Ed·ward Is·land (prins′ ed′wərd ī′lənd), a province in eastern Canada. *Capital:* Charlottetown.

prince·ly (prins′lē), **1** of a prince or his rank;

royal: *the princely families of Europe.* **2** like a prince; noble: *a princely manner.* **3** fit for a prince; magnificent: *Some actors earn princely salaries.* *adjective,* **prince·li·er, prince·li·est.**

prin·cess (prin′ses), **1** a daughter of a king or queen; daughter of a king's or queen's son. **2** a wife or widow of a prince. *noun, plural* **prin·cess·es.**

prin·ci·pal (prin′sə pəl), **1** main; chief; most important: *Chicago is the principal city of Illinois.* **2** the chief person; one who gives orders. **3** the head of a school. **4** a sum of money on which interest is paid. **1** *adjective,* **2-4** *noun.*

prin·ci·pal·ly (prin′sə pə lē), for the most part; above all; chiefly. *adverb.*

prin·ci·ple (prin′sə pəl), **1** a basic truth or law; truth that is a foundation for other truths: *the principle of free speech.* **2** a rule of action or conduct: *I make it a principle to save some money each week.* **3** a rule of science explaining how things act: *the principle by which a machine works.* *noun.*

print (print), **1** to use type or other inked surface to transfer words, pictures, or the like onto paper. Books, magazines, newspapers, and pamphlets are printed. **2** to cause to be printed; publish: *to print books. Most newspapers are printed daily.* **3** words, pictures, or the like transferred onto paper by type or other inked surface: *The book had very large print.* **4** to make letters the way they look in print instead of writing them: *Print your name clearly. Most children learn to print before learning to write.* **5** to mark cloth or paper with patterns or designs: *This machine prints wallpaper.* **6** a kind of cloth with a pattern pressed on it: *She has two dresses made of print.* **7** a picture made in a special way; printed picture or design. **8** to stamp; produce marks or figures by pressure; impress. **9** a mark made by pressing or stamping, such as a footprint. **10** a photograph produced from a negative. **1,2,4,5,8** *verb,* **3,6,7,9,10** *noun.*

print·er (prin′tər), **1** a person whose business or work is printing or setting type. **2** a machine that prints, controlled by a computer. *noun.*

print·ing (prin′ting), **1** the producing of books, newspapers, magazines, or pamphlets by transferring words, pictures, or the like from type or other inked surface. **2** printed words. **3** letters made like those in print. *noun.*

printing press, a machine for printing.

print·out (print′out′), paper on which a computer has written information with a printer: *This printout lists the name and age of everyone in the class. noun.*

pri·or (prī′ər), coming before; earlier: *I can't go with you because I have a prior engagement.* *adjective.*

prior to, earlier than; before.

pri·or·i·ty (prī ôr′ə tē), greater importance; coming before in order or importance: *Fire engines have priority over other traffic. noun, plural* **pri·or·i·ties.**

prism (priz′əm), a transparent solid object with

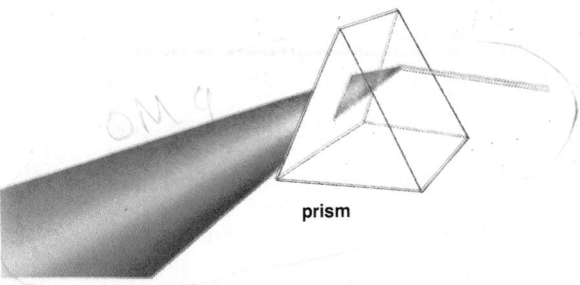

prism

two ends that are triangles and three sides that are rectangles. A prism separates white light passing through it into the colors of the rainbow. *noun.*

pris·on (priz′n), a public building in which criminals are confined: *The convicted killer was sentenced to prison for life. noun.*

pris·on·er (priz′n ər), **1** a person who is under arrest or held in a jail or prison. **2** a person taken by the enemy in war. *noun.*

pris·sy (pris′ē), too careful; too fussy. *adjective,* **pris·si·er, pris·si·est.**

pri·va·cy (prī′və sē), **1** the condition of being private; being away from others: *in the privacy of one's home.* **2** secrecy: *He told me his reasons in strict privacy. noun.*

pri·vate (prī′vit), **1** not for the public; for one person or a few special people: *a private road, a private house, a private letter.* **2** personal; not public: *the private life of a king, a private opinion.* **3** secret; confidential: *News reached her through private channels.* **4** having no public office: *a private citizen.* **5** a soldier or marine of the lowest rank: *His brother was promoted from private to corporal last week.* **1-4** *adjective,* **5** *noun.*

in private, secretly: *The rebels met in private to plot against the government.*

pri·va·teer (prī′və tir′), an armed ship owned by civilians. Formerly, the United States government commissioned privateers to attack and capture enemy ships. *noun.*

pri·va·tion (prī vā′shən), a lack of the comforts or necessities of life; hardship: *People suffered many privations during the war. noun.*

priv·i·lege (priv′ə lij), a special right, advantage, or favor: *My sister has the privilege of driving the family car. noun.*

priv·i·leged (priv′ə lijd), having some privilege or privileges: *Kings and queens are privileged people.* *adjective.*

priv·y (priv′ē), private. *adjective.*

privy to, having secret or private knowledge of: *The Vice-President was privy to the plans of the President.*

prize[1] (prīz), **1** a reward won after trying against other people: *Prizes will be given for the three best stories.* **2** given as a prize: *He saved the prize money for his college education.* **3** worthy of a prize: *prize vegetables.* **1** *noun,* **2,3** *adjective.*

prize[2] (prīz), a thing or person captured in war, especially an enemy's ship and its cargo taken at sea. *noun.*

prize[3] (prīz), to value highly: *She prizes her new bicycle. verb,* **priz·es, prized, priz·ing.**

prize·fight (prīz'fīt'), a boxing match between prizefighters. *noun.*

prize·fight·er (prīz'fī'tər), a person who fights or boxes for money. *noun.*

pro[1] (prō), **1** in favor of; for: *We talked about the problem pro and con.* **2** a reason in favor of. The pros and cons of a question are the arguments for and against it. **1** *adverb,* **2** *noun, plural* **pros.**

pro[2] (prō), **1** a professional. **2** professional. **1** *noun, plural* **pros;** **2** *adjective.*

prob·a·bil·i·ty (prob'ə bil'ə tē), **1** the quality or fact of being likely or probable; good chance: *There is a probability of rain.* **2** something likely to happen: *A storm is a probability for tomorrow. noun, plural* **prob·a·bil·i·ties.**

in all probability, probably: *In all probability I will go with you.*

prob·a·ble (prob'ə bəl), **1** likely to happen: *Cooler weather is probable after this shower.* **2** likely to be true: *Something he ate is the probable cause of his upset stomach. adjective.*

prob·a·bly (prob'ə blē), more likely than not. *adverb.*

pro·ba·tion (prō bā'shən), a trial or testing of conduct, character, or qualifications: *Instead of a prison sentence, the prisoner was allowed to remain free on probation for as long as his behavior remained good. noun.*

probe (prōb), **1** to search into; examine thoroughly; investigate: *I probed my memory for her name.* **2** a thorough examination; investigation: *a probe of illegal gambling.* **3** a slender instrument for exploring something. A doctor or dentist uses a probe to explore the depth or direction of a wound or cavity. A Geiger counter uses a probe to detect the amount of radiation in radioactive matter, such as rock. **4** a spacecraft carrying scientific instruments to record or report back information about planets or other objects in outer space: *a lunar probe.* **5** to examine with a probe. **1,5** *verb,* **probes, probed, prob·ing;** **2-4** *noun.*

prob·lem (prob'ləm), **1** a question; difficult question: *How to do away with poverty is a problem that concerns the government.* **2** a matter of doubt or difficulty: *The president of a large company has to deal with many problems.* **3** something to be worked out: *a problem in arithmetic.* **4** causing difficulty: *a problem child.* **1-3** *noun,* **4** *adjective.*

pro·ce·dure (prə sē'jər), a way of doing things: *What is your procedure in making bread? noun.*

pro·ceed (prə sēd'), **1** to go on after having stopped; move forward: *Please proceed with your story.* **2** to carry on any activity: *I proceeded to light the fire.* **3** to come forth; issue; go out: *Heat proceeds from fire. verb.*

pro·ceed·ing (prə sē'ding), **1** what is done; action; conduct. **2 proceedings, a** the action in a case in a court of law. **b** a record of what was done at the meetings of a society or club. *noun.*

pro·ceeds (prō'sēdz'), the money obtained from a sale or some other activity or transaction: *The proceeds from the school play will be used to buy a new curtain for the stage. noun plural.*

proc·ess (pros'es), **1** a set of actions done in a certain order: *By what process is cloth made from wool?* **2** to treat or prepare by some special method: *This cloth has been processed to make it waterproof.* **1** *noun, plural* **proc·ess·es;** **2** *verb.*

in process, 1 in the course or condition: *In process of time the house will be finished.* **2** in the course or condition of being done: *The author has just finished her first book and has a second one in process.*

pro·ces·sion (prə sesh'ən), **1** something that moves forward; persons marching or riding: *a funeral procession.* **2** an orderly moving forward: *We formed lines to march in procession onto the platform. noun.*

pro·claim (prə klām'), to make known publicly and officially; declare publicly: *War was proclaimed. The President proclaimed this week as National Dog Week. verb.*

proc·la·ma·tion (prok'lə mā'shən), an official announcement; public declaration: *The queen issued a proclamation ending the war. noun.*

pro·cure (prə kyùr'), **1** to get by care or effort; obtain; secure: *to procure a position in a bank. It is hard to procure water in a desert.* **2** to bring about; cause: *The lawyer procured the prisoner's release. verb,* **pro·cures, pro·cured, pro·cur·ing.**

prod (prod), **1** to poke or jab with something pointed: *to prod an animal with a stick.* **2** to stir up; urge on; goad: *My parents keep prodding me to clean my room.* **3** a poke; thrust: *That prod in the ribs hurt.* **4** a stick with a sharp point; goad. **1,2** *verb,* **prods, prod·ded, prod·ding;** **3,4** *noun.*

prod·i·gal (prod'ə gəl), **1** spending too much; wasting money or other things; wasteful: *America has been prodigal of its forests.* **2** a person who is wasteful or extravagant: *The father welcomed the prodigal back home.* **1** *adjective,* **2** *noun.*

pro·di·gious (prə dij'əs), very great; huge; vast: *The ocean contains a prodigious amount of water. adjective.*

prod·i·gy (prod'ə jē), a marvel; wonder. A child prodigy is a child that is remarkably brilliant in some way. *noun, plural* **prod·i·gies.**

pro·duce (prə düs' or prə dyüs' for 1-4; prō'düs or prō'dyüs for 5), **1** to make; bring into existence: *This factory produces stoves.* **2** to bring about; cause: *Hard work produces success.* **3** to bring forth; supply; yield: *Hens produce eggs.* **4** to bring forward; show: *Produce your proof. Our class produced a play.* **5** farm products, especially

fruits and vegetables. 1-4 *verb*, **pro·duc·es,
pro·duced, pro·duc·ing;** 5 *noun*.

pro·duc·er (prə dü′sər *or* prə dyü′sər), **1** a
person who produces, especially a person who
grows or manufactures things that are used by
others. **2** a person in charge of presenting a play,
a motion picture, or a television or radio show. **3** a
living thing that can make its own food from
minerals, water, and sunlight. All green plants and
some bacteria are producers. *noun*.

prod·uct (prod′əkt), **1** that which is produced;
result of work or of growth: *factory products, farm
products.* **2** a number resulting from multiplying
two or more numbers together: *40 is the product
of 5 and 8. noun.*

pro·duc·tion (prə duk′shən), **1** the act of
producing; manufacture: *the production of
automobiles.* **2** something that is produced: *the
yearly production of a farm. noun.*

pro·duc·tive (prə duk′tiv), **1** producing much;
fertile: *a productive farm, a productive writer.*
2 producing food or other useful articles: *Farming
is productive labor. adjective.*

pro·fane (prə fān′), **1** without respect for God or
holy things: *profane language.* **2** to treat holy things
with disrespect or abuse: *to profane a church by
stabling horses in it.* **1** *adjective,* **2** *verb,* **pro·fanes,
pro·faned, pro·fan·ing.**

pro·fan·i·ty (prə fan′ə tē), **1** swearing; use of
profane language. **2** a being profane; lack of
reverence. *noun, plural* **pro·fan·i·ties.**

pro·fess (prə fes′), **1** to claim to have; claim: *She
professed the greatest respect for the law. I don't
profess to be an expert in chemistry.* **2** to declare
openly: *He professed his loyalty to the United
States. verb.*

pro·fes·sion (prə fesh′ən), **1** an occupation
requiring special education, such as law,
medicine, teaching, or the ministry. **2** the people
engaged in such an occupation: *The medical
profession favors this law.* **3** an open declaration;
act of professing: *a profession of friendship, a
profession of faith. noun.*

pro·fes·sion·al (prə fesh′ə nəl), **1** of or having
something to do with a profession: *The surgeon
showed great professional skill during the operation.*
2 engaged in a profession: *A lawyer or a doctor is
a professional person.* **3** a person who works at a
profession; a professional man or woman.
4 making a business or trade of something which
others do for pleasure: *professional musicians.* **5** a
person who does this. **1,2,4** *adjective,* **3,5** *noun.*

pro·fes·sor (prə fes′ər), a teacher of the highest
rank in a college or university. *noun.*

pro·fi·cient (prə fish′ənt), skilled; expert;
advanced in any art, science, or subject: *She was
very proficient in music. adjective.*

pro·file (prō′fīl), **1** a side view, especially of the
human face. **2** an outline. *noun.*

prof·it (prof′it), **1** the gain from a business; what
is left when the cost of goods and of carrying on
the business is subtracted from the amount of
money taken in: *The profits in this business are not*

a hat	i it	oi oil	ch child	a in about
ā age	ī ice	ou out	ng long	e in taken
ä far	o hot	u cup	sh she	ə = { i in pencil
e let	ō open	ů put	th thin	o in lemon
ē equal	ô order	ü rule	₮H then	u in circus
ėr term			zh measure	

large. **2** to make a gain from business; make a
profit. **3** an advantage; benefit: *What profit is there
in worrying?* **4** to get advantage; gain; benefit: *A
wise person profits from mistakes.* **1,3** *noun,* **2,4**
verb.

prof·it·a·ble (prof′ə tə bəl), **1** yielding profit: *The
sale held by the Girl Scouts was very profitable.*
2 useful; giving a gain or benefit: *We spent a
profitable afternoon in the library. adjective.*

pro·found (prə found′), **1** felt strongly; very
great: *profound despair, profound sympathy.*
2 going far deeper than what is easily understood;
having or showing great knowledge or
understanding: *a profound book, a profound
thinker. adjective.*

pro·fuse (prə fyüs′), **1** very abundant: *profuse
thanks.* **2** spending or giving freely; extravagant:
He was profuse in his praise of the book. adjective.

pro·fu·sion (prə fyü′zhən), a very large quantity;
abundance: *a profusion of books, a profusion of
roses. noun.*

pro·gram (prō′gram), **1** a list of items or events
set down in order with a list of the performers.
There are concert programs, theater programs,
and programs of a meeting. **2** the items making up
an entertainment: *The entire program was
delightful.* **3** a broadcast on radio or television: *a
news program.* **4** a plan of what is to be done: *a
school program, a business program, a government
program.* **5** a set of instructions that tells a
computer how to do a certain job. **6** to prepare a
set of instructions for a computer, so that it will do
a certain job. **1-5** *noun,* **6** *verb,* **pro·grams,
pro·grammed, pro·gram·ming.**

pro·gram·mer (prō′gram′ər), a person who
prepares a computer program or programs. *noun.*

prog·ress (prog′res *for 1 and 3;* prə gres′ *for 2
and 4*), **1** an advance; growth; development;

profile (definition 1)

489

improvement: *the progress of science. The class showed rapid progress in its studies.* **2** to get better; advance; develop: *We progress in learning step by step.* **3** a moving forward; going ahead: *We made rapid progress on our journey.* **4** to move forward; go ahead: *The building of the new school progressed quickly during the summer.* 1,3 *noun,* 2,4 *verb.*

pro·gres·sion (prə gresh′ən), a moving forward; going ahead: *Creeping is a slow method of progression. noun.*

pro·gres·sive (prə gres′iv), **1** making progress; advancing to something better; improving: *a progressive nation.* **2** favoring progress; wanting improvement or reform in government, religion, or business. **3** a person who favors improvement and reform in government, religion, or business: *Our doctor is a progressive in her beliefs.* 1,2 *adjective,* 3 *noun.*

pro·hib·it (prō hib′it), **1** to forbid by law or authority: *Picking flowers in the park is prohibited.* **2** to prevent: *Rainy weather and fog prohibited flying. verb.*

pro·hi·bi·tion (prō′ə bish′ən), **1** the act of prohibiting or forbidding: *The prohibition of swimming in the city's reservoirs is sensible.* **2** a law or laws against making or selling liquor. *noun.*

proj·ect (proj′ekt *for 1,2 and 5;* prə jekt′ *for 3 and 4*), **1** a plan; scheme: *a project for slum clearance.* **2** an undertaking; special assignment. **3** to cause to fall on a surface: *Motion pictures are projected on the screen. The tree projects a shadow on the grass.* **4** to stick out: *The rocky point projects far into the water.* **5** a group of apartment buildings built and run as a unit, especially with government support: *They live in a big housing project.* 1,2,5 *noun,* 3,4 *verb.*

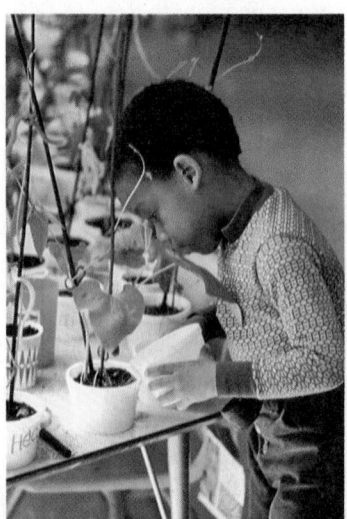

project (definition 2)
He watered the plants in the class science **project.**

pro·jec·tile (prə jek′təl), any object that can be thrown, hurled, or shot, such as a stone or bullet. *noun.*

pro·jec·tion (prə jek′shən), **1** a part that projects or sticks out: *rocky projections on the face of a*

cliff. **2** a sticking out. **3** a throwing or casting forward: *the projection of a shell from a cannon, the projection of a photographic image on a screen. noun.*

pro·jec·tor (prə jek′tər), an apparatus for projecting a picture on a screen. *noun.*

pro·lif·ic (prə lif′ik), **1** producing many offspring: *Rabbits are prolific.* **2** producing much: *a prolific tree, a prolific garden, a prolific writer. adjective.*

pro·long (prə lông′), to make longer; extend; stretch: *Good care may prolong a sick person's life. verb.*

prom (prom), a formal dance given by a college or high-school class. *noun.*

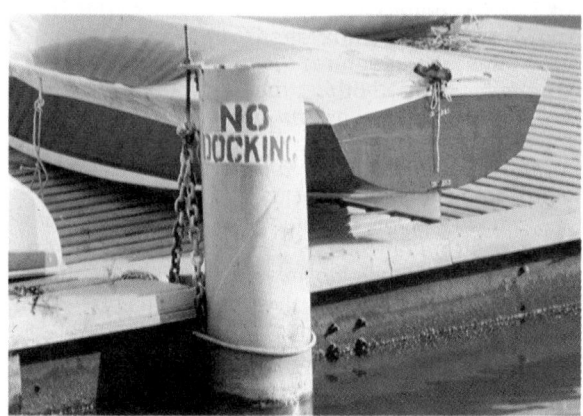

prohibit (definition 1)—Docking boats at the pier was **prohibited.**

prom·e·nade (prom′ə nād′ *or* prom′ə näd′), **1** a walk for pleasure or for show: *They took a promenade in their fine clothes.* **2** a public place for such a walk: *The resort had a promenade along the beach. noun.*

prom·i·nence (prom′ə nəns), **1** a being prominent, distinguished, or conspicuous: *the prominence of Washington as a leader, the prominence of football as a sport.* **2** something that juts out or projects, especially upward. A hill is a prominence. *noun.*

prom·i·nent (prom′ə nənt), **1** well-known; important: *a prominent citizen.* **2** easy to see: *I hung the picture in a prominent place in the living room.* **3** standing out; projecting: *Some insects have prominent eyes. adjective.*

prom·ise (prom′is), **1** words said or written, binding a person to do or not to do something: *You can count on her to keep her promise.* **2** to give one's word; make a promise: *They promised to stay till we came.* **3** an indication of what may be expected: *The clouds give promise of rain.* **4** an indication of giving hope of success in the future: *She shows promise as a musician.* **5** to give hope; give hope of: *The rainbow promises fair weather.* 1,3,4 *noun,* 2,5 *verb,* **prom·is·es, prom·ised, prom·is·ing.**

prom·is·ing (prom′ə sing), giving hope of success in the future; likely to turn out well: *The promising young pianist has a great deal of talent. adjective.*

a hat	i it	oi oil	ch child		a in about
ā age	ī ice	ou out	ng long		e in taken
ä far	o hot	u cup	sh she	ə =	i in pencil
e let	ō open	u̇ put	th thin		o in lemon
ē equal	ô order	ü rule	ŦH then		u in circus
ėr term			zh measure		

promontory—A **promontory** rose high above the river.

prom·on·to·ry (prom′ən tôr′ē), a high point of land or rock extending into a body of water; headland. *noun, plural* **prom·on·to·ries.**

pro·mote (prə mōt′), 1 to raise in rank or importance: *Pupils who pass this test will be promoted to the next higher grade.* 2 to help to grow or develop; help to success: *A kindly feeling toward other countries will promote peace.* 3 to recommend the use of; try to sell by advertising: *A series of TV commercials promotes the new soap.* *verb,* **pro·motes, pro·mot·ed, pro·mot·ing.**

pro·mo·tion (prə mō′shən), 1 an advance in rank or importance: *The clerk was given a promotion and an increase in salary.* 2 a helping to grow or develop; helping along to success: *They are active in the promotion of better health care. noun.*

prompt (prompt), 1 quick; on time; ready and willing: *to be prompt to obey.* 2 done at once; made without delay: *a prompt answer.* 3 to cause someone to do something: *His curiosity prompted him to ask questions.* 4 to remind a speaker or actor of the words or actions needed: *Please prompt me if I forget my lines.* 1,2 *adjective,* 3,4 *verb.*

prone (prōn), 1 inclined; liable: *He is prone to forget to do his chores.* 2 lying down, usually with the face down: *He lay prone on the bed, sound asleep. adjective.*

prong (prông), one of the pointed ends of a fork or antler. *noun.*

prong·horn (prông′hôrn′), an animal very much like an antelope, living on the plains of western North America. *noun, plural* **prong·horns** or **prong·horn.**

pro·noun (prō′noun), a word used to indicate without naming, such as *you, it, they, him, we, whose, this,* or *whoever;* word used instead of a noun. In "John and Mary did not go because they were sick," *they* is a pronoun used in the second part of the sentence to avoid repeating *John and Mary. noun.*

pro·nounce (prə nouns′), 1 to make the sounds of; speak: *Pronounce your words clearly.* 2 to state or declare in a solemn or positive way: *The doctor pronounced her cured. The judge pronounced* sentence on the prisoner. *verb,* **pro·nounc·es, pro·nounced, pro·nounc·ing.**

pro·nounced (prə nounst′), strongly marked; decided: *She has pronounced opinions on politics. adjective.*

pron·to (pron′tō), quickly; immediately; promptly: *They got the job done pronto. adverb.*

pro·nun·ci·a·tion (prə nun′sē ā′shən), 1 a way of pronouncing. This book gives the pronunciation of each main word. 2 a making the sounds of words; speaking. *noun.*

proof (prüf), 1 a way or means of showing beyond doubt the truth of something: *Is what you say a guess or have you proof?* 2 an act of testing; trial: *That box looks big enough; but let us put it to the proof.* 3 of tested value against something: *This fabric is wrinkle-proof.* 1,2 *noun,* 3 *adjective.*

proof·read (prüf′rēd′), to read and mark errors to be corrected. *verb,* **proof·reads, proof·read** (prüf′red′), **proof·read·ing.**

prop (prop), 1 to hold up by placing a support under or against: *Prop the clothes line with a stick. He was propped up in bed with pillows.* 2 a thing or person used to support another: *I used the book as a prop behind my painting.* 1 *verb,* **props, propped, prop·ping;** 2 *noun.*

prop·a·gan·da (prop′ə gan′də), 1 organized efforts to spread opinions or beliefs: *Propaganda is most effective where there is no freedom of the press.* 2 the opinions or beliefs spread by such efforts: *During the war, the enemy spread false propaganda about us. noun.*

prop·a·gate (prop′ə gāt), to produce offspring; reproduce: *Trees propagate themselves by seeds. verb,* **prop·a·gates, prop·a·gat·ed, prop·a·gat·ing.**

pro·pel (prə pel′), to drive forward; force ahead: *to propel a boat by oars, a person propelled by ambition. verb,* **pro·pels, pro·pelled, pro·pel·ling.**

pronghorn—about 3 feet (1 meter) high at the shoulder

pro·pel·lant (prə pel′ənt), something that propels, especially the fuel of a rocket. *noun.*

pro·pel·ler (prə pel′ər), a revolving part with blades, for propelling boats and aircraft. *noun.*

prop·er (prop′ər), **1** right for the occasion; fitting: *Night is the proper time to sleep.* **2** in the strict sense of the word: *Puerto Rico is not part of the United States proper.* **3** decent; respectable: *proper conduct. adjective.*

prop·er·ly (prop′ər lē), **1** in a proper, correct, or suitable manner: *Eat properly.* **2** strictly: *Properly speaking, a whale is not a fish. adverb.*

proper noun, a word that names a particular person, place, or thing. *Maria, George, Chicago,* and *Monday* are proper nouns. A proper noun always begins with a capital letter.

prop·er·ty (prop′ər tē), **1** a thing or things owned; possession or possessions: *This house is her property. That book is my property; please return it to me.* **2** a piece of land or real estate: *He owns some property out West.* **3** a quality or power belonging specially to something: *Soap has the property of removing dirt. Copper has several important properties. noun, plural* **prop·er·ties.**

proph·e·cy (prof′ə sē), **1** telling what will happen; foretelling future events. **2** a thing told about the future. *noun, plural* **proph·e·cies.**

proph·e·sy (prof′ə sī), **1** to tell what will happen; foretell; predict: *The fortuneteller prophesied that I would have good luck in the future.* **2** to speak when or as if inspired by God. *verb,* **proph·e·sies, proph·e·sied, proph·e·sy·ing.**

proph·et (prof′it), **1** a person who tells what will happen: *Don't be a bad-luck prophet.* **2** a religious leader who speaks as the voice of God: *Jeremiah was a prophet of the Old Testament. noun.*

pro·por·tion (prə pôr′shən), **1** the relation of two things; a size, number, or amount compared to another: *Each girl's pay will be in proportion to the work she does. Mix water and orange juice in the proportions of three to one by adding three measures of water to every measure of orange juice.* **2** a proper relation between parts: *The dog's short legs were not in proportion to its long body.* **3** to fit one thing to another so that they go together: *The designs in that rug are well proportioned.* **4** a part; share: *A large proportion of Nevada is desert.*

proportion (definition 1) She was tiny in **proportion** to the dog.

propeller of a ship

5 proportions, **a** size; extent: *He left an art collection of considerable proportions.* **b** dimensions: *The dining room of the castle had the proportions of our entire apartment.* 1,2,4,5 *noun,* 3 *verb.*

pro·pos·al (prə pō′zəl), **1** a plan; scheme; suggestion: *The club will now hear this member's proposal.* **2** an offer of marriage. **3** the act of proposing: *Proposal is easier than performance. noun.*

pro·pose (prə pōz′), **1** to put forward; suggest: *She proposed that we take turns at the swing.* **2** to intend; plan: *She proposes to save half of all she earns.* **3** to make an offer of marriage. *verb,* **pro·pos·es, pro·posed, pro·pos·ing.**

prop·o·si·tion (prop′ə zish′ən), **1** what is offered to be considered; proposal: *She made a proposition to buy out her partner's interest in the store.* **2** a statement that is to be proved true. EXAMPLE: Resolved: that our school should have a bank. *noun.*

pro·pri·e·tor (prə prī′ə tər), an owner. *noun.*

pro·pul·sion (prə pul′shən), **1** a driving forward or onward. **2** a propelling force or impulse: *Most large aircraft are powered by propulsion of jet engines. noun.*

prose (prōz), the ordinary form of spoken or written language; plain language not arranged in verses. *noun.*

pros·e·cute (pros′ə kyüt), to bring before a court of law: *Reckless drivers will be prosecuted. verb,* **pros·e·cutes, pros·e·cut·ed, pros·e·cut·ing.**

pros·e·cu·tion (pros′ə kyü′shən), **1** the carrying on of a lawsuit: *The prosecution will be stopped if the stolen money is returned.* **2** the side that starts action against another in a court of law. The prosecution makes certain charges against the defense. *noun.*

pros·pect (pros′pekt), **1** the act of looking forward; expectation: *The prospect of a vacation is pleasant.* **2** outlook for the future: *Without a high school education the prospect of getting a good job is poor.* **3** to search or look: *to prospect for gold.* **4** a person who may become a customer, buyer, or candidate: *The salesman called on several prospects.* 1,2,4 *noun,* 3 *verb.*

pro·spec·tive (prə spek′tiv), expected; likely to be: *a prospective customer, a prospective raise in pay. adjective.*

pros·pec·tor (pros′pek tər), a person who explores or examines a region, searching for gold, silver, oil, uranium, or other valuable resources. *noun.*

pros·per (pros′pər), to be successful; have good fortune; flourish: *Their business prospered. verb.*

pros·per·i·ty (pros per′ə tē), success; good fortune; prosperous condition: *a time of peace and prosperity. noun.*

pros·per·ous (pros′pər əs), successful; thriving; doing well; fortunate: *a prosperous merchant. adjective.*

pros·trate (pros′trāt), 1 to lay down flat; cast down: *The captives prostrated themselves before the conqueror.* 2 lying flat with face downward: *They were humbly prostrate in prayer.* 3 lying flat: *I stumbled and fell prostrate on the floor.* 4 to make very weak or helpless; exhaust: *Sickness often prostrates people.* 5 overcome; helpless: *They were prostrate with grief.* 1,4 *verb,* **pros·trates, pros·trat·ed, pros·trat·ing;** 2,3,5 *adjective.*

pro·tect (prə tekt′), to shield from harm or danger; shelter; defend; guard: *Proper food protects a person's health. verb.*

pro·tec·tion (prə tek′shən), 1 the act of protecting; condition of being kept from harm; defense: *We have a large dog for our protection.* 2 a thing or person that prevents damage: *A hat is a protection from the sun. noun.*

pro·tec·tive (prə tek′tiv), 1 protecting; being a defense: *the hard protective covering of a turtle.* 2 preventing injury to those around: *a protective device on a machine. adjective.*

pro·tec·tor (prə tek′tər), a person or thing that protects; defender. *noun.*

pro·tein (prō′tēn), one of the substances containing nitrogen which are a necessary part of the cells of animals and plants. Foods such as meat, milk, cheese, eggs, and beans contain protein. *noun.*

pro·test (prō′test *for 1;* prə test′ *for 2 and 3*), 1 a statement that denies or objects strongly: *They yielded only after protest.* 2 to make objections; object: *I protested against having to wash the dishes.* 3 to declare solemnly; assert: *The accused speeder protested her innocence.* 1 *noun,* 2,3 *verb.* **under protest,** unwillingly; though objecting.

Prot·es·tant (prot′ə stənt), 1 a member of any of certain Christian churches which split off from the Roman Catholic Church. 2 of Protestants or their religion. 1 *noun,* 2 *adjective.*

pro·tist (prō′tist), a living thing that has characteristics both of animals and of plants, or of neither. Protists are usually one-celled. Amebas and many algae are protists. *noun.*

pro·ton (prō′ton), a tiny particle having one unit of positive electricity. Protons occur in the nuclei of atoms. *noun.*

a hat	**i** it	**oi** oil	**ch** child	a in about
ā age	**ī** ice	**ou** out	**ng** long	e in taken
ä far	**o** hot	**u** cup	**sh** she	ə = { i in pencil
e let	**ō** open	**ů** put	**th** thin	o in lemon
ē equal	**ô** order	**ü** rule	**ŦH** then	u in circus
ėr term			**zh** measure	

pro·to·plasm (prō′tə plaz′əm), living matter; the living substance of all plant, animal, and other cells. Protoplasm is a colorless substance somewhat like white of egg. *noun.*

pro·to·zo·an (prō′tə zō′ən), a living thing that is like an animal, but that has only one cell and is so small it cannot be seen without a microscope. Most protozoans live in water. They are not animals or plants but another kind of life called protists. Amebas and paramecia are protozoans. *noun, plural* **pro·to·zo·ans** *or* **pro·to·zo·a** (prō′tə zō′ə).

pro·trude (prō trüd′), to stick out; project: *Her teeth protrude too far. verb,* **pro·trudes, pro·trud·ed, pro·trud·ing.**

proud (proud), 1 having pride in oneself or one's achievements. 2 feeling or showing pleasure or satisfaction in something connected with oneself or others: *I am proud to have been chosen to be class president.* 3 having respect for oneself or one's position: *The poor family was too proud to ask for charity.* 4 grand; magnificent: *The big ship was a proud sight. adjective.*
proud of, thinking well of; being well satisfied with: *to be proud of oneself, to be proud of one's family.*

prove (prüv), 1 to show that a thing is true and right: *Prove your statement.* 2 to turn out; be found to be: *The book proved interesting.* 3 to try out; test: *to prove a new product. verb,* **proves, proved, proved** *or* **prov·en, prov·ing.**

prov·en (prü′vən), proved. See **prove.** *verb.*

prov·erb (prov′ėrb′), a short, wise saying used for a long time by many people. "Haste makes waste" is a proverb. *noun.*

pro·vide (prə vīd′), 1 to give what is needed or wanted; supply; furnish: *The school provided inexpensive lunches for students.* 2 to take care for the future: *They saved money to provide for their old age.* 3 to state as a condition: *Our club's rules provide that dues must be paid monthly. verb,* **pro·vides, pro·vid·ed, pro·vid·ing.**

pro·vid·ed (prə vī′did), on the condition that; if: *She will go provided her friends can go also. conjunction.*

prov·i·dence (prov′ə dəns), God's care and help: *Trusting in providence, the Pilgrims sailed for the unknown world. noun.*

protist

Prov·i·dence (prov′ə dəns), the capital of Rhode Island. *noun.*

prov·i·dent (prov′ə dənt), careful in providing for the future; having or showing foresight: *Provident people save some money for the future. adjective.*

prov·ince (prov′əns), one of the main divisions of a country. Canada is divided into provinces instead of into states. *noun.*

pro·vin·cial (prə vin′shəl), of a province: *provincial government. adjective.*

pro·vi·sion (prə vizh′ən), **1** a statement making a condition: *Our apartment lease has a provision that no pets are allowed.* **2** the act of providing; preparation: *They made provision for their children's education.* **3 provisions,** a supply of food and drinks: *After a long winter the settlers were low on provisions.* **4** to supply with provisions: *The cabin was well provisioned with canned goods.* 1-3 *noun,* 4 *verb.*

prov·o·ca·tion (prov′ə kā′shən), something that stirs one up; cause of anger: *Their insults were a provocation. noun.*

provocation—He kicked his brother without **provocation.**

pro·voke (prə vōk′), **1** to make angry: *She provoked him by her teasing.* **2** to stir up; excite: *An insult provokes a person to anger.* **3** to call forth; bring about; cause: *The senator's speech provoked much discussion. verb,* **pro·vokes, pro·voked, pro·vok·ing.**

prow (prou), the pointed front part of a ship or boat; bow. *noun.*

prowl (proul), to go about slowly and secretly, like an animal hunting for something to eat or a thief looking for something to steal: *Many wild animals prowl at night. verb.*

prox·y (prok′sē), agent; substitute: *The mayor sent a proxy to the meeting to act in his place. noun, plural* **prox·ies.**

pru·dence (prüd′ns), wise thought before acting; good judgment. *noun.*

pru·dent (prüd′nt), planning carefully ahead of time; sensible: *Prudent people save part of their wages. adjective.*

prune[1] (prün), a kind of sweet plum that is dried: *We had stewed prunes for breakfast. noun.*

prune[2] (prün), to cut off parts of a tree or bush: *We pruned branches from our apple tree to improve next year's fruit. verb,* **prunes, pruned, prun·ing.**

pry[1] (prī), to look, peer, or inquire into something, especially someone's private business. *verb,* **pries, pried, pry·ing.**

pry[2] (prī), **1** to raise or move by force: *I used a large screwdriver to pry open the window.* **2** to get with much effort: *We finally pried the secret out of him. verb,* **pries, pried, pry·ing.**

P.S., postscript.

psalm (säm), a sacred song or poem, especially one of the Psalms of the Old Testament. *noun.*

pshaw (shô), an exclamation expressing impatience, contempt, or dislike. *interjection, noun.*

psy·chi·a·trist (sī kī′ə trist), a doctor who treats mental and emotional disorders. *noun.*

psy·cho·log·i·cal (sī′kə loj′ə kəl), having to do with the mind: *Doctors think his problem is psychological rather than physical. adjective.*

psy·chol·o·gist (sī kol′ə jist), a person who is an expert in psychology. *noun.*

psy·chol·o·gy (sī kol′ə jē), the science of the mind. Psychology deals with actions, emotions, and thoughts. *noun.*

pt., pint. *plural* **pt.** or **pts.**

ptar·mi·gan (tär′mə gən), a plump bird that looks somewhat like a chicken, found in mountainous and cold regions. *noun, plural* **ptar·mi·gans** or **ptar·mi·gan.**

ptarmigan
about 13 inches
(33 centimeters)
long

pub·lic (pub′lik), **1** of or for the people: *a public meeting, public libraries.* **2** all the people: *The public should be informed when there is danger of a serious epidemic.* **3** busy with the affairs or service of the people: *a public official.* **4** known to many or all; not private: *Though he tried to keep it secret, the actor's illness soon became public knowledge.* 1,3,4 *adjective,* 2 *noun.*

in public, publicly; openly; not in private or secret: *Stand up in public for what you believe.*

pub·li·ca·tion (pub′lə kā′shən), **1** a book, newspaper, or magazine; anything that is published: *This newspaper is a weekly publication.* **2** the printing and selling of books, newspapers, or magazines. *noun.*

pub·lic·i·ty (pub lis′ə tē), **1** public notice, especially attention gained by giving out information: *The new movie received favorable publicity in newspapers and on TV.* **2** measures used for getting, or the process of getting, public notice: *I worked on the publicity for the concert. noun.*

pub·lic·ly (pub′lik lē), **1** in a public manner; openly: *She admitted her error publicly.* **2** by the public: *a publicly approved project. adverb.*

public opinion, the opinion of the people in a country or community: *to make a survey of public opinion.*

public school, 1 (in the United States) a free school supported by taxes. **2** (in Great Britain) a private boarding school.

pub·lish (pub′lish), to prepare and offer a book, newspaper, magazine, or other printed material for sale or distribution. *verb.*

pub·lish·er (pub′li shər), a person or company whose business is to produce and sell books, newspapers, magazines, or other printed material: *Look at the bottom of the title page of this book for the publisher's name. noun.*

puck (puk), a hard, black rubber disk used in the game of ice hockey. *noun.*

puck·er (puk′ər), to draw into wrinkles or folds: *to pucker one's brow, to pucker cloth in sewing. verb.*

pucker
She **puckered** her lips.

pud·ding (púd′ing), a soft, cooked food, usually sweet, such as rice pudding. *noun.*

pud·dle (pud′l), **1** a small pool of water, especially dirty water: *a puddle of rain water.* **2** a small pool of any liquid: *a puddle of ink. noun.*

pudg·y (puj′ē), short and fat or thick: *The plump baby had pudgy hands. adjective,* **pudg·i·er, pudg·i·est.**

pueb·lo (pweb′lō), **1** an Indian village consisting of homes grouped together to form a large building which is several stories high. Pueblos are built of adobe and stone and usually have flat roofs. **2 Pueblo,** a member of an Indian tribe in the southwestern United States and northern Mexico living in such villages. *noun, plural* **pueb·los.**

[*Pueblo* was borrowed from a Spanish word meaning both "village" and "people."]

Puer·to Ri·can (pwer′tō rē′kən), **1** of or

a hat	**i** it	**oi** oil	**ch** child	a in about
ā age	**ī** ice	**ou** out	**ng** long	e in taken
ä far	**o** hot	**u** cup	**sh** she	ə = { i in pencil
e let	**ō** open	**ù** put	**th** thin	o in lemon
ē equal	**ô** order	**ü** rule	**ŦH** then	u in circus
ėr term			**zh** measure	

having something to do with Puerto Rico or its people. **2** a person born or living in Puerto Rico.

Puer·to Ri·co (pwer′tō rē′kō), an island in the eastern part of the West Indies, associated with the United States in foreign affairs, but ruling itself in local affairs. *Abbreviation:* P.R. or PR *Capital:* San Juan.

[The Spanish phrase *puerto rico,* meaning "rich port," was originally given to the capital of the island. Later, the name was given to the whole island, and the capital was given a new name, San Juan.]

puff (definition 6)
Some toads **puff** out their throats to make loud calls.

puff (puf), **1** to give out short, quick blasts of air, smoke, or the like: *I puffed on the fire to make it burn better. Please don't puff smoke in my direction.* **2** a short, quick blast: *A puff of wind blew my hat off.* **3** to breathe quick and hard: *She puffed as she climbed the stairs.* **4** to give out puffs; move with puffs: *The old steam engine stood puffing in the station. The steamboat puffed around the bend in the river.* **5** to smoke: *to puff a cigar.* **6** to swell: *My broken toe puffed up to twice its usual size.* **7** a soft, round mass: *a puff of cotton, a puff of hair.* **8** a small pad for putting powder on the skin. **9** a light pastry filled with whipped cream, jam, or the like: *a cream puff.* 1,3-6 *verb,* 2,7-9 *noun.*

puf·fin (puf′ən), a sea bird of northern waters, having a thick body, a large head, and a bill of several colors. *noun.*

puffin
about 14 inches (36 centimeters) long

puff·y (puf′ē), puffed out; swollen: *My eyes were puffy from crying. adjective,* **puff·i·er, puff·i·est.**

pug nose (pug′ nōz′), a short, turned-up nose.

pull (pul), **1** to move something in a direction toward oneself, usually with effort or force: *Pull the door open. I pulled the sled uphill.* **2** to take hold of and tug: *to pull a person's hair, to pull at someone's sleeve.* **3** to take hold of and draw out with the fingers or a tool: *to pull weeds. She pulled out the nails with the claw of a hammer. The dentist decided to pull my bad tooth.* **4** to move; go: *A strange car pulled into our driveway.* **5** to tear; rip: *The baby pulled the toy to pieces.* **6** to stretch too far; strain: *I pulled a muscle in my leg while skiing.* **7** the act of pulling; tug: *The boy gave a pull at the rope.* **8** an effort of pulling; effort: *It was a hard pull to get up the hill.* 1-6 *verb,* 7,8 *noun.*

pull oneself together, to get control of one's mind or energies: *I stopped crying and started to pull myself together.*

pull over, to bring a vehicle to the side of the road and stop: *We had to pull over and change a flat tire.*

pull through, to get through a difficult or dangerous situation: *The doctor thinks that the patient will pull through.*

pul·let (pul′it), a young hen, usually less than a year old. *noun.*

pul·ley (pul′ē), a wheel with a grooved rim in which a rope can run, and so lift weights, or change the direction of a pull: *Our flag is raised to the top of a pole by a rope and two pulleys. noun, plural* **pul·leys.**

pulley

pulp (pulp), **1** the soft, fleshy part of any fruit or vegetable. **2** the soft inner part of a tooth, containing blood vessels and nerves. **3** any soft, wet mass. Paper is made from wood ground to a pulp. *noun.*

pul·pit (pul′pit), a platform in a church from which the minister preaches. *noun.*

pul·sate (pul′sāt), to beat; throb: *The heart pulsates many times each minute. verb,* **pul·sates, pul·sat·ed, pul·sat·ing.**

pulse (puls), **1** the beating of the arteries caused by the rush of blood that the heart pumps into

them. By feeling your pulse in the artery of your wrist, you can count the number of times your heart beats each minute. **2** any regular, measured beat: *the pulse of an engine.* **3** to beat; throb; vibrate: *My heart pulsed with joy.* 1,2 *noun,* 3 *verb,* **puls·es, pulsed, puls·ing.**

pul·ve·rize (pul′və rīz′), **1** to grind to powder or dust. **2** to break to pieces; demolish. *verb,* **pul·ve·riz·es, pul·ve·rized, pul·ve·riz·ing.**

pu·ma (pyü′mə *or* pü′mə), a large cat with brownish-yellow fur, that lives in parts of North and South America. Other names for it are mountain lion, cougar, and panther. *noun.*

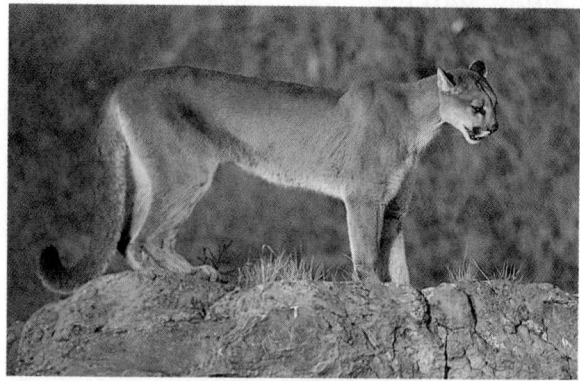

puma—about 8 feet (2½ meters) long with the tail

pum·ice (pum′is), a light, glassy rock having many tiny holes in it. Pumice comes from volcanoes and is used for cleaning and polishing. *noun.*

pump (pump), **1** a machine or device for forcing liquids or gases into or out of things. A gasoline pump makes gasoline flow from a storage tank into the tank of a vehicle. **2** to move liquids or gases with a pump: *to pump water from a well.* **3** to blow air into: *Pump up the car's tires.* **4** to get information out of: *Don't let them pump you.* 1 *noun,* 2-4 *verb.*

pump (definition 1)
As the handle is raised, the plunger moves downward, forcing water through valve A and out the spout. As the handle is pushed down, the plunger moves upward, pulling water up through valve B from the shaft.

PLUNGER
SPOUT
VALVE A
VALVE B
SHAFT TO WELL

pum·per·nick·el (pum′pər nik′əl), a heavy, dark, slightly sour bread made from whole, coarse rye. *noun.*

pump·kin (pump′kin *or* pung′kin), the large, roundish, orange fruit of a trailing vine, used for making pies and for jack-o'-lanterns. *noun.*

pun (pun), **1** the humorous use of a word where it can have different meanings: *"We must all hang together or we shall all hang separately"* is a famous

pun by Benjamin Franklin. **2** to make puns.
1 *noun,* **2** *verb,* **puns, punned, pun·ning.**

punch[1] (punch), **1** to hit with the fists: *to punch someone on the arm.* **2** a quick thrust or blow: *The fighter took a punch to the jaw.* **3** a tool for making holes. **4** to pierce a hole in: *The conductor punched the ticket.* **5** to herd or drive cattle: *Cowboys punch cows for a living.* **1,4,5** *verb,* **2,3** *noun,* plural **punch·es.**

punch[2] (punch), a drink made of different liquids, often fruit juices, mixed together. *noun, plural* **punch·es.**

[*Punch*[2] originally was a drink made up of five different ingredients. The word comes from a word from an ancient language of India, meaning "five."]

punc·tu·al (pungk′chü əl), prompt; on time: *He is punctual to the minute. adjective.*

punc·tu·ate (pungk′chü āt), to use periods, commas, and other marks in writing or printing to help make the meaning clear. *verb,* **punc·tu·ates, punc·tu·at·ed, punc·tu·at·ing.**

punc·tu·a·tion (pungk′chü ā′shən), the use of periods, commas, and other marks to help make the meaning of a sentence clear. Punctuation does for writing or printing what pauses and change of voice do for speech. *noun.*

punctuation mark, a mark used in writing or printing to help make the meaning clear. Periods, commas, question marks, semicolons, and colons are punctuation marks.

punc·ture (pungk′chər), **1** a hole made by something pointed: *A puncture made by a nail caused the flat tire.* **2** to make such a hole in: *A sharp rock punctured the bottom of the canoe.* **1** *noun,* **2** *verb,* **punc·tures, punc·tured, punc·tur·ing.**

pun·gent (pun′jənt), sharp; biting: *a pungent pickle, pungent criticism, a pungent wit. adjective.*

pun·ish (pun′ish), to cause pain, loss, or discomfort to for some fault or offense: *The parents punished the naughty children. verb.*

pun·ish·a·ble (pun′i shə bəl), deserving or subject to punishment: *The crime is punishable by ten years in prison. adjective.*

pun·ish·ment (pun′ish mənt), **1** a punishing; being punished: *Judges determine punishment for crimes that are committed.* **2** a penalty given for a fault or offense: *Her punishment for stealing was a year in prison. noun.*

punt (punt), **1** to kick a football before it touches the ground after dropping it from the hands. **2** such a kick. **1** *verb,* **2** *noun.*

pu·ny (pyü′nē), weak; of less than usual size, strength, or importance: *One of the newborn puppies was so puny we feared it might not live. adjective,* **pu·ni·er, pu·ni·est.**

pup (pup), **1** a young dog; puppy. **2** a young fox, wolf, coyote, or seal. *noun.*

pu·pa (pyü′pə), the form of an insect while it is changing from a wormlike larva into an adult. Many pupae are enclosed in a tough case or cocoon and can't move about. A caterpillar

pupa—silk moth cocoons and **pupa**

becomes a pupa and then a butterfly or moth. *noun, plural* **pu·pae** (pyü′pē), **pu·pas.**

pu·pil[1] (pyü′pəl), a person who is learning in school or is being taught by someone. *noun.*
[*Pupil*[1] comes from Latin words meaning "an orphan." Originally these words meant "a little boy" and "a little girl."]

pu·pil[2] (pyü′pəl), the opening in the center of the eye which looks like a black spot. The pupil is the only place where light can enter the eye. *noun.*

Word History

pupil[2] *Pupil*[2] comes from a Latin word meaning "a little doll." The center of the eye was called this because when you look into the eye of another person you can see a tiny image of yourself.

pup·pet (pup′it), **1** a figure made to look like a person or animal and moved by wires, strings, or the hands. **2** anybody who is not independent, waits to be told how to act, and does what somebody else says. *noun.*

puppet show, a play performed with puppets on a small stage.

pup·py (pup′ē), a young dog. *noun, plural* **pup·pies.**

pur·chase (pėr′chəs), **1** to get by paying a price; buy: *We purchased a new car.* **2** a thing bought: *That hat was a very good purchase.* **1** *verb,* **pur·chas·es, pur·chased, pur·chas·ing;** **2** *noun.*

pure (pyùr), **1** not mixed with anything else; genuine: *pure gold.* **2** perfectly clean; not dirty: *pure water.* **3** nothing else than; mere: *They won* *by pure luck.* **4** with no evil; without sin: *a pure mind. adjective,* **pur·er, pur·est.**

pure·bred (pyur′bred′), of pure breed; having ancestors known to have all belonged to one breed: *purebred cows. adjective.*

purge (pėrj), to wash away all that is not clean; remove what is harmful: *We must purge the city of dishonest officials. verb,* **purg·es, purged, purg·ing.**

pur·i·fi·ca·tion (pyur′ə fə kā′shən), a purifying; being purified. *noun.*

pur·i·fy (pyur′ə fī), to make pure: *Filters are used to purify water. verb,* **pur·i·fies, pu·ri·fied, pu·ri·fy·ing.**

Pur·i·tan (pyur′ə tən), a person who wanted simpler forms of worship and stricter morals than others did in the Protestant Church during the 1500's and 1600's. Many Puritans settled in New England. *noun.*

pur·i·ty (pyur′ə tē), **1** freedom from dirt or other substances; cleanness: *Tests were made to assure the purity of the town's water supply.* **2** freedom from evil; innocence: *a person of purity and goodness. noun.*

pur·ple (pėr′pəl), **1** a dark color that is a mixture of red and blue. **2** having this color: *purple grapes.* **1** *noun,* **2** *adjective.*

pur·plish (pėr′plish), somewhat purple. *adjective.*

pur·port (pər pôrt′ *for* 1; pėr′pôrt *for* 2), **1** to claim or declare: *The letter purported to be from the governor.* **2** the meaning; main idea: *The purport of her letter was that she could not come.* **1** *verb,* **2** *noun.*

pur·pose (pėr′pəs), a plan; aim; intention; something one has in mind to get or do: *Her purpose in coming to see us was to ask for a donation to the hospital fund. noun.*

on purpose, with a purpose; not by accident: *He tripped me on purpose.*

pur·pose·ful (pėr′pəs fəl), having a purpose: *She hurried about in a purposeful way, getting her work done quickly. adjective.*

pur·pose·ly (pėr′pəs lē), on purpose: *Did you leave the door open purposely? adverb.*

purr (pėr), **1** a low, murmuring sound such as a cat makes when pleased. **2** to make this sound. **1** *noun,* **2** *verb.*

purse (pėrs), **1** a small bag or container to hold coins, usually carried in a handbag or pocket. **2** a woman's handbag. **3** a sum of money: *A purse was made up for the victims of the fire.* **4** to draw together; press into folds or wrinkles: *She pursed her lips and whistled.* **1-3** *noun,* **4** *verb,* **purs·es, pursed, purs·ing.**

pur·sue (pər sü′), **1** to follow to catch or kill; chase: *The dogs pursued the rabbit.* **2** to follow; proceed along: *He pursued a wise course by taking no chances.* **3** to strive for; try to get; seek: *to pursue pleasure.* **4** to carry on; keep on with: *She pursued the study of music for four years. verb,* **pur·sues, pur·sued, pur·su·ing.**

pur·su·er (pər sü′ər), a person who pursues. *noun.*

pur·suit (pər süt′), **1** the act of pursuing; chase: *The dog is in pursuit of the cat.* **2** an occupation: *Fishing is his favorite pursuit; reading is mine. noun.*

pus (pus), a thick, yellowish-white liquid found in infected sores. *noun.*

push (push), **1** to press against something so as to move it away from oneself: *Push the door; don't pull it.* **2** to force one's way: *We pushed through the crowd.* **3** to make go forward: *Please push this job and get it done this week.* **4** to urge the use or purchase of: *That auto maker is pushing its small cars this year.* **5** a force; power to succeed: *She has plenty of push.* **6** the act of pushing: *Give the door a push.* **1-4** *verb,* **5,6** *noun, plural* **push·es.**

push·cart (push′kärt′), a light cart pushed by hand: *The peddler's pushcart was filled with fruit. noun.*

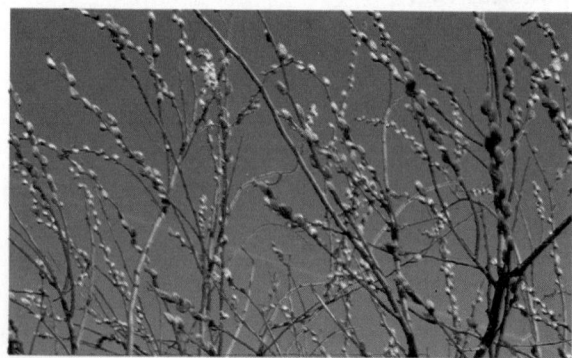

pushup

push·up (push′up′), an exercise done by lying face down and raising the body with the arms while keeping the back straight and the toes on the ground. *noun.*

puss (pus), a cat. *noun, plural* **puss·es.**

puss·y (pus′ē), a cat. *noun, plural* **puss·ies.**

pussy willow, a small North American willow with furry gray catkins that bloom early in spring.

pussy willows

put (put), **1** to place; lay; set; cause to be in some place or position: *I put sugar in my tea. Put away your toys. Put on your coat.* **2** to cause to be in some condition or situation: *Put your room in order. I put myself under the care of a doctor.* **3** to express: *The teacher puts things clearly.* **4** to apply: *I put my writing skill to good use.* **5** to impose: *to put a tax on gasoline. verb,* **puts, put, put·ting.**

put across, to get accepted or understood: *He could not put across his point of view to the audience.*

put down, 1 to put an end to: *The rebellion was quickly put down.* **2** to write down.

put in, to spend time: *Put in a full day of work.*

put off, to lay aside; make wait: *We put off our meeting for a week.*

put on, 1 to present on a stage; produce: *The class put on a play.* **2** to take on or add to oneself: *to put on weight.* **3** to pretend: *I put on an expression of innocence.* **4** to apply or exert: *They put on pressure to try to make me change my mind.*

put out, 1 to make stop burning; extinguish: *The firefighters put out the fire.* **2** to provoke; offend: *I was quite put out by her lateness.*

put through, to carry out with success: *The Congresswoman put her bill through Congress.*

put up, 1 to offer: *to put up a house for sale.* **2** to give or show: *to put up a brave front.* **3** to build: *Several new houses were put up across from ours.* **4** to preserve food by canning or other means: *We put up six jars of blackberries.* **5** to provide lodging and food for: *They put us up for the night.* **6** to get a person to do: *to put someone up to mischief.*

put up with, to bear with patience; endure.

pu·trid (pyü′trid), rotten; foul: *The meat became putrid in the hot sun. adjective.*

putt (put), **1** to strike a golf ball gently and carefully in an effort to make it roll into the hole. **2** the stroke itself: *A good putt requires control.* 1 *verb,* 2 *noun.*

put·ter[1] (put′ər), to keep busy in an aimless or useless way: *I like to putter around the garden. verb.*

putt·er[2] (put′ər), a golf club used in putting. *noun.*

put·ty (put′ē), **1** a soft, doughlike mixture that hardens as it dries. Putty is used to fasten glass in window frames and to fill holes and cracks in walls and woodwork. **2** to stop up, fill up, or cover with putty: *We puttied the holes in the woodwork.* 1 *noun,* 2 *verb,* **put·ties, put·tied, put·ty·ing.**

puz·zle (puz′əl), **1** a hard problem: *How to get all my things into one suitcase is a puzzle.* **2** a problem

or task to be done for fun: *A famous Chinese puzzle has seven pieces of wood to fit together.* **3** to make unable to understand something; confuse: *How the cat got out puzzled us.* 1,2 *noun,* 3 *verb,* **puz·zles, puz·zled, puz·zling.**

puzzle over, to think hard about; try hard to do or work out: *I puzzled over a hard math problem for a long time before I got the right answer.*

Pyg·my (pig′mē), one of a group of people living in Africa who are less than 5 feet (a meter and a half) tall. *noun, plural* **Pyg·mies.**

pyramid (definition 2)
At the left is a skyscraper shaped like a **pyramid.** Below are stone **pyramids** in Egypt.

puzzle (definition 3)
The shape of the statue **puzzled** him.

pyr·a·mid (pir′ə mid), **1** a solid figure with a base and with triangular sides that meet in a point. **2** anything having the form of a pyramid. *noun.*

py·thon (pī′thon), a very large snake of Asia, Africa, and Australia that kills its prey by squeezing. *noun.*

P

Q q

Q or q (kyü), the 17th letter of the English alphabet. *Q* is followed by *u* in most English words. *noun, plural* Q's or q's.

qt., quart. *plural* qt. or qts.

quack[1] (kwak), 1 the sound a duck makes. 2 to make such a sound. 1 *noun,* 2 *verb.*

quack[2] (kwak), a dishonest person who pretends to be a doctor. *noun.*

quad·ri·lat·er·al (kwod′rə lat′ər əl), a figure having four sides and four angles. Squares and rectangles are quadrilaterals. *noun.*

quadrilaterals

quad·ru·ped (kwod′rə ped), an animal that has four feet. *noun.*

qua·dru·plet (kwo drü′plit), one of four children born at the same time of the same mother. *noun.*

quail[1] (kwāl), a plump, wild bird that is hunted and used for food. A bobwhite is one kind of quail. *noun, plural* quail or quails.

quail[1]
about 10 inches
(25 centimeters)
long

quail[2] (kwāl), to be afraid; lose courage; shrink back with fear: *They quailed at the sight of the rattlesnake. verb.*

quaint (kwānt), strange or odd in an interesting, pleasing, or amusing way: *Old photographs seem quaint to us today. adjective.*

quake (kwāk), 1 to shake; tremble: *They quaked with fear.* 2 an earthquake. 1 *verb,* quakes, quaked, quak·ing; 2 *noun.*

Quak·er (kwā′kər), a member of a Christian group which observes simple religious services. Quakers are opposed to war and to taking oaths. *noun.*

qual·i·fi·ca·tion (kwol′ə fə kā′shən), 1 that which makes a person fit for a job, task, office, or function: *To know the way is one qualification for a guide.* 2 that which limits or changes, and makes less free and full: *They accepted the plan with only one qualification. noun.*

qual·i·fy (kwol′ə fī), 1 to make or become fit for a job, task, office, or function: *He qualified for a driver's license.* 2 to limit; make less strong; change somewhat: *Qualify your statement that dogs are loyal by adding "usually." verb,* qual·i·fies, qual·i·fied, qual·i·fy·ing.

qual·i·ty (kwol′ə tē), 1 something special about a person or object that makes it what it is: *One quality of iron is hardness; one quality of sugar is sweetness. She has many fine qualities.* 2 a grade of excellence: *food of poor quality. noun, plural* qual·i·ties.

qualm (kwäm), a sudden disturbing feeling in the mind; uneasiness; misgiving or doubt: *I had no qualms about playing instead of working on such a sunny day. noun.*

quan·ti·ty (kwon′tə tē), 1 an amount: *Use equal quantities of nuts and raisins in the cake.* 2 a large amount; large number: *The baker buys flour in quantity. She owns quantities of books. noun, plural* quan·ti·ties.

quar·an·tine (kwôr′ən tēn′), 1 to keep a person, animal, plant, or ship away from others for a time to prevent the spread of an infectious disease: *People with smallpox were quarantined.* 2 the condition of being quarantined: *The ship was in quarantine because several of the crew had smallpox.* 1 *verb,* quar·an·tines, quar·an·tined, quar·an·tin·ing; 2 *noun.*

[*Quarantine* comes from an Italian word meaning "forty." Ships returning to Italy from Egypt and the Middle East were kept in certain ports for forty days. This was to make sure that no diseases were carried into Italy. The word *quarantine* was first applied to this period of time that the ships were under examination.]

quar·rel (kwôr′əl), 1 an angry dispute; fight with words: *The children had a quarrel over the division of the candy.* 2 to fight with words; dispute or disagree angrily: *The two friends quarreled and now they don't speak to each other.* 1 *noun,* 2 *verb.*

quar·rel·some (kwôr′əl səm), too ready to quarrel; fond of fighting and disputing: *A quarrelsome person has few friends. adjective.*

quar·ry (kwôr′ē), a place where stone is dug, cut, or blasted out for use in building. *noun, plural* quar·ries.

quart (kwôrt), 1 a unit for measuring liquids, equal to one fourth of a gallon: *a quart of milk.* 2 a unit for measuring dry things, equal to one eighth of a peck: *a quart of berries. noun.*

quar·ter (kwôr′tər), **1** one of four equal parts; half of a half; one fourth: *a quarter of an apple. A quarter of an hour is 15 minutes.* **2** to divide into fourths: *She quartered the apple.* **3** a coin of the United States and Canada equal to 25 cents. Four quarters make one dollar. **4** one of four equal periods of play in certain games, such as football, basketball, or soccer. **5** one fourth of a year; 3 months: *Many savings banks pay interest every quarter.* **6** one of the four periods of the moon, lasting about 7 days each. **7** a region; section; place: *The quarter where they live is near the railroad.* **8 quarters,** a place to live or stay in: *The circus has its winter quarters in the South.* 1,3-8 *noun,* 2 *verb.*

quar·ter·back (kwôr′tər bak′), a player who stands behind the center in football. The quarterback begins each play by handing the ball to a running back, passing it to a teammate, or running with it himself. *noun.*

quar·ter·ly (kwôr′tər lē), **1** four times a year: *to make quarterly payments on one's insurance.* **2** once each quarter of a year: *Some magazines are published quarterly.* 1 *adjective,* 2 *adverb.*

quar·tet or **quar·tette** (kwôr tet′), **1** a group of four singers or players performing together. **2** a piece of music for four voices or instruments. *noun.*

quartz (kwôrts), a very hard kind of rock. Common quartz is colorless and transparent, but agate, flint, and many other colored stones are also quartz. *noun.*

quartz
common **quartz**

qua·sar (kwā′sär *or* kwā′zär), any of many heavenly bodies that look like stars but give off as much energy as whole galaxies. Quasars are thought to be the centers of extremely distant galaxies. *noun.*
[*Quasar* was formed by joining parts of the words *quasi,* meaning "almost," and *stellar,* meaning "like a star."]

qua·ver (kwā′vər), **1** to shake; tremble: *The animal quavered with fear.* **2** a trembling of the voice: *After the accident the driver spoke with a quaver.* 1 *verb,* 2 *noun.*

a hat	**i** it	**oi** oil	**ch** child	a in about
ā age	**ī** ice	**ou** out	**ng** long	e in taken
ä far	**o** hot	**u** cup	**sh** she	ə = i in pencil
e let	**ō** open	**ù** put	**th** thin	o in lemon
ē equal	**ô** order	**ü** rule	**ŦH** then	u in circus
ėr term			**zh** measure	

quay (kē), a solid landing place for ships, often built of stone. *noun.*

Que·bec (kwi bek′), **1** a province in eastern Canada. **2** its capital. *noun.*

queen (kwēn), **1** the wife of a king. **2** a woman who rules a country and its people. **3** a woman who is very beautiful or important: *the queen of society.* **4** a female bee or ant that lays eggs. There is usually only one queen in a hive of bees. **5** a playing card with the picture of a queen on it. It is above a jack and below a king. **6** the most powerful piece in the game of chess. A queen can move in any straight or diagonal row across any number of empty squares. *noun.*

queer (kwir), strange; odd; peculiar: *That was a queer remark for her to make. adjective.*

quell (kwel), to put down; overcome: *The police quelled the riot. verb.*

quench (kwench), **1** to put an end to; stop. **2** to drown out; put out: *We quenched the fire with water. verb.*

quer·y (kwir′ē), **1** a question: *She had a query about the high cost of our trip.* **2** to ask; ask about; inquire into: *The teacher queried my reason for being late.* **3** to express doubt about: *Some of us queried the accuracy of the vote.* 1 *noun,* plural **quer·ies;** 2,3 *verb,* **quer·ies, quer·ied, quer·y·ing.**

quest (kwest), a search; hunt: *She went to the library on a quest for something to read. noun.*
in quest of, trying to find; looking for: *In 1849 people rushed to California in quest of gold.*

ques·tion (kwes′chən), **1** a thing asked in order to find out: *The teacher answered the children's questions about the story.* **2** to ask in order to find out: *Then the teacher questioned the children about what happened in the story.* **3** a matter of doubt or dispute: *A question arose about who owned the football.* **4** to doubt; dispute: *I question the truth of their story.* **5** a problem; matter to be talked over, investigated, or considered: *Several family members raised the question of whether they need a new car.* 1,3,5 *noun,* 2,4 *verb.*
out of the question, impossible; not to be considered: *Our teacher said that postponing the test was out of the question.*
without question, without a doubt: *That is without question the best book I've ever read.*

ques·tion·a·ble (kwes′chə nə bəl), open to question; doubtful; uncertain: *Whether your statement is true is questionable. adjective.*

question mark, a mark (?) put after a question in writing or printing.

ques·tion·naire (kwes′chə ner′ *or* kwes′chə nar′), a written or printed list of

Q

questions used to gather information, obtain a sample of opinion, and the like. *noun.*

queue (kyü), a number of persons, automobiles, or trucks waiting their turn in a line. *noun.*

Word History

queue *Queue* was borrowed directly from a French word. It can be traced back to a Latin word meaning "tail." A line of people was thought to be something like the tail of an animal, since one gets in line at the end, or tail, of the line.

queue—There was a long **queue** at the drinking fountain.

quick (kwik), **1** fast and sudden; swift: *The cat made a quick jump. Many weeds have a quick growth.* **2** not patient; hasty: *My brother has a quick temper.* **3** lively; ready; active: *a quick wit.* **4** quickly: *Find the book for me quick.* **5** the tender, sensitive flesh under a fingernail or toenail: *Some people bite their nails down to the quick.* 1-3 *adjective,* 4 *adverb,* 5 *noun.*

quick·en (kwik/ən), **1** to move more quickly; hasten: *Quicken your pace.* **2** to stir up; make alive: *She quickened the hot ashes into flames. Reading adventure stories quickens my imagination.* **3** to become more active or alive: *His pulse quickened. verb.*

quick·sand (kwik/sand/), a very deep, soft, wet sand that will not hold up a person's weight. Quicksand may swallow up people and animals. *noun.*

quick-wit·ted (kwik/wit/id), having a quick mind; clever: *She gave a quick-witted answer to my question. adjective.*

qui·et (kwi/ət), **1** making no sound; with little or no noise: *quiet footsteps, a quiet room.* **2** still; moving very little: *a quiet river.* **3** at rest; not busy: *a quiet evening at home.* **4** peaceful; gentle: *a quiet mind, quiet manners.* **5** a state of rest; stillness; peace: *to read in quiet.* **6** to make or become quiet: *Soft words quieted the frightened child. The wind quieted down.* 1-4 *adjective,* 5 *noun,* 6 *verb.*

quill (kwil), **1** a large stiff feather. **2** a pen made from a feather. **3** a stiff sharp hair or spine like the end of a feather. A porcupine has quills on its back. *noun.*

quilt (kwilt), **1** a cover for a bed, usually made of two pieces of cloth with a soft pad between, held in place by stitching. **2** to make quilts: *The sewing group quilts on Wednesday afternoon.* **3** to stitch together with a soft lining: *to quilt a jacket.* 1 *noun,* 2,3 *verb.*

qui·nine (kwi/nin), a bitter medicine used for malaria and fevers. *noun.*

quin·tet or **quin·tette** (kwin tet/), **1** a group of five singers or players performing together. **2** a piece of music for five voices or instruments. *noun.*

quin·tu·plet (kwin tup/lit, kwin tü/plit, *or* kwin tyü/plit), one of five children born at the same time of the same mother. *noun.*

quit (kwit), **1** to stop: *They quit work at five.* **2** to leave: *to quit one's job. He quit college after one year. verb,* **quits, quit, quit·ting.**

quite (kwit), **1** completely; entirely: *a hat quite out of fashion. I am quite alone.* **2** really; truly: *quite a change in the weather.* **3** very; rather; somewhat: *It is quite hot. adverb.*

quits (kwits). **call it quits,** to stop doing something; give up: *The baseball field was so muddy we called it quits and went home. adjective.*

quit·ter (kwit/ər), a person who shirks or gives up easily. *noun.*

quiv·er[1] (kwiv/ər), **1** to shake; shiver; tremble: *to quiver with excitement.* **2** a shaking or trembling: *A quiver of his mouth showed that he was about to cry.* 1 *verb,* 2 *noun.*

quiv·er[2] (kwiv/ər), a case to hold arrows. *noun.*

quiz (kwiz), **1** a short or informal test: *Each week the teacher gives us a quiz in spelling.* **2** to examine by questions; test the knowledge of: *Each week the teacher quizzes our class in spelling.* 1 *noun,* plural **quiz·zes;** 2 *verb,* **quiz·zes, quizzed, quiz·zing.**

quo·ta (kwō/tə), the share of a total due from or to a particular district, state, or person: *Each class had its quota of tickets to sell for the school fair. noun.*

quo·ta·tion (kwō tā/shən), somebody's words repeated exactly by another person; passage quoted from a book or speech. *noun.*

"The only way to have a friend is to be one."

—*Emerson*

quotation from Ralph Waldo Emerson's *Essays*

quotation mark, one of a pair of marks (" ") put at the beginning and end of a quotation.

quote (kwōt), **1** to repeat exactly the words of another or a passage from a book: *The newspaper quoted the mayor.* **2** a quotation. 1 *verb,* **quotes, quot·ed, quot·ing;** 2 *noun.*

quo·tient (kwō/shənt), a number arrived at by dividing one number by another: *If you divide 26 by 2, the quotient is 13. noun.*

R r

a hat	i it	oi oil	ch child	⎧ a in about
ā age	ī ice	ou out	ng long	⎪ e in taken
ä far	o hot	u cup	sh she	ə = ⎨ i in pencil
e let	ō open	u̇ put	th thin	⎪ o in lemon
ē equal	ô order	ü rule	ᴛH then	⎩ u in circus
ėr term			zh measure	

R or **r** (är), the 18th letter of the English alphabet. *noun, plural* **R's** or **r's.**

the three R's, reading, writing, and arithmetic. The three R's were called this because reading, writing, and arithmetic were humorously spelled reading, 'riting, and 'rithmetic.

rab·bi (rab′ī), a teacher of the Jewish religion; leader of a Jewish congregation. *noun, plural* **rab·bis.**

[*Rabbi* comes from a Hebrew word meaning "my master."]

rab·bit (rab′it), **1** an animal about as big as a cat, with soft fur and long ears. A rabbit can make long jumps. Rabbits are sometimes raised for food or fur. **2** its fur. *noun.*

rab·ble (rab′əl), **1** a disorderly crowd; mob. **2 the rabble,** the lower class of persons: *The proud nobles scorned the rabble. noun.*

ra·bies (rā′bēz), a disease of warm-blooded animals that causes damage to brain cells and paralyzes muscles. Human beings can get rabies from the bite or saliva of an infected animal. Unless it is prevented with a serum, rabies causes death. *noun.*

rac·coon (ra kün′), **1** a small, grayish animal with a bushy ringed tail, that lives in wooded areas near water, and is active at night. **2** its fur. *noun.* Also spelled **racoon.**

Word History

raccoon *Raccoon* comes from a Powhatan Indian word meaning "he scratches with the hands." The animal was probably called this because it scratches trees and digs to find food.

raccoon (definition 1)
32 inches (81 centimeters) long with the tail

race[1] (rās), **1** any contest of speed: *a horse race, a boat race.* **2** to run to see who will win. **3** to run a race with; try to beat in a contest of speed: *I'll race you home.* **4** to run, move, or go swiftly: *I raced home from school.* **5** to make go faster than necessary: *Don't race the motor.* **1** *noun,* **2-5** *verb,* **rac·es, raced, rac·ing.**

race[2] (rās), **1** a great division of all human beings that passes on certain physical characteristics from one generation to another. **2** a group of persons, animals, or plants having the same ancestors, far back in the past: *All people belong to the human race. noun.*

race·horse (rās′hôrs′), a horse bred, trained, or kept for racing. *noun.*

rac·er (rā′sər), **1** a person, animal, boat, or car that takes part in races. **2** a large, harmless North American snake that can move very rapidly. *noun.*

race·track (rās′trak′), a track laid out for racing, usually round or oval. *noun.*

ra·cial (rā′shəl), **1** having something to do with a race of persons, animals, or plants; characteristic of a race: *racial traits.* **2** of or involving races: *racial discrimination. adjective.*

rack (rak), **1** a frame with bars, shelves, or pegs to hold, arrange, or keep things on: *She placed the screwdriver on the tool rack.* **2** an instrument once used for torturing people by stretching them. **3** to hurt very much: *The accident victim was racked with pain.* **1,2** *noun,* **3** *verb.*

rack up, to score: *Our team racked up 14 points.*

rack·et[1] (rak′it), **1** a loud noise; din; loud talk: *Don't make a racket when others are reading.* **2** a dishonest scheme for getting money from people, often by threatening to hurt them or what belongs to them. *noun.*

rack·et[2] (rak′it), an oval wooden or metal frame with a network of strings and a handle. It is used to hit the ball in games like tennis. *noun.* Also spelled **racquet.**

[A racket is held with the handle resting against the palm of the hand. The word comes from an Arabic word meaning "the palm of the hand."]

ra·coon (ra kün′). See **raccoon.** *noun.*

rac·quet (rak′it). See **racket**[2]. *noun.*

rac·quet·ball (rak′it bôl′), a game played in a

racquetball

R

court with four walls, using a hollow rubber ball and a racket with a short handle. *noun.*

ra·dar (rā′där), an instrument for determining the distance, direction, and speed of unseen objects by the reflection of radio waves. *noun.*
[*Radar* comes from the words *radio detecting and ranging,* which describe what this instrument does. It was formed by combining the first two letters of *radio* and the first letter of each of the other words.]

ra·di·ance (rā′dē əns), brightness: *They sat in the garden enjoying the radiance of the sunshine.* *noun.*

ra·di·ant (rā′dē ənt), **1** shining; bright; beaming: *A radiant smile lit up her face.* **2** sent off in rays from some source; radiated: *A fire produces radiant heat. adjective.*

radiant energy, energy in the form of waves. Heat, light, X rays, and radio waves are forms of radiant energy.

ra·di·ate (rā′dē āt), **1** to give out rays of: *The sun radiates light and heat.* **2** to come out in rays: *Heat radiates from hot steam pipes.* **3** to give out; send forth: *His face radiates joy.* **4** to spread out from a center: *Roads radiate from the city in every direction. verb,* **ra·di·ates, ra·di·at·ed, ra·di·at·ing.**

ra·di·a·tion (rā′dē ā′shən), **1** the giving out of rays, as of light or heat. **2** the rays sent or given out. **3** the rays or tiny particles that are given off by the atoms of a radioactive substance; radioactivity. This sort of radiation can be harmful to living tissue. *noun.*

ra·di·a·tor (rā′dē ā′tər), **1** a device for heating a room, consisting of pipes through which hot water or steam passes. **2** a device for cooling water. The radiator of an automobile gives off heat very fast and so cools the water inside it. *noun.*

rad·i·cal (rad′ə kəl), **1** going to the root; fundamental: *To lose weight I had to make radical changes in my eating habits.* **2** extreme; favoring extreme changes or reforms. **3** a person who favors extreme changes or reforms; person with extreme opinions. **1,2** *adjective,* **3** *noun.*

ra·di·i (rā′dē ī), more than one radius. *noun plural.*

ra·di·o (rā′dē ō), **1** a way of sending and receiving sounds without using wires to connect the sender and the receiver: *Music is broadcast by radio.* **2** the device on which these sounds may be heard or from which they may be sent. **3** of radio; used in radio; sent by radio: *I enjoy listening to radio programs.* **4** to transmit or send out by radio: *The ship radioed a call for help.* **1,2** *noun, plural* **ra·di·os** for 2; **3** *adjective,* **4** *verb.*

ra·di·o·ac·tive (rā′dē ō ak′tiv), of, having, or caused by radioactivity. Radium and uranium are radioactive metals. *adjective.*

ra·di·o·ac·tiv·i·ty (rā′dē ō ak tiv′ə tē), **1** the property that certain metals have of giving off rays or tiny particles from their atomic nuclei. **2** the rays or particles given off. *noun.*

radio wave, a wave of radiant electrical energy.

Radio waves are produced for use in radio and television broadcasting, radar, and microwave ovens.

rad·ish (rad′ish), the small, crisp, red or white root of a garden plant. Radishes are eaten as a raw vegetable. *noun, plural* **rad·ish·es.**

ra·di·um (rā′dē əm), a radioactive metal, used in treating cancer. Radium is a chemical element. *noun.*

ra·di·us (rā′dē əs), **1** any line going straight from the center to the outside of a circle or a sphere. Any spoke of a wheel is a radius. **2** a circular area measured by the length of its radius: *The explosion could be heard within a radius of ten miles. noun, plural* **ra·di·i** or **ra·di·us·es.**

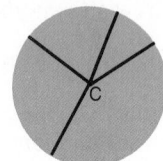
radius (definition 1)
Each line from C
(center) is a **radius.**

raf·fle (raf′əl), **1** a sale in which many people each pay a small sum for a chance to win a prize. **2** to sell an article in a raffle. **1** *noun,* **2** *verb,* **raf·fles, raf·fled, raf·fling.**

raft (raft), a floating platform made of wood or other material. A rubber **life raft** is held up by a tube filled with air. *noun.*

raft·er (raf′tər), a slanting beam of a roof. *noun.*

RAFTER   RAFTER

rag (rag), **1** a piece of cloth, often made from a scrap of old or torn material: *Use a clean rag to rub this mirror bright.* **2 rags,** tattered or worn-out clothes: *The beggar was dressed in rags.* **3** made from rags: *a rag doll, a rag rug.* **1,2** *noun,* **3** *adjective.*

rage (rāj), **1** violent anger: *His voice quivered with rage.* **2** to talk or act violently; storm: *Keep your*

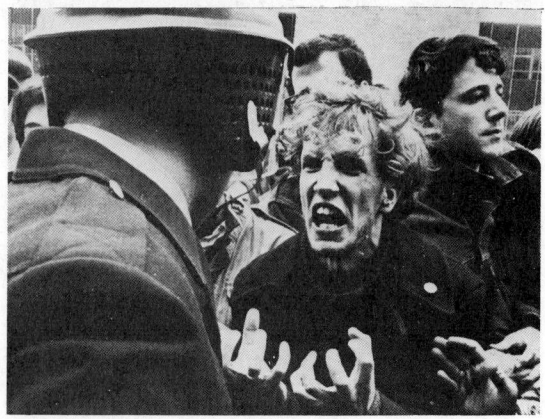
rage (definition 1)—He seethed with **rage.**

temper; don't rage. The fire raged through the forest. **3 all the rage** or **the rage,** what everybody wants for a short time; the fashion: *Red ties were all the rage last year.* 1,3 *noun,* 2 *verb,* **rag·es, raged, rag·ing.**

rag·ged (rag′id), **1** worn or torn into rags: *The refugees were hungry and wore ragged clothing.* **2** wearing torn or badly worn-out clothing: *Ragged children begged for food in the ruined city.* **3** not smooth and tidy; rough: *The child patted the old dog's ragged coat.* **4** having loose shreds or bits: *a ragged wound. adjective.*

rag·weed (rag′wēd′), a coarse weed whose pollen is one of the most common causes of hay fever. *noun.*

raid (rād), **1** an attack; a sudden attack: *The pirates planned a raid on the harbor.* **2** to attack suddenly: *The enemy raided our camp.* **3** an entering and seizing what is inside: *The hungry girls made a raid on the refrigerator.* **4** to force a way into; enter and seize what is in: *The police raided the house looking for stolen jewels.* 1,3 *noun,* 2,4 *verb.*

rail[1] (rāl), **1** a bar of wood or metal used to support, protect, or separate. There are stair rails, fence rails, and altar rails. **2** one of a pair of steel bars laid parallel on ties as a track for a train or other vehicle. **3** a railroad: *We travel by rail and by boat. noun.*

rail[2] (rāl), to complain bitterly: *They railed at their hard luck. verb.*

rail·ing (rā′ling), **1** a fence made of rails. **2** a rail used as a guard or support on a stairway or platform; handrail. *noun.*

rail·road (rāl′rōd′), **1** a road or track with parallel steel rails on which the wheels of the cars go. Engines pull trains on railroads. **2** the tracks, stations, trains, and the people who manage them. **3** to work on a railroad. 1,2 *noun,* 3 *verb.*

rail·way (rāl′wā′), **1** a railroad. **2** a track made of rails. *noun.*

rai·ment (rā′mənt), an old word for clothing; garments. *noun.*

rain (rān), **1** the water falling in drops from the clouds: *The rain spattered the windows.* **2** the fall of such drops: *A hard rain began to come down.* **3** to fall in drops of water: *It rained all day.* **4** a thick, fast fall of anything: *A rain of petals fell from the blossoming apple tree.* **5** to fall like rain: *Sparks rained down from the burning building.* **6** to send like rain: *The guests rained rice on the bride and groom.* 1,2,4 *noun,* 3,5,6 *verb.*
rain out, to delay or cancel because of rain: *Today's game was rained out, and will be played tomorrow.*

rain·bow (rān′bō′), an arch of colored light seen in the sky opposite the sun, or in mist or spray. The seven colors of the rainbow are violet, indigo, blue, green, yellow, orange, and red. Rainbows occur when the sun's rays are bent and reflected by drops of water. *noun.*

rain·coat (rān′kōt′), a waterproof coat worn for protection from rain. *noun.*

a hat	i it	oi oil	ch child	a in about
ā age	ī ice	ou out	ng long	e in taken
ä far	o hot	u cup	sh she	ə = i in pencil
e let	ō open	ù put	th thin	o in lemon
ē equal	ô order	ü rule	�241H then	u in circus
ėr term			zh measure	

rain·drop (rān′drop′), a drop of rain. *noun.*

rain·fall (rān′fôl′), **1** a shower of rain. **2** the amount of water in the form of rain, sleet, or snow that falls within a given time: *The yearly rainfall in New York is much greater than that in Arizona. noun.*

rain forest, a very thick forest in a place where rain is very heavy all through the year. Rain forests are usually in tropical areas.

rain·storm (rān′stôrm′), a storm with much rain. *noun.*

rain·y (rā′nē), **1** having rain; having much rain: *April is a rainy month.* **2** wet with rain: *rainy streets. adjective,* **rain·i·er, rain·i·est.**

raise (rāz), **1** to lift up; put up: *to raise the flag. Children in school raise their hands to answer a question.* **2** to cause to rise: *The automobiles raised a cloud of dust. Dough for bread is raised by yeast.* **3** to put into a higher position; promote: *The store clerk was raised to manager.* **4** to make higher or larger; increase in degree, amount, price, or pay: *That store has raised its prices again. Raise your voice.* **5** an increase in amount, price, or pay: *I got a raise in my allowance.* **6** to bring or gather together: *We helped to raise money for a hospital.* **7** to bring up; make grow; help to grow: *The farmer raises chickens and corn. Parents raise their children.* **8** to cause; bring about: *A funny remark raises a laugh.* **9** to build; build up; set up: *They raised a monument to the famous poet.* 1-4,6-9 *verb,* **rais·es, raised, rais·ing;** 5 *noun.*

rai·sin (rā′zn), a sweet, dried grape. *noun.*

ra·jah or **ra·ja** (rä′jə), a ruler or chief in India, and in some other Eastern countries. *noun.*
[*Rajah* comes from a word from an ancient language of India, meaning "king."]

rake (rāk), **1** a long-handled tool having a bar at one end with teeth in it. A rake is used for smoothing the soil or gathering together loose leaves, hay, or straw. **2** to move with a rake: *Rake the leaves off the grass.* **3** to make clear, clean, or smooth with a rake: *Rake the yard.* **4** to search carefully: *She raked the newspaper ads, hoping to find a bicycle for sale.* 1 *noun,* 2-4 *verb,* **rakes, raked, rak·ing.**

Ra·leigh (rô′lē), the capital of North Carolina. *noun.*

ral·ly (ral′ē), **1** to bring together; bring together again; get in order again: *The commander was able to rally the fleeing troops.* **2** to come together for a common purpose or action: *The people rallied to rebuild the dike before the river flooded their homes.* **3** to come to help: *She rallied to the side of her injured friend.* **4** to recover health and strength: *My sick friend has begun to rally.* **5** a

R

meeting of many people for a particular purpose: *We all attended the rally in support of the candidate for president.* 1-4 *verb*, **ral·lies, ral·lied, ral·ly·ing;** 5 *noun, plural* **ral·lies.**

ram (ram), **1** a male sheep. **2** to butt against; strike head-on; strike violently: *One ship rammed the other ship.* **3** to push hard; drive down or in by heavy blows: *He rammed the post into the ground.* **4** a machine or part of a machine that strikes heavy blows. A **battering ram** knocks walls down. 1,4 *noun*, 2,3 *verb*, **rams, rammed, ram·ming.**

ram (definition 1)
about 2 feet (60 centimeters) high at the shoulder

RAM, random access memory. This is a part of a computer in which information and instructions can be stored temporarily. Everything stored there is equally available, and items can be removed from this memory or added to it at any time.

ram·ble (ram′bəl), **1** to wander about: *We rambled here and there through the woods.* **2** a walk for pleasure, not to go to any special place. **3** to talk or write about first one thing and then another with no clear connections. 1,3 *verb*, **ram·bles, ram·bled, ram·bling;** 2 *noun.*

ram·bling (ram′bling), **1** wandering about. **2** going from one thing to another without clear connections: *The rambling speech bored us.* **3** growing or extending in irregular ways and various directions: *They live in a rambling old farmhouse. Rambling roses frame the front porch.* *adjective.*

ramp (ramp), a sloping way connecting two different levels, especially of a building or road; slope: *The passengers walked up the ramp to board their plane. noun.*

ram·page (ram′pāj *for 1;* ram pāj′ *for 2*), **1** a fit of rushing wildly about; spell of violent behavior. **2** to rush wildly about; behave violently. 1 *noun*, 2 *verb*, **ram·pag·es, ram·paged, ram·pag·ing.**

ram·part (ram′pärt), a wide bank of earth, often with a wall on top, built around a fort to help defend it. *noun.*

ram·rod (ram′rod′), **1** a rod for ramming down the ammunition in a gun that is loaded from the muzzle. **2** a rod for cleaning the barrel of a gun. *noun.*

ran (ran). See **run.** *The dog ran after the cat. verb.*

ranch (ranch), **1** a very large farm and its buildings. Many ranches are used for raising cattle. **2** to work on a ranch; manage a ranch. 1 *noun*, 2 *verb.*

ranch·er (ran′chər), a person who owns, manages, or works on a ranch. *noun.*

ran·dom (ran′dəm), by chance; with no plan: *I don't know the answer, but I'll take a random guess. adjective.*

at random, by chance: *She took a book at random from the shelf.*

rang (rang). See **ring²**. *The telephone rang. verb.*

range (rānj), **1** the distance between certain limits; extent: *There is a wide range of colors to choose from. A dog has a greater range of hearing than a person.* **2** to extend between certain limits: *The prices ranged from $5 to $20.* **3** the greatest distance at which something can operate or go: *This missile has a range of 1500 miles.* **4** a place to practice shooting: *a rifle range.* **5** the land used for grazing. **6** to wander over; rove; roam: *Dinosaurs once ranged the earth. Our talk ranged over all that had happened on our vacation.* **7** a row or line of mountains: *Mount Rainier is in the Cascade Range.* **8** a row or line: *ranges of books in perfect order.* **9** a stove for cooking: *Gas and electric ranges have replaced the coal and wood range.* 1,3-5,7-9 *noun*, 2,6 *verb*, **rang·es, ranged, rang·ing.**

rang·er (rān′jər), **1** a person employed to guard a forest. **2** one of a body of armed troops employed in ranging over a region to police it. *noun.*

rank¹ (rangk), **1** a row or line, usually of soldiers, placed side by side. **2 ranks** or **the rank and file, a** common soldiers. **b** common people. **3** to arrange in a row or line. **4** a position; grade; class: *The rank of major is higher than the rank of captain.* **5** a high position: *A duke is a man of rank.* **6** to have a certain place or position in relation to other persons or things: *I ranked high on the spelling test.* 1,2,4,5 *noun*, 3,6 *verb.*

rank² (rangk), having an unpleasant, strong smell or taste: *rank meat, rank tobacco. adjective.*

ran·kle (rang′kəl), to cause anger; continue to give pain: *The memory of the insult still rankles me. verb*, **ran·kles, ran·kled, ran·kling.**

ran·sack (ran′sak), **1** to search thoroughly through: *We ransacked the house for my lost ring.* **2** to rob; plunder: *The invading army ransacked the city and carried off its treasures. verb.*

ran·som (ran′səm), **1** the price paid or demanded before a captive is set free: *The robber held the travelers for ransom.* **2** to obtain the release of a captive by paying a price: *They ransomed the kidnaped child with a great sum of money.* **3** the freeing of a captive by paying the price that is demanded: *the ransom of a prisoner.* 1,3 *noun*, 2 *verb.*

rap (rap), **1** a light, sharp knock; a quick, light blow: *We heard a rap on the window.* **2** to knock sharply; tap: *The chairman rapped on the table for order.* 1 *noun*, 2 *verb*, **raps, rapped, rap·ping.**

rap·id (rap′id), **1** very quick; swift: *a rapid walk, a rapid worker.* **2 rapids,** a part of a river where the rapid (definition 2)—The raft was swept along by the **rapids**.

a hat	i it	oi oil	ch child	a in about
ã age	ī ice	ou out	ng long	e in taken
ä far	o hot	u cup	sh she	ə = i in pencil
e let	ō open	u̇ put	th thin	o in lemon
ē equal	ô order	ü rule	ŦH then	u in circus
ėr term			zh measure	

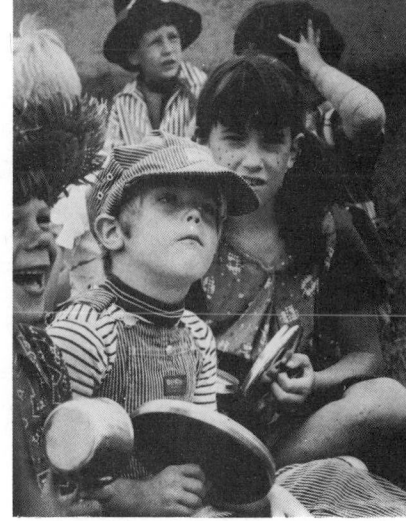

rapt
He listened with
rapt attention.

water rushes quickly, often over rocks lying near the surface. 1 *adjective,* 2 *noun.*

ra·pid·i·ty (rə pid′ə tē), quickness; swiftness; speed. *noun.*

rapt (rapt), showing extreme interest or total enjoyment: *a rapt smile, rapt attention. adjective.*

rap·ture (rap′chər), a very great joy; extreme happiness: *The children watched in rapture as the magician pulled a rabbit out of a hat. noun.*

rap·tur·ous (rap′chər əs), full of great joy; feeling and expressing great happiness. *adjective.*

rare[1] (rer *or* rar), 1 seldom seen, found, or happening: *Snow is rare in Florida. She collects rare coins.* 2 unusually good: *Edison had rare powers as an inventor.* 3 thin; not dense: *The higher we go above the earth, the rarer the air is. adjective,* **rar·er, rar·est.**

rare[1] (definition 1)—This picture shows both sides of a **rare** Jewish coin that is almost 1900 years old.

rare[2] (rer *or* rar), not cooked much: *a rare steak. adjective,* **rar·er, rar·est.**

rare·ly (rer′lē *or* rar′lē), seldom; not often: *A person who is usually on time is rarely late. adverb.*

rar·i·ty (rer′ə tē *or* rar′ə tē), 1 something rare: *A person over a hundred years old is a rarity.* 2 scarcity: *The rarity of diamonds makes them valuable. noun, plural* **rar·i·ties.**

ras·cal (ras′kəl), 1 a bad, dishonest person. 2 a mischievous person: *That little rascal ate all the cookies. noun.*

rash[1] (rash), too hasty; careless; reckless; taking too much risk: *It is rash to cross the street without looking both ways. adjective.*

rash[2] (rash), 1 a breaking out with many small red spots on the skin. Scarlet fever causes a rash. 2 an outbreak: *There was a rash of bank robberies last week. noun.*

rasp (rasp), 1 to make a harsh, grating sound: *The file rasped as she worked.* 2 a harsh, grating sound: *The rasp in his voice was due to a sore throat.* 3 to grate on; irritate: *Their constant quarreling began to rasp my nerves.* 1,3 *verb,* 2 *noun.*

rasp·ber·ry (raz′ber′ē), a small fruit that grows on bushes. Raspberries are usually red or black, but some kinds are white or yellow. They are good to eat. *noun, plural* **rasp·ber·ries.**

rat (rat), 1 a long-tailed gnawing animal like a mouse, but larger. Rats are gray, black, brown, or white. 2 a mean, hateful person. *noun.*
smell a rat, to suspect a trick or scheme.

rate (rāt), 1 quantity, amount, or degree, measured in proportion to something else: *The car was going at the rate of 40 miles an hour.* 2 a price: *We pay the regular rate.* 3 to put a value on: *We rated the house as worth $60,000.* 4 to consider; regard: *He was rated as one of the richest men in town.* 5 class; grade: *first rate, second rate.* 6 to be ranked; be considered: *She rates high as a musician.* 1,2,5 *noun,* 3,4,6 *verb,* **rates, rat·ed, rat·ing.**
at any rate, anyway; in any case.

rath·er (raŦH′ər), 1 more willingly: *I would rather go today than tomorrow.* 2 more properly; with better reason: *This is rather for your parents to decide than for you.* 3 more truly or correctly: *We sat up till one o'clock Monday night, or, rather, Tuesday morning.* 4 to some extent; somewhat; more than a little: *After working so long he was rather tired. adverb.*

507

rat·i·fi·ca·tion (rat/ə fə kā/shən), an approval; confirmation: *The peace treaty was sent to the senate for ratification.* noun.

rat·i·fy (rat/ə fī), to approve; confirm: *The two countries will ratify the agreement made by their representatives.* verb, **rat·i·fies, rat·i·fied, rat·i·fy·ing.**

ra·ti·o (rā/shē ō), **1** the relation between two numbers or quantities meant when we say *times as many* or *times as much.* "They have sheep and cows in the ratio of 10 to 3" means that they have ten sheep for every three cows, or 3⅓ times as many sheep as cows. **2** a quotient. The ratio between two quantities is the number of times one contains the other. The ratio of 3 to 6 is ⅜ or ½; the ratio of 6 to 3 is ⁶⁄₃ or 2. The ratios of 3 to 5 and 6 to 10 are the same. *noun, plural* **ra·ti·os.**

ra·tion (rash/ən *or* rā/shən), **1** a fixed allowance of food; daily allowance of food for a person or animal. **2** a portion of anything dealt out: *After the flood, church workers gave out rations of food to homeless people.* **3** to allow only certain amounts to: *Because gasoline was scarce, the government decided to ration drivers to 10 gallons per week.* **4** to distribute in limited amounts: *Food was rationed to the public during the war.* 1,2 noun, 3,4 verb.

ra·tion·al (rash/ə nəl), **1** sensible; reasonable; reasoned out: *When very angry, people seldom act in a rational way.* **2** able to think and reason clearly: *Human beings are rational animals.* **3** of reason; based on reasoning: *There is a rational explanation for thunder and lightning.* adjective.

rat·tle (rat/l), **1** to make or cause to make a number of short, sharp sounds: *The window rattled in the wind.* **2** a number of short, sharp sounds: *The driver was annoyed by the rattle of bottles in the back seat of the car.* **3** to move with short, sharp sounds: *The old car rattled down the street.* **4** a toy or instrument that makes a noise when it is shaken: *The baby shook the rattle.* **5** the series of horny pieces at the end of a rattlesnake's tail. **6** to talk or say quickly; talk on and on: *She rattled off the names of all the planets.* **7** to disturb; confuse; upset: *I was so rattled that I forgot my speech.* 1,3,6,7 verb, **rat·tles, rat·tled, rat·tling;** 2,4,5 noun.

rat·tler (rat/lər), a rattlesnake. noun.

rat·tle·snake (rat/l snāk/), a poisonous snake with a thick body and a broad head, that makes a buzzing noise with rattles at the end of its tail. noun.

rau·cous (rô/kəs), hoarse; harsh-sounding: *We heard the raucous caw of a crow.* adjective.

rav·age (rav/ij), **1** to lay waste; damage greatly; destroy. **2** violence; destruction; great damage: *the ravages of war.* 1 verb, **rav·ag·es, rav·aged, rav·ag·ing;** 2 noun.

rave (rāv), **1** to talk wildly. An excited, angry person may rave. **2** to talk with great enthusiasm: *They raved about the food.* verb, **raves, raved, rav·ing.**

rav·el (rav/əl), to fray; separate into threads: *The sweater has raveled at the elbow.* verb.

ra·ven (rā/vən), **1** a large black bird like a crow but larger. **2** deep glossy black: *raven hair.* 1 noun, 2 adjective.

rav·en·ous (rav/ə nəs), **1** very hungry: *I hadn't eaten all day and was ravenous.* **2** greedy. adjective.

ra·vine (rə vēn/), a long, deep, narrow valley: *The river had worn a ravine between the two hills.* noun.

rav·ish (rav/ish), **1** to fill with delight: *I was ravished by the beauty of the countryside.* **2** to carry off by force: *The wolf ravished the lamb from the flock.* verb.

rav·ish·ing (rav/i shing), very delightful; enchanting: *jewels of ravishing beauty.* adjective.

raw (rô), **1** not cooked: *raw meat.* **2** in the natural state; not manufactured, treated, or prepared: *Raw milk has not been pasteurized.* **3** not experienced; not trained: *Six months ago these well-trained soldiers were raw recruits.* **4** damp and cold: *A raw wind was blowing from the ocean.* **5** with the skin off; sore: *There was a raw spot on the horse where the harness rubbed.* adjective.

raw·hide (rô/hīd/), **1** the skin of cattle that has not been tanned. **2** a rope or whip made of this. noun.

raw material, a substance in its natural state; any product that comes from mines, farms, forests, or the like before it is prepared for use in factories, mills, and similar places. Coal, coffee beans, iron ore, cotton, and hides are raw materials.

ray¹ (rā), **1** a line or beam of light: *rays of the sun.* **2** a line or stream of heat, light, or other radiant energy. **3** a thin line like a ray, coming out from a center. **4** a part like a ray. The petals of a daisy and the arms of a starfish are rays. **5** a slight trace; faint gleam: *A ray of hope pierced our gloom.* **6** a part of a line stretching from a fixed point on the line but having no end point. noun.

ravage (definition 1)—The forest was **ravaged** by fire.

ray² —up to 12 feet (3½ meters) long with the tail

a hat	i it	oi oil	ch child	a in about
ā age	ī ice	ou out	ng long	e in taken
ä far	o hot	u cup	sh she	ə = i in pencil
e let	ō open	u̇ put	th thin	o in lemon
ē equal	ô order	ü rule	ŦH then	u in circus
ėr term			zh measure	

ray² (rā), a fish with a wide, flat body and very wide fins. *noun.*

ray·on (rā′on), a fiber or fabric made from cellulose, and used instead of silk, cotton, and other similar fabrics. *noun.*

raze (rāz), to tear down; destroy completely: *The old school was razed to the ground, and a new one was built. verb,* **raz·es, razed, raz·ing.**

ra·zor (rā′zər), a tool with one or more sharp blades for shaving. *noun.*

rd., road.

R.D., Rural Delivery.

re-, a prefix meaning: **1** again: *Reopen means to open again.* **2** back: *Repay means to pay back.*

reach (rēch), **1** to get to; arrive at; come to: *Your letter reached me yesterday. We reached an agreement.* **2** to stretch out or hold out an arm or a hand: *He reached in the dark and turned on the lights.* **3** to stretch; extend: *The United States reaches from ocean to ocean.* **4** to touch: *I cannot reach the top of the wall. The anchor reached bottom.* **5** to stretch out to touch or seize something; try to get: *I reached for the rope.* **6** to get in touch with someone: *I could not reach you by telephone.* **7** a reaching; stretching out: *By a long reach, the drowning man grasped the rope.* **8** the extent or distance of reaching: *Food and water were left within reach of the sick dog.* **9** range; power; capacity: *I'm afraid this difficult lesson is beyond my reach.* **10** a long stretch or extent: *There are vast reaches of snow in the Antarctic.* **1-6** *verb,* **7-10** *noun, plural* **reach·es.**

re·act (rē akt′), **1** to act back; have an effect on the one that is acting: *Unkindness often reacts on the unkind person.* **2** to act in response: *Dogs react to kindness by showing affection. verb.*

react against, to act unfavorably toward or take an unfavorable attitude toward: *Some individuals react against fads.*

re·ac·tion (rē ak′shən), an action in response to some influence: *Our reaction to a joke is to laugh. The doctor observed carefully the patient's reactions to the tests. noun.*

re·ac·tor (rē ak′tər), a device for splitting atoms to produce atomic energy without causing an explosion. *noun.*

read¹ (rēd), **1** to get the meaning of writing or print: *to read a book. The blind read by touching special raised print with their fingertips.* **2** to learn from writing or print: *I read of the event in the paper.* **3** to speak out loud the words of writing or print: *Please read this story to me.* **4** to show by letters, figures, or signs: *The thermometer reads 70 degrees. The ticket reads "From New York to Boston."* **5** to get the real meaning of; understand: *She seemed to read my thoughts.* **6** to give the meaning of; interpret: *The fortuneteller told my future by reading tea leaves. verb,* **reads, read** (red), **read·ing.**

read² (red), **1** having knowledge gained by reading; informed: *He is widely read in history.* **2** See **read¹**. *I read that book last year.* **1** *adjective,* **2** *verb.*

read·a·ble (rē′də bəl), easy to read; interesting: *This is a readable story with an exciting plot. adjective.*

read·er (rē′dər), **1** a person who reads. **2** a book for learning and practicing reading. *noun.*

read·i·ly (red′l ē), **1** quickly: *The bright student answered readily.* **2** easily: *This information can be readily located in your science book.* **3** willingly: *He came with us readily. adverb.*

read·i·ness (red′ē nis), **1** a being ready: *Everything is in readiness for the party.* **2** quickness; promptness. **3** willingness. *noun.*

read·ing (rē′ding), **1** getting the meaning of written or printed words. **2** a speaking out loud of written or printed words. **3** the written or printed matter read or to be read: *I have a lot of reading to do this weekend.* **4** the amount shown by letters, figures, or signs on the scale of an instrument: *The reading of the thermometer was 96 degrees. noun.*

read·y (red′ē), **1** prepared for action or use at once; prepared: *Dinner is ready. We were ready to start at nine.* **2** willing: *I am ready to forget our argument.* **3** quick; prompt: *She has a ready wit.* **4** likely; liable: *Don't be too ready to find fault.* **5** easy to get at; easy to reach: *We always keep some ready money in the house.* **6** to make ready; prepare: *The expedition readied itself during the summer.* **1-5** *adjective,* **read·i·er, read·i·est;** **6** *verb,* **read·ies, read·ied, read·y·ing.**

read·y-made (red′ē mād′), ready for immediate use; made for anybody who will buy: *This store sells ready-made clothes. adjective.*

re·al (rē′əl), **1** not imagined; not made up; actually existing; true: *The explorer told us about a real adventure he had while on an expedition.* **2** not imitation; genuine: *This bracelet is made of real gold.* **3** very; extremely: *Come again real soon.* **1,2** *adjective,* **3** *adverb.*

R

509

real estate, land together with the buildings, fences, trees, water, and minerals that belong with it.

re·al·is·tic (rē′ə lis′tik), **1** like the real thing; lifelike: *The speaker gave a very realistic picture of life a hundred years ago.* **2** seeing things as they really are; practical: *She wanted to buy a used car, but decided to be realistic and save her money for college. adjective.*

re·al·i·ty (rē al′ə tē), **1** actual existence; true state of affairs: *I doubt the reality of what I saw; I must have dreamed it.* **2** a real thing; actual fact: *Slaughter and destruction are the terrible realities of war. noun, plural* **re·al·i·ties.**

in reality, really; in fact: *We thought she was serious, but in reality she was joking.*

re·al·i·za·tion (rē′ə lə zā′shən), **1** a realizing or being realized: *Becoming a football player was the realization of his hopes.* **2** an understanding: *The explorers had a full realization of the dangers they would face. noun.*

re·al·ize (rē′ə līz), **1** to understand clearly: *I realize how hard you worked.* **2** to make real: *Her uncle's present made it possible for her to realize the dream of going to college. verb,* **re·al·iz·es, re·al·ized, re·al·iz·ing.**

re·al·ly (rē′ə lē), **1** actually; truly; in fact: *We all should learn to accept things as they really are.* **2** indeed: *Oh, really? adverb.*

realm (relm), **1** a kingdom: *The power of the realm was in the king's hands.* **2** a particular field of something: *the realm of biology, the realm of poetry. noun.*

ream (rēm), 480, 500, or 516 sheets of paper of the same size and quality. *noun.*

reap (rēp), **1** to cut grain. **2** to gather a crop. **3** to cut grain or gather a crop from: *They reaped the field.* **4** to get as a return or reward: *Kind acts often reap happy smiles. verb.*

reap·er (rē′pər), a person or machine that cuts grain or gathers a crop. *noun.*

re·ap·pear (rē′ə pir′), to come into sight again. *verb.*

rear[1] (rir), **1** the back part; back: *The kitchen is in the rear of the house.* **2** at the back; in the back: *Leave by the rear door of the bus.* **1** *noun,* **2** *adjective.*

rear[2] (rir), **1** to make grow; help to grow; bring up: *They reared their children to respect others.* **2** to raise; lift up: *The snake reared its head.* **3** (of an animal) to rise on the hind legs. *verb.*

rear admiral, a naval officer next in rank above a captain.

re·ar·range (rē′ə rānj′), **1** to arrange in a new or different way: *They rearranged the furniture for the party.* **2** to arrange again: *I had to rearrange my papers after the wind blew them on the floor. verb,* **re·ar·rang·es, re·ar·ranged, re·ar·rang·ing.**

rea·son (rē′zn), **1** a cause; motive: *I have my reasons for doing it this way.* **2** an explanation: *What is your reason for being so late?* **3** to think things out; solve new problems: *Most animals can't reason.* **4** the power to think: *He was so angry*

he temporarily lost his reason. **5** to consider; discuss; argue: *If you reason with them they may change their minds.* **1,2,4** *noun,* **3,5** *verb.*

stand to reason, to be reasonable and sensible: *It stands to reason that you can't do your best if you're tired.*

rea·son·a·ble (rē′zn ə bəl), **1** according to reason; sensible; not foolish: *When we are angry, we do not always act in a reasonable way.* **2** not asking too much; fair; just: *He is a reasonable person.* **3** not high in price; inexpensive: *We bought this television set for a very reasonable price.* **4** able to reason: *Human beings are reasonable animals. adjective.*

rea·son·a·bly (rē′zn ə blē), in a reasonable manner; with reason. *adverb.*

rea·son·ing (rē′zn ing), **1** the process of drawing conclusions from facts. **2** reasons; arguments. *noun.*

re·as·sure (rē′ə shủr′), **1** to restore to confidence: *The calmness of the crew during the storm reassured the ship's passengers.* **2** to assure again or anew. *verb,* **re·as·sures, re·as·sured, re·as·sur·ing.**

reb·el (reb′əl *for 1 and 2;* ri bel′ *for 3 and 4*), **1** a person who resists or fights against authority instead of obeying: *The rebels armed themselves against the government.* **2** defying law or authority: *a rebel army.* **3** to resist or fight against law or authority: *Unfair taxes made the colonists rebel.* **4** to feel a great dislike or opposition: *We rebelled at having to stay in on so fine a day.* **1** *noun,* **2** *adjective,* **3,4** *verb,* **reb·els, re·belled, re·bel·ling.**

[*Rebel* comes from a Latin word meaning "one who makes war again." This usually referred to a person who had already been conquered in war, but kept on fighting anyway, hoping to regain freedom.]

re·bel·lion (ri bel′yən), **1** a fight against one's government; revolt: *The American colonists were in rebellion against the British king.* **2** an act of resistance: *The prisoners rose in rebellion against their guards. noun.*

re·bel·lious (ri bel′yəs), **1** defying authority; acting like a rebel: *The rebellious troops marched*

rear[2] (definition 3)
The spirited
horse **reared.**

on the capital. **2** hard to manage; hard to treat; disobedient: *The rebellious child would not obey the rules. adjective.*

re·born (rē bôrn′), born again. *adjective.*

re·bound (ri bound′ *for 1;* rē′bound′ *for 2*), **1** to spring back. **2** a springing back: *You hit the ball on the rebound in handball.* **1** *verb,* **2** *noun.*

re·buff (ri buf′), **1** a blunt or sudden check to a person who makes advances, offers help, or makes a request: *Her offer to help met with a rebuff.* **2** to give a sudden check to: *The friendly dog was rebuffed by a kick.* **1** *noun,* **2** *verb.*

rebuff
(definition 1)

re·build (rē bild′), to build again or anew. *verb,* **re·builds, re·built, re·build·ing.**

re·built (rē bilt′). See **rebuild.** *verb.*

re·buke (ri byük′), **1** to express disapproval of; reprove: *The teacher rebuked the child for throwing paper on the floor.* **2** an expression of disapproval; scolding: *The child feared the teacher's rebuke.* **1** *verb,* **re·bukes, re·buked, re·buk·ing;* **2** *noun.*

re·call (ri kôl′ *for 1,2, and 3;* ri kôl′ *or* rē′kôl′ *for 4*), **1** to call back to mind; remember: *I can recall stories read to me when I was very young.* **2** to call back; order back: *The doctor was recalled to the hospital.* **3** to call back a vehicle in order to replace or repair a defective part. **4** the act of calling back; fact of being called back: *The manufacturer ordered the recall of several thousand cars that had faulty headlights.* **1-3** *verb,* **4** *noun.*

re·cap·ture (rē kap′chər), to capture again; have again: *The soldiers recaptured the fort. verb,*

re·cap·tures, re·cap·tured, re·cap·tur·ing.

re·cede (ri sēd′), to go backward; move backward: *When the tide receded, we dug for clams. verb,* **re·cedes, re·ced·ed, re·ced·ing.**

re·ceipt (ri sēt′), **1** a written statement that money, a package, or a letter has been received: *Sign the receipt for this parcel.* **2** to write on a bill or invoice that something has been received or paid for: *Pay the bill and ask the grocer to receipt it.* **3 receipts,** the money received: *Our expenses were less than our receipts.* **4** a receiving: *His receipt of the good news was a pleasant surprise.* **1,3,4** *noun,* **2** *verb.*

re·ceive (ri sēv′), **1** to take or get something offered or sent: *It's nice to receive a gift. He received a letter today.* **2** to take or let into the mind; accept: *She received many new ideas from reading books.* **3** to experience; suffer; endure: *He received a punishment for cheating.* **4** to let into one's house or society; welcome: *The people of the neighborhood were glad to receive the new couple.* **5** (in radio or television) to change radio waves broadcast through the air into sounds, or sounds and pictures: *Our television receives well since we had a new antenna put on. verb,* **re·ceives, re·ceived, re·ceiv·ing.**

re·ceiv·er (ri sē′vər), **1** a person who receives: *The receiver of a gift should thank the giver.* **2** a thing that receives: *Public telephones have coin receivers for nickels, dimes, and quarters.* **3** a part of the telephone held to the ear. **4** a device that receives sounds, or sounds and pictures, sent by radio waves: *a radio receiver, a television receiver. noun.*

re·cent (rē′snt), **1** done or made not long ago: *This chair is a recent purchase.* **2** not long past; modern: *The recent period of history includes several wars. adjective.*

re·cep·ta·cle (ri sep′tə kəl), any container or place used to put things in. Bags, baskets, and vaults are all receptacles. *noun.*

re·cep·tion (ri sep′shən), **1** an act or manner of receiving: *She got a warm reception from her friend.* **2** a party or entertainment to welcome people: *Our school gave a reception for our new principal.* **3** the quality of the sound in a radio or sound and picture in a television set: *Reception was poor because we were so far from the transmitter. noun.*

re·cep·tion·ist (ri sep′shə nist), a person employed in an office to receive callers: *The receptionist directed me to the right office. noun.*

re·cep·tive (ri sep′tiv), able, quick, or ready to receive ideas, suggestions, or impressions: *a receptive mind. adjective.*

R

re·cess (rē′ses *or* ri ses′ *for 1 and 3;* ri ses′ *for 2*), **1** the time during which work stops: *Our school has an hour's recess at noon.* **2** to take a break; interrupt work for a time: *The committee recessed for lunch.* **3** a part of a wall or other flat surface set back from the rest: *The bench was in the recess of the wall.* 1,3 *noun,* 2 *verb.*

re·ces·sion (ri sesh′ən), a time when business activity is somewhat slow and some people are out of work. It is shorter and less extreme than a depression. *noun.*

rec·i·pe (res′ə pē), **1** a set of directions for preparing something to eat: *Please give me your recipe for cookies.* **2** a set of directions for preparing anything or reaching some result: *a recipe for happiness. noun.*

re·cip·i·ent (ri sip′ē ənt), a person who receives something: *The recipients of the prizes had their names printed in the paper. noun.*

re·cit·al (ri sī′tl), **1** a telling of facts in detail; account: *I hope that my lengthy recital of my problems hasn't bored you.* **2** a musical entertainment, usually given by a single performer: *My music teacher will give a recital Tuesday afternoon. noun.*

rec·i·ta·tion (res′ə tā′shən), a repeating something from memory before an audience. *noun.*

re·cite (ri sīt′), **1** to say over; repeat: *He can recite that poem from memory.* **2** to give an account of in detail: *She recited the day's adventures. verb,* **re·cites, re·cit·ed, re·cit·ing.**

reck·less (rek′lis), rash; heedless; careless: *Reckless driving causes many automobile accidents. adjective.*

reck·on (rek′ən), **1** to find the number or value of; count: *Reckon the cost before you decide.* **2** to think or consider: *He is reckoned to be the best speller in the class. verb.*

reck·on·ing (rek′ə ning), **1** a count; calculation: *By my reckoning we are miles from home.* **2** the settling of an account: *a day of reckoning.* **3** the calculation of the position of a ship or aircraft. *noun.*

re·claim (ri klām′), **1** to bring back to a useful, good condition: *The farmer reclaimed the swamp by draining it.* **2** to get from discarded things: *to reclaim rubber from old tires.* **3** to demand or ask for the return of: *She reclaimed her luggage at the end of the trip. verb.*

rec·la·ma·tion (rek′lə mā′shən), a bringing back to a useful, good condition: *the reclamation of deserts by irrigation. noun.*

re·cline (ri klīn′), to lean back; lie down. *verb,* **re·clines, re·clined, re·clin·ing.**

re·clin·er (ri klī′nər), a comfortable armchair with a seat and back that change position so that a person can lean back comfortably. *noun.*

rec·luse (rek′lüs *or* ri klüs′), a person who lives shut up or away from the world. *noun.*

rec·og·ni·tion (rek′əg nish′ən), **1** a knowing again or being known again: *With a good disguise he escaped recognition.* **2** an admitting or accepting that something is true: *We insisted on complete recognition of our rights.* **3** a favorable notice; attention: *The actor soon won recognition from the public. noun.*

rec·og·nize (rek′əg nīz), **1** to know again: *You have grown so much that I scarcely recognized you.* **2** to accept as true; admit; acknowledge: *They recognized and did their duty. verb,* **rec·og·niz·es, rec·og·nized, rec·og·niz·ing.**

re·coil (ri koil′), **1** to draw back; shrink back: *Most people would recoil at seeing a snake in the path.* **2** to spring back: *The gun recoiled after I fired it.* **3** a springing back: *The recoil of the shotgun hurt my shoulder.* 1,2 *verb,* 3 *noun.*

rec·ol·lect (rek′ə lekt′), to remember: *As I recollect, I had measles when I was about four. verb.*

rec·ol·lec·tion (rek′ə lek′shən), memory; remembrance: *This has been the hottest summer within my recollection. noun.*

rec·om·mend (rek′ə mend′), **1** to speak in favor of; suggest favorably: *The teacher recommended her for the job. Can you recommend a good adventure story?* **2** to advise: *The doctor recommended that the patient stay in bed. verb.*

rec·om·men·da·tion (rek′ə men dā′shən), **1** the act of recommending: *We went to that movie at your recommendation.* **2** words of advice: *What is the doctor's recommendation? noun.*

rec·om·pense (rek′əm pens), **1** to reward; pay back; pay a person: *The travelers recompensed the man who carried their luggage.* **2** to make a fair return for an action, anything lost, damage done, or hurt received: *The insurance company recompensed her for the loss of her car.* **3** a payment; reward; return: *She received $2000 in recompense for the loss of her car.* 1,2 *verb,* **rec·om·pens·es, rec·om·pensed, rec·om·pens·ing;** 3 *noun.*

rec·on·cile (rek′ən sīl), **1** to make friends again: *The children had quarreled but were soon reconciled.* **2** to make agree; bring into harmony: *It is impossible to reconcile their story with the facts. verb,* **rec·on·ciles, rec·on·ciled, rec·on·cil·ing.**

rec·on·cil·i·a·tion (rek′ən sil′ē ā′shən), a bringing together again in friendship. *noun.*

recline—He **reclined** on a park bench.

rec·on·noi·ter (rek′ə noi′tər *or* rē′kə noi′tər), to approach and examine or observe in order to learn something: *Our scouts will reconnoiter the enemy's position before we attack. verb.*

re·con·struct (rē′kən strukt′), to construct again; rebuild; make over: *After the earthquake, many buildings had to be reconstructed. verb.*

re·cord (ri kôrd′ *for 1 and 4;* rek′ərd *for 2,3,5, and 6*), **1** to put into writing or some other permanent form for future use: *Record what the speaker says. We record history in books.* **2** the thing written or kept: *I kept a record of my expenses on the trip.* **3** a thin, flat disk with grooves from which a phonograph can produce music, words, or other sounds that were previously copied. **4** to copy music, words, or other sounds on such a disk or on a specially treated tape for future use. **5** the known facts about what a person or thing has done: *She has a fine record at school.* **6** the best yet done; best amount, rate, or speed yet reached: *Who holds the record for the high jump?* 1,4 *verb,* 2,3,5,6 *noun.*

re·cord·er (ri kôr′dər), **1** a person whose business is to make and keep records. **2** a machine or part of a machine that records. The recorder of a cash register adds up and prints the amount of sales made. **3** a tape recorder. **4** a wooden musical instrument somewhat like a flute. *noun.*

recorder
(definition 4)

re·cord·ing (ri kôr′ding), a record used on a phonograph, or a plastic tape used on a tape recorder. *noun.*

rec·ord play·er (rek′ərd plā′ər), an instrument that reproduces sounds from records; phonograph.

re·count[1] (ri kount′), to tell in detail; give an account of: *He recounted all the happenings of the day. verb.*

re·count[2] *or* **re-count** (rē kount′ *for 1;* rē′kount′ *for 2*), **1** to count again: *I recounted the money to make certain it was the right amount.* **2** a second count: *The defeated candidate demanded a recount of the votes.* 1 *verb,* 2 *noun.*

re·course (rē′kôrs), **1** the act of turning to for help or protection; appealing: *Our recourse in illness is to a doctor.* **2** a person or thing appealed to or turned to for help or protection: *His only recourse in trouble was his family. noun.*

re·cov·er (ri kuv′ər), **1** to get back something lost, taken away, stolen, or sent out: *After the argument, I needed time to recover my temper. The police recovered the stolen car.* **2** to make up for something lost or damaged: *I hurried, trying to recover lost time.* **3** to get well; get back to a normal condition: *She is recovering from a cold. verb.*

re·cov·er (rē kuv′ər), to put a new cover on: *We had our couch re-covered. verb.*

re·cov·er·y (ri kuv′ər ē), **1** a coming back to health or normal condition: *She had a rapid recovery after surgery.* **2** a getting back something that was lost, taken away, stolen, or sent out: *The owner of the stolen property was happy about its quick recovery from the thieves by the police.* **3** a getting back to a proper position or condition: *He started to fall, but made a quick recovery. noun, plural* **re·cov·er·ies.**

rec·re·a·tion (rek′rē ā′shən), play; amusement. Gardening, sports, games, and reading are all forms of recreation. *noun.*

re·cross (rē krôs′), to cross again: *On our hike we had to cross and recross a winding creek several times. verb.*

re·cruit (ri krüt′), **1** a newly enlisted member of one of the armed forces. **2** to get men and women to join one of the armed forces. **3** a new member of any group or class: *The Nature Club needs recruits.* **4** to get new members; get people to join: *We need to recruit players to replace those who left the team.* 1,3 *noun,* 2,4 *verb.*

rec·tan·gle (rek′tang′gəl), a four-sided figure with four right angles. *noun.*

rectangles

rec·tan·gu·lar (rek tang′gyə lər), shaped like a rectangle. *adjective.*

rec·ti·fy (rek′tə fī), to make right; put right; adjust; remedy: *The storekeeper admitted her mistake and was willing to rectify it. verb,* **rec·ti·fies, rec·ti·fied, rec·ti·fy·ing.**

rec·tor (rek′tər), a clergyman who is in charge of a parish or congregation. *noun.*

a hat	i it	oi oil	ch child	ə = { a in about
ā age	ī ice	ou out	ng long	e in taken
ä far	o hot	u cup	sh she	i in pencil
e let	ō open	ů put	th thin	o in lemon
ē equal	ô order	ü rule	ŦH then	u in circus
ėr term			zh measure	

re·cur (ri kèr′), to come up again; occur again; be repeated: *Leap year recurs every four years.* *verb,* **re·curs, re·curred, re·cur·ring.**

re·cy·cle (rē sī′kəl), to treat or process something in order that it may be used again. Paper, aluminum, and glass products are commonly recycled. *verb,* **re·cy·cles, re·cy·cled, re·cy·cling.**

recycle—She brought in old cans so that they could be **recycled.**

red (red), **1** the color of blood or of a ruby. **2** having this color: *a red rose.* **3 Red,** a Communist or, sometimes, any extreme radical. 1,3 *noun,* 2 *adjective.*
see red, to become very angry: *I saw red and before I knew it I had hit him hard.*

red blood cell, a cell in the blood that carries oxygen from the lungs to various parts of the body. Red blood cells give fresh blood its red color.

red·cap (red′kap′), a porter at a railroad or bus station whose uniform usually includes a red cap. *noun.*

red·coat (red′kōt′), (in former times) a British soldier. *noun.*

Red Cross, an international organization to care for the sick and wounded in war, and to relieve suffering caused by floods, fires, earthquakes, and other disasters. Its badge is a red cross on a white background.

red·den (red′n), **1** to make or become red. **2** to blush: *She reddened with embarrassment at her mistake. verb.*

red·dish (red′ish), somewhat red. *adjective.*

re·deem (ri dēm′), **1** to pay off: *We redeemed the mortgage.* **2** to make up for: *A very good feature will sometimes redeem several bad ones.* **3** to set free; rescue; save; deliver: *redeemed from sin. verb.*

re·demp·tion (ri demp′shən), **1** the act of buying back; paying off: *the redemption of a loan.* **2** deliverance; rescue. **3** deliverance from sin; salvation. *noun.*

red·head·ed (red′hed′id), having red hair. *adjective.*

red-hot (red′hot′), very hot: *a red-hot stove, a red-hot temper. adjective.*

re·dis·cov·er (rē′dis kuv′ər), to discover again: *I rediscovered some books that I used to like very much. verb.*

re·dou·ble (rē dub′əl), to double back: *The fox redoubled on its trail to escape the hunters. verb,* **re·dou·bles, re·dou·bled, re·dou·bling.**

re·dress (ri dres′ *for 1;* rē′dres *for 2*), **1** to set right; repair; remedy: *King Arthur tried to redress wrongs in his kingdom.* **2** a setting right; relief: *Anyone who has been injured deserves redress.* 1 *verb,* 2 *noun.*

re·duce (ri düs′ *or* ri dyüs′), **1** to make less; make smaller; decrease: *We have reduced expenses this year. She is trying to reduce her weight.* **2** to become less in weight: *His doctor advised him to reduce.* **3** to bring down; lower: *Their misfortunes reduced them to poverty.* **4** to change to another form: *The chalk was reduced to powder. If you reduce 3 ft., 6 in. to inches you have 42 inches. verb,* **re·duc·es, re·duced, re·duc·ing.**

re·duc·tion (ri duk′shən), **1** a reducing or being reduced: *a reduction of ten pounds in weight.* **2** the amount by which a thing is reduced: *The reduction in cost was $5. noun.*

red·wood (red′wùd′), **1** a very large evergreen tree found along the coasts of California and Oregon. Redwoods are the tallest living trees. **2** its brownish-red wood. *noun.*

reed (rēd), **1** a kind of tall grass that grows in wet places. Reeds have hollow, jointed stalks. **2** a thin piece of wood, metal, or plastic in a musical instrument that produces sound when air is blown over it. *noun.*

reed instrument, a musical instrument that makes sound by means of a vibrating reed or reeds. Oboes, clarinets, English horns, and saxophones are reed instruments.

reef[1]—a photograph of the Great Barrier **Reef** along the coast of Australia, as viewed from an airplane

reef[1] (rēf), a narrow ridge of rocks, sand, or coral at or near the surface of water. *noun.*

reef[2] (rēf), **1** the part of a sail that can be rolled or folded up to reduce its size. **2** to reduce the size

of a sail by rolling or folding up a part of it.
1 *noun,* 2 *verb.*

reek (rēk), **1** a strong, unpleasant smell: *We noticed the reek of cooking cabbage as we entered the hall.* **2** to send out a strong, unpleasant smell: *The beach reeks of dead fish.* 1 *noun,* 2 *verb.*

reel¹ (rēl), **1** a roller or spool for winding fish line, wire, hose, film, or anything that can be wound. **2** something wound on a reel: *two reels of motion-picture film.* **3** to wind on a reel. **4** to draw with a reel or by winding: *She reeled in a fish.* 1,2 *noun,* 3,4 *verb.*

reel off, to say, write, or make in a quick, easy way: *He can reel off stories by the hour.*

reel² (rēl), **1** to suddenly sway or stagger from a blow or shock: *She reeled when the ball struck her.* **2** to sway in standing or walking: *The dazed boy reeled down the street.* **3** to be in a whirl; be dizzy: *My head was reeling after the fast dance. verb.*

reel³ (rēl), **1** a lively dance. **2** the music for it. *noun.*

re·e·lect or **re-e·lect** (rē′i lekt′), to elect again. *verb.*

re·e·lec·tion or **re-e·lec·tion** (rē′i lek′shən), an election again; election for the second time. *noun.*

re·en·ter or **re-en·ter** (rē en′tər), to enter again; go in again: *The spacecraft reentered the earth's atmosphere. verb.*

re·en·try (rē en′trē), an entering again or returning, especially of a rocket or spacecraft into the earth's atmosphere. *noun, plural* **re·en·tries.**

re-en·try (rē en′trē). See **reentry.** *noun, plural* **re-en·tries.**

re·fer (ri fėr′), **1** to send or direct for information, help, or action: *Our teacher referred us to the librarian for some help with our questions.* **2** to hand over; submit: *Let's refer the dispute to the umpire.* **3** to turn for information or help: *A person refers to a dictionary to find the meaning of words.* **4** to direct attention to or speak about: *The speaker referred to the Bible. verb,* **re·fers, re·ferred, re·fer·ring.**

ref·e·ree (ref′ə rē′), **1** a person who rules on the plays in some games: *The referee tossed the ball up between the two centers to start the basketball game.* **2** to act as a referee. 1 *noun,* 2 *verb,* **ref·e·rees, ref·e·reed, ref·e·ree·ing.**

ref·er·ence (ref′ər əns), **1** a direction of the attention: *The report contained many references to newspaper articles.* **2** a statement referred to: *You will find that reference on page 16.* **3** used for information or help: *A dictionary is a reference book.* **4** a person who can give information about another person's character or ability: *He gave his principal as a reference.* **5** a statement about someone's character or ability: *When she left the company, she received an excellent reference from her boss.* **6** relation; respect: *Everyone, without reference to age, was asked to volunteer during the emergency.* 1,2,4-6 *noun,* 3 *adjective.*

make reference to, to mention: *Don't make any reference to the bad news.*

re·fill (rē fil′ *for 1;* rē′fil′ *for 2 and 3*), **1** to fill again: *I refilled my glass with milk.* **2** something to refill with: *Refills can be bought for some kinds of pens and pencils.* **3** a filling again: *I ran out of medicine and got a refill of my prescription.* 1 *verb,* 2,3 *noun.*

re·fine (ri fīn′), **1** to make pure: *Sugar, oil, and metals are refined before they are used.* **2** to make better or more exact: *She worked to refine her skill in writing. verb,* **re·fines, re·fined, re·fin·ing.**

re·fined (ri fīnd′), **1** freed from impurities: *refined sugar.* **2** showing education and good taste; well-bred: *refined tastes, refined manners, a refined voice. adjective.*

re·fine·ment (ri fīn′mənt), **1** fine quality of feeling, taste, manners, or language: *Good manners and correct speech are marks of refinement.* **2** the act or result of refining: *Gasoline is produced by the refinement of petroleum. noun.*

re·fin·er·y (ri fī′nər ē), a building and machinery for purifying sugar, petroleum, or other things. *noun, plural* **re·fin·er·ies.**

refinery

re·fit (rē fit′), to fit, prepare, or equip for use again: *The old ship was refitted for the voyage. verb,* **re·fits, re·fit·ted, re·fit·ting.**

re·flect (ri flekt′), **1** to turn back or throw back light, heat, sound, or the like: *A white roof reflects the heat of the sun.* **2** to give back an image of: *The mirror reflects my face.* **3** to think; think carefully: *Take time to reflect before making a decision.* **4** to cast blame: *The children's spoiled behavior reflected on their parents.* **5** to bring or give back: *A brave act reflects credit on the person who does it. verb.*

re·flec·tion (ri flek′shən), **1** the throwing back of light, heat, sound, or the like: *The reflection of sunlight by sand and water can cause a sunburn.* **2** something reflected: *I thought I saw a light in the window, but it was just a reflection of car headlights.* **3** a likeness; image: *I looked at my reflection in the mirror.* **4** thinking; careful thinking: *On reflection, the plan seemed too dangerous.* **5** a remark or action that casts blame: *The children's bad behavior was a reflection on their parents. noun.*

re·flec·tor (ri flek′tər), any thing, surface, or device that reflects light, heat, sound, or the like, especially a piece of glass or metal for reflecting light in a particular direction. *noun.*

re·flex (rē′fleks), an automatic action that takes place when some nerve cells are stimulated. Sneezing and shivering are reflexes. *noun, plural* **re·flex·es.**

re·fo·rest (rē fôr′ist), to plant again with trees. *verb.*

re·form (ri fôrm′), **1** to make better; improve by removing faults: *Some prisons try to reform criminals instead of just punishing them.* **2** to become better: *They promised to reform if given another chance.* **3** an improvement; change intended to be an improvement: *The new government made many reforms.* **1,2** *verb,* **3** *noun.*

ref·or·ma·tion (ref′ər mā′shən), a change for the better; improvement. *noun.*

re·form·a·to·ry (ri fôr′mə tôr′ē), an institution that is both a school and a prison for young people who have broken the law. *noun, plural* **re·form·a·to·ries.**

re·form·er (ri fôr′mər), a person who reforms, or tries to reform, some state of affairs, custom, or practice. *noun.*

re·fract (ri frakt′), to bend something, such as a ray of light or sound waves, from a straight course. Water refracts light. *verb.*

refract
Because water **refracts** light, the ruler appears bent.

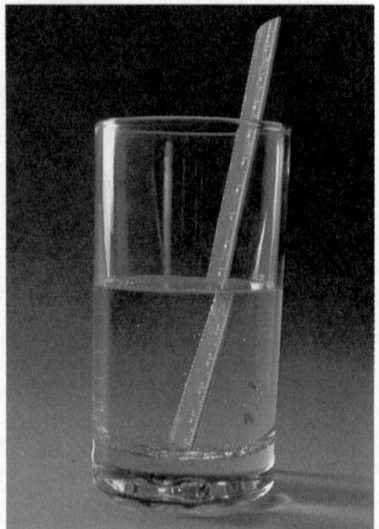

re·frain[1] (ri frān′), to hold oneself back: *Refrain from wrongdoing. verb.*

re·frain[2] (ri frān′), a phrase or verse repeated regularly in a song or poem. In "The Star-Spangled Banner" the refrain is "O'er the land of the free and the home of the brave." *noun.*

re·fresh (ri fresh′), to make fresh again; renew: *His bath refreshed him. She refreshed her memory by a glance at the book. verb.*

re·fresh·ing (ri fresh′ing), able to refresh: *a cool, refreshing drink. adjective.*

re·fresh·ment (ri fresh′mənt), **1** a thing that refreshes: *Fruit juice was the only refreshment served.* **2 refreshments,** food or drink: *Cake and lemonade were the refreshments at our party. noun.*

re·frig·e·rate (ri frij′ə rāt′), to make or keep cold: *Milk, meat, fruit juice, and ice cream must be refrigerated to prevent spoiling. verb,* **re·frig·e·rates, re·frig·e·rat·ed, re·frig·e·rat·ing.**

re·frig·e·ra·tor (ri frij′ə rā′tər), an appliance or room that keeps food or other things cold. *noun.*

re·fu·el (rē fyü′əl), **1** to supply with fuel again. **2** to take on fuel again. *verb.*

ref·uge (ref′yüj), shelter or protection from danger or trouble. *noun.*

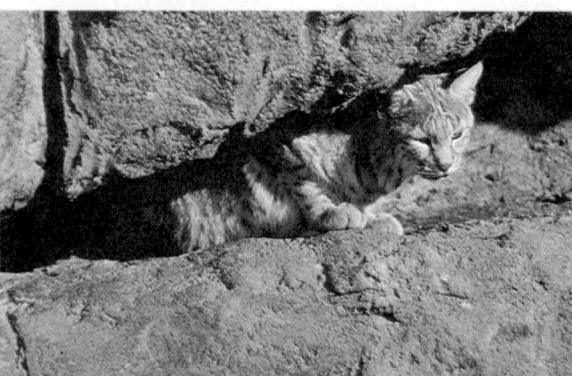

refuge—The bobcat took **refuge** in the rocks.

ref·u·gee (ref′yə jē′), a person who flees to another country for safety from war or from persecution: *Refugees from the war were cared for in neighboring countries. noun.*

re·fund (ri fund′ *for 1;* rē′fund *for 2 and 3*), **1** to pay back: *If these shoes do not wear well, the shop will refund your money.* **2** a return of money paid: *When the show had to be called off, refunds were given to ticket holders.* **3** the money paid back: *I put my tax refund in a savings account.* **1** *verb,* **2,3** *noun.*

re·fus·al (ri fyü′zəl), the act of refusing: *a refusal to lend money. noun.*

re·fuse[1] (ri fyüz′), **1** to say no to: *He refuses the offer. The teacher refused me permission to leave class early.* **2** to say no: *She is free to refuse.* **3** to say one will not do, give, or allow something: *They refuse to obey. verb,* **re·fus·es, re·fused, re·fus·ing.**

ref·use[2] (ref′yüs), useless stuff; waste; rubbish: *The street-cleaning department took away all refuse from the streets. noun.*

re·fute (ri fyüt′), to show a claim, opinion, or argument to be false or incorrect: *He refuted the rumor with facts.* verb, **re·futes, re·fut·ed, re·fut·ing.**

re·gain (ri gān′), 1 to get again; recover: *After the illness, she regained her health quickly.* 2 to get back to; reach again: *You can regain the main road by turning left two miles ahead.* verb.

re·gal (rē′gəl), belonging to or fit for a king or queen; splendid; magnificent: *A regal banquet was given for visiting world leaders.* adjective.

re·gale (ri gāl′), to entertain very well; delight with something pleasing: *Grandmother regaled us with exciting stories about her travels in Africa.* verb, **re·gales, re·galed, re·gal·ing.**

re·gard (ri gärd′), 1 to think of; consider: *Our school band is regarded as the best in the state.* 2 to care for; respect: *Please regard the rights of others.* 3 thoughtfulness for others and their feelings; care: *Have regard for the feelings of others.* 4 to look at; look closely at; watch: *The cat regarded me anxiously when I picked up her kittens.* 5 good opinion; esteem: *The teacher has high regard for your ability.* 6 **regards,** good wishes; greetings: *She sends her regards.* 1,2,4 verb, 3,5,6 noun.

re·gard·ing (ri gär′ding), concerning; about: *A letter regarding the field trip to the museum was sent to parents.* preposition.

re·gard·less (ri gärd′lis), with no concern for; in spite of: *The bridge will be built, regardless of the cost.* adjective.

re·gime (ri zhēm′ or rā zhēm′), a system of government or rule: *the Communist regime in China.* noun.

reg·i·ment (rej′ə mənt), the part of an army commanded by a colonel. Two or more battalions make a regiment. noun.

Re·gi·na (ri jī′nə), the capital of Saskatchewan, Canada. noun.

re·gion (rē′jən), 1 any large part of the earth's surface: *the region of the equator.* 2 a place; space; area: *an unhealthful region, a mountainous region.* 3 a part of the body: *the region of the heart.* noun.

re·gion·al (rē′jə nəl), having to do with or in a particular region: *a regional weather forecast.* adjective.

reg·is·ter (rej′ə stər), 1 to write in a list or record: *Register the names of the new pupils.* 2 to have one's name written in a list or record: *You must register before you can vote.* 3 a list; record: *A register of attendance is kept in our school.* 4 a book in which a list or record is kept: *After we signed the hotel register, we were shown to our rooms.* 5 to have a letter, package, or other mail recorded in the post office, paying extra postage for special care in delivering: *She registered the letter containing the check.* 6 a thing that records. A cash register shows the amount of money taken in. 7 to indicate; record: *The thermometer registers 90*

a hat	i it	oi oil	ch child	a in about
ā age	ī ice	ou out	ng long	e in taken
ä far	o hot	u cup	sh she	ə = { i in pencil
e let	ō open	u̇ put	th thin	o in lemon
ē equal	ô order	ü rule	ᴛʜ then	u in circus
ėr term			zh measure	

degrees. 8 to show surprise, joy, anger, or other feeling by the expression on one's face or by actions: *She registered no emotion when I gave her the bad news.* 9 an opening in a wall or floor that has a device to control the amount of air coming from a furnace or central air conditioner. 1,2,5,7,8 verb, 3,4,6,9 noun.

reg·is·tra·tion (rej′ə strā′shən), 1 the act of registering: *Registration of new students is next Monday.* 2 an entry in a register or a document that shows that something is registered: *The police officer asked to see our car registration.* 3 the number of people registered: *Registration for camp is higher than last year.* noun.

re·gret (ri gret′), 1 to feel sorry for or about: *We regretted his absence.* 2 a feeling of being sorry; sorrow; sense of loss: *I left my friends behind with deep regret.* 3 **regrets,** a polite reply refusing an invitation: *She could not come to the party, but she sent regrets.* 1 verb, **re·grets, re·gret·ted, re·gret·ting;** 2,3 noun.

re·gret·ful (ri gret′fəl), sorry; sorrowful; feeling or expressing regret: *I got a regretful letter from him, saying that he could not visit us.* adjective.

re·gret·ta·ble (ri gret′ə bəl), deserving or giving cause for regret: *It is regrettable that our neighborhood school is being closed.* adjective.

reg·u·lar (reg′yə lər), 1 fixed by custom or rule; usual: *Six o'clock was her regular hour of rising.* 2 coming again and again at the same time: *I make regular visits to the dentist.* 3 steady; habitual: *A regular customer trades often at the same store.* 4 well-balanced; even in size, spacing, or speed: *regular teeth, regular breathing.* adjective.

reg·u·lar·i·ty (reg′yə lar′ə tē), a being regular; steadiness: *The seasons come and go with regularity.* noun.

reg·u·late (reg′yə lāt), 1 to control by rule, principle, or system: *The government regulates the coining of money.* 2 to put in condition to work properly: *My watch is losing time; I will have to have it regulated.* 3 to keep at a stated level, amount, or rate; control; adjust: *A thermostat regulates the temperature of the room.* verb, **reg·u·lates, reg·u·lat·ed, reg·u·lat·ing.**

reg·u·la·tion (reg′yə lā′shən), 1 a controlling or a being controlled by rule, principle, or system: *The regulation of trucks that travel between states is carried out by the federal government.* 2 a rule; law: *traffic regulations.* noun.

re·hears·al (ri hėr′səl), a rehearsing; a practicing to prepare for a public performance. noun.

re·hearse (ri hėrs′), to practice for a public performance: *We rehearsed our parts for the play.* verb, **re·hears·es, re·hearsed, re·hears·ing.**

R

reign (rān), **1** the period of power of a ruler: *The queen's reign lasted fifty years.* **2** to rule: *A king reigns over his kingdom.* **3** the act of ruling; royal power: *The reign of a wise ruler benefits the country.* **4** to exist everywhere; prevail: *On a still night silence reigns.* 1,3 *noun,* 2,4 *verb.*

rein (rān), **1** a long, narrow strap or line fastened to a bridle or bit, and used to guide and control an animal. The reins are held in the hands of the driver or rider. **2** a means of control and direction: *When the President was ill, the Vice-President took the reins of government.* **3** to guide and control: *She reined her galloping horse hard to the left, trying to miss a low branch.* 1,2 *noun,* 3 *verb.*

rein·deer (rān′dir′), a large deer with branching antlers that lives in northern regions. It is used to pull sleighs and also for meat, milk, and hides. Reindeer living in North America are called caribou. *noun, plural* **rein·deer.**

re·in·force (rē′in fôrs′), **1** to strengthen with new force or materials: *More supports were added to reinforce the bridge.* **2** to strengthen by adding troops, warships, or planes: *The general reinforced the small force guarding the town.* *verb,* **re·in·forc·es, re·in·forced, re·in·forc·ing.**

re·in·force·ment (rē′in fôrs′mənt), **1** a strengthening; being strengthened: *Reinforcement of the rafters was necessary to repair the roof.* **2** something that strengthens: *I tried to find more facts to use as reinforcements for my argument.* **3** reinforcements, extra soldiers, warships, or planes: *Reinforcements were sent to the battlefield.* *noun.*

re·ject (ri jekt′), **1** to refuse to take; turn down: *She rejected our help. He tried to join the army but was rejected because of poor health.* **2** to throw away: *Reject all apples with soft spots.* *verb.*

re·jec·tion (ri jek′shən), a rejecting or being rejected: *The inspector ordered the rejection of the faulty parts.* *noun.*

re·joice (ri jois′), to be glad; be filled with joy: *I rejoiced to hear of her success.* *verb,* **re·joic·es, re·joiced, re·joic·ing.**

re·join (rē join′), to join again; unite again: *After my telephone conversation, I rejoined my friends in the kitchen.* *verb.*

re·lapse (ri laps′), **1** to fall or slip back into a former state or way of acting: *After one cry of surprise, he relapsed into silence.* **2** a falling or slipping back into a former state or way of acting: *She seemed to be getting over her illness but had a relapse.* 1 *verb,* **re·laps·es, re·lapsed, re·laps·ing;** 2 *noun.*

re·late (ri lāt′), **1** to give an account of; tell: *The traveler related her adventures.* **2** to connect in thought or meaning: *"Better" and "best" are related to "good."* *verb,* **re·lates, re·lat·ed, re·lat·ing.**

re·lat·ed (ri lā′tid), belonging to the same family: *Cousins are related.* *adjective.*

re·la·tion (ri lā′shən), **1** a connection in thought or meaning: *Your answer has no relation to the question.* **2** the connection or dealings between persons, groups, or countries: *The relation of twins is a close one. Our firm has business relations with their firm.* **3** a person who belongs to the same family as another; relative. *noun.*

re·la·tion·ship (ri lā′shən ship), **1** a connection: *What is the relationship of clouds to rain?* **2** the condition of belonging to the same family. **3** the state that exists between people or groups that deal with each other: *I have good relationships with all of my teachers this year.* *noun.*

rel·a·tive (rel′ə tiv), **1** a person who belongs to the same family as another, such as a father, brother, aunt, nephew, or cousin. **2** compared to each other: *We discussed the relative advantages of city and country life.* **3** depending for meaning on a relation to something else: *East is a relative term; for example, Chicago is east of California but west of New York.* 1 *noun,* 2,3 *adjective.*
relative to, 1 about; concerning: *The teacher asked me some questions relative to my plans for the summer.* **2** in comparison with; in proportion to; for: *He is strong relative to his size.*

rel·a·tive·ly (rel′ə tiv lē), in relation to something else; comparatively: *You are relatively tall for your age.* *adverb.*

re·lax (ri laks′), **1** to loosen up; make or become less stiff or firm: *Relax your muscles to rest them. Relax when you dance.* **2** to make or become less strict or severe; lessen in force: *Discipline is relaxed on the last day of school.* **3** to relieve or be relieved from work, effort, or worry: *We relaxed during the holidays. Relax! Everything will be all right.* *verb.*

re·lax·a·tion (rē′lak sā′shən), **1** a loosening: *the relaxation of the muscles.* **2** a lessening of strictness, severity, or force: *the relaxation of discipline over the holidays.* **3** recreation; amusement: *Walking and reading are relaxations.* *noun.*

re·lay (rē′lā *for 1;* rē′lā *or* ri lā′ *for 2*), **1** a fresh supply: *New relays of firefighters were sent in.* **2** to take and carry farther: *Please relay this message to your parents.* 1 *noun,* 2 *verb,* **re·lays, re·layed, re·lay·ing.**

re·lay race (rē′lā rās′), a race in which each member of a team runs or swims only a certain part of the distance.

relay race—The runner on the left is finishing his part of the race. While still running, he hands a thin, metal rod to his teammate on the right.

re·lease (ri lēs′), **1** to let go: *Release the catch and the box will open.* **2** to let loose; set free: *She released him from his promise.* **3** a letting go; setting free: *The end of the war brought the release of the prisoners.* 1,2 *verb,* **re·leas·es, re·leased, re·leas·ing;** 3 *noun.*

re·lent (ri lent′), to become less harsh; be more tender and merciful: *After I pleaded for hours, my parents finally relented and let me go on the trip. verb.*

re·lent·less (ri lent′lis), without pity; not relenting; harsh: *The storm raged all night with relentless fury. adjective.*

rel·e·vant (rel′ə vənt), connected with the matter in hand; to the point: *relevant questions. adjective.*

re·li·a·ble (ri lī′ə bəl), worthy of trust; able to be depended on: *Send her to the bank for the money; she is reliable. adjective.*

re·li·ance (ri lī′əns), trust; confidence: *I have complete reliance in my friend. noun.*

rel·ic (rel′ik), a thing left from the past. *noun.*

relic—These **relics** found in Israel are more than 3000 years old. At the top is a jar; the three pieces below are oil lamps.

re·lief (ri lēf′), **1** the lessening of, or freeing from, a pain, burden, or difficulty: *It was a relief to hear I had passed the exam.* **2** something that lessens or frees from pain, burden, or difficulty; aid; help: *Relief was quickly sent to the sufferers from the great fire.* **3** freedom from a post of duty: *The nurse was on duty all day with only a short period of relief.* **4** someone who relieves another from duty: *The watchman's relief arrives at seven.* **5** a figure or design that stands out from a surface in sculpture, on coins, or the like. *noun.*

on relief, receiving money to live on from public funds: *Many of those who lost their jobs had to go on relief.*

relief map, a map that shows the different heights of a surface by using shading, colors, or solid materials such as clay.

re·lieve (ri lēv′), **1** to make less; make easier; reduce the pain or trouble of: *What will relieve a headache? We telephoned to relieve our parents' uneasiness.* **2** to set free: *Your coming relieves me of writing a long letter.* **3** to free a person on duty by taking his or her place: *The cashier waited for someone to relieve him so he could eat lunch. verb,* **re·lieves, re·lieved, re·liev·ing.**

re·li·gion (ri lij′ən), **1** belief in and worship of God or gods. **2** a particular system of faith and worship: *the Christian religion, the Moslem religion. noun.*

re·li·gious (ri lij′əs), **1** having to do with religion: *religious meetings, religious books, religious differences.* **2** much interested in religion; devoted to religion: *They are a religious family; they pray before each meal. adjective.*

re·lin·quish (ri ling′kwish), to give up; let go: *The small dog relinquished its bone to the big dog. verb.*

relief (definition 5)

rel·ish (rel′ish), **1** something to add flavor to food. Olives and pickles are relishes. **2** liking; enjoyment: *We watched the old movie with great relish.* **3** to like the taste of; like; enjoy: *That cat relishes cream.* 1,2 *noun,* 3 *verb.*

re·load (rē lōd′), to load again. *verb.*

re·luc·tance (ri luk′təns), unwillingness; slowness in action because of unwillingness: *She took part in the game with reluctance. noun.*

a hat	**i** it	**oi** oil	**ch** child	a in about	
ā age	**ī** ice	**ou** out	**ng** long	e in taken	
ä far	**o** hot	**u** cup	**sh** she	ə =	i in pencil
e let	**ō** open	**u̇** put	**th** thin	o in lemon	
ē equal	**ô** order	**ü** rule	**ŦH** then	u in circus	
ėr term			**zh** measure		

re·luc·tant (ri luk′tənt), unwilling; slow to act because unwilling: *The teacher led the reluctant student to the principal. I am reluctant to go out in very cold weather. adjective.*

re·ly (ri lī′), to depend; trust: *Rely on your own efforts. I relied upon your promise. verb,* **re·lies, re·lied, re·ly·ing.**

re·main (ri mān′), **1** to continue in a place; stay: *We shall remain at the lake till September.* **2** to continue; last; keep on: *The town remains the same year after year.* **3** to be left: *A few apples remain on the tree. If you take 2 from 5, 3 remains.* **4 remains, a** what is left: *The remains of the meal were fed to the dog.* **b** a dead body: *Washington's remains are buried at Mount Vernon.* *1-3 verb, 4 noun.*

re·main·der (ri mān′dər), the part left over; rest: *If you take 2 from 9 the remainder is 7. After studying an hour, she spent the remainder of the afternoon playing. noun.*

re·mark (ri märk′), **1** to say in a few words; state; comment: *She remarked that it was a beautiful day.* **2** something said in a few words; short statement: *The president of the club made a few remarks.* *1 verb, 2 noun.*

re·mark·a·ble (ri mär′kə bəl), worthy of notice; unusual: *He has a remarkable memory for names and faces. adjective.*

re·mark·a·bly (ri mär′kə blē), unusually: *The day of the blizzard was remarkably cold. adverb.*

rem·e·dy (rem′ə dē), **1** a means of removing or relieving diseases or any bad condition; cure: *Aspirin is used as a remedy for headaches.* **2** to cure; put right; make right: *A nap remedied my weariness.* *1 noun, plural* **rem·e·dies;** *2 verb,* **rem·e·dies, rem·e·died, rem·e·dy·ing.**

re·mem·ber (ri mem′bər), **1** to call back to mind: *I can't remember that man's name.* **2** to keep in mind; take care not to forget: *Remember me when I am gone.* **3** to keep in mind as deserving a reward or gift; make a gift to: *Uncle remembered us in his will. verb.*

re·mem·brance (ri mem′brəns), **1** the act of remembering; memory: *I hold my old friend in fond remembrance.* **2** a keepsake; any thing or action that makes one remember a person; souvenir. *noun.*

re·mind (ri mīnd′), to make one think of something; cause to remember: *This picture reminds me of a story I heard. verb.*

re·mind·er (ri mīn′dər), something to help one remember: *The notes taped to my mirror are reminders of things I need to do. noun.*

re·mit (ri mit′), **1** to send money to a person or place: *Please remit payment as soon as possible.* **2** to stop from carrying out; cancel: *The governor is remitting the prisoner's punishment.* **3** to make less; decrease: *After we had rowed the boat into calm water, we remitted our efforts. verb,* **re·mits, re·mit·ted, re·mit·ting.**

rem·nant (rem′nənt), a small part left: *a remnant of silk. This town has only a remnant of its former population. noun.*

re·mod·el (rē mod′l), to make over; change or alter: *The old barn was remodeled into a house. verb.*

re·morse (ri môrs′), a deep, painful regret for having done wrong: *I felt remorse for hurting my friend's feelings, so I apologized. noun.*

re·mote (ri mōt′), **1** far away; far off: *The North Pole is a remote part of the world.* **2** out of the way; secluded: *Mail comes to this remote village only once a week.* **3** distant: *She is a remote relative; a third cousin, to be exact.* **4** slight; faint: *I haven't the remotest idea what you mean. adjective,* **re·mot·er, re·mot·est.**

re·mov·al (ri mü′vəl), **1** a taking away: *We made arrangements for the removal of the dead tree.* **2** a change of place: *The store announced its removal to larger quarters. noun.*

re·move (ri müv′), **1** to move from a place or position; take off; take away: *Remove your hat.* **2** to get rid of; put an end to: *The demonstration removed any doubts we had about the invention's usefulness.* **3** to dismiss from an office or position: *The mayor removed the chief of police for failing to do his duty. verb,* **re·moves, re·moved, re·mov·ing.**

re·name (rē nām′), to give a new name to; name again: *They bought a used boat and renamed it "Seagull." verb,* **re·names, re·named, re·nam·ing.**

rend (rend), to pull apart violently; tear; split: *Lightning rent the tree. verb,* **rends, rent, rend·ing.**

ren·der (ren′dər), **1** to cause to become; make: *Fright rendered me speechless.* **2** to give; do: *to render a suggestion. She rendered us a great service by her help.* **3** to play or sing music. *verb.*

ren·dez·vous (rän′də vü), an appointment to meet at a fixed place or time; meeting by agreement: *A rendezvous in orbit was planned for the two spacecraft. noun, plural* **ren·dez·vous** (rän′də vüz).

ren·e·gade (ren′ə gād), a deserter from a religious faith, political party, or other group; traitor. *noun.*

re·new (ri nü′ *or* ri nyü′), **1** to make new again; make like new; restore: *Rain renews the greenness of the fields.* **2** to begin again; say, do, or give again: *She renewed her efforts to fix the broken bicycle.* **3** to replace with new material or a new thing of the same sort; fill again: *to renew a prescription. The well renews itself no matter how much water is taken away.* **4** to give or get for a new period: *We renewed the lease for another year. verb.*

re·new·al (ri nü′əl *or* ri nyü′əl), a renewing or being renewed: *When hot weather comes, there will be a renewal of interest in swimming. noun.*

re·nounce (ri nouns′), **1** to give up; give up entirely; declare that one gives up: *He renounces his claim to the money.* **2** to cast off; refuse to recognize as one's own: *The people renounced the dictator. verb,* **re·nounc·es, re·nounced, re·nounc·ing.**

renovate—They are **renovating** the building.

a hat	i it	oi oil	ch child		a in about
ā age	ī ice	ou out	ng long		e in taken
ä far	o hot	u cup	sh she	ə =	i in pencil
e let	ō open	u̇ put	th thin		o in lemon
ē equal	ô order	ü rule	ᴛH then		u in circus
ėr term			zh measure		

ren·o·vate (ren′ə vāt), to make like new; restore to good condition. *verb,* **ren·o·vates, ren·o·vat·ed, ren·o·vat·ing.**

re·nown (ri noun′), fame: *A doctor who finds a cure for a disease wins renown. noun.*

re·nowned (ri nound′), famous: *a renowned scientist. adjective.*

rent[1] (rent), **1** the money paid for the use of property: *My apartment is small, but the rent is low.* **2** to pay for the use of property: *Her parents rented a movie for her party.* **3** to receive money for the use of property: *The hardware store rents some tools.* **4** to be rented: *This car rents for $20 a day.* **1** *noun,* **2-4** *verb.*

for rent, available in return for rent paid: *That vacant apartment is for rent.*

rent[2] (rent), **1** a torn place; tear; split: *There is a rent in your pants.* **2** See **rend.** *The tree was rent by the wind.* **1** *noun,* **2** *verb.*

rent·al (ren′tl), an amount received or paid as rent: *The yearly rental of her house is $5000. noun.*

re·o·pen (rē ō′pən), **1** to open again: *School will reopen in September.* **2** to discuss again or further: *The matter is settled and cannot be reopened. verb.*

re·or·gan·ize (rē ôr′gə nīz), to organize anew; form again; arrange in a new way: *Classes will be reorganized after the first four weeks of school.* *verb,* **re·or·gan·iz·es, re·or·gan·ized, re·or·gan·iz·ing.**

re·paid (ri pād′). See **repay.** *I repaid the money I had borrowed. All debts should be repaid. verb.*

re·pair (ri per′ *or* ri par′), **1** to put in good condition again; mend: *He repairs shoes.* **2** an act of repairing or the work of repairing: *Repairs on the school building are made during the summer.* **3** a condition; state; shape: *The house was in very bad repair.* **1** *verb,* **2,3** *noun.*

re·pair·man (ri per′man′ *or* ri par′man′), a person whose work is repairing something. *noun, plural* **re·pair·men.**

rep·a·ra·tion (rep′ə rā′shən), a giving of compensation for wrong or injury done: *France demanded reparations from Germany after World War I. noun.*

re·past (ri past′), a meal; food: *Breakfast at our house is a light repast. noun.*

re·pay (ri pā′), **1** to pay back; give back: *When can you repay me? She repaid the money she had borrowed.* **2** to make return for: *No thanks can repay such kindness.* **3** to make return to: *The boy's success repaid the teacher for her efforts. verb,* **re·pays, re·paid, re·pay·ing.**

re·peal (ri pēl′), **1** to take back; withdraw; do away with: *The law was finally repealed.* **2** the act of repealing; withdrawal; abolition: *He voted for the repeal of that law.* **1** *verb,* **2** *noun.*

re·peat (ri pēt′), **1** to do or make again: *to repeat an error.* **2** to say again: *to repeat a word for emphasis.* **3** to say over; recite: *She can repeat many poems from memory.* **4** to tell to another or others: *I promised not to repeat the secret.* **5** a thing repeated: *a television repeat.* **1-4** *verb,* **5** *noun.*

re·peat·ed (ri pē′tid), said, done, or made more than once: *Her repeated efforts at last won success. adjective.*

re·pel (ri pel′), **1** to force back; drive back; drive away: *They repelled the enemy attack.* **2** to keep off or out: *Rubber repels moisture.* **3** to force apart or away: *The like poles of two magnets repel each other.* **4** to be displeasing to; cause dislike in: *Spiders and worms repel me. verb,* **re·pels, re·pelled, re·pel·ling.**

re·pel·lent (ri pel′ənt), anything that repels: *We sprayed ourselves with insect repellent to protect ourselves from the mosquitoes. noun.*

re·pent (ri pent′), **1** to feel sorry for doing wrong and seek forgiveness: *The thief repented.* **2** to feel sorry for; regret: *They bought a white rug and repented their choice. verb.*

re·pent·ant (ri pen′tənt), feeling regret; sorry for doing wrong. *adjective.*

rep·e·ti·tion (rep′ə tish′ən), a repeating; doing again; saying again: *Repetition helps learning. Any repetition of the offense will be punished. noun.*

re·place (ri plās′), **1** to fill or take the place of: *A substitute replaced our teacher.* **2** to get another in place of: *I will replace the cup I broke.* **3** to put back; put in place again: *Replace the books on the shelves. verb,* **re·plac·es, re·placed, re·plac·ing.**

re·place·ment (ri plās′mənt), **1** a replacing or being replaced: *The law required the replacement of all wooden freight cars by steel cars.* **2** something or someone that replaces: *She is a replacement for our usual shortstop. noun.*

re·play (rē plā′ *for 1;* rē′plā′ *for 2 and 3*), **1** to play something again. **2** something, such as a game, played again. **3** a showing again of a videotape recording of a part of a game broadcast on television: *We saw the touchdown again on the replay.* **1** *verb,* **2,3** *noun.*

re·plen·ish (ri plen′ish), to fill again; provide a

R

new supply for: *Once our natural resources are used up, we cannot replenish them.* verb.

rep·li·ca (rep′lə kə), a copy; reproduction: *The young artist made a replica of the famous painting.* noun.

re·ply (ri plī′), **1** to answer by words or action: *He replied with a shout. The enemy replied to the attack with heavy gun fire.* **2** something said or done as an answer: *I didn't hear your reply to the question.* **1** verb, **re·plies, re·plied, re·ply·ing;** **2** noun, plural **re·plies.**

re·port (ri pôrt′), **1** a statement or description, especially one that is public or formal: *My mother wrote a report for her company on how to increase sales.* **2** to make a report of; make known; tell: *The radio reports the news and weather. The treasurer of our club reports that all dues are paid.* **3** to present oneself: *Report for work at eight o'clock.* **1** noun, **2,3** verb.

report card, a written report sent regularly by a school to parents or guardians, giving information on a student's work and behavior.

re·port·er (ri pôr′tər), a person who gathers and reports news for a newspaper, magazine, or radio or television station. noun.

re·pose (ri pōz′), **1** rest; sleep. **2** to lie at rest: *The cat reposed upon the cushion.* **1** noun, **2** verb, **re·pos·es, re·posed, re·pos·ing.**

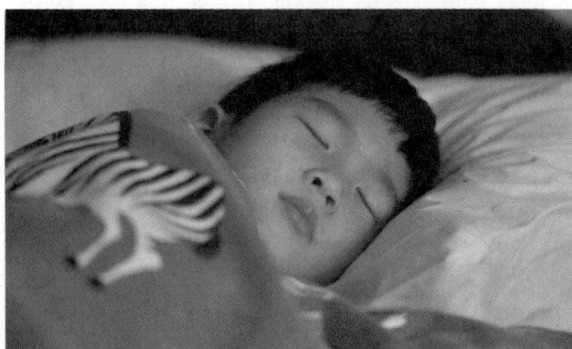

repose (definition 1)—Do not disturb his **repose.**

rep·re·sent (rep′ri zent′), **1** to stand for; be a sign or symbol of. **2** to act in place of; speak and act for: *Elected officials represent the voters.* **3** to show in a picture; give a likeness of; portray: *This painting represents the signing of the Declaration of Independence.* verb.

rep·re·sen·ta·tion (rep′ri zen tā′shən), **1** the act of representing. **2** the condition or fact of being represented: *"Taxation without representation is tyranny."* **3** a likeness; picture; model. noun.

rep·re·sent·a·tive (rep′ri zen′tə tiv), **1** a person appointed or elected to act or speak for others: *He is the club's representative at the convention.* **2 Representative,** a member of the House of Representatives. **3** having its citizens represented by chosen persons: *a representative government.* **4** serving as an example of; typical: *Oak and maple are representative American hardwoods.* **1,2** noun, **3,4** adjective.

re·press (ri pres′), to prevent from acting; check: *She repressed an impulse to cough.* verb.

re·pres·sion (ri presh′ən), a preventing from action; checking: *The repression of a laugh made him choke.* noun.

re·proach (ri prōch′), to blame: *They reproached me for being late.* verb.

re·proach·ful (ri prōch′fəl), full of blame; expressing disapproval: *a reproachful look.* adjective.

re·pro·duce (rē′prə düs′ or rē′prə dyüs′), **1** to make a copy of: *Can you reproduce my handwriting?* **2** to produce offspring: *Most plants reproduce by seeds.* verb, **re·pro·duc·es, re·pro·duced, re·pro·duc·ing.**

re·pro·duc·tion (rē′prə duk′shən), **1** a reproducing; being reproduced: *the reproduction of sounds by a phonograph.* **2** a copy: *a reproduction of a famous painting.* **3** the process by which living things produce offspring. noun.

reproduction (definition 2)—The girl has a small **reproduction** of a jet plane.

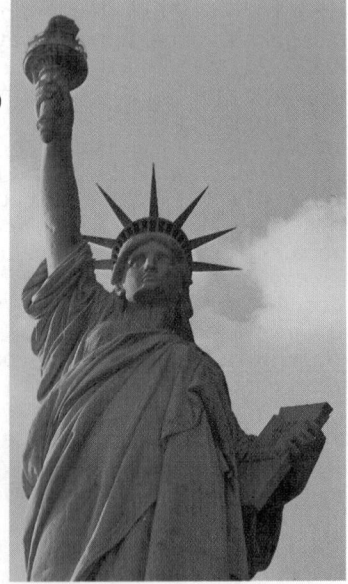

represent (definition 1) The statue of Liberty **represents** freedom.

re·proof (ri prüf′), words of blame or disapproval; blame. *noun.*

re·prove (ri prüv′), to find fault with; scold: *I reproved the children for teasing the cat. verb,* **re·proves, re·proved, re·prov·ing.**

rep·tile (rep′tīl *or* rep′təl), one of a group of cold-blooded animals that have backbones and lungs and are usually covered with scales. Snakes, lizards, turtles, alligators, and crocodiles are reptiles. *noun.*
[*Reptile* comes from a Latin word meaning "to crawl" or "to creep."]

re·pub·lic (ri pub′lik), **1** a government in which the citizens elect representatives to manage the government, which is usually headed by a president. **2** a nation or state that has such a government. The United States and Mexico are republics. *noun.*
[*Republic* comes from two Latin words meaning "public thing," that is, something that belongs to the people.]

re·pub·li·can (ri pub′lə kən), **1** of a republic; like that of a republic: *Many countries have a republican form of government.* **2** a person who favors a republic: *The republicans fought to overthrow the king.* **3 Republican, a** of the Republican Party. **b** a member of the Republican Party. 1,3a *adjective,* 2,3b *noun.*

Republican Party, one of the two main political parties in the United States.

re·pulse (ri puls′), to drive back; repel: *Our soldiers repulsed the enemy. verb,* **re·puls·es, re·pulsed, re·puls·ing.**

re·pul·sive (ri pul′siv), causing disgust or strong dislike: *the repulsive smell of a skunk. adjective.*

rep·u·ta·ble (rep′yə tə bəl), having a good reputation; well thought of: *a reputable citizen. adjective.*

rep·u·ta·tion (rep′yə tā′shən), **1** what people think and say the character of a person or thing is; character in the opinion of others; name: *This store has an excellent reputation for fair dealing.* **2** a good name; good reputation: *Cheating at the game ruined that player's reputation. noun.*

re·pute (ri pyüt′), **1** reputation: *This is a district of bad repute because there are so many robberies here.* **2** to consider; suppose; suppose to be: *He is reputed the richest man in the city.* 1 *noun,* 2 *verb,* **re·putes, re·put·ed, re·put·ing.**

re·quest (ri kwest′), **1** to ask for; ask as a favor: *She requested a loan from her friend.* **2** to ask: *He requested her to go with him.* **3** the act of asking: *Your request for a ticket was made too late.* **4** what is asked for: *She granted my request.* 1,2 *verb,* 3,4 *noun.*

re·quire (ri kwīr′), **1** to need: *We require more spoons for our party.* **2** to demand; order; command: *The rules required us all to be present. verb,* **re·quires, re·quired, re·quir·ing.**

re·quire·ment (ri kwīr′mənt), **1** a need; thing needed: *Patience is a requirement in teaching.* **2** a demand; thing demanded: *That school has a requirement that students wear uniforms. noun.*

reptiles

re·ran (rē ran′). See **rerun.** *They ran a mile yesterday and reran the same distance today. verb.*

re·read (rē rēd′), to read again: *to reread a good book. verb,* **re·reads, re·read** (rē red′), **re·read·ing.**

re·run (rē run′ for 1; rē′run′ for 2), **1** to run again: *The race was a tie and had to be rerun.* **2** a television program or motion-picture film that is shown again. 1 *verb,* **re·runs, re·ran, re·run, re·run·ning;** 2 *noun.*

res·cue (res′kyü), **1** to save from danger, capture, or harm; free; deliver: *to rescue someone from drowning.* **2** a saving or freeing from harm or danger: *The fireman was praised for his brave rescue of the children in the burning house. A dog was chasing our cat when your sister came to the rescue.* 1 *verb,* **res·cues, res·cued, res·cu·ing;** 2 *noun.*

res·cu·er (res′kyü ər), one that rescues. *noun.*

re·search (ri sėrch′ *or* rē′sėrch′), **1** a careful hunting for facts or truth; inquiry; investigation: *Medical research has done much to lessen disease.* **2** to hunt for facts or truth about; investigate: *My father is researching the history of our family.* 1 *noun, plural* **re·search·es;** 2 *verb.*

re·sem·blance (re zem′bləns), likeness; similar appearance: *Twins often show great resemblance. noun.*

R

resemble—The domes on this building **resemble** onions.

re·sem·ble (ri zem′bəl), to be like; be similar to. *verb*, **re·sem·bles, re·sem·bled, re·sem·bling.**

re·sent (ri zent′), to feel injured and angry at; feel bitter and annoyed about: *I resent the lies you have been telling about me. verb.*

re·sent·ful (ri zent′fəl), feeling resentment; injured and angry; showing resentment. *adjective.*

re·sent·ment (ri zent′mənt), the feeling that one has at being injured or insulted; anger; bitterness: *Everyone feels resentment at being treated unfairly. noun.*

res·er·va·tion (rez′ər vā′shən), **1** a doubt, especially one not expressed: *I did not mention it, but I had reservations about staying out so late.* **2** a limiting condition: *We accepted the plan completely, without reservations.* **3** land set aside by the government for a special purpose: *an Indian reservation.* **4** an arrangement to have a room, a seat, or the like held in advance for one's use later on: *to make a reservation for a room at a motel. noun.*

re·serve (ri zėrv′), **1** to keep back; keep to oneself: *Mother reserved judgment until she had heard both sides of the argument.* **2** to set apart: *He reserves his evenings to spend them with his family.* **3** to save for use later: *Reserve enough money for your fare home.* **4** to arrange to have set aside for the use of a particular person or persons: *to reserve a table at a restaurant.* **5** something kept back for future use; store: *a reserve of food or energy. Banks must keep a reserve of money.* **6 reserves,** members of the armed forces not assigned to duty, but ready to serve when needed: *The reserves will be sent to help the soldiers fighting at the front.* **7** a silent manner that keeps people from making friends easily. 1-4 *verb,* **re·serves, re·served, re·serv·ing;** 5-7 *noun.*

re·served (ri zėrvd′), **1** kept back; set apart: *a reserved seat at a football game.* **2** inclined to keep to oneself: *A reserved person does not make friends easily. adjective.*

res·er·voir (rez′ər vwär), a place where water is collected and stored for use. *noun.*

reservoir

re·side (ri zīd′), to live in or at a place for a long time; dwell: *This family has resided in our town for 100 years. verb,* **re·sides, re·sid·ed, re·sid·ing.**

res·i·dence (rez′ə dəns), **1** a house or home; the place where a person lives: *The President's residence is the White House in Washington, D.C.* **2** a residing; living; dwelling: *Long residence in France made them very fond of the French.* **3** the period of residing in a place: *They spent a residence of ten years in France. noun.*

res·i·dent (rez′ə dənt), a person living in a place, not a visitor: *The residents of the town are proud of its new library. noun.*

res·i·den·tial (rez′ə den′shəl), of or having something to do with homes; suitable for homes or residences: *They live in a large residential district outside the city. adjective.*

res·i·due (rez′ə dü or rez′ə dyü), what remains after a part is taken; remainder: *The syrup had dried up, leaving a sticky residue. noun.*

re·sign (ri zīn′), to give up a job, office, or position: *The editor resigned her position on the school paper. verb.*

resign oneself, to submit quietly; yield: *He had to resign himself to a week in bed when he hurt his back.*

res·ig·na·tion (rez′ig nā′shən), the act of resigning: *There have been so many resignations from the committee that a new one must be formed. noun.*

re·signed (ri zīnd′), accepting what comes without complaint. *adjective.*

res·in (rez′n), a sticky, yellow or brown

substance that flows from some trees. Resin is used in medicine and in varnishes and plastics. *noun.*

re·sist (ri zist′), **1** to act against; fight against; oppose: *She resisted the plan to close our neighborhood library.* **2** to keep from doing something; struggle successfully against: *I could not resist laughing.* **3** to withstand the action or effect of: *A healthy body resists disease. verb.*

re·sist·ance (ri zis′təns), **1** the act of resisting: *The bank clerk made no resistance to the robbers.* **2** the power to resist: *Some people have very little resistance to colds.* **3** an opposition; opposing force; thing or act that resists: *Air resistance makes a feather fall more slowly than a pin. noun.*

re·sist·ant (ri zis′tənt), resisting. *adjective.*

res·o·lute (rez′ə lüt), determined; firm: *She was resolute in her attempt to climb to the top of the mountain. adjective.*

res·o·lu·tion (rez′ə lü′shən), **1** a decision; making up one's mind to do or not do something: *He made a resolution to get up early.* **2** the power of holding firmly to a purpose; determination: *The pioneers' resolution overcame their hardships. noun.*

re·solve (ri zolv′), **1** to make up one's mind; determine; decide: *I resolved to do better work in the future.* **2** to answer and explain; solve: *Their letter resolved all our doubts. verb,* **re·solves, re·solved, re·solv·ing.**

re·solved (ri zolvd′), determined; firm; resolute. *adjective.*

res·o·nant (rez′n ənt), full; rich; vibrating: *The singer's resonant voice filled the auditorium. adjective.*

re·sort (ri zôrt′), **1** a place people go to for recreation: *There are many summer resorts in the mountains.* **2** to turn for help: *When discussion doesn't solve a problem, some people resort to arguing and even fighting.* **3** a person or thing turned to for help: *Friends are the best resort in trouble.* **1,3** *noun,* **2** *verb.*

re·sound (ri zound′), **1** to sound loudly: *TVs resound from every apartment.* **2** to be filled with sound: *The room resounded with the children's shouts. verb.*

re·source (ri sôrs′ *or* rē′sôrs), **1** any supply that will meet a need. We have resources of money, of knowledge, and of strength. **2 resources,** the actual and possible wealth of a country: *natural resources, human resources.* **3** any means of getting success or getting out of trouble: *Climbing a tree is a cat's resource when chased by a dog. noun.*

re·source·ful (ri sôrs′fəl), good at thinking of ways to do things. *adjective.*

re·spect (ri spekt′), **1** honor; esteem: *The children always showed great respect for their grandparents.* **2** to feel or show honor or esteem for: *We respect an honest person.* **3** care; consideration: *We should show respect for school buildings, parks, and other public property.* **4** to care for; show consideration for: *Respect the ideas and feelings of others.* **5 respects,** expressions of

respect; regards: *Give them my respects. We must pay our respects to the governor.* **6** a feature; point; matter; detail: *The plan is unwise in many respects.* **7** relation; reference: *We must plan with respect to the future.* **1,3,5-7** *noun,* **2,4** *verb.*

re·spect·a·ble (ri spek′tə bəl), **1** worthy of respect; having a good reputation: *They are very respectable people.* **2** fairly good; moderate in size or quality: *His record in school was always respectable, but never brilliant.* **3** good enough to use; fit to be seen: *respectable clothes. adjective.*

re·spect·ful (ri spekt′fəl), showing respect; polite: *I always try to be respectful to older people. adjective.*

re·spec·tive (ri spek′tiv), belonging to each; particular; individual: *The classes went to their respective rooms. adjective.*

re·spec·tive·ly (ri spek′tiv lē), each in turn or in the order mentioned: *Pat, José, and Kathy are 6, 8, and 10 years old, respectively. adverb.*

res·pi·ra·tion (res′pə rā′shən), act of breathing in and out: *A bad cold can make respiration difficult. noun.*

res·pi·ra·tor (res′pə rā′tər), a device used to help a person breathe. Respirators are used in giving artificial respiration. *noun.*

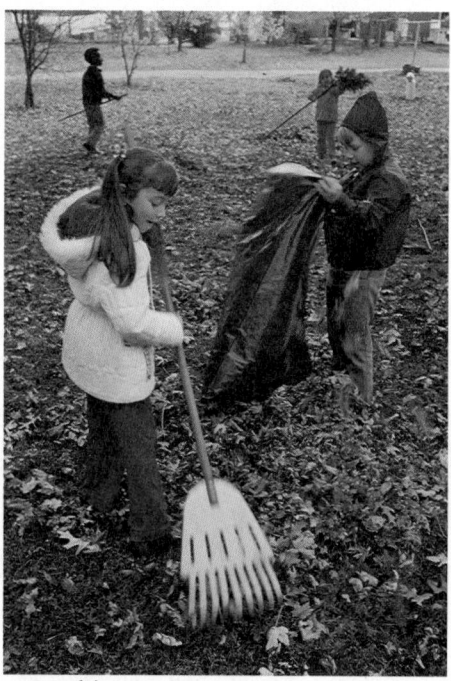

resourceful
The **resourceful** children raked leaves to earn money.

res·pir·a·to·ry (res′pər ə tôr′ē), having something to do with breathing. The lungs are respiratory organs. *adjective.*

res·pite (res′pit), a time of relief and rest; lull: *A thick cloud brought a respite from the glare of the sun. noun.*

re·splend·ent (ri splen′dənt), very bright; shining; splendid: *a face resplendent with joy. adjective.*

re·spond (ri spond′), 1 to answer; reply: *He responded briefly to the question.* 2 to act in answer; react: *A dog responds to kind treatment by loving its owner. She responded quickly to the medicine and was well in a few days. verb.*

re·sponse (ri spons′), 1 an answer by word or act: *Her response to my letter was prompt. She laughed in response to his joke.* 2 a reaction by a living thing to some change in its surroundings: *When you step into a bright light, the pupils of your eyes grow smaller in response. noun.*

re·spon·si·bil·i·ty (ri spon′sə bil′ə tē), 1 a being responsible; sense of duty: *We agreed to share responsibility for planning the party.* 2 a thing for which one is responsible: *Keeping my room clean and feeding the cat are my responsibilities. noun, plural* **re·spon·si·bil·i·ties.**

re·spon·si·ble (ri spon′sə bəl), 1 having the duty or obligation of taking care of someone or something: *You are responsible for keeping your room cleaned up.* 2 being the cause; being the reason: *Rain was responsible for the small attendance.* 3 trustworthy; reliable: *The class chose a responsible pupil to take care of its money.* 4 involving duties or obligations: *The President holds a very responsible position. adjective.*

re·spon·sive (ri spon′siv), 1 making answer; responding: *a responsive glance.* 2 easily moved; responding readily: *Pets are responsive to kindness. adjective.*

rest¹ (rest), 1 sleep: *The children had a good night's rest.* 2 to be still or quiet; sleep: *Lie down and rest.* 3 ease after work or effort; freedom from trouble, pain, or the like: *After mowing the lawn, I needed rest.* 4 a time of ease and freedom from activity or trouble: *I left the swimming pool for a short rest.* 5 to be free from work, effort, care, or trouble: *Some people like to rest on weekends.* 6 an absence of motion; stillness: *The ball came to rest at her feet. The lake was at rest.* 7 to give ease to; refresh by stillness: *Stop and rest your horse.* 8 to place or be placed for support; lie; lay; lean: *He rested his rake against the fence. The roof of the porch rests on columns.* 9 a support; something to lean on: *A barber's chair often has a rest for the feet.* 10 to look; be fixed: *Our eyes rested on the open book.* 11 a pause in music. 12 a mark to show such a pause. 1,3,4,6,9,11,12 *noun,* 2,5,7,8,10 *verb.*

rest² (rest), 1 what is left; those that are left: *The sun was out in the morning but it rained for the rest of the day. One horse was running ahead of the rest.* 2 to continue to be; remain: *The final decision rests with you.* 1 *noun,* 2 *verb.*

res·taur·ant (res′tər ənt *or* res′tə ränt′), a place to buy and eat a meal. *noun.*

[The word *restaurant* was borrowed from a French word. It can be traced back to a Latin word meaning "to restore." The idea is that in a restaurant one can restore one's strength by eating. The English word *restore* comes from the same Latin word.]

rest·ful (rest′fəl), 1 full of rest; giving rest: *She had a restful nap.* 2 quiet; peaceful. *adjective.*

rest·less (rest′lis), 1 unable to rest; not still or quiet; uneasy: *The dog was restless, as if it sensed some danger.* 2 without rest or sleep; not restful: *The sick child passed a restless night. adjective.*

res·to·ra·tion (res′tə rā′shən), 1 a bringing back to a former condition: *the restoration of order after rioting.* 2 something restored: *The house we slept in was a restoration of a colonial mansion. noun.*

re·store (ri stôr′), 1 to bring back; establish again: *The police restored order.* 2 to bring back to a former condition or to a normal condition: *The old house has been restored. He is restored to health.* 3 to give back; put back: *She restored the money she had found to its owner. verb,* **re·stores, re·stored, re·stor·ing.**

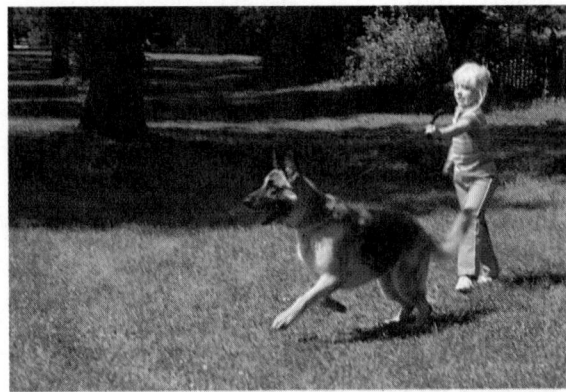

restrain
She had a hard time **restraining** the large dog.

re·strain (ri strān′), to hold back; keep down; keep in check; keep within limits: *I could not restrain my curiosity to see what was in the box. We restrained the excited dog when guests came. verb.*

[*Restrain* comes from a Latin word meaning "to tie tightly" or "to bind fast." Another English word, *restrict,* comes from the same Latin word.]

| WHOLE | HALF | QUARTER | EIGHTH | SIXTEENTH |

rest¹ (definition 12)—different types of **rests**

re·straint (ri strānt′), a restraining or being restrained: *Violent people sometimes need restraint. noun.*

re·strict (ri strikt′), to keep within limits; confine:

Our club membership is restricted to only twelve people. verb.

re·stric·tion (ri strik′shən), **1** something that restricts; limiting condition or rule: *The restrictions on the use of the playground are: No fighting; no damaging property.* **2** a restricting or being restricted: *This park is open to the public without restriction. noun.*

rest room, a washroom or bathroom in a public building.

re·sult (ri zult′), **1** what happens because of something; outcome: *The result of the fall was a broken leg.* **2** a good or useful effect: *The new medicine got results.* **3** to happen because of something: *Sickness may result from eating spoiled food.* **4** to have as a consequence; end: *Eating spoiled food may result in sickness.* **1,2** *noun,* **3,4** *verb.*

re·sume (ri züm′), **1** to begin again; go on: *Resume reading where we left off.* **2** to take again: *Those standing may resume their seats. verb,* **re·sumes, re·sumed, re·sum·ing.**

re·sump·tion (ri zump′shən), a resuming: *the resumption of duties after absence. noun.*

res·ur·rec·tion (rez′ə rek′shən), **1** a coming to life again; rising from the dead. **2 Resurrection,** the rising again of Jesus after His death and burial. *noun.*

re·tail (rē′tāl), **1** the sale of goods in small quantities directly to the user: *Our grocer buys at wholesale and sells at retail.* **2** having to do with sale in small quantities: *a retail merchant, a retail price of $40.* **3** to sell or be sold in small quantities: *They retail these jackets at $30 each.* **1** *noun,* **2** *adjective,* **3** *verb.*

re·tain (ri tān′), **1** to continue to have or hold; keep: *A china teapot retains heat for quite a long time. Our baseball team retained a lead throughout the game.* **2** to hire by payment of a fee: *I retained the best lawyer in the state. verb.*

re·tal·i·ate (ri tal′ē āt), to pay back a wrong or injury; return like for like, usually to return evil for evil: *If we insult them, they will retaliate. verb,* **re·tal·i·ates, re·tal·i·at·ed, re·tal·i·at·ing.**

re·tard·ed (ri tär′did), slow in mental development. *adjective.*

re·tell (rē tel′), to tell again: *The story was better when she retold it than when we heard it the first time. verb,* **re·tells, re·told, re·tel·ing.**

ret·i·na (ret′n ə), a lining at the back of the eyeball that is sensitive to light and receives the images of things looked at. *noun.*

re·tire (ri tīr′), **1** to give up an office or occupation: *Our teachers retire at 65.* **2** to go back; retreat: *The enemy retired before the advance of our troops.* **3** to go to bed: *We retire early. verb,* **re·tires, re·tired, re·tir·ing.**

re·tired (ri tīrd′), withdrawn from one's occupation or office: *a retired teacher. adjective.*

re·tire·ment (ri tīr′mənt), a retiring; withdrawal: *The teacher's retirement from teaching was regretted by the school. noun.*

re·tir·ing (ri tī′ring), shrinking from society or

a hat	i it	oi oil	ch child	a in about
ā age	ī ice	ou out	ng long	e in taken
ä far	o hot	u cup	sh she	ə = i in pencil
e let	ō open	u̇ put	th thin	o in lemon
ē equal	ô order	ü rule	ŦH then	u in circus
ėr term			zh measure	

publicity; shy: *Our neighbor is a quiet, retiring person. adjective.*

re·told (rē tōld′). See retell. *He has retold the same joke three times today. verb.*

re·tort (ri tôrt′), **1** to reply quickly or sharply: *"It's none of your business," he retorted.* **2** a sharp or witty reply: *"Why are your teeth so sharp?" asked Red Ridinghood. "The better to eat you with," was the wolf's retort.* **1** *verb,* **2** *noun.*

re·trace (ri trās′), to go back over: *We retraced our steps to where we started. verb,* **re·trac·es, re·traced, re·trac·ing.**

re·tract (ri trakt′), **1** to draw back or in: *The dog snarled and retracted its lips.* **2** to withdraw; take back: *to retract an offer, to retract an opinion. verb.*

re·treat (ri trēt′), **1** to go back; move back; withdraw: *The enemy retreated before the advance of our soldiers.* **2** the act of going back or withdrawing: *The army's retreat was orderly.* **3** a signal for retreat: *The drums beat a retreat.* **4** a safe, quiet place; place of rest or refuge: *She went to her mountain retreat for the weekend.* **1** *verb,* **2-4** *noun.*

re·trieve (ri trēv′), **1** to get again; recover: *to retrieve a lost pocketbook.* **2** to find and bring back killed or wounded game: *Some dogs can be trained to retrieve game. verb,* **re·trieves, re·trieved, re·triev·ing.**

re·triev·er (ri trē′vər), a dog of any of various breeds that can be trained to find killed or wounded game and bring it to a hunter. *noun.*

re·turn (ri tėrn′), **1** to go back; come back; happen again: *Return home at once. My sister will return this summer.* **2** a going back; coming back; happening again: *We look forward all winter to our return to the country. We wish you many happy returns of your birthday.* **3** to bring back; give back; send back; put back; pay back: *Return that book to the library. I left a message for her to return my telephone call.* **4** a bringing back; giving back; sending back; putting back; paying back: *Such bad behavior was a poor return for kindness.* **5** profit; amount received: *The returns from the sale were more than a hundred dollars.* **6** a report; account: *The election returns are all in. I must make out my income-tax return.* **7** to report or announce officially: *The jury returned a verdict of guilty.* **8** of or for a return: *a return ticket to the point of starting.* **1,3,7** *verb,* **2,4-6** *noun,* **8** *adjective.*

in return, as a return: *If you let me use your skates, I'll lend you my skis in return.*

re·un·ion (rē yü′nyən), a coming together again: *We have a family reunion at Thanksgiving. noun.*

re·u·nite (rē′yü nīt′), to bring together again; come together again: *The two friends were reunited after a long separation.* verb, **re·u·nites, re·u·nit·ed, re·u·nit·ing.**

Rev., Reverend.

re·veal (ri vēl′), 1 to make known: *Promise never to reveal my secret.* 2 to display; show: *His smile revealed his even white teeth.* verb.

rev·eil·le (rev′ə lē), a signal on a bugle or drum to waken members of the armed forces in the morning: *The bugler blew reveille.* noun.
[*Reveille* comes from a French word meaning "wake up!"]

rev·el (rev′əl), 1 to take great pleasure: *The children revel in country life.* 2 a noisy good time; merrymaking: *A parade and fireworks were planned for the Fourth of July revels.* 3 to make merry. 1,3 verb, **rev·els, rev·eled, rev·el·ing;** 2 noun.

rev·e·la·tion (rev′ə lā′shən), 1 the act of making known: *We all waited for the revelation of the winner's name.* 2 a thing made known: *Her true nature was a revelation to me.* noun.

re·venge (ri venj′), 1 harm done in return for a wrong; vengeance; returning evil for evil: *a blow struck in revenge.* 2 to do harm in return for: *I will revenge that insult.* 1 noun, 2 verb, **re·veng·es, re·venged, re·veng·ing.**
be revenged or **revenge oneself,** to get revenge: *He swore to be revenged for the wrongs done to him.*

rev·e·nue (rev′ə nü or rev′ə nyü), money coming in; income: *The government got much revenue from taxes last year.* noun.

re·vere (ri vir′), to love and respect deeply; honor greatly; show reverence for: *People revered the great saint.* verb, **re·veres, re·vered, re·ver·ing.**

rev·er·ence (rev′ər əns), a feeling of deep respect, mixed with wonder, fear, and love. noun.

Rev·er·end (rev′ər ənd), a title for members of the clergy: *The Reverend Thomas A. Johnson.* adjective.

rev·er·ent (rev′ər ənt), feeling reverence; showing reverence: *a reverent prayer.* adjective.

rev·er·ie (rev′ər ē), dreamy thoughts; dreamy thinking of pleasant things: *She was so lost in reverie that she did not hear the bell ring and was late for class.* noun.

re·verse (ri vėrs′), 1 the opposite or contrary: *She did the reverse of what I suggested.* 2 turned backward; opposite or contrary in position or direction: *Play the reverse side of that phonograph record.* 3 the back: *His name is on the reverse of the medal.* 4 to turn the other way; turn inside out; turn upside down: *Reverse your order in line.* 5 an arrangement of gears that reverses the movement of machinery: *Put the car in reverse and back up.* 6 to change to the opposite; repeal: *The higher court reversed the lower court's decision.* 7 a change to bad fortune; setback: *The business used to be profitable but has recently met with reverses.* 1,3,5,7 noun, 2 adjective, 4,6 verb, **re·vers·es, re·versed, re·vers·ing.**

re·vert (ri vėrt′), to go back; return: *My thoughts reverted to the last time that I had seen her.* verb.

re·view (ri vyü′), 1 to look at again; study again: *Review today's lesson for tomorrow.* 2 a looking at again; studying again; thinking over: *a review of the past year's major events.* 3 to examine; inspect: *A higher court may review the decisions of a lower court.* 4 an examination; inspection: *A review of the troops will be held during the general's visit to the camp.* 5 an opinion or judgment of a book, play, concert, or the like, giving its good and bad points. 6 to examine and give an opinion or judgment of: *She reviews books for a living.* 1,3,6 verb, 2,4,5 noun.

re·vise (ri vīz′), 1 to read carefully in order to correct; look over and change; examine and improve: *She has revised the long story she wrote to make it shorter.* 2 to change; alter: *I revised my opinion of the plan.* verb, **re·vis·es, re·vised, re·vis·ing.**

re·viv·al (ri vī′vəl), 1 a bringing or coming back to style or use: *There has been a revival of interest in folk music.* 2 special services or efforts made to awaken or increase interest in religion. noun.

re·vive (ri vīv′), 1 to bring back or come back to life or consciousness: *The lifeguard revived the half-drowned swimmer.* 2 to restore; make or become fresh: *Hot cocoa revived us after a long, cold walk.* 3 to bring back or come back to notice, use, fashion, memory, or activity: *An old play is sometimes revived on the stage.* verb, **re·vives, re·vived, re·viv·ing.**

re·voke (ri vōk′), to take back; repeal; cancel; withdraw: *to revoke a driver's license.* verb, **re·vokes, re·voked, re·vok·ing.**

re·volt (ri vōlt′), 1 the act or state of rebelling: *One cause of the revolt was unfair taxes.* 2 to turn away from and fight against a leader; rise against the government's authority: *The people revolted against the dictator.* 3 to cause to feel disgust: *Senseless cruelty revolts me.* 1 noun, 2,3 verb.

rev·o·lu·tion (rev′ə lü′shən), 1 a complete change in government: *The American Revolution gave independence to the colonies.* 2 a complete change: *The automobile caused a revolution in ways of traveling.* 3 a movement in a circle or curve around some point: *One revolution of the earth around the sun takes a year.* 4 the act or fact of turning around a center: *The wheel of the motor turns at a rate of more than one thousand revolutions a minute.* noun.

rev·o·lu·tion·ar·y (rev′ə lü′shə ner′ē), 1 of or connected with a political revolution: *revolutionary speeches, revolutionary leaders.* 2 bringing or causing great changes: *Radio and television were two revolutionary inventions of this century.* adjective.

Revolutionary War, the war fought by the American colonies from 1775 to 1783 to gain their independence from England.

rev·o·lu·tion·ize (rev′ə lü′shə nīz′), to change completely; produce a very great change in: *The automobile and television revolutionized people's* *lives here in America.* verb, **rev·o·lu·tion·iz·es, rev·o·lu·tion·ized, rev·o·lu·tion·iz·ing.**

re·volve (ri volv′), **1** to move in a curve around a point; move in a circle: *The moon revolves around the earth.* **2** to turn round a center: *The wheels of a moving car revolve.* verb, **re·volves, re·volved, re·volv·ing.**

re·volv·er (ri vol′vər), a pistol in which the part that holds the bullets turns each time a shot is fired. A revolver can be fired several times without being loaded again. noun.

re·ward (ri wôrd′), **1** a return made for something done: *A summer at camp was her reward for high grades.* **2** money payment given or offered. Rewards are given for the capture of criminals and the return of lost property. **3** to give a reward to: *They rewarded me for finding their lost dog.* **4** to give a reward for: *Her display at the science fair was rewarded with a trip to New York.* **1,2** noun, **3,4** verb.

re·word (rē wėrd′), to put in other words. verb.

re·write (rē rīt′), to write again; write in a different form. verb, **re·writes, re·wrote** (rē rōt′), **re·writ·ten** (rē rit′n), **re·writ·ing.**

R.F.D., Rural Free Delivery.

rheu·mat·ic fe·ver (rü mat′ik fē′vər), a disease most often of children that causes fever, pain in the joints, and often damage to the heart.

rheu·ma·tism (rü′mə tiz′əm), a disease that causes soreness, swelling, and stiffness of the joints or muscles. noun.

Rhine (rīn), a river in western Europe. noun.

rhi·no (rī′nō), a rhinoceros. noun, plural **rhi·nos** or **rhi·no.**

rhi·noc·er·os (rī nos′ər əs), a large, thick-skinned animal of Africa and Asia with hoofs and with one or two upright horns on the snout. Rhinoceroses eat grass and other plants. noun, plural **rhi·noc·er·os·es** or **rhi·noc·er·os.**

Word History

rhinoceros *Rhinoceros* comes from two Greek words meaning "nose" and "horn."

rhinoceros—about 5½ feet (1½ meters) high at the shoulder

a hat	i it	oi oil	ch child	⎧ a in about
ā age	ī ice	ou out	ng long	⎪ e in taken
ä far	o hot	u cup	sh she	ə = ⎨ i in pencil
e let	ō open	ů put	th thin	⎪ o in lemon
ē equal	ô order	ü rule	ŦH then	⎩ u in circus
ėr term			zh measure	

Rhode Is·land (rōd′ ī′lənd), one of the northeastern states of the United States. *Abbreviation:* R.I. or RI *Capital:* Providence. [*Rhode Island* probably got its name from Rhodes, an island in the eastern Mediterranean Sea. The name was originally given to Aquidneck Island in Narragansett Bay because it was thought to be about the size of the island of Rhodes.]

rho·do·den·dron (rō′də den′drən), an evergreen shrub with leathery leaves and clusters of showy pink, purple, or white flowers. noun.

Word History

rhododendron *Rhododendron* comes from two Greek words meaning "rose tree."

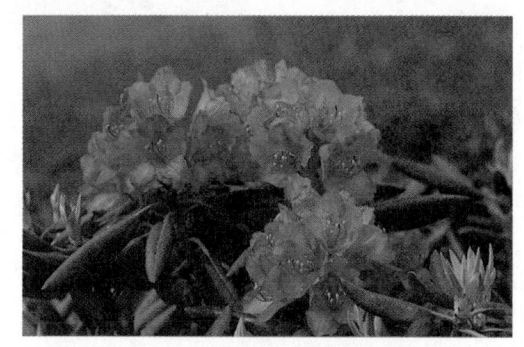

rhom·bus (rom′bəs), a parallelogram with equal sides. A rhombus usually has angles that are greater or less than a right angle. noun, plural **rhom·bus·es** or **rhom·bi** (rom′bī).

rhombuses

rhu·barb (rü′bärb), the sour stalks of a garden plant having very large, poisonous leaves. The stalks are used for making sauce or pies. noun.

rhyme (rīm), **1** to sound alike in the last part: *"Long" and "song" rhyme. "Go to bed" rhymes with "sleepy head."* **2** a word or line having the same last sound as another: *"Cat" is a rhyme for "mat." "Hey! diddle, diddle" and "The cat and the fiddle" are rhymes.* **3** verses or poetry with a regular return of similar sounds. **4** an agreement in the final sounds of words or lines. **5** to make rhymes. **6** to use a word with another that rhymes

R

with it: *to rhyme "love" and "dove."* 1,5,6 *verb*, **rhymes, rhymed, rhym·ing;** 2-4 *noun*.

rhythm (riᴛʜ′əm), any movement with a regular repetition of a beat, accent, rise and fall, or the like: *the rhythm of dancing, the rhythm of music, the rhythm of the tides. noun.*

rhyth·mic (riᴛʜ′mik), rhythmical: *the rhythmic beat of the heart. adjective.*

rhyth·mi·cal (riᴛʜ′mə kəl), having rhythm; of rhythm: *the rhythmical sound of the music. adjective.*

RI, Rhode Island (used with postal Zip Code).

R.I., Rhode Island.

rib (rib), **1** one of the curved bones that go from the backbone around the heart and lungs to the front of the body. **2** something like a rib. The curved timbers in a ship's frame are called ribs. The thick vein of a leaf is also called a rib. An umbrella has ribs. *noun.*

rib (definition 2)—The curved pieces of wood on the canoe are **ribs.**

rib·bon (rib′ən), **1** a strip or band of silk, satin, paper, or other material, used for decorating and tying things: *The gift was tied with a big, red ribbon.* **2** anything like such a strip: *a typewriter ribbon. The flag was torn to ribbons by the windstorm. noun.*

rice (rīs), the grain of a kind of cereal grass, or the plant that it grows on. Rice is grown in warm climates and is an important food in India, China, and Japan. *noun.*

rich (rich), **1** having much money, land, goods, or other property: *That movie star is a rich man.* **2** the **rich,** rich people. **3** abounding; well supplied: *a country rich in oil.* **4** fertile; producing much: *a rich*

soil, *a rich mine.* **5** valuable; worthy: *a rich harvest, a rich suggestion.* **6** containing plenty of butter, eggs, and flavoring: *a rich cake.* **7** deep; full: *a rich red, a rich tone.* 1,3-7 *adjective,* 2 *noun.*

rich·es (rich′iz), wealth; abundance of property; much money, land, or goods. *noun plural.*

Rich·mond (rich′mənd), the capital of Virginia. *noun.*

rick·et·y (rik′ə tē), **1** weak; liable to fall or break down; shaky: *a rickety old chair.* **2** feeble in the joints. *adjective.*

ric·o·chet (rik′ə shā′), **1** the skipping or jumping motion of an object after it bounces or glances off a flat surface: *the ricochet of a stone thrown along the surface of water.* **2** to move in this way: *The bullets struck the ground and ricocheted through the grass.* 1 *noun,* 2 *verb,* **ric·o·chets, ric·o·cheted** (rik′ə shād′), **ric·o·chet·ing** (rik′ə shā′ing).

rid (rid), to make free: *What will rid a house of mice? verb,* **rids, rid** or **rid·ded, rid·ding.**

get rid of, 1 to get free from: *I can't get rid of this cold.* **2** to do away with: *Poison will get rid of the ants.*

rid·den (rid′n). See **ride.** *I had ridden my horse all day. verb.*

rid·dle¹ (rid′l), a puzzling question, statement, or problem. EXAMPLE: When is a door not a door? ANSWER: When it is ajar. *noun.*

rid·dle² (rid′l), to pierce with holes: *Insects had riddled the old tree stump. verb,* **rid·dles, rid·dled, rid·dling.**

ride (rīd), **1** to sit on a horse and make it go. **2** to sit on something and make it go: *to ride a camel, to ride a bicycle.* **3** to be carried along: *to ride on a train, to ride in a car.* **4** to be carried on: *The eagle rides the wind. The raft rode the waves.* **5** a trip on horseback, in an automobile, on a train, or on any other thing that carries: *On Sundays we take a ride into the country.* **6** to carry; cause to ride: *She rode her little brother piggyback.* **7** a machine that carries people a short distance for their amusement: *The carnival had a roller coaster, a Ferris wheel, and other rides.* 1-4,6 *verb,* **rides, rode, rid·den, rid·ing;** 5,7 *noun.*

rid·er (rī′dər), a person who rides: *The West is famous for its riders. noun.*

ridge (rij), **1** the long and narrow upper part of something: *the ridge of an animal's back.* **2** a line where two sloping surfaces meet: *the ridge of a roof.* **3** a long, narrow chain of hills or mountains: *the Blue Ridge of the Appalachian Mountains.* **4** any raised narrow strip: *the ridges in plowed ground, the ridges on corduroy cloth. noun.*

rid·i·cule (rid′ə kyül), **1** to laugh at; make fun of: *Many people ridiculed the Wright brothers' airplane.* **2** laughter in mockery; words or actions that make fun of somebody or something: *I was hurt by the ridicule of my classmates.* 1 *verb,* **rid·i·cules, rid·i·culed, rid·i·cul·ing;** 2 *noun.*

ri·dic·u·lous (ri dik′yə ləs), deserving ridicule; absurd; laughable: *It would be ridiculous to walk backward all the time. adjective.*

ri·fle¹ (rī′fəl), a gun with spiral grooves in its long

barrel which spin the bullet, giving the gun greater accuracy. A rifle is usually fired from the shoulder. *noun.*

ri·fle² (rī′fəl), to search thoroughly and rob; ransack: *Someone has rifled my locker. verb,* **ri·fles, ri·fled, ri·fling.**

rift (rift), a split; break; crack: *There's a rift in the clouds; perhaps the sun will come out soon. noun.*

rig (rig), **1** to fit a ship with masts, sails, and ropes; fit out: *It took us 20 minutes to rig our sailboat.* **2** an arrangement of masts and sails on a ship. A schooner has a fore-and-aft rig; that is, the sails are set lengthwise on the ship. **3** an outfit; equipment: *a camper's rig, an oil-drilling rig.* **4** to fit out; equip: *to rig out a football team with uniforms.* **5** to dress: *On Halloween the children rig themselves up in funny clothes.* **6** a set of clothes; costume: *His rig consisted of a silk hat and overalls.* **7** to put together in a hurry or by using odds and ends: *The girls rigged up a tent in the yard with a rope and a blanket.* **8** to arrange in an unfair way: *The race was rigged.* 1,4,5,7,8 *verb,* **rigs, rigged, rig·ging;** 2,3,6 *noun.*

rig·ging (rig′ing), **1** the ropes, chains, and cables used to support and work the masts and sails on a ship. **2** equipment; gear; apparatus: *The stage crew handled the rigging for the school play. noun.*

right (rīt), **1** good; just; lawful: *She did the right thing when she told the truth.* **2** in a way that is good, just, or lawful: *He acted right when he told the truth.* **3** that which is right, just, good, true: *Do right, not wrong.* **4** a just claim; something that is due to a person: *Each member of the club has a right to vote. I demanded my rights.* **5** correct; true: *the right answer.* **6** correctly; truly: *She guessed right.* **7** fitting; suitable; proper: *Learn to say the right thing at the right time.* **8** properly; well: *It's faster to do a job right the first time.* **9** well; healthy; in good condition: *I don't feel right; I think I'm getting the flu.* **10** meant to be seen; most important: *the right side of cloth.* **11** to make correct; set right: *to right a wrong.* **12** to put right; get into the proper position: *The boys righted the boat. The ship righted after the big wave passed.* **13** belonging to the side that is turned east when the main side is turned north; opposite of left. You have a right hand and a left hand. **14** to the right hand: *to turn right.* **15** the right-hand side: *Turn to your right.* **16** exactly: *Your cap is right where you left it.* **17** at once; immediately: *Stop playing right now.* **18** in a straight line; directly: *Look me right in the eye.* **19** completely: *My hat was knocked right off.* 1,5,7,9,10,13 *adjective,* 2,6,8,14, 16-19 *adverb,* 3,4,15 *noun,* 11,12 *verb.*

right away, at once; immediately.

right angle, an angle of 90 degrees. The angles in a square or in the capital letters F, L, and T are right angles.

right angles

right·eous (rī′chəs), **1** doing right; virtuous; behaving justly: *A righteous person treats others with kindness.* **2** proper; just; right: *righteous anger. adjective.*

right·ful (rīt′fəl), **1** according to law; by right: *the rightful owner of this dog.* **2** just and right; proper: *I took my rightful place alongside the others. adjective.*

right-hand (rīt′hand′), **1** on the right. **2** of, for, or with the right hand. **3** most helpful or useful: *He is the scoutmaster's right-hand man. adjective.*

right-hand·ed (rīt′han′did), using the right hand more easily and more readily than the left. *adjective.*

right·ly (rīt′lē), **1** justly; fairly: *She was rightly upset by their behavior.* **2** correctly: *She guessed rightly that it would rain. adverb.*

rig·id (rij′id), **1** stiff; firm; not bending: *Hold your arm rigid.* **2** strict; not changing: *In our home, it is a rigid rule to wash one's hands before eating. adjective.*

rig·or (rig′ər), harshness; severity: *the rigor of a long, cold winter. noun.*

rig·or·ous (rig′ər əs), very severe; harsh; strict: *the rigorous discipline in the army. adjective.*

rim (rim), **1** an edge, border, or margin on or around anything: *the rim of a wheel, the rim of a cup.* **2** to form a rim around: *Wildflowers and grasses rimmed the little pool.* 1 *noun,* 2 *verb,* **rims, rimmed, rim·ming.**

rind (rīnd), a firm outer covering. We do not eat the rind of oranges, melons, and cheese. *noun.*

ring¹ (ring), **1** a circle: *You can tell the age of a tree by counting the number of rings in its wood; one ring grows every year. The children danced in a ring.* **2** a thin circle of metal or other material: *a wedding ring, a key ring, a napkin ring.* **3** to put a ring around; enclose; form a circle around: *Rosebushes ringed the backyard.* **4** an enclosed space for races or games: *a circus ring, a boxing ring.* **5** a group of people working together for a selfish or bad purpose: *The police arrested a ring of smugglers.* 1,2,4,5 *noun,* 3 *verb,* **rings, ringed, ring·ing.**

ring² (ring), **1** to give forth a clear sound, as a bell does: *Did the telephone ring?* **2** to cause to give forth a clear, ringing sound: *Ring the bell.* **3** to cause a bell to sound: *I rang for the clerk.* **4** the sound of a bell: *Did you hear a ring?* **5** a sound like that of a bell: *On a cold night we can hear the ring of skates on ice.* **6** to hear a sound like that of a bell ringing: *My ears ring.* **7** to sound loudly: *The room rang with laughter.* **8** to seem; appear to be: *Her words rang true.* **9** to call up on a telephone: *I'll ring you tomorrow.* **10** a call on the telephone:

a hat	i it	oi oil	ch child	a in about
ā age	ī ice	ou out	ng long	e in taken
ä far	o hot	u cup	sh she	ə = i in pencil
e let	ō open	ù put	th thin	o in lemon
ē equal	ô order	ü rule	‡H then	u in circus
ėr term			zh measure	

R

531

I'll give you a ring tonight. 1-3,6-9 *verb,* **rings, rang, rung, ring·ing;** 4,5,10 *noun.*

ring·lead·er (ring′lē′dər), a person who leads others in opposition to authority or law: *The ringleaders of the mutiny were placed in irons.* *noun.*

ring·let (ring′lit), a curl: *The baby's hair was in ringlets. noun.*

ring·side (ring′sīd′), **1** a place just outside a ring or arena, especially at a circus or fight. **2** a place affording a close view. *noun.*

ring·worm (ring′wėrm′), a contagious skin disease, often causing round discolored patches on the scalp or other areas. It is caused by a fungus. *noun.*

rink (ringk), **1** a sheet of ice for skating. **2** a smooth floor for roller-skating. *noun.*

rinse (rins), **1** to wash with clean water: *Rinse all the soap out of your hair after you wash it.* **2** to wash lightly: *Rinse your mouth with warm water.* **3** a rinsing: *Give the plate a final rinse in hot water.* 1,2 *verb,* **rins·es, rinsed, rins·ing;** 3 *noun.*

Ri·o de Ja·nei·ro (rē′ō dā zhə ner′ō), a city in Brazil.

ri·ot (rī′ət), **1** a disturbance; confusion; disorder; a wild, violent public disturbance: *a riot in a prison.* **2** to behave in a wild, disorderly way. **3** a bright display: *The garden was a riot of color.* **4** a very funny person or performance: *She was a riot at the party.* 1,3,4 *noun,* 2 *verb.*

run riot, 1 to run wild; act without restraint: *The crowd ran riot and could not be controlled.* **2** to grow wildly in bright display: *The daisies run riot in this field.*

ri·ot·ous (rī′ə təs), **1** taking part in a riot: *The leaders of the riotous mob were arrested.* **2** noisily cheerful; disorderly: *Sounds of riotous glee came from the playhouse. adjective.*

rip (rip), **1** to cut roughly; tear apart; tear off: *I ripped the cover off the box.* **2** to cut or pull out the threads in the seams of a garment. **3** a torn place; seam burst in a garment: *Please sew up this rip in my sleeve.* **4** to move fast or violently: *Fire ripped through the building.* 1,2,4 *verb,* **rips, ripped, rip·ping;** 3 *noun.*

ripe (rīp), **1** full-grown and ready to be gathered and eaten: *a ripe fruit, ripe grain, ripe vegetables.* **2** ready: *a country ripe for revolution. adjective,* **rip·er, rip·est.**

rip·en (rī′pən), to become ripe; make ripe. *verb.*

rip·ple (rip′əl), **1** a very little wave: *Throw a stone into still water and watch the ripples spread in rings.* **2** anything that seems like a tiny wave. **3** a sound that reminds one of little waves: *a ripple of laughter in the crowd.* **4** to make little ripples on: *A breeze rippled the water.* 1-3 *noun,* 4 *verb,* **rip·ples, rip·pled, rip·pling.**

rise (rīz), **1** to get up from a lying, sitting, or kneeling position; stand up; get up: *Please rise from your seat when you recite.* **2** to get up from sleep or rest: *I rise at 7 every morning.* **3** to go up; come up: *The kite rises in the air. Mercury rises in a thermometer on a hot day.* **4** to go higher;

increase: *Butter rose five cents in price. The wind rose rapidly. My anger rose at that remark.* **5** a going up; increase: *a rise in prices, the rise of a balloon.* **6** to advance in importance or rank: *He rose from office clerk to president of the company.* **7** to slope upward: *Hills rise in the distance.* **8** an upward slope: *The rise of the hill is gradual. The house is situated on a rise.* **9** to come above the horizon: *The sun rises in the morning.* **10** to start; begin: *The river rises from a spring. Quarrels often rise from trifles.* **11** the origin; beginning: *the rise of a river, the rise of a storm, the rise of a new problem.* **12** to become more cheerful; improve: *Our spirits rose at the good news.* **13** to revolt; rebel: *The peasants rose against the nobles.* **14** to grow larger and lighter; swell: *Yeast makes dough rise.* 1-4,6,7,9,10,12-14 *verb,* **ris·es, rose, ris·en, ris·ing;** 5,8,11 *noun.*

give rise to, to bring about; start; begin; cause: *Their sudden wealth gave rise to rumors about where the money came from.*

ris·en (riz′n). See **rise.** *The sun had risen long before I woke up. verb.*

risk (risk), **1** a chance of harm or loss; danger: *There is less risk of getting sick if you eat properly.* **2** to expose to the chance of harm or loss: *You risk your neck trying to climb that tree.* **3** to take the risk of: *They risked defeat in fighting the larger army.* 1 *noun,* 2,3 *verb.*

run a risk or **take a risk,** to expose oneself to the chance of harm or loss: *You run the risk of losing your money in that scheme.*

risk·y (ris′kē), full of risk; dangerous. *adjective,* **risk·i·er, risk·i·est.**

rite (rīt), a solemn ceremony. Most religions have rites for marriage and burial. Secret societies have their special rites. *noun.*

rit·u·al (rich′ü əl), a form or system of rites. The rites of marriage and burial are part of the ritual of most religions. *noun.*

ri·val (rī′vəl), **1** a person who wants and tries to get the same thing as another; one who tries to equal or do better than another: *The two girls were rivals for the same class office.* **2** wanting the same thing as another; being a rival: *The rival supermarkets both cut their prices.* **3** to try to equal or outdo: *The sisters rivaled each other in the tennis tournament.* **4** to equal; match: *The sunset rivaled the sunrise in beauty.* 1 *noun,* 2 *adjective,* 3,4 *verb.*

ri·val·ry (rī′vəl rē), an effort to obtain something another person wants; competition: *There is rivalry among business firms for trade. noun, plural* **ri·val·ries.**

ripple (definition 2)
ripples in sand

riv·er (riv′ər), **1** a large natural stream of water that flows into a lake, ocean, or the like. **2** any abundant stream or flow: *Rivers of mud and lava flowed from the volcano. noun.*

riv·er·bank (riv′ər bangk′), the ground bordering a river. *noun.*

riv·er·bed (riv′ər bed′), the channel or bed in which a river flows. *noun.*

riv·er·boat (riv′ər bōt′), a boat for use on a river, usually having a flat bottom. *noun.*

riv·er·side (riv′ər sīd′), the bank of a river: *We walked along the riverside. noun.*

riv·et (riv′it), **1** a metal bolt with a head at one end. The end opposite the head is hammered to form another head after it is passed through the things to be joined. Rivets are often used to fasten heavy steel beams together. **2** to fasten with a rivet or rivets. **3** to fasten firmly; fix firmly: *Their eyes were riveted on the speaker.* **1** *noun,* **2,3** *verb.*

rivet (def. 1)

riv·u·let (riv′yə lit), a very small stream. *noun.*

roach (rōch), an insect often found in kitchens or around water pipes; cockroach. *noun, plural* **roach·es.**

road (rōd), **1** a way between places; way made for automobiles, trucks, or other vehicles to travel on: *the road from New York to Boston.* **2** a way: *the road to ruin, a road to peace. noun.*

road·bed (rōd′bed′), the foundation for a road or for railroad tracks. *noun.*

road map, a flat drawing of a part of the earth's surface showing roads for automobile travel.

roadrunner—about 24 inches (61 centimeters) long

road·run·ner (rōd′run′ər), a bird of the deserts of the southwestern United States, that has a long tail and a thick crest. It can run very fast. *noun.*

road·side (rōd′sīd′), **1** the side of a road: *Flowers grew along the roadside.* **2** beside a road: *a roadside inn.* **1** *noun,* **2** *adjective.*

road·way (rōd′wā′), a road. *noun.*

roam (rōm), to go about with no special plan or aim; wander: *to roam through the fields. verb.*

roan (rōn), a horse with a red, brown, or black coat with white hairs mixed in. *noun.*

a hat	i it	oi oil	ch child		a in about
ā age	ī ice	ou out	ng long		e in taken
ä far	o hot	u cup	sh she	ə =	i in pencil
e let	ō open	ù put	th thin		o in lemon
ē equal	ô order	ü rule	ᴛʜ then		u in circus
ėr term			zh measure		

roar (rôr), **1** to make a loud deep sound; make a loud noise: *The lion roared. The wind roared at the windows.* **2** a loud deep sound; loud noise: *the roar of the cannon, a roar of laughter.* **3** to laugh loudly: *The audience roared at the clown.* **1,3** *verb,* **2** *noun.*

roast (rōst), **1** to cook by the dry heat of an oven, an open fire, or hot charcoal: *I will roast the meat for an hour. We roasted marshmallows at camp.* **2** a piece of baked meat; piece of meat to be roasted. **3** roasted: *roast beef, roast pork.* **4** to prepare by heating: *to roast coffee beans, to roast a metal ore.* **5** to make or become very hot: *I am roasting in this heavy coat.* **1,4,5** *verb,* **2** *noun,* **3** *adjective.*

rob (rob), to take away from by force; steal: *Thieves robbed the bank of thousands of dollars. verb,* **robs, robbed, rob·bing.**

rob·ber (rob′ər), a person who robs; thief. *noun.*

rob·ber·y (rob′ər ē), the act of robbing; theft; stealing: *a bank robbery. noun, plural* **rob·ber·ies.**

robe (rōb), **1** a long, loose, outer garment: *I wore a robe over my pajamas.* **2** a garment that shows rank or office: *a judge's robe, the queen's robes of state.* **3** to put a robe on; dress: *They robed themselves all in white.* **1,2** *noun,* **3** *verb,* **robes, robed, rob·ing.**

rob·in (rob′ən), a large North American bird with a reddish breast. *noun.*

ro·bot (rō′bot *or* rō′bət), a machine with moving parts controlled by a computer. The computer makes it possible for the machine to carry out long and complicated sets of jobs, over and over, without a person to control it. Robots are sometimes built to look like human beings, though they can have any shape or size. *noun.*

Word History

robot *Robot* comes from a word from Czechoslovakia meaning "work."

R

ro·bust (rō bust′ or rō′bust), strong and healthy; sturdy: *a robust person, a robust mind. adjective.*

rock[1] (rok), **1** a large mass of stone: *The ship was wrecked on the rocks.* **2** a piece of stone: *She threw a rock in the lake.* **3** any hard mineral matter that is not metal; stone. The earth's crust is made up of rock under a layer of soil. **4** something firm like a rock; support; defense: *She was a rock when I needed strong support. noun.*

rock[2] (rok), **1** to move backward and forward, or from side to side; sway: *My chair rocks. The waves rocked the ship.* **2** a rocking movement. **3** rock'n'roll. *1 verb, 2,3 noun.*

rock·er (rok′ər), **1** one of the curved pieces on which a cradle or rocking chair rocks. **2** a rocking chair. *noun.*

rock·et (rok′it), **1** a device consisting of a tube open at one end in which an explosive or fuel is rapidly burned. The burning explosive or fuel creates gases that escape from the open end and force the tube and whatever is attached to it upward or forward. Some rockets, such as those used in fireworks displays, shoot into the air and burst into showers of sparks. Larger rockets are used in weapons of war and to send spacecraft beyond the earth's atmosphere. **2** to go like a rocket; move very, very fast: *The singing group rocketed to fame with its first hit record. The racing car rocketed across the finish line. 1 noun, 2 verb.*

Rock·ies (rok′ēz), the Rocky Mountains. *noun plural.*

rocking chair, a chair mounted on rockers, or on springs, so that it can rock back and forth.

rocking horse, a toy horse on rockers or on springs for children to ride.

rock·'n'·roll (rok′ən rōl′), **1** a kind of popular music with a strong beat and simple melody. **2** a lively dance done to this music. *noun.*

rock salt, the common salt got from mines; salt in large crystals. Rock salt is often used to melt ice on roads and sidewalks.

rock·y[1] (rok′ē), full of rocks: *a rocky shore. adjective,* **rock·i·er, rock·i·est.**

rock·y[2] (rok′ē), shaky; likely to rock: *That table seems a bit rocky to me; put a piece of wood under the short leg. adjective,* **rock·i·er, rock·i·est.**

Rocky Mountains, a group of high mountains in western North America.

rod (rod), **1** a thin straight pole or bar of wood, metal, or plastic: *a fishing rod, a curtain rod.* **2** a stick used to beat or punish. **3** a unit of length equal to 5½ yards or 16½ feet. A square rod is 30¼ square yards or 272¼ square feet. *noun.*

rode (rōd). See **ride.** *We rode ten miles yesterday. verb.*

ro·dent (rōd′nt), any of a group of animals with large front teeth that are used for gnawing. Rats, mice, and squirrels are rodents. *noun.*

ro·de·o (rō′dē ō or rō dā′ō), a contest or exhibition of skill in roping cattle or riding horses and bulls. *noun, plural* **ro·de·os.**

roe[1] (rō), a small deer of Europe and Asia. *noun, plural* **roes** or **roe.**

roe[2] (rō), fish eggs. *noun.*

rogue (rōg), **1** a tricky or dishonest person; rascal. **2** a mischievous person: *The little rogue has his grandpa's glasses on.* **3** an animal with a savage nature that lives apart from the herd: *An elephant that is a rogue is very dangerous. noun.*

rogues' gallery, a collection of photographs of known criminals.

ro·guish (rō′gish), **1** dishonest; having to do with rogues. **2** playfully mischievous: *with a roguish twinkle in his eyes. adjective.*

role (rōl), **1** an actor's part in a play: *She played the leading role in the school play.* **2** a part played in real life: *The parental role is one of love and guidance. noun.*

roll (rōl), **1** to move along by turning over and over: *The ball rolled away.* **2** to turn round and round on itself or on something else; wrap; be wrapped round: *She rolled the string into a ball. The boy rolled himself up in a blanket.* **3** something rolled up: *a roll of film, a roll of paper.* **4** a rounded or rolled-up mass: *a roll of cookie dough.* **5** to move on wheels: *to roll a baby carriage. The automobile rolls along.* **6** to move smoothly; sweep along: *Waves roll in on the beach. The years roll on.* **7** to move with a side-to-side motion: *to roll one's eyes. The ship rolled in the waves.* **8** the act of rolling; motion from side to side: *The ship's roll made many people sick.* **9** to turn over, or over and over: *The horse rolled in the dust.* **10** to rise and fall again and again: *rolling country, rolling waves.* **11** to make flat or smooth with a roller; spread out with a rolling pin: *Roll the dough thin for these cookies.* **12** to make deep, loud sounds: *Thunder rolls.* **13** a deep, loud sound: *the roll of thunder.* **14** to beat a drum with rapid, continuous strokes.

rodents

15 a rapid, continuous beating on a drum. 16 to trill: *to roll your r's.* 17 a list of names; list: *I will call the roll to find out who is absent.* 18 a kind of bread or cake: *a sweet roll.* 1,2,5-7,9-12,14, 16 *verb*, 3,4,8,13,15,17,18 *noun.*

roll up, to pile up; increase: *Bills roll up fast.*

roll call, a calling of a list of names to find out who is present.

roll·er (rō′lər), 1 a thing that rolls, especially a small wheel: *Some articles of furniture have rollers under the legs.* 2 a cylinder on which something is rolled along or rolled up. Window shades go up and down on rollers. Hair is curled on rollers. 3 a cylinder of metal, stone, or wood used for smoothing, spreading, pressing, or crushing: *A heavy roller was used to smooth the tennis court. The paint was applied with a small roller.* 4 a long, swelling wave: *Rollers broke on the beach. noun.*

roller coaster, a railway for amusement, consisting of inclined tracks along which small cars roll and make sudden drops and turns.

roller skate, a shoe or metal base with four small wheels, used for skating on a floor, sidewalk, or other smooth surface.

roll·er-skate (rō′lər skāt′), to move on roller skates: *The children roller-skated to the park. verb,* **roll·er-skates, roll·er-skat·ed, roll·er-skat·ing.**

rolling pin, a cylinder of wood, plastic, or glass with a handle at each end, for rolling out dough.

ro·ly-po·ly (rō′lē pō′lē), short and plump: *He was a roly-poly baby. adjective.*

ROM, read-only memory. This is a part of a computer in which information and instructions are stored permanently. Everything stored there can be copied and used, but nothing can be added to this memory or removed from it.

Ro·man (rō′mən), 1 of or having something to do with Rome. 2 a person born or living in Rome. 3 a citizen of ancient Rome. 4 of or having something to do with the Roman Catholic Church. 5 **roman,** the style of type most used in printing and typewriting. This sentence is in roman. 1,4 *adjective,* 2,3,5 *noun.*

Roman Catholic, 1 of, having something to do with, or belonging to the Christian church that recognizes the pope as the supreme head. 2 a member of this church.

ro·mance (rō mans′), 1 a love story. 2 a story or poem telling of heroes and their adventures: *They loved reading the romances about King Arthur and his knights.* 3 a quality of love, adventure, mystery, or daring: *The children dreamed of traveling in search of romance.* 4 a love affair: *My older brother is having a romance with the girl next door. noun.*

Ro·ma·ni·a (rō mā′nē ə), a country in southeastern Europe. *noun.*

Roman numerals, the numerals like XXIII, LVI, and MDCCLX, in which I = 1, V = 5, X = 10, L = 50, C = 100, D = 500, and M = 1000.

ro·man·tic (rō man′tik), 1 full of love, adventure, mystery, or daring: *He likes to read romantic tales of love and war. She thinks it would be romantic to*

be an explorer. 2 having ideas or feelings filled with thoughts of love: *The old couple remembered the days when they were young and romantic.* 3 suited to or bringing to mind thoughts of love: *The band played soft, romantic music. adjective.*

Rome (rōm), 1 a city in southern Europe, the capital of Italy. 2 an ancient city in the same place, the capital of an ancient empire. *noun.*

romp (romp), 1 to play in a rough, boisterous way; rush, tumble, and punch in play: *On rainy days the children liked to romp in the basement.* 2 a rough, lively play or frolic: *The children had a romp on the beach.* 1 *verb,* 2 *noun.*

roof (rüf), 1 the top covering of a building. 2 something like it: *the roof of a cave, the roof of a car, the roof of the mouth.* 3 to cover with or as if with a roof: *Tall trees roofed the road through the woods.* 1,2 *noun, plural* **roofs;** 3 *verb.*

roof·ing (rü′fing), material used for roofs. Shingles are a common roofing for houses. *noun.*

rook[1] (rük), a European bird much like a crow that often nests in trees near buildings. *noun.*

rook[2] (rük), one of the pieces in the game of chess. A rook can move in a straight line across any number of empty squares. *noun.*

rook·ie (rük′ē), 1 an inexperienced person; beginner. 2 a player in his or her first year of professional sport. *noun.*

room (rüm), 1 a part of a house, or other building, with walls of its own: *a dining room.* 2 the people in a room: *The whole room laughed.* 3 space: *The street was so crowded that the cars did not have room to move. There is room for one more in the automobile.* 4 an opportunity: *There is room for improvement in her work.* 5 to occupy a room; live in a room: *Three girls from our town roomed together at college.* 1-4 *noun,* 5 *verb.*

room·er (rü′mər), a person who lives in a rented room or rooms in another's house; lodger. *noun.*

room·i·ness (rü′mē nis), ample space; abundance of room: *We all liked the roominess of our new house. noun.*

room·mate (rüm′māt′), a person who shares a room with another or others. *noun.*

room·y (rü′mē), large; spacious; having plenty of room: *Her new apartment is quite roomy. adjective,* **room·i·er, room·i·est.**

roost (rüst), 1 a bar, pole, or perch on which birds rest or sleep. 2 to sit as birds do on a roost; settle for the night. 3 a place for birds to roost in. 1,3 *noun,* 2 *verb.*

roost·er (rü′stər), a full-grown male chicken. *noun.*

root[1] (rüt), 1 a part of a plant that grows down into the soil, to hold the plant in place, to absorb water

R

and food from the soil, and often to store food. **2** something like a root in shape, position, or use: *the root of a tooth, the roots of the hair.* **3** a part from which other things grow and develop; cause; source: *"The love of money is the root of all evil."* **4** to become fixed in the ground; send out roots and begin to grow: *Some plants root more quickly than others.* **5** to fix firmly: *He was rooted to the spot by surprise.* **6** to pull, tear, or dig up or out by the roots; get rid of completely: *We spent hours rooting up weeds from the garden.* **7** a word from which other words are made. *Room* is the root of *roominess, roomer, roommate,* and *roomy.* 1-3,7 *noun,* 4-6 *verb.*

root² (rüt), **1** to dig with the snout: *The pigs rooted up the garden.* **2** to rummage: *She rooted through the closet looking for her old shoes. verb.*

root³ (rüt), to cheer or support a team or a member of a team enthusiastically. *verb.*

root beer, a soft drink flavored with the juice of the roots of certain plants.

rope (rōp), **1** a strong thick line or cord made by twisting smaller cords together. **2** to tie, bind, or fasten with a rope. **3** to enclose or mark off with a rope: *In winter, they rope off the entrance to the beach.* **4** to catch a horse, calf, or other animal with a lasso. **5** a number of things twisted or strung together: *a rope of onions, a rope of pearls.* 1,5 *noun,* 2-4 *verb,* **ropes, roped, rop·ing.**

ro·sar·y (rō′zər ē), **1** a string of beads for keeping count in saying a series of prayers. **2** a series of prayers. *noun, plural* **ro·sar·ies.**

rose¹ (rōz), **1** a flower that grows on a bush with thorny stems. Roses are red, pink, white, or yellow and usually smell very sweet. **2** pinkish-red: *Her dress was rose.* 1 *noun,* 2 *adjective.*

rose² (rōz). See **rise.** *The cat rose and stretched. verb.*

rose·bud (rōz′bud′), the bud of a rose. *noun.*

rose·bush (rōz′bush′), a shrub or vine that bears roses. *noun, plural* **rose·bush·es.**

rosette on a prize ribbon

ro·sette (rō zet′), an ornament shaped like a rose. Rosettes are often made of ribbon. *noun.*

Rosh Ha·sha·nah or **Rosh Ha·sha·na** (rosh′ hə shä′nə), the Jewish New Year. It usually occurs in September.

ros·in (roz′n), a hard, yellow substance that remains when turpentine is evaporated from pine resin. Rosin is rubbed on violin bows, and on the shoes of acrobats and ballet dancers to keep them from slipping. *noun.*

ros·y (rō′zē), **1** like a rose; pinkish-red: *rosy cheeks.* **2** bright; cheerful: *a rosy future. adjective,* **ros·i·er, ros·i·est.**

rot (rot), **1** to become rotten; decay; spoil: *So much rain will make the fruit rot.* **2** a process of rotting; decay. **3** any of several diseases of plants and animals. 1 *verb,* **rots, rot·ted, rot·ting;** 2,3 *noun.*

ro·tate (rō′tāt), **1** to move around a center or axis; turn in a circle; revolve. Wheels, tops, and the earth rotate. **2** to change in a regular order; cause to take turns: *Farmers rotate their crops in order to keep the soil productive. verb,* **ro·tates, ro·tat·ed, ro·tat·ing.**

[*Rotate* comes from a Latin word meaning "wheel." Other English words from the same Latin root include *rotation* and *rotor.*]

ro·ta·tion (rō tā′shən), a turning round a center; turning in a circle: *the rotation of a top. The earth's rotation causes night and day. noun.*

rotation of crops, the varying from year to year of crops grown in the same field to keep the soil from losing its fertility.

ro·tor (rō′tər), **1** the rotating part of a machine or apparatus. **2** a system of rotating blades by which a helicopter is able to fly. *noun.*

rotor (definition 2)

rot·ten (rot′n), **1** decayed; spoiled: *a rotten egg.* **2** weak; unsound; not in good condition: *rotten beams in a floor.* **3** bad; nasty: *The weather was rotten yesterday. He had a rotten cold all last week. adjective.*

rouge (rüzh), a red powder, paste, or liquid for coloring the cheeks. *noun.*

rough (ruf), **1** not smooth; not level; not even: *rough boards, the rough bark of oak trees.* **2** stormy: *rough weather, a rough sea.* **3** likely to hurt others; harsh; not gentle: *rough manners.* **4** without polish or fine finish: *rough diamonds.* **5** not completed; done as a first try; without details: *a rough drawing, a rough idea.* **6** coarse and tangled: *rough fur, a dog with a rough coat of hair.* **7** unpleasant; hard; severe: *She had a rough time in the hospital.* **8** roughly: *Those older boys play too rough for me.* 1-7 *adjective,* 8 *adverb.*

rough it, to live without comforts and

conveniences: *They have been roughing it in the woods this summer.*

rough up, 1 to make rough: *A strong wind roughed up the waves.* **2** to beat; treat roughly: *The angry mob roughed up the burglary suspect.*

rough·en (ruf′ən), to make rough; become rough. *verb.*

rough·house (ruf′hous′), **1** rough play; rowdy conduct; disorderly behavior: *The teacher warned us that there was too much roughhouse on the playground.* **2** to act in a rough, disorderly way: *The children were roughhousing in the family room.* **1** *noun,* **2** *verb,* **rough·hous·es, rough·housed, rough·hous·ing.**

rough·ly (ruf′lē), **1** in a rough manner: *They pushed him roughly out the door.* **2** approximately: *From New York to Los Angeles is roughly three thousand miles. adverb.*

round (round), **1** shaped like a ball or circle or tree trunk: *Oranges are round. A ring is round. Most candles are round.* **2** anything shaped like a ball or circle or tree trunk. The rungs of a ladder are sometimes called rounds. **3** plump: *The baby had round cheeks.* **4** to make or become round: *The carpenter rounded the corners of the table.* **5** around: *Wheels go round. They built a fence round the yard.* **6** to go around; make a turn to the other side of: *The car rounded the corner at high speed.* **7 rounds,** a fixed course ending where it begins: *The watchman makes his rounds of the building.* **8** a series of duties or events; routine: *a round of pleasures, a round of duties.* **9** a section of a game or sport: *a round in a boxing match, a round of cards.* **10** a complete game or unit: *They played a round of golf this morning.* **11** a firing of guns by a group of soldiers at the same time. **12** the powder or bullets for one such firing, or for a single shot: *Three rounds of ammunition were left in the rifle.* **13** an act that a number of people do together: *a round of cheers. She was greeted by a round of applause.* **14** a short song sung by several persons or groups beginning one after the other. "Row, Row, Row Your Boat" is a round. **15** full; complete; large: *a round dozen, a good round sum of money.* **16** to change a number to the nearest hundredth, tenth, ten, hundred, and so on. 7578 rounded to the nearest hundred would be 7600. **1,3,15** *adjective,* **2,7-14** *noun,* **4,6,16** *verb,* **5** *adverb,* **5** *preposition.*

round up, 1 to drive or bring cattle or horses together: *The cowboys rounded up the cattle.* **2** to gather together; collect: *to round up some kids to play baseball.*

round·a·bout (round′ə bout′), not straight or direct: *a roundabout route, in a roundabout way. adjective.*

round·house (round′hous′), a circular building for storing or repairing locomotives. It is built about a platform that turns around. *noun, plural* **round·hous·es** (round′hou′ziz).

round number, a number in even tens, hundreds, thousands, and so on. 3874 in round numbers would be 3900 or 4000.

round-shoul·dered (round′shōl′dərd), having the shoulders bent forward. *adjective.*

round trip, a trip to a place and back again.

round·up (round′up′), **1** the act of driving or bringing cattle together from long distances. **2** any similar gathering: *a roundup of old friends. noun.*

rouse (rouz), **1** to wake up; awake: *I was roused by the ring of the telephone.* **2** to excite; stir up: *She was roused to anger by the insult. verb,* **rous·es, roused, rous·ing.**

rout[1] (rout), **1** the flight of a defeated army in disorder: *The enemy's retreat soon became a rout.* **2** to put to flight: *Our soldiers routed the enemy.* **3** a complete defeat: *The baseball game ended in a rout for our team.* **4** to defeat completely: *The baseball team routed its opponents by a score of ten to one.* **1,3** *noun,* **2,4** *verb.*

rout[2] (rout), **1** to dig out; get by searching. **2** to put out; force out: *Mother routed us out of bed early the day of the picnic. verb.*

route (rüt *or* rout), **1** a way to go; road: *Will you go to the coast by the northern route?* **2** to send by a certain way or road: *The signs routed us around the construction work and over a side road.* **3** a fixed, regular course or area of a person making deliveries or sales: *a newspaper route, a milk route.* **1,3** *noun,* **2** *verb,* **routes, rout·ed, rout·ing.**

rou·tine (rü tēn′), **1** a fixed, regular method of doing things; usual doing of the same things in the same way: *Getting up and going to bed are parts of your daily routine.* **2** using routine: *routine methods.* **1** *noun,* **2** *adjective.*

rove (rōv), to wander; wander about; roam: *She loved to rove through the woods near her house. verb,* **roves, roved, rov·ing.**

rov·er (rō′vər), a wanderer. *noun.*

row[1] (rō), a line of people or things: *The children stood in a row in front of the row of chairs. Corn is planted in rows. noun.*

row[2] (rō), **1** to use oars to move a boat: *Row to the island.* **2** to carry in a rowboat: *Row us to the island.* **3** a trip in a rowboat: *It's only a short row to the island.* **1,2** *verb,* **3** *noun.*

row[3] (rou), a noisy quarrel; noise: *The children had a row over the bicycle. What's all this row about? noun.*

row·boat (rō′bōt′), a boat moved by oars. *noun.*

row·dy (rou′dē), **1** a rough, disorderly, quarrelsome person: *The rowdies were ordered to leave the gym.* **2** rough; disorderly; quarrelsome: *The gym was full of a rowdy group of kids.* **1** *noun, plural* **row·dies;** **2** *adjective,* **row·di·er, row·di·est.**

roy·al (roi′əl), **1** of kings and queens: *the royal*

family. **2** belonging to a king or queen: *royal power, a royal palace.* **3** from or by a king or queen: *a royal command.* **4** of a kingdom: *a royal army or navy.* **5** suitable for a king or queen; splendid: *a royal welcome, a royal feast.* **6** like a king or queen; noble; majestic: *The lion is a royal beast. adjective.*

roy·al·ty (roi′əl tē), **1** a royal person; royal persons. Kings, queens, princes, and princesses are royalty. **2** the rank or dignity of a king or queen; royal power: *The crown is the symbol of royalty. noun.*

rub (rub), **1** to move one thing back and forth against another: *Rub your hands to warm them. He rubbed soap on his hands.* **2** to push and press along the surface of: *The nurse rubbed my sore back. That door rubs on the floor.* **3** to make or bring by rubbing: *to rub silver bright.* **4** to clean, smooth, or polish by moving one thing firmly against another: *Rub the silver with a soft cloth.* **5** the act of rubbing: *Give the silver a rub with the polish.* **1-4** *verb,* **rubs, rubbed, rub·bing; 5** *noun.*

rub·ber (rub′ər), **1** an elastic substance made from the juice of certain tropical plants or by a chemical process. Rubber will not let air or water through. **2 rubbers,** low-cut overshoes made of rubber. **3** made of rubber: *a rubber tire.* **1,2** *noun,* **3** *adjective.*

rubber band, a circular strip of rubber, used to hold things together.

rubber stamp, a stamp made of rubber, used with ink for printing dates, signatures, or other special imprints.

rub·bish (rub′ish), **1** trash; waste; worthless or useless stuff: *Pick up the rubbish and burn it.* **2** silly words and thoughts; nonsense: *Gossip is often a lot of rubbish. noun.*

rubble—The construction crew cleared away the **rubble** left by the earthquake.

rub·ble (rub′əl), rough broken stone or bricks. *noun.*

ru·by (rü′bē), **1** a clear, hard, deep-red precious stone. Real rubies are very rare. **2** deep, glowing red: *ruby lips, ruby wine.* **1** *noun, plural* **ru·bies; 2** *adjective.*

ruck·us (ruk′əs), a noisy disturbance or uproar; row: *The children were making a ruckus in the family room. noun.*

rud·der (rud′ər), **1** a movable flat piece of wood or metal at the rear end of a boat or ship by which it is steered. **2** a similar piece on an aircraft. *noun.*

rudder
(definition 1, left;
definition 2, right)

rud·dy (rud′ē), having a fresh, healthy, red look: *ruddy cheeks. adjective,* **rud·di·er, rud·di·est.**

rude (rüd), **1** impolite; not courteous: *It is rude to stare at people or to point.* **2** rough; coarse; roughly made or done: *Prehistoric people made rude tools from stone. adjective,* **rud·er, rud·est.**

rude·ness (rüd′nis), roughness; coarseness; bad manners; violence: *His rudeness is inexcusable. noun.*

rue (rü), to be sorry for; regret: *She will rue the day she left school. verb,* **rues, rued, ru·ing.**

rue·ful (rü′fəl), **1** sorrowful; unhappy; mournful: *a rueful expression.* **2** causing sorrow or pity: *a rueful sight. adjective.*

ruff (ruf), **1** a deep frill stiff enough to stand out, worn around the neck by men and women in the 1500's and 1600's. **2** a collar of specially marked feathers or hairs on the neck of a bird or other animal. *noun.*

ruff (definition 1)

ruf·fi·an (ruf/ē ən), a rough, brutal, or cruel person. *noun.*

ruf·fle (ruf/əl), **1** to make rough or uneven; wrinkle: *A breeze ruffled the lake. The hen ruffled its feathers when the dog barked.* **2** a strip of cloth, ribbon, or lace gathered along one edge and used for trimming. **3** to disturb; annoy: *Nothing can ruffle her calm temper.* **1,3** *verb,* **ruf·fles, ruf·fled, ruf·fling; 2** *noun.*

rug (rug), a heavy floor covering: *a rag rug, a fur rug. Rugs usually cover only part of a room's floor. noun.*

rug·ged (rug/id), **1** covered with rough edges; rough and uneven: *rugged rocks, rugged ground.* **2** sturdy and vigorous; able to do and endure much: *Pioneers were rugged people.* **3** strong and irregular: *rugged features.* **4** harsh; stern: *rugged times.* **5** stormy: *rugged weather. adjective.*

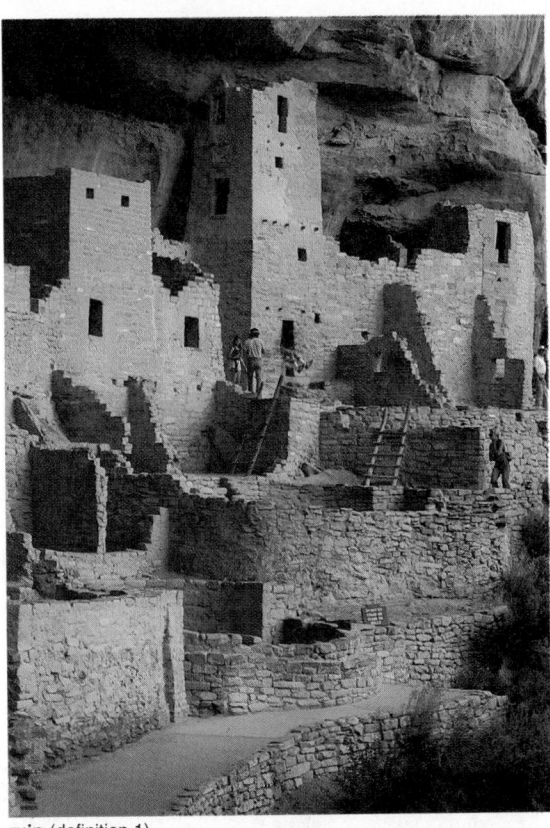

ruin (definition 1)
There are **ruins** of cliff dwellings in Mesa Verde National Park.

ru·in (rü/ən), **1** Often, **ruins.** that which is left after a building or wall has fallen to pieces: *the ruins of an ancient city. That ruin was once a famous castle.* **2** very great damage; destruction; overthrow: *The ruin of property caused by the earthquake was enormous. His enemies planned the duke's ruin.* **3** a fallen or decayed condition: *The house had gone to ruin from neglect.* **4** the cause of destruction, decay, or downfall: *Reckless spending will be your ruin.* **5** to destroy; spoil: *The rain ruined our picnic.* **1-4** *noun,* **5** *verb.*

a hat	i it	oi oil	ch child	a in about
ā age	ī ice	ou out	ng long	e in taken
ä far	o hot	u cup	sh she	ə = i in pencil
e let	ō open	u̇ put	th thin	o in lemon
ē equal	ô order	ü rule	ᴛʜ then	u in circus
ėr term			zh measure	

ru·in·ous (rü/ə nəs), bringing ruin; causing destruction: *The heavy frost in late spring was ruinous to the crops. adjective.*

rule (rül), **1** a statement of what to do and what not to do; principle governing conduct or action: *Obey the rules of the game.* **2** to decide: *My parents ruled in my favor in the dispute between my sister and me. The judge ruled against them.* **3** to control; govern: *The majority rules in a democracy.* **4** a control; government: *the rule of the majority.* **5** the period of power of a ruler; reign: *The Revolutionary War took place during the rule of George III.* **6** a regular method; thing that usually happens or is done; what is usually true: *Fair weather is the rule in June.* **7** a straight strip of wood, metal, or plastic used to measure or as a guide in drawing; ruler. **8** to mark with lines: *She used a ruler to rule the paper.* **1,4-7** *noun,* **2,3,8** *verb,* **rules, ruled, rul·ing.**

as a rule, usually: *As a rule, hail falls in summer rather than in winter.*

rule out, to decide against: *He did not rule out a possible camping trip this summer.*

rul·er (rü/lər), **1** a person who rules: *George III was the ruler of England during the Revolutionary War.* **2** a straight strip of wood, metal, or plastic used in drawing lines or in measuring. *noun.*

rum (rum), a strong alcoholic drink made from sugar cane or molasses. *noun.*

Ru·ma·ni·a (rü mā/nē ə). See **Romania.** *noun.*

rum·ble (rum/bəl), **1** to make a deep, heavy, continuous sound: *Thunder was rumbling in the distance.* **2** a deep, heavy, continuous sound: *We hear the far-off rumble of thunder.* **3** to move with such a sound: *The train rumbled along over the tracks.* **1,3** *verb,* **rum·bles, rum·bled, rum·bling; 2** *noun.*

rum·mage (rum/ij), **1** to search thoroughly by moving things about: *I rummaged in my drawer for a pair of gloves.* **2** a thorough search in which things are moved about: *After a rummage through three drawers I found my gloves.* **1** *verb,* **rum·mag·es, rum·maged, rum·mag·ing; 2** *noun.*

rummage sale, a sale of odds and ends or old clothing, usually held to raise money for charity.

rum·my (rum/ē), a card game in which points are scored by forming sets of three or more cards. *noun.*

ru·mor (rü/mər), **1** a story or statement talked of as news without any proof that it is true: *The rumor spread that a new school would be built here.* **2** vague, general talk: *Rumor has it that the new girl went to school in France.* **3** to tell or spread by rumor: *It was rumored that the*

539

government was going to increase taxes. 1,2 *noun,* 3 *verb.*

rump (rump), the hind part of the body of an animal, where the legs join the back. A rump steak is a cut of beef from this part. *noun.*

rum·ple (rum′pəl), to wrinkle; crush; crumple: *rumple sheets of paper, rumple a suit. verb,* **rum·ples, rum·pled, rum·pling.**

rum·pus (rum′pəs), a noisy disturbance or uproar; row: *The children were making a rumpus in the family room. noun.*

run (run), **1** to go by moving the legs quickly; go faster than walking: *A horse can run faster than a person.* **2** to go in a hurry; hasten: *Run for help.* **3** to make a quick trip: *Let's run over to the lake for the weekend.* **4** to escape; flee: *Run for your life.* **5** to cause to run; cause to move: *to run a horse up and down the track.* **6** to do by running: *to run errands.* **7** to go; move; keep going: *This train runs from Chicago to St. Louis. Does your watch run well?* **8** to creep; grow; climb: *Vines run along the sides of the brick wall.* **9** to pass or cause to pass quickly: *The thought that I might forget my speech ran through my mind.* **10** to stretch; extend: *Shelves run along the walls. The road runs from New York to Atlanta.* **11** to drive; force; thrust: *He ran a splinter into his hand.* **12** to flow; flow with: *Blood runs from a cut. The street ran oil after an oil truck overturned.* **13** to discharge fluid, mucus, or pus: *My nose runs whenever I have a cold.* **14** to get; become; pass into a certain condition: *Never run into debt. The well ran dry.* **15** to spread: *The color ran when the shirt was washed.* **16** to continue; last: *a lease to run two years.* **17** to take part in a race or contest: *Since he has a sore foot, he won't be able to run in the race tomorrow.* **18** to be a candidate for election: *He will run for President.* **19** to expose oneself to: *to run a risk of taking cold.* **20** to move or cause to move easily or smoothly; operate or cause to operate: *The engine ran all day without overheating. Can you run this machine?* **21** the act of running: *to set out at a run. The dog came on the run.* **22** a trip, especially a regular trip over a certain route: *The train makes a run of one hundred miles in two hours.* **23** a quick trip: *Let's take a run over to the lake this afternoon.* **24** to conduct; manage: *to run a business.* **25** a unit of score in baseball: *Our team made three runs in the third inning of the game.* **26** a time; period; spell: *a run of good luck, a run of wet weather.* **27** a series of regular performances: *This play has had a run of two years.* **28** the freedom to go over or through, or to use: *The guests were given the run of the house.* **29** to go about in without control: *The children were allowed to run about the streets.* **30** to drop stitches; become unraveled: *Nylon stockings often run.* **31** a place where stitches have slipped out or become undone: *a run in a stocking.* **32** to get past or through: *Enemy ships tried to run the blockade.* **33** to be suffering from: *to run a fever, to run a temperature.* 1-20,24,29,30,32,33 *verb,* **runs, ran, run, run·ning;** 21-23,25-28,31 *noun.*

in the long run, on the whole; in the end: *In the long run we will have to investigate the mystery.*

run across, to meet by chance: *I ran across an old friend in town today.*

run down, 1 to stop going or working: *The clock has run down.* **2** to knock down by running against: *We stand a good chance of being run down by a car in this traffic.* **3** to say bad things about: *to run down a person, to run down the food at a restaurant.* **4** to make tired or ill: *She is run down from working too hard.*

run into, 1 to meet by chance: *I ran into an old friend at the library.* **2** to crash into: *A large steamship ran into the tugboat.*

run out, to come to an end: *After three minutes his time ran out on the telephone call.*

run out of, to use up; have no more: *Mother ran out of eggs and had to borrow some from her neighbor.*

run over, 1 to ride or drive over: *The car ran over some glass.* **2** to overflow: *The waiter filled my cup too full and the coffee ran over onto the table.*

run through, 1 to spend fast and foolishly: *My cousin ran through a whole week's allowance in one day.* **2** to make a hole through; pierce: *A nail ran through the tire.* **3** to review or rehearse: *The teacher ran through the homework assignment a second time.*

run·a·way (run′ə wā′), **1** a person or animal that runs away. **2** running with nobody to guide or stop it; out of control: *a runaway horse.* 1 *noun,* 2 *adjective.*

run-down (run′doun′), **1** tired; sick: *People who don't eat the right food may become run-down.* **2** falling to pieces; partly ruined: *a run-down old building. adjective.*

rung[1] (rung). See **ring**[2]. *The bell has rung. verb.*

rung[2] (rung), **1** a round rod or bar used as a step of a ladder. **2** a crosspiece set between the legs of a chair or as part of the back or arm of a chair. *noun.*

rung[2]—left (definition 1); right (definition 2)

run·ner (run′ər), **1** a person, animal, or thing that runs; racer: *A runner arrived out of breath.* **2** in baseball, a player on the team at bat who either is on base or is running to the next base. **3** one of the narrow pieces upon which a sleigh, sled, or ice skate slides. **4** a long narrow strip: *We have a runner of carpet in our hall, and runners of linen and lace on bureaus.* **5** a slender stem that takes

a hat	i it	oi oil	ch child	a in about
ā age	ī ice	ou out	ng long	e in taken
ä far	o hot	u cup	sh she	ə = { i in pencil
e let	ō open	u̇ put	th thin	o in lemon
ē equal	ô order	ü rule	ᴛʜ then	u in circus
ėr term			zh measure	

runner (definitions 1, 2, 3, and 5)

root along the ground, thus producing new plants. Strawberry plants spread by runners. *noun.*

run·ner-up (run′ər up′), a player or team that takes second place in a contest. *noun.*

run·ning (run′ing), **1** the act of a person, animal, or thing that runs: *Running is good exercise.* **2** flowing: *I heard the running water of the falls.* **3** continuous; going or carried on continuously: *She made running comments as she showed the slides.* **4** discharging fluid, mucus, or pus: *a running sore. I usually have a running nose when I have a cold.* **5** performed with or during a run: *I made a running jump off the bank into the river.* 1 *noun,* 2-5 *adjective.*

running mate, a candidate in an election who is paired with another candidate from the same political party who is running for a more important office.

run·ny (run′ē), running: *A runny nose and red, runny eyes are symptoms of a cold. adjective,* **run·ni·er, run·ni·est.**

runt (runt), an animal, person, or plant which is smaller than the usual size. *noun.*

run·way (run′wā′), a smooth, level strip of land on which aircraft land and take off. *noun.*

rup·ture (rup′chər), **1** a breaking or being broken: *The rupture of a blood vessel usually causes the mark of a bruise.* **2** to break; burst: *There was a bluish mark on his thigh where a blood vessel ruptured.* 1 *noun,* 2 *verb,* **rup·tures, rup·tured, rup·tur·ing.**

rur·al (rur′əl), in the country; belonging to the country; like that of the country: *a rural school, rural roads. adjective.*

rural delivery or **rural free delivery,** a free delivery of mail in country districts by regular mail carriers.

rural route, a mail route for the free delivery of mail in country areas.

ruse (rüz), a trick or scheme to mislead others. *noun.*

rush[1] (rush), **1** to move with speed or force: *The river rushed past.* **2** to send, push, or force with speed or haste: *Rush this order, please.* **3** to go or act with great haste: *They rush into things without knowing anything about them.* **4** to attack with much speed and force: *The soldiers rushed the enemy.* **5** the act of rushing; dash: *The rush of the flood swept everything before it.* **6** busy haste; hurry: *the rush of city life. What is your rush? Wait a minute.* **7** a great or sudden effort of many people to go somewhere or get something: *a gold rush. The Christmas rush is hard on clerks.* **8** requiring speed: *A rush order must be filled at once.* 1-4 *verb,* 5-7 *noun, plural* **rush·es;** 8 *adjective.*

rush[2]

rush[2] (rush), a grasslike plant with a hollow stem that grows in wet soil or marshy places. The seats of chairs are sometimes made from the stems of rushes. *noun, plural* **rush·es.**

rush hour, the time of day when traffic is heaviest or when trains and buses are most crowded.

R

541

russet—The leaves in the fall are scarlet, yellow, and **russet**.

rus·set (rus′it), yellowish-brown; reddish-brown: *the scarlet, yellow, and russet leaves of autumn. adjective.*

Rus·sia (rush′ə), **1** a country in eastern Europe and northwestern Asia. It was formerly a large part of the Soviet Union. **2** the Soviet Union, a former country reaching from eastern Europe across Asia to the Pacific Ocean. It was made up of 15 republics. *noun.*

Rus·sian (rush′ən), **1** of or having something to do with Russia, its people, or their language. **2** a person born or living in Russia. **3** the chief language of Russia. **1** *adjective,* **2,3** *noun.*

rust (rust), **1** the reddish-brown or orange coating that forms on iron or steel when exposed to air or moisture. **2** to cover or become covered with this: *Don't let the tools rust by leaving them out in the rain.* **3** a plant disease that spots leaves and stems. **1,3** *noun,* **2** *verb.*

rus·tic (rus′tik), belonging to the country; rural; suitable for the country: *The play had a rustic setting. adjective.*

rus·tle (rus′əl), **1** a light, soft sound of things gently rubbing together: *The breeze caused a rustle of the leaves.* **2** to make or cause to make this sound: *Leaves rustled in the breeze. The wind rustled the papers.* **3** to steal cattle or horses: *The sheriff arrested the men who had rustled the cattle from the ranch.* **1** *noun,* **2,3** *verb,* **rus·tles, rus·tled, rus·tling.**

rustle up, 1 to gather; find: *If I am to go on the trip, I must rustle up some money.* **2** to get ready; prepare: *The cook rustled up some food.*

rus·tler (rus′lər), a cattle thief. *noun.*

rust·y (rus′tē), **1** covered with rust; rusted: *a rusty knife.* **2** made by rust: *a rusty spot.* **3** no longer good or effective from lack of use or practice: *My skating is rusty because I haven't skated all winter. adjective,* **rust·i·er, rust·i·est.**

rut (rut), **1** a track made in the ground by wheels: *A car went over the curb and made ruts in our lawn.* **2** to make ruts in: *Our lawn was rutted by a car that went over the curb.* **3** a fixed or established way of acting; boring routine: *Some people become so set in their ways that they get in a rut.* **1,3** *noun,* **2** *verb,* **ruts, rut·ted, rut·ting.**

ruth·less (rüth′lis), having no pity; showing no mercy; cruel: *a ruthless dictator. adjective.*

rye (rī), **1** the grain of a kind of cereal grass, or the plant that it grows on. Rye grows in cool climates and is used for making flour and as food for farm animals. **2** made from rye grain or flour: *rye bread.* **3** a bread made from rye flour: *She ordered a ham sandwich on rye.* **1,3** *noun,* **2** *adjective.*

S s

S or **s** (es), the 19th letter of the English alphabet. *noun, plural* **S's** or **s's.**

S or **S.,** **1** south. **2** southern.

Sab·bath (sab′əth), the day of the week used for rest and worship. Sunday is the Christian Sabbath. Saturday is the Jewish Sabbath. *noun.* [*Sabbath* comes from a Hebrew word meaning "to rest."]

sa·ber (sā′bər), a heavy, curved sword with a sharp edge, used by cavalry. *noun.* [*Saber* comes from a Hungarian word meaning "to cut."]

sa·ber-toothed ti·ger (sā′bər tütht′ tī′gər), a large, prehistoric animal something like a tiger. Two of its upper front teeth were very long and curved.

saber-toothed tiger
about 7 feet (2 meters) long with the tail

sable (definition 1)
about 1½ feet (45 centimeters) long without the tail

sa·ble (sā′bəl), **1** a flesh-eating animal somewhat like a weasel but larger. It has dark-brown, glossy fur. **2** its fur. Sable is one of the most costly furs. *noun.*

sab·o·tage (sab′ə täzh), **1** damage done to property, machinery, bridges, railroads, or the like, especially by enemy agents. **2** to damage or destroy deliberately. **1** *noun,* **2** *verb,* **sab·o·tag·es, sab·o·taged, sab·o·tag·ing.**

sac (sak), a part like a bag in an animal or plant, often one that holds liquids. *noun.*

sa·chem (sā′chəm), the chief of a North American Indian tribe. *noun.*

sack[1] (sak), **1** a large bag made of coarse cloth. Sacks are used for holding grain, flour, potatoes, and charcoal. **2** such a bag with what is in it: *two sacks of corn.* **3** any bag with what is in it: *a sack of candy. noun.*

sack[2] (sak), **1** to plunder a captured city: *The soldiers sacked the town.* **2** the act of plundering a captured city. **1** *verb,* **2** *noun.*

sac·ra·ment (sak′rə mənt), a solemn religious ceremony of the Christian church. Baptism is a sacrament. *noun.*

Sac·ra·men·to (sak′rə men′tō), the capital of California. *noun.*

sa·cred (sā′krid), **1** belonging to or dedicated to God; holy: *A church is a sacred building.* **2** connected with religion; religious: *sacred music.* **3** worthy of reverence: *the sacred memory of a dead hero. adjective.*

sac·ri·fice (sak′rə fīs), **1** the act of offering to a god. **2** the thing offered: *The ancient Hebrews killed animals on the altars as sacrifices to God.* **3** to give or offer to a god. **4** a giving up of one thing for another: *Our teacher does not approve of any sacrifice of studies to sports.* **5** to give up: *to sacrifice one's life for another.* **6** a loss: *They sold their house at a sacrifice because they needed the money.* **1,2,4,6** *noun,* **3,5** *verb,* **sac·ri·fic·es, sac·ri·ficed, sac·ri·fic·ing.**

sacrifice (definition 3)
The ancient Greeks **sacrificed** animals to their gods.

sad (sad), **1** not happy; full of sorrow: *You feel sad if your best friend goes away.* **2** causing sorrow: *The death of a pet is a sad loss. adjective,* **sad·der, sad·dest.**

sad·den (sad′n), to make or become sad: *The bad news saddened her. verb.*

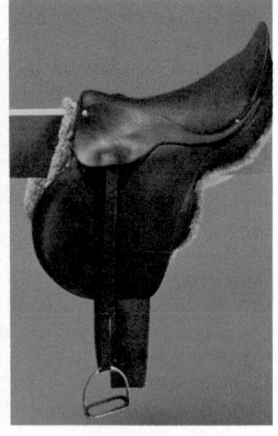

saddles (definition 1)
Western **saddle**   English **saddle**

sad·dle (sad′l), **1** a seat for a rider on a horse's back, on a bicycle, or on other like things. **2** a thing shaped like a saddle. A ridge between two mountain peaks is called a saddle. **3** to put a saddle on: *Saddle the horse.* 1,2 *noun,* 3 *verb,* **sad·dles, sad·dled, sad·dling.**
in the saddle, in a position of control.
sad·dle·bag (sad′l bag′), one of a pair of bags laid over an animal's back behind the saddle, or over the rear fender of a bicycle or motorcycle. *noun.*
sad·ness (sad′nis), a being sad: *A feeling of sadness came over us when our friends moved away. noun.*
sa·fa·ri (sə fär′ē), a journey or hunting expedition in eastern Africa. *noun, plural* **sa·fa·ris.**
[*Safari* comes from an east African word meaning "a journey."]
safe (sāf), **1** free from harm or danger: *Keep money in a safe place.* **2** not harmed: *She returned from the mountain-climbing expedition safe and sound.* **3** out of danger; secure: *We feel safe with the dog in the house.* **4** not causing harm or danger: *Is it safe to leave the house unlocked? A soft rubber ball is a safe plaything.* **5** careful: *a safe guess, a safe move.* **6** that can be depended on: *a safe guide.* **7** (in baseball) reaching a base without being put out. **8** a place or container for keeping things safe. 1-7 *adjective,* **saf·er, saf·est;** 8 *noun.*
safe·guard (sāf′gärd′), **1** to keep safe; guard against hurt or danger; protect: *Pure food laws safeguard our health.* **2** a protection; defense: *Keeping clean is a safeguard against disease.* 1 *verb,* 2 *noun.*
safe·keep·ing (sāf′kē′ping), protection; keeping safe; care. *noun.*
safe·ty (sāf′tē), freedom from harm or danger: *There is a lifeguard at the swimming pool to assure your safety. noun.*
safety belt, a belt or set of belts fastened to the seat or frame of a car or airplane. It helps hold the user in the seat in case of a crash or jolt; seat belt.

safety pin, a pin bent back on itself to form a kind of spring. A guard covers the point of the pin, and prevents the pin from being accidentally unfastened.
sag (sag), **1** to sink, bend, or hang down unevenly under weight or pressure: *The wooden bridge sagged in the middle as the travelers crossed it.* **2** to become less firm or elastic; yield through weakness, weariness, or lack of effort; droop; sink: *Our courage sagged. verb,* **sags, sagged, sag·ging.**
sa·ga (sä′gə), any story of heroic deeds. *noun.*
sage[1] (sāj), a wise man. *noun.*
sage[2] (sāj), the dried leaves of a plant, used as a seasoning in food. *noun.*
sage·brush (sāj′brush′), a grayish-green, bushy plant, common on the dry plains of western North America. *noun.*
sa·gua·ro (sə gwär′ō), a very tall, branching cactus that grows in Arizona and nearby regions. *noun, plural* **sa·gua·ros.**

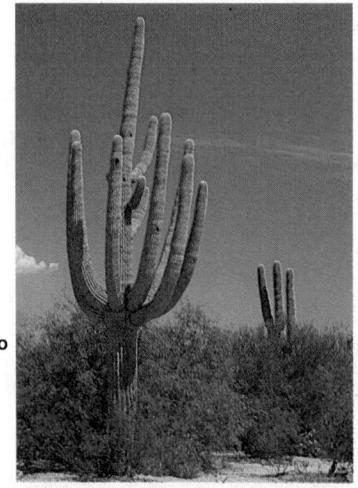

saguaro

Sa·har·a (sə her′ə *or* sə har′ə), a very large desert in northern Africa. *noun.*
said (sed), **1** See **say.** *He said he would come. She had said "No" every time.* **2** named or mentioned before: *the said witness, the said sum of money.* 1 *verb,* 2 *adjective.*
sail (sāl), **1** a piece of cloth that catches the wind to make a ship move on the water. **2** something like a sail, such as the part of a windmill that catches the wind. **3** a trip on a boat with sails: *Let's go for a sail.* **4** to travel on water by the action of wind on sails. **5** to travel on a steamship. **6** to move smoothly like a ship with sails: *The swans sail along the lake. The eagle sailed by. The dancers sailed across the room.* **7** to sail upon, over, or through: *to sail the seas.* **8** to manage a ship or boat: *The boys are learning to sail.* **9** to begin a trip by water: *She sailed from New York.* 1-3 *noun,* 4-9 *verb.*
sail·boat (sāl′bōt′), a boat that is moved by sails. Schooners and sloops are kinds of sailboats. *noun.*

sail·or (sā′lər), **1** a person whose work is handling a boat or other vessel. **2** a member of a ship's crew. Members of the United States Navy who are not officers are called sailors. **3** like a sailor's: *Her blouse has a sailor collar.* **1,2** *noun,* **3** *adjective.*

saint (sānt), **1** a very holy person. **2** a person declared to be a saint by a church. **3** a person who is very humble, patient, or like a saint in other ways. *noun.*

Saint Ber·nard (sānt′ bər närd′), a big, brown-and-white dog with a large head. This dog was first bred by monks to rescue travelers lost in the Swiss Alps.

saint·ly (sānt′lē), like a saint; very holy; very good. *adjective,* **saint·li·er, saint·li·est.**

sake (sāk), **1** cause; account; interest: *Do not go to any trouble for our sakes.* **2** purpose; end: *We moved to the country for the sake of peace and quiet. noun.*

sal·ad (sal′əd), raw green vegetables, such as lettuce and celery, served with a dressing. Often cold meat, fish, eggs, cooked vegetables, or fruits are used along with, or instead of, the raw green vegetables. *noun.*

sal·a·man·der (sal′ə man′dər), an animal shaped like a lizard, but belonging to the same group as frogs and toads. Salamanders live in damp places. *noun.*

salamander—about 5 inches (13 centimeters) long

sa·la·mi (sə lä′mē), a kind of thick sausage, often flavored with garlic. It is usually sliced and eaten cold. *noun, plural* **sa·la·mis.**

sal·ar·y (sal′ər ē), a fixed sum of money paid for work done: *Her yearly salary was $25,000. noun, plural* **sal·ar·ies.**
[*Salary* comes from a Latin word meaning "money given to soldiers for buying salt." In ancient times salt was scarce, and therefore very expensive.]

sale (sāl), **1** the act of selling; exchange of goods for money: *the sale of a house.* **2 sales,** the amount sold: *Today's sales were larger than yesterday's.* **3** a selling at lower prices than usual: *This store is having a sale on suits. noun.*
for sale, to be sold: *That car is for sale.*
on sale, for sale at lower prices than usual: *The grocer has coffee on sale today.*

Sa·lem (sā′ləm), the capital of Oregon. *noun.*

a hat	i it	oi oil	ch child	⎧ a in about
ā age	ī ice	ou out	ng long	e in taken
ä far	o hot	u cup	sh she	ə = ⎨ i in pencil
e let	ō open	u̇ put	th thin	o in lemon
ē equal	ô order	ü rule	ᴛʜ then	⎩ u in circus
ėr term			zh measure	

sales·clerk (sālz′klėrk′), a person whose work is selling in a store. *noun.*

sales·man (sālz′mən), a person whose work is selling. *noun, plural* **sales·men.**

sales·per·son (sālz′pėr′sən), a person whose work is selling, especially in a store. *noun.*

sales·wom·an (sālz′wům′ən), a woman whose work is selling. *noun, plural* **sales·wom·en.**

sa·li·va (sə lī′və), the liquid produced by glands in the mouth to keep it moist, help in chewing, and start digestion. *noun.*

sal·i·var·y (sal′ə ver′ē), of or producing saliva: *the salivary glands. adjective.*

sal·low (sal′ō), having a sickly, yellowish color: *a sallow complexion. adjective.*

sal·ly (sal′ē), **1** to rush forth suddenly; go out; set out briskly: *We sallied forth at dawn.* **2** a sudden rushing forth: *The men in the fort made a brave sally.* **1** *verb,* **sal·lies, sal·lied, sal·ly·ing; 2** *noun, plural* **sal·lies.**

salm·on (sam′ən), **1** a large food fish with silvery scales and yellowish-pink flesh. **2** yellowish-pink. **1** *noun, plural* **salm·on** or **salm·ons; 2** *adjective.*

salmon (definition 1)—up to 19 inches (48 centimeters) long

sa·loon (sə lün′), a place where alcoholic drinks are sold and drunk. *noun.*

salt (sôlt), **1** a white substance found in the earth and in sea water. Salt is used to season and preserve food. **2** containing salt: *The ocean is a great body of salt water.* **3** to season with salt; sprinkle with salt: *We salted the popcorn before eating it.* **4** a chemical compound of a metal and an acid. Baking soda is a salt. **1,4** *noun,* **2** *adjective,* **3** *verb.*
salt away or **salt down, 1** to pack with salt to preserve: *The fish were salted down in a barrel.* **2** to store away: *She is salting away money for her retirement.*

Salt Lake City, the capital of Utah.

salt·wa·ter (sôlt′wô′tər), **1** consisting of or containing salt water: *a saltwater solution.* **2** living in the sea or in water like seawater: *saltwater fish. adjective.*

S

salt·y (sôl′tē), containing salt; tasting of salt. Sweat and tears are salty. *adjective,* **salt·i·er, salt·i·est.**

sal·u·ta·tion (sal′yə tā′shən), **1** a greeting; saluting: *The man raised his hand in salutation.* **2** something said, written, or done to salute. You begin a letter with a salutation, such as "Dear Mr. Jones" or "Dear Sue." *noun.*

sa·lute (sə lüt′), **1** to honor in a formal manner by raising the hand to the head, by firing guns, or by dipping flags: *We salute the flag every day at school. The soldier saluted the officer.* **2** to meet with kind words, a bow, a kiss, or other greeting; greet: *The old gentleman walked along the avenue saluting his friends.* **3** the act of saluting; sign of welcome or honor: *The queen gracefully acknowledged the salutes of the crowd.* **4** the position of the hand or a gun in saluting. 1,2 *verb,* **sa·lutes, sa·lut·ed, sa·lut·ing;** 3,4 *noun.* [*Salute* comes from a Latin word meaning "to wish good health to" or "to greet."]

sal·vage (sal′vij), **1** the act of saving a ship or its cargo from wreck or capture. **2** the rescue of property from fire, flood, or shipwreck. **3** to save from fire, flood, or shipwreck. 1,2 *noun,* 3 *verb,* **sal·vag·es, sal·vaged, sal·vag·ing.**

sal·va·tion (sal vā′shən), **1** a saving; being saved. **2** a person or thing that saves. **3** a saving of the soul; deliverance from sin and from punishment for sin. *noun.*

salve (sav), **1** a soft, greasy substance put on wounds and sores; healing ointment: *Is this salve good for burns?* **2** to put salve on. **3** to soothe; smooth over: *She salved her conscience by the thought that her lie harmed no one.* 1 *noun,* 2,3 *verb,* **salves, salved, salv·ing.**

same (sām), **1** not another: *We came back the same way we went.* **2** just alike; not different: *Her name and mine are the same.* **3** not changed: *It is the same beautiful place.* **4** the same person or thing. **5 the same,** in the same manner: *"Sea" and "see" are pronounced the same.* 1-3 *adjective,* 4 *pronoun,* 5 *adverb.*

all the same, regardless; nevertheless: *All the same, I'm glad to be at home again.*

just the same, 1 in the same manner: *The stairs creaked just the same as ever.* **2** nevertheless: *Just the same, I am planning to go.*

sam·pan (sam′pan), a kind of small boat used in China, Japan, and nearby regions. A sampan is sculled by one or more oars at the stern; it usually has a single sail. *noun.*

sam·ple (sam′pəl), **1** a part to show what the rest is like; one thing to show what the others are like: *Here are some samples of drapery material for you to choose from.* **2** to take a part of; test a part of: *We sampled the cake and found it very good.* 1 *noun,* 2 *verb,* **sam·ples, sam·pled, sam·pling.**

San An·dre·as Fault (san än drā′əs fôlt′), a large break in the earth's crust located in California. It is a center of earthquake activity.

San An·to·ni·o (san an tō′nē ō), a city in Texas.

san·a·to·ri·um (san′ə tôr′ē əm), a place for treating people who are sick or recovering from an illness. *noun.*

sanc·tion (sangk′shən), permission with authority; support; approval: *You need the owner's sanction to cross this property. noun.*

sanc·tu·ar·y (sangk′chü er′ē), **1** a sacred place. A church is a sanctuary. **2** refuge or protection: *We found sanctuary from the storm in an abandoned cabin.* **3** a place of refuge or protection: *a wildlife sanctuary. noun, plural* **sanc·tu·ar·ies.**

sand (sand), **1** tiny grains of broken rock: *the sands of the seashore, the sands of the desert.* **2** to spread sand over: *The highway department sanded the icy road.* **3** to scrape, smooth, polish, or clean with sand or sandpaper: *to sand the edges of a piece of wood.* 1 *noun,* 2,3 *verb.*

san·dal (san′dl), a kind of shoe made of a sole fastened to the foot by straps. *noun.*

san·dal·wood (san′dl wüd′), the fragrant wood of certain trees of Asia, used for making boxes, fans, and other items, and burned as incense. *noun.*

sand·bag (sand′bag′), **1** a bag filled with sand. Sandbags are used to hold back flood waters and as ballast on balloons. **2** to furnish with sandbags: *Several home owners sandbagged their driveways to keep the rising waters out of their houses.* 1 *noun,* 2 *verb,* **sand·bags, sand·bagged, sand·bag·ging.**

sand·bar (sand′bär′), a ridge of sand in a river or along a shore, formed by the action of tides or currents. *noun.*

sand·box (sand′boks′), a box for holding sand, especially for children to play in. *noun, plural* **sand·box·es.**

San Di·e·go (san dē ā′gō), a city in California.

sand·pa·per (sand′pā′pər), **1** a strong paper with sand glued on it, used for smoothing, cleaning, or polishing. **2** to smooth, clean, or polish with sandpaper. 1 *noun,* 2 *verb.*

sampan

sandpiper—about 9 inches (23 centimeters) long

sand·pip·er (sand′pī′pər), a small bird with a long bill, living on sandy shores. *noun.*

sand·stone (sand′stōn′), a kind of rock formed mostly of sand. *noun.*

sand·storm (sand′stôrm′), a storm of wind that bears along clouds of sand. *noun.*

sand·wich (sand′wich), **1** two or more slices of bread with meat, jelly, cheese, or some other filling between them. **2** to put in between: *I was sandwiched between two large boxes in the back seat of the car.* 1 *noun, plural* **sand·wich·es;** 2 *verb.*
[*Sandwich* was named for the fourth Earl of Sandwich, a British official who lived from 1718 to 1792. He is said to have invented this kind of food so that he would not have to stop in the middle of a card game to eat a regular meal.]

sand·y (san′dē), **1** containing sand; consisting of sand: *sandy soil.* **2** covered with sand: *Most of the shore is rocky, but there is a sandy beach.* **3** yellowish-red: *She has sandy hair. adjective,* **sand·i·er, sand·i·est.**

sane (sān), **1** having a healthy mind; not crazy. **2** having or showing good sense; sensible: *A person with a sane attitude toward driving doesn't take chances. adjective,* **san·er, san·est.**

sang (sang). See **sing.** *The bird sang for us yesterday. verb.*

san·i·tar·i·um (san′ə ter′ē əm), a sanatorium. *noun.*

san·i·tar·y (san′ə ter′ē), **1** of or having to do with health; favorable to health; preventing disease: *sanitary regulations in a hospital.* **2** free from dirt and filth: *Food should be kept in a sanitary place. adjective.*

san·i·ta·tion (san′ə tā′shən), the working out of ways to improve health conditions; practical application of sanitary measures. *noun.*

san·i·ty (san′ə tē), **1** soundness of mind; mental health. **2** soundness of judgment; sensibleness. *noun.*

San Juan (san wän′), the capital of Puerto Rico.

sank (sangk). See **sink.** *The ship sank before help reached it. verb.*

San·ta Claus (san′tə klôz′), the saint of Christmas giving. He is pictured as a fat, jolly, old man with a white beard, dressed in a fur-trimmed red suit.

San·ta Fe (san′tə fā′), the capital of New Mexico.

São Pau·lo (soun pou′lu̇), a city in Brazil.

sap¹ (sap), the liquid that circulates through a plant, carrying water and food as blood does in animals. Rising sap carries water and dissolved minerals; sap going downward carries water and dissolved food. *noun.*

sap² (sap), to weaken; use up: *The extreme heat and humidity sapped her strength. verb,* **saps, sapped, sap·ping.**

sap·ling (sap′ling), a young tree. *noun.*

sap·phire (saf′īr), **1** a hard, clear, bright-blue precious stone. **2** bright-blue: *a sapphire sky.* 1 *noun,* 2 *adjective.*

sar·casm (sär′kaz əm), **1** a sneering or cutting remark. **2** the act of making fun of a person to hurt his or her feelings; harsh or bitter irony: *"How unselfish you are!" said the girl in sarcasm as her sister took the biggest piece of cake. noun.*
[*Sarcasm* comes from a Greek word meaning "to speak bitterly" or "to tear the flesh."]

sar·cas·tic (sär kas′tik), using sarcasm; sneering; bitterly cutting: *"Don't hurry!" was my brother's sarcastic comment as I slowly dressed. adjective.*

sar·dine (sär dēn′), one of several kinds of small fish preserved in oil for food. *noun, plural* **sar·dines** or **sar·dine.**

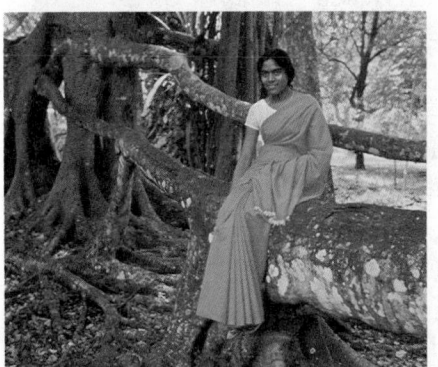

sari

sa·ri (sär′ē), a long piece of cotton or silk worn wound around the body with one end thrown over the head or shoulder. It is the outer garment of Hindu women. *noun, plural* **sa·ris.**

sash¹ (sash), a long, broad strip of cloth or ribbon, worn as an ornament around the waist or over one shoulder. *noun, plural* **sash·es.**

S

sash[2] (sash), a frame for the glass of a window or door. *noun, plural* **sash·es.**

Sa·skatch·e·wan (sa skach′ə won), a province in south central Canada. *Capital:* Regina. *noun.*

sass (sas), **1** rudeness; back talk. **2** to be rude or disrespectful to: *The little girl sassed her mother.* **1** *noun,* **2** *verb.*

sas·sa·fras (sas′ə fras), **1** a slender American tree that has fragrant, yellow flowers and bluish-black fruit. **2** the dried bark of its root, used in medicine and to flavor tea, candy, soft drinks, and the like. *noun.*

sas·sy (sas′ē), rude. *adjective,* **sas·si·er, sas·si·est.**

sat (sat). See **sit.** *Yesterday we sat inside for several hours, waiting for the rain to stop. The cat has sat at that mouse hole for hours. verb.*

Sat., Saturday.

Sa·tan (sāt′n), (in the Jewish and Christian religions) the supreme evil spirit; the Devil. *noun.*
[*Satan* comes from a Hebrew word meaning "enemy."]

satch·el (sach′əl), a small bag, especially one for carrying clothes or books. *noun.*

sat·el·lite (sat′l īt), **1** a heavenly body that revolves around a planet; a moon. The moon is a satellite of the earth. **2** an artificial object shot by a rocket into an orbit around the earth or other heavenly body. Such satellites are used to send weather and other scientific information back to earth; they also transmit television programs across the earth. **3** a country that claims to be independent but is actually under the control of another. *noun.*

satellite (definition 2)—an environmental research **satellite**

sat·in (sat′n), **1** a silk or rayon cloth with one very smooth, glossy side. **2** of satin; like satin; smooth and glossy. **1** *noun,* **2** *adjective.*

sat·is·fac·tion (sat′i sfak′shən), **1** the condition of being satisfied, or pleased and contented: *She felt satisfaction at having done well.* **2** anything that makes us feel pleased or contented: *It is a great satisfaction to have things turn out just the way you want. noun.*

sat·is·fac·tor·i·ly (sat′i sfak′tər ə lē), in a satisfactory manner. *adverb.*

sat·is·fac·tor·y (sat′i sfak′tər ē), satisfying; good enough to satisfy; adequate: *If you do*

satisfactory work in the fourth grade, you will pass to the fifth grade. *adjective.*

sat·is·fy (sat′i sfī), **1** to give enough to; fulfill desires, hopes, or demands; put an end to needs or wants: *He satisfied his hunger with a sandwich and milk.* **2** to make contented; please: *Are you satisfied now?* **3** to pay; make right: *After the accident he satisfied all claims for the damage he had caused.* **4** to set free from doubt; convince: *She is satisfied that it was an accident. verb,* **sat·is·fies, sat·is·fied, sat·is·fy·ing.**

sat·u·rate (sach′ə rāt′), to soak thoroughly; fill full: *During the fog, the air was saturated with moisture. verb,* **sat·u·rates, sat·u·rat·ed, sat·u·rat·ing.**

Sat·ur·day (sat′ər dē), the seventh day of the week; the day after Friday. *noun.*
[*Saturday* comes from an earlier English word meaning "Saturn's day." It referred to the planet Saturn.]

Sat·urn (sat′ərn), **1** the Roman god of agriculture. **2** the second largest planet. Saturn has a system of many rings around it. *noun.*

sauce (sôs), **1** something, usually a liquid, served with or on food to make it taste better. We eat mint sauce with lamb, egg sauce with fish, and many different sauces with ice cream. **2** stewed fruit: *cranberry sauce. noun.*

sauce·pan (sôs′pan′), a small pan with a handle, used for stewing and boiling. *noun.*

sau·cer (sô′sər), a shallow dish to set a cup on. *noun.*

sau·cy (sô′sē), showing lack of respect; rude: *saucy language, saucy conduct. adjective,* **sau·ci·er, sau·ci·est.**

Sa·u·di A·ra·bi·a (sä ü′dē ə rā′bē ə), a country in southwestern Asia.

sauer·kraut (sour′krout′), cabbage cut fine, salted, and allowed to sour. *noun.*
[*Sauerkraut* comes from two German words meaning "sour" and "cabbage."]

saun·ter (sôn′tər), **1** to walk along slowly and happily; stroll: *People sauntered through the park on summer evenings.* **2** a stroll. **1** *verb,* **2** *noun.*

sau·sage (sô′sij), chopped pork, beef, or other meats, seasoned and usually stuffed into a thin tube. *noun.*

sav·age (sav′ij), **1** a member of a primitive, uncivilized people. **2** fierce; cruel; ready to fight: *a savage dog.* **3** a fierce, brutal, or cruel person. **4** wild or rugged: *savage mountain scenery.* **1,3** *noun,* **2,4** *adjective.*

sav·age·ry (sav′ij rē), **1** fierceness; cruelty; brutality. **2** wildness. **3** an uncivilized condition. *noun, plural* **sav·age·ries.**

sa·van·na or **sa·van·nah** (sə van′ə), a grassy plain with few or no trees, especially one in the southern United States or near the tropics. *noun.*

save (sāv), **1** to make or keep safe; rescue or protect from harm, danger, loss, or the like; rescue: *The dog saved the boy's life. We covered the plants with straw to save them from the frost.* **2** to lay aside; store up: *to save money, to save* rubber bands. **3** to keep from spending or wasting: *We took the shortcut to save time.* **4** to avoid expense or waste: *Save in every way you can.* **5** to prevent; make less: *to save work, to save trouble.* **6** to treat carefully to keep in good condition: *Save your strength for the big race. verb,* **saves, saved, sav·ing.**

sav·ing (sā′ving), **1** tending to save up money; avoiding waste; economical. **2 savings,** money saved. **3** a way of saving money or time: *It will be a saving to take this shortcut.* **1** *adjective,* **2,3** *noun.*

sav·ior (sā′vyər), a person who saves or rescues. *noun.*

sa·vor (sā′vər), to enjoy the taste or smell of; enjoy very much: *We savored the soup. verb.*

sa·vor·y (sā′vər ē), pleasing in taste or smell: *The savory smell of roasting turkey greeted us as we entered the house. adjective.*

saw¹ (sô), **1** a tool for cutting, made of a thin blade with sharp teeth on the edge. **2** to cut or be cut with a saw: *to saw wood. Pine saws more easily than oak.* **1** *noun,* **2** *verb,* **saws, sawed, sawed** or **sawn, saw·ing.**

saw² (sô). See **see.** *I saw a robin yesterday. verb.*

saw·dust (sô′dust′), particles of wood made by sawing. *noun.*

saw·horse (sô′hôrs′), a frame for holding wood that is being sawed. *noun.*

saw·mill (sô′mil′), a building where machines saw timber into planks or boards. *noun.*

sawn (sôn), sawed. See **saw**¹. *verb.*

saxophone

sax·o·phone (sak′sə fōn), a brass musical wind instrument with keys for the fingers and a reed mouthpiece. *noun.*
[*Saxophone* was formed from the name of its Belgian inventor, Adolphe Sax, who lived from 1814 to 1894, and a Greek word meaning "sound."]

say (sā), **1** to speak: *What did you say? "Thank you,"* she said. **2** to put into words; declare: *Say*

a hat	i it	oi oil	ch child		a in about
ā age	ī ice	ou out	ng long		e in taken
ä far	o hot	u cup	sh she	ə =	i in pencil
e let	ō open	u̇ put	th thin		o in lemon
ē equal	ô order	ü rule	ŦH then		u in circus
ėr term			zh measure		

what you think. **3** to recite; repeat: *Say your prayers.* **4** about; approximately: *You can learn to dance in, say, ten lessons.* **5** a chance to say something: *If you have all had your say, we will vote on the matter.* **6** power; authority: *Who has the final say in this matter?* **1-3** *verb,* **says, said, say·ing; 4** *adverb,* **5,6** *noun.*

say·ing (sā′ing), **1** something said; statement. **2** a proverb: *"Haste makes waste"* is a saying. *noun.*

says (sez). See **say.** *He says he'll be late. verb.*

SC, South Carolina (used with postal Zip Code).

S.C., South Carolina.

scab (skab), a crust that forms over a sore as it heals: *A scab started to form on my scraped knee. noun.*

scab·bard (skab′ərd), a sheath or case for the blade of a sword, dagger, or knife. *noun.*

scaf·fold (skaf′əld), **1** a temporary structure for holding workers and materials. **2** a raised platform on which criminals are put to death. *noun.*

scaffold (definition 1)—used to bring materials to the various floors of a building under construction

scald (skôld), **1** to burn with hot liquid or steam: *I scalded myself with hot grease.* **2** to pour boiling liquid over: *Scald the dishes before drying them.* **3** to heat almost to boiling, but not quite: *Scald the milk. verb.*

scale¹ (skāl), **1** the dish or pan of a balance. **2 scales,** a balance; instrument for weighing: *She weighed some meat on the scales. noun.*

scale² (skāl), **1** one of the thin, flat, hard plates forming the outer covering of some fish, snakes, and lizards. **2** a thin layer like a scale: *My sunburn caused my skin to peel off in scales.* **3** to remove scales from: *She scaled the fish with a knife.* **4** to come off in scales: *The paint is scaling.* **1,2** *noun,* **3,4** *verb,* **scales, scaled, scal·ing.**

S

549

scale³ (skāl), **1** a series of steps or degrees; scheme of graded amounts: *The salary scale for this job ranges from $12,000 to $15,000.* **2** a series of marks made along a line at regular distances to use in measuring. A thermometer has a scale. **3** the size of a plan, map, drawing, or model compared with what it represents: *This map is drawn to the scale of one inch for each 100 miles.* **4** relative size or extent: *An ambassador must entertain on a large scale.* **5** to reduce by a certain amount in relation to other amounts: *To draw this map, mileage was scaled down to one inch for each 100 miles.* **6** (in music) a series of tones ascending or descending in pitch: *She practices scales on the piano.* **7** to climb: *They scaled the wall by ladders.* 1-4,6 *noun,* 5,7 *verb,* **scales, scaled, scal·ing.**

sca·lene tri·an·gle (skā′lēn′ trī′ang′gəl), a triangle that has three sides unequal.

scalene triangles

scallop (definition 1) shell up to 3 inches (8 centimeters) long

scal·lop (skol′əp), **1** a shellfish somewhat like a clam. In some kinds the large muscle that opens and closes the shell is good to eat. **2** to bake with sauce and bread crumbs in a dish: *scalloped oysters, scalloped tomatoes.* **3** one of a series of curves on the edge of anything: *This cuff has scallops.* **4** to make with such curves: *She scalloped the edge of the quilt.* 1,3 *noun,* 2,4 *verb.*

scalp (skalp), **1** the skin on the top and back of the head, usually covered with hair. **2** to cut or tear the scalp from. 1 *noun,* 2 *verb.*

scal·y (skā′lē), covered with scales; having scales like a fish: *This iron pipe is scaly with rust.* *adjective,* **scal·i·er, scal·i·est.**

scamp (skamp), a rascal; rogue. *noun.*

scam·per (skam′pər), to run quickly: *The mice scampered away when the cat came.* *verb.*

scan (skan), to look at closely; examine with care: *You should scan every word of the contract before you sign it.* *verb,* **scans, scanned, scan·ning.**

scan·dal (skan′dl), **1** a shameful action that brings disgrace or shocks public opinion: *It was a scandal for the city treasurer to take tax money for personal use.* **2** public talk about a person which will hurt that person's reputation; evil gossip; slander. *noun.*

scan·dal·ize (skan′dl īz), to offend by something thought to be wrong or improper; shock: *Our*

great-grandparents would be scandalized by many of the things we do today. *verb,* **scan·dal·iz·es, scan·dal·ized, scan·dal·iz·ing.**

scan·dal·ous (skan′dl əs), **1** disgraceful; shameful; shocking. **2** spreading scandal or slander: *a scandalous piece of gossip.* *adjective.*

Scan·di·na·vi·a (skan′də nā′vē ə), a region of northwestern Europe that includes Norway, Sweden, Denmark, and sometimes Finland and Iceland. *noun.*

Scan·di·na·vi·an (skan′də nā′vē ən), **1** of Scandinavia, its people, or their languages. **2** a person born or living in Scandinavia. **3** the languages of Denmark, Iceland, Norway, and Sweden. 1 *adjective,* 2,3 *noun.*

Word Source

Scandinavian languages gave many words to English. Here are some of the words that have come from Scandinavian:

anger	get	nay	sister	tungsten
auk	geyser	nickel	ski	ugly
calf²	guest	odd	skirt	viking
clip¹	husband	outlaw	skull	weak
egg¹	leak	reindeer	sky	wheeze
egg²	lemming	saga	tight	window
fiord	loft	scale¹	troll²	wing
flaw	low¹	scare	trust	wrong
floe	nag¹			

---

scant (skant), **1** not enough in size or quantity: *Her coat was short and scant.* **2** barely enough; barely full; bare: *Use a scant cup of butter in the cake. You have a scant hour to pack.* *adjective.*

scant·y (skan′tē), barely enough; meager: *Drought caused a scanty harvest.* *adjective,* **scant·i·er, scant·i·est.**

scar (skär), **1** a mark left by a healed cut, wound, burn, or sore: *My vaccination scar is small.* **2** any mark like this: *See the scars your shoes have made on the chair.* **3** to mark with a scar: *He scarred the wood with the hammer when he missed the nail.* 1,2 *noun,* 3 *verb,* **scars, scarred, scar·ring.**

scarce (skers or skars), hard to get; rare: *Very old stamps are scarce.* *adjective,* **scarc·er, scarc·est.**

scarce·ly (skers′lē or skars′lē), **1** not quite; barely: *We could scarcely see the ship through the thick fog.* **2** decidedly not: *He can scarcely have said that.* *adverb.*

scar·ci·ty (sker′sə tē or skar′sə tē), too small a supply; lack; rarity: *There is a scarcity of nurses.* *noun, plural* **scar·ci·ties.**

scare (sker or skar), **1** to frighten: *We were scared and ran away.* **2** a fright: *I had a sudden scare when I saw a dog running toward me.* **3** a widespread state of fright or panic: *a bomb scare at the airport. Such scares are often exaggerated and without foundation or reason.* **4** to frighten away; drive off: *The watchdog scared away the robber by barking.* 1,4 *verb,* **scares, scared, scar·ing;** 2,3 *noun.*

scare·crow (sker′krō′ *or* skar′krō′), a figure of a person dressed in old clothes, set in a field to frighten birds away from growing crops. *noun.*

scarf (skärf), a long, broad strip of silk, lace, or other material, worn about the neck, shoulders, or head. *noun, plural* **scarfs, scarves** (skärvz).

scar·let (skär′lit), very bright red. *adjective.*

scarlet fever, a disease most often of children that causes a scarlet rash, sore throat, and fever. You can catch scarlet fever if you are around someone who has it.

scar·y (sker′ē *or* skar′ē), causing fright or alarm: *scary sounds, a scary movie. adjective,* **scar·i·er, scar·i·est.**

scat (skat), an exclamation used to make an animal run away. *interjection.*
[*Scat* may have been formed by joining parts of the words *hiss* and *cat.*]

scat·ter (skat′ər), **1** to throw here and there; sprinkle: *I scattered salt on the sidewalk to melt the ice.* **2** to separate and drive off in different directions: *The police scattered the disorderly crowd.* **3** to separate and go in different directions: *The chickens scattered in fright when the truck honked at them. verb.*

scav·en·ger (skav′ən jər), an animal that feeds on dead and decaying animals or plants. Vultures are scavengers. *noun.*

scene (sēn), **1** the time, place, and circumstances of a play or story: *The scene of the book is laid in Boston in the year 1775.* **2** a place where something happens or takes place: *the scene of an accident.* **3** the painted screens or hangings used in a theater to represent places; scenery: *The scene represents a city street.* **4** a part of an act of a play: *The king comes to the castle in Act I, Scene 2.* **5** a view; picture: *The white sailboats in the blue water made a pretty scene.* **6** a show of strong feeling in front of others: *The child kicked and screamed and made a dreadful scene. noun.*

scen·er·y (sē′nər ē), **1** the general appearance of a place: *She enjoys mountain scenery very much.* **2** the painted hangings or screens used in a theater to represent places: *The scenery pictures a garden in the moonlight. noun.*

scen·ic (sē′nik), **1** of or having something to do with natural scenery: *The scenic splendors of Yellowstone National Park are famous.* **2** having much fine scenery: *a scenic highway. adjective.*

scent (sent), **1** a smell: *The scent of roses filled the air.* **2** to smell: *The dog scented a rabbit and ran off after it.* **3** the sense of smell: *Many dogs have a keen scent.* **4** a smell left in passing: *The dogs followed the fox by the scent.* **5** a means by which a thing or a person can be traced: *The police are on the scent of the thieves.* **6** to have a suspicion of; be aware of: *I scent a trick in their offer.* **7** perfume: *She used too much scent.* **8** to fill with odor; perfume: *scented writing paper.* **1,3-5,7** *noun,* **2,6,8** *verb.*

scep·ter (sep′tər), the rod or staff carried by a ruler as a symbol of royal power or authority. *noun.*

a	hat	i	it	oi	oil	ch	child		a in about
ā	age	ī	ice	ou	out	ng	long		e in taken
ä	far	o	hot	u	cup	sh	she	ə =	i in pencil
e	let	ō	open	u̇	put	th	thin		o in lemon
ē	equal	ô	order	ü	rule	ᵺ	then		u in circus
ėr	term					zh	measure		

sched·ule (skej′ül), **1** a written or printed statement of details; list: *a television program schedule, an airline schedule.* **2** to plan or arrange something for a definite time or date: *We scheduled our vacation for August.* **3** the time for doing something, for arriving at a place, or the like: *The bus was an hour behind schedule.* **1,3** *noun,* **2** *verb,* **sched·ules, sched·uled, sched·ul·ing.**

scheme (skēm), **1** a program of action; plan: *He has a scheme for extracting salt from sea water.* **2** a plot: *a scheme to cheat the government.* **3** to plan; plot: *They were scheming to smuggle the stolen jewels into the country.* **4** a system of connected things, parts, or thoughts: *The color scheme of the room is blue and gold.* **1,2,4** *noun,* **3** *verb,* **schemes, schemed, schem·ing.**

schol·ar (skol′ər), **1** a person having much knowledge: *The professor was a famous scholar.* **2** a pupil at school; learner. *noun.*

schol·ar·ly (skol′ər lē), **1** of a scholar; like that of a scholar: *scholarly habits.* **2** having much knowledge: *a scholarly person. adjective.*

schol·ar·ship (skol′ər ship), **1** the possession of knowledge gained by study; quality of learning and knowledge. **2** money given to help a student continue his or her studies: *The college offered her a scholarship of one thousand dollars. noun.*

school[1] (skül), **1** a place for teaching and learning: *Children go to school to learn.* **2** learning in school; instruction: *Most children start school when they are about five years old.* **3** regular meetings of teachers and pupils for teaching and learning. **4** a time or period of such meetings: *to stay after school.* **5** pupils who are taught and their teachers: *Our school will be in a new building next fall.* **6** a group of people holding the same beliefs or opinions: *the French school of painting.* **7** a particular department or group in a university: *a medical school, a law school.* **8** to teach; train; discipline: *School yourself to control your temper.*

scepter
At her coronation, Queen Elizabeth II held a **scepter** in her right hand.

S

9 of or having something to do with a school or schools. 1-7 *noun,* 8 *verb,* 9 *adjective.*

school² (skül), a large number of the same kind of fish or water animals swimming together: *a school of mackerel. noun.*

school·book (skül′bůk′), a book for study in schools; textbook. *noun.*

school·boy (skül′boi′), a boy attending school. *noun.*

school·child (skül′chīld′), a schoolboy or schoolgirl. *noun, plural* **school·chil·dren** (skül′chil′drən).

school·girl (skül′gėrl′), a girl attending school. *noun.*

school·house (skül′hous′), a building used as a school. *noun, plural* **school·hous·es** (skül′hou′ziz).

school·ing (skü′ling), instruction in school; education received at school. *noun.*

school·mas·ter (skül′mas′tər), a man who teaches in a school, or is its principal. *noun.*

school·mate (skül′māt′), a companion at school. *noun.*

school·mis·tress (skül′mis′tris), a woman who teaches in a school, or is its principal. *noun, plural* **school·mis·tress·es.**

school·room (skül′rüm′), a room in which pupils are taught. *noun.*

school·teach·er (skül′tē′chər), a person who teaches in a school. *noun.*

school·work (skül′wėrk′), a student's lessons and assignments. *noun.*

school·yard (skül′yärd′), a piece of ground around or near a school, used for play or games. *noun.*

schoon·er (skü′nər), a ship with two or more masts and sails set lengthwise. *noun.*

schooner

schwa (shwä), **1** an unstressed vowel sound such as *a* in *about* or *o* in *lemon.* **2** the symbol ə, used to represent this sound. *noun.*

sci·ence (sī′əns), **1** knowledge based on observed facts and tested truths arranged in an orderly system. **2** a branch of such knowledge. Biology, chemistry, physics, and astronomy are **natural sciences.** Economics is a **social science.** *noun.*

science fiction, a story or novel that combines science and imagination. Science fiction deals with life in the future, on other galaxies, or the like, and makes much use of the latest discoveries of science.

sci·en·tif·ic (sī′ən tif′ik), **1** using the facts and laws of science: *a scientific method, scientific farming.* **2** of or having something to do with science; used in science: *scientific books, scientific instruments. adjective.*

sci·en·tist (sī′ən tist), a person who has expert knowledge of some branch of science. Persons specially trained in and familiar with the facts and laws of such fields of study as biology, chemistry, mathematics, physics, geology, and astronomy are scientists. *noun.*

scis·sors (siz′ərz), a tool or instrument for cutting that has two sharp blades so fastened that they will work toward each other. *noun plural or singular.*

scoff (skôf), to make fun to show one does not believe something; mock: *We scoffed at the idea of swimming in three inches of water. verb.*

scold (skōld), to find fault with; blame with angry words: *She scolded the kids for making such a mess. verb.*

scoop (sküp), **1** a tool like a small shovel for dipping out or shoveling up things. A kitchen utensil to take out flour or sugar is a scoop. **2** the part of a dredge or steam shovel that holds coal, sand, or other like things. **3** the amount taken up at one time by a scoop: *Use two scoops of flour and one of sugar.* **4** to take up or out with a scoop, or as a scoop does: *You scoop up snow with your hands to make snowballs.* **5** to hollow out; dig out; make by scooping: *The children scooped holes in the sand.* **6** the publishing or broadcasting of a piece of news before a rival newspaper, magazine, or television or radio station does. 1-3,6 *noun,* 4,5 *verb.*

scoot (süt), to go quickly; dart: *He scooted out the door. verb.*

scoot·er (skü′tər), a child's vehicle consisting of a board for the feet between two wheels, one in front of the other, steered by a long, upright handlebar. It is moved by pushing one foot against the ground. *noun.*

scope (skōp), the extent or range of understanding or mental activity: *The scope of the child's interests was enlarged from reading many books. noun.*

scorch (skôrch), **1** to burn slightly; burn on the outside: *The cake tastes scorched.* **2** a slight burn. **3** to dry up; wither: *The grass is scorched by so much hot sunshine.* 1,3 *verb,* 2 *noun, plural* **scorch·es.**

score (skôr), **1** the record of points made in a game, contest, or test: *The score was 9 to 2 in favor of our school.* **2** to make as points in a game, contest, or test: *score two runs in the second inning.* **3** to keep a record of the number of points made in a game or contest: *The teacher will appoint some pupil to score for both sides.* **4** a group or set of twenty: *A score or more were* *present at the party.* **5** a written or printed piece of music arranged for different instruments or voices: *She was studying the score of the piece she was learning to play.* 1,4,5 *noun,* 2,3 *verb,* **scores, scored, scor·ing.**

settle a score, to get even for an injury or wrong: *He had an old score to settle.*

score·board (skôr′bôrd′), a large board on which the scores of a ball game, horse race, or the like are posted. *noun.*

scorn (skôrn), **1** to look down upon; think of as mean or low; despise: *Most people scorn tattletales.* **2** a feeling that a person or act is mean or low; contempt: *Most pupils feel scorn for those who cheat.* 1 *verb,* 2 *noun.*

scorn·ful (skôrn′fəl), showing contempt; mocking; full of scorn: *They spoke of our old car in a scornful way.* *adjective.*

scor·pi·on (skôr′pē ən), a small animal belonging to the same group as the spider and having a poisonous sting in its tail. *noun.*

scorpion—about 4 inches (10 centimeters) long

Scotch (skoch), Scottish. *adjective, noun.*

Scotch tape, a trademark for a very thin, transparent or opaque adhesive tape used for mending or sealing.

Scot·land (skot′lənd), the division of Great Britain north of England. *noun.*

Scot·tish (skot′ish), **1** of or having something to do with Scotland, its people, or their language. **2** the people of Scotland. **3** the form of English spoken by the people of Scotland. 1 *adjective,* 2 *noun plural,* 3 *noun singular.*

scoun·drel (skoun′drəl), a very bad person without honor or good principles; villain; rascal: *The scoundrels set fire to the barn. noun.*

scour[1] (skour), to clean or polish by hard rubbing: *I scoured the sink with cleanser. verb.*

scour[2] (skour), to move quickly over or through in search or pursuit: *We scoured the house for my pet snake. verb.*

scourge (skėrj), **1** to punish. **2** some thing or person that causes great trouble or misfortune. Formerly, an outbreak of disease was called a scourge. 1 *verb,* **scourg·es, scourged, scourg·ing;** 2 *noun.*

scout (skout), **1** a person sent to find out what the enemy is doing. A scout usually wears a uniform; a spy does not. **2** a thing that acts as a scout. Some ships and airplanes are scouts. **3** to act as

a hat	**i** it	**oi** oil	**ch** child	a in about
ā age	**ī** ice	**ou** out	**ng** long	e in taken
ä far	**o** hot	**u** cup	**sh** she	**ə =** i in pencil
e let	**ō** open	**u̇** put	**th** thin	o in lemon
ē equal	**ô** order	**ü** rule	**ŦH** then	u in circus
ėr term			**zh** measure	

a scout; hunt around to find something: *Go and scout for firewood for the picnic.* **4** a person belonging to the Boy Scouts or Girl Scouts. 1,2,4 *noun,* 3 *verb.*

scout·mas·ter (skout′mas′tər), an adult in charge of a troop of Boy Scouts. *noun.*

scow (skou), a large boat with a flat bottom used to carry freight, sand, or other like things. *noun.*

scowl (skoul), **1** to look angry or sullen by lowering the eyebrows; frown: *She scowled at the man who stepped on her toes.* **2** an angry, sullen look; frown. 1 *verb,* 2 *noun.*

scrag·gly (skrag′lē), rough or irregular; ragged. *adjective,* **scrag·gli·er, scrag·gli·est.**

scraggly
His hair and beard are **scraggly.**

scram·ble (skram′bəl), **1** to make one's way by climbing or crawling: *We scrambled up the steep, rocky hill.* **2** a climb or walk over rough ground: *It was a long scramble through bushes and over rocks to the top of the hill.* **3** to struggle with others for something: *The players scrambled to get the ball.* **4** a struggle to possess: *the scramble for wealth and power.* **5** scrambling; any disorderly struggle or activity: *The pile of boys on the football seemed a wild scramble of arms and legs.* **6** to mix together in a confused way: *to scramble letters of the alphabet in order to create a code.* **7** to cook eggs with the whites and yolks mixed together. 1,3,6,7 *verb,* **scram·bles, scram·bled, scram·bling;** 2,4,5 *noun.*

scrap[1] (skrap), **1** a small piece; little bit; small part left over: *The cook gave some scraps of meat to the dog. Put the scraps of paper in the wastebasket.* **2** to make into scraps; break up. **3** to throw aside as useless or worn out. 1 *noun,* 2,3 *verb,* **scraps, scrapped, scrap·ping.**

scrap[2] (skrap), **1** a fight, quarrel, or struggle: *The dogs growled and then got into a scrap over a bone.* **2** to fight, quarrel, or struggle: *Those two dogs are always scrapping.* 1 *noun,* 2 *verb,* **scraps, scrapped, scrap·ping.**

scrap·book (skrap′bu̇k′), a book in which pictures or clippings are pasted and kept. *noun.*

scrape (skrāp), **1** to rub with something sharp or

S

rough; make smooth or clean by doing this: *Scrape your muddy shoes with this old knife.* 2 to remove by rubbing with something sharp or rough: *We need to scrape the peeling paint off the house before we repaint it.* 3 to scratch or graze by rubbing against something rough: *She fell and scraped her knee on the sidewalk.* 4 a scraped place. 5 to rub with a harsh sound: *The branch scraped against the window.* 6 a harsh, grating sound: *the scrape of the bow of a violin.* 7 to collect by scraping or with difficulty: *I was so hungry I scraped every crumb from my plate. I've finally scraped together enough money for a bicycle.* 8 a difficulty; position hard to get out of: *Children often get into scrapes.* 1-3,5,7 *verb,* **scrapes, scraped, scrap·ing;** 4,6,8 *noun.*

scrap·er (skrā′pər), a tool for scraping: *We removed the loose paint with a scraper. noun.*

scratch (skrach), 1 to break, mark, or cut slightly with something sharp or rough: *Your feet have scratched the chair.* 2 a mark made by scratching: *There are deep scratches on this desk.* 3 to tear or dig with the nails or claws: *The cat scratched me.* 4 a very slight cut: *That scratch on your hand will soon be well.* 5 to rub or scrape to relieve itching: *Don't scratch your mosquito bites.* 6 to rub with a harsh noise; rub: *I scratched the match on a rock.* 7 the sound of scratching: *the scratch of a pen.* 8 to scrape out; strike out; draw a line through. 1,3,5,6,8 *verb,* 2,4,7 *noun, plural* **scratch·es.**
from scratch, with no advantages; from the beginning: *They had to borrow money and start their business from scratch.*

scratch·y (skrach′ē), likely or apt to scratch or scrape: *He wore a scratchy wool sweater. adjective,* **scratch·i·er, scratch·i·est.**

scrawl (skrôl), 1 to write or draw poorly or carelessly. 2 poor, careless handwriting. 1 *verb,* 2 *noun.*

scraw·ny (skrô′nē), lean; thin; skinny: *Turkeys have scrawny necks. adjective,* **scraw·ni·er, scraw·ni·est.**

scream (skrēm), 1 to make a loud, sharp, piercing cry. People scream in fright, in anger, and in excitement. 2 a loud, sharp, piercing cry. 1 *verb,* 2 *noun.*

screech (skrēch), 1 to cry out sharply in a high voice; shriek: *Someone screeched, "Help! Help!"* 2 a shrill, harsh scream or sound: *The screeches brought the police.* 1 *verb,* 2 *noun, plural* **screech·es.**

screen (skrēn), 1 a covered frame that hides, protects, or separates: *We keep the trunk behind a screen.* 2 wire woven together with small openings in between: *We have screens at the windows to keep out flies.* 3 anything like a screen: *A screen of trees hides our house from the road.* 4 to shelter, protect, or hide with, or as with, a screen: *We have screened our porch to keep out flies.* 5 a flat, white surface on which motion pictures or slides are shown. 6 motion pictures; the movie industry: *a star of the screen, stage, and television.* 7 a glass surface on which television pictures, computer

information, or video game diagrams appear. 8 the information shown by a computer at any particular moment, or any particular diagram shown by a video game machine: *If you score enough points now, you get another turn on a different screen.* 9 a sieve for sifting sand, gravel, coal, seed, or other like things. 10 to sift with a screen or as with a screen: *to screen sand. Many government agencies screen their employees for loyalty.* 1-3,5-7,8,9 *noun,* 4,10 *verb.*

screw (skrü), 1 a slender piece of metal with a ridge twisted evenly around its length. It has a slot in its flat or rounded head for a screwdriver to fit into, and a sharp point at the other end. 2 a cylinder with a ridge winding around it. 3 to turn as one turns a screw; twist: *to screw a lid on a jar.* 4 to fasten or tighten with a screw or screws: *The carpenter screwed the hinges to the door.* 5 a propeller that moves a boat or ship. 1,2,5 *noun,* 3,4 *verb.*

screw·driv·er (skrü′drī′vər), a tool for putting in or taking out screws by turning them. *noun.*

scrib·ble (skrib′əl), 1 to write or draw carelessly or hastily. 2 something scribbled. 1 *verb,* **scrib·bles, scrib·bled, scrib·bling;** 2 *noun.*

scribe (skrīb), a person whose occupation is writing. Before printing was invented, there were many scribes. *noun.*

scribes at work

scrim·mage (skrim′ij), a play in football that takes place when the two teams are lined up and the ball is snapped back. *noun.*

scrimp (skrimp), to be very economical: *They scrimped and saved to buy a new motorboat. verb.*

script (skript), 1 handwriting; written letters, figures, signs, or characters. 2 a style of printing that looks like handwriting. 3 the manuscript of a play, actor's part, or radio or television broadcast. *noun.*

Scrip·ture (skrip′chər), 1 the Bible. 2 the **Scriptures** or the **Holy Scriptures,** the Bible. 3 **scripture,** any sacred writing. *noun.*

scroll (definition 1)

a hat	i it	oi oil	ch child	(a in about
ā age	ī ice	ou out	ng long	e in taken
ä far	o hot	u cup	sh she	ə = { i in pencil
e let	ō open	ů put	th thin	o in lemon
ē equal	ô order	ü rule	ŦH then	u in circus
ėr term			zh measure	

oars used, one on each side, by a single rower. **3** to make a boat go by a scull or by sculls. **1,2** *noun,* **3** *verb.*

sculp·tor (skulp′tər), a person who carves or models figures. Sculptors make statues of marble and bronze. *noun.*

sculp·ture (skulp′chər), **1** the art of carving or modeling figures. Sculpture includes the cutting of statues from blocks of marble, stone, or wood, casting in bronze, and modeling in clay or wax. **2** to make figures this way; carve or model. **3** sculptured work; piece of such work: *There are many famous sculptures in the museums.* **1,3** *noun,* **2** *verb,* **sculp·tures, sculp·tured, sculp·tur·ing.**

scum (skum), **1** a thin layer that rises to the top of a liquid: *Green scum floated on the pond.* **2** an undesirable person or persons. *noun.*

scur·ry (skėr′ē), **1** to run quickly; scamper; hurry: *We could hear the mice scurry about in the walls.* **2** a hasty running; hurrying: *With much fuss and scurry, we at last got started.* **1** *verb,* **scur·ries, scur·ried, scur·ry·ing;** **2** *noun.*

scur·vy (skėr′vē), **1** a disease caused by a lack of vegetables and fruits. It causes swollen and bleeding gums, extreme weakness, and spots that look like bruises on the skin. Scurvy used to be common among sailors when they had little to eat except bread and salt meat. **2** mean; contemptible; base: *a scurvy fellow, a scurvy trick.* **1** *noun,* **2** *adjective,* **scur·vi·er, scur·vi·est.**

scut·tle¹ (skut′l), to scamper; scurry: *The dogs scuttled off into the woods.* *verb,* **scut·tles, scut·tled, scut·tling.**

scut·tle² (skut′l), to cut holes through the bottom or sides of a ship to sink it: *After the pirates captured the ship, they scuttled it.* *verb,* **scut·tles, scut·tled, scut·tling.**

scythe (sīŦH), a long, slightly curved blade on a long handle, used for mowing or reaping. *noun.*

SD, South Dakota (used with postal Zip Code).

S.Dak., South Dakota.

SE or **S.E.,** **1** southeast. **2** southeastern.

sea (sē), **1** the great body of salt water that covers almost three fourths of the earth's surface; the ocean. **2** any large body of salt water, smaller than an ocean: *the North Sea, the Mediterranean Sea.* **3** a large, heavy wave: *A high sea swept over the ship's deck.* **4** the swell of the ocean: *a heavy sea.* **5** an overwhelming amount or number: *a sea of trouble. noun.*

at sea, 1 out on the sea: *We were at sea out of sight of land for ten days.* **2** puzzled; confused: *I can't understand this problem; I'm all at sea.*

go to sea, to become a sailor: *The captain had gone to sea when he was barely seventeen.*

scroll (skrōl), **1** a roll of parchment or paper, especially one with writing on it. **2** an ornament resembling a partly unrolled sheet of paper, or having a spiral or coiled form. *noun.*

scrounge (skrounj), to search about for what one can find that is useful. *verb,* **scroung·es, scrounged, scroung·ing.**

scrub¹ (skrub), **1** to rub hard; wash or clean by rubbing: *The floor needs to be scrubbed with a brush and soap.* **2** a scrubbing: *Give your face and hands a good scrub.* **1** *verb,* **scrubs, scrubbed, scrub·bing;** **2** *noun.*

scrub² (skrub), **1** low, stunted trees or shrubs. **2** anything small or below the usual size: *The stray we found is a little scrub of a dog.* **3** small; poor; inferior. A scrub ball team is made up of inferior, substitute, or untrained players. **1,2** *noun,* **3** *adjective.*

scruff (skruf), the skin at the back of the neck; the back of the neck. *noun.*

scrump·tious (skrump′shəs), very pleasing or satisfying, especially to the taste or smell; delightful: *a scrumptious meal. adjective.*

scrunch (skrunch), **1** to crush; squeeze; crumple: *He scrunched the wad of paper in his fist.* **2** to crouch: *He scrunched way down in his seat. verb.*

scru·ple (skrü′pəl), a feeling of uneasiness that keeps a person from doing something: *She has scruples about ever telling a lie. noun.*

scru·pu·lous (skrü′pyə ləs), **1** very careful to do what is right. **2** attending thoroughly to details; very careful: *A restaurant has to be scrupulous about cleanliness. adjective.*

scu·ba (skü′bə), portable breathing equipment, including one or more tanks of compressed air, used by underwater swimmers or divers. *noun.* [*Scuba* comes from the words *self contained underwater breathing apparatus.* It was formed by using the first letter of each of those words.]

scuff (skuf), **1** to walk without lifting the feet; shuffle. **2** to wear or injure the surface of by hard use: *to scuff one's shoes. verb.*

scuf·fle (skuf′əl), **1** to struggle or fight in a rough, confused manner: *The children were scuffling over the ball.* **2** a confused, rough struggle or fight: *I lost my hat in the scuffle.* **1** *verb,* **scuf·fles, scuf·fled, scuf·fling;** **2** *noun.*

scull (skul), **1** an oar worked with a side twist over the end of a boat to make it go. **2** one of a pair of

555

sea anemone
commonly about 2 to 4 inches (6 to 10 centimeters) in diameter

sea a·nem·o·ne (ə nem′ə nē), a small, flowerlike sea animal with a fleshy, cylindrical body and a mouth surrounded by many brightly colored tentacles.

sea·board (sē′bôrd′), the land near the sea; seacoast; seashore: *New York City is on the Atlantic seaboard. noun.*

sea·coast (sē′kōst′), the land along the sea: *the seacoast of North America. noun.*

sea·far·ing (sē′fer′ing *or* sē′far′ing), going, traveling, or working on the sea: *a hardy seafaring people. adjective.*

sea·food (sē′füd′), any saltwater fish and shellfish that are good to eat. *noun.*

sea·go·ing (sē′gō′ing), **1** going by sea; seafaring: *I come from a seagoing family.* **2** fit for going to sea: *a seagoing tugboat. adjective.*

sea gull, any gull, especially one living on or near the sea.

sea horse, a small fish with a head that looks somewhat like a horse's head.

sea horse
up to 12 inches
(30 centimeters)
long

seal[1] (sēl), **1** a design or pattern, used to show ownership or authority. **2** a piece of wax or very soft metal on which such a design is pressed or stamped. Seals were attached in former times to important government papers. **3** a stamp for marking things with such a design. **4** to mark with a seal: *The treaty was signed and sealed by both governments.* **5** to close very tightly; fasten: *Seal the letter before mailing it. I sealed the jars of fruit.*

Her promise sealed her lips. **6** a thing that fastens or closes something tightly: *The jar of instant coffee was covered with a seal.* **7** to settle; determine: *The judge's words sealed the prisoner's fate.* **8** to give a sign that a thing is true: *They sealed their bargain by shaking hands.* **9** a special kind of stamp: *Christmas seals.* 1-3,6,9 *noun,* 4,5,7,8 *verb.*

seal[2] (sēl), **1** a sea animal with large flippers, usually living in cold regions. Some kinds have very valuable fur. **2** its fur. *noun, plural* **seals** *or* **seal.**

sea level, the surface of the sea. Mountains, plains, and ocean beds are measured as so many feet or meters above or below sea level.

sea lion, a large seal of the Pacific coast.

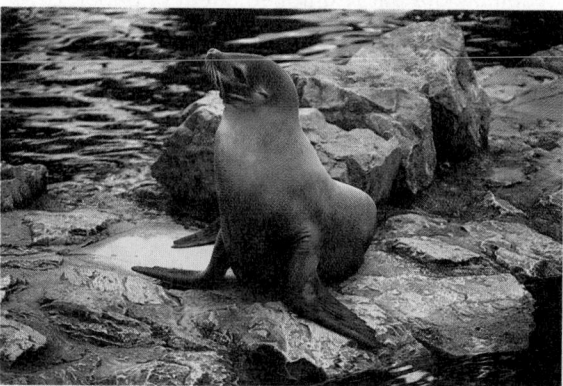

sea lion—about 8 feet (2½ meters) long

seal·skin (sēl′skin′), the skin or fur of the seal, prepared for use. *noun.*

seam (sēm), **1** the line formed by sewing together two pieces of cloth, canvas, leather, and the like: *the seams of a coat, the seams of a sail.* **2** any line where edges join: *The seams of the boat must be filled in or they will leak.* **3** any mark or line like a seam: *The old sword cut had left a seam in his face.* **4** to mark with seams, furrows, wrinkles, and the like; scar: *Her face was seamed by age.* 1-3 *noun,* 4 *verb.*

sea·man (sē′mən), **1** a sailor. **2** a sailor who is not an officer. *noun, plural* **sea·men.**

seam·stress (sēm′stris), a woman whose work is sewing. *noun, plural* **seam·stress·es.**

sea·plane (sē′plān′), an airplane that can rise from and land on water. Seaplanes have floats instead of wheels. *noun.*

sea·port (sē′pôrt′), a port or harbor on the seacoast; city or town with a harbor that ships can reach from the sea: *San Francisco is a seaport. noun.*

sear (sir), **1** to burn the surface of: *The hot iron seared my hand.* **2** to dry up; wither. *verb.*

search (sėrch), **1** to try to find by looking; seek; look for something: *We searched all day for the lost kitten.* **2** to look through; go over carefully; examine, especially for something concealed: *The police searched the prisoners to see if they had weapons.* **3** the act of searching; examination: *She* *found her book after a long search.* 1,2 *verb,* 3 *noun, plural* **search·es.**

in search of, trying to find; looking for: *The children went in search of their lost dog.*

search·ing (sėr′ching), examining carefully; thorough: *a searching look, a searching examination. adjective.*

search·light (sėrch′līt′), 1 a device that can throw a very bright beam of light in any direction desired. 2 the beam of light thrown by this device. *noun.*

sea·shell (sē′shel′), the shell of any shellfish, such as an oyster or clam. *noun.*

sea·shore (sē′shôr′), the land at the edge of a sea; shore. *noun.*

sea·sick (sē′sik′), sick because of a ship's motion. *adjective.*

sea·side (sē′sīd′), 1 the seashore. 2 of or at the seaside: *a seaside hotel.* 1 *noun,* 2 *adjective.*

sea·son (sē′zn), 1 one of the four periods of the year; spring, summer, autumn, or winter. 2 any period of time marked by something special: *the holiday season, the harvest season.* 3 to improve the flavor of: *Season your egg with salt.* 1,2 *noun,* 3 *verb.*

sea·son·al (sē′zn əl), having to do with the seasons; depending on a season; happening at regular intervals: *Heavy rains are seasonal in Asia and Africa. adjective.*

sea·son·ing (sē′zn ing), something that gives a better flavor: *Salt, pepper, and spices are seasonings. noun.*

seat (sēt), 1 a thing to sit on. Chairs, benches, and stools are seats. *Take a seat, please.* 2 a place to sit: *Can you find a seat on the train?* 3 a place in which one has the right to sit. When we say that someone has a seat in Congress, we mean that that person is a member of Congress. 4 that part of a chair, bench, stool, and the like, on which one sits: *This bench has a broken seat.* 5 that part of the body on which one sits, or the clothing covering it: *The seat of her jeans is patched.* 6 to set or place on a seat: *Please seat yourself in a comfortable chair.* 7 to have seats for: *Our school auditorium seats one thousand pupils.* 8 an established place or center: *A university is a seat of learning. The seat of our government is in Washington, D.C.* 1-5,8 *noun,* 6,7 *verb.*

seat belt, a belt attached to the seat of an automobile or airplane, used to hold a person in the seat in the event of a crash, jolt, or bump.

sea·ward (sē′wərd), toward the sea: *Our house faces seaward. adjective, adverb.*

sea·wa·ter (sē′wô′tər), the salt water of the sea or ocean: *I would rather swim in seawater than in the hotel pool. noun.*

sea·way (sē′wā′), an inland waterway that is deep enough to permit ocean shipping: *Ocean-going freighters reach Detroit by passing through the St. Lawrence Seaway. noun.*

sea·weed (sē′wēd′), any plant or any living thing like a plant growing in the sea. *noun.*

sec. or **sec,** second or seconds.

a hat	**i** it	**oi** oil	**ch** child	a in about
ā age	**ī** ice	**ou** out	**ng** long	e in taken
ä far	**o** hot	**u** cup	**sh** she	ə = i in pencil
e let	**ō** open	**u̇** put	**th** thin	o in lemon
ē equal	**ô** order	**ü** rule	**ᴛH** then	u in circus
ėr term			**zh** measure	

se·cede (si sēd′), to withdraw from a group or country: *Some southern states seceded from the United States during the Civil War. verb,* **se·cedes, se·ced·ed, se·ced·ing.**

se·clud·ed (si klü′did), shut off from others; undisturbed: *a secluded cottage in the woods. adjective.*

se·clu·sion (si klü′zhən), a keeping apart or being shut off from others; retirement: *She lives in seclusion apart from her friends. noun.*

sec·ond[1] (sek′ənd), 1 next after the first: *the second seat from the front, a second child.* 2 below the first; inferior: *the second officer on a ship, cloth of second quality.* 3 another; other: *Please give me a second chance.* 4 in the second group, division, rank, or place; secondly: *I finished second in the tennis finals.* 5 a person or thing that is second: *You won the first prize; I won the second.* 6 **seconds, a** goods below first quality: *These stockings are seconds and have some slight defects.* **b** a second portion of food: *After I finished eating what was on my plate I went back for seconds.* 7 a person who supports or aids another: *The prizefighter had a second.* 8 to support; back up; assist: *One member made a motion to adjourn the meeting, and another seconded it.* 1-3 *adjective,* 4 *adverb,* 5-7 *noun,* 8 *verb.*

sec·ond[2] (sek′ənd), one of the 60 very short equal periods of time that make up a minute. *noun.*

sec·ond·ar·y (sek′ən der′ē), 1 next after the first in order, place, time, or importance: *A secondary industry uses products produced by other industries as its raw materials.* 2 having less importance: *Reading fast is secondary to reading well. adjective.*

secondary accent, 1 an accent in a word that is stronger than no accent but weaker than the strongest accent. The second syllable of *ab bre′vi a′ tion* has a secondary accent. 2 the mark (′) used to show this.

secondary school, a school attended after elementary school or junior high school; high school.

sec·ond-class (sek′ənd klas′), 1 of or belonging to the class next after the first: *second-class mail.* 2 by the second grade of passenger seating and service offered by a ship, airplane, or train: *We could afford only to travel second-class.* 3 of inferior grade, quality, or position: *second-class goods.* 1,3 *adjective,* 2 *adverb.*

sec·ond·hand (sek′ənd hand′), 1 not original; obtained from another: *secondhand information.* 2 not new; used already by another: *a secondhand car.* 3 dealing in used goods: *a secondhand clothing store. adjective.*

S

sec·ond·ly (sek′ənd lē), in the second place. *adverb.*

se·cre·cy (sē′krə sē), 1 the condition of being secret or being kept secret: *Plans for the birthday party were made in the greatest secrecy.* 2 the ability to keep things secret: *Secrecy was necessary to keep them from finding out our plans for the party.* *noun.*

se·cret (sē′krit), 1 kept from the knowledge of others: *a secret errand, a secret weapon.* 2 known only to a few: *a secret sign.* 3 kept from sight; hidden: *a secret drawer.* 4 working or acting in secret: *the secret police, a secret agent.* 5 something secret or hidden: *Can you keep a secret?* 6 a hidden cause or reason: *I wish I knew the secret of her success.* 1-4 *adjective,* 5,6 *noun.*

in secret, secretly; privately; not openly: *I have said nothing in secret that I would not say openly.*

sec·re·tar·y (sek′rə ter′ē), 1 a person who writes letters and keeps records for a person, company, club, committee, and the like: *Our club has a secretary who keeps the minutes of the meeting.* 2 a person who has charge of a department of the government. The Secretary of the Treasury is the head of the Treasury Department. 3 a writing desk with a set of drawers, and often with shelves for books. *noun, plural* **sec·re·tar·ies.**

se·crete[1] (si krēt′), to keep secret; hide: *She secreted money in a cupboard.* *verb,* **se·cretes, se·cret·ed, se·cret·ing.**

se·crete[2] (si krēt′), produce and give out: *Glands in the mouth secrete saliva.* *verb,* **se·cretes, se·cret·ed, se·cret·ing.**

sect (sekt), a group of people having the same principles, beliefs, or opinions: *Each religious sect in the town had its own church.* *noun.*

sec·tion (sek′shən), 1 a part cut off; part; division; slice: *Cut the pie into eight equal sections.* 2 a division of a book, newspaper, law, or the like: *He always turns to the sports section first. Our arithmetic book has several sections on fractions.* 3 a region; part of a country, city, community, or group: *the business section of a town.* 4 to cut into sections; divide into sections: *to section an orange.* 1-3 *noun,* 4 *verb.*

sec·tor (sek′tər), any section, zone, or region: *Our new house is located in the northern sector of the city. noun.*

se·cure (si kyùr′), 1 safe against loss, attack, escape, or danger: *This is a secure hiding place.* 2 to make safe; protect: *You cannot secure yourself against all risks and dangers.* 3 sure; certain; that can be counted on: *We know in advance that our victory is secure.* 4 free from care or fear: *He hoped for a secure old age.* 5 firmly fastened; not liable to break or fall: *The boards of this bridge do not look secure.* 6 to make firm or fast: *Secure the locks on the doors and windows.* 7 to get; obtain: *We have secured our tickets for the school play.* 1,3-5 *adjective,* 2,6,7 *verb,* **se·cures, se·cured, se·cur·ing.**

se·cur·i·ty (si kyùr′ə tē), 1 freedom from danger, care, or fear; feeling or condition of being safe: *It* gave us a sense of security to have the lifeguard nearby while we swam. 2 something that secures or makes safe: *My watchdog is a security against burglars.* 3 something given to another as a guarantee of good faith or of a future action: *She used her car as security for the loan. noun.*

se·dan (si dan′), a closed automobile seating four or more persons. *noun.*

sedan chair, a covered chair carried on poles by two men. Sedan chairs were much used during the 1600's and 1700's.

sedan chair

sedge (sej), a grasslike plant that grows chiefly in wet places. *noun.*

sed·i·ment (sed′ə mənt), 1 any matter that settles to the bottom of a liquid: *Sediment often collects at the bottom of hot-water tanks.* 2 the earth and stones deposited by water, wind, or ice: *When the river overflows, it leaves sediment on the land it covers. noun.*

sed·i·men·tar·y (sed′ə men′tər ē), formed by the depositing of sediment. Sandstone is a sedimentary rock. *adjective.*

see (sē), 1 to look at; be aware of by using the eyes: *See that black cloud.* 2 to have the power of sight: *The blind do not see.* 3 to understand; be aware of with the mind: *I see what you mean.* 4 to find out: *I will see what needs to be done.* 5 to take care; make sure: *See that the work is done properly.* 6 to have knowledge or experience of: *That coat has seen hard wear.* 7 to go with; attend; escort: *She saw her friend home safely.* 8 to call on: *I went to see a friend.* 9 to receive a visit from: *She is too ill to see anyone.* 10 to visit; attend: *We saw the new book fair. verb,* **sees, saw, seen, see·ing.**

see through, 1 to understand the real character or hidden purpose of: *I saw through their excuses.* 2 to go through with; finish: *I mean to see this job through.*

see to, to look after; take care of: *They saw to it that their children had good educations.*

seed (sēd), 1 a part of a plant from which another plant like it can grow. A seed has a protective outer coat. Inside this is the part that will grow into a new plant, with a supply of food to be used during that growth. *We planted seeds in the garden. Part of every crop is saved for seed.* 2 to sow with seeds; scatter seeds over: *The farmer seeded the field with corn. Dandelions seed themselves.* 3 to remove the seeds from: *I seeded the grapes.* 4 the source or beginning of anything: *the seeds of trouble.* 1,4 *noun, plural* **seeds** *or* **seed**; 2,3 *verb.*

seed·case (sēd′kās′), any pod or other dry, hollow fruit that contains seeds. *noun.*

seed·ling (sēd′ling), a young plant grown from a seed: *I dug up the seedlings and transplanted them into the garden. noun.*

seek (sēk), 1 to try to find; look for; hunt; search: *to seek for something lost. We are seeking a new home.* 2 to try to get: *Some people seek wealth. Friends sought her advice.* 3 to try; attempt: *Nations are seeking to make peace with one another. verb,* **seeks, sought, seek·ing.**

seem (sēm), 1 to look like; appear to be: *This apple seemed good but was rotten inside. The dog seems to like that bone. Does this room seem hot to you?* 2 to appear to oneself: *I still seem to hear the music. verb.*

seem·ing·ly (sē′ming lē), so it appears; as far as appearances go; apparently: *This hill is, seemingly, the highest around here. adverb.*

seen (sēn). See **see.** *Have you seen Father? verb.*

seep (sēp), to leak slowly; trickle; ooze: *Water seeps through sand. verb.*

see·saw (sē′sô′), 1 a plank resting on a support near its middle so that the ends can move up and down. 2 a children's game in which the children sit at opposite ends of such a plank and move up and down. 3 to move up and down on such a plank: *The two children seesawed in the playground.* 1,2 *noun,* 3 *verb.*

seethe (sēᴛʜ), to be excited; be disturbed: *She seethed with anger at being unjustly fired from her job. verb,* **seethes, seethed, seeth·ing.**

seg·ment (seg′mənt), a piece or part cut off, marked off, or broken off; division; section: *An orange is easily pulled apart into its segments. A line can be divided into segments. noun.*

seg·re·gate (seg′rə gāt), to separate people of different races by having separate schools, restaurants, theaters, and the like. *verb,* **seg·re·gates, seg·re·gat·ed, seg·re·gat·ing.**

seg·re·ga·tion (seg′rə gā′shən), the separation of people of different races, especially in schools, restaurants, and other public places. *noun.*

seine (sān), a fishing net that hangs straight down in the water. A seine has floats at the upper edge and weights at the lower. *noun.*

seis·mo·graph (sīz′mə graf), an instrument for recording earthquakes. *noun.*

seize (sēz), 1 to take hold of suddenly; clutch; grasp: *In fright I seized her arm.* 2 to take possession of by force: *The soldiers seized the city. verb,* **seiz·es, seized, seiz·ing.**

sei·zure (sē′zhər), 1 the act of seizing: *The seizure of the smuggled jewels by government agents was reported in yesterday's newspaper.* 2 a sudden attack of disease: *He died of a heart seizure. noun.*

sel·dom (sel′dəm), rarely; not often: *I am seldom ill. adverb.*

se·lect (si lekt′), 1 to choose; pick out: *Select the book you want.* 2 picked as best; chosen specially:

a hat	**i** it	**oi** oil	**ch** child	⎡ a in about
ā age	**ī** ice	**ou** out	**ng** long	e in taken
ä far	**o** hot	**u** cup	**sh** she	ə = ⎨ i in pencil
e let	**ō** open	**ù** put	**th** thin	o in lemon
ē equal	**ô** order	**ü** rule	**ᴛʜ** then	⎣ u in circus
ėr term			**zh** measure	

She is one of a select group of skiers chosen to compete. 1 *verb,* 2 *adjective.*

se·lec·tion (si lek′shən), 1 a choice: *This library has a good selection of mystery stories.* 2 a person, thing, or group chosen: *This book of stories is my selection.* 3 the condition of being chosen: *Her selection as a candidate was certain. noun.*

self (self), 1 one's own person: *Your self is you. My self is I.* 2 the character of a person; nature of a person or thing: *She does not seem like her former self. noun, plural* **selves.**

self-, a prefix meaning: 1 of or over oneself: *Self-control means control over oneself.* 2 by or in oneself: *Self-confidence means confidence in oneself.* 3 to or for oneself: *Self-addressed means addressed to oneself.* 4 automatic; automatically: A *self-winding watch is a watch that winds itself automatically.*

self-ad·dressed (self′ə drest′), addressed to oneself: *Send a self-addressed envelope along with your order. adjective.*

self-con·fi·dence (self′kon′fə dəns), a belief in one's own ability, power, or judgment; confidence in oneself. *noun.*

self-con·scious (self′kon′shəs), embarrassed, especially by the presence of other people or by the opinions one believes other people have of one; shy: *I always feel self-conscious when I'm among people I don't know. adjective.*

seine—African fishermen using a **seine.** It is lowered into the water and pulled to shore.

self-con·trol (self′kən trōl′), the control of one's own actions or feelings. *noun.*

self-de·fense (self′di fens′), a defense of one's own person, property, or reputation: *After he'd been hit, he fought back in self-defense. noun.*

self-gov·ern·ment (self′guv′ərn mənt), the government of a group by its own members: *We*

S

have self-government through our elected representatives. noun.

self·ish (sel′fish), caring too much for oneself; caring too little for others. *Selfish people put their own interests first.* adjective.

self-re·spect (self′ri spekt′), respect for oneself; proper pride. noun.

self·same (self′sām′), very same: *We study the selfsame books that you do.* adjective.

sell (sel), **1** to exchange for money or other payment: *We plan to sell our house.* **2** to deal in; keep for sale: *The butcher sells meat.* **3** to be on sale; be sold: *Strawberries sell at a high price in January.* verb, **sells, sold, sell·ing.**

sell·er (sel′ər), a person who sells: *A druggist is a seller of drugs.* noun.

selves (selvz), more than one self: *She has two selves—one that likes to save money and one that likes to spend it.* noun plural.

sem·a·phore (sem′ə fôr), a device for signaling. Railroad semaphores are posts with colored lights or movable arms. Hand-held flags in different positions are another kind of semaphore, used chiefly on ships. noun.

se·mes·ter (sə mes′tər), a division, often one half, of a school year: *My brother will graduate from college at the end of the spring semester.* noun.

semi-, a prefix meaning: **1** half: *Semicircle means half a circle.* **2** partly: *Semisolid means partly solid.* **3** twice: *Semimonthly means twice a month.*

sem·i·cir·cle (sem′i sèr′kəl), a half of a circle: *We sat in a semicircle around the fire.* noun.

sem·i·co·lon (sem′i kō′lən), a mark of punctuation (;) that shows a separation not so complete as that shown by a period. EXAMPLE: *We arrived much later than we had intended; consequently there was almost no time left for swimming.* noun.

sem·i·fi·nal (sem′i fī′nl), **1** of or having to do with the two games, rounds, or matches that come before the final one in a tournament: *Our team lost in the semifinal game.* **2** Often, **semifinals.** one of these two games: *The team that will face the state champions defeated our team in the semifinals.* **1** adjective, **2** noun.

sem·i·nar·y (sem′ə ner′ē), a school or college for training students to be priests, ministers, or rabbis. noun, plural **sem·i·nar·ies.**

sen·ate (sen′it), **1** a governing or lawmaking assembly. The highest council of state in ancient Rome was called the senate. **2** the upper and smaller branch of an assembly that makes laws. The Congress of the United States is the Senate and the House of Representatives. noun.

sen·a·tor (sen′ə tər), **1** a member of a senate. **2 Senator,** a member of the United States Senate. noun.

send (send), **1** to cause to go from one place to another: *to send someone for a doctor, to send someone on an errand.* **2** to cause to be carried: *We sent the package by air mail.* **3** to cause to come, occur, or be: *Send help at once.* **4** to drive;

throw: *The volcano sent clouds of smoke into the air.* verb, **sends, sent, send·ing.**

send out for, to send someone to bring: *We got so hungry we sent out for a pizza.*

Sen·e·gal (sen′ə gôl′), a country in western Africa. noun.

sen·ior (sē′nyər), **1** the older. The word *senior* is used of a father whose son has the same name. *John Parker, Senior, is the father of John Parker, Junior.* **2** older: *a senior citizen.* **3** an older person: *I am my sister's senior by seven years.* **4** higher in rank or longer in service: *Mr. Jones is the senior member of the firm of Jones and Brown.* **5** a student who is a member of the graduating class of a high school or college. **6** of the last year of high school or college: *the senior class, the senior prom.* **1,2,4,6** adjective, **3,5** noun.

se·ñor (sā nyôr′), a Spanish word meaning: **1** Mr. or sir. **2** a man. noun, plural **se·ño·res** (sā nyôr′ās).

se·ño·ra (sā nyôr′ä), a Spanish word meaning: **1** Mrs. or madam. **2** a married woman. noun, plural **se·ño·ras.**

se·ño·ri·ta (sā′nyō rē′tä), a Spanish word meaning: **1** Miss. **2** an unmarried girl or woman. noun, plural **se·ño·ri·tas.**

sen·sa·tion (sen sā′shən), **1** the action of the senses; power to see, hear, feel, taste, or smell: *Blindness is the loss of the sensation of sight.* **2** a feeling: *Ice gives a sensation of coldness. I have a sensation of dizziness when I walk along cliffs.* **3** a strong or excited feeling: *The announcement of peace caused a sensation throughout the nation.* noun.

sen·sa·tion·al (sen sā′shə nəl), **1** very good or exciting; outstanding; spectacular: *The player's sensational catch made the crowd cheer.* **2** arousing or trying to arouse strong or excited feeling: *a sensational newspaper story.* adjective.

sense (sens), **1** a power of a living thing to know what happens outside itself. Sight, smell, taste, hearing, and touch are senses. *A dog has a keen sense of smell.* **2** a feeling: *The extra lock on the door gives us a sense of security.* **3** to feel; understand: *I sense that you would rather not go.* **4** an understanding; appreciation: *Everyone thinks he has a good sense of humor.* **5 senses,** a clear or sound state of mind: *They must be out of their senses to climb that steep cliff.* **6** judgment; intelligence: *She had the good sense to stay out of the argument.* **7** a reason; use: *What's the sense of going out in the rain?* **8** a meaning: *What sense does the word have in each sentence?* **1,2,4-8** noun, **3** verb, **sens·es, sensed, sens·ing.**

make sense, to have a meaning; be reasonable: *"Cow cat bless Monday" doesn't make sense.*

sense·less (sens′lis), **1** unconscious: *A hard blow on the head knocked him senseless.* **2** foolish; stupid: *a senseless idea.* adjective.

sen·si·bil·i·ty (sen′sə bil′ə tē), the ability to feel or perceive: *Some drugs lessen a person's sensibilities.* noun, plural **sen·si·bil·i·ties.**

sen·si·ble (sen′sə bəl), having good sense;

showing good judgment; wise: *She is too sensible to do anything foolish. adjective.*

sen·si·tive (sen′sə tiv), **1** receiving impressions readily: *The eye is sensitive to light.* **2** easily affected or influenced: *The mercury in the thermometer is sensitive to changes in temperature.* **3** easily hurt or offended: *to be sensitive about one's weight. adjective.*

sen·sor·y (sen′sər ē), of or having to do with sensation or the senses. The eyes and ears are sensory organs. *adjective.*

sent (sent). See **send.** *They sent the trunks last week. She was sent on an errand. verb.*

sen·tence (sen′təns), **1** a word or group of words that makes a statement, a request, a question, a command, or an exclamation. Written sentences begin with capital letters and end with a period, a question mark, or an exclamation mark. EXAMPLES: *The books are heavy. Please hand me a pencil. Is this yours? Come in. Good morning, class. Ouch!* **2** a decision by a judge on the punishment of a criminal: *By the sentence of the court the thief spent five years in prison.* **3** the punishment itself: *The thief received a sentence of five years in prison.* **4** to give a punishment to: *The judge sentenced the thief to five years in prison.* 1-3 *noun,* 4 *verb,* **sen·tenc·es, sen·tenced, sen·tenc·ing.**

sen·ti·ment (sen′tə mənt), **1** a mixture of thought and feeling. Admiration, patriotism, and loyalty are sentiments. **2** feeling, especially tender feeling: *Birthdays are times for sentiment. noun.*

sen·ti·men·tal (sen′tə men′tl), **1** having or showing much tender feeling: *sentimental poetry.* **2** likely to act from feelings rather than from reason: *a sentimental person.* **3** of sentiment; dependent on sentiment: *These old family photographs have sentimental value. adjective.*

sen·ti·nel (sen′tə nəl), a person stationed to keep watch and guard against surprise attacks: *"Who goes there?" said the sentinel. noun.*

sen·try (sen′trē), a soldier stationed at a place to keep watch and guard against surprise attacks: *The sentry at the gate saluted the officer and let him pass. noun, plural* **sen·tries.**

Seoul (sōl), the capital of South Korea. *noun.*

se·pal (sē′pəl), one of the leaflike parts which make up the calyx, or outer covering, of a flower. In a carnation, the sepals make a green cup at the base of the flower. In a tulip, the sepals are bright, just like the petals. *noun.*

sep·a·rate (sep′ə rāt′ *for 1-4;* sep′ər it *for 5 and 6*), **1** to keep apart; divide; be between: *The Atlantic Ocean separates America from Europe.* **2** to go, draw, or come apart: *The children separated in all directions. The rope separated under the strain.* **3** to put or set apart; keep away: *Separate your books from mine.* **4** to live apart. A husband and wife may separate by agreement or by order of a court. **5** apart from others: *in a separate room.* **6** divided; not joined: *separate seats.* 1-4 *verb,* **sep·a·rates, sep·a·rat·ed, sep·a·rat·ing;** 5,6 *adjective.*

a hat	**i** it	**oi** oil	**ch** child	⎧ a in about
ā age	**ī** ice	**ou** out	**ng** long	e in taken
ä far	**o** hot	**u** cup	**sh** she	ə = ⎨ i in pencil
e let	**ō** open	**ů** put	**th** thin	o in lemon
ē equal	**ô** order	**ü** rule	**ᴛʜ** then	⎩ u in circus
ėr term			**zh** measure	

sep·a·ra·tion (sep′ə rā′shən), **1** the act of separating; dividing; taking apart. **2** the condition of being apart; being separated: *The friends were glad to meet after so long a separation. noun.*

Sept., September.

Sep·tem·ber (sep tem′bər), the ninth month of the year. It has 30 days. *noun.* [*September,* the Latin name for this month, came from a Latin word meaning "seven." The month was called this because it was the seventh month in the ancient Roman calendar.]

se·quel (sē′kwəl), a complete story continuing an earlier one about the same characters: *"Son of Lassie" is a sequel to the movie "Lassie Come Home." noun.*

se·quence (sē′kwəns), **1** the coming of one thing after another; succession; order of succession: *Arrange the names in alphabetical sequence.* **2** a connected series: *a sequence of lessons on one subject. noun.*

se·quoi·a (si kwoi′ə), an evergreen tree of California that bears cones and grows to a height of over 300 feet. *noun.* [The sequoia was named in honor of Sequoya, a Cherokee Indian who invented a way of writing his own language. He lived from 1770 to 1843.]

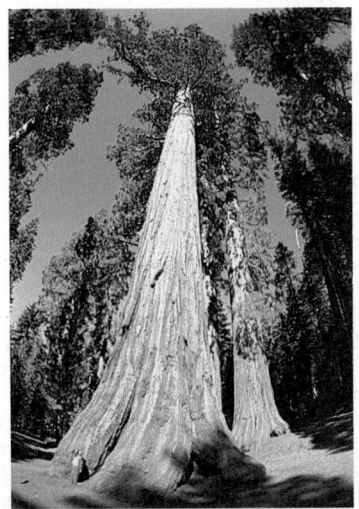

sequoias

se·ra·pe (sə rä′pē), a shawl or blanket, often having bright colors, worn by Spanish Americans. *noun.*

ser·e·nade (ser′ə nād′), **1** music played or sung outdoors at night, especially by a lover under his sweetheart's window. **2** to sing or play to in this way. 1 *noun,* 2 *verb,* **ser·e·nades, ser·e·nad·ed, ser·e·nad·ing.**

se·rene (sə rēn′), peaceful; calm: *She sat on the beach with a serene smile, listening to the waves.* adjective.

se·ren·i·ty (sə ren′ə tē), quiet peace; calmness: *I enjoyed the serenity of the quiet woods after the busy week.* noun.

serf (sėrf), in the Middle Ages, a slave who could not be sold off the land but passed from one owner to another with the land. noun.

ser·geant (sär′jənt), **1** an army or marine officer ranking next above a corporal. **2** an officer in the air force next above the highest grade of airman. **3** a police officer ranking next above an ordinary policeman. noun.

ser·i·al (sir′ē əl), a story published in installments in a magazine or newspaper, or televised as a series of individual programs. Formerly, radio and movie serials were popular. noun.

ser·ies (sir′ēz), **1** a number of similar things that follow one another in a row: *We put our names in an alphabetical series. A series of rainy days spoiled their vacation.* **2** a television program shown at a regular time: *I watched the new mystery series last night.* noun, plural **ser·ies.**

ser·i·ous (sir′ē əs), **1** thoughtful; grave: *a serious face.* **2** not fooling; in earnest; sincere: *Are you joking or serious?* **3** important; needing thought: *Choice of one's life work is a serious matter.* **4** important because it may do much harm; dangerous: *The patient was in serious condition.* adjective.

ser·mon (sėr′mən), **1** a public talk on religion or something connected with religion, usually given by a member of the clergy. **2** a serious talk about conduct or duty: *After the guests left, the children got a sermon on their table manners.* noun.

ser·pent (sėr′pənt), a snake, especially a big snake. noun.

ser·um (sir′əm), **1** the clear, pale-yellow, watery part that separates from blood when it clots. **2** a liquid used to prevent or cure a disease, obtained from the blood of an animal that has been made immune to the disease. Polio vaccine is a serum. noun.

serv·ant (sėr′vənt), **1** a person employed in a household. Cooks and nursemaids are servants. **2** a person employed by another. Police and firefighters are public servants. noun.

serve (sėrv), **1** to work for; be a servant to; work: *to serve a worthwhile cause, to serve customers in a store, to serve in the army.* **2** to bring food to: *The waiter served us.* **3** to put food or drink on the table: *The waitress served the soup. Dinner is served.* **4** to supply; furnish; supply with something needed: *The dairy serves us with milk.* **5** to supply enough for: *One pie will serve six persons.* **6** to be useful; be what is needed; be used: *A flat stone served as a table.* **7** to pass; spend: *The thief served a term in prison.* **8** to deliver; present: *She was served with a notice to appear in court.* **9** to put the ball in play by hitting it in volleyball, and games played with a racket, such as tennis. **10** the act of serving the ball in volleyball, and games played with a racket, such as tennis. 1-9 verb, **serves, served, serv·ing;** 10 noun.

serve one right, to be just what one deserves: *The punishment served him right.*

serv·ice (sėr′vis), **1** a helpful act or acts; aid; being useful to others: *They performed many services for their community.* **2** a business or system that supplies something useful or necessary: *Bus service was good.* **3** occupation or employment as a servant: *She is in service with a wealthy family.* **4** a department of government or public employment, or the persons working in it: *the diplomatic service.* **5** the army, navy, or air force: *We were in the service together.* **6** a religious meeting; religious ceremony: *They attend services on Friday evening. The marriage service was performed at the home of the bride.* **7** the manner of serving food or the food served: *The service in this restaurant is excellent.* **8** a number of things to be used together at the table: *a silver tea service.* **9** to make fit for service; keep fit for service: *The mechanic serviced our automobile.* **10** the act of serving the ball in volleyball, and games played with a racket, such as tennis. 1-8,10 noun, 9 verb, **serv·ic·es, serv·iced, serv·ic·ing.**

serv·ice·a·ble (sėr′vi sə bəl), useful for a long time; able to stand much use: *We want to buy a serviceable used car.* adjective.

serv·ice·man (sėr′vis man′), **1** a member of the armed forces. **2** a person who maintains or repairs machinery or equipment: *We called a serviceman to fix our dryer.* noun, plural **serv·ice·men.**

service station, filling station.

serv·ing (sėr′ving), a portion of food served to a person at one time; helping. noun.

ser·vi·tude (sėr′və tüd or sėr′və tyüd), **1** slavery; bondage. **2** forced labor as a punishment: *The criminal was sentenced to five years' servitude.* noun.

ses·a·me (ses′ə mē), the small seeds of a tropical plant. They are used in bread, candy, and other foods, and in making an oil used in cooking. noun.

ses·sion (sesh′ən), **1** a sitting or meeting of a court, council, or legislature: *We attended one session of the trial.* **2** the term or period of such sittings: *This year's session of Congress was unusually long.* **3** the meeting of a group for a special purpose: *The singer was late for the recording session.* noun.

in session, meeting: *Congress is now in session.*

set (set), **1** to put in some place; put; place: *Set the box on its end.* **2** to put in the right place, position, or condition for use; arrange; put in proper order: *Set the table for dinner. Set the clock. The doctor set my broken leg.* **3** to cause to be; put in some condition or relation: *A spark set the woods on fire. The slaves were set free.* **4** to fix; arrange; appoint: *The teacher set a time limit for the examination.* **5** fixed or appointed beforehand; established: *a set time for meals. There are set rules to the game of chess.* **6** ready: *I am all set to try again.* **7** to provide for others to follow: *to set a* good example. **8** to put in a fixed, rigid, or settled state: *She set her jaw in determination.* **9** stubbornly fixed: *They are set in their ways and are unwilling to change their views.* **10** to become fixed; make or become firm or hard: *Jelly sets as it cools.* **11** to go down; sink: *The sun sets in the west.* **12** a group; things or people belonging together: *a set of dishes.* **13** the scenery of a play or for a motion picture. **14** a device for receiving radio or television signals that turns them into sounds and pictures: *We have a TV set in the basement.* **15** a form; shape; the way a thing is put or placed: *There was a stubborn set to her jaw.* **16** to begin to move; start: *She set to work.* **17** a group of numbers or other items which are alike in some way. All even numbers form a set, and any number that can be divided by 2 is a member of this set. 1-4,7,8,10,11,16 *verb,* **sets, set, set·ting;** 5,6,9 *adjective,* 12-15,17 *noun.*

set about, to start work upon; begin: *to set about washing.*

set down, to put into writing.

set forth, 1 to make known; express; declare: *She set forth her opinions on the subject.* **2** to start to go: *He set forth on a trip around the world.*

set in, to begin: *Winter set in early.*

set off, 1 to explode: *to set off a string of firecrackers.* **2** to start to go: *to set off for home.* **3** to increase by contrast: *The green dress set off her red hair.*

set on or **set upon,** to attack: *They were set on by a pack of dogs.*

set up, 1 to build: *to set up a monument.* **2** to begin; start: *He sold his old business and set up a new one.*

set·back (set′bak′), a check to progress; reverse: *The team suffered a setback when its best player became sick. noun.*

set·tee (se tē′), a sofa or long bench with a back and, usually, arms. *noun.*

settee

set·ter (set′ər), a long-haired hunting dog, trained to stand motionless and point its nose toward the game that it scents. *noun.*

set·ting (set′ing), **1** a frame or other thing in which something is set. The mounting of a jewel is a setting. **2** the place and time of a story, play, or motion picture: *The setting was a garden in England in the 1860's.* **3** See **set.** *You may help me by setting the table.* 1,2 *noun,* 3 *verb.*

set·tle (set′l), **1** to determine; decide; agree upon:

Let's settle this argument. Have you settled on a day for the picnic? **2** to put or be put in order; arrange: *I must settle all my affairs before going away for the winter.* **3** to pay: *We have settled all our bills.* **4** to take up residence in a new country or place: *Our cousin intends to settle in California.* **5** to establish colonies in: *The English settled New England.* **6** to come to rest in a particular place; become set or fixed: *My cold has settled in my lungs.* **7** to place in or come to a desired or comfortable position: *The cat settled itself in the chair for a nap.* **8** to make quiet; become quiet: *This medicine will settle your stomach.* **9** to go down; sink: *Our house has settled several inches since it was built. verb,* **set·tles, set·tled, set·tling.**

settle down, to calm down; become quiet: *The children began to settle down for a nap.*

set·tle·ment (set′l mənt), **1** a putting in order; arrangement: *No settlement of the dispute is possible unless each side yields some point.* **2** a payment: *Settlement of all claims against the company will be made shortly.* **3** the settling of persons in a new country: *The settlement of the English along the Atlantic coast gave England claim to that section.* **4** colony: *England had many settlements along the Atlantic coast.* **5** a group of buildings and the people living in them: *Ships brought supplies to the colonists' settlements.* **6** a place in a poor, neglected neighborhood where work for its improvement is carried on: *Hull House is a famous settlement in Chicago. noun.*

set·tler (set′lər), a person who settles in a new country. *noun.*

sev·en (sev′ən), one more than six; 7. *noun, adjective.*

sev·en·teen (sev′ən tēn′), seven more than ten; 17. *noun, adjective.*

sev·en·teenth (sev′ən tēnth′), **1** next after the 16th. **2** one of 17 equal parts. *adjective, noun.*

setter—about 2 feet (60 centimeters) high at the shoulder

S

sev·enth (sev'ənth), **1** next after the sixth: *Saturday is the seventh day of the week.* **2** one of seven equal parts: *A day is one seventh of a week.* *adjective, noun.*

sev·en·ti·eth (sev'ən tē ith), **1** next after the 69th. **2** one of 70 equal parts. *adjective, noun.*

sev·en·ty (sev'ən tē), seven times ten; 70. *noun, plural* **sev·en·ties;** *adjective.*

sev·er (sev'ər), **1** to cut apart; cut off: *I severed the rope with a knife.* **2** to break off: *The two nations severed friendly relations.* *verb.*

sev·er·al (sev'ər əl), more than two or three but not many; some; a few: *to gain several pounds. Several have given their consent. adjective, noun.*

se·vere (sə vir'), **1** very strict; stern; harsh: *The judge imposed a severe sentence on the criminal.* **2** sharp; violent: *I have a severe headache.* **3** serious; dangerous: *a severe illness.* **4** difficult: *The new car had to pass severe safety tests.* *adjective,* **se·ver·er, se·ver·est.**

severe (definition 2)
The **severe** weather made driving dangerous.

se·ver·i·ty (sə ver'ə tē), **1** strictness; sternness; harshness: *The severity of the punishment seemed unfair to many people.* **2** violence; sharpness: *the severity of storms, the severity of pain, the severity of grief.* **3** seriousness: *We did not realize the severity of her illness. noun.*

sew (sō), **1** to work with a needle and thread. You can sew by hand or with a machine. **2** to fasten with stitches: *to sew on a button, to sew a hem on a sewing machine.* **3** to close with stitches: *The doctor sewed up the wound. verb,* **sews, sewed, sewed** or **sewn, sew·ing.**

sew·age (sü'ij), the waste matter which passes through sewers. *noun.*

sew·er (sü'ər), an underground drain to carry off waste water and refuse. *noun.*

sew·ing (sō'ing), **1** work done with a needle and thread. **2** something to be sewed. *noun.*

sewing machine, a machine for sewing or stitching cloth.

sewn (sōn), sewed. See **sew.** *She has sewn patches on her jeans. verb.*

sex (seks), **1** one of the two basic kinds of human beings and many other living things. The two kinds are males and females. **2** the character of being male or female: *The list of members of the club was arranged by age and by sex. noun, plural* **sex·es.**

sex·tant (sek'stənt), an instrument used by navigators to determine the position of a ship or aircraft. *noun.*

shab·by (shab'ē), **1** much worn: *His old suit looks shabby.* **2** wearing old or much worn clothes: *She is always shabby.* **3** mean; not generous; unfair: *That's a shabby way to treat a friend.* *adjective,* **shab·bi·er, shab·bi·est.**

shack (shak), a roughly built hut or cabin: *We built a shack of old boards in the backyard. noun.*

shack·le (shak'əl), **1** a metal band fastened around the ankle or wrist of a prisoner or slave. Shackles are usually fastened to each other, the wall, or the floor by chains. **2** to put shackles on. **3** anything that prevents freedom of action or thought: *Fear and prejudice are shackles.* **4** to restrain; hamper. 1,3 *noun,* 2,4 *verb,* **shack·les, shack·led, shack·ling.**

shad (shad), a saltwater food fish related to the herring. Shad are common along the northern Atlantic coast. *noun, plural* **shad** or **shads.**

shade (shād), **1** a partly dark place, not in the sunshine: *Let's sit in the shade of that tree.* **2** a slight darkness or coolness given by something that cuts off light: *Big, leafy trees cast shade.* **3** something that shuts out light: *Pull down the shades of the windows.* **4** to keep light from: *A big hat shades the eyes.* **5** lightness or darkness of color: *I want to see silks in all shades of blue.* **6** a very small difference; little bit: *Your coat is a shade longer than your dress.* 1-3,5,6 *noun,* 4 *verb,* **shades, shad·ed, shad·ing.**

shad·ing (shā'ding), the use of variation in black or color to give the effect of shade or depth in a picture. *noun.*

shading—Shading gives more shape to the ball on the right.

shad·ow (shad'ō), **1** the shade made by some person, animal, or thing. Sometimes your shadow is much longer than you are, and sometimes it is much shorter. **2** Often, **shadows.** darkness; partial shade: *There was someone lurking in the shadows.* **3** a little bit; small degree; slight suggestion: *He is innocent beyond a shadow of a doubt.* **4** to follow closely, usually secretly: *The detective shadowed the suspected burglar.* 1-3 *noun,* 4 *verb.*

shad·ow·y (shad'ō ē), like a shadow; dim; faint: *shadowy outlines in the pale moonlight. adjective.*

shad·y (shā'dē), **1** in the shade: *We sat in a shady spot.* **2** giving shade: *We sat under a shady tree.* **3** of doubtful honesty or character: *They were* *arrested for being involved in a shady business deal.* adjective, **shad·i·er, shad·i·est.**

shaft (shaft), **1** a bar to support parts of a machine that turn, or to help move parts. **2** a deep passage sunk in the earth. The entrance to a mine is called a shaft. **3** a passage that is like a well; long, narrow space: *an elevator shaft.* **4** an arrow, spear, or lance. **5** the long, slender stem of an arrow, spear, or lance. **6** a ray or beam of light: *We saw shafts of light through the leaves.* **7** the long, straight handle of a hammer, ax, golf club, or the like. **8** the main part of a column. *noun.*

shag·gy (shag′ē), **1** covered with a thick, rough mass of hair or wool, or something resembling them: *a shaggy dog.* **2** long, thick, and rough: *My cousin has shaggy eyebrows.* adjective, **shag·gi·er, shag·gi·est.**

shake (shāk), **1** to move quickly backwards and forwards, up and down, or from side to side: *to shake a rug. The baby shook the rattle. The branches of the old tree shook in the wind.* **2** to bring, throw, or scatter by or as if by movement: *She shook the snow off her clothes.* **3** to clasp hands in greeting another: *to shake hands.* **4** to tremble or make tremble: *The kitten was shaking with cold. The explosion shook the whole town.* **5** to disturb; upset; make less firm or sure: *His lie shook my faith in his honesty.* **6** the act of shaking: *A shake of her head was the answer.* 1-5 *verb,* **shakes, shook, shak·en, shak·ing;** 6 *noun.*

shake up, 1 to shake hard: *Shake up a mixture of oil and vinegar for the salad.* **2** to jar in body or nerves: *I was much shaken up by the experience.*

shak·er (shā′kər), a container for salt, pepper, or the like, having a top with holes in it. *noun.*

shak·y (shā′kē), **1** shaking: *a shaky voice.* **2** liable to break down; weak: *a shaky porch.* **3** not reliable; not to be depended on: *a shaky bank, a shaky supporter.* adjective, **shak·i·er, shak·i·est.**

shale (shāl), a rock formed from hardened clay or mud in thin layers that split easily. *noun.*

shall (shal). *Shall* is used to express future time, command, obligation, and necessity. *We shall come soon. You shall go to the party, I promise you. Shall I drink the milk? verb, past tense* **should.**

shal·low (shal′ō), **1** not deep: *shallow water, a shallow dish, a shallow mind.* **2 shallows,** a shallow place: *The children splashed in the shallows of the pond.* 1 *adjective,* 2 *noun.*

sham (sham), **1** a fraud; pretense: *Their claim to be descended from royalty is a sham.* **2** false; pretended; imitation: *a sham battle fought for practice, sham antiques.* **3** to pretend: *He shammed sickness so he wouldn't have to work.* 1 *noun,* 2 *adjective,* 3 *verb,* **shams, shammed, sham·ming.**

sham·ble (sham′bəl), to walk awkwardly or unsteadily: *The exhausted hikers shambled into camp. verb,* **sham·bles, sham·bled, sham·bling.**

sham·bles (sham′bəlz), confusion; mess; general disorder: *They made a shambles of the clean room. noun plural or singular.*

a hat	i it	oi oil	ch child		a in about
ā age	ī ice	ou out	ng long		e in taken
ä far	o hot	u cup	sh she	ə =	i in pencil
e let	ō open	u̇ put	th thin		o in lemon
ē equal	ô order	ü rule	ŦH then		u in circus
ėr term			zh measure		

shame (shām), **1** a painful feeling of having done something wrong, improper, or silly: *to blush with shame.* **2** to cause to feel shame: *My silly mistake shamed me.* **3** to drive or force by shame: *I was shamed into cleaning my room after guests saw it.* **4** a disgrace; dishonor: *to bring shame to one's family.* **5** to bring disgrace upon: *to shame one's family.* **6** a fact to be sorry about; pity: *It is a shame to be so wasteful. What a shame you can't come to the party!* 1,4,6 *noun,* 2,3,5 *verb,* **shames, shamed, sham·ing.**

put to shame, 1 to make ashamed; disgrace: *Her bad behavior put her family to shame.* **2** to be better than; surpass: *His careful work put the rest to shame.*

shame·ful (shām′fəl), causing shame; bringing disgrace: *We were shocked by his shameful behavior. adjective.*

shame·less (shām′lis), without shame: *She was a shameless liar. adjective.*

sham·poo (sham pü′), **1** to wash the hair. **2** a washing of the hair. **3** a preparation used for shampooing. 1 *verb,* **sham·poos, sham·pooed, sham·poo·ing;** 2,3 *noun, plural* **sham·poos.**

sham·rock (sham′rok), **1** a bright-green leaf that is divided into three parts. The shamrock is the national emblem of Ireland. **2** a plant, such as white clover, that has leaves like this. *noun.*

Word History

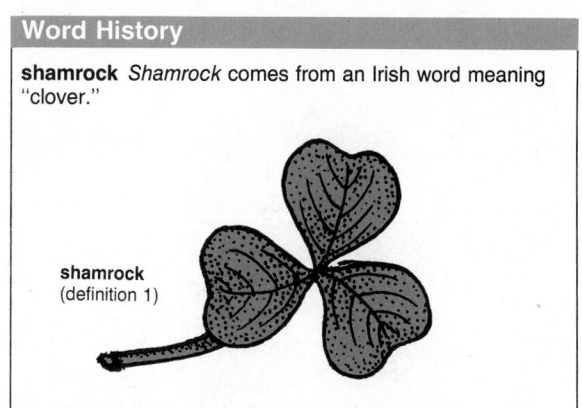

shamrock *Shamrock* comes from an Irish word meaning "clover."

shamrock
(definition 1)

Shang·hai (shang′hī′), a city in China. *noun.*

shank (shangk), a cut of meat from the upper part of the leg of an animal. *noun.*

shan't (shant), shall not.

shan·ty (shan′tē), a roughly built hut or cabin. *noun, plural* **shan·ties.**

shape (shāp), **1** a form; figure; appearance: *An apple is different in shape from a banana. A witch was supposed to take the shape of a cat or a bat. A white shape stood beside his bed.* **2** to form: *The*

S

child shapes clay into balls. **3** to develop; take shape: *Her plan is shaping well.* **4** condition: *Athletes exercise to keep themselves in good shape.* **5** order; definite form; proper arrangement: *Take time to get your thoughts into shape.* 1,4,5 *noun*, 2,3 *verb*, **shapes, shaped, shap·ing.**

shape up, 1 to take on a certain form or appearance; develop: *Our school project is shaping up well.* **2** to behave properly; do what is expected: *You will have to shape up if you want to pass this course.*

take shape, to have or take on a definite form: *The general outline of the novel began to take shape.*

shape·less (shāp′lis), **1** without definite shape: *a shapeless old hat.* **2** having a shape that is not attractive: *a shapeless figure. adjective.*

shape·ly (shāp′lē), having a pleasing shape. *adjective*, **shape·li·er, shape·li·est.**

share (sher *or* shar), **1** the part belonging to one person; part; portion: *Each child received an equal share of the property. You've done more than your share of the work.* **2** each of the parts into which the ownership of a company or corporation is divided: *The ownership of this railroad is divided into several million shares.* **3** to use together; enjoy together; have in common: *The sisters share the same room.* **4** to divide into parts, each taking a part: *The child shared his candy with his sister.* **5** to have a share; take part: *Everyone shared in making the picnic a success.* 1,2 *noun*, 3-5 *verb*, **shares, shared, shar·ing.**

shark[1] (shärk), a large and ferocious fish that eats other fish. Certain kinds are sometimes dangerous to human beings. *noun.*

shark[1]—The diver is photographing a great white **shark**. This is a very dangerous kind of **shark**, which may reach a length of 25 feet (7½ meters) or more.

shark[2] (shärk), a dishonest person who preys on others. *noun.*

sharp (shärp), **1** having a thin cutting edge or a fine point: *a sharp knife.* **2** having a point; not rounded: *a sharp corner on a box.* **3** with a sudden change of direction: *a sharp turn.* **4** very cold: *a sharp wind.* **5** severe; biting: *sharp words.* **6** feeling

somewhat like a cut or prick; acting keenly on the senses: *a sharp taste, a sharp pain.* **7** clear; distinct: *the sharp contrast between black and white.* **8** watchful; alert; aware of things: *The sentry kept a sharp watch for the enemy. The dog has sharp ears.* **9** quick in mind; shrewd; clever: *a sharp lawyer.* **10** promptly; exactly: *Come at one o'clock sharp.* **11** in a sharp manner; in an alert manner; keenly: *Look sharp!* **12** high in pitch; shrill: *a sharp voice.* **13** above the true pitch in music: *to sing sharp.* **14** a tone one half step above natural pitch: *Play a C sharp.* **15** the sign in music (♯) that shows this. 1-9,12 *adjective*, 10,11,13 *adverb*, 14,15 *noun.*

sharp·en (shär′pən), to make or become sharp: *Sharpen the pencil. Sharpen your wits. verb.*

sharp·shoot·er (shärp′shü′tər), a person who shoots very well, especially with a rifle. *noun.*

shat·ter (shat′ər), **1** to break into pieces: *A stone shattered the window.* **2** to destroy; disturb greatly: *Our hopes for a picnic were shattered by the rain. verb.*

shave (shāv), **1** to remove hair with a razor; cut hair from the face, chin, or some other part of a person's body with a razor: *Father shaves every day. The actor shaved his head in order to portray a bald man.* **2** a cutting off of hair with a razor. **3** to cut off in thin slices: *She shaved the chocolate.* **4** a narrow miss or escape: *The car missed her, but it was a close shave.* 1,3 *verb*, **shaves, shaved, shaved** *or* **shav·en, shav·ing;** 2,4 *noun.*

shav·en (shā′vən), **1** shaved: *a clean-shaven face.* **2** shaved. See **shave.** *He had shaven an hour earlier.* 1 *adjective*, 2 *verb.*

shav·ing (shā′ving), **1** a very thin piece or slice: *Shavings of wood are cut off by a plane.* **2** the act or process of cutting hair from the face, chin, or some other part of a person's body with a razor: *He washed his face after shaving. noun.*

shawl (shôl), a square or oblong piece of cloth to be worn about the shoulders or head. *noun.*

she (shē), **1** the girl, woman, or female animal spoken about or mentioned before: *My sister says she likes to read and her reading helps her in school.* **2** anything thought of as female and spoken about or mentioned before: *She was a fine old ship.* **3** a female: *Is the baby a he or a she?* 1,2 *pronoun, plural* **they;** 3 *noun.*

sheaf (shēf), a bundle of things of the same sort: *a sheaf of arrows. They were bringing sheaves of wheat. noun, plural* **sheaves.**

shear (shir), **1** to cut the wool or fleece from: *to shear sheep.* **2** to cut close; cut off; cut: *The airplane's wing was sheared off in the accident. verb*, **shears, sheared, sheared** *or* **shorn, shear·ing.**

shears (shirz), **1** large scissors: *barber's shears.* **2** any cutting instrument resembling scissors: *grass shears, tin shears. noun plural.*

sheath (shēth), **1** a case or covering for the blade of a sword, dagger, or knife. **2** any similar covering, especially on an animal or plant. *noun, plural* **sheaths** (shēᴛʜz *or* shēths).

sheathe (shēⱦH), **1** to put a sword, dagger, or knife into a sheath. **2** to enclose in a case or covering: *a mummy sheathed in linen, doors sheathed in metal. verb,* **sheathes, sheathed, sheath·ing.**

sheaves (shēvz), more than one sheaf. *noun plural.*

shed[1] (shed), a building used for the shelter or storage of goods or vehicles, usually having only one story: *The rake is in the tool shed. noun.*

shed[2] (shed), **1** to pour out; let flow: *to shed tears, to shed blood.* **2** to throw off: *The snake sheds its skin. The umbrella sheds water.* **3** to send out; give forth: *The sun sheds light. verb,* **sheds, shed, shed·ding.**

she'd (shēd), **1** she had. **2** she would.

sheen (shēn), brightness; luster: *Satin and polished silver have a sheen. noun.*

sheep (shēp), an animal with a thick coat and hoofs that chews its cud. Sheep are somewhat like goats and cattle, and they are raised for wool, meat, and skin. *noun, plural* **sheep.**

sheep dog, a collie or other dog trained to help a shepherd watch and tend sheep.

sheep·ish (shē′pish), awkwardly bashful or embarrassed: *a sheepish smile. adjective.*

sheep·skin (shēp′skin′), the skin of a sheep, especially with the wool on it. *noun.*

sheer (shir), **1** very thin; almost transparent: *Those sheer curtains will let the light through.* **2** unmixed with anything else; complete: *sheer nonsense, sheer weariness.* **3** straight up and down; steep. *adjective.*

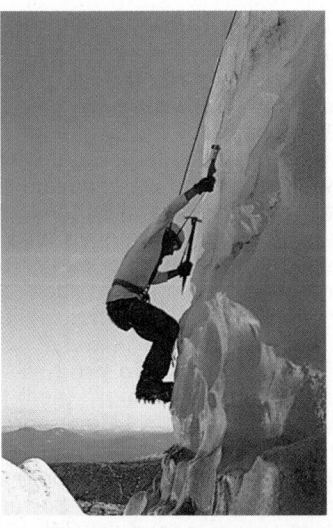

sheer (definition 3) Ropes and picks are necessary when climbing the **sheer** wall of a glacier.

sheet (shēt), **1** a large piece of cloth, usually of linen or cotton, used to sleep on or under. **2** a broad, thin piece of anything: *a sheet of glass.* **3** a single piece of paper. **4** a broad, flat surface: *There was a sheet of ice on the windshield. noun.*

sheik (shēk), an Arab chief or head of a family, village, or tribe. *noun.*

[*Sheik* comes from an Arabic word originally meaning "old man."]

a hat	i it	oi oil	ch child	a in about
ā age	ī ice	ou out	ng long	e in taken
ä far	o hot	u cup	sh she	ə = i in pencil
e let	ō open	u̇ put	th thin	o in lemon
ē equal	ô order	ü rule	ⱦH then	u in circus
ėr term			zh measure	

shelf (shelf), **1** a thin, flat piece of wood, stone, metal, or other material, fastened to a wall or frame to hold things, such as books or dishes. **2** anything like a shelf: *The ship hit a shelf of coral. noun, plural* **shelves.**

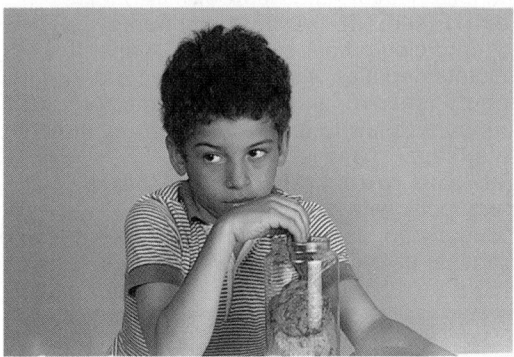

sheepish—He looked **sheepish** when he was caught taking another cookie.

shell (shel), **1** the hard outside covering of certain animals. Oysters, turtles, and beetles all have shells. **2** the hard outside covering of a nut, seed, or fruit. **3** the hard outside covering of an egg. **4** to take out of a shell: *The cook is shelling peas.* **5** to separate grains of corn from the cob. **6** something like a shell. The framework of a house, a very light racing boat, and a hollow baked dough for pastry are all called shells. **7** a case filled with gunpowder to be fired from a rifle, pistol, or cannon. **8** to fire cannon at; bombard with shells: *The enemy shelled the town.* 1-3,6,7 *noun,* 4,5,8 *verb.*

shell out, to hand over money; pay out: *We had to shell out five dollars for the movie.*

she'll (shēl), **1** she shall. **2** she will.

shel·lac (shə lak′), **1** a kind of varnish made from resin dissolved in alcohol. Shellac dries rapidly to give wood, metal, and other materials a smooth, shiny appearance, and protection from air and moisture. **2** to put shellac on. 1 *noun,* 2 *verb,* **shel·lacs, shel·lacked, shel·lack·ing.**

shell·fish (shel′fish′), a water animal with a shell. Oysters, clams, crabs, and lobsters are shellfish. *noun, plural* **shell·fish** or **shell·fish·es.**

shel·ter (shel′tər), **1** something that covers or protects from weather, danger, or attack: *Trees are a shelter from the sun.* **2** to protect; shield; hide: *to shelter runaway slaves.* **3** protection; refuge: *We took shelter from the storm in a barn.* **4** a temporary place of shelter for poor or homeless people, or for animals without owners. 1,3,4 *noun,* 2 *verb.*

S

shelve (shelv), **1** to put on a shelf: *My job is shelving books at the library.* **2** to lay aside: *Let us shelve that argument.* verb, **shelves, shelved, shelv·ing.**

shelves (shelvz), more than one shelf. *noun plural.*

shep·herd (shep′ərd), **1** a person who takes care of sheep. **2** to take care of: *to shepherd a flock.* **3** to guide; direct: *The teacher shepherded the class safely out of the burning building.* **1** *noun*, **2,3** *verb.*

shep·herd·ess (shep′ər dis), a woman who takes care of sheep. *noun, plural* **shep·herd·ess·es.**

sher·bet (shėr′bət), a frozen dessert made of fruit juice, sugar, and water or milk. *noun.*

sher·iff (sher′if), the most important law-enforcing officer of a county. A sheriff appoints deputies who help to keep order. *noun.*

sher·ry (sher′ē), a strong wine. Its color varies from pale yellow to brown. *noun, plural* **sher·ries.**

she's (shēz), **1** she is. **2** she has.

Shet·land po·ny (shet′lənd pō′nē), a small, sturdy pony with a rough coat.
[The pony got its name from the Shetland Islands, northeast of Scotland, where it was first bred.]

Shetland pony
32 to 46 inches (81 to 117 centimeters) high at the shoulder

shied (shīd). See **shy.** *The horse shied and threw the rider. It had never shied like that before.* verb.

shield (shēld), **1** a piece of armor carried on the arm to protect the body in battle. **2** anything used to protect: *I turned up my collar as a shield against the cold wind.* **3** something shaped like a shield. A police officer's badge and a coat of arms are called shields. **4** to protect; defend: *They shielded me from unjust punishment.* **1-3** *noun*, **4** *verb.*

shift (shift), **1** to move or change from one place, position, or person, to another; change: *I shifted the heavy bag from one hand to the other. Don't try to shift the blame to someone else. The wind has shifted to the southeast.* **2** a change of direction, position, or attitude: *a shift of the mind, a shift in policy.* **3** a group of workers who work during the same period of time: *The night shift begins work at 12:30 a.m.* **4** the time during which such a group works: *She is on the night shift this week.* **5** to manage to get along: *He left home at an early age and had to shift for himself.* **6** to change the position of gears, as in an automobile. **1,5,6** *verb*, **2-4** *noun.*

shift·less (shift′lis), lazy; inefficient: *The shiftless fellow refused to work.* adjective.

shift·y (shif′tē), tricky; not straightforward: *The burglary suspect gave shifty answers to the police.* adjective, **shift·i·er, shift·i·est.**

shil·ling (shil′ing), a former British coin equal to 12 pence. Twenty shillings made one pound. *noun.*

shim·mer (shim′ər), **1** to gleam faintly: *Both the sea and the sand shimmered in the moonlight.* **2** a faint gleam or shine. **1** *verb*, **2** *noun.*

shin (shin), **1** the front part of the leg from the knee to the ankle. **2** to climb by holding tight with the arms and legs and pulling oneself up: *I shinned up the tree.* **1** *noun*, **2** *verb*, **shins, shinned, shin·ning.**

shine (shīn), **1** to send out light; be bright with light; glow: *The sun shines. His face is shining with soap and water.* **2** light; brightness: *the shine of a lamp.* **3** luster; polish: *the shine of a new penny.* **4** fair weather; sunshine: *We'll be there rain or shine.* **5** to do very well; be bright: *She shines at sports. He is a shining athlete.* **6** to make bright; polish: *I have to shine my shoes.* **1,5,6** *verb*, **shines, shone** or **shined, shin·ing; 2-4** *noun.*

shin·gle (shing′gəl), **1** a thin piece of wood or other material, used to cover roofs and walls. Shingles are laid in overlapping rows with the thicker ends showing. **2** to cover with such pieces: *to shingle a roof.* **1** *noun*, **2** *verb*, **shin·gles, shin·gled, shin·gling.**

shin·ny (shin′ē), to climb by holding tight with the arms and legs and pulling oneself up: *He shinnied up the tree.* verb, **shin·nies, shin·nied, shin·ny·ing.**

shin·y (shī′nē), **1** reflecting light; bright: *A new penny is shiny.* **2** worn to a glossy smoothness: *a coat shiny from hard wear.* adjective, **shin·i·er, shin·i·est.**

ship (ship), **1** any large boat which can travel on oceans and deep waterways. Freighters, passenger liners, and oil tankers are common kinds of ships. **2** an airship, airplane, or spacecraft. **3** to send or carry from one place to another by a ship, train, truck, or airplane: *Did he ship it by express or by freight?* **4** to take a job on a ship: *He shipped as cook.* **1,2** *noun*, **3,4** *verb*, **ships, shipped, ship·ping.**

-ship, a suffix meaning: **1** the office, position, or occupation of _____: Governor*ship* means *the office of* governor. **2** the quality or condition of being _____: Partner*ship* means *the condition of being* a partner. **3** the act, power, or skill of _____: Workman*ship* means *the skill of* a workman.

ship·board (ship′bôrd′). **on shipboard,** on or inside a ship. *noun.*

ship·load (ship′lōd′), a full load for a ship. *noun.*

ship·ment (ship′mənt), **1** the act of shipping goods: *The oranges were crated for shipment.* **2** the goods sent at one time to a person or company: *We received two shipments of boxes from the factory.* noun.

ship·per (ship′ər), a person who ships goods. *noun.*

ship·ping (ship′ing), **1** the sending of goods by ship, train, truck, or airplane. **2** ships: *Much of the world's shipping passes through the Panama Canal each year. noun.*

ship·shape (ship′shāp′), trim; tidy; in good order: *We made the house shipshape before the visitor arrived. adjective.*

ship·wreck (ship′rek′), **1** the destruction or loss of a ship: *Only two people were saved from the shipwreck.* **2** a wrecked ship: *At low tide several old shipwrecks could be seen.* **3** to suffer shipwreck: *They shipwrecked on the rocks.* **1,2** *noun,* **3** *verb.*

ship·yard (ship′yärd′), a place near the water where ships are built or repaired. *noun.*

shirk (shėrk), to avoid or get out of doing (work or a duty): *You will lose your job if you continue to shirk responsibility. verb.*

THE BABY-SITTER CERTAINLY **SHIRKED** HER DUTIES!

shirt (shėrt), a piece of clothing for the upper part of the body. A shirt usually has a collar, long or short sleeves, and an opening in the front which is closed by buttons. *noun.*

shiv·er (shiv′ər), **1** to shake with cold, fear, or excitement: *I shivered in the cold wind.* **2** a shaking from cold, fear, or excitement: *A shiver ran down my back as I waited for the roller coaster ride to begin.* **1** *verb,* **2** *noun.*

shoal (shōl), **1** a place in a sea, lake, or river where the water is shallow. **2** a sandbank or sandbar that makes the water shallow: *The ship was wrecked on the shoals. noun.*

shock¹ (shok), **1** a sudden, violent shake, blow, or crash: *Earthquake shocks are often felt in Japan. The two trains collided with a terrible shock.* **2** a sudden, violent, or upsetting disturbance: *Her death was a great shock to her family.* **3** to cause to feel surprise, horror, or disgust: *That child's bad language shocks everyone.* **4** a great weakening of the body that sometimes causes a person to become unconscious. Shock may set in after a severe injury, great loss of blood, or after a person suddenly becomes very upset. **5** the feeling or physical effects produced by an electric current passing through the body. **6** to give an electric shock to: *That lamp shocked me when I*

touched it with my wet hands. **1,2,4,5** *noun,* **3,6** *verb.*

shock² (shok), a group of stalks of corn or bundles of grain set up on end together. *noun.*

shock³ (shok), a thick, bushy mass: *An untidy shock of red hair stuck out from under his cap. noun.*

shock·ing (shok′ing), **1** causing very painful feelings or surprise: *We heard the shocking news of the airplane crash.* **2** causing disgust or horror: *The crimes of the convicted murderers were shocking. adjective.*

shod (shod). See **shoe.** *The blacksmith shod the horses. verb.*

shoe (shü), **1** an outer covering for a person's foot. Shoes are often made of leather and usually have a stiff sole and a heel. **2** a horseshoe. **3** to furnish with a shoe or shoes: *A blacksmith shoes horses. Her feet were shod with silver slippers.* **1,2** *noun,* **3** *verb,* **shoes, shod, shoe·ing.**

shoe·lace (shü′lās′), a cord or a strip of leather or other material for fastening a shoe. *noun.*

shoe·mak·er (shü′mā′kər), a person who makes or mends shoes. *noun.*

shoe·string (shü′string′), **1** a shoelace. **2** a very small amount of money: *They started in business on a shoestring. noun.*

shone (shōn). See **shine.** *The sun shone all last week. It has not shone since. verb.*

shoo (shü), **1** an exclamation used to scare or drive away animals or small children: *"Shoo! You children get away from that cake!"* **2** to scare or drive away: *Shoo those flies away.* **1** *interjection,* **2** *verb,* **shoos, shooed, shoo·ing.**

shook (shúk). See **shake.** *They shook hands. verb.*

shoot (shüt), **1** to hit with a bullet, an arrow, or the like: *He shot a rabbit.* **2** to send swiftly: *A bow shoots an arrow. She shot question after question at us.* **3** to fire or use a gun or other shooting weapon: *to shoot a rifle. We shot at the target.* **4** to send a bullet: *This gun shoots straight.* **5** to move suddenly and rapidly: *A car shot by us. Flames shoot up from a burning house. Pain shot up his arm from his hurt finger.* **6** to pass quickly along, through, over, or under: *Only a shallow boat can shoot this stretch of rapids.* **7** to come forth from the ground; grow; grow rapidly: *Buds shoot forth in the spring. The corn is shooting up in the warm weather.* **8** a new part growing out; young branch: *See the new shoots on that bush.* **9** to send a ball, puck, or the like toward the goal while scoring or trying to score: *We put up a basketball hoop and shot baskets for practice.* **10** to take a picture with a camera; photograph: *I shot several views of the*

a hat	i it	oi oil	ch child		a in about
ā age	ī ice	ou out	ng long		e in taken
ä far	o hot	u cup	sh she	ə =	i in pencil
e let	ō open	ú put	th thin		o in lemon
ē equal	ô order	ü rule	ᴛʜ then		u in circus
ėr term			zh measure		

mountains. 1-7,9,10 *verb,* **shoots, shot,
shoot·ing;** 8 *noun.*

shooting star, a meteor seen falling or darting
through the sky at night.

shop (shop), **1** a place where things are sold;
store: *a small dress shop.* **2** to visit stores to look at
or to buy things: *We shopped all morning for a
coat.* **3** a place where things are made or repaired:
He works in a carpenter's shop. **4** a place where a
certain kind of work is done: *We get our hair cut at
a barber shop.* 1,3,4 *noun,* 2 *verb,* **shops,
shopped, shop·ping.**

shop·keep·er (shop'kē'pər), a person who
owns or manages a shop or store. *noun.*

shop·lift (shop'lift'), to steal goods from a store
while pretending to be a customer. *verb.*

shop·per (shop'ər), a person who visits stores to
look at and buy things. *noun.*

shop·ping (shop'ing), the act of visiting stores to
look at or to buy things: *I do the shopping on
Saturdays. noun.*

shopping center, a group of stores built as a
unit on or near a main road. Most shopping
centers have large areas for parking automobiles.

shore (shôr), **1** the land at the edge of a sea, lake,
or large river. **2** the land: *After so many months at
sea, it was good to be on shore again. noun.*
  off shore, in or on the water, not far from the
  shore: *The yacht was anchored off shore.*

shore·line (shôr'līn'), the line where shore and
water meet: *The shoreline changes during every big
storm. noun.*

shorn (shôrn). See **shear.** *The sheep was shorn of
its wool. verb.*

short (shôrt), **1** not long; of small extent from end
to end: *a short time, a short life, a short street.* **2** not
tall: *a short man, short grass.* **3** not having enough;
not coming up to the right amount, measure, or
standard: *We are short of food. I would like to buy
this, but I am short by a dime.* **4** so brief as to be
rude: *She was so short with me that I felt hurt.*
5 failing to reach the point aimed at: *The arrows
landed just short of the target.* **6** suddenly: *The horse
stopped short.* **7** A **short vowel** is a vowel like *a* in
hat, e in *leg, i* in *it, o* in *hot,* or *u* in *hut.* **8 shorts,
a** short pants that do not reach the knees. **b** a
similar kind of men's or boys' underwear.
1-4,7 *adjective,* 5,6 *adverb,* 8 *noun.*
  cut short, to end suddenly: *We cut short our
  vacation because of the bad weather.*
  fall short, to fail to reach: *The ball fell short of
  her.*
  for short, in order to make shorter: *Robert was
  called Rob for short.*
  in short, briefly: *I will give you the details later; in
  short, the party has been canceled.*
  run short, 1 not have enough: *Let me know if
  you run short of money before then.* **2** not be
  enough: *Our food supply ran short.*
  short of, 1 not up to; less than: *Nothing short of
  your best work will satisfy me.* **2** not having enough
  of: *He is short of funds right now.*

short·age (shôr'tij), lack; too small an amount:

*There is a shortage of grain because of poor crops.
noun.*

short circuit, a side circuit of electricity like that
formed when insulation wears off wires which
touch each other. A short circuit may blow a fuse
or cause a fire.

short·com·ing (shôrt'kum'ing), a fault; defect:
Rudeness is a serious shortcoming. noun.

short·cut (shôrt'kut'), a quicker way: *To save
time we took a shortcut through some vacant lots.
noun.*

short·en (shôrt'n), **1** to make shorter; cut off: *The
new highway shortens the trip. I had my coat
shortened.* **2** to become shorter: *The days
shortened and soon snow began to fall. verb.*

short·en·ing (shôrt'n ing), butter, lard, vegetable
oil, or other fat, used to make pastry or cake crisp
or easily crumbling. *noun.*

short·hand (shôrt'hand'), **1** a method of rapid
writing which uses symbols in place of letters,
sounds, and words. **2** writing in such symbols.
noun.

shorthand (definition 2) for "Your letter was received
today." (Century 21 system)

short·horn (shôrt'hôrn'), a breed of cattle with
short horns, raised for beef. *noun.*

short·ly (shôrt'lē), in a short time; before long;
soon: *I will be with you shortly. adverb.*

short·sight·ed (shôrt'sī'tid), **1** nearsighted; not
able to see far. **2** not taking careful thought for the
future: *It was shortsighted of us not to bring
umbrellas or raincoats on our trip. adjective.*

short·stop (shôrt'stop'), a baseball player
stationed between second and third base. *noun.*

short·tem·pered (shôrt'tem'pərd), easily made
angry; quick-tempered. *adjective.*

shot[1] (shot), **1** the firing of a gun or other weapon:
We heard two shots. **2** the tiny balls of lead or steel
fired from a shotgun. **3** a single ball of lead or
steel for a gun or cannon. **4** an attempt to hit by
shooting: *That was a good shot, and it hit the
mark.* **5** the distance a weapon can shoot; range:
We were within rifle shot of the fort. **6** a person
who shoots: *He is a good shot.* **7** something like a
shot. An aimed stroke or throw in a game is
sometimes called a shot. **8** a dose of a drug in the
form of an injection: *I hardly felt the needle when
the doctor gave me a shot of penicillin.* **9** an
attempt; try: *I think I'll take a shot at that job.
noun, plural* **shots** or (for definition 3) **shot.**

shot[2] (shot), **1** See **shoot.** *I shot the gun.* **2** woven
so as to show a play of colors: *blue silk shot with
gold.* 1 *verb,* 2 *adjective.*

shot·gun (shot'gun'), a long gun with no
grooves in its barrel, for firing cartridges filled
with small shot that sprays over a wide area.
noun.

should (shůd), **1** See **shall. 2** ought to: *You*

should try to make fewer mistakes. **3** *Should* is used to express uncertainty. *If it should rain, I won't go. verb.*

shoul·der (shōl′dər), **1** the part of the body to which an arm, foreleg, or wing is attached. **2** the part of a piece of clothing that covers a shoulder: *I tore the shoulder of my jacket.* **3 shoulders,** the two shoulders and the upper part of the back: *The man carried a trunk on his shoulders.* **4** to bear a burden or blame: *She shouldered the responsibility of sending her niece through college.* **5** the edge of a road: *When a tire went flat, we pulled onto the shoulder to fix it.* **6** to push with the shoulders: *She shouldered her way through the crowd.* 1-3,5 *noun,* 4,6 *verb.*

shoulder blade, the flat bone of either shoulder, in the upper back.

should·n't (shud′nt), should not.

shout (shout), **1** to call or yell loudly: *I shouted for help when the boat sank. Somebody shouted, "Fire!" The crowd shouted with laughter.* **2** a loud call or yell: *I heard their shouts for help.* 1 *verb,* 2 *noun.*

shove (shuv), **1** to push; move forward or along by force from behind: *Help me shove this bookcase into place.* **2** to push roughly or rudely against: *The people shoved to get on the crowded car.* **3** a push: *We gave the boat a shove which sent it far out into the water.* 1,2 *verb,* **shoves, shoved, shov·ing;** 3 *noun.*

shov·el (shuv′əl), **1** a tool with a broad scoop, used to lift and throw loose matter: *a snow shovel, a coal shovel. A steam shovel is worked by steam.* **2** to lift and throw with a shovel: *She shoveled the snow from the walk.* **3** to make with a shovel: *They shoveled a path through the snow.* **4** to throw or lift as if with a shovel: *The hungry girl shoveled the food into her mouth.* 1 *noun,* 2-4 *verb.*

show (shō), **1** to let be seen; put in sight: *She showed me her rock collection. The dog showed its teeth.* **2** to be in sight; appear; be seen: *The hole in his sock shows above his shoe. Amusement showed in his face.* **3** to point out: *She showed us the way to town.* **4** to direct; guide: *Show them out.* **5** to make clear to; explain to: *The teacher showed the children how to do the problem.* **6** to grant; give: *The governor was asked to show mercy and pardon the criminal.* **7** a display: *The jewels made a fine show.* **8** a display for effect: *He put on a show of learning to impress us.* **9** any kind of public exhibition or display: *We are going to the flower show and to the automobile show.* **10** a play, motion picture, or television program: *We saw a good show on television last night.* 1-6 *verb,* **shows, showed, shown** or **showed, show·ing;** 7-10 *noun.*

show off, to make a show of; display one's good points or abilities: *to show off new clothes. My little sister likes to show off by doing cartwheels when we have company.*

show up, to put in an appearance: *We were going to play ball, but the other team didn't show up.*

show·er (shou′ər), **1** a short fall of rain. **2** to wet

a hat	i it	oi oil	ch child	a in about
ā age	ī ice	ou out	ng long	e in taken
ä far	o hot	u cup	sh she	ə = i in pencil
e let	ō open	ů put	th thin	o in lemon
ē equal	ô order	ü rule	ᵀH then	u in circus
ėr term			zh measure	

with a shower; sprinkle; spray: *Water from the broken hose showered those standing nearby.* **3** anything like a fall of rain: *a shower of hail, a shower of tears, a shower of sparks from an engine.* **4** to give generously or in large amounts: *Her rich aunt showered gifts upon her.* **5** a bath in which water pours down on the body from an overhead nozzle. **6** to take such a bath: *I shower every morning.* 1,3,5 *noun,* 2,4,6 *verb.*

shown (shōn), showed. See **show.** *She has shown us how to play the game. We were shown many tricks. verb.*

show-off (shō′ôf′), a person who shows off in an effort to attract attention: *He is a terrible show-off who keeps doing stunts to make people watch him. noun.*

show·y (shō′ē), **1** making a display; likely to attract attention: *A peony is a showy flower.* **2** too bright and flashy to be in good taste. *adjective,* **show·i·er, show·i·est.**

shrank (shrangk). See **shrink.** *That shirt shrank in the wash. verb.*

shred (shred), **1** a very small piece torn off or cut off; very narrow strip; scrap: *The wind tore the sail to shreds.* **2** a bit; fragment; particle: *There's not a shred of evidence that he took the money.* **3** to tear or cut into small pieces: *He shredded the lettuce for the salad.* 1,2 *noun,* 3 *verb,* **shreds, shred·ded** or **shred, shred·ding.**

shrew (shrü), a small animal like a mouse, that has a long snout and brownish fur. Shrews eat insects and worms. *noun.*

shrew
about 6 inches (15 centimeters) long with the tail

shrewd (shrüd), having a sharp mind; clever: *She is a shrewd store manager with a talent for knowing what the public wants to buy. adjective.*

shriek (shrēk), **1** a loud, sharp, shrill sound: *Shrieks of laughter greeted the clown's tricks.* **2** to make a loud, sharp, shrill sound. People sometimes shriek because of terror, anger, pain, or amusement. **1** *noun,* **2** *verb.*

shrill (shril), having a high pitch; high and sharp in sound; piercing: *Crickets and katydids make shrill noises. adjective.*

shril·ly (shril′lē), in shrill tones: *A bird called shrilly to its mate. adverb.*

shrimp (shrimp), **1** a small shellfish with a long tail. Some shrimp are used for food. **2** a small, short, or unimportant person. *noun, plural* **shrimp** or **shrimps** for definition 1.

shrimp (definition 1)—about 2 inches (6 centimeters) long

shrine (shrīn), a sacred place; place where sacred things are kept. A shrine may be the tomb of a saint, an altar in a church, or a box holding a holy object. *noun.*

shrink (shringk), **1** to draw back: *I shrank from the large, hissing snake. They were shy people who shrank from strangers.* **2** to make or become smaller: *The heat of the dryer shrank my wool socks. verb,* **shrinks, shrank** or **shrunk, shrunk** or **shrunk·en, shrink·ing.**

shriv·el (shriv′əl), to dry up; wither; shrink and wrinkle: *The hot sunshine shriveled the grass. verb.*

shroud (shroud), **1** a cloth or garment in which a dead person is wrapped for burial. **2** something that covers, conceals, or veils: *The fog was a shroud over the city.* **3** to cover; conceal; veil: *The earth is shrouded in darkness.* **4** a rope from a mast to the side of a ship. Shrouds help support the mast. **1,2,4** *noun,* **3** *verb.*

shrub (shrub), a woody plant smaller than a tree, usually with many separate stems starting from or near the ground; bush. *noun.*

shrub·ber·y (shrub′ər ē), a group of shrubs: *Shrubbery hid the house from the street. noun.*

shrug (shrug), **1** to raise the shoulders as an expression of doubt or lack of interest: *He shrugged his shoulders when I asked him which team he wanted to win.* **2** a raising the shoulders in this way: *She replied with a shrug.* **1** *verb,* **shrugs, shrugged, shrug·ging;** **2** *noun.*

shrunk (shrungk). See **shrink.** *These woolen socks have shrunk and I can't get them on. verb.*

shrunk·en (shrung′kən), **1** grown smaller; shriveled: *I threw away the shrunken orange.* **2** See **shrink.** **1** *adjective,* **2** *verb.*

shuck (shuk), **1** a husk; pod: *I shelled the peas and threw away the shucks.* **2** to remove the outer covering from: *I shucked the corn before cooking it.* **1** *noun,* **2** *verb.*

shucks (shuks), an exclamation of disappointment or disgust: *Shucks! My shoelace just broke. interjection.*

shud·der (shud′ər), **1** to tremble with horror, fear, or cold: *I shudder at the sight of snakes.* **2** a trembling; quivering: *A shudder went through me when I saw the snake.* **1** *verb,* **2** *noun.*

shuf·fle (shuf′əl), **1** to scrape or drag the feet while walking: *We shuffled along the slippery sidewalk.* **2** a scraping or dragging movement of the feet: *The old beggar walked with a shuffle.* **3** to mix cards so as to change the order. **4** to move this way and that: *to shuffle a stack of papers.* **1,3,4** *verb,* **shuf·fles, shuf·fled, shuf·fling;** **2** *noun.*

shun (shun), to keep away from; avoid: *She shuns housework. verb,* **shuns, shunned, shun·ning.**

shush (shush), **1** to hush; to stop making noise: *The librarian asked them to shush.* **2** hush! stop the noise! **1** *verb,* **2** *interjection.*

shut (shut), **1** to close a container or opening by pushing or pulling a lid, door, or some part into place: *to shut a box, to shut a window.* **2** to bring together the parts of: *Shut your eyes. Shut the book.* **3** to close tight; close securely; close doors or other openings of: *We shut the house for the winter by boarding up the windows.* **4** to become closed; be closed: *The baby's mouth shut and she refused to eat any more.* **5** to enclose; confine; keep from going out: *The canary was shut in its cage. verb,* **shuts, shut, shut·ting.**

shut down, to close a factory or the like for a time; stop work: *We've got to shut down until there is a demand for our product.*

shut off, to turn off; close; check: *Shut off the radio. Police shut off traffic on the flooded road.*

shut out, 1 to keep from coming in: *The curtains shut out the light.* **2** to defeat a team without allowing it to score: *The pitcher shut out the other team, limiting them to three hits.*

shut up, 1 to shut the doors and windows of. **2** to stop talking: *It was rude of you to tell me to shut up.*

shut·out (shut′out′), a defeat of a team without allowing it to score. *noun.*

shut·ter (shut′ər), **1** a movable cover for a window: *We closed the shutters as the storm approached.* **2** a device in a camera that opens and closes to allow light to reach the film and produce a picture. *noun.*

shut·tle (shut′l), **1** a device used in weaving that carries the thread back and forth across the piece being woven. **2** the sliding holder for the lower thread in a sewing machine, which moves back and forth once for each stitch. **3** to move quickly to and fro: *We shuttled between our old and our new house many times on moving day.* **4** a bus, train, or airplane that runs regularly back and forth over a short distance. **5** a space shuttle.

1,2,4,5 *noun*, 3 *verb*, **shut·tles, shut·tled, shut·tling.**

shy (shī), **1** uncomfortable in company; bashful: *He is shy and dislikes parties.* **2** easily frightened away; timid: *A deer is a shy animal.* **3** to jump back or to the side suddenly, as when startled: *The horse shied at the newspaper blowing along the ground.* **4** not having enough; short: *I am shy of cash this week.* 1,2,4 *adjective*, **shy·er, shy·est,** or **shi·er, shi·est;** 3 *verb*, **shies, shied, shy·ing.**

a hat	i it	oi oil	ch child	a in about
ā age	ī ice	ou out	ng long	e in taken
ä far	o hot	u cup	sh she	ə = { i in pencil
e let	ō open	u̇ put	th thin	o in lemon
ē equal	ô order	ü rule	ᴛʜ then	u in circus
ėr term			zh measure	

shy (definition 3)

Si·ber·i·a (sī bir′ē ə), a region in northern Asia. It is a part of Russia. *noun.*

sic (sik), **1** to attack. Sic is usually a command to a dog. *Sic that squirrel!* **2** to excite to attack: *If you don't leave me alone, I'll sic my dog on you. verb,* **sics, sicced, sic·cing.**

sick (sik), **1** in poor health; having some disease; ill. **2** vomiting or feeling as though about to vomit: *The motion of the boat made me sick.* **3 the sick,** sick people: *The sick need special care.* **4** weary; tired: *I'm sick of school.* **5** affected by sorrow, longing, disgust, or other strong emotions: *It makes me sick to think I almost caused a serious accident.* 1,2,4,5 *adjective*, 3 *noun.*

sick·en (sik′ən), to make or become sick: *The sight of blood sickens some people. The bird sickened from being kept in a cage. verb.*

sick·le (sik′əl), a tool with a curved blade on a short handle, used to cut grass. *noun.*

sick·ly (sik′lē), **1** often sick; not strong; not healthy: *The baby was sickly and required a lot of medical care.* **2** of or caused by sickness: *Her skin is a sickly yellow. adjective,* **sick·li·er, sick·li·est.**

sick·ness (sik′nis), illness; poor health; disease: *There has been more sickness than usual this winter. noun, plural* **sick·ness·es.**

side (sīd), **1** a surface or line that forms the boundary of something: *A cube has six square sides. A square has four sides.* **2** a surface of an object that is not the front, back, top, or bottom:

There is a door at the side of the house. **3** either of the two surfaces of paper or cloth: *Write only on one side of the paper.* **4** a particular surface: *the outer and inner sides of a hollow ball, the side of the moon toward the earth.* **5** the slope of a hill or mountain: *The side of the hill was very steep.* **6** either the right or the left part of a thing; either part or region beyond a central line: *the east side of a city, our side of the street.* **7** either the right or the left part of the body: *I felt a sharp pain in my side.* **8** a group of persons who oppose another group: *Both sides are ready for the contest. We'll choose sides for a game of softball.* **9** a position or point of view that is opposed to others: *Let's hear your side of the argument. There are several sides to this problem.* **10** a part of a family line: *He is English on his mother's side and Spanish on his father's side.* **11** at one side; on one side: *a side door, the side aisles of a theater.* **12** from one side: *a side view.* **13** toward one side: *a side glance.* **14** less important: *Let's deal with the main problem and forget the side issues for now.* **15 side with,** to take the part of; agree with: *The sisters always side with each other.* 1-10 *noun*, 11-14 *adjective*, 15 *verb*, **sides, sid·ed, sid·ing.**

by one's side, near one: *My family was by my side during my illness.*

side by side, beside one another: *They walked side by side.*

side effect, an additional effect, usually one that is unpleasant: *Many drugs produce side effects such as headache or upset stomach in some people.*

side·line (sīd′līn′), **1** a line that marks the side of a playing field. **2 sidelines,** the space just outside one of these lines: *to watch a game from the sidelines.* **3** an additional line of goods, business, or activity: *My mother is a teacher, but she trains dogs as a sideline. noun.*

side·long (sīd′lông′), to one side; toward the side. *adjective.*

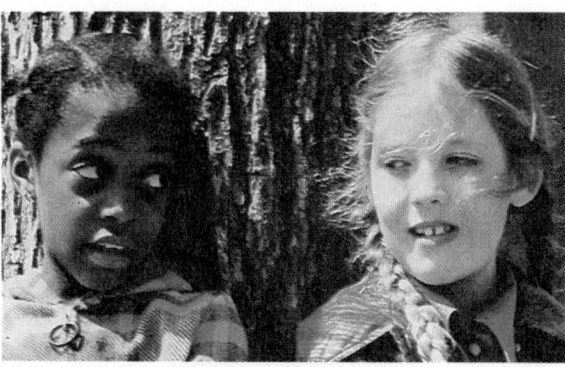

sidelong—They gave each other **sidelong** glances.

S

side·show (sīd′shō′), a small show in connection with a main one: *the sideshow of a circus. noun.*

side·step (sīd′step′), **1** to step aside: *I sidestepped the puddle of water.* **2** to get away from; avoid: *She would never sidestep a responsibility. verb,* **side·steps, side·stepped, side·step·ping.**

side·track (sīd′trak′), to put aside; turn aside: *The teacher refused to be sidetracked by questions on other subjects. verb.*
[Another meaning of *sidetrack* is "a short track onto which a train may be switched." The word came to mean "to put or turn aside."]

side·walk (sīd′wôk′), a place to walk at the side of a street, usually paved. *noun.*

side·ways (sīd′wāz′), **1** to one side; toward one side: *to walk sideways.* **2** from one side: *a sideways glimpse.* **3** with one side toward the front: *to stand sideways, to place a book sideways on a shelf. adverb, adjective.*

side·wise (sīd′wīz′), sideways. *adverb, adjective.*

siege (sēj), **1** the surrounding of a fortified place by an army trying to capture it: *The castle was under siege for several weeks before its defenders gave up.* **2** any long-continued attack: *I had a siege of illness that lasted for several months. noun.*

si·er·ra (sē er′ə), a chain or ridge of jagged hills or mountains. *noun.*

sierra *Sierra* was borrowed from a Spanish word originally meaning "a saw." Jagged mountain peaks were thought to look like the teeth of a saw.

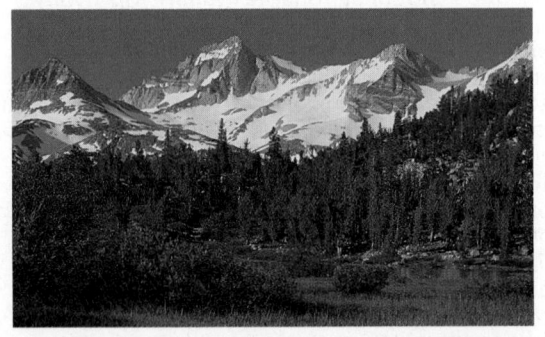

Si·er·ra Le·o·ne (sē er′ə lē ō′nē), a country in western Africa.

si·es·ta (sē es′tə), a nap or rest taken at noon or in the afternoon. *noun.*

sieve (siv), a utensil having holes that let liquids and smaller pieces pass through, but not the larger pieces: *Shaking flour through a sieve removes lumps. noun.*

sift (sift), **1** to separate large pieces from small by shaking in a sieve: *Sift the gravel and put the larger stones in another pile.* **2** to put through a sieve: *Sift powdered sugar on the top of the cake.* **3** to fall through, or as if through, a sieve: *The snow sifted softly down.* **4** to examine very carefully: *The jury sifted the evidence before making its decision. verb.*

sigh (sī), **1** to let out a very long, deep breath because one is sad, tired, or relieved: *We heard her sigh with relief.* **2** the act or sound of sighing: *a sigh of relief.* **3** to make a sound like a sigh: *The wind sighed in the treetops.* **1,3** *verb,* **2** *noun.*

sight (sīt), **1** the power of seeing: *Birds have better sight than dogs.* **2** the act of seeing; look: *love at first sight.* **3** the range of seeing: *Land was in sight.* **4** a thing seen; view; glimpse: *I can't stand the sight of blood.* **5** something worth seeing: *Niagara Falls is one of the sights of the world.* **6** something that looks bad or odd: *Your room is a sight.* **7** to see: *The lifeboat drifted for several days before the survivors sighted land.* **8** a device to guide the eye in taking aim or observing: *the sights on a rifle.* **9** to take aim or look at by means of a sight: *I sighted carefully and fired at the target.* **1-6,8** *noun,* **7,9** *verb.*

catch sight of, to see: *I caught sight of her.*

out of sight of, 1 where one cannot see: *Columbus was out of sight of land for several weeks.* **2** where one cannot be seen by: *out of sight of the neighbors.*

sight·ing (sī′ting), a seeing; being seen: *The newspaper reported the sighting of a comet. noun.*

sight·less (sīt′lis), blind. *adjective.*

sight·see·ing (sīt′sē′ing), a going around to see objects or places of interest: *a weekend of sightseeing. noun.*

sight·se·er (sīt′sē′ər), a person who goes around to see objects or places of interest: *There are a lot of sightseers at Niagara Falls. noun.*

sign (sīn), **1** any mark or thing used to mean, stand for, or point out something: *The sign reads, "Keep off the grass." The signs for add, subtract, multiply, and divide are +, −, ×, and ÷.* **2** to write one's name on. A person signs a letter, a note promising to pay a debt, or a check. We sign for telegrams or parcels. **3** a motion or gesture used to mean, stand for, or point out something: *She made the sign of the cross. A nod is a sign of agreement. We talked to the deaf man by signs.* **4** an indication: *There are no signs of life about the house.* **5** an indication of a coming event: *Dawn is the first sign of a new day. The coming of robins is a sign of spring.* **6** a trace: *The hunters found signs of deer.* **1,3-6** *noun,* **2** *verb.*

sign off, to stop broadcasting: *That radio station signs off at midnight.*

sign up, to enlist or join by written agreement: *I signed up as a member of the scouts.*

sig·nal (sig′nəl), **1** a sign giving notice of something: *A red light is a signal of danger.* **2** to make a signal or signals to: *She signaled the car to stop by raising her hand.* **3** to make known by a signal or signals: *A bell signals the end of a school period.* **4** used as a signal or in signaling: *a signal flag.* **5** an electrical wave or current that carries sounds and pictures to be received by a radio, television set, or the like. **1,5** *noun,* **2,3** *verb,* **4** *adjective.*

sig·na·ture (sig′nə chər), **1** a person's name written by that person. **2** the signs printed at the beginning of a staff to show the pitch, key, and time of a piece of music. *noun.*

sign·board (sīn′bôrd′), a board having a sign, notice, or advertisement on it. *noun.*

sig·net (sig′nit), a small seal used to stamp documents: *The order was sealed with the king's signet. noun.*

sig·nif·i·cance (sig nif′ə kəns), **1** importance: *The President wants to see you on a matter of significance.* **2** a meaning: *I understood the significance of her look. noun.*

sig·nif·i·cant (sig nif′ə kənt), **1** full of meaning; important: *The landing of men on the moon was a significant event in human history.* **2** having or expressing a hidden meaning: *A significant nod from his friend warned him to stop talking. adjective.*

sig·ni·fy (sig′nə fī), **1** to be a sign of; mean: *"Oh!" signifies surprise.* **2** to make known by signs, words, or actions: *They waved to signify that they saw us. verb,* **sig·ni·fies, sig·ni·fied, sig·ni·fy·ing.**

sign language, a language in which motions, especially of the hands, stand for words and ideas.

sign·post (sīn′pōst′), a post having signs, notices, or directions on it. *noun.*

si·lence (sī′ləns), **1** an absence of sound or noise; stillness: *The teacher asked for silence.* **2** a keeping still; not talking: *His silence made us think he agreed with the plan.* **3** to stop the noise of; make silent; quiet: *Please silence that barking dog.* **1,2** *noun,* **3** *verb,* **si·lenc·es, si·lenced, si·lenc·ing.**

si·lent (sī′lənt), **1** quiet; still; noiseless: *a silent house.* **2** not speaking; saying little or nothing: *The stranger was silent about his early life. Pupils must be silent during the study hour.* **3** not spoken; not said out loud: *a silent prayer. The "e" in "time" is a silent letter. adjective.*

sil·hou·ette (sil′ü et′), **1** a picture that is cut out of black paper or filled in with some single color to form an outline. **2** a dark image outlined against a lighter background: *At night the silhouettes of*

a hat	i it	oi oil	ch child	⎧ a in about
ā age	ī ice	ou out	ng long	e in taken
ä far	o hot	u cup	sh she	ə = ⎨ i in pencil
e let	ō open	u̇ put	th thin	o in lemon
ē equal	ô order	ü rule	ŦH then	⎩ u in circus
ėr term			zh measure	

silhouette
(definition 1)

silhouette (definition 3)
The roosting gulls were **silhouetted** against the sky.

skyscrapers could be seen against the moonlit sky. **3** to show in outline. **1,2** *noun,* **3** *verb,* **sil·hou·ettes, sil·hou·et·ted, sil·hou·et·ting.**

sil·i·con (sil′ə kən), a very common chemical element that is always found combined with oxygen or other elements. Sand and most rocks and soils contain silicon. It is used in computer chips, transistors, and other products. *noun.*

silk (silk), **1** a fine, soft thread spun by silkworms. **2** a cloth made from this thread. **3** a fiber like silk, produced by spiders to make webs. **4** anything like silk. The glossy threads at the end of an ear of corn are called **corn silk. 5** of silk; like silk: *She sewed the silk dress with silk thread.* **1-4** *noun,* **5** *adjective.*

silk·en (sil′kən), **1** made of silk: *The king wore silken robes.* **2** like silk; smooth, soft, and glossy: *silken hair. adjective.*

silk·worm (silk′wėrm′), a moth caterpillar that spins silk to make a cocoon. *noun.*

silk·y (sil′kē), like silk; smooth, soft, and glossy: *A kitten has silky fur. adjective,* **silk·i·er, silk·i·est.**

sill (sil), a piece of wood or stone across the bottom of a door or window frame. *noun.*

sil·ly (sil′ē), without sense or reason; foolish; ridiculous: *It's silly to be afraid of harmless insects like moths.* adjective, **sil·li·er, sil·li·est.**

si·lo (sī′lō), a tall, round, airtight building in which green food for farm animals can be stored without spoiling. *noun, plural* **si·los.**
[*Silo* was borrowed directly from a Spanish word. It can be traced back to a Greek word meaning "grain cellar."]

silo—A tall **silo** stood close to the barn.

silt (silt), very fine particles of earth and sand carried by moving water: *The harbor is being choked with silt.* noun.

sil·ver (sil′vər), **1** a shining white precious metal that is a chemical element. Silver is used to make coins, jewelry, spoons, knives, and forks. **2** coins made of this or a similar metal: *a pocketful of silver.* **3** knives, forks, spoons, or dishes made of or coated with silver: *I polished the silver so it could be used for Thanksgiving dinner.* **4** made of or covered with silver: *a silver spoon.* **5** shining whitish-gray: *a silver slipper.* 1-3 *noun,* 4,5 *adjective.*

sil·ver·smith (sil′vər smith′), a person who makes articles of silver. *noun.*

sil·ver·ware (sil′vər wer′ *or* sil′vər wãr′), knives, forks, or spoons made of silver or a less precious metal: *We set the table with our everyday silverware unless we are having company.* noun.

sil·ver·y (sil′vər ē), like silver; like that of silver: *Grandmother has beautiful, silvery hair. We polished the metal to a silvery gleam.* adjective.

sim·i·lar (sim′ə lər), much the same; alike; like: *The children in that family are very similar in appearance.* adjective.

sim·i·lar·i·ty (sim′ə lar′ə tē), a likeness; resemblance: *There is a remarkable similarity between your handwriting and hers.* noun, plural **sim·i·lar·i·ties.**

sim·i·le (sim′ə lē), the comparing of two different things or ideas using words such as *like* or *as. A face like marble* and *as brave as a lion* are similes. *noun.*

sim·mer (sim′ər), **1** to keep at or just below the boiling point; boil gently: *Simmer the milk, do not boil it. The soup should simmer for a few hours to improve its taste.* **2** to be on the point of just breaking out: *simmering rebellion. I simmered with anger, but said nothing.* verb.

sim·ple (sim′pəl), **1** easy to do or understand: *a simple problem. This book is in simple language.* **2** without ornament; not rich or showy; plain: *simple food, simple clothing.* **3** having few parts; not complex: *A pair of pliers is a simple device.* **4** natural; not showing off: *The famous scientist had a pleasant, simple manner.* **5** stupid; dull; having little mental ability: *"Simple Simon met a pieman."* adjective, **sim·pler, sim·plest.**

simple machine, a basic mechanical device which increases force or changes its direction. The lever, wedge, and screw are simple machines. Many parts of more complicated machines are based on simple machines.

sim·ple·ton (sim′pəl tən), a stupid or silly person; fool. *noun.*

sim·plic·i·ty (sim plis′ə tē), **1** a being simple: *Simplicity of design can keep building costs low.* **2** freedom from difficulty; clearness: *The simplicity of that book makes it suitable for children.* **3** plainness: *Hospital rooms are furnished with simplicity.* noun.

sim·pli·fy (sim′plə fī), to make plainer or easier; make simple or more simple: *The rules of the game were simplified for younger children.* verb, **sim·pli·fies, sim·pli·fied, sim·pli·fy·ing.**

sim·ply (sim′plē), **1** in a simple manner: *to explain a problem simply.* **2** without much ornament; plainly: *She was simply dressed in blue jeans and a sweater.* **3** merely; only: *We simply need a little information.* **4** absolutely: *The cool, sunny day was simply perfect for hiking.* adverb.

si·mul·ta·ne·ous (sī′məl tā′nē əs), done, existing, or happening at the same time: *The two simultaneous shots sounded like one.* adjective.

sin (sin), **1** a breaking the law of God on purpose. **2** to break the law of God. **3** wrongdoing of any kind; immoral act. Lying, stealing, dishonesty, and cruelty are sins. 1,3 *noun,* 2 *verb,* **sins, sinned, sin·ning.**

since (sins), **1** from a past time till now: *The sun has been up since five.* **2** after the time that; from the time when: *He has been home only once since he went to New York.* **3** after: *She has worked hard since she left school.* **4** from then till now: *I caught cold Saturday and have been in bed ever since.* **5** at some time between then and now: *He at first refused the position, but has since accepted it.* **6** before now; ago: *The ancient city had long since been deserted.* **7** because: *Go, since you are bored.* 1 *preposition,* 2,3,7 *conjunction,* 4-6 *adverb.*

sin·cere (sin sir′), honest; real; genuine: *I gave them my sincere thanks for all their help. I made a sincere effort to pass my exams.* adjective, **sin·cer·er, sin·cer·est.**

sin·cer·i·ty (sin ser′ə tē), honesty; truthfulness: *We do business with him because of his sincerity.* noun.

sin·ew (sin′yü), a tough, strong band or cord that joins muscle to bone; tendon. *noun.*

sin·ful (sin′fəl), full of sin; wicked; wrong: *a sinful person, a sinful act. adjective.*

sing (sing), **1** to make music with the voice: *You sing very well.* **2** to make pleasant, musical sounds: *Birds sing.* **3** to make a ringing, whistling, humming, or buzzing sound: *The teakettle sang on the stove. verb,* **sings, sang** or **sung, sung, sing·ing.**

Sing·a·pore (sing′ə pôr), an island country off the coast of southeastern Asia. *noun.*

singe (sinj), to burn a little: *A spark from the fireplace singed the rug. I singed my finger on the hot iron. verb,* **sing·es, singed, singe·ing.**

sing·er (sing′ər), a person or bird that sings: *Our canary is a fine singer. noun.*

sin·gle (sing′gəl), **1** one and no more; only one: *The spider hung by a single thread.* **2** for only one; individual: *The sisters share one room with two single beds in it.* **3** not married: *a single man.* **4** to pick from others: *She was singled out for praise.* **5** (in baseball) a hit that allows the batter to reach first base. 1-3 *adjective,* 4 *verb,* **sin·gles, sin·gled, sin·gling;** 5 *noun.*

single file, a line of persons or things arranged one behind another: *to march in single file.*

sin·gle-hand·ed (sing′gəl han′did), without help from others. *adjective, adverb.*

single-handed
She tamed lions and tigers **single-handed.**

sin·gly (sing′glē), by itself; separately: *Let us consider each point singly. adverb.*

sin·gu·lar (sing′gyə lər), **1** one in number. *Dog is singular; dogs is plural.* **2** a form of a word to show that it means no more than one. *Ox is the singular of oxen.* **3** strange; queer; peculiar: *The detectives were puzzled by the singular nature of the crime.* 1,3 *adjective,* 2 *noun.*

sin·is·ter (sin′ə stər), **1** showing ill will; threatening: *a sinister rumor, a sinister look.* **2** bad; evil; dishonest: *a sinister plan. adjective.*

sink (singk), **1** to go down; fall slowly; go lower

a hat	**i** it	**oi** oil	**ch** child	(a in about
ā age	**ī** ice	**ou** out	**ng** long	e in taken
ä far	**o** hot	**u** cup	**sh** she	ə = i in pencil
e let	**ō** open	**u̇** put	**th** thin	o in lemon
ē equal	**ô** order	**ü** rule	**ŦH** then	u in circus
ėr term			**zh** measure	

and lower: *The sun is sinking in the west.* **2** to go or make go under: *The ship sank. The submarine sank two ships.* **3** to make or become lower or weaker: *Her voice sank to a whisper.* **4** to pass gradually into sleep, silence, or the like: *The injured person sank into unconsciousness.* **5** to go deeply: *Let the lessons sink into your mind.* **6** to make go deep; dig: *They are sinking a well.* **7** a shallow basin or tub with a pipe to drain it: *The dishes are in the kitchen sink.* 1-6 *verb,* **sinks, sank** or **sunk, sunk, sink·ing;** 7 *noun.*

sin·ner (sin′ər), a person who sins or does wrong: *The sinner who repented was forgiven. noun.*

si·nus (sī′nəs), one of the spaces inside the bones in the front of the skull. The sinuses connect with the nose and may become infected by cold germs. *noun, plural* **si·nus·es.**

sip (sip), **1** to drink little by little: *She sipped her tea.* **2** a very small drink: *She took a sip.* 1 *verb,* **sips, sipped, sip·ping;** 2 *noun.*

siphon
(definition 1)
The arrows show the direction of flow of the liquid.

si·phon (sī′fən), **1** a bent tube through which liquid can be drawn over the edge of one container into another at a lower level by air pressure. **2** to draw off or pass through a siphon: *They siphoned some gasoline from their car to ours.* 1 *noun,* 2 *verb.*

sinister (definition 2)
A **sinister** character can add suspense to a movie.

© 1980 Darth Vader from THE EMPIRE STRIKES BACK

S

577

sir (sér), **1** a polite title used in writing or speaking to any man: *"Thank you for helping me, sir."* **2 Sir,** the title of a knight: *Sir Walter Scott.* noun.

sire (sīr), **1** a male parent; father: *Lightning was the sire of the racehorse Danger.* **2** to be the father of: *Lightning sired Danger.* **3** a title of respect formerly used to a great noble and now used to a king: *"Good morning, Sire," said the page to the king.* **1,3** noun, **2** verb, **sires, sired, sir·ing.**

si·ren (sī'rən), a device that makes a loud, shrill sound: *A police car went past, siren wailing and lights flashing.* noun.

sir·up (sir'əp *or* sér'əp). See **syrup.** noun.

sis (sis), sister. noun.

sis·sy (sis'ē), a weak or cowardly person; coward: *They called me a sissy when I said I thought fighting was a waste of time.* noun, plural **sis·sies.**

sis·ter (sis'tər), **1** a daughter of the same parents. A girl is a sister to the other children of her parents. **2** a female member of the same group, club, union, or religious organization. noun.

sis·ter·hood (sis'tər hüd), **1** a bond between sisters; feeling of sister for sister: *There was a strong feeling of sisterhood among the women who worked together for the right to vote.* **2** an association of women with some common aim, interest, or profession. noun.

sis·ter-in-law (sis'tər in lô'), **1** the sister of one's husband or wife. **2** the wife of one's brother. noun, plural **sis·ters-in-law.**

sis·ter·ly (sis'tər lē), of or like a sister; friendly; kindly: *My friend took a sisterly interest in helping me solve my problem.* adjective.

sit (sit), **1** to rest on the lower part of the body, with the weight off the feet: *She sat in a chair.* **2** to seat; cause to sit: *I sat the child in the chair.* **3** to be placed; be: *The clock has sat on that shelf for years.* **4** to perch: *The birds were sitting on the fence rail.* **5** to cover eggs so that they will hatch; brood: *The hen will sit until the eggs are ready to hatch.* **6** to take care of children while their parents are away for a short time: *I sit for the woman next door while she's at work.* verb, **sits, sat, sit·ting.**

sit down, to take a seat; sit: *We sat down by the roadside to have our picnic.*

sit in or **sit in on,** to take part in a game, meeting, or the like: *He sat in on our discussion but did not vote.*

sit up, 1 to raise the body to a sitting position: *Stop slumping and sit up on your chair.* **2** to keep such a position: *The sick man was able to sit up while eating.* **3** to stay up instead of going to bed: *They sat up talking all night.*

site (sīt), the position or place of anything: *The site for the new school has not yet been chosen.* noun.

sit·ter (sit'ər), a baby-sitter. noun.

sit·ting (sit'ing), **1** a meeting or session of a court of law, legislature, commission, or anything of the sort: *The hearing lasted through six sittings.* **2** the time of remaining seated: *He read five chapters at one sitting.* noun.

sitting room, a room to sit in; parlor; living room.

sit·u·ate (sich'ü āt), to place or locate: *The school is situated so that it can be reached easily from all parts of town.* verb, **sit·u·ates, sit·u·at·ed, sit·u·at·ing.**

sit·u·a·tion (sich'ü ā'shən), **1** circumstances; case; condition: *It is a very disagreeable situation to be alone and without money in a strange city.* **2** a position; location: *Our house has a beautiful situation on a hill.* noun.

sit-up (sit'up'), an exercise done by lying on the back and then sitting up without raising the feet: *She does 30 sit-ups every morning.* noun.

sit-up

six (siks), one more than five; 6: *Six apples are half a dozen apples.* noun, plural **six·es;** adjective.

six-pack (siks'pak'), a cardboard or plastic container holding six bottles, cans, or other items sold as a unit: *a six-pack of apple juice.* noun.

six·pence (siks'pəns), **1** six British pennies; 6 pence. **2** a former British coin having this value. noun.

six-shoot·er (siks'shü'tər), a revolver that can fire six shots without being loaded again. noun.

six·teen (sik'stēn'), six more than ten; 16: *There are sixteen ounces in a pound.* noun, adjective.

six·teenth (sik'stēnth'), **1** next after the 15th. **2** one of 16 equal parts: *An ounce is one sixteenth of a pound.* adjective, noun.

sixth (siksth), **1** next after the fifth. **2** one of six equal parts. adjective, noun.

six·ti·eth (sik'stē ith), **1** next after the 59th. **2** one of 60 equal parts. adjective, noun.

six·ty (sik'stē), six times ten; 60. noun, plural **six·ties;** adjective.

siz·a·ble (sī'zə bəl), fairly large: *a sizable bruise, a sizable fortune.* Also spelled **sizeable.** adjective.

size (sīz), **1** the amount of surface or space a thing takes up: *The two boys are the same size.* **2** an amount, number, or quantity; extent: *The city's population has grown in size.* **3** one of a series of measures: *His collar size is fourteen.* **4 size up,** to form an opinion of: *We sized up the candidates before we voted.* **1-3** noun, **4** verb, **siz·es, sized, siz·ing.**

size·a·ble (sī'zə bəl). See **sizable.** adjective.

siz·zle (siz'əl), **1** to make a hissing sound, as fat does when it is frying or burning. **2** a hissing

sound. 1 *verb*, **siz·zles, siz·zled, siz·zling;**
2 *noun*.

skate¹ (skāt), **1** a frame with a blade fixed to a shoe so that a person can glide over ice. **2** a roller skate. **3** to glide or move along on skates.
1,2 *noun*, 3 *verb*, **skates, skat·ed, skat·ing.**
[*Skate¹* comes from a Dutch word. Skates with iron blades apparently were first made by the Dutch.]

skate² (skāt), a broad, flat fish with very wide fins. *noun*, *plural* **skates** or **skate.**

skate²—up to 8 feet (2½ meters) long with the tail

skate·board (skāt′bôrd′), **1** a narrow board with roller-skate wheels attached to each end, used for gliding or moving on any hard surface. **2** to ride on a skateboard. 1 *noun*, 2 *verb*.

skat·er (skā′tər), a person who skates. *noun*.

skein (skān), a small bundle of yarn or thread. *noun*.

skeins of yarn

skel·e·tal (skel′ə təl), of or like a skeleton; attached to the skeleton: *skeletal muscles*. *adjective*.

skel·e·ton (skel′ə tən), **1** the framework of bones inside the body that supports the muscles and organs of any animal having a backbone. **2** a frame: *the steel skeleton of a building. noun.*
[*Skeleton* comes from a Greek word meaning "dried up." The Greeks used this same word to mean "a mummy" or "a skeleton."]

skeleton key, a key made to open many locks.

skep·tic (skep′tik), a person who does not believe easily; doubter. *noun*.

skep·ti·cal (skep′tə kəl), not believing easily; inclined to doubt; questioning the truth of theories and apparent facts. *adjective*.

sketch (skech), **1** a rough, quickly done drawing, painting, or design. **2** to make a sketch of

something; draw roughly. **3** a short description, story, or play. 1,3 *noun*, *plural* **sketch·es;** 2 *verb*.

sketch·y (skech′ē), **1** having or giving only outlines or main features. **2** incomplete; done very roughly: *The first news bulletins gave only a sketchy account of the disaster. adjective,* **sketch·i·er, sketch·i·est.**

ski (skē), **1** one of a pair of long, flat, slender pieces of hard wood, plastic, or metal that can be fastened to the shoes or boots to enable a person to glide over snow. **2** a similar object used to glide over water; water ski. **3** to glide over the snow or water on skis. 1,2 *noun*, *plural* **skis** or **ski;** 3 *verb*, **skis, skied, ski·ing.**
[*Ski* was borrowed directly from a Norwegian word.]

skid (skid), **1** to slip or slide sideways while moving: *The car skidded on the slippery road*. **2** a sideways slip or slide: *The car went into a skid on the icy road*. 1 *verb*, **skids, skid·ded, skid·ding;** 2 *noun*.

ski·er (skē′ər), a person who skies. *noun*.

skies (skīz). See **sky.** *The skies are cloudy. noun plural*.

skiff (skif), **1** a light rowboat. **2** a small, light boat. *noun*.

skill (skil), an ability to do something well, especially an ability gained by practice or knowledge: *It takes great skill to tune a piano. noun*.

skilled (skild), **1** having skill; trained; experienced: *A carpenter is a skilled worker*. **2** showing skill; requiring skill: *Plastering is skilled labor. adjective*.

skil·let (skil′it), a shallow pan with a handle, used for frying; frying pan. *noun*.

skill·ful or **skil·ful** (skil′fəl), **1** having skill; expert: *a skillful surgeon*. **2** showing skill: *That is a skillful piece of work. adjective*.

skim (skim), **1** to remove from the top: *The cook skims the fat from the soup*. **2** to take something from the top of: *The dairy skims milk to remove the cream for making butter*. **3** to move or cause to move lightly over something: *You can skim a flat stone over the water*. **4** to read hastily; read with omissions: *It took me an hour to skim the book. verb*, **skims, skimmed, skim·ming.**

skim milk or **skimmed milk,** milk from which the cream has been removed.

skimp·y (skim′pē), scanty; not enough: *I was hungry all afternoon after my skimpy lunch. adjective,* **skimp·i·er, skimp·i·est.**

skin (skin), **1** the outer covering of human and animal bodies, plants, fruits, and seeds: *Their skin was tanned from playing in the sun. Peach*

skins are fuzzy. **2** a hide; pelt: *The skin of a calf makes soft leather.* **3** to take the skin off: *She fell and skinned her knee. The hunter skinned the deer.* 1,2 *noun,* 3 *verb,* **skins, skinned, skin·ning.**
by the skin of one's teeth, very narrowly; barely: *She got home by the skin of her teeth before it rained.*

skin diver, a person skilled in skin diving.

skin diving, the sport of swimming underwater with a face mask, rubber flippers, and often a portable breathing device.

skin·ny (skin′ē), very thin; very lean: *You will get skinny if you don't eat more.* adjective, **skin·ni·er, skin·ni·est.**

skip (skip), **1** to leap lightly; spring; jump: *The children skipped merrily down the street.* **2** to leap lightly over: *The girls skipped rope.* **3** a light spring, jump, or leap: *The child gave a skip of joy.* **4** to send or go bounding along a surface; skim: *I like to skip stones on the lake.* **5** to pass over; fail to notice; omit: *Skip any questions you can't answer.* **6** to move ahead in school by being promoted into a grade ahead of the next one: *to skip third grade.* 1,2,4-6 *verb,* **skips, skipped, skip·ping;** 3 *noun.*

skip·per (skip′ər), **1** the captain of a ship, especially of a small trading or fishing boat. **2** any captain or leader. *noun.*

skir·mish (skėr′mish), **1** a slight fight between small groups: *The scouts of our army had a skirmish with a small group of the enemy.* **2** any slight conflict, argument, or contest: *The children had a skirmish over whose turn it was to play.* **3** to take part in a skirmish. 1,2 *noun, plural* **skir·mish·es;** 3 *verb.*

skirt (skėrt), **1** the part of a dress that hangs from the waist. **2** a woman's or girl's garment that hangs from the waist. **3** to pass along the border or edge of: *The new highway skirts the city instead of going through it.* 1,2 *noun,* 3 *verb.*

skit (skit), a short play that often contains humor: *a television skit. noun.*

skit·ter (skit′ər), to move lightly or quickly; skip or skim along a surface: *The rabbit skittered across the road. verb.*

skulk (skulk), to keep out of sight to avoid danger, work, or duty; hide for a bad purpose; sneak; lurk. *verb.*

skull (skul), the bony framework of the head and face in human beings and other animals with backbones. The skull encloses and protects the brain. *noun.*

skunk (skungk), **1** a black, bushy-tailed animal of North America about the size of a cat, usually with white stripes along the back. Skunks spray out a strong, unpleasant-smelling liquid when they are frightened or attacked. **2** the fur of this animal. **3** a mean, unpleasant person. *noun.*

sky (skī), **1** the space overhead that seems to cover the earth like a bowl; the area of clouds; the heavens: *a blue sky, a cloudy sky.* **2** heaven. *noun, plural* **skies.**
[*Sky* comes from an old Norse word meaning "cloud."]

skydiving

sky·div·ing (skī′dī′ving), the act or sport of diving from an airplane and dropping for a great distance before opening a parachute. *noun.*

sky·lark (skī′lärk′), **1** a small bird of Europe that sings very sweetly as it flies toward the sky. **2** to play; frolic: *The children were skylarking in the orchard.* 1 *noun,* 2 *verb.*

sky·light (skī′līt′), a window in a roof or ceiling. *noun.*

sky·line (skī′līn′), **1** the line at which earth and sky seem to meet; horizon. **2** the outline of mountains, trees, or buildings, as seen against the sky: *The tall buildings of New York make a remarkable skyline. noun.*

sky·rock·et (skī′rok′it), **1** a type of fireworks that goes up high in the air and bursts into a shower of stars and sparks. **2** to rise suddenly; rise much and quickly: *The movie star skyrocketed to fame. The price of sugar has skyrocketed.* 1 *noun,* 2 *verb.*

sky·scrap·er (skī′skrā′pər), a very tall building. *noun.*

slab (slab), a broad, flat, thick piece of stone, wood, meat, or anything solid: *This sidewalk is made of slabs of stone. The butcher cut slices from the slab of bacon. noun.*

slack (slak), **1** not tight or firm; loose: *a slack rope.* **2** the part that hangs loose: *Pull in the slack of the rope.* **3** slow: *The horse was moving at a slack pace.* 1,3 *adjective,* 2 *noun.*

slack·en (slak′ən), **1** to make or become slower: *We didn't slacken our efforts until the work was done.* **2** to make or become looser: *Slacken the rope; it is too tight. verb.*

slacks (slaks), trousers for casual wear. *noun plural.*

slain (slān). See **slay.** *The sheep were slain by wolves. verb.*

slam (slam), **1** to shut with force and noise; close with a bang: *She slammed the window down. The door slammed.* **2** to throw, push, hit, or move with force: *That car slammed into a truck.* **3** a violent and noisy closing or striking; bang: *The door blew shut with a slam.* 1,2 *verb,* **slams, slammed, slam·ming;** 3 *noun.*

slan·der (slan′dər), **1** a false spoken statement meant to harm a person's reputation: *The* *candidate for mayor accused his opponent of slander.* **2** to talk falsely about. **1** *noun,* **2** *verb.*

slang (slang), words, phrases, or meanings not used when speaking or writing formal English. Slang is often very lively and expressive and is used in talk between friends, but it is not usually proper in school themes. Slang is mostly made up of new words or meanings that are popular for only a short time. *noun.*

Word History

slang The word *slang* itself first appeared as a slang term.

a	hat	i	it	oi	oil	ch	child		a in about
ā	age	ī	ice	ou	out	ng	long		e in taken
ä	far	o	hot	u	cup	sh	she	ə =	i in pencil
e	let	ō	open	ů	put	th	thin		o in lemon
ē	equal	ô	order	ü	rule	ŦH	then		u in circus
ėr	term					zh	measure		

into thin, smooth layers. Slate is used to cover roofs and for blackboards. **2** a thin piece of this rock. Schoolchildren used to write on slates. *noun.*

slaugh·ter (slô′tər), **1** the killing of an animal or animals for food; butchering: *the slaughter of a steer, to fatten hogs for slaughter.* **2** brutal killing; much or needless killing: *The battle resulted in a frightful slaughter.* **3** to kill an animal or animals for food; butcher: *Millions of cattle are slaughtered every year in the stockyards.* **4** to kill brutally; kill in large numbers. **1,2** *noun,* **3,4** *verb.*

slave (slāv), **1** a person who is owned by another. **2** a person who is controlled or ruled by some desire, habit, or influence: *a slave of drink, a slave to one's emotions.* **3** to work like a slave: *We slaved all day cleaning the house.* **4** of slaves; done by slaves: *slave labor.* **1,2** *noun,* **3** *verb,* **slaves, slaved, slav·ing;** **4** *adjective.*

slav·er·y (slā′vər ē), **1** the condition of being a slave. **2** the custom of owning slaves. Where slavery is permitted, certain people own other people. **3** hard work like that of a slave. *noun.*

slav·ish (slā′vish), **1** weakly submitting; like slaves; fit for slaves: *slavish obedience.* **2** lacking originality and independence: *a slavish reproduction. adjective.*

slay (slā), to kill with violence: *A hunter slays wild animals. verb,* **slays, slew, slain, slay·ing.**

sled (sled), **1** a framework mounted on runners used for sliding on snow or ice. Sleds pulled by dogs are in common use in the Arctic. **2** to ride or coast on a sled. **1** *noun,* **2** *verb,* **sleds, sled·ded, sled·ding.**

sledge·ham·mer (slej′ham′ər), a large, heavy hammer, usually swung with both hands. *noun.*

sleek (slēk), **1** soft and glossy; smooth: *sleek hair.* **2** having smooth, soft skin, hair, or fur: *a sleek cat.* **3** to smooth: *He sleeked down his hair.* **1,2** *adjective,* **3** *verb.*

slant (slant), **1** to slope: *Most handwriting slants to the right.* **2** a sloping direction, position, or movement: *The roof has a sharp slant.* **1** *verb,* **2** *noun.*

slap (slap), **1** a blow with the open hand or with something flat. **2** to strike with the open hand or with something flat: *He slapped at the fly with a folded newspaper. I slapped the table with my hand.* **3** to put or throw with force: *She slapped the book down on the table.* **1** *noun,* **2,3** *verb,* **slaps, slapped, slap·ping.**

slash (slash), **1** to cut something with a sweeping blow of a sword, knife, or whip: *She slashed at the vines growing across the path.* **2** a cutting stroke: *the slash of a sword.* **3** a cut or wound made by such a stroke; a gash: *When the screwdriver slipped, it made a deep slash on his thumb.* **4** to cut down severely; reduce a great deal: *Salaries were slashed when business became bad.* **5** a sharp cutting down; great reduction: *a slash in prices.* **1,4** *verb,* **2,3,5** *noun, plural* **slash·es.**

slat (slat), a long, thin, narrow piece of wood, metal, or plastic: *the slats of a Venetian blind. noun.*

slate (slāt), **1** a bluish-gray rock that splits easily

slat—The child peered at the stranger through the **slats.**

sleep (slēp), **1** to rest body and mind; be without ordinary thought or movement: *We sleep at night. Most animals sleep.* **2** a rest of body and mind occurring naturally and regularly: *Many people need eight hours of sleep a day.* **1** *verb,* **sleeps, slept, sleep·ing;** **2** *noun.*

sleep·i·ly (slē′pə lē), in a sleepy manner: *The baby opened its eyes sleepily.* *adverb.*

sleeping bag, a long, warmly lined or padded cloth bag, used for sleeping in a tent or outdoors.

sleeping car, a railroad car with berths for passengers to sleep in.

sleep·less (slēp′lis), without sleep; not sleeping; restless: *The hot weather caused me to have a sleepless night.* *adjective.*

sleep·y (slē′pē), **1** ready to go to sleep; inclined to sleep: *He never gets enough rest and is always sleepy.* **2** quiet; not active: *There was nothing to do in the sleepy little mountain town.* *adjective,* **sleep·i·er, sleep·i·est.**

sleet (slēt), **1** half-frozen rain. Sleet forms when rain falls through a layer of cold air. **2** to come down in sleet: *It sleeted; then it snowed; then it rained.* **1** *noun,* **2** *verb.*

sleeve (slēv), the part of a garment that covers the arm. *noun.*

sleigh (slā), a carriage or cart mounted on runners for use on snow or ice. *noun.*

slen·der (slen′dər), **1** long and thin; not big around; slim: *a slender child. A pencil is a slender piece of wood.* **2** slight; small: *a slender meal, a slender income, a slender hope.* *adjective.*

slept (slept). See **sleep.** *The child slept soundly. I haven't slept well for weeks.* *verb.*

slew (slü). See **slay.** *Jack slew the giant.* *verb.*

slice (slīs), **1** a thin, flat, broad piece cut from something: *a slice of bread, a slice of meat, a slice of cake.* **2** to cut into slices: *Slice the bread.* **3** to cut off as a slice: *Slice a piece of cake for her.* **4** to cut through or across: *The boat sliced the waves.* **1** *noun,* **2-4** *verb,* **slic·es, sliced, slic·ing.**

slick (slik), **1** sleek; smooth: *slick hair.* **2** to make sleek or smooth. **3** slippery; greasy: *a road slick with ice.* **4** a smooth place or spot. Oil makes a slick on the surface of water. **1,3** *adjective,* **2** *verb,* **4** *noun.*

slid (slid). See **slide.** *The snow slid down the mountainside. She has slid past us.* *verb.*

slide (slīd), **1** to move or cause to move smoothly, as a sled moves on snow or ice: *The bureau drawers slide in and out.* **2** to move or cause to move quietly or secretly: *I slid behind the curtain. He slid his hand into his pocket.* **3** to slip, as when losing one's footing: *The car slid into the ditch.* **4** the act of sliding: *The children each take a slide in turn.* **5** a smooth surface for sliding on: *a playground slide, a toboggan slide.* **6** a mass of snow and ice or dirt and rocks sliding down: *The slide cut off the valley from the rest of the world.* **7** a small, thin sheet of glass or plastic. Objects are put on slides in order to look at them under a microscope. Slides of photographic film with pictures on them are put in a projector and shown on a screen. **1-3** *verb,* **slides, slid, slid·ing; 4-7** *noun.*

slight (slīt), **1** not much; not important; small: *I have a slight headache.* **2** not big around; slender: *a slight child.* **3** to pay too little attention to; neglect: *I felt slighted because I was not asked to the party.* **1,2** *adjective,* **3** *verb.*

slight·ly (slīt′lē), to a slight degree; somewhat; a little: *I knew him slightly.* *adverb.*

slim (slim), **1** slender; thin: *He was very slim, being 6 feet tall and weighing only 130 pounds.* **2** small; slight; weak: *We had a slim attendance at the football game because of the rain.* **3** to make or become slim or slender: *to slim one's figure with a strict diet.* **1,2** *adjective,* **slim·mer, slim·mest; 3** *verb,* **slims, slimmed, slim·ming.**
[*Slim* comes from a Dutch word meaning "bad."]

slime (slīm), **1** soft, sticky mud or something like it: *Thick slime surrounded the edge of the stagnant pool.* **2** a sticky substance given off by certain animals, such as snails, slugs, and fish. *noun.*

slim·y (slī′mē), covered with slime: *The pond is too slimy to swim in.* *adjective,* **slim·i·er, slim·i·est.**

sling (sling), **1** a strip of leather with a string fastened to each end, for throwing stones. **2** to throw with a sling. **3** to throw; cast; hurl: *I slung the bag of oats into the truck.* **4** a hanging loop of cloth fastened around the neck to support a hurt arm. **5** a rope, band, or chain by which heavy objects are lifted, carried, or held: *We lowered the heavy boxes over the railing by a sling.* **6** to hang in a sling; hang so as to swing loosely: *The bag was slung over her shoulder.* **1,4,5** *noun,* **2,3,6** *verb,* **slings, slung, sling·ing.**

sling·shot (sling′shot′), a Y-shaped stick with a rubber band fastened to its prongs, used to shoot pebbles. *noun.*

slink (slingk), to move in a secret, guilty manner; sneak: *After stealing the meat, the dog slunk away.* *verb,* **slinks, slunk, slink·ing.**

slip[1] (slip), **1** to move or cause to move smoothly, quietly, easily, or quickly: *She slipped out of the room. I slipped the bolt into place and locked the door.* **2** to slide; move out of place: *The knife slipped and cut him.* **3** to slide suddenly and lose one's balance: *He slipped and fell on the icy sidewalk.* **4** a slipping: *My broken leg was caused by a slip on a banana peel.* **5** to put or take something easily or quickly: *Slip on your coat and come with us. Slip off your shoes.* **6** a sleeveless garment worn under a dress. **7** to pass without notice; pass through neglect; escape: *Don't let this opportunity slip.* **8** to get loose from; get away from; escape from: *The dog has slipped its collar. Your name has slipped my mind.* **9** to make a mistake or error: *I slipped and mailed the wrong letter.* **10** a mistake; error: *He makes slips in pronouncing words. That remark was a slip of the tongue.* **1-3,5,7-9** *verb,* **slips, slipped, slip·ping; 4,6,10** *noun.*

let slip, to tell without meaning to: *Don't let the secret slip about the surprise party.*

slip up, to make a mistake or error: *I slipped up on that problem and got the answer all wrong.*

slip² (slip), **1** a narrow strip of paper, wood, or other material. **2** a small branch or twig cut from a plant to grow a new plant: *She has promised us slips from that bush. noun.*

slip·per (slip′ər), a light, low shoe that is slipped on easily: *a pair of bedroom slippers. noun.*

slip·per·y (slip′ər ē), **1** causing or likely to cause slipping: *A wet street is slippery. The steps are slippery with ice.* **2** slipping away easily: *Wet soap is slippery.* **3** not to be depended on; tricky. *adjective,* **slip·per·i·er, slip·per·i·est.**

slit (slit), **1** to cut or tear along a line; make a long, straight cut or tear in: *to slit cloth into strips, to slit a skirt to make a pocket.* **2** a straight, narrow cut, tear, or opening: *a slit in a bag, the slit in a mailbox.* **1** *verb,* **slits, slit, slit·ting;** **2** *noun.*

slith·er (sliŦн′ər), to go with a sliding motion: *The snake slithered into the weeds. verb.*

sliv·er (sliv′ər), a long, thin piece that has been split off, broken off, or cut off; splinter. *noun.*

slob·ber (slob′ər), **1** to let liquid run out from the mouth; drool: *Don't let the dog slobber all over my pants.* **2** liquid running out from the mouth. **1** *verb,* **2** *noun.*

slo·gan (slō′gən), a word or phrase used by a business, political party, or any group to advertise its purpose; motto: *"Service with a smile" was the store's slogan. noun.*

sloop (slüp), a sailboat having one mast and at least two sails, one before the mast and the other behind it. *noun.*

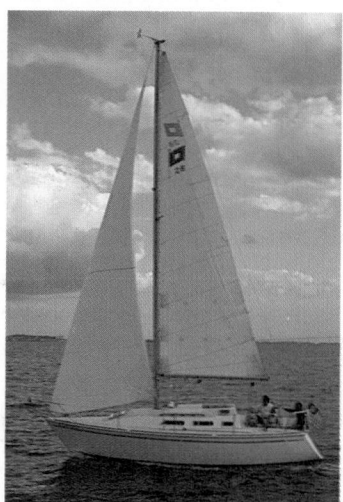

sloop

slop (slop), **1** to spill liquid upon; spill; splash: *I slopped water on the floor.* **2** a liquid carelessly spilled or splashed about. **1** *verb,* **slops, slopped, slop·ping;** **2** *noun.*

slope (slōp), **1** to go up or down at an angle; slant: *The land slopes toward the sea. That house has a sloping roof.* **2** any line, surface, or land that goes up or down from a level: *If you roll a ball up a slope, it will roll down again.* **3** the amount of slant:

a hat	i it	oi oil	ch child	a in about
ā age	ī ice	ou out	ng long	e in taken
ä far	o hot	u cup	sh she	ə = i in pencil
e let	ō open	u̇ put	th thin	o in lemon
ē equal	ô order	ü rule	ŦH then	u in circus
ėr term			zh measure	

The floor of the theater has a slope of four feet from the back seats to the front seats. **1** *verb,* **slopes, sloped, slop·ing;** **2,3** *noun.*

slop·py (slop′ē), **1** very wet: *sloppy weather.* **2** careless: *sloppy work.* **3** untidy; not neat: *sloppy clothes. adjective,* **slop·pi·er, slop·pi·est.**

slosh (slosh), to splash in slush, mud, or water: *The children sloshed through the puddles. verb.*

slot (slot), **1** a small, narrow opening: *Put your money in the slot to get a candy bar from this machine.* **2** to make a slot or slots in. **1** *noun,* **2** *verb,* **slots, slot·ted, slot·ting.**

sloth (slôth *or* slōth), a very slow-moving animal of South and Central America that hangs upside down from tree branches. *noun.*

Word History

sloth The word *sloth* also means "laziness" and "slowness." It comes from an old English word meaning "slow."

sloth—about 2 feet (60 centimeters) long

slouch (slouch), **1** to stand, sit, walk, or move in an awkward, drooping manner: *She slouched in her chair.* **2** a bending forward of head and shoulders; awkward, drooping way of standing, sitting, or walking. **3** an awkward, careless, or inefficient person: *He is no slouch when it comes to hard work.* **1** *verb,* **2,3** *noun, plural* **slouch·es.**

Slo·ve·ni·a (slō vē′nē ə), a country in southeastern Europe. *noun.*

slov·en·ly (sluv′ən lē), untidy, dirty, or careless in dress, appearance, habits, or work. *adjective,* **slov·en·li·er, slov·en·li·est.**

slow (slō), **1** taking a long time; taking longer than usual; not fast or quick: *a slow journey. He is slow to anger.* **2** moving with little speed or with less speed than others: *The slow runners couldn't keep up.* **3** showing time earlier than the correct time:

S

The clock was slow and I was late for school. **4** to make or become slower: *Cars should slow up when they pass a school.* **5** in a slow manner or way; slowly: *Drive slow past a school.* **6** not quick to understand: *a slow pupil.* 1-3,6 *adjective*, 4 *verb*, 5 *adverb*.

slow·poke (slō′pōk′), a very slow person or thing: *My brother is a slowpoke who is always late.* *noun.*

slug[1] (slug), **1** a slow-moving animal like a snail, without a shell or with only a partially developed shell. Slugs live mostly in forests, gardens, and damp places, and feed on plants. **2** a piece of lead or other metal for firing from a gun. **3** a round metal piece or counterfeit coin illegally inserted in a machine instead of a genuine coin. *noun.*

slug[1] (definition 1) about 1 inch (2½ centimeters) long

slug[2] (slug), **1** to hit hard. **2** a hard blow with the fist. 1 *verb*, **slugs, slugged, slug·ging;** 2 *noun.*

slug·gish (slug′ish), slow-moving; not active: *When I stay up late, I am often sluggish the next day. adjective.*

sluice (slüs), **1** a gate that controls the flow of water through a channel. When the water behind a dam gets too high, the sluices are opened. **2** a long, sloping trough through which water flows, used to wash gold from sand, dirt, or gravel. *noun.*

slum (slum), a run-down, overcrowded part of a city or town. Poverty, dirt, and unhealthy living conditions are common in the slums. *noun.*

slum·ber (slum′bər), **1** to sleep lightly; doze: *The baby slumbers away the hours.* **2** a light sleep: *I awoke from my slumber.* 1 *verb*, 2 *noun.*

slump (slump), **1** to drop heavily; fall suddenly: *to slump into a chair.* **2** a heavy or sudden fall: *a slump in prices.* **3** to slouch. 1,3 *verb*, 2 *noun.*

slung (slung). See **sling.** *They slung some stones and ran away. She has slung the bag over her shoulder. verb.*

slunk (slungk). See **slink.** *The dog slunk away ashamed. verb.*

slur (slėr), **1** to pronounce in an incomplete or indistinct way: *Many persons slur "How do you do."* **2** a blot or stain upon reputation; insulting remark: *a slur on a person's good name.* 1 *verb*, **slurs, slurred, slur·ring;** 2 *noun.*

slurp (slėrp), **1** to eat or drink with a noisy gurgling sound. **2** a noisy gurgling sound. 1 *verb*, 2 *noun.*

slush (slush), partly melted snow; snow and water mixed. *noun.*

sly (slī), **1** skillful in deceiving others; tricky: *He was very sly in pretending to be unable to help get the job done.* **2** playfully mischievous or knowing: *Waiting for the surprise party to begin, the children exchanged many sly looks and smiles.* **3 on the sly,** in a sly way; secretly: *The teacher caught me reading a comic book on the sly.* 1,2 *adjective*, **sly·er, sly·est,** or **sli·er, sli·est;** 3 *noun.*

sly·ly (slī′lē), in a sly manner. *adverb.*

smack[1] (smak), **1** a trace; touch: *The old sailor still had a smack of the sea about him.* **2** to have a taste, trace, or touch (of): *That plan smacks of dishonesty.* 1 *noun*, 2 *verb.*

smack[2] (smak), **1** to open the lips quickly so as to make a sharp sound: *He smacked his lips at the thought of cake.* **2** the sharp sound made in this way. **3** to kiss loudly. **4** a loud kiss. **5** to slap: *She smacked the horse on its rump.* **6** directly: *He rode the bicycle smack into the hedge.* 1,3,5 *verb*, 2,4 *noun*, 6 *adverb.*

small (smôl), **1** not large; little; not large as compared with other things of the same kind: *A cottage is a small house.* **2** not great in amount, value, time, or strength: *a small dose, small hope of success. The cent is our smallest coin.* **3** not important: *This is only a small matter now.* **4** mean; unkind: *A person with a small nature is not generous.* **5** that part which is small; a small, slender, or narrow part: *the small of the back.* 1-4 *adjective*, 5 *noun.*

small intestine, the long, winding tube between the stomach and the large intestine. The small intestine receives partly digested food from the stomach, completes the process of digesting the food, and passes the useful parts of it into the blood.

small letter, an ordinary letter, not a capital.

small·pox (smôl′poks′), a disease that causes fever and a rash of sores like blisters on the skin. The rash often leaves permanent scars shaped like little pits. Unless you are vaccinated against smallpox, you can catch the disease if you are around someone who has it. *noun.*

smart (smärt), **1** to feel or cause sharp pain: *The wind made her eyes smart.* **2** to feel distress or irritation: *She smarted from the scolding.* **3** keen; active; lively: *They walked at a smart pace.* **4** clever; bright: *a smart student.* **5** fresh and neat; in good order: *a smart uniform.* **6** stylish; fashionable: *smart new clothes.* 1,2 *verb*, 3-6 *adjective.*

smart al·eck (smärt′ al′ik), a person who is too pleased with herself or himself and very unpleasant to other people.

smash (smash), **1** to break or be broken into pieces with violence and noise: *to smash a window with a stone. The dish smashed.* **2** to rush or strike violently; crash: *The car smashed into the tree.* **3** a violent breaking; shattering; crash: *Two cars were involved in the smash.* **4** the sound of a smash or crash: *The smash of broken glass makes me very nervous.* 1,2 *verb,* 3,4 *noun, plural* **smash·es.**

smear (smir), **1** to cover or stain with anything sticky, greasy, or dirty: *My clothes are smeared with mud.* **2** to rub or spread oil, grease, or paint. **3** a mark or stain left by smearing: *There are smears of paint on the wallpaper.* **4** to receive a mark or stain; be smeared: *Wet paint smears easily.* **5** to harm; soil; spoil: *Enemies tried to smear his reputation, but his friends knew better than to believe them.* 1,2,4,5 *verb,* 3 *noun.*

smell (smel), **1** to detect or recognize by breathing in through the nose: *Can you smell the smoke?* **2** the sense of smelling: *Smell is keener in dogs than in people.* **3** to use the nose to smell; sniff: *Smell this rose.* **4** an odor: *The smell of burning rubber is not pleasant.* **5** to give out a smell: *The garden smelled of roses.* **6** to give out a bad smell: *That dirty, wet dog smells; take him outside.* 1,3,5,6 *verb,* **smells, smelled** or **smelt, smell·ing;** 2,4 *noun.*

smell·y (smel′ē), having or giving out a strong or unpleasant smell: *Rotten fish are smelly. adjective,* **smell·i·er, smell·i·est.**

smelt[1] (smelt), to melt ore in order to get the metal out of it. *verb.*

smelt[2] (smelt), a small food fish with silvery scales. *noun, plural* **smelt** or **smelts.**

smelt[3] (smelt), smelled. See **smell.** *verb.*

smile (smīl), **1** to look pleased or amused; show pleasure, favor, kindness, or amusement by an upward curve of the mouth. **2** to show scorn or disdain by a curve of the mouth: *to smile bitterly.* **3** the act of smiling: *She gave a friendly smile as she came in.* 1,2 *verb,* **smiles, smiled, smil·ing;** 3 *noun.*

smirk (smėrk), **1** to smile in a silly or self-satisfied way. **2** a silly or self-satisfied smile. 1 *verb,* 2 *noun.*

smite (smīt), to strike; strike hard; hit hard: *The hero smote the giant with his sword. verb,* **smites, smote, smit·ten, smit·ing.**

smith (smith), **1** a person who makes or shapes things out of metal. **2** a blacksmith. *noun.*

smith·e·reens (smiтн′ə rēnz′), bits; small pieces: *The glass was smashed to smithereens. noun plural.*

smith·y (smith′ē), the workshop of a smith, especially a blacksmith. *noun, plural* **smith·ies.**

smit·ten (smit′n). See **smite.** *I was smitten with curiosity. verb.*

smock (smok), a loose outer garment worn to protect clothing. *noun.*

a hat	i it	oi oil	ch child	a in about
ā age	ī ice	ou out	ng long	e in taken
ä far	o hot	u cup	sh she	ə = i in pencil
e let	ō open	u̇ put	th thin	o in lemon
ē equal	ô order	ü rule	тн then	u in circus
ėr term			zh measure	

smog (smog), a combination of smoke and fog in the air: *Automobile exhaust fumes are a major cause of smog. noun.*
[*Smog* was formed by joining parts of the words *smoke* and *fog.*]

smog·gy (smog′ē), full of smog: *She breathed in the smoggy air and began to cough. adjective,* **smog·gi·er, smog·gi·est.**

smoke (smōk), **1** a mixture of gases and carbon that can be seen rising in a cloud from anything burning. **2** to give off smoke or steam, or something like it: *The fireplace smokes.* **3** to draw the smoke from a pipe, cigar, or cigarette into the mouth and puff it out again. **4** an act or period of smoking tobacco: *He went outside for a smoke.* **5** to preserve meat or fish by treating it with smoke. 1,4 *noun,* 2,3,5 *verb,* **smokes, smoked, smok·ing.**

smoke out, to drive out by smoke: *We tried to smoke the woodchuck out of its hole.*

smoke·house (smōk′hous′), a building or place in which meat or fish is treated with smoke to keep it from spoiling. *noun, plural* **smoke·hous·es** (smōk′hou′ziz).

smok·er (smō′kər), a person who smokes tobacco. *noun.*

smoke·stack (smōk′stak′), a tall chimney. *noun.*

smok·y (smō′kē), **1** giving off much smoke: *The smoky campfire made us cough.* **2** full of smoke: *The kitchen became smoky when we broiled the steak.* **3** darkened or stained with smoke. **4** like smoke or suggesting smoke: *a smoky gray, a smoky taste. adjective,* **smok·i·er, smok·i·est.**

smol·der (smōl′dər), **1** to burn and smoke without flame: *The campfire smoldered for hours after the blaze died down.* **2** to exist or continue without being let out or expressed: *The people's discontent smoldered for years before it broke out into open rebellion. verb.* Also spelled **smoulder.**

smooth (smüтн), **1** having an even surface, like glass, silk, or still water; flat; level: *The table was made of smooth, polished walnut.* **2** free from unevenness or roughness: *smooth sailing.* **3** without lumps: *He stirred the sauce until it was smooth.* **4** to make smooth or smoother; make flat, even, or level: *I smoothed out the ball of paper and read it.* **5** to make easy: *Your tact smoothed the way to an agreement.* **6** polished; pleasant; polite: *That salesclerk has a smooth manner.* 1-3,6 *adjective,* 4,5 *verb.*

smooth down, to calm; soothe: *I tried to smooth down my parents' anger.*

smooth·ly (smüтн′lē), in a smooth manner: *The engine ran smoothly. adverb.*

S

smote (smōt). See **smite.** *The blacksmith smote the horseshoe with a hammer. verb.*

smoth·er (smuŦH′ər), **1** to make unable to get air; kill by keeping air from: *The gas almost smothered the coal miners but they got out in time.* **2** to be unable to breathe freely; suffocate: *We are smothering in this stuffy room.* **3** to cover thickly: *In the fall the grass is smothered with leaves.* **4** to put out by covering thickly: *Smother the fire with sand before you leave.* **5** to keep back; check: *I smothered a cough. verb.*

smoul·der (smōl′dər). See **smolder.** *verb.*

smudge (smuj), **1** a dirty mark; smear. **2** to mark with dirty streaks; smear: *The child's drawing was smudged.* 1 *noun,* 2 *verb,* **smudg·es, smudged, smudg·ing.**

smug (smug), self-satisfied; too pleased with one's own goodness, cleverness, or accomplishments: *Nothing disturbs the smug beliefs of some prim, narrow-minded people. adjective,* **smug·ger, smug·gest.**

smug·gle (smug′əl), **1** to bring in or take out of a country secretly and against the law: *It is a crime to smuggle goods into the United States.* **2** to bring, take, or put secretly: *I tried to smuggle my puppy into the house. verb,* **smug·gles, smug·gled, smug·gling.**

smug·gler (smug′lər), a person who smuggles. *noun.*

snack (snak), **1** a small amount of food eaten between meals: *She had a snack of cheese and crackers after school.* **2** to eat a small amount between meals: *He snacked on ice cream and cookies while he watched TV.* 1 *noun,* 2 *verb.*

snag (snag), **1** a tree or branch held fast in a river or lake. Snags are dangerous to boats. **2** any sharp or rough projecting point, such as the broken end of a branch. **3** to catch on a snag: *I snagged my sweater on a nail.* **4** a hidden or unexpected obstacle: *Our plans hit a snag, and we had to change them.* 1,2,4 *noun,* 3 *verb,* **snags, snagged, snag·ging.**

snail (snāl), **1** a small animal with a soft body that crawls very slowly. Most snails have shells on their backs into which they can pull back for protection. **2** a lazy, slow-moving person. *noun.*

snail (definition 1)—about 2 inches (6 centimeters) long

snake (snāk), **1** a long, slender, crawling reptile with a dry, scaly skin and no legs. Some snakes are poisonous. **2** a sly, treacherous person. **3** to move, wind, or curve like a snake: *The narrow road snaked through the mountains.* 1,2 *noun,* 3 *verb,* **snakes, snaked, snak·ing.**

snap (snap), **1** to make or cause to make a sudden, sharp sound: *This wood snaps as it burns.* **2** a quick, sharp sound: *The box shut with a snap.* **3** to break suddenly or sharply: *The violin string snapped because it was fastened too tight.* **4** a sudden breaking or the sound of breaking: *One snap made the knife useless.* **5** to make a sudden, quick bite or snatch: *The turtle snapped at the child's hand. The dog snapped up the meat.* **6** to seize suddenly; grab: *We snapped up several bargains at the sale. She snapped at the chance to go.* **7** a quick, sudden bite or snatch: *The dog made a snap at a fly.* **8** to speak quickly and sharply: *"Silence!" snapped the captain.* **9** to move quickly and sharply: *The soldiers snapped to attention. You better snap it up or you'll never get the job done.* **10** A **cold snap** is a few days of cold weather. **11** made or done suddenly: *A snap judgment is likely to be wrong.* **12** a fastener; clasp: *One of the snaps of your dress is unfastened.* **13** a thin, crisp cooky: *We ate lemon snaps after school.* **14** to take a snapshot of. **15** an easy job or piece of work: *Building the model was a snap.* 1,3,5,6,8,9,14 *verb,* **snaps, snapped, snap·ping;** 2,4,7,10,12,13,15 *noun,* 11 *adjective.*

snap·drag·on (snap′drag′ən), a garden plant with spikes of showy flowers of various colors. *noun.*

snapping turtle, a large American freshwater turtle that has powerful jaws with which it snaps at its prey.

snapping turtle—up to 18½ inches (46 centimeters) long

snap·shot (snap′shot′), a photograph taken in an instant with a small camera. *noun.*

snare (sner *or* snar), **1** a noose for catching small animals and birds: *The boys made snares to catch rabbits.* **2** to catch with or as if with a snare; trap: *They snared a rabbit.* 1 *noun,* 2 *verb,* **snares, snared, snar·ing.**

snare drum

snare drum, a small drum with strings stretched across the bottom to make a rattling sound.

snarl[1] (snärl), **1** to growl sharply and show one's teeth: *The dog snarled at the stranger.* **2** a sharp, angry growl. **3** to say or express with a snarl: *The bully snarled out threats.* **4** a sharp, angry remark: *She replied with a nasty snarl.* 1,3 *verb,* 2,4 *noun.*

snarl[2] (snärl), **1** a tangle: *He was brushing the snarls out of his hair.* **2** to tangle or become tangled: *The kitten snarled the yarn by playing with it.* **3** a confused situation; confusion: *An accident caused a snarl in traffic.* **4** to confuse: *The snow snarled traffic for hours.* 1,3 *noun,* 2,4 *verb.*

snatch (snach), **1** to seize suddenly: *The hawk snatched the chicken and flew away.* **2** the act of snatching: *The boy made a snatch at the ball.* **3** a small amount; bit; scrap: *We heard snatches of their conversation as they raised their voices from time to time.* 1 *verb,* 2,3 *noun,* plural **snatch·es.**

snatch at, 1 to try to seize or grasp; seize; grasp: *I snatched at the rail as I fell.* **2** to take advantage of eagerly: *She snatched at the chance to travel.*

sneak (snēk), **1** to move, take, or get in a sly, secret way: *The children sneaked the puppy into the house.* **2** to come or go like a thief or a person who is ashamed to be seen: *She sneaked in by the back way.* **3** a person who sneaks; sneaking, cowardly person. **4** sly and secret: *The enemy made a sneak attack.* 1,2 *verb,* 3 *noun,* 4 *adjective.*

sneak·ers (snē'kərz), light canvas shoes with rubber soles, used for games and sports. *noun plural.*

sneak·y (snē'kē), like a person ashamed to be seen. *adjective,* **sneak·i·er, sneak·i·est.**

sneer (snir), **1** to show scorn or contempt by looks or words: *People sneered at claims that a machine could be made to fly.* **2** a look or words expressing scorn or contempt: *The Wright brothers ignored people's sneers and built an airplane.* 1 *verb,* 2 *noun.*

sneeze (snēz), **1** to force air suddenly and violently through the nose and mouth. A person with a cold often sneezes. *The pepper made her sneeze.* **2** a sudden, violent forcing of air through the nose and mouth. 1 *verb,* **sneez·es, sneezed, sneez·ing;** 2 *noun.*

snick·er (snik'ər), **1** a sly or silly laugh; giggle. **2** to laugh in this way: *The children were snickering to each other.* 1 *noun,* 2 *verb.*

sniff (snif), **1** to draw air through the nose in short, quick breaths that can be heard: *The man who had a cold was sniffing.* **2** to smell with sniffs: *The dog sniffed at the stranger.* **3** an act or sound of sniffing: *He cleared his nose with a loud sniff.* **4** a single breathing in of something; breath. 1,2 *verb,* 3,4 *noun.*

snif·fle (snif'əl), **1** to sniff again and again as one does from a cold in the head or in trying to stop crying. **2** a sniffling; a loud sniff. **3** the sniffles, a slight cold in the head. 1 *verb,* **snif·fles, snif·fled, snif·fling;** 2,3 *noun.*

snip (snip), **1** to cut with a small, quick stroke or series of strokes with scissors: *She snipped the thread.* **2** the act of snipping: *With a few snips, she had cut her hair.* **3** a small piece cut off: *Pick up the snips of thread from the floor.* 1 *verb,* **snips, snipped, snip·ping;** 2,3 *noun.*

snipe (snīp), **1** a marsh bird with a long bill. **2** to shoot at an enemy one at a time from a hidden place. 1 *noun,* plural **snipes** or **snipe;** 2 *verb,* **snipes, sniped, snip·ing.**

snip·er (snī'pər), a hidden sharpshooter. *noun.*

snob (snob), a person who cares too much for rank, wealth, or position, and too little for real merit. *noun.*

snob·bish (snob'ish), of a snob; like a snob: *a snobbish pride in being wealthy. adjective.*

snoop (snüp), **1** to go about in a sneaking, prying way; pry. **2** a person who snoops. 1 *verb,* 2 *noun.*

S

snoop (definition 1)
He had a bad habit of **snooping** into other people's business.

snoot·y (snü′tē), having too high an opinion of oneself; apt to look down on others. *adjective,* **snoot·i·er, snoot·i·est.**

snooze (snüz), **1** to sleep; doze; take a nap: *The dog snoozed on the porch in the sun.* **2** a doze; nap. **1** *verb,* **snooz·es, snoozed, snooz·ing; 2** *noun.*

snore (snôr), **1** to breathe during sleep with a harsh, rough sound: *The child had a stuffy nose and snored all night.* **2** the sound made. **1** *verb,* **snores, snored, snor·ing; 2** *noun.*

snor·kel (snôr′kəl), a curved tube which enables swimmers to breathe under water while swimming near the surface. *noun.*

snort (snôrt), **1** to force the breath violently through the nose with a loud, harsh sound: *The horse snorted.* **2** an act or sound of snorting: *The horse leaped up with a loud snort.* **1** *verb,* **2** *noun.*

snout (snout), **1** the part of an animal's head that extends forward and contains the nose, mouth, and jaws. Pigs, dogs, and crocodiles have snouts. **2** anything like an animal's snout. *noun.*

snow (snō), **1** frozen water vapor in soft, white flakes that fall to earth and spread upon it as a white layer. **2** a fall of snow: *We had a heavy snow yesterday.* **3** to fall as snow: *It is snowing in the mountains, and will probably start to snow here soon.* **1,2** *noun,* **3** *verb.*

snow in, to shut in by snow: *The mountain village was snowed in for almost a week after the blizzard.*

snow·ball (snō′bôl′), **1** a ball made of snow pressed together. **2** a shrub with white flowers in large clusters like balls. *noun.*

snow·bank (snō′bangk′), a large mass or drift of snow, especially at the side of a road. *noun.*

snow·capped (snō′kapt′), having its top covered with snow: *a snowcapped mountain.* *adjective.*

snow·drift (snō′drift′), a bank of snow piled up by the wind: *Huge snowdrifts blocked the road.* *noun.*

snow·fall (snō′fôl′), **1** a fall of snow. **2** the amount of snow falling within a certain time and area: *The snowfall in that one storm was 16 inches.* *noun.*

snow·flake (snō′flāk′), a small, feathery piece of snow. *noun.*

snowflakes (magnified many times)

snow·man (snō′man′), a mass of snow made into a figure somewhat like that of a person. *noun, plural* **snow·men.**

snow·mo·bile (snō′mō bēl′), a vehicle used in traveling on snow. Wooden runners in front are steered by handlebars. A snowmobile is powered by an engine. *noun.*

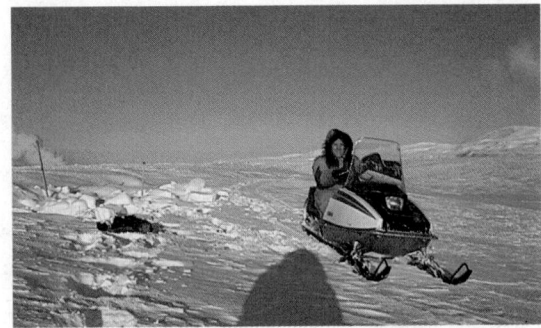

snowmobile

snow·plow (snō′plou′), a machine for clearing away snow from streets, railroad tracks, and roads. *noun.*

snow·shoe (snō′shü′), a light wooden frame with strips of leather stretched across it. Trappers in the far North wear snowshoes on their feet to keep from sinking in deep, soft snow. *noun.*

snowshoe—hunters on **snowshoes** stalking deer in deep snow

snow·storm (snō′stôrm′), a storm with much snow. *noun.*

snow·y (snō′ē), **1** having snow: *a snowy day.* **2** covered with snow: *The snowy trees looked lovely the day after the storm.* **3** like snow; white as snow: *The old woman has snowy hair.* *adjective,* **snow·i·er, snow·i·est.**

snub (snub), **1** to treat coldly, scornfully, or with contempt: *Ever since we argued, my neighbor snubs me when we meet.* **2** cold, scornful, or disdainful treatment. **3** short and turned up at the tip: *He has a snub nose.* **1** *verb,* **snubs, snubbed, snub·bing; 2** *noun,* **3** *adjective.*

snuff[1] (snuf), **1** to draw in through the nose; draw up into the nose: *He snuffs up steam to relieve a* cold. **2** to sniff; smell: *The dog snuffed at the tracks of the fox.* **3** powdered tobacco to be taken into the nose. 1,2 *verb,* 3 *noun.*

snuff² (snuf), to put out a candle. *verb.*

snuf·fle (snuf′əl), **1** to breathe noisily through the nose like a person with a cold in the head. **2** the act or sound of breathing like this. **3** to smell; sniff. 1,3 *verb,* **snuf·fles, snuf·fled, snuf·fling;** 2 *noun.*

snug (snug), **1** comfortable; warm; sheltered: *The cat has found a snug corner behind the stove.* **2** neat; trim; compact: *The cabins on the boat are snug.* **3** fitting closely: *That coat is a little too snug.* *adjective,* **snug·ger, snug·gest.**

snug·gle (snug′əl), to nestle; cuddle: *The kittens snuggled together in the basket.* verb, **snug·gles, snug·gled, snug·gling.**

so (sō), **1** in that way; in the same way or degree: *Hold your pen so. Do not walk so fast.* **2** as stated; true: *Is that really so?* **3** in such a way; to such a degree: *He is not so tall as his brother.* **4** very: *You are so kind.* **5** very much: *My head aches so.* **6** therefore: *The dog seemed hungry; so we fed it.* **7** *So* is sometimes used alone to ask a question or to exclaim: *So! late again! The train is late. So?* **8** more or less: *It weighs a pound or so.* 1,3-6 *adverb,* 2 *adjective,* 7 *interjection,* 8 *pronoun.*
and so, 1 likewise; also: *He is here, and so is she.* **2** accordingly: *I said I would go, and so I shall.*
so as or **so that,** with the result or purpose: *I go to bed early so as to get enough sleep. The boy studies so that he will do well.*

soak (sōk), **1** to make or become very wet; wet through: *The rain soaked my clothes.* **2** to let remain in water or other liquid until wet clear through: *Soak the clothes all night before you wash them.* **3** to go; enter; make its way: *Water will soak through the earth.* **4** the act or process of soaking: *Give the clothes a long soak.* 1-3 *verb,* 4 *noun.*
soak up, to take up; suck: *Sponges soak up water.*

soap (sōp), **1** a substance used for washing, usually made of a fat and lye. **2** to rub with soap: *Soap your hands well.* 1 *noun,* 2 *verb.*

soap·suds (sōp′sudz′), bubbles and foam made with soap and water. *noun plural.*

soap·y (sō′pē), **1** containing soap: *She washed her hands in soapy water.* **2** of or like soap: *The water has a soapy taste. adjective,* **soap·i·er, soap·i·est.**

soar (sôr), **1** to fly at a great height; fly upward: *The eagle soared without flapping its wings.* **2** to rise beyond what is common and ordinary: *Prices are soaring. Her hopes soared when she was called in for a job interview. verb.*

sob (sob), **1** to cry or sigh with short, quick breaths: *"I have lost my penny," the child sobbed.* **2** a catching of short, quick breaths because of grief or some other emotion. **3** to make a sound like this: *The wind sobbed.* **4** to say or express with quick, short breaths: *He sobbed out his sad story.* 1,3,4 *verb,* **sobs, sobbed, sob·bing;** 2 *noun.*

so·ber (sō′bər), **1** not drunk. **2** temperate; moderate: *The Puritans led sober, hard-working*

a hat	i it	oi oil	ch child		a in about
ā age	ī ice	ou out	ng long		e in taken
ä far	o hot	u cup	sh she	ə =	i in pencil
e let	ō open	ů put	th thin		o in lemon
ē equal	ô order	ü rule	ᵺ then		u in circus
ėr term			zh measure		

lives. **3** quiet; serious; solemn: *He looked sober at the thought of missing the picnic.* **4** to make or become sober: *The class sobered when the teacher entered the room.* 1-3 *adjective,* 4 *verb.*

so-called (sō′kôld′), called so, but really not so: *Her so-called friend hasn't phoned her. adjective.*

soc·cer (sok′ər), a game played between two teams of eleven players each, using a round ball. The ball may be struck with any part of the body except the hands and arms. Players score by hitting the ball through a goal at either end of the field. *noun.*

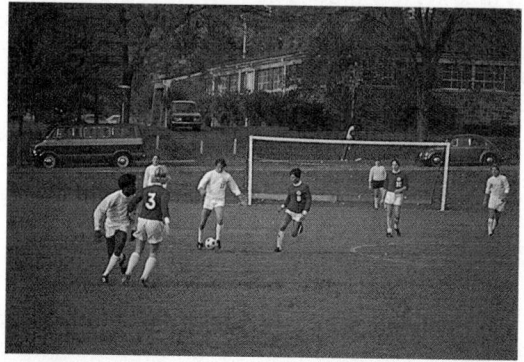

soccer

so·cia·ble (sō′shə bəl), **1** liking company; friendly: *They are a sociable family and entertain a great deal.* **2** with conversation and companionship: *We had a sociable afternoon together. adjective.*

so·cial (sō′shəl), **1** concerned with human beings as a group: *social customs, social problems.* **2** living or liking to live with others: *People are social beings.* **3** for companionship or friendliness: *They belong to several social clubs.* **4** liking company: *She has a social nature.* **5** connected with fashionable society: *The mayor and his wife are the social leaders of our town.* **6** a social gathering or party. 1-5 *adjective,* 6 *noun.*

so·cial·ism (sō′shə liz′əm), a system in which the means of production and distribution of goods are owned and controlled by the government or by the community as a whole. *noun.*

so·cial·ist (sō′shə list), a person who favors or supports socialism. *noun.*

social security, a system of federal insurance for retired persons and their dependents. Social security includes a health insurance program for aged people.

social studies, the study of people, their activities, customs, and institutions. History, economics, geography, and civics are social studies.

S

so·ci·e·ty (sə sī′ə tē), **1** a group of persons joined together for a common purpose or by common interests. A club, a lodge, or an association may be called a society. **2** all the people; human beings living together as a group: *Society must work hard for world peace.* **3** company; companionship: *I enjoy your society.* **4** fashionable people or their doings: *His parents are leaders of society. noun, plural* **so·ci·e·ties.**

sock[1] (sok), a short, close-fitting knitted covering of wool, cotton, or other fabric for the foot and leg, especially one that reaches about halfway to the knee. *noun.*

sock[2] (sok), **1** to strike or hit hard: *He socked me on the jaw.* **2** a hard blow: *He gave me a sock on the jaw.* **1** *verb,* **2** *noun.*

sock·et (sok′it), a hollow part or piece for receiving and holding something. A candlestick has a socket for a candle. A light bulb is screwed into a socket. Your eyes are set in sockets. *noun.*

sod (sod), **1** any ground covered with grass. **2** a piece or layer of this containing the grass and its roots. **3** to cover with sods: *We must have the bare spots of our lawn sodded.* **1,2** *noun,* **3** *verb,* **sods, sod·ded, sod·ding.**

sod (definition 2)—The pioneer family lived in a house made of **sod.**

so·da (sō′də), **1** baking soda. **2** soda water flavored with fruit juice or syrup, and often containing ice cream. *noun.*

soda fountain, a counter with places for holding soda water, flavored syrups, ice cream, and soft drinks.

soda pop, a bubbling soft drink.

soda water, water charged with carbon dioxide to make it bubble and fizz.

sod·den (sod′n), thoroughly wet; soaked through: *sodden clothes, a sodden rug. adjective.*

so·di·um (sō′dē əm), a soft, silver-white metal that occurs naturally only in combination with other substances. Sodium is a chemical element. Salt and baking soda contain sodium. *noun.*

so·di·um chlo·ride (sō′dē əm klôr′īd), a white substance used to season food; salt.

so·fa (sō′fə), a long, upholstered seat or couch having a back and arms. *noun.*

soft (sôft), **1** not hard; not stiff; yielding easily to touch: *Feathers, cotton, and wool are soft.* **2** not hard compared with other things of the same sort: *Pine is softer than oak. Lead is softer than steel.* **3** smooth; pleasant to the touch; not rough or coarse: *The kitten's fur is soft.* **4** quietly pleasant; mild: *a soft spring morning, the soft light of candles.* **5** gentle; kind; tender: *He has a soft heart.* **6** weak; not in condition: *He became soft from lack of exercise.* **7** free from minerals that keep soap from forming suds: *It is easy to wash clothes in soft water. adjective.*

soft·ball (sôft′bôl′), **1** a kind of baseball that is played on a smaller field, with a larger and softer ball and lighter bats. A softball must be pitched underhand. **2** the ball used in this game. *noun.*

soft coal, coal that burns with a yellow, smoky flame; bituminous coal.

soft drink, a sweetened, flavored drink, made with soda water and containing no alcohol.

soft·en (sôf′ən), to make or become softer: *Lotion softens the skin. verb.*

soft·ware (sôft′wer′ *or* sôft′war′), instructions for a computer; programs. *noun.*

soft·wood (sôft′wud′), any wood that is easily cut. Pine is a softwood; oak is a hardwood. *noun.*

sog·gy (sog′ē), **1** soaked; thoroughly wet: *The wash on the line was soggy from the rain.* **2** damp and heavy: *We could not eat the soggy bread. adjective,* **sog·gi·er, sog·gi·est.**

soil[1] (soil), **1** the ground; earth; dirt: *Roses grow best in rich soil.* **2** a land; country: *This is my native soil. noun.*

soil[2] (soil), to make or become dirty: *He soiled his clean clothes. verb.*

so·journ (sō′jėrn′), **1** to dwell for a time: *The Jews sojourned in the land of Egypt.* **2** a brief stay; stay that is not permanent: *During his sojourn in Paris his French improved.* **1** *verb,* **2** *noun.*

so·lar (sō′lər), **1** of the sun: *a solar eclipse.* **2** measured by the earth's motion in relation to the sun: *solar time.* **3** working by means of the sun's light or heat. A **solar cell** traps sunlight and changes it into electrical energy. *adjective.*

solar system, the sun and all the planets, satellites, and comets that revolve around it.

sold (sōld). See **sell.** *She sold her car a week ago. She has sold it to a friend. verb.*

sol·der (sod′ər), **1** a metal that can be melted and used for joining or mending metal surfaces or parts. **2** to fasten, mend, or join with such a metal: *She soldered the broken wires together.* **1** *noun,* **2** *verb.*

sol·dier (sōl′jər), **1** a person who serves in an army. **2** a person in the army who is not a commissioned officer. *noun.*

sole[1] (sōl), **1** one and only; single: *He was the sole heir to the fortune when his aunt died.* **2** only: *We three were the sole survivors from the wreck.* **3** not shared with others; of or for only one person or group: *That company has the sole right to make this drug. adjective.*

sole[2] (sōl), **1** the bottom or under surface of the foot. **2** the bottom of a shoe, slipper, or boot. **3** to

put a sole on: *I must have my shoes soled.*
1,2 *noun,* 3 *verb,* **soles, soled, sol·ing.**

sole³ (sōl), a flatfish much used for food. *noun,*
plural **sole** or **soles.**

sole·ly (sōl′lē), **1** alone: *I am solely responsible
for providing the lunch.* **2** only: *Bananas grow
outdoors solely in warm climates. adverb.*

sol·emn (sol′əm), **1** serious; grave; earnest: *a
solemn voice. He gave his solemn promise to do
better.* **2** causing serious thoughts: *The organ
played solemn music. adjective.*

a hat	i it	oi oil	ch child	⎧ a in about
ā age	ī ice	ou out	ng long	e in taken
ä far	o hot	u cup	sh she	ə = ⎨ i in pencil
e let	ō open	u̇ put	th thin	o in lemon
ē equal	ô order	ü rule	ᴛʜ then	⎩ u in circus
ėr term			zh measure	

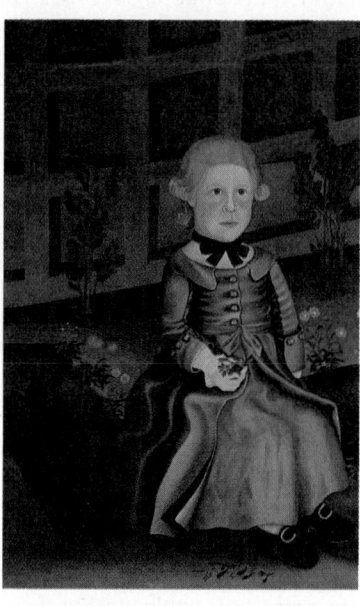

solemn
(definition 1)
The child
looked very
solemn.

so·lem·ni·ty (sə lem′nə tē), a solemn feeling;
seriousness; impressiveness: *The solemnity of the
occasion was felt even by the children. noun.*

so·lic·it (sə lis′it), **1** to ask earnestly; try to get:
*The new store is soliciting customers through
newspaper advertising.* **2** to make appeals or
requests: *to solicit for contributions to a charity.
verb.*

sol·id (sol′id), **1** a substance that is not a liquid or
a gas. Iron, wood, and ice are solids. **2** not liquid
or gaseous: *Water becomes solid when it freezes.*
3 in the form of a solid; not liquid: *After I had my
tooth pulled, I couldn't eat solid food.* **4** not hollow:
A bar of iron is solid; a pipe is hollow. **5** strongly
put together; hard; firm: *They were glad to leave
the boat and put their feet on solid ground.* **6** alike
throughout: *The cloth is a solid blue.* **7** that can be
depended on: *They are solid citizens.* **8** unbroken;
without interruption; continuous: *I spent a solid
hour on my arithmetic.* **9** completely: *The subway
was packed solid with commuters.* **1** *noun,*
2-8 *adjective,* **9** *adverb.*

so·lid·i·fy (sə lid′ə fī), to make or become solid;
harden: *The melted butter solidified as it cooled.*
verb, **so·lid·i·fies, so·lid·i·fied, so·lid·i·fy·ing.**

sol·i·tar·y (sol′ə ter′ē), **1** alone; single; only: *A
solitary rider was seen in the distance.* **2** without
companions; away from people; lonely: *She leads*

a solitary life in her cabin in the mountains.
adjective.

sol·i·tude (sol′ə tüd *or* sol′ə tyüd), a being alone:
I like solitude in the evening so that I can read.
noun.

so·lo (sō′lō), **1** a piece of music for one voice or
instrument: *She sang three solos.* **2** arranged for
one voice or instrument: *He played the solo part.*
3 without a partner, teacher, or associate; alone:
The flying student made her first solo flight.
1 *noun, plural* **so·los; 2,3** *adjective.*

so·lo·ist (sō′lō ist), a person who performs a
solo. *noun.*

sol·u·ble (sol′yə bəl), capable of being dissolved
or made into liquid: *Salt is soluble in water.*
adjective.

so·lu·tion (sə lü′shən), **1** the solving of a
problem: *That problem was hard; its solution
required many hours.* **2** an explanation: *The police
are seeking a solution of the crime.* **3** a liquid or
mixture formed by dissolving: *Every time you put
sugar in lemonade you are making a solution.*
noun.

solve (solv), to find the answer to; clear up;
explain: *The detective solved the mystery. He has
solved all the problems in the lesson. verb,* **solves,
solved, solv·ing.**

So·ma·li·a (sə mä′lyə), a country in eastern
Africa. *noun.*

som·ber (som′bər), **1** dark; gloomy: *A cloudy
winter day is somber.* **2** sad; dismal: *His losses
made him very somber. adjective.*

som·brer·o (som brer′ō), a broad-brimmed hat
worn in the southwestern United States, Mexico,
and Spain. *noun, plural* **som·brer·os.**

Word History

sombrero *Sombrero* was borrowed from a Spanish word.
It can be traced back to two Latin words meaning "under"
and "shade." The wide brim of a sombrero casts
considerable shade.

S

some (sum), **1** certain or particular, but not known or named: *Some dogs are larger than others.* **2** a number of: *Ask some people to help you.* **3** a quantity of: *Drink some milk.* **4** a certain number or quantity: *She kept some and gave the rest away.* **5** a; any: *Can't you find some person who will help you?* **6** about: *Some twenty people asked for work.* **7** very big, bad, good, or the like; remarkable of its kind: *That is some dog you've got.* 1-3,5,7 *adjective,* 4 *pronoun,* 6 *adverb.*

some·bod·y (sum'bod'ē), **1** a person not known or named; some person; someone: *Somebody has taken my pen.* **2** a person of importance: *This restaurant treats you as if you are really somebody.* 1 *pronoun,* 2 *noun, plural* **some·bod·ies.**

some·day (sum'dā), at some future time. *adverb.*

some·how (sum'hou), in a way not known or not stated; in one way or another: *I'll finish this work somehow. adverb.*

some·one (sum'wun), some person; somebody: *Someone has to lock up the house. pronoun.*

some·place (sum'plās), in or to some place; somewhere: *They went someplace for the weekend. adverb.*

som·er·sault (sum'ər sôlt), **1** a run or jump, turning the heels over the head. **2** to run or jump, turning the heels over the head: *Do you know how to somersault?* 1 *noun,* 2 *verb.*

some·thing (sum'thing), **1** some thing; a particular thing not named or known: *I'm sure I've forgotten something.* **2** a part; a certain amount; a little: *There is something of his father in his smile.* **3** somewhat; to some extent or degree: *She and her sister look something alike.* 1,2 *noun,* 3 *adverb.*

some·time (sum'tīm), **1** at one time or another: *Come to see us sometime.* **2** at an indefinite point of time: *It happened sometime last March or April. adverb.*

some·times (sum'tīmz), now and then; at times: *They come to visit sometimes. adverb.*

some·what (sum'hwot), **1** to some degree; slightly: *My hat is somewhat like yours.* **2** some part; some amount: *The large gift came as somewhat of a surprise.* 1 *adverb,* 2 *noun.*

some·where (sum'hwer *or* sum'hwar), **1** in or to some place; in or to one place or another: *It is somewhere about the house.* **2** at some time: *It happened somewhere in the past. adverb.*

son (sun), a male child. A boy or man is the son of his father and mother. *noun.*

so·nar (sō'när), a device for finding the depth of water and locating underwater objects. Sonar sends sound waves into water, which return when they strike the bottom or any object. *noun.* [*Sonar* comes from the words *sound navigation ranging,* which describe what this device does. It was formed from the first two letters of *sound* and *navigation* and the first letter of *ranging.*]

so·na·ta (sə nä'tə), a piece of music for one or two instruments, having three or four movements in contrasted rhythms but related keys. *noun.*

song (sông), **1** something to sing; short poem set to music. **2** a sound like music made by a bird: *the*

song of the canary. **3** poetry that has a musical sound. *noun.*

for a song, very cheap: *I bought this for a song.*

song·bird (sông'bėrd'), a bird that sings. *noun.*

son·ic (son'ik), of sound waves. *adjective.*

son-in-law (sun'in lô'), the husband of one's daughter. *noun, plural* **sons-in-law.**

son·net (son'it), a short poem, especially one of 14 lines with rhyme. *noun.*

so·no·rous (sə nôr'əs), **1** giving out or having a deep, loud sound: *a big, sonorous church bell.* **2** full and rich in sound: *a sonorous voice. adjective.*

soon (sün), **1** in a short time; before long: *I will see you again soon.* **2** before the usual or expected time; early: *Why have you come so soon?* **3** promptly; quickly: *As soon as I hear, I will let you know.* **4** readily; willingly: *I would as soon get it over with. adverb.*

soot (sut), a black substance in the smoke from burning coal, wood, oil, or other fuel. Soot makes smoke dark and collects on the inside of chimneys. *noun.*

soothe (süŦH), **1** to quiet; calm; comfort: *The father soothed the crying child.* **2** to make less painful; ease: *Heat soothes some aches; cold soothes others. verb,* **soothes, soothed, sooth·ing.**

sooth·say·er (süth'sā'ər), a person who claims to tell what will happen. *noun.*

sop (sop), **1** to dip or soak: *to sop bread in milk.* **2** to take up water or other liquid: *Please sop up that water with a cloth. verb,* **sops, sopped, sop·ping.**

sopping wet, thoroughly wet, or drenched.

sop, sopping wet
The baby mountain lions were **sopping wet** after the rainstorm.

so·phis·ti·cat·ed (sə fis'tə kā'tid), knowing how to get on in the world; not simple in one's tastes or ideas: *Her sophisticated tastes are the result of having lived in several countries. adjective.*

soph·o·more (sof'ə môr), a student in the second year of high school or college. *noun.*

so·pran·o (sə pran'ō), **1** the highest female or boys' singing voice. **2** a singer with such a voice. **3** a part sung by such a voice. *noun, plural* **so·pran·os.**

sor·cer·er (sôr'sər ər), a person who supposedly

practices magic with the aid of evil spirits; magician. *noun.*

sor·cer·ess (sôr′sər is), a woman who supposedly practices magic with the aid of evil spirits; witch. *noun, plural* **sor·cer·ess·es.**

sor·cer·y (sôr′sər ē), magic thought to be performed by the aid of evil spirits; witchcraft: *The prince had been changed into a lion by sorcery.* *noun.*

sore (sôr), **1** painful; aching; smarting: *a sore finger.* **2** a painful place on the body where the skin or flesh is broken or bruised. **3** offended; angered: *She is sore at having to stay home.* **4** causing misery, anger, or offense: *Their defeat is a sore subject with the members of the team.* 1,3,4 *adjective,* **sor·er, sor·est;** 2 *noun.*

so·ror·i·ty (sə rôr′ə tē), a club or society of women or girls, especially at a college. *noun, plural* **so·ro·ri·ties.**

sor·rel (sôr′əl), a plant with sour leaves. *noun.*

sor·row (sor′ō), **1** grief; sadness; regret: *We felt sorrow at the loss of our kitten.* **2** a cause of grief or sadness; trouble; suffering; misfortune: *His sorrows have aged him.* **3** to feel or show grief, sadness, or regret; be sad; feel sorrow: *She sorrowed over the lost money.* 1,2 *noun,* 3 *verb.*

sor·row·ful (sor′ə fəl), **1** full of sorrow; feeling sorrow; sad: *He has been sorrowful since his best friend moved away.* **2** causing sorrow: *A funeral is a sorrowful occasion. adjective.*

sor·ry (sor′ē), **1** feeling pity, regret, or sympathy; sad: *I am sorry that you are sick.* **2** wretched; poor; pitiful: *The hungry, shivering dog was a sorry sight. adjective,* **sor·ri·er, sor·ri·est.**

sort (sôrt), **1** a kind; class: *What sort of work do you do? I like this sort of candy best.* **2** to arrange by kinds or classes; arrange in order: *Sort these cards according to their colors.* **3** to separate from others; put: *The farmer sorted out the best apples for eating.* 1 *noun,* 2,3 *verb.*

out of sorts, ill, cross, or uncomfortable.

sort of, somewhat; rather: *In spite of his faults, I sort of like him.*

S·O·S (es′ō′es′), an urgent call for help.

sought (sôt). See **seek.** *For days she sought a job. He was sought and found. verb.*

soul (sōl), **1** the spiritual part of a human being, believed to be the source of thought, feeling, and action. Many religions teach that the soul is separate from the body and never dies. **2** energy of mind or feelings; spirit: *She puts her whole soul into her work.* **3** the cause of inspiration and energy: *Florence Nightingale was the soul of the movement to reform nursing.* **4** a special feeling or spirit of black American culture, expressed especially through music. **5** a person: *Don't tell a soul. noun.*

sound[1] (sound), **1** what can be heard: *the sound of music, the sound of thunder.* **2** energy in the form of waves passing through a vibrating substance such as air. This energy is heard as sound. **3** one of the simple elements that make up speech: *a vowel sound.* **4** to make or cause to

make a sound or noise: *The wind sounds like an animal howling.* **5** to pronounce or be pronounced: *"Dough" and "doe" sound just alike.* **6** to order or direct by a sound: *Sound the retreat.* **7** to make known; announce; utter: *The trumpets sounded the call to battle. Everyone sounded his praises.* **8** to seem: *That answer sounds wrong to me.* 1-3 *noun,* 4-8 *verb.*

sound[2] (sound), **1** free from disease; healthy: *a sound body, a sound mind.* **2** free from injury, decay, or defect: *sound walls, a sound ship, sound fruit.* **3** strong; safe; secure: *a sound business firm.* **4** correct; right; reasonable; reliable: *sound advice.* **5** deep; heavy: *a sound sleep.* **6** thorough; complete: *a sound defeat.* **7** deeply; thoroughly: *He was sound asleep.* 1-6 *adjective,* 7 *adverb.*

sound[3] (sound), **1** to measure the depth of water by letting down a weight fastened on the end of a line. **2** to try to find out the views of; test; examine: *We sounded our landlady on the subject of having pets in the apartment. verb.*

sound[4] (sound), **1** a long, narrow channel of water joining two larger bodies of water, or between the mainland and an island: *Long Island Sound.* **2** an inlet or arm of the sea: *Puget Sound. noun.*

sound·less (sound′lis), without sound; making no sound: *soundless footsteps. adjective.*

sound·ly (sound′lē), **1** deeply; heavily: *The tired child slept soundly.* **2** vigorously; thoroughly: *We were scolded soundly. adverb.*

sound·proof (sound′prüf′), **1** not letting sound pass through. **2** to make soundproof: *The halls at school are soundproofed.* 1 *adjective,* 2 *verb.*

soup (süp), a liquid food made by boiling meat, vegetables, or fish in water, milk, or the like. *noun.*

sour (sour), **1** having a taste like vinegar or lemon juice; sharp and biting: *This green fruit is sour.* **2** fermented; spoiled: *sour milk.* **3** disagreeable; bad-tempered; cross: *a sour face, a sour remark.* **4** to make sour; become sour; turn sour: *The milk soured while it stood in the hot sun.* **5** to make or become cross, bad-tempered, or disagreeable. 1-3 *adjective,* 4,5 *verb.*

source (sôrs), **1** a person or place from which anything comes or is obtained: *A newspaper gets news from many sources. Mines are the chief source of diamonds.* **2** the beginning of a brook or river; fountain; spring. *noun.*

south (south), **1** the direction to one's right as one faces the rising sun; direction just opposite north. **2** toward the south; farther toward the south: *Drive south forty miles.* **3** from the south: *a south wind.* **4** in the south: *the south window of the house.* **5** the part of any country toward the south.

a hat	i it	oi oil	ch child	a in about
ā age	ī ice	ou out	ng long	e in taken
ä far	o hot	u cup	sh she	ə = i in pencil
e let	ō open	u̇ put	th thin	o in lemon
ē equal	ô order	ü rule	ᴛʜ then	u in circus
ėr term			zh measure	

S

6 the South, the southern part of the United States; the states south of Pennsylvania, the Ohio River, and Missouri. 1,5,6 *noun,* 2-4 *adjective,* 2 *adverb.*

south of, further south than: *New York is south of Boston.*

South Africa, Republic of, a country in southern Africa.

South America, a continent southeast of North America and west of the Atlantic Ocean. It is the fourth largest continent; only Asia, Africa, and North America are larger. Brazil, Argentina, and Peru are countries in South America.

South American, 1 of South America; having something to do with South America or its people; from South America. **2** a person born or living in South America.

South Car·o·li·na (south′ kar′ə lī′nə), one of the southeastern states of the United States. *Abbreviation:* S.C. or SC *Capital:* Columbia. [*South Carolina* was named in honor of Charles I, king of England, who lived from 1600 to 1649. His name in Latin is Carolus.]

South Da·ko·ta (south′ də kō′tə), one of the midwestern states of the United States. *Abbreviation:* S.Dak. or SD *Capital:* Pierre. [*South Dakota* got its name from an American Indian tribe, the Dakota, meaning "allies" or "friends."]

south·east (south′ēst′), **1** halfway between south and east. **2** a southeast direction. **3** a place that is in the southeast part or direction. **4** toward the southeast. **5** from the southeast: *a southeast wind.* **6** in the southeast: *the southeast district.* 1,5,6 *adjective,* 2,3 *noun,* 4 *adverb.*

south·east·ern (south′ē′stərn), **1** toward the southeast. **2** from the southeast. **3** of the southeast. *adjective.*

south·er·ly (su͞ᴛн′ər lē), **1** toward the south: *We hiked in a southerly direction.* **2** from the south: *a southerly wind. adjective, adverb.*

south·ern (su͞ᴛн′ərn), **1** toward the south: *the southern side of a building.* **2** from the south: *a southern breeze.* **3** of or in the south: *They have traveled in southern countries.* **4 Southern,** of or in the southern part of the United States: *a Southern city. adjective.*

south·ern·er (su͞ᴛн′ər nər), **1** a person born or living in the south. **2 Southerner,** a person born or living in the southern part of the United States. *noun.*

south·ern·most (su͞ᴛн′ərn mōst), farthest south. *adjective.*

South Korea, a country in eastern Asia.

south·paw (south′pô′), **1** a left-handed baseball pitcher. **2** any left-handed person. *noun.*

South Pole, the southern end of the earth's axis.

south·ward (south′wərd), toward the south; south: *I walked southward. The orchard is on the southward slope of the hill. adverb, adjective.*

south·wards (south′wərdz), southward. *adverb.*

south·west (south′west′), **1** halfway between

south and west. **2** a southwest direction. **3** a place that is in the southwest part or direction. **4 the Southwest,** the southwestern part of the United States, especially Texas, New Mexico, Oklahoma, Arizona, and, sometimes, southern California. **5** toward the southwest. **6** from the southwest: *a southwest wind.* **7** in the southwest. 1,6,7 *adjective,* 2-4 *noun,* 5 *adverb.*

south·west·er (south′wes′tər *for 1;* sou′wes′tər *for 2*), **1** a wind or storm from the southwest. **2** a waterproof hat with a broad brim behind to protect the neck. *noun.* Also spelled **sou'wester.**

southwester
(definition 2)

south·west·ern (south′wes′tərn), **1** toward the southwest. **2** from the southwest. **3** of or in the southwest. *adjective.*

sou·ve·nir (sü′və nir′), something given or kept for remembrance; keepsake: *She bought a pair of moccasins as a souvenir of her trip out West. noun.*

sou'west·er (sou′wes′tər), southwester. *noun.*

sove·reign (sov′rən), **1** the supreme ruler; king or queen; monarch. Queen Victoria was the sovereign of Great Britain from 1837 to 1901. **2** having supreme rank, power, or authority: *a sovereign prince.* **3** independent of the control of other governments: *When the thirteen colonies won the Revolutionary War, America became a sovereign nation.* 1 *noun,* 2,3 *adjective.*

sove·reign·ty (sov′rən tē), **1** supreme power or authority: *The revolutionaries rejected the sovereignty of the king.* **2** freedom from outside control; independence in power or authority: *Satellite countries lack full sovereignty. noun.*

So·vi·et (sō′vē et), of or having to do with the Soviet Union: *Soviet villages. adjective.*

Soviet Union, a former country reaching from eastern Europe across Asia to the Pacific Ocean. It broke up into several countries in 1991.

sow[1] (sō), **1** to scatter seed on the ground; plant seed; plant seed in: *She sowed grass seed in the yard.* **2** to scatter anything; spread abroad: *The*

rebels sowed discontent among the people. verb,
sows, sowed, sown or **sowed, sow·ing.**

sow² (sou), a fully grown female pig. *noun.*

sown (sōn). See **sow¹**. *The field had been sown with oats. verb.*

sox (soks), socks; stockings. *noun plural.*

soy·bean (soi′bēn′), a bean widely grown in Asia and North America that is an important source of food. Its oil is removed and used in margarine and paints. The remaining meal is fed to livestock or made into flour. *noun.*

soy sauce (soi′ sôs′), a Chinese and Japanese sauce for fish, meat, and the like, made from soybeans.
[*Soy* comes from a Japanese word. It can be traced back to two Chinese words meaning "soybean oil."]

space (spās), **1** the unlimited room or place extending in all directions: *The earth moves through space.* **2** a limited place or room: *Is there space in the car for another person?* **3** outer space: *the conquest and exploration of space, a rocket launched into space.* **4** of or having to do with outer space: *a space satellite, space flight, space vehicles.* **5** a distance: *The road is bad for a space of two miles.* **6** a length of time: *The flowers died in the space of a day.* **7** to separate by spaces: *Space your words evenly when you write.* 1-3,5,6 *noun,* 4 *adjective,* 7 *verb,* **spac·es, spaced, spac·ing.**

space age, the current period in history, as marked by the advances made in the exploration of outer space.

space·craft (spās′kraft′), a vehicle or vehicles used for flight in outer space. *noun, plural* **space·craft.**

space·ship (spās′ship′), spacecraft. *noun.*

space shuttle, a spacecraft with wings, which can orbit the earth, land like an airplane, and be used again. A space shuttle has two rockets and a large fuel tank which drop off after use in launching the spacecraft.

space shuttle

a hat	i it	oi oil	ch child	⎧ a in about
ā age	ī ice	ou out	ng long	e in taken
ä far	o hot	u cup	sh she	ə = ⎨ i in pencil
e let	ō open	ủ put	th thin	o in lemon
ē equal	ô order	ü rule	ŦH then	⎩ u in circus
ėr term			zh measure	

space·suit (spās′süt′), an airtight suit that protects travelers in outer space from radiation, heat, and lack of oxygen. *noun.*

space·walk (spās′wôk′), the act of moving or floating in space while outside a spacecraft. *noun.*

spa·cious (spā′shəs), containing much space; with plenty of room: *a spacious house. adjective.*

spade¹ (spād), **1** a tool for digging, with an iron blade which can be pressed into the ground with the foot. **2** to dig with a spade: *Spade up the garden.* 1 *noun,* 2 *verb,* **spades, spad·ed, spad·ing.**

spade² (spād), **1** a figure shaped like this: ♠. **2** a playing card with one or more figures shaped like this. *noun.*

spa·ghet·ti (spə get′ē), dry, slender lengths of the same mixture of flour and water as macaroni. Spaghetti is thinner than macaroni and not hollow. *noun.*
[*Spaghetti* comes from an Italian word, originally meaning "thin strings."]

Spain (spān), a country in southwestern Europe. *noun.*

span (definition 4)

span (span), **1** the part between two supports: *The bridge crossed the river in a single span.* **2** the distance between two supports: *The arch had a fifty-foot span.* **3** a space of time, often short or limited: *the span of human life.* **4** to extend over: *A bridge spanned the river.* **5** to measure by the hand spread out: *This post can be spanned by one's two hands.* **6** the distance between the tip of a person's thumb and the tip of the little finger when the hand is spread out. 1-3,6 *noun,* 4,5 *verb,* **spans, spanned, span·ning.**

S

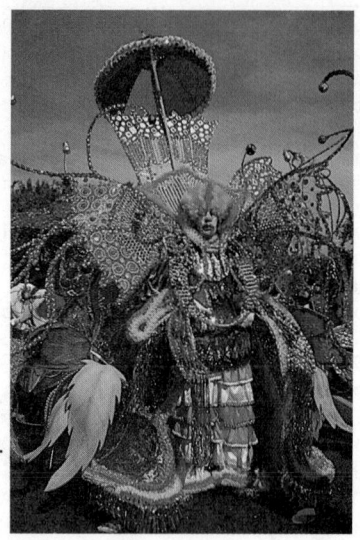

spangle (definition 1)
This costume is
covered with **spangles**.

span·gle (spang′gəl), a small piece of glittering metal used for decoration. *noun.*

Span·iard (span′yərd), a person born or living in Spain. *noun.*

span·iel (span′yəl), a dog, usually of small or medium size, with long, silky hair and drooping ears. *noun.*

[*Spaniel* was shortened from an old French word meaning "a Spanish dog." The spaniel first came from Spain.]

Span·ish (span′ish), **1** of or having something to do with Spain, its people, or their language. **2** the people of Spain. **3** the language of Spain. Spanish is spoken also in Mexico, most parts of Central America and South America, and many other places. **1** *adjective,* **2** *noun plural,* **3** *noun singular.*

Word Source

Spanish is the official language in many areas, including Mexico and most of South America and Central America. Here are words that have come into English from Spanish. Those that have come from Mexican Spanish are marked with the sign *.

alligator	corral	*mustang	siesta
armadillo	fiesta	Nevada	silo
*bronco	Florida	patio	sombrero
burro	hacienda	piñata	*stampede
*cafeteria	hammock	plaza	*taco
California	lariat	poncho	tornado
cargo	lasso	pueblo	tortilla
castanet	mesa	ranch	tuna
*chaps	Montana	rodeo	vanilla
Colorado	mosquito	sierra	

---

spank (spangk), to strike with the open hand or a flat object: *She was spanked for being naughty. verb.*

spank·ing (spang′king), a striking with the open hand or a flat object. *noun.*

spar[1] (spär), a stout pole used to support or extend the sails of a ship; mast, yard, or boom of a ship. *noun.*

spar[2] (spär), **1** to make motions of attack and defense with the arms and fists; box. **2** to argue: *Two people were sparring about who would win the election. verb,* **spars, sparred, spar·ring.**

spare (sper *or* spar), **1** to show mercy to; refrain from harming or destroying: *He spared his enemy. Her jokes spared no one, not even herself.* **2** to make a person free from labor or pain: *They did the work to spare you the trouble.* **3** to get along without; omit; do without: *I can't spare the car today, so you'll have to take the bus.* **4** to use in small quantities or not at all; be saving of: *to spare no expense.* **5** free for other use: *spare time.* **6** extra; in reserve: *a spare tire.* **7** an extra thing or part: *We had a spare in the trunk in case of a flat tire.* **8** thin; lean: *Lincoln was a tall, spare man.* **9** small in quantity; scanty: *I'm still hungry after that spare meal.* **10** the knocking down of all the pins in bowling with two balls. **1-4** *verb,* **spares, spared, spar·ing; 5,6,8,9** *adjective,* **spar·er, spar·est; 7,10** *noun.*

spar·ing (sper′ing *or* spar′ing), economical; frugal: *a sparing use of sugar. adjective.*

spark (spärk), **1** a small bit of fire: *The burning wood threw off sparks.* **2** the flash given off when electricity jumps across an open space. An electric spark ignites the gasoline vapor in the engine of an automobile. **3** a bright flash; gleam: *We saw a spark of light through the trees.* **4** to flash; gleam; sparkle. **5** a small amount: *I haven't a spark of interest in the plan.* **6** a glittering bit: *The moving sparks we saw were fireflies.* **7** to send out small bits of fire; produce sparks. **1-3,5,6** *noun,* **4,7** *verb.*

spar·kle (spär′kəl), **1** to send out little sparks: *The fireworks sparkled.* **2** a little spark. **3** to shine; glitter; flash: *The jewels in the crown sparkled.* **4** a shine; glitter; flash: *the sparkle of someone's eyes.* **5** to be brilliant; be lively: *This author's wit sparkles.* **1,3,5** *verb,* **spar·kles, spar·kled, spar·kling; 2,4** *noun.*

spar·kler (spär′klər), a firework that shoots out many bright sparks when it is lit. *noun.*

spar·kling (spär′kling), **1** shining; glittering: *sparkling stars.* **2** brilliant: *She has a sparkling wit. adjective.*

spar·row (spar′ō), a small brownish-gray bird. Sparrows are common in North and South America but are also found in Europe, Asia, and Africa. *noun.*

sparse (spärs), thinly scattered; occurring here and there: *a sparse population, sparse hair. adjective,* **spars·er, spars·est.**

spasm (spaz′əm), **1** a sudden, abnormal, uncontrollable contraction of a muscle or muscles: *The sick dog kept twitching its legs in a spasm.* **2** any sudden, brief fit or spell of unusual energy or activity: *a spasm of enthusiasm, a spasm of laughter. noun.*

spat[1] (spat), a slight quarrel. *noun.*

spat[2] (spat). See **spit**[1]. *The cat spat at me. verb.*

spat·ter (spat′ər), **1** to scatter or dash in drops: *to spatter mud.* **2** to fall in drops: *Rain spatters on the sidewalk.* **3** the act or sound of spattering: *We listened to the spatter of the rain on the roof.* **4** a spot caused by something splashed. 1,2 *verb*, 3,4 *noun.*

spat·u·la (spach′ə lə), a tool with a broad, flat, flexible blade, used for spreading, scraping, or stirring soft substances such as putty, cake frosting, or the like. A wider kind of spatula is used to lift cooked food from a pan. *noun.*

spatula—using a **spatula** to frost a cake

spawn (spôn), **1** the eggs of fish, frogs, shellfish, and other animals growing or living in water. **2** the young newly hatched from these eggs. **3** to produce eggs. 1,2 *noun*, 3 *verb.*

speak (spēk), **1** to say words; talk: *A person with a cold often has trouble speaking distinctly.* **2** to make a speech: *Who is going to speak at the meeting?* **3** to say; tell; express; make known: *Speak the truth. Their eyes speak of suffering.* **4** to use a language: *Do you speak French? verb*, **speaks, spoke, spo·ken, speak·ing.**

speak for, to speak in the interest of; represent: *Why don't you speak for yourself instead of having others speak for you?*

speak of, to mention; refer to: *She spoke of this matter to me. Speaking of school, how do you like the new gym? I have no complaints to speak of.*

speak out or **speak up,** to speak loudly, clearly, or freely: *No one dared to speak out against the big bully. The children all spoke up in favor of having a party.*

speak·er (spē′kər), **1** a person who speaks. **2** a person who presides over an assembly: *the Speaker of the House of Representatives.* **3** a loudspeaker. *noun.*

spear[1] (spir), **1** a weapon with a long shaft and a sharp-pointed head. **2** to pierce with a spear: *to spear a fish.* **3** to pierce or stab with anything sharp: *to spear string beans with a fork.* 1 *noun*, 2,3 *verb.*

spear[2] (spir), a sprout or shoot of a plant: *a spear of grass. noun.*

spear·head (spir′hed′), **1** the sharp-pointed striking end of a spear. **2** to lead or clear the way for; head: *Our group spearheaded the efforts to clean up the lake.* 1 *noun*, 2 *verb.*

spear·mint (spir′mint′), a kind of mint grown for its oil which is used for flavoring. *noun.*

a hat	i it	oi oil	ch child	a in about
ā age	ī ice	ou out	ng long	e in taken
ä far	o hot	u cup	sh she	ə = { i in pencil
e let	ō open	ù put	th thin	o in lemon
ē equal	ô order	ü rule	ʈʜ then	u in circus
ér term			zh measure	

spe·cial (spesh′əl), **1** of a particular kind; distinct from others; not general: *A safe has a special lock. Have you any special color in mind for your new coat?* **2** more than ordinary; unusual; exceptional: *Lions and tigers are a topic of special interest.* **3** having a particular purpose, function, or use: *Send the letter by a special messenger.* **4** something special in importance, price, interest, or the like: *The store advertised a special on raincoats. We watched a TV special on whales.* 1-3 *adjective*, 4 *noun.*

spe·cial·ist (spesh′ə list), a person who pursues one particular branch of study, business, or occupation. A heart specialist is a doctor who treats diseases of the heart. *noun.*

spe·cial·ize (spesh′ə līz), to pursue some special branch of study or work: *Some doctors specialize in taking care of children. verb*, **spe·cial·iz·es, spe·cial·ized, spe·cial·iz·ing.**

spe·cial·ly (spesh′ə lē), in a special manner or degree; particularly; unusually. *adverb.*

spe·cial·ty (spesh′əl tē), **1** a special study; special line of work, profession, or trade: *American history is the specialty of my social studies teacher.* **2** a product or article to which special attention is given: *This store makes a specialty of children's clothes. noun, plural* **spe·cial·ties.**

spe·cies (spē′shēz), a group of related living things that have certain basic characteristics in common. Wheat is a species of grass. The lion is one species of cat. *noun, plural* **spe·cies.**

spe·cif·ic (spi sif′ik), definite; precise; particular: *There was no specific reason for the quarrel. adjective.*

spe·cif·i·cal·ly (spi sif′ik lē), in a specific way; definitely: *The doctor told her specifically not to eat eggs. adverb.*

spec·i·fi·ca·tion (spes′ə fə kā′shən), **1** a detailed statement of particulars: *She made careful specification as to the kinds of cake and candy for her party.* **2 specifications,** a detailed description of the dimensions or materials for a building, road, dam, boat, or like thing to be made or built. *noun.*

spec·i·fy (spes′ə fī), to mention or name definitely: *Did you specify any particular time for us to call? He delivered the paper as specified. verb,* **spec·i·fies, spec·i·fied, spec·i·fy·ing.**

spec·i·men (spes′ə mən), one of a group or class taken to show what the others are like; sample: *He collects specimens of all kinds of rocks. noun.*

speck (spek), **1** a small spot; stain: *Can you clean the specks off this wallpaper?* **2** a tiny bit; particle: *a speck in the eye. noun.*

speck·le (spek′əl), **1** a small spot or mark: *This hen is gray with white speckles.* **2** to mark with small spots: *The shirt was speckled with paint.* **1** *noun,* **2** *verb,* **speck·les, speck·led, speck·ling.**

speck·led (spek′əld), marked with small spots: *A speckled bird flew out of the bush. adjective.*

spec·ta·cle (spek′tə kəl), **1** a public show or display: *The parade was a fine spectacle.* **2 spectacles,** eyeglasses. *noun.*

spec·tac·u·lar (spek tak′yə lər), making a great display: *Motion pictures present spectacular scenes like battles, processions, storms, or races. adjective.*

spectacular—The sunset was **spectacular.**

spec·ta·tor (spek′tā tər), a person who looks on without taking part: *There were many spectators at the game. noun.*

spec·trum (spek′trəm), the band of colors formed when a beam of light is passed through a prism or is broken up by other means. A rainbow has all the colors of the spectrum: red, orange, yellow, green, blue, indigo, and violet. *noun,* plural **spec·tra** (spek′trə), **spec·trums.**

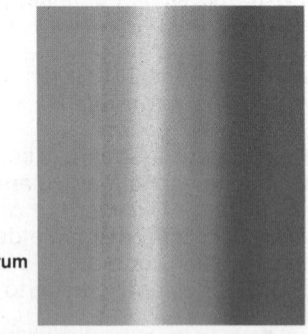
spectrum

spec·u·late (spek′yə lāt), **1** to think carefully; reflect; meditate; consider: *The philosopher speculated about time and space.* **2** to buy or sell when there is a large risk: *He became poor after speculating in what turned out to be worthless oil wells. verb,* **spec·u·lates, spec·u·lat·ed, spec·u·lat·ing.**

spec·u·la·tion (spek′yə lā′shən), **1** careful thought; reflection: *Former speculations about electricity were often mere guesses.* **2** a buying or selling when there is a large risk: *Her speculations in the stock market made her a thousand dollars. noun.*

sped (sped). See **speed.** *The police car sped down the road. verb.*

speech (spēch), **1** the act of speaking; talk: *Human beings express their thoughts by speech.* **2** the power of speaking: *Animals lack speech.* **3** a manner of speaking; dialect or language: *I could tell by their speech that they were from the South. The native speech of most Americans is English.* **4** what is said; the words spoken: *We made the usual farewell speeches.* **5** a public talk: *The President gave an excellent speech. noun, plural* **speech·es.**

speech·less (spēch′lis), **1** not able to speak: *I was speechless with anger.* **2** silent: *Her frown gave a speechless message. adjective.*

speed (spēd), **1** swift or rapid movement: *The cat pounced on the mouse with amazing speed.* **2** to go fast: *The boat sped over the water.* **3** to make go fast: *Let's all help speed the work.* **4** a rate of movement: *The children ran at full speed.* **5** to go faster than is safe or lawful: *The car was stopped for speeding.* **1,4** *noun,* **2,3,5** *verb,* **speeds, sped** or **speed·ed, speed·ing.**

speed·i·ly (spē′dl ē), quickly; with speed; soon. *adverb.*

speed·om·e·ter (spē dom′ə tər), an instrument to indicate speed. Automobiles have speedometers. *noun.*

speed·way (spēd′wā′), a road or track for automobile or motorcycle racing. *noun.*

speed·y (spē′dē), fast; rapid; quick; swift: *speedy workers, a speedy change, a speedy decision. adjective,* **speed·i·er, speed·i·est.**

spell[1] (spel), **1** to write or say the letters of a word in order: *Some words are easy to spell. We learn to spell in school.* **2** to make up or form the letters of a word: *C-a-t spells cat.* **3** to mean: *Those clouds spell a storm. verb,* **spells, spelled** or **spelt, spell·ing.**

spell[2] (spel), **1** a word or set of words supposed to have magic power. **2** a fascination; charm: *We were under the spell of the beautiful music. noun.*

spell[3] (spel), **1** a period of work or duty: *The sailor's spell at the wheel was four hours.* **2** a period or time of anything: *The child has spells of coughing. There was a long spell of rainy weather in August.* **3** to work in place of another person for a while: *I'll spell you at cutting the grass.* **1,2** *noun,* **3** *verb,* **spells, spelled, spell·ing.**

spell·bound (spel′bound′), too interested to move; fascinated; enchanted: *The children were spellbound by the circus performance. adjective.*

spell·er (spel′ər), **1** a person who spells words. **2** a book for teaching spelling. *noun.*

spell·ing (spel′ing), **1** the writing or saying of the letters of a word in order: *She is poor at spelling.* **2** the way a word is spelled: *"Ax" has two spellings, "ax" and "axe." noun.*

spelt (spelt), spelled. See **spell**[1]. *verb.*

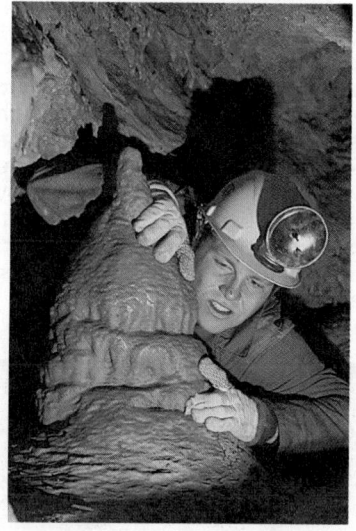
spelunker

a hat	i it	oi oil	ch child		a in about
ā age	ī ice	ou out	ng long		e in taken
ä far	o hot	u cup	sh she	ə =	i in pencil
e let	ō open	u̇ put	th thin		o in lemon
ē equal	ô order	ü rule	ŦH then		u in circus
ėr term			zh measure		

spe·lunk·er (spi lung′kər), a person who explores and makes maps of caves. *noun*.

spend (spend), **1** to pay out: *I spent ten dollars shopping for food today.* **2** to use; use up: *Spend more time on that lesson.* **3** to pass: *We spent last summer at the seashore.* **4** to wear out: *The storm has spent its force. verb,* **spends, spent, spend·ing.**

spend·thrift (spend′thrift′), **1** a person who wastes money. **2** wasteful. 1 *noun,* 2 *adjective.*

spent (spent), **1** See **spend.** *Saturday was spent at the beach.* **2** used up. **3** worn out; tired: *a spent swimmer, a spent horse.* 1 *verb,* 2,3 *adjective.*

sperm cell (spėrm′ sel′), a cell in a male for producing young when combined with an egg cell.

sperm whale (spėrm′ hwāl′), a large whale with a square head that is valuable for its oil.

sperm whale—capturing a **sperm whale**

spew (spyü), to throw out; throw forth; vomit. *verb.*

sphere (sfir), **1** a round solid object. Every point on the surface of a sphere is the same distance from the center. **2** a ball; globe. The sun, moon, earth, and stars are spheres. A baseball is a sphere. **3** the place or surroundings in which a person or thing exists, acts, or works: *A teacher's sphere is the classroom.* **4** a range; extent; region: *England's sphere of influence. noun.*

sphinx (sfingks), **1** a statue of a lion's body with the head of a man, ram, or hawk. The **Great Sphinx** is a huge statue with a man's head and a lion's body, near Cairo, Egypt. **2 Sphinx,** (in Greek mythology) a monster with the head of a woman, the body of a lion, and wings. The Sphinx proposed a riddle to everyone who passed by and killed those unable to guess it. **3** a puzzling, mysterious person. *noun, plural* **sphinx·es.**

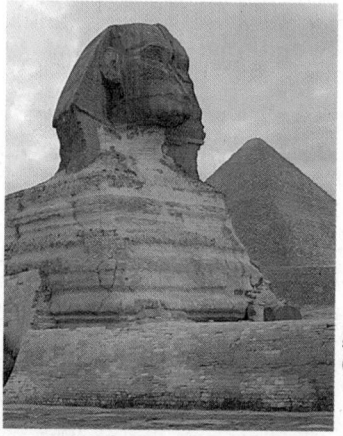
sphinx
(definition 1)

spice (spīs), **1** a seasoning. Pepper, cinnamon, cloves, ginger, and nutmeg are common spices. **2** to put spice in; season: *spiced peaches.* **3** something that adds flavor or interest: *"Variety is the spice of life."* 1,3 *noun,* 2 *verb,* **spic·es, spiced, spic·ing.**

spick-and-span (spik′ən span′), new; fresh; spruce; smart; neat and clean: *a spick-and-span room. adjective.*

spic·y (spī′sē), **1** flavored with spice: *The cookies were rich and spicy.* **2** like spice: *Those apples have a spicy smell and taste. adjective,* **spic·i·er, spic·i·est.**

spi·der (spī′dər), **1** a small animal with eight legs,

sphere
(definition 2)

S

no wings, and a body divided into two parts. Many spiders spin webs to catch insects for food. **2** a kind of pan used for frying. *noun.*

spied (spīd). See **spy.** *She spied her friend in the crowd. Who spied on us? verb.*

spig·ot (spig′ət), a faucet. *noun.*

spike[1] (spīk), **1** a large, strong nail. **2** to fasten with spikes: *The work crew laid the track by spiking the rails to the ties.* **3** a sharp-pointed piece of metal: *fence spikes. The baseball players wore shoes with spikes.* **4** to provide with spikes: *The runners wore spiked shoes to keep from slipping.* **5** to pierce or injure with a spike. 1,3 *noun,* 2,4,5 *verb,* **spikes, spiked, spik·ing.**

spike[2] (spīk), **1** an ear of grain. **2** a long, pointed flower cluster. *noun.*

spill (spil), **1** to let liquid or any loose matter run or fall: *to spill milk, to spill salt.* **2** to fall or flow out: *Water spilled from the pail.* **3** to cause to fall from a horse, car, boat, or the like: *The boat upset and spilled us into the water.* **4** a fall: *He took a bad spill trying to ride that horse.* 1-3 *verb,* **spills, spilled** or **spilt, spill·ing;** 4 *noun.*

spilt (spilt), spilled. See **spill.** *verb.*

spin (definition 3)—She **spun** the wool into yarn.

spin (spin), **1** to turn or cause to turn around rapidly: *The wheels are spinning. The child spun the top.* **2** to feel as if one were whirling around; feel dizzy: *My head is spinning.* **3** to draw out and twist cotton, flax, or wool into thread. **4** to make a thread, web, or cocoon by giving out from the body sticky material that hardens into thread. A spider spins a web. **5** to produce; draw out; tell: *They sat around the campfire spinning stories.* **6** the act of spinning. **7** a rapid run, ride, or drive: *Get your bicycle and come for a spin with me.* **8** to run, ride, or drive rapidly. **9** a rapid turning around of an airplane as it falls. 1-5,8 *verb,* **spins, spun, spin·ning;** 6,7,9 *noun.*

spin·ach (spin′ich), the green leaves of a garden plant, cooked and eaten as a vegetable or used uncooked in a salad. *noun.*

spi·nal (spī′nl), of the spine or backbone; having to do with the backbone. *adjective.*

spinal column, the backbone.

spinal cord, the thick, whitish cord of nerve tissue in the backbone or spine. Nerves to various parts of the body branch off from the spinal cord.

spin·dle (spin′dl), **1** a rod or pin used in spinning to twist, wind, and hold thread. **2** any rod or pin that turns around or on which something turns. Axles and shafts are spindles. *noun.*

spin·dly (spind′lē), very long and slender; too tall and thin: *a spindly plant. adjective,* **spin·dli·er, spin·dli·est.**

spindly—The seedlings on the left are **spindly** because they have not received as much light as those on the right.

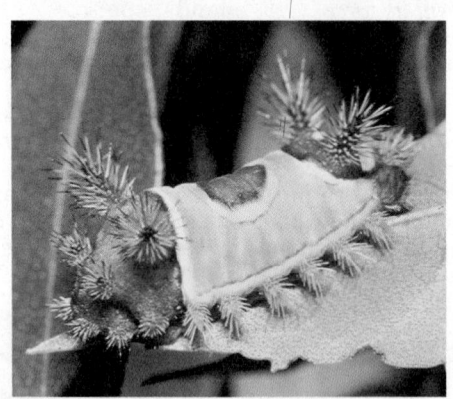

spine (definition 2)
This kind of caterpillar has many **spines.**

spine (spīn), **1** the series of small bones down the middle of the back; backbone. **2** a stiff, sharp-pointed growth on plants or animals. The thorns of a cactus and the quills of a porcupine are spines. *noun.*

spine·less (spīn′lis), **1** having no spine: *A turtle is spineless.* **2** without courage: *a spineless coward.* **3** having no spines: *a spineless cactus. adjective.*

spin·ner (spin′ər), a thing that spins. *noun.*

spinning wheel, a large wheel with a spindle, arranged for spinning cotton, flax, or wool into thread or yarn.

spin·ster (spin′stər), a woman who has not married. *noun.*

spin·y (spī′nē), **1** covered with spines; thorny: *a spiny cactus.* **2** stiff and sharp-pointed: *the spiny quills of a porcupine. adjective,* **spin·i·er, spin·i·est.**

600

spiral (definition 2)

spi·ral (spī′rəl), **1** a winding and gradually widening coil. A watch spring is a spiral. The thread of a screw is a spiral. **2** winding; coiled: *a spiral staircase. Some seashells have a spiral shape.* **3** to move in a spiral: *The flaming airplane spiraled to earth.* **1** *noun,* **2** *adjective,* **3** *verb.*

spire (spīr), **1** the top part of a tower or steeple that narrows to a point. **2** anything tapering and pointed: *The sun shone on the mountain's rocky spires. noun.*

spire (definition 1)—The cathedral has a tall **spire.**

spir·it (spir′it), **1** the soul: *Some religions teach that at death the spirit leaves the body.* **2** a human being's moral, religious, or emotional nature. **3** a supernatural being. God is a spirit. Ghosts and fairies are spirits. **4 spirits, a** a state of mind; disposition; temper: *I am in good spirits.* **b** a strong alcoholic liquor. Whiskey or brandy is called spirits. **5** a person; personality: *You have been a brave spirit. She is a moving spirit in the community.* **6** a feeling that stirs up and rouses: *A spirit of progress is good for people.* **7** courage; vigor; liveliness: *A racehorse must have spirit.* **8** what is really meant as opposed to what is said or written: *The spirit of a law is more important than its words.* **9** to carry away or off secretly: *The gold has been spirited away.* **1-8** *noun,* **9** *verb.*
out of spirits, sad; gloomy.

spir·it·ed (spir′ə tid), lively; dashing; brave: *a spirited racehorse. adjective.*

spir·i·tu·al (spir′ə chü əl), **1** of or having something to do with the spirit or spirits. **2** sacred; religious: *a spiritual leader.* **3** a religious song which originated among the Negroes of the southern United States. **1,2** *adjective,* **3** *noun.*

spit[1] (spit), **1** to throw out saliva, bits of food, or the like from the mouth. **2** to hurl: *A gun spits fire. The crew spat curses.* **3** the liquid produced in the mouth; saliva. **4** to make a spitting sound: *The cat spits when angry.* **1,2,4** *verb,* **spits, spat** or **spit, spit·ting; 3** *noun.*

spit[2] (spit), a sharp-pointed, slender rod or bar on which meat is roasted. *noun.*

spite (spīt), **1** ill will; grudge: *He broke my new radio out of spite.* **2** to show ill will toward; annoy: *They let the weeds grow in their yard to spite their neighbors.* **1** *noun,* **2** *verb,* **spites, spit·ed, spit·ing.**
in spite of, not prevented by: *The schools were open in spite of the snowstorm.*

spite·ful (spīt′fəl), full of spite; eager to annoy; behaving with ill will. *adjective.*

splash (splash), **1** to cause water, mud, or the like to fly about so as to wet or soil: *The swimmers splashed each other with water.* **2** to dash liquid about: *The baby likes to splash in the tub.* **3** to dash in scattered masses or drops: *The waves splashed on the beach.* **4** to wet, spatter, or soil: *Our car is all splashed with mud.* **5** the act or sound of splashing; splashing: *The boat upset with a loud splash.* **6** a spot of liquid splashed upon a thing: *She has splashes of grease on her clothes.* **1-4** *verb,* **5,6** *noun, plural* **splash·es.**

splash·down (splash′doun′), the landing of a capsule or other spacecraft in the ocean after reentry. *noun.*

splat·ter (splat′ər), **1** to splash; spatter. **2** a splash; spatter. **1** *verb,* **2** *noun.*

splen·did (splen′did), **1** brilliant; glorious; magnificent; grand: *a splendid sunset, a splendid palace, splendid jewels, a splendid victory.* **2** very good; fine; excellent: *a splendid chance. adjective.*

splen·dor (splen′dər), **1** great brightness; brilliant light: *The sun set in a golden splendor.* **2** a magnificent show; pomp; glory. *noun.*

splice (splīs), **1** to join ropes by weaving together ends which have been pulled out into separate strands. **2** to join two pieces of timber by overlapping. **3** to join film, tape, or wire by gluing or cementing the ends. **4** a joining of ropes, timbers, film, or the like, by splicing: *How neat a splice can you make?* **1-3** *verb,* **splic·es, spliced, splic·ing; 4** *noun.*

S

splint (splint), **1** an arrangement of wood, metal, or plaster to hold a broken bone in place. **2** a thin strip of wood, such as is used in making baskets. *noun.*

splin·ter (splin′tər), **1** a thin, sharp piece of wood, bone, glass, or the like: *I have a splinter in my hand. The mirror broke into splinters.* **2** to split or break into thin, sharp pieces: *to splinter wood with an ax. The mirror splintered.* **1** *noun,* **2** *verb.*

split (split), **1** to break or cut from end to end, or in layers: *We split the logs into firewood. The baker split the cake and filled it with jelly.* **2** to separate into parts; divide: *The huge tree split when it was struck by lightning. Let's split the cost of the dinner between us.* **3** a division in a group, party, or faction: *There was a split in the club for a time, but harmony was soon restored.* **4** a splitting; break; crack: *Frost caused the split in the rock.* **5** an acrobatic trick of sinking to the floor with the legs spread far apart in opposite directions. **6** to divide a molecule or atomic nucleus into two or more smaller parts. **1,2,6** *verb,* **splits, split, split·ting;** **3-5** *noun.*

split (definition 5)

splotch (sploch), a large, irregular spot; splash: *The butterfly had orange wings with splotches of white. noun, plural* **splotch·es.**

splurge (splėrj), to spend more money than one should: *We splurged and ate at a fancy restaurant. verb,* **splurg·es, splurged, splurg·ing.**

splut·ter (splut′ər), **1** to talk in a hasty, confused way: *She was so excited she spluttered the good news.* **2** to make spitting or popping noises; sputter: *The bacon was spluttering in the hot frying pan. verb.*

spoil (spoil), **1** to damage or injure something so as to make it unfit or useless; ruin; destroy: *The rain spoiled the picnic.* **2** to be damaged; become bad or unfit for use: *The fruit spoiled because I kept it too long.* **3** to injure the character or disposition of: *They spoiled the children by always giving in to their demands.* **4 spoils,** things taken by force; things won: *The soldiers carried the spoils back to their own land.* **1-3** *verb,* **spoils, spoiled** or **spoilt, spoil·ing;** **4** *noun.*

spoilt (spoilt), spoiled. See **spoil.** *verb.*

spoke¹ (spōk). See **speak.** *She spoke about that yesterday. verb.*

spoke² (spōk), one of the bars that connect the center of a wheel to the rim. *noun.*

spo·ken (spō′kən), **1** See **speak.** *She has spoken about coming to visit.* **2** expressed with the mouth; uttered; told: *There were no written directions for the test, only spoken ones.* **1** *verb,* **2** *adjective.*

spokes·man (spōks′mən), a person who speaks for another or others: *I am the spokesman for my class in the student council. noun, plural* **spokes·men.**

sponge (definition 1)
This **sponge** is a bright orange color.

sponge (spunj), **1** a water animal with a light, elastic skeleton having many holes in it. Most sponges live in large colonies on the bottom of the ocean. **2** the skeleton of this animal, used in bathing or cleaning. **3** a similar article made artificially of rubber or plastic. **4** to wipe or rub with a wet sponge; make clean or damp in this way: *Sponge up the spilled water. Sponge the mud spots off the car.* **5** to live or profit at the expense of another in a selfish way: *They are sponging on their relatives instead of working.* **1-3** *noun,* **4,5** *verb,* **spong·es, sponged, spong·ing.**

sponge cake, a light, spongy cake made with eggs, sugar, and flour, but no shortening.

spon·gy (spun′jē), **1** like a sponge; soft, light, and full of holes: *spongy moss, spongy dough.* **2** hard and full of holes: *a spongy rock. adjective,* **spon·gi·er, spon·gi·est.**

spon·sor (spon′sər), **1** a person who is responsible for a person or thing: *the sponsor of a law, the sponsor of a student applying for a scholarship.* **2** a person who stands with the parents at an infant's baptism, agreeing to assist in the child's religious upbringing if necessary; godfather or godmother. **3** a company, store, or other business firm that pays the costs of a radio or television program advertising its products. **4** to act as sponsor for: *The parents' organization at school sponsors our scout troop.* **1-3** *noun,* **4** *verb.*

spon·ta·ne·ous (spon tā′nē əs), of one's own choice; natural; of itself: *Both sides burst into spontaneous cheers at the skillful play. adjective.*

spook (spük), a ghost. *noun.*

spook·y (spü′kē), strange and frightening; suggesting the presence of ghosts: *The old house looked spooky. adjective,* **spook·i·er, spook·i·est.**

spool (spül), a cylinder of wood, plastic, or metal on which thread or wire is wound. *noun.*

spoon (spün), 1 a utensil consisting of a small, shallow bowl at the end of a handle. Spoons are used to take up or stir food or drink. 2 to take up in a spoon: *He spooned great heaps of food onto his plate.* 1 *noun*, 2 *verb.*

spoon·bill (spün′bil′), a long-legged, pink wading bird that has a long, flat bill with a spoon-shaped tip. *noun.*

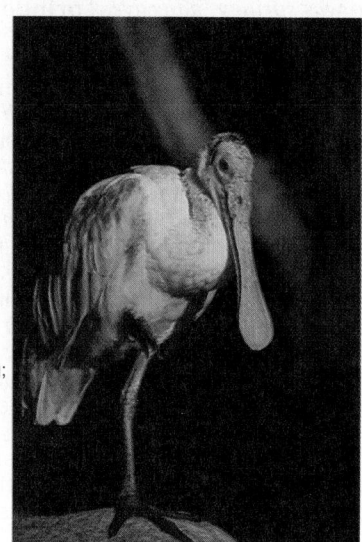

spoonbill
about 30 inches
(75 centimeters) long;
wingspread about
5 feet (1½ meters)

spoon·ful (spün′fùl), as much as a spoon can hold. *noun, plural* **spoon·fuls.**

spore (spôr), a special kind of cell. A spore produced by a living thing can grow into a new living thing. Ferns, mosses, and molds produce spores. *noun.*

sport (spôrt), 1 a game or contest requiring some skill and usually a certain amount of physical exercise. Baseball, golf, football, tennis, swimming, racing, hunting, and fishing are outdoor sports; bowling and basketball are indoor sports. 2 any pastime or amusement: *They hunted wild animals for sport.* 3 a person who behaves in a fair and honorable manner and is a good loser: *to be a sport. noun.*

sport·ing (spôr′ting), 1 playing fair: *It was a sporting gesture for the loser to shake the winner's hand.* 2 offering the kind of risk that is fair and even: *The inexperienced team hardly had a sporting chance of winning. adjective.*

sports (spôrts), of or suitable for sports: *That fancy hotel doesn't allow guests to wear sports clothes in the dining room. adjective.*

sports·cast·er (spôrts′kas′tər), a person who does the spoken part of a broadcast sporting event. *noun.*

sports·man (spôrts′mən), 1 a person who takes part in or is interested in sports, especially hunting or fishing. 2 a person who plays fair. *noun, plural* **sports·men.**

sports·man·ship (spôrts′mən ship), 1 the

a hat	i it	oi oil	ch child	a in about
ā age	ī ice	ou out	ng long	e in taken
ä far	o hot	u cup	sh she	ə = i in pencil
e let	ō open	ù put	th thin	o in lemon
ē equal	ô order	ü rule	ᴛʜ then	u in circus
ėr term			zh measure	

qualities or conduct of a sportsman; fair play. 2 ability in sports. *noun.*

sports·writ·er (spôrts′rī′tər), a journalist who writes about sports. *noun.*

spot (spot), 1 a small mark or stain that discolors or disfigures: *You have grease spots on your suit. That spot on her arm is a bruise.* 2 a blemish or flaw in character or reputation: *His record is without spot.* 3 a small part unlike the rest: *The shirt is blue with white spots.* 4 to make or become spotted: *I have spotted the tablecloth.* 5 a place: *From this spot you can see the ocean.* 6 to pick out; find out; recognize: *I spotted my sister in the crowd. The teacher spotted every mistake in my paper.* 7 a figure or dot on playing cards, dominoes, or dice to show their kind and value. 1-3,5,7 *noun*, 4,6 *verb*, **spots, spot·ted, spot·ting.**

on the spot, 1 at the very place where needed: *Several detectives were sent to investigate the robbery on the spot.* 2 at once: *Your orders will be carried out on the spot.* 3 in trouble or difficulty: *He put me on the spot by asking a question I could not answer.*

spot·less (spot′lis), without a spot: *a spotless white shirt. adjective.*

spot·light (spot′līt′), 1 a strong light thrown upon a particular place or person. 2 a lamp that gives the light: *a spotlight in a theater.* 3 to light up with a spotlight or spotlights: *At night the baseball field is spotlighted.* 4 public notice; anything that directs attention on a person or thing: *Movie stars are often in the spotlight.* 1,2,4 *noun*, 3 *verb.*

spot·ty (spot′ē), 1 having spots; spotted. 2 not of uniform quality: *Your work is spotty. adjective,* **spot·ti·er, spot·ti·est.**

spouse (spous), a husband or wife: *Mr. Smith is Mrs. Smith's spouse, and she is his spouse. noun.*

spout (spout), 1 to throw out a liquid in a stream or spray: *The fountain spouted up high. A whale spouts water when it breathes.* 2 to flow out with force: *Water spouted from a break in the pipe.* 3 a stream; jet: *A spout of water shot up from the hole in the pipe.* 4 a pipe for carrying off water: *Rain runs down a spout from our roof to the ground.* 5 a tube or lip by which liquid is poured. 6 to speak in loud and very emotional tones: *The inexperienced actor spouted his lines.* 1,2,6 *verb*, 3-5 *noun.*

sprain (sprān), 1 to stretch or tear the tissue that holds the bones together at a joint by a sudden twist or wrench: *I sprained my ankle.* 2 an injury caused by a sudden twist or wrench: *The sprain took a long time to heal.* 1 *verb*, 2 *noun.*

sprang (sprang). See **spring.** *She sprang from her chair. verb.*

S

sprawl (sprôl), **1** to lie or sit with the arms and legs spread out, especially in an awkward manner: *The children were sprawled in front of the TV.* **2** to spread out in an irregular or awkward manner: *His large handwriting sprawled across the page. verb.*

spray[1] (sprā), **1** a liquid going through the air in small drops: *We were wet with the sea spray.* **2** something like this: *A spray of bullets hit the target.* **3** an instrument that sends a liquid out as spray. **4** to sprinkle; scatter spray on: *Spray the apple tree to kill the worms.* 1-3 *noun,* 4 *verb.*

spray[2] (sprā), a small branch or piece of some plant with its leaves, flowers, or fruit: *a spray of lilacs, a spray of berries. noun.*

spread (spred), **1** to cover or cause to cover a large or larger area; stretch out; unfold; open out: *We spread rugs on the floor. He spread his arms. The bird spread its wings.* **2** to move farther apart: *Spread out your fingers.* **3** to extend; lie: *Fields of corn spread out before us.* **4** to scatter; distribute: *We spread the news. She spread grain for the chickens.* **5** to put as a thin layer; cover with a thin layer: *I spread jam on the bread. This paint spreads easily.* **6** the act of spreading: *to fight the spread of infection, to encourage the spread of knowledge.* **7** the width; extent; amount of spreading: *The spread of the airplane's wings was sixty feet.* **8** a covering for a bed or table. **9** a soft food to spread on bread, crackers, or the like. Butter and jam are spreads. 1-5 *verb,* **spreads, spread, spread·ing;** 6-9 *noun.*

spree (sprē), a period of activity, fun, or pleasure, especially when done to excess: *I went on a buying spree. noun.*

sprig (sprig), a shoot, twig, or small branch: *a sprig of lilac. noun.*

spright·ly (sprīt'lē), lively; gay: *a sprightly kitten. adjective,* **spright·li·er, spright·li·est.**

spring (spring), **1** to leap or jump; rise or move suddenly and lightly: *The dog sprang at the thief. I sprang to my feet.* **2** a leap or jump: *She made a spring over the fence.* **3** to fly back or away: *The door sprang open.* **4** to cause to spring; cause to act by a spring: *They planned to spring a trap on their enemy.* **5** an elastic device that returns to its original shape after being pulled or held out of shape. Beds have wire springs. The spring in a clock makes it go. **6** an elastic quality: *There is no spring left in these old rubber bands.* **7** the season when plants begin to grow; season of the year between winter and summer: *Robins return in the spring.* **8** of or for spring; coming in spring. Spring wheat is wheat sown in the spring. *Tulips are spring flowers.* **9** a small stream of water coming from the earth. **10** to come from some source; arise; grow: *A wind has sprung up. Plants spring from seeds.* **11** to begin to move, act, or grow suddenly; burst forth: *Towns spring up where oil is discovered.* **12** to bring out, produce, or make suddenly: *to spring a surprise on someone.* **13** to crack, split, bend, strain, or break: *The door was sprung and wouldn't close.* 1,3,4,10-13 *verb,*

springs, sprang or sprung, spring·ing; 2,5-7,9 *noun,* 8 *adjective.*

spring·board, (spring'bôrd'), a board used to give added spring in diving, jumping, and vaulting. *noun.*

Spring·field (spring'fēld'), the capital of Illinois. *noun.*

spring·time (spring'tīm'), the season of spring: *Flowers bloom in the springtime. noun.*

spring·y (spring'ē), full of bounce; elastic: *Her step was springy. adjective,* **spring·i·er, spring·i·est.**

sprin·kle (spring'kəl), **1** to scatter in drops or tiny bits: *I sprinkled sand on the icy sidewalk.* **2** to spray or cover with small drops: *She sprinkled the flowers with water.* **3** a sprinkling; small quantity: *The cook put a sprinkle of nuts on the cake.* **4** to rain a little. **5** a light rain. 1,2,4 *verb,* **sprin·kles, sprin·kled, sprin·kling;** 3,5 *noun.*

sprin·kler (spring'klər), a device for sprinkling water on gardens and lawns. *noun.*

sprin·kling (spring'kling), a small amount scattered here and there: *He has a sprinkling of gray hair. noun.*

sprint (sprint), **1** to run at top speed for a short distance. **2** a short race at top speed. 1 *verb,* 2 *noun.*

sprock·et (sprok'it), **1** one of a set of parts sticking out from the rim of a wheel and arranged to fit into the links of a chain. The sprockets keep

spring (definitions 1, 2, 5, 7, and 8)

sprocket (definitions 1 and 2)

a hat	i it	oi oil	ch child	a in about
ā age	ī ice	ou out	ng long	e in taken
ä far	o hot	u cup	sh she	ə = i in pencil
e let	ō open	ů put	th thin	o in lemon
ē equal	ô order	ü rule	ŦH then	u in circus
ėr term			zh measure	

the chain from slipping. **2** a wheel made with sprockets, sometimes called a **sprocket wheel.** *noun.*

sprout (sprout), **1** to begin to grow; shoot forth: *Seeds sprout. Buds sprout in the spring.* **2** the shoot of a plant: *The gardener was setting out sprouts.* **1** *verb,* **2** *noun.*

spruce[1] (sprüs), **1** a kind of evergreen tree with leaves shaped like needles. **2** its wood. *noun.*

spruce[2] (sprüs), **1** neat; trim: *You look very spruce in your new suit.* **2** to make spruce; become spruce: *He spruced himself up for dinner.* **1** *adjective,* **spruc·er, spruc·est;** **2** *verb,* **spruc·es, spruced, spruc·ing.**

sprung (sprung). See **spring.** *The mouse sprung the trap. The trap was sprung. verb.*

spry (sprī), lively; nimble: *The spry old woman traveled all over the country. adjective,* **spry·er, spry·est,** or **spri·er, spri·est.**

spud (spud), a potato. *noun.*

spun (spun). See **spin.** *The car skidded and spun on the ice. The thread was spun from silk. verb.*

spunk (spungk), courage; pluck; spirit: *a little puppy full of spunk. noun.*

spur (spėr), **1** a metal point or pointed wheel worn on a rider's heel for urging a horse on. **2** to prick with spurs: *The riders spurred their horses on.* **3** something like a spur; point sticking out: *A spur of rock stuck out from the mountain.* **4** anything that urges on; goad: *Ambition was the spur that made him work.* **5** to urge on: *Anger spurred her to speak unkindly.* **1,3,4** *noun,* **2,5** *verb,* **spurs, spurred, spur·ring.**

spur (definition 1)

spurn (spėrn), to refuse with scorn; scorn: *The judge spurned the bribe. verb.*

spurt (spėrt), **1** to flow suddenly in a stream or jet; gush out; squirt: *Water spurted from the fountain.* **2** a sudden rushing forth; jet: *a spurt of blood from a cut.* **3** a great increase of effort or activity for a short time: *To win the race he put on a spurt of speed.* **4** to put forth great energy for a short time; show great activity for a short time: *The runners spurted near the end of the race.* **1,4** *verb,* **2,3** *noun.*

sput·ter (sput′ər), **1** to make spitting or popping noises: *fat sputtering in the frying pan. The firecrackers sputtered.* **2** to talk in a hasty, confused way: *In his embarrassment, he began to sputter and make silly excuses. verb.*

spy (spī), **1** a person who keeps secret watch on the actions of others. **2** a person who tries to get information about the enemy, usually in time of war, by visiting the enemy's territory in disguise. **3** to keep secret watch: *He saw two men spying on him from behind a tree.* **4** to act as a spy; be a spy. **5** to catch sight of; see: *She was the first to spy the mountains on the horizon.* **1,2** *noun, plural* **spies;** **3-5** *verb,* **spies, spied, spy·ing.**

spy·glass (spī′glas′), a small telescope. *noun, plural* **spy·glass·es.**

sq. or **sq,** square.

squab (skwob), a young pigeon. *noun.*

squab·ble (skwob′əl), **1** a petty, noisy quarrel: *Children's squabbles annoy their parents.* **2** to take part in a petty, noisy quarrel: *I won't squabble over a nickel.* **1** *noun,* **2** *verb,* **squab·bles, squab·bled, squab·bling.**

squad (skwod), **1** a small number of soldiers grouped for drill, inspection, or work. A squad is the smallest part of an army. **2** any small group of persons working together: *A squad of children cleaned up the yard. noun.*

squad·ron (skwod′rən), **1** a part of a naval fleet used for special service: *a destroyer squadron.* **2** a formation of eight or more airplanes that fly or fight together. **3** a unit of cavalry. **4** any group. *noun.*

squal·id (skwol′id), very dirty; degraded; wretched: *a squalid tenement. adjective.*

squall[1] (skwôl), a sudden, violent gust of wind, often with rain, snow, or sleet. *noun.*

squall[2] (skwôl), **1** to cry out loudly; scream violently: *The baby squalled.* **2** a loud, harsh cry: *The parrot's squall was heard all over the house.* **1** *verb,* **2** *noun.*

squal·or (skwol′ər), misery and dirt; filth. *noun.*

squan·der (skwon′dər), to spend foolishly; waste: *to squander time and money. verb.*

605

S

square (skwer *or* skwar), **1** a figure with four equal sides and four right angles (□). **2** having this shape: *a square box. This table is square.* **3** anything having this shape or nearly this shape: *I gave the child a square of chocolate.* **4** to make square in shape: *to square the corners of a board.* **5** an open space in a city or town bounded by streets on four sides, often planted with grass or trees: *There is a fountain in the square opposite the city hall.* **6** any similar open space, such as at the meeting of streets. **7** having length and width. A square meter is the area of a square whose edges are each one meter long. **8** the sum when a number is multiplied by itself: *9 is the square of 3.* **9** forming a right angle: *This table has four square corners.* **10** an instrument shaped like a T or an L, used for drawing right angles and testing the squareness of anything. **11** to make straight, level, or even: *to square a picture on a wall.* **12** to adjust; settle: *Let us square our accounts.* **13** to agree; conform: *My thoughts on the subject square with yours.* **14** just; fair; honest: *You will get a square deal at this shop.* **15** satisfying: *At our house we have three square meals each day.* 1,3,5,6,8,10 *noun*, 2,7,9,14,15 *adjective*, **squar·er, squar·est;** 4,11-13 *verb*, **squares, squared, squar·ing.**

square dance, a dance done by groups of four couples in a square formation. The dancers form different patterns according to the directions of a caller.

square knot, a knot firmly joining two loose ends of rope or cord. Each end is formed into a loop which both encloses and passes through the other.

square knot

squash[1] (skwosh), **1** to press until soft or flat; crush: *She squashed the bug. This package was squashed in the mail.* **2** a game somewhat like handball and tennis, played in a walled court with rackets and a hollow rubber ball. 1 *verb*, 2 *noun*.

squash[2] (skwosh), the fruit of a trailing garden vine, eaten as a vegetable. Squash have different shapes and colors, usually yellow, green, or white. *noun, plural* **squash** or **squash·es.**
[*Squash*[2] comes from a Narragansett Indian word meaning "the green things that may be eaten raw."]

squat (skwot), **1** to crouch on the heels: *She was squatting on the grass watching a caterpillar.* **2** to settle on another's land without title or right. **3** to settle on public land to acquire ownership of it.

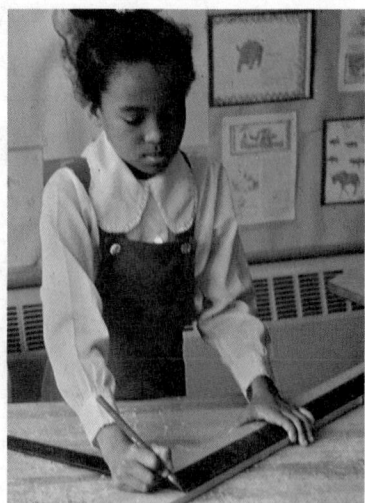

square (definition 10)

4 short and thick; low and broad: *That is a squat teapot.* 1-3 *verb*, **squats, squat·ted** or **squat, squat·ting;** 4 *adjective*, **squat·ter, squat·test.**

squaw (skwô), a North American Indian woman or wife. The use of this word is often considered offensive. *noun.*

squawk (skwôk), **1** to make a loud, harsh sound: *Hens and ducks squawk when frightened.* **2** a loud, harsh sound. **3** to complain loudly: *They squawked about the large repair bill.* **4** a loud complaint. 1,3 *verb*, 2,4 *noun.*

squeak (skwēk), **1** to make a short, sharp, shrill sound: *A mouse squeaks.* **2** such a sound: *We heard the squeak of the stairs.* 1 *verb*, 2 *noun.*

squeak·y (skwē′kē), squeaking: *a squeaky door. adjective,* **squeak·i·er, squeak·i·est.**

squeal (skwēl), **1** to make a long, sharp, shrill cry: *A pig squeals when it is hurt.* **2** such a cry. **3** to inform on another: *One thief squealed on the others.* 1,3 *verb*, 2 *noun.*

squeeze (skwēz), **1** to press hard: *Don't squeeze the kitten, or you will hurt it.* **2** a tight pressure: *She gave her sister's arm a squeeze.* **3** to hug: *He squeezed his child.* **4** to force by pressing: *I can't squeeze another thing into my trunk.* **5** to force out by pressure: *I squeezed the juice from two lemons.* **6** to force a way: *He squeezed through the crowd.* **7** a crush; crowd: *It's a tight squeeze to get five people in that little car.* 1,3-6 *verb*, **squeez·es, squeezed, squeez·ing;** 2,7 *noun.*

squid (skwid), a sea animal that looks something like an octopus but having a pair of tail fins and

squid—this type up to 8 feet (2½ meters) long with arms

606

ten arms instead of eight. It is a mollusk. *noun,
plural* **squids** or **squid.**

squig·gle (skwig′əl), **1** a wiggly twist or curve:
The child drew squiggles on the paper. **2** to twist
and turn about; squirm; wriggle: *The puppy
squiggled in my arms.* **1** *noun,* **2** *verb,* **squig·gles,
squig·gled, squig·gling.**
[*Squiggle* was formed by joining parts of the words
squirm and *wriggle.*]

squinch (skwinch), to squeeze together; squint: *I
squinched my eyes and tried to read the distant sign.*
verb.
[*Squinch* was probably formed by joining parts of
the words *squint* and *pinch.*]

squint (skwint), **1** to look with the eyes partly
closed. **2** a sidelong look; hasty look: *The squint
she gave me indicated she doubted my story.* **3** to
look sideways. **1,3** *verb,* **2** *noun.*

squint (definition 1)
The bright sunlight
made him **squint.**

squire (definition 2)—a **squire** attending a knight

squire (skwīr), **1** (in Great Britain) a country
gentleman, especially the chief landowner in a
district. **2** a young man of noble family who
attended a knight till he himself was made a
knight. *noun.*

squirm (skwėrm), to wriggle; writhe; twist: *The
restless girl squirmed in her seat. verb.*

squir·rel (skwėr′əl), **1** a small, bushy-tailed
animal that usually lives in trees and eats nuts.
2 its gray, reddish, or dark-brown fur. *noun.*

squirt (skwėrt), **1** to force out liquid through a

narrow opening: *to squirt water through a tube.* **2** to
come out in a jet or stream: *Water squirted from
the hose.* **3** a jet of liquid: *I soaked her with squirts
from the hose.* **1,2** *verb,* **3** *noun.*

squirt gun, a water pistol.

squish (skwish), **1** to press out something soft
and wet; ooze: *The mud squished between my toes.*
2 the sound of something soft and wet being
pressed: *the squish of wet shoes.* **3** to make such a
sound: *My wet shoes squished as I walked.*
1,3 *verb,* **2** *noun.*

Sr., Senior.

Sri Lan·ka (srē′ läng′kə), an island country in
the Indian Ocean.

St., 1 Saint. **2** Street.

stab (stab), **1** to pierce or wound with a pointed
weapon: *He was stabbed with a knife.* **2** a thrust or
blow made with something pointed; jab: *I made a
stab at the meat with my fork.* **3** a wound made by
stabbing. **4** a sudden, sharp feeling: *He felt a stab
of pain when he moved his arm.* **5** a try; attempt:
*I've never skied before but I would like to take a
stab at it.* **1** *verb,* **stabs, stabbed, stab·bing;**
2-5 *noun.*

sta·bil·i·ty (stə bil′ə tē), firmness; permanence;
steadfastness: *A brick wall has more stability than
a light wooden fence. She has the stability to see the
job through to its completion. noun.*

sta·ble[1] (stā′bəl), **1** a building where horses or
cattle are kept and fed: *She took riding lessons at
the stable.* **2** a group of animals housed in such a
building: *a stable of racehorses.* **3** to put or keep in
a stable. **1,2** *noun,* **3** *verb,* **sta·bles, sta·bled,
sta·bling.**

sta·ble[2] (stā′bəl), **1** not likely to move or change
position; steady; firm: *We held the ladder to make
it perfectly stable for the painter.* **2** not likely to fall
or be overturned: *a stable government. adjective.*

stack (stak), **1** a large pile of hay or straw.
Haystacks are often round and arranged so as to
shed water. **2** a pile of anything: *a stack of wood.*
3 to pile or arrange in a stack: *to stack hay, to
stack guns.* **4** a chimney. **1,2,4** *noun,* **3** *verb.*

sta·di·um (stā′dē əm), a large building, usually
without a roof, having rows of seats surrounding a
playing field. *noun.*

staff (staf), **1** a stick; pole; rod: *The old man
leaned on his staff. The flag hangs on a staff.*
2 something that supports or sustains. Bread is
called the staff of life because it will support life.
3 a group assisting a chief; group of employees:
Our school has a staff of twenty teachers. **4** to
provide with employees. **5** the five lines and the
four spaces between them on which music is
written. **1-3,5** *noun,* **4** *verb.*

a hat	i it	oi oil	ch child	a in about
ā age	ī ice	ou out	ng long	e in taken
ä far	o hot	u cup	sh she	i in pencil
e let	ō open	u̇ put	th thin	o in lemon
ē equal	ô order	ü rule	ŦH then	u in circus
ėr term			zh measure	

607

stag (stag), a full-grown male deer. *noun.*

stage (stāj), **1** one step or degree in a process; period of development. Frogs pass through a tadpole stage. **2** the raised platform in a theater on which the actors perform. **3 the stage,** the theater; the drama; actor's profession: *to write for the stage.* **4** the scene of action: *Bunker Hill was the stage of a famous battle.* **5** to arrange: *The play was very well staged. The class staged a surprise party for the teacher's birthday.* **6** a section of a rocket or missile having its own engine and fuel. A three-stage rocket has three engines, one in each stage, which separate one after another from the rocket after use. **7** a stagecoach. 1-4,6,7 *noun,* 5 *verb,* **stag·es, staged, stag·ing.**

stage·coach (stāj′kōch′), a coach pulled by horses and carrying passengers, mail, and parcels over a regular route. *noun.*

stag·ger (stag′ər), **1** to sway or reel from weakness, a heavy load, or being drunk: *I staggered and fell under the heavy load of books.* **2** to make sway or reel: *The blow staggered him for a moment.* **3** a swaying or reeling movement: *She walked with a stagger after spinning around.* **4** to confuse or shock greatly; overwhelm: *She was staggered by the news of her friend's death.* **5** to arrange to take place at different times: *Vacations were staggered so that only one person was away at a time.* 1,2,4,5 *verb,* 3 *noun.*

stagger (definition 2)
The news that he had lost his entire fortune **staggered** him.

stag·nant (stag′nənt), **1** not running or flowing; foul from standing still: *stagnant air, stagnant water.* **2** not active; sluggish: *During the summer, business is often stagnant. adjective.*

stain (stān), **1** to soil; spot: *The tablecloth is stained where food has been spilled.* **2** a spot: *I have an ink stain on my shirt.* **3** to spot by wrongdoing or disgrace; dishonor: *His crimes stained the family honor.* **4** a mark of disgrace; dishonor: *His character is without stain.* **5** to color; dye: *She stained the chair green.* **6** a coloring or dye: *Paint the table with a brown stain.* 1,3,5 *verb,* 2,4,6 *noun.*

stained glass

stained glass (stānd′ glas′), colored glass used in sheets or fitted pieces to form a picture or design. Church windows are often made of stained glass.

stain·less steel (stān′lis stēl′), steel containing a good deal of chromium, making it very resistant to rust. Knives, forks, and spoons are often made of stainless steel.

stair (ster *or* star), **1** one of a series of steps for going from one level or floor to another. **2 stairs,** a set of such steps: *the top of the stairs. noun.*

stair·case (ster′kās′ *or* star′kās′), a flight of stairs with its framework; stairs. *noun.*

stair·way (ster′wā′ *or* star′wā′), a way up and down by stairs; stairs: *the back stairway. noun.*

stake[1] (stāk), **1** a stick or post pointed at one end for driving into the ground. **2** to fasten to a stake or with a stake: *to stake down a tent.* **3** to mark with stakes; mark the boundaries of: *The miners staked out their claims.* 1 *noun,* 2,3 *verb,* **stakes, staked, stak·ing.**

stake[2] (stāk), **1** to risk money or something valuable on the result of a game or on any chance: *She staked five dollars on the black horse.* **2** money risked; what is staked: *The gamblers played for high stakes.* **3** the prize in a race or contest: *The stakes were divided up among the winners.* **4** something to gain or lose; an interest; a share in a property: *Each of us has a stake in the future of our country.* 1 *verb,* **stakes, staked, stak·ing;** 2-4 *noun.*

at stake, to be won or lost: *Your health is at stake when you smoke.*

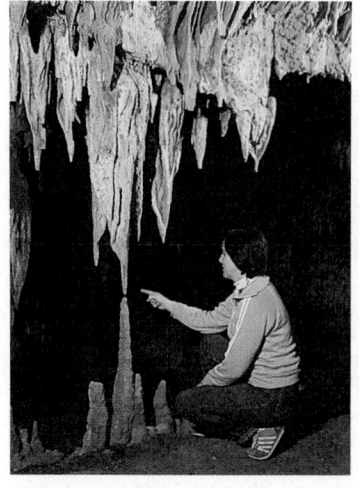

stalactites and stalagmites

a hat	i it	oi oil	ch child		a in about
ā age	ī ice	ou out	ng long		e in taken
ä far	o hot	u cup	sh she	ə =	i in pencil
e let	ō open	u̇ put	th thin		o in lemon
ē equal	ô order	ü rule	ᴛʜ then		u in circus
ėr term			zh measure		

sta·lac·tite (stə lak′tīt), a formation of stone, shaped like an icicle, hanging from the roof of a cave. It is formed by dripping water. *noun.*

sta·lag·mite (stə lag′mīt), a formation of stone, shaped like a cone, built up on the floor of a cave. It is formed by water dripping from a stalactite. *noun.*

stale (stāl), **1** not fresh: *stale bread.* **2** no longer new or interesting: *a stale joke.* **3** out of condition: *The tennis player practiced every day to avoid becoming stale. adjective,* **stal·er, stal·est.**

stalk[1] (stôk), **1** the main stem of a plant. **2** any slender, supporting part of a plant or animal. A flower may have a stalk. The eyes of a lobster are on stalks. *noun.*

stalk[2] (stôk), **1** to hunt by following silently and carefully: *The hungry lion stalked a zebra.* **2** to walk in a slow, stiff, or proud manner: *She stalked into the room and threw herself into a chair.* **3** a stalking. 1,2 *verb,* 3 *noun.*

stall[1] (stôl), **1** a place for one animal in a barn or stable. **2** a small place for selling things: *At the public market different things were sold in different stalls under one big roof.* **3** to put or keep in a stall: *The horses were safely stalled.* **4** to stop or bring to a standstill, usually accidentally: *The engine stalled. We were stalled in the mud.* 1,2 *noun,* 3,4 *verb.*

stall[2] (stôl), **1** to delay: *You have been stalling long enough.* **2** a pretense to avoid doing something: *Her excuse was just a stall.* 1 *verb,* 2 *noun.*

stal·lion (stal′yən), a male horse. *noun.*

stal·wart (stôl′wərt), **1** strongly built. **2** strong and brave: *a stalwart knight.* **3** firm; steadfast: *a stalwart refusal. adjective.*

sta·men (stā′mən), the part of a flower that contains the pollen. A stamen consists of an anther supported by a slender stem called a filament. The stamens are surrounded by the petals. *noun.*

stam·i·na (stam′ə nə), strength; endurance: *He didn't have enough stamina to enter the race. noun.*

stam·mer (stam′ər), **1** to repeat the same sound in an effort to speak; hesitate in speaking. People may stammer when nervous, embarrassed, or afraid. **2** to say in this manner: *She stammered an excuse.* **3** a stammering; stuttering: *He has a nervous stammer.* 1,2 *verb,* 3 *noun.*

stamp (stamp), **1** a small piece of paper with a sticky back that is put on letters, papers, or parcels to show that a charge has been paid; postage stamp. **2** to put a stamp on: *to stamp a letter.* **3** to bring down one's foot with force: *He stamped his foot in anger. I stamped on the spider.* **4** the act of stamping: *The horse gave a stamp of its hoof.* **5** to pound; crush; trample; tread: *Stamp out the fire.* **6** an instrument that cuts, shapes, or impresses a design on paper, wax, or metal; thing that puts a mark on: *The rubber stamp had her name on it.* **7** the mark made by such an instrument. **8** to make a mark on: *She stamped the papers with the date.* 1,4,6,7 *noun,* 2,3,5,8 *verb.*

stam·pede (stam pēd′), **1** a sudden scattering or headlong flight of a frightened herd of cattle or horses. **2** any headlong flight of a large group: *a stampede of a frightened crowd from a burning building.* **3** to scatter or cause to scatter suddenly: *The frightened cattle began to stampede.* 1,2 *noun,* 3 *verb,* **stam·pedes, stam·ped·ed, stam·ped·ing.**
[*Stampede* comes from a Mexican Spanish word. It can be traced back to a Spanish word meaning "to stamp."]

stand (stand), **1** to be upright on one's feet: *Don't stand if you are tired, but sit down.* **2** to rise to one's feet: *The children stood to salute the flag.* **3** to set upright; be located: *Stand the box here. The box stands here.* **4** to be in a certain place, rank, or scale: *Pillars stand on each side of the door. He stood first in his class in mathematics.* **5** to take or keep a certain position: *"Stand back!" called the policeman to the crowd.* **6** to be in a special condition: *She stands innocent of the crime. The poor child stood in need of food and clothing.* **7** to

stamen—The flower had yellow **stamens.**

think or act in a certain way: *How does your group stand on tax reform?* **8** to be unchanged; hold good; remain the same: *The rule against being late will stand.* **9** to stay in place; last: *The old house has stood for a hundred years.* **10** to put up with; bear; endure: *I can't stand that singer. This plant cannot stand the cold.* **11** to stop moving; halt; stop: *The cars stood and waited for the light to change.* **12** a stop for defense: *We made a last stand against the enemy.* **13** a place where a person stands; position: *The monitor took her stand in the hall.* **14** a raised place where people can sit or stand: *The mayor sat on the reviewing stand at the parade.* **15** something to put things on or in: *Leave your wet umbrella in the stand in the hall.* **16** a place or fixtures for a small business: *a newspaper stand, a fruit stand.* **17** a group of growing trees or plants: *a stand of timber.* 1-11 *verb,* **stands, stood, stand·ing;** 12-17 *noun.*

stand by, 1 to be near. **2** to side with; help; support: *to stand by a friend.* **3** to be or get ready for use or action: *The radio operator was ordered to stand by.*

stand for, 1 to represent; mean: *What does the abbreviation "St." stand for?* **2** to be on the side of; take the part of; uphold: *Our school stands for fair play.* **3** to put up with: *The teacher said she would not stand for talking during class.*

stand out, 1 to project: *His ears stood out.* **2** to be noticeable or prominent: *Certain facts stand out.*

stand up for, to take the part of; defend; support: *to stand up for a friend.*

stand up to, to meet or face boldly: *to stand up to an enemy.*

stan·dard (stan′dərd), **1** anything taken as a basis of comparison; model: *Your work is not up to the class standard.* **2** used as a standard; according to rule: *standard spelling, standard pronunciation.* **3** having recognized excellence or authority: *Use a standard encyclopedia to look up the facts for your report.* **4** a flag, emblem, or symbol: *The dragon was the standard of China.* 1,4 *noun,* 2,3 *adjective.*

stan·dard·ize (stan′dər dīz), to make standard in size, shape, weight, quality, or strength: *Bicycle tires are standardized. verb,* **stan·dard·iz·es, stan·dard·ized, stan·dard·iz·ing.**

stand·ing (stan′ding), **1** position; reputation: *a person of good standing.* **2** duration: *a friendship of long standing.* **3** straight up; erect: *standing timber.* **4** done from an erect position: *a standing jump.* **5** established; permanent: *a standing invitation, a standing army.* **6** not flowing; stagnant: *standing water.* 1,2 *noun,* 3-6 *adjective.*

stand·point (stand′point′), a point of view; mental attitude: *From my standpoint, you are wrong. noun.*

stand·still (stand′stil′), a complete stop; halt. *noun.*

stank (stangk). See **stink.** *The dead fish stank. verb.*

stan·za (stan′zə), a group of lines of poetry, usually four or more, arranged according to a fixed plan; verse of a poem: *They sang the first and last stanzas of "America." noun.*

sta·ple[1] (stā′pəl), **1** a piece of metal with pointed ends bent into a U shape. Staples are driven into wood to hold hooks, wiring, and insulation. **2** a bent piece of wire used to hold together papers or parts of a book. **3** to fasten with staples: *to staple pages together.* 1,2 *noun,* 3 *verb,* **sta·ples, sta·pled, sta·pling.**

sta·ple[2] (stā′pəl), **1** the most important or principal article grown or manufactured in a place: *Cotton is the staple in many Southern states.* **2** most important; principal: *Bread is a staple food.* **3** a product, especially a food sold and used all the time. Bread, milk, sugar, and salt are common staples in this country. 1,3 *noun,* 2 *adjective.*

sta·pler (stā′plər), a device for fastening papers together with wire staples. *noun.*

star (stär), **1** any heavenly body appearing as a bright point in the sky at night and shining by its own light. A star is a mass of very hot gas. Some stars are smaller than the earth, while others are several million times as large as the sun. **2** a figure having five or more points, like these: ☆ ✩ . **3** a person having brilliant qualities: *an athletic star.* **4** a famous person in some art or profession, especially one who plays the lead in a performance: *a movie star.* **5** chief; best; leading; excellent: *the star player on a football team.* **6** to be a leading performer; be prominent; excel: *She has starred in many motion pictures.* 1-4 *noun,* 5 *adjective,* 6 *verb,* **stars, starred, star·ring.**

star·board (stär′bərd), **1** the right side of a ship, boat, or aircraft when you are facing forward. **2** on the right side of a ship, boat, or aircraft. 1 *noun,* 2 *adjective.*

starch (stärch), **1** a white, tasteless food substance. Potatoes, wheat, rice, and corn contain much starch. **2** a preparation of it used to stiffen clothes or curtains. **3** to stiffen clothes or curtains with starch. 1,2 *noun,* 3 *verb.*

starch·y (stär′chē), **1** like starch; containing starch: *Rice is a starchy food.* **2** stiffened with starch: *My collar is too starchy. adjective,* **starch·i·er, starch·i·est.**

stare (ster *or* star), **1** to look long and directly with the eyes wide open. A person stares in wonder, surprise, stupidity, curiosity, or from rudeness. *The little girl stared at the toys in the window.* **2** a long and direct look with the eyes wide open: *The doll's eyes were set in an unchanging stare.* 1 *verb,* **stares, stared, star·ing;** 2 *noun.*

star·fish (stär′fish′), a star-shaped sea animal

starfish—about 4 inches
(10 centimeters) across

with a flattened body. Starfish are not fish. *noun, plural* **star·fish** or **star·fish·es.**

stark (stärk), **1** downright; complete: *That fool is talking stark nonsense.* **2** entirely; completely: *The boys went swimming stark naked.* **3** barren; bare; desolate. 1,3 *adjective,* 2 *adverb.*

stark (definition 3)—Mars has a very **stark** landscape.

star·light (stär′līt′), the light from the stars. *noun.*

star·ling (stär′ling), a common European and American bird with a plump body and glossy, dark feathers. It flies in large flocks. *noun.*

starling
about 8 inches
(20 centimeters) long

star·lit (stär′lit′), lighted by the stars: *a starlit night. adjective.*

star·ry (stär′ē), **1** lighted by stars; containing many stars: *a starry sky.* **2** shining like stars: *starry eyes. adjective,* **star·ri·er, star·ri·est.**

Stars and Stripes, the flag of the United States.

star·ship (stär′ship′), (in stories) a vehicle that can travel through outer space from one planet or star to another; spaceship. *noun.*

Star-Span·gled Ban·ner (stär′spang′gəld ban′ər), **1** the national anthem of the United States. **2** the flag of the United States.

start (stärt), **1** to begin to move, go, or act: *The train started on time.* **2** to begin: *School starts next week. I started reading my book.* **3** to set going; put into action: *to start a car, to start a fire.* **4** a setting

in motion: *We pushed the car to give the motor a start.* **5** a beginning to move, go, or act: *to see a race from start to finish.* **6** to move suddenly: *I started in surprise.* **7** a sudden movement; jerk: *I awoke with a start.* 1-3,6 *verb,* 4,5,7 *noun.*

start·er (stär′tər), **1** an electric motor for starting the engine of a vehicle. **2** a person who gives the signal for starting: *the starter of a race. noun.*

star·tle (stär′tl), to frighten suddenly; surprise: *The dog jumped at the girl and startled her. verb,* **star·tles, star·tled, star·tling.**

star·va·tion (stär vā′shən), a suffering from extreme hunger; being starved: *Starvation caused his death. noun.*

starve (stärv), **1** to suffer or die because of hunger: *People are starving in that country.* **2** to weaken or kill with hunger: *The enemy starved the men in the fort into surrendering.* **3** to feel very hungry: *I'm starving. Let's eat. verb,* **starves, starved, starv·ing.**

starve for, to suffer from lack of: *That lonely child is starving for affection.*

stash (stash), to hide or put away for safekeeping or future use: *The thieves stashed the money in the attic. verb.*

state (stāt), **1** the condition of a person or thing. *Ice is water in a solid state. The crowd was in a state of excitement. The house is in a bad state of repair.* **2** a group of people occupying a given area and organized under a government; nation: *The state of Israel is an independent country.* **3** one of several organized political groups of people which together form a nation: *The state of Alaska is in the United States.* **4** of or having to do with a state: *a state road, state police.* **5** to tell in speech or writing; express; say: *State your opinion of the new school rules.* 1-3 *noun,* 4 *adjective,* 5 *verb,* **states, stat·ed, stat·ing.**

stat·ed (stā′tid), fixed; settled: *School begins daily at a stated time. adjective.*

state·ly (stāt′lē), having dignity; grand; majestic: *The Capitol at Washington is a stately building. adjective,* **state·li·er, state·li·est.**

state·ment (stāt′mənt), **1** something stated; account; report: *Her statement was correct.* **2** the act of stating; manner of stating something: *The statement of an idea helps me to remember it.* **3** a single instruction given to a computer; command. *noun.*

states·man (stāts′mən), a person skilled in the management of public or national affairs: *Statesmen from many nations met to discuss possible solutions to serious world problems. noun, plural* **states·men.**

stat·ic (stat′ik), **1** at rest; standing still: *Life does*

S

not remain static, but changes constantly. **2** the crackling noise that sometimes comes from radios. Static is produced by electrical disturbances. **1** *adjective,* **2** *noun.*

static electricity, an electric charge which sometimes builds up on objects which rub against each other. Static electricity often occurs when people comb their hair.

sta·tion (stā′shən), **1** a place to stand in; place which a person is appointed to occupy in the performance of some duty: *The policeman took his station at the corner.* **2** a building or place used for a definite purpose: *The suspects were taken to the police station for questioning. Coast Guard stations are equipped with boats and aircraft to rescue people from the water.* **3** a building where buses or trains regularly pick up and unload passengers and baggage. **4** the place or equipment for sending out or receiving programs or messages by radio or television. **5** to place: *She stationed herself at the door to collect tickets. The soldier was stationed at Fort Hays.* **1-4** *noun,* **5** *verb.*

sta·tion·ar·y (stā′shə ner′ē), **1** having a fixed station or place; not movable: *A furnace is stationary.* **2** standing still; not moving: *A parked car is stationary.* **3** without change: *The population of this town has been stationary for ten years at about 5000 people. adjective.*

sta·tion·er·y (stā′shə ner′ē), writing materials such as paper and envelopes. *noun.*

station wagon, an automobile with a rear door for loading and unloading and seats in the rear that can be folded down, for use as a light truck.

sta·tis·tics (stə tis′tiks), facts in the form of numbers. Statistics are collected to give information about people, weather, businesses, and many other things. *noun plural.*

stat·ue (stach′ü), an image of a person or animal carved in stone or wood, cast in bronze, or modeled in clay or wax: *Nearly every city has a statue of some famous person. noun.*

stat·ure (stach′ər), **1** height: *a young woman of average stature.* **2** development; physical, mental, or moral growth; accomplishment: *Thomas Jefferson was a man of great stature among his countrymen. noun.*

sta·tus (stā′təs), **1** social or professional position; rank: *the status of a judge.* **2** condition; state: *Diplomats are interested in the status of world affairs. noun.*

stat·ute (stach′üt), a law: *The statutes for the United States are made by Congress. noun.*

staunch (stônch), loyal; faithful: *A few staunch friends stood by him when he was in trouble. adjective.*

stave (stāv), **1** one of the curved pieces of wood which form the sides of a barrel, tub, or the like. **2 stave off,** to put off; keep back; delay or prevent: *The lost campers ate birds' eggs to stave off starvation.* **1** *noun,* **2** *verb,* **staves, staved** or **stove, stav·ing.**

stay[1] (stā), **1** to remain; continue to be: *Stay still. Stay here till I tell you to move. The cat stayed out*

all night. Shall I go or stay? **2** to live for a while; dwell: *She is staying with her aunt for a few weeks.* **3** a period of time spent: *Our stay at the seashore was much too short.* **1,2** *verb,* **3** *noun.*

stay[2] (stā), **1** a strong rope, often made of wire, which supports the mast of a ship. **2** any rope or chain attached to something to steady it. *noun.*

stead (sted), place: *Our regular baby-sitter could not come, but sent her brother in her stead. noun.*

stead·fast (sted′fast′), firmly fixed; constant; not moving or changing: *The girls were steadfast companions for many years. The cat watched the caged bird with a steadfast gaze. adjective.*

stead·i·ly (sted′l ē), in a steady manner: *She improved steadily in her schoolwork. adverb.*

stead·i·ness (sted′ē nis), a being steady; firmness. *noun.*

stead·y (sted′ē), **1** changing very little; regular: *steady speed, a steady gain in value.* **2** firmly fixed; firm; not swaying or shaking: *This post is steady as a rock. Hold the ladder steady.* **3** not easily excited; calm: *Pilots who test new aircraft must have steady nerves.* **4** to make or become steady; keep steady: *Steady the ladder while I climb to the roof.* **1-3** *adjective,* **stead·i·er, stead·i·est; 4** *verb,* **stead·ies, stead·ied, stead·y·ing.**

steak (stāk), a slice of meat or fish for broiling or frying. *Steak often means beefsteak. noun.*

steal (stēl), **1** to take something that does not belong to one; take dishonestly: *Robbers stole the money.* **2** to take, get, or do secretly: *She stole time from her lessons to read a story.* **3** to move secretly or quietly: *She had stolen softly out of the house.* **4** (in baseball) to run to second base, third base, or home plate, as the pitcher throws the ball to the catcher. *verb,* **steals, stole, sto·len, steal·ing.**

stealth (stelth), a secret or sly action: *He obtained the letter by stealth, taking it while nobody was in the room. noun.*

stealth·y (stel′thē), done in a secret manner; secret; sly: *The cat crept in a stealthy way toward the bird. adjective,* **stealth·i·er, stealth·i·est.**

steam (stēm), **1** water in the form of vapor or gas. Boiling water gives off steam. Steam is used to produce electricity, and for heating and cooking. **2** to give off steam: *The cup of coffee was steaming.* **3** to move by steam: *The ship steamed off.* **4** to apply steam to: *I steam vegetables to cook them. Steam those curtains to get the wrinkles out.* **5** power; energy; force: *I have worked all day and am running out of steam.* **1,5** *noun,* **2-4** *verb.*

let off steam, to get rid of energy or express feelings: *During recess the children ran around the playground to let off steam.*

steam·boat (stēm′bōt′), a boat moved by steam. In former times, steamboats carried passengers and cargo on large rivers. *noun.*

steam engine, an engine worked by steam. Steam engines were used to drive locomotives, ships, and large machines.

steam·er (stē′mər), a steamboat; steamship. *noun.*

steam·roll·er (stēm′rō′lər), a heavy roller, used to crush and level materials in making roads. Steamrollers were formerly run by steam but are now usually run by a gasoline or diesel engine. *noun.*

steam·ship (stēm′ship′), a ship moved by steam. *noun.*

steam shovel, a machine for digging, formerly run by steam but now usually by an engine burning gasoline or oil.

steed (stēd), a horse, especially a spirited riding horse or a horse used in war. *noun.*

steel (stēl), **1** iron mixed with carbon so that it is very hard, strong, and tough. Most tools are made from steel. **2** made of steel: *Steel beams are used in skyscrapers and bridges.* **3** to make hard or strong like steel: *I tried to steel myself against possible failure.* 1 *noun,* 2 *adjective,* 3 *verb.*

steel wool, a pad of long, fine steel threads. Steel wool is used in cleaning or polishing surfaces.

steep[1] (stēp), **1** having a sharp slope; almost straight up and down: *The hill is steep.* **2** too high; unreasonable: *a steep price. adjective.*

steep[2] (stēp), to soak: *Let the tea steep in boiling water for five minutes. verb.*

stee·ple (stē′pəl), a high tower on a church, that usually narrows to a point at the top. *noun.*

steer[1] (stir), **1** to guide the course of: *to steer a car.* **2** to be guided: *This car steers easily.* **3** to direct one's way or course: *Steer for the harbor. Steer away from trouble. verb.*

steer[2] (stir), a young male of cattle raised for beef, usually two to four years old. *noun.*

steg·o·sau·rus (steg′ə sôr′əs), a very large plant-eating dinosaur with bony plates and spikes along the back and tail. *noun, plural* **steg·o·sau·ri** (steg′ə·sôr′ī).

Word History

stegosaurus *Stegosaurus* comes from two Greek words meaning "roof" and "lizard." The animal was named this because the growths on its back were thought to look or be like parts of the roof of a building.

stegosaurus about 18 feet (5½ meters) long

stem[1] (stem), **1** the main supporting part of a plant above the ground. The stem holds up the branches. The trunk of a tree and the stalks of corn are stems. **2** the part of a flower, a fruit, or a leaf that joins it to the plant or tree. **3** anything like

a hat	i it	oi oil	ch child		a in about
ā age	ī ice	ou out	ng long		e in taken
ä far	o hot	u cup	sh she	ə =	i in pencil
e let	ō open	u̇ put	th thin		o in lemon
ē equal	ô order	ü rule	ᵺ then		u in circus
ėr term			zh measure		

the stem of a plant: *the stem of a goblet, the stem of a pipe.* **4** to grow out; come from; develop: *Our difficulties stem from poor planning.* 1-3 *noun,* 4 *verb,* **stems, stemmed, stem·ming.**

stem[2] (stem), to stop; check; dam up: *I put a tight bandage on the cut to stem the flow of blood. verb,* **stems, stemmed, stem·ming.**

stench (stench), a very bad smell; stink: *the stench of a garbage dump. noun.*

sten·cil (sten′səl), **1** a thin sheet of metal, paper, or cardboard, having letters or designs cut through it. When it is laid on a surface and ink or color is spread on, these letters or designs are made on the surface. **2** to mark, paint, or make with a stencil: *to stencil one's name on a box.* 1 *noun,* 2 *verb.*

step (step), **1** a movement made by lifting the foot and putting it down again in a new position; one motion of the leg in walking, running, or dancing. **2** the distance covered by one such movement: *I was three steps from the phone when it stopped ringing.* **3** to move the legs as in walking, running, or dancing: *Step lively!* **4** a short distance; little way: *The school is only a step from our house.* **5** to walk a short distance: *Step this way.* **6** a way of walking or dancing: *My dance instructor taught me several new steps.* **7** to measure off by taking steps: *Step off the distance from the door to the window.* **8** to put the foot down: *Don't step on that bug.* **9** the sound made by putting the foot down: *I hear steps upstairs.* **10** a place for the foot in going up or coming down. A stair or a rung of a ladder is a step. **11** a footprint: *I see steps in the mud.* **12** an action: *Choosing where to go was the first step in planning our vacation.* **13** a degree in a scale; grade in rank: *A colonel is two steps above a captain.* 1,2,4,6,9-13 *noun,* 3,5,7,8 *verb,* **steps, stepped, step·ping.**

in step, moving the same leg at the same time as another person does: *Band members must learn to march in step.*

keep step, to move the same leg at the same time as another person does.

out of step, not in step.

step up, to make go faster or higher; increase: *to step up the production of automobiles, to step up the pressure in a boiler.*

take steps, to put into effect or carry out measures considered to be necessary or desirable: *The principal took steps to stop needless absence from school.*

step·fa·ther (step′fä′ᵺər), a man who has married one's mother after the death or divorce of one's real father. *noun.*

step·lad·der (step′lad′ər), a ladder with flat

S

steps instead of rungs, and a folding support attached to the back by hinges. *noun.*

step·moth·er (step′muᴛн′ər), a woman who has married one's father after the death or divorce of one's real mother. *noun.*

ster·e·o (ster′ē ō *or* stir′ē ō), a record player giving the effect of lifelike sound by using two or more sets of equipment. *noun, plural* **ster·e·os.**

ster·ile (ster′əl), free from living germs: *Bandages should be kept sterile. adjective.*

ster·i·lize (ster′ə līz), to make free from living germs: *The water had to be sterilized by boiling to make it fit to drink. verb,* **ster·i·liz·es, ster·i·lized, ster·i·liz·ing.**

ster·ling (stėr′ling), **1** containing 92.5 percent pure silver. *Sterling* is stamped on solid silver knives, forks, spoons, and jewelry. **2** genuine; reliable: *A job with so many responsibilities requires a person of sterling character. adjective.*

stern[1] (stėrn), severe; strict; harsh: *Our teacher's stern frown silenced us. adjective.*

stern[2] (stėrn), the rear part of a ship or boat. *noun.*

steth·o·scope (steth′ə skōp), an instrument used to hear the sounds produced in the lungs, heart, or other part of the body. *noun.*

stethoscope
veterinarian using a
stethoscope

stew (stü *or* styü), **1** to cook by slow boiling: *The cook stewed the chicken for a long time.* **2** food cooked by slow boiling: *beef stew.* **1** *verb,* **2** *noun.*

stew·ard (stü′ərd *or* styü′ərd), a man employed on an airplane or ship to look after passengers. *noun.*

stew·ard·ess (stü′ər dis *or* styü′ər dis), a woman employed on an airplane or ship to look after passengers. *noun, plural* **stew·ard·ess·es.**

stick[1] (stik), **1** a long, thin piece of wood: *Put some sticks on the fire.* **2** such a piece of wood shaped for a special use: *a walking stick.* **3** something like a stick in shape: *a stick of candy. noun.*

stick[2] (stik), **1** to pierce with a pointed instrument; stab: *She stuck her fork into the potato.* **2** to fasten by pushing the point or end into or through something: *He stuck a flower in his buttonhole.* **3** to

put into a position: *Don't stick your head out of the window.* **4** to come out from; extend: *The sweater shrank so that my arms stick out of the sleeves.* **5** to fasten; attach: *Stick a stamp on the letter.* **6** to keep close: *The puppy stuck to my heels.* **7** to be or become fastened; become fixed; be at a standstill: *Our car stuck in the mud. Two pages of the book stuck together.* **8** to keep on; hold fast: *Let's stick to the task until we've finished it.* **9** to puzzle: *That problem in arithmetic stuck me.* **10** to take advantage of; burden: *I got stuck washing dishes when everyone else went out. verb,* **sticks, stuck, stick·ing.**

stick up for, to stand up for; support; defend: *Stick up for your friends when they are in trouble.*

stick·ball (stik′bôl′), a form of baseball played with a rubber ball and a stick or broom handle for a bat. *noun.*

stick·er (stik′ər), a label that has gum or glue on the back of it so that it can be fastened to something. *noun.*

stick·y (stik′ē), **1** apt to stick: *sticky candy.* **2** covered with a layer of material that will stick: *Adhesive tape is sticky. adjective,* **stick·i·er, stick·i·est.**

stiff (stif), **1** not easily bent: *He wore a stiff collar.* **2** not able to move or be moved easily: *My neck is stiff. The hinges on this old door are stiff.* **3** firm: *Beat the egg whites until they are stiff.* **4** not easy or natural in manner; formal: *The magician made a stiff bow to the audience.* **5** strong: *a stiff breeze.* **6** hard to deal with; hard: *a stiff test.* **7** more than seems suitable: *They are asking a stiff price for their house.* **8** very much; extremely: *I was scared stiff.* **1-7** *adjective,* **8** *adverb.*

stiff·en (stif′ən), to make or become stiff: *I stiffened the shirt with starch. She stiffened with anger. The wind is stiffening. verb.*

sti·fle (stī′fəl), **1** to stop the breath of; smother: *The smoke stifled the firefighters.* **2** to be unable to breathe freely: *I am stifling in this close room.* **3** to keep back; stop: *The conversation was boring and I had to stifle a few yawns. verb,* **sti·fles, sti·fled, sti·fling.**

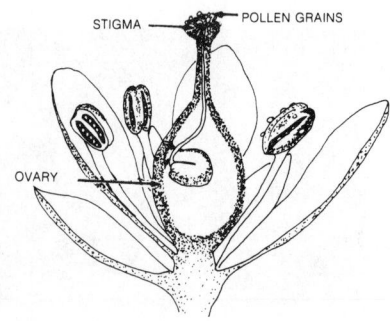

STIGMA — POLLEN GRAINS
OVARY

stigma

stig·ma (stig′mə), the part of the pistil of a plant which receives the pollen. *noun.*

still (stil), **1** without motion: *Sit still. The lake is still today.* **2** without noise; quiet: *a still night. The room was so still that you could have heard a pin drop.* **3** to make or become quiet: *A lullaby stilled* the baby's crying. *The storm stilled.* **4** even; yet: *You can read still better if you will try.* **5** in spite of it; nevertheless: *Proof was given, but they still doubted. She has many friends; still she likes to stay home.* **6** at or until the present, or some other stated time: *Was the store still open? Were they still up when you got here last night?* 1,2 *adjective,* 3 *verb,* 4-6 *adverb.*

stilt (stilt), one of a pair of poles, each with a support for the foot at some distance above the ground. Stilts are used in walking through shallow water, or by children for amusement. *noun.*

stilt·ed (stil′tid), stiffly dignified: *a stilted manner of speaking. adjective.*

stim·u·lant (stim′yə lənt), **1** a food, drug, or medicine that speeds up the activity of the body or some part of the body for a short time. Tea and coffee are stimulants. **2** something that excites, stirs, or stimulates: *Advertising is a stimulant to sales. noun.*

stim·u·late (stim′yə lāt), to stir up; rouse to action: *The new factory helped to stimulate growth in the town. verb,* **stim·u·lates, stim·u·lat·ed, stim·u·lat·ing.**

stim·u·lus (stim′yə ləs), **1** something that stirs to action or effort: *A need for money was the stimulus that led me to look for a summer job.* **2** something that causes a reaction in a living thing: *The stimulus of a bright light makes the pupils of the eyes become smaller. noun, plural* **stim·u·li** (stim′yə lī).

sting (sting), **1** to prick with a small point; wound: *Bees, wasps, and hornets sting. A bee stung her.* **2** a prick; wound: *The wasp sting began to swell.* **3** a stinger. **4** to pain sharply: *I was stung by the insult.* **5** a sharp pain: *The ball team felt the sting of defeat.* **6** to cause a feeling like that of a sting: *Mustard stings the tongue.* 1,4,6 *verb,* **stings, stung, sting·ing;** 2,3,5 *noun.*

sting·er (sting′ər), the sharp-pointed part of an insect or animal that pricks or wounds and often poisons; sting. *noun.*

stin·gi·ness (stin′jē nis), an unwillingness to spend or give money. *noun.*

stin·gy (stin′jē), unwilling to spend or give money; not generous: *He tried to save money without being stingy. adjective,* **stin·gi·er, stin·gi·est.**

stink (stingk), **1** a very bad smell. **2** to have a bad smell: *Decaying fish stink.* 1 *noun,* 2 *verb,* **stinks, stank** or **stunk, stunk, stink·ing.**

stir (stėr), **1** to mix by moving around with a spoon, stick, or some device: *Stir the sugar in the lemonade.* **2** to move: *The wind stirs the leaves.* **3** to move about: *No one was stirring in the house.* **4** to affect strongly; set going; excite: *Don't stir up trouble.* **5** a movement: *There was a stir in the bushes where the children were hiding.* **6** an excitement: *The queen's coming caused a great stir.* **7** the act of stirring: *Give the mixture a hard stir.* 1-4 *verb,* **stirs, stirred, stir·ring;** 5-7 *noun.*

stir·ring (stėr′ing), lively; exciting: *She gave a stirring speech about freedom. adjective.*

a hat	**i** it	**oi** oil	**ch** child		a in about	
ā age	**ī** ice	**ou** out	**ng** long		e in taken	
ä far	**o** hot	**u** cup	**sh** she	**ə =**	i in pencil	
e let	**ō** open	**u̇** put	**th** thin		o in lemon	
ē equal	**ô** order	**ü** rule	**ŦH** then		u in circus	
ėr term			**zh** measure			

stir·rup (stėr′əp), a support for the rider's foot, that hangs from a saddle. *noun.*

stirrup *Stirrup* comes from two older English words meaning "a climbing up" and "rope." Originally a stirrup was a loop of rope that hung from the saddle.

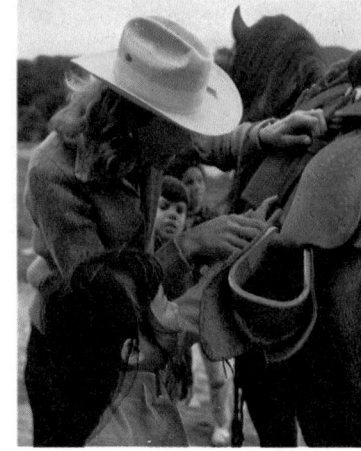

stirrup on a Western saddle

stitch (stich), **1** one complete movement of a threaded needle in sewing: *Take short stitches so the seam will be strong.* **2** one complete movement in knitting, crocheting, or embroidering. **3** a loop of thread or yarn made by a stitch: *Rip out these long stitches. The doctor took the stitches out of my cut.* **4** to make stitches in; fasten with stitches: *I stitched a patch on my jeans. The doctor stitched the cut.* **5** to sew. 1-3 *noun, plural* **stitch·es;** 4,5 *verb.*

St. John's (sānt jonz′), the capital of Newfoundland, Canada.

stock (stok), **1** things for use or for sale; supply used as it is needed: *This store keeps a large stock of toys.* **2** cattle or other farm animals; livestock: *The farm was sold with all its stock.* **3** to lay in a supply of; supply: *Our camp is well stocked with food for a short stay.* **4** to get or keep regularly for use or for sale: *A toy store stocks toys.* **5** kept on hand regularly for use or for sale: *Nails and screws are stock items in a hardware store.* **6** the shares in a company. The profits of a company are divided among the owners of stock. **7** the people who have come from the same ancestor; family: *The senator is from old New England stock.* **8** a part used as a support or handle: *the stock of a rifle.* **9 the stocks,** a framework with holes for

stock (definition 9)
the **stocks**

the feet, and sometimes for the hands, used as a punishment. 1,2,6-9 *noun,* 3,4 *verb,* 5 *adjective.*
in stock, on hand; ready for use or sale: *The store has many brands of canned goods in stock.*
out of stock, no longer on hand; lacking: *That item is out of stock, but we should have some more soon.*
stock·ade (sto kād′), a defense or pen made of large, strong posts fixed upright in the ground: *A heavy stockade around the cabins protected the pioneers from attack. noun.*
stock·ing (stok′ing), a close-fitting knitted covering of nylon, cotton, or other fabric for the foot and leg. *noun.*
stock·y (stok′ē), having a solid or sturdy form or build; thick for its height: *a stocky little child. adjective,* **stock·i·er, stock·i·est.**
stock·yard (stok′yärd′), a place with pens and sheds to keep cattle, sheep, hogs, and horses in before shipping or slaughtering them. *noun.*
stole (stōl). See **steal.** *Who stole my money? verb.*
sto·len (stō′lən). See **steal.** *The money was stolen by a thief. verb.*
stom·ach (stum′ək), 1 the large muscular bag in the body which receives swallowed food, and digests some of it before passing it on to the intestines. 2 the part of the body containing the stomach: *The ball hit me in the stomach.* 3 to put up with; bear; endure: *I cannot stomach violent movies.* 4 a liking: *I have no stomach for killing harmless creatures.* 1,2,4 *noun,* 3 *verb.*
stomp (stomp), 1 to stamp with the foot: *The crowd cheered and stomped.* 2 such a stamping: *the stomp of heavy boots.* 1 *verb,* 2 *noun.*
stone (stōn), 1 the hard mineral matter of which rocks are made up; hard matter that is not metal. Stone, such as granite and marble, is much used in building. 2 a piece of rock: *The children threw stones into the pond.* 3 made of stone: *a stone wall, a stone house.* 4 a gem; jewel: *The royal diamonds are fine stones.* 5 to throw stones at; drive by throwing stones: *The cruel children stoned the dog.* 6 a hard seed: *peach stones.* 1,2,4,6 *noun,* 3 *adjective,* 5 *verb,* **stones, stoned, ston·ing.**
Stone Age, the earliest known period of human culture, in which people used tools and weapons made from stone.

ston·y (stō′nē), 1 having many stones: *The beach is stony.* 2 without expression or feeling: *After our argument, when we met she would give me a stony stare. adjective,* **ston·i·er, ston·i·est.**
stood (stud). See **stand.** *I stood on the corner for five minutes. I had stood in line all morning to buy tickets to the game. verb.*
stool (stül), 1 a seat without back or arms. 2 a similar article used to rest the feet on. *noun.*
stoop[1] (stüp), 1 to bend forward: *I stooped to pick up the money.* 2 a forward bend: *She walks with a stoop.* 3 to carry head and shoulders bent forward: *The old man stoops.* 4 to lower oneself: *He stooped to cheating.* 1,3,4 *verb,* 2 *noun.*
stoop[2] (stüp), a porch or platform at the entrance of a house. *noun.*
stop (stop), 1 to keep from moving or doing: *She stopped the car. I stopped the child from breaking the toy.* 2 to put an end to; check: *to stop a noise.* 3 to stay; halt: *She stopped at the bank for a few minutes.* 4 to come to an end; quit; leave off: *The rain stopped. The baby stopped crying.* 5 to close up or block; plug: *Grease and vegetable peelings have stopped up the drain in the sink. This cold has stopped up my nose.* 6 the act of coming to a stop: *Her sudden stop startled us. The singing came to a stop.* 7 a place where a stop is made: *a bus stop.* 8 something that blocks, hinders, or checks: *a door stop.* 1-5 *verb,* **stops, stopped, stop·ping;** 6-8 *noun.*
stop·light (stop′līt′), 1 a red light at the rear end of a vehicle, that turns on when the brakes are put on. 2 a traffic light. *noun.*
stop·page (stop′ij), an act of stopping: *The foreman called for a stoppage of operations to oil the machinery. noun.*
stop·per (stop′ər), a plug or cork for closing the opening of a bottle, tube, or container. *noun.*
stop·watch (stop′woch′), a watch which has a hand that can be stopped or started at any instant. A stopwatch indicates fractions of a second and is used for timing races. *noun, plural* **stop·watch·es.**
stor·age (stôr′ij), 1 the act or fact of storing goods: *the storage of furs in summertime.* 2 the condition of being stored. Cold storage is used to keep eggs and meat from spoiling. 3 a place for storing: *She has put her furniture in storage.* 4 the part of a computer in which information and instructions are stored; memory. *noun.*
storage battery, a battery that can be charged again, after it has discharged its electricity, by passing an electric current through it. Automobiles have storage batteries.
store (stôr), 1 a place where goods are kept for sale: *a clothing store.* 2 something put away for use later; supply; stock: *We have a large store of frozen food in the freezer.* 3 to put away for use later; lay up: *The squirrel stores away nuts.* 1,2 *noun,* 3 *verb,* **stores, stored, stor·ing.**
in store, to be expected; waiting to happen: *Lots of new experiences were in store for us.*
store·house (stôr′hous′), 1 a place where things

are stored: *After the harvest the storehouses were full.* **2** a person or place very much like this: *a storehouse of ideas. A library is a storehouse of information. noun, plural* **store·hous·es** (stôr′hou′ziz).

store·keep·er (stôr′kē′pər), a person who has charge of a store. *noun.*

store·room (stôr′rüm′), a room where things are stored. *noun.*

stork (stôrk), a large bird with long legs for wading, a long neck, and a long bill. Storks are found in most warm parts of the world. *noun.*

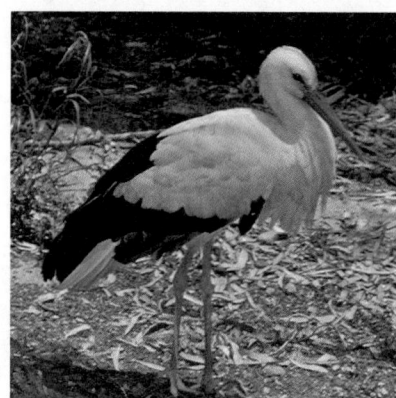

stork
about 3 feet
(1 meter) high

storm (stôrm), **1** a strong wind, usually with heavy rain, snow, or hail, and sometimes with thunder and lightning. **2** to blow hard; rain; snow; hail: *It stormed all night.* **3** a violent outburst or disturbance: *a storm of tears, a storm of angry words.* **4** to rush violently: *I stormed from the room in anger.* **5** to attack violently: *The enemy stormed the castle.* **6** a violent attack: *The castle was taken by storm.* **1,3,6** *noun,* **2,4,5** *verb.*

storm·y (stôr′mē), **1** having storms; likely to have storms; troubled by storms: *a stormy sea, stormy weather, a stormy night.* **2** rough and disturbed; violent: *They had stormy quarrels. adjective,* **storm·i·er, storm·i·est.**

sto·ry[1] (stôr′ē), **1** an account of some happening or group of happenings: *Tell us the story of your life.* **2** such an account, either true or made-up, intended to interest the reader or hearer; tale: *fairy stories, stories of adventure.* **3** a falsehood: *That's not true; you're telling stories. noun, plural* **sto·ries.**

sto·ry[2] (stôr′ē), all the rooms or space on one level of a building; floor: *That building has nine stories. noun, plural* **sto·ries.**

sto·ry·tell·er (stôr′ē tel′ər), a person who tells stories: *A good storyteller is able to create pictures in the minds of listeners and readers. noun.*

stout (stout), **1** fat and large: *That boy could run faster if he weren't so stout.* **2** strongly built; firm; strong: *The fort has stout walls.* **3** brave; bold: *Robin Hood was a stout fellow. adjective.*

stove[1] (stōv), an appliance for cooking or heating. There are electric, gas, oil, wood, and coal stoves. *noun.*

stove[2] (stōv). See **stave.** *They barely stove off starvation when they were lost in the forest. verb.*

stove·pipe (stōv′pīp′), a metal pipe that carries smoke and gases from a stove to a chimney. *noun.*

stow (stō), **1** to pack: *The cargo was stowed in the ship's hold.* **2** to pack things closely in; fill by packing: *The girls stowed their packs with supplies for the hike. verb.*

stow away, to hide on a ship, airplane, train, or bus to get a free ride or to make an escape.

stow·a·way (stō′ə wā′), a person who hides on a ship, airplane, train, or bus to get a free ride or to make an escape. *noun.*

St. Paul (sānt pôl′), the capital of Minnesota.

strad·dle (strad′l), **1** to walk, stand, or sit with the legs wide apart: *to straddle over a fence watching cars go by.* **2** to have a leg on each side of a horse, bicycle, chair, ditch, or the like. *verb,* **strad·dles, strad·dled, strad·dling.**

strag·gle (strag′əl), **1** to wander from or lag behind one's group, a leader, or the like: *Several hikers straggled into camp a half hour after the others.* **2** to spread out in an irregular way: *Vines straggled over the yard. verb,* **strag·gles, strag·gled, strag·gling.**

strag·gler (strag′lər), a person or thing that lags behind: *Several stragglers entered the theater after the play had started. noun.*

straight (strāt), **1** without a bend or curve: *a straight line, a straight path, straight hair.* **2** in a line; directly: *Walk straight. Go straight home.* **3** going in a line; direct: *a straight course, a straight throw.* **4** frank; honest; upright: *a straight answer.* **5** frankly; honestly; uprightly: *Live straight.* **6** right; correct: *straight thinking, a straight thinker.* **7** in proper order or condition: *Set the room straight. Our accounts are straight.* **8** showing no emotion or humor: *I kept a straight face, though I wanted to laugh.* **1,3,4,6-8** *adjective,* **2,5** *adverb.*

straight·en (strāt′n), **1** to make or become straight: *He straightened the bent pin.* **2** to put in the proper order or condition: *straighten out accounts. Straighten up your room. verb.*

straight·for·ward (strāt′fôr′wərd), honest; frank: *a straightforward answer. adjective.*

strain[1] (strān), **1** to draw tight; stretch: *The weight strained the rope.* **2** to pull hard: *The dog strained at its leash.* **3** any force or weight that stretches: *The strain on the rope made it break.* **4** to stretch as much as possible: *She strained the truth in telling that story.* **5** to injure by too much effort or by stretching: *The runner strained her leg.* **6** an injury caused by too much effort or by stretching: *The injury to his back was only a slight strain.* **7** any

strain¹ (definition 5)
The runners **strained** every muscle to reach the finish line.

severe or wearing pressure: *The strain of overwork can make you ill.* **8** to use to the utmost. **9** to press or pour through a strainer: *Babies eat food that has been strained.* 1,2,4,5,8,9 *verb*, 3,6,7 *noun*.

strain² (strān), **1** a family line; stock: *I am proud of my Irish strain.* **2** an inherited quality: *There is a strain of musical talent in that family. noun.*

strain·er (strā′nər), a utensil having holes that lets liquids and smaller pieces pass through, but not the larger pieces. *noun.*

strait (strāt), **1** a narrow channel connecting two larger bodies of water: *The Strait of Gibraltar connects the Mediterranean Sea and the Atlantic Ocean.* **2 straits,** difficulty; need; distress: *The family is in desperate straits for money. noun.*

strand¹ (strand), **1** to leave in a helpless position: *She was stranded a thousand miles from home with no money.* **2** to run aground; drive on the shore: *The ship was stranded on the rocks. verb.*

strand² (strand), **1** one of the threads, strings, or wires that are twisted together to make a rope or cable. **2** a thread or string: *a strand of hair, a strand of pearls. noun.*

strange (strānj), **1** unusual; odd; peculiar: *a strange experience, strange clothing, a strange quiet.* **2** not known, seen, or heard of before; not familiar: *She is moving to a strange place. A strange cat is on our steps.* **3** out of place; not at home: *The poor child felt strange in the palace. adjective,* **strang·er, strang·est.**

stran·ger (strān′jər), **1** a person not known, seen, or heard of before: *She is a stranger to us.* **2** a person or thing new to a place: *I am a stranger in New York.* **3** a person from another country: *The king received the stranger with kindness. noun.*

stran·gle (strang′gəl), **1** to kill by squeezing the throat to stop the breath. **2** to choke; suffocate: *This tight collar is nearly strangling me. verb,* **stran·gles, stran·gled, stran·gling.**

strap (strap), **1** a narrow strip of leather, cloth, or other material used for fastening things or holding things together: *Put a strap around the trunk. The strap on my sandal broke.* **2** to fasten with a strap: *We strapped the trunk.* 1 *noun*, 2 *verb*, **straps, strapped, strap·ping.**

strap·ping (strap′ing), tall, strong, and healthy: *a fine, strapping youngster. adjective.*

stra·ta (strā′tə). See **stratum.** *noun plural.*

strat·a·gem (strat′ə jəm), a scheme or trick for deceiving an enemy; trick; trickery: *The spy got into the country by the stratagem of pretending to be a student. noun.*

stra·te·gic (strə tē′jik), **1** of strategy; based on strategy; useful in strategy: *a strategic retreat.* **2** important in strategy: *The air force is a strategic link in our national defense. adjective.*

strat·e·gy (strat′ə jē), **1** planning and directing of military movements and operations. **2** the skillful planning and management of anything: *Strategy helped our team win the game. noun, plural* **strat·e·gies.**

stra·tum (strā′təm), a layer of material, especially one of several parallel layers placed one upon another: *In digging the well, the men struck first a stratum of sand, then several strata of rock. noun, plural* **stra·ta** *or* **stra·tums.**

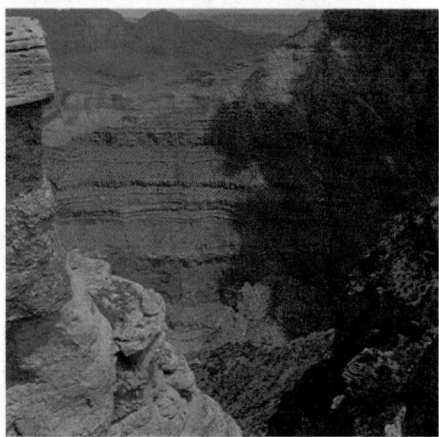

stratum—Many different **strata** of rock were visible in the canyon walls.

stra·tus cloud (strā′təs), a low, horizontal cloud that forms a gray layer over a large area.

straw (strô), **1** the stalks or stems of grain after drying and threshing. Straw is used for bedding for horses and cows, for making hats, and for many other purposes. **2** a hollow stem or stalk; something like it. Straws made of plastic or waxed paper are used for sucking up drinks. **3** made of straw: *a straw hat.* 1,2 *noun*, 3 *adjective.*

straw·ber·ry (strô′ber′ē), the small, juicy, red fruit of a plant that grows close to the ground. Strawberries are good to eat. *noun, plural* **straw·ber·ries.**

stray (strā), **1** to lose one's way; wander; roam: *Our dog has strayed off somewhere.* **2** wandering; lost: *A stray cat is crying at the door.* **3** a wanderer; lost animal: *That cat is a stray that we took in.* **4** scattered; here and there: *The beach was empty except for a few stray swimmers.* 1 *verb*, 2,4 *adjective*, 3 *noun.*

streak (strēk), **1** a long, thin mark or line: *You have a streak of dirt on your face. We saw the* *streaks of lightning.* **2** an element of one's character: *She has a streak of humor, although she looks very serious.* **3** to put long, thin marks or lines on: *The children streaked their faces with watercolors.* **4** a short period: *a streak of bad luck.* **5** to move very fast; go at full speed: *She streaked past us to win the race.* 1,2,4 *noun,* 3,5 *verb.*

like a streak, very fast: *When her dog saw her, it ran like a streak to greet her.*

stream (strēm), **1** a flow of water in a channel or bed. Small rivers and large brooks are both called streams. *Because of the lack of rain many streams dried up.* **2** any steady flow: *a stream of lava, a stream of light, a stream of words.* **3** to flow: *Rain water streamed down the gutters.* **4** to move steadily; move swiftly: *The crowd streamed out of the theater.* **5** to float or wave: *The flags streamed in the wind.* 1,2 *noun,* 3-5 *verb.*

stream·er (strē′mər), **1** any long, narrow flowing thing: *Streamers of colored paper decorated the gym for the dance.* **2** a long, narrow flag. *noun.*

stream·line (strēm′līn′), to bring up to date; make more efficient: *Efforts have been made to streamline train service between New York and Washington, D.C. verb,* **stream·lines, stream·lined, stream·lin·ing.**

stream·lined (strēm′līnd′), having a shape that offers the least possible resistance to air or water. The fastest automobiles, airplanes, and trains have streamlined bodies. *adjective.*

street (strēt), **1** a road in a city or town, usually with buildings on both sides. **2** the people who live in the buildings on a street: *The whole street came to the party. noun.*

street·car (strēt′kär′), a car that runs on rails in the streets and carries passengers. *noun.*

street·light (strēt′līt′), a powerful lamp that lights a street or public area of a city or town. *noun.*

strength (strengkth), **1** the quality of being strong; power; force; vigor: *I do not have the strength to lift that heavy box. Steel is valued for its strength.* **2** the power to resist force or to endure: *the strength of a fort, the strength of a rope.* **3** degree of strength; intensity: *Some flavorings lose their strength in cooking. noun.*

strength·en (strengk′thən), to make or grow stronger: *Daily exercise strengthens my muscles. verb.*

stren·u·ous (stren′yü əs), **1** very active: *We had a strenuous day moving into our new house.* **2** full of energy: *Beavers are strenuous workers.* **3** needing much energy or effort: *Running is strenuous exercise. adjective.*

strep throat (strep′ thrōt′), an infection that causes a very sore throat.

stress (stres), **1** great pressure or force, especially a force that can cause damage to a structure: *The roof collapsed under the stress of the heavy snow.* **2** tension, pressure, or strain which affects the mind and body: *A person's blood pressure may increase under stress.* **3** importance; emphasis: *That school lays stress upon arithmetic and reading.*

a hat	i it	oi oil	ch child	a in about
ā age	ī ice	ou out	ng long	e in taken
ä far	o hot	u cup	sh she	ə = i in pencil
e let	ō open	ů put	th thin	o in lemon
ē equal	ô order	ü rule	ŦH then	u in circus
ėr term			zh measure	

4 to lay stress on; emphasize: *Stress the important words of a sentence.* **5** the greater force or stronger tone of voice given to certain syllables or words; accent. In *zero,* the stress is on the first syllable. **6** to pronounce with stress: *"Accept" is stressed on the second syllable.* 1-3,5 *noun, plural* **stress·es;** 4,6 *verb.*

stretch (strech), **1** to draw out; extend to full length: *The bird stretched its wings. She stretched herself out on the grass to rest.* **2** to extend one's body or arms and legs: *I stretched out on the couch.* **3** to continue over a distance; extend from one place to another; fill space; spread: *The forest stretches for miles.* **4** to reach out; hold out: *The child stretched out a hand for the candy.* **5** to draw out to greater size: *Stretch this shoe a little.* **6** to become longer or wider without breaking: *Rubber stretches.* **7** to draw tight; strain: *to stretch a rubber band until it breaks.* **8** to exaggerate: *to stretch the truth.* **9** an unbroken length; extent: *A stretch of sand hills lay between the road and the ocean.* **10** a continuous length of time: *He worked for a stretch of five hours.* **11** the act of stretching; condition of being stretched: *With a stretch I was able to reach the high shelf.* 1-8 *verb,* 9-11 *noun, plural* **stretch·es.**

stretch·er (strech′ər), canvas stretched on a frame for carrying the sick, wounded, or dead. *noun.*

strew (strü), **1** to scatter; sprinkle: *She strewed seeds in her garden.* **2** to cover with something scattered or sprinkled: *In fall the ground was strewed with colorful leaves. verb,* **strews, strewed, strewed** or **strewn, strew·ing.**

strewn (strün), strewed. See **strew.** *verb.*

strick·en (strik′ən), **1** hit, wounded, or affected by a weapon, disease, trouble, sorrow, or the like: *a stricken deer. They fled from the stricken city. The stricken man was taken immediately to a hospital.* **2** struck. See **strike.** 1 *adjective,* 2 *verb.*

strict (strikt), **1** very careful in following a rule or in making others follow it: *Our teacher is strict but fair.* **2** harsh; severe: *a strict parent, strict discipline.* **3** exact; precise: *He told the strict truth.* **4** perfect; complete; absolute: *The secret was told in strict confidence. adjective.*
[*Strict* comes from a Latin word meaning "to tie tight." Other English words from the same Latin root are *strain*[1] and *strait.*]

strid·den (strid′n). See **stride.** *He had stridden away angrily. verb.*

stride (strīd), **1** to walk with long steps: *She strode rapidly down the street.* **2** to pass with one long step: *I strode over the brook.* **3** a long step: *The child could not keep up with his father's stride.* **4** to sit or stand with one leg on each side of: *to stride a fence.* 1,2,4 *verb,* **strides, strode, strid·den, strid·ing;** 3 *noun.*

make great strides or **make rapid strides,** to make great progress; advance rapidly: *Under a new teacher the class is making great strides in math.*

strife (strīf), quarreling; fighting: *bitter strife between rivals. noun.*

strike (strīk), **1** to hit: *to strike a person in anger. The ship struck a rock.* **2** to give; deal forth or out: *to strike a blow in self-defense.* **3** to set or be set on fire by hitting or rubbing: *Strike a match.* **4** to have a strong effect on the mind or feelings of; impress: *The plan strikes me as silly.* **5** to sound: *The clock strikes twelve times at noon.* **6** to find or come upon suddenly: *After drilling several holes, they finally struck oil.* **7** a sudden success in finding rich ore in mining or oil in boring: *They made a rich strike in the Yukon.* **8** to stop work to get better pay, shorter hours, or to force an employer to meet some other demand: *The coal miners struck when the company refused to improve safety conditions in the mines.* **9** a stopping work in this way: *The workers were home for six weeks during the strike last year.* **10** a baseball pitched through the strike zone but not swung at, any pitch that is swung at and missed, or any pitch that is hit foul under the rules of the game. After three strikes, a batter is out. **11** the knocking down of all the pins in bowling with one ball. 1-6,8 *verb,* **strikes, struck, struck** or **strick·en, strik·ing;** 7,9-11 *noun.*

on strike, stopping work to get more pay, shorter hours, or to force an employer to meet some other demand: *Most of the workers voted to go on strike.*

strike out, 1 to remove; cross out: *Strike out the incorrect answers.* **2** in baseball, to put out or be put out on three strikes: *Two batters struck out.*

strike up, to begin: *The two girls struck up a friendship.*

strike zone, (in baseball) the zone or area above home plate, between the batter's knees and armpits, through which a pitch must be thrown to be called a strike.

strik·ing (strī′king), **1** attracting attention; very noticeable: *a striking color, a striking performance.* **2** on strike: *The striking miners will soon return to work. adjective.*

string (string), **1** a small cord or very thin rope: *The package is tied with red string.* **2** a cord or thread with things on it: *She wore a string of beads around her neck.* **3** to put on a string: *The child is stringing beads.* **4** a special cord or wire for musical instruments or bows: *the strings of a violin.* **5 strings,** violins, cellos, and other stringed instruments. **6** to furnish with strings: *She had her tennis racket strung.* **7** anything used for tying: *apron strings.* **8** to tie with string or rope; hang with a string or rope: *We dry herbs by stringing them from rafters in the barn.* **9** to stretch or extend from one point to another: *Telephone wires and cables are strung on telephone poles or placed*

underground. **10** a number of things in a line or row: *A string of cars came down the street.* 1,2,4,5,7,10 *noun,* 3,6,8,9 *verb,* **strings, strung, strung** or **stringed, string·ing.**

string bean, a long, green or yellow pod containing smooth, somewhat flat seeds. String beans grow on bushes or vines and are eaten as a vegetable.

stringed in·stru·ment (stringd′ in′strə mənt), a musical instrument having strings, played either with a bow or by plucking. A harp, a violin, and a guitar are stringed instruments.

string·y (string′ē), like a string or strings: *a person with stringy hair. adjective,* **string·i·er, string·i·est.**

strip[1] (strip), **1** to make bare or naked; undress. **2** to take off the covering of: *They stripped the logs by removing the bark.* **3** to remove; pull off: *The birds stripped the fruit from the trees.* **4** to rob: *Thieves stripped the house of everything valuable. verb,* **strips, stripped, strip·ping.**

strip[2] (strip), a long, narrow, flat piece of cloth, paper, bark, or the like. *noun.*

stripe (strīp), **1** a line or long, narrow part of different color, material, or the like: *A tiger has stripes. The American flag has thirteen stripes.* **2** to mark with stripes: *The stick of candy was striped with red.* 1 *noun,* 2 *verb,* **stripes, striped, strip·ing.**

striped (strīpt), having stripes; marked with stripes: *He wore a striped shirt. adjective.*

strip mining, a form of mining in which a mine is operated from the surface of the earth by stripping away the layers of rock and soil that cover the mineral which is then taken.

strive (strīv), to try hard; work hard: *Strive to succeed. verb,* **strives, strove** or **strived, striv·en, striv·ing.**

striv·en (striv′ən). See **strive.** *She has striven hard to make the business a success. verb.*

strode (strōd). See **stride.** *He strode into the room. verb.*

stroke[1] (strōk), **1** the act of striking; blow: *I drove in the nail with several strokes of the hammer. The house was hit by a stroke of lightning.* **2** the sound made by striking: *We arrived at the stroke of three o'clock.* **3** an unexpected happening or instance of something: *Finding my lost ring was a stroke of good luck.* **4** a single complete movement to be made again and again: *He rowed with a strong stroke of the oars.* **5** a movement or mark made by a pen, pencil, or brush: *She writes with a heavy down stroke.* **6** a very successful effort; feat: *a stroke of genius.* **7** a single effort; act: *I felt lazy and didn't do a stroke of work all day.* **8** a sudden attack of illness, especially a paralysis caused by injury to the brain when a blood vessel breaks or becomes blocked. *noun.*

stroke[2] (strōk), **1** to move the hand gently along: *She likes to stroke her kitten.* **2** such a movement: *I brushed the crumbs away with one stroke.* 1 *verb,* **strokes, stroked, strok·ing;** 2 *noun.*

stroll (strōl), **1** to take a quiet walk for pleasure;

walk: *We strolled through the park after dinner.* **2** a leisurely walk: *We went for a stroll in the park.* 1 *verb,* 2 *noun.*

stroll·er (strō′lər), a kind of light baby carriage in which a small child sits erect. *noun.*

strong (strông), **1** having a great deal of force or power: *A strong person can lift heavy things.* **2** having good bodily strength or health: *Several months after the operation she was well and strong again.* **3** able to last; not easy to break: *a strong rope.* **4** having great mental force; not easily influenced: *a strong will.* **5** having great force or effectiveness: *a strong argument.* **6** having a lot of a particular quality: *Strong tea has more flavor than weak tea. adjective,* **strong·er** (strông′gər), **strong·est** (strông′gəst).

strong·hold (strông′hōld′), a strong place; safe place; fort: *The robbers have a stronghold in the mountains. noun.*

strove (strōv). See **strive.** *They strove hard, but did not win the game. verb.*

struck (struk). See **strike.** *The clock struck four. The barn was struck by lightning. verb.*

struc·tur·al (struk′chər əl), **1** used in building. Structural steel is steel made into beams and girders. **2** of or having to do with structure or structures: *Ferns and daisies have structural differences. adjective.*

struc·ture (struk′chər), **1** a building; something built: *The city hall is a large stone structure.* **2** anything composed of parts arranged together: *The human body is a wonderful structure.* **3** the way parts are put together; manner of building; construction: *The structure of the school was excellent.* **4** the arrangement of parts: *the structure of an atom, the structure of a flower. noun.*

strug·gle (strug′əl), **1** to make great efforts with the body; try hard; work hard against difficulties: *The poor have to struggle for a living. The swimmer struggled against the tide. I struggled to keep back my tears.* **2** great effort; hard work: *It was a struggle for them to send their six children to college.* **3** to fight: *The dog struggled fiercely with the wildcat.* **4** a fighting; conflict: *The struggle between the two enemy countries went on for years.* 1,3 *verb,* **strug·gles, strug·gled, strug·gling;** 2,4 *noun.*

strum (strum), to play by running the fingers lightly or carelessly across the strings or keys: *to strum a guitar. verb,* **strums, strummed, strum·ming.**

strung (strung). See **string.** *The children strung the beads according to size. The vines had been strung on poles. verb.*

strut (strut), to walk in a vain, important manner: *The rooster struts about the barnyard. verb,* **struts, strut·ted, strut·ting.**

stub (stub), **1** a short piece that is left: *the stub of a pencil.* **2** the short piece of a ticket or of each check in a checkbook, kept as a record. **3** to strike one's toe against something: *I stubbed my toe on a rock.* 1,2 *noun,* 3 *verb,* **stubs, stubbed, stub·bing.**

stub·ble (stub′əl), **1** the lower ends of stalks of grain left in the ground after the grain is cut: *The stubble hurt her bare feet.* **2** any short, rough growth, especially a short growth of beard: *Since he had not shaved for three days, there was stubble on his face. noun.*

stub·born (stub′ərn), **1** fixed in purpose or opinion; not giving in to argument or requests: *The stubborn child refused to listen to reasons for not going out in the rain.* **2** hard to deal with: *a stubborn cough. adjective.*

stub·by (stub′ē), short and thick: *stubby fingers. adjective,* **stub·bi·er, stub·bi·est.**

stuc·co (stuk′ō), **1** plaster for covering the outer walls of buildings. **2** to cover with stucco: *We had our house stuccoed last year.* 1 *noun, plural* **stuc·coes** or **stuc·cos;** 2 *verb.*

stuck (stuk). See **stick².** *She stuck her arm out of the car window. We were stuck in the mud. verb.*

stuck-up (stuk′up′), too proud; conceited; haughty: *We didn't join that group at the party because they seemed stuck-up. adjective.*

stud (stud), **1** a head of a nail, knob, or the like, sticking out from a surface: *The belt was ornamented with silver studs.* **2** to set with studs or something like studs: *The crown was studded with jewels.* **3** to be set or scattered over: *Little islands studded the harbor.* 1 *noun,* 2,3 *verb,* **studs, stud·ded, stud·ding.**

stud (definition 1)—**studs** on a dog's collar

stu·dent (stüd′nt *or* styüd′nt), **1** a person who studies: *She is a student of birds.* **2** a person who is studying in a school, college, or university: *That high school has 3000 students. noun.* [*Student* comes from a Latin word meaning "to study." The original meaning of the Latin root was "to be eager." Other English words from the same root include *studio, studious,* and *study.*]

stu·di·o (stü′dē ō *or* styü′dē ō), **1** the workroom of a painter, sculptor, photographer, or other

S

artist. **2** a place where motion pictures are made. **3** a place from which a radio or television program is broadcast. *noun, plural* **stu·di·os.**

stu·di·ous (stü′dē əs *or* styü′dē əs), fond of study: *That studious boy likes school. adjective.*

stud·y (stud′ē), **1** the effort to learn by reading or thinking: *After an hour's hard study, I knew my lesson.* **2** to try to learn: *She studied her spelling lesson for half an hour. He is studying to be a doctor.* **3** a careful examination; investigation: *A careful study of the map showed us the shortest way home.* **4** to examine carefully: *We studied the map to find the shortest road home.* **5** a subject that is studied; branch of learning. History, music, and law are studies. **6** a room for study, reading, or writing: *The author was at work in her study.* **7** to consider with care; think out; plan: *The mayor is studying ways to cut expenses.* **1,3,5,6** *noun, plural* **stud·ies; 2,4,7** *verb,* **stud·ies, stud·ied, stud·y·ing.**

stuff (stuf), **1** what a thing is made of; material: *She bought some white stuff for curtains.* **2** belongings; goods: *She was told to move her stuff out of the room.* **3** worthless material; useless things: *Their attic is full of old stuff.* **4** qualities of character: *The girl has good stuff in her.* **5** to pack full; fill: *I stuffed the pillow with feathers.* **6** to stop up; block; choke up: *My head is stuffed up by a cold.* **7** to fill the skin of a dead animal to make it look as it did when alive: *We saw many stuffed birds at the museum.* **8** to prepare meat, fowl, or vegetables by filling with stuffing: *to stuff a turkey, to stuff peppers.* **9** to force; push; thrust: *I stuffed my things into a closet.* **10** to fill too much with food: *I stuffed myself at dinner last night.* **1-4** *noun,* **5-10** *verb.*

stuff·ing (stuf′ing), **1** material used to fill or pack something: *The stuffing is coming out of the pillow.* **2** a seasoned mixture of bread crumbs with sausage or oysters, chestnuts, or some other food, used to stuff a chicken, turkey, fish, or other animal before cooking. *noun.*

stuff·y (stuf′ē), **1** lacking fresh air: *a stuffy room.* **2** lacking freshness or interest; dull: *a stuffy speech.* **3** stopped up: *A cold makes my head feel stuffy. adjective,* **stuff·i·er, stuff·i·est.**

stum·ble (stum′bəl), **1** to slip or trip by striking the foot against something: *to stumble over a stool in the dark.* **2** to walk in an unsteady way: *The tired hikers stumbled along.* **3** to speak or act in a clumsy or hesitating way: *The actors made many blunders as they stumbled through the play.* **4** to come by accident or chance: *While in the country, she stumbled upon some fine old pieces of furniture. verb,* **stum·bles, stum·bled, stum·bling.**

stump (stump), **1** the lower end of a tree or plant left after the main part is cut off: *We sat on top of a stump.* **2** anything left after the main or important part is removed: *the stump of a pencil, the stump of a candle. The dog wagged its stump of a tail.* **3** to make unable to answer or do; cause to be at a loss: *The riddle stumped me.* **1,2** *noun,* **3** *verb.*

stun (stun), **1** to make senseless; knock unconscious: *He was stunned by the fall.* **2** to daze; bewilder; shock; overwhelm: *She was stunned by the news of her friend's death. verb,* **stuns, stunned, stun·ning.**

stung (stung). See **sting.** *A wasp stung him. He was stung on the neck. verb.*

stunk (stungk). See **stink.** *The garbage dump stunk. The rotten eggs had stunk up the kitchen. verb.*

stun·ning (stun′ing), **1** excellent; very attractive; good-looking: *a stunning outfit.* **2** shocking; bewildering: *a stunning blow. adjective.*

stunt¹ (stunt), to check in growth or development: *Lack of proper food stunts a child. verb.*

stunt¹—This tree has been **stunted.**

stunt²

stunt² (stunt), a feat to attract attention; unusual performance or trick: *Circus riders perform stunts on horseback. noun.*

stu·pen·dous (stü pen′dəs *or* styü pen′dəs), amazing; marvelous; immense: *Niagara Falls is a stupendous sight. adjective.*

stu·pid (stü′pid *or* styü′pid), **1** not intelligent; dull: *a stupid person, a stupid remark.* **2** not interesting; boring: *a stupid book. adjective.*
[*Stupid* comes from a Latin word meaning "to be amazed." From the original meaning, the meaning "slow in understanding" developed.]

stu·pid·i·ty (stü pid′ə tē *or* styü pid′ə tē), lack of intelligence. *noun.*

stu·por (stü′pər *or* styü′pər), a dazed condition; loss or lessening of the power to feel: *I lay in a stupor for some time after I was hit on the head. noun.*

stur·dy (stėr′dē), **1** strong; stout: *a sturdy child, a sturdy chair.* **2** firm; not yielding: *The enemy put up a sturdy defense. adjective,* **stur·di·er, stur·di·est.**

stur·geon (stėr′jən), a large food fish whose body has a tough skin with rows of bony plates. *noun, plural* **stur·geon** *or* **stur·geons.**

sturgeon—up to 14 feet (4 meters) long

stut·ter (stut′ər), **1** to repeat the same sound in an effort to speak. People may stutter when nervous, embarrassed, or afraid. **2** the act or habit of stuttering: *to speak with a stutter.* **1** *verb,* **2** *noun.*

style (stīl), **1** fashion: *My clothes are out of style.* **2** a manner; method; way: *the Gothic style of architecture. She learned several styles of swimming.* **3** a way of writing or speaking: *Books for children should have a clear, easy style.* **4** good style: *She dresses in style.* **5** to design according to a fashion: *His suits are styled by a famous designer.* **6** to name; call: *She styles herself a poet.* **1-4** *noun,* **5,6** *verb,* **styles, styled, styl·ing.**

styl·ish (stī′lish), having style; in the current fashion; fashionable: *stylish clothes. adjective.*

sub¹ (sub), **1** a substitute: *My mother taught as a sub in school today.* **2** to act as a substitute: *My mother subbed for our regular teacher in school today.* **1** *noun,* **2** *verb,* **subs, subbed, sub·bing.**

sub² (sub), a submarine. *noun.*

sub-, a prefix meaning: **1** under; below: *A subnormal temperature means a temperature that is below normal.* **2** down; further; again: *Subdivide means to divide again.* **3** near; nearly: *a subtropical climate means a climate that is nearly tropical.* **4** lower; less important: *Subcommittee means a lower or less important committee.*

sub·di·vide (sub′də vīd′), to divide again; divide into smaller parts: *A builder bought the farm, subdivided it into lots, and built homes on them. verb,* **sub·di·vides, sub·di·vid·ed, sub·di·vid·ing.**

sub·di·vi·sion (sub′də vizh′ən), a tract of land divided into building lots. *noun.*

sub·due (səb dü′ *or* səb dyü′), **1** to overcome by force; conquer: *The government forces subdued the rebels.* **2** to keep down; hold back: *We subdued a desire to laugh. verb,* **sub·dues, sub·dued, sub·du·ing.**

sub·head (sub′hed′), **1** a less important heading or title: *Many magazine articles have subheads.* **2** a less important division of a heading or title. Lesson subheads are often indicated by numbers or letters in parentheses, such as (1) and (a). *noun.*

sub·head·ing (sub′hed′ing), a subhead. *noun.*

sub·ject (sub′jikt *for* 1-4,7-10; səb jekt′ *for* 5 *and* 6), **1** something thought about, discussed, or studied; topic: *The subject for our composition was "An Exciting Moment."* **2** something learned or taught; course of study in some branch of knowledge: *English, science, and arithmetic are some of the subjects we take up in school.* **3** a person who is under the power, control, or influence of another: *The people are the subjects of the king.* **4** under the power or influence of: *We are subject to our country's laws.* **5** to bring under some power or influence: *Rome subjected all Italy to its rule.* **6** to cause to experience or undergo something: *The school subjected new students to many tests.* **7** a person or thing that experiences or undergoes something: *Rabbits and mice are subjects of medical experiments.* **8** likely to have: *I am subject to colds.* **9** depending on; on the condition of: *I bought the car subject to your approval.* **10** the word or group of words about which something is said in a sentence. *I* is the subject of the following sentences: I see the cat. I am seen by the cat. I can see. **1-3,7,10** *noun,* **4,8,9** *adjective,* **5,6** *verb.*

sub·lime (sə blīm′), noble; majestic; grand: *From the train we could view the sublime mountain scenery. adjective.*

sub·ma·rine (sub′mə rēn′ *for* 1; sub′mə rēn′ *for* 2), **1** a boat that can go under water. Submarines are used in warfare for attacking enemy ships and launching guided missiles. **2** under the surface of the sea; underwater: *submarine plants, submarine warfare.* **1** *noun,* **2** *adjective.*

sub·merge (səb mėrj′), **1** to put under water; cover with water: *A big wave submerged us. At high tide this path is submerged.* **2** to go below the surface of the water: *The submarine submerged to*

a hat	**i** it	**oi** oil	**ch** child	a in about
ā age	**ī** ice	**ou** out	**ng** long	e in taken
ä far	**o** hot	**u** cup	**sh** she	**ə =** i in pencil
e let	**ō** open	**ů** put	**th** thin	o in lemon
ē equal	**ô** order	**ü** rule	**TH** then	u in circus
ėr term			**zh** measure	

escape enemy attack. *verb,* **sub·merg·es, sub·merged, sub·merg·ing.**

sub·mis·sion (səb mish′ən), **1** a yielding to the power, control, or authority of another: *The defeated general showed his submission by giving up his sword.* **2** humble obedience: *He bowed in submission to the king's order. noun.*

sub·mis·sive (səb mis′iv), yielding to the power, control, or authority of another; obedient; humble. *adjective.*

sub·mit (səb mit′), **1** to yield to the power, control, or authority of some person or group; surrender; yield: *They submitted to the wishes of the majority.* **2** to refer to the consideration or judgment of another or others: *The secretary submitted a report of the last meeting. verb,* **sub·mits, sub·mit·ted, sub·mit·ting.**

sub·or·di·nate (sə bôrd′n it), **1** lower in rank: *In the army, lieutenants are subordinate to captains.* **2** having less importance; dependent; secondary: *An assistant has a subordinate position.* **3** a subordinate person or thing: *Our supervisor does not always take the advice of her subordinates.* **1,2** *adjective,* **3** *noun.*

sub·scribe (səb skrīb′), **1** to promise to take and pay for: *We subscribe to several magazines.* **2** to give one's consent or approval; agree: *She does not subscribe to my opinion. verb,* **sub·scribes, sub·scribed, sub·scrib·ing.**

sub·scrib·er (səb skrī′bər), a person who subscribes: *The magazines make a special offer to new subscribers. noun.*

sub·scrip·tion (səb skrip′shən), **1** the act of subscribing. **2** the right to receive something, obtained by paying a certain sum: *My subscription to the newspaper expired. noun.*

sub·se·quent (sub′sə kwənt), coming after; following after; later: *Subsequent events proved that she was right. The story will be continued in subsequent chapters. adjective.*

sub·se·quent·ly (sub′sə kwənt lē), afterward; later. *adverb.*

sub·set (sub′set′), (in mathematics) a set, each of whose members is a member of a second set: *Fourth graders are a subset of the set which includes all students attending elementary school. noun.*

sub·side (səb sīd′), **1** to grow less; die down; become less active: *The waves subsided when the wind stopped. Her fever subsided after she took the medicine.* **2** to sink to a lower level: *Several days after the rain stopped, the flood waters subsided. verb,* **sub·sides, sub·sid·ed, sub·sid·ing.**

sub·stance (sub′stəns), **1** what a thing consists of; matter; material: *Ice and water are the same substance in different forms.* **2** the main or important part of anything: *The substance of an education is its effect on your life, not just learning lessons.* **3** the real meaning: *Give the substance of the speech in your own words. noun.*

sub·stan·tial (səb stan′shəl), **1** real; actual: *People and things are substantial; dreams and ghosts are not.* **2** strong; firm; solid: *That house is substantial enough to last a hundred years.* **3** large;

important; ample: *Your work shows substantial improvement.* **4** in the main; in substance: *The stories told by the children were in substantial agreement. adjective.*

sub·stan·tial·ly (səb stan′shə lē), **1** mainly: *This report is substantially correct.* **2** really; actually. **3** solidly; strongly: *a substantially built house. adverb.*

sub·sti·tute (sub′stə tüt *or* sub′stə tyüt), **1** a thing used instead of another; person taking the place of another: *Margarine is a common substitute for butter.* **2** to put in the place of another: *We substituted brown sugar for molasses in these cookies.* **3** to take the place of another: *The principal substituted for our teacher, who is ill.* **1** *noun,* **2,3** *verb,* **sub·sti·tutes, sub·sti·tut·ed, sub·sti·tut·ing.**

sub·sti·tu·tion (sub′stə tü′shən *or* sub′stə tyü′shən), the use of one thing for another; putting one person or thing in place of another; taking the place of another. *noun.*

sub·tle (sut′l), **1** not obvious; delicate; fine: *There is a subtle odor of burning leaves in the fall air. Subtle jokes are often hard to understand.* **2** having a quick mind; clever: *She is a subtle observer of slight differences in things.* **3** sly; crafty; tricky: *a subtle scheme to get some money. adjective,* **sub·tler, sub·tlest.**

sub·tract (səb trakt′), to take away: *Subtract 2 from 10 and you have 8. verb.*

sub·trac·tion (səb trak′shən), the operation of subtracting one number from another: $10 - 2 = 8$ *is a simple subtraction. noun.*

sub·tra·hend (sub′trə hend), a number to be subtracted from another: *In $10 - 2 = 8$, the subtrahend is 2. noun.*

sub·urb (sub′ėrb′), a district, town, or village just outside or near a city: *Many people who work in the city live in the suburbs. noun.*

sub·ur·ban (sə bėr′bən), having to do with a suburb; in a suburb: *We have excellent suburban train service. adjective.*

sub·way (sub′wā′), an underground electric railroad running beneath the surface of the streets in a city. *noun.*

subway

suc·ceed (sək sēd′), **1** to turn out well; do well; have success: *The plan succeeded.* **2** to come next after; follow; take the place of: *John Adams succeeded Washington as President. Week succeeds week. verb.*

suc·cess (sək ses′), **1** a favorable result; wished-for ending; good fortune: *Success in school comes from intelligence and work.* **2** the gaining of wealth or position: *She has had success in business.* **3** a person or thing that succeeds: *The circus was a great success. noun, plural* **suc·cess·es.**

suc·cess·ful (sək ses′fəl), having success; ending in success; prosperous; fortunate: *The books of a successful writer are liked by the public. adjective.*

suc·ces·sion (sək sesh′ən), **1** a group of things happening one after another; series: *A succession of accidents spoiled our automobile trip.* **2** the coming of one person or thing after another. **3** the right of succeeding to an office, property, or rank: *There was a dispute about the rightful succession to the throne.* **4** the order or arrangement of persons having such a right of succeeding: *The queen's oldest son is next in succession to the throne. noun.*

in succession, one after another: *We visited our sick friend several days in succession.*

suc·ces·sive (sək ses′iv), coming one after another; following in order: *It has rained for three successive days. adjective.*

suc·ces·sor (sək ses′ər), one who follows or succeeds another in office, position, or ownership of property; thing that comes after another in a series: *John Adams was Washington's successor as President. noun.*

such (such), **1** of that kind; of the same kind or degree: *We had never seen such a sight.* **2** of a particular kind; of the kind that: *The child had such a fever that she nearly died.* **3** of the kind already spoken of or suggested: *She does not like tea and coffee and such drinks.* **4** so great, so bad, or so good: *They are such liars! Such weather!* **5** a person or thing of that kind; persons or things of that kind: *There were rowboats, canoes, surfboards, and such on sale at the store last week.* **6** so very: *We had such good times last summer.* **1-4** *adjective,* **5** *pronoun,* **6** *adverb.*

such as, 1 similar to; like: *A good friend such as you is rare.* **2** for example: *members of the dog family, such as the wolf and the fox.*

suck (suk), **1** to draw into the mouth: *Lemonade can be sucked through a straw.* **2** to draw something from with the mouth: *suck oranges.* **3** to draw in; take in: *The fan sucked the smoke from the room. Plants suck up moisture from the earth. A sponge sucks in water.* **4** to hold in the mouth and lick: *The child sucked a lollipop. verb.*

suck·er (suk′ər), **1** a piece of hard candy, usually on the end of a small stick; lollipop. **2** a part of the body of some animals for sucking and holding fast. **3** a person easy to fool or to deceive. *noun.*

suc·tion (suk′shən), the process of drawing liquids or gases into a space by sucking out or removing part of the air from that space. We draw liquid through a straw by suction. Vacuum cleaners work by suction. *noun.*

Su·dan (sü dan′), a country in northeastern Africa. *noun.*

sud·den (sud′n), **1** not expected: *a sudden stop, a sudden storm, a sudden idea.* **2** quick; rapid: *The cat made a sudden jump at the mouse. adjective.*

all of a sudden, unexpectedly or quickly.

suds (sudz), **1** soapy water. **2** bubbles and foam on soapy water; soapsuds. *noun plural.*

sue (sü), to start a lawsuit against: *She sued the driver of the car that hit her. verb,* **sues, sued, su·ing.**

suede (swād), a soft leather that has a velvety surface on one or both sides. *noun.*

su·et (sü′it), the hard fat of cattle or sheep. Suet is used in cooking and for making tallow. *noun.*

suf·fer (suf′ər), **1** to have or feel pain, grief, or injury: *She suffered a broken leg while skiing.* **2** to experience harm or loss: *Crops suffered during the dry spell.* **3** to bear with patiently; endure: *I will not suffer such insults. verb.*

suf·fer·ing (suf′ər ing), the experiencing of pain: *Hunger causes suffering. noun.*

suf·fi·cient (sə fish′ənt), as much as is needed; enough: *The poor child did not have sufficient clothing for the winter. adjective.*

suf·fi·cient·ly (sə fish′ənt lē), as much as is needed; enough. *adverb.*

a hat	**i** it	**oi** oil	**ch** child	a in about
ā age	**ī** ice	**ou** out	**ng** long	e in taken
ä far	**o** hot	**u** cup	**sh** she	ə = { i in pencil
e let	**ō** open	**u̇** put	**th** thin	o in lemon
ē equal	**ô** order	**ü** rule	**ᵺ** then	u in circus
ėr term			**zh** measure	

sucker (definition 2)
The octopus has **suckers** on its tentacles.

S

suf·fix (suf′iks), a letter, syllable, or syllables put at the end of a word to change its meaning or to make another word, as *-ly* in *badly*, *-ness* in *goodness*, and *-ful* in *spoonful*. *noun, plural* **suf·fix·es.**

Word History

suffix *Suffix* comes from a Latin word meaning "to fasten upon."

builder
dreamy
childish
respectable
agreement

---

suf·fo·cate (suf′ə kāt), **1** to kill by stopping the breath: *Thick smoke suffocated several people in the burning building.* **2** to keep from breathing; hinder in breathing: *I was suffocating under too many blankets.* **3** to die for lack of air: *The diver suffocated when his air line became twisted. verb,* **suf·fo·cates, suf·fo·cat·ed, suf·fo·cat·ing.**

suf·frage (suf′rij), the right to vote: *The United States granted suffrage to women in 1920. noun.*

sug·ar (shüg′ər), **1** a sweet substance obtained chiefly from sugar cane or sugar beets and widely used in food products. **2** to put sugar in or on; sweeten with sugar: *Sugar your tea.* **1** *noun,* **2** *verb.*

[*Sugar* can be traced back to a word from an ancient language of India meaning originally "grit." Juice from sugarcane dried in the form of a sandy grit on its stalks.]

sugar beet, a large white beet from which sugar is made.

sugar beet

sug·ar·cane (shüg′ər kān′), a very tall grass with a strong, jointed stem and long, flat leaves, growing in warm regions. Sugarcane is the chief source of sugar. *noun.*

sugar maple, a kind of maple tree. Maple sugar and maple syrup are made from the sweet sap of this tree.

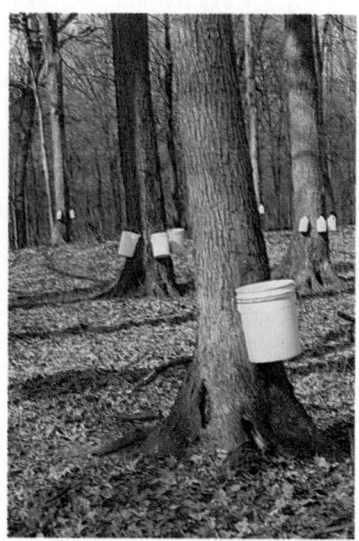
sugar maples
being tapped

sug·gest (səg jest′ *or* sə jest′), **1** to bring to mind; call up the thought of: *The thought of summer suggests swimming, tennis, and hot weather.* **2** to put forward; propose: *She suggested a swim, and we all agreed.* **3** to show in an indirect way; hint: *His yawns suggested that he would like to go to bed. verb.*

sug·ges·tion (səg jes′chən *or* sə jes′chən), **1** the act of suggesting: *The suggestion of a swim made the children jump with joy.* **2** a thing suggested: *The picnic was an excellent suggestion.* **3** a very small amount; slight trace: *She spoke with just a suggestion of a French accent. noun.*

su·i·cide (sü′ə sīd), **1** killing oneself on purpose. **2** a person who kills himself or herself on purpose. *noun.*

commit suicide, to kill oneself on purpose.

suit (süt), **1** a set of clothes to be worn together. A man's suit consists of a coat, pants, and sometimes a vest. A woman's suit consists of a coat and either a skirt or pants. **2** a case in a court of law: *She started a suit to collect the money she was owed.* **3** to be good for; agree with: *A cold climate suits apples and wheat, but not oranges and tea.* **4** to be convenient; please; satisfy: *Which time suits you best? It is hard to suit everybody.* **5** to be becoming to: *That blue sweater suits you.* **6** one of the four sets of cards (spades, hearts, diamonds, and clubs) that make up a deck. **1,2,6** *noun,* **3-5** *verb.*

suit·a·ble (sü′tə bəl), right for the occasion; fitting; proper: *Simple clothes are suitable for school wear. adjective.*

suit·case (süt′kās′), a flat traveling bag. *noun.*

suite (swēt), **1** a set of connected rooms to be used by one person or family: *She has a suite of rooms at the hotel—a living room, bedroom, and bath.* **2** a set of furniture that matches. *noun.*

sui·tor (sü′tər), a man who is courting a woman: *The princess had many suitors. noun.*

sul·fur (sul′fər), a light-yellow substance that is used in making matches and gunpowder. Sulfur is a chemical element. *noun.* Also spelled **sulphur.**

sulk (sulk), to be sulky. *verb.*

sulk·y (sul′kē), **1** silent because of bad humor; sullen: *Some people become sulky when they cannot have their own way.* **2** a light carriage with two wheels, for one person. 1 *adjective,* **sulk·i·er, sulk·i·est;** 2 *noun, plural* **sulk·ies.**

sulky (definition 2)

sul·len (sul′ən), **1** silent because of bad humor or anger: *The sullen child wouldn't even speak to me.* **2** gloomy; dismal: *The sullen skies threatened rain. adjective.*

sul·phur (sul′fər). See **sulfur.** *noun.*

sul·tan (sult′n), the ruler of certain Moslem countries. *noun.*

sul·try (sul′trē), hot, close, and moist: *We expect some sultry weather during July. adjective,* **sul·tri·er, sul·tri·est.**

sum (sum), **1** an amount of money: *We paid a large sum for our new house.* **2** a number arrived at by adding two or more numbers together: *The sum of 2 and 3 and 4 is 9.* **3** the whole amount; total amount: *The sum of scientific knowledge has increased greatly in this century.* **4 sum up,** to express or tell briefly: *Sum up the main points of the lesson in three sentences. The judge summed up the evidence.* 1-3 *noun,* 4 *verb,* **sums, summed, sum·ming.**

su·mac (sü′mak *or* shü′mak), a shrub or small tree which has divided leaves that turn scarlet in the autumn and clusters of red or white fruit. Some sumacs are poisonous to the touch. *noun.*

sum·ma·rize (sum′ə rīz′), to make a summary of; give only the main points of; express briefly: *to summarize the story of a book. verb,* **sum·ma·riz·es, sum·ma·rized, sum·ma·riz·ing.**

sum·mar·y (sum′ər ē), a brief statement giving the main points: *This history book has a summary at the end of each chapter. noun, plural* **sum·mar·ies.**

sum·mer (sum′ər), **1** the warmest season of the year; season of the year between spring and autumn. **2** of or for summer; coming in summer: *summer heat, summer clothes, summer holidays.* 1 *noun,* 2 *adjective.*

sum·mer·time (sum′ər tīm′), the summer season; summer. *noun.*

sum·mit (sum′it), the highest point; top: *the summit of a mountain, to reach the summit of success. noun.*

summit
The **summit** rose above the clouds.

sum·mon (sum′ən), **1** to call with authority; order to come; send for: *I was summoned to the principal's office.* **2** to stir to action; rouse: *We summoned our courage and entered the deserted house. verb.*

sum·mons (sum′ənz), **1** a formal order or notice to appear before a court of law or judge, especially to answer a charge: *I received a summons for speeding.* **2** an urgent call; a summoning command, message, or signal: *I hurried in response to my friend's summons for help. noun, plural* **sum·mons·es.**

sumac

S

sump·tu·ous (sump′chü əs), costly; magnificent; rich: *sumptuous jewels, a sumptuous banquet.* *adjective.*

sun (sun), **1** the brightest object in the sky; the star around which the earth and the other planets revolve, and which supplies them with light and heat. **2** the light and warmth of the sun: *The cat likes to sit in the sun.* **3** to put in the light and warmth of the sun: *The swimmers sunned themselves on the beach.* **4** any heavenly body like the sun; star. 1,2,4 *noun,* 3 *verb,* **suns, sunned, sun·ning.**

Sun., Sunday.

sun·beam (sun′bēm′), a ray of sunlight: *A sunbeam brightened the child's hair to gold. noun.*

sun·bon·net (sun′bon′it), a large bonnet that shades the face and neck. *noun.*

sun·burn (sun′bern′), **1** a burning of the skin by the sun's rays. A sunburn is often red and painful. **2** to burn the skin by the sun's rays: *He is sunburned from a day on the beach.* **3** to become burned by the sun: *Her skin sunburns quickly.* 1 *noun,* 2,3 *verb,* **sun·burns, sun·burned** or **sun·burnt, sun·burn·ing.**

sun·burnt (sun′bernt′), sunburned. See **sunburn.** *verb.*

sun·dae (sun′dē), a dish of ice cream with syrup, crushed fruits, or nuts over it. *noun.*

Sun·day (sun′dē), the first day of the week. *noun.*
[*Sunday* comes from an earlier English word meaning "day of the sun."]

Sunday school, 1 a school held on Sunday for teaching religion. **2** its members.

sun·di·al (sun′dī′əl), an instrument for telling the time of day by the position of a shadow cast by the sun. The sun strikes an upright pointer, casting a shadow onto a dial indicating the hours. *noun.*

sundial—This picture was taken at one o'clock.

sun·down (sun′doun′), sunset: *We'll be home by sundown. noun.*

sun·fish (sun′fish′), a small, freshwater fish of North America, used for food. *noun, plural* **sun·fish** or **sun·fish·es.**

sun·flow·er (sun′flou′ər), a large yellow flower with a brown center, that grows on a very tall

sunflowers

plant. Sunflower seeds are used as food and to produce oil for cooking. *noun.*

sung (sung). See **sing.** *Many songs were sung at the concert. verb.*

sun·glass·es (sun′glas′iz), eyeglasses to protect the eyes from the glare of the sun. They are made of colored glass or plastic. *noun plural.*

sunk (sungk). See **sink.** *The ship had sunk to the bottom. verb.*

sunk·en (sung′kən), **1** that has sunk: *a sunken ship.* **2** submerged; underwater: *a sunken rock.* **3** lower than the surrounding level: *We walked down three steps to the sunken garden.* **4** fallen in; hollow: *After the long illness the patient's cheeks were sunken. adjective.*

sun·light (sun′līt′), the light of the sun: *We hung the wash out to dry in the sunlight. noun.*

sun·lit (sun′lit′), lighted by the sun. *adjective.*

sun·ny (sun′ē), **1** having much sunshine or sunlight: *a sunny day.* **2** bright; cheerful; happy: *The baby gave a sunny smile. adjective,* **sun·ni·er, sun·ni·est.**

sun·rise (sun′rīz′), the first appearance of the sun at the beginning of day. *noun.*

sun·set (sun′set′), the last appearance of the sun at the end of day. *noun.*

sun·shine (sun′shīn′), the light of the sun. *noun.*

sun·spot (sun′spot′), one of the dark spots that appear from time to time on the surface of the sun. Sunspots cannot be seen without special equipment. *noun.*

sun·stroke (sun′strōk′), a sudden illness with fever and dry skin that is caused by too much heat from the sun. *noun.*

sun·tan (sun′tan′), the brown color of a person's skin caused by being in the sun. *noun.*

sun·up (sun′up′), sunrise. *noun.*

su·per (sü′pər), **1** excellent: *We thought the movie was super and stayed to see it again.* **2** special; more than normal: *super powers, super heroes. adjective.*

su·perb (sù pėrb′), very fine; first-rate; excellent: *The singer gave a superb performance. adjective.*

su·per·fi·cial (sü′pər fish′əl), **1** on the surface; at the surface: *His burns were superficial and soon healed.* **2** not thorough; shallow: *Girls used to receive only a superficial education. adjective.*

su·per·high·way (sü′pər hī′wā), a highway for fast traveling. *noun.*

su·per·in·tend (sü′pər in tend′), to oversee and direct work or workers; manage a place or institution. *verb.*

su·per·in·tend·ent (sü′pər in ten′dənt), a person who oversees, directs, or manages; supervisor: *a superintendent of schools, a superintendent of a factory. noun.*

su·per·i·or (sə pir′ē ər), **1** above the average; very good; excellent: *superior work in school.* **2** higher in quality; better; greater: *We lost the game to a superior team.* **3** higher in position, rank, or importance: *a superior officer.* **4** a person who is superior in rank, position, or ability: *As a violin player, he has no superior. A captain is a lieutenant's superior.* **5** showing a feeling of being above others; proud: *Her superior attitude caused her to be disliked.* **1-3,5** *adjective,* **4** *noun.*

superior to, 1 higher than; above: *Apes are considered superior to most other animals in intelligence.* **2** better than; greater than: *This restaurant's food is superior to any other.*

Su·per·i·or (sə pir′ē ər), **Lake,** one of the five Great Lakes. *noun.*

su·per·i·or·i·ty (sə pir′ē ôr′ə tē), a superior state or quality: *The tennis team showed its superiority by winning all its matches this year. noun.*

su·per·la·tive (sə pėr′lə tiv), **1** of the highest kind; above all others; supreme: *superlative skills, superlative wisdom.* **2** a form of a word or combination of words to show the extreme degree or greatest amount. *Fastest* is the superlative of *fast. Best* is the superlative of *good. Most quickly* is the superlative of *quickly.* **1** *adjective,* **2** *noun.*

su·per·man (sü′pər man′), a person having more than human powers. *noun, plural* **su·per·men.**

su·per·mar·ket (sü′pər mär′kit), a large store for groceries and household articles in which customers select items from open shelves and pay for them just before leaving. *noun.*

su·per·nat·ur·al (sü′pər nach′ər əl), above or beyond the forces or laws of nature; having to do with God, angels, ghosts, or the like: *The movie was about ghosts, demons, and other supernatural beings. adjective.*

su·per·son·ic (sü′pər son′ik), **1** faster than the speed of sound in air: *supersonic travel.* **2** able to move at a speed greater than the speed of sound: *a supersonic jet. adjective.*

su·per·sti·tion (sü′pər stish′ən), a belief or practice that is based on fear or hope, not on reason or fact: *A common superstition is the belief that 13 is an unlucky number. noun.*

su·per·sti·tious (sü′pər stish′əs), full of

a hat	**i** it	**oi** oil	**ch** child	[a in about
ā age	**ī** ice	**ou** out	**ng** long	e in taken
ä far	**o** hot	**u** cup	**sh** she	ə = { i in pencil
e let	**ō** open	**ù** put	**th** thin	o in lemon
ē equal	**ô** order	**ü** rule	**ŦH** then	[u in circus
ėr term			**zh** measure	

superstitions; likely to believe superstitions; caused by superstitions: *a superstitious habit, a superstitious belief. adjective.*

su·per·vise (sü′pər vīz), to look after and direct work, workers, or a process; oversee; manage: *Morning recess is supervised by teachers. verb,* **su·per·vis·es, su·per·vised, su·per·vis·ing.**

su·per·vi·sion (sü′pər vīzh′ən), management; direction: *The house was built under the careful supervision of an architect. noun.*

su·per·vi·sor (sü′pər vī′zər), a person who supervises: *The music supervisor has charge of the school band, chorus, and orchestra. noun.*

sup·per (sup′ər), the evening meal; meal eaten early in the evening if dinner is near noon, or late in the evening if dinner is at six or later. *noun.* [*Supper* comes from an older French word meaning "soup." When the main meal of the day is eaten earlier, and called dinner, supper is often a light meal including soup.]

sup·per·time (sup′ər tīm′), the time at which supper is served. *noun.*

sup·plant (sə plant′), **1** to take the place of: *Machinery has supplanted hand labor in making shoes.* **2** to take the place of by unfair methods: *The queen's cousin plotted to supplant her. verb.*

sup·ple (sup′əl), **1** bending easily: *a supple birch tree, supple leather, a supple dancer.* **2** readily adapting to different ideas, circumstances, or people: *The children's supple natures will enable them to make friends quickly in their new neighborhood. adjective,* **sup·pler, sup·plest.**

supple
(definition 1)

S

sup·ple·ment (sup′lə mənt *for 1;* sup′lə ment *for 2*), **1** something added to complete a thing, or to make it larger or better: *We get a supplement to our encyclopedia every year.* **2** to add to; complete: *I supplement my diet with vitamin pills.* 1 *noun,* 2 *verb.*

sup·ply (sə plī′), **1** to furnish; provide: *The school supplies books for the children.* **2** a quantity ready for use; stock; store: *We have a large supply of vegetables in the freezer.* **3 supplies,** the food and equipment necessary for an army, expedition, or the like. 1 *verb,* **sup·plies, sup·plied, sup·ply·ing;** 2,3 *noun, plural* **sup·plies.**

sup·port (sə pôrt′), **1** to keep from falling; hold up: *Walls support the roof.* **2** to provide for: *Parents usually support their children.* **3** to be in favor of; back: *She supports the proposed law.* **4** to help prove; bear out: *The facts support his claim.* **5** help; aid: *He needs the support of a scholarship.* **6** a person or thing that holds something up; prop: *The neck is the support of the head.* 1-4 *verb,* 5,6 *noun.*

sup·pose (sə pōz′), **1** to consider as possible: *Suppose we are late, what will the teacher say?* **2** to believe; think; imagine: *I suppose she will come as usual.* **3** to expect; require: *I'm supposed to go home right after school. verb,* **sup·pos·es, sup·posed, sup·pos·ing.**

sup·posed (sə pōzd′), considered as possible or probable; accepted as true: *The supposed beggar was really a prince. adjective.*

sup·pos·ing (sə pō′zing), if: *Supposing it rains, shall we go? conjunction.*

sup·press (sə pres′), **1** to put an end to; put down; stop by force: *to suppress a riot.* **2** to keep in; hold back; keep from appearing: *She suppressed a yawn. verb.*

sup·pres·sion (sə presh′ən), **1** a putting down by force or authority; putting an end to: *Troops were used in the suppression of the revolt.* **2** a keeping in; holding back: *The suppression of facts may be as dishonest as the telling of lies. noun.*

su·preme (sə prēm′), **1** highest in rank or authority: *a supreme ruler.* **2** highest in degree; greatest; utmost; extreme: *With supreme effort, we moved the piano. adjective.*

Supreme Being, God.

Supreme Court, the highest court in the United States, which meets at Washington, D.C. It consists of a chief justice and eight associate justices.

sure (shur), **1** free from doubt; certain: *Are you sure you locked the door? Make sure you have the key.* **2** to be trusted; safe; reliable: *The only sure way of sending a message during the storm was by radio.* **3** firm: *stand on sure ground.* **4** certain to come, to be, or to happen: *It is sure to snow this winter.* **5** surely. 1-4 *adjective,* **sur·er, sur·est;** 5 *adverb.*

sure-foot·ed (shur′fut′id), not liable to stumble, slip, or fall. *adjective.*

sure·ly (shur′lē), certainly; of course: *Surely you must come again. adverb.*

surf (serf), the waves of the sea breaking on the shore. *noun.*

sur·face (ser′fis), **1** the outside of anything: *the surface of a golf ball. An egg has a smooth surface.* **2** the top of the ground or soil, or of a body of water or other liquid: *The stone sank beneath the surface of the water.* **3** the outward appearance: *She seems rough, but you will find her very kind below the surface.* **4** to put a top layer on; make smooth: *The town must surface this road.* **5** to rise to the top of water: *The submarine surfaced.* 1-3 *noun,* 4,5 *verb,* **sur·fac·es, sur·faced, sur·fac·ing.**

surf·board (serf′bôrd′), a long, narrow board for riding the surf. *noun.*

surf·ing (ser′fing), the act or sport of riding the surf on a surfboard. *noun.*

surfing

sure-footed
Mules need to be **sure-footed** on the canyon trail.

surge (sėrj), **1** to rise and fall; move like waves: *A wave surged over us. The crowd surged through the streets.* **2** a swelling motion; a sweep or rush, especially of waves: *Our boat was upset by a surge of water.* **3** something like a wave: *a surge of anger.* **1** *verb,* **surg·es, surged, surg·ing; 2,3** *noun.*

sur·geon (sėr′jən), a doctor who performs operations: *A surgeon removed my tonsils. noun.*

sur·ger·y (sėr′jər ē), the art and science of treating diseases or injuries by operations and instruments: *Flu can be treated with medicine, but a ruptured appendix requires surgery. noun.*

sur·gi·cal (sėr′jə kəl), **1** of surgery: *a surgical patient.* **2** used in surgery: *surgical instruments. adjective.*

Sur·i·nam (sur′ə nam), a country in northern South America. *noun.*

sur·ly (sėr′lē), bad-tempered and unfriendly; rude; gruff: *They got a surly answer from their grouchy neighbor. adjective,* **sur·li·er, sur·li·est.**

sur·mise (sər mīz′), **1** to guess: *We surmised that the delay was caused by some accident.* **2** a guessing: *His guilt was a matter of surmise; there was no proof.* **1** *verb,* **sur·mis·es, sur·mised, sur·mis·ing; 2** *noun.*

sur·name (sėr′nām′), a last name; family name: *Stein is the surname of Judith Stein. noun.*

sur·pass (sər pas′), to do better than; be greater than; excel: *She surpasses her sister in arithmetic. verb.*

sur·plus (sėr′pləs), **1** an amount over and above what is needed; extra quantity left over; excess: *The bank keeps a large surplus of money in reserve.* **2** more than is needed; extra; excess: *Surplus wheat is put in storage or shipped abroad.* **1** *noun,* *plural* **sur·plus·es; 2** *adjective.*

sur·prise (sər prīz′), **1** the feeling caused by something that happens suddenly or unexpectedly; astonishment; wonder: *His face showed surprise at the news.* **2** to cause to feel surprise; astonish: *The victory surprised us.* **3** something unexpected: *Our grandparents always have a surprise for us when we visit them.* **4** surprising; not expected; coming suddenly and without warning: *a surprise party, a surprise visit.* **5** to catch unprepared; come upon suddenly: *The enemy surprised the fort during the night.* **6** the act of coming upon suddenly; catching unprepared: *The fort was captured by surprise.* **1,3,6** *noun,* **2,5** *verb,* **sur·pris·es, sur·prised, sur·pris·ing; 4** *adjective.*

sur·pris·ing (sər prī′zing), causing surprise or wonder: *a surprising recovery. adjective.*

sur·ren·der (sə ren′dər), **1** to give up; yield: *The captain had to surrender to the enemy. As the storm got worse, we surrendered all hope of going camping.* **2** the act of surrendering: *The surrender of the fort came at dawn.* **1** *verb,* **2** *noun.*

sur·round (sə round′), to shut in on all sides; extend around; enclose: *A high fence surrounds the field. verb.*

sur·round·ings (sə roun′dingz), surrounding

a hat	i it	oi oil	ch child	⌠a in about
ā age	ī ice	ou out	ng long	⎪e in taken
ä far	o hot	u cup	sh she	ə = ⎨i in pencil
e let	ō open	u̇ put	th thin	⎪o in lemon
ē equal	ô order	ü rule	␪H then	⌡u in circus
ėr term			zh measure	

things or conditions: *We enjoyed the peaceful surroundings at the cabin in the mountains. noun plural.*

sur·veil·lance (sər vā′ləns), a watch kept over a person: *The police kept the criminal under surveillance. noun.*

sur·vey (sər vā′ for 1 and 4; sėr′vā for 2, 3, and 5), **1** to look over; view; examine: *The buyers surveyed the goods offered for sale.* **2** a general look; view; examination; inspection: *We were pleased with our first survey of the house.* **3** a formal or official study, poll, or inspection: *The school board made a survey of public opinion about the new textbooks.* **4** to measure for size, shape, position, or boundaries: *The land is being surveyed before it is divided into house lots.* **5** a careful measurement: *A survey showed that the northern boundary was not correct.* **1,4** *verb,* **2,3,5** *noun, plural* **sur·veys.**

sur·vey·or (sər vā′ər), a person who surveys land. *noun.*

sur·viv·al (sər vī′vəl), **1** the act or fact of surviving; continuance of life; living or lasting longer than others. **2** a person, thing, custom, or belief that has lasted from an earlier time: *Many superstitions are survivals of ancient times. noun.*

sur·vive (sər vīv′), **1** to live longer than: *He survived his wife by three years.* **2** to remain alive after: *The crops survived the dry weather.* **3** to continue to live or exist; remain: *These cave paintings have survived for over 15,000 years. verb,* **sur·vives, sur·vived, sur·viv·ing.**

sur·vi·vor (sər vī′vər), a person or other living thing that survives; thing that continues to exist: *There were two survivors from the plane crash. noun.*

sus·cep·ti·ble (sə sep′tə bəl), easily influenced by feelings or emotions; very sensitive: *Poetry appealed to his susceptible nature. adjective.*
susceptible of, capable of receiving, undergoing, or being affected by: *Her plan is susceptible of a great deal of improvement.*
susceptible to, easily affected by; liable to; open to: *Young children are susceptible to many diseases. Vain people are susceptible to flattery.*

sus·pect (sə spekt′ for 1-3; sus′pekt for 4), **1** to imagine to be so; think likely; suppose: *I suspect that they have been delayed.* **2** to believe to be guilty, false, or bad without proof: *The police suspected them of being thieves.* **3** to feel no confidence in; doubt: *Her guilty look made me suspect the truth of her excuse.* **4** a person believed to be guilty: *The police have arrested two suspects in connection with the bank robbery.* **1-3** *verb,* **4** *noun.*

S

sus·pend (sə spend′), **1** to hang by fastening to something above: *The lamp was suspended from the ceiling.* **2** to hold in place as if by hanging: *We saw the smoke suspended in the still air.* **3** to stop for a while: *We suspended building operations during the winter.* **4** to keep or prevent someone from attending school, being on a team, doing a job, or the like, for a short time: *They were suspended from school for a week for bad conduct.* **5** to cancel temporarily: *The judge suspended her driver's license.* verb.

Word History

suspend *Suspend* comes from a Latin word meaning "to hang up." Other English words from the same root include *suspenders, suspense,* and *suspension.*

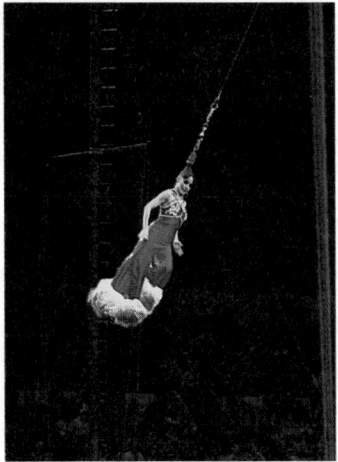

suspend (definition 1)
It must hurt
to be **suspended**
by your hair.

sus·pend·ers (sə spen′dərz), straps worn over the shoulders to hold up the trousers. *noun plural.*

sus·pense (sə spens′), **1** the condition of being uncertain: *The detective story kept me in suspense until the last chapter.* **2** anxious uncertainty; anxiety: *The class waited in suspense while the teacher graded the tests.* noun.

sus·pen·sion (sə spen′shən), a suspending or being suspended: *the suspension of a driver's license for speeding.* noun.

suspension bridge, a bridge hung on cables or chains between towers.

sus·pi·cion (sə spish′ən), **1** the state of mind of a person who suspects; suspecting: *The real thief tried to turn suspicion toward others.* **2** the condition of being suspected. **3** a belief, feeling, or thought: *I have a suspicion that the weather will be very hot today.* noun.

above suspicion, not to be suspected: *My friend is honest and, therefore, above suspicion.*

on suspicion, because of being suspected: *They were arrested on suspicion of robbery.*

under suspicion, suspected.

sus·pi·cious (sə spish′əs), **1** causing one to

suspect: *Someone suspicious was hanging around the house.* **2** feeling suspicion; suspecting: *Our dog is suspicious of strangers.* **3** showing suspicion: *The dog gave suspicious sniffs at my leg.* adjective.

sus·tain (sə stān′), **1** to keep up; keep going: *His cheerfulness sustained us through our troubles.* **2** to suffer; experience: *She sustained a great loss in the death of her husband.* verb.

SW or **S.W., 1** southwest. **2** southwestern.

swag·ger (swag′ər), to walk with a bold, rude, or superior air; strut about or show off in a conceited or bragging way: *The villain in the play swaggered onto the stage.* verb.

swal·low[1] (swol′ō), **1** to take into the stomach through the throat: *We swallow all our food and drink.* **2** to take in; absorb: *The waves swallowed up the swimmer.* **3** to believe too easily; accept without question or suspicion: *No one will swallow that ridiculous story.* **4** to keep back; keep from expressing: *She swallowed her displeasure and smiled.* **5** a swallowing: *I took the bitter medicine at one swallow.* **6** an amount swallowed at one time: *There are only about four swallows of water left in the bottle.* **1-4** verb, **5,6** noun.

swal·low[2] (swol′ō), a small bird that has long, pointed wings and can fly very fast. Some kinds have deeply forked tails. noun.

swallows[2]—about 7 inches (18 centimeters) long

swam (swam). See **swim.** *We swam all afternoon.* verb.

swamp (swomp), **1** wet, soft land: *We will drain the swamp on our farm so that we can plant crops there.* **2** to fill with water and sink: *The waves swamped the boat.* **3** to overwhelm as by a flood; make helpless: *to be swamped with homework.* **1** noun, **2,3** verb.

suspension bridge

swamp·y (swom′pē), **1** like a swamp; soft and wet: *The front yard is swampy from the heavy rain.* **2** containing swamps: *a swampy region.* *adjective,* **swamp·i·er, swamp·i·est.**

swan (swon), a large, graceful water bird with a long, slender, curving neck. The adult is usually pure white. *noun.*

swap (swop), to trade: *The children swapped toys.* *verb,* **swaps, swapped, swap·ping.**

swarm (swôrm), **1** a group of bees that leave a hive and fly off together to start a new colony. **2** to fly off together in this way to start a new colony of bees. **3** a large group of insects, animals, or people moving about together: *Swarms of children played in the park.* **4** to fly or move about in great numbers; be in very great numbers: *The mosquitoes swarmed about us.* **5** to be crowded: *The lobby of the theater swarmed with people during intermission.* **1,3** *noun,* **2,4,5** *verb.*

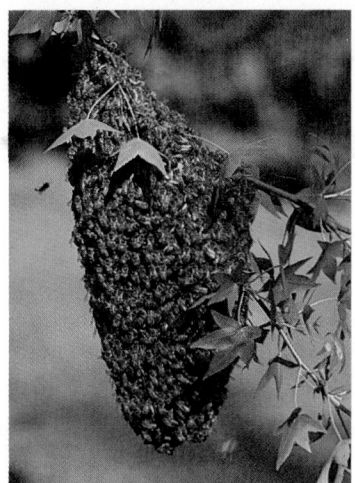

swarm
(definition 1)

swat (swot), to hit sharply or violently: *to swat a fly. verb,* **swats, swat·ted, swat·ting.**

sway (swā), **1** to swing or cause to swing back and forth; swing from side to side, or to one side: *The dancers swayed to the music.* **2** a swinging back and forth or from side to side: *The sway of the pail caused some milk to spill out.* **3** to change in opinion or feeling: *Nothing could sway him after he had made up his mind.* **4** to influence; control; rule: *The speaker's words swayed the audience.* **5** an influence, control, or rule: *a country under the sway of a dictator.* **1,3,4** *verb,* **2,5** *noun.*

swear (swer *or* swar), **1** to make a solemn statement, appealing to God or some other sacred being or object: *A witness at a trial is asked, "Do you swear to tell the truth, the whole truth, and nothing but the truth, so help you God?"* **2** to promise; vow: *The governor swore to uphold the constitution. I swear I will tell no one.* **3** to bind by an oath; require to promise: *Members of the club were sworn to secrecy.* **4** to use profane language; curse: *The pirates raged and swore when they were captured. verb,* **swears, swore, sworn, swear·ing.**

a hat	i it	oi oil	ch child	⎧ a in about
ā age	ī ice	ou out	ng long	⎪ e in taken
ä far	o hot	u cup	sh she	ə = ⎨ i in pencil
e let	ō open	u̇ put	th thin	⎪ o in lemon
ē equal	ô order	ü rule	ŦH then	⎩ u in circus
ėr term			zh measure	

sweat (swet), **1** moisture coming through the pores of the skin: *After mowing the lawn she wiped the sweat from her face.* **2** to give out moisture through the pores of the skin: *We sweated because it was very hot.* **3** a fit or condition of sweating: *I was in a cold sweat from fear.* **4** moisture given out by something or gathered on its surface. **5** to give out moisture; collect moisture from the air: *A pitcher of ice water sweats on a hot day.* **1,3,4** *noun,* **2,5** *verb,* **sweats, sweat·ed** or **sweat, sweat·ing.**

sweat·er (swet′ər), a knitted article of clothing made of wool, cotton, nylon, or the like, worn on the upper part of the body. *noun.*

sweat shirt, a heavy shirt with long sleeves, worn especially to keep warm before and after exercise.

sweat·y (swet′ē), covered or wet with sweat: *After moving the boxes we were all sweaty.* *adjective,* **sweat·i·er, sweat·i·est.**

Swe·den (swēd′n), a country in northern Europe. *noun.*

sweep (swēp), **1** to clean or clear a floor, deck, or the like with a broom or brush; use a broom or something like one to remove dirt: *The campers swept the floor of their cabin every morning.* **2** to move, drive, or take away with a broom or as with a broom or brush: *They swept the dust into a pan. The wind sweeps the snow into drifts.* **3** to remove with a sweeping motion; carry along: *A flood swept away the bridge.* **4** an act of sweeping: *I need to give the room a good sweep.* **5** to pass over with a steady movement: *Her fingers swept the strings of the harp. His eyes swept the crowd, looking for his friend.* **6** to move swiftly; pass swiftly: *The hawk swept down on the mouse. The wind sweeps over the valley.* **7** a steady, driving motion or swift onward course of something: *the sweep of the wind across the prairie.* **8** to move or extend in a long course or curve: *The shore sweeps to the south for miles.* **9** a swinging or curving motion: *He cut the grass with strong sweeps of his scythe.* **10** a continuous extent; stretch: *The house looks upon a wide sweep of farming country.* **11** a person who sweeps chimneys or streets. **1-3,5,6,8** *verb,* **sweeps, swept, sweep·ing;** **4,7,9-11** *noun.*

sweep·er (swē′pər), a person or thing that sweeps: *a carpet sweeper. noun.*

sweep·ing (swē′ping), **1** passing over a wide space: *Her sweeping glance took in the whole room.* **2** having wide range: *a sweeping victory, a sweeping statement. adjective.*

sweep·ings (swē′pingz), dust or scraps swept out or up. *noun plural.*

S

sweep·stakes (swēp′stāks′), a system of gambling on horse races or other contests. People buy tickets, and the money they pay goes to the holder or holders of winning tickets. *noun.*

sweet (swēt), **1** having a taste like sugar or honey: *Pears are much sweeter than lemons.* **2** having a pleasant taste or smell: *Perfume is sweet.* **3** pleasant; agreeable: *a sweet child, a sweet smile, sweet music.* **4** fresh; not sour, salty, bitter, or spoiled: *sweet cream.* **5 sweets,** candy or other sweet things. **6** in a sweet manner. 1-4 *adjective,* 5 *noun,* 6 *adverb.*

sweet corn, a kind of corn eaten by people when it is young and tender.

sweet·en (swēt′n), to make or become sweet: *He sweetened his coffee with sugar. verb.*

sweet·en·er (swēt′n ər), a substance that sweetens something: *Do you prefer sugar or an artificial sweetener? noun.*

sweet·en·ing (swēt′n ing), something that sweetens. Sugar is a sweetening. *noun.*

sweet·heart (swēt′härt′), a loved one; lover. *noun.*

sweet pea, a climbing plant with delicate, fragrant flowers of various colors.

sweet potato, the sweet, thick, yellow or reddish root of a vine grown in warm regions. Sweet potatoes are used as a vegetable or in pies.

sweet tooth, a fondness for sweets.

swell (swel), **1** to grow bigger; make bigger: *Bread dough swells as it rises. The bee sting had swelled his finger.* **2** to be larger or thicker in a particular place; stick out: *A barrel swells in the middle.* **3** to increase in amount, degree, or force: *Investments may swell into a fortune.* **4** the act of swelling; increase in amount, degree, or force. **5** a long, unbroken wave or waves: *The boat rocked in the swell.* **6** to grow louder; make louder: *The sound swelled to a roar. All joined in to swell the chorus.* **7** stylish; grand. **8** excellent; very satisfactory. 1-3,6 *verb,* **swells, swelled, swelled** or **swol·len, swell·ing;** 4,5 *noun,* 7,8 *adjective.*

swell·ing (swel′ing), an increase in size; swollen part: *There is a swelling on her head where she bumped it. noun.*

swel·ter (swel′tər), to suffer from heat. *verb.*

swept (swept). See **sweep.** *He swept the room. It was swept clean. verb.*

swept-back (swept′bak′), extending outward and sharply backward. Most fast airplanes have swept-back wings. *adjective.*

swept-back—an airplane with **swept-back** wings

swerve (swėrv), **1** to turn aside: *The car swerved sharply to avoid hitting the truck.* **2** a turning aside: *The swerve of the ball made it hard to hit.* 1 *verb,* **swerves, swerved, swerv·ing;** 2 *noun.*

swift (swift), **1** moving very fast; able to move very fast: *a swift automobile.* **2** coming or happening quickly: *a swift answer.* **3** quick, rapid, or prompt to act: *He is swift to repay a kindness.* **4** in a swift manner. **5** a small bird with long wings. A swift looks somewhat like a swallow. 1-3 *adjective,* 4 *adverb,* 5 *noun.*

swift (definition 5) about 5 inches (13 centimeters) long

swim (swim), **1** to move along on or in the water by using arms, legs, or fins: *Fish swim. Most girls and boys like to swim.* **2** to swim across: *He swam the river.* **3** to float: *The roast lamb was swimming in gravy.* **4** to be overflowed or flooded with: *His eyes were swimming with tears.* **5** an act, time, motion, or distance of swimming: *Her swim had tired her. She had had an hour's swim.* **6 the swim,** activities; what is going on: *An active and sociable person likes to be in the swim.* **7** to go smoothly; glide: *Clouds swam across the sky.* **8** to be dizzy; whirl: *The heat and noise made my head swim.* 1-4,7,8 *verb,* **swims, swam, swum, swim·ming;** 5,6 *noun.*

swim·mer (swim′ər), a person or animal that swims. *noun.*

swim·suit (swim′süt′), a bathing suit. *noun.*

swin·dle (swin′dl), **1** to cheat; defraud: *Honest storekeepers do not swindle their customers.* **2** a cheating act; fraud. 1 *verb,* **swin·dles, swin·dled, swin·dling;** 2 *noun.*

swin·dler (swin′dlər), a person who cheats or defrauds. *noun.*

swine (swīn), a hog or pig. *noun, plural* **swine.**

swing (swing), **1** to move back and forth, especially with a regular motion: *We swing our arms as we walk.* **2** to move or cause to move in a curve: *to swing a bat, to swing a golf club.* **3** the act or manner of swinging: *With a mighty swing, the batter hit a home run.* **4** a seat hung from ropes or chains in which one may sit and swing. **5** to hang: *We swung the hammock between two trees.* **6** to move with a free, swaying motion: *The children came swinging down the street.* **7** movement; activity: *It's hard to get into the swing of school after vacation.* **8** a marked, swinging rhythm: *The* song "Dixie" has a swing. 1,2,5,6 *verb*, **swings, swung, swing·ing;** 3,4,7,8 *noun*.

in full swing, going on actively and completely: *By five o'clock the party was in full swing.*

swipe (swīp), **1** a sweeping stroke: *I made two swipes at the golf ball without hitting it.* **2** to strike with a sweeping blow: *He swiped at the mosquito, but missed it.* **3** to steal: *Someone swiped her bike.* 1 *noun,* 2,3 *verb,* **swipes, swiped, swip·ing.**

swirl (swėrl), **1** to move or drive along with a twisting motion; whirl: *dust swirling in the air, a stream swirling over rocks.* **2** a swirling movement; whirl; eddy. **3** a twist or curl: *There was a swirl of whipped cream on top of the sundae.* 1 *verb,* 2,3 *noun.*

swish (swish), **1** to move or cause to move with a thin, light, hissing or brushing sound: *The whip swished through the air. The child swished the stick.* **2** to make such a sound: *The long gown swished as she danced across the floor.* **3** a swishing movement or sound: *the swish of little waves on the shore.* 1,2 *verb,* 3 *noun, plural* **swish·es.**

Swiss (swis), **1** of or having to do with Switzerland or its people: *the Swiss lakes.* **2** a person born or living in Switzerland. **3** the people of Switzerland. 1 *adjective,* 2 *noun singular,* 3 *noun plural.*

switch (swich), **1** a slender stick used in whipping. **2** to whip; strike: *I switched the horse to make it gallop.* **3** a stroke; lash: *The big dog knocked a vase off the table with a switch of its tail.* **4** to move or swing like a switch: *The horse switched its tail to drive off the flies.* **5** a device for making or breaking a connection in an electric circuit. **6** a pair of movable rails by which a train is shifted from one track to another. **7** to shift by using a switch: *to switch railroad cars from one track to another.* **8** to turn on or turn off by using a switch: *Switch off the light.* **9** to change or shift: *to switch places. They switched hats.* **10** a change; turn; shift: *a last-minute switch in plans.* 1,3,5,6,10 *noun, plural* **switch·es;** 2,4,7-9 *verb.*

switch·board (swich′bôrd′), a panel with electric switches and plugs for connecting telephone lines. *noun.*

Swit·zer·land (swit′sər lənd), a country in central Europe. *noun.*

swiv·el (swiv′əl), **1** a fastening that allows the thing fastened to turn around freely. **2** to turn on a fastening like this. 1 *noun,* 2 *verb,* **swiv·els, swiv·eled, swiv·el·ing.**

swivel (definition 1)

swol·len (swō′lən), **1** swelled: *a swollen ankle.* **2** See **swell.** *Her ankle has swollen considerably since she fell.* 1 *adjective,* 2 *verb.*

swoon (swün), to faint: *He swoons at the sight of blood. verb.*

a hat	**i** it	**oi** oil	**ch** child	a in about
ā age	**ī** ice	**ou** out	**ng** long	e in taken
ä far	**o** hot	**u** cup	**sh** she	ə = i in pencil
e let	**ō** open	**u̇** put	**th** thin	o in lemon
ē equal	**ô** order	**ü** rule	**ŦH** then	u in circus
ėr term			**zh** measure	

swoop (swüp), **1** to come down with a rush, as a hawk does; sweep rapidly down upon in a sudden attack: *Bats swooped down from the roof of the cave.* **2** a rapid downward sweep; sudden, swift descent or attack: *With one swoop the hawk seized the chicken and flew away.* **3** to snatch: *The nurse swooped up the running child.* 1,3 *verb,* 2 *noun.*

sword (sôrd), a weapon, usually metal, with a long, sharp blade fixed in a handle or hilt. *noun.*

sword·fish (sôrd′fish′), a very large sea fish that has a swordlike bone sticking out from its upper jaw. *noun, plural* **sword·fish** or **sword·fish·es.**

swordfish—up to 15 feet (4½ meters) long

swords·man (sôrdz′mən), **1** a person skilled in using a sword. **2** a person using a sword. *noun, plural* **swords·men.**

swore (swôr). See **swear.** *I swore to keep my friend's secret. verb.*

sworn (swôrn), **1** See **swear.** *A solemn oath of loyalty was sworn by all the knights.* **2** declared or promised with an oath: *We have her sworn statement before us.* 1 *verb,* 2 *adjective.*

swum (swum). See **swim.** *I have never swum before. verb.*

swung (swung). See **swing.** *He swung his arms as he walked. The door had swung open. verb.*

syc·a·more (sik′ə môr), a kind of shade tree with large leaves and light-colored bark that peels off in tiny scales. *noun.*

syl·lab·ic (sə lab′ik), **1** of, having to do with, or made up of syllables. **2** forming a separate syllable by itself. The second *l* sound in *little* (lit′l) is syllabic. *adjective.*

syl·lab·i·cate (sə lab′ə kāt), to divide into syllables. *verb,* **syl·lab·i·cates, syl·lab·i·cat·ed, syl·lab·i·cat·ing.**

syl·lab·i·ca·tion (sə lab′ə kā′shən), division into syllables. *noun.*

syl·la·ble (sil′ə bəl), **1** a word or part of a word pronounced as a unit. A syllable is usually made up of a vowel alone or a vowel with one or more consonants. There are three syllables (sil, ə, and

S

bəl) in the pronunciation of the word *syllable.* Certain consonant sounds may be used as a vowel sound in syllables, such as the (l) in *bottle* (bot′l) or the (n) in *hidden* (hid′n). **2** a letter or group of letters representing a syllable in writing and printing. *Strength* has only one syllable; *ap prox i mate* has four syllables. *noun.*

sym·bol (sim′bəl), something that stands for or represents something else: *The lion is the symbol of courage; the lamb, of meekness; the olive branch, of peace; the cross, of Christianity. The marks +, −, ×, and ÷ are symbols for add, subtract, multiply, and divide. noun.*

sym·bol·ic (sim bol′ik), expressed by a symbol or symbols; using symbols: *Writing is a symbolic form of expression. adjective.*

sym·bol·ize (sim′bə līz), **1** to be a symbol of; stand for; represent: *A dove symbolizes peace.* **2** to represent by a symbol or symbols: *The Indians and the settlers symbolized their friendship by smoking the peace pipe. verb,* **sym·bol·iz·es, sym·bol·ized, sym·bol·iz·ing.**

sym·met·ric (si met′rik), having a balanced form or arrangement: *symmetric patterns. adjective.*

sym·met·ri·cal (si met′rə kəl), having a balanced form or arrangement: *symmetrical figures. adjective.*

sym·me·try (sim′ə trē), **1** a regular, balanced form or arrangement on opposite sides of a line or around a center. **2** a well-balanced arrangement of parts; harmony: *A swollen cheek spoiled the symmetry of his face. noun.*

symmetry (definition 1)—two kinds of **symmetry**

sym·pa·thet·ic (sim′pə thet′ik), **1** having or showing kind feelings toward others; sympathizing: *She is an unselfish and sympathetic friend.* **2** approving; agreeing: *The teacher was sympathetic to the class's plan for a trip to the museum. adjective.*

sym·pa·thet·i·cal·ly (sim′pə thet′ik lē), in a sympathetic way; with kindness: *The doctor spoke sympathetically while bandaging my injured leg. adverb.*

sym·pa·thize (sim′pə thīz), **1** to feel or show sympathy: *The boy sympathized with his little sister who had hurt herself.* **2** to share in or agree with a feeling or opinion: *Her parents sympathize with her plans to be a painter. verb,* **sym·pa·thiz·es, sym·pa·thized, sym·pa·thiz·ing.**

sym·pa·thy (sim′pə thē), **1** a sharing another's sorrow or trouble: *We feel sympathy for a person who is ill.* **2** having the same feeling: *The sympathy between the twins was so great that they always smiled or cried at the same things.* **3** agreement; favor: *I am in sympathy with your plan. noun, plural* **sym·pa·thies.**

sym·pho·ny (sim′fə nē), **1** an elaborate musical composition for an orchestra. **2** a large orchestra that plays symphonies, made up of brass, woodwind, percussion, and stringed instruments. **3** a harmony of colors: *In autumn the woods are a symphony in red, brown, and yellow. noun, plural* **sym·pho·nies.**

symp·tom (simp′təm), a sign; indication: *Fever is a symptom of illness. noun.*

syn·a·gogue (sin′ə gôg), a building used by Jews for religious instruction and worship. *noun.*

syn·o·nym (sin′ə nim), a word that means the same or nearly the same as another word. *Keen* is a synonym of *sharp. noun.*

syn·on·y·mous (si non′ə məs), having the same or nearly the same meaning. "Little" and "small" are synonymous. *adjective.*

syn·thet·ic (sin thet′ik), not natural; made by people; made by chemical processes: *synthetic rubber. Nylon is a synthetic fiber. adjective.*

Syr·i·a (sir′ē ə), a country in southwestern Asia. *noun.*

syr·up (sir′əp *or* sėr′əp), a sweet, thick liquid. Sugar boiled with water or fruit juices makes a syrup. A cough syrup contains medicine to relieve coughing. Maple syrup is made from the sap of maple trees. *noun.* Also spelled **sirup.** [*Syrup* comes from an Arabic word meaning "a drink."]

sys·tem (sis′təm), **1** a set of things or parts forming a whole: *a mountain system, a railroad system, the digestive system, the nervous system.* **2** an ordered group of facts, principles, or beliefs: *a system of government, a system of education.* **3** a plan; scheme; method: *She has a system for getting the work done in half the time.* **4** an orderly way of getting things done: *He works by a system, not by chance. noun.*

sys·tem·at·ic (sis′tə mat′ik), **1** according to a system; having a system, method, or plan: *systematic work.* **2** orderly in arranging things or in getting things done: *a very systematic person. adjective.*

sys·tem·at·i·cal·ly (sis′tə mat′ik lē), with system; according to some plan or method. *adverb.*

a hat	i it	oi oil	ch child	⎧ a in about
ā age	ī ice	ou out	ng long	e in taken
ä far	o hot	u cup	sh she	ə = ⎨ i in pencil
e let	ō open	u̇ put	th thin	o in lemon
ē equal	ô order	ü rule	ᵺ then	⎩ u in circus
ėr term			zh measure	

T t

T or **t** (tē), the 20th letter of the English alphabet. *noun, plural* **T's** or **t's.**

T. or **T,** ton or tons.

tab (tab), a small flap. Tabs stick out from caps to cover the ears, from cards used in filing, and from envelopes or cans for opening them. *noun.*

tab·er·nac·le (tab′ər nak′əl), **1** a place of worship for a large group of people. **2 Tabernacle,** the covered, wooden framework used by the Jews as a place of worship during their journey from Egypt to Palestine. *noun.*

ta·ble (tā′bəl), **1** a piece of furniture having a smooth, flat top on legs. **2** the food put on a table to be eaten: *Our hosts set a good table.* **3** the persons seated at a table: *The whole table joined in the conversation.* **4** information in a very brief form; list: *The table of contents is in the front of the book. He is studying the multiplication table. noun.*

at table, having a meal; eating: *We were at table when my brother arrived.*

turn the tables, to reverse conditions or circumstances completely: *They won the first game but we turned the tables on them and won the second.*

ta·ble·cloth (tā′bəl klôth′), a cloth for covering a table: *Spread the tablecloth and set the table for dinner. noun, plural* **ta·ble·cloths** (tā′bəl klôᵺz′ or tā′bəl klôths′).

ta·ble·land (tā′bəl land′), a high plain; plateau. *noun.*

ta·ble·spoon (tā′bəl spün′), **1** a large spoon used to serve food. **2** a unit of measure in cooking equal to 3 teaspoons or one half fluid ounce. *noun.*

ta·ble·spoon·ful (tā′bəl spün′fu̇l), as much as a tablespoon holds. *noun, plural* **ta·ble·spoon·fuls.**

tab·let (tab′lit), **1** a thin, flat sheet of stone, wood, ivory, or other material, used to write or draw on. The ancient Romans used tablets as we use pads of paper. **2** a number of sheets of writing paper fastened together at the edge. **3** a small, flat surface with an inscription. **4** a small, flat piece of medicine or candy: *That box contains twelve aspirin tablets. noun.*

table tennis, a game played on a large table marked somewhat like a tennis court, using small wooden paddles and a light, hollow, plastic ball; Ping-Pong.

tack (tak), **1** a short, sharp-pointed nail or pin having a broad, flat head: *We bought some carpet tacks.* **2** to fasten with tacks: *She tacked mosquito netting over the windows.* **3** to attach; add: *He tacked a postscript to the end of the letter.* **4** to sail in a zigzag course against the wind: *The ship was tacking, trying to make the harbor.* **5** a course of action or conduct: *Ordering rather than asking her to help was the wrong tack to take.* **1,5** *noun,* **2-4** *verb.*

tack·le (tak′əl), **1** equipment; apparatus; gear. **Fishing tackle** means the rod, line, hooks, or other equipment used in catching fish. **2** ropes and pulleys for lifting, lowering, and moving heavy things. The sails of a ship are raised and moved by tackle. **3** to try to deal with: *We have a difficult problem to tackle.* **4** to lay hold of; seize: *I tackled the boy with the football and pulled him to the ground.* **5** the act of tackling. **6** a football player between the guard and the end on either side of the line. **1,2,5,6** *noun,* **3,4** *verb,* **tack·les, tack·led, tack·ling.**

ta·co (tä′kō), a tortilla filled with chopped meat, chicken, or cheese, and served hot. *noun, plural* **ta·cos.**

tact (takt), the ability to say and do the right things; skill in dealing with people or handling difficult situations: *Father's tact kept him from talking about things likely to be unpleasant to his guests. noun.*

tact·ful (takt′fəl), having or showing tact: *A tactful reply does not hurt a person's feelings. adjective.*

tac·tics (tak′tiks), **1** the art or science of arranging military or naval forces, or of putting them in a certain position. **2** the operations themselves: *The tactics of pretending to retreat*

tablet (definition 1)

T

fooled the enemy. **3** the ways to gain advantage or success; methods: *When coaxing failed, they changed their tactics and began to threaten. noun.*

tad·pole (tad′pōl′), a very young frog or toad, at the stage when it has a tail and lives in water. *noun.*

tadpole at different stages of growth

taf·fy (taf′ē), a kind of chewy candy. *noun.*

tag¹ (tag), **1** a piece of card, paper, leather, or the like, to be tied or fastened to something: *Each coat in the store has a tag with the price mark on it.* **2** to supply with a tag or tags: *All her trunks and suitcases are tagged with her name and address. The saleswomen tagged all the clothing that was on sale.* **3** to follow closely: *The baby tagged after his brother.* **1** *noun,* **2,3** *verb,* **tags, tagged, tag·ging.**

tag² (tag), **1** a children's game in which one player who is "it" chases the others and tries to touch them. The first one touched is then "it" and must chase the others. **2** to touch or tap with the hand. **3** in baseball, to touch a runner with the ball to make an out. **4** in baseball, the act of touching a runner with the ball to make an out. **1,4** *noun,* **2,3** *verb,* **tags, tagged, tag·ging.**

tail (tāl), **1** the part that sticks out from the back of an animal's body. Rabbits have short tails. Mice have long tails. **2** something like an animal's tail: *Rags tied together made the tail of my kite.* **3** the part at the rear of an airplane. **4** the hind part of anything; back; rear: *A crowd of children formed the tail of the parade.* **5 tails,** the reverse side of a coin. **6** to follow closely and secretly: *The police tailed the suspected killer.* **7** coming from behind: *a tail wind.* **1-5** *noun,* **6** *verb,* **7** *adjective.*

tai·lor (tā′lər), **1** a person whose business is making, altering, or repairing clothes. **2** to make by tailor's work: *The suit was well tailored.* **1** *noun,* **2** *verb.*

tail·spin (tāl′spin′), a downward movement of an airplane with the nose first and the tail spinning in a circle above. *noun.*

taint (tānt), **1** a stain or spot; trace of decay, corruption, or disgrace: *No taint of scandal ever touched the mayor.* **2** to spoil: *Meat taints if left too long in a warm place. Rumors about taking bribes tainted the judge's reputation.* **1** *noun,* **2** *verb.*

Tai·wan (tī′wän′), an island country off the coast of eastern Asia. *noun.*

Ta·jik·i·stan (tä jēk′ə stän), a country in western Asia. *noun.*

take (tāk), **1** to hold onto: *I took her hand when we crossed the street.* **2** to seize; capture: *Wild animals are taken in traps.* **3** to accept: *Take my advice. The dealer won't take a cent less for the car.* **4** to receive: *I took the gift with a smile of thanks.* **5** to win: *Our team took six games. He took first prize.* **6** to get; have: *to take a seat.* **7** to absorb: *Wool takes dye well.* **8** to use; make use of: *We took a train to go to Boston.* **9** to eat or drink; swallow: *They took tea with us yesterday.* **10** to let oneself have; indulge in: *Are you taking a vacation this year? He took a nap.* **11** to put up with; stand: *People from the south often find it hard to take cold weather.* **12** to study: *She plans to take art next year.* **13** to need; require: *It takes time and patience to learn how to play the piano.* **14** to choose; select: *Take the shortest way home.* **15** to remove: *Please take the wastebasket away and empty it.* **16** to subtract: *If you take 2 from 7, you have 5.* **17** to go with; escort: *He likes to take his dog out for a walk.* **18** to carry: *Take your lunch along.* **19** to do; make; obtain by a special method: *Take a walk. Please take my photograph.* **20** to feel: *She takes pride in her schoolwork.* **21** to act; have effect: *The inoculation did not take.* **22** to suppose: *I take it you won't go to school since you feel sick.* **23** to regard; consider: *Let us take an example.* **24** to engage; hire; lease: *They have taken a cottage by the seashore for a month.* **25** to receive and pay for; receive regularly: *to take a newspaper.* **26** to become affected by: *Try not to take cold. verb.* **takes, took, tak·en, tak·ing.**

take after, to be like; resemble: *She takes after her mother.*

take back, to withdraw; retract: *I apologized and took back my rude remark.*

take in, 1 to make smaller: *Please take in the waist of my pants.* **2** to understand: *She took in the situation at a glance.*

take off, 1 to rise from the ground or water into the air: *The airplane took off smoothly.* **2** to rush off: *I took off at the first sign of trouble.*

take on, to agree to do; take upon oneself: *I plan to take on more jobs when school lets out this June.*

take over, to get control or ownership of: *A large corporation has taken over our local grocery store.*

take to, 1 to form a liking for: *We took to one another right away.* **2** to go to: *The cat took to the woods and became wild.*

take up, 1 to soak up; absorb: *A sponge takes up liquid.* **2** to make shorter: *The tailor took up the hem of the dress.* **3** to begin; undertake: *He took up piano lessons in the summer.*

tak·en (tā′kən). See **take.** *I have taken this toy from the shelf. verb.*

take·off (tāk′ôf′), a rising from the ground or water into the air, as in an aircraft. *noun.*

tale (tāl), **1** a story: *Grandfather told the children tales of his boyhood.* **2** a falsehood; lie. *noun.*

tell tales, to tell something that will get a person into trouble.

tal·ent (tal′ənt), a special natural ability; ability: *She has a talent for music. noun.*

tal·ent·ed (tal′ən tid), having natural ability; gifted: *a talented musician. adjective.*

talk (tôk), **1** to use words; speak: *Baby is learning to talk.* **2** to use a language in speaking: *Can you talk French?* **3** the use of words; spoken words; speech; conversation: *The old friends met for a good talk.* **4** an informal speech: *The coach gave the team a talk about the need for more team spirit.* **5** to bring, put, drive, or influence by talk: *We talked her into joining the club.* **6** to discuss: *They talked politics all evening.* **7** to spread ideas by other means than speech: *Some people talk with their hands.* **8** to spread rumors; gossip: *I try never to talk about anyone, because the facts could prove me wrong.* 1,2,5-8 *verb*, 3,4 *noun*.

talk over, to speak about; discuss: *We need to talk over this important decision.*

talk·a·tive (tô′kə tiv), having the habit of talking a great deal; fond of talking: *He is a merry, talkative old man who knows everyone on our street. adjective.*

tall (tôl), **1** higher than the average; high: *New York has many tall buildings.* **2** having the height of; in height: *The tree is a hundred feet tall.* **3** hard to believe; exaggerated: *That is a pretty tall story. adjective.*

Tal·la·has·see (tal′ə has′ē), the capital of Florida. *noun.*

tal·low (tal′ō), the fat of sheep and cattle after it has been melted. Tallow is used for making candles and soap. *noun.*

tal·ly (tal′ē), **1** something, such as a sheet or pad of paper, on which a score or account is kept. **2** a mark made for a certain number of objects in keeping account. **3** to mark on a tally; count up: *Will you tally the score?* **4** to agree; correspond: *Your account tallied with mine.* 1,2 *noun*, plural **tal·lies;** 3,4 *verb*, **tal·lies, tal·lied, tal·ly·ing.**

tal·on (tal′ən), the claw of a bird of prey; claw. *noun.*

talons

ta·ma·le (tə mä′lē), a Mexican food made of cornmeal and minced meat, seasoned with red peppers, wrapped in corn husks, and roasted or steamed. *noun.*

[*Tamale* was borrowed directly from a Mexican Spanish word. It can be traced back to an American Indian word.]

tam·bou·rine (tam′bə rēn′), a small, shallow drum with jingling metal disks around the side, played by striking it with the knuckles or by shaking it. *noun.*

tame (tām), **1** taken from the wild state and made obedient: *a tame bear.* **2** gentle; without fear: *The*

a hat	**i** it	**oi** oil	**ch** child	a in about
ā age	**ī** ice	**ou** out	**ng** long	e in taken
ä far	**o** hot	**u** cup	**sh** she	ə = i in pencil
e let	**ō** open	**ù** put	**th** thin	o in lemon
ē equal	**ô** order	**ü** rule	**ŦH** then	u in circus
ėr term			**zh** measure	

birds are so tame that they will eat from our hands. **3** to make or become tame: *The lion was tamed for the circus.* 1,2 *adjective*, **tam·er, tam·est;** 3 *verb*, **tames, tamed, tam·ing.**

tam·per (tam′pər), to meddle; meddle in an improper way: *Do not tamper with the lock. verb.*

tan (tan), **1** yellowish-brown: *tan shoes.* **2** the brown color of a person's skin caused by being in the sun and air: *His arms and legs had a dark tan.* **3** to make or become brown by exposure to sun and air: *Sun and wind had tanned her face. If you lie on the beach in the sun you will tan.* **4** to make a hide into leather by soaking in a special liquid. 1 *adjective*, **tan·ner, tan·nest;** 2 *noun*, 3,4 *verb*, **tans, tanned, tan·ning.**

tandem

tan·dem (tan′dəm), a bicycle with two seats, one behind the other. *noun.*

tang (tang), a strong taste or flavor: *the tang of mustard. noun.*

tambourine

tan·ge·rine (tan′jə rēn′), the reddish-orange, juicy fruit of a tree grown in warm climates. Tangerines look somewhat like small oranges. They have a very loose peel, and their segments separate easily. *noun.*
[*Tangerine* comes from the name of Tangier, a seaport in Morocco, northern Africa. The fruit was originally called "Tangerine orange" because it looked like an orange and was first exported from Tangier.]

tan·gle (tang′gəl), **1** to twist and twine together in a confused mass: *The kitten had tangled the ball of twine.* **2** a confused or twisted mass: *The climbing vines are all one tangle and need to be pruned and tied up.* **3** a bewildering confusion; mess: *We tried to sort out the truth from a tangle of lies.* 1 *verb,* **tan·gles, tan·gled, tan·gling;** 2,3 *noun.*

tank (tangk), **1** a large container for liquid or gas. An automobile has a fuel tank. **2** to put or store in a tank: *The plane tanked up on gas.* **3** a heavily armored combat vehicle carrying machine guns and usually a cannon, moving on an endless track on each side. Tanks can travel over rough ground, fallen trees, and other obstacles. 1,3 *noun,* 2 *verb.*

tank·er (tang′kər), a ship, airplane, or truck with tanks for carrying oil or other liquid. *noun.*

tan·ner (tan′ər), a person whose work is making hides into leather by tanning them. *noun.*

tan·ta·lize (tan′tl īz), to torment by keeping something desired in sight but out of reach; tease by holding out hopes that are repeatedly disappointed: *They tantalized the hungry dog by pretending to feed it. verb,* **tan·ta·liz·es, tan·ta·lized, tan·ta·liz·ing.**
[*Tantalize* was formed from the name of Tantalus, a king in Greek myths. His punishment in the world of the dead was having to stand up to his chin in water under branches filled with fruit. Yet, whenever he tried to drink or eat, the water or fruit drew back from his reach.]

tan·trum (tan′trəm), a fit of bad temper: *Little children sometimes have tantrums when they do not get what they want. noun.*

Tan·za·ni·a (tan′zə nē′ə), a country in eastern Africa. *noun.*

tap¹ (tap), **1** to strike lightly: *I tapped on the window.* **2** a light blow: *There was a tap at the door.* **3** to make, put, or move by light blows: *to tap a message, to tap a rhythm, to tap the ashes out of a pipe.* 1,3 *verb,* **taps, tapped, tap·ping;** 2 *noun.*

tap² (tap), **1** a stopper or plug to close a hole in a barrel containing liquid. **2** a means of turning on or off a flow of liquid; faucet. **3** to make a hole in to let out liquid: *to tap sugar maples.* **4** to cut in on or connect with, usually in secret: *The spy tapped the scientist's telephone to find out about the new weapon.* 1,2 *noun,* 3,4 *verb,* **taps, tapped, tap·ping.**
on tap, ready for use: *I keep an extra box of stationery on tap so that I will never find that*

I have run out of it unexpectedly.

tape (tāp), **1** a long, narrow strip of cloth, paper, plastic, or some other material: *fancy tape to tie packages. Put the bandage on with adhesive tape.* **2** something like such a strip. The strip stretched across the finish line in a race is called the tape. **3** to fasten with tape; wrap with tape: *The doctor taped up the wound.* **4** a plastic tape on which sounds or images can be recorded. **5** to record on such a tape: *The parade was taped to show on a television news program in the evening.* 1,2,4 *noun,* 3,5 *verb,* **tapes, taped, tap·ing.**

tape deck, the mechanical part of a tape recorder, used with a separate amplifier and speaker system or in connection with a computer.

tape measure, a long strip of cloth or steel marked in inches and feet, or in metric units, for measuring.

ta·per (tā′pər), **1** to make or become gradually smaller toward one end: *The church spire tapers off to a point.* **2** to grow less gradually; diminish: *Their business tapered to nothing as people moved away. verb.*

tape-re·cord (tāp′ri kôrd′), to record on a tape recorder. *verb.*

tape recorder, a machine that records sound on plastic tape and plays the sound back after it is recorded.

tap·es·try (tap′ə strē), a fabric with pictures or designs woven in it, used to hang on walls or to cover furniture. *noun, plural* **tap·es·tries.**

tapestry

tape·worm (tāp′wėrm′), a long, flat worm that lives in the intestines of people and animals. *noun.*

tap·i·o·ca (tap′ē ō′kə), a starchy food obtained from the root of a tropical plant. It is used for puddings. *noun.*

tapir—about 3 feet (1 meter) high at the shoulder

ta·pir (tā′pər), a large piglike animal of tropical America and southern Asia with hoofs and a flexible snout. *noun.*

tap·root (tap′rüt′), a main root growing downward. *noun.*

taps (taps), a signal on a bugle or drum to put out lights at night. Taps are also sounded at military funerals. *noun plural.*

tar (tär), **1** a black, sticky substance obtained from wood or coal. Tar is used to cover and patch roads and roofs. **2** to cover with tar: *The workers tarred our roof last week.* **3** the brownish-black residue from the smoke of cigarettes, cigars, or pipes. 1,3 *noun*, 2 *verb*, **tars, tarred, tar·ring.**
tar and feather, to pour heated tar on and cover with feathers as a punishment.

ta·ran·tu·la (tə ran′chə lə), a large, hairy, poisonous spider whose bite is painful but not dangerous. *noun.*
[*Tarantula* comes from the name of Taranto, a seaport in southeastern Italy where the spider is commonly found.]

tarantula—body 1 to 2 inches (2½ to 6 centimeters) long

tar·dy (tär′dē), behind time; late: *I was tardy for school yesterday. adjective,* **tar·di·er, tar·di·est.**

tar·get (tär′git), **1** a mark for shooting at; thing aimed at. A target is often a circle, but anything may be used as a target. **2** a person or thing that is laughed at or criticized: *Their crazy plan was the target of many jokes.* **3** any aim one tries to

achieve; goal: *The city championship is our team's target. noun.*

tar·iff (tar′if), **1** a list of duties or taxes on imports or exports. **2** any duty or tax in such a list: *There is a very high tariff on imported jewelry. noun.*

tar·nish (tär′nish), **1** to dull the luster or brightness of: *Salt will tarnish silver.* **2** to lose luster or brightness: *The brass doorknobs tarnished because we did not polish them.* **3** a dull coating, especially on silver: *Silver polish will remove the tarnish from those spoons.* 1,2 *verb*, 3 *noun.*

taro

ta·ro (tär′ō), a plant grown in the Pacific islands and other tropical regions. Its starchy root is used as food. *noun, plural* **ta·ros.**

tar·pau·lin (tär pô′lən), a sheet of canvas, plastic, or other strong waterproof material, used as a protective covering. *noun.*

tarpaulin—The motorcycle is covered with a **tarpaulin.**

tar·pon (tär′pon), a large, silver-colored fish found in the warmer parts of the Atlantic Ocean. *noun, plural* **tar·pon** or **tar·pons.**

tar·ry (tar′ē), **1** to remain; stay: *We tarried another day to see all the sights.* **2** to wait; delay:

T

Why do you tarry so long? verb, **tar·ries,
tar·ried, tar·ry·ing.**

tart[1] (tärt), **1** having a sharp taste; sour: *Some
apples are tart.* **2** sharp: *A tart reply is sometimes
impolite. adjective.*

tart[2] (tärt), a pastry filled with cooked fruit, jam, or
the like. In Canada and the United States, a tart is
small and open on the top so that the fruit shows;
in England, any fruit pie is a tart. *noun.*

tar·tan (tärt′n), a plaid woolen cloth. Each
Scottish clan has its own pattern of tartan. *noun.*

tar·tar (tär′tər), a substance that collects on the
teeth. If not removed by brushing the teeth, tartar
will harden into a crust. *noun.*

tartar sauce, a sauce made of mayonnaise
mixed with finely chopped pickles, onions, olives,
and herbs. It is usually used with fish.

task (task), work to be done; piece of work; duty:
His task is to set the table. noun.

take to task, to blame, scold, or reprove: *The
teacher took the student to task for not studying.*

tas·sel (tas′əl), **1** a hanging bunch of threads,
small cords, beads, or the like, fastened together
at one end. **2** something like this: *Corn has tassels.
noun.*

taste (tāst), **1** flavor; what is special about
something to the sense organs of the mouth.
Sweet, sour, salt, and bitter are the four most
important tastes. *I think this milk is sour; it has a
funny taste.* **2** to try the flavor of something by
taking a little into the mouth: *The cook tastes
everything to see if it is right.* **3** the sense by which
one is aware of the flavor of things. **4** to get the
flavor of by the sense of taste: *I taste almond in
this cake.* **5** to have a particular flavor: *The soup
tastes of onion.* **6** to eat or drink a little bit of: *The
children barely tasted their breakfast the day they
went to the circus.* **7** a little bit; sample: *Give me
just a taste of the pudding. The snowstorm will give
you a taste of northern winter.* **8** to experience;
have: *Having tasted freedom, the bird would not
return to its cage.* **9** a liking: *Suit your own taste.*
10 the ability to know and enjoy what is beautiful
and excellent: *Some people have taste in art.* **11** a
manner or style that shows such ability: *Their
house is furnished in excellent taste.* 1,3,7,9-11
noun, 2,4-6,8 *verb,* **tastes, tast·ed, tast·ing.**

taste buds, very small bumps on the tongue that
let you know how things taste.

taste·less (tāst′lis), **1** without taste: *Some hot
foods are tasteless and unpleasant when they
become cold.* **2** without good taste; in poor taste.
adjective.

tast·y (tā′stē), tasting good; pleasing to the taste.
adjective, **tast·i·er, tast·i·est.**

tat·ter (tat′ər), a torn piece; rag: *After the storm
the flag hung in tatters upon the mast. noun.*

tat·tered (tat′ərd), **1** torn; ragged. **2** wearing torn
or ragged clothes. *adjective.*

tat·tle (tat′l), to tell tales or secrets. *verb,*
tat·tles, tat·tled, tat·tling.

tat·tle·tale (tat′l tāl′), a person who tells tales
on others; person who reveals private or secret
matters from ill will. *noun.*

tat·too (ta tü′), **1** to mark the skin with designs or
patterns by pricking it and putting in colors: *The
sailor had a ship tattooed on his arm.* **2** a mark or
design tattooed on the skin. 1 *verb,* 2 *noun, plural*
tat·toos.

taught (tôt). See **teach.** *That teacher taught my
mother. She has taught science for years. verb.*

taunt (tônt), **1** to make fun of in a bitter or
insulting way; mock; jeer at: *My classmates taunted
me for being teacher's pet.* **2** a bitter or insulting
remark; mocking; jeering. 1 *verb,* 2 *noun.*

taut (tôt), **1** drawn tight: *Make sure the rope is taut.*
2 showing strain; tense: *The shock strained his taut
nerves to the breaking point. adjective.*

tav·ern (tav′ərn), **1** a place where alcoholic drinks
are sold and drunk. **2** (in former times) an inn.
noun.

taw·ny (tô′nē), brownish-yellow. *adjective,*
taw·ni·er, taw·ni·est.

tawny—The lion has a **tawny** coat of hair.

tax (taks), **1** money paid by people for the support
of the government and the cost of public works
and services. **2** to put a tax on. People who own
property are taxed in order to provide clean
streets, good roads, protection against crime, and
free education. **3** a heavy burden, duty, or
demand; strain: *Climbing stairs is a tax on a weak
heart.* **4** to lay a heavy burden on; be hard for:
*The work taxed my strength. Reading in a poor
light taxes the eyes.* 1,3 *noun, plural* **tax·es** for 1;
2,4 *verb.*

tax·a·tion (tak sā′shən), **1** the act or system of
taxing: *Taxation is necessary to provide roads,
schools, and police.* **2** the amount people pay for
the support of the government; taxes. *noun.*

tax·i (tak′sē), **1** a taxicab. **2** to ride in a taxi. **3** to
move slowly on the ground or water: *The airplane
taxied off the field after landing.* 1 *noun, plural*
tax·is or **tax·ies;** 2,3 *verb,* **tax·is** or **tax·ies,
tax·ied, tax·i·ing** or **tax·y·ing.**

tax·i·cab (tak′sē kab′), an automobile for hire,
usually with a meter for recording the fare. *noun.*

tax·pay·er (taks′pā′ər), a person who pays a tax
or is required by law to do so. *noun.*

TB, tuberculosis.

tbsp., tablespoon or tablespoons.

tea (tē), **1** a common drink made by pouring boiling water over the dried and prepared leaves of a shrub grown chiefly in China, Japan, and India. **2** the leaves themselves. **3** the shrub these leaves grow on. **4** a drink made from some other plant or from meat: *sage tea.* **Beef tea** is a strong broth made from beef. **5** a light meal in the late afternoon or early evening, at which tea is served. **6** an afternoon reception at which tea is served. *noun.*
[*Tea* comes from a Chinese word.]

teach (tēch), **1** to help to learn; show how to do; make understand: *He is teaching his dog to shake hands.* **2** to give lessons in: *He teaches music.* **3** to give lessons; act as teacher: *She teaches for a living. verb,* **teach·es, taught, teach·ing.**

teach·er (tē′chər), a person who teaches, especially one who teaches in a school. *noun.*

teach·ing (tē′ching), **1** the work or profession of a teacher. **2** what is taught: *religious teachings. noun.*

tea·cup (tē′kup′), a cup for drinking tea. *noun.*

tea·ket·tle (tē′ket′l), a kettle with a handle and a spout for heating water. *noun.*

teal (tēl), a small wild duck that is related to the mallard. *noun, plural* **teal** or **teals.**

teal—about 14 inches (36 centimeters) long

team (tēm), **1** a number of people working or acting together, especially one of the sides in a game or a match: *He is on the football team, and I am on the debating team.* **2** two or more horses or other animals harnessed together to work. **3** to join together in a team: *Everybody teamed up to clean the room after the party.* **1,2** *noun,* **3** *verb.*

team·mate (tēm′māt′), a fellow member of a team. *noun.*

team·ster (tēm′stər), a person whose work is hauling things with a truck. *noun.*

team·work (tēm′wėrk′), the acting together of a number of people to make the work of a group successful and effective: *Football requires teamwork even more than individual skill. noun.*

tea·pot (tē′pot′), a container with a handle and a spout for making and serving tea. *noun.*

tear[1] (tir), a drop of salty water coming from the eye. *noun.*

in tears, shedding tears or crying: *The baby is in tears because he is hungry.*

tear[2] (ter *or* tar), **1** to pull apart by force: *to tear a box open. I tore the paper in half.* **2** to make by pulling apart: *She tore a hole in her jeans.* **3** to pull hard; pull violently: *Tear out the page.* **4** to cut badly; wound: *The jagged stone tore my skin.* **5** to become torn: *Lace tears easily.* **6** a torn place: *She has a tear in her jacket.* **7** to move with great force or haste: *An automobile came tearing down the road.* **1-5,7** *verb,* **tears, tore, torn, tear·ing;** **6** *noun.*

tear down, to destroy: *to tear down an old building.*

tear·ful (tir′fəl), **1** full of tears; weeping. **2** causing tears; sad: *Getting lost was a tearful experience. adjective.*

tease (tēz), **1** to worry by jokes, questions, requests, or the like; annoy: *The children teased the dog until it snapped at them.* **2** a person who teases. **1** *verb,* **teas·es, teased, teas·ing;** **2** *noun.*

tea·spoon (tē′spün′), **1** a small spoon often used to stir tea or coffee. **2** a unit of measure in cooking equal to one-third tablespoon. *noun.*

tea·spoon·ful (tē′spün′fül), as much as a teaspoon holds. *noun, plural* **tea·spoon·fuls.**

team (definition 2)—a **team** of 33 mules

tech·ni·cal (tek′nə kəl), **1** of or having something to do with a mechanical or industrial art or with applied science: *This technical school trains engineers, chemists, and architects.* **2** of or having something to do with the special facts of a science or art: *"Transistor" and "protein" are technical words.* **3** of or having to do with the method or ability of an artist's performance: *Her singing showed technical skill, but her voice was weak. adjective.*

tech·ni·cian (tek nish′ən), a person who knows the technical details and methods of a subject or a job. *noun.*

tech·nique (tek nēk′), 1 the method or ability of an artist's performance; technical skill: *The pianist's technique was excellent.* 2 a special method or system used to do something. *noun.*
[*Technique* was borrowed directly from a French word. It can be traced back to a Greek word meaning "art," "skill," or "craft." Other English words from the same Greek root include *technical, technician, technological, technologist,* and *technology.*]

tech·no·log·i·cal (tek′nə loj′ə kəl), of technology; used in technology: *Inventions make technological advances possible.* *adjective.*

tech·nol·o·gist (tek nol′ə jist), a person skilled in mechanical and industrial methods; person who uses scientific knowledge to do a job. *noun.*

tech·nol·o·gy (tek nol′ə jē), 1 the use of scientific knowledge to solve practical problems. 2 the practical methods used to solve problems. 3 the science of technical methods used in industry: *He studied at a school of technology.* *noun, plural* **tech·nol·o·gies** for 2.

ted·dy bear (ted′ē ber′ *or* ted′ē bar′), a child's furry toy bear.

Word History

teddy bear The word *teddy* comes from *Teddy,* a nickname for Theodore Roosevelt. He was President of the United States from 1901 to 1909. A cartoon showed him refusing to shoot a bear cub when he was hunting. Soon, stuffed toy animals were being sold that came to be known as "teddy bears."

DRAWING THE LINE IN MISSISSIPPI

te·di·ous (tē′dē əs *or* tē′jəs), long and tiring: *A boring talk that you cannot understand is tedious.* *adjective.*

tee (tē), 1 a mark or place where a player starts to play each hole in golf. 2 a short wooden or plastic peg on which a golf ball can be placed and then hit. 3 **tee off,** to hit a golf ball from a tee. 1,2 *noun,* 3 *verb,* **tees, teed, tee·ing.**

teem (tēm), to be full; abound; swarm: *The swamp teemed with mosquitoes.* *verb.*

teen·age (tēn′āj′), 1 of or for a teenager or teenagers: *This store has all the latest teenage fashions.* 2 in one's teens; being a teenager: *They have two teenage daughters.* *adjective.*

teen·ag·er (tēn′ā′jər), a person in his or her teens. *noun.*

teens (tēnz), the years of life from 13 to 19. *noun plural.*

tee shirt, See **T-shirt.**

tee·ter (tē′tər), to rock unsteadily; sway. *verb.*

tee·ter-tot·ter (tē′tər tot′ər), a seesaw. *noun.*

teeth (tēth), more than one tooth: *You often show your teeth when you smile. noun plural.*
in the teeth of, straight against; in the face of: *He advanced in the teeth of the wind.*

teethe (tēᴛн), to grow teeth; cut teeth: *Babies teethe. verb,* **teethes, teethed, teeth·ing.**

tel·e·cast (tel′ə kast′), 1 to broadcast by television. 2 a television program. 1 *verb,* **tel·e·casts, tel·e·cast** *or* **tel·e·cast·ed, tel·e·cast·ing;** 2 *noun.*

tel·e·gram (tel′ə gram), a message sent by telegraph: *Father sent a telegram to wish me a happy birthday. noun.*

tel·e·graph (tel′ə graf), 1 a way of sending coded messages over wires by means of electricity. 2 a device used for sending these messages. 3 to send a message by telegraph: *Mother telegraphed congratulations to the bride and groom.* 1,2 *noun,* 3 *verb.*

tel·e·phone (tel′ə fōn), 1 an instrument for talking between distant points over wires by means of electricity. 2 to talk through a telephone; send a message by telephone. 3 to make a telephone call to. 1 *noun,* 2,3 *verb,* **tel·e·phones, tel·e·phoned, tel·e·phon·ing.**
[*Telephone* was formed from two Greek words meaning "far off," and "sound" or "voice."]

telephone book or **telephone directory,** a list of names, addresses, and telephone numbers.

tel·e·scope (tel′ə skōp), 1 an instrument for making distant objects appear nearer and larger. The stars are studied by means of telescopes. 2 to force together, one inside another, like the sliding tubes of some telescopes: *When the two railroad trains crashed into each other, the cars were telescoped.* 3 to be forced together in this way. 1 *noun,* 2,3 *verb,* **tel·e·scopes, tel·e·scoped, tel·e·scop·ing.**

tel·e·vise (tel′ə vīz), to send by television: *Will they televise today's game? verb,* **tel·e·vis·es, tel·e·vised, tel·e·vis·ing.**

tel·e·vi·sion (tel′ə vizh′ən), 1 a way of sending

and receiving over wires or through the air pictures of things and events and the sounds that go with them. **2** a device on which these pictures and sounds may be seen and heard. *noun.*

tell (tel), **1** to put in words; say: *Tell us a story. Tell the truth.* **2** to tell to; inform: *Tell us about it.* **3** to make known: *Don't tell where the candy is.* **4** to recognize; know: *I can't tell which house is yours.* **5** to say to; order; command: *Do as you are told. verb,* **tells, told, tell·ing.**

tell off, to scold: *She really told me off when she found out I took her book.*

tell on, to inform on; tell tales about: *Please don't tell on me.*

tell·er (tel′ər), **1** a person who tells: *Our teacher is a good teller of stories.* **2** a bank cashier who takes in, gives out, and counts money. *noun.*

tem·per (tem′pər), **1** a state of mind; disposition; condition: *a sweet temper. She was in no temper to be kept waiting.* **2** an angry state of mind: *to fly into a temper. In my temper I slammed the door.* **3** a calm state of mind: *He became angry and lost his temper.* **4** to soften; make less severe: *Temper justice with mercy.* **1-3** *noun,* **4** *verb.*

tem·per·a·ment (tem′pər ə mənt), a person's nature; makeup; disposition: *a nervous temperament. noun.*

tem·per·a·men·tal (tem′pər ə men′tl), likely to have sudden changes of mood; easily irritated; sensitive: *A temperamental person can be hard to live with. adjective.*

tem·per·ance (tem′pər əns), a being moderate in action, speech, or habits; self-control: *Temperance should be applied not only to food and drink but also to work and play. noun.*

tem·per·ate (tem′pər it), **1** not very hot, and not very cold: *Seattle has a temperate climate.* **2** moderate; using self-control: *She spoke in a quiet, temperate manner. adjective.*

tem·per·a·ture (tem′pər ə chər), **1** the degree of heat or cold. The temperature of freezing water is 32 degrees Fahrenheit, or 0 degrees Celsius. **2** a body temperature higher than normal (98.6 degrees Fahrenheit, or 37 degrees Celsius): *A sick person may have a temperature. noun.*

tem·pest (tem′pist), a violent storm with much wind. *noun.*

tempest
The **tempest** drove the ship southward.

a hat	i it	oi oil	ch child		a in about
ā age	ī ice	ou out	ng long		e in taken
ä far	o hot	u cup	sh she	ə =	i in pencil
e let	ō open	u̇ put	th thin		o in lemon
ē equal	ô order	ü rule	ᵀH then		u in circus
ėr term			zh measure		

tem·pes·tu·ous (tem pes′chü əs), **1** stormy: *It was a tempestuous night.* **2** violent: *a tempestuous fit of anger. adjective.*

tem·ple[1] (tem′pəl), **1** a building used for the service or worship of a god or gods: *Greek temples were beautifully built.* **2** any building set apart for worship, especially a Jewish synagogue. *noun.*

tem·ple[2] (tem′pəl), the flattened part on either side of the forehead. *noun.*

temple[2]—Sometimes you can feel your pulse at your **temple.**

tem·po (tem′pō), the rate of speed at which a piece of music is played: *The song was played in a very fast tempo. noun, plural* **tem·pos.**

tem·po·rar·i·ly (tem′pə rer′ə lē), for a short time; for the present: *They are living in a hotel temporarily. adverb.*

tem·po·rar·y (tem′pə rer′ē), lasting for a short time only: *This is just a temporary job. adjective.*

tempt (tempt), **1** to make or try to make a person do something: *Extreme hunger can tempt a person to steal food.* **2** to appeal strongly to; attract. **3** to

tempt (definition 2)—The delicious-looking ice cream **tempted** him.

call forth; provoke: *It is tempting fate to try to cross the lake in that old boat.* verb.

temp·ta·tion (temp tā′shən), **1** a tempting: *No temptation could make her break her promise.* **2** a being tempted: *The Lord's Prayer says, "Lead us not into temptation."* **3** a thing that tempts: *Money left carelessly about is a temptation.* noun.

ten (ten), one more than nine; 10. noun, adjective.

te·na·cious (ti nā′shəs), **1** holding fast: *the tenacious jaws of a bulldog.* **2** stubborn; persistent: *a tenacious salesman.* adjective.

ten·ant (ten′ənt), a person paying rent for the use of land, a building, or space in a building belonging to another person: *That building has apartments for one hundred tenants.* noun.

tend[1] (tend), **1** to be apt; be likely to: *Fruit tends to decay. I tend to sleep late on weekends.* **2** to move toward; lead: *The road tends to the south here.* verb.

tend[2] (tend), to take care of; look after; attend to: *He tends the store for his parents. The shepherd tends the flock of sheep.* verb.

ten·den·cy (ten′dən sē), a natural inclination to do something: *a tendency to oversleep. Wood has a tendency to swell if it gets wet.* noun, plural **ten·den·cies.**

ten·der[1] (ten′dər), **1** not hard or tough; soft: *The meat is tender. Stones hurt the little child's tender feet.* **2** delicate; not strong and hardy: *The leaves in spring are green and tender.* **3** kind; affectionate; loving: *She spoke tender words to the baby.* **4** gentle; not rough or crude: *He patted the dog with tender hands.* **5** young: *She came to live here at the tender age of five.* **6** painful; sore: *a tender wound. Automobiles are a tender subject with Dad since he wrecked his.* **7** feeling pain or grief easily: *a person with a tender heart.* adjective.

ten·der[2] (ten′dər), to offer formally: *She tendered her resignation.* verb.

ten·der·foot (ten′dər fut′), **1** a person not used to rough living and hardships. **2** an inexperienced person; beginner. noun, plural **ten·der·foots, ten·der·feet** (ten′dər fēt′).

[Another meaning of *tenderfoot* is "a newcomer to the pioneer life of the western United States." It was first used around the time of the gold rush to California in 1849.]

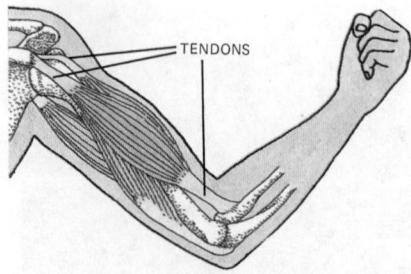
TENDONS

ten·don (ten′dən), a tough, strong band or cord of tissue that joins a muscle to a bone; sinew. noun.

ten·e·ment (ten′ə mənt), an old building, especially in a poor section of a city. A tenement is divided into sets of rooms occupied by separate families. noun.

Tenn., Tennessee.

Ten·nes·see (ten′ə sē′), one of the south central states of the United States. *Abbreviation:* Tenn. or TN *Capital:* Nashville. noun.

[*Tennessee* got its name from a Cherokee Indian village called Tanasie.]

ten·nis (ten′is), a game played by two or four players on a special court, in which a ball is hit back and forth over a net with a racket. noun.

ten·or (ten′ər), **1** the highest singing voice of a man. **2** a singer with such a voice. **3** the part sung by such a voice. noun.

tense[1] (tens), **1** stretched tight; strained to stiffness: *a tense rope, a face tense with pain.* **2** to stretch tight; stiffen: *She tensed her muscles for the leap.* **3** having, showing, or causing strain: *tense nerves, a tense look, a tense moment.* **1,3** adjective, **tens·er, tens·est; 2** verb, **tens·es, tensed, tens·ing.**

tense[2] (tens), the form of a verb that shows the time of the action or state expressed by the verb. *I dance* is in the present tense. *I danced* is in the past tense. *I will dance* is in the future tense. noun.

ten·sion (ten′shən), **1** a stretching; a stretched condition: *The tension of the bow gives speed to the arrow.* **2** a strain: *Tension is sometimes brought on by overwork.* noun.

tent (tent), a movable shelter made of canvas or nylon supported by a pole or poles. noun.

ten·ta·cle (ten′tə kəl), a long, slender, flexible growth on the head or around the mouth of an animal, used to touch, hold, or move: *Jellyfish have many stinging tentacles.* noun.

tenth (tenth), **1** next after the ninth. **2** one of ten equal parts. adjective, noun.

te·pee (tē′pē), a tent used by North American Indians, made of hides sewn together and stretched over poles arranged in the shape of a cone. noun.

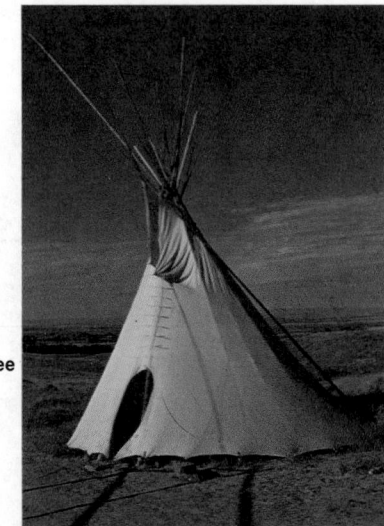
tepee

tep·id (tep′id), slightly warm; lukewarm: *By the time I arrived at the breakfast table my tea was tepid. adjective.*

term (tėrm), **1** a word or group of words used in connection with some special subject, science, art, or business: *medical terms.* "*Acid,*" "*base,*" and "*salt*" *are terms commonly used in chemistry.* **2** to name; call: *He might be termed handsome.* **3** a set period of time; length of time that a thing lasts: *The President's term of office is four years.* **4** one of the periods into which the school year is divided: *Most schools have a fall term and a spring term.* **5 terms, a** conditions: *The terms of the peace were very hard for the defeated nation.* **b** personal relations: *We are on very good terms with all our neighbors.* **6** the numerator or denominator in a fraction: *4/12 reduced to lowest terms is ⅓.* **1,3-6** *noun,* **2** *verb.*

ter·mi·nal (tėr′mə nəl), **1** the end; end part. A terminal is either end of a railroad line, bus line, airline, or shipping route where sheds, hangars, garages, and stations to handle freight and passengers are located. **2** a device for making an electrical connection: *the terminals of a battery.* **3** a device by which a person and a computer may communicate. A terminal usually has a keyboard like a typewriter and a screen like a television. *noun.*

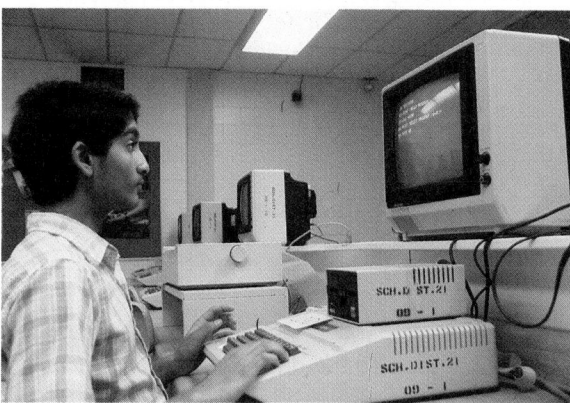

terminal (definition 3)—He worked steadily at his **terminal.**

ter·mi·nate (tėr′mə nāt), to bring or come to an end: *The lawyers terminated their partnership and each opened a separate office. verb,* **ter·mi·nates, ter·mi·nat·ed, ter·mi·nat·ing.**

ter·mi·na·tion (tėr′mə nā′shən), an ending; end: *Termination of the contract left both parties free to do business elsewhere. noun.*

ter·mite (tėr′mīt), an insect with a soft, pale body. Termites live in colonies somewhat like ants and eat wood, paper, and other material containing cellulose. They are very destructive to buildings, furniture, and books. *noun.*

tern (tėrn), a sea bird related to the gulls but with a more slender body and bill and usually a long, forked tail. *noun.*

ter·race (ter′is), **1** a paved outdoor space near a house for lounging or dining. **2** a flat, raised piece of land with straight or sloping sides. Terraces are often made one above the other in hilly areas to create more space for raising crops. *noun.*

a hat	i it	oi oil	ch child	a in about
ā age	ī ice	ou out	ng long	e in taken
ä far	o hot	u cup	sh she	ə = i in pencil
e let	ō open	ů put	th thin	o in lemon
ē equal	ô order	ü rule	ŦH then	u in circus
ėr term			zh measure	

Word History

terrace *Terrace* comes from a Latin word meaning "earth" or "land." Other English words from the same Latin root are *terrain, terrarium, terrier,* and *territory.*

terrace (definition 2)
Terraces make it possible to farm steep hills.

ter·rain (tə rān′), an area of land, especially its natural features: *The hilly, rocky terrain of the island made hiking difficult. noun.*

ter·rar·i·um (tə rer′ē əm), a glass enclosure in which plants or small land animals are kept. *noun.*

ter·ri·ble (ter′ə bəl), causing great fear; dreadful; awful: *The terrible storm destroyed many lives. adjective.*

ter·ri·bly (ter′ə blē), **1** in a terrible manner; dreadfully: *Thunder crashed terribly during the storm.* **2** extremely; very: *I am terribly sorry I stepped on your toes. adverb.*

tern—16 inches (41 centimeters) long

T

terrier | that

ter·ri·er (ter′ē ər), a small, active, intelligent dog that was once used to chase prey into its burrow. Well-known kinds include fox terriers, Irish terriers, and Scotch terriers. *noun.*

ter·rif·ic (tə rif′ik), **1** causing great fear; terrifying: *A terrific earthquake shook Japan.* **2** very great or severe: *A terrific hot spell ruined many of the crops.* **3** very good; wonderful: *She is a terrific tennis player. adjective.*

ter·ri·fy (ter′ə fī), to fill with great fear; frighten very much: *The sight of a large bear terrified the campers.* verb, **ter·ri·fies, ter·ri·fied, ter·ri·fy·ing.**

ter·ri·to·ry (ter′ə tôr′ē), **1** land; region: *Much territory in the northern part of Africa is desert.* **2** land belonging to a government; land under the rule of a distant government: *Alaska was a territory of the United States until 1958.* **3** an area, such as a nesting ground, in which an animal lives and from which it keeps out others of its kind. *noun, plural* **ter·ri·to·ries.**

ter·ror (ter′ər), **1** great fear: *The child has a terror of thunder.* **2** a cause of great fear: *Pirates were once the terror of the sea. noun.*

ter·ror·ize (ter′ə rīz′), to fill with terror: *The sight of the growling dog terrorized the little child.* verb, **ter·ror·iz·es, ter·ror·ized, ter·ror·iz·ing.**

test (test), **1** an examination; trial: *The teacher gave us a test in arithmetic. People who want a license to drive an automobile must pass a test.* **2** a means of trial: *Trouble is a test of character.* **3** an examination of a substance to see what it is or what it contains: *A test showed that the water was pure.* **4** to put to a test of any kind; try out: *That water was tested for purity. The doctor tested the girl's eyes.* 1-3 *noun,* 4 *verb.*

tes·ta·ment (tes′tə mənt), **1** written instructions telling what to do with a person's property after the person dies; will. **2 Testament,** one of the two parts into which the Bible is divided; the Old Testament or the New Testament. *noun.*

tes·ti·fy (tes′tə fī), to give evidence; say as a witness; declare: *The witness testified that the speeding car had crashed into the truck. Other witnesses were unwilling to testify.* verb, **tes·ti·fies, tes·ti·fied, tes·ti·fy·ing.**

tes·ti·mo·ny (tes′tə mō′nē), **1** a statement used for evidence or proof: *A witness gave testimony that the accused man was at home all day.* **2** evidence: *The dry, brown grass was testimony to a hot summer with very little rain. noun, plural* **tes·ti·mo·nies.**

test tube, a thin glass tube closed at one end, used in making chemical tests.

tet·a·nus (tet′n əs), a disease caused by a certain germ entering the body through a wound. Tetanus produces very painful stiffness of muscles, and it sometimes results in death. You can be protected against it by a series of shots. *noun.*

teth·er (teᴛн′ər), **1** a rope or chain for fastening an animal so that it can graze or move only within a certain limit: *The cow had broken its tether and was in the garden.* **2** to fasten with a tether: *The horse is tethered to a stake.* 1 *noun,* 2 *verb.*

Tex., Texas.

Tex·as (tek′səs), one of the southwestern states of the United States. *Abbreviation:* Tex. or TX *Capital:* Austin. *noun.*
[*Texas* got its name from a group of American Indians living in the area who were called *Tejas* by the Spanish. This name came from an American Indian word meaning "friends" or "allies."]

text (tekst), **1** the main body of reading matter in a book: *This history book contains 300 pages of text, and about 50 pages of maps and pictures.* **2** the original words of a writer. A text is often changed here and there when it is copied. **3** a short passage in the Bible: *The minister preached on the text "Blessed are the merciful."* **4** a topic; subject: *Town improvement was the speaker's text.* **5** a textbook. *noun.*

text·book (tekst′bůk′), a book for regular study by pupils. Most books used in school are textbooks. *noun.*

tex·tile (tek′stəl *or* tek′stīl), a woven fabric; cloth: *Beautiful textiles are sold in Paris. noun.*

tex·ture (teks′chər), the feel that cloth or other things have because of their structure: *Velvet has a soft, smooth texture. noun.*

-th¹, a suffix meaning: number _____in order or position in a series. Six*th* means *number* six *in order or position in a series.* The suffix -eth is used to form numbers like *fiftieth* and *sixtieth.*

-th², a suffix meaning: **1** the act or process of _____ing: Grow*th* means *the act or process of* grow*ing.* **2** the quality, state, or condition of being _____: Tru*th* means *the quality, state, or condition of being* true.

Thai·land (tī′land′), a country in southeastern Asia. *noun.*

than (ᴛнan), **1** in comparison with: *She is taller than her sister.* **2** compared to that which: *You know better than I do. conjunction.*

thank (thangk), **1** to say that one is pleased and grateful for something given or done: *She thanked her teacher for helping her.* **2 thanks, a** I thank you: *Thanks for your good wishes.* **b** a feeling or expression of gratitude: *You have our thanks for everything you have done.* **3** to blame: *You have yourself to thank if you eat too much.* 1,3 *verb,* 2 *noun.*

thanks to, owing to or because of: *Thanks to his efforts, the garden is a great success.*

thank·ful (thangk′fəl), feeling thanks; grateful: *I am thankful for your help. adjective.*

thank·less (thangk′lis), **1** ungrateful: *The thankless child expressed no appreciation for our gift.* **2** not likely to get thanks: *Giving advice can be a thankless act. adjective.*

Thanks·giv·ing Day (thangks giv′ing dā′), a day set apart as a holiday on which to give thanks for past blessings. In the United States, Thanksgiving Day is the fourth Thursday in November.

that (ᴛнat), **1** *That* is used to point out some

person or thing or idea. We use *this* for the thing nearer us, and *that* for the thing farther away from us. *Do you know that woman? Shall we buy this book or that one? I like that better.* **2** *That* is also used to connect a group of words. *I know that 6 and 4 are 10.* **3** *That* is used to show purpose. *Study that you may learn.* **4** *That* is used to show result. *I ran so fast that I was five minutes early.* **5** who; whom: *Is he the man that sells dogs? She is the girl that you saw in school.* **6** which: *Bring the box that will hold most.* **7** on which; at or in which: *It was the day that school began. The year that we went to England was 1980.* **8** to such an extent; to such a degree; so: *The baby cannot stay up that long.* 1 *adjective, plural* **those;** 1,5-7 *pronoun, plural* **those;** 2-4 *conjunction;* 8 *adverb.*

thatch (thach), **1** straw, rushes, or the like, used as a roof or covering. **2** to make or cover with thatch. 1 *noun,* 2 *verb.*

thatch (definition 2)—This man is **thatching** a roof.

that'll (ᴛʜat'l), that will.

that's (ᴛʜats), that is.

thaw (thô), **1** to melt ice, snow, or anything frozen; free from frost: *The sun will thaw the ice on the streets. It thawed early last spring.* **2** weather above the freezing point (32 degrees Fahrenheit, or 0 degrees Celsius); time of melting: *In January we usually have a thaw.* **3** to make or become less cold: *After shoveling snow, I thawed my hands and feet in front of the fire.* 1,3 *verb,* 2 *noun.*

the[1] (ᴛʜə, ᴛʜi, *or* ᴛʜē), a certain; a particular: *The dog I saw had no tail. The girl driving the car is my sister. definite article.*

the[2] (ᴛʜə *or* ᴛʜi), by how much; by that much: *The longer you work, the more you get. The later I sit up, the sleepier I become. adverb.*

the·a·ter *or* **the·a·tre** (thē′ə tər), **1** a place where plays are acted or motion pictures are shown. **2** plays; writing, acting in, or producing plays; drama: *He was interested in the theater and tried to write plays himself. noun.*

the·at·ri·cal (thē at′rə kəl), of or having something to do with the theater or actors: *theatrical performances, a theatrical company. adjective.*

thee (ᴛʜē), an old word meaning **you.** "Bless thee" means "bless you." *pronoun.*

theft (theft), the act of stealing: *The prisoner was jailed for theft. noun.*

their (ᴛʜer *or* ᴛʜar), of them; belonging to them: *I like their house. adjective.*

theirs (ᴛʜerz *or* ᴛʜarz), the one or ones belonging to them: *Our house is white; theirs is brown. pronoun.*

them (ᴛʜem), the persons, animals, or things spoken about: *The books are new; take care of them. pronoun.*

theme (thēm), **1** a subject; topic: *The theme of her speech was equal rights for all Americans.* **2** a short written composition: *Our school themes must be written in ink and on white paper.* **3** the principal melody in a piece of music. *noun.*

them·selves (ᴛʜem selvz′), **1** *Themselves* is used to make a statement stronger. *The teachers themselves said the test was too hard.* **2** *Themselves* is used instead of *them* in cases like: *They hurt themselves sliding downhill.* **3** their normal or usual selves: *The children are sick and are not themselves this morning. pronoun.*

then (ᴛʜen), **1** at that time: *Father talked of his childhood, and recalled that prices were lower then.* **2** that time: *By then we shall know the result of the election.* **3** soon afterward: *The noise stopped and then began again.* **4** next in time or place: *First comes spring, then summer.* **5** at another time: *Now one team was ahead and then the other.* **6** also; besides: *The circus is too good to miss, and then it costs very little.* **7** in that case; therefore: *If she painted the best picture, then she should receive the first prize.* 1,3-7 *adverb,* 2 *noun.*

the·ol·o·gy (thē ol′ə jē), **1** teachings concerning God and His relations to human beings and to the universe. **2** the study of religion and religious beliefs. *noun, plural* **the·ol·o·gies.**

the·o·ry (thē′ər ē), **1** an explanation of something, based on observation and reasoning: *According to one scientific theory of life, the more complicated animals developed from the simpler ones.* **2** the principles or methods of a science or art rather than its practice: *Before she began to compose, she studied music theory.* **3** an idea or opinion about something: *I think the fire was started by a careless smoker. What is your theory? noun, plural* **the·o·ries.**

ther·a·pist (ther′ə pist), a person who specializes in some form of therapy: *The therapist showed me how to do exercises that would strengthen my injured leg. noun.*

ther·a·py (ther′ə pē), the treatment of diseases, injuries, or disorders. *noun.*

there (ᴛʜer *or* ᴛʜar), **1** in that place; at that place; at that point: *Sit there. Finish reading the page and* *stop there.* **2** to or into that place: *We are going there tomorrow.* **3** that place: *We go to New York first and from there to Boston.* **4** in that matter: *You are mistaken there.* **5** *There* is also used in sentences in which the verb comes before its subject. *There are three new houses on our street. Is there a drugstore near here?* **6** *There* is used to call attention to some person or thing. *There goes the bell.* **7** *There* is also used to express some feeling. *There, there! Don't cry.* 1,2,4-6 *adverb,* 3 *noun,* 7 *interjection.*

there·a·bouts (ᴛʜer′ə bouts′ *or* ᴛʜar′ə bouts′), **1** near that place: *She lives in the main part of town, on Front Street or thereabouts.* **2** near that time: *He went home in the late afternoon, at 5 o'clock or thereabouts.* **3** near that number or amount: *It was very cold and the temperature fell to zero or thereabouts. adverb.*

there·af·ter (ᴛʜer af′tər *or* ᴛʜar af′tər), after that; afterward: *He was very ill as a child and was considered delicate thereafter. adverb.*

there·by (ᴛʜer bī′ *or* ᴛʜar bī′), by means of that; in that way: *He wished to travel and thereby study the customs of other countries. adverb.*

there·fore (ᴛʜer′fôr *or* ᴛʜar′fôr), for that reason; as a result of that: *She had to work last night and therefore had little time to study. adverb.*

there's (ᴛʜerz *or* ᴛʜarz), there is.

ther·mom·e·ter (thər mom′ə tər), an instrument for measuring temperature. Most thermometers contain mercury or alcohol in a narrow tube. When the temperature outside goes up, the liquid rises by expanding; when the temperature goes down, the liquid drops by contracting. *noun.* [*Thermometer* was formed from two Greek words meaning "heat" and "measure."]

ther·mos (ther′məs), a container made with a vacuum between its inner and outer walls so that its contents remain hot or cold for a long time. *noun, plural* **ther·mos·es.**

ther·mo·stat (ther′mə stat), an automatic device for regulating temperature: *Most furnaces and ovens are controlled by thermostats. noun.*

these (ᴛʜēz). *These* is used to point out persons, things, or ideas. *These girls helped me. These are my books. These two problems are hard. adjective, pronoun plural* of **this.**

they (ᴛʜā), **1** the persons, animals, things, or ideas spoken about: *I had three books yesterday. Do you know where they are? They are on the table.* **2** some people; any people; persons: *They say we should have a new school. pronoun plural.*

they'd (ᴛʜād), **1** they had. **2** they would.

they'll (ᴛʜāl), **1** they will. **2** they shall.

they're (ᴛʜer *or* ᴛʜar), they are.

they've (ᴛʜāv), they have.

thick (thik), **1** with much space from one side to the opposite side; not thin: *The castle has thick stone walls.* **2** measuring between two opposite sides: *This brick is 8 inches long, 4 inches wide, and 2½ inches thick.* **3** closely packed together; dense: *a thick forest, thick smoke. The air was thick with insects.* **4** like glue or syrup; not like

water: *Thick liquids pour much more slowly than thin liquids.* **5** not clear in sound; hoarse: *She had a thick voice because of a cold.* **6** stupid; dull: *I couldn't get the lesson through my thick head.* **7** thickly: *The cars came thick and fast.* **8** the hardest part; place where there is the most danger or activity: *They were in the thick of the fight.* 1-6 *adjective,* 7 *adverb,* 8 *noun.*

through thick and thin, in good times and bad: *They were friends through thick and thin.*

thick·en (thik′ən), to make thick or thicker; become thick or thicker: *The cook thickens the gravy with flour. The pudding will thicken as it cools. verb.*

thick·et (thik′it), shrubs, bushes, or small trees growing close together: *We crawled into the thicket and hid. noun.*

thick·ly (thik′lē), in a thick manner; densely: *Most of New York City is thickly settled. Weeds grow thickly in the rich soil. adverb.*

thick·ness (thik′nis), **1** a being thick: *The thickness of the walls shuts out all sound.* **2** the distance between two opposite sides; the third measurement of a solid, not length nor width: *The length of the board is 10 feet, the width 6 inches, the thickness 2 inches.* **3** a layer: *The pad was made up of three thicknesses of cloth. noun, plural* **thick·ness·es.**

thief (thēf), a person who steals, especially one who steals secretly and usually without using force: *A thief stole the bicycle from the yard. noun, plural* **thieves.**

thieve (thēv), to steal: *She saw a student thieving at school today. verb,* **thieves, thieved, thiev·ing.**

thieves (thēvz), more than one thief. *noun plural.*

thigh (thī), the part of the leg between the hip and the knee. *noun.*

thim·ble (thim′bəl), a small metal or plastic cap worn on the finger to protect it when pushing the needle in sewing. *noun.*

thimble

thin (thin), **1** with little space from one side to the opposite side; not thick: *thin paper, thin wire. The ice on the pond is too thin for skating.* **2** having little flesh; slender; lean: *a thin person.* **3** not closely packed together; not dense: *thin hair. The air on the tops of high mountains is thin.* **4** like water; not like glue or syrup; not as thick as usual: *This gravy is too thin.* **5** not deep or strong: *The sickly child had a thin, shrill voice.* **6** easily seen through; flimsy: *It was a thin excuse that* *satisfied no one.* **7** make thin; become thin: *Starvation had thinned their cheeks.* 1-6 *adjective,* **thin·ner, thin·nest;** 7 *verb,* **thins, thinned, thin·ning.**

thine (ᵺīn), an old word meaning: **1** yours. "It is thine" means "it is yours." **2** your (used only before a vowel or *h*). "Thine eyes" means "your eyes." **1** *pronoun,* **2** *adjective.*

thing (thing), **1** any object or substance; what you can see or hear or touch or taste or smell: *All the things in the house were burned. Put these things away.* **2 things,** personal belongings: *I packed my things and took the train.* **3** whatever is spoken of, thought of, or done: *It was a good thing to do. That is a strange thing to think of. A strange thing happened.* **4** a matter; affair: *Let's settle this thing between us. How are things going?* **5** a person or animal: *I felt sorry for the poor thing. noun.*

think (thingk), **1** to form an idea in the mind: *I want to think about that question before I answer it.* **2** to have in the mind: *He thought that he would go.* **3** to have an opinion; believe: *Do you think it will rain? We thought it might snow.* **4** to consider: *They think their child a genius. verb,* **thinks, thought, think·ing.**

think of, 1 to imagine: *She doesn't like apple pie. Think of that!* **2** to remember: *I can't think of his name.*

third (ᵺėrd), **1** next after the second: *C is the third letter of the alphabet.* **2** one of three equal parts: *We divided the cake into thirds. adjective, noun.*

thirst (ᵺėrst), **1** a dry, uncomfortable feeling in the mouth or throat caused by having had nothing to drink: *The traveler in the desert suffered from thirst.* **2** a desire for something to drink: *She satisfied her thirst with a glass of water.* **3** a strong desire: *to have a thirst for adventure.* **4** to have a strong desire: *Some people thirst for power.* 1-3 *noun,* 4 *verb.*

thirst·y (ᵺėr′stē), **1** feeling thirst; having thirst: *The dog is thirsty; please give it some water.* **2** without water or moisture; dry: *The land was as thirsty as a desert. adjective,* **thirst·i·er, thirst·i·est.**

thir·teen (ᵺėr′tēn′), three more than ten; 13. *noun, adjective.*

thir·teenth (ᵺėr′tēnth′), **1** next after the 12th. **2** one of 13 equal parts. *adjective, noun.*

thir·ti·eth (ᵺėr′tē ith), **1** next after the 29th. **2** one of 30 equal parts: *A day is about one thirtieth of a month. adjective, noun.*

thir·ty (ᵺėr′tē), three times ten; 30. *noun, plural* **thir·ties;** *adjective.*

this (ᵺis), **1** *This* is used to point out some person, thing, or idea as present, or near, or spoken of before. We use *that* for the thing farther away from us and *this* for the thing nearer us. *This is my brother. Shall we buy this or that? School begins at eight this year.* **2** to such an extent or degree; so: *You can have this much.* 1 *adjective, pronoun, plural* **these;** 2 *adverb.*

this'll (ᵺis′əl), this will.

thistle

this·tle (this′əl), a plant with a prickly stalk and leaves and usually with purple flowers. *noun.*

tho or **tho'** (ᵺō), though. *conjunction, adverb.*

thong (thông), a narrow strip of leather, especially one used as a fastening: *The ancient Greeks laced their sandals on with thongs. noun.*

tho·rax (thôr′aks), **1** the part of the body between the neck and the abdomen; chest. It contains the heart and the lungs. **2** the second of the three parts of the body of an insect. It is between the head and the abdomen. *noun, plural* **tho·rax·es.**

thorax (definition 1, left, and definition 2, right)

thorn (thôrn), **1** a sharp point on a stem or branch of a tree or other plant: *Roses have thorns.* **2** a tree or other plant with thorns. *noun.*

thorn·y (thôr′nē), **1** full of thorns: *I scratched my hands on the thorny bush.* **2** troublesome; annoying: *It took her a long time to solve the thorny problem. adjective,* **thorn·i·er, thorn·i·est.**

thor·ough (thėr′ō), **1** complete: *Please make a thorough search for the lost money.* **2** doing all that should be done: *The doctor was very thorough in examining the patient. adjective.*

thor·ough·bred (thėr′ō bred′), **1** of pure breed: *The farmer had a fine herd of thoroughbred cattle.*

2 a thoroughbred animal, most often a horse. **1** *adjective*, **2** *noun*.

thor·ough·fare (thėr′ō fer′ *or* thėr′ō far′), **1** a passage, road, or street open at both ends: *A city street is a public thoroughfare.* **2** a main road; highway: *The interstate highway that goes from Chicago to San Francisco is one of the main thoroughfares in the United States. noun.*

those (ŦHōz). *Those* is used to point out persons, things, or ideas. *Those girls helped me. Those are my books. Those two problems are hard. adjective, pronoun plural* of **that.**

thou (ŦHou), an old word meaning **you:** *Be thou with me. pronoun singular.*

though (ŦHō), **1** in spite of the fact that: *Though it was pouring, the girls went to school.* **2** even if: *Though I fail, I shall try again.* **3** however: *I am sorry for our quarrel; you began it, though.* **1,2** *conjunction,* **3** *adverb.* Also spelled **tho** or **tho'.**

as though, as if: *You look as though you were tired.*

thought (thôt), **1** what a person thinks; idea; notion: *Her thought was to have a picnic.* **2** the process of thinking: *Thought helps us solve problems.* **3** care; attention; regard: *Show some thought for others than yourself.* **4** See **think.** *We thought it would snow yesterday.* **1-3** *noun,* **4** *verb.*

thought·ful (thôt′fəl), **1** full of thought; thinking. **2** careful of others; considerate: *She is always thoughtful of her parents. adjective.*

thoughtful (definition 1)
The boys looked **thoughtful** as they played checkers.

thought·less (thôt′lis), **1** without thought; doing things without thinking; careless: *Thoughtless drivers cause many automobile accidents.* **2** showing little or no care or regard for others: *It is thoughtless of them to keep us waiting so long. adjective.*

thou·sand (thou′znd), ten hundred; 1000. *noun, adjective.*

thou·sandth (thou′zndth), **1** next after the 999th. **2** one of 1000 equal parts. *adjective, noun.*

thrash (thrash), **1** to beat: *I'd like to thrash whoever broke my camera.* **2** to move violently; toss: *Unable to sleep, I thrashed about in bed.* **3** to thresh wheat, rye, or other grain. *verb.*

thrash·er (thrash′ər), a North American songbird that has a long tail and is somewhat like a thrush. *noun.*

thread (thred), **1** a fine cord made of strands of cotton, silk, wool, nylon, or the like, spun and twisted together. You sew with thread. **2** to pass a thread through: *Can you thread a needle? I threaded beads onto a string.* **3** something long and slender like a thread: *The spider hung by a thread. A thread of light came through the crack in the door.* **4** the main thought that connects the parts of a story or speech: *Something distracted her and she lost the thread of their conversation.* **5** to make one's way through; make one's way carefully: *He threaded his way through the crowd.* **6** the sloping ridge that winds around a bolt, screw, or pipe joint. The thread of a nut interlocks with the thread of a bolt. **1,3,4,6** *noun,* **2,5** *verb.*

thread·bare (thred′ber′ *or* thred′bar′), **1** worn thin; worn so much that the threads show: *I threw away the threadbare coat.* **2** old and worn: *Saying "I forgot" is a threadbare excuse. adjective.*

threat (thret), **1** a statement of what will be done to hurt or punish someone: *The teacher's threat to keep the class after school stopped the noise.* **2** a sign or cause of possible harm or worry: *Black clouds held the threat of rain. Pollution is a threat to our health. noun.*

threat·en (thret′n), **1** to make a threat against; say what will be done to hurt or punish: *The teacher threatened to fail all the students that did no homework.* **2** to give warning of coming trouble: *Black clouds threaten rain.* **3** to be a cause of possible harm or worry to: *A flood threatened the city. verb.*

three (thrē), one more than two; 3. Three feet make one yard. *noun, adjective.*

thresh (thresh), **1** to separate the grain or seeds from wheat, rye, or other grain. Nowadays most farmers use a machine to thresh their wheat. **2** to toss about; thrash. *verb.*

thresh·er (thresh′ər), a person or thing that threshes, especially a person or machine that threshes wheat, rye, or other grain. *noun.*

thresh·old (thresh′ōld), **1** a piece of wood or stone under a door. **2** a doorway. **3** the point of entering; beginning point: *The scientist was on the threshold of an important discovery. noun.*

threw (thrü). See **throw.** *He threw the ball at me. verb.*

thrice (thrīs), three times: *He knocked thrice. adverb.*

thrift (thrift), the careful management of money; the habit of saving: *By thrift they managed to get along on their small income. A savings account encourages thrift. noun.*

thrift·y (thrif′tē), careful in spending; economical; saving: *a thrifty shopper. adjective,* **thrift·i·er, thrift·i·est.**

thrill (thril), **1** a shivering, exciting feeling: *She gets a thrill whenever she sees a parade.* **2** to give a shivering, exciting feeling to: *Stories of adventure thrilled him.* **3** to have a shivering, exciting feeling:

The children thrilled at the sight of the parade. **4** to tremble: *Her voice thrilled with excitement.* **1** *noun,* **2-4** *verb.*

thrill·er (thril′ər), a thing that thrills, especially a story, play, television program, or motion picture filled with excitement and suspense. *noun.*

thrive (thrīv), to be successful; grow rich; grow strong; prosper: *Flowers will not thrive without sunshine.* *verb,* **thrives, throve** or **thrived, thrived** or **thriv·en** (thriv′ən), **thriv·ing.**

throat (thrōt), **1** the front of the neck: *The coat was buttoned up to her throat.* **2** the passage from the mouth to the stomach or the lungs: *A chicken bone got stuck in the dog's throat.* **3** any narrow passage: *The throat of the valley was blocked by fallen rocks.* *noun.*

throb (throb), **1** to beat rapidly or strongly: *The long climb up the hill made her heart throb. The wounded arm throbbed with pain.* **2** a rapid or strong beat: *A throb of pain shot through his head.* **1** *verb,* **throbs, throbbed, throb·bing;** **2** *noun.*

throne (thrōn), **1** the chair on which a king, queen, bishop, or other person of high rank sits during ceremonies. **2** the power or authority of a king, queen, or other ruler: *The throne of England commands respect but does not command armies.* *noun.*

throng (thrông), **1** a crowd; multitude. **2** to crowd; fill with a crowd: *People thronged the theater to see the new movie.* **3** to come together in a crowd; go or press in large numbers: *The people thronged to see the parade.* **1** *noun,* **2,3** *verb.*

throt·tle (throt′l), **1** a valve for regulating the supply of steam or gasoline to an engine. **2** a lever or pedal working such a valve. The throttle of a car is called an accelerator. **3** to choke; strangle: *The thief throttled the dog to keep it from barking.* **1,2** *noun,* **3** *verb,* **throt·tles, throt·tled, throt·tling.**

through (thrü), **1** from end to end of; from side to side of; between the parts of: *They drove through a snowstorm. I bored holes through a board.* **2** from beginning to end; from one side to the other: *She read the book all the way through.* **3** here and there in; over: *We traveled through New England and saw many old towns.* **4** because of; by reason of: *The family refused help through pride.* **5** by means of: *I learned of the new book through my teacher.* **6** completely: *I walked home in the rain and my clothes are wet through.* **7** going all the way without change: *a through train from New York to Chicago.* **8** having reached the end of; finished with: *We are through school at three o'clock.* **9** having reached the end; finished: *I will soon be through.* **10** allowing movement or passage through without stopping: *Is this a through street?* **1,3-5,8** *preposition,* **2,6** *adverb,* **7,9,10** *adjective.* Also spelled **thru.**

through·out (thrü out′), **1** all the way through; through all; in every part of: *The Fourth of July is celebrated throughout the United States.* **2** in every part: *The house is well built throughout.* **1** *preposition,* **2** *adverb.*

a hat	i it	oi oil	ch child	ə = { a in about
ā age	ī ice	ou out	ng long	e in taken
ä far	o hot	u cup	sh she	i in pencil
e let	ō open	ù put	th thin	o in lemon
ē equal	ô order	ü rule	ᴛʜ then	u in circus
ėr term			zh measure	

throve (thrōv). See **thrive.** *The plants throve in the rich soil.* *verb.*

throw (thrō), **1** to send through the air forcefully; hurl: *to throw a ball. I threw water on the fire.* **2** the act of throwing; a cast, toss, or hurl: *That was a good throw from left field to the catcher.* **3** to cause to fall: *The wrestler threw his opponent. I was thrown by a horse.* **4** to put carelessly or in haste: *I threw a coat over my shoulders.* **5** to move a lever or switch that connects or disconnects parts of a mechanism. **1,3-5** *verb,* **throws, threw, thrown, throw·ing;** **2** *noun.*

throw away, 1 to get rid of; discard: *Throw away those old shoes.* **2** to waste: *Don't throw away your opportunities.*

throw in, to add as a gift: *Our grocer often throws in an extra apple or two.*

throw off, to cause to lose: *The fox threw the hounds off its trail by doubling back several times.*

throw out, to get rid of; discard: *Let's throw out this broken old toy.*

throw up, to bring up food from the stomach; vomit.

thrown (thrōn). See **throw.** *She has thrown her old toys away.* *verb.*

thru (thrü). See **through.** *preposition, adverb, adjective.*

thrush (thrush), any of a large group of songbirds that includes the robin and the bluebird. *noun, plural* **thrush·es.**

thrust (thrust), **1** to push with force: *He thrust his hands into his pockets.* **2** a push with force: *She hid the book behind the pillow with a quick thrust.* **3** to stab; pierce: *I thrust the knife into the apple.* **4** a stab: *A thrust with the pin broke the balloon.* **1,3** *verb,* **thrusts, thrust, thrust·ing;** **2,4** *noun.*

thud (thud), **1** a dull sound. A heavy blow or fall may cause a thud. *The book hit the floor with a thud.* **2** to hit, move, or strike with a thud: *The heavy box fell and thudded on the floor.* **1** *noun,* **2** *verb,* **thuds, thud·ded, thud·ding.**

thug (thug), a rough, violent criminal. *noun.*

thumb (thum), **1** the short, thick finger of the hand. **2** the part that covers the thumb: *There was a hole in the thumb of the mitten.* **3** to turn the pages of rapidly, with a thumb or as if with a thumb: *I didn't read the book; I just thumbed through it.* **4** to ask for or get a free ride by holding up a thumb to motorists. **1,2** *noun,* **3,4** *verb.*

under one's thumb, under one's power or influence: *Several members of the club are under the president's thumb.*

thumb·tack (thum′tak′), a tack with a broad, flat head, that can be pressed into a wall or board with the thumb. *noun.*

thump (thump), **1** to strike with something thick and heavy; pound: *She thumped the table with her fist.* **2** a blow with something thick and heavy; heavy knock: *a thump on the head.* **3** the dull sound made by a blow, knock, or fall: *We heard a thump when the book fell.* **4** to beat violently: *His heart thumped as he walked past the cemetery at night.* **1,4** *verb,* **2,3** *noun.*

thun·der (thun′dər), **1** the loud noise that accompanies or follows a flash of lightning. It is caused by a disturbance of the air resulting from the discharge of electricity. **2** to give forth thunder: *It thundered a few times, but no rain fell.* **3** any noise like thunder: *the thunder of Niagara Falls, a thunder of applause.* **4** to make a noise like thunder: *The cannon thundered throughout the night.* **1,3** *noun,* **2,4** *verb.*

thun·der·bolt (thun′dər bōlt′), **1** a flash of lightning and the thunder that accompanies or follows it. **2** something sudden, startling, and terrible: *The news of the accident came as a thunderbolt. noun.*

thun·der·clap (thun′dər klap⌐), a loud crash of thunder. *noun.*

thun·der·cloud (thun′dər kloud′), a dark cloud that brings thunder and lightning. *noun.*

thun·der·head (thun′dər hed′), one of the round, swelling, very high clouds that often develop into thunderclouds. *noun.*

thunderhead

thun·der·ous (thun′dər əs), **1** producing thunder. **2** making a noise like thunder: *The famous actor received a thunderous burst of applause at the end of the play. adjective.*

thun·der·show·er (thun′dər shou′ər), a shower with thunder and lightning. *noun.*

thun·der·storm (thun′dər stôrm′), a storm with thunder and lightning. *noun.*

thun·der·struck (thun′dər struk′), overcome as if hit by a thunderbolt; astonished; amazed: *We were thunderstruck by the news of war. adjective.*

Thurs. or **Thur.,** Thursday.

Thurs·day (thėrz′dē), the fifth day of the week;
the day after Wednesday. *noun.*
[*Thursday* comes from an earlier English word meaning "Thur's day." Thur or Thunor is the name of a Norse god of thunder.]

thus (ᴛʜus), **1** in this way; in the following manner: *The speaker spoke thus: "Ladies and Gentlemen, parents, fellow students."* **2** therefore: *We hurried and thus arrived on time.* **3** to this extent; to this degree; so: *Thus far he is enjoying his studies. adverb.*

thwart (thwôrt), **1** to oppose and defeat; keep from doing something: *Lack of money thwarted her plans for college.* **2** a seat across a boat, on which a rower sits. **1** *verb,* **2** *noun.*

thy (ᴛʜī), an old word meaning **your.** "Thy name" means "your name." *adjective.*

thyme (tīm), a small plant with sweet-smelling leaves. The leaves are used for seasoning. *noun.*

thy·roid (thī′roid), a gland in the neck that affects growth and metabolism. *noun.*

thy·self (ᴛʜī self′), an old word meaning **yourself.** *pronoun.*

tick[1] (tik), **1** a sound made by a clock or watch. **2** to make such a sound: *The clock ticked.* **3** to mark off: *The clock ticked away the minutes.* **4** a small mark. We use √ or / as a tick. *I put a tick next to each chore I had completed on the list.* **5** to mark with a tick; check: *She ticked off the items one by one.* **1,4** *noun,* **2,3,5** *verb.*

tick[2] (tik), a tiny eight-legged animal, related to the spider, that lives on animals and sucks their blood. *noun.*

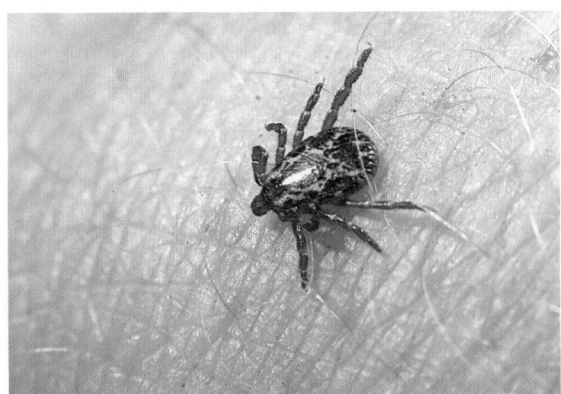

tick[2]—about ¼ inch (5 millimeters) long

tick·et (tik′it), **1** a card or piece of paper that gives its holder a right or privilege: *a ticket to the theater.* **2** a written order to appear in court, given to a person accused of breaking a traffic law or a parking regulation: *a ticket for speeding, a parking ticket.* **3** to give a written order to appear in court: *The cars were ticketed for illegal parking.* **4** a card or piece of paper attached to something to show its price, what it is or consists of, or some similar information. **5** to put a ticket on: *All items are ticketed with the price.* **6** the list of candidates to be voted on that belong to one political party: *the Democratic ticket.* **1,2,4,6** *noun,* **3,5** *verb.*

tick·le (tik′əl), **1** to touch lightly, causing little thrills, shivers, or wriggles: *He tickled the baby's feet and made her laugh.* **2** to have a feeling like this: *My nose tickles from the dust.* **3** a tingling or itching feeling. **4** to amuse; excite pleasantly: *The funny story tickled me.* 1,2,4 *verb*, **tick·les, tick·led, tick·ling;** 3 *noun.*

tick·lish (tik′lish), **1** sensitive to tickling: *The bottoms of the feet are ticklish.* **2** requiring careful handling; delicate; risky: *Telling your friends their faults is a ticklish business. adjective.*

tick-tack-toe (tik′tak tō′), a game in which two players alternate putting circles or crosses in a figure of nine squares. The object is to be the first to fill three squares in a row with your mark. *noun.*

tid·al (tī′dl), of tides; having tides; caused by tides. A tidal river is affected by the ocean's tide. *adjective.*

tidal wave, a large, destructive ocean wave produced by an earthquake or strong wind.

tid·bit (tid′bit′), a very pleasing bit of food, news, or information. *noun.*

tide (tīd), **1** the rise and fall of the ocean about every twelve hours, caused by the pull of the moon and the sun: *We go swimming at high tide; at low tide we dig clams.* **2** anything that rises and falls like the tide: *the tide of public opinion.* **3 tide over,** to help along for a time: *His savings will tide him over his illness.* 1,2 *noun,* 3 *verb,* **tides, tid·ed, tid·ing.**

ti·di·ness (tī′dē nis), neatness. *noun.*

ti·dings (tī′dingz), news; information: *joyful tidings. noun plural.*

ti·dy (tī′dē), **1** neat and in order: *a tidy room.* **2** to make neat; put in order: *We tidied the room.* **3** considerable; fairly large: *$500 is a tidy sum of money.* 1,3 *adjective,* **ti·di·er, ti·di·est;** 2 *verb,* **ti·dies, ti·died, ti·dy·ing.**

tie (tī), **1** to fasten with string or the like; bind: *Please tie this package.* **2** to arrange to form a bow or knot: *We tied red ribbons on the party favors.* **3** to fasten; form a bow: *That ribbon doesn't tie well.* **4** to tighten and fasten the string or strings of: *to tie one's shoes.* **5** a necktie: *He always wears a shirt and tie.* **6** a thing that ties; fastening; bond; connection: *family ties, ties of friendship.* **7** a heavy piece of timber or iron. The rails of a railroad track rest on ties. **8** an equality in points: *The game ended in a tie, 3 to 3.* **9** to make the same score; be equal in points: *The two teams tied.* 1-4,9 *verb,* **ties, tied, ty·ing;** 5-8 *noun.*

tie up, 1 to hinder; stop: *The stalled truck tied up traffic for half an hour.* **2** to be very busy: *I can't go tomorrow; I'm all tied up.*

tier (tir), one of several rows one above another: *tiers of seats in a football stadium. noun.*

ti·ger (tī′gər), a large cat of Asia with dull-yellow fur striped with black. *noun.*

tight (tīt), **1** firm; held firmly; packed or put together firmly: *a tight knot.* **2** firmly: *The rope was tied too tight.* **3** fitting closely; close: *tight clothing.* **4** not having much time: *With such a tight*

schedule, he isn't able to take a vacation this month. **5** not letting water, air, or gas in or out: *The tight roof kept rain from leaking in.* **6** hard to deal with or manage; difficult: *A lie got her in a tight spot.* **7** almost even; close: *It was a tight race.* **8** hard to get; scarce: *Money is tight just now.* **9** stingy: *He is tight with his money.* 1,3-9 *adjective,* 2 *adverb.*

tight·en (tīt′n), to make or become tight: *He tightened his belt. The rope tightened as I pulled it. verb.*

tight·rope (tīt′rōp′), a rope stretched tight on which acrobats perform. *noun.*

tightrope

tights (tīts), a tight-fitting garment, usually covering the lower part of the body and the legs, worn by acrobats, dancers, or gymnasts. *noun plural.*

tight·wad (tīt′wod′), a stingy person. *noun.*

ti·gress (tī′gris), a female tiger. *noun, plural* **ti·gress·es.**

tile (tīl), **1** a thin piece of baked clay, stone, or

tiger—about 9 feet (2½ meters) long with the tail

plastic. Tiles are used for covering roofs, paving floors, and ornamenting. **2** to put tiles on or in: *to tile a bathroom floor.* 1 *noun,* 2 *verb,* **tiles, tiled, til·ing.**

till[1] (til), until; up to the time of; up to the time when: *The child played till eight. Walk till you come to a white house.* *preposition, conjunction.*

till[2] (til), to cultivate land; plow: *Farmers till before planting.* *verb.*

till[3] (til), a small drawer for money under or behind a counter. *noun.*

till·er (til′ər), a bar or handle used to turn the rudder in steering a boat. *noun.*

tilt (tilt), **1** to tip or cause to tip; slope; slant: *You tilt your head forward when you bow.* **2** a slope; slant: *the tilt of a wobbly table.* **3** to fight with lances. Knights used to tilt on horseback. 1,3 *verb,* 2 *noun.*

full tilt, at full speed; with full force: *The wagon ran full tilt down the hill.*

tim·ber (tim′bər), **1** wood for building and making things. Houses, ships, and furniture are made from timber. **2** a large piece of wood used in building. Beams and rafters are timbers. **3** trees or forests that could provide wood for building: *Half their land is covered with timber.* *noun.*

tim·ber·line (tim′bər līn′), the line beyond which trees will not grow on mountains and in the polar regions because of the cold. *noun.*

timberline

time (tīm), **1** all the days there have been or ever will be; the past, present, and future. Time is measured in years, months, days, hours, minutes, and seconds. **2** a part of the past, present, or future: *A minute is a short time. A long time ago people lived in caves.* **3** a period of history; age: *We are living in the time of space exploration.* **4** some point in time: *The time the game begins is two o'clock, November 8. What time is it right now?* **5** the right part or point of time: *It is time to eat dinner.* **6** an occasion: *This time we will succeed.* **7** a way of counting the hours that pass: *standard time, daylight-saving time.* **8** a condition of life: *War brings hard times.* **9** an experience during a certain period: *Everyone had a good time at the party.* **10** the rate of movement in music; rhythm:

march time, waltz time. **11** to measure the speed of: *I timed the horse at half a mile per minute.* **12** to do at regular times; do in rhythm with; set the time of: *The dancers time their steps to the music.* **13** to set, regulate, or adjust: *The clock was timed to ring at 7:00.* **14 times,** multiplied by. The sign for this in arithmetic is ×. *Four times three is twelve. Twenty is five times four.* 1-10 *noun,* 11-13 *verb,* **times, timed, tim·ing;** 14 *preposition.*

at times, now and then; once in a while; sometimes: *At times, I wish I were taller.*

bide one's time, to wait for a good chance: *If you bide your time you will probably get a better buy.*

for the time being, for the present; for now: *The baby is asleep for the time being.*

from time to time, now and then; once in a while: *From time to time we visit my grandparents.*

in no time, shortly; before long: *We hurried and arrived home in no time.*

in time, 1 after a while: *I think that in time we may win.* **2** soon enough: *Will she arrive in time to have dinner with us?* **3** in the right rate of movement in music, dancing, or marching: *We clapped in time to the music.*

keep time, 1 (of a watch or clock) to go correctly: *My watch keeps good time.* **2** to sound or move at the right rate: *The marchers kept time to the music.*

on time, 1 at the right time; not late: *We get to school on time each day.* **2** with time in which to pay; on credit: *He bought a car on time.*

tell time, to know what time it is by the clock.

time after time or **time and again,** again and again: *I made the same mistake time after time.*

time line, a straight line which represents a certain length of time. Along the line are printed important historical dates and the events that happened on those dates.

time·ly (tīm′lē), at the right time: *The timely arrival of the firemen prevented the fire from destroying the building.* *adjective,* **time·li·er, time·li·est.**

time·piece (tīm′pēs′), a clock or watch. *noun.*

tim·er (tī′mər), a device like a clock that tells when a certain amount of time has passed: *The timer rang when the cake had baked for 38 minutes.* *noun.*

time·ta·ble (tīm′tā′bəl), a schedule showing the times when trains, boats, buses, or airplanes come and go. *noun.*

tim·id (tim′id), easily frightened; shy: *The timid child was afraid of other children.* *adjective.*

ti·mid·i·ty (tə mid′ə tē), timid behavior; shyness. *noun.*

tim·ing (tī′ming), the proper control of the time or speed of something to get the greatest effect: *Timing is important when you swing your bat at a baseball.* *noun.*

tin (tin), **1** a soft, silvery-white metal. Tin is used to plate other metals and is mixed with other metals to form alloys. Tin is a chemical element. **2** made of or lined with tin: *tin cans.* **3** any can, box, or pan made of or lined with tin: *a pie tin.* 1,3 *noun,* 2 *adjective.*

tin·der (tin′dər), a material used to catch fire from a spark: *Before matches were invented people struck flint and steel together to light tinder. noun.*

tin·foil (tin′foil′), a very thin sheet of aluminum, tin, or tin and lead, used as a wrapping for candy, tobacco, or similar articles. *noun.*

tinge (tinj), **1** to color slightly: *The dawn sky was tinged with pink.* **2** a slight coloring or tint: *There was a tinge of red in the leaves.* 1 *verb,* **ting·es, tinged, tinge·ing** or **ting·ing;** 2 *noun.*

tinge (definition 2)—The water reflected a **tinge** of pink from the sunset.

tin·gle (ting′gəl), **1** to have a feeling of thrills or a pricking, stinging feeling: *He tingled with excitement on his first airplane trip.* **2** a pricking, stinging feeling: *The cold caused a tingle in my fingers.* 1 *verb,* **tin·gles, tin·gled, tin·gling;** 2 *noun.*

tink·er (ting′kər), **1** a person who mends pots, pans, kettles, and other metal household articles. **2** to work or repair in an unskilled or clumsy way: *The children were tinkering with the clock and broke it.* **3** to work or keep busy in a rather useless way: *I was tinkering in my workshop.* 1 *noun,* 2,3 *verb.*

tin·kle (ting′kəl), **1** to make or cause to make short, light, ringing sounds: *Little bells tinkle. She tinkled the side of the glass with her spoon.* **2** a series of short, light, ringing sounds: *the tinkle of sleigh bells.* 1 *verb,* **tin·kles, tin·kled, tin·kling;** 2 *noun.*

tin·sel (tin′səl), **1** very thin sheets, strips, or threads of glittering metal or plastic, used to trim Christmas trees. **2** anything showy but having little value. *noun.*

tint (tint), **1** a shade of a color: *The picture was painted in several tints of blue.* **2** a delicate or pale color. **3** to put a tint on; color slightly: *The walls were tinted gray.* 1,2 *noun,* 3 *verb.*

ti·ny (tī′nē), very small: *a tiny baby chicken. adjective,* **ti·ni·er, ti·ni·est.**

tip[1] (tip), **1** the end part; end: *the tips of the fingers.* **2** a small piece put on the end of something: *to buy rubber tips to put on the legs of a stool.* **3** to put a tip on; furnish with a tip: *spears tipped with steel.* 1,2 *noun,* 3 *verb,* **tips, tipped, tip·ping.**

a hat	i it	oi oil	ch child	⎧ a in about
ā age	ī ice	ou out	ng long	e in taken
ä far	o hot	u cup	sh she	ə = i in pencil
e let	ō open	u̇ put	th thin	o in lemon
ē equal	ô order	ü rule	ᵺ then	⎩ u in circus
ėr term			zh measure	

tip[2] (tip), **1** to slope; slant: *She tipped the table toward her.* **2** to upset; overturn: *I tipped over my glass of water.* **3** to take off a hat in greeting: *The old gentleman tipped his hat to his neighbor. verb,* **tips, tipped, tip·ping.**

tip[3] (tip), **1** a small present of money in return for service: *She gave the waiter a tip.* **2** to give a small present of money to: *Did you tip the porter?* **3** a useful hint; helpful information: *Someone gave me a tip about pitching the tent where trees would shade it.* 1,3 *noun,* 2 *verb,* **tips, tipped, tip·ping.**

tip off, 1 to give secret information to: *They tipped me off about a good bargain.* **2** to warn: *Someone tipped off the criminals and they escaped.*

tip·toe (tip′tō′), **1** the tips of the toes. **2** to walk on the tips of the toes: *She tiptoed quietly up the stairs.* 1 *noun,* 2 *verb,* **tip·toes, tip·toed, tip·toe·ing.**

tip·top (tip′top′), **1** the very top; highest point. **2** first-rate; excellent: *I'm in tiptop shape.* 1 *noun,* 2 *adjective.*

tire[1] (tīr), to make or become weary: *The work tires me. The old dog tired easily. verb,* **tires, tired, tir·ing.**

tire[2] (tīr), a band of rubber around a wheel. Some tires have inner tubes for holding air; others hold the air in the tire itself or are made of solid rubber. *Put more air in the tires. noun.*

tired (tīrd), weary; wearied; exhausted: *I'm tired, but I must get back to work. adjective.*

tire·less (tīr′lis), **1** never becoming tired; requiring little rest: *a tireless worker.* **2** never stopping: *tireless efforts. adjective.*

tire·some (tīr′səm), tiring; not interesting: *a tiresome speech. adjective.*

tis·sue (tish′ü), **1** the substance that forms the parts of living things. **2** a group of the same type of cells working together to do the same job: *muscle tissue, brain tissue.* **3** a thin, soft paper that absorbs moisture easily. *noun.*

tissue paper, a very thin, soft paper, used for wrapping or covering things.

ti·tle (tī′tl), **1** the name of a book, poem, picture, song, and the like: *"Goldilocks and the Three Bears" is the title of a famous story for little children.* **2** a name showing rank, occupation, or condition in life. King, duke, lord, countess, captain, doctor, professor, Madame, and Miss are titles. **3** a first-place position; championship: *He won the school tennis title.* **4** a written deed showing a legal right to the possession of property. When a house is sold, the seller gives title to the buyer. *noun.*

title page, the page at the front of a book giving the title, the author's name, and the publisher.

T

tit·ter (tit′ər), to laugh nervously; giggle: *The students tittered when their teacher stumbled. verb.*

TN, Tennessee (used with postal Zip Code).

to (tü, tu̇, *or* tə), **1** in the direction of: *Go to the right.* **2** as far as; until: *This apple is rotten to the core. I will be your friend to the end.* **3** for the purpose of; for: *She soon came to the rescue.* **4** into: *She tore the letter to pieces.* **5** along with; with: *We danced to the music.* **6** compared with: *The score was 9 to 5.* **7** in agreement with: *Going without food is not to my liking.* **8** on; against: *Fasten it to the wall. They danced cheek to cheek.* **9** about; concerning: *What did he say to that?* **10** *To* is used to show action toward. *Give the book to me. Speak to her.* **11** *To* is used with verbs. *He likes to read. The birds began to sing. preposition.*

toad (tōd), a small animal somewhat like a frog, that lives most of the time on land rather than in water. Toads have a rough, brown skin that suggests a lump of earth. *noun.*

toad·stool (tōd′stül′), a poisonous mushroom. *noun.*

toast¹ (tōst), **1** slices of bread browned by heat. **2** to brown by heat: *We toasted the bread.* **3** to heat thoroughly: *He toasted his feet before the open fire.* **1** *noun,* **2,3** *verb.*

toast² (tōst), **1** to wish good fortune to before drinking; drink to the health of: *We toasted our hosts.* **2** the act of drinking to the health of a person or thing. **3** a popular or celebrated person: *The actor was the toast of the town.* **1** *verb,* **2,3** *noun.*

toast·er (tō′stər), a thing that toasts: *Turn on the electric toaster. noun.*

to·bac·co (tə bak′ō), **1** the prepared leaves of certain plants, used for smoking or chewing or as snuff. **2** one of these plants. *noun, plural* **to·bac·cos** or **to·bac·coes.**

toboggan
(definition 2)

to·bog·gan (tə bog′ən), **1** a long, narrow, flat sled without runners. The front of a toboggan curves upwards. **2** to slide downhill on such a sled. **1** *noun,* **2** *verb.*

[*Toboggan* comes from a word used by French settlers in Canada. They got the word from the American Indian name for the sled.]

to·day (tə dā′), **1** this day; the present time: *Today is Wednesday.* **2** on or during this day: *What are you doing today?* **3** at the present time; now:

Pollution is a problem today. **1** *noun,* **2,3** *adverb.*

tod·dle (tod′l), to walk with short, unsteady steps, as a baby does. *verb,* **tod·dles, tod·dled, tod·dling.**

toe (tō), **1** one of the five end parts of the foot. **2** the part of a stocking, shoe, or slipper that covers the toes: *to have a hole in the toe of a sock.* **3** to touch or reach with the toes: *Toe this line.* **1,2** *noun,* **3** *verb,* **toes, toed, toe·ing.**

toe·nail (tō′nāl′), the nail growing on a toe. *noun.*

to·geth·er (tə geŦH′ər), **1** with each other; in company: *They were standing together.* **2** with united action; in cooperation: *Let's work together and get the job done quickly.* **3** into one gathering, company, mass, or body: *The principal called the school together. The tailor will sew these pieces together and make a suit.* **4** at the same time: *Rain and snow were falling together.* **5** without a stop or break; continuously: *He reads for hours together.* **6** taken or considered as a whole: *This one cost more than all the others together. adverb.*

toil (toil), **1** hard work; labor. **2** to work hard: *to toil with one's hands for a living.* **3** to move with difficulty, pain, or weariness: *Carrying heavy loads, they toiled up the hill.* **1** *noun,* **2,3** *verb.*

toil (definition 1)

toi·let (toi′lit), **1** a bathroom. **2** a porcelain bowl with a seat attached and with a drain at the bottom to flush the bowl clean. Waste matter from the body is disposed of in a toilet. **3** the process of dressing. Bathing, combing the hair, and putting on one's clothes are all parts of one's toilet. *I made a hurried toilet.* **4** of or for the toilet: *Combs and brushes are toilet articles.* **1-3** *noun,* **4** *adjective.*

to·ken (tō′kən), **1** a mark or sign of something; symbol: *I gave her my ring as a token of friendship.* **2** a piece of metal stamped for a higher value than the metal is worth. Tokens are used on some buses and subways instead of money. **3** a piece of metal or plastic indicating a right or privilege: *This token will admit you to the swimming pool. noun.*

Tokyo | tongs

To·ky·o (tō′kē ō), the capital of Japan. *noun.*

told (tōld). See **tell.** *You told me that last week. We were told to wait. verb.*

tol·er·a·ble (tol′ər ə bəl), **1** able to be endured; bearable: *The pain has become tolerable.* **2** fairly good: *My grandparents are in tolerable health.* *adjective.*

tol·er·ance (tol′ər əns), a willingness to be patient toward people whose opinions or ways differ from one's own: *The principal's tolerance of their bad behavior surprised us. noun.*

tol·er·ant (tol′ər ənt), willing to let other people do as they think best; willing to endure beliefs and actions of which one does not approve: *to be tolerant toward all religious beliefs. adjective.*

tol·er·ate (tol′ə rāt′), **1** to allow; permit: *The teacher won't tolerate any disorder.* **2** to bear; endure; put up with: *I cannot tolerate swimming in icy water. verb,* **tol·e·rates, tol·e·rat·ed, tol·e·rat·ing.**

toll[1] (tōl), **1** to sound with single strokes slowly and regularly repeated: *On Sunday all the church bells toll.* **2** a stroke or sound of a bell being tolled. **1** *verb,* **2** *noun.*

toll[2] (tōl), **1** a tax or fee paid for some right or privilege: *We pay a toll when we use that bridge.* **2** a charge for a certain service. There is a toll on long-distance telephone calls. *noun.*

toll·booth (tōl′büth′), a place where tolls are collected before or after going over a bridge, road, or turnpike or through a tunnel. *noun, plural* **toll·booths** (tōl′büฮ̄z′ *or* tōl′büths′).

toll·gate (tōl′gāt′), a tollbooth. *noun.*

toll road, a road on which tolls are charged; turnpike.

tom·a·hawk (tom′ə hôk), a light ax used by North American Indians as a weapon and a tool. *noun.*

tomahawks

to·ma·to (tə mā′tō *or* tə mä′tō), a juicy, red or yellow fruit eaten as a vegetable, either raw or cooked. Tomatoes grow on a spreading garden plant that has hairy leaves and stems and yellow flowers. *noun, plural* **to·ma·toes.**

tomb (tüm), a grave or vault for a dead body, often above ground. *noun.*

a hat	i it	oi oil	ch child	a in about
ā age	ī ice	ou out	ng long	e in taken
ä far	o hot	u cup	sh she	ə = i in pencil
e let	ō open	ů put	th thin	o in lemon
ē equal	ô order	ü rule	ฮ̄н then	u in circus
ėr term			zh measure	

tom·boy (tom′boi′), a girl who likes to take part in so-called boys' games and activities. *noun.*

tomb·stone (tüm′stōn′), a stone that marks a tomb or grave. *noun.*

tom·cat (tom′kat′), a male cat. *noun.*

to·mor·row (tə môr′ō), **1** the day after today: *Today is Thursday; tomorrow will be Friday.* **2** the near future: *Houses of tomorrow may all be heated by the sun.* **3** on the day after today: *I'll see you tomorrow.* **1,2** *noun,* **3** *adverb.*

tom-tom (tom′tom′), a kind of drum, usually beaten with the hands. *noun.*

ton (tun), a unit of weight equal to 2000 pounds in the United States and Canada, and 2240 pounds in Great Britain. A **long ton** is 2240 pounds; a **short ton** is 2000 pounds. A **metric ton** is 1000 kilograms. *noun.*

tone (tōn), **1** any sound considered with reference to its quality, pitch, strength, or source: *angry tones, gentle tones, the deep tone of an organ.* **2** the quality of sound: *a voice that is soft in tone.* **3** a musical sound, especially one of definite pitch and character. **4** the difference in pitch between two notes. C and D are one tone apart. **5** a manner of speaking or writing: *I disliked their disrespectful tone.* **6** spirit; character; style: *A tone of quiet elegance prevails in their home.* **7** a normal, healthy condition; vigor: *Regular exercise will keep your body in tone.* **8** a shade of color: *The room is furnished in tones of brown.* **9** **tone down,** to soften: *Tone down your voice.* **1-8** *noun,* **9** *verb,* **tones, toned, ton·ing.**

tongs (tôngz), a tool with two arms that are joined, used for holding or lifting. Different kinds of tongs are used for picking up ice, logs, sugar, and other things. *noun plural.*

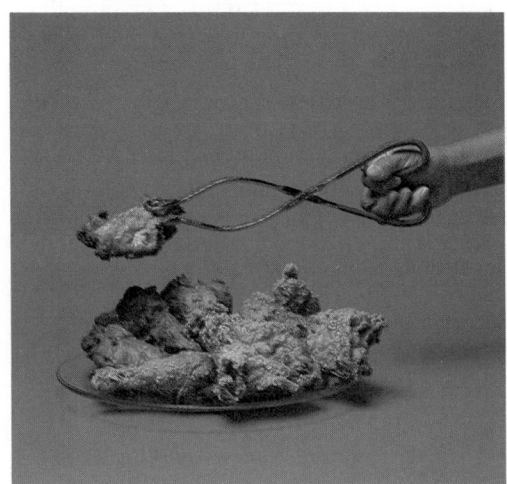

tongs

T

659

tongue (tung), **1** the movable piece of flesh in the mouth. The tongue is used in tasting and, by people, for talking. **2** an animal's tongue used as food: *We ate cold tongue and salad.* **3** the power of speech: *Have you lost your tongue?* **4** a way of speaking; speech; talk: *My friend has a quick tongue.* **5** the language of a people: *the English tongue.* **6** something shaped or used like a tongue: *Tongues of flame leaped from the fire.* **7** the strip of leather under the laces of a shoe. *noun.*
hold one's tongue, to keep quiet; be silent: *Try to hold your tongue while someone else is talking.*

tongue-tied (tung′tīd′), unable to speak, especially because of shyness, embarrassment, surprise, or shock. *adjective.*

ton·ic (ton′ik), something that improves health or strength: *Fresh air and exercise are splendid tonics. noun.*

to·night (tə nīt′), **1** the night of this day; this night: *I must finish this work by tonight.* **2** on or during this night: *Do you think it will snow tonight?* **1** *noun,* **2** *adverb.*

ton·nage (tun′ij), weight in tons. *noun.*

ton·sil (ton′səl), either of the two small, oval masses of tissue on the sides of the throat, just back of the mouth. *noun.*

TONSIL

ton·sil·li·tis (ton′sə lī′tis), soreness and swelling of the tonsils. *noun.*

too (tü), **1** also; besides: *The dog is hungry, and thirsty too. We, too, are going away.* **2** more than what is proper or enough: *I ate too much.* **3** very; exceedingly: *I am only too glad to help. adverb.*

took (tùk). See take. *She took the car an hour ago. verb.*

tool (tül), **1** a knife, hammer, saw, shovel, or any instrument used in doing work: *Plumbers, mechanics, carpenters, and shoemakers need tools.* **2** a person or thing used by another like a tool: *Books are a scholar's tools.* **3** to work or shape with a tool: *to tool beautiful designs in leather with a knife.* **1,2** *noun,* **3** *verb.*

tool·box (tül′boks′), a box in which tools and sometimes such things as small parts are kept. *noun, plural* **tool·box·es.**

toot (tüt), **1** the sound of a horn, whistle, or other wind instrument. **2** to give forth a short blast of sound: *He heard the train whistle toot three times.* **3** to sound a horn, whistle, or other wind

instrument in short blasts. **1** *noun,* **2,3** *verb.*

tooth (tüth), **1** one of the hard, bonelike parts in the mouth, used for biting and chewing. **2** something like a tooth. Each one of the projecting parts of a comb, rake, or saw is a tooth. *noun, plural* **teeth.**

CROWN
ENAMEL
GUM
PULP
DENTIN
ROOTS
BONE

tooth (definition 1)

tooth·ache (tüth′āk′), a pain in a tooth. *noun.*

tooth·brush (tüth′brush′), a small brush for cleaning the teeth. *noun, plural* **tooth·brush·es.**

toothed (tütht *or* tüŧнd), **1** having teeth. **2** notched: *the toothed surface of a gear. adjective.*

tooth·paste (tüth′pāst′), a paste used in cleaning the teeth. *noun.*

tooth·pick (tüth′pik′), a small, pointed piece of wood or plastic for removing bits of food from between the teeth. *noun.*

top[1] (top), **1** the highest point or part: *the top of a mountain.* **2** the upper part, end, or surface: *the top of a table, a shoe top.* **3** the highest or leading place or rank: *She is at the top of her class.* **4** the highest point, pitch, or degree: *They were yelling at the top of their voices.* **5** the part of a plant that grows above ground: *Beet tops are somewhat like spinach.* **6** the cover of a bottle, can, or the like. **7** an article of clothing worn on the upper body: *a pajama top. She wore a blue top yesterday.* **8** highest; greatest: *the top shelf. The runners set off at top speed.* **9** to put a top on: *I will top the box.* **10** to be on top of; be the top of: *A church tops the hill.* **11** to reach the top of: *Call me when you see a gray car topping the hill.* **12** to rise high; rise above: *The sun topped the horizon.* **13** to be higher or greater than; do better than; outdo; excel: *His story topped all the rest.* **14** to remove the top part of: *to top a tree.* **1-7** *noun,* **8** *adjective,* **9-14** *verb,* **tops, topped, top·ping.**

top[2] (top), a toy that spins on a point. *noun.*

to·paz (tō′paz), a hard precious stone that occurs in crystals of various forms and colors. Clear yellow topaz is used in jewelry. *noun, plural* **to·paz·es.**

top·coat (top′kōt′), a lightweight overcoat. *noun.*

To·pe·ka (tə pē′kə), the capital of Kansas. *noun.*

top·ic (top′ik), a subject that people think, write,

or talk about: *I chose women's rights as the topic for my report. noun.*

topic sentence, a sentence that expresses the main idea in a paragraph.

top·most (top′mōst), highest: *I need a ladder to reach the apples on the topmost branches. adjective.*

to·pog·ra·phy (tə pog′rə fē), **1** the accurate and detailed description of places. **2** the surface features of a place or region. The topography of a region includes hills, valleys, streams, lakes, bridges, tunnels, and roads. *noun.*

top·ple (top′əl), **1** to fall forward; tumble down: *The chimney toppled over on the roof.* **2** to throw over or down; overturn: *The wind toppled the tree. verb,* **top·ples, top·pled, top·pling.**

top·soil (top′soil′), the upper part of the soil; surface soil: *Farmers need rich topsoil for their crops. noun.*

top·sy-tur·vy (top′sē tėr′vē), **1** upside down. **2** in confusion or disorder: *On moving day everything in the house was topsy-turvy. adverb, adjective.*

To·rah (tôr′ə), **1** the entire body of Jewish law and tradition. **2** the first five books of the Old Testament. *noun.*

torch (tôrch), **1** a light to be carried around or stuck in a holder on a wall. A piece of pine wood or anything that burns easily makes a good torch. **2** a device that shoots out a very hot flame. A torch is used to melt metal and burn off paint. *noun, plural* **torch·es.**

torch (definition 2)
a **torch** being used
to thaw a frozen pipe

tore (tôr). See **tear**[2]. *I tore my jeans. verb.*

tor·ment (tôr ment′ *for 1 and 4;* tôr′ment *for 2 and 3*), **1** to cause very great pain to: *Severe headaches tormented him.* **2** a cause of very great pain: *A bad burn can be a torment.* **3** a very great pain: *She suffered torments from her toothache.* **4** to worry or annoy very much: *Don't torment me with silly questions.* **1,4** *verb,* **2,3** *noun.*

tor·men·tor (tôr men′tər), a person or thing that torments. *noun.*

torn (tôrn). See **tear**[2]. *I had torn up the plant by*

a hat	i it	oi oil	ch child	a in about
ā age	ī ice	ou out	ng long	e in taken
ä far	o hot	u cup	sh she	ə = i in pencil
e let	ō open	u̇ put	th thin	o in lemon
ē equal	ô order	ü rule	ᵺ then	u in circus
ėr term			zh measure	

the roots. The coat was torn at the elbow. verb.

tor·na·do (tôr nā′dō), a very violent and destructive whirlwind. A tornado extends down from a mass of dark clouds as a twisting funnel and moves over the land in a narrow path. *noun, plural* **tor·na·does** or **tor·na·dos.**
[*Tornado* comes from a Latin word meaning "to thunder." Originally in English the word referred to a severe tropical thunderstorm.]

tornado in Nebraska

To·ron·to (tə ron′tō), the capital of Ontario, Canada. *noun.*

tor·pe·do (tôr pē′dō), **1** a large cigar-shaped metal tube that contains explosives and travels through water by its own power. **2** to attack or destroy with a torpedo or torpedoes: *After the warship was torpedoed, it sank.* **1** *noun, plural* **tor·pe·does; 2** *verb,* **tor·pe·does, tor·pe·doed, tor·pe·do·ing.**

tor·rent (tôr′ənt), **1** a violent, rushing stream of water: *The torrent dashed over the rocks.* **2** a heavy downpour. **3** any violent, rushing stream; flood: *a torrent of lava, a torrent of words. noun.*

torrent (definition 2)—The rain came down in a **torrent.**

T

tor·rid (tôr′id), very hot: *In this area July is usually a torrid month. adjective.*

tor·til·la (tôr tē′yə), a thin, flat, round cake made of cornmeal, commonly eaten in Spanish America. Tortillas are baked on a flat surface and served hot. *noun.*
[*Tortilla* was borrowed from a Spanish word meaning "a small cake."]

tor·toise (tôr′təs), **1** a turtle with a high, arched shell that lives only on land. **2** any turtle. *noun, plural* **tor·tois·es** or **tor·toise.**

tor·ture (tôr′chər), **1** the act of causing very severe pain to a person or an animal. Torture has been used to make people give evidence about crimes, or to make them confess. **2** very severe pain: *You can suffer tortures from a toothache.* **3** to cause very severe pain to: *It is cruel to torture animals.* **1,2** *noun,* **3** *verb,* **tor·tures, tor·tured, tor·tur·ing.**

toss (tôs), **1** to throw lightly with the palm of the hand upward; cast; fling: *She tossed the ball to me.* **2** to throw about; pitch about: *The ship was tossed by the waves. He tossed in bed all night.* **3** to lift quickly; throw upward: *She tossed her head.* **4** to throw a coin to decide something by the side that falls upward. **5** a throw; tossing: *A toss of a coin decided who should play first.* **1-4** *verb,* **5** *noun, plural* **toss·es.**

tot (tot), a little child. *noun.*

to·tal (tō′tl), **1** whole; entire: *The total cost of the house and land will be $90,000.* **2** the whole amount; sum: *Our expenses reached a total of $100. The total of 6 and 8 and 4 is 18.* **3** to find the sum of; add: *Total that column of figures.* **4** to reach an amount of; amount to: *The money spent yearly on chewing gum totals millions of dollars.* **5** complete: *The lights went out and we were in total darkness.* **1,5** *adjective,* **2** *noun,* **3,4** *verb.*

to·tal·ly (tō′tl ē), completely; entirely; wholly: *We were totally unprepared for a surprise attack. adverb.*

tote (tōt), to carry. *verb,* **totes, tot·ed, tot·ing.**

to·tem (tō′təm), **1** a natural object, often an animal, taken as the emblem of a tribe, clan, or family. **2** the image of such an object. Totems are often carved and painted on poles. *noun.*

totem pole, a pole carved and painted with images of totems, set up by the Indians of the northwestern coast of North America, especially in front of their houses.

tot·ter (tot′ər), **1** to walk with shaky, unsteady steps: *The baby tottered across the room.* **2** to be unsteady; shake as if about to fall: *The old wall tottered in the gale and fell. verb.*

tou·can (tü′kan), a bright-colored bird of warm regions in Central and South America, with a very large beak. *noun.*

touch (tuch), **1** to put the hand or some other part of the body on or against and feel: *I touched the soft, furry kitten.* **2** to put one thing against another: *He touched the post with his umbrella.* **3** to be against; come against: *Your sleeve is touching the butter.* **4** a touching or being touched: *A*

bubble bursts at a touch. **5** the sense by which a person perceives things by feeling, handling, or coming against them: *The blind develop a keen touch.* **6** the feeling caused by touching something; feel: *Worms and fish have a slimy touch.* **7** communication; connection: *She kept in touch with her family while she was overseas.* **8** a slight amount; little bit: *We had a touch of frost.* **9** a slight attack: *The child has a touch of fever.* **10** a light, delicate stroke with a brush, pencil, or pen; detail: *The artist finished the picture with a few touches.* **11** to strike lightly or gently: *She touched the strings of the harp to see if it was in tune.* **12** to injure slightly: *The flowers were touched by the frost.* **13** to affect with some feeling: *The sad story touched our hearts.* **14** to use: *He won't touch liquor or tobacco.* **1-3,11-14** *verb,* **4-10** *noun, plural* **touch·es.**

touch down, to land an aircraft: *The pilot touched down at a small country airfield.*

touch on or **touch upon,** to mention; treat lightly: *Our conversation touched on many subjects.*

touch up, to change a little; improve: *The photographer touched up a photograph.*

touch·down (tuch′doun′), a score of six points made in football by putting the ball on or beyond the opponents' goal line. *noun.*

touch football, a game having rules similar to those of football except that the person carrying the ball is touched rather than tackled.

touch·ing (tuch′ing), arousing tender feeling: *"A Christmas Carol" is a touching story. adjective.*

touch·y (tuch′ē), easily hurt or offended; apt to take offense at trifles: *He is tired and very touchy this afternoon. adjective,* **touch·i·er, touch·i·est.**

tough (tuf), **1** bending without breaking: *Leather is tough; cardboard is not.* **2** hard to cut, tear, or chew: *The steak was so tough I couldn't eat it.* **3** strong; hardy: *a tough plant. Donkeys are tough little animals and can carry big loads.* **4** hard; difficult: *Dragging the load uphill was tough work for the horses.* **5** hard to influence; stubborn: *a tough person to deal with.* **6** rough; disorderly: *That is a tough neighborhood.* **7** a rough person: *A gang of toughs attacked them.* **1-6** *adjective,* **7** *noun.*

tough·en (tuf′ən), to make or become tough: *I toughened my muscles by doing exercises. My*

toucan
25 inches
(64 centimeters) long

muscles finally toughened. verb.

tour (tur), **1** to travel through; travel from place to place: *Last year they toured Mexico.* **2** a long journey: *The family made a tour through Europe.* **3** a short journey; a walk around: *Our class made a tour of the historic old battlefield.* **4** to walk around in: *The class will tour the museum.* 1,4 *verb*, 2,3 *noun*.

tour·ist (tur′ist), a person traveling for pleasure: *Each year many tourists go to Canada. noun.*

tour·na·ment (ter′nə mənt), **1** a contest of many persons in some sport: *a golf tournament.* **2** a contest between two groups of knights on horseback who fought for a prize. *noun.*

tour·ni·quet (tur′nə kit), something used to stop bleeding by pressing a blood vessel, such as a bandage tightened by twisting with a stick. *noun.*

tourniquet

tow (tō), **1** to pull by a rope or chain: *The tug is towing three barges.* **2** the act of towing: *We telephoned for a tow when our car engine stopped running.* 1 *verb*, 2 *noun*.

in tow, being pulled by a rope or chain: *The motorboat had the sailboat in tow.*

to·ward (tôrd *or* tə wôrd′), **1** in the direction of; to: *He walked toward the north.* **2** turned or directed to; facing: *to lie with one's face toward the wall.* **3** with regard to; about; concerning: *What is her attitude toward the building of a new library?* **4** near: *Toward morning the storm ended.* **5** for: *Will you give something toward our new hospital? preposition.*

to·wards (tôrdz *or* tə wôrdz′), toward. *preposition.*

tow·el (tou′əl), a piece of cloth or paper for wiping and drying something wet. We have hand towels, bath towels, and dish towels. *noun.*

tow·er (tou′ər), **1** a high structure. A tower may stand alone or form part of a church, castle, or other building. Some towers are forts or prisons. **2** to rise high up: *The new skyscraper towers over the older buildings.* 1 *noun*, 2 *verb.*

tow·er·ing (tou′ər ing), **1** very high: *a towering peak.* **2** very great: *Making electricity from atomic power is a towering achievement.* **3** very violent: *a towering rage. adjective.*

a hat	**i** it	**oi** oil	**ch** child	⎡ a in about
ā age	**ī** ice	**ou** out	**ng** long	⎥ e in taken
ä far	**o** hot	**u** cup	**sh** she	ə = ⎨ i in pencil
e let	**ō** open	**u̇** put	**th** thin	⎥ o in lemon
ē equal	**ô** order	**ü** rule	**ᴛʜ** then	⎣ u in circus
ėr term			**zh** measure	

town (toun), **1** a large group of houses and buildings, smaller than a city: *Do you live in a town or in the country?* **2** any large place with many people living in it: *I hear that Boston is a fine town. noun.*

town cri·er (toun′ krī′ər), (in former times) a person who called out the news on the streets of a city or town.

town hall, a building used for a town's business.

towns·folk (tounz′fōk′), the people of a town. *noun.*

town·ship (toun′ship), a part of a county in the United States and Canada having certain powers of government. *noun.*

towns·peo·ple (tounz′pē′pəl), the people of a town. *noun.*

tox·ic (tok′sik), poisonous: *Fumes from an automobile are toxic. adjective.*

Word History

toxic *Toxic* comes from a Latin word meaning "poison."

toxic—This mushroom is **toxic**.

toy (toi), **1** something for a child to play with; plaything. Dolls are toys; so are electric trains. **2** a thing that has little value or importance. **3** to amuse oneself; play; trifle: *I toyed with my pencil. Don't toy with matches.* 1,2 *noun*, 3 *verb.*

trace (trās), **1** a mark or sign of the former existence of something: *The explorer found traces of an ancient city.* **2** a footprint or other mark left; track; trail: *We saw traces of rabbits and squirrels on the snow.* **3** to follow by means of marks, tracks, or clues: *The police trace missing persons. The dog traced the fox to its den.* **4** to follow the course of: *We traced the river to its source. The Aldens trace their family back three hundred years*

T

to John Alden, one of the Pilgrims. **5** a very small amount; little bit: *There was not a trace of gray in her hair.* **6** to draw; mark out: *The spy traced a plan of the fort.* **7** to copy by following the lines of with a pencil or pen: *He put thin paper over the map and traced it.* 1,2,5 *noun,* 3,4,6,7 *verb,* **trac·es, traced, trac·ing.**

tra·che·a (trā′kē ə), the windpipe. *noun, plural* **tra·che·ae** (trā′kē ē′), **tra·che·as.**

trac·ing (trā′sing), a copy of something made by putting thin paper over it and following the lines of it with a pencil or pen. *noun.*

track (trak), **1** a pair of parallel metal rails for cars to run on: *railroad tracks.* **2** a mark left: *The dirt road showed many automobile tracks.* **3** a footprint: *We saw bear tracks near the camp.* **4** to follow by means of footprints, smell, or any mark left by anything that has passed by: *We tracked the deer and photographed it.* **5** to bring snow or mud into a place on one's feet: *He tracked mud into the house.* **6** a path; trail; rough road: *A track runs through the woods to the farmhouse.* **7** a course for running or racing. **8** the contests in running, jumping, throwing, and similar sports performed around or inside a track: *I'm trying out for track this year.* **9** one of the endless belts of linked steel plates on which a tank, bulldozer, or tractor moves. 1-3,6-9 *noun,* 4,5 *verb.*

keep track of, to keep within one's sight or attention: *There was so much noise it was difficult for me to keep track of what you said.*

track (definition 7)

track·less (trak′lis), without paths or trails: *The region near the South Pole is a trackless wilderness.* *adjective.*

track meet, a series of contests in running, jumping, throwing, and similar sports.

tract (trakt), **1** a stretch of land or water; area: *A tract of desert land has little value.* **2** a system of related parts or organs in the body. The stomach and intestines are parts of the digestive tract. *noun.*

trac·tion (trak′shən), friction: *Wheels slip on ice because there is too little traction.* *noun.*

trac·tor (trak′tər), a heavy motor vehicle which moves on wheels or on two endless tracks. A

tractor is used for pulling a wagon, plow, or other vehicle along roads or over fields. *noun.*

trade (trād), **1** a buying and selling; exchange of goods; commerce: *The United States has much trade with foreign countries.* **2** to buy and sell; exchange goods; be in commerce: *Some American companies trade all over the world.* **3** an exchange: *an even trade.* **4** to exchange; make an exchange: *He traded a stick of gum for a ride on her bicycle. If you don't like your book, I'll trade with you.* **5** a kind of work; business, especially one requiring skilled work: *the carpenter's trade.* **6** the people in the same kind of work or business: *Carpenters, plumbers, and electricians are all members of the building trade.* 1,3,5,6 *noun,* 2,4 *verb,* **trades, trad·ed, trad·ing.**

trade in, to give an automobile, refrigerator, or other article as payment or part payment for something, especially for a newer model.

trade-in (trād′in′), a thing given or accepted as payment or part payment for something, especially for a newer model. *noun.*

trade·mark (trād′märk′), a mark, picture, name, word, symbol, design, or letters owned and used by a manufacturer or seller. A trademark identifies the product for the buyer. *noun.*

trad·er (trā′dər), a person who trades: *The trappers sold furs to traders. noun.*

trades·man (trādz′mən), a storekeeper; shopkeeper. *noun, plural* **trades·men.**

trade wind, a wind blowing steadily from east to west toward the equator.

trading post, a store or station of a trader, especially on the frontier or in unsettled country. Trading posts used to exchange food, weapons, clothes, and other articles for hides and furs.

tra·di·tion (trə dish′ən), **1** the handing down of beliefs, opinions, customs, and stories from parents to children, especially by word of mouth or by practice. **2** what is handed down in this way: *According to the old tradition, the first American flag was made by Betsy Ross. noun.*

tra·di·tion·al (trə dish′ə nəl), **1** of tradition; handed down by tradition: *Shaking hands upon meeting is a traditional custom.* **2** according to tradition: *traditional furniture.* **3** customary: *A Memorial Day parade is traditional in almost every town. adjective.*

traf·fic (traf′ik), **1** people, automobiles, trucks, airplanes, ships, or the like coming and going along a way of travel: *Police control the traffic in large cities.* **2** a buying and selling; trade: *Governments are trying to stop the illegal drug traffic.* **3** to carry on trade; buy; sell; exchange: *The traders trafficked with the islanders for pearls.* **4** the business done by a railroad line, steamship line, or airline; number of passengers or amount of freight carried. 1,2,4 *noun,* 3 *verb,* **traf·fics, traf·ficked, traf·fick·ing.**

traffic light, a set of electric lights used to control traffic at a corner or intersection. The lights are usually colored red for stop, green for go, and yellow for caution. They are flashed automatically every few seconds or minutes.

trag·e·dy (traj′ə dē), **1** a serious play having an unhappy ending. **2** a very sad or terrible happening: *Her sudden death was a tragedy to her friends. noun, plural* **trag·e·dies.**

trag·ic (traj′ik), **1** of tragedy; having something to do with tragedy: *a tragic actor, a tragic poet.* **2** very sad; dreadful: *a tragic death, a tragic accident. adjective.*

trail (trāl), **1** a path across a wild or unsettled region: *The scouts followed mountain trails for days.* **2** a track or smell: *The dogs found the trail of the rabbit.* **3** to hunt by track or smell: *The dogs trailed the rabbit.* **4** anything that follows along behind: *As the car sped down the road, it left a trail of dust behind it.* **5** to follow along behind; follow: *The dog trailed its master constantly.* **6** to pull or drag along behind: *The child trailed a toy horse.* **7** to grow along: *Poison ivy trailed by the road.* **8** to follow, fall, or lag behind, as in a race, game, or the like: *Our team trailed by three runs with one turn at bat left.* 1,2,4 *noun,* 3,5-8 *verb.*

trail·er (trā′lər), **1** a vehicle used for carrying freight. It is usually pulled by a truck. **2** a vehicle like a house on wheels usually pulled by an automobile. When parked, it is used as a house or office. *noun.*

train (definition 3)—He carried the train of her gown.

train (trān), **1** a connected line of railroad cars moving along together: *A very long freight train of 100 cars rolled by.* **2** a line of people, animals, wagons, trucks, or the like, moving along together: *The early settlers crossed the continent by wagon train.* **3** a part that hangs down and drags along. **4** a group of followers: *the king and his train.* **5** a continuous series of events or ideas: *A long train of misfortunes overcame the hero. I lost my train of thought when I was interrupted.* **6** to bring up; rear; teach: *They trained their child to be thoughtful of others.* **7** to make skillful by teaching and practice: *to train people as nurses. Saint Bernard dogs were trained to hunt for travelers lost in the snow.* **8** to make or become fit by exercise and diet: *The runners trained for races.* **9** to point; aim: *to train guns upon a fort.* **10** to bring into a particular position; make grow in a particular way:

We trained the vines around the post. 1-5 *noun,* 6-10 *verb.*

train·er (trā′nər), a person who trains athletes, horses, or other animals to take part in competition or to perform. *noun.*

train·ing (trā′ning), **1** practical education in some art, profession, or trade: *training for teachers.* **2** the development of strength and endurance: *physical training.* **3** good condition maintained by exercise and care: *The athlete kept in training by not overeating and not smoking. noun.*

train·man (trān′mən), a brakeman or railroad worker in a train crew, of lower rank than a conductor. *noun, plural* **train·men.**

trait (trāt), a quality of mind or character; feature; characteristic: *Courage, love of fair play, and common sense are desirable traits. noun.*

trai·tor (trā′tər), **1** a person who betrays his or her country: *Benedict Arnold became a traitor by helping the British during the Revolutionary War.* **2** a person who betrays a trust, a duty, or a friend. *noun.*

tramp (tramp), **1** to walk heavily: *They tramped across the floor in their heavy boots.* **2** to step heavily on: *He tramped on the flowers.* **3** the sound of a heavy step: *the tramp of marching feet.* **4** to walk; go on foot: *The hikers tramped through the mountains.* **5** a long, steady walk; hike: *The friends took a tramp together over the hills.* **6** a person who wanders about and lives by begging or doing odd jobs. 1,2,4 *verb,* 3,5,6 *noun.*

tram·ple (tram′pəl), **1** to walk or step heavily on; crush: *The cattle got loose and trampled the farmer's crops.* **2** to walk or step heavily; tramp: *Don't trample on the flowers. verb,* **tram·ples, tram·pled, tram·pling.**

tram·po·line (tram′pə lēn′), a piece of canvas or other sturdy fabric stretched on a metal frame, used for tumbling. *noun.*

trampoline

T

trance (trans), **1** a condition somewhat like sleep in which a person no longer responds to the surroundings. A person may be in a trance from some illnesses or from hypnotism. Some people can put themselves into trances. **2** a condition like daydreaming or a trance: *She sat in a trance, watching the flames in the fireplace. noun.*

tran·quil (trang′kwəl), calm; peaceful; quiet: *the tranquil morning air. adjective.*

tran·quil·iz·er (trang′kwə lī′zər), a drug that relaxes muscles, reduces tension, and lowers blood pressure. *noun.*

tran·quil·li·ty (trang kwil′ə tē), a tranquil condition; calmness; peacefulness; quiet: *They wanted only to live in peace and tranquillity. noun.*

trans-, a prefix meaning: **1** across; over; through: *Transcontinental means across the continent.* **2** in or to a different place or position: *Transplant means to plant in a different place.*

trans·act (tran zakt′), to attend to; manage; do; carry on: *He transacts business daily. verb.*

trans·ac·tion (tran zak′shən), the carrying on of business: *She attends to the transaction of important matters herself. noun.*

trans·at·lan·tic (tran′sət lan′tik), crossing the Atlantic: *a transatlantic ocean liner. adjective.*

trans·con·ti·nen·tal (tran′skon tə nen′tl), crossing a continent: *a transcontinental railroad. adjective.*

trans·fer (tran sfėr′ *for 1 and 3;* tran′sfėr *for 2 and 4*), **1** to change or move from one person or place to another: *The clerk was transferred to another department. Please have my trunks transferred to the Union Station.* **2** a transferring or being transferred: *a transfer to a different school.* **3** to change from one bus, train, or the like, to another: *On our way into the city we transferred from a train to a bus.* **4** a ticket allowing a passenger to change from one bus, train, or the like, to another. **1,3** *verb,* **trans·fers, trans·ferred, trans·fer·ring; 2,4** *noun.*

trans·form (tran sfôrm′), **1** to change in form or appearance: *The blizzard transformed the bushes into mounds of white.* **2** to change in condition, nature, or character: *A tadpole becomes transformed into a frog. verb.*

trans·for·ma·tion (tran′sfər mā′shən), a transforming: *the transformation of a caterpillar into a butterfly. noun.*

trans·fu·sion (tran sfyü′zhən), the transferring of blood from one person or animal to another: *The injured driver was bleeding badly and needed a transfusion at once. noun.*

tran·sis·tor (tran zis′tər), a small electronic device used to control or amplify the flow of electrons in an electric circuit. Transistors are used in radios, television sets, computers, and other electronic equipment. *noun.*

transistor—Replacing tubes (left) with **transistors** (right) allows radios and televisions to be made smaller.

tran·sit (tran′sit), a carrying across or through: *The goods were damaged in transit. noun.*

tran·si·tion (tran zish′ən), a change or passing from one condition, place, or thing to another: *Lincoln's life was a transition from poverty to power. noun.*

trans·late (tran slāt′), to change from one language into another: *to translate a book from French into English. verb,* **trans·lates, trans·lat·ed, trans·lat·ing.**

trans·la·tion (tran slā′shən), **1** a changing into another language: *the translation of the Bible from Hebrew to English.* **2** the result of translating; version: *a Spanish translation of a book. noun.*

trans·la·tor (tran slā′tər), a person who translates. *noun.*

trans·lu·cent (tran slü′snt), letting light through, but not easily seen through: *Frosted glass is translucent. adjective.*

transform (definition 2)
The movie was about a man who was **transformed** into a wolf.

translucent—The window on the left is transparent. The window on the right is **translucent**.

trans·mis·sion (tran smish′ən), **1** a sending over; passing on; passing along; letting through: *Mosquitoes are the only means of transmission of malaria.* **2** the part of an automobile or other motor vehicle that transmits power from the engine to the rear or front axle by the use of gears. **3** the passing through space of radio or television waves from the transmitting station to the receiving station: *When transmission is good, even foreign stations can be heard.* *noun.*

trans·mit (tran smit′), **1** to send over; pass on; pass along; let through: *I will transmit the money by special messenger. Rats transmit disease.* **2** to send out signals, voice, music, or pictures by radio or television: *Some station is transmitting every hour of the day.* *verb,* **trans·mits, trans·mit·ted, trans·mit·ting.**

trans·mit·ter (tran smit′ər), a device that sends out sounds, or sounds and pictures, by radio waves or by electric current: *Radio stations and television stations have transmitters.* *noun.*

tran·som (tran′səm), a window or panel over a door or other window, usually hinged for opening. *noun.*

trans·par·ent (tran sper′ənt *or* tran spar′ənt), **1** letting light through so that things on the other side can be clearly seen: *Window glass is transparent.* **2** easily seen through or detected; obvious: *A transparent excuse doesn't fool anyone.* *adjective.*

trans·plant (tran splant′ *for 1 and 2;* tran′splant *for 3*), **1** to plant again in a different place: *We start the flowers indoors and then transplant them to the garden.* **2** to transfer skin, an organ, or the like from one person, animal, or part of the body to another: *to transplant a kidney.* **3** the transfer of skin, an organ, or the like from one person, animal, or part of the body to another: *a heart transplant.* **1,2** *verb,* **3** *noun.*

trans·port (tran spôrt′ *for 1;* tran′spôrt *for 2 and 3*), **1** to carry from one place to another: *Wheat is transported from the farms to the mills.* **2** a carrying from one place to another: *Trucks are much used for transport.* **3** a ship used to carry troops and supplies. **1** *verb,* **2,3** *noun.*

trans·por·ta·tion (tran′spər tā′shən), **1** a transporting or a being transported: *The railroad allows free transportation for a certain amount of a passenger's baggage.* **2** a means of transport: *When the bus broke down, we had no other transportation to school.* *noun.*

trap (trap), **1** a thing or means for catching animals: *The mouse was caught in a trap.* **2** a trick or other means for catching someone off guard: *The police set traps to catch the robbers.* **3** to catch in a trap: *We trapped a squirrel in our yard and released it in the woods.* **1,2** *noun,* **3** *verb,* **traps, trapped, trap·ping.**

trap·door (trap′dôr′), a door in a floor or roof. *noun.*

tra·peze (trə pēz′), a short, horizontal bar hung by ropes like a swing, used in gymnasiums and circuses. *noun.*

a hat	i it	oi oil	ch child	⌠a in about
ā age	ī ice	ou out	ng long	⎪e in taken
ä far	o hot	u cup	sh she	ə = ⎨i in pencil
e let	ō open	ů put	th thin	⎪o in lemon
ē equal	ô order	ü rule	ᴛʜ then	⌡u in circus
ėr term			zh measure	

trapezoids

trap·e·zoid (trap′ə zoid), a figure having two sides parallel and two sides not parallel. *noun.*

trap·per (trap′ər), a person who traps, especially one who traps wild animals for their furs. *noun.*

trash (trash), anything of little or no worth; worthless stuff; rubbish; garbage: *We cleaned the house and garage and threw out ten boxes of trash.* *noun.*

trav·el (trav′əl), **1** to go from one place to another; journey: *She is traveling in Europe this summer.* **2** a going in trains, airplanes, ships, cars, and the like, from one place to another: *She loves travel.* **3** to move; proceed; pass: *Sound travels in waves.* **1,3** *verb,* **2** *noun.*

trav·el·er (trav′ə lər), a person who travels. *noun.*

trawl (trôl), **1** a net dragged along the bottom of the sea. **2** to fish or catch fish with a net by dragging it along the bottom of the sea. **1** *noun,* **2** *verb.*

tray (trā), a flat, shallow holder or container with a rim around it: *The waiter carries the dishes on a tray.* *noun.*

treach·er·ous (trech′ər əs), **1** not to be trusted; not faithful; not loyal: *The treacherous soldier carried reports to the enemy.* **2** having a false appearance of strength or security; not reliable; deceiving: *That thin ice is treacherous.* *adjective.*

treach·er·y (trech′ər ē), a breaking of faith; treacherous behavior; deceit: *King Arthur's kingdom was destroyed by treachery.* *noun.*

tread (tred), **1** to walk; step; set the foot down: *Don't tread on the flower beds. He trod a narrow path through the woods.* **2** to press under the feet; trample; crush: *In Italy, we watched people tread grapes to make wine.* **3** a way of walking; step: *to walk with a heavy tread.* **4** the part of stairs or a ladder that a person steps on: *The stair treads were covered with rubber to prevent slipping.* **5** the part of a wheel or tire that touches the ground: *The treads of rubber tires have grooves to improve traction.* **1,2** *verb,* **treads, trod, trod·den** *or* **trod, tread·ing;** **3-5** *noun.*

trea·dle (tred′l), a lever or pedal worked by the foot to operate a machine. *noun.*

tread·mill (tred′mil′), **1** a device that operates by having a person or animal walk on the moving steps of a wheel or on an endless belt. Treadmills were once used to grind grain. Today a treadmill may be used for walking or jogging exercise. **2** any wearisome or monotonous round of work or of life. *noun.*

trea·son (trē′zn), a being false to one's country or ruler. Helping the enemies of one's country is treason. *noun.*

treas·ure (trezh′ər), **1** wealth or riches stored up; valuable things: *The pirates buried treasure along the coast.* **2** any thing or person that is much loved or valued: *The silver teapot was my parents' chief treasure.* **3** to value highly: *She treasures her train more than all her other toys.* 1,2 *noun,* 3 *verb,* **treas·ures, treas·ured, treas·ur·ing.**

treas·ur·er (trezh′ər ər), a person in charge of money. The treasurer of a club pays its bills. *noun.*

treas·ur·y (trezh′ər ē), **1** (in former times) a place where money was kept. **2** money owned; funds: *We voted to pay for the party out of the club treasury.* **3** **Treasury,** the department of the government that has charge of the income and expenses of a country. The Treasury of the United States collects federal taxes, mints money, supervises national banks, and prevents counterfeiting. *noun, plural* **treas·ur·ies.**

treat (trēt), **1** to act toward: *The children treated the puppy with care.* **2** to think of; consider; regard: *She treated her mistake as a joke.* **3** to deal with to relieve or cure: *The dentist is treating my toothache.* **4** to deal with to bring about some special result: *to treat drinking water to remove impurities.* **5** to deal with; discuss: *The article treated the subject thoroughly.* **6** to give food, drink, or amusement to: *She treated her friends to ice cream.* **7** a gift of food, drink, or amusement: *"This is my treat," she said.* **8** to pay the cost of a treat or entertainment: *I'll treat for lunch today.* **9** anything that gives pleasure: *Being in the country was a treat to the city children.* 1-6,8 *verb,* 7,9 *noun.*

treat·ment (trēt′mənt), **1** the act or process of treating: *My cold won't respond to treatment.* **2** a way of treating: *This cat has suffered from bad treatment.* **3** a thing done or used to treat a disease or condition: *Doctors are always investigating new treatments for cancer. noun.*

trea·ty (trē′tē), a formal agreement, especially one between nations, signed and approved by each nation. *noun, plural* **trea·ties.**

tre·ble (treb′əl), **1** three times: *His salary is treble mine.* **2** to make or become three times as much: *She trebled her money by buying a dog for $25 and selling it for $75.* 1 *adjective,* 2 *verb,* **tre·bles, tre·bled, tre·bling.**

tree (trē), **1** a large plant with a woody trunk and usually having branches and leaves at some distance from the ground. **2** an object often made of wood or resembling a tree, used for some special purpose: *a clothes tree.* **3** anything like a tree: *a family tree.* **4** to chase up a tree: *The cat was treed by a dog.* 1-3 *noun,* 4 *verb,* **trees, treed, tree·ing.**

tree frog—up to 2 inches (6 centimeters) long

tree frog, any of various small frogs that live in trees and have gripping disks or suckers on their toes.

tree·less (trē′lis), without trees: *a treeless plain. adjective.*

tree·top (trē′top′), the top or uppermost part of a tree. *noun.*

trek (trek), **1** to travel slowly by any means; travel: *The pioneers trekked across the great western plains by covered wagon.* **2** a journey: *It was a long trek over the mountains.* 1 *verb,* **treks, trekked, trek·king;** 2 *noun.*

trel·lis (trel′is), a frame of light strips of wood or metal crossing one another with open spaces in between; lattice, especially one supporting growing vines. *noun, plural* **trel·lis·es.**

trellis
The vine is climbing up the **trellis.**

trem·ble (trem′bəl), **1** to shake because of fear, excitement, weakness, cold, or the like: *The child's voice trembled with fear. My hands trembled from the cold.* **2** to move gently: *The leaves trembled in the breeze.* **3** a trembling: *There was a tremble in her voice as she began to recite.* 1,2 *verb,* **trem·bles, trem·bled, trem·bling;** 3 *noun.*

tre·men·dous (tri men′dəs), **1** dreadful; very

severe: *The army suffered a tremendous defeat.*
2 enormous; very great: *That is a tremendous house for a family of three. adjective.*
[*Tremendous* comes from a Latin word meaning "to be trembled at." Other English words from the same Latin root are *tremble* and *tremor.*]

trem·or (trem′ər), **1** a shaking or trembling which you cannot control: *a nervous tremor in the voice.* **2** a shaking or vibrating movement. An earthquake is sometimes called an earth tremor. *noun.*

trench (trench), **1** a long, narrow ditch with earth thrown up in front to protect soldiers. **2** a ditch; deep furrow: *to dig a trench for a sewer pipe.* **3** a long, deep, narrow area like a valley or canyon in the ocean floor: *The deepest trenches of the Pacific Ocean are much deeper than the Grand Canyon. noun, plural* **trench·es.**

trend (trend), **1** the general direction; course; tendency: *The trend of modern living is away from many old customs.* **2** to have a general direction; tend; run: *Modern life trends toward less formal customs.* **1** *noun,* **2** *verb.*

Tren·ton (tren′tən), the capital of New Jersey. *noun.*

tres·pass (tres′pəs *or* tres′pas), **1** to go on somebody's property without any right: *The farmer put up "No Trespassing" signs to keep hunters off his farm.* **2** to do wrong; sin. **3** a wrong; sin: *"Forgive us our trespasses as we forgive those who trespass against us."* **1,2** *verb,* **3** *noun, plural* **tres·pass·es.**

tress (tres), a lock, curl, or braid of hair: *golden tresses. noun, plural* **tress·es.**

tres·tle (tres′əl), a framework of steel or wood used as a bridge to support railroad tracks or a road. *noun.*

trestle

tri·al (trī′əl), **1** the examining and deciding of a case in court: *The suspect was brought to trial.* **2** the process of trying or testing: *The mechanic gave the motor another trial to see if it would start.* **3** trouble: hardship: *The pioneers suffered many trials. noun.*

on trial, 1 being tried or tested: *He is employed for two weeks on trial.* **2** being tried in a court of law: *The suspect goes on trial next Monday.*

tri·an·gle (trī′ang′gəl), **1** a figure having three sides and three angles. **2** something having this shape. **3** a musical instrument made of a steel bar

bent into this shape and struck with a steel rod. *noun.*

tri·an·gu·lar (trī ang′gyə lər), shaped like a triangle; three-cornered. *adjective.*

trib·al (trī′bəl), of a tribe: *tribal customs. adjective.*

tribe (trīb), a group of people sharing the same customs, language, and ancestors, forming a community under one leader or group of leaders. *noun.*

tribes·man (trībz′mən), a member of a tribe. *noun, plural* **tribes·men.**

trib·u·tar·y (trib′yə ter′ē), a stream or river that flows into a larger body of water: *The Ohio River is one of the tributaries of the Mississippi River. noun, plural* **trib·u·tar·ies.**

trib·ute (trib′yüt), something done or given to show thanks or respect; compliment: *Labor Day is a tribute to workers. noun.*

tri·cer·a·tops (trī ser′ə tops), a dinosaur with a large horn above each eye and a smaller horn on the nose, and a long and powerful tail. *noun, plural* **tri·cer·a·tops·es.**

Word History

triceratops *Triceratops* comes from three Greek words meaning "three," "horn," and "face."

triceratops—about 25 feet (8 meters) long

triangles (definition 1)

T

trick (trik), **1** something done to deceive or cheat: *The false message was a trick to get her to leave the house.* **2** to deceive; cheat: *We were tricked into buying a stolen car.* **3** a clever act; feat of skill: *We enjoyed the tricks of the trained animals.* **4** the best way of doing or dealing with something: *She is teaching me the trick of restoring old furniture.* **5** a piece of mischief; prank; joke: *Hiding my lunch was a mean trick.* **6** the cards played in one round of a card game. 1,3-6 *noun,* 2 *verb.*

trick·er·y (trik′ər ē), the use of tricks; deception; cheating: *He tried to sell me a bicycle with a broken chain, but I saw through his trickery. noun.*

trick·le (trik′əl), **1** to flow or fall in drops or in a small stream: *Tears trickled down her cheeks. The brook trickled through the valley.* **2** a small flow or stream. **3** to come, go, pass, or move slowly and unevenly: *An hour before the show started, people began to trickle into the theater.* 1,3 *verb,* **trick·les, trick·led, trick·ling;** 2 *noun.*

trick·y (trik′ē), **1** full of tricks; deceiving: *a tricky person.* **2** not doing what is expected; dangerous or difficult to deal with: *The back door has a tricky lock. adjective,* **trick·i·er, trick·i·est.**

tri·cy·cle (trī′sə kəl), a three-wheeled vehicle worked by pedals. Children often ride tricycles before they are old enough for bicycles. *noun.*

tried (trīd), **1** tested; proved: *a person of tried abilities.* **2** See **try.** *I tried to call you. We have tried both those games.* 1 *adjective,* 2 *verb.*

tries (trīz), **1** more than one try: *After several tries, I gave up.* **2** See **try.** *He tries to please.* 1 *noun,* 2 *verb.*

tri·fle (trī′fəl), **1** a thing that is of very little value or small importance. **2** a small amount; little bit: *She was a trifle late. The picture cost only a trifle.* **3** to play or toy with; handle: *He trifled with his pencil.* 1,2 *noun,* 3 *verb,* **tri·fles, tri·fled, tri·fling.**

tri·fling (trī′fling), having little value; not important; small: *The friends treated their quarrel as only a trifling matter. adjective.*

trig·ger (trig′ər), **1** the small lever pulled back by the finger in firing a gun. **2** to begin; start: *I broke the glass that triggered the fire alarm.* 1 *noun,* 2 *verb.*

trill (tril), **1** to sing, play, sound, or speak with a trembling sound: *Some birds trill their songs.* **2** the act or sound of trilling. 1 *verb,* 2 *noun.*

trim (trim), **1** to put in good order; make neat by cutting away parts: *The gardener trims the hedge. The barber trimmed my hair.* **2** neat; in good condition or order: *The entire family works together to keep a trim house.* **3** good condition or order: *Is our team in trim for the game?* **4** to decorate: *The children were trimming the Christmas tree.* **5** anything used to trim or decorate: *the trim on a coat.* **6** to arrange the sails to fit wind and direction. 1,4,6 *verb,* **trims, trimmed, trim·ming;** 2 *adjective,* **trim·mer, trim·mest;** 3,5 *noun.*

trim·ming (trim′ing), **1** anything used to trim or decorate; ornament: *trimming for a dress.* **2 trimmings, a** the parts cut away: *trimmings from a hedge.* **b** everything needed to make something complete and festive: *We ate turkey with all the trimmings. noun.*

trin·ket (tring′kit), any small fancy article, bit of jewelry, or the like: *The baby played with the trinkets on the bracelet. noun.*

tri·o (trē′ō), **1** a piece of music for three voices or instruments. **2** a group of three singers or players performing together. *noun, plural* **tri·os.**

trip (trip), **1** a journey; voyage: *a trip to Europe.* **2** to stumble: *He tripped on the stairs.* **3** to cause to stumble and fall: *The loose board on the stairs tripped her.* **4** to make a mistake; do something wrong: *He tripped on that difficult question.* **5** to cause to make a mistake: *The difficult question tripped me.* **6** to take light, quick steps: *The children came tripping down the path to meet us.* 1 *noun,* 2-6 *verb,* **trips, tripped, trip·ping.**

tri·ple (trip′əl), **1** three times as much or as many: *a triple portion of cake, to get triple pay.* **2** having three parts: *a triple crown.* **3** to make or become three times as much or as many: *The number of club members has tripled this year.* **4** (in baseball) a hit that allows the batter to reach third base. **5** to make such a hit in baseball. 1,2 *adjective,* 3, 5 *verb,* **tri·ples, tri·pled, tri·pling;** 4 *noun.*

tri·plet (trip′lit), one of three children born at the same time to the same mother. *noun.*

tri·pod (trī′pod), a three-legged support or stand for a camera, telescope, or the like. *noun.*

tripod—She put her camera on a **tripod.**

tri·umph (trī′umf), **1** victory; success: *final triumph over the enemy. The exploration of outer space is a great triumph of modern science.* **2** to gain victory; win success: *Our team triumphed over theirs.* **3** joy because of victory or success: *We welcomed the team home with cheers of triumph.* 1,3 *noun,* 2 *verb.*

tri·um·phant (trī um′fənt), **1** victorious; successful: *a triumphant army.* **2** joyful because of victory or success: *The winners spoke in triumphant tones about their skillful play. adjective.*

triv·i·al (triv′ē əl), not important: *Your composition has only a few trivial mistakes.* *adjective.*

trod (trod). See **tread**. *He just trod on my toe. The path was trod by many feet.* *verb.*

trod·den (trod′n). See **tread**. *The cattle had trodden down the corn.* *verb.*

troll¹ (trōl), **1** a song whose parts are sung in succession; round: *"Three Blind Mice" is a well-known troll.* **2** to fish with a moving line, usually by trailing the line behind the boat near the surface: *I trolled for bass.* **1** *noun,* **2** *verb.*

troll¹
(definition 1)
and **troll²**

troll² (trōl), (in stories) an ugly giant or dwarf living in caves or underground. *noun.*

trol·ley (trol′ē), a grooved wheel at the end of a pole which moves against a wire to carry electricity to an electric engine. A **trolley car** or **trolley bus** is a streetcar or bus having such a wheel. *noun, plural* **trol·leys.**

trom·bone (trom′bōn *or* trom bōn′), a brass wind instrument with a long sliding piece for changing the length of the tube to produce various tones. *noun.*

trombone

a hat	**i** it	**oi** oil	**ch** child		a in about
ā age	**ī** ice	**ou** out	**ng** long		e in taken
ä far	**o** hot	**u** cup	**sh** she	**ə** =	i in pencil
e let	**ō** open	** u̇** put	**th** thin		o in lemon
ē equal	**ô** order	**ü** rule	**ᴛʜ** then		u in circus
ėr term			**zh** measure		

troop (trüp), **1** a group or band of persons: *a troop of children.* **2 troops,** soldiers: *The government sent troops to put down the revolt.* **3** to gather or move in a group: *The children trooped after their teacher.* **1,2** *noun,* **3** *verb.*

troop·er (trü′pər), **1** a soldier in the cavalry. **2** a mounted police officer. The state police of some states are called troopers, because they used to ride horses. *noun.*

tro·phy (trō′fē), an award, often in the form of a statue or cup, given as a sign of victory. A trophy is often awarded as a prize in a race or contest. *noun, plural* **tro·phies.**

trophy
He won the
tennis **trophy.**

trop·i·cal (trop′ə kəl), of or like the tropics: *tropical heat. Bananas are tropical fruit. adjective.*

trop·ics (trop′iks), regions near the equator. The hottest parts of the earth are in the tropics. *noun plural.*

trot (trot), **1** a gait of a horse and some other four-footed animals between a walk and a run. In a trot, the right forefoot and the left hind foot are lifted at the same time. **2** to ride at a trot: *The riders trotted home.* **3** to go or cause to go at a trot: *The pony trotted through the field. We trotted our horses through the woods.* **4** to run, but not fast: *The child trotted after me.* **5** a slow running. **1,5** *noun,* **2-4** *verb,* **trots, trot·ted, trot·ting.**

trou·ble (trub′əl), **1** distress; worry; difficulty: *The noisy students made trouble for their teacher.* **2** to cause distress or worry to; disturb: *Lack of business troubled the grocer. I am troubled by headaches.* **3** something that causes worry or distress; problem: *His troubles began when his car* broke down in a rainstorm. **4** extra work; bother; effort: *Take the trouble to do careful work.* **5** to require extra work or effort of: *May I trouble you to pass the sugar?* **6** an illness; disease: *The patient suffered from heart trouble.* 1,3,4,6 *noun,* 2,5 *verb,* **trou·bles, trou·bled, trou·bling.**

trou·ble·some (trub′əl səm), causing trouble; annoying; full of trouble: *Last year we had noisy, troublesome neighbors. adjective.*

trough (trôf), a long, narrow container for holding food or water: *He led the horses to the watering trough. noun.*

trounce (trouns), to beat; thrash: *The victors trounced the losing team. verb,* **trounc·es, trounced, trounc·ing.**

troupe (trüp), a band or company, especially a group of actors, singers, or acrobats. *noun.*

trou·sers (trou′zərz), a two-legged outer article of clothing reaching from the waist to the ankles; pants. *noun plural.*

trout (trout), a freshwater food fish that is related to the salmon. *noun, plural* **trout** or **trouts.**

trow·el (trou′əl), **1** a tool with a broad, flat blade for spreading or smoothing plaster or mortar. **2** a tool with a curved blade for taking up plants or loosening dirt. *noun.*

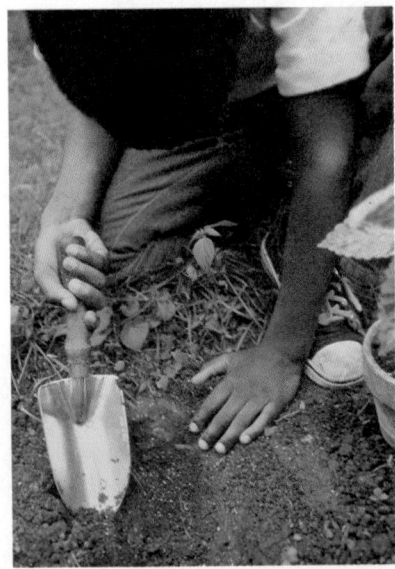

trowel
(definition 2)

troy weight (troi′ wāt′), a standard system of weights used for gems and precious metals. One pound troy equals a little over four fifths of an ordinary pound. 12 troy ounces = 1 troy pound.

tru·ant (trü′ənt), a student who stays away from school without permission. *noun.*

truce (trüs), a stop in fighting; peace for a short time: *A truce was declared between the two armies for a week. noun.*

truck (truk), **1** a strongly built motor vehicle for carrying heavy loads. **2** to carry on a truck: *to truck freight to the warehouse.* 1 *noun,* 2 *verb.* [*Truck* is believed to come from a Greek word meaning "wheel."]

trudge (truj), **1** to walk wearily or with effort: *She trudged slowly through the deep snow.* **2** a hard or weary walk: *It was a long trudge up the hill.* 1 *verb,* **trudg·es, trudged, trudg·ing;** 2 *noun.*

true (trü), **1** correct; right; accurate; not false: *It is true that 4 and 6 are 10. The story I told is true; I did not make it up.* **2** real; genuine: *true courage.* **3** faithful; loyal: *my truest friend, true to your promises.* **4** in a true manner; truly; exactly: *Your words ring true.* 1-3 *adjective,* **tru·er, tru·est;** 4 *adverb.*

tru·ly (trü′lē), **1** in a true manner; exactly; rightly; faithfully: *Tell me truly what you think.* **2** really; in fact: *It was truly a beautiful sight. adverb.*

trumpet (definition 1)

trum·pet (trum′pit), **1** a brass wind instrument that has a powerful tone, commonly a curved tube with a flaring bell at one end. **2** a thing shaped like a trumpet. Ear trumpets were once used to help persons who were not able to hear well. **3** a sound like that of a trumpet. **4** to make a sound like that of a trumpet: *An elephant trumpeted.* **5** to announce loudly or widely: *They trumpeted the news all over town.* 1-3 *noun,* 4,5 *verb.*

trun·dle (trun′dl), **1** to roll along; push along: *The worker trundled a wheelbarrow up a ramp.* **2** a trundle bed. 1 *verb,* **trun·dles, trun·dled, trun·dling;** 2 *noun.*

trundle bed, a low bed movable on small wheels.

trunk (trungk), **1** the main stem of a tree, from which the branches and roots grow. **2** a big, sturdy box with a hinged lid, for holding clothes and other articles when traveling. **3** an enclosed compartment usually in the rear of an automobile: *The spare tire and the jack are in the trunk.* **4** a human or animal body, not including the head, arms, and legs. **5** the long, flexible snout of an elephant: *The elephant picked up peanuts and put them in its mouth with its trunk.* **6 trunks,** very short pants worn by males for swimming, boxing, and the like. *noun.*

trust (trust), **1** a firm belief in the honesty,

truthfulness, justice, or power of a person or thing; faith: *The children put trust in their parents.* **2** to believe firmly in the honesty, truth, justice, or power of; have faith in: *They are people you can trust.* **3** to rely on; depend on: *If you can't trust your memory, write things down.* **4** to hope; believe: *I trust you will soon feel better.* **5** the duty or responsibility that a person takes on when given confidence or authority: *Congress has a public trust.* **6** keeping; care: *The will was left in her trust.* 1,5,6 *noun,* 2-4 *verb.*

trus·tee (tru stē′), a person responsible for the property or affairs of another person or of an institution: *A trustee will manage the children's property until they grow up. noun.*

trust·ful (trust′fəl), ready to confide; ready to have faith; trusting; believing: *That trustful boy would lend money to anyone. adjective.*

trust·wor·thy (trust′wėr′FHē), able to be depended on; reliable: *The class chose a trustworthy student for treasurer. adjective.*

trust·y (trus′tē), **1** able to be depended on; reliable: *She left her new car with a trusty friend.* **2** a prisoner who is given special privileges because of good behavior. 1 *adjective,* **trust·i·er, trust·i·est;** 2 *noun, plural* **trust·ies.**

truth (trüth), **1** that which is true: *Tell the truth.* **2** the quality or nature of being true, exact, honest, sincere, or loyal: *The jury doubted the truth of the statements of the witness. noun, plural* **truths** (trüFHz *or* trüths).

truth·ful (trüth′fəl), telling the truth: *a truthful person. You can count on her for a truthful report. adjective.*

try (trī), **1** to attempt; make an effort: *He tried to do the work. Try harder if you wish to succeed.* **2** to find out about by using; experiment on or with; test: *Try this candy and see if you like it.* **3** an attempt: *Each girl had three tries at the high jump.* **4** to judge in a court of law: *They were tried and found guilty of robbery.* 1,2,4 *verb,* **tries, tried, try·ing;** 3 *noun, plural* **tries.**

try on, to put on to test the fit or looks: *I tried on several coats.*

try out, 1 to test or sample: *Try out this new recipe for apple pie.* **2** to show someone how well you can do: *I tried out for the swimming team.*

try·ing (trī′ing), hard to bear; annoying; distressing: *a long, hot, trying drive. adjective.*

try·out (trī′out′), a test made to determine fitness for a specific purpose: *Tryouts for our football team will start a week after school opens. noun.*

T-shirt (tē′shėrt′), **1** a light, close-fitting knitted shirt with short sleeves and no collar. **2** an undershirt resembling this. *noun.*

tsp., teaspoon or teaspoons.

tsu·na·mi (sü nä′mē *or* tsü nä′mē), a very large and destructive ocean wave caused by an underwater earthquake. *noun, plural* **tsu·na·mis** *or* **tsu·na·mi.**

[*Tsunami* comes from two Japanese words meaning "harbor wave."]

a hat	**i** it	**oi** oil	**ch** child	(a in about
ā age	**ī** ice	**ou** out	**ng** long	e in taken
ä far	**o** hot	**u** cup	**sh** she	ə = { i in pencil
e let	**ō** open	**u̇** put	**th** thin	o in lemon
ē equal	**ô** order	**ü** rule	**TH** then	u in circus
ėr term			**zh** measure	

tub (tub), **1** a large, open container for washing or bathing. **2** a round container for holding butter, lard, or something similar. *noun.*

tu·ba (tü′bə *or* tyü′bə), a large brass wind instrument that has a very deep tone. *noun.*

tuba

tube (tüb *or* tyüb), **1** a long pipe of metal, glass, rubber, plastic, or other material. Tubes are used to hold or carry liquids or gases. **2** a small cylinder of plastic or thin, easily bent metal with a cap that screws on the open end, used for holding toothpaste, ointment, paint, or some similar material. **3** an inner tube. **4** a pipe or tunnel through which something travels: *The railroad runs under the river in a tube.* **5** anything like a tube: *the bronchial tubes. noun.*

tu·ber (tü′bər *or* tyü′bər), the thick part of an underground stem. A potato is a tuber. *noun.*

tu·ber·cu·lo·sis (tü bėr′kyə lō′sis *or* tyü bėr′kyə lō′sis), a disease that destroys various tissues of the body, but most often the lungs. You can catch tuberculosis if you are around someone who has it. *noun.*

tuck (tuk), **1** to thrust into some narrow space or into some out-of-the-way place: *She tucked the book under her arm. He tucked the letter in his pocket.* **2** to thrust the edge or end of something closely into place: *Tuck your shirt in. He tucked a napkin under his chin.* **3** to cover snugly: *Tuck the children in bed.* **4** a fold sewed in an article of clothing: *The pants were too big, so I put a tuck in them.* 1-3 *verb,* 4 *noun.*

Tues., Tuesday.

Tues·day (tüz′dē *or* tyüz′dē), the third day of the week; the day after Monday. *noun.*

[*Tuesday* comes from an earlier English word

meaning "Tiw's day." Tiw is the name of the ancient German god of war.]

tuft (tuft), a bunch of feathers, hair, grass, or other soft and flexible things, held together at one end: *The goat had a tuft of hair on its chin. noun.*

tug (tug), **1** to pull with force or effort; pull hard: *We tugged the boat in to shore. The dog tugged at the rope.* **2** a hard pull: *The baby gave a tug at my hair.* **3** a tugboat. 1 *verb,* **tugs, tugged, tug·ging;** 2,3 *noun.*

tug·boat (tug′bōt′), a small, powerful boat used to tow or push other boats. *noun.*

tug-of-war (tug′əv wôr′ *or* tug′ə wôr′), **1** a contest between two teams pulling at the ends of a rope, each trying to drag the other over a line marked between them. **2** any hard struggle. *noun,* plural **tugs-of-war.**

tu·i·tion (tü ish′ən *or* tyü ish′ən), the money paid for instruction: *The college raised its tuition $300. noun.*

tu·lip (tü′lip *or* tyü′lip), a plant having long, narrow leaves and cup-shaped flowers of various colors. Tulips grow from bulbs and bloom in the spring. *noun.*

Word History

tulip *Tulip* comes from a Persian word meaning "turban." It was called this because the flower resembles a turban.

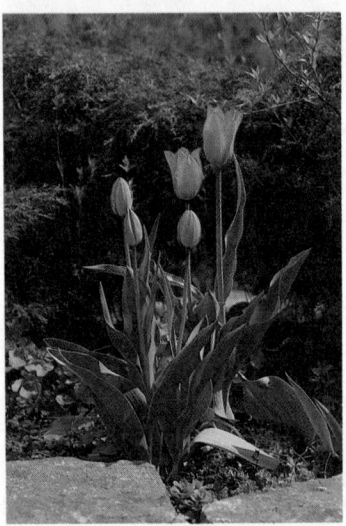

tulips

tum·ble (tum′bəl), **1** to fall headfirst or in a helpless way: *The child tumbled down the stairs.* **2** a fall by tumbling: *The tumble only bruised the child.* **3** to roll or toss about: *The sick child tumbled restlessly in the bed.* **4** to move in a hurried or awkward way: *He tumbled out of bed.* **5** to perform leaps, somersaults, or other acrobatic tricks. 1,3-5 *verb,* **tum·bles, tum·bled, tum·bling;** 2 *noun.*

tum·ble-down (tum′bəl doun′), ready to fall down; not in good condition: *a tumble-down shack in the mountains. adjective.*

tum·bler (tum′blər), **1** a person who performs leaps or springs; acrobat. **2** a drinking glass. *noun.*

tum·ble·weed (tum′bəl wēd′), a plant growing in the western United States, that breaks off from its roots and is blown about by the wind. *noun.*

tum·my (tum′ē), the stomach. *noun, plural* **tum·mies.**

tu·mor (tü′mər *or* tyü′mər), a growth of cells or tissue in the body that is not normal. *noun.*

tu·mult (tü′mult *or* tyü′mult), **1** noise; uproar: *The sailors' voices could not be heard above the tumult of the storm.* **2** a violent disturbance or disorder: *The shout of "Fire!" caused a tumult in the theater. noun.*

tu·na (tü′nə), a large sea fish used for food. It sometimes grows to a length of ten feet or more. *noun, plural* **tu·na** *or* **tu·nas.**

tun·dra (tun′drə), a vast, level, treeless plain in the arctic regions. The ground beneath its surface is frozen even in summer. Much of Alaska and northern Canada is tundra. *noun.*

tune (tün *or* tyün), **1** a piece of music; air or melody: *popular tunes.* **2** the proper pitch: *The piano is out of tune. Please sing in tune.* **3** an outlook or manner: *They'll change their tune when they see this.* **4** agreement; harmony: *I hope my ideas are in tune with the times.* **5** to adjust to the proper pitch: *We should have the piano tuned.* 1-4 *noun,* 5 *verb,* **tunes, tuned, tun·ing.**
tune in, to adjust a radio or television set to hear or see what is wanted: *to tune in an out-of-town station.*
tune up, to put an engine or other mechanism into the best working order.

tune·ful (tün′fəl *or* tyün′fəl), musical; melodious: *A robin has a tuneful song. adjective.*

tung·sten (tung′stən), a rare metal used in making steel and for electric light bulb filaments. *noun.*

tu·nic (tü′nik *or* tyü′nik), **1** an article of clothing like a long shirt, worn by the ancient Greeks and Romans. **2** a short, close-fitting coat, especially one worn by soldiers or police officers. *noun.*

tuning fork, a small steel instrument with two prongs. When struck, it makes a musical tone of a certain pitch that can be used to tune musical instruments.

tuning fork

Tu·ni·sia (tü nē′zhə *or* tyü nē′zhə), a country in northern Africa. *noun.*

tun·nel (tun′l), **1** an underground passage: *The railroad passes under the mountain through a tunnel.* **2** to make an underground passage: *The mole tunneled in the ground.* **1** *noun,* **2** *verb.*

tur·ban (tėr′bən), **1** a scarf wound around the head or around a cap, worn by men in parts of India and in some other countries. **2** any hat or headdress like this. *noun.*

tur·bine (tėr′bən), an engine containing a wheel with paddles or blades, that is caused to rotate by the pressure of rapidly flowing water, steam, or air. Turbines are often used to turn generators that produce electric power. *noun.*

tur·bu·lence (tėr′byə ləns), disturbance; disorder; commotion: *Air turbulence causes discomfort for some aircraft passengers. noun.*

tur·bu·lent (tėr′byə lənt), **1** causing a disturbance; disorderly: *a turbulent mob.* **2** stormy: *turbulent weather. adjective.*

tu·reen (tə rēn′), a deep, covered dish for serving soup. *noun.*

turf (tėrf), the upper surface of the soil covered with grass and other small plants, including their roots and the soil clinging to them; sod. *noun.*

Turk (tėrk), a person born or living in Turkey. *noun.*

tur·key (tėr′kē), **1** a large North American bird with brown or white feathers and a bare head and neck. **2** its flesh, used for food. *noun, plural* **tur·keys.**

talk turkey, to speak in a frank, blunt way: *Let's talk turkey—how much do you want for your bike?*

Tur·key (tėr′kē), a country in western Asia and southeastern Europe. *noun.*

Turk·ish (tėr′kish), **1** of or having something to do with Turkey, its people, or their language. **2** the language of Turkey. **1** *adjective,* **2** *noun.*

Word Source

Some **Turkish** words that have come into the English language are <u>coffee</u>, <u>horde</u>, <u>jackal</u>, <u>sherbet</u>, <u>turban</u>, and <u>yogurt</u>.

Turk·men·i·stan (tėrk men′ə stän), a country in western Asia. *noun.*

tur·moil (tėr′moil), a commotion; disturbance; disorder: *Moving put us in a turmoil. noun.*

turn (tėrn), **1** to move or cause to move round as a wheel does; spin: *The merry-go-round turned.* **2** a motion like that of a wheel: *At each turn the screw goes in further.* **3** to move part way around; change from one side to the other: *Turn over on your back.* **4** to take or cause to take a new direction: *The road turns to the north here.* **5** to move to the other side of; go round; get beyond: *She turned the corner.* **6** a change of direction: *A turn to the left brought him in front of us.* **7** a place where there is a change in direction: *a turn in the road.* **8** to change; cause to become; change and

a hat	**i** it	**oi** oil	**ch** child	a in about
ā age	**ī** ice	**ou** out	**ng** long	e in taken
ä far	**o** hot	**u** cup	**sh** she	ə = { i in pencil
e let	**ō** open	**ù** put	**th** thin	o in lemon
ē equal	**ô** order	**ü** rule	**ᴛʜ** then	u in circus
ėr term			**zh** measure	

turban (definition 1)

become: *The bitter cold turned his hands blue. He turned pale with fright.* **9** a change: *Matters have taken a turn for the worse. The patient has taken a turn for the better.* **10** to spoil; sour: *Hot weather turns milk.* **11** a time or chance to do something: *It is her turn to bat.* **12** a deed; act: *One good turn deserves another.* **13** a walk, drive, or ride: *We all enjoyed a turn in the park before dinner.* **14** to make or become sick: *The sight of blood turns my stomach.* **1,3-5,8,10,14** *verb,* **2,6,7,9,11-13** *noun.*

in turn, in proper order: *Each should go in turn.*

take turns, to act one after another in proper order: *They took turns watching the baby.*

turn down, 1 to fold down: *to turn down the covers on the bed.* **2** to refuse: *to turn down a plan.* **3** to reduce the amount, volume, or brightness of something by turning a control switch: *Turn down the gas. Turn down the sound on the radio, please.*

turn in, 1 to go to bed: *It's late and I'm going to turn in now.* **2** to give or give back: *to turn in homework, to turn in a library book.* **3** to exchange: *to turn in an old car for a new one.*

turn off, 1 to shut off: *Is the tap turned off or do I hear the water dripping?* **2** to put out a light: *Turn off the lights.*

turn on, 1 to start the flow of; put on. **2** to put on a light. **3** to attack; resist; oppose: *The cat turned on the dog that was chasing it.* **4** to depend on: *The success of the picnic turns on the weather.*

turn out, 1 to put out; shut off: *Turn out that big spotlight.* **2** to come out; go out: *Everyone turned out for the circus.* **3** to make; produce: *This author*

T

turns out two novels a year. **4** to result; end: *How did the game turn out?* **5** to be found or known: *The rumor turned out to be true.*

turn over, 1 to give; hand over; transfer: *to turn over a job to someone.* **2** to think carefully about; consider in different ways: *to turn over an idea in the mind.*

turn up, 1 to appear; arrive: *An old friend has turned up.* **2** to increase the amount, volume, or brightness of something by turning a control switch: *Turn up the gas. Turn up the sound on the TV, please.*

tur·nip (tėr′nəp), the large, fleshy, roundish root of a garden plant, eaten as a vegetable. *noun.*

turn·out (tėrn′out′), a gathering of people: *There was a large turnout at the picnic. noun.*

turn·pike (tėrn′pīk′), **1** a highway on which tolls are charged; toll road. **2** any main highway. *noun.*

turn·stile (tėrn′stīl′), a gate with bars that turn, set in an entrance or exit. A turnstile allows one person through at a time. *noun.*

turnstile

turn·ta·ble (tėrn′tā′bəl), the round, rotating platform of a phonograph upon which records are placed. *noun.*

tur·pen·tine (tėr′pən tīn), an oil obtained from various cone-bearing trees and used in mixing paints and varnishes. *noun.*

tur·quoise (tėr′koiz *or* tėr′kwoiz), **1** a clear blue or greenish-blue precious stone, used in jewelry. **2** greenish-blue. **1** *noun,* **2** *adjective.*
[*Turquoise* comes from an old French word meaning "Turkish." It was called Turkish stone because it was first brought into Europe through a Turkish territory.]

tur·ret (tėr′it), **1** a small tower, often on the corner of a building. **2** any of various low, rotating, armored structures that have guns mounted in them, as on a warship or tank. *noun.*

tur·tle (tėr′tl), **1** a reptile with a soft, rounded body enclosed in a hard shell into which many kinds can draw their head, legs, and tail. Turtles live in fresh water, in salt water, and on land.

Those living on land are often called tortoises. **2** a mark that can be moved about on a computer screen by instructions in LOGO and certain other computer languages. *noun.*

tur·tle·neck (tėr′tl nek′), a knitted article of clothing with a high, close-fitting collar, usually worn turned down over itself. *noun.*

tusk (tusk), a very long, pointed tooth that sticks out of the mouth. Elephants, walruses, and wild boars have tusks. *noun.*

tus·sle (tus′əl), **1** to struggle; wrestle; scuffle: *They tussled over the ball.* **2** a severe struggle or hard contest: *We thought the game would be easy, but it turned into a long, hard tussle.* **1** *verb,* **tus·sles, tus·sled, tus·sling;** **2** *noun.*

tut (tut), an exclamation used to express impatience, anger, or dislike. *interjection.*

tu·tor (tü′tər *or* tyü′tər), **1** a private teacher. **2** to teach; instruct: *Students are sometimes tutored at home when they are sick.* **1** *noun,* **2** *verb.*

tutor (definition 1)—The **tutor** listened as the boy read aloud.

TV, television.

twang (twang), **1** a sharp ringing sound: *The bow made a twang when I shot the arrow.* **2** to make a sharp ringing sound: *The banjos twanged.* **3** a sharp nasal tone: *The visitor spoke with a twang.* **4** to speak with a sharp nasal tone. **1,3** *noun,* **2,4** *verb.*

turrets (definition 1)

tweed (definition 1)

a hat	i it	oi oil	ch child	a in about
ā age	ī ice	ou out	ng long	e in taken
ä far	o hot	u cup	sh she	ə = { i in pencil
e let	ō open	u̇ put	th thin	o in lemon
ē equal	ô order	ü rule	ŦH then	u in circus
ėr term			zh measure	

tweed (twēd), **1** a woolen cloth with a rough surface. Tweed usually has two or more colors woven together. **2 tweeds,** clothes made of tweed. *noun.*

tweet (twēt), **1** the sound made by a bird: *We heard the "tweet, tweet" from a nest in the tree.* **2** to make a tweet or tweets: *Birds tweeted softly.* **1** *noun, interjection,* **2** *verb.*

tweez·ers (twē′zərz), small tongs for pulling out hairs, picking up small objects, or the like: *Father pulled the splinter from my foot with tweezers. noun plural.*

twelfth (twelfth), **1** next after the 11th. **2** one of 12 equal parts. *adjective, noun.*

twelve (twelv), one more than 11; 12. A year has twelve months. *noun, adjective.*

twen·ti·eth (twen′tē ith), **1** next after the 19th. **2** one of 20 equal parts. *adjective, noun.*

twen·ty (twen′tē), two times ten; 20. *noun, plural* **twen·ties;** *adjective.*

twice (twīs), **1** two times: *I have already called you twice.* **2** doubly: *This story is twice as long as the last one. adverb.*

twid·dle (twid′l), to twirl: *twiddle one's pencil. verb,* **twid·dles, twid·dled, twid·dling.**

twig (twig), a very small branch of a tree or bush: *Dry twigs are good to start a fire with. noun.*

twi·light (twī′līt′), the faint light reflected from the sky before sunrise and after sunset. *noun.*

twin (twin), **1** one of two children born at the same time to the same mother. Twins sometimes look exactly alike. **2** being a twin: *Have you met my twin sister?* **3** one of two things that are exactly alike. **4** being one of two things very much or exactly alike: *Twin candlesticks stood on the shelf.* **1,3** *noun,* **2,4** *adjective.*

twine (twīn), **1** a strong thread or string made of two or more strands twisted together. **2** to twist together: *We twined holly into wreaths.* **3** to wind: *The vine twines around the tree.* **1** *noun,* **2,3** *verb,* **twines, twined, twin·ing.**

twinge (twinj), a sudden, sharp pain: *a twinge of rheumatism, a twinge of remorse. noun.*
[*Twinge* comes from an older English word meaning "to pinch."]

twin·kle (twing′kəl), **1** to shine with quick little gleams: *The stars twinkled. His eyes twinkled when he laughed.* **2** a sparkle; gleam; shine: *She has a merry twinkle in her eye.* **1** *verb,* **twin·kles, twin·kled, twin·kling;** **2** *noun.*

twin·kling (twing′kling), a very brief period; an instant: *The mouse vanished in a twinkling. noun.*

twirl (twėrl), **1** to revolve rapidly; spin; whirl: *The skater twirled like a top.* **2** a twirling; spin; whirl; turn: *a twirl in a dance.* **1** *verb,* **2** *noun.*

twist (twist), **1** to turn with a winding motion; wind: *I twisted the cap off the jar.* **2** to wind together; wind: *This rope is twisted from many threads.* **3** to bend; curve; turn: *to twist a piece of wire into a loop.* **4** a curve; bend; turn: *The path is full of twists.* **5** to force out of shape or place: *I fell and twisted my ankle.* **6** to change the meaning of: *Don't twist what I say into something completely different.* **7** a twisting; being twisted. **1-3,5,6** *verb,* **4,7** *noun.*

twist·er (twis′tər), a whirlwind; tornado. *noun.*

twitch (twich), **1** to move with a quick jerk: *The cat's paw twitched when I touched it.* **2** a quick, jerky movement of some part of the body. **1** *verb,* **2** *noun, plural* **twitch·es.**

twit·ter (twit′ər), **1** a sound made by birds; chirping. **2** to make such a sound: *Birds begin to twitter just before sunrise.* **3** an excited condition: *My nerves are in a twitter when I have to speak in public.* **4** to tremble with excitement. **1,3** *noun,* **2,4** *verb.*

two (tü), one more than one; 2. We count one, two, three, four. *noun, plural* **twos;** *adjective.*

TX, Texas (used with postal Zip Code).

twine (definition 3)
Vines **twined** around the fence.

T

677

-ty[1], a suffix meaning: _____ tens: Seven*ty* means seven *tens*.

-ty[2], a suffix meaning the quality, condition, or fact of being _____: Safe*ty* means *the condition or quality of being* safe. The form *-ity* is often used instead of *-ty*, as in *timidity*.

ty·ing (tī′ing). See **tie**. *He is tying his shoes. verb.*

type (tīp), **1** a kind, sort, or group alike in some important way: *three types of local government. She is the type of person I like, kind and friendly.* **2** a set of wooden or metal pieces having on their upper surfaces raised letters for use in printing: *to set the manuscript of a book in type.* **3** to write with a typewriter: *to type a letter asking for a job.* **4** to find out the kind of; classify: *to type a person's blood.* *1,2 noun, 3,4 verb,* **types, typed, typ·ing.**

type·writ·er (tīp′rī′tər), a machine for writing which makes letters, numbers, and other symbols that are similar to printed ones. When the keys of a typewriter keyboard are struck or touched, they are pressed against an inked ribbon onto a sheet of paper. *noun.*

type·writ·ten (tīp′rit′n), written with a typewriter: *a typewritten letter. adjective.*

ty·phoid fe·ver (tī′foid fē′vər), an infectious and often fatal disease that causes a high fever and soreness and swelling of the intestine. The germs that cause typhoid fever enter the body with impure food or water. People can be inoculated against the disease.

ty·phoon (tī fün′), a storm with violent wind and, usually, very heavy rain. Typhoons occur in the western Pacific Ocean. *noun.*
[*Typhoon* comes from two Chinese words meaning "big wind."]

typ·i·cal (tip′ə kəl), showing the features or characteristics of a group or kind: *The typical Thanksgiving dinner consists of turkey, cranberry sauce, several vegetables, and mince or pumpkin pie. adjective.*

typ·ist (tī′pist), a person operating a typewriter, especially for a living. *noun.*

ty·ran·ni·cal (tə ran′ə kəl), cruel; unjust; of or like a tyrant: *a tyrannical ruler. adjective.*

ty·ran·no·sau·rus (ti ran′ə sôr′əs), a huge, prehistoric, flesh-eating dinosaur that lived in North America and walked erect on two hind legs. *noun, plural* **ty·ran·no·sau·rus·es.**

Word History

tyrannosaurus The name for this dinosaur comes from two Greek words meaning "tyrant" and "lizard."

tyrannosaurus—about 19 feet (6 meters) tall

tyr·an·ny (tir′ə nē), **1** a cruel or unjust use of power: *Cinderella escaped from the tyranny of her stepmother.* **2** government by an absolute ruler. *noun.*

ty·rant (tī′rənt), **1** a cruel or unjust ruler. **2** any person who uses power cruelly or unjustly: *A good teacher is never a tyrant. noun.*

U u

a hat	**i** it	**oi** oil	**ch** child	⎧ a in about
ā age	**ī** ice	**ou** out	**ng** long	e in taken
ä far	**o** hot	**u** cup	**sh** she	**ə** = ⎨ i in pencil
e let	**ō** open	**u̇** put	**th** thin	o in lemon
ē equal	**ô** order	**ü** rule	**ŦH** then	⎩ u in circus
ėr term			**zh** measure	

U or **u** (yü), the 21st letter of the English alphabet. *noun, plural* **U's** *or* **u's.**

ud·der (ud/ər), the baglike part that hangs down from the belly of a cow, female goat, or other female animal. Milk comes from the udder. *noun.*

UFO (yü/ef ō/), an unidentified flying object, reported seen in the sky over many different parts of the world. *noun, plural* **UFOs** *or* **UFO's.**

U·gan·da (ü gan/də *or* yü gan/də), a country in eastern Africa. *noun.*

ugh (ug *or* u), a word used to express strong dislike, disgust, or horror: *Ugh! Beets! interjection.*

ug·li·ness (ug/lē nis), an ugly appearance. *noun.*

ug·ly (ug/lē), **1** very unpleasant to look at: *an ugly house.* **2** disagreeable; unpleasant; bad; offensive: *an ugly smell, ugly language.* **3** threatening; dangerous: *an ugly wound.* **4** cross; bad-tempered; quarrelsome: *Several people seemed to be in an ugly mood. adjective,* **ug·li·er, ug·li·est.**

U·kraine (yü krān/), a country in eastern Europe. *noun.*

u·ku·le·le (yü/kə lā/lē), a small guitar having four strings. *noun.*

Word History

ukulele *Ukulele* was borrowed from a Hawaiian word. It is made up of two words meaning "leaping flea." This may have been the nickname for a person who helped make the ukulele popular in Hawaii.

ul·ti·mate (ul/tə mit), **1** last; final: *The ultimate result of driving too fast might be a serious accident.* **2** basic; fundamental: *The brain is the ultimate source of ideas. adjective.*

um·brel·la (um brel/ə), a light, folding frame covered with cloth or plastic, used as a protection against rain or sun. *noun.*
[*Umbrella* comes from an Italian word. It can be traced back to a Latin word meaning "shade."]

um·pire (um/pīr), **1** a person who rules on the plays in a game: *The umpire called the player safe.* **2** to act as umpire. **1** *noun,* **2** *verb,* **um·pires, um·pired, um·pir·ing.**

UN or **U.N.,** United Nations.

un-, a prefix meaning: **1** not: *Unchanged* means *not* changed. **2** to do the opposite of: *Unfasten* means *to do the opposite of* fasten. *Undress* means *to do the opposite of* dress.

un·a·ble (un ā/bəl), not able: *A newborn baby is unable to walk or talk. adjective.*

ugly (definition 3)—The **ugly** sky signaled that a storm was coming.

un·ac·cent·ed (un ak/sen tid), not pronounced with force; not accented. In *unattended* the second and fourth syllables are unaccented. *adjective.*

un·ac·count·a·ble (un/ə koun/tə bəl), **1** not able to be accounted for or explained: *He had an unaccountable feeling that something was wrong.* **2** not responsible: *A wild animal is unaccountable for its actions. adjective.*

un·ac·cus·tomed (un/ə kus/təmd), **1** not accustomed: *Polar bears are unaccustomed to hot weather.* **2** not familiar; unusual or strange: *He was unaccustomed to the routine of his new job. adjective.*

un·a·fraid (un/ə frād/), not afraid; fearless: *In spite of the danger, we were unafraid. adjective.*

un·aid·ed (un ā/did), not aided; without help. *adjective.*

u·nan·i·mous (yü nan/ə məs), **1** in complete agreement; agreed: *The children were unanimous in their wish to go to the beach.* **2** showing complete agreement: *She was elected by a unanimous vote. adjective.*
[*Unanimous* comes from a Latin word meaning "of one mind."]

un·armed (un ärmd/), without weapons: *an unarmed robber. adjective.*

un·as·sum·ing (un/ə sü/ming), modest; not

U

unattended | uncover

putting on airs: *The people of the village were delighted by the unassuming manners of the king and queen. adjective.*

un·at·tend·ed (un′ə ten′did), **1** alone; not accompanied: *The king arrived unattended.* **2** not taken care of; not attended to: *The baby was left unattended. adjective.*

un·a·void·a·ble (un′ə voi′də bəl), not able to be avoided: *an unavoidable delay, an unavoidable accident. adjective.*

un·a·ware (un′ə wer′ *or* un′ə war′), **1** not aware; unconscious: *We were unaware of the approaching storm.* **2** unawares. **1** *adjective,* **2** *adverb.*

unaware (definition 1)—The painter was **unaware** of the cow licking his picture.

un·a·wares (un′ə werz′ *or* un′ə warz′), **1** without being expected; by surprise: *She came in and caught us unawares.* **2** without knowing: *to approach danger unawares. adverb.*

un·bear·a·ble (un ber′ə bəl *or* un bar′ə bəl), not able to be suffered or endured: *The pain from a severe toothache is almost unbearable. adjective.*

un·beat·en (un bēt′n), **1** not defeated. **2** not traveled: *unbeaten paths. adjective.*

un·be·com·ing (un′bi kum′ing), **1** not becoming; not flattering: *unbecoming clothes.* **2** not fitting; not proper: *unbecoming behavior. adjective.*

un·be·liev·a·ble (un′bi lē′və bəl), not able to be believed: *He told an unbelievable story. adjective.*

un·born (un bôrn′), not yet born; still to come; of the future: *unborn generations. adjective.*

un·break·a·ble (un brā′kə bəl), not breakable; not easily broken: *Some plastic phonograph records are unbreakable. adjective.*

un·bro·ken (un brō′kən), **1** not broken; whole: *an unbroken dish.* **2** continuous; not interrupted: *He had eight hours of unbroken sleep.* **3** not tamed: *an unbroken colt. adjective.*

un·buck·le (un buk′əl), **1** to unfasten the buckle or buckles of. **2** to unfasten. *verb,* **un·buck·les, un·buck·led, un·buck·ling.**

un·but·ton (un but′n), to unfasten the button or buttons of. *verb.*

un·called-for (un kôld′fôr′), **1** unnecessary and improper: *an uncalled-for remark.* **2** not called for. *adjective.*

un·can·ny (un kan′ē), strange and mysterious; weird: *The trees took uncanny shapes in the half darkness. adjective.*

un·cer·tain (un sėrt′n), **1** not certain; doubtful: *She came so late that she was uncertain of her welcome.* **2** likely to change; not to be depended on: *This dog has an uncertain temper. adjective.*

un·cer·tain·ty (un sėrt′n tē), **1** uncertain state or condition; doubt: *There was some uncertainty as to our plans.* **2** something uncertain: *When we'll be coming is still an uncertainty. noun, plural* **un·cer·tain·ties.**

un·chain (un chān′), to let loose; set free. *verb.*

un·changed (un chānjd′), not changed; the same: *unchanged tradition. adjective.*

un·civ·i·lized (un siv′ə līzd), not civilized; barbarous; savage: *uncivilized manners. The cave dwellers of Europe were uncivilized people of the Stone Age. adjective.*

un·cle (ung′kəl), **1** a brother of one's father or mother. **2** the husband of one's aunt. *noun.*

un·clear (un klir′), not clear; confusing; vague: *Your directions were unclear and we got lost. adjective.*

un·coil (un koil′), to unwind. *verb.*

un·com·fort·a·ble (un kum′fər tə bəl), **1** not comfortable: *an uncomfortable chair.* **2** troubled; not at ease: *I felt uncomfortable when they stared at me. adjective.*

un·com·mon (un kom′ən), rare; unusual: *Snow is uncommon in Florida. adjective.*

un·con·cerned (un′kən sėrnd′), **1** free from care or anxiety: *She seemed quite unconcerned about the small cut on her finger.* **2** not interested; indifferent: *They were unconcerned with the election next week. adjective.*

un·con·di·tion·al (un′kən dish′ə nəl), without conditions; absolute: *The enemy refused our demand for unconditional surrender. adjective.*

un·con·scious (un kon′shəs), **1** not able to feel or think; not conscious: *He was knocked unconscious by the blow.* **2** not aware: *Unconscious of the time, she kept on reading and missed her piano lesson.* **3** not meant; not intended: *Her rude remark was unconscious. adjective.*

un·con·sti·tu·tion·al (un′kon stə tü′shə nəl *or* un′kon stə tyü′shə nəl), not allowed by a constitution; not in agreement with a constitution: *The judges declared the law unconstitutional. adjective.*

un·con·trol·la·ble (un′kən trō′lə bəl), not able to be controlled; beyond control: *I had an uncontrollable urge to laugh. adjective.*

un·cooked (un kùkt′), not cooked; raw. *adjective.*

un·couth (un küth′), awkward; clumsy; crude: *uncouth manners. adjective.*

un·cov·er (un kuv′ər), **1** to remove the cover from: *I uncovered the pot.* **2** to reveal; expose; make known: *The reporter uncovered a scandal. verb.*

680

un·cul·ti·vat·ed (un kul′tə vā′tid), wild; not developed or cultivated: *uncultivated land.* *adjective.*

un·curl (un kėrl′), to straighten out. *verb.*

un·daunt·ed (un dôn′tid), not afraid; not discouraged; fearless: *The skier was undaunted by the bad fall she suffered in the first race. adjective.*

un·de·cid·ed (un′di sī′did), 1 not decided; not settled: *Our schedule is still undecided.* 2 not having one's mind made up: *I am undecided about which book to buy. adjective.*

un·de·ni·a·ble (un′di nī′ə bəl), plain; certain; not able to be denied: *undeniable facts. adjective.*

un·der (un′dər), 1 below; beneath: *The book fell under the table. The swimmer went under.* 2 lower: *the under lip.* 3 lower than; lower down than; not so high as: *There was a tiny bruise just under his eye.* 4 less than: *The coat will cost under twenty dollars.* 5 according to; because of: *under the law. We acted under orders. The class learned a great deal under her teaching.* 6 during the rule or time of: *England under Queen Victoria.* 1,3-6 *preposition,* 1 *adverb,* 2 *adjective.*

under-, a prefix meaning: 1 below; beneath: *Under*line the title of a book means to draw a line *below* the title. An *under*ground passage means a passage that is *beneath* the ground. 2 not enough; not sufficiently: *Under*nourished people means people who are *not sufficiently* nourished.

un·der·brush (un′dər brush′), bushes, shrubs, and small trees growing under large trees in woods or forests. *noun.*

un·der·clothes (un′dər klōz′), underwear. *noun plural.*

un·der·cur·rent (un′dər kėr′ənt), a current below the surface of a body of water. *noun.*

un·der·de·vel·oped (un′dər di vel′əpt), 1 not normally developed: *underdeveloped muscles.* 2 poorly developed in industry and way of living: *The underdeveloped countries need trained workers. adjective.*

underdeveloped (definition 2)
In some **underdeveloped** countries people harvest grain by hand.

un·der·dog (un′dər dôg′), a person or group having the worst of any struggle; person or group expected to be the loser. *noun.*

un·der·fed (un′dər fed′), fed too little; not well

nourished: *The stray cat looked underfed. adjective.*

un·der·foot (un′dər fu̇t′), 1 under one's feet; on the ground; underneath: *The leaves crunched underfoot.* 2 in the way: *She complained because the cat was always underfoot. adverb.*

un·der·go (un′dər gō′), to go through; experience; be subjected to: *The town is undergoing many changes as more and more people are moving in. The pioneers underwent many hardships. verb,* **un·der·goes, un·der·went, un·der·gone, un·der·go·ing.**

un·der·gone (un′dər gôn′). See **undergo.** *The town has undergone many changes. verb.*

un·der·ground (un′dər ground′ for 1 and 4; un′dər ground′ for 2, 3, 5, and 6), 1 beneath the surface of the ground: *Miners work underground.* 2 being, working, or used beneath the surface of the ground: *an underground passage.* 3 a place or space beneath the surface of the ground: *In London the subway system is called the underground.* 4 in secrecy: into concealment: *The thief went underground after the robbery.* 5 secret: *The revolt against the government was an underground plot.* 6 a secret organization working against an unpopular government, especially during military occupation: *The French underground protected many American fliers shot down over France during World War II.* 1,4 *adverb,* 2,5 *adjective,* 3,6 *noun.*

un·der·growth (un′dər grōth′), bushes, shrubs, and small trees growing under large trees in woods or forests. *noun.*

un·der·hand (un′dər hand′), 1 secret; sly; not open or honest. 2 secretly; slyly. 3 with the hand below the shoulder: *to pitch underhand, an underhand pitch.* 1,3 *adjective,* 2,3 *adverb.*

un·der·hand·ed (un′dər han′did), secret; sly; not open or honest: *an underhanded trick. adjective.*

un·der·line (un′dər līn′), to draw a line under: *In writing, we underline titles of books. verb,* **un·der·lines, un·der·lined, un·der·lin·ing.**

un·der·mine (un′dər mīn′), 1 to dig under or wear away the foundations of: *The waves had undermined the cliff.* 2 to weaken by secret or unfair means: *Nasty rumors undermined his reputation.* 3 to weaken or destroy gradually: *Many severe colds had undermined her health. verb,* **un·der·mines, un·der·mined, un·der·min·ing.**

un·der·neath (un′dər nēth′), beneath; below; under: *We can sit underneath this tree. Someone was pushing underneath. preposition, adverb.*

un·der·nour·ished (un′dər nėr′isht), not getting enough good food: *An undernourished* *child needs plenty of healthy food. adjective.*

un·der·pants (un′dər pants′), shorts or panties worn next to the skin under other clothing. *noun plural.*

un·der·pass (un′dər pas′), a path underneath; road under railroad tracks or under another road. *noun, plural* **un·der·pass·es.**

un·der·priv·i·leged (un′dər priv′ə lijd), having fewer advantages than most people have, especially because of poverty: *Underprivileged people need our help. adjective.*

un·der·rate (un′dər rāt′), to rate or estimate too low; put too low a value on: *Don't underrate this team; it usually wins. verb,* **un·der·rates, un·der·rat·ed, un·der·rat·ing.**

un·der·sea (un′dər sē′), being, working, or used beneath the surface of the sea: *an undersea cable, undersea exploration. adjective.*

un·der·shirt (un′dər shėrt′), a shirt worn next to the skin under other clothing. *noun.*

un·der·side (un′dər sīd′), the surface lying underneath; bottom side: *The underside of the stone was covered with ants. noun.*

un·der·stand (un′dər stand′), **1** to get the meaning of: *Now I understand the teacher's question.* **2** to know well: *My parents understand Russian.* **3** to be informed; learn: *I understand that she is moving to another town.* **4** to take as a fact; believe: *It is understood that you will come.* **5** to be sympathetic; show patience toward: *When I have a problem, I know my friend will understand. A good teacher understands children. verb,* **un·der·stands, un·der·stood, un·der·stand·ing.**

un·der·stand·ing (un′dər stan′ding), **1** comprehension; knowledge: *She has a clear understanding of the problem.* **2** intelligence; the ability to learn and know: *That scholar is a man of understanding.* **3** able to understand; intelligent and sympathetic: *an understanding reply.* **4** knowledge of each other's meaning and wishes: *You and I must come to an understanding.* **1,2,4** *noun,* **3** *adjective.*

un·der·stood (un′dər stůd′). See **understand.** *Have you understood the lesson? I understood what she said. verb.*

un·der·take (un′dər tāk′), **1** to try; attempt: *to undertake to reach home before dark.* **2** to agree to do; take upon oneself: *I will undertake the feeding of your dogs while you are away. verb,* **un·der·takes, un·der·took, un·der·tak·en, un·der·tak·ing.**

un·der·tak·en (un′dər tā′kən). See **undertake.** *She has undertaken more than she can do. verb.*

un·der·tak·er (un′dər tā′kər), a person who prepares the dead for burial and takes charge of funerals. *noun.*

un·der·tak·ing (un′dər tā′king), something undertaken; task; enterprise: *Starting your own business is a large undertaking. noun.*

un·der·tone (un′dər tōn′), **1** a low or very quiet tone: *to talk in undertones.* **2** something beneath the surface: *An undertone of sadness crept into her*

voice despite the happy occasion. noun.

un·der·took (un′dər tůk′). See **undertake.** *He failed because he undertook more than he could do. verb.*

un·der·tow (un′dər tō′), a strong current below the surface of the water, moving in a direction different from that of the surface current. *noun.*

un·der·wa·ter (un′dər wô′tər), **1** below the surface of the water: *an underwater current, to swim underwater.* **2** made for use under the water: *A submarine is an underwater boat.* **1,2** *adjective,* **1** *adverb.*

un·der·wear (un′dər wer′ *or* un′dər war′), clothing worn under one's outer clothes, especially next to the skin. *noun.*

un·der·weight (un′dər wāt′), having too little weight; below the normal or required weight. *adjective.*

un·der·went (un′dər went′). See **undergo.** *Transportation underwent a great change with the development of the automobile. verb.*

un·de·sir·a·ble (un′di zī′rə bəl), objectionable; disagreeable: *The drug was taken off the market because it had undesirable effects on persons who used it. adjective.*

un·did (un did′). See **undo.** *I undid my shoes. The fire in the artist's studio undid many years of work. verb.*

un·dis·put·ed (un′dis pyü′tid), not disputed; not doubted. *adjective.*

un·dis·turbed (un′dis tėrbd′), not disturbed; not troubled; calm: *The sleeping children were undisturbed by the noise. adjective.*

un·do (un dü′), **1** to unfasten; untie: *Please undo the package. I undid the string.* **2** to wipe out; cancel; destroy: *Workers repair the road each year, but heavy winter storms undo their work. verb,* **un·does** (un duz′), **un·did, un·done, un·do·ing.**

un·do·ing (un dü′ing), **1** a wiping out; canceling; destroying. **2** a cause of destruction or ruin: *Gambling was this man's undoing. noun.*

un·done (un dun′), **1** not done; not finished. **2** untied; unfastened. **3** See **undo.** **1,2** *adjective,* **3** *verb.*

un·doubt·ed (un dou′tid), not doubted; accepted as true: *She is the undoubted winner. adjective.*

un·doubt·ed·ly (un dou′tid lē), beyond doubt; certainly: *He is undoubtedly the best speller in class. adverb.*

un·dress (un dres′), to take the clothes off; strip. *verb.*

un·due (un dü′ *or* un dyü′), **1** not fitting; improper; not right: *They made rude, undue remarks about people in the restaurant.* **2** too great; too much: *Some people give undue importance to money. adjective.*

un·du·ly (un dü′lē *or* un dyü′lē), excessively; too much: *The treatment of the prisoners was unduly harsh. adverb.*

un·dy·ing (un dī′ing), deathless; immortal; eternal: *undying fame, undying beauty. adjective.*

un·earth (un ėrth′), **1** to dig up: *The scientists unearthed a buried city.* **2** to discover; find out: *The* *police unearthed the evidence. verb.*

un·eas·i·ly (un ē′zə lē), in an uneasy manner; restlessly. *adverb.*

un·eas·i·ness (un ē′zē nis), a lack of ease or comfort; restlessness; anxiety. *noun.*

un·eas·y (un ē′zē), **1** restless; disturbed; anxious: *They were uneasy when the children didn't come home for dinner.* **2** not comfortable: *I had an uneasy sleep.* **3** not easy in manner; awkward: *The speaker seemed nervous and uneasy. adjective,* **un·eas·i·er, un·eas·i·est.**

un·ed·u·cat·ed (un ej′ə kā′tid), not educated; not taught or trained. *adjective.*

un·em·ployed (un′em ploid′), **1** not employed; not in use: *an unemployed skill.* **2** not having a job; having no work: *an unemployed person.* **3 the unemployed,** people out of work: *Some of the unemployed sought aid from the government.* 1,2 *adjective,* 3 *noun.*

un·em·ploy·ment (un′em ploi′mənt), lack of employment; being out of work. *noun.*

un·end·ing (un en′ding), never ending; endless; continuous: *an unending struggle, the unending change of the seasons. adjective.*

un·e·qual (un ē′kwəl), **1** not the same in amount, size, number, or value: *unequal sums of money.* **2** not fair; one-sided: *an unequal contest.* **3** not enough; not adequate: *Their strength was unequal to the task. adjective.*

un·e·ven (un ē′vən), **1** not level: *uneven ground.* **2** not equal: *an uneven contest.* **3** leaving a remainder of 1 when divided by 2; odd: *1, 3, 5, 7, and 9 are uneven numbers. adjective.*

un·ex·pect·ed (un′ek spek′tid), not expected: *We had an unexpected, but welcome, visit from our grandmother last week. adjective.*

un·fail·ing (un fā′ling), **1** never failing; always ready when needed; loyal: *an unfailing friend.* **2** never running short: *an unfailing supply of water. adjective.*

un·fair (un fer′ *or* un far′), unjust: *an unfair decision. It was unfair of you to trick him. adjective.*

un·faith·ful (un fāth′fəl), not faithful; not true to duty or one's promises; faithless. *adjective.*

un·fa·mil·iar (un′fə mil′yər), **1** not well known; unusual; strange: *That face is unfamiliar to me.* **2** not acquainted: *He is unfamiliar with the Greek language. adjective.*

un·fas·ten (un fas′n), to undo; untie; loosen; open: *Don't unfasten your seat belt yet. verb.*

un·fa·vor·a·ble (un fā′vər ə bəl), not favorable; harmful: *The forecast for tomorrow is for unfavorable weather. adjective.*

un·feel·ing (un fē′ling), cruel; hardhearted: *a cold, unfeeling person. adjective.*

un·fin·ished (un fin′isht), **1** not finished; not complete: *unfinished homework, an unfinished symphony.* **2** without some special finish; rough; not polished or painted: *unfinished furniture. adjective.*

un·fit (un fit′), **1** not fit; not suitable: *This moldy bread is unfit to eat.* **2** not healthy and strong; in poor physical condition: *He was unfit for the hard work. adjective.*

un·fold (un fōld′), **1** to open the folds of; spread out: *to unfold a napkin, to unfold your arms.* **2** to reveal; show; explain: *to unfold the plot of a story.* **3** to open; develop: *Buds unfold into flowers. verb.*

un·fore·seen (un′fôr sēn′), not known beforehand; unexpected: *There was an unforeseen delay. adjective.*

un·for·get·ta·ble (un′fər get′ə bəl), not able to be forgotten; worth remembering: *Winning the contest was an unforgettable experience. adjective.*

un·for·giv·a·ble (un′fər giv′ə bəl), not to be forgiven; inexcusable: *Such cruelty is unforgivable. adjective.*

un·for·tu·nate (un fôr′chə nit), not lucky; having bad luck: *She had an unfortunate accident. adjective.*

un·friend·ly (un frend′lē), **1** not friendly: *The unfriendly dog growled at me.* **2** not favorable: *The play received unfriendly reviews. adjective,* **un·friend·li·er, un·friend·li·est.**

un·furl (un fėrl′), to spread out; shake out; unfold: *Unfurl the sail. The flag unfurled. verb.*

un·fur·nished (un fėr′nisht), not furnished; without furniture: *an unfurnished room. adjective.*

un·gain·ly (un gān′lē), awkward; clumsy: *Long arms and large hands can give a person an ungainly appearance. adjective,* **un·gain·li·er, un·gain·li·est.**

ungainly—The newborn camel was very **ungainly.**

un·grate·ful (un grāt′fəl), not grateful; not thankful: *I don't want to seem ungrateful, but I don't need your help. adjective.*

un·guard·ed (un gär′did), **1** not protected: *an unguarded camp.* **2** careless: *In an unguarded moment, she gave away the secret. adjective.*

un·hand (un hand′), to let go; take the hands

a hat	**i** it	**oi** oil	**ch** child		a in about
ā age	**ī** ice	**ou** out	**ng** long		e in taken
ä far	**o** hot	**u** cup	**sh** she	ə =	i in pencil
e let	**ō** open	**ù** put	**th** thin		o in lemon
ē equal	**ô** order	**ü** rule	**ŦH** then		u in circus
ėr term			**zh** measure		

from; release: *Unhand me at once! verb.*

un·hap·pi·ly (un hap′ə lē), **1** not happily: *to live unhappily.* **2** unfortunately: *Unhappily I missed seeing him. adverb.*

un·hap·pi·ness (un hap′ē nis), sadness; sorrow: *We felt great unhappiness when our dog died. noun.*

un·hap·py (un hap′ē), **1** without gladness; sad; sorrowful: *an unhappy face.* **2** unlucky: *an unhappy accident.* **3** not suitable: *an unhappy selection of colors. adjective,* **un·hap·pi·er, un·hap·pi·est.**

un·harmed (un härmd′), not harmed; not injured. *adjective.*

un·health·y (un hel′thē), **1** not possessing good health; not well: *an unhealthy child.* **2** coming from or showing poor health: *an unhealthy paleness.* **3** hurtful to health; not healthful: *an unhealthy climate. adjective,* **un·health·i·er, un·health·i·est.**

un·heard (un hèrd′), not listened to; not heard: *My advice went unheard. adjective.*

un·heard-of (un hèrd′uv′), **1** never heard of; unknown: *The electric light was unheard-of 200 years ago.* **2** not known before: *unheard-of prices, unheard-of bad manners. adjective.*

un·heed·ed (un hē′did), not heeded; unnoticed; disregarded: *My warning was unheeded. adjective.*

un·hitch (un hich′), to free from being hitched; unfasten: *She unhitched the wagon from her bicycle so she could ride faster. verb.*

un·hook (un hùk′), **1** to loosen from a hook. **2** to undo by loosening a hook or hooks. **3** to become unhooked; become undone. *verb.*

U·NI·CEF (yü′nə sef), United Nations Children's Fund. *noun.*

u·ni·corn (yü′nə kôrn), an imaginary animal like a horse, but having a single, long horn in its forehead. *noun.*

unicycle—Learning to balance a **unicycle** takes practice.

u·ni·cy·cle (yü′nə sī′kəl), a vehicle pedaled like a bicycle but with only one wheel. *noun.*

u·ni·den·ti·fied (un′ī den′tə fīd), not identified; not recognized. *adjective.*

u·ni·form (yü′nə fôrm), **1** always the same; not changing: *The earth turns at a uniform rate.* **2** all alike; not varying: *All the bricks have a uniform size.* **3** the clothes worn by the members of a group when on duty. Soldiers, police officers, and nurses wear uniforms so that they may be easily recognized. **1,2** *adjective,* **3** *noun.*

u·ni·form·i·ty (yü′nə fôr′mə tē), a uniform condition or character; sameness throughout. *noun, plural* **u·ni·form·i·ties.**

u·ni·fy (yü′nə fī), to unite; make or form into one: *Several small states were unified into one nation. verb,* **u·ni·fies, u·ni·fied, u·ni·fy·ing.**

un·im·por·tant (un′im pôrt′nt), not important; insignificant; trifling: *The cost of the gift is unimportant; it is the thought that counts. adjective.*

un·in·hab·it·ed (un′in hab′ə tid), not lived in; without inhabitants: *an uninhabited wilderness. adjective.*

un·in·tel·li·gi·ble (un′in tel′ə jə bəl), not able to be understood: *There was so much static on the radio that the whole program was unintelligible. adjective.*

un·in·ter·est·ing (un in′tər ə sting), not interesting: *I didn't finish the book because it was uninteresting. adjective.*

un·ion (yü′nyən), **1** a joining of two or more persons or things into one: *The United States was formed by the union of thirteen former British colonies.* **2** a group of persons, states, or nations joined for some common purpose; combination: *the Soviet Union.* **3** the **Union,** the United States. **4** a group of workers joined together to protect and promote their interests; labor union. *noun.* [*Union* comes from a Latin word meaning "one." Other English words from the same root include *unique, unit, unite,* and *unity.*]

u·nique (yü nēk′), **1** having no like or equal; being the only one of its kind: *a unique specimen of rock, a unique experience. The astronaut described his experience as unique.* **2** very uncommon or unusual; rare; remarkable: *His style of singing is rather unique. adjective.*

Word History

unicorn *Unicorn* comes from two Latin words meaning "one horn."

unison—The runners moved **in unison**.

a hat	i it	oi oil	ch child	(a in about
ā age	ī ice	ou out	ng long	e in taken
ä far	o hot	u cup	sh she	ə = { i in pencil
e let	ō open	ů put	th thin	o in lemon
ē equal	ô order	ü rule	ᴛʜ then	(u in circus
ėr term			zh measure	

u·ni·son (yü′nə sən), **in unison,** together; as one: *At the party we sang "Happy Birthday" in unison. noun.*

u·nit (yü′nit), **1** a single thing or person. **2** any group of things or persons considered as one: *The family is a social unit.* **3** one of the individuals or groups of which a whole is composed: *The body consists of units called cells.* **4** a standard quantity or amount: *A foot is a unit of length; a pound is a unit of weight.* **5** a machine or part of a machine that has a specific purpose: *This furnace is old; we may need a new unit.* **6** a special part, division, or section: *Tomorrow the teacher is going to ask us questions about the stories we have read in this unit. noun.*

u·nite (yü nīt′), to join together; make one; become one: *Several firms were united to form one company. verb,* **u·nites, u·nit·ed, u·nit·ing.**

United Kingdom, a country in northwestern Europe made up of Great Britain and Northern Ireland.

United Nations, 1 a worldwide organization established in 1945 to promote world peace and economic and social welfare. Its headquarters is in New York City. **2** the nations that belong to this organization.

United States, a country in North America, extending from the Atlantic to the Pacific and from the Gulf of Mexico to Canada. Alaska, the 49th state, lies northwest of Canada. Hawaii, the 50th state, is an island group in the Pacific.

United States of America, the United States.

u·ni·ty (yü′nə tē), **1** oneness: *The group's unity of purpose helped them get results.* **2** harmony: *Brothers and sisters should live together in unity. noun, plural* **u·ni·ties.**

u·ni·ver·sal (yü′nə vėr′səl), **1** of all; belonging to all; concerning all; done by all: *Food is a universal need.* **2** existing everywhere: *The law of gravity is universal. adjective.*

u·ni·ver·sal·ly (yü′nə vėr′sə lē), **1** in every instance; without exception. **2** everywhere. *adverb.*

u·ni·verse (yü′nə vėrs′), all things; everything there is. Our world is but a small part of the universe. *noun.*

u·ni·ver·si·ty (yü′nə vėr′sə tē), an institution of higher education. Universities usually have schools of law, medicine, teaching, and business, as well as colleges for general instruction. *noun, plural* **u·ni·ver·si·ties.**

un·just (un just′), not just; not fair: *Punishing someone for no reason would be unjust. adjective.*

un·kempt (un kempt′), **1** not combed: *unkempt hair.* **2** neglected; untidy: *unkempt clothes, an unkempt appearance. adjective.*

un·kind (un kīnd′), harsh; cruel: *I resented their unkind remarks about my friend. adjective.*

un·kind·ly (un kīnd′lē), in an unkind way; harshly: *They spoke unkindly of my friend. adverb.*

un·known (un nōn′), **1** not known; not familiar; strange; unexplored: *the dark, unknown depths of the sea.* **2** a person or thing that is unknown: *The diver descended into the unknown.* **1** *adjective,* **2** *noun.*

un·lace (un lās′), to undo the laces of: *She unlaced her shoes. verb,* **un·lac·es, un·laced, un·lac·ing.**

un·law·ful (un lô′fəl), against the law; forbidden; illegal: *Littering the highway is unlawful. adjective.*

un·learn·ed (un lėr′nid *for 1;* un lėrnd′ *for 2),* **1** not educated; ignorant: *They were unlearned and could not read or write.* **2** not learned; known without being learned: *Swallowing is unlearned behavior. adjective.*

un·less (un les′), if not; except if: *I won't go unless you do. conjunction.*

un·like (un līk′), **1** not like; different: *The two problems are quite unlike.* **2** different from: *One kitten was acting unlike the others.* **1** *adjective,* **2** *preposition.*

un·like·ly (un līk′lē), **1** not likely; not probable: *She is unlikely to win the race.* **2** not likely to succeed: *an unlikely undertaking. adjective,* **un·like·li·er, un·like·li·est.**

un·lim·it·ed (un lim′ə tid), without limits. *adjective.*

un·load (un lōd′), **1** to take a load from: *They unloaded the car. They unloaded boxes from the truck.* **2** to remove powder, shot, bullets, or shells from a gun. *verb.*

un·lock (un lok′), **1** to open the lock of; open anything firmly closed: *I unlocked the door.* **2** to disclose; reveal: *Science has unlocked the mystery of the atom. verb.*

un·luck·y (un luk′ē), not lucky; unfortunate; bringing bad luck. *adjective,* **un·luck·i·er, un·luck·i·est.**

un·manned (un mand′), without a crew: *an unmanned space flight. adjective.*

un·mar·ried (un mar′ēd), not married; single. *adjective.*

un·mis·tak·a·ble (un′mə stā′kə bəl), not able to

U

be mistaken or misunderstood; clear; plain; evident: *The artist's talent was unmistakable.* adjective.

un·moved (un müvd′), **1** not moved; firm: *They tried to convince me, but I was unmoved by their arguments.* **2** not disturbed; indifferent: *Their sad tale left me unmoved.* adjective.

un·nat·ur·al (un nach′ər əl), not natural; not normal: *It is unnatural for a dog to climb a tree.* adjective.

un·nec·es·sar·y (un nes′ə ser′ē), not necessary; needless: *A coat is unnecessary on such a warm day.* adjective.

un·nerve (un nėrv′), to deprive of firmness or self-control: *The sight of blood unnerves some people.* verb, **un·nerves, un·nerved, un·nerv·ing.**

un·no·ticed (un nō′tist), not noticed; not observed; not receiving any attention: *I slipped into the room unnoticed.* adjective.

un·num·bered (un num′bərd), **1** not numbered; not counted: *The theater seats were unnumbered.* **2** too many to count: *There are unnumbered fish in the ocean.* adjective.

un·ob·served (un′əb zėrvd′), not observed; not noticed; disregarded: *The thief was unobserved as he left the building.* adjective.

un·oc·cu·pied (un ok′yə pīd), **1** not occupied; vacant: *The driver pulled her car into the unoccupied parking space.* **2** not busy; not in use; idle: *I enjoy being busy; I don't like being unoccupied.* adjective.

un·of·fi·cial (un′ə fish′əl), not official: *That's the unofficial report, but we are waiting for further facts.* adjective.

un·pack (un pak′), **1** to take out things packed in a box, trunk, or other container: *I unpacked my clothes.* **2** to take things out of: *to unpack a trunk.* verb.

un·paid (un pād′), not paid: *Their unpaid bills amounted to $200.* adjective.

un·par·al·leled (un par′ə leld), having no parallel; unequaled; matchless: *an unparalleled achievement.* adjective.

un·pleas·ant (un plez′nt), not pleasant; disagreeable: *an unpleasant odor.* adjective.

un·pop·u·lar (un pop′yə lər), not popular; not generally liked; disliked. adjective.

un·pre·dict·a·ble (un′pri dik′tə bəl), not able to be predicted; uncertain: *How a game would turn out between such evenly matched teams was unpredictable.* adjective.

un·pre·pared (un′pri perd′ or un′pri pard′), **1** not made ready; not worked out ahead: *an unprepared speech.* **2** not ready: *a person unprepared to answer.* adjective.

un·prin·ci·pled (un prin′sə pəld), lacking good moral principles; bad. adjective.

un·ques·tion·a·ble (un kwes′chə nə bəl), beyond dispute or doubt; certain: *Being tall is an unquestionable advantage to a basketball player.* adjective.

un·ques·tion·a·bly (un kwes′chə nə blē), beyond dispute or doubt; certainly. adverb.

un·rav·el (un rav′əl), **1** to separate the threads of; pull apart: *My sweater is unraveling. The cat unraveled the ball of yarn.* **2** to bring out of a tangled state: *The detective unraveled the mystery.* verb.

un·re·al (un rē′əl), not real; imaginary; fanciful: *In the bright morning sunlight, our fears of last night's storm seemed unreal.* adjective.

un·rea·son·a·ble (un rē′zn ə bəl), **1** not reasonable: *an unreasonable dislike of animals.* **2** not moderate; excessive: *They spend an unreasonable amount of money on clothes.* adjective.

un·re·li·a·ble (un′ri lī′ə bəl), not reliable; not to be depended on; irresponsible: *Don't count on them to help; they're unreliable.* adjective.

un·rest (un rest′), restlessness; dissatisfaction; lack of ease and quiet: *The government's injustices caused political unrest among the people.* noun.

un·ri·valed (un rī′vəld), having no rival; without an equal: *She is the unrivaled champion.* adjective.

un·roll (un rōl′), **1** to open or become open; spread out: *I unrolled my sleeping bag.* **2** to reveal; display; make known: *The movie unrolls a tale of mystery and adventure.* verb.

un·rul·y (un rü′lē), hard to rule or control; lawless: *The unruly horse threw its rider. The unruly mob stormed the palace.* adjective, **un·rul·i·er, un·rul·i·est.**

un·safe (un sāf′), dangerous: *Swimming all alone is unsafe.* adjective.

un·said (un sed′), not said: *Everything he had meant to say remained unsaid.* adjective.

un·sat·is·fac·tor·y (un′sat i sfak′tər ē), not good enough to satisfy: *Your work is unsatisfactory because there are too many mistakes.* adjective.

un·sat·is·fied (un sat′i sfīd), not satisfied; not contented: *The tiny meal left me unsatisfied.* adjective.

un·scram·ble (un skram′bəl), to change from confusion to order: *After the wind died down, I unscrambled the papers that had blown on the floor.* verb, **un·scram·bles, un·scram·bled, un·scram·bling.**

un·screw (un skrü′), **1** to take out the screw or screws from. **2** to loosen or take off by turning: *to unscrew an electric light bulb.* verb.

un·scru·pu·lous (un skrü′pyə ləs), not careful about right or wrong; without principles: *The unscrupulous student cheated on the test.* adjective.

un·seat (un sēt′), **1** to displace from a seat. **2** to throw a rider from a saddle. **3** to remove from office: *to unseat a senator, to unseat a government.* verb.

un·seem·ly (un sēm′lē), not proper; not suitable: *Laughter is often unseemly in a courtroom.* adjective, **un·seem·li·er, un·seem·li·est.**

un·seen (un sēn′), **1** not seen: unnoticed: *an unseen error.* **2** not able to be seen; invisible: *an unseen spirit.* adjective.

un·self·ish (un sel′fish), caring for others;

generous: *an unselfish person. adjective.*

un·set·tle (un set′l), to disturb; make or become unstable; shake; weaken: *The shock unsettled my nerves. verb,* **un·set·tles, un·set·tled, un·set·tling.**

un·set·tled (un set′ld), **1** disordered; not in proper condition or order: *We've just moved in, so the house is still unsettled.* **2** not paid; not adjusted: *He was out of work and worried about unsettled bills.* **3** not determined or decided: *an unsettled question.* **4** not inhabited: *Some parts of the world are still unsettled. adjective.*

un·shak·en (un shā′kən), not shaken; firm: *unshaken courage, an unshaken belief in liberty. adjective.*

un·sheathe (un shēᴛн′), to draw a sword, knife, or the like from a sheath. *verb,* **un·sheathes, un·sheathed, un·sheath·ing.**

un·sight·ly (un sīt′lē), ugly or unpleasant to look at: *The room was an unsightly mess. adjective.*

un·skilled (un skild′), **1** not skilled; not trained; not expert: *unskilled workers, an unskilled athlete.* **2** not requiring special skills or training: *unskilled labor. adjective.*

un·skill·ful (un skil′fəl), awkward; clumsy: *an unskillful attempt to ski. adjective.*

un·solved (un solvd′), not solved; not explained: *an unsolved mystery. adjective.*

un·sound (un sound′), **1** not sound; not in good condition: *unsound walls, an unsound business, an unsound mind.* **2** not based on truth or fact: *an unsound doctrine, an unsound theory.* **3** not restful; disturbed: *an unsound sleep. adjective.*

un·speak·a·ble (un spē′kə bəl), **1** not able to be expressed in words: *unspeakable joy.* **2** extremely bad; so bad that it is not spoken of: *an unspeakable crime. adjective.*

un·speak·a·bly (un spē′kə blē), beyond words; extremely: *unspeakably rude. adverb.*

un·sta·ble (un stā′bəl), **1** not stable; unsteady; shaky: *That stool with a cracked leg is very unstable.* **2** easily overthrown: *an unstable government. adjective.*

un·stead·i·ly (un sted′l ē), in an unsteady manner; without steadiness: *He walked unsteadily. adverb.*

un·stead·y (un sted′ē), **1** not steady; shaky: *an unsteady voice, an unsteady flame.* **2** likely to change; not reliable: *an unsteady mind, unsteady winds. adjective,* **un·stead·i·er, un·stead·i·est.**

un·stressed (un strest′), unaccented. In *upward,* the second syllable is unstressed. *adjective.*

un·suc·cess·ful (un′sək ses′fəl), not successful; having no success: *My attempts at juggling were unsuccessful. adjective.*

un·suit·a·ble (un sü′tə bəl), not suitable; unfit: *an unsuitable remark, unsuitable behavior. adjective.*

un·sure (un shùr′), not sure; uncertain: *I was unsure about how to spell the word. adjective.*

un·sus·pect·ing (un′sə spek′ting), not suspecting; not suspicious: *an unsuspecting victim. adjective.*

a hat	i it	oi oil	ch child	a in about
ā age	ī ice	ou out	ng long	e in taken
ä far	o hot	u cup	sh she	ə = i in pencil
e let	ō open	ù put	th thin	o in lemon
ē equal	ô order	ü rule	ᴛн then	u in circus
ėr term			zh measure	

un·tan·gle (un tang′gəl), **1** to take the tangles out of: *Combing will untangle your hair.* **2** to clear up or straighten out: *We untangled the mystery. verb,* **un·tan·gles, un·tan·gled, un·tan·gling.**

un·think·a·ble (un thing′kə bəl), not able to be imagined: *an unthinkable disaster. adjective.*

un·think·ing (un thing′king), not thinking; thoughtless; careless: *My unthinking remark hurt my friend's feelings. adjective.*

un·ti·dy (un tī′dē), not neat; not in order: *an untidy house. adjective,* **un·ti·di·er, un·ti·di·est.**

un·tie (un tī′), to loosen; unfasten; undo: *to untie a knot. She was untying bundles. verb,* **un·ties, un·tied, un·ty·ing.**

un·til (un til′), **1** up to the time of: *It was cold from November until April.* **2** up to the time when: *We waited until the sun had set.* **3** before: *She did not leave until morning.* **4** to the degree or place that: *I worked until I was too tired to do more.* **1,3** *preposition,* **2,4** *conjunction.*

un·tir·ing (un tī′ring), tireless: *an untiring runner, untiring efforts to succeed. adjective.*

un·told (un tōld′), **1** not told; not revealed: *an untold secret.* **2** too many or too much to be counted: *There are untold stars in the sky.* **3** very great: *untold wealth. Wars do untold damage. adjective.*

un·touched (un tucht′), not touched: *The cat left the milk untouched. The miser was untouched by the poor man's story. adjective.*

un·trained (un trānd′), not trained; without discipline or education: *Babies have untrained minds. adjective.*

un·true (un trü′), **1** not true to the facts; false: *The story was untrue.* **2** not faithful; disloyal: *His friend was untrue. adjective.*

un·truth·ful (un trüth′fəl), not telling the truth: *An untruthful person tells lies. An untruthful story is a lie. adjective.*

un·used (un yüzd′ *for 1,2;* un yüst′ *for 3*), **1** not in use; not being used: *an unused room.* **2** never having been used: *unused drinking cups.* **3** not accustomed: *The actor's hands were unused to labor. adjective.*

un·u·su·al (un yü′zhü əl), not in common use; not common; rare; beyond the ordinary: *an unusual adventure, an unusual color. adjective.*

un·veil (un vāl′), to remove a veil from; uncover; disclose; reveal: *The sun broke through the mist and unveiled the mountains. verb.*

un·want·ed (un won′tid), not wanted: *unwanted responsibilities, unwanted advice. adjective.*

un·wel·come (un wel′kəm), not welcome; not wanted: *The bees were unwelcome guests at our picnic. adjective.*

U

unwieldy
an **unwieldy** spacesuit

un·wield·y (un wēl′dē), hard to handle or manage; bulky and clumsy: *a large, unwieldy package. adjective.*

un·will·ing (un wil′ing), not willing; not consenting: *They were unwilling to help. adjective.*

un·wind (un wīnd′), 1 to unroll or become unrolled; uncoil or become uncoiled: *to unwind a ball of string.* 2 to relax: *After working all day, she needed to unwind. verb,* **un·winds, un·wound, un·wind·ing.**

un·wise (un wīz′), not wise; not showing good judgment; foolish: *It is unwise to delay going to the doctor if you are sick. adjective.*

un·wit·ting·ly (un wit′ing lē), not knowingly; unconsciously; not intentionally. *adverb.*

un·wor·thy (un wėr′ŦHē), not worthy; not deserving: *Such a silly story is unworthy of belief. adjective,* **un·wor·thi·er, un·wor·thi·est.**

un·wound (un wound′). See **unwind.** *I unwound the ball of string. verb.*

un·wrap (un rap′), to remove a wrapping from; open. *verb,* **un·wraps, un·wrapped, un·wrap·ping.**

un·yield·ing (un yēl′ding), firm; not giving in: *My parents were unyielding in their refusal. adjective.*

up (up), 1 to a higher place or condition: *The butterfly flew up. Prices have gone up.* 2 in a higher place or condition: *We live up in a skyscraper. The sun is up.* 3 to a higher place on; at a higher place in: *The cat ran up the tree.* 4 along: *They walked up the street.* 5 to, near, or at the upper part of: *We sailed up the river.* 6 out of bed: *The children were up at dawn. Please get up before you are late.* 7 completely; entirely: *The house burned up.* 8 at an end; over: *His time is up now.* 9 to or in an even position; not back of: *to catch up in a race.*

Keep up with the times. 10 at bat in baseball: *Am I up?* 11 offered or proposed: *Our house is up for sale. 1,2,6,7,9 adverb, 2,6,8,10,11 adjective, 3-5 preposition.*

up to, 1 doing; about to do: *She is up to some mischief.* 2 equal to; capable of doing: *Do you feel up to going out so soon after being sick?*

up·held (up held′). See **uphold.** *The higher court upheld the lower court's decision. verb.*

up·hill (up′hil′ *for 1 and 3;* up′hil′ *for 2*), 1 up the slope of a hill; upward: *It is an uphill road all the way.* 2 upward: *We walked a mile uphill.* 3 difficult: *an uphill fight. 1,3 adjective, 2 adverb.*

up·hold (up hōld′), 1 to give support to; confirm: *The principal upheld the teacher's decision.* 2 to hold up; not let down; support: *We uphold the*

up (definitions 1, 2, and 5)

good name of our school. *verb,* **up·holds,**
up·held, up·hold·ing.

up·hol·ster (up hōl′stər), to provide seats or
other furniture with coverings, springs, or stuffing:
to upholster a sofa. verb.

up·hol·ster·y (up hōl′stər ē), **1** the materials
used for covering seats or other furniture: *That
chair comes with cloth, plastic, or leather
upholstery.* **2** the business of upholstering. *noun.*

up·keep (up′kēp′), the act of keeping in good
condition; maintenance: *the upkeep of a house.*
noun.

up·land (up′lənd), **1** high land. **2** of high land;
living or growing on high land: *upland flowers.*
1 *noun,* **2** *adjective.*

up·lift (up lift′), to improve the moral, emotional,
or social condition of: *I was uplifted by his
encouraging words. verb.*

up·on (ə pôn′), on: *I sat upon the rug. preposition.*

up·per (up′ər), higher: *the upper lip, the upper
floor, the upper notes of a singer's voice. adjective.*

upper hand, control; advantage: *Do what the
doctor says or that cold may get the upper hand.*

up·per·most (up′ər mōst), **1** highest: *She climbed
to the uppermost branch.* **2** most prominent; having
the most force or influence: *Your safety was
uppermost in my mind. adjective.*

up·right (up′rīt′), **1** standing up straight; erect:
an upright post. **2** straight up: *Hold yourself
upright.* **3** good; honest: *an upright citizen.* **1,3**
adjective, **2** *adverb.*

up·ris·ing (up′rī′zing), a revolt: *a prison
uprising. noun.*

up·roar (up′rôr′), **1** a confused, disturbed, or
excited state: *There was an uproar over the large
tax increase.* **2** a loud or confused noise: *There was
an uproar as our team scored the winning run.*
noun.

up·root (up rüt′), **1** to tear up by the roots: *The
storm uprooted many trees.* **2** to remove
completely: *Many families were uprooted from
their homes because of the flood. verb.*

up·set (up set′ for 1,3, and 5; up′set′ for 2,4, and
6), **1** to tip over; overturn: *I upset my glass of milk.
Moving about in a boat may upset it.* **2** tipped over;
overturned: *The upset glass rolled off the table.* **3** to
disturb greatly; disorder: *Rain upset our plans for
a picnic. The bad news upset me.* **4** greatly
disturbed; disordered: *an upset stomach.* **5** to
defeat unexpectedly in a contest: *The independent
candidate upset the mayor in the election.* **6** an
unexpected defeat: *The hockey team suffered an
upset.* **1,3,5** *verb,* **up·sets, up·set, up·set·ting;**
2,4 *adjective,* **6** *noun.*

up·shot (up′shot′), a conclusion; result: *The
upshot of our discussion was a better understanding
of one another. noun.*

up·side down (up′sīd′ doun′), **1** having what
should be on top at the bottom: *The pie fell upside
down on the floor.* **2** in or into complete disorder:
The children turned the house upside down.

up·stairs (up′sterz′ or up′starz′), **1** up the
stairs: *The boy ran upstairs.* **2** on or to an upper

a hat	**i** it	**oi** oil	**ch** child	a in about
ā age	**ī** ice	**ou** out	**ng** long	e in taken
ä far	**o** hot	**u** cup	**sh** she	ə = { i in pencil
e let	**ō** open	**ù** put	**th** thin	o in lemon
ē equal	**ô** order	**ü** rule	**ŦH** then	u in circus
ėr term			**zh** measure	

floor: *She lives upstairs. He is waiting in an upstairs
hall.* **3** the upper floor or floors: *That small cottage
has no upstairs.* **1,2** *adverb,* **2** *adjective,* **3** *noun.*

up·start (up′stärt′), **1** a person who has
suddenly risen from a humble position to wealth,
power, or importance. **2** a person who is very
bold, conceited, and unpleasant. *noun.*

up·stream (up′strēm′), against the current of a
stream; up a stream: *It is hard to swim upstream.
We had an upstream campsite. adverb, adjective.*

up-to-date (up′tə dāt′), **1** extending to the
present time: *an up-to-date bank balance.*
2 keeping up with the times in style or ideas;
modern: *an up-to-date store. adjective.*

up·town (up′toun′), to or in the upper or higher
part of a town or city; away from the main
business section of a town or city: *Let's go
uptown. I use an uptown bank. adverb, adjective.*

up·turn (up′tėrn′), **1** an upward turn: *The
airplane made a sudden upturn to avoid the
mountain.* **2** an improvement: *As business
improved, his income took an upturn. noun.*

up·turned (up tėrnd′), turned upward: *The rain
fell on their upturned faces. adjective.*

up·ward (up′wərd), **1** toward a higher place: *She
climbed upward until she reached the apple.*
2 moving toward a higher place: *the upward flight
of a bird.* **3** toward a higher or greater rank,
amount, age, or the like: *From ten years of age
upward, she had studied French.* **4** above; more:
*Children of twelve years and upward must pay full
fare.* **1,3,4** *adverb,* **2** *adjective.*

upward of, more than: *Repairs to the car will cost
upward of $100.*

up·wards (up′wərdz), upward. *adverb.*

u·ra·ni·um (yü rā′nē əm), a heavy, white,
radioactive metal used as a source of atomic
energy. Uranium is a chemical element. *noun.*

Ur·a·nus (yùr′ə nəs *or* yə rā′nəs), the third
largest planet in the solar system and the seventh
in distance from the sun. *noun.*

Uranus

ur·ban (ėr′bən), **1** of or having something to do with cities or towns: *an urban district, urban planning.* **2** living in a city or cities: *Most urban people are familiar with pollution. adjective.*

ur·chin (ėr′chən), a small child, especially one who gets into trouble or who is ragged and dirty. *noun.*

urge (ėrj), **1** to push; force; drive: *The rider urged on his horse with whip and spurs. Hunger urged me to find some food.* **2** a driving force or impulse: *I had an urge to see my old friend again.* **3** to ask earnestly; plead with: *She urged us to stay longer.* **4** to plead or argue earnestly for; recommend strongly: *I urged the acceptance of the new plan.* 1,3,4 *verb,* **urg·es, urged, urg·ing;** 2 *noun.*

ur·gent (ėr′jənt), demanding immediate action or attention; pressing: *an urgent duty, an urgent message. adjective.*

ur·ine (yür′ən), a liquid waste product that is separated from the blood by the kidneys, goes to the bladder, and is discharged from the body. *noun.*

urn (ėrn), **1** a vase with a base. Urns have been used since ancient times to hold the ashes of the dead. **2** a coffeepot or teapot with a faucet, used for making or serving coffee or tea at the table. *noun.*

Ur·u·guay (yür′ə gwā *or* yür′ə gwī), a country in southeastern South America. *noun.*

us (us). *We* and *us* mean the person speaking plus the person or persons addressed or spoken about. *Can you help us? Mother went with us to the theater. pronoun.*

U.S., the United States.

U.S.A., the United States of America.

us·a·ble (yü′zə bəl), able to be used; fit for use: *The broken toy was no longer usable. adjective.*

us·age (yü′sij *or* yü′zij), **1** a manner or way of using; treatment: *This car has had rough usage.* **2** the usual way of using words: *The usage of the best writers and speakers determines what is good English. noun.*

use (yüz *for 1 and 2;* yüs *for 3-10),* **1** to put into action or service: *We use our legs in walking. We use spoons to eat soup.* **2** to finish; consume: *We've used all our money.* **3** a using: *the use of tools.* **4** a being used: *methods long out of use.* **5** usefulness: *a thing of no practical use.* **6** a purpose that a thing is used for: *to find a new use for something.* **7** the way of using: *poor use of material.* **8** a need; occasion: *A camper has use for a hatchet. I had no further use for it.* **9** the power of using; ability to use: *to lose the use of an arm.* **10** the right or privilege of using: *I have the use of a friend's boat this summer.* 1,2 *verb,* **us·es, used, us·ing;** 3-10 *noun.*

used to (yüst′ tü′), **1** accustomed to: *Southerners are not used to cold weather.* **2** formerly did: *I used to have a bicycle, but now I don't.*

used (yüzd), not new; that has belonged to someone else: *a used car. adjective.*

use·ful (yüs′fəl), of use; giving service; helpful: *a useful suggestion. They made themselves useful about the house. adjective.*

use·less (yüs′lis), of no use; worthless: *Snowshoes are useless in the desert. adjective.*

us·er (yü′zər), one that uses. *noun.*

ush·er (ush′ər), **1** a person who shows people to their seats in a church, theater, or public hall. **2** to conduct; escort; show: *We ushered our guests to the door.* 1 *noun,* 2 *verb.*

u·su·al (yü′zhü əl), commonly seen, found, or happening; ordinary; customary: *Snow is usual in the Rocky Mountains during winter. His usual bedtime is 8 p.m. adjective.*

as usual, in the usual manner; at the usual time; in the usual way: *We met, as usual, very late.*

u·su·al·ly (yü′zhü ə lē), commonly; ordinarily: *We usually eat dinner at six. adverb.*

UT, Utah (used with postal Zip Code).

Ut., Utah.

U·tah (yü′tô *or* yü′tä), one of the western states of the United States. *Abbreviation:* Ut. or UT *Capital:* Salt Lake City. *noun.*

[*Utah* got its name from the Ute, an American Indian tribe that lived in the area. The name of the tribe may have come from a Ute word meaning "person" or "people."]

u·ten·sil (yü ten′səl), **1** a container or implement used for practical purposes. Pots and pans are kitchen utensils. **2** an implement or tool used for some special purpose. Pens and pencils are writing utensils. *noun.*

[*Utensil* comes from a Latin word meaning "able to be used."]

u·til·i·ty (yü til′ə tē), **1** usefulness: *I appreciate the utility of owning a car.* **2** a company that performs a public service. Railroads, bus lines, and gas and electric companies are utilities. **3** the service provided by such a company. *noun, plural* **u·til·i·ties.**

u·ti·lize (yü′tl īz), to make use of; put to some practical use: *The cook will utilize the bones to make soup. verb,* **u·ti·liz·es, u·ti·lized, u·ti·liz·ing.**

ut·most (ut′mōst), **1** greatest possible; greatest; highest: *Eating proper food is of the utmost importance to health.* **2** farthest; extreme: *She walked to the utmost edge of the cliff.* **3** the extreme limit; the most that is possible: *He enjoyed himself to the utmost at the circus.* 1,2 *adjective,* 3 *noun.*

ut·ter[1] (ut′ər), complete; total; absolute: *When the lights went out we were in utter darkness. adjective.*

ut·ter[2] (ut′ər), **1** to speak; make known; express: *"Good-by" was the last word she uttered.* **2** to give out or forth: *She uttered a sigh of relief. verb.*

ut·ter·ly (ut′ər lē), completely; totally; absolutely: *I was utterly delighted with my present. adverb.*

Uz·bek·i·stan (üz′bek′ə stän), a country in western Asia. *noun.*

Vv

a hat	i it	oi oil	ch child	(a in about
ā age	ī ice	ou out	ng long	e in taken
ä far	o hot	u cup	sh she	ə = { i in pencil
e let	ō open	u̇ put	th thin	o in lemon
ē equal	ô order	ü rule	ℸH then	(u in circus
ėr term			zh measure	

V or **v** (vē), the 22nd letter of the English alphabet. *noun, plural* **V's** or **v's.**

V or **v.,** volt or volts.

VA, Virginia (used with postal Zip Code).

Va., Virginia.

va·can·cy (vā′kən sē), **1** an unoccupied position: *The retirement of two clerks made two vacancies in the store.* **2** a room, space, or apartment for rent: *There was a vacancy in the motel. There was a vacancy in the parking lot. noun, plural* **va·can·cies.**

va·cant (vā′kənt), **1** not occupied or filled; empty: *a vacant house, a vacant space.* **2** empty of thought or intelligence: *When I asked her a question, she just gave me a vacant smile. adjective.*

va·cate (vā′kāt), to go away from and leave empty; make vacant: *They will vacate the house at the end of the month. verb,* **va·cates, va·cat·ed, va·cat·ing.**

va·ca·tion (vā kā′shən), a time of rest from school, business, or other duties: *Our school has a spring vacation each year. noun.*

vac·ci·nate (vak′sə nāt), to give a person a vaccine by a shot or other means to protect against a disease. People who are vaccinated against measles, whooping cough, diphtheria, and tetanus will not get these diseases. *verb,* **vac·ci·nates, vac·ci·nat·ed, vac·ci·nat·ing.**

vac·ci·na·tion (vak′sə nā′shən), the act of vaccinating: *Vaccination has made smallpox a very rare disease. noun.*

vac·cine (vak′sēn′ *or* vak sēn′), a preparation of dead or weakened germs of a particular disease. A vaccine is given by a shot or other means to prevent or lessen the effects of a disease. Vaccines are used against polio, mumps, measles, and other diseases. *noun.*
[*Vaccine* comes from a Latin word meaning "of a cow." It was called this because the vaccine used against smallpox was obtained from cows.]

vac·u·um (vak′yü əm *or* vak′yüm), **1** an empty space without even air in it. A perfect vacuum has yet to be found or created. **2** a space which has almost no air or other matter in it. Outer space is a vacuum of this sort. **3** to clean with a vacuum cleaner: *I vacuumed the rugs.* **1,2** *noun,* **3** *verb.*

vacuum cleaner, a machine for cleaning carpets, curtains, floors, or the like, by suction.

vag·a·bond (vag′ə bond), **1** an idle wanderer; tramp. **2** wandering: *The gypsies lead a vagabond life.* **1** *noun,* **2** *adjective.*

vague (vāg), not definite; not clear; not distinct: *In a fog everything looks vague. His vague statement confused them. adjective,* **va·guer, va·guest.**

vain (vān), **1** having too much pride in one's looks, ability, or achievements: *Some good-looking people are vain.* **2** of no use; unsuccessful: *I made vain attempts to reach her by telephone. adjective.*
in vain, without effect or without success: *Their shouts for help were in vain, for no one could hear them.*

val·en·tine (val′ən tīn), **1** a greeting card or small gift sent on Valentine's Day. **2** a sweetheart chosen on this day: *Will you be my valentine? noun.*

valentine
(definition 1)

Valentine's Day, February 14, the day on which valentines are exchanged.

val·et (val′it *or* val′ā), **1** a servant who takes care of a man's clothes and gives him personal service. **2** a worker in a hotel who cleans or presses clothes. *noun.*

val·iant (val′yənt), brave; courageous: *A neighbor's valiant efforts saved the children from the burning building. adjective.*

val·id (val′id), **1** supported by facts or authority; true: *She had valid reasons for her objections to the plan.* **2** legally acceptable; binding; having legal force: *A contract made by a minor child is not valid. adjective.*

val·ley (val′ē), **1** low land between hills or mountains. Most large valleys have rivers running through them. **2** a wide region drained by a great river system: *the Mississippi valley. noun, plural* **val·leys.**

val·or (val′ər), bravery; courage: *The soldier was given a medal for valor in battle. noun.*

val·u·a·ble (val′yü ə bəl), **1** having value; being worth something: *valuable information, a valuable friend.* **2** worth much money: *a valuable ring.* **3 valuables,** articles of value: *She keeps her jewelry and other valuables in a safe.* **1,2** *adjective,* **3** *noun.*

V

valuation | vary

val·u·a·tion (val′yü ā′shən), **1** value estimated or determined: *The jeweler's valuation of the necklace was $10,000.* **2** an estimating or determining of the value of something. *noun.*

val·ue (val′yü), **1** the real worth; proper price: *We bought the house for less than its value.* **2** worth; usefulness or importance: *She appreciated the value of a good education. He researched the value of applying cold to burns.* **3** to estimate the worth of: *The land is valued at $5000.* **4** an estimated worth: *The dealer placed a value of $500 on the old car.* **5** to think highly of; regard highly: *Since he was an expert, his opinion was valued.* 1,2,4 *noun,* 3,5 *verb,* **val·ues, val·ued, val·u·ing.**

valve (valv), **1** a movable part that controls the flow of a liquid or gas through a pipe by opening and closing the passage. A faucet contains a valve. **2** a part of the body that works like a valve. The valves of the heart are membranes that control the flow of blood into and out of the heart. *noun.*

vam·pire (vam′pīr), (in stories) a dead body that comes to life at night and sucks the blood of people while they sleep. *noun.*

van (van), **1** a covered truck for moving household goods or animals: *The movers loaded our furniture into the van.* **2** a small, enclosed truck designed for light hauling or for recreation. *noun.*

van·dal (van′dl), a person who destroys or damages beautiful or valuable things on purpose: *Vandals had thrown paint on the statues in the park. noun.*
[Our word *vandal* comes from the name of the Vandals, an uncivilized people who invaded parts of Europe and Africa long ago. In A.D. 455 they captured and looted the city of Rome.]

van·dal·ism (van′dl iz′əm), the destroying or damaging of beautiful or valuable things on purpose: *They were arrested for breaking windows and other acts of vandalism. noun.*

vane (vān), **1** a flat piece of metal or wood that turns around a rod; weather vane. Vanes are often placed on the tops of buildings; they turn

vane (definition 1)

with the wind and show its direction. **2** a blade of a windmill, of a propeller, or the like. *noun.*

va·nil·la (və nil′ə), a flavoring used in ice cream, candy, cakes, and cookies. It is made from the bean of a tropical plant. *noun.*

van·ish (van′ish), **1** to disappear; disappear suddenly: *The sun vanished behind a cloud.* **2** to pass away; cease to be: *Dinosaurs have vanished from the earth. verb.*

van·i·ty (van′ə tē), too much pride in one's looks or ability: *Good looks or talent sometimes cause vanity. noun.*

van·quish (vang′kwish), to conquer; defeat; overcome: *The champion had vanquished all challengers. verb.*

va·por (vā′pər), **1** steam from boiling water; moisture in the air that can be seen; fog; mist: *I could see the vapor from my breath in the cool morning air.* **2** a gas formed from a substance that is usually a liquid or a solid: *We could smell the gasoline vapor as the gas tank of the car was being filled. noun.*

va·por·iz·er (vā′pə rī′zər), a device that changes a liquid into a vapor. One kind of vaporizer releases steam into a room in order to ease the breathing of someone with a cold. *noun.*

var·i·a·ble (ver′ē ə bəl *or* var′ē ə bəl), **1** apt to change; changeable; uncertain: *variable winds. The weather is more variable in New York than it is in California.* **2** able to be changed: *The speed of that electric fan is variable.* **3** something that is likely to vary or change: *A number of variables influence the weather.* 1,2 *adjective,* 3 *noun.*

var·i·a·tion (ver′ē ā′shən *or* var′ē ā′shən), **1** a change or difference: *There were variations of several degrees in the temperature in different parts of the city.* **2** a changed or different form: *Which variation of this wallpaper pattern do you like best? noun.*

var·ied (ver′ēd *or* var′ēd), of different kinds; having variety: *a varied assortment of candies. adjective.*

va·ri·e·ty (və rī′ə tē), **1** a lack of sameness; difference or change: *Variety prevents boredom.* **2** a number of different kinds: *This shop has a variety of toys.* **3** a kind or sort: *Which varieties of cake did you buy? noun, plural* **va·ri·e·ties.**

var·i·ous (ver′ē əs *or* var′ē əs), **1** different; differing from one another: *There are various opinions as to how to raise children.* **2** several; many: *We looked at various houses, but have decided to buy this one. adjective.*

var·nish (vär′nish), **1** a liquid that gives a smooth, glossy appearance to wood, metal, or the like. Varnish is often made from resin dissolved in oil or alcohol. **2** the smooth hard surface made by this liquid when it dries: *The varnish on the table was scratched.* **3** to put varnish on: *They varnished the wood floors of the house.* 1,2 *noun, plural* **var·nish·es;** 3 *verb.*

var·y (ver′ē *or* var′ē), **1** to change; make or become different: *The driver can vary the speed of an automobile.* **2** to be different; differ: *Stars vary*

692

in brightness. verb, **var·ies, var·ied, var·y·ing.**

vase (vās), a container used for ornament or to hold flowers. A vase is usually round, narrowing at the top and bottom. *noun.*

vas·sal (vas′əl), a person who held land from a lord or superior, to whom in return he gave help in war or some other service. A great noble could be a vassal of the king and have many other vassals of his own. *noun.*

vast (vast), very, very large; immense: *Texas and Alaska cover vast territories. A billion dollars is a vast amount of money. adjective.*

vat (vat), a tank; large container for liquids: *a vat of dye. noun.*

Vat·i·can (vat′ə kən), **1** the buildings grouped about the palace of the pope in Rome. **2** the government, office, or authority of the pope. *noun.*

vault[1] (vôlt), **1** an arched roof or ceiling; series of arches. **2** a place for storing valuable things and keeping them safe. Vaults are often made of steel. *noun.*

vault[1] (definition 1)
vault of a cathedral

vault[2] (vôlt), **1** to jump or leap, especially to jump over something, using the hands or a pole: *She vaulted the fence.* **2** such a jump or leap: *He excels at the pole vault.* **1** *verb,* **2** *noun.*

veal (vēl), meat from a calf. *noun.*

veer (vir), to change in direction; shift; turn: *The wind veered to the south. verb.*

vege·ta·ble (vej′tə bəl *or* vej′ə tə bəl), **1** a plant whose fruit, seeds, leaves, roots, or other parts are used for food: *We grow vegetables such as peas, corn, lettuce, and beets in our garden.* **2** the part of such a plant which is used for food: *Shall we have broccoli or spinach for a vegetable at dinner tonight?* **3** any plant: *Does this substance come from a vegetable or a mineral?* **4** of plants; like plants; having something to do with plants: *the vegetable kingdom, vegetable life.* **5** of or made from vegetables: *vegetable soup.* **1-3** *noun,* **4,5** *adjective.*

veg·e·tar·i·an (vej′ə ter′ē ən *or* vej′ə tar′ē ən), **1** a person who eats vegetables but no meat. **2** containing or serving no meat: *a vegetarian diet, a vegetarian restaurant.* **1** *noun,* **2** *adjective.*

veg·e·ta·tion (vej′ə tā′shən), plant life; growing plants: *There is not much vegetation in deserts. noun.*

ve·he·ment (vē′ə mənt), **1** having or showing strong feeling: *loud and vehement quarrels.* **2** forceful; violent: *a vehement burst of energy. adjective.*

ve·hi·cle (vē′ə kəl), a means of carrying or transporting, such as a car, carriage, cart, wagon, or sled. Automobiles and trucks are motor vehicles. Rockets and satellites are space vehicles. *noun.*

veil (vāl), **1** a piece of very thin material worn to protect or hide the face, or as an ornament. **2** a piece of material worn so as to fall over the head and shoulders. **3** to cover with a veil: *Some Moslem women veil their faces before going into public.* **4** anything that screens or hides: *A veil of clouds hid the sun.* **5** to cover; hide: *Fog veiled the shore. The spy veiled his plans in secrecy.* **1,2,4** *noun,* **3,5** *verb.*

vein (vān), **1** one of the blood vessels that carry blood to the heart from all parts of the body. **2** a rib of a leaf or of an insect's wing. **3** a crack or layer in rock filled with a different material: *The miners went deep into the earth searching for veins of gold.* **4** any streak or marking of a different shade or color in wood or marble. **5** a state of mind; mood: *The guests chatted among themselves in a relaxed vein. noun.*

vein (definition 2)—**veins** of a leaf

ve·loc·i·ty (və los′ə tē), **1** swiftness; quickness: *The car sped by with such velocity that the driver's face was just a blur.* **2** the rate of motion; speed: *The velocity of light is about 186,000 miles per second. noun, plural* **ve·loc·i·ties.**

vel·vet (vel′vit), **1** a very soft cloth with short raised threads on one side. Velvet may be made of silk, rayon, nylon, or cotton, or some combination of these. **2** made of velvet: *a velvet jacket.* **3** like velvet: *Our kitten has soft, velvet paws.* **1** *noun,* **2,3** *adjective.*

vel·vet·y (vel′və tē), smooth and soft like velvet. *adjective.*

vend (vend), to sell; peddle: *They were vending fruit from a cart. verb.*

vend·ing ma·chine (ven′ding mə shēn′), a machine from which one obtains candy, stamps, or other small articles when a coin is dropped in.

ven·dor (ven′dər), a seller; peddler. *noun.*

vendor

ven·e·rate (ven′ə rāt′), to regard with reverence; revere: *He venerates his father's memory. verb,* **ven·e·rates, ven·e·rat·ed, ven·e·rat·ing.**

ven·e·ra·tion (ven′ə rā′shən), deep respect; reverence. *noun.*

Ve·ne·tian blind (və nē′shən blīnd′), a window blind made of many horizontal slats. The blind can be raised and lowered, or the slats can be tilted so that they overlap, to regulate the light that is let in.

Ven·e·zue·la (ven′ə zwā′lə), a country in northern South America. *noun.*

venge·ance (ven′jəns), revenge; punishment in return for a wrong: *She swore vengeance against her hateful enemies. noun.*

with a vengeance, with great force or violence: *By six o'clock it was raining with a vengeance.*

ven·i·son (ven′ə sən), deer meat; flesh of a deer, used for food. *noun.*

ven·om (ven′əm), the poison of some snakes, spiders, scorpions, lizards, and similar animals. *noun.*

vent (vent), **1** a hole; opening, especially one serving as an outlet: *He used a pencil to make air vents in the box top so his frog could breathe.* **2** an outlet; way out: *Her great energy found vent in hard work. They gave vent to their grief in tears.* **3** to let out; express freely: *Don't vent your anger on the dog.* **1,2** *noun,* **3** *verb.*

ven·ti·late (ven′tl āt), to change the air in: *We ventilate a room by opening windows. verb,* **ven·ti·lates, ven·ti·lat·ed, ven·ti·lat·ing.** [*Ventilate* comes from a Latin word meaning "wind[1]."]

ven·ti·la·tion (ven′tl ā′shən), **1** a change of air; act or process of supplying with fresh air. **2** a means of supplying fresh air: *Air conditioning provides ventilation in the summer. noun.*

ven·ti·la·tor (ven′tl ā′tər), any device or other means for changing the air in a room, vehicle, or other space. Ventilators may be fans or air conditioners. *noun.*

ven·tri·cle (ven′trə kəl), either of the two lower chambers of the heart. A ventricle receives blood from an upper chamber and forces it into the arteries. *noun.*

ven·ture (ven′chər), **1** a risky or daring undertaking: *The explorers hoped to find gold on their venture into the wilderness.* **2** to expose to risk or danger: *She ventured her life to rescue me.* **3** to dare: *No one ventured to interrupt the speaker.* **4** to dare to come or go: *They ventured out on the thin ice and fell through.* **5** to dare to say or make: *He ventured an objection.* **1** *noun,* **2-5** *verb,* **ven·tures, ven·tured, ven·tur·ing.**

Ve·nus (vē′nəs), **1** the Roman goddess of love and beauty. **2** the second planet in distance from the sun and the one that comes closest to the earth. From the earth Venus is the most brilliant of the planets. *noun.*

ve·ran·da (və ran′də), a large porch along one or more sides of a house or other building. *noun.*

veranda

verb (vėrb), a word that tells what is or what is done; part of speech that expresses action or being. *Do, go, come, be, sit, think, know,* and *eat* are verbs. *noun.*

ver·bal (vėr′bəl), **1** in words; of words: *A description is a verbal picture.* **2** expressed in spoken words; oral: *a verbal promise. adjective.*

ver·dict (vėr′dikt), the decision of a jury: *The jury returned a verdict of "Not guilty." noun.*

verge (vėrj), the point at which something begins or happens; brink: *Their business is on the verge of ruin. noun.*

ver·i·fy (ver′ə fī), **1** to prove to be true; confirm:

The driver's report of the accident was verified by two women who had seen it happen. **2** to test the correctness of; check the accuracy of: *You can verify the spelling of a word by looking in a dictionary. verb,* **ver·i·fies, ver·i·fied, ver·i·fy·ing.**

ver·mil·ion (vər mil′yən), bright-red. *adjective.*

ver·min (vėr′mən), small animals that are troublesome or destructive. Fleas, lice, rats, and mice are vermin. *noun plural or singular.*

Ver·mont (vər mont′), one of the northeastern states of the United States. *Abbreviation:* Vt. or VT *Capital:* Montpelier. *noun.*
[*Vermont* was formed from two French words meaning "green mountain."]

ver·sa·tile (vėr′sə təl), able to do many things well: *She is a versatile student who is skilled at science, art, mathematics, English, German, and history. adjective.*

verse (vėrs), **1** poetry; lines of words with a regularly repeated accent and often with rhyme. **2** a single line of poetry. **3** a group of lines of poetry: *Sing the first verse of "America."* **4** a short division of a chapter in the Bible. *noun.*

versed (vėrst), experienced; practiced; skilled: *Our doctor is well versed in the latest medical developments. adjective.*

ver·sion (vėr′zhən), **1** one particular statement, account, or description: *Each of the three girls gave her own version of what happened.* **2** a translation from one language to another: *Though the story was originally written in German, I read an English version. noun.*

ver·te·bra (vėr′tə brə), any of the many bones that make up the backbone. *noun, plural* **ver·te·brae** (vėr′tə brē), **ver·te·bras.**

a hat	i it	oi oil	ch child	a in about
ā age	ī ice	ou out	ng long	e in taken
ä far	o hot	u cup	sh she	ə = i in pencil
e let	ō open	u̇ put	th thin	o in lemon
ē equal	ô order	ü rule	ŦH then	u in circus
ėr term			zh measure	

ver·te·brate (vėr′tə brit), **1** an animal that has a backbone. Fishes, amphibians, reptiles, birds, and mammals are vertebrates. **2** having a backbone: *Whales, pigeons, lizards and trout are vertebrate animals.* **1** *noun,* **2** *adjective.*

ver·tex (vėr′teks), **1** the point opposite to and farthest away from the base of a triangle, pyramid, or the like. **2** the point where the two sides of an angle meet. *noun, plural* **ver·tex·es, ver·ti·ces** (vėr′tə sēz).

ver·ti·cal (vėr′tə kəl), straight up and down; perpendicular to a level surface; upright. A person standing up straight is in a vertical position. *adjective.*

ver·y (ver′ē), **1** much; greatly; extremely: *The sunshine is very hot in July.* **2** absolute; exactly: *He stood in the very same place for an hour.* **3** same: *The very people who supported the plan are against it now.* **4** nothing else than; mere: *The very thought of summer vacation makes her happy.* **5** absolute; complete: *The storm meant the very end of our hopes for a picnic.* **6** actual: *They were caught in the very act of stealing.* **1,2** *adverb,* **3-6** *adjective.*

ves·pers or **Ves·pers** (ves′pərz), a church service held in the late afternoon or early evening. *noun plural.*

ves·sel (ves′əl), **1** a ship; large boat: *Ocean liners and other vessels are usually docked by tugboats.* **2** a hollow holder or container. Cups, bowls, pitchers, bottles, barrels, and tubs are vessels. **3** a tube carrying blood or other fluid. Veins and arteries are blood vessels. *noun.*

vest (vest), **1** a short, sleeveless garment worn over a shirt or blouse. **2** to furnish with powers, authority, rights, or functions: *The Congress of the United States is vested with the power to make laws.* **1** *noun,* **2** *verb.*

ves·tige (ves′tij), all that remains; trace: *The explorers discovered vestiges of an ancient civilization. noun.*

vest·ment (vest′mənt), garment worn by a member of the clergy in performing sacred duties. *noun.*

vet[1] (vet), a veterinarian. *noun.*

vet[2] (vet), a veteran. *noun.*

vet·er·an (vet′ər ən), **1** a person who has served in the armed forces. **2** a person who has had much experience in some position or occupation: *a veteran of Congress.* **3** having had much experience: *a veteran teacher, veteran troops.* **1,2** *noun,* **3** *adjective.*

vet·er·i·nar·i·an (vet′ər ə ner′ē ən *or* vet′ər ə nar′ē ən), a doctor or surgeon who treats animals. *noun.*

Word History

vertebra *Vertebra* can be traced back to a Latin word meaning "to turn." Having separate vertebrae in the backbone instead of a single, solid bone allows the body to turn or bend easily.

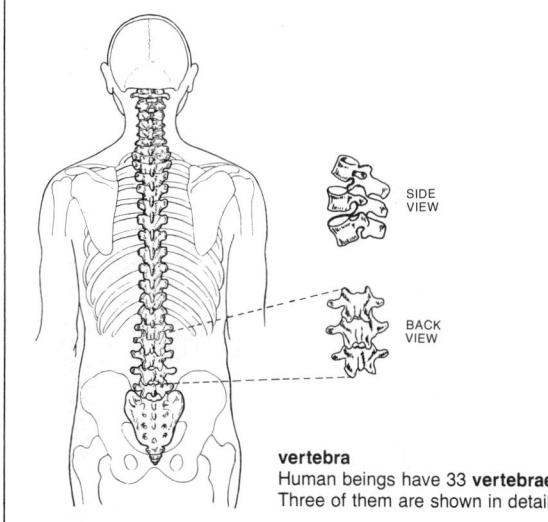

SIDE VIEW

BACK VIEW

vertebra
Human beings have 33 **vertebrae.**
Three of them are shown in detail.

V

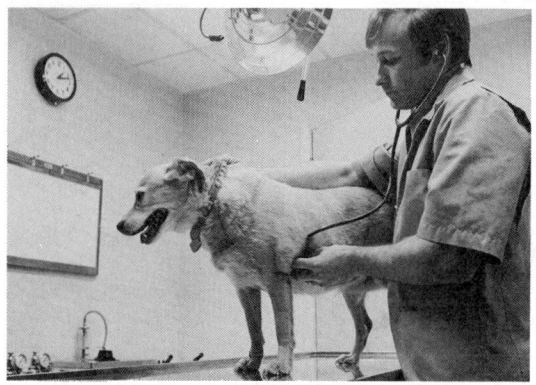

veterinary—A veterinarian practices
veterinary medicine.

vet·er·i·nar·y (vet′ər ə ner′ē), having something to do with the medical or surgical treatment of animals. *adjective.*

ve·to (vē′tō), **1** the right or power to forbid or prevent: *The President has the power of veto over most bills passed in Congress.* **2** the use of this right or power: *The governor's veto kept the bill from becoming a law.* **3** a prohibition; refusal of consent: *Our plan met with a veto from the boss.* **4** to refuse to consent to: *Her parents vetoed her plan to buy a car.* 1-3 *noun, plural* **ve·toes;** 4 *verb.*
[*Veto* comes from a Latin word meaning "I forbid." Originally, it was used by officials who represented the people in ancient Rome to oppose proposed laws.]

vex (veks), to annoy; anger by trifles; provoke: *It is vexing to have to wait for somebody. verb.*

vex·a·tion (vek sā′shən), **1** an annoyance; being made angry by trifles: *Their faces showed their vexation at the delay.* **2** a thing that annoys: *Rain on Saturday was a vexation to the children. noun.*

vi·a (vī′ə *or* vē′ə), by way of; by a route that passes through: *We are going from New York to Paris via London. preposition.*

vi·a·duct (vī′ə dukt), a bridge for carrying a road or railroad over a valley, a part of a city, a river, or the like. *noun.*

vi·al (vī′əl), a small glass or plastic bottle for holding medicines or the like. *noun.*

vi·brate (vī′brāt), to move rapidly back and forth: *A piano string vibrates and makes a sound when a key is struck. verb,* **vi·brates, vi·brat·ed, vi·brat·ing.**

vi·bra·tion (vī brā′shən), a rapid movement back and forth; quivering motion; vibrating: *The buses shake the house so much that we feel the vibration. noun.*

vice (vīs), **1** an evil habit or tendency: *Lying and cruelty are vices.* **2** a fault; bad habit: *They believed that gambling was a vice. noun.*

vice-pres·i·dent (vīs′prez′ə dənt), an officer next in rank to the president, who takes the president's place when necessary. If the President of the United States dies or resigns, the Vice-President becomes President. *noun.*

vice·roy (vīs′roi), a person who rules a country or province, acting as the king's or queen's representative. *noun.*

vi·ce ver·sa (vī′sə vėr′sə), the other way round: *John blamed Mary, and vice versa (Mary blamed John).*

vi·cin·i·ty (və sin′ə tē), the region near or about a place; neighborhood: *There are no houses for sale in this vicinity. noun, plural* **vi·cin·i·ties.**

vi·cious (vish′əs), **1** very violent or cruel: *They were accused of a vicious crime.* **2** likely to attack; dangerous: *a vicious animal.* **3** showing a strong desire to harm someone; spiteful: *I won't listen to such vicious gossip.* **4** unpleasantly severe: *a vicious headache. adjective.*

vic·tim (vik′təm), **1** a person or animal sacrificed, injured, or destroyed: *victims of war, victims of an accident.* **2** a person badly treated or taken advantage of: *The swindlers had tricked their victims into giving them large sums of money. noun.*

vic·tor (vik′tər), a winner; conqueror. *noun.*

Vic·to·ri·a (vik tôr′ē ə), the capital of British Columbia, Canada. *noun.*

vic·to·ri·ous (vik tôr′ē əs), **1** conquering; having won a victory: *a victorious team.* **2** having something to do with victory; ending in victory: *The team gave a victorious shout as the winning run scored. adjective.*

vic·to·ry (vik′tər ē), the defeat of an enemy or opponent: *The game ended in a victory for our school. noun, plural* **vic·to·ries.**

vid·e·o (vid′ē ō), **1** having to do with the picture in television: *The video part of the program was off for several minutes because of problems at the TV station.* **2** having or using a television screen or a screen like that of a television: *The computer has prepared this information for video display. adjective.*
[*Video* comes from a Latin word meaning "I see."]

video game, any of many games played on electronic machines that produce changing pictures and sounds, or that cause a television set to produce such pictures and sounds. A player uses mechanical devices to control these changes in ways that depend on the rules of the particular game.

vid·e·o·tape (vid′ē ō tāp′), **1** a magnetic tape that records and reproduces both sound and picture for television. **2** to record on videotape: *The football game was videotaped and shown on television later in the day.* 1 *noun,* 2 *verb,* **vid·e·o·tapes, vid·e·o·taped, vid·e·o·tap·ing.**

Vi·et·nam (vē et′näm′), a country in southeastern Asia. *noun.*

view (vyü), **1** the act of seeing; sight: *It was our first view of the ocean.* **2** the range at which the eye can see something: *A ship came into view.* **3** to see; look at: *They viewed the scene with pleasure.* **4** a thing seen; scene: *The view from the top of the hill is beautiful.* **5** a picture of some scene: *Various views of the coast hung on the walls.* **6** a mental picture; idea: *This book will give* you a general view of the way the pioneers lived. **7** a way of looking at or considering a matter; opinion: *What are your views on the subject?* **8** to consider; regard: *The plan was viewed favorably.* 1,2,4-7 *noun,* 3,8 *verb.*

in view, 1 in sight: *As the noise grew louder, the airplane came in view.* **2** under consideration: *Keep the teacher's advice in view as you try to improve your work.*

in view of, considering; because of: *In view of the fact that she is the best player on the team, she should be the captain.*

on view, to be seen; open for people to see: *The exhibit is on view from 9 a.m. to 5 p.m.*

view·er (vyü′ər), a person who views something, especially television. *noun.*

view·point (vyü′point′), a way of thinking about something; attitude of mind; point of view: *A heavy rain that is good from the viewpoint of farmers may be bad from the viewpoint of tourists.* *noun.*

vig·il (vij′əl), a keeping awake during the usual hours of sleep for some purpose; act of watching; watch: *All night the parents kept vigil over the sick child. noun.*

vig·i·lance (vij′ə ləns), watchfulness; alertness: *Constant vigilance while driving helps to prevent accidents. noun.*

vig·i·lant (vij′ə lənt), watchful; alert; wide-awake: *The dog kept vigilant guard over the flock of sheep. adjective.*

vig·or (vig′ər), **1** active strength or force: *The principal argued with vigor that the new school should have a library.* **2** healthy energy or power: *After a long sleep, we felt rested and full of vigor. noun.*

vig·or·ous (vig′ər əs), full of vigor; strong and active; energetic: *The old man is still vigorous and lively. Doctors wage a vigorous war against disease. adjective.*

vi·king or **Vi·king** (vī′king), one of the daring seamen from northwest Europe who raided the coasts of Europe during the A.D. 700's, 800's, and 900's. The vikings were great warriors and explorers. They even came to North America. *noun.*

vile (vīl), **1** very bad: *The weather today was vile—rainy, windy, and cold.* **2** foul; disgusting: *A vile smell hung in the air around the garbage dump.* **3** evil; immoral: *a vile crime. adjective,* **vil·er, vil·est.**

vil·la (vil′ə), a house in the country or suburbs, or sometimes at the seashore. A villa is usually a large or elegant residence. *noun.*

vil·lage (vil′ij), **1** a group of houses, usually smaller than a town. **2** the people of a village: *The whole village was out to see the fire. noun.*

vil·lag·er (vil′i jər), a person who lives in a village. *noun.*

vil·lain (vil′ən), a very wicked person: *At the end of the story, the villain was caught and punished. noun.*

vim (vim), force; energy; vigor: *The campers were*

a hat	i it	oi oil	ch child		a in about
ā age	ī ice	ou out	ng long		e in taken
ä far	o hot	u cup	sh she	ə =	i in pencil
e let	ō open	u̇ put	th thin		o in lemon
ē equal	ô order	ü rule	ᴛʜ then		u in circus
ėr term			zh measure		

full of vim after a good night's sleep. *noun.*

vin·di·cate (vin′də kāt), **1** to clear from suspicion, dishonor, or any charge of wrongdoing: *The verdict of "Not guilty" vindicated them.* **2** to defend successfully against opposition; uphold; justify: *The heir vindicated her claim to the fortune. verb,* **vin·di·cates, vin·di·cat·ed, vin·di·cat·ing.**

vine (vīn), **1** any plant with a long, slender stem that grows along the ground or that climbs by attaching itself to a wall, tree, or other support. Melons and pumpkins grow on vines. Ivy is a vine. **2** a grapevine. *noun.*

vin·e·gar (vin′ə gər), a sour liquid produced by the fermenting of cider, wine, beer, ale, or the like. Vinegar is used in salad dressing, in flavoring food, and in preserving food. *noun.* [*Vinegar* comes from two French words meaning "sour wine."]

vine·yard (vin′yərd), a place planted with grapevines. *noun.*

vi·nyl (vī′nl), any of various tough plastics, used in floor coverings, toys, and phonograph records. *noun.*

vi·o·la (vē ō′lə), a musical instrument shaped like a violin, but slightly larger, and lower in pitch. *noun.*

vi·o·late (vī′ə lāt), to break a law, rule, agreement, promise, or instructions; act contrary to; fail to perform: *Speeding violates the traffic laws. verb,* **vi·o·lates, vi·o·lat·ed, vi·o·lat·ing.**

vi·o·la·tion (vī′ə lā′shən), a breaking of a law, rule, agreement, promise, or instructions: *He was fined $10 for his violation of the traffic law. noun.*

vi·o·la·tor (vī′ə lā′tər), a person who violates. *noun.*

villain
Only a **villain** would stomp on your hand when you're clinging to a cliff.

V

vi·o·lence (vī′ə ləns), **1** strong force; great force: *She slammed the door with violence.* **2** rough or harmful action or treatment: *the violence of war. The dictator ruled with violence. noun.*

vi·o·lent (vī′ə lənt), **1** acting or done with strong, rough force: *a violent blow.* **2** caused by strong, rough force: *a violent death.* **3** showing or caused by very strong feeling: *violent language, a violent rage. adjective.*

vi·o·let (vī′ə lit), **1** a small plant with purple, blue, yellow, or white flowers. Many violets grow wild and bloom in the early spring. **2** bluish-purple. **1** *noun*, **2** *adjective.*

vi·o·lin (vī′ə lin′), a musical instrument with four strings played with a bow. *noun.*

violin—The boy is playing a **viola**; the girl is playing a **violin**.

vi·o·lin·ist (vī′ə lin′ist), a person who plays the violin. *noun.*

vi·o·lon·cel·lo (vī′ə lən chel′ō), a cello. *noun, plural* **vi·o·lon·cel·los.**

vi·per (vī′pər), **1** a poisonous snake, especially one with a thick body. **2** a spiteful, treacherous person. *noun.*

vir·gin (vėr′jən), **1** pure; in the original condition; not yet changed or used: *virgin snow, a virgin forest.* **2** a maiden. **1** *adjective,* **2** *noun.*

Vir·gin·ia (vər jin′yə), one of the southeastern states of the United States. *Abbreviation:* Va. or VA *Capital:* Richmond. *noun.*
[*Virginia* was formed in 1584 from a Latin word meaning "virgin." The area was named in honor of Elizabeth I of England, who lived from 1533 to 1603. She was called the Virgin Queen.]

Virgin Islands, a group of islands in the West Indies, several of which belong to the United States.

vir·tu·al (vėr′chü əl), real; actual; being something in effect, though not so in name; for all practical purposes: *The battle was won with so great a loss of soldiers that it was a virtual defeat. adjective.*

vir·tu·al·ly (vėr′chü ə lē), really; actually; in effect, though not in name: *If you travel by jet plane, New York and London are virtually neighbors. adverb.*

vir·tue (vėr′chü), **1** goodness; moral excellence: *a person of the highest virtue.* **2** a particular kind of moral excellence: *Justice is a virtue.* **3** a good quality: *They praised the virtues of their small car. noun.*

vir·tu·ous (vėr′chü əs), having or showing virtue; good; honest; just: *virtuous conduct, a virtuous life. adjective.*

vi·rus (vī′rəs), a very tiny thing that causes a disease. Viruses are so small that they cannot be seen through most microscopes. They can reproduce only inside the cells of living things. Viruses cause rabies, polio, chicken pox, the common cold, and many other infectious diseases of people, animals, and plants. *noun, plural* **vi·rus·es.**

Word History

virus *Virus* was borrowed from a Latin word meaning "poison."

virus—two types of **viruses**, 50,000 times actual size. The pictures were taken with a special, very powerful microscope.

vise

vise (vīs), a tool having two jaws opened and closed by a screw, used to hold an object firmly while work is being done on it. *noun.*

vis·i·bil·i·ty (viz′ə bil′ə tē), **1** the condition or

visibility (definition 1)—Reflective tape on his clothes and motorcycle increases the **visibility** of this rider.

a hat	**i** it	**oi** oil	**ch** child	a in about
ā age	**ī** ice	**ou** out	**ng** long	e in taken
ä far	**o** hot	**u** cup	**sh** she	ə = i in pencil
e let	**ō** open	**ù** put	**th** thin	o in lemon
ē equal	**ô** order	**ü** rule	**ŦH** then	u in circus
ėr term			**zh** measure	

quality of being visible: *She put lights and reflectors on her bicycle to increase its visibility.* **2** the distance at which things are visible: *Fog and rain decreased visibility to about 50 feet.* noun.

vis·i·ble (viz′ə bəl), **1** able to be seen: *The shore was barely visible through the fog.* **2** apparent; obvious: *There has been visible improvement in his work since he changed schools.* adjective.

vis·i·bly (viz′ə blē), clearly; plainly: *After the long hike the children were visibly weary.* adverb.

vi·sion (vizh′ən), **1** the power of seeing; sense of sight: *I have to wear glasses because my vision is poor.* **2** something that is seen: *The vision of the table loaded with food made our mouths water.* **3** the power of seeing with the imagination or by clear thinking, especially seeing what the future may bring: *The founder of this company was a person of great vision.* **4** something seen with the imagination, in a dream, or in one's thoughts: *The gambler had visions of great wealth.* noun.

vis·it (viz′it), **1** to go to see; come to see: *Would you like to visit New Orleans?* **2** to make a call; stay with; make a stay; be a guest: *I visited my friend last week.* **3** an act of visiting; short stay: *My aunt paid us a visit last week.* 1,2 verb, 3 noun.

vis·i·tor (viz′ə tər), a person who visits; person who is visiting; guest: *Visitors from the East arrived last night.* noun.

vi·sor (vī′zər), **1** the brim of a cap, that sticks out in front. **2** a shade above a windshield, that can be lowered to shield the eyes from the sun. noun.

vis·ta (vis′tə), a view seen through a narrow opening or passage: *Between the two rows of trees I saw a vista of the lake.* noun.

vis·u·al (vizh′ü əl), of sight; for sight; by sight: *Being nearsighted is a visual defect.* adjective.

vi·tal (vī′tl), **1** of life; having something to do with life: *Growth and decay are vital processes.* **2** necessary to life: *Eating is a vital function. The heart is a vital organ.* **3** very important; basic; very necessary: *Pure water is vital to the welfare of a community.* adjective.

vi·tal·i·ty (vī tal′ə tē), strength or vigor of mind or body: *Exercise helps maintain vitality.* noun.

vi·ta·min (vī′tə mən), **1** any of certain special substances necessary in small amounts for the normal growth and proper nourishment of the body. Vitamins are found especially in milk, butter, raw fruits and vegetables, cod-liver oil, and the outside part of wheat and other grains. Lack of vitamins causes certain diseases as well as generally poor health. **2** of or containing vitamins: *a vitamin tablet.* 1 noun, 2 adjective.

vitamin A, a vitamin found in milk, butter, cod-liver oil, egg yolk, green and yellow vegetables, and liver. Vitamin A increases the resistance of the body to infection and helps vision at night.

vitamin C, a vitamin found in oranges, lemons, tomatoes, and leafy green vegetables. Vitamin C cannot be stored in the body and must be replaced regularly.

vitamin D, a vitamin found in cod-liver oil, milk, and egg yolk, that is necessary for the growth and health of bones and teeth.

vi·va·cious (vī vā′shəs *or* vi vā′shəs), lively; sprightly; animated; gay: *a vivacious manner, a vivacious person.* adjective.

viv·id (viv′id), **1** strikingly bright; brilliant; strong

visor (definition 1)

vivid (definition 1)—**vivid** colors

V

and clear. **2** like life; giving clear ideas of life: *Her description of the party was so vivid that I almost felt I had been there.* **3** strong and distinct: *I have a vivid memory of the fire.* **4** very active; lively: *a vivid imagination. adjective.*

vo·cab·u·lar·y (vō kab′yə ler′ē), **1** all the words used by a person or group of people: *Reading will increase your vocabulary. The vocabulary of science has grown tremendously in the past 20 years.* **2** a list of words, usually in alphabetical order, with their meanings: *There is a vocabulary in the back of our French book. noun, plural* **vo·cab·u·lar·ies.**

vo·cal (vō′kəl), **1** of the voice; having to do with the voice or speaking: *The tongue is a vocal organ.* **2** made with the voice: *I like vocal music better than instrumental. adjective.*

vocal cords, two bands of elastic tissue in the throat. When they are pulled tight, the passage of breath between them causes them to vibrate, producing the sound of the voice.

vo·ca·tion (vō kā′shən), a particular occupation, business, profession, or trade: *Architecture is her vocation. noun.*

vod·ka (vod′kə), a strong alcoholic drink made from potatoes, rye, barley, or corn. *noun.*

vogue (vōg), **1** the fashion: *Hoop skirts were in vogue more than 100 years ago.* **2** popularity: *That song had a great vogue at one time. noun.*

voice (vois), **1** a sound made through the mouth, especially by people in speaking, singing, or shouting: *The voices of the children could be heard coming from the playground.* **2** the power to make sounds through the mouth: *His voice was gone because of a sore throat.* **3** ability as a singer: *That child has a very good voice.* **4** to express; utter: *They voiced their approval.* **5** expression: *They gave voice to their joy.* **6** the right to express an opinion or choice: *Have we any voice in this matter at all?* 1-3,5,6 *noun,* 4 *verb,* **voic·es, voiced, voic·ing.**

void (void), **1** an empty space: *The death of his dog left an aching void in the boy's heart.* **2** empty; vacant: *a void space.* **3** without force; not binding in law: *Any contract made by a child is void.* 1 *noun,* 2,3 *adjective.*

vol·can·ic (vol kan′ik), **1** of or caused by a volcano; having to do with volcanoes: *a volcanic eruption.* **2** like a volcano; liable to break out violently: *a volcanic temper. adjective.*

vol·ca·no (vol kā′nō), **1** an opening in the earth's crust through which steam, ashes, and lava are sometimes forced out. **2** a cone-shaped hill or mountain around this opening, built up of the material that is forced out. *noun, plural* **vol·ca·noes** or **vol·ca·nos.**
[*Volcano* comes from the Latin name of Vulcan, the Roman god of fire.]

vol·ley (vol′ē), **1** a shower of stones, bullets, or other missiles: *A volley of arrows rained down upon the attacking knights.* **2** to hit or kick a ball without letting it touch the ground: *They volleyed the tennis ball back and forth.* 1 *noun, plural* **vol·leys;** 2 *verb.*

volleyball (definition 1)

vol·ley·ball (vol′ē bôl′), **1** a game played by two teams of players with a large ball and a high net. The ball is hit with the hands or forearms back and forth over the net without letting it touch the ground. **2** the ball used in this game. *noun.*

volt (vōlt), the unit for measuring electric force. *noun.*
[*Volt* was named for Alessandro Volta, who lived from 1745 to 1827. He was an Italian scientist who invented one of the first electric batteries.]

volt·age (vōl′tij), electric force, measured in volts. A current of high voltage is used in transmitting electric power over long distances. *noun.*

vol·u·ble (vol′yə bəl), ready to talk much; having the habit of talking much: *She is a voluble speaker. adjective.*

vol·ume (vol′yəm), **1** a book: *We own a library of five hundred volumes.* **2** a book forming part of a set or series: *You can find what you want to know in the ninth volume of this encyclopedia.* **3** the amount of space anything contains or fills: *The storeroom has a volume of 400 cubic feet.* **4** an amount of sound; loudness: *Please turn the volume down on the stereo. noun.*

vol·un·tar·i·ly (vol′ən ter′ə lē), of one's own choice; without being made to or forced to: *I was surprised when they voluntarily agreed to help me. I didn't even have to ask them. adverb.*

vol·un·tar·y (vol′ən ter′ē), **1** acting, done, made, or given of one's own choice; not forced; not required: *a voluntary worker. My decision to quit my job was voluntary.* **2** intended; done on purpose: *Voluntary disobedience will be punished.* **3** controlled by the will: *Talking is voluntary; hiccupping is not voluntary. adjective.*

vol·un·teer (vol′ən tir′), **1** a person who enters any branch of the armed forces by choice; one who is not drafted. Some soldiers are volunteers. **2** to offer one's services: *She volunteered for the committee.* **3** to offer freely: *He volunteered to help.* **4** of volunteers; serving as a volunteer: *a volunteer fire department, a volunteer firefighter.* 1 *noun,* 2,3 *verb,* 4 *adjective.*

vom·it (vom′it), **1** to throw up what has been eaten. **2** the substance thrown up from the stomach. 1 *verb,* 2 *noun.*

voo·doo (vü′dü′), a religion that came from Africa, made up of strange practices that include the use of witchcraft and magic. *noun.*

vote (vōt), **1** a formal expression of a choice about a proposal, a motion, or a candidate for office. In an election the person receiving the most votes is elected. **2** the right to give such an expression: *In this club, only members who have paid all their dues have the vote.* **3** the act or process of voting: *We took a vote on where to go for vacation.* **4** to give a vote: *I voted for that senator.* **5** to pass, determine, or grant by voting: *Money for a new school was voted by the board.* **1-3** *noun,* **4,5** *verb,* **votes, vot·ed, vot·ing.**

vot·er (vō′tər), **1** a person who votes. **2** a person who has the right to vote: *Women have been voters in the United States only since 1920. noun.*

vouch (vouch), to be responsible; give a guarantee: *I can vouch for the truth of the story. verb.*

vow (vou), **1** a solemn promise: *a vow of secrecy, marriage vows.* **2** to make a vow: *The knight vowed loyalty to the king.* **1** *noun,* **2** *verb.*

vow·el (vou′əl), **1** a speech sound that is spelled by the letters *a, e, i, o, u,* and sometimes *y.* **2** a letter or combination of letters that stands for a vowel sound. *noun.*

voy·age (voi′ij), **1** a journey by water; cruise: *We had a pleasant voyage to England.* **2** a journey through the air or through space: *the earth's voyage around the sun.* **3** to make or take a voyage; go by sea or air: *We voyaged across the Atlantic Ocean.* **1,2** *noun,* **3** *verb,* **voy·ag·es, voy·aged, voy·ag·ing.**

voy·ag·er (voi′i jər), a person who makes a voyage; traveler. *noun.*

VT, Vermont (used with postal Zip Code).

Vt., Vermont.

vul·gar (vul′gər), showing a lack of good breeding, manners, or taste; not refined; coarse: *to use vulgar language. adjective.*

a hat	i it	oi oil	ch child	⎧ a in about
ā age	ī ice	ou out	ng long	e in taken
ä far	o hot	u cup	sh she	ə = ⎨ i in pencil
e let	ō open	u̇ put	th thin	o in lemon
ē equal	ô order	ü rule	ŦH then	⎩ u in circus
ėr term			zh measure	

vul·gar·i·ty (vul gar′ə tē), **1** a lack of good breeding, manners, or taste; lack of refinement; coarseness. **2** a vulgar act or word: *Their vulgarities annoyed me terribly. noun, plural* **vul·gar·i·ties.**

vul·ner·a·ble (vul′nər ə bəl), **1** capable of being wounded or injured; open to attack: *The army's retreat left the city vulnerable to attack by the enemy.* **2** sensitive to criticism, temptations, or influences: *Most people are vulnerable to ridicule. adjective.*

vul·ture (vul′chər), a large bird of prey related to eagles and hawks that eats the flesh of dead animals. Vultures usually do not have feathers on their heads and necks. *noun.*

vultures—about 2½ feet (76 centimeters) long

V

W w

W or w (dub′əl yü), the 23rd letter of the English alphabet. *noun, plural* **W's** or **w's.**

W or W., 1 watt or watts. 2 west. 3 western.

WA, Washington (used with postal Zip Code).

wad (wod), 1 a small, soft, compact mass: *a wad of chewing gum. I plugged my ears with wads of cotton.* 2 to make into a wad: *I wadded up the paper and threw it away.* 3 a large, rolled bundle of paper money. 1,3 *noun,* 2 *verb,* **wads, wad·ded, wad·ding.**

wad·dle (wod′l), 1 to walk with short steps and an awkward, swaying motion, as a duck does: *The small child waddled from the house carrying a large toy.* 2 an awkward, swaying way of walking: *He imitated the waddle of a duck.* 1 *verb,* **wad·dles, wad·dled, wad·dling;** 2 *noun.*

wade (wād), 1 to walk through water, snow, sand, mud, or anything that hinders free motion: *to wade across a brook.* 2 to make one's way with difficulty: *Must I wade through that dull book?* 3 to get across or pass through by wading: *We waded the stream. verb,* **wades, wad·ed, wad·ing.**

wa·fer (wā′fər), a flat, dry food made of flour and water baked together. *noun.*

waf·fle (wof′əl), a cake made of batter and cooked in a special griddle that makes the cakes very thin in places, usually eaten while hot with butter and syrup. *noun.*

waft (waft), 1 to carry over water or through air: *The waves wafted the boat to shore.* 2 a breath or puff of air, wind, or scent: *A waft of fresh air came through the open window.* 3 a waving movement: *a waft of the hand.* 1 *verb,* 2,3 *noun.*

wag (wag), 1 to move from side to side or up and down: *A dog wags its tail.* 2 a wagging motion: *My dog greeted me with a wag of its tail.* 1 *verb,* **wags, wagged, wag·ging;** 2 *noun.*

wage (wāj), 1 Usually, **wages.** the money paid for work done, especially work paid for by the hour: *He receives a weekly wage of $300.* 2 to carry on: *Doctors wage war against disease.* 1 *noun,* 2 *verb,* **wag·es, waged, wag·ing.**

wa·ger (wā′jər), 1 to make a bet; bet; gamble: *I'll wager the black horse will win the race.* 2 the act of betting; bet: *The wager of $10 was promptly paid.* 1 *verb,* 2 *noun.*

wag·gle (wag′əl), to move quickly and repeatedly from side to side; wag. *verb,* **wag·gles, wag·gled, wag·gling.**

wag·on (wag′ən), 1 a four-wheeled vehicle for carrying loads, usually pulled by a horse: *a milk wagon.* 2 a child's toy cart. *noun.*

waif (wāf), 1 a homeless or neglected child. 2 anything without an owner; stray thing or animal. *noun.*

wail (wāl), 1 to cry loud and long because of grief or pain: *The baby wailed.* 2 a long cry of grief or pain: *The baby woke up with a wail.* 3 a sound like such a cry: *the wail of a coyote.* 1 *verb,* 2,3 *noun.*

waist (wāst), the part of the body between the ribs and the hips. *noun.*

waist·coat (wāst′kōt′ or wes′kit), a man's vest. *noun.*

wait (wāt), 1 to stay or stop doing something till someone comes or something happens: *Let's wait in the shade.* 2 the act or time of waiting: *I had a long wait at the doctor's office.* 3 to be left undone; be put off: *That matter can wait until tomorrow.* 4 to delay or put off: *Please wait dinner for me.* 1,3,4 *verb,* 2 *noun.*

lie in wait, to stay hidden ready to attack: *Robbers lay in wait for the travelers.*

wait on or **wait upon,** 1 to be a servant to: *wait on hotel guests.* 2 to serve as a waiter or waitress: *to wait on several tables of diners.* 3 to call upon a superior: *The duke waited upon the queen.*

wait·er (wā′tər), a man who serves or brings food to people in a restaurant. *noun.*

wai·tress (wā′tris), a woman who serves or brings food to people in a restaurant. *noun, plural* **wai·tress·es.**

wake¹ (wāk), 1 to stop sleeping: *I usually wake at dawn. She wakes at seven every morning.* 2 to cause to stop sleeping: *The noise of the traffic always wakes the baby. Wake him up early.* 3 to make or become alive or active: *He needs some interest to wake him up. Flowers wake in the spring.* 4 a watch kept beside the body of a dead person before its burial. 1,2,3 *verb,* **wakes, waked** or **woke, waked, wak·ing;** 4 *noun.*

wake² (wāk), the track left behind a moving ship. *noun.*

wake·ful (wāk′fəl), 1 not able to sleep: *a wakeful baby.* 2 without sleep: *to spend a wakeful night. adjective.*

wak·en (wā′kən), to wake. *verb.*

Wales (wālz), a division of Great Britain in the southwestern part. *noun.*

walk (wôk), 1 to go on foot. In walking, a person always has one foot on the ground. *Walk down to the post office with me.* 2 to go over, on, or through: *We walked the length of the trail.* 3 the slowest gait of a four-legged animal, in which at least two feet are always on the ground. 4 to cause to go at a walk; make go slowly: *The rider walked the horse up the hill.* 5 the act of walking, especially for pleasure or exercise: *We went for a walk in the country.* 6 to accompany or escort in walking; to conduct while walking: *to walk a guest to the door. I walk the dog every morning.* 7 a distance to walk: *The library is a twenty-minute walk from our house.* 8 a way of walking; gait: *We could tell she was happy from her lively walk.* 9 a place for walking: *There are many pretty walks in the park.* 10 (in baseball) to go or cause to go to first base after four balls. 11 (in baseball) a going to first base after the pitcher has thrown four balls. 1,2,4,6,10 *verb,* 3,5,7-9,11 *noun.*

walk·ie-talk·ie (wô′kē tô′kē), a small, portable radio set that can be used to receive and send messages. It is operated by a battery and has an antenna. *noun.*

walk·way (wôk′wā′), **1** a structure for walking on: *an overhead steel walkway.* **2** path; walk: *a walkway between houses. noun.*

wall (wôl), **1** the side of a room or building: *to wallpaper a bedroom wall, the brick wall of a house.* **2** the side part of any hollow thing: *the wall of the stomach.* **3** a structure of stone, brick, or other material built up to enclose, divide, support, or protect. Cities used to be surrounded by high walls to keep out enemies. **4** anything like a wall in looks or use: *The flood came in a wall of water twelve feet high.* **5** to enclose, divide, protect, or fill with a wall: *The garden is walled. They walled up the old doorway.* 1-4 *noun,* 5 *verb.*

wal·let (wol′it), a small, flat case for carrying paper money or cards in one's pocket; billfold. *noun.*

wal·lop (wol′əp), **1** to beat soundly; thrash. **2** to hit very hard: *The batter walloped a home run over the fence.* **3** a very hard blow: *The wallop knocked me down.* 1,2 *verb,* 3 *noun.*

wal·low (wol′ō), to roll about; flounder: *The pigs wallowed in the mud. The boat wallowed helplessly in the stormy sea. verb.*

wall·pa·per (wôl′pā′pər), **1** paper, usually printed with a pattern in color, for pasting on and covering walls. **2** to put wallpaper on: *We are going to wallpaper my bedroom.* 1 *noun,* 2 *verb.*

wal·nut (wôl′nut), **1** a rather large, almost round nut with a division between the two halves. The meat of the walnut is eaten by itself or used in cakes and cookies. **2** tree it grows on. **3** the wood of this tree. Some kinds of walnut are used in making furniture. *noun.*

wal·rus (wôl′rəs), a large sea animal of the arctic regions, resembling a seal but having long tusks. Walruses are hunted for their hides, ivory tusks, and blubber oil. *noun, plural* **wal·rus·es** or **wal·rus.**

Word History

walrus *Walrus* comes from two Dutch words meaning "whale" and "horse."

walruses—up to 11 feet (3½ meters) long

a hat	**i** it	**oi** oil	**ch** child	⎧ a in about
ā age	**ī** ice	**ou** out	**ng** long	⎪ e in taken
ä far	**o** hot	**u** cup	**sh** she	ə = ⎨ i in pencil
e let	**ō** open	**u̇** put	**th** thin	⎪ o in lemon
ē equal	**ô** order	**ü** rule	**ŦH** then	⎩ u in circus
ėr term			**zh** measure	

waltz (wôlts), **1** a smooth, even, gliding dance with three beats to a measure. **2** the music for it. **3** to dance a waltz. 1,2 *noun, plural* **waltz·es;** 3 *verb.*

wam·pum (wom′pəm), beads made from shells, formerly used by North American Indians as money and for ornament. *noun.*

wampum

wan (won), **1** pale: *Her face looked wan after her long illness.* **2** faint; weak; looking worn or tired: *The sick boy gave the doctor a wan smile. adjective,* **wan·ner, wan·nest.**

wand (wond), a slender stick or rod: *The magician waved her wand and a rabbit popped out of the hat. noun.*

wan·der (won′dər), **1** to move here and there without any special purpose: *We wandered around the fair, looking at exhibits.* **2** to go from the right way; stray: *The dog wandered off and got lost. The speaker wandered away from the subject. verb.*

wan·der·er (won′dər ər), a person or animal that wanders. *noun.*

wane (wān), **1** to lose size; become smaller gradually: *The moon wanes after it has become full.* **2** to lose power, influence, or importance: *Many great empires have waned. verb,* **wanes, waned, wan·ing.**

want (wont), **1** to wish for; wish: *We want a new car. I want to become an engineer.* **2** a thing desired or needed: *They live simply and have few wants.* **3** to lack; be without: *The fund for a new hospital wants only a few thousand dollars of the sum needed.* **4** a lack; need; condition of being without something desired or needed: *The plant died from want of water.* **5** to need: *That plant wants water.* **6** a lack of food, clothing, or shelter; great poverty: *The old couple are now in want.* 1,3,5 *verb,* 2,4,6 *noun.*

want·ing (won′ting), **1** lacking; missing: *The*

machine had some of its parts *wanting*. **2** not satisfactory; not coming up to a standard or need: *Some people are wanting in courtesy. The vegetables were weighed and found wanting. adjective.*

war (wôr), **1** fighting carried on by armed force between nations or parts of a nation. **2** any fighting or struggle; conflict; strife: *Doctors carry on war against disease.* **3** to fight; make war: *Germany warred against France.* **1,2** *noun,* **3** *verb,* **wars, warred, war·ring.**

war·ble (wôr′bəl), **1** to sing in a quick, vibrating, tuneful way: *Birds warbled in the trees.* **2** to make a sound something like a bird warbling: *The brook warbled over its rocky bed.* **3** a bird's song or a sound like it: *the warble of a canary.* **1,2** *verb,* **war·bles, war·bled, war·bling;** **3** *noun.*

war·bler (wôr′blər), any of several kinds of small songbirds, often brightly colored. *noun.*

warbler—5 inches (13 centimeters) long

ward (wôrd), **1** a division of a hospital or prison. **2** one of the parts or districts into which a city or town is divided for purposes of government. **3** a person under the care of a guardian or of a court. **4 ward off,** to keep away or turn aside: *He warded off the blow with his arm.* **1-3** *noun,* **4** *verb.*

-ward, a suffix meaning: toward _____: Back*ward* means *toward* the back. Home*ward* means *toward* home.

ward·en (wôrd′n), **1** a keeper; guard. The person in charge of a prison is called the warden. **2** an official who enforces certain laws and regulations: *a game warden, a fire warden. noun.*

ward·robe (wôrd′rōb′), **1** a stock of clothes: *a summer wardrobe.* **2** a room, closet, or piece of furniture for holding clothes. *noun.*

ware (wer *or* war), **1 wares,** articles for sale; manufactured goods: *Household wares are on the third floor at this store.* **2** a kind of manufactured thing or article for sale: *copper ware.* **3** earthenware; pottery: *porcelain ware. noun.*

ware·house (wer′hous′ *or* war′hous′), a place where goods are kept; storehouse. *noun, plural* **ware·hous·es** (wer′hou′ziz *or* war′hou′ziz).

war·fare (wôr′fer′ *or* wôr′far′), war; fighting. *noun.*

war·i·ly (wer′ə le *or* war′ə lē), cautiously; with care: *We climbed warily up the dangerous path. adverb.*

war·like (wôr′līk′), **1** fit for war; ready for war; fond of war: *a warlike nation.* **2** threatening war; hostile: *a warlike speech. adjective.*

warm (wôrm), **1** more hot than cold; giving forth gentle heat: *a warm fire. She sat in the warm sunshine.* **2** having a feeling of heat: *be warm from running.* **3** able to keep body heat in: *We wear warm clothes in winter.* **4** having or showing lively feelings; enthusiastic: *a warm welcome, a warm friend, a warm heart.* **5** (in games, treasure hunts, and the like) getting close to what one is looking for. **6** to make or become warm: *warm a room.* **7** to make or become cheered, interested, or friendly: *The speaker warmed to his subject.* **1-5** *adjective,* **6,7** *verb.*

warm up, 1 to heat or cook again: *This morning we warmed up yesterday's oatmeal.* **2** to practice or exercise for a few minutes before a game or contest.

warm-blood·ed (wôrm′blud′id), having blood that stays at about the same temperature no matter what the temperature is of the air or water around the animal. Cats are warm-blooded; snakes are cold-blooded. *adjective.*

warmth (wôrmth), **1** a being warm: *We enjoyed the warmth of the open fire.* **2** a warm feeling: *the warmth of our host's welcome.* **3** liveliness of feelings or emotions: *She spoke with warmth of the natural beauty of the mountains. noun.*

warm-up (wôrm′up′), the practice or exercise taken for a few minutes before a game or contest. *noun.*

warn (wôrn), **1** to give notice to in advance about possible danger, evil, or harm; put on guard; caution: *The clouds warned us that a storm was coming.* **2** to give notice to; inform: *The whistle warned visitors that the ship was ready to sail. verb.*

warn·ing (wôr′ning), something that warns; notice given in advance: *Let this experience be a warning to you to be more careful in the future. noun.*

warp (definition 3)

warp (wôrp), **1** to bend or twist out of shape: *This old floor has warped so that it is not level.* **2** to make not as it should be; cause not to work as it should: *Suspicions can warp our judgment.* **3** the threads running lengthwise in a fabric. The warp is crossed by the woof. **1,2** *verb,* **3** *noun.*

war·path (wôr′path′), the way taken by a fighting group of North American Indians. *noun, plural* **war·paths** (wôr′paᴛнz′ *or* wôr′paths′).

on the warpath, ready for war; ready for a fight:

The two enemy tribes are on the warpath again.

war·rant (wôr′ənt), **1** a reason which gives a right; authority: *They had no warrant for their action.* **2** a written order giving authority for something: *The police obtained a warrant to search the house.* **3** to give a good reason for; justify: *Nothing can warrant such rudeness.* **4** to give one's word for; guarantee; promise: *The company warranted the quality of their cameras.* 1,2 *noun,* 3,4 *verb.*

war·ri·or (wôr′ē ər), a person experienced in fighting battles. *noun.*

war·ship (wôr′ship′), a ship armed for war. *noun.*

wart (wôrt), a small, hard lump on the skin. *noun.*

war·y (wer′ē *or* war′ē), **1** on one's guard against danger or being deceived: *They were wary of walking alone at night in that neighborhood.* **2** cautious; careful: *We gave wary answers to all of the stranger's questions.* *adjective,* **war·i·er, war·i·est.**

was (woz *or* wuz). *Was* is a form of **be.** *Once there was a queen. I was late to school yesterday. She was going to study. The candy was eaten.* *verb.*

wash (wosh), **1** to clean with water: *to wash one's face, to wash dishes, to wash clothes.* **2** to remove dirt, stains, paint, or the like by or as by scrubbing with soap and water: *Can you wash that spot out?* **3** to wash oneself; wash one's face and hands: *You should always wash before eating.* **4** to wash clothes: *I have to wash today.* **5** a washing or being washed: *This floor needs a good wash.* **6** a quantity of clothes washed or to be washed: *Take the wash from the dryer.* **7** to carry or be carried along or away by water or other liquid: *Wood is often washed ashore by waves. The road washed out during the storm.* **8** to wear by water: *The cliffs are being slowly washed away by the waves.* **9** the motion, rush, or sound of water: *We listened to the wash of the waves against the boat.* **10** a liquid for special use: *a mouth wash, a hair wash.* 1-4,7,8 *verb,* 5,6,9,10 *noun, plural* **wash·es.**

Wash., Washington.

wash·a·ble (wosh′ə bəl), able to be washed without damage: *washable fabrics.* *adjective.*

wash·bowl (wosh′bōl′), a bowl for holding water to wash one's face and hands. *noun.*

wash·cloth (wosh′klôth′), a small cloth for washing oneself. *noun, plural* **wash·cloths** (wosh′klôᵺz′ *or* wosh′klôths′).

wash·er (wosh′ər), **1** a person or machine that washes. **2** a flat ring of metal, rubber, leather, or the like. Washers are used to provide tightness or to avoid friction at joints, especially with nuts and bolts. *noun.*

washer (definition 2)

wash·ing (wosh′ing), clothes washed or to be washed: *send washing to the laundry.* *noun.*

washing machine, a machine that washes clothes.

Wash·ing·ton (wosh′ing tən), **1** the capital of the United States, covering the entire District of Columbia. Washington is situated along the Potomac River between Maryland and Virginia. **2** one of the Pacific states of the United States. *Abbreviation:* Wash. or WA *Capital:* Olympia. *noun.*
[The city and the state of *Washington* were both named in honor of George Washington, the first president of the United States. He lived from 1732 to 1799.]

wash·out (wosh′out′), **1** a hole where earth has been washed away by water. **2** a disappointment; failure: *The party was a complete washout.* *noun.*

wash·room (wosh′rüm′), a room with a sink and a toilet, usually a public bathroom. *noun.*

was·n't (woz′nt *or* wuz′nt), was not.

wasp (wosp), an insect that has a slender body and a powerful sting. Hornets and yellow jackets are kinds of wasps. *noun.*

wasps on their nest (about life-size)

waste (wāst), **1** to make poor use of; spend uselessly; fail to get full value or benefit from: *Though they had much work to do, they wasted their time doing nothing.* **2** a poor use; useless spending; failure to get the most out of something: *Buying that suit was a waste of money; it is already starting to wear out.* **3** thrown away as useless or worthless: *a pile of waste lumber.* **4** useless or worthless material; stuff to be thrown away. Garbage or sewage is waste. **5** the material which the body gets rid of because it cannot be digested or used. **6** left over; not used: *waste food.* **7** stuff that is left over. Bunches of cotton waste are used

W

to clean machinery. **8** a desert; wilderness: *We traveled through treeless wastes.* **9** to wear down little by little; destroy gradually: *The patient was wasted by disease.* **10** to become weak or thin, especially because of disease. **11** to spoil; ruin; destroy: *The soldiers wasted the fields and towns of the enemy.* 1,9-11 *verb,* **wastes, wast·ed, wast·ing;** 2,4,5,7,8 *noun,* 3,6 *adjective.*

waste·bas·ket (wāst′bas′kit), a basket or other container for wastepaper or other trash. *noun.*

waste·ful (wāst′fəl), using or spending too much: *to be wasteful of water. adjective.*

waste·land (wāst′land′), land that is not cultivated and does not produce anything. *noun.*

waste·pa·per (wāst′pā′pər), paper thrown away or to be thrown away as useless or worthless. *noun.*

watch (woch), **1** to look carefully: *The medical students watched while the surgeon performed the operation.* **2** to look at: *Are you watching that show on television? We watched the kittens play.* **3** to look or wait with care and attention; be very careful: *She watched for a chance to cross the street.* **4** a careful looking; attitude of attention: *a tornado watch. I kept watch for the taxi we had telephoned for.* **5** to keep guard over: *The police watched the burglary suspect for several days. The sentry watched all through the night.* **6** a protecting; guarding: *She kept watch over the house while we were gone.* **7** a person or persons kept to guard: *A call for help aroused the night watch.* **8** a period of time for guarding: *a watch in the night.* **9** a device for telling time, small enough to be carried in a pocket or worn on the wrist. 1-3,5 *verb,* 4,6-9 *noun, plural* **watch·es.**

watch out, to be careful: *Watch out for cars when you cross the street.*

watch·dog (woch′dôg′), a dog kept to guard property. *noun.*

watch·ful (woch′fəl), wide-awake; watching carefully: *You should always be watchful for cars when you cross the street. adjective.*

watch·man (woch′mən), a person who keeps watch; guard: *A watchman guards the bank at night. noun, plural* **watch·men.**

watch·tow·er (woch′tou′ər), a tower from which a person watches for enemies, fires, ships, or any approaching danger. *noun.*

watch·word (woch′werd′), a secret word that allows a person to pass a guard; password: *We gave the watchword, and the guard let us pass. noun.*

wa·ter (wô′tər), **1** the liquid that fills the ocean, rivers, lakes, and ponds, and falls from the sky as rain. **2** a liquid like water. When you cry, water runs from your eyes. **3** to sprinkle or wet with water: *I watered the grass.* **4** to give water to; supply with water: *After we returned from our ride, we fed and watered the horses.* **5** to weaken by adding water: *It is against the law to sell milk that has been watered.* **6** to fill with water; discharge water: *Strong sunlight will make your eyes water. The cake made my mouth water.* **7** done or used in

or on water: *water sports.* **8** growing or living in or near water: *water plants, water insects.* 1,2 *noun,* 3-6 *verb,* 7,8 *adjective.*

throw cold water on, to discourage: *My parents threw cold water on my plan to camp in the mountains by myself.*

tread water, to keep oneself from sinking by moving the feet up and down in a treading motion.

water buffalo, a buffalo of Asia, often used to pull loads.

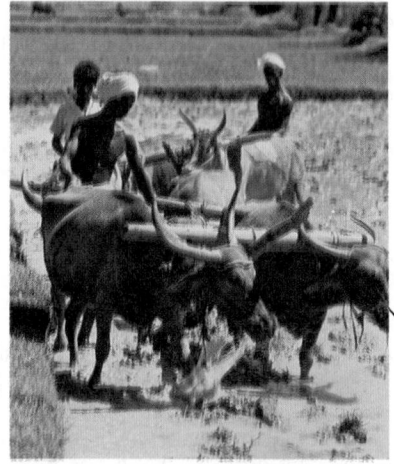

water buffaloes
5 feet (1½ meters)
high at the shoulder

wa·ter·col·or (wô′tər kul′ər), **1** a paint mixed with water instead of oil. **2** the art of painting with watercolors. **3** a picture made with watercolors. *noun.*

watercolor (definition 3)

wa·ter·cress (wot′ər kres′), a plant that grows in water and has crisp leaves which are used for salad. *noun.*

water cycle, a cycle in nature by which water evaporates from oceans, lakes, and rivers and returns to them as rain or snow.

wa·ter·fall (wô′tər fôl′), a fall of water from a high place. *noun.*

wa·ter·front (wô′tər frunt′), land at the water's

edge, especially the part of a city beside a river, lake, or harbor. *noun.*

water hole, a hole in the ground where water collects; small pond; pool.

water lily, a water plant having flat, floating leaves and showy, fragrant flowers. The flowers of the common American water lily are white, or sometimes pink.

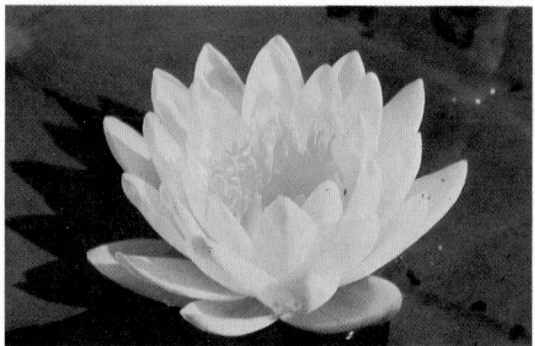

water lily

wa·ter·logged (wô′tər logd′), so full of water that it will barely float. *adjective.*

wa·ter·mel·on (wô′tər mel′ən), a large, juicy melon with red or pink pulp and a hard, green rind. It grows on a vine. *noun.*

water moccasin, a poisonous snake that is found in the southern part of the United States and lives in swamps and along streams; cottonmouth.

water pistol, a toy pistol that shoots water; squirt gun.

water power, the power from flowing or falling water. Water power can be used to drive machinery and to generate electricity.

wa·ter·proof (wô′tər prüf′), 1 able to keep water from coming through: *An umbrella should be waterproof.* 2 to make waterproof: *These hiking shoes have been waterproofed.* 1 *adjective,* 2 *verb.*

wa·ter·shed (wô′tər shed′), 1 the ridge between the regions drained by two different river systems. On one side of a watershed, rivers and streams flow in one direction; on the other side, they flow in the opposite direction. 2 the region drained by one river system. *noun.*

water ski, one of a pair of skis for gliding over water while being towed at the end of a rope by a motorboat.

wa·ter-ski (wô′tər skē′), to glide over the water on water skis. *verb,* **wa·ter-skis, wa·ter-skied, wa·ter-ski·ing.**

wa·ter·tight (wô′tər tīt′), so tight that no water can get in or out. Ships are often divided into watertight compartments. *adjective.*

wa·ter·way (wô′tər wā′), 1 a river, canal, or other body of water that ships can go on. 2 a channel for water. *noun.*

water wheel, a wheel turned by water and used to drive machinery.

wa·ter·works (wô′tər wėrks′), 1 a system of pipes, reservoirs, and pumps for supplying a city with water. 2 a building with machinery for pumping water. *noun plural or singular.*

wa·ter·y (wô′tər ē), 1 full of water; wet: *watery soil.* 2 full of tears; tearful: *watery eyes.* 3 containing too much water: *watery soup.* 4 of water; like water: *A blister is filled with a watery fluid.* *adjective,* **wa·ter·i·er, wa·ter·i·est.**

watt (wot), a unit of electric power: *My lamp uses 60 watts; my toaster uses 1000 watts. noun.* [The *watt* was named for James Watt, who lived from 1736 to 1819. He was a Scottish engineer and inventor who perfected the steam engine.]

wave (wāv), 1 a moving ridge or swell of water: *The raft rose and fell on the waves.* 2 any movement like this. Light, heat, and sound travel in waves. 3 a swell or sudden increase of some condition or emotion; flood or rush of anything: *A wave of cold weather is sweeping over the country. The announcement brought a wave of enthusiasm.* 4 to move as waves do; move up and down or back and forth; sway: *The tall grass waved in the breeze.* 5 to cause to move or sway back and forth or up and down: *to wave a flag. Wave your hand.* 6 to signal or direct by moving the hand or an object back and forth: *The children waved good-by to their parents. The police officer waved the speeding driver to the side of the road.* 7 the act of waving: *a wave of the hand.* 8 a curve or series of curves: *waves in a person's hair.* 9 to have or cause to have a wavelike form: *to wave one's hair. Her hair waves naturally.* 1-3,7,8 *noun,* 4-6,9 *verb,* **waves, waved, wav·ing.**

wave·length (wāv′lengkth′ *or* wāv′length′), the distance between a point on one wave and a point in the same position on the next wave. *noun.*

wa·ver (wā′vər), 1 to move back and forth, especially in an unsteady way; flutter: *Butterflies hovered and wavered among the flower blossoms.* 2 to flicker: *a wavering light.* 3 to be undecided; hesitate: *We are still wavering between a picnic and a trip to the zoo.* 4 an act of wavering. 1-3 *verb,* 4 *noun.*

wav·y (wā′vē), having waves or curves: *a wavy line, wavy hair. adjective,* **wav·i·er, wav·i·est.**

wax[1] (waks), 1 a yellowish substance made by bees for constructing their honeycomb. Wax is hard when cold, but can be easily shaped when warm. 2 any substance like this. Most of the wax used for candles is really paraffin. 3 a substance containing wax for polishing floors, furniture, cars, or the like. 4 to rub, stiffen, or polish with wax or something like wax: *We wax that floor each month.* 1-3 *noun, plural* **wax·es** for 2 and 3; 4 *verb.*

W

wax² (waks), to grow bigger or greater; increase: *The moon waxes till it becomes full, and then wanes. verb.*

wax·y (wak′sē), **1** like wax: *The floor had a smooth, waxy surface.* **2** made of wax; containing wax; covered with wax: *a waxy solution. adjective,* **wax·i·er, wax·i·est.**

way (wā), **1** a manner; style: *I decided to wear my hair in a new way.* **2** a means; method: *Scientists are finding new ways to prevent disease.* **3** a point; feature; detail; respect: *The plan is bad in several ways.* **4** a direction: *Look this way.* **5** a coming or going; moving along a course: *Our guide led the way through the museum.* **6** distance: *The sun is a long way off.* **7** a path; road; means of moving along a course: *The scouts found a way through the forest.* **8** a space for passing or going ahead: *Please clear a way for us to get through.* **9** a habit; custom: *She's always on time; it's her way.* **10** one's wish; will: *Just once I'd like to have my own way.* **11** a condition; state: *The patient was in a bad way.* **12** at or to a distance; far: *The cloud of smoke stretched way out to the pier.* 1-11 *noun,* 12 *adverb.*

by the way, incidentally; in that connection: *By the way, the school library has several interesting new books.*

by way of, 1 by the route of; through: *She went to India by way of Japan.* **2** as; for: *By way of an answer he just nodded.*

give way, 1 to retreat; make way; yield. **2** to break down or fail: *The old bridge finally gave way and collapsed.* **3** to abandon oneself to emotion: *to give way to despair.*

make way, to give space for passing or going ahead; make room: *Automobiles must make way for a fire engine.*

way, give way (definition 1)
Neither goat would **give way** and let the other pass.

way·far·er (wā′fer′ər *or* wā′far′ər), a traveler, especially a person who travels on foot. *noun.*

way·laid (wā′lād′). See **waylay.** *I waylaid him when he entered the meeting. verb.*

way·lay (wā′lā′), **1** to lie in wait for; attack on the way: *Bandits waylaid travelers and robbed*

them. **2** to stop a person on his or her way: *Newspaper reporters waylaid the mayor and asked her many questions. verb,* **way·lays, way·laid, way·lay·ing.**

way·side (wā′sīd′), the edge of a road or path: *We ate lunch on the wayside. noun.*

we (wē), **1** the persons speaking: *We are glad to see you.* **2** the person speaking. An author, a ruler, or a judge sometimes uses *we* to mean *I.* *pronoun plural.*

weak (wēk), **1** lacking bodily strength: *He was too weak to lift the chair.* **2** easily broken or torn: *My foot went through a weak board in the floor.* **3** lacking great mental force: *A person with a weak character is easily influenced by others.* **4** lacking force or effectiveness: *a weak law.* **5** not having much of a particular quality: *Weak tea has less flavor than strong tea. adjective.*

weak·en (wē′kən), to make or become weak or weaker: *You can weaken tea by adding water. We are almost to the top of the mountain; let's not weaken now. verb.*

weak·ling (wēk′ling), a weak person or animal. *noun.*

weak·ly (wēk′lē), **1** in a weak manner: *He called weakly for help.* **2** weak; feeble; sickly: *a weakly animal.* 1 *adverb,* 2 *adjective,* **weak·li·er, weak·li·est.**

weak·ness (wēk′nis), **1** a being weak; lack of power, force, or vigor: *Weakness kept him in bed.* **2** a weak point; slight fault: *Putting things off is her weakness.* **3** fondness; a liking that one is a little ashamed of: *a weakness for sweets. noun, plural* **weak·ness·es.**

wealth (welth), **1** riches; many valuable possessions; property: *people of wealth, the wealth of a city.* **2** a large quantity; abundance: *a wealth of hair, a wealth of words. noun.*

wealth·y (wel′thē), having wealth; rich. *adjective,* **wealth·i·er, wealth·i·est.**

wean (wēn), to accustom a child or young animal to food other than its mother's milk. *verb.*

weap·on (wep′ən), **1** any object or instrument used in fighting. Swords, spears, arrows, clubs, guns, cannons, and shields are weapons. Animals use claws, horns, teeth, and stings as weapons. **2** any means of attack or defense: *Drugs are effective weapons against many diseases. noun.*

wear (wer *or* war), **1** to have on the body: *to wear a coat, to wear a beard, to wear black, to wear a ring.* **2** to have; show: *The gloomy old house wore an air of sadness.* **3** a wearing; being worn: *Clothing for summer wear is being shown in the shops. This suit has been in constant wear for two years.* **4** things worn or to be worn; clothing: *The store sells children's wear.* **5** to last long; give good service: *These jeans wear well. Their friendship wore well.* **6** to use up; be used up: *The pencil is worn to a stub.* **7** to damage or become damaged by use, weather, or the like: *The waves are wearing the beach away.* **8** damage from use: *The rug shows wear.* **9** to make by rubbing, scraping, or washing away: *Walking wore a hole in my left* *shoe.* 1,2,5-7,9 *verb*, **wears, wore, worn, wear·ing;** 3,4,8 *noun.*

wear off, to become less, slowly and gradually: *The excitement of playing with the new toys soon wore off.*

wear out, 1 to wear or use until no longer fit for use: *These shoes are worn out.* **2** to tire out; weary: *She is worn out by too much work.*

wear·i·ly (wir′ə lē), in a weary manner: *The tired hikers walked slowly and wearily along the road.* *adverb.*

wear·i·ness (wir′ē nis), weary condition; tired feeling: *After tramping all day the hikers were overcome with weariness.* *noun.*

wear·i·some (wir′ē səm), wearying; tiring; tiresome: *a long, boring, and wearisome tale.* *adjective.*

wear·y (wir′ē), **1** tired: *weary feet, a weary brain.* **2** to make or become tired: *Walking all day wearied the tourists.* **1** *adjective,* **wear·i·er, wear·i·est; 2** *verb,* **wear·ies, wear·ied, wear·y·ing.**

wea·sel (wē′zəl), a small, quick, animal with a slender body and short legs. Weasels eat many small animals such as mice, rats, and birds. *noun.*

weasel—about 16 inches (41 centimeters) long with the tail

weath·er (weᴛн′ər), **1** the condition of the air at a certain place and time. Weather includes facts about temperature, wind, and moisture. **2** to expose to the weather; change from the effect of the weather: *Wood turns gray if weathered for a long time.* **3** to go or come through safely: *The ship weathered the storm.* **1** *noun,* 2,3 *verb.*

weath·er·beat·en (weᴛн′ər bēt′n), worn or toughened by the wind, rain, and other forces of the weather: *a seaman's weather-beaten face, a weather-beaten old barn.* *adjective.*

weath·er·cock (weᴛн′ər kok′), a weather vane, especially one in the shape of a rooster. *noun.*

weath·er·ing (weᴛн′ər ing), a changing by the action of weather: *Weathering can turn rock into sand.* *noun.*

weath·er·man (weᴛн′ər man′), a person who forecasts the weather, especially on radio or television. *noun, plural* **weath·er·men.**

weather vane, a flat piece of metal or wood that turns around a rod. Weather vanes are often

weather vane

placed on the tops of buildings. They turn with the wind and show its direction.

weave (wēv), **1** to form threads or strips into a thing or fabric. People weave thread into cloth, straw into hats, and reeds into baskets. **2** to make out of thread, strips, or strands of the same material: *A spider weaves a web. She is weaving a rug.* **3** a method or pattern of weaving: *Homespun is a cloth of coarse weave.* **4** to go by twisting and turning: *a car weaving in and out of traffic.* 1,2,4 *verb,* **weaves, wove** or **weaved, woven** or **weaved, weav·ing;** 3 *noun.*

weave (definition 1)—She **wove** thread into beautiful cloth.

W

709

weav·er (wē′vər), **1** a person who weaves. **2** a person whose work is weaving. *noun.*

web (web), **1** a woven net of very tiny threads like silk spun by a spider. **2** a whole piece of cloth made at one time. **3** anything like a web: *a web of lies.* **4** the skin joining the toes of swimming birds such as ducks and of other water animals such as frogs and beavers. *noun.*

web (definition 1)—a spider **web**

webbed (webd), having the toes joined by a web. Ducks have webbed feet. *adjective.*

web-foot·ed (web′fůt′id), having the toes joined by a web. Geese are web-footed birds. *adjective.*

wed (wed), **1** to marry. **2** to unite. *verb,* **weds, wed·ded, wed·ded** or **wed, wed·ding.**

we'd (wēd), **1** we had. **2** we should. **3** we would.

Wed., Wednesday.

wed·ded (wed′id), **1** married. **2** united. **3** devoted. *adjective.*

wed·ding (wed′ing), **1** a marriage ceremony. **2** an anniversary of it. A golden wedding is the fiftieth anniversary of a marriage. *noun.*

wedge (definition 1)—He used a **wedge** to split the stump.

wedge (wej), **1** a piece of wood or metal thick at one end and tapering to a thin edge at the other. A wedge is driven in between objects to be separated or into anything to be split. **2** something shaped like a wedge or used like a wedge: *a wedge of pie. Wild geese fly in a wedge.* **3** to split or separate with a wedge: *He wedged the log apart*

with a sledgehammer. **4** to fasten or tighten with a wedge: *Before bringing the heavy cartons into the kitchen, we wedged the door open with a flat piece of wood.* **5** to thrust or pack in tightly; squeeze: *She wedged herself through the narrow opening. The hiker's foot was wedged between the rocks.* **1,2** *noun,* **3-5** *verb,* **wedg·es, wedged, wedg·ing.**

wed·lock (wed′lok), married life; marriage. *noun.*

Wednes·day (wenz′dē), the fourth day of the week; the day after Tuesday. *noun.* [*Wednesday* comes from an earlier English word meaning "Woden's day." Woden was one of the most important of the old English gods.]

wee (wē), very small; tiny: *the wee infant in the baby carriage, to have a wee bit of a headache. adjective,* **we·er, we·est.**

weed (wēd), **1** a useless or troublesome plant: *Weeds choked out the vegetables and flowers in the garden.* **2** to take weeds out of: *Please weed the garden now.* **1** *noun,* **2** *verb.*

weed out, to remove as useless or worthless: *I weeded out the old magazines that I no longer wanted.*

weed·y (wē′dē), full of weeds: *a weedy garden. adjective,* **weed·i·er, weed·i·est.**

wee hours, the early morning hours.

week (wēk), **1** seven days, one after another: *On Tuesday my mother left on a business trip and will be gone for a week.* **2** the time from Sunday through Saturday: *He is away most of the week but comes home on Sundays.* **3** the working days of a seven-day period: *A school week is usually five days. noun.*

week·day (wēk′dā′), any day of the week except Sunday or (now often) Saturday. *noun.*

week·end (wēk′end′), Saturday and Sunday as a time for recreation or visiting: *We plan to spend this weekend in the country. noun.*

week·ly (wēk′lē), **1** of a week; for a week; lasting a week: *Her weekly wage is $100.* **2** done or published once a week: *I subscribe to several weekly magazines. She writes a weekly letter to her grandmother.* **3** once each week; every week: *I play tennis weekly.* **4** a newspaper or magazine published once a week. **1,2** *adjective,* **3** *adverb,* **4** *noun, plural* **week·lies.**

weep (wēp), to cry; shed tears: *I wept for joy when I won the award. verb,* **weeps, wept, weep·ing.**

wee·vil (wē′vəl), a small beetle whose larvae eat grain, nuts, fruits, or the stems of leaves. Weevils do much damage to grain and cotton crops. *noun.*

weft (weft), in weaving, the woof. *noun.*

weigh (wā), **1** to find out how heavy a thing is: *I weigh myself to see if I have gained any weight since last week. The grocer weighed the bag of apples.* **2** to have as a measure by weight: *I weigh 110 pounds.* **3** to bend by weight; burden: *The boughs of the apple tree are weighed down with fruit. They were weighed down with many troubles.* **4** to bear down; be a burden: *Don't let this mistake weigh on your mind.* **5** to balance in the mind;

consider carefully: *He weighs his words before speaking.* **6** to lift up an anchor: *The ship weighed anchor and sailed away.* verb.

weight (wāt), **1** how heavy a thing is; amount a thing weighs: *The dog's weight is 50 pounds.* **2** the force with which an object is drawn toward the earth or some other heavenly body. This force is felt as heaviness. *An astronaut who weighs 180 pounds on earth has a weight of only 30 pounds on the moon, because the moon draws matter with much less force than the earth does.* **3** a unit for measuring how much a thing weighs, such as a pound or kilogram. **4** a piece of metal having a known heaviness, used in weighing things: *a pound weight.* **5** a heavy object used to hold something in place: *A weight keeps the papers in one place on my desk.* **6** load; burden: *The pillars support the weight of the roof. The good news took a weight off my mind.* **7** influence; importance; value: *the weight of public opinion.* noun.

weight·less (wāt′lis), **1** having little or no weight: *weightless snow.* **2** being free from the pull of gravity. adjective.

a hat	i it	oi oil	ch child	a in about
ā age	ī ice	ou out	ng long	e in taken
ä far	o hot	u cup	sh she	ə = { i in pencil
e let	ō open	u̇ put	th thin	o in lemon
ē equal	ô order	ü rule	ŦH then	u in circus
ėr term			zh measure	

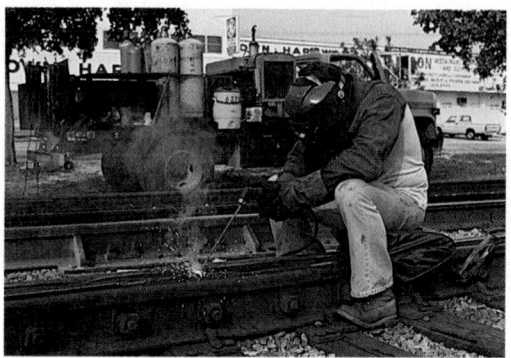
weld (definition 1)—The worker is **welding** a railroad track.

weld (weld), **1** to join pieces of metal or plastic together by bringing the parts that touch to the melting point, so that they flow together and become one piece in cooling. **2** a welded joint. **1** verb, **2** noun.

wel·fare (wel′fer′ *or* wel′far′), **1** health, happiness, and prosperity; being well; doing well: *My uncle asked about the welfare of everyone in our family.* **2** the aid provided by the government to poor or needy people. noun.

on welfare, receiving aid from the government because of hardship or need.

well[1] (wel), **1** all right; in a satisfactory, favorable, or good manner: *Is everything going well at school? The job was well done.* **2** satisfactory; good; right: *It is well you came along.* **3** thoroughly: *He knew the lesson well. Shake the medicine well before taking it.* **4** much; to a considerable degree: *The fair brought in well over a hundred dollars.* **5** fairly; reasonably: *I couldn't very well refuse their request.* **6** healthy; in good health: *I am very well.* **7** *Well* is sometimes used to show mild surprise or merely to fill in. *Well! Well! Here she is. Well, I'm not sure.* **1,3-5** adverb, **bet·ter, best; 2,6** adjective, **7** interjection.

well[2] (wel), **1** a hole dug or bored in the ground to get water, oil, or gas: *I pumped a bucket of water from the well.* **2** a spring; fountain; source: *This book is a well of ideas.* **3** a shaft for stairs or elevator, extending through the floors of a building. **4** to spring; rise; gush: *Water wells from a spring beneath the rock. Tears welled up in the child's eyes.* **1-3** noun, **4** verb.

we'll (wēl), **1** we shall. **2** we will.

well-bal·anced (wel′bal′ənst), rightly balanced, adjusted, or regulated: *A well-balanced diet includes plenty of fruit and vegetables.* adjective.

well-be·haved (wel′bi hāvd′), showing good manners or conduct: *The children were well-behaved.* adjective.

weightless (definition 2)—Astronauts know what it is like to float in space while in a **weightless** condition.

weight·y (wā′tē), **1** heavy: *a weighty suitcase.* **2** important; serious: *This is indeed a weighty problem.* adjective, **weight·i·er, weight·i·est.**

weird (wird), **1** frightening; mysterious; wild: *We were awakened by a weird shriek.* **2** odd; fantastic; of strange appearance: *The shadows made weird figures on the wall.* adjective.

wel·come (wel′kəm), **1** to greet kindly: *We always welcome guests at our house.* **2** a kind reception: *You will always have a welcome here.* **3** to receive gladly: *We welcome new ideas.* **4** gladly received: *a welcome visitor, a welcome letter, a welcome rest from work.* **5** gladly or freely permitted: *You are welcome to pick the flowers.* **6** You say "You are welcome" when someone thanks you. **7** exclamation of friendly greeting: *Welcome, everyone!* **1,3** verb, **wel·comes, wel·comed, wel·com·ing; 2** noun, **4-6** adjective, **7** interjection.

well·be·ing (wel′bē′ing), welfare; health and happiness: *Our mayor and city council have concern for the well-being of the citizens. noun.*

well-bred (wel′bred′), well brought up; having or showing good manners. *adjective.*

well-known (wel′nōn′), **1** clearly known; familiar: *a well-known fact, a well-known performer.* **2** generally or widely known; famous: *a well-known actor. adjective.*

well-man·nered (wel′man′ərd), polite; courteous: *A well-mannered person always remembers to say "please" and "thank you." adjective.*

well-nigh (wel′nī′), very nearly; almost: *It was well-nigh midnight before we arrived home. adverb.*

well-to-do (wel′tə dü′), having enough money to live well; prosperous. *adjective.*

welt (welt), a streak or ridge made on the skin, often by a blow. *noun.*

went (went). See **go.** *I went home promptly after school. verb.*

wept (wept). See **weep.** *The children wept over the loss of their dog. verb.*

were (wėr). *Were is a form of* **be.** *Once upon a time there were dragons. They were going to finish early. Our plans for a picnic were upset by the rain. verb.*

we're (wir), we are.

weren't (wėrnt), were not.

were·wolf (wir′wùlf′), (in stories) a person who changes into a wolf at certain times. *noun, plural* **were·wolves** (wir′wùlvz′).

west (west), **1** the direction of the sunset. **2** toward the west; farther toward the west: *Walk west three blocks.* **3** coming from the west: *a warm west wind.* **4** in the west: *The kitchen is in the west wing of the house.* **5** the part of any country toward the west. **6 the West, a** the western part of the United States. **b** the countries in Europe and America as distinguished from those in Asia. 1,5,6 *noun,* 2-4 *adjective,* 2 *adverb.*

west of, farther west than: *Kansas is west of Pennsylvania.*

West Bank, part of Jordan west of the Jordan River. It has been controlled by Israel since 1967.

west·er·ly (wes′tər lē), **1** toward the west: *They were heading in a westerly direction.* **2** from the west: *a westerly wind. adjective, adverb.*

west·ern (wes′tərn), **1** toward the west: *We sailed to the western shore of the island.* **2** from the west: *There is a western wind blowing today.* **3** of or in the west: *Wyoming is one of our western states.* **4 Western, a** of or in the western part of the United States. **b** of or in the countries in Europe or America. **5** a story, motion picture, or television show about life in the western part of the United States, especially cowboy life. 1-4 *adjective,* 5 *noun.*

West Germany, a former country in Europe.

West Indies, islands in the Atlantic Ocean between Florida and South America.

West Virginia, one of the southeastern states of the United States. *Abbreviation:* W.Va. or WV *Capital:* Charleston.

[*West Virginia* got its name from the state of Virginia. After the beginning of the Civil War, the western part of the state of Virginia formed its own government. It became a separate state in 1863.]

west·ward (west′wərd), toward the west; west: *I walked westward. The orchard is on the westward slope of the hill. adverb, adjective.*

west·wards (west′wərdz), westward. *adverb.*

wet (wet), **1** covered or soaked with water or other liquid: *wet hands, a wet sponge.* **2** not yet dry: *Don't touch wet paint.* **3** to make wet: *Wet the cloth and wipe off the window.* **4** rainy: *wet weather.* **5** wetness; rain: *Come in out of the wet.* 1,2,4 *adjective,* **wet·ter, wet·test;** 3 *verb,* **wets, wet** or **wet·ted, wet·ting;** 5 *noun.*

we've (wēv), we have.

whack (hwak), **1** a sharp, noisy blow: *She hit the ball with a whack.* **2** to strike with such a blow: *The batter whacked at the ball and hit it out of the park.* 1 *noun,* 2 *verb.*

whale[1] (hwāl), a very large animal that lives in the sea. Whales look like fish but are really mammals and breathe air. *noun, plural* **whales** or **whale.**

whale[2] (hwāl), to whip severely; beat; thrash. *verb,* **whales, whaled, whal·ing.**

whales
1. blue whale—up to 100 feet (30 meters) long
2. humpback whale—about 45 feet (24 meters) long
3. Minke whale—about 28 feet (8 meters) long
4. sperm whale—about 50 feet (15 meters) long

whale·bone (hwāl′bōn′), an elastic, horny substance growing in place of teeth in the upper jaw of certain whales. Thin strips of whalebone were used for stiffening in clothing. *noun.*

whal·er (hwā′lər), **1** a hunter of whales. **2** a ship used for hunting and catching whales. *noun.*

whal·ing (hwā′ling), the hunting and catching of whales. *noun.*

wharf (hwôrf), a platform built on the shore or out from the shore, beside which ships can load and unload. *noun, plural* **wharves** (hwôrvz) or **wharfs.**

what (hwot), **1** *What is used in asking questions about persons or things. What is your name? What time is it?* **2** that which: *I know what you mean. Put* back what money is left. **3** whatever; anything that; any that: *Do what you please. Take what supplies you will need.* **4** how much; how: *What does it matter?* **5** *What* is often used to show surprise, liking, dislike, or other feeling. *What a pity! What happy times! What! Are you late again?* 1-3 *pronoun*, 1-3,5 *adjective*, 4,5 *adverb*, 5 *interjection*.

what·ev·er (hwot ev′ər), **1** anything that: *Do whatever you like.* **2** any person or thing that; any: *Take whatever books you need.* **3** no matter what: *Do it, whatever happens. Whatever excuse you make will not be accepted.* **4** *Whatever* is used for emphasis instead of *what. Whatever do you mean?* 1,3,4 *pronoun*, 2,3 *adjective*.

what's (hwots), **1** what is: *What's the latest news?* **2** what has: *What's been going on here lately?*

what·so·ev·er (hwot′sō ev′ər), whatever. *pronoun, adjective.*

wheat (hwēt), the grain of a kind of cereal grass, or the plant that it grows on. The grain is used to make flour. *noun.*

whee·dle (hwē′dl), **1** to persuade by flattery, smooth words, or caresses; coax: *The children wheedled their parents into letting them go to the picnic.* **2** to get by wheedling: *They finally wheedled the secret out of me. verb,* **whee·dles, whee·dled, whee·dling.**

wheel (hwēl), **1** a round frame that turns on its center. **2** anything round like a wheel or moving like one. A ship's wheel is used in steering. Clay is shaped into dishes on a potter's wheel. **3** to turn: *She wheeled around when I called her name.* **4** to move on wheels: *I wheeled the load of bricks on the wheelbarrow.* 1,2 *noun*, 3,4 *verb.*

at the wheel, at the steering wheel of an automobile.

wheel and axle, an axle on which a wheel is fastened. It is used to lift weights by winding a rope onto the axle as the wheel is turned.

wheel and axle

wheel·bar·row (hwēl′bar′ō), a small vehicle which has one wheel at the front and two handles at the back. A wheelbarrow holds a small load which one person can push. *noun.*

wheel·chair (hwēl′cher′ or hwēl′char′), a chair on wheels, used by people who are sick or unable to walk. A wheelchair can be moved by the person sitting in it. *noun.*

wheel·ie (hwē′lē), a stunt in which a moving bicycle, motorcycle, or car is balanced only on its back wheel or wheels. *noun.*

a hat	i it	oi oil	ch child		a in about
ā age	ī ice	ou out	ng long		e in taken
ä far	o hot	u cup	sh she	ə =	i in pencil
e let	ō open	u̇ put	th thin		o in lemon
ē equal	ô order	ü rule	ŦH then		u in circus
ėr term			zh measure		

wheeze (hwēz), **1** to breathe with difficulty and a whistling sound. **2** a whistling sound caused by difficult breathing. **3** to make a sound like this: *The old engine wheezed.* 1,3 *verb,* **wheez·es, wheezed, wheez·ing;** 2 *noun.*

whelk (hwelk), a sea animal with a spiral shell. One kind is used for food in Europe. *noun.*

whelks—The shells are 2 to 3 inches (6 to 8 centimeters) long.

when (hwen), **1** at what time: *When does school close?* **2** at the time that: *Stand up when your name is called.* **3** at any time that: *The dog comes when it is called.* **4** at which time; and then: *We had just started on our walk when it began to rain.* **5** although: *We have only three books when we need five.* **6** what time; which time: *Since when have they had a car?* 1 *adverb*, 2-5 *conjunction*, 6 *pronoun.*

when·ev·er (hwen ev′ər), when; at whatever time; at any time that: *Please come whenever you wish. You may come whenever possible. conjunction, adverb.*

where (hwer *or* hwar), **1** in what place; at what place: *Where do you live? Where is she?* **2** to what place: *Where are you going?* **3** from what place: *Where did you get that story?* **4** what place: *Where did it come from?* **5** in which; at which: *That is the house where I was born.* **6** to which: *I know the place where he is going.* **7** in what way; in what respect: *Where is the harm in trying?* **8** in the place in which; at the place at which: *Your coat is where you left it.* **9** to the place to which: *I will go where you go.* 1-3,7 *adverb*, 4 *noun*, 5,6,8,9 *conjunction.*

where·a·bouts (hwer′ə bouts′ *or* hwar′ə bouts′), **1** where; near what place: *Whereabouts are my books?* **2** a place where a person or thing is: *Do you know the whereabouts of the cottage?* 1 *adverb, conjunction*, 2 *noun.*

where·as (hwer az′ *or* hwar az′), but; while; on the contrary: *Some children like school, whereas*

W

others do not like school at all. conjunction.

where·by (hwer bī′ or hwar bī′), by what; by which: *There is no other way whereby she can do it. adverb, conjunction.*

where·up·on (hwer′ə pôn′ or hwar′ə pôn′), at which; after which: *He handed me a box, whereupon I opened it. conjunction.*

wher·ev·er (hwer ev′ər or hwar ev′ər), where; to whatever place; in whatever place: *Sit wherever you like. Wherever did he go? conjunction, adverb.*

whet (hwet), **1** to sharpen by rubbing: *to whet a knife.* **2** to make keen or eager: *The smell of food whetted my appetite. An exciting story whets your interest. verb,* **whets, whet·ted, whet·ting.**

wheth·er (hweŦH′ər), **1** *Whether* is used in expressing choices. *It matters little whether we go or stay. He does not know whether to work or rest.* **2** if: *He asked whether he might be excused.* **3** either: *Whether sick or well, she is always cheerful. conjunction.*

whew (hwyü), a word expressing surprise or dismay: *Whew! it's cold! interjection.*

whey (hwā), the watery part of milk that separates from the curd when milk sours or when cheese is made. *noun.*

which (hwich), **1** *Which* is used in asking questions about persons or things. *Which is the best plan? Which book do you want to read?* **2** *Which* is also used in connecting a group of words with some other word in the sentence. *Read the book which you have. Be careful which way you turn.* **3** the one that; any that: *Here are three boxes. Choose which you like best.* **1-3** *pronoun,* **1,2** *adjective.*

which·ev·er (hwich ev′ər), **1** any one; any that: *Take whichever you want. Buy whichever hat you like.* **2** no matter which: *Whichever you choose will be fine. Whichever side wins, I shall be satisfied. pronoun, adjective.*

whiff (hwif), **1** a slight puff; gust; breath: *A whiff of smoke blew in my face.* **2** a slight smell; a puff of air having an odor: *I took a whiff of the rose. noun.*

while (hwīl), **1** time; space of time: *They kept us waiting a long while. The mail came a while ago.* **2** during the time that; in the time that; as: *While I was speaking, he said nothing. Summer is pleasant while it lasts.* **3** although: *While I like the color of the hat, I do not like its shape.* **4** to pass or spend in some easy or pleasant manner: *We whiled away the day at the beach.* **1** *noun,* **2,3** *conjunction,* **4** *verb,* **whiles, whiled, whil·ing.** **worth one's while,** worth one's time, attention, or effort: *If you help me with the painting, I'll make it worth your while—I'll pay you ten dollars.*

whim (hwim), a sudden fancy or notion: *I had a whim to take a plane somewhere. noun.*

whim·per (hwim′pər), **1** to cry with low, broken sounds, in the way that a sick child or dog does. **2** a whimpering cry. **1** *verb,* **2** *noun.*

whim·si·cal (hwim′zə kəl), having many odd notions or fancies; fanciful; odd: *a whimsical drawing of a boy on a stork. adjective.*

whine (hwīn), **1** to make a low, complaining cry or sound: *The dog whined to go out with us.* **2** a low, complaining cry or sound. **3** to complain in a cross, childish way: *Some people are always whining about trifles.* **1,3** *verb,* **whines, whined, whin·ing;** **2** *noun.*

whin·ny (hwin′ē), **1** the sound that a horse makes. **2** to make such a sound. **1** *noun, plural* **whin·nies;** **2** *verb,* **whin·nies, whin·nied, whin·ny·ing.**

whip (hwip), **1** a thing to strike or beat with, usually a stick or handle with a lash at the end. **2** to strike; beat: *The jockey whipped the horse to make it go faster.* **3** to move, put, or pull quickly and suddenly: *She whipped off her coat.* **4** to defeat in a fight or contest: *She whipped her opponent in the election.* **5** to beat cream, eggs, or the like to a froth. **1** *noun,* **2-5** *verb,* **whips, whipped, whip·ping.**

whip·lash (hwip′lash′), **1** the lash of a whip. **2** an injury to the neck caused by a sudden jolt that snaps the head backward and then forward. A driver whose car is hit hard from behind may suffer whiplash. *noun, plural* **whip·lash·es.**

whippoorwill—about 10 inches (25 centimeters) long

whip·poor·will (hwip′ər wil′), a North American bird whose call sounds somewhat like its name. It is active at night or twilight. *noun.*

whir (hwėr), **1** a noise that sounds like whir-r-r: *the whir of machinery.* **2** to move quickly with such

whimsical

a noise: *The motor whirs.* **1** *noun,* **2** *verb,* **whirs, whirred, whir·ring.** Also spelled **whirr.**

whirl (hwėrl), **1** to turn or swing round and round; spin: *The leaves whirled in the wind.* **2** to move round and round: *to whirl a lasso. We whirled about the room.* **3** to move or carry quickly: *We were whirled away in an airplane.* **4** a whirling movement: *The dancer suddenly made a whirl.* **5** a dizzy or confused condition: *My thoughts are in a whirl.* **1-3** *verb,* **4,5** *noun.*

whirl·i·gig (hwėr′li gig′), a toy that whirls or spins. *noun.*

whirligig

whirl·pool (hwėrl′pül′), a current of water whirling round and round rapidly and violently. *noun.*

whirl·wind (hwėrl′wind′), **1** a current of air whirling violently round and round; whirling storm of wind. **2** very fast; marked by great speed: *a whirlwind tour of several foreign countries.* **1** *noun,* **2** *adjective.*

whirr (hwėr). See **whir.** *noun, verb.*

whisk (hwisk), **1** to sweep or brush from a surface: *She whisked the crumbs from the table.* **2** a quick sweep: *He brushed away the dirt with a few whisks of the broom.* **3** to move quickly: *The mouse whisked into its hole. I whisked the letter out of sight.* **4** a light, quick movement. **5** to beat cream, eggs, or the like to a froth. **1,3,5** *verb,* **2,4** *noun.*

whisk broom, a small broom for brushing clothes.

whisk·er (hwis′kər), **1** one of the hairs growing on a man's face. **2 whiskers,** the hair or part of a beard that grows on a man's cheeks. **3** a long, stiff hair growing near the mouth of a cat, rat, or other animal. *noun.*

whis·key (hwis′kē), a strong alcoholic drink made from such grains as rye, barley, or corn. *noun, plural* **whis·keys.**

whis·ky (hwis′kē), whiskey. *noun, plural* **whis·kies.**

whis·per (hwis′pər), **1** to speak very softly and low. **2** a very soft, low spoken sound. **3** to speak to in a whisper: *I whispered to my friend in class.* **4** to

a hat	**i** it	**oi** oil	**ch** child	a in about
ā age	**ī** ice	**ou** out	**ng** long	e in taken
ä far	**o** hot	**u** cup	**sh** she	ə = i in pencil
e let	**ō** open	**ù** put	**th** thin	o in lemon
ē equal	**ô** order	**ü** rule	**ҭн** then	u in circus
ėr term			**zh** measure	

make a soft, rustling sound: *The wind whispered in the pines.* **5** a soft, rustling sound: *The wind was so gentle that we could hear the whisper of the leaves.* **1,3,4** *verb,* **2,5** *noun.*

whis·tle (hwis′əl), **1** to make a clear, shrill sound by forcing breath through one's teeth or through rounded lips: *The girl whistled and her dog ran to her.* **2** a sound made by whistling. **3** an instrument for making whistling sounds. Whistles usually consist of a tube through which air or steam is blown. **4** to blow a whistle: *The policeman whistled for the automobile to stop. The engineer whistled to warn the people at the train crossing.* **5** to produce by whistling: *to whistle a tune.* **6** to move with a shrill sound: *The wind whistled around the house.* **1,4-6** *verb,* **whis·tles, whis·tled, whis·tling; 2,3** *noun.*

white (hwīt), **1** the color of snow, salt, or the paper on which this book is printed. **2** having this color: *My grandparents have white hair.* **3** the part that is white or whitish: *Take the whites of four eggs.* **4** pale: *They turned white with fear.* **5** light-colored: *a white wine, white meat.* **6** having a light-colored skin. **7** a person who has light-colored skin. **8** snowy: *We had a white Christmas.* **1,3,7** *noun,* **2,4-6,8** *adjective,* **whit·er, whit·est.**

white blood cell, a colorless cell in the blood that destroys disease germs.

white·cap (hwīt′kap′), a wave with a foaming white crest. *noun.*

whitecaps

white flag, a plain white flag that means "We have quit fighting," or "We give up."

White·horse (hwīt′hôrs′), the capital of Yukon Territory, Canada. *noun.*

white-hot (hwīt′hot′), white with heat; extremely hot: *The coals were white-hot.* *adjective.*

White House, 1 the official residence of the President of the United States, in Washington,

W

D.C. **2** the office, authority, or opinion of the President of the United States.

white lie, a lie about some small matter; polite or harmless lie: *I told a white lie about liking his painting.*

whit·en (hwīt′n), to make white; become white: *Sunshine helps to whiten clothes. A person's hair whitens with age. verb.*

white·wash (hwīt′wosh′), **1** a liquid for whitening walls, woodwork, or other surfaces. Whitewash is usually made of lime and water. **2** to whiten with whitewash. **3** to cover up the faults or mistakes of: *They tried to whitewash the crime.* 1 *noun,* 2,3 *verb.*

whit·ish (hwī′tish), somewhat white. *adjective.*

whit·tle (hwit′l), **1** to cut shavings or chips from wood with a knife, usually for fun. **2** to cut or shape with a knife: *The class learned how to whittle animals from wood. verb,* **whit·tles, whit·tled, whit·tling.**

whiz (hwiz), **1** to move or rush with a humming or hissing sound: *An arrow whizzed past his head.* **2** a very clever person; expert: *a computer whiz.* 1 *verb,* **whiz·zes, whizzed, whiz·zing;** 2 *noun,* plural **whiz·zes.**

who (hü), **1** *Who* is used in asking questions about persons. *Who goes there? Who is your friend? Who told you?* **2** *Who* is also used in connecting a group of words with some word that refers to a person in the sentence. *The girl who spoke is my best friend. We saw people who were working in the fields.* **3** the person that; any person that; one that: *Who is not for us is against us. pronoun.*

whoa (hwō *or* wō), stop: *"Whoa there!" said the cowgirl to her horse. interjection.*

who'd (hüd), **1** who had. **2** who would.

who·ev·er (hü ev′ər), **1** who; any person that: *Whoever wants the book may have it.* **2** no matter who: *Whoever else leaves you, I won't. pronoun.*

whole (hōl), **1** having all its parts; complete: *They gave us a whole set of dishes.* **2** full; entire: *He worked the whole day. We ate the whole melon.* **3** all of a thing; the total: *Three thirds make a whole.* **4** in one piece: *The dog swallowed the meat whole.* 1,2,4 *adjective,* 3 *noun.*

as a whole, as one complete thing; altogether: *The group as a whole protested.*

on the whole, 1 considering everything: *On the whole, it appears that our team doesn't have a chance to win the championship.* **2** generally; mostly: *On the whole, I enjoy sports.*

whole·heart·ed (hōl′här′tid), enthusiastic; earnest; hearty; devoted: *The school gave the team its wholehearted support. adjective.*

whole number, a number such as 1, 2, 3, 4, 5, and so on, which is not a fraction or a mixed number. 15 and 106 are whole numbers; ½ and ⅞ are fractions; 1⅜ and 23⅔ are mixed numbers.

whole·sale (hōl′sāl′), **1** the sale of goods in large quantities, usually to storekeepers or others who will in turn sell them to users: *Our grocer buys at wholesale and sells at retail.* **2** having to do with selling in large quantities: *a wholesale*

merchant, *a wholesale price of $20.* **3** to sell in large quantities: *They wholesale these jackets at $10 each.* 1 *noun,* 2 *adjective,* 3 *verb,* **whole·sales, whole·saled, whole·sal·ing.**

whole·some (hōl′səm), **1** healthful; good for the health: *Milk is a wholesome food.* **2** healthy-looking; suggesting health: *a clean, wholesome face.* **3** good for the mind or morals: *The students had a wholesome interest in learning. adjective.*

whole-wheat (hōl′hwēt′), **1** made of the entire wheat kernel: *whole-wheat flour.* **2** made from whole-wheat flour: *whole-wheat bread. adjective.*

who'll (hül), **1** who will. **2** who shall.

whol·ly (hō′lē), completely; entirely; totally: *The patient was wholly cured. adverb.*

whom (hüm), what person; which person. *Whom is a form of who, just as him is a form of he. Whom do you like best? He does not know whom to believe. The girl to whom I spoke is my cousin. pronoun.*

whoop (hüp), **1** a loud cry or shout: *The winner gave a whoop of joy.* **2** to shout loudly. **3** the loud, gasping sound a person with whooping cough makes after a fit of coughing. **4** to make this noise. 1,3 *noun,* 2,4 *verb.*

whoop·ing cough (hüp′ing kôf′), a disease most often of children that causes fits of coughing that end with a loud, gasping sound. Unless you are vaccinated against whooping cough, you can catch the disease if you are around someone who has it.

whooping crane, a large white crane having a loud, hoarse cry. It is now almost extinct.

whoosh (hwush *or* hwüsh), **1** a dull, soft, hissing sound like that of something rushing through the air. **2** to make a sound like this. 1 *noun,* 2 *verb.*

whop·per (hwop′ər), **1** something very large: *The fish I caught was a whopper.* **2** a big lie: *She was punished for telling such a whopper. noun.*

who's (hüz), **1** who is. **2** who has.

whose (hüz), of whom; of which: *The girl whose work got the prize is very talented. Whose book is this? pronoun.*

why (hwī), **1** for what reason: *Why did the baby cry? I do not know why they are late.* **2** because of which: *That is the reason why we left.* **3** *Why* is sometimes used to show surprise, doubt, or just to fill in, without adding any important meaning to what is said. *Why, it's all gone! Why, yes, I will do it for you if you wish.* 1 *adverb,* 1,2 *conjunction,* 3 *interjection.*

WI, Wisconsin (used with postal Zip Code).

wick (wik), a cord of twisted thread on an oil lamp or candle. When the wick is lit, it draws the oil or melted wax up to be burned. *noun.*

wick·ed (wik′id), **1** bad; evil; sinful: *a wicked person, wicked deeds.* **2** mischievous; playfully sly: *a wicked smile.* **3** unpleasant; severe: *A wicked snowstorm swept through the state. adjective.*

wick·ed·ness (wik′id nis), **1** sin; being wicked. **2** a wicked thing or act. *noun,* plural **wick·ed·ness·es.**

wick·er (wik′ər), **1** thin twigs or other easily bent material woven together to make baskets and furniture. **2** made of wicker: *a wicker chair.* **1** *noun,* **2** *adjective.*

Word History

wicker *Wicker* comes from a Scandinavian word meaning "a willow branch." Willow branches are commonly used in wicker furniture.

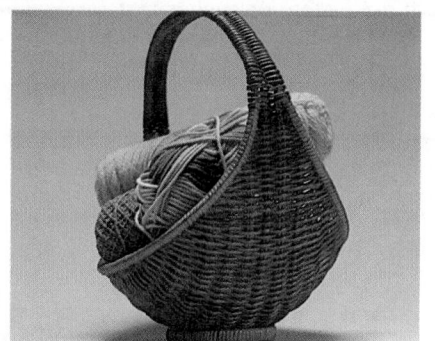

wicker
(definition 2)

a hat	i it	oi oil	ch child	a in about
ā age	ī ice	ou out	ng long	e in taken
ä far	o hot	u cup	sh she	ə = { i in pencil
e let	ō open	u̇ put	th thin	o in lemon
ē equal	ô order	ü rule	ŦH then	u in circus
ėr term			zh measure	

wick·et (wik′it), (in croquet) a wire arch stuck in the ground to knock the ball through. *noun.*

wide (wīd), **1** filling much space from side to side; not narrow; broad: *a wide street. The ship sailed across the wide ocean. They went forth into the wide world.* **2** extending a certain distance from side to side: *The door is three feet wide.* **3** over a large space or region: *to travel far and wide.* **4** having great range; including many different things: *A trip around the world gives wide experience.* **5** far open: *The child stared with wide eyes.* **6** to the full extent: *Open your mouth wide. The gates stand wide open.* **7** far from a named point or object: *The club raised little money; it was wide of its goal. The shot was wide of the mark.* **1,2,4,5,7** *adjective,* **wid·er, wid·est; 3,6** *adverb.*

wide-a·wake (wīd′ə wāk′), **1** fully awake; with the eyes wide open. **2** alert; knowing: *The mountain climber was wide-awake to the dangers of the climb. adjective.*

wide-eyed (wīd′īd′), with the eyes wide open: *The children watched the baby rabbits with wide-eyed interest. adjective.*

wide·ly (wīd′lē), to a wide extent: *It was once widely believed that butter soothed burns. That actress is widely known. adverb.*

wid·en (wīd′n), to make or become wide or wider: *We widened the path through the forest. The river widens as it flows. verb.*

wide·spread (wīd′spred′), **1** spread widely: *widespread wings.* **2** spread over a wide space: *a widespread flood.* **3** occurring in many places or among many persons far apart: *a widespread belief. adjective.*

wid·ow (wid′ō), **1** a woman whose husband is dead and who has not married again. **2** to make a widow of: *She was widowed in May.* **1** *noun,* **2** *verb.*

wid·ow·er (wid′ō ər), a man whose wife is dead and who has not married again. *noun.*

width (width), **1** how wide a thing is; distance across; breadth: *The room is 12 feet in width.* **2** a piece of a certain width: *Two widths of cloth will make the curtains. noun.*

wield (wēld), to hold and use; manage; control: *The worker wielded a hammer. A writer wields the pen. The people wield the power in a democracy. verb.*

wicket

wie·ner (wē′nər), a reddish sausage; frankfurter. *noun.*
[*Wiener* comes from a German word meaning "of Vienna." This type of sausage is a specialty of Vienna, a city in Austria.]

wife (wīf), a married woman. *noun, plural* **wives.**
[*Wife* comes from an earlier English word, which originally meant "woman."]

wig (wig), an artificial covering of natural or false hair for the head. *noun.*

wig·gle (wig′əl), **1** to wriggle; move with short, quick movements from side to side: *The puppy wiggled out of my arms.* **2** such a movement. **1** *verb,* **wig·gles, wig·gled, wig·gling; 2** *noun.*

wig·gly (wig′lē), **1** moving from side to side with quick, short movements: *I couldn't hold the wiggly puppy.* **2** having curves or waves; wavy: *There were wiggly lines on the wallpaper. adjective,* **wig·gli·er, wig·gli·est.**

wig·wag (wig′wag′), **1** to signal by movements of arms, flags, or lights, according to a code. **2** such signaling. **1** *verb,* **wig·wags, wig·wagged, wig·wag·ging; 2** *noun.*

wig·wam (wig′wom), a hut of poles covered with

wigwam

W

bark, mats, or skins, made by certain North American Indians. *noun.*

wild (wīld), **1** living or growing naturally; not grown, tamed, or cultivated by people: *The tiger is a wild animal.* **2 wilds,** wild country. **3** not in proper control or order; uncontrolled; not disciplined: *The children were wild during the teacher's absence.* **4** not civilized; savage: *He is reading about the wild tribes of ancient times in Europe.* **5** violent: *a wild snowstorm. Wild waves came roaring onto the shore.* **6** rash; crazy: *The child had the wild idea that horses could fly.* **7** very eager; enthusiastic: *They were wild about animals.* **8** far from the mark: *The shortstop made a wild throw to first base.* **9** in a wild manner; to a wild degree: *Daisies grew wild in the field.* 1,3-8 *adjective,* 2 *noun,* 9 *adverb.*

wild·cat (wīld′kat′), a wild animal like a common cat, but larger. A lynx is one kind of wildcat. *noun.*

wil·der·ness (wil′dər nis), a wild place; region with no people living in it. *noun, plural* **wil·der·ness·es.**

wild·fire (wīld′fīr′), a fire that is hard to put out. *noun.*
like wildfire, very rapidly: *The news spread like wildfire.*

wild·flow·er (wīld′flou′ər), any flowering plant that grows wild in woods or fields. *noun.*

wild fowl, birds ordinarily hunted, such as wild ducks or geese, partridges, quails, and pheasants.

wild·life (wīld′līf′), wild animals and plants: *The campers saw many kinds of wildlife. noun.*

will[1] (wil), **1** am going to; is going to; are going to: *He will come tomorrow.* **2** am willing to; is willing to; are willing to: *I will go if you do.* **3** to be able to; can: *The pail will hold four gallons.* **4** must: *Don't argue with me; you will do it at once. verb, past tense* **would.**

will[2] (wil), **1** the power of the mind to decide and do: *A good leader must have a strong will.* **2** to decide by using this power; use the will: *She willed to keep awake.* **3** purpose; determination: *Although very ill, the patient had the will to live.* **4** a wish; desire: *Elections express the will of the people.* **5** a legal statement of a person's wishes about what shall be done with property left after the person's death. **6** to give by such a statement: *They willed all their property to their children.* 1,3-5 *noun,* 2,6 *verb.*

will·ful (wil′fəl), **1** wanting or taking one's own way; stubborn. **2** intended; done on purpose: *willful murder, willful waste. adjective.*

will·ing (wil′ing), **1** ready; consenting: *He is willing to wait.* **2** cheerfully ready: *She is a willing helper. adjective.*

wil·low (wil′ō), a kind of tree or shrub with tough, slender branches and narrow leaves. The branches of most willows bend easily and are used to make furniture and baskets. *noun.*

will·pow·er (wil′pou′ər), strength of will; firmness; determination: *She had the willpower not*

to go along with silly suggestions. *noun.*

wilt (wilt), **1** to become limp and drooping; wither: *Flowers wilt when they do not get enough water.* **2** to lose strength and vigor: *The hikers wilted after walking 15 miles. verb.*

wil·y (wī′lē), tricky; cunning; crafty; sly: *The wily thief got away. adjective,* **wil·i·er, wil·i·est.**

win (win), **1** to be successful over others; get victory or success: *We all hope our team will win.* **2** to get victory or success in: *He won the race.* **3** a success; victory: *We had five wins and no defeats.* **4** to get by effort, ability, or skill; gain: *to win fame, to win a prize.* 1,2,4 *verb,* **wins, won, win·ning;** 3 *noun.*

wince (wins), to draw back suddenly; flinch slightly: *I winced when the dentist's drill touched my tooth. verb,* **winc·es, winced, winc·ing.**

winch (winch), a machine for lifting or pulling, turned by hand with a crank or by an engine. *noun, plural* **winch·es.**

winch

wind[1] (wind), **1** air in motion. The wind varies in force from a slight breeze to a strong gale. *Winds of ninety miles an hour were blowing.* **2** breath; power of breathing: *A runner needs good wind.* **3** to put out of breath; cause difficulty in breathing:

willful (definition 1)
The **willful** donkey would not obey its owner.

Walking up the steep hill winded the hiker.
1,2 *noun,* 3 *verb.*

get wind of, to find out about; get a hint of: *Don't let Mother get wind of our plans for a surprise party on her birthday.*

wind[2] (wīnd), **1** to move this way and that; go in a crooked way; change direction; turn: *A brook winds through the woods. We wound our way through the narrow streets.* **2** to fold, wrap, or place about something: *She wound her arms around her new puppy.* **3** to cover with something put, wrapped, or folded around: *The patient's arm was wound with bandages.* **4** to roll into a ball or on a spool: *We took turns winding yarn. Thread comes wound on spools.* **5** to twist or turn around something: *The vine winds around a pole.* **6** to make some machine go by turning some part of it: *to wind a clock. verb,* **winds, wound, wind·ing.**

wind up, 1 to end; settle; conclude: *The committee wound up its meeting in time for dinner.* **2** (in baseball) to make a swinging movement of the arms while twisting the body just before pitching the ball.

wind·break (wind′brāk′), a shelter from the wind: *We pitched our tent next to the stone wall, so that it would serve as a windbreak. noun.*

Wind·break·er (wind′brā′kər), a trademark for a short jacket of wool, nylon, or the like, with a tight-fitting band at the waist and cuffs. *noun.*

wind·fall (wind′fôl′), **1** fruit blown down by the wind. **2** an unexpected piece of good luck: *Finding this job was a windfall. noun.*

wind·ing (wīn′ding), bending; turning: *narrow, winding streets. adjective.*

wind instrument (wind), a musical instrument sounded by blowing air into it. Horns, flutes, and trombones are wind instruments.

wind·lass (wind′ləs), a machine for pulling or lifting things. The windlass is a kind of winch used to hoist water from a well or an anchor out of the water. *noun, plural* **wind·lass·es.**

wind·mill (wind′mil′), a mill or machine worked by the action of the wind upon a wheel of vanes or sails mounted on a tower. Windmills are used to pump water, grind grain, and produce electricity. *noun.*

win·dow (win′dō), an opening in an outer wall or roof of a building, or in a vehicle, that lets in air or light. It is usually a wooden or metal frame that surrounds panes of glass or plastic. *noun.* [*Window* comes from two old Norse words meaning "wind" and "eye."]

win·dow·pane (win′dō pān′), a piece of glass or plastic in a window. *noun.*

win·dow·sill (win′dō sil′), a piece of wood or stone across the bottom of a window. *noun.*

wind·pipe (wind′pīp′), the passage by which air is carried from the throat to the lungs; trachea. *noun.*

wind·shield (wind′shēld′), a sheet of glass or plastic on the front of automobiles, motorcycles, and other vehicles, to keep the wind off the driver or passengers. *noun.*

wind·storm (wind′stôrm′), a storm with much wind but little or no rain. *noun.*

wind·swept (wind′swept′), open to the full force of the wind: *a windswept hillside. adjective.*

wind·up (wīnd′up′), **1** a winding up; end: *The windup of the movie was very exciting.* **2** a series of swinging and twisting movements of the arm and body made by a baseball pitcher just before pitching the ball. *noun.*

wind·y (win′dē), having much wind: *a windy street, windy weather. adjective,* **wind·i·er, wind·i·est.**

wine (wīn), an alcoholic drink made from the fermented juice of grapes or other fruit. *noun.*

wing (wing), **1** one of the movable parts of a bird, insect, or bat used in flying, or a similar part in a bird or insect that does not fly. Birds have one pair of wings; insects have usually two pairs. **2** anything like a wing in shape or use: *the wings of an airplane.* **3** a part that sticks out from the main part of a building: *The house has a wing at each side.* **4** either of the spaces to the right or left of the stage in a theater. **5** a player on either the right or left side of the center in hockey, soccer, and some other games. **6** to fly: *Modern airliners wing from continent to continent.* **7** to wound in the wing or arm: *The bullet winged the bird but did not kill it.* 1-5 *noun,* 6,7 *verb.*

on the wing, in flight.

wing—a bird **on the wing**

winged (wingd *or* wing′id), having wings: *A gnat is a winged insect. adjective.*

wing·spread (wing′spred′), the distance between the tips of the wings when they are spread. *noun.*

wink (wingk), **1** to close the eyes and open them

again quickly: *The bright light made me wink.* **2** to close and open one eye on purpose as a hint or signal: *I winked at my sister to keep still.* **3** a winking: *I gave them a friendly wink.* **4** to twinkle: *The stars winked.* **5** a very short time: *quick as a wink.* 1,2,4 *verb,* 3,5 *noun.*

win·ner (win′ər), a person or thing that wins: *The winner of the contest got a prize. noun.*

win·ning (win′ing), **1** victorious; successful: *a winning team.* **2** charming; attractive: *a winning smile.* **3 winnings,** what is won: *The gamblers pocketed their winnings.* 1,2 *adjective,* 3 *noun.*

Win·ni·peg (win′ə peg), the capital of Manitoba, Canada. *noun.*

win·ter (win′tər), **1** the coldest season of the year; season of the year between fall and spring. **2** of or for the winter; coming in winter: *winter clothes, winter weather.* **3** to pass the winter: *Robins winter in the South.* **4** to keep or feed during winter: *We wintered our cattle in the warm valley.* 1 *noun,* 2 *adjective,* 3,4 *verb.*

win·ter·green (win′tər grēn′), a small evergreen plant with bright-red berries. An oil made from its leaves is used in medicine and candy. *noun.*

win·ter·time (win′tər tīm′), the season of winter: *I like to ski in the wintertime. noun.*

win·try (win′trē), **1** of winter; like winter: *wintry weather, a wintry sky.* **2** not warm or friendly; chilly: *a wintry manner, a wintry smile, a wintry greeting. adjective,* **win·tri·er, win·tri·est.**

wintry (definition 1)—a **wintry** day

wipe (wīp), **1** to rub in order to clean or dry: *We wipe our shoes on the mat. We wipe the dishes with a towel.* **2** to take away, off, or out by rubbing: *Wipe away your tears. I wiped off the dust.* **3** the

act of wiping: *He gave his face a hasty wipe.* 1,2 *verb,* **wipes, wiped, wip·ing;** 3 *noun.*

wipe out, to destroy completely: *Whole cities have been wiped out by volcanoes.*

wip·er (wī′pər), a thing used for wiping: *All cars have windshield wipers. noun.*

wire (wīr), **1** metal drawn out into a thin rod or thread: *a telephone wire.* **2** made of wire: *a wire fence.* **3** to supply with wire: *to wire a house for electricity.* **4** to fasten with wire: *She wired the two pieces together.* **5** telegraph: *He sent a message by wire.* **6** to telegraph: *She wired a birthday greeting.* **7** a telegram: *The news of his arrival came in a wire.* 1,5,7 *noun,* 2 *adjective,* 3,4,6 *verb,* **wires, wired, wir·ing.**

wire·less (wīr′lis), **1** using no wires; transmitting by radio waves instead of by electric wires. **2** radio. 1 *adjective,* 2 *noun, plural* **wire·less·es.**

wire·tap (wīr′tap′), to make a secret connection with telephone or telegraph wires to listen to or to record the messages sent over them: *They wiretapped the phones of the embassy. verb,* **wire·taps, wire·tapped, wire·tap·ping.**

wire·tap·ping (wīr′tap′ing), the making of a secret connection with telephone or telegraph wires to listen to or to record the messages sent over them. *noun.*

wir·ing (wī′ring), a system of wires to carry an electric current. *noun.*

wir·y (wī′rē), **1** like wire: *Our terrier has a wiry coat.* **2** lean, strong, and tough: *The gymnast had a small, wiry body. adjective,* **wir·i·er, wir·i·est.**

Wis., Wisconsin.

Wis·con·sin (wi skon′sən), one of the north central states of the United States. *Abbreviation:* Wis. or WI *Capital:* Madison. *noun.*

[*Wisconsin* may have come from *Ouisconsing,* a French form of the American Indian name of the Wisconsin River.]

wis·dom (wiz′dəm), a being wise; knowledge and good judgment based on experience: *The leader's wisdom guided the group through difficulties. noun.*

wise (wīz), **1** having or showing knowledge and good judgment: *a wise judge, wise advice, wise plans.* **2** having knowledge or information: *The old senator was wise in the ways of politics. adjective,* **wis·er, wis·est.**

wise·crack (wīz′krak′), a witty and sometimes insulting remark or reply. *noun.*

wish (wish), **1** to have a desire; want: *Do you wish to go home? They wished for a new house.* **2** a desire; need: *I have no wish to be rich. What is your wish?* **3** a saying of something desired: *Please give them my best wishes for a happy New Year.* **4** to wish something for someone; have a hope for: *We wish peace for all people. I wish you a happy New Year.* **5** a thing wished for: *She got her wish.* 1,4 *verb,* 2,3,5 *noun, plural* **wish·es.**

wish·bone (wish′bōn′), the forked bone in the front of the breastbone in poultry and other birds. *noun.*

[The wishbone is called this because of the custom of two people making a wish while breaking the bone by pulling on the two ends. It is believed that the person left with the longer piece of bone will get his or her wish.]

wish·ful (wish′fəl), having or expressing a wish; desiring: *His boast about winning the race was only wishful thinking. adjective.*

wisp (wisp), **1** a small bit or bunch of something: *a wisp of fluff, a wisp of hair.* **2** a tiny puff of smoke, steam, or the like: *Wisps of steam rose from the boiling water. noun.*

wisp·y (wis′pē), like a wisp; thin; slight: *wispy feathers, wispy clouds. adjective,* **wisp·i·er, wisp·i·est.**

wis·ter·i·a (wi stir′ē ə), a climbing shrub with large, drooping clusters of purple, blue, or white flowers. *noun.*
[*Wisteria* was named for Caspar Wistar, an American doctor who lived from 1761 to 1818.]

wist·ful (wist′fəl), longing; yearning. *adjective.*

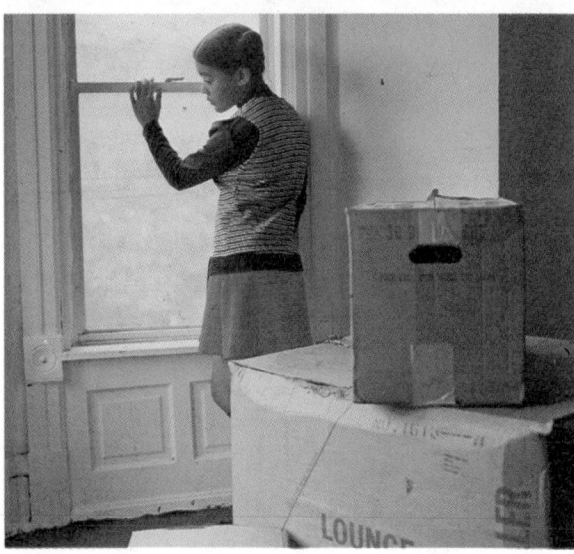
wistful—Her **wistful** expression showed her sadness at moving away.

wit (wit), **1** the power to perceive quickly and express cleverly ideas that are unusual, striking, and amusing: *Her wit made even troubles seem amusing.* **2** a person with such power: *Benjamin Franklin was a wit.* **3** understanding; mind; sense: *People with quick wits learn easily. You can answer the riddle if you keep your wits about you. The beggar did not have wit enough to earn a living. noun.*

witch (wich), **1** a woman that was believed to have magic power. Witches generally used their power to do evil. **2** an ugly old woman. *noun, plural* **witch·es.**

witch·craft (wich′kraft′), what a witch does or is believed to be able to do; magic power. *noun.*

with (wiᴛʜ *or* with). *With* shows that persons or things are taken together in some way. **1** in the company of: *Come with me.* **2** among: *They will mix with the crowd.* **3** having: *He is a man with brains. She received a telegram with good news.* **4** by means of: *I cut the meat with a knife.* **5** using;

showing: *Work with care.* **6** added to: *Do you want sugar with your tea?* **7** in regard to: *We are pleased with the house.* **8** in proportion to: *Her pay increased with her skill.* **9** because of: *The child is shaking with cold.* **10** in the keeping or service of: *Leave the dog with me.* **11** on the side of; for: *They are with us in our plan.* **12** from: *I hate to part with my favorite things.* **13** against: *The English fought with the Germans.* **14** in spite of: *With all his weight he was not a strong man. preposition.*

with·draw (wiᴛʜ drô′ *or* with drô′), **1** to draw back; draw away. **2** to take back; remove: *She withdrew all her savings from the bank.* **3** to go away: *She withdrew from the room. verb,* **with·draws, with·drew, with·drawn, with·draw·ing.**

withdraw (definition 1)—The turtle **withdrew** its head into its shell.

with·draw·al (wiᴛʜ drô′əl *or* with drô′əl), a withdrawing or being withdrawn: *a withdrawal of money from a bank account. noun.*

with·drawn (wiᴛʜ drôn′ *or* with drôn′). See **withdraw.** *She has withdrawn all her savings from the bank. verb.*

with·drew (wiᴛʜ drü′ *or* with drü′). See **withdraw.** *The coach withdrew the player from the game when he was hurt. verb.*

with·er (wiᴛʜ′ər), to make or become dry and lifeless; dry up; fade; shrivel: *The hot sun withers the grass. Flowers wither after they are cut. verb.*

with·held (with held′ *or* wiᴛʜ held′). See **withhold.** *The witness withheld information from the police. verb.*

with·hold (with hōld′ *or* wiᴛʜ hōld′), to refuse to give: *There will be no school play if the principal withholds consent. verb,* **with·holds, with·held, with·hold·ing.**

with·in (wiᴛʜ in′ *or* with in′), **1** not beyond; inside the limits of; not more than: *The task was within*

W

their power. **2** in or into the inner part of; inside of: *By the use of X rays, doctors can see within the body.* **3** in or into the inner part; inside: *The house has been painted within and without.* 1,2 *preposition,* 3 *adverb.*

with·out (wiŦH out′ *or* with out′), **1** with no; not having; free from; lacking: *A cat walks without noise. I drink tea without sugar.* **2** so as to leave out, avoid, or neglect: *She walked past without noticing us.* **3** outside of; beyond: *Children were playing within and without the house.* **4** outside; on the outside: *The house is painted without and within.* 1-3 *preposition,* 4 *adverb.*

with·stand (with stand′ *or* wiŦH stand′), to stand against; hold out against; resist; oppose, especially successfully; endure: *The pioneers had to withstand hardships in their move West. These shoes will withstand hard wear. verb,* **with·stands, with·stood, with·stand·ing.**

with·stood (with stud′ *or* wiŦH stud′). See **withstand.** *The family withstood many hardships. verb.*

wit·less (wit′lis), lacking sense; stupid; foolish: *Crossing the street without looking in both directions is a witless thing to do. adjective.*

wit·ness (wit′nis), **1** a person who saw something happen; spectator: *There were several witnesses to the accident.* **2** to see: *He witnessed the accident.* **3** a person who takes an oath to tell the truth in a court of law. **4** evidence; testimony: *A person who gives false witness in court may be fined or jailed.* **5** to testify to; give evidence of: *Her whole manner witnessed her surprise.* **6** a person who signs a document to show that he or she saw the writer of the document sign it. **7** to sign a document as witness: *to witness a will.* 1,3,4,6 *noun, plural* **wit·ness·es;** 2,5,7 *verb.*

wit·ty (wit′ē), full of wit; clever and amusing: *A witty person makes witty remarks. adjective,* **wit·ti·er, wit·ti·est.**

wives (wīvz), more than one wife. *noun plural.*

wiz·ard (wiz′ərd), **1** a man that was believed to have magic power. **2** a very clever person; expert: *She is a wizard at mathematics. noun.*

wk., week.

wob·ble (wob′əl), **1** to move unsteadily from side to side; shake; tremble: *A baby wobbles when it begins to walk alone.* **2** a wobbling motion. 1 *verb,* **wob·bles, wob·bled, wob·bling;** 2 *noun.*

wob·bly (wob′lē), unsteady; shaky; wavering. *adjective,* **wob·bli·er, wob·bli·est.**

woe (wō), great grief, trouble, or distress: *the woes of sickness and poverty. noun.*

woe·be·gone (wō′bi gôn′), looking sad or unhappy. *adjective.*

woe·ful (wō′fəl), full of woe; sad; sorrowful; wretched: *The lost child had a woeful expression. adjective.*

woke (wōk). See **wake**[1]. *I woke before they did. verb.*

wolf (wulf), **1** a wild animal somewhat like a dog. Wolves sometimes kill sheep and other livestock, but they almost never attack human beings. **2** to

eat greedily: *The starving man wolfed down the food.* 1 *noun, plural* **wolves;** 2 *verb.*

wolf·hound (wulf′hound′), a large dog of any of various kinds once used in hunting wolves. *noun.*

wol·ve·rine *or* **wol·ve·rene** (wul′və rēn′), a heavily built, meat-eating animal, something like a badger, living in the northern parts of the world. *noun.*

wolverine—about 3½ feet (1 meter) long with the tail

wolves (wulvz), more than one wolf. *noun plural.*

wom·an (wum′ən), **1** an adult female person. When a girl grows up, she becomes a woman. **2** a female follower, servant, or employee: *The princess told her woman to wait outside. noun, plural* **wom·en.**
[*Woman* comes from an earlier English word *wifman.* This was formed from words meaning "woman or wife" and "a human being." Look at the word history for *man.*]

wom·an·hood (wum′ən hud), **1** the condition or time of being a woman: *The girl was about to enter womanhood.* **2** the character or qualities of a woman. *noun.*

wom·an·kind (wum′ən kīnd′), women as a group. *noun.*

wom·an·li·ness (wum′ən lē nis), womanly quality; womanly behavior. *noun.*

wom·an·ly (wum′ən lē), having qualities that are by tradition admired in a woman: *womanly sympathy and understanding. adjective.*

wom·en (wim′ən), more than one woman. *noun plural.*

Wom·en's Lib·e·ra·tion (wim′ənz lib′ə rā′shən), the efforts of women to achieve equality for women in all areas of life.

won (wun). See **win.** *Which side won yesterday? We have won four games. verb.*

won·der (wun′dər), **1** a strange and surprising thing or event: *The Grand Canyon is one of the wonders of the world. It is a wonder that he refused such a good offer.* **2** the feeling caused by what is strange and surprising: *The baby looked with wonder at the snow.* **3** to be surprised or astonished: *I shouldn't wonder if she wins the prize.* **4** to be curious about; wish to know: *I wonder what time it is.* 1,2 *noun,* 3,4 *verb.*

won·der·ful (wun′dər fəl), **1** causing wonder; marvelous; remarkable: *a wonderful adventure, the* *wonderful creations of nature.* **2** excellent; splendid; fine: *We had a wonderful time at the party. adjective.*

won·der·ing·ly (wun′dər ing lē), in a curious or surprised way; with wonder: *to look wonderingly at a strange sight. adverb.*

won·der·land (wun′dər land′), a land or place full of wonders. *noun.*

won·der·ment (wun′dər mənt), wonder; surprise: *He stared at the huge bear in wonderment. noun.*

won·drous (wun′drəs), wonderful. *adjective.*

won't (wōnt), will not.

woo (wü), **1** to make love to; seek to marry. **2** to seek to win; try to get: *Some people woo fame; some woo wealth.* **3** to try to persuade. *verb,* **woos, wooed, woo·ing.**

wood (wud), **1** the hard substance beneath the bark of trees and shrubs. Wood is used for making houses, boats, boxes, and furniture. **2** trees cut up for use: *The carpenter brought wood to build a playhouse. Put some wood on the fire.* **3** made of wood; wooden: *a wood house.* **4 woods,** a large number of growing trees; small forest: *We walked through the woods behind the farm.* **1,2,4** *noun,* **3** *adjective.*

wood·chuck (wud′chuk′), a small animal with a thick body, short legs, and a bushy tail; groundhog. Woodchucks grow fat in summer and sleep in their holes in the ground all winter. *noun.*

woodchuck—about 2 feet (60 centimeters) long with the tail

wood·cut·ter (wud′kut·ər), a person who cuts down trees or chops wood. *noun.*

wood·ed (wud′id), covered with trees: *The house stood on a wooded hill. adjective.*

wood·en (wud′n), **1** made of wood. **2** stiff as wood; awkward. **3** dull; lifeless: *a face with a wooden expression. adjective.*

wood·land (wud′lənd), land covered with trees. *noun.*

wood·peck·er (wud′pek·ər), a bird with a hard, pointed bill for pecking holes in trees to get insects. *noun.*

wood·pile (wud′pīl′), a pile of wood, especially wood for fuel. *noun.*

wood·shed (wud′shed′), a shed for storing wood. *noun.*

woods·man (wudz′mən), **1** a person used to life in the woods and skilled in hunting, fishing, trapping, and the like. **2** a person whose work is cutting down trees; lumberjack. *noun, plural* **woods·men.**

wood·wind (wud′wind′), any of a group of wind instruments which were originally made of wood, but are now often made of metal or plastic. Clarinets, flutes, oboes, and bassoons are woodwinds. *noun.*

wood·work (wud′wėrk′), things made of wood; wooden parts inside a house, especially doors, stairs, and moldings. *noun.*

wood·work·ing (wud′wėr′king), a making or shaping things of wood: *He is skilled in woodworking. noun.*

wood·y (wud′ē), **1** having many trees; covered with trees: *a woody hillside.* **2** consisting of wood: *the woody parts of a shrub. adjective,* **wood·i·er, wood·i·est.**

woof (wüf), the threads running from side to side across a woven fabric. The woof crosses the warp. *noun.*

wool (wul), **1** the soft curly hair or fur of sheep and some other animals. **2** short, thick, curly hair. **3** something like wool. **4** yarn, cloth, or garments made of wool: *People in cold climates often wear wool in the winter. noun.*

wool·en (wul′ən), **1** made of wool: *a woolen suit.* **2** cloth made of wool. **3 woolens,** cloth or clothing made of wool: *We put our woolens in plastic bags to protect them against moths.* **4** of wool; having something to do with wool; that makes things from wool: *a woolen mill.* **1,4** *adjective,* **2,3** *noun.*

wool·ly (wul′ē), **1** consisting of wool: *the woolly coat of a sheep.* **2** like wool. **3** covered with wool or

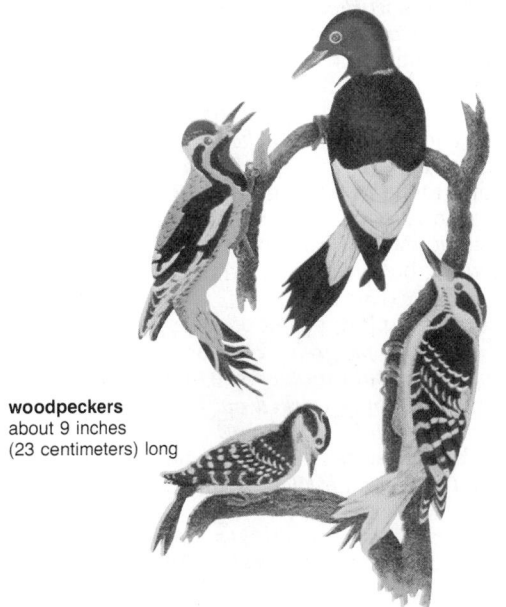

woodpeckers
about 9 inches
(23 centimeters) long

a hat	**i** it	**oi** oil	**ch** child		a in about
ā age	**ī** ice	**ou** out	**ng** long		e in taken
ä far	**o** hot	**u** cup	**sh** she	**ə =**	i in pencil
e let	**ō** open	**ù** put	**th** thin		o in lemon
ē equal	**ô** order	**ü** rule	**ŦH** then		u in circus
ėr term			**zh** measure		

W

wooly | worm

something like it. *adjective,* **wool·li·er, wool·li·est.**

wool·y (wul/ē), woolly. *adjective,* **wool·i·er, wool·i·est.**

word (wėrd), **1** a sound or a group of sounds that has meaning and is a unit of speech. We speak words when we talk. **2** the writing or printing that stands for a word: *This page is filled with words.* **3** **words,** angry talk; quarrel; dispute: *I had sharp words with them.* **4** a short talk: *May I have a word with you?* **5** a brief expression: *The teacher gave us a word of advice.* **6** a command; order: *On a ship, the captain's word is law.* **7** a promise: *She kept her word. He is a man of his word.* **8** news: *I have had no word from them in months.* **9** to put into words: *She worded the message clearly.* 1-8 *noun,* 9 *verb.*

word history, an account or explanation of the origin and history of a word; etymology.

word·ing (wėr/ding), a way of saying a thing; choice of words; use of words: *Careful wording helps you make clear to others what you really mean. noun.*

word·y (wėr/dē), using too many words. *adjective,* **word·i·er, word·i·est.**

wore (wôr). See **wear.** *I wore out my shoes in two months. verb.*

work (wėrk), **1** effort in doing or making something: *Gardening can be hard work.* **2** something to do; occupation; employment: *My friend is out of work.* **3** something made or done; result of effort: *The artist considers that picture to be his greatest work.* **4** that on which effort is put: *We carried our work out onto the porch.* **5** **works,** the moving parts of a machine: *the works of a watch.* **6** to do work; labor: *Most people must work to earn money.* **7** to work for pay; be employed: *She works at an airplane factory.* **8** to put effort on: *They worked their farm with success.* **9** to act; operate: *This pump will not work. The plan worked well.* **10** to cause to do work: *That company works its employees hard.* **11** to make or get by effort: *I worked my way across the room in the dark. He worked his way through college.* **12** to bring about; cause; do: *The plan worked harm.* **13** to go slowly or with effort: *The ship worked up the rocky coast.* **14** to become up, round, loose, or the like: *The handle has worked loose.* **15** to make: *She worked a piece of copper into a tray.* **16** the result of a force moving an object through a distance. In science, work is said to be done only if something moves. Pushing against a wall does not do work, but lifting your hand does. 1-5,16 *noun,* 6-15 *verb.*

work out, 1 to plan; develop: *Each group must work out its own program.* **2** to solve: *I have to work out a few math problems.* **3** to turn out; succeed: *Everything worked out fine. My part-time job after school didn't work out.*

work·a·ble (wėr/kə bəl), able to be used or put into effect: *a workable plan, workable theories. adjective.*

work·bench (wėrk/bench/), a strong, heavy table used by a carpenter, or by any person who

works with tools and materials. *noun, plural* **work·bench·es.**

work·book (wėrk/buk/), a book containing outlines for the study of some subject or questions to be answered; book in which a pupil answers questions and does some written work. *noun.*

work·er (wėr/kər), **1** a person that works. **2** a bee, ant, wasp, or other insect that works for its community and usually does not produce young. *noun.*

work·ing (wėr/king), **1** that works: *The class constructed a working model of a helicopter.* **2** of, for, or used in working: *working hours, working clothes. adjective.*

work·man (wėrk/mən), **1** a worker. **2** a person who works with his or her hands or with machines. *noun, plural* **work·men.**

work·man·ship (wėrk/mən ship), **1** the art or skill in a worker or in the work done: *Good workmanship requires long practice.* **2** the quality or manner of work. *noun.*

work·out (wėrk/out/), exercise; practice: *They had a good workout running around the track before breakfast. noun.*

work·room (wėrk/rüm/), a room where work is done. *noun.*

work·shop (wėrk/shop/), **1** a shop or building where work is done. **2** a group of people working on or studying a special project: *a teachers' workshop. noun.*

work·ta·ble (wėrk/tā/bəl), a table to work at. *noun.*

world (wėrld), **1** the earth: *Ships can sail around the world.* **2** all of certain parts, people, or things of the earth: *the insect world, the world of books, the world of fashion.* **3** all people; the public: *The whole world knows it.* **4** the things of this life and the people devoted to them: *Some monks and nuns live apart from the world.* **5** any planet, especially when considered as inhabited: *Has the earth ever been visited by creatures from another world?* **6** a great deal; very much; large amount: *Sunshine does children a world of good. noun.*

world·ly (wėrld/lē), of this world; not of heaven: *worldly wealth. adjective.*

World War I, a war fought from 1914 to 1918. The United States, Great Britain, France, Russia, and their allies were on one side; Germany, Austria-Hungary, and their allies were on the other side.

World War II, a war fought from 1939 to 1945. The United States, Great Britain, the Soviet Union, and their allies were on one side; Germany, Italy, Japan, and their allies were on the other side.

world·wide (wėrld/wīd/), **1** spread throughout the world: *Pollution is becoming a worldwide problem.* **2** throughout the world: *The news spread worldwide.* 1 *adjective,* 2 *adverb.*

worm (wėrm), **1** a small, slender, crawling or creeping animal. Most worms have soft bodies and no legs. **2** something like a worm in shape or movement, such as the thread of a screw. **3** to move like a worm; crawl or creep like a worm: *The children wormed their way under the fence.* **4** to get by persistent and secret means: *They wormed the information out of him.* **5** a weak, disgusting, or pitiful person. **6 worms,** a disease caused by worms in the body: *Our dog was cured of a bad case of worms.* 1,2,5,6 *noun,* 3,4 *verb.*

worm·y (wėr′mē), **1** having worms; containing many worms: *wormy apples.* **2** damaged by worms: *wormy wood. adjective,* **worm·i·er, worm·i·est.**

worn (wôrn), **1** See **wear.** *I have worn these jeans all week.* **2** damaged by use: *worn rugs.* **3** tired; wearied: *The sick man's face was worn.* 1 *verb,* 2,3 *adjective.*

worn-out (wôrn′out′), **1** very worn from long, hard use; worn or used until useless or in poor condition: *a worn-out lawn mower, worn-out shoes, a worn-out sweater.* **2** very tired; exhausted: *a worn-out horse. adjective.*

wor·ri·some (wèr′ē səm), causing worry: *a worrisome problem. adjective.*

wor·ry (wėr′ē), **1** to feel anxious; be uneasy: *Don't worry about little things. They will worry if we are late.* **2** to make anxious; trouble: *The problem worried him.* **3** care; anxiety; trouble; uneasiness: *Worry kept her awake.* **4** to annoy; bother; vex: *Don't worry me right now with so many questions.* **5** to seize and shake with the teeth; bite at; snap at: *The cat worried the mouse.* 1,2,4,5 *verb,* **wor·ries, wor·ried, wor·ry·ing;** 3 *noun, plural* **wor·ries.**

worse (wėrs), **1** less well; more ill: *The patient seems even worse today.* **2** less good; more evil: *Disobeying your parents was bad enough, but lying to them about it was worse.* **3** in a more severe or evil manner or degree: *It is raining worse than ever today.* **4** that which is worse: *The loss of their property was terrible, but worse followed.* 1,2 *adjective, comparative of* **bad;** 3 *adverb,* 4 *noun.*

wor·ship (wėr′ship), **1** great honor and respect: *the worship of God.* **2** to pay great honor and respect to: *to worship God.* **3** ceremonies or services in honor of God. Prayers and hymns are part of worship. **4** to take part in a religious service. **5** to consider extremely precious; hold very dear; adore: *A miser worships money. She worships her mother.* 1,3 *noun,* 2,4,5 *verb.*

wor·ship·er (wėr′ship ər), a person who worships: *The church was filled with worshipers. noun.*

worst (wėrst), **1** least well; most ill: *This is the worst I've been since I got sick.* **2** least good; most evil: *That was the worst movie I've ever seen.* **3** in the worst manner or degree: *The children behave worst when they are tired.* **4** that which is worst: *Today was bad, but the worst is yet to come.* **5** to beat; defeat: *to worst an enemy.* 1,2 *adjective, superlative of* **bad;** 3 *adverb,* 4 *noun,* 5 *verb.*

worth (wėrth), **1** good or important enough for; deserving of: *That book is worth reading. New York is a city worth visiting.* **2** merit; usefulness;

importance: *We should read books of real worth.* **3** value: *She got her money's worth out of that coat.* **4** quantity that a certain amount will buy: *He bought a dollar's worth of stamps.* **5** equal in value to: *This book is worth five dollars. That toy is worth little.* **6** having property that amounts to: *That man is worth millions.* 1,5,6 *preposition,* 2-4 *noun.*

worth·less (wėrth′lis), without worth; good-for-nothing; useless: *Throw those worthless, broken toys away. adjective.*

worth·while (wėrth′hwīl′), worth time, attention, or trouble; having real merit: *This is a worthwhile book; you should read it. adjective.*

wor·thy (wėr′ᴛʜē), **1** having worth or merit: *Helping the poor is a worthy cause.* **2** deserving; meriting: *Her courage was worthy of high praise. adjective,* **wor·thi·er, wor·thi·est.**

would (wùd), **1** See **will¹.** *She said that she would come. They would go in spite of our warning.* **2** *Would* is also used: **a** to express future time: *Would he never go?* **b** to express action done again and again: *The children would play for hours on the beach.* **c** to express a wish: *I would I were rich.* **d** to sound more polite than *will* sounds: *Would you help us, please? verb.*

would·n't (wùd′nt), would not.

wound¹ (wünd), **1** a hurt or injury caused by cutting, stabbing, or shooting: *a knife wound, a bullet wound.* **2** to injure by cutting, stabbing, or shooting; hurt: *The hunter wounded the deer.* **3** any hurt or injury to feelings or reputation: *Being fired from a job can be a wound to a person's pride.* **4** to injure in feelings or reputation: *Their unkind words wounded me.* 1,3 *noun,* 2,4 *verb.*

wound² (wound). See **wind².** *I wound the string into a tight ball. It is wound too loosely. verb.*

wove (wōv). See **weave.** *The spider wove a new web after the first was destroyed. verb.*

wo·ven (wō′vən). See **weave.** *This cloth is closely woven. verb.*

wow (wou), an exclamation of surprise, joy, or wonder: *Wow! I can sure use a gift like that. interjection.*

wran·gle (rang′gəl), **1** to argue or dispute in a noisy or angry way; quarrel: *The children wrangled about who should wash the dog.* **2** (in the western United States and Canada) to herd or tend horses or cattle on the range. *verb,* **wran·gles, wran·gled, wran·gling.**

wrap (rap), **1** to cover by winding or folding something around: *She wrapped herself in a shawl.* **2** to wind or fold as a covering: *Wrap a shawl around yourself.* **3** to cover with paper and tie up or fasten: *Have you wrapped her birthday presents*

W

yet? **4** to cover; hide: *The mountain peak is wrapped in clouds.* **5** an outer covering. Shawls, scarfs, coats, and furs are wraps. 1-4 *verb,* **wraps, wrapped, wrap·ping;** 5 *noun.*

wrapped up in, devoted to; thinking chiefly of: *She is so wrapped up in her work that she never sees her old friends any more.*

wrap·per (rap′ər), **1** a person or thing that wraps. **2** a covering or cover: *Some magazines are mailed in paper wrappers. noun.*

wrap·ping (rap′ing), paper, cloth, or the like in which something is wrapped. *noun.*

wrath (rath), very great anger; rage. *noun.*

wrath·ful (rath′fəl), very angry; showing wrath: *The wrathful lion turned on the hunters. His wrathful eyes flashed. adjective.*

wreak (rēk), **1** to give expression to; work off feelings or desires: *I wreaked my anger on my brother by yelling at him.* **2** to inflict vengeance or punishment. *verb.*

wreath (rēth), **1** a ring of flowers or leaves twisted together: *There were wreaths in the windows at Christmas.* **2** something suggesting a wreath: *a wreath of smoke. noun, plural* **wreaths** (rēṯHz).

wreathe (rēṯH), **1** to make into a wreath: *The children wreathed a chain of daisies.* **2** to decorate or adorn with wreaths: *The inside of the schoolhouse was wreathed with flowers for the graduation ceremony.* **3** to make a ring around; encircle: *Mist wreathes the hills. verb,* **wreathes, wreathed, wreath·ing.**

wreck (rek), **1** the destruction of a ship, building, train, automobile, truck, or airplane: *The hurricane caused many wrecks. Reckless driving causes many wrecks on the highway.* **2** any destruction or serious injury: *Heavy rains caused the wreck of many crops.* **3** what is left of anything that has been destroyed or much injured: *The waves cast the wreck of a ship upon the shore.* **4** to cause the wreck of; destroy; ruin: *A broken rail wrecked the freight train just outside of town.* **5** a person who has lost his or her health or money: *He was a wreck from overwork.* 1-3,5 *noun,* 4 *verb.*

wreck·age (rek′ij), **1** what is left by a wreck or wrecks: *The shore was covered with the wreckage of the ship.* **2** the act of wrecking: *They felt defeated by the wreckage of their plans. noun.*

wreck·er (rek′ər), **1** a person whose work is tearing down buildings. **2** a person, car, train, or machine that removes wrecks. **3** a person or ship that recovers wrecked or disabled ships or their cargoes. *noun.*

wren (ren), a small songbird with a slender bill and a short tail. Wrens often build their nests near houses. *noun.*

wrench (rench), **1** a violent twist or twisting pull: *She broke the branch off the tree with a sudden wrench.* **2** to twist or pull violently: *She wrenched the knob off when she was trying to open the door. The policeman wrenched the gun out of the man's hand.* **3** to injure by twisting: *She wrenched her back doing gymnastics.* **4** an injury caused by twisting: *He gave his ankle a wrench when he*

jumped off the car. **5** a source of grief or sorrow: *It was a wrench to leave our old home.* **6** a tool to hold and turn nuts, bolts, pieces of pipe, or the like. 1,4-6 *noun, plural* **wrench·es;** 2,3 *verb.*

wrest (rest), **1** to twist, pull, or tear away with force; wrench away: *She bravely wrested the knife from the attacker.* **2** to take by force: *An enemy wrested the power from the duke. verb.*

wres·tle (res′əl), **1** to try to throw or force an opponent to the ground. **2** a wrestling match. **3** to struggle: *I have been wrestling with this problem for an hour.* 1,3 *verb,* **wres·tles, wres·tled, wres·tling;** 2 *noun.*

wres·tler (res′lər), a person who wrestles, especially as a sport. *noun.*

wres·tling (res′ling), a sport or contest in which two opponents try to throw or force each other to the ground. The rules for wrestling do not allow using the fists or certain holds on the body. *noun.*

wretch (rech), **1** a very unfortunate or unhappy person. **2** a very bad person. *noun, plural* **wretch·es.**

wretch·ed (rech′id), **1** very unfortunate or unhappy. **2** very unsatisfactory; miserable: *a wretched hut.* **3** very bad: *a wretched traitor. adjective.*

wrig·gle (rig′əl), **1** to twist and turn: *Children wriggle when they are restless.* **2** to move by twisting and turning: *The worm wriggled out of my hand when I tried to put it on the hook.* **3** to make one's way by slyness and tricks: *That child can wriggle out of any difficulty.* **4** a wriggling motion. 1-3 *verb,* **wrig·gles, wrig·gled, wrig·gling;** 4 *noun.*

wring (ring), **1** to twist with force; squeeze hard: *Wring out your wet bathing suit.* **2** to get by twisting or squeezing; force out: *The boy wrung water from his wet bathing suit.* **3** to get by force, effort, or persuasion: *to wring a secret out of someone.* **4** to clasp and hold firmly: *She wrung her old friend's hand.* **5** to cause pain or pity in: *Their poverty wrung his heart.* **6** a twist or squeeze. 1-5 *verb,* **wrings, wrung, wring·ing;** 6 *noun.*

wring·er (ring′ər), a machine for squeezing water from wet clothes. *noun.*

wrin·kle (ring′kəl), **1** a ridge; fold: *the wrinkles in an old person's face, to press out the wrinkles in a shirt.* **2** to make a wrinkle or wrinkles in: *She*

wren—about 5 inches (13 centimeters) long with the tail

wrinkled her forehead. **3** to have wrinkles; acquire wrinkles: *This shirt will not wrinkle.* 1 *noun,* 2,3 *verb,* **wrin·kles, wrin·kled, wrin·kling.**

wrist (rist), the joint connecting hand and arm. *noun.*

wrist·watch (rist′woch′), a small watch worn on the wrist. *noun, plural* **wrist·watch·es.**

writ (rit), **1** something written; piece of writing. The Bible is sometimes called Holy Writ. **2** a formal order directing a person to do or not to do something: *A writ from the judge ordered the prisoner's release from jail. noun.*

write (rīt), **1** to make letters or words with pen, pencil, or chalk: *You can read and write.* **2** to mark with letters or words: *Please write on both sides of the paper.* **3** to put down the letters or words of: *Write your name and address.* **4** to make up stories, books, poems, articles, or the like; compose: *He writes for magazines.* **5** to be a writer: *Her ambition was to write.* **6** to write a letter: *I write to my friend every week.* **7** to write a letter to: *She wrote her parents that she would be home for New Year's.* **8** to show plainly: *Fear was written on his face. verb,* **writes, wrote, writ·ten, writ·ing.**

write down, to put into writing: *I will write down your directions.*

write out, 1 to put in writing: *He wrote out a check.* **2** to write in full: *He wrote out his speech and memorized it.*

write up, to write a description or account of, especially a full or detailed account: *The reporter wrote up his interview with the mayor for the newspaper.*

writ·er (rī′tər), **1** a person who writes. **2** a person whose occupation is writing; author. *noun.*

writhe (rīŦH), **1** to twist and turn; twist about: *to writhe in pain. The snake writhed along the branch.* **2** to suffer mentally; be very uncomfortable. *verb,* **writhes, writhed, writh·ing.**

"The Wrestlers," George Loks. Museum of Fine Arts, Boston. Charles Henry Hayden Fund

writhe (definition 1)—The wrestlers **writhed** on the mat.

writ·ing (rī′ting), **1** the act of making letters or words with pen, pencil, chalk, or the like. **2** a written form: *Put your ideas in writing.* **3** handwriting: *Your writing is hard to read.* **4** something written; a letter, paper, document, or the like. **5** a literary work; book or other literary production: *the writings of Benjamin Franklin. noun.*

writ·ten (rit′n). See **write.** *I have written a letter. verb.*

wrong (rông), **1** not right; bad: *Stealing is wrong.* **2** not true; not correct; not what it should be: *She gave the wrong answer.* **3** not proper; not suitable: *Heavy boots would be the wrong thing to wear for tennis.* **4** out of order: *Something is wrong with the car.* **5** badly; in an incorrect way: *I did my homework wrong and had to do it over.* **6** anything not right; wrong thing or action: *Two wrongs do not make a right.* **7** an injury; harm: *You can do an innocent person a wrong by spreading false rumors.* **8** to do wrong to; treat unfairly; injure: *It is often hard to forgive someone who has wronged you.* **9** not meant to be seen; least important: *the wrong side of cloth.* 1-4,9 *adjective,* 5 *adverb,* 6,7 *noun,* 8 *verb.*

go wrong, 1 to turn out badly: *Everything went wrong today.* **2** to stop being good and become bad: *The cashier went wrong and stole money from the cash register.*

in the wrong, at fault; guilty: *I was in the wrong.*

wrong·do·er (rông′dü′ər), a person who does wrong. *noun.*

wrong·do·ing (rông′dü′ing), a doing wrong: *The thief was guilty of wrongdoing. noun.*

wrong·ful (rông′fəl), **1** wrong. **2** unlawful. *adjective.*

wrote (rōt). See **write.** *He wrote his mother a long letter last week. verb.*

wrought (rôt), **1** made: *The gate was wrought with great skill.* **2** formed by hammering: *wrought iron. adjective.*

wrung (rung). See **wring.** *She wrung out the wet cloth and hung it up. Her heart is wrung with pity for the poor. verb.*

wry (rī), twisted; turned to one side: *She made a wry face to show her disgust. adjective,* **wri·er, wri·est.**

WV, West Virginia (used with postal Zip Code).

W.Va., West Virginia.

WY, Wyoming (used with postal Zip Code).

Wyo., Wyoming.

Wy·o·ming (wī ō′ming), one of the western states of the United States. *Abbreviation:* Wyo. or WY *Capital:* Cheyenne. *noun.*

[*Wyoming* got its name from Wyoming Valley, Pennsylvania. The name *Wyoming* comes from a Delaware Indian word meaning "upon the great plain." It became popular after a poem called "Gertrude of Wyoming" was published. A member of Congress proposed it as the name of the western land that became the state of Wyoming.]

a	hat	i	it	oi	oil	ch	child		a in about
ā	age	ī	ice	ou	out	ng	long		e in taken
ä	far	o	hot	u	cup	sh	she	ə =	i in pencil
e	let	ō	open	ů	put	th	thin		o in lemon
ē	equal	ô	order	ü	rule	ŦH	then		u in circus
ėr	term					zh	measure		

W

X-ray (definition 1)—They **X-rayed** the snake and found light bulbs.

X or **x** (eks), **1** the 24th letter of the English alphabet. **2** an unknown quantity. **3** a mark that shows a place on a map or diagram: *X marks the spot where gold is buried. noun, plural* **X's** or **x's.**

Xer·ox (zir′oks), **1** a trademark for a process of copying letters or other documents by making photographic prints of them. **2** to make a copy or copies of something by using a Xerox copying machine. **1** *noun,* **2** *verb.*

Xmas (kris′məs *or* ek′sməs), Christmas. *noun.*

X ray, 1 a ray which can go through substances that rays of light cannot penetrate. X rays are used to locate breaks in bones or decay in teeth, and to treat certain diseases. **2** a photograph made by means of X rays.

X-ray (eks′rā′), **1** to examine, photograph, or treat with X rays. **2** of, by, or having something to do with X rays: *an X-ray examination of one's teeth.* **1** *verb,* **2** *adjective.*

xy·lo·phone (zī′lə fōn), a musical instrument consisting of two rows of wooden bars of varying lengths, which are sounded by striking with wooden hammers. *noun.*

Word History

xylophone *Xylophone* was formed from two Greek words meaning "wood" and "sound."

Y or **y** (wī), **1** the 25th letter of the English alphabet. **2** anything shaped like a Y. *noun, plural* **Y's** or **y's.**

-y¹, a suffix meaning: **1** full of ____: Bump*y* means *full of* bumps. **2** containing ____: Salt*y* means *containing* salt. **3** having ____: Cloud*y* means *having* clouds. **4** inclined to ____: Sleep*y* means *inclined to* sleep. **5** like ____: Dream*y* means *like* a dream.

-y², a suffix meaning: **1** a small ____: Doll*y* means *a small* doll. **2** dear ____: Padd*y* means *dear* dad.

yacht (yot), a boat for pleasure trips or for racing. *noun.*
[*Yacht* comes from an old Dutch word meaning "a chasing ship." The boat was called this because it originally was a kind of light, fast ship suitable for chasing other ships.]

yak (yak), a long-haired animal like an ox that

yak—about 5½ feet (1½ meters) high at the shoulder

lives in central Asia. It is raised for its meat, milk, and hair. *noun.*

yam (yam), **1** the thick, sweet, orange root of a vine of warm regions, eaten as a vegetable. **2** the sweet potato: *We like candied yams. noun.*
[*Yam* comes from a west African word meaning "to eat."]

yank (yangk), **1** to pull with a sudden motion; jerk; tug: *She yanked the weeds out of the flower bed.* **2** a sudden pull; jerk; tug: *I gave the door a yank, and it flew open.* **1** *verb,* **2** *noun.*

Yan·kee (yang′kē), **1** a person born or living in New England. **2** a person born or living in the

North, especially during the Civil War. **3** a person born or living in the United States; American. *noun.*

yap (yap), **1** a quick, sharp bark; yelp. **2** to bark in a quick, sharp way; yelp: *The little dog yapped at me.* **1** *noun,* **2** *verb,* **yaps, yapped, yap·ping.**

yard[1] (yärd), **1** a piece of ground near or around a house, barn, school, or other building: *You can play outside, but you must not leave the yard.* **2** a piece of enclosed ground for some special purpose or business: *a chicken yard.* **3** a space with many tracks where railroad cars are stored, shifted around, serviced, or made up into new trains: *My dad works in the railroad yards. noun.*

yard[2] (yärd), **1** a unit of length equal to 36 inches; 3 feet: *I bought three yards of blue cloth for curtains.* **2** a beam or pole fastened across a mast and used to support a sail. *noun.*

yard·stick (yärd/stik/), a stick one yard long, used for measuring. *noun.*

yarn (yärn), **1** any spun thread, especially that prepared for weaving or knitting: *I'm knitting a scarf from this yarn.* **2** a tale; story: *The old sailor made up his yarns as he told them. noun.*

yawn (yôn), **1** to open the mouth wide because one is sleepy, tired, or bored. **2** the act of opening the mouth in this way. **3** to open wide: *The canyon yawned in front of us.* **1,3** *verb,* **2** *noun.*

yd., yard. *plural* **yd.** *or* **yds.**

ye (yē), an old word meaning **you.** *If ye are thirsty, drink. pronoun.*

yea (yā), **1** yes. **2** indeed. **3** a vote or voter in favor of something: *The yeas outnumber the nays, so the plan is approved.* **1,2** *adverb,* **3** *noun.*

yeah (ye, ya, *or* ye/ə), yes. *adverb.*

year (yir), **1** 12 months or 365 days; January 1 to December 31. Leap year has 366 days. **2** 12 months counted from any point: *I will see you again a year from today.* **3** the part of a year spent in a certain activity: *Our school year is 9 months.* **4** the amount of time it takes a planet to go once around the sun. *noun.*

year·book (yir/bùk/), a book or report published every year. Yearbooks often report facts of the year. The graduating class in a school or college usually publishes a yearbook, with pictures of its members. *noun.*

year·ling (yir/ling), an animal one year old. *noun.*

year·ly (yir/lē), **1** once a year; in every year: *I take a yearly trip to New York.* **2** for a year: *She wants to earn a yearly salary of $30,000.* **1,2** *adjective,* **1** *adverb.*

yearn (yėrn), to feel a longing or desire; desire earnestly: *He yearns for home. verb.*

yearn·ing (yėr/ning), an earnest or strong desire; longing: *a yearning to be popular. noun.*

year-round (yir/round/), throughout the year: *She lives here year-round. adjective, adverb.*

yeast (yēst), the substance that causes bread dough to rise and beer to ferment. Yeast consists of many tiny one-celled fungi that grow quickly in any material containing sugar. *noun.*

yell (yel), **1** to cry out with a strong, loud sound: *I*

a hat	i it	oi oil	ch child	a in about
ā age	ī ice	ou out	ng long	e in taken
ä far	o hot	u cup	sh she	ə = i in pencil
e let	ō open	ù put	th thin	o in lemon
ē equal	ô order	ü rule	ᴛʜ then	u in circus
ėr term			zh measure	

yelled with pain when the door slammed on my finger. **2** a strong, loud cry. **3** a special shout or cheer used by a school or college at sports events. **1** *verb,* **2,3** *noun.*

yel·low (yel/ō), **1** the color of gold, butter, or ripe lemons. **2** having this color. **3** to make or become yellow: *Paper yellows with age.* **4** the yolk of an egg. **5** cowardly. **1,4** *noun,* **2,5** *adjective,* **3** *verb.*

yellow fever, a dangerous, infectious disease of warm climates that causes high fever and turns the skin yellow. It is transmitted by the bite of a certain kind of mosquito. Yellow fever was once common in some southern parts of the United States.

yel·low·ish (yel/ō ish), somewhat yellow. *adjective.*

yellow jacket, a wasp marked with bright yellow.

Yellow Pages, a telephone book or section of a telephone book that is printed on yellow paper and lists businesses and professional people. The kinds of business are listed alphabetically, and so are the names within each kind.

yelp (yelp), **1** the quick, sharp bark or cry of a dog or fox. **2** to make such a bark or cry. **1** *noun,* **2** *verb.*

Yem·en (yem/ən), a country in Arabia, in southwestern Asia. *noun.*

yen (yen), the unit of money in Japan. *noun, plural* **yen.**

yes (yes), **1** a word used to show agreement or consent: *Yes, five and two are seven. When he asked me if I'd go, I said, "Yes."* **2** a vote for; person voting for: *The yeses won.* **3** and what is more: *"Your work is good, yes, very good," said the teacher.* **1,3** *adverb,* **2** *noun, plural* **yes·es** *or* **yes·ses.**

yes·ter·day (yes/tər dē), **1** the day before today: *Yesterday was cold and rainy.* **2** on the day before today: *It rained yesterday.* **3** the recent past: *We are often amused by the fashions of yesterday.* **1,3** *noun,* **2** *adverb.*

yet (yet), **1** up to the present time; thus far: *The work is not yet finished.* **2** now; at this time: *Don't go yet.* **3** then; at that time: *It was not yet dark.* **4** still; even now: *She is doing her homework yet.* **5** sometime: *I may yet get rich.* **6** additionally; again: *Let us try yet one more time.* **7** even: *The teacher threatens yet more punishment unless I behave better.* **8** but: *The work is good, yet it could be better.* **1-8** *adverb,* **8** *conjunction.*

yew (yü), an evergreen tree of Europe and Asia. Some kinds of yew are now widely grown in the United States as shrubs. *noun.*

yield (yēld), **1** to produce: *This land yields good*

crops. *Mines yield ore.* **2** the amount yielded; product: *This year's yield from the silver mine was very large.* **3** to give; grant: *Her parents yielded their consent to her plans.* **4** to give up; surrender: *The enemy yielded to our soldiers.* **5** to give way: *Traffic on a side street should yield to traffic on a highway.* 1,3-5 *verb,* 2 *noun.*

yip (yip), **1** to bark or yelp sharply. **2** a sharp, barking sound. 1 *verb,* **yips, yipped, yip·ping;** 2 *noun.*

yo·del (yō′dl), **1** to sing with frequent changes from the ordinary voice to a forced shrill voice and back again. **2** the act or sound of yodeling. 1 *verb,* **yo·dels, yo·deled** or **yo·delled, yo·del·ing** or **yo·del·ling;** 2 *noun.*

yo·gurt (yō′gərt), a kind of liquid food made from milk, thickened by the action of bacteria. Yogurt is often sweetened and flavored. *noun.*
[*Yogurt* comes from a Turkish word. The food was originally made in Turkey and other countries of the Middle East.]

yoke (yōk), **1** a wooden frame to fasten two work animals together. **2** a pair of animals fastened together with a yoke: *The plow was drawn by a yoke of oxen.* **3** to put a yoke on; fasten with a yoke: *The farmer yoked the oxen before hitching them to the wagon.* **4** a part of a garment fitting the neck and shoulders closely. 1,2,4 *noun,* *plural* **yokes** for 1 and 4, **yoke** or **yokes** for 2; 3 *verb,* **yokes, yoked, yok·ing.**

yolk (yōk), the yellow part of an egg. *noun.*
[*Yolk* comes from an older English word meaning "yellow."]

Yom Kip·pur (yom kip′ər or yom ki pür′), a Jewish fast day of atoning for sins. It occurs ten days after Rosh Hashanah, the Jewish New Year.

yon (yon), yonder. *adjective, adverb.*

yon·der (yon′dər), **1** over there; within sight, but not near: *Look at that wild duck yonder!* **2** situated over there; being within sight, but not near: *On yonder hill stands a castle.* 1 *adverb,* 2 *adjective.*

yore (yôr). **of yore,** long past; now long since gone: *Plague was common in days of yore. noun.*

you (yü or yə), **1** the person or persons spoken to: *Are you ready? Then you may go.* **2** one; anybody: *You never can tell. pronoun singular or plural.*

you'd (yüd or yəd), **1** you had. **2** you would.

you'll (yül or yəl), **1** you will. **2** you shall.

young (yung), **1** in the early part of life or growth; not old: *A puppy is a young dog.* **2** young ones; offspring: *An animal will fight to protect its young.* **3** having the looks or qualities of youth or of a young person: *She looks and acts young for her age.* **4** of youth; early: *Grandmother told us stories of her young days.* **5** in an early stage; not far advanced: *The night was still young when they left the party.* 1,3-5 *adjective,* **young·er** (yung′gər), **young·est** (yung′gist); 2 *noun.*

young·ster (yung′stər), **1** a child: *Those youngsters live next door.* **2** a young person: *The old woman was as spry as a youngster. noun.*

your (yür or yər), **1** belonging to you: *Wash your hands.* **2** having to do with you: *We enjoyed your*

visit. **3** *Your* is used as part of some titles. *Your Highness, Your Lordship, Your Honor. adjective.*

you're (yür or yər), you are.

yours (yürz), **1** the one or ones belonging to you: *This pencil is yours. My hands are clean; yours are dirty.* **2** at your service: *I am yours to command.* **3** *Yours* is used at the end of a letter with some other word. *Yours truly. pronoun singular or plural.*

your·self (yür self′ or yər self′), **1** *Yourself* is used to make a statement stronger. *You yourself know the story is not true.* **2** *Yourself* is used instead of *you* in cases like: *Did you hurt yourself? Can you teach yourself this song? Try to do it by yourself.* **3** your real self: *Now that your cold is better, you'll feel like yourself again. pronoun, plural* **your·selves.**

your·selves (yür selvz′ or yər selvz′). See **yourself.** *Do this yourselves. pronoun plural.*

youth (yüth), **1** the fact or quality of being young: *In spite of her youth, she has already traveled widely.* **2** the time between childhood and adulthood. **3** a young man. **4** young people. *noun, plural* **youths** (yüths or yüᴛʜz), **youth.**

youth·ful (yüth′fəl), **1** young. **2** of youth: *youthful energy, youthful pleasures.* **3** lively; fresh; having the looks or qualities of youth: *My grandmother has a very gay and youthful spirit. adjective.*

you've (yüv or yəv), you have.

yowl (youl), **1** a long, loud, wailing cry; howl. **2** to howl: *That dog is always yowling.* 1 *noun,* 2 *verb.*

yo·yo (yō′yō), a small wheel-shaped toy made up of two wooden or plastic disks joined by a peg. A yoyo can be spun out and reeled back to the hand by means of a string that is wound around the peg. *noun, plural* **yo·yos.**

yr., year. *plural* **yr.** or **yrs.**

yuc·ca (yuk′ə), a plant found in dry, warm regions of North and Central America. It has stiff, narrow leaves and white, bell-shaped flowers. *noun.*

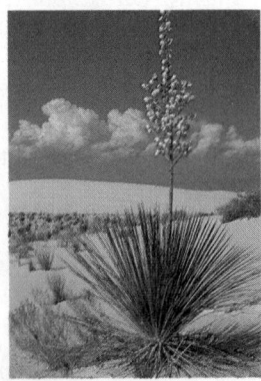
yucca

Yu·go·sla·vi·a (yü′gō slä′vē ə), a country in southeastern Europe. *noun.*

Yu·kon Ter·ri·to·ry (yü′kon ter′ə tôr′ē), a territory in northwestern Canada. *Capital:* Whitehorse.

yule or **Yule** (yül), **1** Christmas. **2** yuletide. *noun.*

yule·tide or **Yule·tide** (yül′tīd′), Christmastime; the Christmas season. *noun.*

Z z

Z or **z** (zē), the 26th and last letter of the English alphabet. *noun, plural* **Z's** or **z's.**

Za·ire (zä ir′), a country in central Africa. *noun.*

Zam·bi·a (zam′bē ə), a country in southern Africa. *noun.*

zeal (zēl), eager desire or effort; earnest enthusiasm: *We worked with zeal to finish the project. noun.*

zeal·ous (zel′əs), full of zeal; eager; earnest: *The children made zealous efforts to clean up the house for the party. adjective.*

ze·bra (zē′brə), a wild animal of Africa that is somewhat like a horse or a donkey but has black and white stripes. *noun, plural* **ze·bras** or **ze·bra.**

ze·bu (zē′bü *or* zē′byü), an animal like an ox but with a large hump. The zebu is a farm animal in Asia and eastern Africa. *noun.*

zebu—up to 5 feet (1½ meters) high at the shoulder

ze·nith (zē′nith), **1** the point in the sky directly overhead. **2** the highest point: *At the zenith of its power Rome ruled all of civilized Europe. noun.*

Zep·pe·lin (zep′ə lən), a large airship shaped like a cigar with pointed ends. It has compartments filled with gas. *noun.*

[*Zeppelin* was named for Count Ferdinand von Zeppelin, the German army officer who invented it. He lived from 1838 to 1917.]

Zeppelin

zer·o (zir′ō), **1** the figure 0: *There are three zeros in 40,006.* **2** the point marked as 0 on the scale of a thermometer. **3** the temperature that corresponds to 0 on the scale of a thermometer. **4** of or at nothing: *The other team's score was zero points.* **5** nothing; a complete absence of quantity: *One minus zero is one.* **6** not any; none at all: *The weather station at the airport announced zero visibility.* 1-3,5 *noun, plural* **zer·os** or **zer·oes;** 4,6 *adjective.*

[*Zero* comes from an Arabic word meaning originally "empty." Zero is a number worth nothing, an "empty" number.]

zest (zest), **1** keen enjoyment; great pleasure: *The hungry children ate with zest.* **2** a pleasant or exciting quality: *Wit gives zest to conversation. noun.*

Zeus (züs), the chief god of the ancient Greeks. The Romans called him Jupiter. *noun.*

zig·zag (zig′zag′), **1** with short, sharp turns from one side to the other: *We traveled in a zigzag direction. The path ran zigzag up the hill.* **2** to move in a zigzag way: *Lightning zigzagged across the sky.* **3** a zigzag line or course. **4** one of the short, sharp turns of a zigzag. 1 *adjective, adverb,* 2 *verb,* **zig·zags, zig·zagged, zig·zag·ging;** 3,4 *noun.*

zigzags
(definition 3)

zil·lion (zil′yən), **1** any very large, indefinite number. **2** very many; a great many: *He knows a zillion jokes.* 1 *noun,* 2 *adjective.*

[*Zillion* is made up of *z,* the last letter of the alphabet, and the last six letters of *million.*]

Zim·ba·bwe (zim bä′bwe), a country in southeastern Africa. *noun.*

zinc (zingk), a bluish-white metal very little

Z

affected by air and moisture. Zinc is used as a coating for iron, in electric batteries, and in paint. It is a chemical element. *noun.*

zin·ni·a (zin′ē ə), a garden plant grown for its showy flowers of many colors. *noun.*
[*Zinnia* was named in honor of Johann Zinn, a German botanist. He lived from 1727 to 1759.]

zip[1] (zip), to move or act quickly or with much energy: *Cars were zipping along the highway. verb,* **zips, zipped, zip·ping.**

zip[2] (zip), to fasten or close with a zipper: *I zipped up my jacket. verb,* **zips, zipped, zip·ping.**

Zip Code, a number which identifies one of the postal delivery areas into which the United States and its larger cities have been divided.
[*Zip* was formed from the first letters of the words *zone improvement plan.*]

zip·per (zip′ər), **1** a fastener in which two rows of metal or plastic teeth can be made to hook together or come apart by pulling on a sliding tab. Zippers are used in clothing, boots, luggage, and the like. **2** to fasten or close with a zipper: *Zipper up your jacket before you go out in the cold.* **1** *noun,* **2** *verb.*

zith·er (zith′ər *or* ziŦH′ər), a musical instrument having 30 to 40 strings, played with the fingers. *noun.*

zither

zo·di·ac (zō′dē ak), an imaginary strip of sky that is divided into 12 equal parts called signs. The signs are named after 12 groups of stars found in them. *noun.*

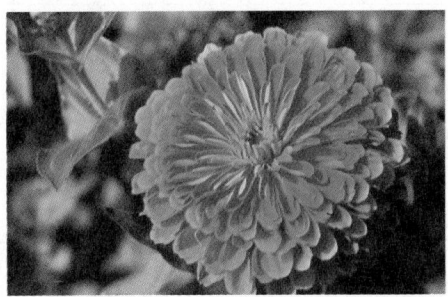
zinnias

zom·bie (zom′bē), a corpse supposedly brought to a condition resembling life by a supernatural power. People who practice voodoo believe in zombies. *noun.*

zone (zōn), **1** any of the five great divisions of the earth's surface, bounded by imaginary lines going around the earth parallel to the equator. Zones differ from each other in climate. **2** any region or area treated or thought of as different from others. A combat zone is a district where fighting is going on. **3** to divide into zones: *The city was zoned for factories and residences.* **1,2** *noun,* **3** *verb,* **zones, zoned, zon·ing.**

zoo (zü), a place where animals are kept and shown: *There are often many tame animals in a children's zoo. noun, plural* **zoos.**

zoo·keep·er (zü′kē′pər), a person who works in a zoo. *noun.*

zo·o·log·i·cal (zō′ə loj′ə kəl), **1** of animals and animal life. **2** having to do with zoology. *adjective.*

zo·ol·o·gist (zō ol′ə jist), a person who is an expert in zoology. *noun.*

zo·ol·o·gy (zō ol′ə jē), the science of animals; the study of animals and animal life. Zoology is a branch of biology. *noun.*
[*Zoology* comes from two Greek words meaning "animal" and "report or discussion."]

zoom (züm), **1** to move rapidly upward or downward: *The airplane zoomed up out of sight.* **2** to move very rapidly: *The car zoomed past us, going 80 miles an hour.* **3** to move or travel with a humming or buzzing sound: *The bumblebee zoomed from flower to flower. verb.*

zuc·chi·ni (zü kē′nē), a kind of dark-green squash shaped like a cucumber. It is eaten as a vegetable. *noun, plural* **zuc·chi·ni** *or* **zuc·chi·nis.**

Picture Credits

Unless otherwise credited, all illustrations and photographs are the property of Scott, Foresman and Company.

How to Use This Dictionary

page 10	**kingfisher**	© Wayne Lankinen / Bruce Coleman Inc.
page 11	**kumquat**	Joe Rychetnik / Photo Researchers
page 18	**gondola**	Adam Woolfitt / Woodfin Camp
page 26	**robot**	Courtesy of Toshiba Corporation
page 38	**conspicuous**	Buck Campbell/FPG International

Dictionary

aardvark Patti Murray / Animals Animals

absurdity Oppenheim, Meret, OBJECT Le Déjeuner en fourrure, 1936. The Museum of Modern Art, New York

accordion Don & Pat Valenti / Tom Stack & Associates

achievement NASA

adder J. Chellman / Animals Animals

adept Lynn Millar / Rapho / Photo Researchers

adorn John Padour

agile Film Stills Archive, The Museum of Modern Art

alligator Lynn M. Stone

aloft Bettmann Newsphotos

anaconda Timothy O'Keefe / Bruce Coleman Inc.

anemometer National Oceanic & Atmospheric Administration

angelfish E. R. Degginger / Bruce Coleman Inc.

anteater Norman Owen Tomalin / Bruce Coleman Inc.

antelope Michael Fogden / Animals Animals

antenna Turtox / Cambosco—Macmillan Science Company, Chicago, Ill.

antique Ford Motor Company

arch Tom Myers

armadillo L.R. Ditto / Bruce Coleman Inc.

aspen Mike Mazzaschi / Stock Boston

aster Gretchen Garner

atoll N. Devore III / Bruce Coleman Inc.

attempt P. C. & Connie Peri

attire Tom Myers

austere "American Gothic," Grant Wood, Friends of American Art Collection. Courtesy of The Art Institute of Chicago.

auk Joe & Carol McDonald / Animals Animals

azalea Gail Nachel

baboon Clem Haagner / Bruce Coleman Inc.

backhand Diane Johnson / Focus West

bacteria Courtesy of Dr. R. Wychoff, National Institutes of Health

badger John H. Gerard

bald eagle From the collection of Cynthia Zilliac

bamboo Lynn M. Stone

barracuda Zig Leszcynski / Animals Animals

basset Walter Chandoha

beagle Robert P. Carr / Bruce Coleman Inc.

beaver © Harry Engles / Bruce Coleman Inc.

beret C. McNee / FPG

bighorn sheep © Harry Engles / Bruce Coleman Inc.

biplane Tom Myers

bison Jeff Foott / Bruce Coleman Inc.

blackbird From the collection of Cynthia Zilliac

blacken Ruth A. Cordner / Root Resources

black-eyed Susan James P. Rowan

blimp John Madeley / R.C. Photo Agency

bloodhound H. Armstrong Roberts

blowhole © Jeff Foott / Bruce Coleman Inc.

bluebird From the collection of Cynthia Zilliac

blue jay Edgar Jones / Bruce Coleman Inc.

boa constrictor James P. Rowan

boar Hans Reinhard / Bruce Coleman Inc.

bobcat John H. Gerard

bobsled Arthur Grace / Stock Boston

boll weevil U.S. Dept. of Agriculture (USDA photo)

bongo Brent Jones

boomerang Bill Noel Kleeman / Tom Stack & Associates

boxer Hans Reinhard / Bruce Coleman Inc.

brand Courtesy of the State Highway Commission of Montana, Helena, Mont.

breadfruit Kevin Schafer / Tom Stack & Associates

breaker David Muench / Click / Chicago Ltd.

breeches The Franklin D. Roosevelt Library

brindle © Leonard Lee Rue III / Animals Animals

bristle Zig Leszcynski / Animals Animals

brontosaurus Courtesy of the Department of Library Services, American Museum of Natural History, No. 2417.

bulldozer Courtesy of Caterpillar Tractor Co.

bullfight Walter S. Clark, Jr.

bust "Sioux Indian Man." Sculpture by Malvina Hoffman. Courtesy of the Field Museum of Natural History, Chicago.

butte James P. Rowan

cable Courtesy of Bell Laboratories

cable car Lynn M. Stone

canoe Walter Chandoha

cardinal Jen & Des Bartlett / Bruce Coleman Inc.

cascade William B. Parker

cattail Gretchen Garner

centipede Don and Pat Valenti

chalice Courtesy of Kremsmunster Abbey, Austria

chameleon Joe McDonald / Animals Animals

chandelier Courtesy of The White House Historical Association. Green Room, 1964.

chaps Moorhouse Collection, University of Oregon

cheetah M.P. Kahl / Bruce Coleman Inc.

Chihuahua Walter Chandoha

chimpanzee Tom Myers

chinchilla Norman C. Tomalin / Bruce Coleman Inc.

chip Courtesy of Western Electric

chrysalis Patti Murray / Animals Animals

clipper Seven Seas Fine Arts (1945) Ltd., London

clover Bob & Miriam Francis / Tom Stack & Associates

cluster © Tom Myers 1985

cobra © Tom Myers

cockatoo John Chellman / Animals Animals

collar From the collection of Gay Russell-Dempsey

comet Courtesy of Hale Observatories

commemorate U.S. Postal Service

competition Neil Leifer / Sports Illustrated, Time Inc.

conch Lynn M. Stone

condor M. A. Chapell / Animals Animals

congregate L & M Photo / FPG

conspicuous © Buck Campbell / FPG

contemplation Detail of portrait of Christina Rossetti by D. G. Rossetti. The Mansell Collection

contort © Pam Hasegawa / Taurus

contraption Michael Boddy / Houston Post

conventional Library of Congress

conveyor belt Tom Myers

cooperate P. C. & Connie Peri

coral Anne L. Doubilet / Animals Animals

coral snake Michael Fogden / Animals Animals (Oxford Scientific Films)

countenance Library of Congress

coyote Jim & Des Bartlett / Bruce Coleman Inc.

crane Lynn M. Stone

crater NASA

crescent A. Upitis Alpha / FPG

crest Hans & Judy Beste / Animals Animals

crevasse Information Canada Photothèque

crocodile James P. Rowan

crocus Gretchen Garner

crossbow Royal MS 14E.IV.f.23. Reproduced by the permission of The British Library Board.

cultivator Grant Heilman / Grant Heilman Photography

curtsy Jean-Claude LeJeune

dachshund Walter Chandoha

dappled Fritz Prenzel / Animals Animals

dazzling Steve White / Photo Design

decoration Library of Congress

decoy Don and Pat Valenti

deface Don Bronstein

dejected Isaac Soyer. "Employment Agency," 1937. Oil. 34¼ x 45 in. Collection of the Whitney Museum of Art. Purchase. Acq. #37.44.

delicate Lynn M. Stone

delta NASA

demolish John Gordon

demonstration Bettmann Newsphotos

derby Barbara Frankel

destroyer U.S. Navy Photo

diminutive From the Collection of Gay Russell-Dempsey Neg. #39108. Courtesy Department Library Services. American Museum of Natural History

dinosaur U.S. Navy Photo

dirigible U.S. Navy Photo

disdainful From the collection of Gay Russell-Dempsey

dismal Thomas W. Putney / Putney Photo Library

distort Mike Mazzaschi / Stock Boston

Doberman pinscher Hans Reinhard / Bruce Coleman Inc.

dodo Brown Brothers

doff "General Washington on a White Charger;" American; National Gallery of Art, Washington; Gift of Edgar William and Bernice Chrysler Garbisch. (Date: first half 19th century; wood; 0.968 x 0.746.)

dolphin © Mickey Gibson / Animals Animals

dome Courtesy of the National Park Service

dormouse Hans Reinhard / Bruce Coleman Inc.

dove K. W. Fink / Bruce Coleman Inc.

dragonfly Lynn M. Stone

driftwood Lynn M. Stone

dromedary © R. Ingo Riepl / Animals Animals

drought Library of Congress

drum major J. M. Mejuto / FPG

dubious "Their Pride," Thomas Hovenden, Courtesy of the Union League Club, New York City. Photograph by Robert S. Crandall.

duffel bag Nina Leen, Life Magazine, © 1945, Time, Inc.

dunes Courtesy of the National Park Service

dwarf Tom Myers

earthquake Library of Congress

eject Frank Siteman / Stock Boston

elephant James P. Rowan

elevator Donald Dietz / Stock Boston

elk Lynn M. Stone

elongate John Tenniel illustration from Lewis Carroll's Alice's Adventures in Wonderland.

engross Horace Bonham: Detail of "Nearing the Issue at the Cockpit." In the collection of The Corcoran Gallery of Art. Museum Purchase, Gallery Fund.

envelope Lynn M. Stone

equilibrium Tom Myers

ermine © Leonard Lee Rue III / Animals Animals

erosion Lynn M. Stone

ethnic Liz Jaquith / Tom Stack & Associates

evergreen (palm) Lynn M. Stone

evergreen (fir) Lynn M. Stone

excavate Stewart M. Green / Tom Stack & Associates

exhibit "Staircase of the Old British Museum, Montague House," George Scharf, the Elder. Trustees of the British Museum.

exotic A. Visage / Gamma-Liaison

expedition Stuart Cohen / Stock Boston

experimental General Motors

extricate The Bettmann Archive

eye Detail of "Queer Fish" by Mabel Dwight. Collection of the Philadelphia Museum of Art, The Harrison Fund.

fad	Wide World
falcon	Arabian American Oil Company
fanciful	From the collection of Gay Russell-Dempsey
fang	D. Lyons / Bruce Coleman Inc.
fault	Peter Menzel / Stock Boston
faun	Culver Pictures
feat	Keystone Press Agency
ferret	Tom McHugh / Photo Researchers
Ferris wheel	Courtesy of the Chicago Historical Society
fez	Brown Brothers
fife	Library of Congress ("Heroes of '76 Marching to the Fight." Lithograph by Currier & Ives, 1876)
figurehead	National Gallery of Art (Index of America Design, Washington D.C.)
fingerprint	FBI
fiord	Tom Stack / Tom Stack & Associates
firefly	S. Kuribayashi / Katherine Young
flamingo	Lynn M. Stone
flexible	From the collection of Gay Russell-Dempsey
flicker	© C. W. Perkins / Animals Animals
flying fish	Jane Burton / Bruce Coleman Inc.
forbidding	C. B. Jones / Taurus
forge	"Trotting Cracks at the Forge," Currier & Ives, 1869. The Henry T. Peters Collection. Museum of the City of New York.
forlorn	Leonard Freed / Magnum Photos
forsythia	Don and Pat Valenti
foxhound	C. L. Sawyer / Bruce Coleman Inc.
fracas	Charles Scribner's Sons (Scribner's Popular History of the U.S., 1897)
freak	John MacGregor / Peter Arnold, Inc.
fronds	Gretchen Garner
furrow	Food & Agricultural Organization
galaxy	© California Institute of Technology
gazelle	M. J. Griffith / Photo Researchers
geometric	Cat. #2 / 4821. Museum of the American Indian, Heye Foundation, N.Y.
geranium	S. Rannels / Grant Heilman Photography
gerbil	E. R. Degginger / Animals Animals
geyser	Don and Pat Valenti
gibbon	© Michael Dick / Animals Animals
Gila monster	Z. Leszczynski / Animals Animals
glacier	Tom Myers
gleeful	Gretchen Garner
gnarled	Karen R. Preuss / Taurus
goatee	Public Archives of Canada
goldenrod	Mark S. Carlson / Tom Stack & Associates
gondola	Adam Woolfitt / Woodfin Camp & Associates, New York
gorilla	Jerry Cooke / Animals Animals
gossamer	S. Kuribayashi / Katherine Young
grackle	Jen & Des Bartlett / Bruce Coleman Inc.
Great Dane	Hans Reinhard / Bruce Coleman Inc.
greyhound	Ken Love / Nawrocki Stock Photos
grimace	Marble bust by X. F. Messerschmidt. Courtesy Österreichische Galerie, Vienna.
grotesque	© Lucasfilm Ltd. (LFL) 1983. All rights reserved.
grouse	Leonard Lee Rue III / Animals Animals
grub	Oxford Scientific Films / Animals Animals
guppy	Hans Reinhard / Bruce Coleman Inc.
gymnast	Dave Black / Focus West
haggard	Library of Congress
halo	George T. Maniates
harmony	Edward Hicks. "Peaceable Kingdom," 1848. Oil on canvas. 17⅞ x 23¹⁵⁄₁₆ in. John S. Phillips Bequest. Courtesy of The Pennsylvania Academy of the Fine Arts.
harrow	Tom Myers
hawk	From the collection of Cynthia Zilliac
hazardous	Bettmann Newsphotos
hedgehog	E. R. Degginger / Bruce Coleman Inc.
helicopter	Tom Myers
heron	From the collection of Cynthia Zilliac
hideous	Boris Karloff in "The Mummy," Universal Pictures. Courtesy of Film Stills Archive, The Museum of Modern Art.
hippopotamus	John Padour
hive	Lynn M. Stone
hogan	Adeline Haaga / Tom Stack & Associates
hollyhock	© Patrick Grace 1982 / Taurus
honeybee	Fred Winner / Gamma-Liaison

hooked	Lynn M. Stone
horned toad	Robert L. Dunne / Bruce Coleman Inc.
horse	Tom Stack / Tom Stack & Associates
hourglass	The Bettmann Archive
houseboat	© M. Timothy O'Keefe / Tom Stack & Associates
hummingbird	Anthony Mercieca / Root Resources
hurdle	Gerry Cranham / Rapho / Photo Researchers
hyacinth	S. Rannels / Grant Heilman Photography
hyena	Frederic / Jacana / Gamma-Liaison
iceberg	United States Coast Guard
iceboat	© 1985 Michael Habichi / Taurus
icebreaker	United States Coast Guard
identical	© Lenore Weber / Taurus
igloo	Information Canada Photothèque
iguana	Zig Leszczynski / Animals Animals
imaginative	From the collection of Gay Russell-Dempsey
immense	C. Bonington / Woodfin Camp & Associates, New York
impala	© Leonard Lee Rue III / Animals Animals
Inca	Peter Cummings / Tom Stack & Associates
incubator	© Herb Snitzer / Stock Boston
inedible	Film Stills Archive, The Museum of Modern Art
infancy	Library of Congress
inherit	Tom Stack / Tom Stack & Associates
inspect	Courtesy of Hughes Aircraft
insulator	Don and Pat Valenti
intent	© Herb Snitzer / Stock Boston
interchange	Tom Myers
isthmus	Fairchild Aerial Surveys Inc.
jackal	E. Lyons / Bruce Coleman Inc.
jaguar	Tom McHugh 1978 / Photo Researchers
jester	From the collection of Carol Hatcher
jewel	Folger Shakespeare Library
jib	© Bob Hahn / Taurus
jointed	Jim Nachel
joust	Courtesy of the Trustees of The British Library
junk	Shostal Associates
Jupiter	NASA
karate	Ellis Herwig / Stock Boston
katydid	Lynn M. Stone
kayak	Information Canada Photothèque
killdeer	David C. Fritts / Animals Animals
kilt	Shostal Associates
kingfisher	© Wayne Lankinen / Bruce Coleman Inc.
koala	Walter S. Clark, Jr.
kumquat	Joe Rychetnik / Photo Researchers
lacrosse	Thomas W. Putney / Putney Photo Library
ladybug	Lynn M. Stone
larva	Turton / Cambosco—Macmillan Science Company, Chicago, Ill
laser	Tom Myers
laurel	From the collection of Cynthia Zilliac
lava	Courtesy of the National Park Service
leech	Oxford Scientific Films / Animals Animals
lei	Peter Menzel / Stock Boston
lemming	Ted Levin / Animals Animals
leopard	Carlton C. McAvey
lichen	William B. Parker
lithe	© 1983 Alec Duncan / Taurus
litter	Rare Book Division. The New York Public Library, Astor, Lenox and Tilden Foundation.
lizard	Z. Leszczynski / Animals Animals
llama	F. Erize / Bruce Coleman Inc.
lock	Tom Myers
locomotive	Tom Myers
longhorn	James P. Rowan
loon	Information Canada Photothèque
lotus	Wayne Lankinen / Bruce Coleman Inc.
low tide	Nova Scotia Information Service
lubricate	© 1939 Loew's Incorporated. Ren. 1966 Metro-Goldwyn-Mayer Inc.
ludicrous	Harry Benson
lute	From the collection of Gay Russell-Dempsey
lynx	Leonard Lee Rue III / Bruce Coleman Inc.
lyre	"Music and Reading Lessons," detail from a cup by Douris. Staatliche Museen zu Berlin, Antiken-Abteilung.
magnificent	Carlton C. McAvey
magnolia	Perry D. Slocum / Earth Scenes

mail	Bashford Dean Memorial Collection, 1929, Metropolitan Museum of Art
mallard	Luke Wade © 1986 / Taurus
mammoth	Copyright Field Museum of Natural History. Artist, Charles R. Knight.
mangrove	James P. Rowan
mantis	© B. G. Murray Jr. / Animals Animals
marathon	Tom Myers 1983
matador	Wendy Wallen
maxim	The White House Historical Association
maze	Colonial Williamsburg
meadowlark	From the collection of Cynthia Zilliac
medal	Courtesy of Georgia Pacific, Hopper Paper Division
megaphone	Shostal Associates
melancholy	George Cochran Lambdin. American 1830–96. "At the Front," 1866. Oil on canvas. 18¼ x 24 in. Acc. #59.314. © 1987 The Detroit Institute of Arts, Founders Society Purchase, Directors Discretionary Fund.
memorial	Vance Henry / Taurus
mesa	Doris DeWitt © 1980 / Stock Boston
mesquite	© Yvonne Freund / Earth Scenes
milkweed	E. R. Degginger / Earth Scenes
mill wheel	Ellis Herwig / Stock Boston
mime	Joan Menschenfreund / Taurus
mimic	Lynn M. Stone
minaret	Shostal Associates
mink	Tom Brakefield / Bruce Coleman Inc.
mistletoe	Hans Reinhard / Bruce Coleman Inc.
misty	William B. Parker
mockingbird	J. Van Wormer / Bruce Coleman Inc.
mongoose	© K. G. Preston-Mafham / Animals Animals
monocle	Film Stills Archive, The Museum of Modern Art
monorail	William B. Parker
moose	© Ray Richardson / Animals Animals
moray	© Ed Robinson / Tom Stack & Associates
mosaic	Bust of Theodora. Scala / Art Resource
mosque	Walter S. Clark, Jr.
moth	Lynn M. Stone
mountain goat	Keith Gunnar / Bruce Coleman Inc.
muff	The Franklin D. Roosevelt Library
mummy	Courtesy of the Field Museum of Natural History, Chicago.
mural	Hal Franklin
musk ox	Leonard Lee Rue III / Bruce Coleman Inc.
muskrat	© Wilfred D. Schurig / Animals Animals
nape	Walter Chandoha
narcissus	Barry L. Runk / Grant Heilman Photography
nasturtium	S. Rannels / Grant Heilman Photography
neon	David Linden
nerve	Minnesota Historical Society
nestle	American 19th century sculpture, Apollo and Diana, William Henry Rinehart. The Metropolitan Museum of Art. Rogers Fund, 1905.
nettle	© B. G. Murray, Jr. / Earth Scenes
newborn	Tom Myers
newt	E. R. Degginger / Bruce Coleman Inc.
niche	© Donald Dietz / Stock Boston
nightingale	Hans Reinhard / Bruce Coleman Inc.
nomad	Courtesy of Exxon Corporation
northern lights	National Oceanic & Atmospheric Administration
noteworthy	Union Pacific Railroad Museum Collection
notorious	Rare Book Division, New York Public Library. Astor, Lenox and Tilden Foundation.
novel	Bob Amft
nucleus	Courtesy of the Carolina Biological Supply Company
nugget	Museum of Natural History, Smithsonian Institution
nuzzle	Film Stills Archive, The Museum of Modern Art
nymph	D. R. Specker / Animals Animals
obelisk	Walter S. Clark, Jr.
obsidian	Breck P. Kent / Earth Scenes
obsolete	The Bettmann Archive
ocelot	Gary Milburn / Tom Stack & Associates
octopus	Jane Burton / Bruce Coleman Inc.
ogre	From the collection of Gay Russell-Dempsey
olive	© Mike Andrews / Earth Scenes
ominous	"Grey and Gold," John Rogers Cox, 1942. The Cleveland Museum of Art. Mr. and Mrs. William H. Marlatt Fund.

opal — E. R. Degginger / Bruce Coleman Inc.

opossum — John H. Gerard

orangutan — Grossa / Jacana / Gamma-Liaison

orchid — Don and Pat Valenti

oriole — Ben Goldstein / Valenti Photography

ornate — Gary Wolinsky / Stock Boston

ostrich — Mark A. Mittelman / Taurus

otter — William B. Parker

outrigger — Bob Frerck / Odyssey Productions

owl — From the collection of Cynthia Zilliac

oxcart — J. Somers / Taurus

pack animal — Jack D. Swenson / Tom Stack & Associates

paddle wheel — © Richard Pasley / Stock Boston

paddy — Walter S. Clark, Jr.

pagoda — J. Kugler / FPG

palmetto — Ronald Orenstein / Earth Scenes

panda — Smithsonian Institution

paramecium — Ed Reschke

parasite — Gail Nachel

passenger pigeon — Watercolor by John Audubon. New York Historical Society

peace pipe — Carlton C. McAvey

pearl — Robert Joslin / Root Resources

peccary — Lynn M. Stone

Pekingese — © Michael & Barbara Reed / Animals Animals

pelican — Lynn M. Stone

penguin — © Suinot / Jacana / Gamma-Liaison

pentagon — U.S. Navy Photo

perplex — © Richard Feiner & Company Inc. By permission of Hal Roach Studio.

pewter — Don and Pat Valenti

pheasant — © A. Duchot / Jacana / Gamma-Liaison

pier — Lynn M. Stone

piñata — © 1983 Alec Duncan / Taurus

pincer — Lynn M. Stone

placid — Lynn M. Stone

planetarium — Adler Planetarium, Chicago

plover — © Gordon Langsbury / Bruce Coleman Inc.

plumage — Walter S. Clark, Jr.

poinsettia — Kitty Kohout / Don and Pat Valenti

poison ivy — Don and Pat Valenti

polar bear — J. Stoll / Jacana / Gamma-Liaison

pole vault — Tom Myers

polyp — © M. Timothy O'Keefe / Tom Stack & Associates

poncho — Owen Franken / Stock Boston

pontoon — © Claire Talpin 1981 / Taurus

poodle — Hans Reinhard / Bruce Coleman Inc.

porcelain — Birthday Group, German Porcelain c. 1771. Artist, Frankenthal after a model by K. G. Luck. Courtesy of the Trustees of the British Museum.

porcupine — © Scott Ransom / Taurus

porpoise — Official photograph, U.S. Navy

portico — Virginia Conservation Commission, Richmond, Va.

portrait — Pocahontas. The National Portrait Gallery, The Smithsonian Institution, Washington, D.C.

potter — Courtesy of the United Nations

pout — Jack Wallen

prairie dog — Lynn M. Stone

prairie schooner — Settlers wagon. Index of American Design. National Gallery of Art.

predatory — From the collection of Cynthia Zilliac

preen — Lynn M. Stone

prickly pear — Lynn M. Stone

profile — Carlton C. McAvey

promontory — George Catlin. "Distant View of Mandan Village," 1832, oil on canvas 11¼ x 14½ in. 1985. 66.379. National Museum of American Art, Smithsonian Institution; Gift of Mrs. Joseph Harrison, Jr.

pronghorn — L. West / Bruce Coleman Inc.

propeller — Newport News Shipbuilding & Drydock Company

proportion — John Tenniel illustration from Lewis Carroll's "Alice's Adventures in Wonderland"

protist — Brian Parker / Tom Stack & Associates

provocation — Film Stills Archive, The Museum of Modern Art

ptarmigan — Lynn M. Stone

pucker — Culver Pictures

puff — Lynn M. Stone

puffin — Gordon Langsbury / Bruce Coleman Inc.

puma — Brian Parker / Tom Stack & Associates

pupa — E. R. Degginger / Animals Animals

pussy willow — Lynn M. Stone

pyramid (building) — Courtesy of Transamerica

pyramid (Egypt) — Walter S. Clark, Jr.

quail — C. W. Schwartz / Animals Animals

quartz — William B. Parker

queue — Copyrighted July 7, 1986, Chicago Tribune Company. All rights reserved, used with permission.

raccoon — © John Shaw / Tom Stack & Associates

racquetball — © Frank Siteman 1985 / Taurus

rage — Bettmann Newsphotos

ram — © Leonard Lee Rue III / Animals Animals

rapid — © Doug Lee / Tom Stack & Associates

rapt — Jerry Howard / Pioneer Press

ravage — Wide World

ray — Doug Wallin / Taurus

rear — Film Stills Archive, The Museum of Modern Art

recline — © John Lei / Stock Boston

reef — Walter S. Clark, Jr.

refuge — Anthony Mercieca / Root Resources

relay — Thomas Hopker / Woodfin Camp & Associates, New York

relief — Roman Emperor in a triumphal chariot drawn by four horses. Capitoline Museum, Art Resource.

represent — Guy Gillette / Photo Researchers

resemble — Klaus D. Francke / Peter Arnold, Inc.

reservoir — Chicago Bridge and Iron Company

restrain — Jack Wallen

rhododendron — Lynn M. Stone

rib — Information Canada Photothèque

roadrunner — Joe McDonald / Animals Animals

robot — Peter Menzel / Stock Boston

rosette — Don and Pat Valenti

rotor — John Madeley / R. C. Photo Agency

rubble — N.O.A.A.

ruin — Tom Myers

rush — Ted Levin / Earth Scenes

russet — Lynn M. Stone

sable — Wayne Lankinen / Bruce Coleman Inc.

sacrifice — Raymond V. Schoder, S. J.

saguaro — © Richard Pasley / Stock Boston

salamander — Lynn M. Stone

salmon — Lynn M. Stone

sampan — Adrienne Gibson / Tom Stack & Associates

sandpiper — From the collection of Cynthia Zilliac

sari — Jean-Claude LeJeune

satellite — NASA

scaffold — Uris Building Corporation

scallop — Oxford Scientific Films / Animals Animals

scepter — Cecil Beaton, London, England

schooner — Stuart Cohen / Stock Boston

scorpion — Rod Planck / Tom Stack & Associates

scribe — Staatsbibliothek, Bremen

sea anemone — Bill Tronca © 1981 / Tom Stack & Associates

sea horse — Jane Burton / Bruce Coleman Inc.

sea lion — Lynn M. Stone

sedan chair — Messrs. Mallett and Son, London

seine — F.D.A.

sequoia — Tom Stack / Tom Stack & Associates

settee — Sheraton Style Settee. Index of American Design. National Gallery of Art, Washington, D.C.

severe — © Bob McKeever 1981 / Tom Stack & Associates

shark — Peter Lake / Sea Library / Tom Stack & Associates

sheer — Jim Yuskavitch / Tom Stack & Associates

Shetland pony — Ralph A. Reinhold / Animals Animals

shrew — Jerry Hennen

shrimp — O. M. Opresko / Taurus

sierra — Dale Jorgenson / Tom Stack & Associates

silo — William B. Parker

single-handed — Carlton C. McAvey

sinister — © Lucasfilm Ltd. (LFL) 1980. All rights reserved. Courtesy of Lucasfilm Ltd.

skate — Bill Tronca / Tom Stack & Associates

skydiving — © Guy Sauvage / Photo Researchers

slat — Janet Edwards / Eastman Kodak Company

sloop — Courtesy of Pearson Yachts.

sloth — © David C. Houston / Bruce Coleman Inc.

slug — Lynn M. Stone

snail — Lynn M. Stone

snapping turtle — © Patti Murray / Animals Animals

snoop — From the collection of Gay Russell-Dempsey

snowflake — National Oceanic & Atmospheric Administration

snowmobile — Randy Hyman / Stock Boston

soccer — A. J. Wright / Taurus

sod — Solomon D. Butcher Collection, Nebraska State Historical Society.

solemn — Detail from "Two Boys in a Garden," attributed to John Duran, © 1770. Courtesy of The Connecticut Historical Society.

sop — Allan Roberts

space shuttle — NASA

spangle — Owen Franken / Stock Boston

spectacular — William B. Parker

spelunker — © 1986 Kerry T. Givens / Tom Stack & Associates

sperm whale — "Capturing a Sperm Whale." Engraving by John Gill, 1835. Courtesy of The New York Historical Society.

sphere — NASA

sphinx — © M. Timothy O'Keefe / Tom Stack & Associates

spin — Walter S. Clark, Jr.

spine — Lynn M. Stone

spire — Salisbury Cathedral, Courtesy of the National Monuments Record.

split — Orville Schell / Jeroboam Inc.

sponge — Barry Parker / Bruce Coleman Inc.

spoonbill — M. Amsterman / Animals Animals

squid — © Fred Bauendam / Peter Arnold, Inc.

squint — Don and Pat Valenti

squire — Pierpont Morgan Library

stained glass — Philip Jon Bailey / Taurus

stalactite — Breck P. Kent / Earth Scenes

stamen — Lynn M. Stone

starfish — William B. Parker

stark — NASA

starling — J. Markham / Bruce Coleman Inc.

stegosaurus — Neg. / Trans. No. V/C336. Charles R. Knight painting. Courtesy Department Library Services, American Museum of Natural History.

stork — Lynn M. Stone

strain — George Silk / Life Picture Service (Life Magazine, Time Inc.)

stunt (tree) — Holsten Bonsai Collection, Brooklyn Botanic Gardens.

stunt (action) — Syndication International

sturgeon — Gary Milburn / Tom Stack & Associates

sucker — © Zig Leszczynski / Animals Animals

sugar beet — Grant Heilman / Grant Heilman Photography

sugar maple — Mary A. Root / Root Resources

sulky — Steve Hansen / Stock Boston

sumac — Leonard Lee Rue III / Earth Scenes

summit — Spencer Swanger / Tom Stack & Associates

sundial — E. R. Degginger / Earth Scenes

supple — Martha Swope

sure-footed — Breck P. Kent / Animals Animals

surfing — Neil Leifer / Sports Illustrated (Sports Illustrated, Time Inc.)

suspend — © 1980 Norman R. Thompson / Taurus

suspension bridge — Gregg Mancuso / Stock Boston

swallow — Leonard Lee Rue III / Tom Stack & Associates

swarm — Tom Myers

swept-back — William B. Parker

swift — James Hancock / Photo Researchers

symmetry — William B. Parker

tablet — "Moses Breaking the Tables of the Law." Detail of an illustration by Gustave Doré, 1866, Doré Gallery, London

tandem — L. L. T. Rhodes / Taurus

tapestry — "The Woodpecker Tapestry," (1885–1887). William Morris. Photo: Woodmansterne / Clive Friend.

tapir — W. Garst / Tom Stack & Associates

tarantula — J. McDonald / Bruce Coleman Inc.

taro — Jen & Des Bartlett / Bruce Coleman Inc.

tawny — Dan Baliotte / Animals Animals

teal	John Gerlach / Animals Animals		tyrannosaurus	Neg. / Trans. No. V/C PK212. Painting by Charles P. Knight. Courtesy of the Department of Library Services, American Museum of Natural History.
team	Caterpillar Tractor Co.			
teddy bear	Neg. #326107. Courtesy Department of Library Services. American Museum of Natural History.		ugly	E.S.S.A.
			unaware	From the collection of Gay Russell-Dempsey
tempest	Etching for "The Rime of the Ancient Mariner," by Gustave Doré. First published in 1875 by the Doré Gallery, London.		underdeveloped	F.A.O.
			ungainly	Tom Myers
tepee	Lynn M. Stone		unicorn	16th century. "The Hunt of the Unicorn," silk and wool, silver and silver gilt threads. From the chateau of Verteiu. The Cloister Collection, Gift of John D. Rockefeller Jr., 1937, Metropolitan Museum of Art
tern	John Gerlach / Animals Animals			
terrace	Spencer Swanger / Tom Stack & Associates			
thatch	Diane K. Lowe / Stock Boston			
thistle	Kitty Kohout / Don and Pat Valenti		unicycle	Tom Myers
thunderhead	Peter Pearson / Click / Chicago Ltd.		unison	UNICEF Collection
tick	Zig Leszcynski / Animals Animals		unwieldy	Republic Aviation Corporation, Farmingdale, Long Island, N.Y.
tiger	Zig Leszcynski / Animals Animals			
tightrope	Shostal Associates		Uranus	NASA (JPL/NASA)
timberline	Lynn M. Stone		valentine	From the collection of Lois Metcalf.
tinge	Lynn M. Stone		vane	H. Armstrong Roberts
toboggan	Tom Myers		vault	Folger Shakespeare Library
toil	"The Gleaners," by Jean F. Millet. Art Resource		vein	Lynn M. Stone
			vendor	"Root Beer Seller," Nicolino Calyo. Museum of the City of New York.
tomahawk	Cat. #17/5088 + 21/1295. Museum of the American Indian, Heye Foundation, N.Y.			
			veranda	Walter S. Clark, Jr.
tornado	E.S.S.A.		villain	"Lone Hand Saunders," Film Still Archive, The Museum of Modern Art.
torrent	UNICEF Collection			
toucan	© John Cheilman / Animals Animals		virus	Gene M. Milbrath, Department of Plant Pathology, University of Illinois.
track	Information Canada Photothèque			
train	From the collection of Cynthia Zilliac		vivid	South African Travel Bureau
transform	Copyright © by Universal Pictures, a Division of Universal City Studios, Inc. Courtesy of MCA Publishing Rights, a Division of MCA Inc.		vulture	Lynn M. Stone
			walrus	Bruce Coleman Inc. (F. Erize)
			wampum	Cat. #5/3150. Museum of the American Indian, Heye Foundation, N.Y.
tree frog	© Bob McKeever 1982 / Tom Stack & Associates			
			warbler	From the collection of Cynthia Zilliac
triceratops	Neg. / Trans. No. PK213. Courtesy of the Department of Library Services, American Museum of Natural History.		wasp	R. E. Pelham / Bruce Coleman Inc.
			water buffalo	Walter S. Clark, Jr.
			watercolor	Prendergast, Maurice. "The East River, 1901." Watercolor 13 3/4 x 19 3/4. Collection of The Museum of Modern Art, New York. Gift of Abby Aldrich Rockefeller.
trophy	Leo Mason / Focus West			
tulips	Don and Pat Valenti			
turban	Walter S. Clark, Jr.			
turrets	Ken Rapalee / Root Resources			

waterlily	Lynn M. Stone
way	From the collection of Gay Russell-Dempsey
weasel	Bob & Clara Calhoun / Bruce Coleman Inc.
weather vane	Index of American Design, National Gallery of Art, Washington, D.C.
weave	Walter S. Clark, Jr.
weightless	NASA
weld	Willie Hill Jr. / Stock Boston
whelk	Lynn M. Stone
whimsical	From the collection of Gay Russell-Dempsey
whippoorwill	From the collection of Cynthia Zilliac
whitecaps	Ann McQueen / Stock Boston
wigwam	Museum of the American Indian, Heye Foundation, N.Y.
willful	From the collection of Gay Russell-Dempsey
wing	Lynn M. Stone
wintry	R. Kluge / Bruce Coleman Inc.
withdraw	Lynn M. Stone
wolverine	Tom McHugh / Photo Researchers
woodchuck	Leonard Lee Rue III / Animals Animals
woodpecker	From the collection of Cynthia Zilliac
wren	Leonard Lee Rue III / Bruce Coleman Inc.
writhe	George Benjamin Luks. "The Wrestlers," 1905. American, 1867–1933. Oil on canvas. 48½ x 66½ in. Charles Henry Hayden Fund. Courtesy Museum of Fine Arts, Boston.
X-ray	John Moran
yak	F.A.O.
yucca	© Bob McKeever / Tom Stack & Associates
zebu	Norman Owen Tomlin / Bruce Coleman Inc.
zeppelin	Wide World
zigzag	Gretchen Garner

Student's Reference Section

Student's Reference Section

The Solar System and the Milky Way

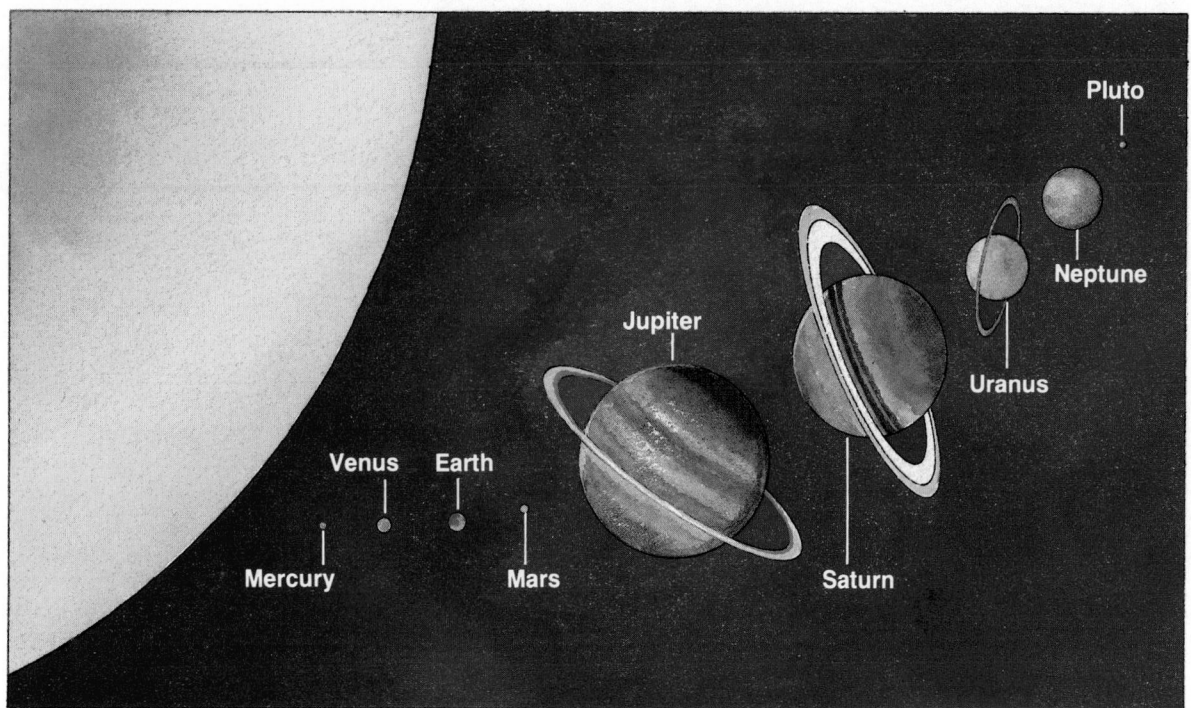

The Solar System

The sun and all of the heavenly bodies that orbit it make up the solar system. Earth is one of nine major planets in the solar system. These planets are shown in the diagram above in order of their distance from the sun. Thousands of minor planets called asteroids also travel around the sun between the orbits of Mars and Jupiter. Comets and meteors are also found in the solar system. More than thirty natural satellites orbit the planets. The moon is the earth's only natural satellite.

The Milky Way

The sun is a star. It is one of a vast group of stars that form our galaxy. A galaxy is a huge cloud of many billions of stars. Galaxies are shaped like disks with a bulge at the center. Since we are inside our galaxy, which is called the Milky Way, we can only see parts of it. The Milky Way is thought to have several arms. Our solar system is located on one of the arms.

   Our galaxy is called the Milky Way because the part of it that we can see appears as a broad, milky-white band of light across the night sky.

Milky Way Galaxy
above, top view; below, side view.
The dot shows the estimated
position of the solar system,
which contains the planet Earth.

The World

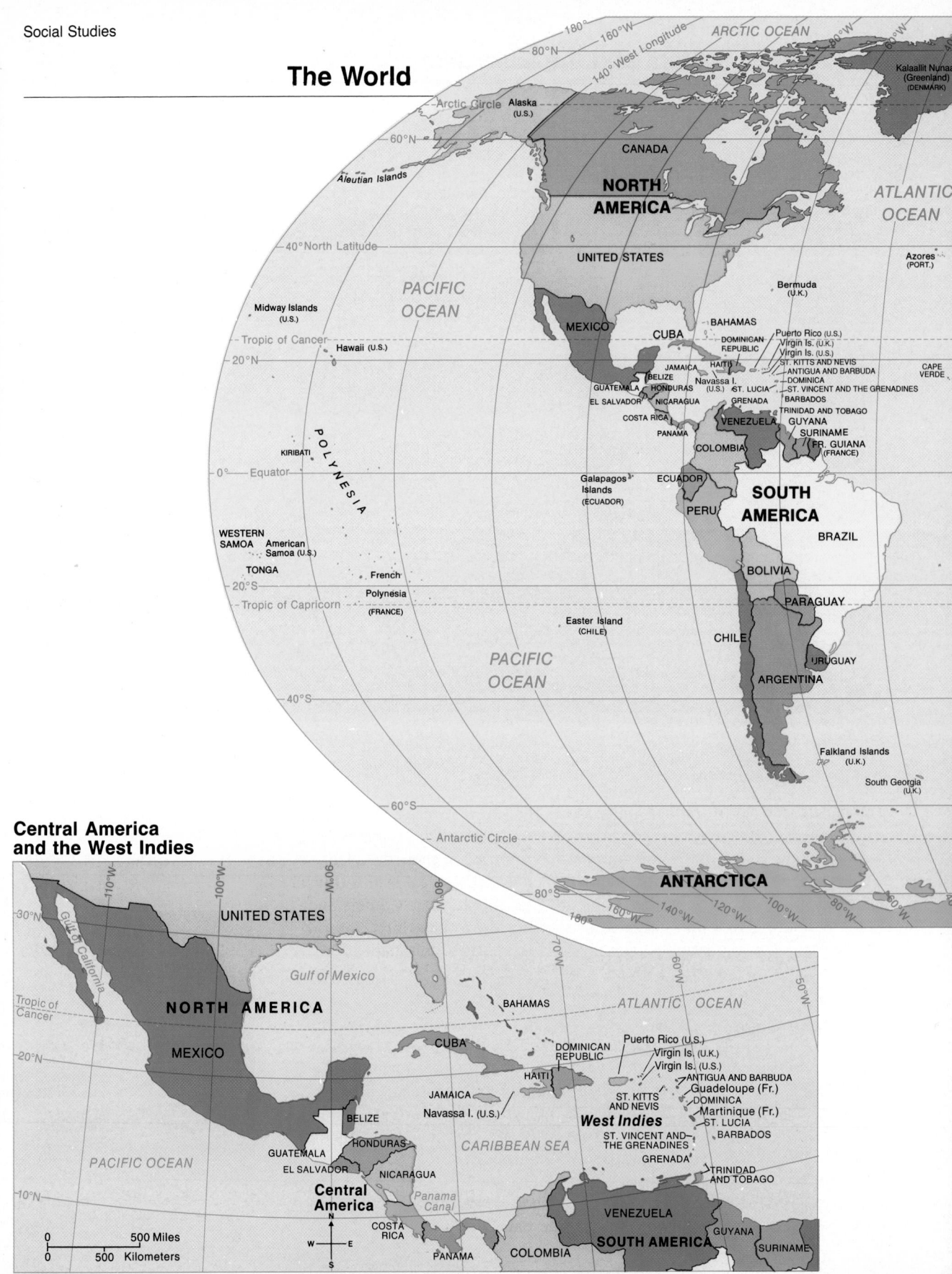

ARCTIC OCEAN

Kalaallit Nunaat
(Greenland)
(DENMARK)

Arctic Circle Alaska
(U.S.)

80°N

60°N

CANADA

**NORTH
AMERICA**

ATLANTIC
OCEAN

Aleutian Islands

40°North Latitude

UNITED STATES

Azores
(PORT.)

PACIFIC
OCEAN

Bermuda
(U.K.)

Midway Islands
(U.S.)

MEXICO

BAHAMAS

Puerto Rico (U.S.)

CAPE
VERDE

Tropic of Cancer

CUBA

DOMINICAN
REPUBLIC

Virgin Is. (U.K.)
Virgin Is. (U.S.)
ST. KITTS AND NEVIS

20°N

Hawaii (U.S.)

HAITI

ANTIGUA AND BARBUDA

JAMAICA

Navassa I.
(U.S.) ST. LUCIA

DOMINICA
ST. VINCENT AND THE GRENADINES

GUATEMALA HONDURAS
EL SALVADOR NICARAGUA

BELIZE

BARBADOS

GRENADA

TRINIDAD AND TOBAGO

COSTA RICA

VENEZUELA

GUYANA
SURINAME

KIRIBATI

PANAMA

COLOMBIA

FR. GUIANA
(FRANCE)

P
O
L
Y
N
E
S
I
A

0° Equator

Galapagos
Islands
(ECUADOR)

ECUADOR

**SOUTH
AMERICA**

PERU

WESTERN
SAMOA American
Samoa (U.S.)

BRAZIL

BOLIVIA

TONGA

French

20°S

Polynesia
(FRANCE)

Tropic of Capricorn

Easter Island
(CHILE)

PARAGUAY

CHILE

URUGUAY

ARGENTINA

PACIFIC
OCEAN

40°S

Falkland Islands
(U.K.)

South Georgia
(U.K.)

60°S

Antarctic Circle

80°S

ANTARCTICA

Central America
and the West Indies

UNITED STATES

30°N

Gulf of California

Gulf of Mexico

NORTH AMERICA

BAHAMAS

ATLANTIC OCEAN

Tropic of
Cancer

MEXICO

CUBA

DOMINICAN
REPUBLIC

Puerto Rico (U.S.)
Virgin Is. (U.K.)
Virgin Is. (U.S.)

20°N

HAITI

ANTIGUA AND BARBUDA

JAMAICA

Guadeloupe (Fr.)

ST. KITTS
AND NEVIS

DOMINICA
Martinique (Fr.)

Navassa I. (U.S.)

BELIZE

West Indies

ST. LUCIA

PACIFIC OCEAN

CARIBBEAN SEA

ST. VINCENT AND
THE GRENADINES

BARBADOS

GUATEMALA HONDURAS

GRENADA

TRINIDAD
AND TOBAGO

EL SALVADOR NICARAGUA

10°N

**Central
America**

N

Panama
Canal

VENEZUELA

GUYANA

COSTA
RICA

W   E

PANAMA

COLOMBIA

SOUTH AMERICA

SURINAME

S

0   500 Miles

0   500 Kilometers

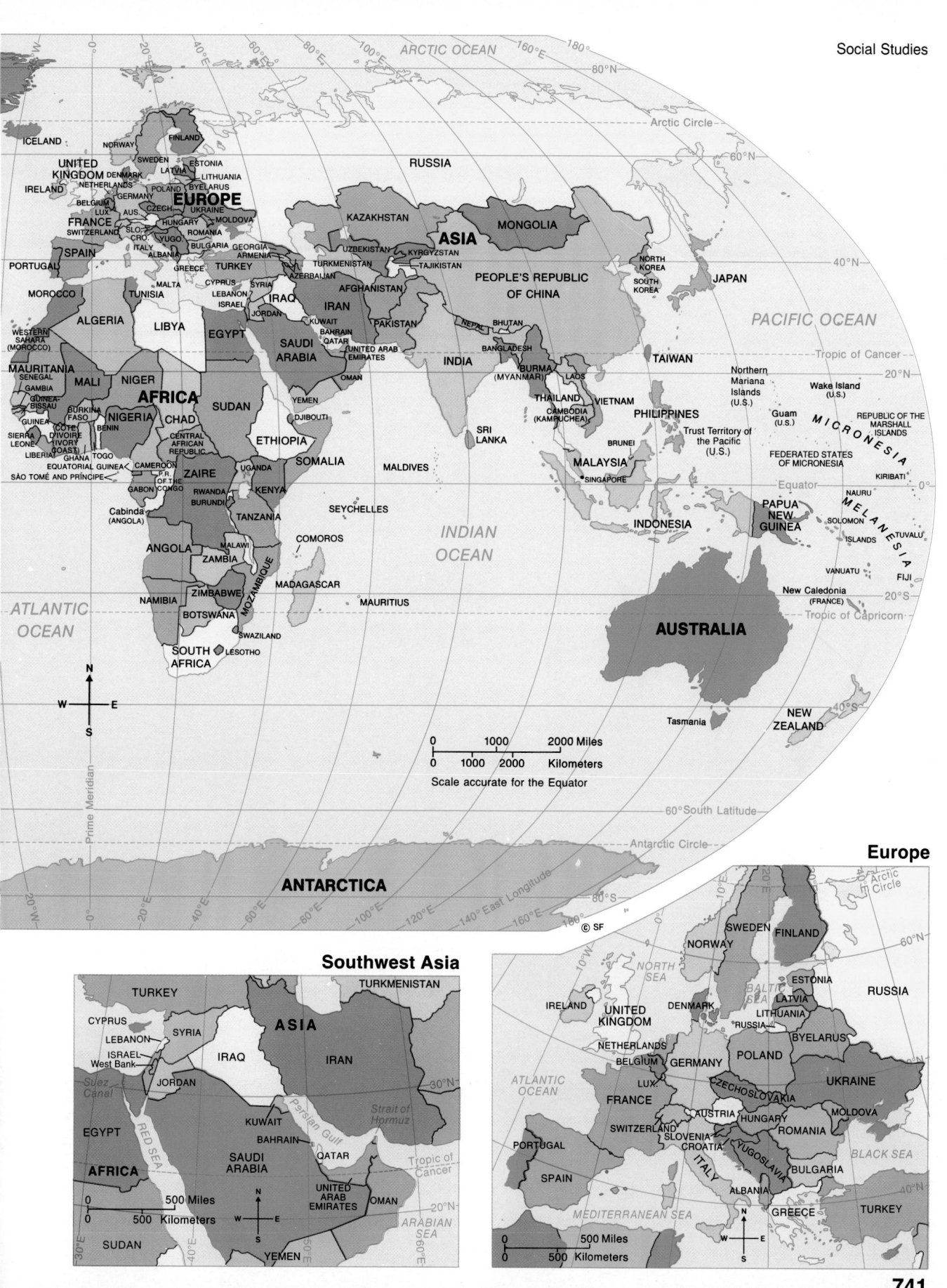

Southwest Asia

Europe

Locating Places

Any place on earth can be located by using hemispheres, latitude lines (parallels) and longitude lines (meridians), or continents and oceans to find it on a globe or map.

Hemispheres

Northern Hemisphere

Western Hemisphere

Southern Hemisphere

Eastern Hemisphere

Latitude and Longitude

Parallels

Meridians

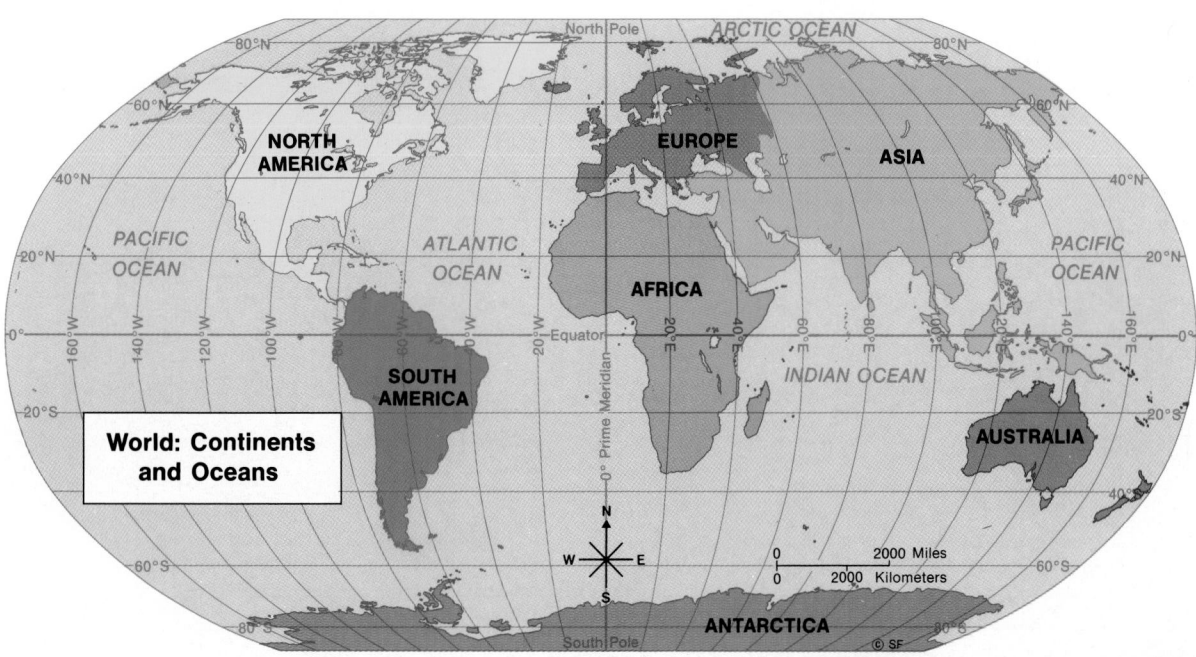

   Latitude lines are imaginary lines numbered in degrees north and south of the equator. The latitude of the equator is 0°, that of the North Pole is 90° North, and that of the South Pole is 90° South.
   Longitude lines are imaginary lines numbered in degrees east and west of the prime meridian, which runs through Greenwich, England, and has a longitude of 0°. The other longitude lines are numbered from 1° to 180° east or west of it.

Continents and Oceans

World: Continents and Oceans

The United States

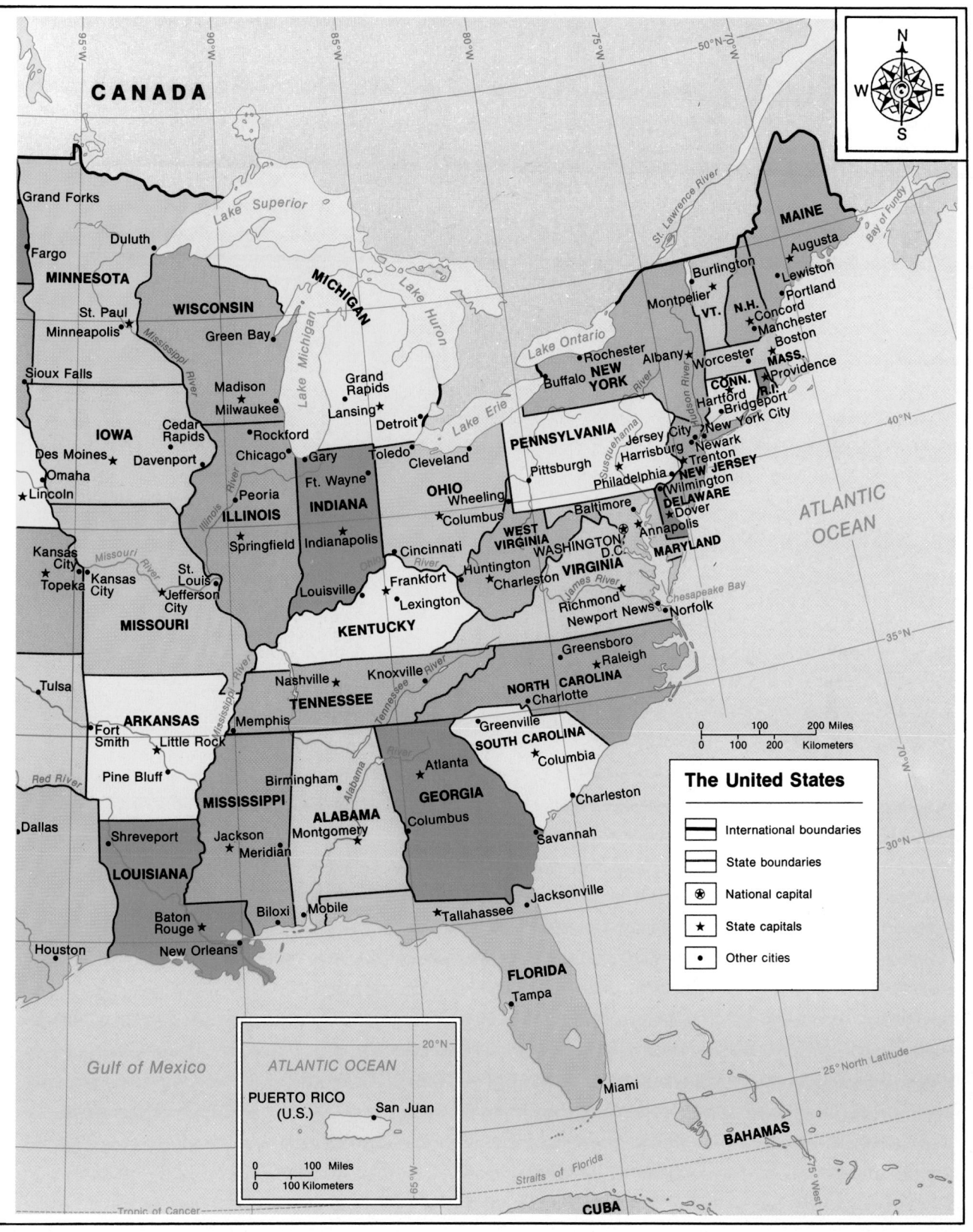

CANADA

Grand Forks
Duluth
Fargo
MINNESOTA
St. Paul
Minneapolis
Sioux Falls
WISCONSIN
Green Bay
Madison
Milwaukee
IOWA
Cedar Rapids
Des Moines
Davenport
Omaha
Lincoln
ILLINOIS
Rockford
Chicago
Gary
Peoria
Springfield
INDIANA
Ft. Wayne
Indianapolis
Kansas City
Topeka
Kansas City
St. Louis
Jefferson City
MISSOURI
Tulsa
ARKANSAS
Fort Smith
Little Rock
Pine Bluff
Dallas
LOUISIANA
Shreveport
Houston
Baton Rouge
New Orleans

MICHIGAN
Lake Superior
Lake Michigan
Lake Huron
Grand Rapids
Lansing
Detroit
Toledo
Cleveland
OHIO
Wheeling
Columbus
Cincinnati
Frankfort
Louisville
Lexington
KENTUCKY
Nashville
Knoxville
TENNESSEE
Memphis
Birmingham
MISSISSIPPI
Jackson
Meridian
ALABAMA
Montgomery
Columbus
GEORGIA
Atlanta
Biloxi
Mobile
Tallahassee
Jacksonville

Lake Ontario
Lake Erie
PENNSYLVANIA
Pittsburgh
Harrisburg
Philadelphia
WEST VIRGINIA
Huntington
Charleston
VIRGINIA
WASHINGTON D.C.
Richmond
Newport News
Norfolk
Rochester
Buffalo
NEW YORK
Albany
Worcester
MAINE
Augusta
Lewiston
Portland
Burlington
Montpelier
VT. N.H.
Concord
Manchester
Boston
MASS.
Providence
CONN.
Hartford
R.I.
Bridgeport
New York City
Jersey City
Newark
Trenton
NEW JERSEY
Wilmington
DELAWARE
Dover
Baltimore
Annapolis
MARYLAND
Chesapeake Bay
ATLANTIC OCEAN
Greensboro
Raleigh
NORTH CAROLINA
Charlotte
Greenville
SOUTH CAROLINA
Columbia
Charleston
Savannah

FLORIDA
Tampa
Miami

Gulf of Mexico
BAHAMAS
CUBA
Straits of Florida

The United States

▬	International boundaries
	State boundaries
⊛	National capital
★	State capitals
•	Other cities

0 100 200 Miles
0 100 200 Kilometers

ATLANTIC OCEAN
20°N
PUERTO RICO (U.S.)
San Juan
0 100 Miles
0 100 Kilometers

Tropic of Cancer

Facts About the Fifty States

Alabama USA 20c — Yellowhammer & Camellia
Alaska USA 20c — Willow Ptarmigan & Forget-Me-Not
Arizona USA 20c — Cactus Wren & Saguaro Cactus Blossom
Arkansas USA 20c — Mockingbird & Apple Blossom
California USA 20c — California Quail & California Poppy
Colorado USA 20c — Lark Bunting & Rocky Mountain Columbine
Connecticut USA 20c — Robin & Mountain Laurel
Delaware USA 20c — Blue Hen Chicken & Peach Blossom

Florida USA 20c — Mockingbird & Orange Blossom
Georgia USA 20c — Brown Thrasher & Cherokee Rose
Hawaii USA 20c — Hawaiian Goose & Hibiscus
Idaho USA 20c — Mountain Bluebird & Syringa
Illinois USA 20c — Cardinal & Violet
Indiana USA 20c — Cardinal & Peony
Iowa USA 20c — Eastern Goldfinch & Wild Rose
Kansas USA 20c — Western Meadowlark & Sunflower

State	U.S. Postal Service Abbreviation	State Capital	State Nickname	Year Admitted to Union	Order of Admission
Alabama	AL	Montgomery	Yellowhammer State	1819	22
Alaska	AK	Juneau	The Last Frontier	1959	49
Arizona	AZ	Phoenix	Grand Canyon State	1912	48
Arkansas	AR	Little Rock	Land of Opportunity	1836	25
California	CA	Sacramento	Golden State	1850	31
Colorado	CO	Denver	Centennial State	1876	38
Connecticut	CT	Hartford	Nutmeg State	1788	5
Delaware	DE	Dover	Diamond State	1787	1
Florida	FL	Tallahassee	Sunshine State	1845	27
Georgia	GA	Atlanta	Peach State	1788	4
Hawaii	HI	Honolulu	Aloha State	1959	50
Idaho	ID	Boise	Gem State	1890	43
Illinois	IL	Springfield	Prairie State	1818	21
Indiana	IN	Indianapolis	Hoosier State	1816	19
Iowa	IA	Des Moines	Hawkeye State	1846	29
Kansas	KS	Topeka	Sunflower State	1861	34
Kentucky	KY	Frankfort	Bluegrass State	1792	15
Louisiana	LA	Baton Rouge	Pelican State	1812	18

Kentucky USA 20c — Cardinal & Goldenrod

Louisiana USA 20c — Brown Pelican & Magnolia

State	U.S. Postal Service Abbreviation	State Capital	State Nickname	Year Admitted to Union	Order of Admission
Maine	ME	Augusta	Pine Tree State	1820	23
Maryland	MD	Annapolis	Free State	1788	7
Massachusetts	MA	Boston	Bay State	1788	6
Michigan	MI	Lansing	Wolverine State	1837	26
Minnesota	MN	St. Paul	North Star State	1858	32
Mississippi	MS	Jackson	Magnolia State	1817	20
Missouri	MO	Jefferson City	Show Me State	1821	24
Montana	MT	Helena	Treasure State	1889	41
Nebraska	NE	Lincoln	Cornhusker State	1867	37
Nevada	NV	Carson City	Silver State	1864	36
New Hampshire	NH	Concord	Granite State	1788	9
New Jersey	NJ	Trenton	Garden State	1787	3
New Mexico	NM	Santa Fe	Land of Enchantment	1912	47
New York	NY	Albany	Empire State	1788	11
North Carolina	NC	Raleigh	Tar Heel State	1789	12
North Dakota	ND	Bismarck	Sioux State	1889	39

State	U.S. Postal Service Abbreviation	State Capital	State Nickname	Year Admitted to Union	Order of Admission
Ohio	OH	Columbus	Buckeye State	1803	17
Oklahoma	OK	Oklahoma City	Sooner State	1907	46
Oregon	OR	Salem	Beaver State	1859	33
Pennsylvania	PA	Harrisburg	Keystone State	1787	2
Rhode Island	RI	Providence	Ocean State	1790	13
South Carolina	SC	Columbia	Palmetto State	1788	8
South Dakota	SD	Pierre	Sunshine State	1889	40
Tennessee	TN	Nashville	Volunteer State	1796	16
Texas	TX	Austin	Lone Star State	1845	28
Utah	UT	Salt Lake City	Beehive State	1896	45
Vermont	VT	Montpelier	Green Mountain State	1791	14
Virginia	VA	Richmond	The Old Dominion	1788	10
Washington	WA	Olympia	Evergreen State	1889	42
West Virginia	WV	Charleston	Mountain State	1863	35
Wisconsin	WI	Madison	Badger State	1848	30
Wyoming	WY	Cheyenne	Equality State	1890	44

The Presidents of the United States

1. George Washington 1789–1797* **2. John Adams** 1797–1801   **3. Thomas Jefferson** 1801–1809

Born in Virginia in 1732, he was the commanding general in the Revolutionary War, and a strong uniting force for the new nation. He was everyone's choice for President. He died in 1799.

Adams was born in Massachusetts in 1735. He was a leader in the Revolution, and was vice-president under Washington. He was the first President to live in the White House. He died in 1826.

Jefferson was born in Virginia in 1743. He wrote the Declaration of Independence. The U.S. doubled its size by buying the Louisiana Territory from France while he was President. He died in 1826.

4. James Madison 1809–1817   **5. James Monroe** 1817–1825   **6. John Quincy Adams** 1825–1829

Madison was born in Virginia in 1751. When he was President, trouble with the British resulted in the War of 1812. During this war, the British captured and burned the capital. He died in 1836.

Monroe was born in Virginia in 1758. He bought Florida from Spain. He also warned the countries of Europe against trying to set up any more colonies in the Americas. He died in 1831.

Born in Massachusetts, he was President when the Erie Canal opened, making it easier to travel west. Later, as a Congressman, he spoke out against slavery. He died in 1848.

7. Andrew Jackson 1829–1837   **8. Martin Van Buren** 1837–1841   **9. William Henry Harrison** 1841

Born in South Carolina in 1767, he gave government jobs to his followers. Eastern Indians were forced to move west of the Mississippi River when he was President. He died in 1845.

Van Buren was born in New York in 1782. When he was President, times were bad. Banks closed and workers lost their jobs. Disputes about the U.S.-Canadian border were settled. He died in 1862.

Harrison was born in Virginia in 1773. He was a popular military hero. He caught cold at his 1841 inauguration and died a month later. He was the first President to die in office.

*Dates following President's name are the dates of his term of office.

10. John Tyler 1841–1845

Born in Virginia in 1790, he had problems with Congress and vetoed many bills. He made peace with the Indians in Florida and signed a pact with China, opening it to traders. He died in 1862.

11. James K. Polk 1845–1849

Born in North Carolina in 1795, he was President when Texas joined the U.S. The Oregon border dispute with England was settled. In the Mexican War, the U.S. gained territory. He died in 1849.

12. Zachary Taylor 1849–1850

Taylor was born in Virginia in 1784. He was a hero of the Mexican War. As President, he opposed slavery in California and other land won in the Mexican War. This angered the South. He died in office in 1850.

13. Millard Fillmore 1850–1853

Fillmore was born in New York in 1800. When he was President there were serious problems over slavery. He failed to solve them. He sent an expedition to begin trade with Japan. He died in 1874.

14. Franklin Pierce 1853–1857

Pierce was born in New Hampshire in 1804. When he was President, a new law let settlers decide on slavery in Kansas and Nebraska. This increased problems between North and South. He died in 1869.

15. James Buchanan 1857–1861

Buchanan was born in 1791 in Pennsylvania. When he was President, the U.S. faced war over slavery. The South threatened to leave the Union, and 7 states did leave. He died in 1868.

16. Abraham Lincoln 1861–1865

Lincoln was born in Kentucky in 1809. He was President during the Civil War. He vowed to preserve the Union. He freed the slaves in the South. In 1865, just after the war's end, he was shot to death.

17. Andrew Johnson 1865–1869

Johnson was born in North Carolina in 1808. He and Congress battled over how state government should be restored in the South. Congress tried to remove him from office, but failed. He died in 1875.

18. Ulysses S. Grant 1869–1877

Born in Ohio in 1822, he was a Civil War hero. He was President when blacks were given voting rights. He gave important jobs to men who proved to be dishonest. He died in 1885.

19. Rutherford B. Hayes
1877–1881

Hayes was born in Ohio in 1822. He withdrew federal troops from the South. He favored civil service reform, and gave government jobs to those best qualified. He died in 1893.

20. James A. Garfield 1881

Born in Ohio in 1831, he tried to bring about government reforms, but Congress opposed him. A disappointed job seeker shot him, and he died from his injuries a few months later, in 1881.

21. Chester A. Arthur 1881–1885

Born in Vermont in 1830, he worked for a fair way to hire qualified workers, not political supporters, for government jobs. The Civil Service Commission was set up as a result. He died in 1886.

22. and 24. Grover Cleveland
1885–1889 and 1893–1897

Born in New Jersey in 1837, he tried to help farmers and factory workers. A law to control interstate trade was passed. During his second term many businesses failed. He died in 1908.

23. Benjamin Harrison
1889–1893

Harrison was born in Ohio in 1833. When he was President, taxes on imported goods were increased. This protected American-made goods from foreign competition. He died in 1901.

25. William McKinley 1897–1901

McKinley was born in Ohio in 1843. The Spanish-American War took place when he was President. The U.S. became a world power. He was shot in 1901, and died eight days later.

26. Theodore Roosevelt
1901–1909

Born in New York in 1858, he saved many forests and wilderness areas. He fought big businesses that controlled key industries such as steel. The Panama Canal was begun. He died in 1919.

27. William Howard Taft
1909–1913

Born in Ohio in 1857, he worked to control abuse of power by big business. The income tax became law when he was President. Later, he was Chief Justice of the Supreme Court. He died in 1930.

28. Woodrow Wilson 1913–1921

Born in Virginia in 1856, he was President during World War I. After the war, his call for a League of Nations to settle disputes succeeded, but the U.S. did not join the League. He died in 1924.

29. Warren G. Harding 1921–1923

Harding was born in Ohio in 1865. He promised to help business. But, he gave jobs to some people who proved to be dishonest. They took bribes, causing problems for Harding. He died in office in 1923.

30. Calvin Coolidge 1923–1929

Coolidge was born in Vermont in 1872. His honesty and thrift gave people renewed confidence in government. Business boomed, and the national debt was reduced. He died in 1933.

31. Herbert Hoover 1929–1933

Hoover was born in Iowa in 1874. The Great Depression began when he was President. Many banks and businesses failed; millions lost their jobs. His efforts to help were not enough. He died in 1964.

32. Franklin D. Roosevelt 1933–1945

Roosevelt was born in New York in 1882. He introduced job programs and social security to fight the Depression. President during World War II, he was elected four times, and died in office in 1945.

33. Harry S. Truman 1945–1953

Born in Missouri in 1884, he ordered the atomic bomb dropped on Japan. After the war, the U.S. joined the United Nations. Truman sent aid to Europe. Later he sent troops to Korea. He died in 1972.

34. Dwight D. Eisenhower 1953–1961

Born in Texas in 1890, he headed the Allied forces in World War II. He helped settle the war in Korea. Segregated schools were declared unlawful while he was President. He died in 1969.

35. John F. Kennedy 1961–1963

Born in Massachusetts in 1917, he was President when a U.S. astronaut first orbited the earth. He and other world leaders signed a nuclear test ban treaty. He was shot to death in 1963.

36. Lyndon B. Johnson 1963–1969

Born in Texas in 1908, he was President when the Civil Rights Act and other programs to help schools and the poor became law. Many U.S. soldiers went to fight in Vietnam. He died in 1973.

37. Richard M. Nixon 1969–1974

Born in California in 1913, he was President when U.S. astronauts landed on the moon. He ended the war in Vietnam. Political scandal clouded his second term. He was the first President to resign.

752

38. Gerald R. Ford 1974–1977

Ford was born in Nebraska in 1913. He was the only President who never won a national election. While he was President, prices rose and many people had no jobs. Ford worked to restore public faith in government.

39. Jimmy Carter 1977–1981

Carter was born in Georgia in 1924. He helped Israel and Egypt agree on a peace treaty. He could not stop prices from rising. When 52 Americans were held hostage in Iran, he tried to obtain their freedom.

40. Ronald Reagan 1981–1989

Reagan was born in Illinois in 1911. He lowered taxes, gave more money to defense, and cut welfare programs. Business got better. Relations with Central America, Libya, and the Middle East caused trouble.

41. George H. W. Bush 1989–1993

Bush was born in Connecticut in 1924. He continued many of Reagan's policies. In 1990 he sent troops to resist Iraq's invasion of Kuwait in the Persian Gulf War. Business conditions got worse, and recession threatened economic progress.

42. Bill Clinton: 1993–

Clinton was born in Arkansas in 1946. Five-term governor of Arkansas, he won the Democratic nomination on the first ballot. His platform promised economic recovery through government investment to stimulate growth.

Facts About the Presidency

Qualifications
at least 35 years old
a natural-born citizen
lived in the United States 14 years

Term of Office
four years, and not more than twice

Inauguration
January 20 after election

Oath of Office
"I do solemnly swear (or affirm) that I will faithfully execute the office of President of the United States, and will to the best of my ability, preserve, protect, and defend the Constitution of the United States."

Time Line of Events in United States History

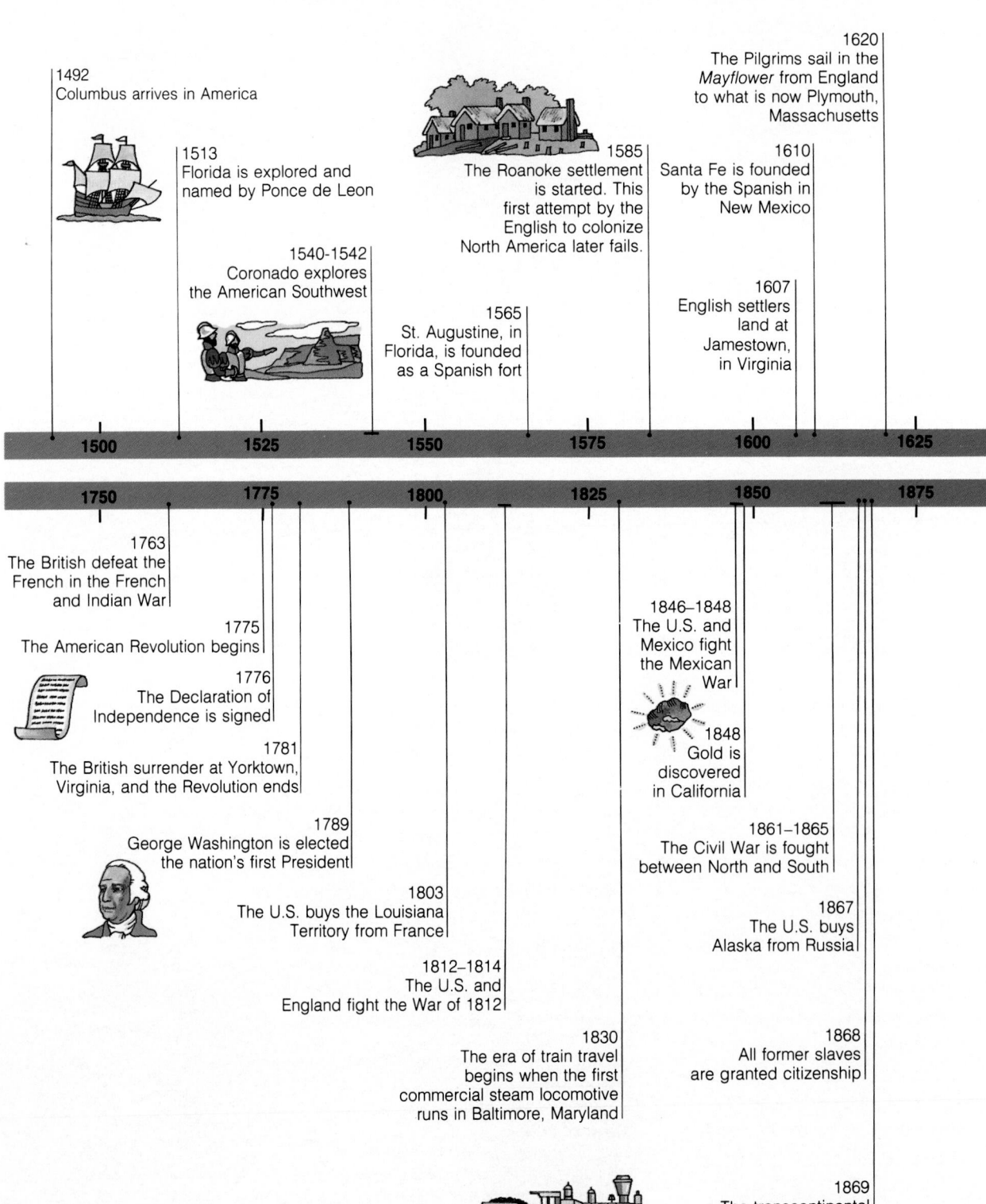

1492
Columbus arrives in America

1513
Florida is explored and
named by Ponce de Leon

1540-1542
Coronado explores
the American Southwest

1585
The Roanoke settlement
is started. This
first attempt by the
English to colonize
North America later fails.

1565
St. Augustine, in
Florida, is founded
as a Spanish fort

1620
The Pilgrims sail in the
Mayflower from England
to what is now Plymouth,
Massachusetts

1610
Santa Fe is founded
by the Spanish in
New Mexico

1607
English settlers
land at
Jamestown,
in Virginia

1500   **1525**   **1550**   **1575**   **1600**   **1625**

1750   **1775**   **1800**   **1825**   **1850**   **1875**

1763
The British defeat the
French in the French
and Indian War

1775
The American Revolution begins

1776
The Declaration of
Independence is signed

1781
The British surrender at Yorktown,
Virginia, and the Revolution ends

1789
George Washington is elected
the nation's first President

1803
The U.S. buys the Louisiana
Territory from France

1812-1814
The U.S. and
England fight the War of 1812

1830
The era of train travel
begins when the first
commercial steam locomotive
runs in Baltimore, Maryland

1846–1848
The U.S. and
Mexico fight
the Mexican
War

1848
Gold is
discovered
in California

1861–1865
The Civil War is fought
between North and South

1867
The U.S. buys
Alaska from Russia

1868
All former slaves
are granted citizenship

1869
The transcontinental
railroad is completed

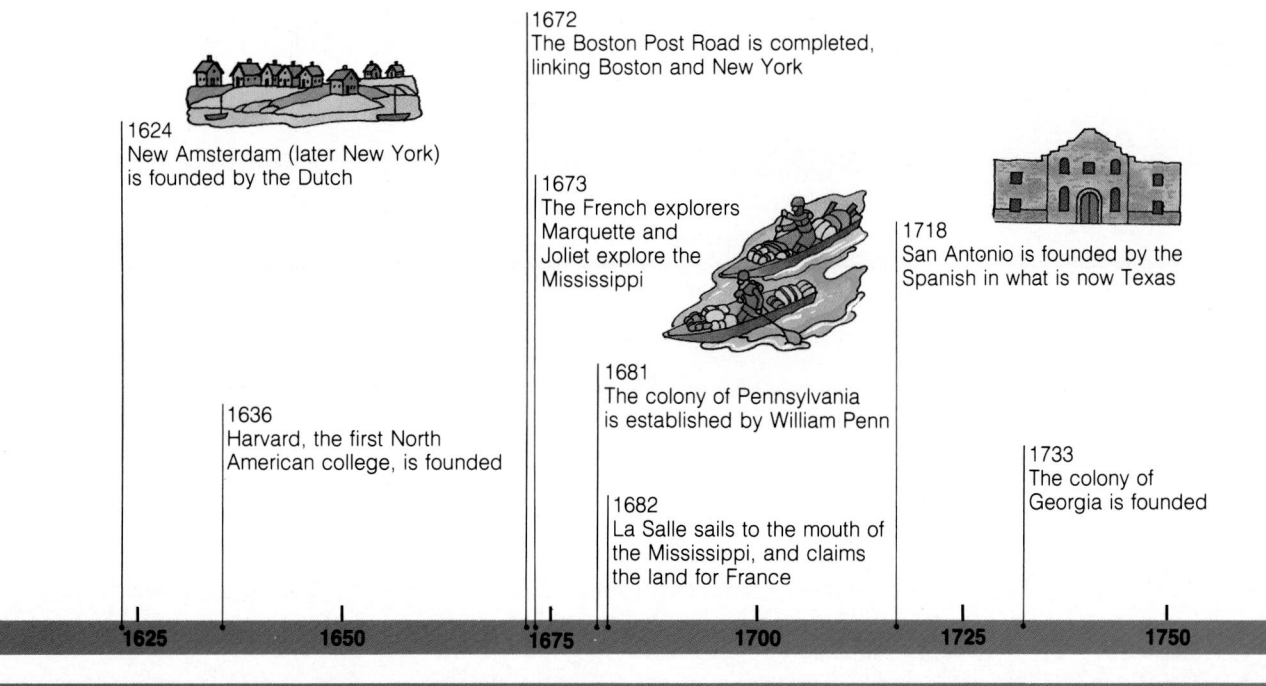

1672
The Boston Post Road is completed,
linking Boston and New York

1624
New Amsterdam (later New York)
is founded by the Dutch

1673
The French explorers
Marquette and
Joliet explore the
Mississippi

1718
San Antonio is founded by the
Spanish in what is now Texas

1636
Harvard, the first North
American college, is founded

1681
The colony of Pennsylvania
is established by William Penn

1733
The colony of
Georgia is founded

1682
La Salle sails to the mouth of
the Mississippi, and claims
the land for France

1625   **1650**   **1675**   **1700**   **1725**   **1750**

1875   **1900**   **1925**   **1950**   **1975**   **2000**

1950–1953
The Korean
War takes
place

1991
The Persian Gulf
War forces Iraq to
withdraw from
Kuwait

1879
Thomas Edison
invents the
electric light
bulb

1941–1945
The U.S.
takes part in
World War II

1981
The first flight of the
space shuttle takes place

1933
President, Roosevelt
starts programs to
end the Depression

1973
The U.S. ends involvement
in the Vietnam War

1876
The telephone
is invented
by Alexander
Graham Bell

1929
The stock market crashes;
many people lose their
jobs and homes

1969
Two U.S. astronauts
land on the moon

1920
Women are granted the
right to vote

1964
U.S. troops sent to Vietnam

1917–1918
The U.S. fights in World War I

1963
Civil rights march on
Washington, D.C., takes place

1914
The Panama Canal is finished

1962
John Glenn is the first American
to orbit the earth

1913
The Model T Ford, the first mass-produced
automobile, is introduced

1903
The Wright Brothers make the first airplane flight

1898
The Spanish-American War takes place

English Words from Other Languages

It may surprise you to learn that most of the words in the English language have come from other languages. These words, from languages all over the world, came into English in various ways.

During its early history, England was invaded by people from other lands. Words from the languages spoken by these invaders became part of the English language. Later, English explorers brought back

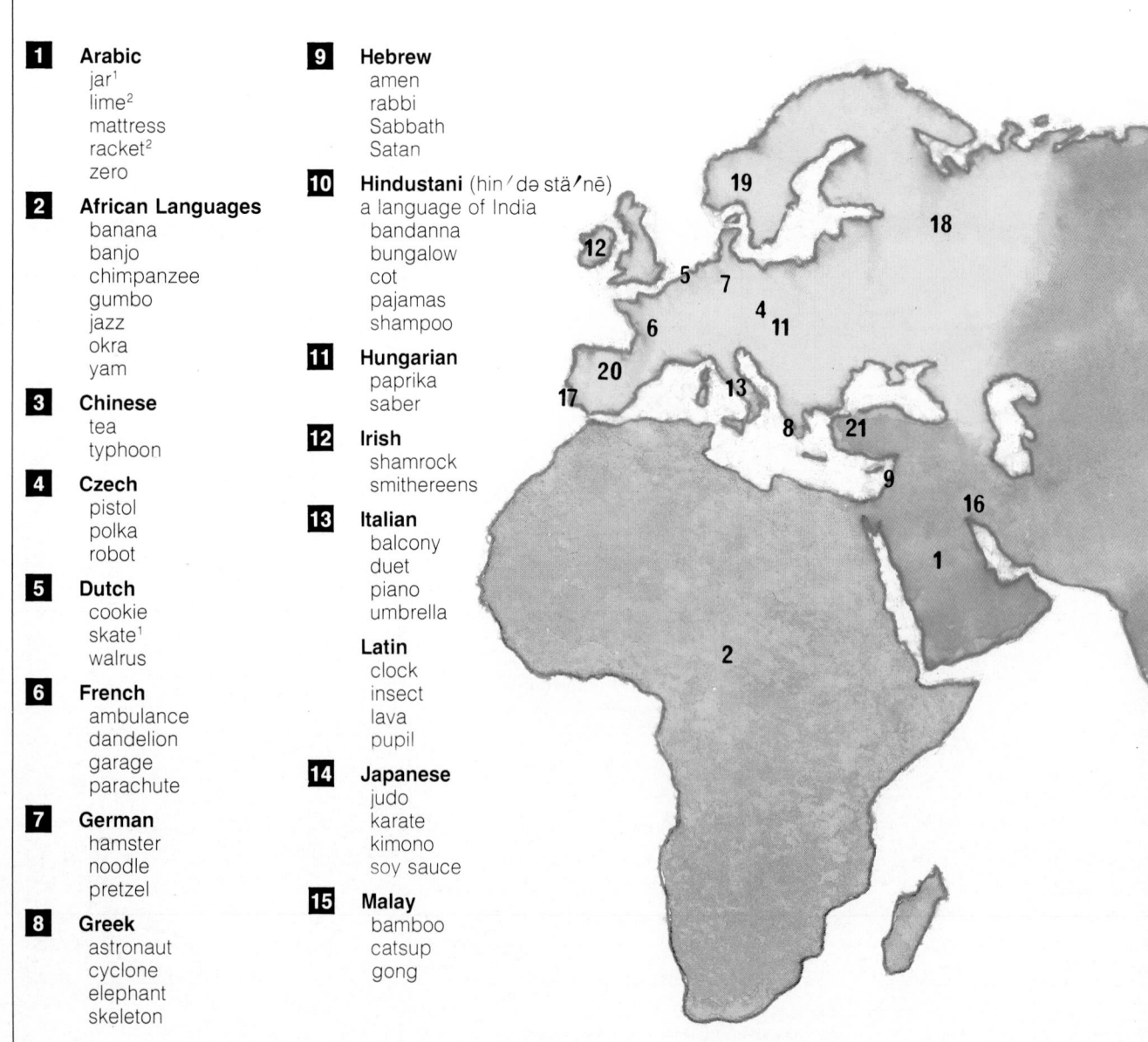

1 Arabic
jar[1]
lime[2]
mattress
racket[2]
zero

2 African Languages
banana
banjo
chimpanzee
gumbo
jazz
okra
yam

3 Chinese
tea
typhoon

4 Czech
pistol
polka
robot

5 Dutch
cookie
skate[1]
walrus

6 French
ambulance
dandelion
garage
parachute

7 German
hamster
noodle
pretzel

8 Greek
astronaut
cyclone
elephant
skeleton

9 Hebrew
amen
rabbi
Sabbath
Satan

10 Hindustani (hin′də stä′nē)
a language of India
bandanna
bungalow
cot
pajamas
shampoo

11 Hungarian
paprika
saber

12 Irish
shamrock
smithereens

13 Italian
balcony
duet
piano
umbrella

Latin
clock
insect
lava
pupil

14 Japanese
judo
karate
kimono
soy sauce

15 Malay
bamboo
catsup
gong

to England words from the lands they visited. Later still, when English colonists settled in other lands, they saw many new and unusual things. They adopted many of the words spoken by the people who were already living there to describe these unfamiliar things.

This borrowing of words from other languages is still going on. At the present time, scientists often borrow words from Latin and ancient Greek to name new scientific developments, inventions, and products.

Here is a small sample of words that have entered English from other languages.

16 **Persian**
the language of Iran
candy
lemon
orange
tulip

17 **Portuguese**
cobra
flamingo
jaguar

18 **Russian**
mammoth
parka

19 **Scandinavian**
egg
ski
sky
window

20 **Spanish**
cargo
patio
plaza
ranch
tuna
vanilla

21 **Turkish**
coffee
sherbet
turban
yogurt

English Words Borrowed from Mexican Spanish

The first explorers of what is today the American Southwest were Spanish. Modern place names, from San Antonio in Texas to San Francisco in California, testify to the Spanish heritage of this vast region. Indeed, before 1836 it was all part of the Republic of Mexico. As English-speaking settlers began to move into the region, they began to borrow and use words from the Spanish speakers they found living there.

Over the years, many kinds of Mexican foods have become popular. *Chocolate* was an early favorite as a hot drink. Spicy *chili* was eaten. Later on, *abalone* became a popular seafood along the Pacific Coast. In more recent years, people all over the United States have learned to eat and enjoy *tacos* and *tamales*.

The Southwest is a rugged, dry land where cattle have been raised for many years. The following sentence contains six words borrowed from Mexican Spanish; look up any of the words in italic type that you don't know:

Out on the open range, where the *coyotes* roam, cattle often *stampeded*, running aimlessly through *mesquite* shrubs until they were herded into a *canyon* by cowboys riding *broncos* and wearing *chaps*.

Other English words borrowed from Mexican Spanish words include *cafeteria*, *mustang*, and *serape*.

English Words from Native American Words

When European settlers arrived in the New World in the 1600s, they found a people who spoke a language very different from any they had ever heard. These settlers began to use the Indian words for the unfamiliar things they saw. Below are a few examples of these words.

Animals

The settlers saw many new and unusual animals in the New World and tried to use the Indian names for many of them.

Indian name	Meaning
moose	"he strips off the bark"
raccoon	"he scratches with his hand"

Other animal names from Native American words include *caribou, chipmunk, peccary, skunk,* and *woodchuck.*

Foods

American Indians not only helped the early settlers plant their first crops, but they gave the newcomers the names for many good things to eat.

Indian name	Meaning
squash	"the green things that may be eaten raw"
pecan	"hard-shelled nut"

Other names for foods from Native American words include *cashew* and *succotash.*

State Names

In many towns throughout the United States, street names, nearby lakes and rivers, and even the towns themselves may have names that are from Native American languages. In fact, more than half of our states have names from Native American words. These include:

Alabama	Kentucky	Mississippi	North Dakota	Tennessee
Illinois	Massachusetts	Missouri	Ohio	Texas
Kansas	Michigan	Nebraska	Oklahoma	Utah

You will find an interesting word history about each of these state names at its entry word in this dictionary.

Words Made from Other Words

In 1943 French scientists Jacques-Yves Cousteau and Emil Gagnan invented an underwater breathing device. This device had an air tank that could be carried on a diver's back. Divers no longer had to be connected by hoses to air at the surface of the water. This new device came to be called *scuba* after the first letters of its full name, *s*elf-*c*ontained *u*nderwater *b*reathing *a*pparatus.

In the 1960s, computers were being used by more and more people. In order to make it easier to tell computers what to do, it was necessary to devise a language, made up mainly of simple commands, such as PRINT, INPUT, GO TO, and so forth. This language was called "*b*eginner's *a*ll-purpose *s*ymbolic *i*nstruction *c*ode." Combining these first letters results in the word BASIC, which suggests also the word *basic,* meaning "fundamental."

Another expression that came into English in this way is *Zip Code.* This is the number that you put after the name of the state on envelopes to be mailed. *Zip* stands for the first letters of "*z*one *i*mprovement *p*lan," the official name of the plan to improve postal service. *Zip Code* also suggests speed, one of the meanings of the word *zip*. Zip Codes were put into use to speed mail delivery, since numbers can be read faster and more easily by Postal Service computers than words can.

You can find other examples of words formed in this way by reading the word histories for *bit*[4], *hi-fi, jeep, laser, radar,* and *sonar.*

Blends: Words Made by Joining Two Words

During the 1800s many factories were built in growing cities. Often these cities were located near oceans or other large bodies of water that produced fog. Smoke from the factories mixed with the fog. By 1905 people had combined letters from *smoke* and *fog* to create a new word—*smog*. This way of combining parts of words is another way that new words come into the English language.

During the 1920s automobile travel increased greatly. Motorists needing overnight shelter began to find small groups of individual cabins conveniently built close to the highway. By 1925 a *mo*tor ho*tel* was known throughout the country as a *motel*.

In recent years scientists have developed ways to give mechanical replacements to people with missing arms or legs. Today an electronic arm can be directly attached to a person's shoulder. The muscles and nerves in the shoulder can control the mechanical arm and can make it move. In this way, *bio*logy has been united with the electr*onic* to create the *bionic*.

For other interesting blends, read the word histories of *chortle*, *quasar*, *squiggle*, *squinch*, and *zillion*.

That's from his**s** and **c**at.

Scat!

Words from People's Names

The next time you're happily munching a graham cracker, take a moment to remember the man for whom it was named. Sylvester Graham was a minister who believed that vegetables, fruits, and grains were the healthiest foods one could eat. In the 1850s he combined whole grain and unsifted wheat flour to make a thin, brittle cracker. Reverend Graham's creation, called the *graham cracker,* went on to become one of the most popular and lasting items ever to grace a grocer's shelf.

There are many other people whose names have become part of our language. Jules Léotard, for example. He was a French trapeze artist who amazed the people of his day with his electrifying aerial work. The tight-fitting garment he wore while performing became very popular also, and other high-wire artists soon imitated it. This costume became known as the *leotard,* in memory of the man who designed and first wore it.

The Earl of Sandwich, an English nobleman, loved to gamble at cards. Often he was too involved in his game to stop for a meal. Sometimes he would ask a servant to bring him something he could nibble on while still playing. One evening he asked for meat and bread. Placing the meat on the bread, the earl created a *sandwich,* a popular meal for busy folks ever since.

Your own state may be named after, or in honor of, a famous historical person. *Pennsylvania* means "Penn's woods." It was named in honor of William Penn, the man who established a colony there. There are names of persons hidden in the names of other states also, including Delaware, Georgia, Louisiana, Maryland, New York, North Carolina, South Carolina, Virginia, and Washington.

There are lots of English words that come from the names of people, including *braille, Celsius, guy, pasteurize, sequoia,* and even your old *teddy bear.*

The Earth: Its Crust (Plates), Mantle, and Core

The earth's crust is its outer layer of rocks, soil, and various minerals. This crust covers the surface of the entire earth, even the part that lies beneath rivers, lakes, and oceans. The crust varies in thickness from about two miles to about twenty miles. The crust is made up of individual sections, called plates, that actually float on the next layer that lies beneath the crust.

crust
mantle
core

This next layer, called the mantle, makes up most of the total mass of the earth. Because it lies so very far below the earth's surface, we know very little about it directly. But scientists believe that it is formed mostly of very hot rock. Below the mantle, at the very center of the earth, lies its core. Scientists believe it is made of molten, or liquid, iron.

The Eruption of a Volcano

lava

pressure   magma   pressure

The inside of the earth is hot enough to melt rock. The drawing shows a pocket of melted rock, called magma, deep underground. Pressure squeezes the magma up through the crust just as you squeeze toothpaste through a tube. Sometimes the magma breaks through to the surface and makes an opening.

Magma that comes out onto the surface of the earth is called lava. During an eruption, lava, gases, rocks, and ashes burst from the opening. After many eruptions, lava, rocks and ash build a mountain called a volcano.

The Water Cycle

The picture of the water cycle shows the paths that fresh water and salt water follow on earth. Water changes from fresh to salt water and back to fresh water, again and again. But the total amount of water on earth stays the same.

In the water cycle, water evaporates from the ocean, leaving the salts behind. This water, which enters the air as water vapor, is fresh water. Moving air carries the water vapor away. Clouds form when water vapor condenses—or changes into tiny drops of water. In time, rain or snow falls from the clouds onto the oceans or land.

Most of the rain or snow that falls on the land or oceans evaporates into the air once more. But some of the rain and snow that falls on the land sinks into the ground and becomes groundwater. Plants use some of this water to live and grow and release the rest of the water into the air as water vapor.

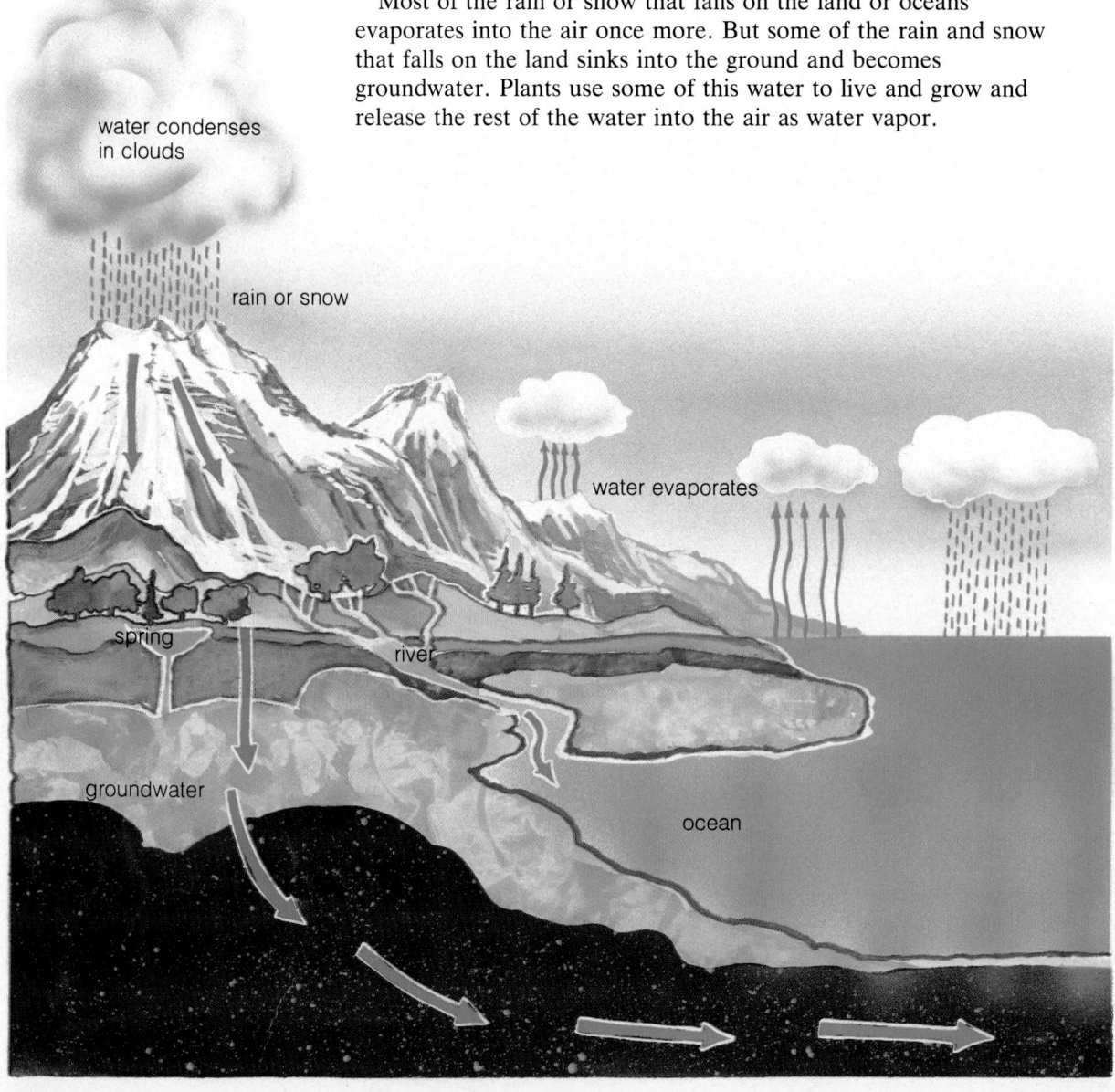

water condenses
in clouds

rain or snow

water evaporates

spring

river

groundwater

ocean

A Food Chain

When several kinds of living things are linked because they use one another as food, this group is called a food chain. The drawing above shows a food chain in a freshwater lake. The arrows point from the thing that is eaten to those that do the eating. The food chain starts with plants, which store food energy from the sun. The plants are eaten by plant-eaters, which are then eaten by meat-eaters. Each living thing in the series is usually larger than the one it feeds on.

Basic Food Groups

You can use the food guide pyramid to help choose healthy foods. Using the plan helps you get the right nutrients, which your body needs. To get all the nutrients your body needs, you need to eat different kinds of food each day. The nutrients in different kinds of food work together to help you stay healthy.

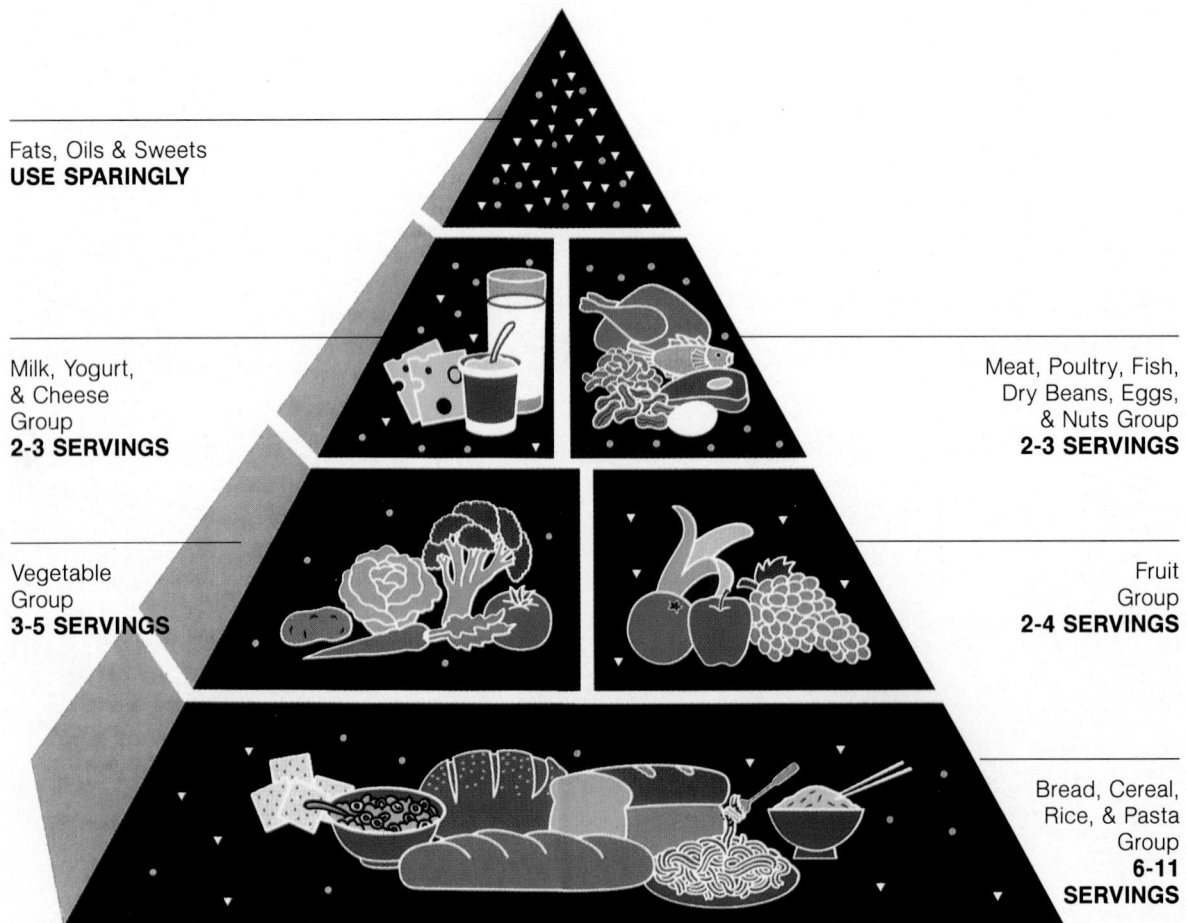

Fats, Oils & Sweets
USE SPARINGLY

Milk, Yogurt,
& Cheese
Group
2-3 SERVINGS

Meat, Poultry, Fish,
Dry Beans, Eggs,
& Nuts Group
2-3 SERVINGS

Vegetable
Group
3-5 SERVINGS

Fruit
Group
2-4 SERVINGS

Bread, Cereal,
Rice, & Pasta
Group
**6-11
SERVINGS**

Bicycle Safety

· Ride a bicycle that is the right size for you.
  (When you sit on the bicycle saddle, your feet should be able to reach flat to the ground.)

· Learn how to ride your bicycle well.

· Ride on the sidewalk if your community allows you to.

· Otherwise, ride on the right-hand side of the street, with, not facing, traffic.

· Ride in single file if you are with other bicycle riders.

· Learn and use the hand signals shown at the right for a left turn, right turn, and stop.

Bicycle Parts to Check

· Check the brakes. Be sure they can stop the bike safely.

· Check the tires. Be sure they have enough air in them.

· Check to see if the horn or bell, and the light on your bike work.

· Make sure your bike has a chain guard and rear reflectors.

left turn

right turn

stop

bell

light

reflector

reflector

tire

tire

chain guard

Metric Measurements

Length

millimeter
(1/1000 of a meter)

centimeter
(1/100 of a meter)

decimeter
(1/10 of a meter)

meter

kilometer
(1000 meters)

A dime is about as <u>thick</u> as a millimeter.

This insect is about one centimeter long.

This crayon is about one decimeter long.

A guitar is about one meter tall.

This bridge is about one kilometer long.

Weight

gram

kilogram
(1000 grams)

This paper clip weighs about one gram.

A roller skate weighs about one kilogram.

Capacity

milliliter
(1/1000 of a liter)

liter

A dropper holds about one milliliter.

One liter is a little more than a quart.

Customary Measurements

Length

inch
(12 inches equal 1 foot)
foot
(3 feet equal 1 yard)
yard
(1760 yards equal 1 mile)
mile

The width of a door is about one yard.

Eight city blocks measure about one mile.

A quarter is about one inch wide.

This ruler is one foot long.

Weight

ounce
(16 ounces equal 1 pound)
pound
(2000 pounds equal 1 ton)
ton

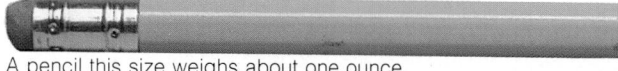

A pencil this size weighs about one ounce.

A small melon weighs about one pound.

A compact car weighs about one ton.

Capacity

cup
(2 cups equal 1 pint)
pint
(2 pints equal 1 quart)
quart
(4 quarts equal 1 gallon)
gallon

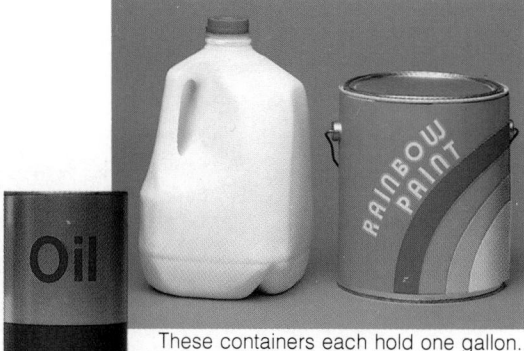

These containers each hold one pint.

These containers each hold one cup.

These containers each hold one quart.

These containers each hold one gallon.

Plane Figures

Circles

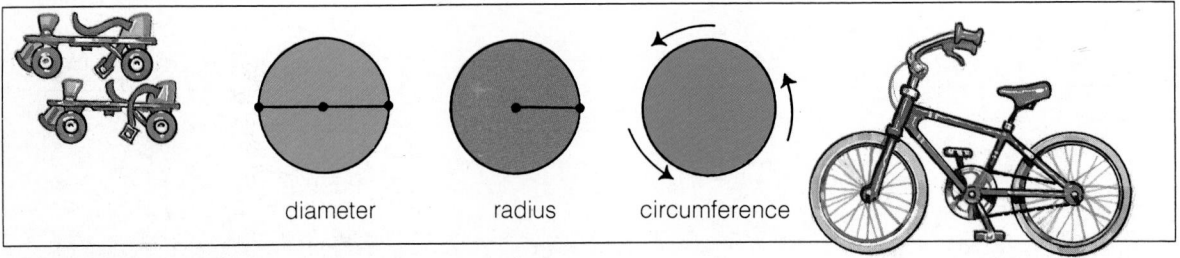

diameter   radius   circumference

Polygons

triangles

quadrilaterals

pentagons

parallelograms

hexagons

rectangles

octagons

squares

|||| Algebra

Arithmetic Operations

$$a(b + c) = ab + ac$$

$$\frac{a}{b} + \frac{c}{d} = \frac{ad + bc}{bd}$$

$$\frac{a + c}{b} = \frac{a}{b} + \frac{c}{b}$$

$$\frac{\frac{a}{b}}{\frac{c}{d}} = \frac{a}{b} \times \frac{d}{c} = \frac{ad}{bc}$$

Exponents and Radicals

$$x^m x^n = x^{m+n}$$

$$\frac{x^m}{x^n} = x^{m-n}$$

$$(x^m)^n = x^{mn}$$

$$x^{-n} = \frac{1}{x^n}$$

$$(xy)^n = x^n y^n$$

$$\left(\frac{x}{y}\right)^n = \frac{x^n}{y^n}$$

$$x^{1/n} = \sqrt[n]{x}$$

$$x^{m/n} = \sqrt[n]{x^m} = \left(\sqrt[n]{x}\right)^m$$

$$\sqrt[n]{xy} = \sqrt[n]{x}\sqrt[n]{y}$$

$$\sqrt[n]{\frac{x}{y}} = \frac{\sqrt[n]{x}}{\sqrt[n]{y}}$$

Factoring Special Polynomials

$$x^2 - y^2 = (x + y)(x - y)$$

$$x^3 + y^3 = (x + y)(x^2 - xy + y^2)$$

$$x^3 - y^3 = (x - y)(x^2 + xy + y^2)$$

Binomial Theorem

$$(x + y)^2 = x^2 + 2xy + y^2 \qquad (x - y)^2 = x^2 - 2xy + y^2$$

$$(x + y)^3 = x^3 + 3x^2y + 3xy^2 + y^3$$

$$(x - y)^3 = x^3 - 3x^2y + 3xy^2 - y^3$$

$$(x + y)^n = x^n + nx^{n-1}y + \frac{n(n-1)}{2}x^{n-2}y^2$$

$$+ \cdots + \binom{n}{k}x^{n-k}y^k + \cdots + nxy^{n-1} + y^n$$

$$\text{where } \binom{n}{k} = \frac{n(n-1)\cdots(n-k+1)}{1 \cdot 2 \cdot 3 \cdot \cdots \cdot k}$$

Quadratic Formula

If $ax^2 + bx + c = 0$, then $x = \dfrac{-b \pm \sqrt{b^2 - 4ac}}{2a}$.

Inequalities and Absolute Value

If $a < b$ and $b < c$, then $a < c$.

If $a < b$, then $a + c < b + c$.

If $a < b$ and $c > 0$, then $ca < cb$.

If $a < b$ and $c < 0$, then $ca > cb$.

If $a > 0$, then

$$|x| = a \quad \text{means} \quad x = a \quad \text{or} \quad x = -a$$

$$|x| < a \quad \text{means} \quad -a < x < a$$

$$|x| > a \quad \text{means} \quad x > a \quad \text{or} \quad x < -a$$

|||| Geometry

Geometric Formulas

Formulas for area A, circumference C, and volume V:

Triangle
$$A = \tfrac{1}{2}bh$$
$$= \tfrac{1}{2}ab\sin\theta$$

Circle
$$A = \pi r^2$$
$$C = 2\pi r$$

Sector of Circle
$$A = \tfrac{1}{2}r^2\theta$$
$$s = r\theta \ (\theta \text{ in radians})$$

  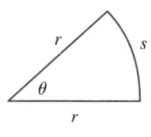

Sphere
$$V = \tfrac{4}{3}\pi r^3$$
$$A = 4\pi r^2$$

Cylinder
$$V = \pi r^2 h$$

Cone
$$V = \tfrac{1}{3}\pi r^2 h$$
$$A = \pi r\sqrt{r^2 + h^2}$$

  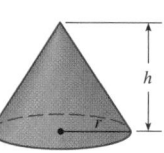

Distance and Midpoint Formulas

Distance between $P_1(x_1, y_1)$ and $P_2(x_2, y_2)$:

$$d = \sqrt{(x_2 - x_1)^2 + (y_2 - y_1)^2}$$

Midpoint of $\overline{P_1 P_2}$: $\left(\dfrac{x_1 + x_2}{2}, \dfrac{y_1 + y_2}{2}\right)$

Lines

Slope of line through $P_1(x_1, y_1)$ and $P_2(x_2, y_2)$:

$$m = \frac{y_2 - y_1}{x_2 - x_1}$$

Point-slope equation of line through $P_1(x_1, y_1)$ with slope m:

$$y - y_1 = m(x - x_1)$$

Slope-intercept equation of line with slope m and y-intercept b:

$$y = mx + b$$

Circles

Equation of the circle with center (h, k) and radius r:

$$(x - h)^2 + (y - k)^2 = r^2$$

S0-AGC-608

||| Trigonometry

Angle Measurement

π radians $= 180°$

$1° = \dfrac{\pi}{180}$ rad $\qquad$ 1 rad $= \dfrac{180°}{\pi}$

$s = r\theta$

(θ in radians)

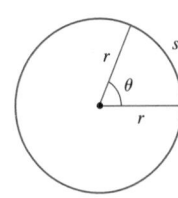

Right Angle Trigonometry

$\sin \theta = \dfrac{\text{opp}}{\text{hyp}} \qquad \csc \theta = \dfrac{\text{hyp}}{\text{opp}}$

$\cos \theta = \dfrac{\text{adj}}{\text{hyp}} \qquad \sec \theta = \dfrac{\text{hyp}}{\text{adj}}$

$\tan \theta = \dfrac{\text{opp}}{\text{adj}} \qquad \cot \theta = \dfrac{\text{adj}}{\text{opp}}$

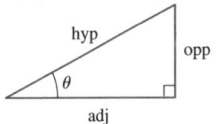

Trigonometric Functions

$\sin \theta = \dfrac{y}{r} \qquad \csc \theta = \dfrac{r}{y}$

$\cos \theta = \dfrac{x}{r} \qquad \sec \theta = \dfrac{r}{x}$

$\tan \theta = \dfrac{y}{x} \qquad \cot \theta = \dfrac{x}{y}$

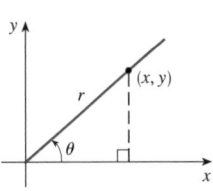

Graphs of Trigonometric Functions

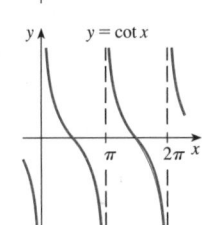

Trigonometric Functions of Important Angles

θ	radians	$\sin \theta$	$\cos \theta$	$\tan \theta$
0°	0	0	1	0
30°	$\pi/6$	$1/2$	$\sqrt{3}/2$	$\sqrt{3}/3$
45°	$\pi/4$	$\sqrt{2}/2$	$\sqrt{2}/2$	1
60°	$\pi/3$	$\sqrt{3}/2$	$1/2$	$\sqrt{3}$
90°	$\pi/2$	1	0	—

Fundamental Identities

$\csc \theta = \dfrac{1}{\sin \theta} \qquad\qquad \sec \theta = \dfrac{1}{\cos \theta}$

$\tan \theta = \dfrac{\sin \theta}{\cos \theta} \qquad\qquad \cot \theta = \dfrac{\cos \theta}{\sin \theta}$

$\cot \theta = \dfrac{1}{\tan \theta} \qquad\qquad \sin^2\theta + \cos^2\theta = 1$

$1 + \tan^2\theta = \sec^2\theta \qquad\qquad 1 + \cot^2\theta = \csc^2\theta$

$\sin(-\theta) = -\sin \theta \qquad\qquad \cos(-\theta) = \cos \theta$

$\tan(-\theta) = -\tan \theta \qquad\qquad \sin\left(\dfrac{\pi}{2} - \theta\right) = \cos \theta$

$\cos\left(\dfrac{\pi}{2} - \theta\right) = \sin \theta \qquad \tan\left(\dfrac{\pi}{2} - \theta\right) = \cot \theta$

The Law of Sines

$\dfrac{\sin A}{a} = \dfrac{\sin B}{b} = \dfrac{\sin C}{c}$

The Law of Cosines

$a^2 = b^2 + c^2 - 2bc \cos A$

$b^2 = a^2 + c^2 - 2ac \cos B$

$c^2 = a^2 + b^2 - 2ab \cos C$

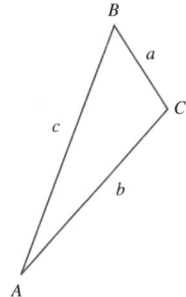

Addition and Subtraction Formulas

$\sin(x + y) = \sin x \cos y + \cos x \sin y$

$\sin(x - y) = \sin x \cos y - \cos x \sin y$

$\cos(x + y) = \cos x \cos y - \sin x \sin y$

$\cos(x - y) = \cos x \cos y + \sin x \sin y$

$\tan(x + y) = \dfrac{\tan x + \tan y}{1 - \tan x \tan y}$

$\tan(x - y) = \dfrac{\tan x - \tan y}{1 + \tan x \tan y}$

Double-Angle Formulas

$\sin 2x = 2 \sin x \cos x$

$\cos 2x = \cos^2x - \sin^2x = 2 \cos^2x - 1 = 1 - 2 \sin^2x$

$\tan 2x = \dfrac{2 \tan x}{1 - \tan^2x}$

Half-Angle Formulas

$\sin^2x = \dfrac{1 - \cos 2x}{2} \qquad \cos^2x = \dfrac{1 + \cos 2x}{2}$

Calculus, University of Michigan Edition

Math 156/255 - Applied Honors Calculus II / III

James Stewart

CENGAGE
Learning™

Australia • Brazil • Japan • Korea • Mexico • Singapore • Spain • United Kingdom • United States

CENGAGE
Learning™

Calculus, University of Michigan Edition: Math 156/255 - Applied Honors Calculus II / III

James Stewart

Executive Editors:
Michele Baird

Maureen Staudt

Michael Stranz

Project Development Manager:
Linda deStefano

Senior Marketing Coordinators:
Sara Mercurio

Lindsay Shapiro

Production/Manufacturing Manager:
Donna M. Brown

PreMedia Services Supervisor:
Rebecca A. Walker

Rights & Permissions Specialist:
Kalina Hintz

Cover Image:
Getty Images*

* Unless otherwise noted, all cover images used by Custom Solutions, a part of Cengage Learning, have been supplied courtesy of Getty Images with the exception of the Earthview cover image, which has been supplied by the National Aeronautics and Space Administration (NASA).

For product information and technology assistance, contact us at
Cengage Learning Customer & Sales Support, 1-800-354-9706

For permission to use material from this text or product,
submit all requests online at **cengage.com/permissions**
Further permissions questions can be emailed to
permissionrequest@cengage.com

ISBN-13: 978-0-495-46194-4

ISBN-10: 0-495-46194-6

Cengage Learning
5191 Natorp Boulevard
Mason, Ohio 45040
USA

Cengage Learning is a leading provider of customized learning solutions with office locations around the globe, including Singapore, the United Kingdom, Australia, Mexico, Brazil, and Japan. Locate your local office at:
international.cengage.com/region

Cengage Learning products are represented in Canada by Nelson Education, Ltd.

For your lifelong learning solutions, visit **custom.cengage.com**

Visit our corporate website at **cengage.com**

Printed in the United States of America

Table of Contents

CHAPTER 5

To compute an area we approximate a region by rectangles and let the number of rectangles become large. The precise area is the limit of these sums of areas of rectangles.

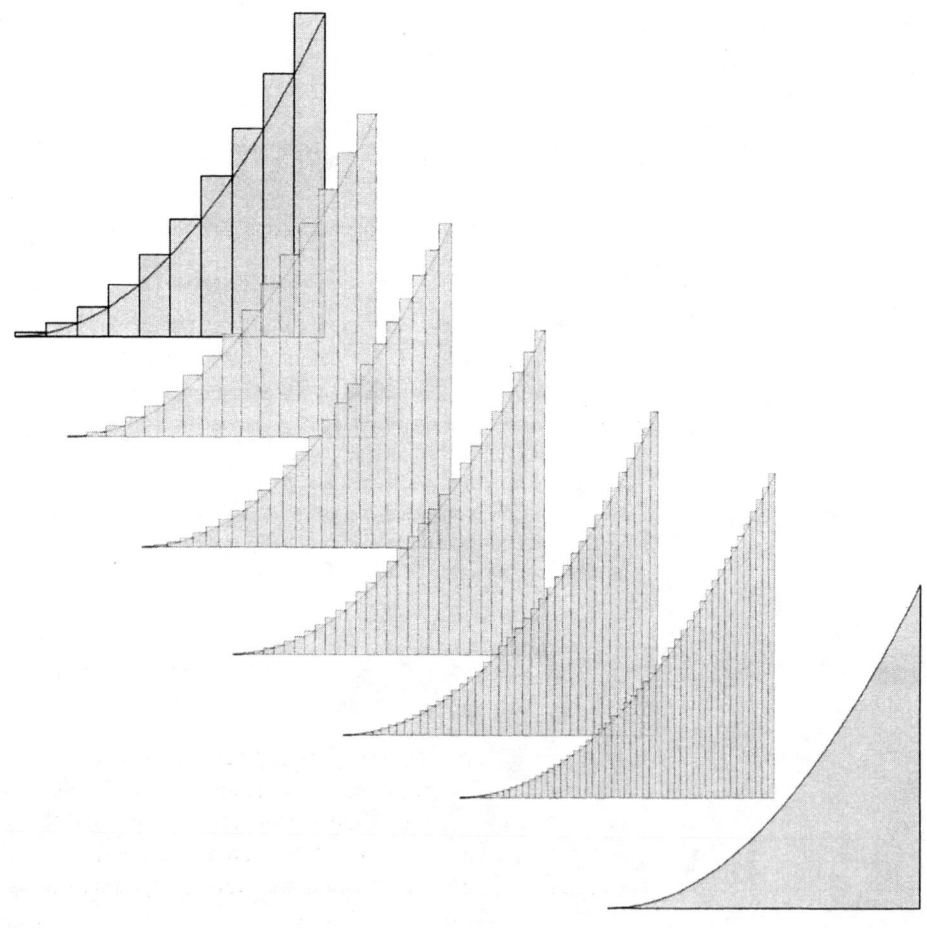

Integrals

|||| Now is a good time to read (or reread) *A Preview of Calculus* (see page 2). It discusses the unifying ideas of calculus and helps put in perspective where we have been and where we are going.

In Chapter 2 we used the tangent and velocity problems to introduce the derivative, which is the central idea in differential calculus. In much the same way, this chapter starts with the area and distance problems and uses them to formulate the idea of a definite integral, which is the basic concept of integral calculus. We will see in Chapters 6 and 9 how to use the integral to solve problems concerning volumes, lengths of curves, population predictions, cardiac output, forces on a dam, work, consumer surplus, and baseball, among many others.

There is a connection between integral calculus and differential calculus. The Fundamental Theorem of Calculus relates the integral to the derivative, and we will see in this chapter that it greatly simplifies the solution of many problems.

5.1 Areas and Distances

In this section we discover that in trying to find the area under a curve or the distance traveled by a car, we end up with the same special type of limit.

The Area Problem

We begin by attempting to solve the *area problem:* Find the area of the region S that lies under the curve $y = f(x)$ from a to b. This means that S, illustrated in Figure 1, is bounded by the graph of a continuous function f [where $f(x) \geqslant 0$], the vertical lines $x = a$ and $x = b$, and the x-axis.

FIGURE 1
$S = \{(x, y) \mid a \leqslant x \leqslant b, 0 \leqslant y \leqslant f(x)\}$

In trying to solve the area problem we have to ask ourselves: What is the meaning of the word *area*? This question is easy to answer for regions with straight sides. For a rectangle, the area is defined as the product of the length and the width. The area of a triangle is half the base times the height. The area of a polygon is found by dividing it into triangles (as in Figure 2) and adding the areas of the triangles.

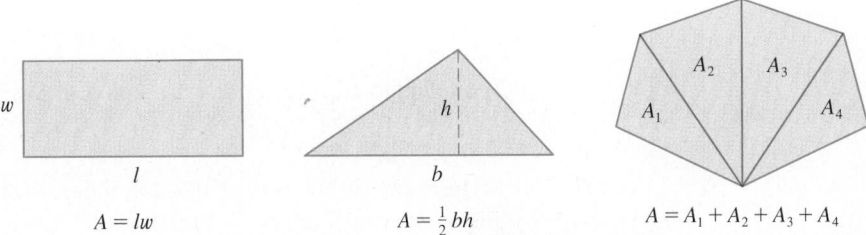

FIGURE 2

$A = lw$ $\qquad A = \frac{1}{2}bh$ $\qquad A = A_1 + A_2 + A_3 + A_4$

However, it isn't so easy to find the area of a region with curved sides. We all have an intuitive idea of what the area of a region is. But part of the area problem is to make this intuitive idea precise by giving an exact definition of area.

Recall that in defining a tangent we first approximated the slope of the tangent line by slopes of secant lines and then we took the limit of these approximations. We pursue a similar idea for areas. We first approximate the region S by rectangles and then we take the limit of the areas of these rectangles as we increase the number of rectangles. The following example illustrates the procedure.

EXAMPLE 1 Use rectangles to estimate the area under the parabola $y = x^2$ from 0 to 1 (the parabolic region S illustrated in Figure 3).

Try placing rectangles to estimate the area.
Resources / Module 6
/ What Is Area?
/ Estimating Area under a Parabola

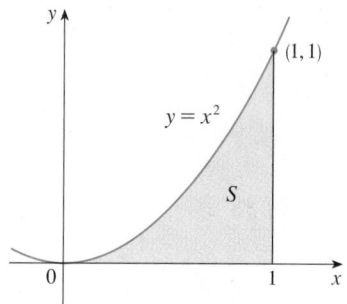

FIGURE 3

SOLUTION We first notice that the area of S must be somewhere between 0 and 1 because S is contained in a square with side length 1, but we can certainly do better than that. Suppose we divide S into four strips S_1, S_2, S_3, and S_4 by drawing the vertical lines $x = \frac{1}{4}$, $x = \frac{1}{2}$, and $x = \frac{3}{4}$ as in Figure 4(a).

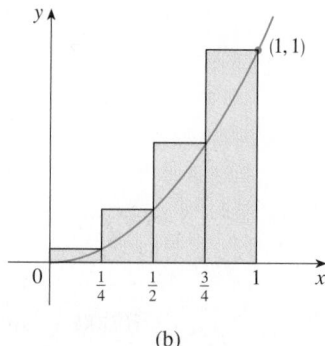

FIGURE 4

(a)

(b)

We can approximate each strip by a rectangle whose base is the same as the strip and whose height is the same as the right edge of the strip [see Figure 4(b)]. In other words, the heights of these rectangles are the values of the function $f(x) = x^2$ at the right end points of the subintervals $[0, \frac{1}{4}]$, $[\frac{1}{4}, \frac{1}{2}]$, $[\frac{1}{2}, \frac{3}{4}]$, and $[\frac{3}{4}, 1]$.

Each rectangle has width $\frac{1}{4}$ and the heights are $\left(\frac{1}{4}\right)^2$, $\left(\frac{1}{2}\right)^2$, $\left(\frac{3}{4}\right)^2$, and 1^2. If we let R_4 be the sum of the areas of these approximating rectangles, we get

$$R_4 = \frac{1}{4} \cdot \left(\frac{1}{4}\right)^2 + \frac{1}{4} \cdot \left(\frac{1}{2}\right)^2 + \frac{1}{4} \cdot \left(\frac{3}{4}\right)^2 + \frac{1}{4} \cdot 1^2 = \frac{15}{32} = 0.46875$$

From Figure 4(b) we see that the area A of S is less than R_4, so

$$A < 0.46875$$

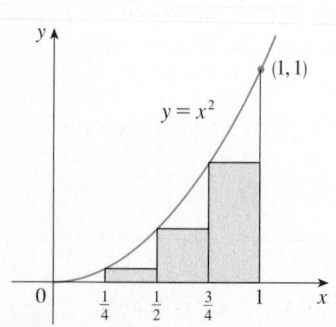

FIGURE 5

Instead of using the rectangles in Figure 4(b) we could use the smaller rectangles in Figure 5 whose heights are the values of f at the left endpoints of the subintervals. (The leftmost rectangle has collapsed because its height is 0.) The sum of the areas of these

approximating rectangles is

$$L_4 = \tfrac{1}{4} \cdot 0^2 + \tfrac{1}{4} \cdot \left(\tfrac{1}{4}\right)^2 + \tfrac{1}{4} \cdot \left(\tfrac{1}{2}\right)^2 + \tfrac{1}{4} \cdot \left(\tfrac{3}{4}\right)^2 = \tfrac{7}{32} = 0.21875$$

We see that the area of S is larger than L_4, so we have lower and upper estimates for A:

$$0.21875 < A < 0.46875$$

We can repeat this procedure with a larger number of strips. Figure 6 shows what happens when we divide the region S into eight strips of equal width.

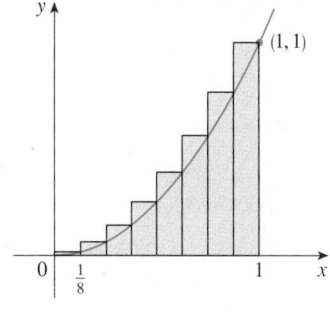

FIGURE 6

Approximating S with eight rectangles

(a) Using left endpoints

(b) Using right endpoints

By computing the sum of the areas of the smaller rectangles (L_8) and the sum of the areas of the larger rectangles (R_8), we obtain better lower and upper estimates for A:

$$0.2734375 < A < 0.3984375$$

n	L_n	R_n
10	0.2850000	0.3850000
20	0.3087500	0.3587500
30	0.3168519	0.3501852
50	0.3234000	0.3434000
100	0.3283500	0.3383500
1000	0.3328335	0.3338335

So one possible answer to the question is to say that the true area of S lies somewhere between 0.2734375 and 0.3984375.

We could obtain better estimates by increasing the number of strips. The table at the left shows the results of similar calculations (with a computer) using n rectangles whose heights are found with left endpoints (L_n) or right endpoints (R_n). In particular, we see by using 50 strips that the area lies between 0.3234 and 0.3434. With 1000 strips we narrow it down even more: A lies between 0.3328335 and 0.3338335. A good estimate is obtained by averaging these numbers: $A \approx 0.3333335$.

From the values in the table in Example 1, it looks as if R_n is approaching $\tfrac{1}{3}$ as n increases. We confirm this in the next example.

EXAMPLE 2 For the region S in Example 1, show that the sum of the areas of the upper approximating rectangles approaches $\tfrac{1}{3}$, that is,

$$\lim_{n \to \infty} R_n = \tfrac{1}{3}$$

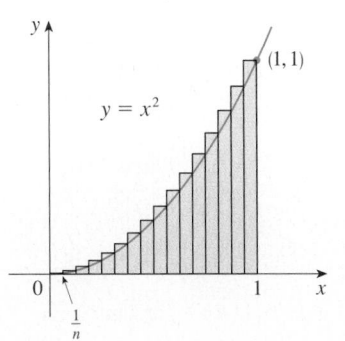

FIGURE 7

SOLUTION R_n is the sum of the areas of the n rectangles in Figure 7. Each rectangle has width $1/n$ and the heights are the values of the function $f(x) = x^2$ at the points $1/n, 2/n, 3/n, \ldots, n/n$; that is, the heights are $(1/n)^2, (2/n)^2, (3/n)^2, \ldots, (n/n)^2$.

Thus

$$R_n = \frac{1}{n}\left(\frac{1}{n}\right)^2 + \frac{1}{n}\left(\frac{2}{n}\right)^2 + \frac{1}{n}\left(\frac{3}{n}\right)^2 + \cdots + \frac{1}{n}\left(\frac{n}{n}\right)^2$$

$$= \frac{1}{n} \cdot \frac{1}{n^2}\left(1^2 + 2^2 + 3^2 + \cdots + n^2\right)$$

$$= \frac{1}{n^3}\left(1^2 + 2^2 + 3^2 + \cdots + n^2\right)$$

The ideas in Examples 1 and 2 are explored in Module 5.1/5.2/8.7 for a variety of functions.

Here we need the formula for the sum of the squares of the first n positive integers:

$\boxed{1}$
$$1^2 + 2^2 + 3^2 + \cdots + n^2 = \frac{n(n + 1)(2n + 1)}{6}$$

Perhaps you have seen this formula before. It is proved in Example 5 in Appendix E. Putting Formula 1 into our expression for R_n, we get

$$R_n = \frac{1}{n^3} \cdot \frac{n(n + 1)(2n + 1)}{6} = \frac{(n + 1)(2n + 1)}{6n^2}$$

Thus, we have

‖‖ Here we are computing the limit of the sequence $\{R_n\}$. Sequences were discussed in *A Preview of Calculus* and will be studied in detail in Chapter 12. Their limits are calculated in the same way as limits at infinity (Section 4.4). In particular, we know that

$$\lim_{n \to \infty} \frac{1}{n} = 0$$

$$\lim_{n \to \infty} R_n = \lim_{n \to \infty} \frac{(n + 1)(2n + 1)}{6n^2}$$

$$= \lim_{n \to \infty} \frac{1}{6}\left(\frac{n + 1}{n}\right)\left(\frac{2n + 1}{n}\right)$$

$$= \lim_{n \to \infty} \frac{1}{6}\left(1 + \frac{1}{n}\right)\left(2 + \frac{1}{n}\right)$$

$$= \frac{1}{6} \cdot 1 \cdot 2 = \frac{1}{3}$$

It can be shown that the lower approximating sums also approach $\frac{1}{3}$, that is,

$$\lim_{n \to \infty} L_n = \frac{1}{3}$$

From Figures 8 and 9 it appears that, as n increases, both L_n and R_n become better and better approximations to the area of S. Therefore, we *define* the area A to be the limit of the

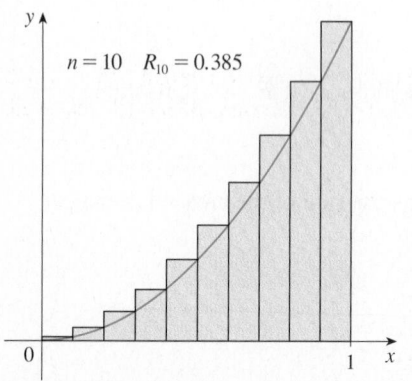

$n = 10 \quad R_{10} = 0.385$

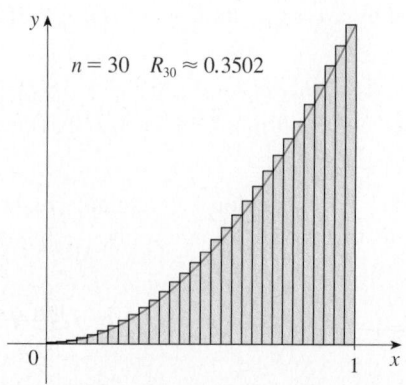

$n = 30 \quad R_{30} \approx 0.3502$

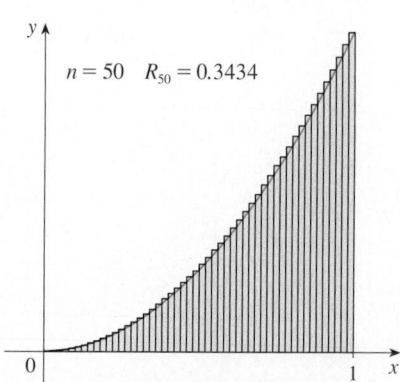

$n = 50 \quad R_{50} = 0.3434$

FIGURE 8

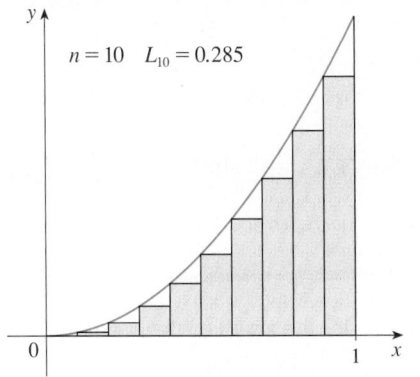

$n = 10 \quad L_{10} = 0.285$

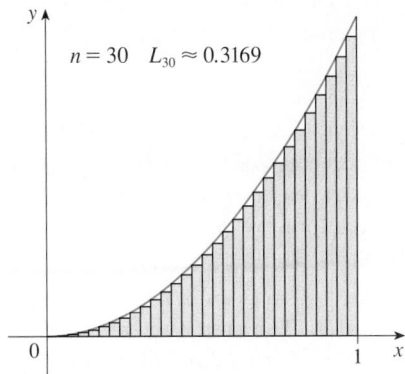

$n = 30 \quad L_{30} \approx 0.3169$

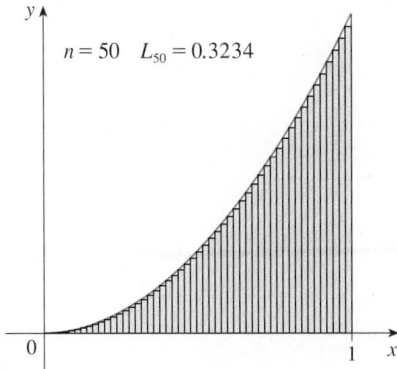

$n = 50 \quad L_{50} = 0.3234$

FIGURE 9

The area is the number that is smaller than all upper sums and larger than all lower sums

sums of the areas of the approximating rectangles, that is,

$$A = \lim_{n \to \infty} R_n = \lim_{n \to \infty} L_n = \tfrac{1}{3}$$

Let's apply the idea of Examples 1 and 2 to the more general region S of Figure 1. We start by subdividing S into n strips $S_1, S_2, \ldots, S_n$ of equal width as in Figure 10. The width of the interval $[a, b]$ is $b - a$, so the width of each of the n strips is

$$\Delta x = \frac{b - a}{n}$$

These strips divide the interval $[a, b]$ into n subintervals

$$[x_0, x_1], \quad [x_1, x_2], \quad [x_2, x_3], \quad \ldots, \quad [x_{n-1}, x_n]$$

where $x_0 = a$ and $x_n = b$. The right endpoints of the subintervals are

$$x_1 = a + \Delta x, \quad x_2 = a + 2\,\Delta x, \quad x_3 = a + 3\,\Delta x, \quad \ldots$$

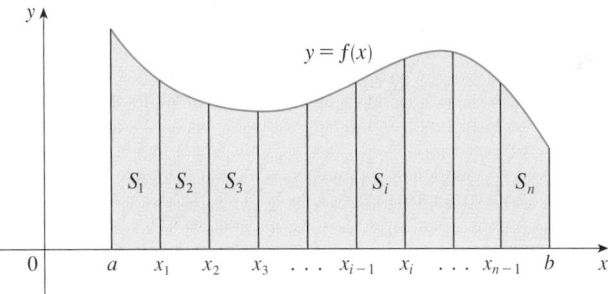

FIGURE 10

Let's approximate the ith strip S_i by a rectangle with width Δx and height $f(x_i)$, which is the value of f at the right endpoint (see Figure 11). Then the area of the ith rectangle

FIGURE 11

(a) $n = 2$

(b) $n = 4$

(c) $n = 8$

(d) $n = 12$

FIGURE 12

is $f(x_i) \, \Delta x$. What we think of intuitively as the area of S is approximated by the sum of the areas of these rectangles, which is

$$R_n = f(x_1) \, \Delta x + f(x_2) \, \Delta x + \cdots + f(x_n) \, \Delta x$$

Figure 12 shows this approximation for $n = 2, 4, 8,$ and 12. Notice that this approximation appears to become better and better as the number of strips increases, that is, as $n \to \infty$. Therefore, we define the area A of the region S in the following way.

> **2 Definition** The **area** A of the region S that lies under the graph of the continuous function f is the limit of the sum of the areas of approximating rectangles:
>
> $$A = \lim_{n \to \infty} R_n = \lim_{n \to \infty} \left[f(x_1) \, \Delta x + f(x_2) \, \Delta x + \cdots + f(x_n) \, \Delta x \right]$$

It can be proved that the limit in Definition 2 always exists, since we are assuming that f is continuous. It can also be shown that we get the same value if we use left endpoints:

$$\boxed{3} \qquad A = \lim_{n \to \infty} L_n = \lim_{n \to \infty} \left[f(x_0) \, \Delta x + f(x_1) \, \Delta x + \cdots + f(x_{n-1}) \, \Delta x \right]$$

In fact, instead of using left endpoints or right endpoints, we could take the height of the ith rectangle to be the value of f at *any* number x_i^* in the ith subinterval $[x_{i-1}, x_i]$. We call the numbers $x_1^*, x_2^*, \ldots, x_n^*$ the **sample points**. Figure 13 shows approximating rectangles when the sample points are not chosen to be endpoints. So a more general expression for the area of S is

$$\boxed{4} \qquad A = \lim_{n \to \infty} \left[f(x_1^*) \, \Delta x + f(x_2^*) \, \Delta x + \cdots + f(x_n^*) \, \Delta x \right]$$

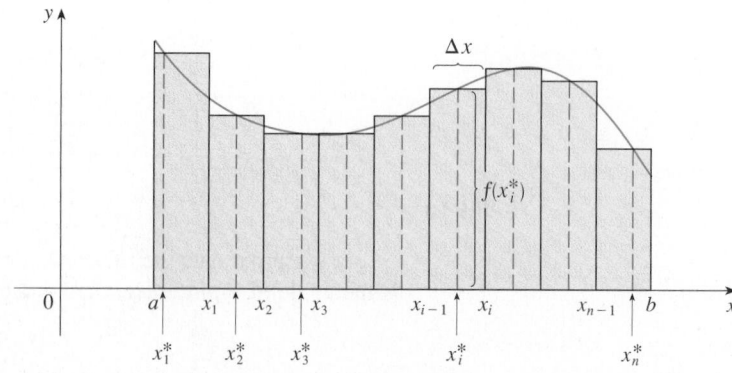

FIGURE 13

This tells us to end with $i = n$.

This tells us to add.

This tells us to start with $i = m$.

$$\sum_{i=m}^{n} f(x_i) \, \Delta x$$

We often use **sigma notation** to write sums with many terms more compactly. For instance,

$$\sum_{i=1}^{n} f(x_i) \, \Delta x = f(x_1) \, \Delta x + f(x_2) \, \Delta x + \cdots + f(x_n) \, \Delta x$$

So the expressions for area in Equations 2, 3, and 4 can be written as follows:

IIII If you need practice with sigma notation, look at the examples and try some of the exercises in Appendix E.

$$A = \lim_{n \to \infty} \sum_{i=1}^{n} f(x_i) \, \Delta x$$

$$A = \lim_{n \to \infty} \sum_{i=1}^{n} f(x_{i-1}) \, \Delta x$$

$$A = \lim_{n \to \infty} \sum_{i=1}^{n} f(x_i^*) \, \Delta x$$

We could also rewrite Formula 1 in the following way:

$$\sum_{i=1}^{n} i^2 = \frac{n(n+1)(2n+1)}{6}$$

EXAMPLE 3 Let A be the area of the region that lies under the graph of $f(x) = \cos x$ between $x = 0$ and $x = b$, where $0 \le b \le \pi/2$.
(a) Using right endpoints, find an expression for A as a limit. Do not evaluate the limit.
(b) Estimate the area for the case $b = \pi/2$ by taking the sample points to be midpoints and using four subintervals.

SOLUTION
(a) Since $a = 0$, the width of a subinterval is

$$\Delta x = \frac{b-0}{n} = \frac{b}{n}$$

So $x_1 = b/n$, $x_2 = 2b/n$, $x_3 = 3b/n$, $x_i = ib/n$, and $x_n = nb/n$. The sum of the areas of the approximating rectangles is

$$R_n = f(x_1) \, \Delta x + f(x_2) \, \Delta x + \cdots + f(x_n) \, \Delta x$$

$$= (\cos x_1) \, \Delta x + (\cos x_2) \, \Delta x + \cdots + (\cos x_n) \, \Delta x$$

$$= \left(\cos \frac{b}{n}\right) \frac{b}{n} + \left(\cos \frac{2b}{n}\right) \frac{b}{n} + \cdots + \left(\cos \frac{nb}{n}\right) \frac{b}{n}$$

According to Definition 2, the area is

$$A = \lim_{n \to \infty} R_n = \lim_{n \to \infty} \frac{b}{n} \left(\cos \frac{b}{n} + \cos \frac{2b}{n} + \cos \frac{3b}{n} + \cdots + \cos \frac{nb}{n}\right)$$

Using sigma notation we could write

$$A = \lim_{n \to \infty} \frac{b}{n} \sum_{i=1}^{n} \cos \frac{ib}{n}$$

It is very difficult to evaluate this limit directly by hand, but with the aid of a computer algebra system it isn't hard (see Exercise 25). In Section 5.3 we will be able to find A more easily using a different method.

FIGURE 14

(b) With $n = 4$ and $b = \pi/2$ we have $\Delta x = (\pi/2)/4 = \pi/8$, so the subintervals are $[0, \pi/8]$, $[\pi/8, \pi/4]$, $[\pi/4, 3\pi/8]$, and $[3\pi/8, \pi/2]$. The midpoints of these subintervals are

$$x_1^* = \frac{\pi}{16} \qquad x_2^* = \frac{3\pi}{16} \qquad x_3^* = \frac{5\pi}{16} \qquad x_4^* = \frac{7\pi}{16}$$

and the sum of the areas of the four approximating rectangles (see Figure 14) is

$$M_4 = \sum_{i=1}^{4} f(x_i^*) \, \Delta x$$

$$= f(\pi/16) \, \Delta x + f(3\pi/16) \, \Delta x + f(5\pi/16) \, \Delta x + f(7\pi/16) \, \Delta x$$

$$= \left(\cos \frac{\pi}{16} \right) \frac{\pi}{8} + \left(\cos \frac{3\pi}{16} \right) \frac{\pi}{8} + \left(\cos \frac{5\pi}{16} \right) \frac{\pi}{8} + \left(\cos \frac{7\pi}{16} \right) \frac{\pi}{8}$$

$$= \frac{\pi}{8} \left(\cos \frac{\pi}{16} + \cos \frac{3\pi}{16} + \cos \frac{5\pi}{16} + \cos \frac{7\pi}{16} \right) \approx 1.006$$

So an estimate for the area is

$$A \approx 1.006$$

▏▏▏ The Distance Problem

Now let's consider the *distance problem:* Find the distance traveled by an object during a certain time period if the velocity of the object is known at all times. (In a sense this is the inverse problem of the velocity problem that we discussed in Section 2.1.) If the velocity remains constant, then the distance problem is easy to solve by means of the formula

$$\text{distance} = \text{velocity} \times \text{time}$$

But if the velocity varies, it's not so easy to find the distance traveled. We investigate the problem in the following example.

EXAMPLE 4 Suppose the odometer on our car is broken and we want to estimate the distance driven over a 30-second time interval. We take speedometer readings every five seconds and record them in the following table:

Time (s)	0	5	10	15	20	25	30
Velocity (mi/h)	17	21	24	29	32	31	28

In order to have the time and the velocity in consistent units, let's convert the velocity readings to feet per second (1 mi/h = 5280/3600 ft/s):

Time (s)	0	5	10	15	20	25	30
Velocity (ft/s)	25	31	35	43	47	46	41

During the first five seconds the velocity doesn't change very much, so we can estimate the distance traveled during that time by assuming that the velocity is constant. If we take the velocity during that time interval to be the initial velocity (25 ft/s), then we obtain the approximate distance traveled during the first five seconds:

$$25 \text{ ft/s} \times 5 \text{ s} = 125 \text{ ft}$$

Similarly, during the second time interval the velocity is approximately constant and we take it to be the velocity when $t = 5$ s. So our estimate for the distance traveled from $t = 5$ s to $t = 10$ s is

$$31 \text{ ft/s} \times 5 \text{ s} = 155 \text{ ft}$$

If we add similar estimates for the other time intervals, we obtain an estimate for the total distance traveled:

$$25 \times 5 + 31 \times 5 + 35 \times 5 + 43 \times 5 + 47 \times 5 + 46 \times 5 = 1135 \text{ ft}$$

We could just as well have used the velocity at the *end* of each time period instead of the velocity at the beginning as our assumed constant velocity. Then our estimate becomes

$$31 \times 5 + 35 \times 5 + 43 \times 5 + 47 \times 5 + 46 \times 5 + 41 \times 5 = 1215 \text{ ft}$$

If we had wanted a more accurate estimate, we could have taken velocity readings every two seconds, or even every second.

Perhaps the calculations in Example 4 remind you of the sums we used earlier to estimate areas. The similarity is explained when we sketch a graph of the velocity function of the car in Figure 15 and draw rectangles whose heights are the initial velocities for each time interval. The area of the first rectangle is $25 \times 5 = 125$, which is also our estimate for the distance traveled in the first five seconds. In fact, the area of each rectangle can be interpreted as a distance because the height represents velocity and the width represents time. The sum of the areas of the rectangles in Figure 15 is $L_6 = 1135$, which is our initial estimate for the total distance traveled.

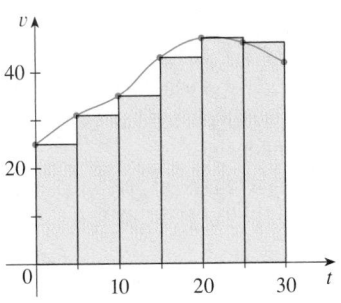

FIGURE 15

In general, suppose an object moves with velocity $v = f(t)$, where $a \leq t \leq b$ and $f(t) \geq 0$ (so the object always moves in the positive direction). We take velocity readings at times $t_0 \, (= a), t_1, t_2, \ldots, t_n \, (= b)$ so that the velocity is approximately constant on each subinterval. If these times are equally spaced, then the time between consecutive readings is $\Delta t = (b - a)/n$. During the first time interval the velocity is approximately $f(t_0)$ and so the distance traveled is approximately $f(t_0) \, \Delta t$. Similarly, the distance traveled during the second time interval is about $f(t_1) \, \Delta t$ and the total distance traveled during the time interval $[a, b]$ is approximately

$$f(t_0) \, \Delta t + f(t_1) \, \Delta t + \cdots + f(t_{n-1}) \, \Delta t = \sum_{i=1}^{n} f(t_{i-1}) \, \Delta t$$

If we use the velocity at right endpoints instead of left endpoints, our estimate for the total distance becomes

$$f(t_1) \, \Delta t + f(t_2) \, \Delta t + \cdots + f(t_n) \, \Delta t = \sum_{i=1}^{n} f(t_i) \, \Delta t$$

The more frequently we measure the velocity, the more accurate our estimates become, so it seems plausible that the *exact* distance d traveled is the *limit* of such expressions:

$$\boxed{5} \qquad\qquad d = \lim_{n \to \infty} \sum_{i=1}^{n} f(t_{i-1}) \, \Delta t = \lim_{n \to \infty} \sum_{i=1}^{n} f(t_i) \, \Delta t$$

We will see in Section 5.4 that this is indeed true.

Because Equation 5 has the same form as our expressions for area in Equations 2 and 3, it follows that the distance traveled is equal to the area under the graph of the velocity function. In Chapters 6 and 9 we will see that other quantities of interest in the natural and social sciences—such as the work done by a variable force or the cardiac output of the heart—can also be interpreted as the area under a curve. So when we compute areas in this chapter, bear in mind that they can be interpreted in a variety of practical ways.

5.1 Exercises

1. (a) By reading values from the given graph of f, use five rectangles to find a lower estimate and an upper estimate for the area under the given graph of f from $x = 0$ to $x = 10$. In each case sketch the rectangles that you use.
(b) Find new estimates using 10 rectangles in each case.

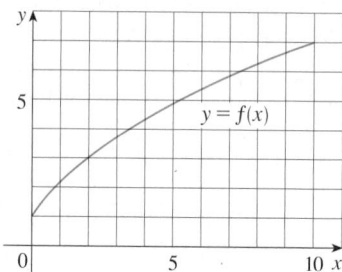

2. (a) Use six rectangles to find estimates of each type for the area under the given graph of f from $x = 0$ to $x = 12$.
   (i) L_6 (sample points are left endpoints)
   (ii) R_6 (sample points are right endpoints)
   (iii) M_6 (sample points are midpoints)
(b) Is L_6 an underestimate or overestimate of the true area?
(c) Is R_6 an underestimate or overestimate of the true area?
(d) Which of the numbers L_6, R_6, or M_6 gives the best estimate? Explain.

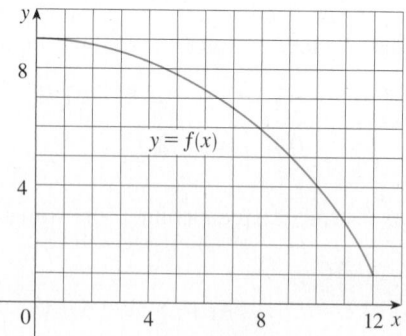

3. (a) Estimate the area under the graph of $f(x) = 1/x$ from $x = 1$ to $x = 5$ using four approximating rectangles and right endpoints. Sketch the graph and the rectangles. Is your estimate an underestimate or an overestimate?
(b) Repeat part (a) using left endpoints.

4. (a) Estimate the area under the graph of $f(x) = 25 - x^2$ from $x = 0$ to $x = 5$ using five approximating rectangles and

right endpoints. Sketch the graph and the rectangles. Is your estimate an underestimate or an overestimate?
(b) Repeat part (a) using left endpoints.

5. (a) Estimate the area under the graph of $f(x) = 1 + x^2$ from $x = -1$ to $x = 2$ using three rectangles and right endpoints. Then improve your estimate by using six rectangles. Sketch the curve and the approximating rectangles.
(b) Repeat part (a) using left endpoints.
(c) Repeat part (a) using midpoints.
(d) From your sketches in parts (a)–(c), which appears to be the best estimate?

6. (a) Graph the function $f(x) = 1/(1 + x^2)$, $-2 \le x \le 2$.
(b) Estimate the area under the graph of f using four approximating rectangles and taking the sample points to be
   (i) right endpoints   (ii) midpoints
   In each case sketch the curve and the rectangles.
(c) Improve your estimates in part (b) by using eight rectangles.

7–8 ▓ With a programmable calculator (or a computer), it is possible to evaluate the expressions for the sums of areas of approximating rectangles, even for large values of n, using looping. (On a TI use the Is> command or a For-EndFor loop, on a Casio use Isz, on an HP or in BASIC use a FOR-NEXT loop.) Compute the sum of the areas of approximating rectangles using equal subintervals and right endpoints for $n = 10, 30$, and 50. Then guess the value of the exact area.

7. The region under $y = \sin x$ from 0 to π

8. The region under $y = 1/x^2$ from 1 to 2

       □   □   □   □   □   □   □   □   □   □   □   □

[CAS] **9.** Some computer algebra systems have commands that will draw approximating rectangles and evaluate the sums of their areas, at least if x_i^* is a left or right endpoint. (For instance, in Maple use leftbox, rightbox, leftsum, and rightsum.)
(a) If $f(x) = \sqrt{x}$, $1 \le x \le 4$, find the left and right sums for $n = 10, 30$, and 50.
(b) Illustrate by graphing the rectangles in part (a).
(c) Show that the exact area under f lies between 4.6 and 4.7.

[CAS] **10.** (a) If $f(x) = \sin(\sin x)$, $0 \le x \le \pi/2$, use the commands discussed in Exercise 9 to find the left and right sums for $n = 10, 30$, and 50.

(b) Illustrate by graphing the rectangles in part (a).
(c) Show that the exact area under f lies between 0.87 and 0.91.

11. The speed of a runner increased steadily during the first three seconds of a race. Her speed at half-second intervals is given in the table. Find lower and upper estimates for the distance that she traveled during these three seconds.

t (s)	0	0.5	1.0	1.5	2.0	2.5	3.0
v (ft/s)	0	6.2	10.8	14.9	18.1	19.4	20.2

12. Speedometer readings for a motorcycle at 12-second intervals are given in the table.
 (a) Estimate the distance traveled by the motorcycle during this time period using the velocities at the beginning of the time intervals.
 (b) Give another estimate using the velocities at the end of the time periods.
 (c) Are your estimates in parts (a) and (b) upper and lower estimates? Explain.

t (s)	0	12	24	36	48	60
v (ft/s)	30	28	25	22	24	27

13. Oil leaked from a tank at a rate of $r(t)$ liters per hour. The rate decreased as time passed and values of the rate at 2-hour time intervals are shown in the table. Find lower and upper estimates for the total amount of oil that leaked out.

t (h)	0	2	4	6	8	10
$r(t)$ (L/h)	8.7	7.6	6.8	6.2	5.7	5.3

14. When we estimate distances from velocity data, it is sometimes necessary to use times $t_0, t_1, t_2, t_3, \ldots$ that are not equally spaced. We can still estimate distances using the time periods $\Delta t_i = t_i - t_{i-1}$. For example, on May 7, 1992, the space shuttle *Endeavour* was launched on mission STS-49, the purpose of which was to install a new perigee kick motor in an Intelsat communications satellite. The table, provided by NASA, gives the velocity data for the shuttle between liftoff and the jettisoning of the solid rocket boosters.

Event	Time (s)	Velocity (ft/s)
Launch	0	0
Begin roll maneuver	10	185
End roll maneuver	15	319
Throttle to 89%	20	447
Throttle to 67%	32	742
Throttle to 104%	59	1325
Maximum dynamic pressure	62	1445
Solid rocket booster separation	125	4151

Use these data to estimate the height above the Earth's surface of the space shuttle *Endeavour,* 62 seconds after liftoff.

15. The velocity graph of a braking car is shown. Use it to estimate the distance traveled by the car while the brakes are applied.

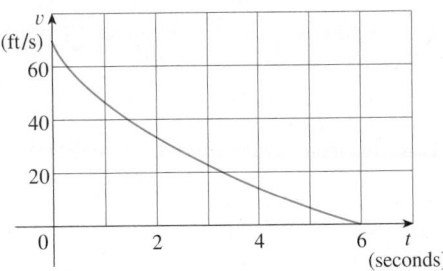

16. The velocity graph of a car accelerating from rest to a speed of 120 km/h over a period of 30 seconds is shown. Estimate the distance traveled during this period.

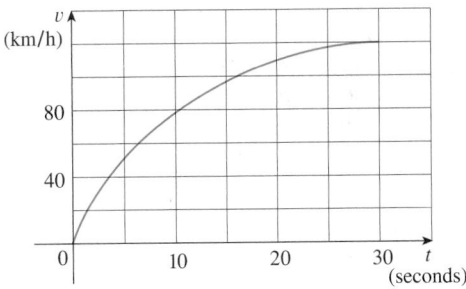

17–19 ||||| Use Definition 2 to find an expression for the area under the graph of f as a limit. Do not evaluate the limit.

17. $f(x) = \sqrt[4]{x}, \quad 1 \le x \le 16$

18. $f(x) = 1 + x^4, \quad 2 \le x \le 5$

19. $f(x) = x \cos x, \quad 0 \le x \le \pi/2$

⬚   ⬚   ⬚   ⬚   ⬚   ⬚   ⬚   ⬚   ⬚   ⬚   ⬚

20–21 ||||| Determine a region whose area is equal to the given limit. Do not evaluate the limit.

20. $\displaystyle \lim_{n \to \infty} \sum_{i=1}^{n} \frac{2}{n} \left(5 + \frac{2i}{n} \right)^{10}$

21. $\displaystyle \lim_{n \to \infty} \sum_{i=1}^{n} \frac{\pi}{4n} \tan \frac{i\pi}{4n}$

⬚   ⬚   ⬚   ⬚   ⬚   ⬚   ⬚   ⬚   ⬚   ⬚   ⬚

22. (a) Use Definition 2 to find an expression for the area under the curve $y = x^3$ from 0 to 1 as a limit.
 (b) The following formula for the sum of the cubes of the first n integers is proved in Appendix E. Use it to evaluate the limit in part (a).

$$1^3 + 2^3 + 3^3 + \cdots + n^3 = \left[\frac{n(n+1)}{2} \right]^2$$

CAS **23.** (a) Express the area under the curve $y = x^5$ from 0 to 2 as a limit.
(b) Use a computer algebra system to find the sum in your expression from part (a).
(c) Evaluate the limit in part (a).

CAS **24.** (a) Express the area under the curve $y = x^4 + 5x^2 + x$ from 2 to 7 as a limit.
(b) Use a computer algebra system to evaluate the sum in part (a).
(c) Use a computer algebra system to find the exact area by evaluating the limit of the expression in part (b).

CAS **25.** Find the exact area under the cosine curve $y = \cos x$ from $x = 0$ to $x = b$, where $0 \leqslant b \leqslant \pi/2$. (Use a computer algebra system both to evaluate the sum and compute the limit in Example 3.) In particular, what is the area if $b = \pi/2$? Compare your answer with the estimate obtained in Example 3(b).

26. (a) Let A_n be the area of a polygon with n equal sides inscribed in a circle with radius r. By dividing the polygon into n congruent triangles with central angle $2\pi/n$, show that
$A_n = \frac{1}{2}nr^2 \sin(2\pi/n)$.
(b) Show that $\lim_{n\to\infty} A_n = \pi r^2$. [*Hint:* Use Equation 3.5.2.]

5.2 The Definite Integral

We saw in Section 5.1 that a limit of the form

$$\boxed{1} \qquad \lim_{n\to\infty} \sum_{i=1}^{n} f(x_i^*)\,\Delta x = \lim_{n\to\infty} \left[f(x_1^*)\,\Delta x + f(x_2^*)\,\Delta x + \cdots + f(x_n^*)\,\Delta x \right]$$

arises when we compute an area. We also saw that it arises when we try to find the distance traveled by an object. It turns out that this same type of limit occurs in a wide variety of situations even when f is not necessarily a positive function. In Chapters 6 and 9 we will see that limits of the form (1) also arise in finding lengths of curves, volumes of solids, centers of mass, force due to water pressure, and work, as well as other quantities. We therefore give this type of limit a special name and notation.

---

2 Definition of a Definite Integral If f is a continuous function defined for $a \leqslant x \leqslant b$, we divide the interval $[a, b]$ into n subintervals of equal width $\Delta x = (b - a)/n$. We let $x_0 \,(= a), x_1, x_2, \ldots, x_n \,(= b)$ be the endpoints of these subintervals and we let $x_1^*, x_2^*, \ldots, x_n^*$ be any **sample points** in these subintervals, so x_i^* lies in the ith subinterval $[x_{i-1}, x_i]$. Then the **definite integral of f from a to b** is

$$\int_a^b f(x)\,dx = \lim_{n\to\infty} \sum_{i=1}^{n} f(x_i^*)\,\Delta x$$

Because we have assumed that f is continuous, it can be proved that the limit in Definition 2 always exists and gives the same value no matter how we choose the sample points x_i^*. (See Note 4 for a precise definition of this type of limit.) If we take the sample points to be right endpoints, then $x_i^* = x_i$ and the definition of an integral becomes

$$\boxed{3} \qquad \int_a^b f(x)\,dx = \lim_{n\to\infty} \sum_{i=1}^{n} f(x_i)\,\Delta x$$

If we choose the sample points to be left endpoints, then $x_i^* = x_{i-1}$ and the definition becomes

$$\int_a^b f(x)\, dx = \lim_{n \to \infty} \sum_{i=1}^{n} f(x_{i-1})\, \Delta x$$

Alternatively, we could choose x_i^* to be the midpoint of the subinterval or any other number between x_{i-1} and x_i.

Although most of the functions that we encounter are continuous, the limit in Definition 2 also exists if f has a finite number of removable or jump discontinuities (but not infinite discontinuities). (See Section 2.5.) So we can also define the definite integral for such functions.

NOTE 1 ◦ The symbol $\int$ was introduced by Leibniz and is called an **integral sign**. It is an elongated S and was chosen because an integral is a limit of sums. In the notation $\int_a^b f(x)\, dx$, $f(x)$ is called the **integrand** and a and b are called the **limits of integration**; a is the **lower limit** and b is the **upper limit**. The symbol dx has no official meaning by itself; $\int_a^b f(x)\, dx$ is all one symbol. The procedure of calculating an integral is called **integration**.

NOTE 2 ◦ The definite integral $\int_a^b f(x)\, dx$ is a number; it does not depend on x. In fact, we could use any letter in place of x without changing the value of the integral:

$$\int_a^b f(x)\, dx = \int_a^b f(t)\, dt = \int_a^b f(r)\, dr$$

NOTE 3 ◦ The sum

$$\sum_{i=1}^{n} f(x_i^*)\, \Delta x$$

|||| Bernhard Riemann received his Ph.D. under the direction of the legendary Gauss at the University of Göttingen and remained there to teach. Gauss, who was not in the habit of praising other mathematicians, spoke of Riemann's "creative, active, truly mathematical mind and gloriously fertile originality." The definition (2) of an integral that we use is due to Riemann. He also made major contributions to the theory of functions of a complex variable, mathematical physics, number theory, and the foundations of geometry. Riemann's broad concept of space and geometry turned out to be the right setting, 50 years later, for Einstein's general relativity theory. Riemann's health was poor throughout his life, and he died of tuberculosis at the age of 39.

that occurs in Definition 2 is called a **Riemann sum** after the German mathematician Bernhard Riemann (1826–1866). We know that if f happens to be positive, then the Riemann sum can be interpreted as a sum of areas of approximating rectangles (see Figure 1). By comparing Definition 2 with the definition of area in Section 5.1, we see that the definite integral $\int_a^b f(x)\, dx$ can be interpreted as the area under the curve $y = f(x)$ from a to b. (See Figure 2.)

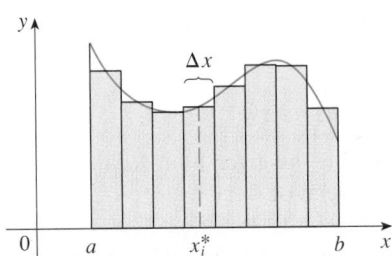

FIGURE 1
If $f(x) \geqslant 0$, the Riemann sum $\Sigma f(x_i^*)\, \Delta x$ is the sum of areas of rectangles.

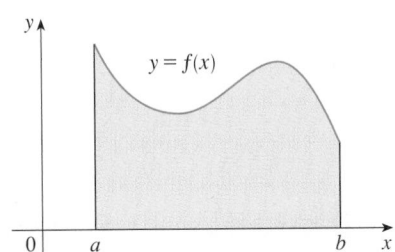

FIGURE 2
If $f(x) \geqslant 0$, the integral $\int_a^b f(x)\, dx$ is the area under the curve $y = f(x)$ from a to b.

FIGURE 3

$\Sigma f(x_i^*) \, \Delta x$ is an approximation to the net area

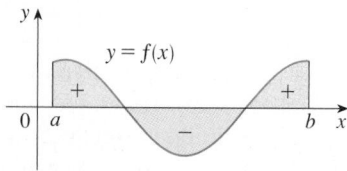

FIGURE 4

$\int_a^b f(x) \, dx$ is the net area

If f takes on both positive and negative values, as in Figure 3, then the Riemann sum is the sum of the areas of the rectangles that lie above the x-axis and the *negatives* of the areas of the rectangles that lie below the x-axis (the areas of the gold rectangles *minus* the areas of the blue rectangles). When we take the limit of such Riemann sums, we get the situation illustrated in Figure 4. A definite integral can be interpreted as a **net area**, that is, a difference of areas:

$$\int_a^b f(x) \, dx = A_1 - A_2$$

where A_1 is the area of the region above the x-axis and below the graph of f, and A_2 is the area of the region below the x-axis and above the graph of f.

NOTE 4 ∘ In the spirit of the precise definition of the limit of a function in Section 2.4, we can write the precise meaning of the limit that defines the integral in Definition 2 as follows:

For every number $\varepsilon > 0$ there is an integer N such that

$$\left| \int_a^b f(x) \, dx - \sum_{i=1}^n f(x_i^*) \, \Delta x \right| < \varepsilon$$

for every integer $n > N$ and for every choice of x_i^* in $[x_{i-1}, x_i]$.

This means that a definite integral can be approximated to within any desired degree of accuracy by a Riemann sum.

NOTE 5 ∘ Although we have defined $\int_a^b f(x) \, dx$ by dividing $[a, b]$ into subintervals of equal width, there are situations in which it is advantageous to work with subintervals of unequal width. For instance, in Exercise 14 in Section 5.1 NASA provided velocity data at times that were not equally spaced, but we were still able to estimate the distance traveled. And there are methods for numerical integration that take advantage of unequal subintervals.

If the subinterval widths are $\Delta x_1, \Delta x_2, \ldots, \Delta x_n$, we have to ensure that all these widths approach 0 in the limiting process. This happens if the largest width, $\max \Delta x_i$, approaches 0. So in this case the definition of a definite integral becomes

$$\int_a^b f(x) \, dx = \lim_{\max \Delta x_i \to 0} \sum_{i=1}^n f(x_i^*) \, \Delta x_i$$

EXAMPLE 1 Express

$$\lim_{n \to \infty} \sum_{i=1}^n (x_i^3 + x_i \sin x_i) \, \Delta x$$

as an integral on the interval $[0, \pi]$.

SOLUTION Comparing the given limit with the limit in Definition 2, we see that they will be identical if we choose

$$f(x) = x^3 + x \sin x \qquad \text{and} \qquad x_i^* = x_i$$

(So the sample points are right endpoints and the given limit is of the form of Equation 3.) We are given that $a = 0$ and $b = \pi$. Therefore, by Definition 2 or Equation 3, we have

$$\lim_{n \to \infty} \sum_{i=1}^n (x_i^3 + x_i \sin x_i) \, \Delta x = \int_0^\pi (x^3 + x \sin x) \, dx$$

Later, when we apply the definite integral to physical situations, it will be important to recognize limits of sums as integrals, as we did in Example 1. When Leibniz chose the notation for an integral, he chose the ingredients as reminders of the limiting process. In general, when we write

$$\lim_{n \to \infty} \sum_{i=1}^{n} f(x_i^*) \, \Delta x = \int_a^b f(x) \, dx$$

we replace $\lim \Sigma$ by $\int$, x_i^* by x, and Δx by dx.

||| Evaluating Integrals

When we use the definition to evaluate a definite integral, we need to know how to work with sums. The following three equations give formulas for sums of powers of positive integers. Equation 4 may be familiar to you from a course in algebra. Equations 5 and 6 were discussed in Section 5.1 and are proved in Appendix E.

4    $$\sum_{i=1}^{n} i = \frac{n(n+1)}{2}$$

5    $$\sum_{i=1}^{n} i^2 = \frac{n(n+1)(2n+1)}{6}$$

6    $$\sum_{i=1}^{n} i^3 = \left[\frac{n(n+1)}{2} \right]^2$$

The remaining formulas are simple rules for working with sigma notation:

7    $$\sum_{i=1}^{n} c = nc$$

||| Formulas 7–10 are proved by writing out each side in expanded form. The left side of Equation 8 is

$$ca_1 + ca_2 + \cdots + ca_n$$

The right side is

$$c(a_1 + a_2 + \cdots + a_n)$$

These are equal by the distributive property. The other formulas are discussed in Appendix E.

8    $$\sum_{i=1}^{n} ca_i = c \sum_{i=1}^{n} a_i$$

9    $$\sum_{i=1}^{n} (a_i + b_i) = \sum_{i=1}^{n} a_i + \sum_{i=1}^{n} b_i$$

10   $$\sum_{i=1}^{n} (a_i - b_i) = \sum_{i=1}^{n} a_i - \sum_{i=1}^{n} b_i$$

EXAMPLE 2

(a) Evaluate the Riemann sum for $f(x) = x^3 - 6x$ taking the sample points to be right endpoints and $a = 0$, $b = 3$, and $n = 6$.

(b) Evaluate $\int_0^3 (x^3 - 6x) \, dx$.

Try more problems like this one.

Resources / Module 6
/ What Is Area?
/ Problems and Tests

SOLUTION

(a) With $n = 6$ the interval width is

$$\Delta x = \frac{b - a}{n} = \frac{3 - 0}{6} = \frac{1}{2}$$

and the right endpoints are $x_1 = 0.5$, $x_2 = 1.0$, $x_3 = 1.5$, $x_4 = 2.0$, $x_5 = 2.5$, and $x_6 = 3.0$. So the Riemann sum is

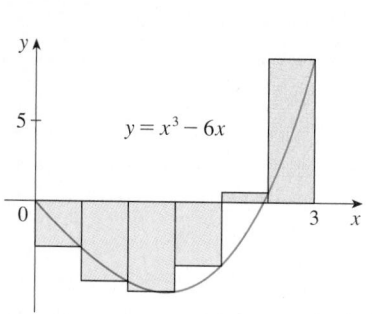

$$R_6 = \sum_{i=1}^{6} f(x_i)\,\Delta x$$

$$= f(0.5)\,\Delta x + f(1.0)\,\Delta x + f(1.5)\,\Delta x + f(2.0)\,\Delta x + f(2.5)\,\Delta x + f(3.0)\,\Delta x$$

$$= \tfrac{1}{2}(-2.875 - 5 - 5.625 - 4 + 0.625 + 9)$$

$$= -3.9375$$

FIGURE 5

Notice that f is not a positive function and so the Riemann sum does not represent a sum of areas of rectangles. But it does represent the sum of the areas of the gold rectangles (above the x-axis) minus the sum of the areas of the blue rectangles (below the x-axis) in Figure 5.

(b) With n subintervals we have

$$\Delta x = \frac{b - a}{n} = \frac{3}{n}$$

Thus $x_0 = 0$, $x_1 = 3/n$, $x_2 = 6/n$, $x_3 = 9/n$, and, in general, $x_i = 3i/n$. Since we are using right endpoints, we can use Equation 3:

|||| In the sum, n is a constant (unlike i), so we can move $3/n$ in front of the Σ sign.

$$\int_0^3 (x^3 - 6x)\,dx = \lim_{n \to \infty} \sum_{i=1}^{n} f(x_i)\,\Delta x = \lim_{n \to \infty} \sum_{i=1}^{n} f\!\left(\frac{3i}{n}\right)\frac{3}{n}$$

$$= \lim_{n \to \infty} \frac{3}{n} \sum_{i=1}^{n} \left[\left(\frac{3i}{n}\right)^3 - 6\left(\frac{3i}{n}\right) \right] \qquad \text{(Equation 8 with } c = 3/n\text{)}$$

$$= \lim_{n \to \infty} \frac{3}{n} \sum_{i=1}^{n} \left[\frac{27}{n^3} i^3 - \frac{18}{n} i \right]$$

$$= \lim_{n \to \infty} \left[\frac{81}{n^4} \sum_{i=1}^{n} i^3 - \frac{54}{n^2} \sum_{i=1}^{n} i \right] \qquad \text{(Equations 10 and 8)}$$

$$= \lim_{n \to \infty} \left\{ \frac{81}{n^4} \left[\frac{n(n + 1)}{2} \right]^2 - \frac{54}{n^2}\frac{n(n + 1)}{2} \right\}$$

$$= \lim_{n \to \infty} \left[\frac{81}{4} \left(1 + \frac{1}{n}\right)^2 - 27\left(1 + \frac{1}{n}\right) \right]$$

$$= \frac{81}{4} - 27 = -\frac{27}{4} = -6.75$$

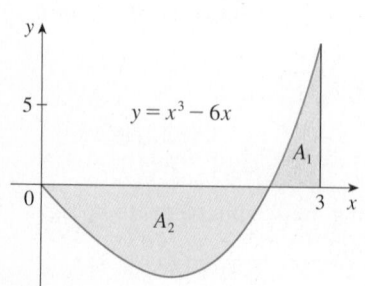

FIGURE 6

$\int_0^3 (x^3 - 6x)\,dx = A_1 - A_2 = -6.75$

This integral can't be interpreted as an area because f takes on both positive and negative values. But it can be interpreted as the difference of areas $A_1 - A_2$, where A_1 and A_2 are shown in Figure 6.

Figure 7 illustrates the calculation by showing the positive and negative terms in the right Riemann sum R_n for $n = 40$. The values in the table show the Riemann sums approaching the exact value of the integral, -6.75, as $n \to \infty$.

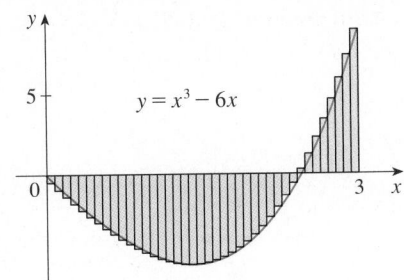

n	R_n
40	-6.3998
100	-6.6130
500	-6.7229
1000	-6.7365
5000	-6.7473

FIGURE 7
$R_{40} \approx -6.3998$

A much simpler method for evaluating the integral in Example 2 will be given in Section 5.3.

|||| Because $f(x) = x^4$ is positive, the integral in Example 3 represents the area shown in Figure 8.

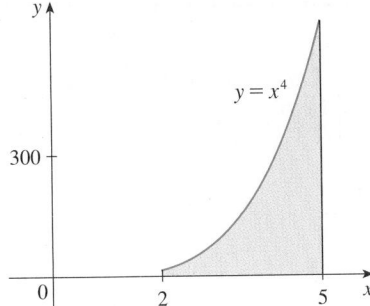

FIGURE 8

EXAMPLE 3
(a) Set up an expression for $\int_2^5 x^4 \, dx$ as a limit of sums.
(b) Use a computer algebra system to evaluate the expression.

SOLUTION
(a) Here we have $f(x) = x^4$, $a = 2$, $b = 5$, and

$$\Delta x = \frac{b - a}{n} = \frac{3}{n}$$

So $x_0 = 2$, $x_1 = 2 + 3/n$, $x_2 = 2 + 6/n$, $x_3 = 2 + 9/n$, and

$$x_i = 2 + \frac{3i}{n}$$

From Equation 3, we get

$$\int_2^5 x^4 \, dx = \lim_{n \to \infty} \sum_{i=1}^{n} f(x_i) \, \Delta x = \lim_{n \to \infty} \sum_{i=1}^{n} f\left(2 + \frac{3i}{n}\right) \frac{3}{n}$$

$$= \lim_{n \to \infty} \frac{3}{n} \sum_{i=1}^{n} \left(2 + \frac{3i}{n}\right)^4$$

(b) If we ask a computer algebra system to evaluate the sum and simplify, we obtain

$$\sum_{i=1}^{n} \left(2 + \frac{3i}{n}\right)^4 = \frac{2062n^4 + 3045n^3 + 1170n^2 - 27}{10n^3}$$

Now we ask the CAS to evaluate the limit:

$$\int_2^5 x^4 \, dx = \lim_{n \to \infty} \frac{3}{n} \sum_{i=1}^{n} \left(2 + \frac{3i}{n}\right)^4 = \lim_{n \to \infty} \frac{3(2062n^4 + 3045n^3 + 1170n^2 - 27)}{10n^4}$$

$$= \frac{3(2062)}{10} = \frac{3093}{5} = 618.6$$

We will learn a much easier method for the evaluation of integrals in the next section.

EXAMPLE 4 Evaluate the following integrals by interpreting each in terms of areas.

(a) $\int_0^1 \sqrt{1 - x^2}\, dx$

(b) $\int_0^3 (x - 1)\, dx$

SOLUTION

(a) Since $f(x) = \sqrt{1 - x^2} \geq 0$, we can interpret this integral as the area under the curve $y = \sqrt{1 - x^2}$ from 0 to 1. But, since $y^2 = 1 - x^2$, we get $x^2 + y^2 = 1$, which shows that the graph of f is the quarter-circle with radius 1 in Figure 9. Therefore

$$\int_0^1 \sqrt{1 - x^2}\, dx = \tfrac{1}{4}\pi(1)^2 = \frac{\pi}{4}$$

(In Section 8.3 we will be able to *prove* that the area of a circle of radius r is πr^2.)

(b) The graph of $y = x - 1$ is the line with slope 1 shown in Figure 10. We compute the integral as the difference of the areas of the two triangles:

$$\int_0^3 (x - 1)\, dx = A_1 - A_2 = \tfrac{1}{2}(2 \cdot 2) - \tfrac{1}{2}(1 \cdot 1) = 1.5$$

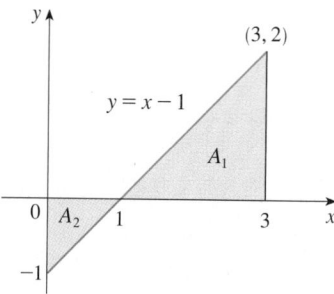

FIGURE 10

FIGURE 9

▏▏▏▏ **The Midpoint Rule**

We often choose the sample point x_i^* to be the right endpoint of the ith subinterval because it is convenient for computing the limit. But if the purpose is to find an *approximation* to an integral, it is usually better to choose x_i^* to be the midpoint of the interval, which we denote by $\bar{x}_i$. Any Riemann sum is an approximation to an integral, but if we use midpoints we get the following approximation.

 Module 5.1/5.2/8.7 shows how the Midpoint Rule estimates improve as n increases.

Midpoint Rule

$$\int_a^b f(x)\, dx \approx \sum_{i=1}^n f(\bar{x}_i)\, \Delta x = \Delta x [f(\bar{x}_1) + \cdots + f(\bar{x}_n)]$$

where $\Delta x = \dfrac{b - a}{n}$

and $\bar{x}_i = \tfrac{1}{2}(x_{i-1} + x_i) = $ midpoint of $[x_{i-1}, x_i]$

EXAMPLE 5 Use the Midpoint Rule with $n = 5$ to approximate $\int_1^2 \dfrac{1}{x}\, dx$.

SOLUTION The endpoints of the five subintervals are 1, 1.2, 1.4, 1.6, 1.8, and 2.0, so the midpoints are 1.1, 1.3, 1.5, 1.7, and 1.9. The width of the subintervals is $\Delta x = (2 - 1)/5 = \frac{1}{5}$, so the Midpoint Rule gives

$$\int_1^2 \frac{1}{x}\,dx \approx \Delta x\,[f(1.1) + f(1.3) + f(1.5) + f(1.7) + f(1.9)]$$

$$= \frac{1}{5}\left(\frac{1}{1.1} + \frac{1}{1.3} + \frac{1}{1.5} + \frac{1}{1.7} + \frac{1}{1.9}\right)$$

$$\approx 0.691908$$

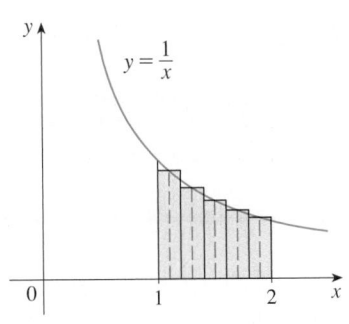

$y = \dfrac{1}{x}$

FIGURE 11

Since $f(x) = 1/x > 0$ for $1 \le x \le 2$, the integral represents an area, and the approximation given by the Midpoint Rule is the sum of the areas of the rectangles shown in Figure 11.

At the moment we don't know how accurate the approximation in Example 5 is, but in Section 8.7 we will learn a method for estimating the error involved in using the Midpoint Rule. At that time we will discuss other methods for approximating definite integrals.

If we apply the Midpoint Rule to the integral in Example 2, we get the picture in Figure 12. The approximation $M_{40} \approx -6.7563$ is much closer to the true value -6.75 than the right endpoint approximation, $R_{40} \approx -6.3998$, shown in Figure 7.

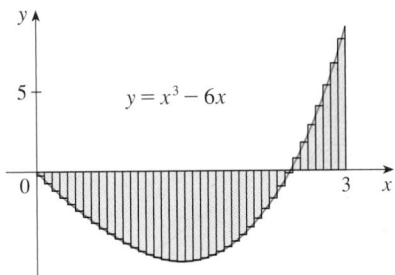

$y = x^3 - 6x$

FIGURE 12

$M_{40} \approx -6.7563$

||| **Properties of the Definite Integral**

When we defined the definite integral $\int_a^b f(x)\,dx$, we implicitly assumed that $a < b$. But the definition as a limit of Riemann sums makes sense even if $a > b$. Notice that if we reverse a and b, then Δx changes from $(b - a)/n$ to $(a - b)/n$. Therefore

$$\int_b^a f(x)\,dx = -\int_a^b f(x)\,dx$$

If $a = b$, then $\Delta x = 0$ and so

$$\int_a^a f(x)\,dx = 0$$

We now develop some basic properties of integrals that will help us to evaluate integrals in a simple manner. We assume that f and g are continuous functions.

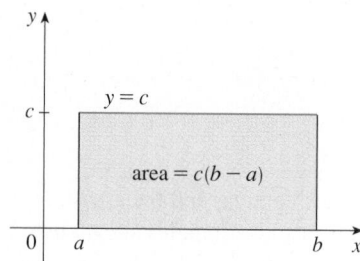

FIGURE 13
$\int_a^b c\,dx = c(b - a)$

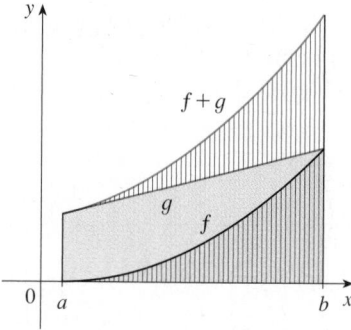

FIGURE 14
$\int_a^b [f(x) + g(x)]\,dx =$
$\int_a^b f(x)\,dx + \int_a^b g(x)\,dx$

|||| Property 3 seems intuitively reasonable because we know that multiplying a function by a positive number c stretches or shrinks its graph vertically by a factor of c. So it stretches or shrinks each approximating rectangle by a factor c and therefore it has the effect of multiplying the area by c.

Properties of the Integral

1. $\displaystyle\int_a^b c\,dx = c(b - a)$,   where c is any constant

2. $\displaystyle\int_a^b [f(x) + g(x)]\,dx = \int_a^b f(x)\,dx + \int_a^b g(x)\,dx$

3. $\displaystyle\int_a^b cf(x)\,dx = c \int_a^b f(x)\,dx$,   where c is any constant

4. $\displaystyle\int_a^b [f(x) - g(x)]\,dx = \int_a^b f(x)\,dx - \int_a^b g(x)\,dx$

Property 1 says that the integral of a constant function $f(x) = c$ is the constant times the length of the interval. If $c > 0$ and $a < b$, this is to be expected because $c(b - a)$ is the area of the shaded rectangle in Figure 13.

Property 2 says that the integral of a sum is the sum of the integrals. For positive functions it says that the area under $f + g$ is the area under f plus the area under g. Figure 14 helps us understand why this is true: In view of how graphical addition works, the corresponding vertical line segments have equal height.

In general, Property 2 follows from Equation 3 and the fact that the limit of a sum is the sum of the limits:

$$\int_a^b [f(x) + g(x)]\,dx = \lim_{n \to \infty} \sum_{i=1}^{n} [f(x_i) + g(x_i)]\,\Delta x$$

$$= \lim_{n \to \infty} \left[\sum_{i=1}^{n} f(x_i)\,\Delta x + \sum_{i=1}^{n} g(x_i)\,\Delta x \right]$$

$$= \lim_{n \to \infty} \sum_{i=1}^{n} f(x_i)\,\Delta x + \lim_{n \to \infty} \sum_{i=1}^{n} g(x_i)\,\Delta x$$

$$= \int_a^b f(x)\,dx + \int_a^b g(x)\,dx$$

Property 3 can be proved in a similar manner and says that the integral of a constant times a function is the constant times the integral of the function. In other words, a constant (but *only* a constant) can be taken in front of an integral sign. Property 4 is proved by writing $f - g = f + (-g)$ and using Properties 2 and 3 with $c = -1$.

EXAMPLE 6 Use the properties of integrals to evaluate $\displaystyle\int_0^1 (4 + 3x^2)\,dx$.

SOLUTION Using Properties 2 and 3 of integrals, we have

$$\int_0^1 (4 + 3x^2)\,dx = \int_0^1 4\,dx + \int_0^1 3x^2\,dx = \int_0^1 4\,dx + 3\int_0^1 x^2\,dx$$

We know from Property 1 that

$$\int_0^1 4\,dx = 4(1 - 0) = 4$$

and we found in Example 2 in Section 5.1 that $\int_0^1 x^2 \, dx = \frac{1}{3}$. So

$$\int_0^1 (4 + 3x^2) \, dx = \int_0^1 4 \, dx + 3 \int_0^1 x^2 \, dx$$

$$= 4 + 3 \cdot \frac{1}{3} = 5$$

The next property tells us how to combine integrals of the same function over adjacent intervals:

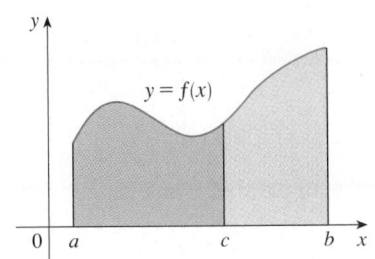

FIGURE 15

> **5.**
> $$\int_a^c f(x) \, dx + \int_c^b f(x) \, dx = \int_a^b f(x) \, dx$$

This is not easy to prove in general, but for the case where $f(x) \geqslant 0$ and $a < c < b$ Property 5 can be seen from the geometric interpretation in Figure 15: The area under $y = f(x)$ from a to c plus the area from c to b is equal to the total area from a to b.

EXAMPLE 7 If it is known that $\int_0^{10} f(x) \, dx = 17$ and $\int_0^8 f(x) \, dx = 12$, find $\int_8^{10} f(x) \, dx$.

SOLUTION By Property 5, we have

$$\int_0^8 f(x) \, dx + \int_8^{10} f(x) \, dx = \int_0^{10} f(x) \, dx$$

so

$$\int_8^{10} f(x) \, dx = \int_0^{10} f(x) \, dx - \int_0^8 f(x) \, dx = 17 - 12 = 5$$

Notice that Properties 1–5 are true whether $a < b$, $a = b$, or $a > b$. The following properties, in which we compare sizes of functions and sizes of integrals, are true only if $a \leqslant b$.

> **Comparison Properties of the Integral**
>
> **6.** If $f(x) \geqslant 0$ for $a \leqslant x \leqslant b$, then $\int_a^b f(x) \, dx \geqslant 0$.
>
> **7.** If $f(x) \geqslant g(x)$ for $a \leqslant x \leqslant b$, then $\int_a^b f(x) \, dx \geqslant \int_a^b g(x) \, dx$.
>
> **8.** If $m \leqslant f(x) \leqslant M$ for $a \leqslant x \leqslant b$, then
>
> $$m(b - a) \leqslant \int_a^b f(x) \, dx \leqslant M(b - a)$$

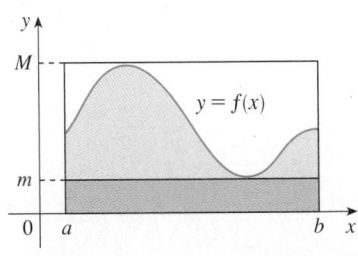

FIGURE 16

If $f(x) \geqslant 0$, then $\int_a^b f(x) \, dx$ represents the area under the graph of f, so the geometric interpretation of Property 6 is simply that areas are positive. But the property can be proved from the definition of an integral (Exercise 64). Property 7 says that a bigger function has a bigger integral. It follows from Properties 6 and 4 because $f - g \geqslant 0$.

Property 8 is illustrated by Figure 16 for the case where $f(x) \geqslant 0$. If f is continuous we could take m and M to be the absolute minimum and maximum values of f on the interval $[a, b]$. In this case Property 8 says that the area under the graph of f is greater than the area of the rectangle with height m and less than the area of the rectangle with height M.

Proof of Property 8 Since $m \le f(x) \le M$, Property 7 gives

$$\int_a^b m \, dx \le \int_a^b f(x) \, dx \le \int_a^b M \, dx$$

Using Property 1 to evaluate the integrals on the left and right sides, we obtain

$$m(b - a) \le \int_a^b f(x) \, dx \le M(b - a)$$

Property 8 is useful when all we want is a rough estimate of the size of an integral without going to the bother of using the Midpoint Rule.

EXAMPLE 8 Use Property 8 to estimate $\int_1^4 \sqrt{x} \, dx$.

SOLUTION Since $f(x) = \sqrt{x}$ is an increasing function, its absolute minimum on $[1, 4]$ is $m = f(1) = 1$ and its absolute maximum on $[1, 4]$ is $M = f(4) = \sqrt{4} = 2$. Thus, Property 8 gives

$$1(4 - 1) \le \int_1^4 \sqrt{x} \, dx \le 2(4 - 1)$$

or

$$3 \le \int_1^4 \sqrt{x} \, dx \le 6$$

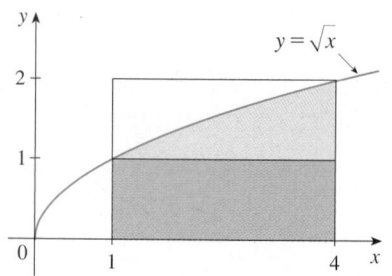

FIGURE 17

The result of Example 8 is illustrated in Figure 17. The area under $y = \sqrt{x}$ from 1 to 4 is greater than the area of the lower rectangle and less than the area of the large rectangle.

5.2 Exercises

1. Evaluate the Riemann sum for $f(x) = 2 - x^2$, $0 \le x \le 2$, with four subintervals, taking the sample points to be right endpoints. Explain, with the aid of a diagram, what the Riemann sum represents.

2. If $f(x) = 3x - 7$, $0 \le x \le 3$, evaluate the Riemann sum with $n = 6$, taking the sample points to be left endpoints. What does the Riemann sum represent? Illustrate with a diagram.

3. If $f(x) = \sqrt{x} - 2$, $1 \le x \le 6$, find the Riemann sum with $n = 5$ correct to six decimal places, taking the sample points to be midpoints. What does the Riemann sum represent? Illustrate with a diagram.

4. (a) Find the Riemann sum for $f(x) = x - 2 \sin 2x$, $0 \le x \le 3$, with six terms, taking the sample points to be right endpoints. (Give your answer correct to six decimal places.)

Explain what the Riemann sum represents with the aid of a sketch.

(b) Repeat part (a) with midpoints as the sample points.

5. The graph of a function f is given. Estimate $\int_0^8 f(x) \, dx$ using four subintervals with (a) right endpoints, (b) left endpoints, and (c) midpoints.

6. The graph of g is shown. Estimate $\int_{-3}^{3} g(x)\,dx$ with six sub-intervals using (a) right endpoints, (b) left endpoints, and (c) midpoints.

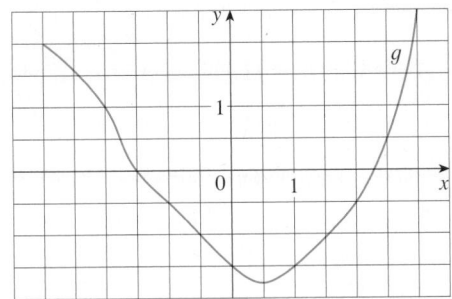

7. A table of values of an increasing function f is shown. Use the table to find lower and upper estimates for $\int_{0}^{25} f(x)\,dx$.

x	0	5	10	15	20	25
$f(x)$	-42	-37	-25	-6	15	36

8. The table gives the values of a function obtained from an experiment. Use them to estimate $\int_{0}^{6} f(x)\,dx$ using three equal subintervals with (a) right endpoints, (b) left endpoints, and (c) midpoints. If the function is known to be a decreasing function, can you say whether your estimates are less than or greater than the exact value of the integral?

x	0	1	2	3	4	5	6
$f(x)$	9.3	9.0	8.3	6.5	2.3	-7.6	-10.5

9–12 ▒ Use the Midpoint Rule with the given value of n to approximate the integral. Round the answer to four decimal places.

9. $\int_{2}^{10} \sqrt{x^3 + 1}\,dx$, $\quad n = 4$

10. $\int_{0}^{\pi} \sec(x/3)\,dx$, $\quad n = 6$

11. $\int_{0}^{1} \sin(x^2)\,dx$, $\quad n = 5$

12. $\int_{1}^{5} \dfrac{x - 1}{x + 1}\,dx$, $\quad n = 4$

[CAS] **13.** If you have a CAS that evaluates midpoint approximations and graphs the corresponding rectangles (use `middlesum` and `middlebox` commands in Maple), check the answer to Exercise 11 and illustrate with a graph. Then repeat with $n = 10$ and $n = 20$.

14. With a programmable calculator or computer (see the instructions for Exercise 7 in Section 5.1), compute the left and right Riemann sums for the function $f(x) = \sin(x^2)$ on the interval $[0, 1]$ with $n = 100$. Explain why these estimates show that

$$0.306 < \int_{0}^{1} \sin(x^2)\,dx < 0.315$$

Deduce that the approximation using the Midpoint Rule with $n = 5$ in Exercise 11 is accurate to two decimal places.

15. Use a calculator or computer to make a table of values of right Riemann sums R_n for the integral $\int_{0}^{\pi} \sin x\,dx$ with $n = 5, 10, 50,$ and 100. What value do these numbers appear to be approaching?

16. Use a calculator or computer to make a table of values of left and right Riemann sums L_n and R_n for the integral $\int_{0}^{2} \sqrt{1 + x^4}\,dx$ with $n = 5, 10, 50,$ and 100. Between what two numbers must the value of the integral lie? Can you make a similar statement for the integral $\int_{-1}^{2} \sqrt{1 + x^4}\,dx$? Explain.

17–20 ▒ Express the limit as a definite integral on the given interval.

17. $\displaystyle\lim_{n \to \infty} \sum_{i=1}^{n} x_i \sin x_i\,\Delta x$, $\quad [0, \pi]$

18. $\displaystyle\lim_{n \to \infty} \sum_{i=1}^{n} \dfrac{x_i}{1 + x_i}\,\Delta x$, $\quad [1, 5]$

19. $\displaystyle\lim_{n \to \infty} \sum_{i=1}^{n} \sqrt{2x_i^* + (x_i^*)^2}\,\Delta x$, $\quad [1, 8]$

20. $\displaystyle\lim_{n \to \infty} \sum_{i=1}^{n} [4 - 3(x_i^*)^2 + 6(x_i^*)^5]\,\Delta x$, $\quad [0, 2]$

21–25 ▒ Use the form of the definition of the integral given in Equation 3 to evaluate the integral.

21. $\displaystyle\int_{-1}^{5} (1 + 3x)\,dx$

22. $\displaystyle\int_{1}^{4} (x^2 + 2x - 5)\,dx$

23. $\displaystyle\int_{0}^{2} (2 - x^2)\,dx$

24. $\displaystyle\int_{0}^{5} (1 + 2x^3)\,dx$

25. $\displaystyle\int_{1}^{2} x^3\,dx$

26. (a) Find an approximation to the integral $\int_{0}^{4} (x^2 - 3x)\,dx$ using a Riemann sum with right endpoints and $n = 8$.
(b) Draw a diagram like Figure 3 to illustrate the approximation in part (a).
(c) Use Equation 3 to evaluate $\int_{0}^{4} (x^2 - 3x)\,dx$.
(d) Interpret the integral in part (c) as a difference of areas and illustrate with a diagram like Figure 4.

27. Prove that $\displaystyle\int_{a}^{b} x\,dx = \dfrac{b^2 - a^2}{2}$.

28. Prove that $\displaystyle\int_{a}^{b} x^2\,dx = \dfrac{b^3 - a^3}{3}$.

29–30 ▒ Express the integral as a limit of Riemann sums. Do not evaluate the limit.

29. $\displaystyle\int_{2}^{6} \dfrac{x}{1 + x^5}\,dx$

30. $\displaystyle\int_{0}^{2\pi} x^2 \sin x\,dx$

CAS 31–32 |||| Express the integral as a limit of sums. Then evaluate, using a computer algebra system to find both the sum and the limit.

31. $\int_0^\pi \sin 5x \, dx$ **32.** $\int_2^{10} x^6 \, dx$

33. The graph of f is shown. Evaluate each integral by interpreting it in terms of areas.

(a) $\int_0^2 f(x) \, dx$ (b) $\int_0^5 f(x) \, dx$

(c) $\int_5^7 f(x) \, dx$ (d) $\int_0^9 f(x) \, dx$

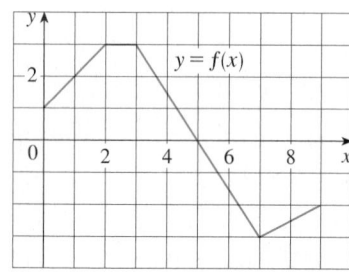

34. The graph of g consists of two straight lines and a semicircle. Use it to evaluate each integral.

(a) $\int_0^2 g(x) \, dx$ (b) $\int_2^6 g(x) \, dx$ (c) $\int_0^7 g(x) \, dx$

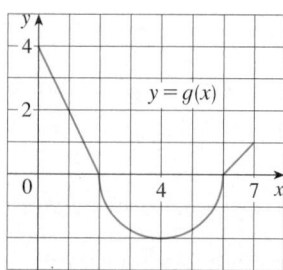

35–40 |||| Evaluate the integral by interpreting it in terms of areas.

35. $\int_0^3 \left(\frac{1}{2}x - 1\right) dx$ **36.** $\int_{-2}^2 \sqrt{4 - x^2} \, dx$

37. $\int_{-3}^0 \left(1 + \sqrt{9 - x^2}\right) dx$ **38.** $\int_{-1}^3 (3 - 2x) \, dx$

39. $\int_{-1}^2 |x| \, dx$ **40.** $\int_0^{10} |x - 5| \, dx$

41. Given that $\int_4^9 \sqrt{x} \, dx = \frac{38}{3}$, what is $\int_9^4 \sqrt{t} \, dt$?

42. Evaluate $\int_1^1 x^2 \cos x \, dx$.

43. In Example 2 in Section 5.1 we showed that $\int_0^1 x^2 \, dx = \frac{1}{3}$. Use this fact and the properties of integrals to evaluate $\int_0^1 (5 - 6x^2) \, dx$.

44. Use the properties of integrals and the result of Example 3 to evaluate $\int_2^5 (1 + 3x^4) \, dx$.

45. Use the results of Exercises 27 and 28 and the properties of integrals to evaluate $\int_1^4 (2x^2 - 3x + 1) \, dx$.

46. Use the result of Exercise 27 and the fact that $\int_0^{\pi/2} \cos x \, dx = 1$ (from Exercise 25 in Section 5.1), together with the properties of integrals, to evaluate $\int_0^{\pi/2} (2 \cos x - 5x) \, dx$.

47. Write as a single integral in the form $\int_a^b f(x) \, dx$:

$$\int_{-2}^2 f(x) \, dx + \int_2^5 f(x) \, dx - \int_{-2}^{-1} f(x) \, dx$$

48. If $\int_1^5 f(x) \, dx = 12$ and $\int_4^5 f(x) \, dx = 3.6$, find $\int_1^4 f(x) \, dx$.

49. If $\int_0^9 f(x) \, dx = 37$ and $\int_0^9 g(x) \, dx = 16$, find $\int_0^9 [2f(x) + 3g(x)] \, dx$.

50. Find $\int_0^5 f(x) \, dx$ if

$$f(x) = \begin{cases} 3 & \text{for } x < 3 \\ x & \text{for } x \geq 3 \end{cases}$$

51–54 |||| Use the properties of integrals to verify the inequality without evaluating the integrals.

51. $\int_0^{\pi/4} \sin^3 x \, dx \leq \int_0^{\pi/4} \sin^2 x \, dx$

52. $\int_1^2 \sqrt{5 - x} \, dx \geq \int_1^2 \sqrt{x + 1} \, dx$

53. $2 \leq \int_{-1}^1 \sqrt{1 + x^2} \, dx \leq 2\sqrt{2}$

54. $\frac{\pi}{6} \leq \int_{\pi/6}^{\pi/2} \sin x \, dx \leq \frac{\pi}{3}$

55–60 |||| Use Property 8 to estimate the value of the integral.

55. $\int_1^2 \frac{1}{x} \, dx$ **56.** $\int_0^2 \sqrt{x^3 + 1} \, dx$

57. $\int_{\pi/4}^{\pi/3} \tan x \, dx$ **58.** $\int_0^2 (x^3 - 3x + 3) \, dx$

59. $\int_{-1}^1 \sqrt{1 + x^4} \, dx$ **60.** $\int_{\pi/4}^{3\pi/4} \sin^2 x \, dx$

61–62 |||| Use properties of integrals, together with Exercises 27 and 28, to prove the inequality.

61. $\int_1^3 \sqrt{x^4 + 1} \, dx \geq \frac{26}{3}$ **62.** $\int_0^{\pi/2} x \sin x \, dx \leq \frac{\pi^2}{8}$

63. Prove Property 3 of integrals.

64. Prove Property 6 of integrals.

65. If f is continuous on $[a, b]$, show that

$$\left| \int_a^b f(x)\, dx \right| \le \int_a^b |f(x)|\, dx$$

[*Hint:* $-|f(x)| \le f(x) \le |f(x)|$.]

66. Use the result of Exercise 65 to show that

$$\left| \int_0^{2\pi} f(x) \sin 2x\, dx \right| \le \int_0^{2\pi} |f(x)|\, dx$$

67–68 ▏ Express the limit as a definite integral.

67. $\lim\limits_{n \to \infty} \sum\limits_{i=1}^{n} \dfrac{i^4}{n^5}$ [*Hint:* Consider $f(x) = x^4$.]

68. $\lim\limits_{n \to \infty} \dfrac{1}{n} \sum\limits_{i=1}^{n} \dfrac{1}{1 + (i/n)^2}$

69. Find $\int_1^2 x^{-2}\, dx$. *Hint:* Choose x_i^* to be the geometric mean of x_{i-1} and x_i (that is, $x_i^* = \sqrt{x_{i-1} x_i}$) and use the identity

$$\frac{1}{m(m+1)} = \frac{1}{m} - \frac{1}{m+1}$$

▐▐▐ DISCOVERY PROJECT

Area Functions

1. (a) Draw the line $y = 2t + 1$ and use geometry to find the area under this line, above the t-axis, and between the vertical lines $t = 1$ and $t = 3$.
   (b) If $x > 1$, let $A(x)$ be the area of the region that lies under the line $y = 2t + 1$ between $t = 1$ and $t = x$. Sketch this region and use geometry to find an expression for $A(x)$.
   (c) Differentiate the area function $A(x)$. What do you notice?

2. (a) If $x \ge -1$, let

$$A(x) = \int_{-1}^{x} (1 + t^2)\, dt$$

   $A(x)$ represents the area of a region. Sketch that region.
   (b) Use the result of Exercise 28 in Section 5.2 to find an expression for $A(x)$.
   (c) Find $A'(x)$. What do you notice?
   (d) If $x \ge -1$ and h is a small positive number, then $A(x + h) - A(x)$ represents the area of a region. Describe and sketch the region.
   (e) Draw a rectangle that approximates the region in part (d). By comparing the areas of these two regions, show that

$$\frac{A(x + h) - A(x)}{h} \approx 1 + x^2$$

   (f) Use part (e) to give an intuitive explanation for the result of part (c).

3. (a) Draw the graph of the function $f(x) = \cos(x^2)$ in the viewing rectangle $[0, 2]$ by $[-1.25, 1.25]$.
   (b) If we define a new function g by

$$g(x) = \int_0^{x} \cos(t^2)\, dt$$

   then $g(x)$ is the area under the graph of f from 0 to x [until $f(x)$ becomes negative, at which point $g(x)$ becomes a difference of areas]. Use part (a) to determine the value of x at which $g(x)$ starts to decrease. [Unlike the integral in Problem 2, it is impossible to evaluate the integral defining g to obtain an explicit expression for $g(x)$.]
   (c) Use the integration command on your calculator or computer to estimate $g(0.2)$, $g(0.4)$, $g(0.6), \ldots, g(1.8)$, $g(2)$. Then use these values to sketch a graph of g.
   (d) Use your graph of g from part (c) to sketch the graph of g' using the interpretation of $g'(x)$ as the slope of a tangent line. How does the graph of g' compare with the graph of f?

4. Suppose f is a continuous function on the interval $[a, b]$ and we define a new function g by the equation

$$g(x) = \int_a^x f(t)\, dt$$

Based on your results in Problems 1–3, conjecture an expression for $g'(x)$.

5.3 The Fundamental Theorem of Calculus

The Fundamental Theorem of Calculus is appropriately named because it establishes a connection between the two branches of calculus: differential calculus and integral calculus. Differential calculus arose from the tangent problem, whereas integral calculus arose from a seemingly unrelated problem, the area problem. Newton's teacher at Cambridge, Isaac Barrow (1630–1677), discovered that these two problems are actually closely related. In fact, he realized that differentiation and integration are inverse processes. The Fundamental Theorem of Calculus gives the precise inverse relationship between the derivative and the integral. It was Newton and Leibniz who exploited this relationship and used it to develop calculus into a systematic mathematical method. In particular, they saw that the Fundamental Theorem enabled them to compute areas and integrals very easily without having to compute them as limits of sums as we did in Sections 5.1 and 5.2.

The first part of the Fundamental Theorem deals with functions defined by an equation of the form

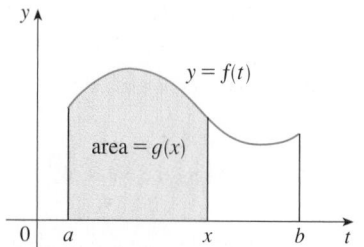

Investigate the area function interactively.
Resources / Module 6
/ Areas and Derivatives
/ Area as a Function

| 1 |

$$g(x) = \int_a^x f(t)\, dt$$

where f is a continuous function on $[a, b]$ and x varies between a and b. Observe that g depends only on x, which appears as the variable upper limit in the integral. If x is a fixed number, then the integral $\int_a^x f(t)\, dt$ is a definite number. If we then let x vary, the number $\int_a^x f(t)\, dt$ also varies and defines a function of x denoted by $g(x)$.

If f happens to be a positive function, then $g(x)$ can be interpreted as the area under the graph of f from a to x, where x can vary from a to b. (Think of g as the "area so far" function; see Figure 1.)

FIGURE 1

EXAMPLE 1 If f is the function whose graph is shown in Figure 2 and $g(x) = \int_0^x f(t)\, dt$, find the values of $g(0), g(1), g(2), g(3), g(4),$ and $g(5)$. Then sketch a rough graph of g.

SOLUTION First we notice that $g(0) = \int_0^0 f(t)\, dt = 0$. From Figure 3 we see that $g(1)$ is the area of a triangle:

$$g(1) = \int_0^1 f(t)\, dt = \tfrac{1}{2}(1 \cdot 2) = 1$$

To find $g(2)$ we add to $g(1)$ the area of a rectangle:

$$g(2) = \int_0^2 f(t)\, dt = \int_0^1 f(t)\, dt + \int_1^2 f(t)\, dt = 1 + (1 \cdot 2) = 3$$

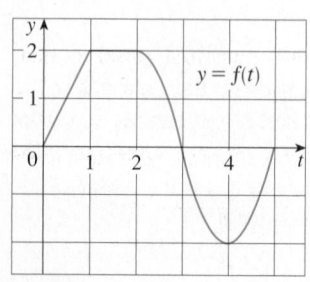

FIGURE 2

We estimate that the area under f from 2 to 3 is about 1.3, so

$$g(3) = g(2) + \int_2^3 f(t)\, dt \approx 3 + 1.3 = 4.3$$

$g(1) = 1$

$g(2) = 3$

$g(3) \approx 4.3$

$g(4) \approx 3$

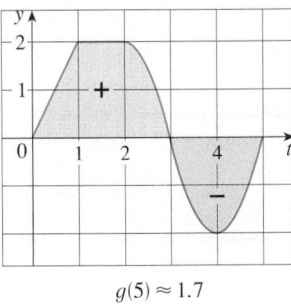

$g(5) \approx 1.7$

FIGURE 3

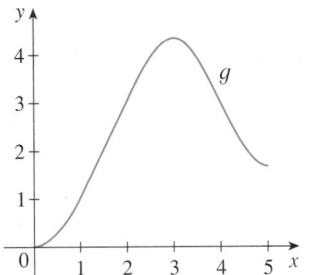

FIGURE 4

$g(x) = \int_a^x f(t)\, dt$

For $t > 3$, $f(t)$ is negative and so we start subtracting areas:

$$g(4) = g(3) + \int_3^4 f(t)\, dt \approx 4.3 + (-1.3) = 3.0$$

$$g(5) = g(4) + \int_4^5 f(t)\, dt \approx 3 + (-1.3) = 1.7$$

We use these values to sketch the graph of g in Figure 4. Notice that, because $f(t)$ is positive for $t < 3$, we keep adding area for $t < 3$ and so g is increasing up to $x = 3$, where it attains a maximum value. For $x > 3$, g decreases because $f(t)$ is negative. ▬

If we take $f(t) = t$ and $a = 0$, then, using Exercise 27 in Section 5.2, we have

$$g(x) = \int_0^x t\, dt = \frac{x^2}{2}$$

Notice that $g'(x) = x$, that is, $g' = f$. In other words, if g is defined as the integral of f by Equation 1, then g turns out to be an antiderivative of f, at least in this case. And if we sketch the derivative of the function g shown in Figure 4 by estimating slopes of tangents, we get a graph like that of f in Figure 2. So we suspect that $g' = f$ in Example 1 too.

To see why this might be generally true we consider any continuous function f with $f(x) \geqslant 0$. Then $g(x) = \int_a^x f(t)\, dt$ can be interpreted as the area under the graph of f from a to x, as in Figure 1.

In order to compute $g'(x)$ from the definition of derivative we first observe that, for $h > 0$, $g(x + h) - g(x)$ is obtained by subtracting areas, so it is the area under the graph of f from x to $x + h$ (the gold area in Figure 5). For small h you can see from the figure that this area is approximately equal to the area of the rectangle with height $f(x)$ and width h:

$$g(x + h) - g(x) \approx hf(x)$$

so

$$\frac{g(x + h) - g(x)}{h} \approx f(x)$$

FIGURE 5

Intuitively, we therefore expect that

$$g'(x) = \lim_{h \to 0} \frac{g(x + h) - g(x)}{h} = f(x)$$

The fact that this is true, even when f is not necessarily positive, is the first part of the Fundamental Theorem of Calculus.

The Fundamental Theorem of Calculus, Part 1 If f is continuous on $[a, b]$, then the function g defined by

$$g(x) = \int_a^x f(t)\, dt \qquad a \leqslant x \leqslant b$$

is continuous on $[a, b]$ and differentiable on (a, b), and $g'(x) = f(x)$.

|||| We abbreviate the name of this theorem as FTC1. In words, it says that the derivative of a definite integral with respect to its upper limit is the integrand evaluated at the upper limit.

Proof If x and $x + h$ are in (a, b), then

$$g(x + h) - g(x) = \int_a^{x+h} f(t)\, dt - \int_a^x f(t)\, dt$$

$$= \left(\int_a^x f(t)\, dt + \int_x^{x+h} f(t)\, dt \right) - \int_a^x f(t)\, dt \qquad \text{(by Property 5)}$$

$$= \int_x^{x+h} f(t)\, dt$$

and so, for $h \neq 0$,

$$\boxed{2} \qquad \frac{g(x + h) - g(x)}{h} = \frac{1}{h} \int_x^{x+h} f(t)\, dt$$

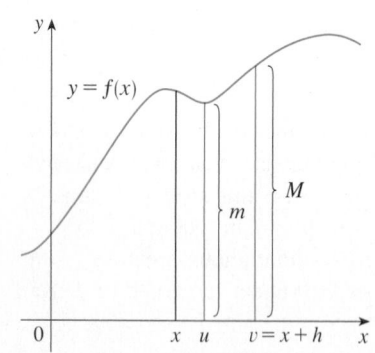

FIGURE 6

For now let us assume that $h > 0$. Since f is continuous on $[x, x + h]$, the Extreme Value Theorem says that there are numbers u and v in $[x, x + h]$ such that $f(u) = m$ and $f(v) = M$, where m and M are the absolute minimum and maximum values of f on $[x, x + h]$. (See Figure 6.)

By Property 8 of integrals, we have

$$mh \leqslant \int_x^{x+h} f(t)\, dt \leqslant Mh$$

that is,

$$f(u)h \leqslant \int_x^{x+h} f(t)\, dt \leqslant f(v)h$$

Since $h > 0$, we can divide this inequality by h:

$$f(u) \leqslant \frac{1}{h} \int_x^{x+h} f(t)\, dt \leqslant f(v)$$

Now we use Equation 2 to replace the middle part of this inequality:

$$\boxed{3} \qquad f(u) \leqslant \frac{g(x + h) - g(x)}{h} \leqslant f(v)$$

Inequality 3 can be proved in a similar manner for the case $h < 0$. (See Exercise 55.)

Now we let $h \to 0$. Then $u \to x$ and $v \to x$, since u and v lie between x and $x + h$. Therefore

$$\lim_{h \to 0} f(u) = \lim_{u \to x} f(u) = f(x)$$

and

$$\lim_{h \to 0} f(v) = \lim_{v \to x} f(v) = f(x)$$

because f is continuous at x. We conclude, from (3) and the Squeeze Theorem, that

$$\boxed{4} \qquad g'(x) = \lim_{h \to 0} \frac{g(x + h) - g(x)}{h} = f(x)$$

If $x = a$ or b, then Equation 4 can be interpreted as a one-sided limit. Then Theorem 3.2.4 (modified for one-sided limits) shows that g is continuous on $[a, b]$.

Using Leibniz notation for derivatives, we can write FTC1 as

$$\boxed{5} \qquad \frac{d}{dx} \int_a^x f(t)\, dt = f(x)$$

when f is continuous. Roughly speaking, Equation 5 says that if we first integrate f and then differentiate the result, we get back to the original function f.

EXAMPLE 2 Find the derivative of the function $g(x) = \int_0^x \sqrt{1 + t^2}\, dt$.

SOLUTION Since $f(t) = \sqrt{1 + t^2}$ is continuous, Part 1 of the Fundamental Theorem of Calculus gives

$$g'(x) = \sqrt{1 + x^2}$$

EXAMPLE 3 Although a formula of the form $g(x) = \int_a^x f(t)\, dt$ may seem like a strange way of defining a function, books on physics, chemistry, and statistics are full of such functions. For instance, the **Fresnel function**

$$S(x) = \int_0^x \sin(\pi t^2/2)\, dt$$

is named after the French physicist Augustin Fresnel (1788–1827), who is famous for his works in optics. This function first appeared in Fresnel's theory of the diffraction of light waves, but more recently it has been applied to the design of highways.

Part 1 of the Fundamental Theorem tells us how to differentiate the Fresnel function:

$$S'(x) = \sin(\pi x^2/2)$$

This means that we can apply all the methods of differential calculus to analyze S (see Exercise 49).

Figure 7 shows the graphs of $f(x) = \sin(\pi x^2/2)$ and the Fresnel function $S(x) = \int_0^x f(t)\,dt$. A computer was used to graph S by computing the value of this integral for many values of x. It does indeed look as if $S(x)$ is the area under the graph of f from 0 to x [until $x \approx 1.4$ when $S(x)$ becomes a difference of areas]. Figure 8 shows a larger part of the graph of S.

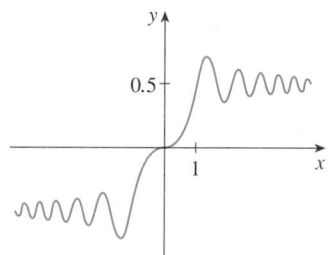

FIGURE 7

$f(x) = \sin(\pi x^2/2)$

$S(x) = \int_0^x \sin(\pi t^2/2)\,dt$

FIGURE 8

The Fresnel function $S(x) = \int_0^x \sin(\pi t^2/2)\,dt$

If we now start with the graph of S in Figure 7 and think about what its derivative should look like, it seems reasonable that $S'(x) = f(x)$. [For instance, S is increasing when $f(x) > 0$ and decreasing when $f(x) < 0$.] So this gives a visual confirmation of Part 1 of the Fundamental Theorem of Calculus.

EXAMPLE 4 Find $\dfrac{d}{dx} \displaystyle\int_1^{x^4} \sec t\,dt$.

SOLUTION Here we have to be careful to use the Chain Rule in conjunction with FTC1. Let $u = x^4$. Then

$$\frac{d}{dx}\int_1^{x^4} \sec t\,dt = \frac{d}{dx}\int_1^{u} \sec t\,dt$$

$$= \frac{d}{du}\left(\int_1^{u} \sec t\,dt\right)\frac{du}{dx} \qquad \text{(by the Chain Rule)}$$

$$= \sec u\,\frac{du}{dx} \qquad \text{(by FTC1)}$$

$$= \sec(x^4)\cdot 4x^3$$

In Section 5.2 we computed integrals from the definition as a limit of Riemann sums and we saw that this procedure is sometimes long and difficult. The second part of the Fundamental Theorem of Calculus, which follows easily from the first part, provides us with a much simpler method for the evaluation of integrals.

The Fundamental Theorem of Calculus, Part 2 If f is continuous on $[a, b]$, then

$$\int_a^b f(x)\,dx = F(b) - F(a)$$

where F is any antiderivative of f, that is, a function such that $F' = f$.

|||| We abbreviate this theorem as FTC2.

Proof Let $g(x) = \int_a^x f(t)\,dt$. We know from Part 1 that $g'(x) = f(x)$; that is, g is an antiderivative of f. If F is any other antiderivative of f on $[a, b]$, then we know from Corollary 4.2.7 that F and g differ by a constant:

$$\boxed{6} \qquad F(x) = g(x) + C$$

for $a < x < b$. But both F and g are continuous on $[a, b]$ and so, by taking limits of both sides of Equation 6 (as $x \to a^+$ and $x \to b^-$), we see that it also holds when $x = a$ and $x = b$.

If we put $x = a$ in the formula for $g(x)$, we get

$$g(a) = \int_a^a f(t)\,dt = 0$$

So, using Equation 6 with $x = b$ and $x = a$, we have

$$F(b) - F(a) = [g(b) + C] - [g(a) + C]$$

$$= g(b) - g(a) = g(b) = \int_a^b f(t)\,dt$$

Part 2 of the Fundamental Theorem states that if we know an antiderivative F of f, then we can evaluate $\int_a^b f(x)\,dx$ simply by subtracting the values of F at the endpoints of the interval $[a, b]$. It's very surprising that $\int_a^b f(x)\,dx$, which was defined by a complicated procedure involving all of the values of $f(x)$ for $a \le x \le b$, can be found by knowing the values of $F(x)$ at only two points, a and b.

Although the theorem may be surprising at first glance, it becomes plausible if we interpret it in physical terms. If $v(t)$ is the velocity of an object and $s(t)$ is its position at time t, then $v(t) = s'(t)$, so s is an antiderivative of v. In Section 5.1 we considered an object that always moves in the positive direction and made the guess that the area under the velocity curve is equal to the distance traveled. In symbols:

$$\int_a^b v(t)\,dt = s(b) - s(a)$$

That is exactly what FTC2 says in this context.

EXAMPLE 5 Evaluate the integral $\int_{-2}^1 x^3\,dx$.

SOLUTION The function $f(x) = x^3$ is continuous on $[-2, 1]$ and we know from Section 4.10 that an antiderivative is $F(x) = \frac{1}{4}x^4$, so Part 2 of the Fundamental Theorem gives

$$\int_{-2}^1 x^3\,dx = F(1) - F(-2) = \tfrac{1}{4}(1)^4 - \tfrac{1}{4}(-2)^4 = -\tfrac{15}{4}$$

Notice that FTC2 says we can use *any* antiderivative F of f. So we may as well use the simplest one, namely $F(x) = \frac{1}{4}x^4$, instead of $\frac{1}{4}x^4 + 7$ or $\frac{1}{4}x^4 + C$.

We often use the notation

$$F(x)\Big]_a^b = F(b) - F(a)$$

So the equation of FTC2 can be written as

$$\int_a^b f(x)\,dx = F(x)\Big]_a^b \qquad \text{where} \qquad F' = f$$

Other common notations are $F(x)\big|_a^b$ and $[F(x)]_a^b$.

EXAMPLE 6 Find the area under the parabola $y = x^2$ from 0 to 1.

SOLUTION An antiderivative of $f(x) = x^2$ is $F(x) = \frac{1}{3}x^3$. The required area A is found using Part 2 of the Fundamental Theorem:

|||| In applying the Fundamental Theorem we use a particular antiderivative F of f. It is not necessary to use the most general antiderivative.

$$A = \int_0^1 x^2\,dx = \frac{x^3}{3}\Big]_0^1 = \frac{1^3}{3} - \frac{0^3}{3} = \frac{1}{3}$$

If you compare the calculation in Example 6 with the one in Example 2 in Section 5.1, you will see that the Fundamental Theorem gives a *much* shorter method.

EXAMPLE 7 Find the area under the cosine curve from 0 to b, where $0 \le b \le \pi/2$.

SOLUTION Since an antiderivative of $f(x) = \cos x$ is $F(x) = \sin x$, we have

$$A = \int_0^b \cos x\,dx = \sin x\Big]_0^b = \sin b - \sin 0 = \sin b$$

In particular, taking $b = \pi/2$, we have proved that the area under the cosine curve from 0 to $\pi/2$ is $\sin(\pi/2) = 1$. (See Figure 9.)

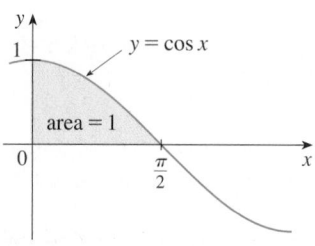

FIGURE 9

When the French mathematician Gilles de Roberval first found the area under the sine and cosine curves in 1635, this was a very challenging problem that required a great deal of ingenuity. If we didn't have the benefit of the Fundamental Theorem, we would have to compute a difficult limit of sums using obscure trigonometric identities (or a computer algebra system as in Exercise 25 in Section 5.1). It was even more difficult for Roberval because the apparatus of limits had not been invented in 1635. But in the 1660s and 1670s, when the Fundamental Theorem was discovered by Barrow and exploited by Newton and Leibniz, such problems became very easy, as you can see from Example 7.

EXAMPLE 8 What is wrong with the following calculation?

$$\int_{-1}^3 \frac{1}{x^2}\,dx = \frac{x^{-1}}{-1}\Big]_{-1}^3 = -\frac{1}{3} - 1 = -\frac{4}{3}$$

SOLUTION To start, we notice that this calculation must be wrong because the answer is negative but $f(x) = 1/x^2 \ge 0$ and Property 6 of integrals says that $\int_a^b f(x)\,dx \ge 0$ when $f \ge 0$. The Fundamental Theorem of Calculus applies to continuous functions. It can't be applied here because $f(x) = 1/x^2$ is not continuous on $[-1, 3]$. In fact, f has an infinite discontinuity at $x = 0$, so

$$\int_{-1}^3 \frac{1}{x^2}\,dx \qquad \text{does not exist}$$

‖ **Differentiation and Integration as Inverse Processes**

We end this section by bringing together the two parts of the Fundamental Theorem.

The Fundamental Theorem of Calculus Suppose f is continuous on $[a, b]$.

1. If $g(x) = \int_a^x f(t)\, dt$, then $g'(x) = f(x)$.

2. $\int_a^b f(x)\, dx = F(b) - F(a)$, where F is any antiderivative of f, that is, $F' = f$.

We noted that Part 1 can be rewritten as

$$\frac{d}{dx} \int_a^x f(t)\, dt = f(x)$$

which says that if f is integrated and then the result is differentiated, we arrive back at the original function f. Since $F'(x) = f(x)$, Part 2 can be rewritten as

$$\int_a^b F'(x)\, dx = F(b) - F(a)$$

This version says that if we take a function F, first differentiate it, and then integrate the result, we arrive back at the original function F, but in the form $F(b) - F(a)$. Taken together, the two parts of the Fundamental Theorem of Calculus say that differentiation and integration are inverse processes. Each undoes what the other does.

The Fundamental Theorem of Calculus is unquestionably the most important theorem in calculus and, indeed, it ranks as one of the great accomplishments of the human mind. Before it was discovered, from the time of Eudoxus and Archimedes to the time of Galileo and Fermat, problems of finding areas, volumes, and lengths of curves were so difficult that only a genius could meet the challenge. But now, armed with the systematic method that Newton and Leibniz fashioned out of the Fundamental Theorem, we will see in the chapters to come that these challenging problems are accessible to all of us.

‖ **5.3 Exercises**

1. Explain exactly what is meant by the statement that "differentiation and integration are inverse processes."

2. Let $g(x) = \int_0^x f(t)\, dt$, where f is the function whose graph is shown.
(a) Evaluate $g(x)$ for $x = 0, 1, 2, 3, 4, 5,$ and 6.
(b) Estimate $g(7)$.
(c) Where does g have a maximum value? Where does it have a minimum value?
(d) Sketch a rough graph of g.

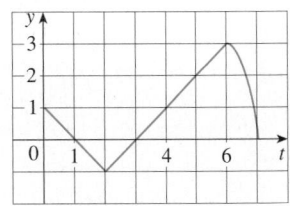

3. Let $g(x) = \int_0^x f(t)\, dt$, where f is the function whose graph is shown.
  (a) Evaluate $g(0)$, $g(1)$, $g(2)$, $g(3)$, and $g(6)$.
  (b) On what interval is g increasing?
  (c) Where does g have a maximum value?
  (d) Sketch a rough graph of g.

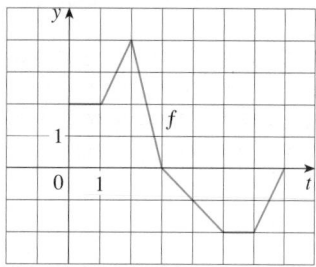

4. Let $g(x) = \int_{-3}^x f(t)\, dt$, where f is the function whose graph is shown.
  (a) Evaluate $g(-3)$ and $g(3)$.
  (b) Estimate $g(-2)$, $g(-1)$, and $g(0)$.
  (c) On what interval is g increasing?
  (d) Where does g have a maximum value?
  (e) Sketch a rough graph of g.
  (f) Use the graph in part (e) to sketch the graph of $g'(x)$. Compare with the graph of f.

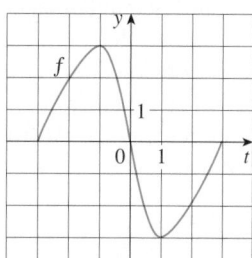

5–6 ‖‖‖ Sketch the area represented by $g(x)$. Then find $g'(x)$ in two ways: (a) by using Part 1 of the Fundamental Theorem and (b) by evaluating the integral using Part 2 and then differentiating.

5. $g(x) = \int_1^x t^2\, dt$

6. $g(x) = \int_0^x \left(1 + \sqrt{t}\right) dt$

7–18 ‖‖‖ Use Part 1 of the Fundamental Theorem of Calculus to find the derivative of the function.

7. $g(x) = \int_0^x \sqrt{1 + 2t}\, dt$

8. $g(x) = \int_1^x (2 + t^4)^5\, dt$

9. $g(y) = \int_2^y t^2 \sin t\, dt$

10. $g(u) = \int_3^u \dfrac{1}{x + x^2}\, dx$

11. $F(x) = \int_x^2 \cos(t^2)\, dt$

$$\left[\text{Hint: } \int_x^2 \cos(t^2)\, dt = -\int_2^x \cos(t^2)\, dt \right]$$

12. $F(x) = \int_x^{10} \tan\theta\, d\theta$

13. $h(x) = \int_2^{1/x} \sin^4 t\, dt$

14. $h(x) = \int_0^{x^2} \sqrt{1 + r^3}\, dr$

15. $y = \int_3^{\sqrt{x}} \dfrac{\cos t}{t}\, dt$

16. $y = \int_1^{\cos x} (t + \sin t)\, dt$

17. $y = \int_{1-3x}^1 \dfrac{u^3}{1 + u^2}\, du$

18. $y = \int_{1/x^2}^0 \sin^3 t\, dt$

19–36 ‖‖‖ Use Part 2 of the Fundamental Theorem of Calculus to evaluate the integral, or explain why it does not exist.

19. $\int_{-1}^3 x^5\, dx$

20. $\int_{-2}^5 6\, dx$

21. $\int_2^8 (4x + 3)\, dx$

22. $\int_0^4 (1 + 3y - y^2)\, dy$

23. $\int_0^1 x^{4/5}\, dx$

24. $\int_1^8 \sqrt[3]{x}\, dx$

25. $\int_1^2 \dfrac{3}{t^4}\, dt$

26. $\int_{-2}^3 x^{-5}\, dx$

27. $\int_{-5}^5 \dfrac{2}{x^3}\, dx$

28. $\int_\pi^{2\pi} \cos\theta\, d\theta$

29. $\int_0^2 x(2 + x^5)\, dx$

30. $\int_1^4 \dfrac{1}{\sqrt{x}}\, dx$

31. $\int_0^{\pi/4} \sec^2 t\, dt$

32. $\int_0^1 \left(3 + x\sqrt{x}\right) dx$

33. $\int_\pi^{2\pi} \csc^2\theta\, d\theta$

34. $\int_0^{\pi/6} \csc\theta \cot\theta\, d\theta$

35. $\int_0^2 f(x)\, dx$ where $f(x) = \begin{cases} x^4 & \text{if } 0 \le x < 1 \\ x^5 & \text{if } 1 \le x \le 2 \end{cases}$

36. $\int_{-\pi}^\pi f(x)\, dx$ where $f(x) = \begin{cases} x & \text{if } -\pi \le x \le 0 \\ \sin x & \text{if } 0 < x \le \pi \end{cases}$

37–40 ‖‖‖ Use a graph to give a rough estimate of the area of the region that lies beneath the given curve. Then find the exact area.

37. $y = \sqrt[3]{x}$, $0 \le x \le 27$

38. $y = x^{-4}$, $1 \le x \le 6$

39. $y = \sin x$, $0 \le x \le \pi$

40. $y = \sec^2 x$, $0 \le x \le \pi/3$

41–42 ▥ Evaluate the integral and interpret it as a difference of areas. Illustrate with a sketch.

41. $\displaystyle\int_{-1}^{2} x^3\,dx$

42. $\displaystyle\int_{\pi/4}^{5\pi/2} \sin x\,dx$

▫ ▫ ▫ ▫ ▫ ▫ ▫ ▫ ▫ ▫

43–46 ▥ Find the derivative of the function.

43. $\displaystyle g(x) = \int_{2x}^{3x} \frac{u^2-1}{u^2+1}\,du$

$$\left[\; \text{Hint: } \int_{2x}^{3x} f(u)\,du = \int_{2x}^{0} f(u)\,du + \int_{0}^{3x} f(u)\,du \right]$$

44. $\displaystyle g(x) = \int_{\tan x}^{x^2} \frac{1}{\sqrt{2+t^4}}\,dt$

45. $\displaystyle y = \int_{\sqrt{x}}^{x^3} \sqrt{t}\,\sin t\,dt$

46. $\displaystyle y = \int_{\cos x}^{5x} \cos(u^2)\,du$

▫ ▫ ▫ ▫ ▫ ▫ ▫ ▫ ▫ ▫

47. If $F(x) = \displaystyle\int_{1}^{x} f(t)\,dt$, where $f(t) = \displaystyle\int_{1}^{t^2} \frac{\sqrt{1+u^4}}{u}\,du$, find $F''(2)$.

48. Find the interval on which the curve

$$y = \int_{0}^{x} \frac{1}{1+t+t^2}\,dt$$

is concave upward.

49. The Fresnel function S was defined in Example 3 and graphed in Figures 7 and 8.
(a) At what values of x does this function have local maximum values?
(b) On what intervals is the function concave upward?
(c) Use a graph to solve the following equation correct to two decimal places:

$$\int_{0}^{x} \sin(\pi t^2/2)\,dt = 0.2$$

CAS **50.** The **sine integral function**

$$\mathrm{Si}(x) = \int_{0}^{x} \frac{\sin t}{t}\,dt$$

is important in electrical engineering. [The integrand $f(t) = (\sin t)/t$ is not defined when $t = 0$, but we know that its limit is 1 when $t \to 0$. So we define $f(0) = 1$ and this makes f a continuous function everywhere.]
(a) Draw the graph of Si.
(b) At what values of x does this function have local maximum values?
(c) Find the coordinates of the first inflection point to the right of the origin.

(d) Does this function have horizontal asymptotes?
(e) Solve the following equation correct to one decimal place:

$$\int_{0}^{x} \frac{\sin t}{t}\,dt = 1$$

51–52 ▥ Let $g(x) = \int_{0}^{x} f(t)\,dt$, where f is the function whose graph is shown.
(a) At what values of x do the local maximum and minimum values of g occur?
(b) Where does g attain its absolute maximum value?
(c) On what intervals is g concave downward?
(d) Sketch the graph of g.

51.

52.

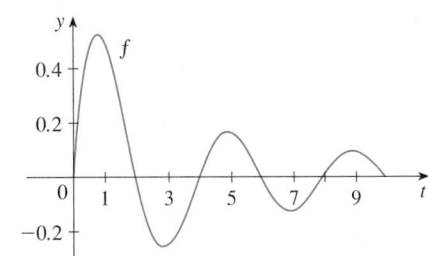

▫ ▫ ▫ ▫ ▫ ▫ ▫ ▫ ▫ ▫ ▫ ▫

53–54 ▥ Evaluate the limit by first recognizing the sum as a Riemann sum for a function defined on $[0, 1]$.

53. $\displaystyle\lim_{n\to\infty} \sum_{i=1}^{n} \frac{i^3}{n^4}$

54. $\displaystyle\lim_{n\to\infty} \frac{1}{n}\left(\sqrt{\frac{1}{n}} + \sqrt{\frac{2}{n}} + \sqrt{\frac{3}{n}} + \cdots + \sqrt{\frac{n}{n}} \right)$

▫ ▫ ▫ ▫ ▫ ▫ ▫ ▫ ▫ ▫ ▫ ▫

55. Justify (3) for the case $h < 0$.

56. If f is continuous and g and h are differentiable functions, find a formula for

$$\frac{d}{dx} \int_{g(x)}^{h(x)} f(t)\,dt$$

57. (a) Show that $1 \leqslant \sqrt{1+x^3} \leqslant 1 + x^3$ for $x \geqslant 0$.
(b) Show that $1 \leqslant \int_{0}^{1} \sqrt{1+x^3}\,dx \leqslant 1.25$.

58. Let

$$f(x) = \begin{cases} 0 & \text{if } x < 0 \\ x & \text{if } 0 \leqslant x \leqslant 1 \\ 2 - x & \text{if } 1 < x \leqslant 2 \\ 0 & \text{if } x > 2 \end{cases}$$

and

$$g(x) = \int_0^x f(t)\, dt$$

(a) Find an expression for $g(x)$ similar to the one for $f(x)$.
(b) Sketch the graphs of f and g.
(c) Where is f differentiable? Where is g differentiable?

59. Find a function f and a number a such that

$$6 + \int_a^x \frac{f(t)}{t^2}\, dt = 2\sqrt{x}$$

for all $x > 0$.

60. Suppose h is a function such that $h(1) = -2$, $h'(1) = 2$, $h''(1) = 3$, $h(2) = 6$, $h'(2) = 5$, $h''(2) = 13$, and h'' is continuous everywhere. Evaluate $\int_1^2 h''(u)\, du$.

61. A manufacturing company owns a major piece of equipment that depreciates at the (continuous) rate $f = f(t)$, where t is the time measured in months since its last overhaul. Because a fixed cost A is incurred each time the machine is overhauled, the company wants to determine the optimal time T (in months) between overhauls.
(a) Explain why $\int_0^t f(s)\, ds$ represents the loss in value of the machine over the period of time t since the last overhaul.
(b) Let $C = C(t)$ be given by

$$C(t) = \frac{1}{t}\left[A + \int_0^t f(s)\, ds\right]$$

What does C represent and why would the company want to minimize C?
(c) Show that C has a minimum value at the numbers $t = T$ where $C(T) = f(T)$.

62. A high-tech company purchases a new computing system whose initial value is V. The system will depreciate at the rate $f = f(t)$ and will accumulate maintenance costs at the rate $g = g(t)$, where t is the time measured in months. The company wants to determine the optimal time to replace the system.
(a) Let

$$C(t) = \frac{1}{t}\int_0^t [f(s) + g(s)]\, ds$$

Show that the critical numbers of C occur at the numbers t where $C(t) = f(t) + g(t)$.
(b) Suppose that

$$f(t) = \begin{cases} \dfrac{V}{15} - \dfrac{V}{450}\,t & \text{if } 0 < t \leqslant 30 \\ 0 & \text{if } t > 30 \end{cases}$$

and

$$g(t) = \frac{Vt^2}{12{,}900} \qquad t > 0$$

Determine the length of time T for the total depreciation $D(t) = \int_0^t f(s)\, ds$ to equal the initial value V.
(c) Determine the absolute minimum of C on $(0, T]$.
(d) Sketch the graphs of C and $f + g$ in the same coordinate system, and verify the result in part (a) in this case.

□   □   □   □   □   □   □   □   □   □   □

The following exercises are intended only for those who have already covered Chapter 7.

63–68 ▏▎▎ Evaluate the integral.

63. $\displaystyle\int_1^9 \frac{1}{2x}\, dx$

64. $\displaystyle\int_0^1 10^x\, dx$

65. $\displaystyle\int_{1/2}^{\sqrt{3}/2} \frac{6}{\sqrt{1 - t^2}}\, dt$

66. $\displaystyle\int_0^1 \frac{4}{t^2 + 1}\, dt$

67. $\displaystyle\int_{-1}^1 e^{u+1}\, du$

68. $\displaystyle\int_1^2 \frac{4 + u^2}{u^3}\, du$

□   □   □   □   □   □   □   □   □   □

5.4 Indefinite Integrals and the Net Change Theorem

We saw in Section 5.3 that the second part of the Fundamental Theorem of Calculus provides a very powerful method for evaluating the definite integral of a function, assuming that we can find an antiderivative of the function. In this section we introduce a notation for antiderivatives, review the formulas for antiderivatives, and use them to evaluate definite integrals. We also reformulate FTC2 in a way that makes it easier to apply to science and engineering problems.

▏▏▏ **Indefinite Integrals**

Both parts of the Fundamental Theorem establish connections between antiderivatives and definite integrals. Part 1 says that if f is continuous, then $\int_a^x f(t)\,dt$ is an antiderivative of f. Part 2 says that $\int_a^b f(x)\,dx$ can be found by evaluating $F(b) - F(a)$, where F is an antiderivative of f.

We need a convenient notation for antiderivatives that makes them easy to work with. Because of the relation given by the Fundamental Theorem between antiderivatives and integrals, the notation $\int f(x)\,dx$ is traditionally used for an antiderivative of f and is called an **indefinite integral**. Thus

$$\int f(x)\,dx = F(x) \qquad \text{means} \qquad F'(x) = f(x)$$

For example, we can write

$$\int x^2\,dx = \frac{x^3}{3} + C \qquad \text{because} \qquad \frac{d}{dx}\left(\frac{x^3}{3} + C\right) = x^2$$

So we can regard an indefinite integral as representing an entire *family* of functions (one antiderivative for each value of the constant C).

⊘   You should distinguish carefully between definite and indefinite integrals. A definite integral $\int_a^b f(x)\,dx$ is a number, whereas an indefinite integral $\int f(x)\,dx$ is a function (or family of functions). The connection between them is given by Part 2 of the Fundamental Theorem. If f is continuous on $[a, b]$, then

$$\int_a^b f(x)\,dx = \int f(x)\,dx \Big]_a^b$$

The effectiveness of the Fundamental Theorem depends on having a supply of antiderivatives of functions. We therefore restate the Table of Antidifferentiation Formulas from Section 4.10, together with a few others, in the notation of indefinite integrals. Any formula can be verified by differentiating the function on the right side and obtaining the integrand. For instance

$$\int \sec^2 x\,dx = \tan x + C \qquad \text{because} \qquad \frac{d}{dx}(\tan x + C) = \sec^2 x$$

1 **Table of Indefinite Integrals**

$$\int cf(x)\,dx = c\int f(x)\,dx \qquad\qquad \int [f(x) + g(x)]\,dx = \int f(x)\,dx + \int g(x)\,dx$$

$$\int k\,dx = kx + C \qquad\qquad \int x^n\,dx = \frac{x^{n+1}}{n+1} + C \quad (n \neq -1)$$

$$\int \sin x\,dx = -\cos x + C \qquad\qquad \int \cos x\,dx = \sin x + C$$

$$\int \sec^2 x\,dx = \tan x + C \qquad\qquad \int \csc^2 x\,dx = -\cot x + C$$

$$\int \sec x \tan x\,dx = \sec x + C \qquad\qquad \int \csc x \cot x\,dx = -\csc x + C$$

Recall from Theorem 4.10.1 that the most general antiderivative *on a given interval* is obtained by adding a constant to a particular antiderivative. **We adopt the convention that when a formula for a general indefinite integral is given, it is valid only on an interval.** Thus, we write

$$\int \frac{1}{x^2} \, dx = -\frac{1}{x} + C$$

with the understanding that it is valid on the interval $(0, \infty)$ or on the interval $(-\infty, 0)$. This is true despite the fact that the general antiderivative of the function $f(x) = 1/x^2$, $x \neq 0$, is

$$F(x) = \begin{cases} -\dfrac{1}{x} + C_1 & \text{if } x < 0 \\[2mm] -\dfrac{1}{x} + C_2 & \text{if } x > 0 \end{cases}$$

|||| The indefinite integral in Example 1 is graphed in Figure 1 for several values of C. The value of C is the y-intercept.

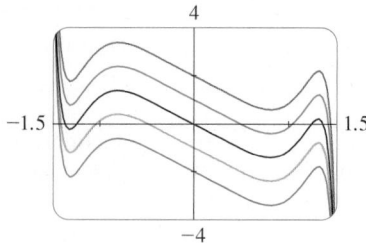

FIGURE 1

EXAMPLE 1 Find the general indefinite integral

$$\int (10x^4 - 2 \sec^2 x) \, dx$$

SOLUTION Using our convention and Table 1, we have

$$\int (10x^4 - 2 \sec^2 x) \, dx = 10 \int x^4 \, dx - 2 \int \sec^2 x \, dx$$

$$= 10 \frac{x^5}{5} - 2 \tan x + C$$

$$= 2x^5 - 2 \tan x + C$$

You should check this answer by differentiating it.

EXAMPLE 2 Evaluate $\displaystyle\int \frac{\cos \theta}{\sin^2 \theta} \, d\theta$.

SOLUTION This indefinite integral isn't immediately apparent in Table 1, so we use trigonometric identities to rewrite the function before integrating:

$$\int \frac{\cos \theta}{\sin^2 \theta} \, d\theta = \int \left(\frac{1}{\sin \theta}\right)\left(\frac{\cos \theta}{\sin \theta}\right) d\theta$$

$$= \int \csc \theta \cot \theta \, d\theta = -\csc \theta + C$$

EXAMPLE 3 Evaluate $\displaystyle\int_0^3 (x^3 - 6x) \, dx$.

SOLUTION Using FTC2 and Table 1, we have

$$\int_0^3 (x^3 - 6x) \, dx = \frac{x^4}{4} - 6\frac{x^2}{2} \bigg]_0^3$$

$$= \left(\tfrac{1}{4} \cdot 3^4 - 3 \cdot 3^2\right) - \left(\tfrac{1}{4} \cdot 0^4 - 3 \cdot 0^2\right)$$

$$= \tfrac{81}{4} - 27 - 0 + 0 = -6.75$$

Compare this calculation with Example 2(b) in Section 5.2.

|||| Figure 2 shows the graph of the integrand in Example 4. We know from Section 5.2 that the value of the integral can be interpreted as the sum of the areas labeled with a plus sign minus the areas labeled with a minus sign.

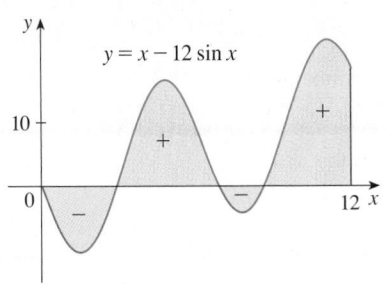

FIGURE 2

EXAMPLE 4 Find $\int_0^{12} (x - 12 \sin x)\, dx$.

SOLUTION The Fundamental Theorem gives

$$\int_0^{12} (x - 12 \sin x)\, dx = \frac{x^2}{2} - 12(-\cos x)\Bigg]_0^{12}$$

$$= \tfrac{1}{2}(12)^2 + 12(\cos 12 - \cos 0)$$

$$= 72 + 12 \cos 12 - 12$$

$$= 60 + 12 \cos 12$$

This is the exact value of the integral. If a decimal approximation is desired, we can use a calculator to approximate $\cos 12$. Doing so, we get

$$\int_0^{12} (x - 12 \sin x)\, dx \approx 70.1262$$

EXAMPLE 5 Evaluate $\int_1^9 \dfrac{2t^2 + t^2 \sqrt{t} - 1}{t^2}\, dt$.

SOLUTION First we need to write the integrand in a simpler form by carrying out the division:

$$\int_1^9 \frac{2t^2 + t^2 \sqrt{t} - 1}{t^2}\, dt = \int_1^9 (2 + t^{1/2} - t^{-2})\, dt$$

$$= 2t + \frac{t^{3/2}}{\frac{3}{2}} - \frac{t^{-1}}{-1}\Bigg]_1^9 = 2t + \tfrac{2}{3}t^{3/2} + \frac{1}{t}\Bigg]_1^9$$

$$= \left[2 \cdot 9 + \tfrac{2}{3}(9)^{3/2} + \tfrac{1}{9}\right] - \left(2 \cdot 1 + \tfrac{2}{3} \cdot 1^{3/2} + \tfrac{1}{1}\right)$$

$$= 18 + 18 + \tfrac{1}{9} - 2 - \tfrac{2}{3} - 1 = 32\tfrac{4}{9}$$

|||| **Applications**

Part 2 of the Fundamental Theorem says that if f is continuous on $[a, b]$, then

$$\int_a^b f(x)\, dx = F(b) - F(a)$$

where F is any antiderivative of f. This means that $F' = f$, so the equation can be rewritten as

$$\int_a^b F'(x)\, dx = F(b) - F(a)$$

We know that $F'(x)$ represents the rate of change of $y = F(x)$ with respect to x and $F(b) - F(a)$ is the change in y when x changes from a to b. [Note that y could, for instance, increase, then decrease, then increase again. Although y might change in both directions, $F(b) - F(a)$ represents the *net* change in y.] So we can reformulate FTC2 in words as follows.

> **The Net Change Theorem** The integral of a rate of change is the net change:
>
> $$\int_a^b F'(x)\,dx = F(b) - F(a)$$

This principle can be applied to all of the rates of change in the natural and social sciences that we discussed in Section 3.4. Here are a few instances of this idea:

○ If $V(t)$ is the volume of water in a reservoir at time t, then its derivative $V'(t)$ is the rate at which water flows into the reservoir at time t. So

$$\int_{t_1}^{t_2} V'(t)\,dt = V(t_2) - V(t_1)$$

is the change in the amount of water in the reservoir between time t_1 and time t_2.

○ If $[C](t)$ is the concentration of the product of a chemical reaction at time t, then the rate of reaction is the derivative $d[C]/dt$. So

$$\int_{t_1}^{t_2} \frac{d[C]}{dt}\,dt = [C](t_2) - [C](t_1)$$

is the change in the concentration of C from time t_1 to time t_2.

○ If the mass of a rod measured from the left end to a point x is $m(x)$, then the linear density is $\rho(x) = m'(x)$. So

$$\int_a^b \rho(x)\,dx = m(b) - m(a)$$

is the mass of the segment of the rod that lies between $x = a$ and $x = b$.

○ If the rate of growth of a population is dn/dt, then

$$\int_{t_1}^{t_2} \frac{dn}{dt}\,dt = n(t_2) - n(t_1)$$

is the net change in population during the time period from t_1 to t_2. (The population increases when births happen and decreases when deaths occur. The net change takes into account both births and deaths.)

○ If $C(x)$ is the cost of producing x units of a commodity, then the marginal cost is the derivative $C'(x)$. So

$$\int_{x_1}^{x_2} C'(x)\,dx = C(x_2) - C(x_1)$$

is the increase in cost when production is increased from x_1 units to x_2 units.

○ If an object moves along a straight line with position function $s(t)$, then its velocity is $v(t) = s'(t)$, so

2
$$\int_{t_1}^{t_2} v(t)\,dt = s(t_2) - s(t_1)$$

is the net change of position, or *displacement,* of the particle during the time period from t_1 to t_2. In Section 5.1 we guessed that this was true for the case where the object moves in the positive direction, but now we have proved that it is always true.

▫ If we want to calculate the distance traveled during the time interval, we have to consider the intervals when $v(t) \geq 0$ (the particle moves to the right) and also the intervals when $v(t) \leq 0$ (the particle moves to the left). In both cases the distance is computed by integrating $|v(t)|$, the speed. Therefore

$$\boxed{3} \qquad \int_{t_1}^{t_2} |v(t)| \, dt = \text{total distance traveled}$$

Figure 3 shows how both displacement and distance traveled can be interpreted in terms of areas under a velocity curve.

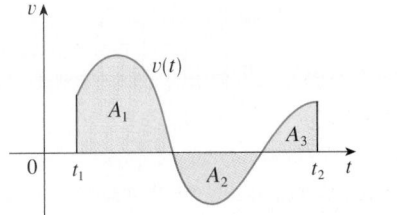

$$\text{displacement} = \int_{t_1}^{t_2} v(t) \, dt = A_1 - A_2 + A_3$$

$$\text{distance} = \int_{t_1}^{t_2} |v(t)| \, dt = A_1 + A_2 + A_3$$

FIGURE 3

▫ The acceleration of the object is $a(t) = v'(t)$, so

$$\int_{t_1}^{t_2} a(t) \, dt = v(t_2) - v(t_1)$$

is the change in velocity from time t_1 to time t_2.

Resources / Module 7
/ Physics and Engineering
/ Start of Spy Tracks

EXAMPLE 6 A particle moves along a line so that its velocity at time t is $v(t) = t^2 - t - 6$ (measured in meters per second).
(a) Find the displacement of the particle during the time period $1 \leq t \leq 4$.
(b) Find the distance traveled during this time period.

SOLUTION
(a) By Equation 2, the displacement is

$$s(4) - s(1) = \int_1^4 v(t) \, dt = \int_1^4 (t^2 - t - 6) \, dt$$

$$= \left[\frac{t^3}{3} - \frac{t^2}{2} - 6t \right]_1^4 = -\frac{9}{2}$$

This means that the particle moved 4.5 m toward the left.

(b) Note that $v(t) = t^2 - t - 6 = (t - 3)(t + 2)$ and so $v(t) \leq 0$ on the interval $[1, 3]$ and $v(t) \geq 0$ on $[3, 4]$. Thus, from Equation 3, the distance traveled is

‖‖‖ To integrate the absolute value of $v(t)$, we use Property 5 of integrals from Section 5.2 to split the integral into two parts, one where $v(t) \leq 0$ and one where $v(t) \geq 0$.

$$\int_1^4 |v(t)| \, dt = \int_1^3 [-v(t)] \, dt + \int_3^4 v(t) \, dt$$

$$= \int_1^3 (-t^2 + t + 6) \, dt + \int_3^4 (t^2 - t - 6) \, dt$$

$$= \left[-\frac{t^3}{3} + \frac{t^2}{2} + 6t \right]_1^3 + \left[\frac{t^3}{3} - \frac{t^2}{2} - 6t \right]_3^4$$

$$= \frac{61}{6} \approx 10.17 \text{ m}$$

EXAMPLE 7 Figure 4 shows the power consumption in the city of San Francisco for a day in September (P is measured in megawatts; t is measured in hours starting at midnight). Estimate the energy used on that day.

FIGURE 4

Pacific Gas & Electric

SOLUTION Power is the rate of change of energy: $P(t) = E'(t)$. So, by the Net Change Theorem,

$$\int_0^{24} P(t)\,dt = \int_0^{24} E'(t)\,dt = E(24) - E(0)$$

is the total amount of energy used that day. We approximate the value of the integral using the Midpoint Rule with 12 subintervals and $\Delta t = 2$:

$$\int_0^{24} P(t)\,dt \approx [P(1) + P(3) + P(5) + \cdots + P(21) + P(23)]\,\Delta t$$

$$\approx (440 + 400 + 420 + 620 + 790 + 840 + 850$$

$$+ 840 + 810 + 690 + 670 + 550)(2)$$

$$= 15{,}840$$

The energy used was approximately 15,840 megawatt-hours.

‖‖ A note on units

How did we know what units to use for energy in Example 7? The integral $\int_0^{24} P(t)\,dt$ is defined as the limit of sums of terms of the form $P(t_i^*)\,\Delta t$. Now $P(t_i^*)$ is measured in megawatts and Δt is measured in hours, so their product is measured in megawatt-hours. The same is true of the limit. In general, the unit of measurement for $\int_a^b f(x)\,dx$ is the product of the unit for $f(x)$ and the unit for x.

‖‖‖ 5.4 Exercises

1–4 ‖‖ Verify by differentiation that the formula is correct.

1. $\int \dfrac{x}{\sqrt{x^2 + 1}}\,dx = \sqrt{x^2 + 1} + C$

2. $\int x \cos x\,dx = x \sin x + \cos x + C$

3. $\int \dfrac{1}{\sqrt{(a^2 - x^2)^3}}\,dx = \dfrac{x}{a^2\sqrt{a^2 - x^2}} + C$

4. $\int \dfrac{1}{x^2\sqrt{x^2 + a^2}}\,dx = -\dfrac{\sqrt{x^2 + a^2}}{a^2 x} + C$

5–14 ‖‖ Find the general indefinite integral.

5. $\int x^{-3/4}\,dx$

6. $\int \sqrt[3]{x}\,dx$

7. $\int (x^3 + 6x + 1)\,dx$

8. $\int x(1 + 2x^4)\,dx$

9. $\displaystyle\int (1 - t)(2 + t^2)\, dt$

10. $\displaystyle\int \left(u^2 + 1 + \frac{1}{u^2} \right) du$

11. $\displaystyle\int (2 - \sqrt{x})^2\, dx$

12. $\displaystyle\int (\sin\theta + 3\cos\theta)\, d\theta$

13. $\displaystyle\int \frac{\sin x}{1 - \sin^2 x}\, dx$

14. $\displaystyle\int \frac{\sin 2x}{\sin x}\, dx$

15–16 ▓ Find the general indefinite integral. Illustrate by graphing several members of the family on the same screen.

15. $\displaystyle\int x\sqrt{x}\, dx$

16. $\displaystyle\int (\cos x - 2\sin x)\, dx$

17–40 ▓ Evaluate the integral.

17. $\displaystyle\int_0^2 (6x^2 - 4x + 5)\, dx$

18. $\displaystyle\int_1^3 (1 + 2x - 4x^3)\, dx$

19. $\displaystyle\int_{-3}^0 (5y^4 - 6y^2 + 14)\, dy$

20. $\displaystyle\int_{-2}^0 (u^5 - u^3 + u^2)\, du$

21. $\displaystyle\int_{-2}^2 (3u + 1)^2\, du$

22. $\displaystyle\int_0^4 (2v + 5)(3v - 1)\, dv$

23. $\displaystyle\int_1^4 \sqrt{t}(1 + t)\, dt$

24. $\displaystyle\int_0^9 \sqrt{2t}\, dt$

25. $\displaystyle\int_{-2}^{-1} \left(4y^3 + \frac{2}{y^3} \right) dy$

26. $\displaystyle\int_1^2 \frac{y + 5y^7}{y^3}\, dy$

27. $\displaystyle\int_0^1 x(\sqrt[3]{x} + \sqrt[4]{x})\, dx$

28. $\displaystyle\int_1^2 \left(x + \frac{1}{x} \right)^2 dx$

29. $\displaystyle\int_1^4 \sqrt{\frac{5}{x}}\, dx$

30. $\displaystyle\int_1^9 \frac{3x - 2}{\sqrt{x}}\, dx$

31. $\displaystyle\int_0^\pi (4\sin\theta - 3\cos\theta)\, d\theta$

32. $\displaystyle\int_{\pi/4}^{\pi/3} \sec\theta\tan\theta\, d\theta$

33. $\displaystyle\int_0^{\pi/4} \frac{1 + \cos^2\theta}{\cos^2\theta}\, d\theta$

34. $\displaystyle\int_0^{\pi/3} \frac{\sin\theta + \sin\theta\tan^2\theta}{\sec^2\theta}\, d\theta$

35. $\displaystyle\int_1^{64} \frac{1 + \sqrt[3]{x}}{\sqrt{x}}\, dx$

36. $\displaystyle\int_0^1 (1 + x^2)^3\, dx$

37. $\displaystyle\int_0^1 (\sqrt[4]{x^5} + \sqrt[5]{x^4})\, dx$

38. $\displaystyle\int_1^8 \frac{x - 1}{\sqrt[3]{x^2}}\, dx$

39. $\displaystyle\int_{-1}^2 (x - 2|x|)\, dx$

40. $\displaystyle\int_0^{3\pi/2} |\sin x|\, dx$

41. Use a graph to estimate the x-intercepts of the curve $y = x + x^2 - x^4$. Then use this information to estimate the area of the region that lies under the curve and above the x-axis.

42. Repeat Exercise 41 for the curve $y = 2x + 3x^4 - 2x^6$.

43. The area of the region that lies to the right of the y-axis and to the left of the parabola $x = 2y - y^2$ (the shaded region in the figure) is given by the integral $\int_0^2 (2y - y^2)\, dy$. (Turn your head clockwise and think of the region as lying below the curve $x = 2y - y^2$ from $y = 0$ to $y = 2$.) Find the area of the region.

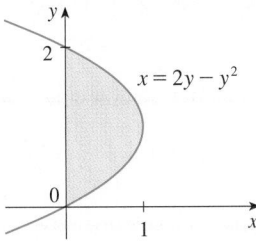

44. The boundaries of the shaded region are the y-axis, the line $y = 1$, and the curve $y = \sqrt[4]{x}$. Find the area of this region by writing x as a function of y and integrating with respect to y (as in Exercise 43).

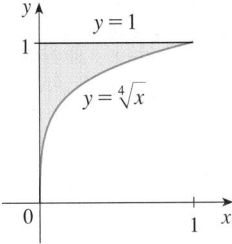

45. If $w'(t)$ is the rate of growth of a child in pounds per year, what does $\int_5^{10} w'(t)\, dt$ represent?

46. The current in a wire is defined as the derivative of the charge: $I(t) = Q'(t)$. (See Example 3 in Section 3.4.) What does $\int_a^b I(t)\, dt$ represent?

47. If oil leaks from a tank at a rate of $r(t)$ gallons per minute at time t, what does $\int_0^{120} r(t)\, dt$ represent?

48. A honeybee population starts with 100 bees and increases at a rate of $n'(t)$ bees per week. What does $100 + \int_0^{15} n'(t)\, dt$ represent?

49. In Section 4.8 we defined the marginal revenue function $R'(x)$ as the derivative of the revenue function $R(x)$, where x is the number of units sold. What does $\int_{1000}^{5000} R'(x)\, dx$ represent?

50. If $f(x)$ is the slope of a trail at a distance of x miles from the start of the trail, what does $\int_3^5 f(x)\, dx$ represent?

51. If x is measured in meters and $f(x)$ is measured in newtons, what are the units for $\int_0^{100} f(x)\, dx$?

52. If the units for x are feet and the units for $a(x)$ are pounds per foot, what are the units for da/dx? What units does $\int_2^8 a(x)\, dx$ have?

53–54 ▓ The velocity function (in meters per second) is given for a particle moving along a line. Find (a) the displacement and (b) the distance traveled by the particle during the given time interval.

53. $v(t) = 3t - 5$, $\quad 0 \leqslant t \leqslant 3$

54. $v(t) = t^2 - 2t - 8$, $\quad 1 \leqslant t \leqslant 6$

55–56 ▓ The acceleration function (in m/s²) and the initial velocity are given for a particle moving along a line. Find (a) the velocity at time t and (b) the distance traveled during the given time interval.

55. $a(t) = t + 4$, $\quad v(0) = 5$, $\quad 0 \leqslant t \leqslant 10$

56. $a(t) = 2t + 3$, $\quad v(0) = -4$, $\quad 0 \leqslant t \leqslant 3$

57. The linear density of a rod of length 4 m is given by $\rho(x) = 9 + 2\sqrt{x}$ measured in kilograms per meter, where x is measured in meters from one end of the rod. Find the total mass of the rod.

58. Water flows from the bottom of a storage tank at a rate of $r(t) = 200 - 4t$ liters per minute, where $0 \leqslant t \leqslant 50$. Find the amount of water that flows from the tank during the first 10 minutes.

59. The velocity of a car was read from its speedometer at 10-second intervals and recorded in the table. Use the Midpoint Rule to estimate the distance traveled by the car.

t (s)	v (mi/h)	t (s)	v (mi/h)
0	0	60	56
10	38	70	53
20	52	80	50
30	58	90	47
40	55	100	45
50	51		

60. Suppose that a volcano is erupting and readings of the rate $r(t)$ at which solid materials are spewed into the atmosphere are given in the table. The time t is measured in seconds and the units for $r(t)$ are tonnes (metric tons) per second.

t	0	1	2	3	4	5	6
$r(t)$	2	10	24	36	46	54	60

(a) Give upper and lower estimates for the quantity $Q(6)$ of erupted materials after 6 seconds.
(b) Use the Midpoint Rule to estimate $Q(6)$.

61. The marginal cost of manufacturing x yards of a certain fabric is $C'(x) = 3 - 0.01x + 0.000006x^2$ (in dollars per yard). Find the increase in cost if the production level is raised from 2000 yards to 4000 yards.

62. Water flows in and out of a storage tank. A graph of the rate of change $r(t)$ of the volume of water in the tank, in liters per day, is shown. If the amount of water in the tank at time $t = 0$ is 25,000 L, use the Midpoint Rule to estimate the amount of water four days later.

63. Economists use a cumulative distribution called a *Lorenz curve* to describe the distribution of income between households in a given country. Typically, a Lorenz curve is defined on [0, 1] with endpoints (0, 0) and (1, 1), and is continuous, increasing, and concave upward. The points on this curve are determined by ranking all households by income and then computing the percentage of households whose income is less than or equal to a given percentage of the total income of the country. For example, the point ($a/100$, $b/100$) is on the Lorenz curve if the bottom $a\%$ of the households receive less than or equal to $b\%$ of the total income. *Absolute equality* of income distribution would occur if the bottom $a\%$ of the households receive $a\%$ of the income, in which case the Lorenz curve would be the line $y = x$. The area between the Lorenz curve and the line $y = x$ measures how much the income distribution differs from absolute equality. The *coefficient of inequality* is the ratio of the area between the Lorenz curve and the line $y = x$ to the area under $y = x$.

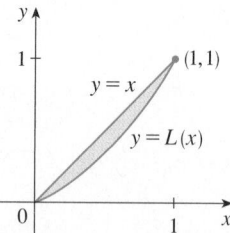

(a) Show that the coefficient of inequality is twice the area between the Lorenz curve and the line $y = x$, that is, show that

$$\text{coefficient of inequality} = 2 \int_0^1 [x - L(x)] \, dx$$

(b) The income distribution for a certain country is represented by the Lorenz curve defined by the equation

$$L(x) = \frac{5}{12}x^2 + \frac{7}{12}x$$

What is the percentage of total income received by the bottom 50% of the households? Find the coefficient of inequality.

64. On May 7, 1992, the space shuttle *Endeavour* was launched on mission STS-49, the purpose of which was to install a new perigee kick motor in an Intelsat communications satellite. The table gives the velocity data for the shuttle between liftoff and the jettisoning of the solid rocket boosters.

Event	Time (s)	Velocity (ft/s)
Launch	0	0
Begin roll maneuver	10	185
End roll maneuver	15	319
Throttle to 89%	20	447
Throttle to 67%	32	742
Throttle to 104%	59	1325
Maximum dynamic pressure	62	1445
Solid rocket booster separation	125	4151

(a) Use a graphing calculator or computer to model these data by a third-degree polynomial.
(b) Use the model in part (a) to estimate the height reached by the *Endeavour*, 125 seconds after liftoff.

The following exercises are intended only for those who have already covered Chapter 7.

65–67 ‖‖ Evaluate the integral.

65. $\displaystyle\int_1^e \frac{x^2 + x + 1}{x}\,dx$

66. $\displaystyle\int_4^9 \left(\sqrt{x} + \frac{1}{\sqrt{x}} \right)^2 dx$

67. $\displaystyle\int \left(x^2 + 1 + \frac{1}{x^2 + 1} \right) dx$

68. The area labeled B is three times the area labeled A. Express b in terms of a.

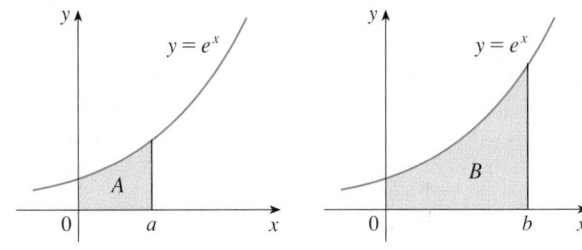

WRITING PROJECT

Newton, Leibniz, and the Invention of Calculus

We sometimes read that the inventors of calculus were Sir Isaac Newton (1642–1727) and Gottfried Wilhelm Leibniz (1646–1716). But we know that the basic ideas behind integration were investigated 2500 years ago by ancient Greeks such as Eudoxus and Archimedes, and methods for finding tangents were pioneered by Pierre Fermat (1601–1665), Isaac Barrow (1630–1677), and others. Barrow, Newton's teacher at Cambridge, was the first to understand the inverse relationship between differentiation and integration. What Newton and Leibniz did was to use this relationship, in the form of the Fundamental Theorem of Calculus, in order to develop calculus into a systematic mathematical discipline. It is in this sense that Newton and Leibniz are credited with the invention of calculus.

Read about the contributions of these men in one or more of the given references and write a report on one of the following three topics. You can include biographical details, but the main thrust of your report should be a description, in some detail, of their methods and notations. In particular, you should consult one of the sourcebooks, which give excerpts from the original publications of Newton and Leibniz, translated from Latin to English.

- The Role of Newton in the Development of Calculus

- The Role of Leibniz in the Development of Calculus

- The Controversy between the Followers of Newton and Leibniz over Priority in the Invention of Calculus

References

1. Carl Boyer and Uta Merzbach, *A History of Mathematics* (New York: Wiley, 1987), Chapter 19.

2. Carl Boyer, *The History of the Calculus and Its Conceptual Development* (New York: Dover, 1959), Chapter V.

3. C. H. Edwards, *The Historical Development of the Calculus* (New York: Springer-Verlag, 1979), Chapters 8 and 9.

4. Howard Eves, *An Introduction to the History of Mathematics,* 6th ed. (New York: Saunders, 1990), Chapter 11.

5. C. C. Gillispie, ed., *Dictionary of Scientific Biography* (New York: Scribner's, 1974). See the article on Leibniz by Joseph Hofmann in Volume VIII and the article on Newton by I. B. Cohen in Volume X.

6. Victor Katz, *A History of Mathematics: An Introduction* (New York: HarperCollins, 1993), Chapter 12.

7. Morris Kline, *Mathematical Thought from Ancient to Modern Times* (New York: Oxford University Press, 1972), Chapter 17.

Sourcebooks

1. John Fauvel and Jeremy Gray, eds., *The History of Mathematics: A Reader* (London: MacMillan Press, 1987), Chapters 12 and 13.

2. D. E. Smith, ed., *A Sourcebook in Mathematics* (New York: Dover, 1959), Chapter V.

3. D. J. Struik, ed., *A Sourcebook in Mathematics, 1200–1800* (Princeton, N.J.: Princeton University Press, 1969), Chapter V.

5.5   The Substitution Rule

Because of the Fundamental Theorem, it's important to be able to find antiderivatives. But our antidifferentiation formulas don't tell us how to evaluate integrals such as

$$\boxed{1} \qquad \int 2x\sqrt{1 + x^2}\, dx$$

To find this integral we use the problem-solving strategy of *introducing something extra.* Here the "something extra" is a new variable; we change from the variable x to a new variable u. Suppose that we let u be the quantity under the root sign in (1), $u = 1 + x^2$. Then the differential of u is $du = 2x\, dx$. Notice that if the dx in the notation for an integral were to be interpreted as a differential, then the differential $2x\, dx$ would occur in (1) and, so, formally, without justifying our calculation, we could write

|||| Differentials were defined in Section 3.10. If $u = f(x)$, then
$$du = f'(x)\, dx$$

$$\boxed{2} \qquad \int 2x\sqrt{1 + x^2}\, dx = \int \sqrt{1 + x^2}\, 2x\, dx = \int \sqrt{u}\, du$$

$$= \tfrac{2}{3}u^{3/2} + C = \tfrac{2}{3}(x^2 + 1)^{3/2} + C$$

But now we can check that we have the correct answer by using the Chain Rule to differentiate the final function of Equation 2:

$$\frac{d}{dx}\left[\tfrac{2}{3}(x^2 + 1)^{3/2} + C\right] = \tfrac{2}{3}\cdot\tfrac{3}{2}(x^2 + 1)^{1/2}\cdot 2x = 2x\sqrt{x^2 + 1}$$

In general, this method works whenever we have an integral that we can write in the form $\int f(g(x))g'(x)\, dx$. Observe that if $F' = f$, then

$$\boxed{3} \qquad \int F'(g(x))g'(x)\, dx = F(g(x)) + C$$

because, by the Chain Rule,

$$\frac{d}{dx}[F(g(x))] = F'(g(x))g'(x)$$

If we make the "change of variable" or "substitution" $u = g(x)$, then from Equation 3 we have

$$\int F'(g(x))g'(x)\,dx = F(g(x)) + C = F(u) + C = \int F'(u)\,du$$

or, writing $F' = f$, we get

$$\int f(g(x))g'(x)\,dx = \int f(u)\,du$$

Thus, we have proved the following rule.

> **4 The Substitution Rule** If $u = g(x)$ is a differentiable function whose range is an interval I and f is continuous on I, then
>
> $$\int f(g(x))g'(x)\,dx = \int f(u)\,du$$

Notice that the Substitution Rule for integration was proved using the Chain Rule for differentiation. Notice also that if $u = g(x)$, then $du = g'(x)\,dx$, so a way to remember the Substitution Rule is to think of dx and du in (4) as differentials.

Thus, the Substitution Rule says: **It is permissible to operate with dx and du after integral signs as if they were differentials.**

EXAMPLE 1 Find $\int x^3 \cos(x^4 + 2)\,dx$.

SOLUTION We make the substitution $u = x^4 + 2$ because its differential is $du = 4x^3\,dx$, which, apart from the constant factor 4, occurs in the integral. Thus, using $x^3\,dx = du/4$ and the Substitution Rule, we have

$$\int x^3 \cos(x^4 + 2)\,dx = \int \cos u \cdot \tfrac{1}{4}\,du = \tfrac{1}{4}\int \cos u\,du$$

$$= \tfrac{1}{4}\sin u + C$$

$$= \tfrac{1}{4}\sin(x^4 + 2) + C$$

||| Check the answer by differentiating it.

Notice that at the final stage we had to return to the original variable x.

The idea behind the Substitution Rule is to replace a relatively complicated integral by a simpler integral. This is accomplished by changing from the original variable x to a new variable u that is a function of x. Thus, in Example 1 we replaced the integral $\int x^3 \cos(x^4 + 2)\,dx$ by the simpler integral $\tfrac{1}{4}\int \cos u\,du$.

The main challenge in using the Substitution Rule is to think of an appropriate substitution. You should try to choose u to be some function in the integrand whose differential also occurs (except for a constant factor). This was the case in Example 1. If that is not possible, try choosing u to be some complicated part of the integrand (perhaps the inner function in a composite function). Finding the right substitution is a bit of an art. It's not unusual to guess wrong; if your first guess doesn't work, try another substitution.

EXAMPLE 2 Evaluate $\int \sqrt{2x + 1}\, dx$.

SOLUTION 1 Let $u = 2x + 1$. Then $du = 2\, dx$, so $dx = du/2$. Thus, the Substitution Rule gives

$$\int \sqrt{2x + 1}\, dx = \int \sqrt{u}\, \frac{du}{2} = \tfrac{1}{2} \int u^{1/2}\, du$$

$$= \frac{1}{2} \cdot \frac{u^{3/2}}{3/2} + C = \tfrac{1}{3} u^{3/2} + C$$

$$= \tfrac{1}{3}(2x + 1)^{3/2} + C$$

SOLUTION 2 Another possible substitution is $u = \sqrt{2x + 1}$. Then

$$du = \frac{dx}{\sqrt{2x + 1}} \qquad \text{so} \qquad dx = \sqrt{2x + 1}\, du = u\, du$$

(Or observe that $u^2 = 2x + 1$, so $2u\, du = 2\, dx$.) Therefore

$$\int \sqrt{2x + 1}\, dx = \int u \cdot u\, du = \int u^2\, du$$

$$= \frac{u^3}{3} + C = \tfrac{1}{3}(2x + 1)^{3/2} + C$$

EXAMPLE 3 Find $\int \dfrac{x}{\sqrt{1 - 4x^2}}\, dx$.

SOLUTION Let $u = 1 - 4x^2$. Then $du = -8x\, dx$, so $x\, dx = -\tfrac{1}{8}\, du$ and

$$\int \frac{x}{\sqrt{1 - 4x^2}}\, dx = -\tfrac{1}{8} \int \frac{du}{\sqrt{u}} = -\tfrac{1}{8} \int u^{-1/2}\, du$$

$$= -\tfrac{1}{8}(2\sqrt{u}) + C = -\tfrac{1}{4}\sqrt{1 - 4x^2} + C$$

The answer to Example 3 could be checked by differentiation, but instead let's check it with a graph. In Figure 1 we have used a computer to graph both the integrand $f(x) = x/\sqrt{1 - 4x^2}$ and its indefinite integral $g(x) = -\tfrac{1}{4}\sqrt{1 - 4x^2}$ (we take the case $C = 0$). Notice that $g(x)$ decreases when $f(x)$ is negative, increases when $f(x)$ is positive, and has its minimum value when $f(x) = 0$. So it seems reasonable, from the graphical evidence, that g is an antiderivative of f.

EXAMPLE 4 Calculate $\int \cos 5x\, dx$.

SOLUTION If we let $u = 5x$, then $du = 5\, dx$, so $dx = \tfrac{1}{5}\, du$. Therefore

$$\int \cos 5x\, dx = \tfrac{1}{5} \int \cos u\, du = \tfrac{1}{5} \sin u + C = \tfrac{1}{5} \sin 5x + C$$

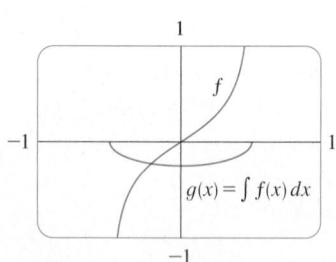

FIGURE 1

$f(x) = \dfrac{x}{\sqrt{1 - 4x^2}}$

$g(x) = \int f(x)\, dx = -\tfrac{1}{4}\sqrt{1 - 4x^2}$

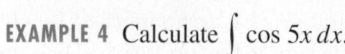

EXAMPLE 5 Find $\int \sqrt{1 + x^2}\, x^5\, dx$.

SOLUTION An appropriate substitution becomes more obvious if we factor x^5 as $x^4 \cdot x$. Let $u = 1 + x^2$. Then $du = 2x\, dx$, so $x\, dx = du/2$. Also $x^2 = u - 1$, so $x^4 = (u - 1)^2$:

$$\int \sqrt{1 + x^2}\, x^5\, dx = \int \sqrt{1 + x^2}\, x^4 \cdot x\, dx$$

$$= \int \sqrt{u}\, (u - 1)^2\, \frac{du}{2} = \tfrac{1}{2} \int \sqrt{u}\, (u^2 - 2u + 1)\, du$$

$$= \tfrac{1}{2} \int (u^{5/2} - 2u^{3/2} + u^{1/2})\, du$$

$$= \tfrac{1}{2}\left(\tfrac{2}{7}u^{7/2} - 2 \cdot \tfrac{2}{5}u^{5/2} + \tfrac{2}{3}u^{3/2}\right) + C$$

$$= \tfrac{1}{7}(1 + x^2)^{7/2} - \tfrac{2}{5}(1 + x^2)^{5/2} + \tfrac{1}{3}(1 + x^2)^{3/2} + C$$

||| **Definite Integrals**

When evaluating a *definite* integral by substitution, two methods are possible. One method is to evaluate the indefinite integral first and then use the Fundamental Theorem. For instance, using the result of Example 2, we have

$$\int_0^4 \sqrt{2x + 1}\, dx = \int \sqrt{2x + 1}\, dx\Big]_0^4 = \tfrac{1}{3}(2x + 1)^{3/2}\Big]_0^4$$

$$= \tfrac{1}{3}(9)^{3/2} - \tfrac{1}{3}(1)^{3/2} = \tfrac{1}{3}(27 - 1) = \tfrac{26}{3}$$

Another method, which is usually preferable, is to change the limits of integration when the variable is changed.

||| This rule says that when using a substitution in a definite integral, we must put everything in terms of the new variable u, not only x and dx but also the limits of integration. The new limits of integration are the values of u that correspond to $x = a$ and $x = b$.

5 The Substitution Rule for Definite Integrals If g' is continuous on $[a, b]$ and f is continuous on the range of $u = g(x)$, then

$$\int_a^b f(g(x))g'(x)\, dx = \int_{g(a)}^{g(b)} f(u)\, du$$

Proof Let F be an antiderivative of f. Then, by (3), $F(g(x))$ is an antiderivative of $f(g(x))g'(x)$, so by Part 2 of the Fundamental Theorem, we have

$$\int_a^b f(g(x))g'(x)\, dx = F(g(x))\Big]_a^b = F(g(b)) - F(g(a))$$

But, applying FTC2 a second time, we also have

$$\int_{g(a)}^{g(b)} f(u)\, du = F(u)\Big]_{g(a)}^{g(b)} = F(g(b)) - F(g(a))$$

EXAMPLE 6 Evaluate $\int_0^4 \sqrt{2x + 1}\, dx$ using (5).

SOLUTION Using the substitution from Solution 1 of Example 2, we have $u = 2x + 1$ and $dx = du/2$. To find the new limits of integration we note that

when $x = 0$, $u = 2(0) + 1 = 1$ and when $x = 4$, $u = 2(4) + 1 = 9$

Therefore

$$\int_0^4 \sqrt{2x + 1}\, dx = \int_1^9 \tfrac{1}{2}\sqrt{u}\, du$$

$$= \tfrac{1}{2} \cdot \tfrac{2}{3} u^{3/2} \Big]_1^9$$

$$= \tfrac{1}{3}(9^{3/2} - 1^{3/2}) = \tfrac{26}{3}$$

‖‖‖ The geometric interpretation of Example 6 is shown in Figure 2. The substitution $u = 2x + 1$ stretches the interval $[0, 4]$ by a factor of 2 and translates it to the right by 1 unit. The Substitution Rule shows that the two areas are equal.

Observe that when using (5) we do not return to the variable x after integrating. We simply evaluate the expression in u between the appropriate values of u.

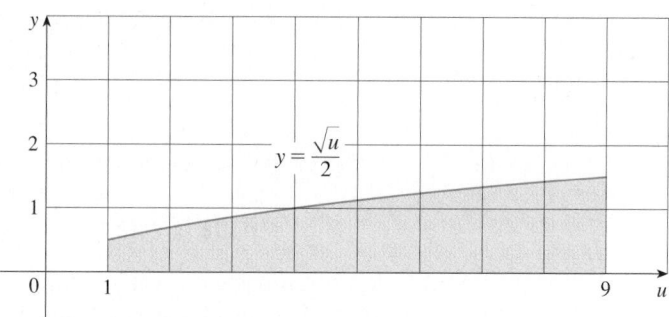

FIGURE 2

EXAMPLE 7 Evaluate $\displaystyle\int_1^2 \frac{dx}{(3 - 5x)^2}$.

‖‖‖ The integral given in Example 7 is an abbreviation for

$$\int_1^2 \frac{1}{(3 - 5x)^2}\, dx$$

SOLUTION Let $u = 3 - 5x$. Then $du = -5\, dx$, so $dx = -du/5$. When $x = 1$, $u = -2$ and when $x = 2$, $u = -7$. Thus

$$\int_1^2 \frac{dx}{(3 - 5x)^2} = -\frac{1}{5}\int_{-2}^{-7} \frac{du}{u^2}$$

$$= -\frac{1}{5}\left[-\frac{1}{u} \right]_{-2}^{-7} = \frac{1}{5u}\Bigg]_{-2}^{-7}$$

$$= \frac{1}{5}\left(-\frac{1}{7} + \frac{1}{2} \right) = \frac{1}{14}$$

‖‖‖ Symmetry

The next theorem uses the Substitution Rule for Definite Integrals (5) to simplify the calculation of integrals of functions that possess symmetry properties.

> **6** **Integrals of Symmetric Functions** Suppose f is continuous on $[-a, a]$.
>
> (a) If f is even $[f(-x) = f(x)]$, then $\int_{-a}^a f(x)\, dx = 2\int_0^a f(x)\, dx$.
>
> (b) If f is odd $[f(-x) = -f(x)]$, then $\int_{-a}^a f(x)\, dx = 0$.

Proof We split the integral in two:

$$\boxed{7} \qquad \int_{-a}^a f(x)\, dx = \int_{-a}^0 f(x)\, dx + \int_0^a f(x)\, dx = -\int_0^{-a} f(x)\, dx + \int_0^a f(x)\, dx$$

In the first integral on the far right side we make the substitution $u = -x$. Then

$du = -dx$ and when $x = -a$, $u = a$. Therefore

$$-\int_0^{-a} f(x)\,dx = -\int_0^a f(-u)(-du) = \int_0^a f(-u)\,du$$

and so Equation 7 becomes

8 $$\int_{-a}^a f(x)\,dx = \int_0^a f(-u)\,du + \int_0^a f(x)\,dx$$

(a) If f is even, then $f(-u) = f(u)$ so Equation 8 gives

$$\int_{-a}^a f(x)\,dx = \int_0^a f(u)\,du + \int_0^a f(x)\,dx = 2\int_0^a f(x)\,dx$$

(b) If f is odd, then $f(-u) = -f(u)$ and so Equation 8 gives

$$\int_{-a}^a f(x)\,dx = -\int_0^a f(u)\,du + \int_0^a f(x)\,dx = 0$$

Theorem 6 is illustrated by Figure 3. For the case where f is positive and even, part (a) says that the area under $y = f(x)$ from $-a$ to a is twice the area from 0 to a because of symmetry. Recall that an integral $\int_a^b f(x)\,dx$ can be expressed as the area above the x-axis and below $y = f(x)$ minus the area below the axis and above the curve. Thus, part (b) says the integral is 0 because the areas cancel.

EXAMPLE 8 Since $f(x) = x^6 + 1$ satisfies $f(-x) = f(x)$, it is even and so

$$\int_{-2}^2 (x^6 + 1)\,dx = 2\int_0^2 (x^6 + 1)\,dx$$

$$= 2\left[\tfrac{1}{7}x^7 + x\right]_0^2 = 2\left(\tfrac{128}{7} + 2\right) = \tfrac{284}{7}$$

EXAMPLE 9 Since $f(x) = (\tan x)/(1 + x^2 + x^4)$ satisfies $f(-x) = -f(x)$, it is odd and so

$$\int_{-1}^1 \frac{\tan x}{1 + x^2 + x^4}\,dx = 0$$

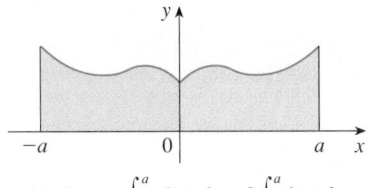

(a) f even, $\int_{-a}^a f(x)\,dx = 2\int_0^a f(x)\,dx$

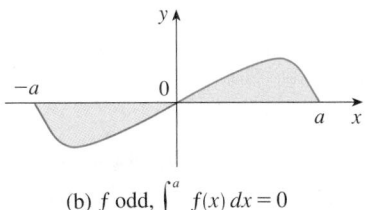

(b) f odd, $\int_{-a}^a f(x)\,dx = 0$

FIGURE 3

5.5 Exercises

1–6 ▦ Evaluate the integral by making the given substitution.

1. $\displaystyle\int \cos 3x\,dx, \quad u = 3x$

2. $\displaystyle\int x(4 + x^2)^{10}\,dx, \quad u = 4 + x^2$

3. $\displaystyle\int x^2\sqrt{x^3 + 1}\,dx, \quad u = x^3 + 1$

4. $\displaystyle\int \frac{\sin\sqrt{x}}{\sqrt{x}}\,dx, \quad u = \sqrt{x}$

5. $\displaystyle\int \frac{4}{(1 + 2x)^3}\,dx, \quad u = 1 + 2x$

6. $\displaystyle\int \cos^4\theta \sin\theta\,d\theta, \quad u = \cos\theta$

7–32 |||| Evaluate the indefinite integral.

7. $\int 2x(x^2 + 3)^4 \, dx$

8. $\int x^2(x^3 + 5)^9 \, dx$

9. $\int (3x - 2)^{20} \, dx$

10. $\int (2 - x)^6 \, dx$

11. $\int \dfrac{1 + 4x}{\sqrt{1 + x + 2x^2}} \, dx$

12. $\int \dfrac{x}{(x^2 + 1)^2} \, dx$

13. $\int \dfrac{3}{(2y + 1)^5} \, dy$

14. $\int \dfrac{1}{(5t + 4)^{2.7}} \, dt$

15. $\int \sqrt{4 - t} \, dt$

16. $\int y^3 \sqrt{2y^4 - 1} \, dy$

17. $\int \sin \pi t \, dt$

18. $\int \sec 2\theta \tan 2\theta \, d\theta$

19. $\int \dfrac{\cos \sqrt{t}}{\sqrt{t}} \, dt$

20. $\int \sqrt{x} \sin(1 + x^{3/2}) \, dx$

21. $\int \cos \theta \sin^6 \theta \, d\theta$

22. $\int (1 + \tan \theta)^5 \sec^2 \theta \, d\theta$

23. $\int \dfrac{z^2}{\sqrt[3]{1 + z^3}} \, dz$

24. $\int \dfrac{ax + b}{\sqrt{ax^2 + 2bx + c}} \, dx$

25. $\int \sqrt{\cot x} \, \csc^2 x \, dx$

26. $\int \dfrac{\cos(\pi/x)}{x^2} \, dx$

27. $\int \sec^3 x \tan x \, dx$

28. $\int \sqrt[3]{x^3 + 1} \, x^5 \, dx$

29. $\int x^a \sqrt{b + cx^{a+1}} \, dx \quad (c \neq 0, a \neq -1)$

30. $\int \sin t \sec^2(\cos t) \, dt$

31. $\int \dfrac{x}{\sqrt[4]{x + 2}} \, dx$

32. $\int \dfrac{x^2}{\sqrt{1 - x}} \, dx$

33–36 |||| Evaluate the indefinite integral. Illustrate and check that your answer is reasonable by graphing both the function and its antiderivative (take $C = 0$).

33. $\int \dfrac{3x - 1}{(3x^2 - 2x + 1)^4} \, dx$

34. $\int \dfrac{x}{\sqrt{x^2 + 1}} \, dx$

35. $\int \sin^3 x \cos x \, dx$

36. $\int \tan^2 \theta \sec^2 \theta \, d\theta$

37–54 |||| Evaluate the definite integral, if it exists.

37. $\int_0^2 (x - 1)^{25} \, dx$

38. $\int_0^7 \sqrt{4 + 3x} \, dx$

39. $\int_0^1 x^2(1 + 2x^3)^5 \, dx$

40. $\int_0^{\sqrt{\pi}} x \cos(x^2) \, dx$

41. $\int_0^\pi \sec^2(t/4) \, dt$

42. $\int_{1/6}^{1/2} \csc \pi t \cot \pi t \, dt$

43. $\int_{-\pi/6}^{\pi/6} \tan^3 \theta \, d\theta$

44. $\int_0^2 \dfrac{dx}{(2x - 3)^2}$

45. $\int_0^{\pi/3} \dfrac{\sin \theta}{\cos^2 \theta} \, d\theta$

46. $\int_{-\pi/2}^{\pi/2} \dfrac{x^2 \sin x}{1 + x^6} \, dx$

47. $\int_0^{13} \dfrac{dx}{\sqrt[3]{(1 + 2x)^2}}$

48. $\int_0^{\pi/2} \cos x \sin(\sin x) \, dx$

49. $\int_1^2 x\sqrt{x - 1} \, dx$

50. $\int_0^4 \dfrac{x}{\sqrt{1 + 2x}} \, dx$

51. $\int_0^4 \dfrac{dx}{(x - 2)^3}$

52. $\int_0^a x\sqrt{a^2 - x^2} \, dx$

53. $\int_0^a x\sqrt{x^2 + a^2} \, dx \quad (a > 0)$

54. $\int_{-a}^a x\sqrt{x^2 + a^2} \, dx$

55–56 |||| Use a graph to give a rough estimate of the area of the region that lies under the given curve. Then find the exact area.

55. $y = \sqrt{2x + 1}, \quad 0 \le x \le 1$

56. $y = 2 \sin x - \sin 2x, \quad 0 \le x \le \pi$

57. Evaluate $\int_{-2}^2 (x + 3)\sqrt{4 - x^2} \, dx$ by writing it as a sum of two integrals and interpreting one of those integrals in terms of an area.

58. Evaluate $\int_0^1 x\sqrt{1 - x^4} \, dx$ by making a substitution and interpreting the resulting integral in terms of an area.

59. Breathing is cyclic and a full respiratory cycle from the beginning of inhalation to the end of exhalation takes about 5 s. The maximum rate of air flow into the lungs is about 0.5 L/s. This explains, in part, why the function $f(t) = \frac{1}{2} \sin(2\pi t/5)$ has often been used to model the rate of air flow into the lungs. Use this model to find the volume of inhaled air in the lungs at time t.

60. Alabama Instruments Company has set up a production line to manufacture a new calculator. The rate of production of these calculators after t weeks is

$$\dfrac{dx}{dt} = 5000\left(1 - \dfrac{100}{(t + 10)^2}\right) \text{ calculators/week}$$

(Notice that production approaches 5000 per week as time goes on, but the initial production is lower because of the workers' unfamiliarity with the new techniques.) Find the number of calculators produced from the beginning of the third week to the end of the fourth week.

61. If f is continuous and $\int_0^4 f(x)\, dx = 10$, find $\int_0^2 f(2x)\, dx$.

62. If f is continuous and $\int_0^9 f(x)\, dx = 4$, find $\int_0^3 xf(x^2)\, dx$.

63. Suppose f is continuous on $\mathbb{R}$.
(a) Prove that

$$\int_a^b f(-x)\, dx = \int_{-b}^{-a} f(x)\, dx$$

For the case where $f(x) \geqslant 0$ and $0 < a < b$, draw a diagram to interpret this equation geometrically as an equality of areas.
(b) Prove that

$$\int_a^b f(x + c)\, dx = \int_{a+c}^{b+c} f(x)\, dx$$

For the case where $f(x) \geqslant 0$, draw a diagram to interpret this equation geometrically as an equality of areas.

64. Show that the area under the graph of $y = \sin\sqrt{x}$ from 0 to 4 is the same as the area under the graph of $y = 2x \sin x$ from 0 to 2.

65. If a and b are positive numbers, show that

$$\int_0^1 x^a(1-x)^b\, dx = \int_0^1 x^b(1-x)^a\, dx$$

66. Use the substitution $u = \pi - x$ to show that

$$\int_0^\pi xf(\sin x)\, dx = \frac{\pi}{2}\int_0^\pi f(\sin x)\, dx$$

The following exercises are intended only for those who have already covered Chapter 7.

67–82 ▓ Evaluate the integral.

67. $\displaystyle\int \frac{dx}{5 - 3x}$

68. $\displaystyle\int \frac{x}{x^2 + 1}\, dx$

69. $\displaystyle\int \frac{(\ln x)^2}{x}\, dx$

70. $\displaystyle\int \frac{\tan^{-1}x}{1 + x^2}\, dx$

71. $\displaystyle\int e^x\sqrt{1 + e^x}\, dx$

72. $\displaystyle\int e^{\cos t}\sin t\, dt$

73. $\displaystyle\int \frac{dx}{x\ln x}$

74. $\displaystyle\int \frac{e^x}{e^x + 1}\, dx$

75. $\displaystyle\int \cot x\, dx$

76. $\displaystyle\int \frac{\sin x}{1 + \cos^2 x}\, dx$

77. $\displaystyle\int \frac{1 + x}{1 + x^2}\, dx$

78. $\displaystyle\int \frac{x}{1 + x^4}\, dx$

79. $\displaystyle\int_1^2 \frac{e^{1/x}}{x^2}\, dx$

80. $\displaystyle\int_0^1 xe^{-x^2}\, dx$

81. $\displaystyle\int_e^{e^4} \frac{dx}{x\sqrt{\ln x}}$

82. $\displaystyle\int_0^{1/2} \frac{\sin^{-1}x}{\sqrt{1 - x^2}}\, dx$

83. Use Exercise 66 to evaluate the integral

$$\int_0^\pi \frac{x\sin x}{1 + \cos^2 x}\, dx$$

5 Review

1. (a) Write an expression for a Riemann sum of a function f. Explain the meaning of the notation that you use.

  (b) If $f(x) \geq 0$, what is the geometric interpretation of a Riemann sum? Illustrate with a diagram.

  (c) If $f(x)$ takes on both positive and negative values, what is the geometric interpretation of a Riemann sum? Illustrate with a diagram.

2. (a) Write the definition of the definite integral of a continuous function from a to b.

  (b) What is the geometric interpretation of $\int_a^b f(x)\, dx$ if $f(x) \geq 0$?

  (c) What is the geometric interpretation of $\int_a^b f(x)\, dx$ if $f(x)$ takes on both positive and negative values? Illustrate with a diagram.

3. State both parts of the Fundamental Theorem of Calculus.

4. (a) State the Net Change Theorem.

  (b) If $r(t)$ is the rate at which water flows into a reservoir, what does $\int_{t_1}^{t_2} r(t)\, dt$ represent?

5. Suppose a particle moves back and forth along a straight line with velocity $v(t)$, measured in feet per second, and acceleration $a(t)$.

  (a) What is the meaning of $\int_{60}^{120} v(t)\, dt$?

  (b) What is the meaning of $\int_{60}^{120} |v(t)|\, dt$?

  (c) What is the meaning of $\int_{60}^{120} a(t)\, dt$?

6. (a) Explain the meaning of the indefinite integral $\int f(x)\, dx$.

  (b) What is the connection between the definite integral $\int_a^b f(x)\, dx$ and the indefinite integral $\int f(x)\, dx$?

7. Explain exactly what is meant by the statement that "differentiation and integration are inverse processes."

8. State the Substitution Rule. In practice, how do you use it?

Determine whether the statement is true or false. If it is true, explain why. If it is false, explain why or give an example that disproves the statement.

1. If f and g are continuous on $[a, b]$, then

$$\int_a^b [f(x) + g(x)]\, dx = \int_a^b f(x)\, dx + \int_a^b g(x)\, dx$$

2. If f and g are continuous on $[a, b]$, then

$$\int_a^b [f(x)g(x)]\, dx = \left(\int_a^b f(x)\, dx \right)\left(\int_a^b g(x)\, dx \right)$$

3. If f is continuous on $[a, b]$, then

$$\int_a^b 5f(x)\, dx = 5 \int_a^b f(x)\, dx$$

4. If f is continuous on $[a, b]$, then

$$\int_a^b x f(x)\, dx = x \int_a^b f(x)\, dx$$

5. If f is continuous on $[a, b]$ and $f(x) \geq 0$, then

$$\int_a^b \sqrt{f(x)}\, dx = \sqrt{\int_a^b f(x)\, dx}$$

6. If f' is continuous on $[1, 3]$, then $\int_1^3 f'(v)\, dv = f(3) - f(1)$.

7. If f and g are continuous and $f(x) \geq g(x)$ for $a \leq x \leq b$, then

$$\int_a^b f(x)\, dx \geq \int_a^b g(x)\, dx$$

8. If f and g are differentiable and $f(x) \geq g(x)$ for $a < x < b$, then $f'(x) \geq g'(x)$ for $a < x < b$.

9. $\displaystyle \int_{-1}^{1} \left(x^5 - 6x^9 + \frac{\sin x}{(1 + x^4)^2} \right) dx = 0$

10. $\displaystyle \int_{-5}^{5} (ax^2 + bx + c)\, dx = 2 \int_0^5 (ax^2 + c)\, dx$

11. $\displaystyle \int_{-2}^{1} \frac{1}{x^4}\, dx = -\frac{3}{8}$

12. $\int_0^2 (x - x^3)\, dx$ represents the area under the curve $y = x - x^3$ from 0 to 2.

13. All continuous functions have derivatives.

14. All continuous functions have antiderivatives.

- EXERCISES -

1. Use the given graph of f to find the Riemann sum with six subintervals. Take the sample points to be (a) left endpoints and (b) midpoints. In each case draw a diagram and explain what the Riemann sum represents.

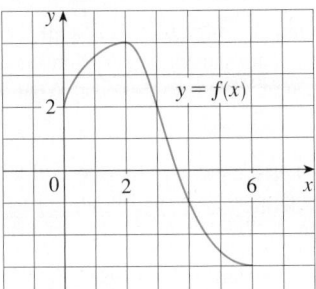

2. (a) Evaluate the Riemann sum for

$$f(x) = x^2 - x \qquad 0 \le x \le 2$$

with four subintervals, taking the sample points to be right endpoints. Explain, with the aid of a diagram, what the Riemann sum represents.

(b) Use the definition of a definite integral (with right endpoints) to calculate the value of the integral

$$\int_0^2 (x^2 - x)\, dx$$

(c) Use the Fundamental Theorem to check your answer to part (b).

(d) Draw a diagram to explain the geometric meaning of the integral in part (b).

3. Evaluate

$$\int_0^1 \left(x + \sqrt{1 - x^2} \right) dx$$

by interpreting it in terms of areas.

4. Express

$$\lim_{n \to \infty} \sum_{i=1}^n \sin x_i\, \Delta x$$

as a definite integral on the interval $[0, \pi]$ and then evaluate the integral.

5. If $\int_0^6 f(x)\, dx = 10$ and $\int_0^4 f(x)\, dx = 7$, find $\int_4^6 f(x)\, dx$.

CAS **6.** (a) Write $\int_1^5 (x + 2x^5)\, dx$ as a limit of Riemann sums, taking the sample points to be right endpoints. Use a computer algebra system to evaluate the sum and to compute the limit.

(b) Use the Fundamental Theorem to check your answer to part (a).

7. The figure shows the graphs of f, f', and $\int_0^x f(t)\, dt$. Identify each graph, and explain your choices.

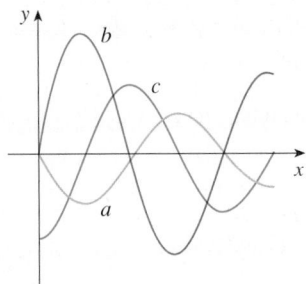

8. Evaluate:

(a) $\displaystyle \int_0^{\pi/2} \frac{d}{dx} \left(\sin \frac{x}{2} \cos \frac{x}{3} \right) dx$

(b) $\displaystyle \frac{d}{dx} \int_0^{\pi/2} \sin \frac{x}{2} \cos \frac{x}{3}\, dx$

(c) $\displaystyle \frac{d}{dx} \int_x^{\pi/2} \sin \frac{t}{2} \cos \frac{t}{3}\, dt$

9–28 ▏▏▏ Evaluate the integral, if it exists.

9. $\displaystyle \int_1^2 (8x^3 + 3x^2)\, dx$

10. $\displaystyle \int_0^T (x^4 - 8x + 7)\, dx$

11. $\displaystyle \int_0^1 (1 - x^9)\, dx$

12. $\displaystyle \int_0^1 (1 - x)^9\, dx$

13. $\displaystyle \int_1^9 \frac{\sqrt{u} - 2u^2}{u}\, du$

14. $\displaystyle \int_0^1 \left(\sqrt[4]{u} + 1 \right)^2 du$

15. $\displaystyle \int_0^1 y(y^2 + 1)^5\, dy$

16. $\displaystyle \int_0^2 y^2\sqrt{1 + y^3}\, dy$

17. $\displaystyle \int_1^5 \frac{dt}{(t - 4)^2}$

18. $\displaystyle \int_0^1 \sin(3\pi t)\, dt$

19. $\displaystyle \int_0^1 v^2 \cos(v^3)\, dv$

20. $\displaystyle \int_{-1}^1 \frac{\sin x}{1 + x^2}\, dx$

21. $\displaystyle \int \frac{x + 2}{\sqrt{x^2 + 4x}}\, dx$

22. $\displaystyle \int \csc^2 3t\, dt$

23. $\displaystyle \int \sin \pi t \cos \pi t\, dt$

24. $\displaystyle \int \sin x \cos(\cos x)\, dx$

25. $\displaystyle \int_0^{\pi/8} \sec 2\theta \tan 2\theta\, d\theta$

26. $\displaystyle \int_0^{\pi/4} (1 + \tan t)^3 \sec^2 t\, dt$

27. $\displaystyle \int_0^3 |x^2 - 4|\, dx$

28. $\displaystyle \int_0^4 |\sqrt{x} - 1|\, dx$

29–30 |||| Evaluate the indefinite integral. Illustrate and check that your answer is reasonable by graphing both the function and its antiderivative (take $C = 0$).

29. $\displaystyle\int \frac{\cos x}{\sqrt{1 + \sin x}}\, dx$

30. $\displaystyle\int \frac{x^3}{\sqrt{x^2 + 1}}\, dx$

31. Use a graph to give a rough estimate of the area of the region that lies under the curve $y = x\sqrt{x}$, $0 \le x \le 4$. Then find the exact area.

32. Graph the function $f(x) = \cos^2 x\, \sin^3 x$ and use the graph to guess the value of the integral $\int_0^{2\pi} f(x)\, dx$. Then evaluate the integral to confirm your guess.

33–38 |||| Find the derivative of the function.

33. $F(x) = \displaystyle\int_1^x \sqrt{1 + t^4}\, dt$

34. $F(x) = \displaystyle\int_\pi^x \tan(s^2)\, ds$

35. $g(x) = \displaystyle\int_0^{x^3} \frac{t}{\sqrt{1 + t^3}}\, dt$

36. $g(x) = \displaystyle\int_1^{\cos x} \sqrt[3]{1 - t^2}\, dt$

37. $y = \displaystyle\int_{\sqrt{x}}^x \frac{\cos\theta}{\theta}\, d\theta$

38. $y = \displaystyle\int_{2x}^{3x+1} \sin(t^4)\, dt$

39–40 |||| Use Property 8 of integrals to estimate the value of the integral.

39. $\displaystyle\int_1^3 \sqrt{x^2 + 3}\, dx$

40. $\displaystyle\int_3^5 \frac{1}{x + 1}\, dx$

41–42 |||| Use the properties of integrals to verify the inequality.

41. $\displaystyle\int_0^1 x^2 \cos x\, dx \le \frac{1}{3}$

42. $\displaystyle\int_{\pi/4}^{\pi/2} \frac{\sin x}{x}\, dx \le \frac{\sqrt{2}}{2}$

43. Use the Midpoint Rule with $n = 5$ to approximate $\int_0^1 \sqrt{1 + x^3}\, dx$.

44. A particle moves along a line with velocity function $v(t) = t^2 - t$, where v is measured in meters per second. Find (a) the displacement and (b) the distance traveled by the particle during the time interval $[0, 5]$.

45. Let $r(t)$ be the rate at which the world's oil is consumed, where t is measured in years starting at $t = 0$ on January 1, 2000, and $r(t)$ is measured in barrels per year. What does $\int_0^3 r(t)\, dt$ represent?

46. A radar gun was used to record the speed of a runner at the times given in the table. Use the Midpoint Rule to estimate the distance the runner covered during those 5 seconds.

t (s)	v (m/s)	t (s)	v (m/s)
0	0	3.0	10.51
0.5	4.67	3.5	10.67
1.0	7.34	4.0	10.76
1.5	8.86	4.5	10.81
2.0	9.73	5.0	10.81
2.5	10.22		

47. A population of honeybees increased at a rate of $r(t)$ bees per week, where the graph of r is as shown. Use the Midpoint Rule with six subintervals to estimate the increase in the bee population during the first 24 weeks.

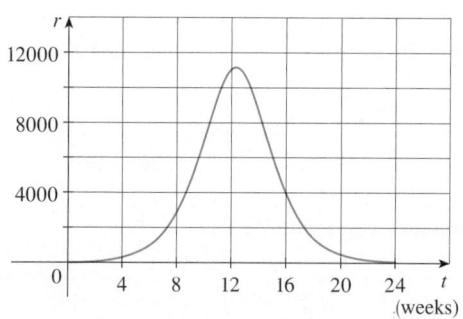

48. Let

$$f(x) = \begin{cases} -x - 1 & \text{if } -3 \le x \le 0 \\ -\sqrt{1 - x^2} & \text{if } 0 \le x \le 1 \end{cases}$$

Evaluate $\int_{-3}^1 f(x)\, dx$ by interpreting the integral as a difference of areas.

49. Find an antiderivative F of $f(x) = x^2 \sin(x^2)$ such that $F(1) = 0$.

50. The Fresnel function $S(x) = \int_0^x \sin\left(\frac{1}{2}\pi t^2\right) dt$ was introduced in Section 5.3. Fresnel also used the function

$$C(x) = \int_0^x \cos\left(\frac{1}{2}\pi t^2\right) dt$$

in his theory of the diffraction of light waves.

(a) On what intervals is C increasing?

(b) On what intervals is C concave upward?

CAS (c) Use a graph to solve the following equation correct to two decimal places:

$$\int_0^x \cos\left(\frac{1}{2}\pi t^2\right) dt = 0.7$$

CAS (d) Plot the graphs of C and S on the same screen. How are these graphs related?

51. If f is a continuous function such that

$$\int_0^x f(t) \, dt = x \sin x + \int_0^x \frac{f(t)}{1 + t^2} \, dt$$

for all x, find an explicit formula for $f(x)$.

52. Find a function f and a value of the constant a such that

$$2 \int_a^x f(t) \, dt = 2 \sin x - 1$$

53. If f' is continuous on $[a, b]$, show that

$$2 \int_a^b f(x) f'(x) \, dx = [f(b)]^2 - [f(a)]^2$$

54. Find $\lim\limits_{h \to 0} \dfrac{1}{h} \displaystyle\int_2^{2+h} \sqrt{1 + t^3} \, dt$.

55. If f is continuous on $[0, 1]$, prove that

$$\int_0^1 f(x) \, dx = \int_0^1 f(1 - x) \, dx$$

56. Evaluate

$$\lim_{n \to \infty} \frac{1}{n} \left[\left(\frac{1}{n}\right)^9 + \left(\frac{2}{n}\right)^9 + \left(\frac{3}{n}\right)^9 + \cdots + \left(\frac{n}{n}\right)^9 \right]$$

PROBLEMS PLUS

Before you look at the solution of the following example, cover it up and first try to solve the problem yourself.

EXAMPLE 1 Evaluate $\displaystyle\lim_{x\to 3}\left(\frac{x}{x-3}\int_3^x \frac{\sin t}{t}\,dt\right)$.

SOLUTION Let's start by having a preliminary look at the ingredients of the function. What happens to the first factor, $x/(x-3)$, when x approaches 3? The numerator approaches 3 and the denominator approaches 0, so we have

$$\frac{x}{x-3}\to\infty \quad\text{as}\quad x\to 3^+ \qquad\text{and}\qquad \frac{x}{x-3}\to-\infty \quad\text{as}\quad x\to 3^-$$

The second factor approaches $\int_3^3 (\sin t)/t\,dt$, which is 0. It's not clear what happens to the function as a whole. (One factor is becoming large while the other is becoming small.) So how do we proceed?

One of the principles of problem solving is *recognizing something familiar*. Is there a part of the function that reminds us of something we've seen before? Well, the integral

|||| The principles of problem solving are discussed on page 58.

$$\int_3^x \frac{\sin t}{t}\,dt$$

has x as its upper limit of integration and that type of integral occurs in Part 1 of the Fundamental Theorem of Calculus:

$$\frac{d}{dx}\int_a^x f(t)\,dt = f(x)$$

This suggests that differentiation might be involved.

Once we start thinking about differentiation, the denominator $(x-3)$ reminds us of something else that should be familiar: One of the forms of the definition of the derivative in Chapter 3 is

$$F'(a) = \lim_{x\to a}\frac{F(x)-F(a)}{x-a}$$

and with $a=3$ this becomes

$$F'(3) = \lim_{x\to 3}\frac{F(x)-F(3)}{x-3}$$

So what is the function F in our situation? Notice that if we define

$$F(x) = \int_3^x \frac{\sin t}{t}\,dt$$

then $F(3)=0$. What about the factor x in the numerator? That's just a red herring, so let's factor it out and put together the calculation:

$$\lim_{x\to 3}\left(\frac{x}{x-3}\int_3^x \frac{\sin t}{t}\,dt\right) = \lim_{x\to 3} x \cdot \lim_{x\to 3}\frac{\displaystyle\int_3^x \frac{\sin t}{t}\,dt}{x-3}$$

|||| Another approach is to use l'Hospital's Rule.

$$= 3\lim_{x\to 3}\frac{F(x)-F(3)}{x-3}$$

$$= 3F'(3)$$

$$= 3\,\frac{\sin 3}{3} \qquad \text{(FTC1)}$$

$$= \sin 3$$

||| PROBLEMS

1. If $x \sin \pi x = \int_0^{x^2} f(t)\, dt$, where f is a continuous function, find $f(4)$.

2. In this problem we approximate the sine function on the interval $[0, \pi]$ by three quadratic functions, each of which has the same zeros as the sine function on this interval.
   (a) Find a quadratic function f such that $f(0) = f(\pi) = 0$ and which has the same maximum value as sin on $[0, \pi]$.
   (b) Find a quadratic function g such that $g(0) = g(\pi) = 0$ and which has the same rate of change as the sine function at 0 and π.
   (c) Find a quadratic function h such that $h(0) = h(\pi) = 0$ and the area under h from 0 to π is the same as for the sine function.
   (d) Illustrate by graphing f, g, h, and the sine function in the same viewing rectangle $[0, \pi]$ by $[0, 1]$. Identify which graph belongs to each function.

3. Show that $\dfrac{1}{17} \leq \displaystyle\int_1^2 \dfrac{1}{1 + x^4}\, dx \leq \dfrac{7}{24}$.

4. Suppose the curve $y = f(x)$ passes through the origin and the point $(1, 1)$. Find the value of the integral $\int_0^1 f'(x)\, dx$.

5. Find a function f such that $f(1) = -1$, $f(4) = 7$, and $f'(x) > 3$ for all x, or prove that such a function cannot exist.

6. (a) Graph several members of the family of functions $f(x) = (2cx - x^2)/c^3$ for $c > 0$ and look at the regions enclosed by these curves and the x-axis. Make a conjecture about how the areas of these regions are related.
   (b) Prove your conjecture in part (a).
   (c) Take another look at the graphs in part (a) and use them to sketch the curve traced out by the vertices (highest points) of the family of functions. Can you guess what kind of curve this is?
   (d) Find the equation of the curve you sketched in part (c).

7. If $f(x) = \displaystyle\int_0^{g(x)} \dfrac{1}{\sqrt{1 + t^3}}\, dt$, where $g(x) = \displaystyle\int_0^{\cos x} [1 + \sin(t^2)]\, dt$, find $f'(\pi/2)$.

8. If $f(x) = \int_0^x x^2 \sin(t^2)\, dt$, find $f'(x)$.

9. Find the interval $[a, b]$ for which the value of the integral $\int_a^b (2 + x - x^2)\, dx$ is a maximum.

10. Use an integral to estimate the sum $\displaystyle\sum_{i=1}^{10000} \sqrt{i}$.

11. (a) Evaluate $\int_0^n [\![x]\!]\, dx$, where n is a positive integer.
    (b) Evaluate $\int_a^b [\![x]\!]\, dx$, where a and b are real numbers with $0 \leq a < b$.

12. Find $\dfrac{d^2}{dx^2} \displaystyle\int_0^x \left(\int_1^{\sin t} \sqrt{1 + u^4}\, du \right) dt$.

13. If f is a differentiable function such that $\int_0^x f(t)\, dt = [f(x)]^2$ for all x, find f.

14. A circular disk of radius r is used in an evaporator and is rotated in a vertical plane. If it is to be partially submerged in the liquid so as to maximize the exposed wetted area of the disk, show that the center of the disk should be positioned at a height $r/\sqrt{1 + \pi^2}$ above the surface of the liquid.

15. Prove that if f is continuous, then $\int_0^x f(u)(x - u)\, du = \int_0^x \left(\int_0^u f(t)\, dt \right) du$.

16. The figure shows a region consisting of all points inside a square that are closer to the center than to the sides of the square. Find the area of the region.

17. Evaluate $\displaystyle\lim_{n \to \infty} \left(\dfrac{1}{\sqrt{n}\sqrt{n+1}} + \dfrac{1}{\sqrt{n}\sqrt{n+2}} + \cdots + \dfrac{1}{\sqrt{n}\sqrt{n+n}} \right)$.

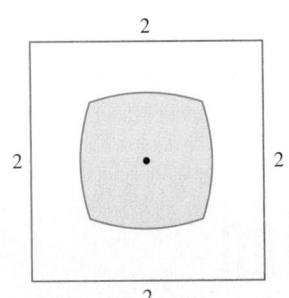

2
2   2
2

FIGURE FOR PROBLEM 16

CHAPTER 6

The volume of a sphere is the
limit of sums of volumes of
approximating cylinders.

Applications of Integration

In this chapter we explore some of the applications of the definite integral by using it to compute areas between curves, volumes of solids, and the work done by a varying force. The common theme is the following general method, which is similar to the one we used to find areas under curves: We break up a quantity Q into a large number of small parts. We next approximate each small part by a quantity of the form $f(x_i^*)\Delta x$ and thus approximate Q by a Riemann sum. Then we take the limit and express Q as an integral. Finally we evaluate the integral using the Fundamental Theorem of Calculus or the Midpoint Rule.

6.1 Areas between Curves

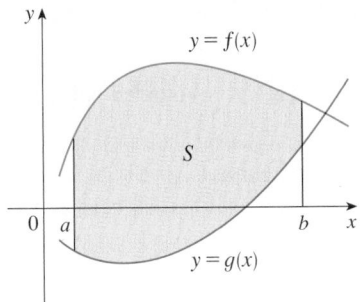

FIGURE 1
$S = \{(x, y) \mid a \leqslant x \leqslant b, g(x) \leqslant y \leqslant f(x)\}$

In Chapter 5 we defined and calculated areas of regions that lie under the graphs of functions. Here we use integrals to find areas of regions that lie between the graphs of two functions.

Consider the region S that lies between two curves $y = f(x)$ and $y = g(x)$ and between the vertical lines $x = a$ and $x = b$, where f and g are continuous functions and $f(x) \geqslant g(x)$ for all x in $[a, b]$. (See Figure 1.)

Just as we did for areas under curves in Section 5.1, we divide S into n strips of equal width and then we approximate the ith strip by a rectangle with base Δx and height $f(x_i^*) - g(x_i^*)$. (See Figure 2. If we like, we could take all of the sample points to be right endpoints, in which case $x_i^* = x_i$.) The Riemann sum

$$\sum_{i=1}^{n} [f(x_i^*) - g(x_i^*)]\Delta x$$

is therefore an approximation to what we intuitively think of as the area of S.

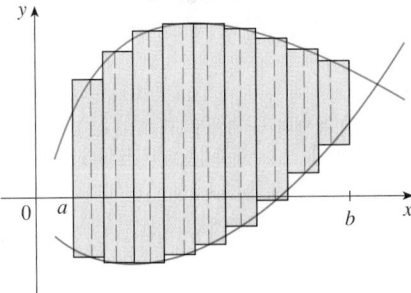

FIGURE 2   (a) Typical rectangle   (b) Approximating rectangles

This approximation appears to become better and better as $n \to \infty$. Therefore, we define the **area** A of S as the limiting value of the sum of the areas of these approximating rectangles.

$$\boxed{1} \qquad A = \lim_{n \to \infty} \sum_{i=1}^{n} [f(x_i^*) - g(x_i^*)]\Delta x$$

We recognize the limit in (1) as the definite integral of $f - g$. Therefore, we have the following formula for area.

---

2 The area A of the region bounded by the curves $y = f(x)$, $y = g(x)$, and the lines $x = a$, $x = b$, where f and g are continuous and $f(x) \geq g(x)$ for all x in $[a, b]$, is

$$A = \int_a^b [f(x) - g(x)]\, dx$$

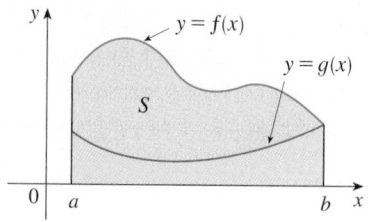

FIGURE 3

$$A = \int_a^b f(x)\, dx - \int_a^b g(x)\, dx$$

Notice that in the special case where $g(x) = 0$, S is the region under the graph of f and our general definition of area (1) reduces to our previous definition (Definition 2 in Section 5.1).

In the case where both f and g are positive, you can see from Figure 3 why (2) is true:

$$A = [\text{area under } y = f(x)] - [\text{area under } y = g(x)]$$

$$= \int_a^b f(x)\, dx - \int_a^b g(x)\, dx = \int_a^b [f(x) - g(x)]\, dx$$

EXAMPLE 1 Find the area of the region bounded above by $y = x^2 + 1$, bounded below by $y = x$, and bounded on the sides by $x = 0$ and $x = 1$.

SOLUTION The region is shown in Figure 4. The upper boundary curve is $y = x^2 + 1$ and the lower boundary curve is $y = x$. So we use the area formula (2) with $f(x) = x^2 + 1$, $g(x) = x$, $a = 0$, and $b = 1$:

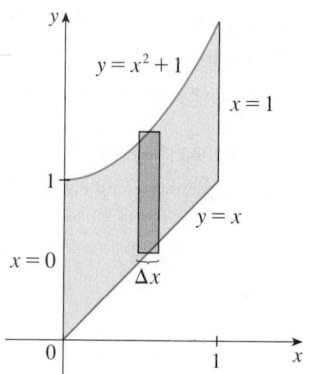

FIGURE 4

$$A = \int_0^1 [(x^2 + 1) - x]\, dx = \int_0^1 (x^2 - x + 1)\, dx$$

$$= \frac{x^3}{3} - \frac{x^2}{2} + x \Big]_0^1 = \frac{1}{3} - \frac{1}{2} + 1 = \frac{5}{6}$$

In Figure 4 we drew a typical approximating rectangle with width Δx as a reminder of the procedure by which the area is defined in (1). In general, when we set up an integral for an area, it's helpful to sketch the region to identify the top curve y_T, the bottom curve y_B, and a typical approximating rectangle as in Figure 5. Then the area of a typical rectangle is $(y_T - y_B)\, \Delta x$ and the equation

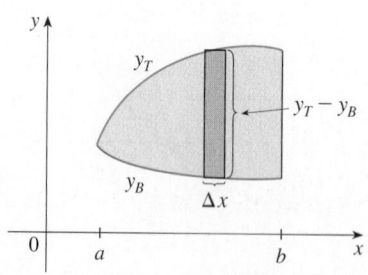

FIGURE 5

$$A = \lim_{n \to \infty} \sum_{i=1}^n (y_T - y_B)\, \Delta x = \int_a^b (y_T - y_B)\, dx$$

summarizes the procedure of adding (in a limiting sense) the areas of all the typical rectangles.

Notice that in Figure 5 the left-hand boundary reduces to a point, whereas in Figure 3 the right-hand boundary reduces to a point. In the next example both of the side boundaries reduce to a point, so the first step is to find a and b.

EXAMPLE 2 Find the area of the region enclosed by the parabolas $y = x^2$ and $y = 2x - x^2$.

SOLUTION We first find the points of intersection of the parabolas by solving their equations simultaneously. This gives $x^2 = 2x - x^2$, or $2x^2 - 2x = 0$. Thus $2x(x - 1) = 0$, so $x = 0$ or 1. The points of intersection are $(0, 0)$ and $(1, 1)$.

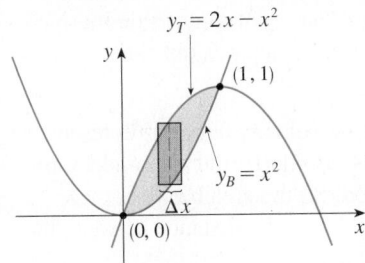

FIGURE 6

We see from Figure 6 that the top and bottom boundaries are

$$y_T = 2x - x^2 \quad \text{and} \quad y_B = x^2$$

The area of a typical rectangle is

$$(y_T - y_B)\,\Delta x = (2x - x^2 - x^2)\,\Delta x$$

and the region lies between $x = 0$ and $x = 1$. So the total area is

$$A = \int_0^1 (2x - 2x^2)\,dx = 2\int_0^1 (x - x^2)\,dx$$

$$= 2\left[\frac{x^2}{2} - \frac{x^3}{3}\right]_0^1$$

$$= 2\left(\frac{1}{2} - \frac{1}{3}\right) = \frac{1}{3}$$

Sometimes it's difficult, or even impossible, to find the points of intersection of two curves exactly. As shown in the following example, we can use a graphing calculator or computer to find approximate values for the intersection points and then proceed as before.

EXAMPLE 3 Find the approximate area of the region bounded by the curves $y = x/\sqrt{x^2 + 1}$ and $y = x^4 - x$.

SOLUTION If we were to try to find the exact intersection points, we would have to solve the equation

$$\frac{x}{\sqrt{x^2 + 1}} = x^4 - x$$

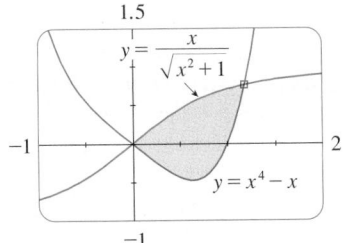

FIGURE 7

This looks like a very difficult equation to solve exactly (in fact, it's impossible), so instead we use a graphing device to draw the graphs of the two curves in Figure 7. One intersection point is the origin. We zoom in toward the other point of intersection and find that $x \approx 1.18$. (If greater accuracy is required, we could use Newton's method or a rootfinder, if available on our graphing device.) Thus, an approximation to the area between the curves is

$$A \approx \int_0^{1.18} \left[\frac{x}{\sqrt{x^2 + 1}} - (x^4 - x)\right]dx$$

To integrate the first term we use the subsitution $u = x^2 + 1$. Then $du = 2x\,dx$, and when $x = 1.18$, we have $u \approx 2.39$. So

$$A \approx \frac{1}{2}\int_1^{2.39} \frac{du}{\sqrt{u}} - \int_0^{1.18} (x^4 - x)\,dx$$

$$= \sqrt{u}\,\Big]_1^{2.39} - \left[\frac{x^5}{5} - \frac{x^2}{2}\right]_0^{1.18}$$

$$= \sqrt{2.39} - 1 - \frac{(1.18)^5}{5} + \frac{(1.18)^2}{2}$$

$$\approx 0.785$$

FIGURE 8

EXAMPLE 4 Figure 8 shows velocity curves for two cars, A and B, that start side by side and move along the same road. What does the area between the curves represent? Use the Midpoint Rule to estimate it.

SOLUTION We know from Section 5.4 that the area under the velocity curve A represents the distance traveled by car A during the first 16 seconds. Similarly, the area under curve B is the distance traveled by car B during that time period. So the area between these curves, which is the difference of the areas under the curves, is the distance between the cars after 16 seconds. We read the velocities from the graph and convert them to feet per second ($1 \text{ mi/h} = \frac{5280}{3600} \text{ ft/s}$).

t	0	2	4	6	8	10	12	14	16
v_A	0	34	54	67	76	84	89	92	95
v_B	0	21	34	44	51	56	60	63	65
$v_A - v_B$	0	13	20	23	25	28	29	29	30

We use the Midpoint Rule with $n = 4$ intervals, so that $\Delta t = 4$. The midpoints of the intervals are $\bar{t}_1 = 2$, $\bar{t}_2 = 6$, $\bar{t}_3 = 10$, and $\bar{t}_4 = 14$. We estimate the distance between the cars after 16 seconds as follows:

$$\int_0^{16} (v_A - v_B) \, dt \approx \Delta t \, [13 + 23 + 28 + 29]$$

$$= 4(93) = 372 \text{ ft}$$

If we are asked to find the area between the curves $y = f(x)$ and $y = g(x)$ where $f(x) \geq g(x)$ for some values of x but $g(x) \geq f(x)$ for other values of x, then we split the given region S into several regions $S_1, S_2, \ldots$ with areas $A_1, A_2, \ldots$ as shown in Figure 9. We then define the area of the region S to be the sum of the areas of the smaller regions $S_1, S_2, \ldots$, that is, $A = A_1 + A_2 + \cdots$. Since

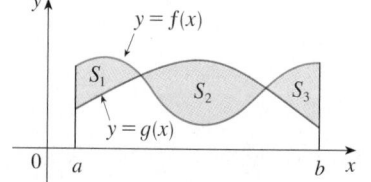

FIGURE 9

$$|f(x) - g(x)| = \begin{cases} f(x) - g(x) & \text{when } f(x) \geq g(x) \\ g(x) - f(x) & \text{when } g(x) \geq f(x) \end{cases}$$

we have the following expression for A.

3 The area between the curves $y = f(x)$ and $y = g(x)$ and between $x = a$ and $x = b$ is

$$A = \int_a^b |f(x) - g(x)| \, dx$$

When evaluating the integral in (3), however, we must still split it into integrals corresponding to $A_1, A_2, \ldots$.

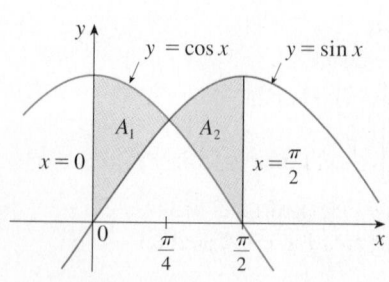

FIGURE 10

EXAMPLE 5 Find the area of the region bounded by the curves $y = \sin x$, $y = \cos x$, $x = 0$, and $x = \pi/2$.

SOLUTION The points of intersection occur when $\sin x = \cos x$, that is, when $x = \pi/4$ (since $0 \leq x \leq \pi/2$). The region is sketched in Figure 10. Observe that $\cos x \geq \sin x$

when $0 \le x \le \pi/4$ but $\sin x \ge \cos x$ when $\pi/4 \le x \le \pi/2$. Therefore, the required area is

$$A = \int_0^{\pi/2} |\cos x - \sin x| \, dx = A_1 + A_2$$

$$= \int_0^{\pi/4} (\cos x - \sin x) \, dx + \int_{\pi/4}^{\pi/2} (\sin x - \cos x) \, dx$$

$$= [\sin x + \cos x]_0^{\pi/4} + [-\cos x - \sin x]_{\pi/4}^{\pi/2}$$

$$= \left(\frac{1}{\sqrt{2}} + \frac{1}{\sqrt{2}} - 0 - 1 \right) + \left(-0 - 1 + \frac{1}{\sqrt{2}} + \frac{1}{\sqrt{2}} \right)$$

$$= 2\sqrt{2} - 2$$

In this particular example we could have saved some work by noticing that the region is symmetric about $x = \pi/4$ and so

$$A = 2A_1 = 2 \int_0^{\pi/4} (\cos x - \sin x) \, dx$$

Some regions are best treated by regarding x as a function of y. If a region is bounded by curves with equations $x = f(y)$, $x = g(y)$, $y = c$, and $y = d$, where f and g are continuous and $f(y) \ge g(y)$ for $c \le y \le d$ (see Figure 11), then its area is

$$A = \int_c^d [f(y) - g(y)] \, dy$$

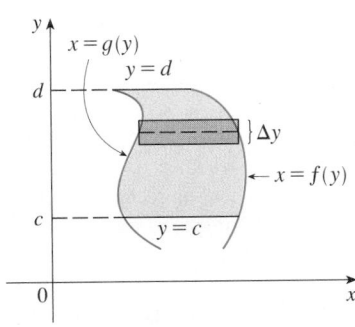

FIGURE 11   **FIGURE 12**

If we write x_R for the right boundary and x_L for the left boundary, then, as Figure 12 illustrates, we have

$$A = \int_c^d (x_R - x_L) \, dy$$

Here a typical approximating rectangle has dimensions $x_R - x_L$ and Δy.

EXAMPLE 6 Find the area enclosed by the line $y = x - 1$ and the parabola $y^2 = 2x + 6$.

SOLUTION By solving the two equations we find that the points of intersection are $(-1, -2)$ and $(5, 4)$. We solve the equation of the parabola for x and notice from Figure 13 that the left and right boundary curves are

$$x_L = \tfrac{1}{2} y^2 - 3 \qquad x_R = y + 1$$

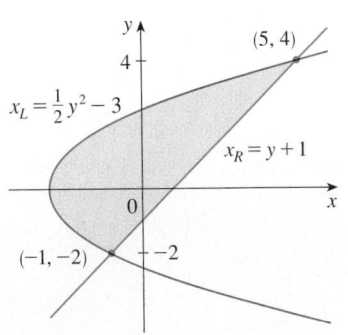

FIGURE 13

We must integrate between the appropriate y-values, $y = -2$ and $y = 4$. Thus

$$A = \int_{-2}^{4} (x_R - x_L)\,dy = \int_{-2}^{4} \left[(y+1) - \left(\tfrac{1}{2}y^2 - 3\right)\right] dy$$

$$= \int_{-2}^{4} \left(-\tfrac{1}{2}y^2 + y + 4\right) dy = -\frac{1}{2}\left(\frac{y^3}{3}\right) + \frac{y^2}{2} + 4y \Big]_{-2}^{4}$$

$$= -\tfrac{1}{6}(64) + 8 + 16 - \left(\tfrac{4}{3} + 2 - 8\right) = 18$$

We could have found the area in Example 6 by integrating with respect to x instead of y, but the calculation is much more involved. It would have meant splitting the region in two and computing the areas labeled A_1 and A_2 in Figure 14. The method we used in Example 6 is *much* easier.

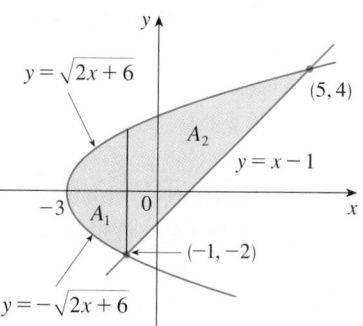

FIGURE 14

6.1 Exercises

1–4 |||| Find the area of the shaded region.

1.

2.

3.

4.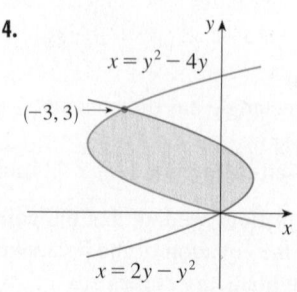

5–26 |||| Sketch the region enclosed by the given curves. Decide whether to integrate with respect to x or y. Draw a typical approximating rectangle and label its height and width. Then find the area of the region.

5. $y = x + 1$, $y = 9 - x^2$, $x = -1$, $x = 2$

6. $y = \sin x$, $y = x$, $x = \pi/2$, $x = \pi$

7. $y = x$, $y = x^2$

8. $y = x^2$, $y = x^4$

9. $y = \sqrt{x+3}$, $y = (x+3)/2$

10. $y = 1 + \sqrt{x}$, $y = (3+x)/3$

11. $y = x^2$, $y^2 = x$

12. $y = x$, $y = \sqrt[3]{x}$

13. $y = 12 - x^2$, $y = x^2 - 6$

14. $y = x^3 - x$, $y = 3x$

15. $y = \sqrt{x}$, $y = \tfrac{1}{2}x$, $x = 9$

16. $y = 8 - x^2$, $y = x^2$, $x = -3$, $x = 3$

17. $x = 2y^2$, $x + y = 1$

18. $4x + y^2 = 12$, $x = y$

19. $x = 1 - y^2$, $x = y^2 - 1$

20. $y = \sin(\pi x/2)$, $y = x$

21. $y = \cos x$, $y = \sin 2x$, $x = 0$, $x = \pi/2$

22. $y = \sin x$, $y = \sin 2x$, $x = 0$, $x = \pi/2$

23. $y = \cos x$, $y = 1 - 2x/\pi$

24. $y = |x|$, $y = x^2 - 2$

25. $y = x$, $x + 2y = 0$, $2x + y = 3$

26. $y = \sin \pi x$, $y = x^2 - x$, $x = 2$

27–28 ||| Use calculus to find the area of the triangle with the given vertices.

27. $(0, 0)$, $(2, 1)$, $(-1, 6)$

28. $(0, 5)$, $(2, -2)$, $(5, 1)$

29–30 ||| Evaluate the integral and interpret it as the area of a region. Sketch the region.

29. $\int_{-1}^{1} |x^3 - x| \, dx$

30. $\int_{0}^{4} |\sqrt{x + 2} - x| \, dx$

31–32 ||| Use the Midpoint Rule with $n = 4$ to approximate the area of the region bounded by the given curves.

31. $y = \sin^2(\pi x/4)$, $y = \cos^2(\pi x/4)$, $0 \le x \le 1$

32. $y = \sqrt[3]{16 - x^3}$, $y = x$, $x = 0$

33–36 ||| Use a graph to find approximate x-coordinates of the points of intersection of the given curves. Then find (approximately) the area of the region bounded by the curves.

33. $y = x^2$, $y = 2 \cos x$

34. $y = x^4$, $y = 3x - x^3$

35. $y = \sqrt{x + 1}$, $y = x^2$

36. $y = x^4 - 1$, $y = x \sin(x^2)$

CAS 37. Use a computer algebra system to find the exact area enclosed by the curves $y = x^5 - 6x^3 + 4x$ and $y = x$.

38. Sketch the region in the xy-plane defined by the inequalities $x - 2y^2 \ge 0$, $1 - x - |y| \ge 0$ and find its area.

39. Racing cars driven by Chris and Kelly are side by side at the start of a race. The table shows the velocities of each car (in miles per hour) during the first ten seconds of the race. Use the Midpoint Rule to estimate how much farther Kelly travels than Chris does during the first ten seconds.

t	v_C	v_K	t	v_C	v_K
0	0	0	6	69	80
1	20	22	7	75	86
2	32	37	8	81	93
3	46	52	9	86	98
4	54	61	10	90	102
5	62	71			

40. The widths (in meters) of a kidney-shaped swimming pool were measured at 2-meter intervals as indicated in the figure. Use the Midpoint Rule to estimate the area of the pool.

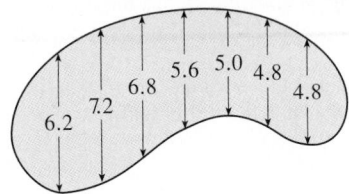

41. Two cars, A and B, start side by side and accelerate from rest. The figure shows the graphs of their velocity functions.
(a) Which car is ahead after one minute? Explain.
(b) What is the meaning of the area of the shaded region?
(c) Which car is ahead after two minutes? Explain.
(d) Estimate the time at which the cars are again side by side.

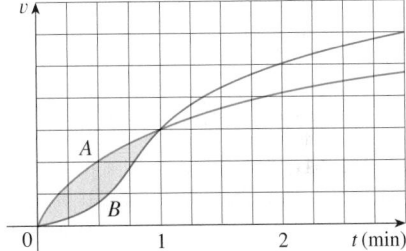

42. The figure shows graphs of the marginal revenue function R' and the marginal cost function C' for a manufacturer. [Recall from Section 4.8 that $R(x)$ and $C(x)$ represent the revenue and cost when x units are manufactured. Assume that R and C are measured in thousands of dollars.] What is the meaning of the area of the shaded region? Use the Midpoint Rule to estimate the value of this quantity.

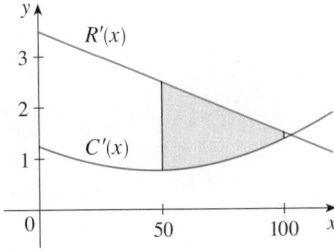

43. The curve with equation $y^2 = x^2(x + 3)$ is called **Tschirn-hausen's cubic**. If you graph this curve you will see that part of the curve forms a loop. Find the area enclosed by the loop.

44. Find the area of the region bounded by the parabola $y = x^2$, the tangent line to this parabola at $(1, 1)$, and the x-axis.

45. Find the number b such that the line $y = b$ divides the region bounded by the curves $y = x^2$ and $y = 4$ into two regions with equal area.

46. (a) Find the number a such that the line $x = a$ bisects the area under the curve $y = 1/x^2$, $1 \le x \le 4$.
(b) Find the number b such that the line $y = b$ bisects the area in part (a).

47. Find the values of c such that the area of the region enclosed by the parabolas $y = x^2 - c^2$ and $y = c^2 - x^2$ is 576.

48. Suppose that $0 < c < \pi/2$. For what value of c is the area of the region enclosed by the curves $y = \cos x$, $y = \cos(x - c)$, and $x = 0$ equal to the area of the region enclosed by the curves $y = \cos(x - c)$, $x = \pi$, and $y = 0$?

The following exercises are intended only for those who have already covered Chapter 7.

49–51 ||| Sketch the region bounded by the given curves and find the area of the region.

49. $y = 1/x$, $y = 1/x^2$, $x = 2$

50. $y = \sin x$, $y = e^x$, $x = 0$, $x = \pi/2$

51. $y = x^2$, $y = 2/(x^2 + 1)$

52. For what values of m do the line $y = mx$ and the curve $y = x/(x^2 + 1)$ enclose a region? Find the area of the region.

6.2 Volumes

In trying to find the volume of a solid we face the same type of problem as in finding areas. We have an intuitive idea of what volume means, but we must make this idea precise by using calculus to give an exact definition of volume.

We start with a simple type of solid called a **cylinder** (or, more precisely, a *right cylinder*). As illustrated in Figure 1(a), a cylinder is bounded by a plane region B_1, called the **base**, and a congruent region B_2 in a parallel plane. The cylinder consists of all points on line segments that are perpendicular to the base and join B_1 to B_2. If the area of the base is A and the height of the cylinder (the distance from B_1 to B_2) is h, then the volume V of the cylinder is defined as

$$V = Ah$$

In particular, if the base is a circle with radius r, then the cylinder is a circular cylinder with volume $V = \pi r^2 h$ [see Figure 1(b)], and if the base is a rectangle with length l and width w, then the cylinder is a rectangular box (also called a *rectangular parallelepiped*) with volume $V = lwh$ [see Figure 1(c)].

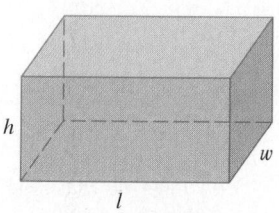

FIGURE 1

(a) Cylinder
$V = Ah$

(b) Circular cylinder
$V = \pi r^2 h$

(c) Rectangular box
$V = lwh$

For a solid S that isn't a cylinder we first "cut" S into pieces and approximate each piece by a cylinder. We estimate the volume of S by adding the volumes of the cylinders. We arrive at the exact volume of S through a limiting process in which the number of pieces becomes large.

We start by intersecting S with a plane and obtaining a plane region that is called a **cross-section** of S. Let $A(x)$ be the area of the cross-section of S in a plane P_x perpendicular to the x-axis and passing through the point x, where $a \le x \le b$. (See Figure 2. Think of slicing S with a knife through x and computing the area of this slice.) The cross-sectional area $A(x)$ will vary as x increases from a to b.

Watch an animation of Figure 2.
Resources / Module 7
/ Volumes
/ Volumes by Cross-Section

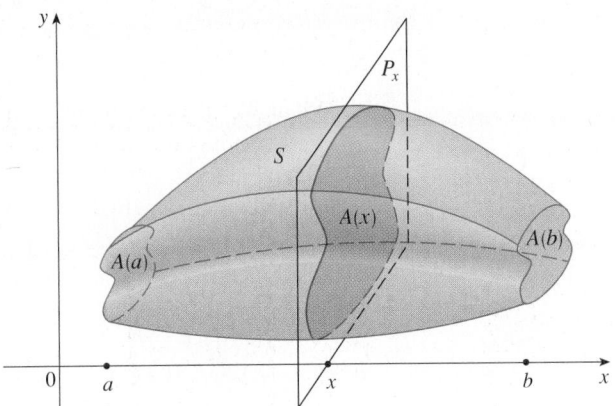

FIGURE 2

Let's divide S into n "slabs" of equal width Δx by using the planes P_{x_1}, P_{x_2}, . . . to slice the solid. (Think of slicing a loaf of bread.) If we choose sample points x_i^* in $[x_{i-1}, x_i]$, we can approximate the ith slab S_i (the part of S that lies between the planes $P_{x_{i-1}}$ and P_{x_i}) by a cylinder with base area $A(x_i^*)$ and "height" Δx. (See Figure 3.)

FIGURE 3

The volume of this cylinder is $A(x_i^*)\,\Delta x$, so an approximation to our intuitive conception of the volume of the ith slab S_i is

$$V(S_i) \approx A(x_i^*)\,\Delta x$$

Adding the volumes of these slabs, we get an approximation to the total volume (that is, what we think of intuitively as the volume):

$$V \approx \sum_{i=1}^{n} A(x_i^*)\,\Delta x$$

This approximation appears to become better and better as $n \to \infty$. (Think of the slices as becoming thinner and thinner.) Therefore, we *define* the volume as the limit of these sums as $n \to \infty$. But we recognize the limit of Riemann sums as a definite integral and so we have the following definition.

|||| It can be proved that this definition is independent of how S is situated with respect to the x-axis. In other words, no matter how we slice S with parallel planes, we always get the same answer for V.

Definition of Volume Let S be a solid that lies between $x = a$ and $x = b$. If the cross-sectional area of S in the plane P_x, through x and perpendicular to the x-axis, is $A(x)$, where A is a continuous function, then the **volume** of S is

$$V = \lim_{n \to \infty} \sum_{i=1}^{n} A(x_i^*) \, \Delta x = \int_a^b A(x) \, dx$$

When we use the volume formula $V = \int_a^b A(x) \, dx$ it is important to remember that $A(x)$ is the area of a moving cross-section obtained by slicing through x perpendicular to the x-axis.

Notice that, for a cylinder, the cross-sectional area is constant: $A(x) = A$ for all x. So our definition of volume gives $V = \int_a^b A \, dx = A(b - a)$; this agrees with the formula $V = Ah$.

EXAMPLE 1 Show that the volume of a sphere of radius r is

$$V = \tfrac{4}{3} \pi r^3$$

SOLUTION If we place the sphere so that its center is at the origin (see Figure 4), then the plane P_x intersects the sphere in a circle whose radius (from the Pythagorean Theorem) is $y = \sqrt{r^2 - x^2}$. So the cross-sectional area is

$$A(x) = \pi y^2 = \pi (r^2 - x^2)$$

Using the definition of volume with $a = -r$ and $b = r$, we have

$$V = \int_{-r}^{r} A(x) \, dx = \int_{-r}^{r} \pi (r^2 - x^2) \, dx$$

$$= 2\pi \int_0^r (r^2 - x^2) \, dx \qquad \text{(The integrand is even.)}$$

$$= 2\pi \left[r^2 x - \frac{x^3}{3} \right]_0^r = 2\pi \left(r^3 - \frac{r^3}{3} \right)$$

$$= \tfrac{4}{3} \pi r^3$$

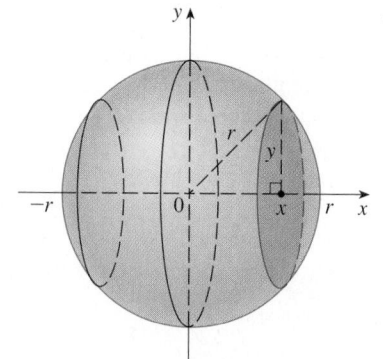

FIGURE 4

Watch an animation of Figure 5.
Resources / Module 7
/ Volumes
/ Volumes

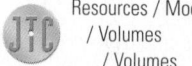

Figure 5 illustrates the definition of volume when the solid is a sphere with radius $r = 1$. From the result of Example 1, we know that the volume of the sphere is $\frac{4}{3} \pi \approx 4.18879$. Here the slabs are circular cylinders, or *disks*, and the three parts of Figure 5

(a) Using 5 disks, $V \approx 4.2726$ (b) Using 10 disks, $V \approx 4.2097$ (c) Using 20 disks, $V \approx 4.1940$

FIGURE 5 Approximating the volume of a sphere with radius 1 show the geometric interpretations of the Riemann sums

$$\sum_{i=1}^{n} A(\bar{x}_i)\, \Delta x = \sum_{i=1}^{n} \pi(1^2 - \bar{x}_i^2)\, \Delta x$$

when $n = 5$, 10, and 20 if we choose the sample points x_i^* to be the midpoints $\bar{x}_i$. Notice that as we increase the number of approximating cylinders, the corresponding Riemann sums become closer to the true volume.

EXAMPLE 2 Find the volume of the solid obtained by rotating about the x-axis the region under the curve $y = \sqrt{x}$ from 0 to 1. Illustrate the definition of volume by sketching a typical approximating cylinder.

SOLUTION The region is shown in Figure 6(a). If we rotate about the x-axis, we get the solid shown in Figure 6(b). When we slice through the point x, we get a disk with radius $\sqrt{x}$. The area of this cross-section is

$$A(x) = \pi\left(\sqrt{x}\right)^2 = \pi x$$

and the volume of the approximating cylinder (a disk with thickness Δx) is

$$A(x)\, \Delta x = \pi x\, \Delta x$$

The solid lies between $x = 0$ and $x = 1$, so its volume is

$$V = \int_0^1 A(x)\, dx = \int_0^1 \pi x\, dx = \pi \frac{x^2}{2}\bigg]_0^1 = \frac{\pi}{2}$$

|||| Did we get a reasonable answer in Example 2? As a check on our work, let's replace the given region by a square with base $[0, 1]$ and height 1. If we rotate this square, we get a cylinder with radius 1, height 1, and volume $\pi \cdot 1^2 \cdot 1 = \pi$. We computed that the given solid has half this volume. That seems about right.

See a volume of revolution being formed.
Resources / Module 7
/ Volumes
/ Volumes of Revolution

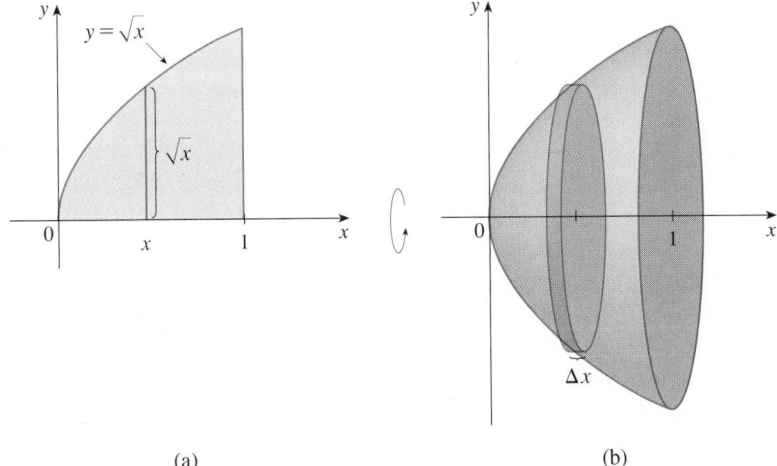

FIGURE 6

(a)   (b)

EXAMPLE 3 Find the volume of the solid obtained by rotating the region bounded by $y = x^3$, $y = 8$, and $x = 0$ about the y-axis.

SOLUTION The region is shown in Figure 7(a) and the resulting solid is shown in Figure 7(b). Because the region is rotated about the y-axis, it makes sense to slice the solid perpendicular to the y-axis and therefore to integrate with respect to y. If we slice at height y, we get a circular disk with radius x, where $x = \sqrt[3]{y}$. So the area of a cross-section through y is

$$A(y) = \pi x^2 = \pi\left(\sqrt[3]{y}\right)^2 = \pi y^{2/3}$$

and the volume of the approximating cylinder pictured in Figure 7(b) is

$$A(y) \, \Delta y = \pi y^{2/3} \, \Delta y$$

Since the solid lies between $y = 0$ and $y = 8$, its volume is

$$V = \int_0^8 A(y) \, dy = \int_0^8 \pi y^{2/3} \, dy$$

$$= \pi \left[\tfrac{3}{5} y^{5/3} \right]_0^8 = \frac{96\pi}{5}$$

 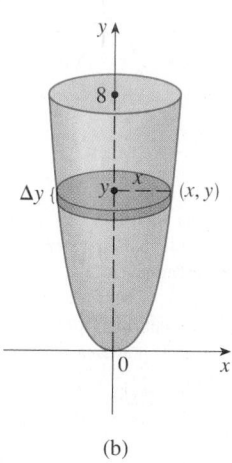

FIGURE 7
  (a)   (b)

EXAMPLE 4 The region $\mathcal{R}$ enclosed by the curves $y = x$ and $y = x^2$ is rotated about the x-axis. Find the volume of the resulting solid.

SOLUTION The curves $y = x$ and $y = x^2$ intersect at the points $(0, 0)$ and $(1, 1)$. The region between them, the solid of rotation, and a cross-section perpendicular to the x-axis are shown in Figure 8. A cross-section in the plane P_x has the shape of a *washer* (an annular ring) with inner radius x^2 and outer radius x, so we find the cross-sectional area by subtracting the area of the inner circle from the area of the outer circle:

$$A(x) = \pi x^2 - \pi (x^2)^2 = \pi (x^2 - x^4)$$

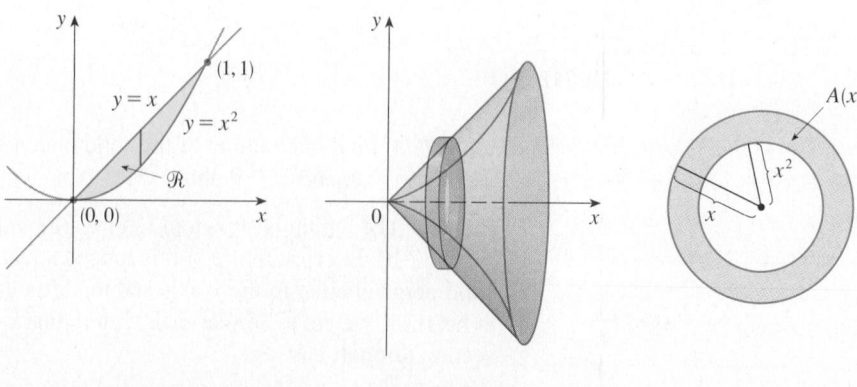

FIGURE 8
  (a)   (b)   (c)

Therefore, we have

$$V = \int_0^1 A(x)\, dx = \int_0^1 \pi(x^2 - x^4)\, dx$$

$$= \pi \left[\frac{x^3}{3} - \frac{x^5}{5} \right]_0^1 = \frac{2\pi}{15}$$

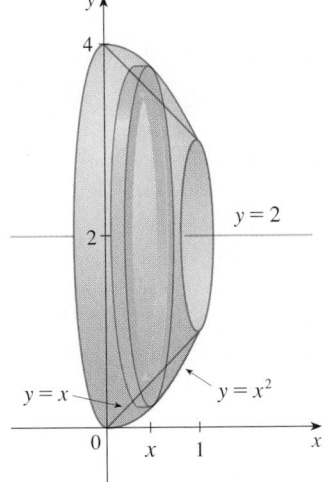

EXAMPLE 5 Find the volume of the solid obtained by rotating the region in Example 4 about the line $y = 2$.

SOLUTION The solid and a cross-section are shown in Figure 9. Again the cross-section is a washer, but this time the inner radius is $2 - x$ and the outer radius is $2 - x^2$. The cross-sectional area is

$$A(x) = \pi(2 - x^2)^2 - \pi(2 - x)^2$$

and so the volume of S is

$$V = \int_0^1 A(x)\, dx = \pi \int_0^1 \left[(2 - x^2)^2 - (2 - x)^2 \right] dx$$

$$= \pi \int_0^1 (x^4 - 5x^2 + 4x)\, dx = \pi \left[\frac{x^5}{5} - 5\frac{x^3}{3} + 4\frac{x^2}{2} \right]_0^1 = \frac{8\pi}{15}$$

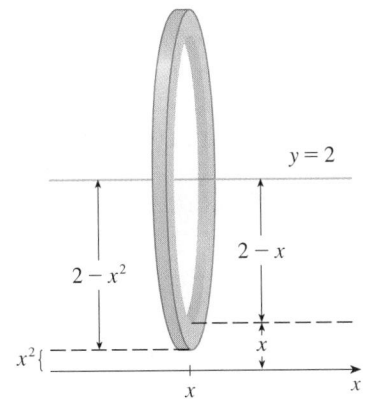

The solids in Examples 1–5 are all called **solids of revolution** because they are obtained by revolving a region about a line. In general, we calculate the volume of a solid of revolution by using the basic defining formula

$$V = \int_a^b A(x)\, dx \qquad \text{or} \qquad V = \int_c^d A(y)\, dy$$

and we find the cross-sectional area $A(x)$ or $A(y)$ in one of the following ways:

▫ If the cross-section is a disk (as in Examples 1–3), we find the radius of the disk (in terms of x or y) and use

$$A = \pi(\text{radius})^2$$

▫ If the cross-section is a washer (as in Examples 4 and 5), we find the inner radius r_{in} and outer radius r_{out} from a sketch (as in Figures 9 and 10) and compute the area of the washer by subtracting the area of the inner disk from the area of the outer disk:

$$A = \pi(\text{outer radius})^2 - \pi(\text{inner radius})^2$$

FIGURE 9

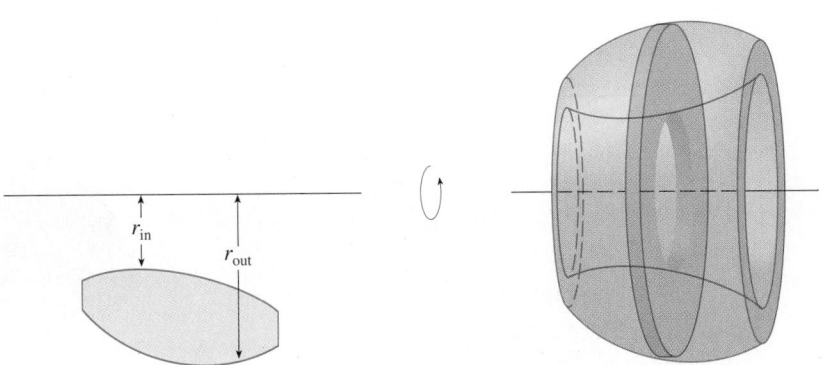

FIGURE 10

The next example gives a further illustration of the procedure.

EXAMPLE 6 Find the volume of the solid obtained by rotating the region in Example 4 about the line $x = -1$.

SOLUTION Figure 11 shows a horizontal cross-section. It is a washer with inner radius $1 + y$ and outer radius $1 + \sqrt{y}$, so the cross-sectional area is

$$A(y) = \pi(\text{outer radius})^2 - \pi(\text{inner radius})^2$$
$$= \pi(1 + \sqrt{y})^2 - \pi(1 + y)^2$$

The volume is

$$V = \int_0^1 A(y)\, dy$$

$$= \pi \int_0^1 \left[(1 + \sqrt{y})^2 - (1 + y)^2\right] dy$$

$$= \pi \int_0^1 \left(2\sqrt{y} - y - y^2\right) dy$$

$$= \pi \left[\frac{4y^{3/2}}{3} - \frac{y^2}{2} - \frac{y^3}{3}\right]_0^1 = \frac{\pi}{2}$$

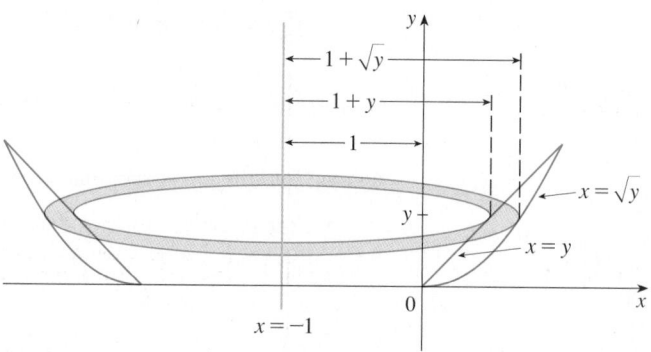

FIGURE 11

We now find the volumes of three solids that are *not* solids of revolution.

EXAMPLE 7 Figure 12 shows a solid with a circular base of radius 1. Parallel cross-sections perpendicular to the base are equilateral triangles. Find the volume of the solid.

FIGURE 12
Computer-generated picture
of the solid in Example 7

SOLUTION Let's take the circle to be $x^2 + y^2 = 1$. The solid, its base, and a typical cross-section at a distance x from the origin are shown in Figure 13.

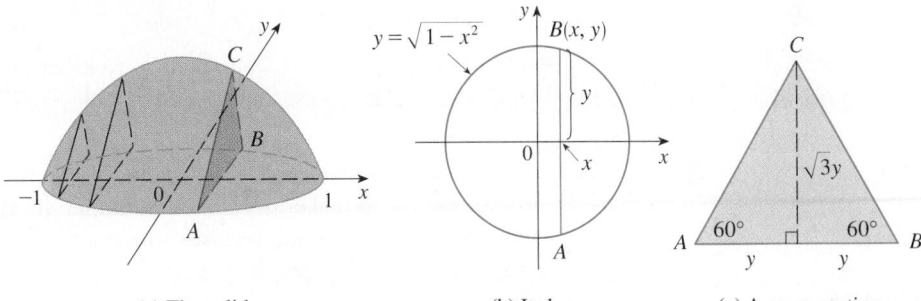

FIGURE 13   (a) The solid   (b) Its base   (c) A cross-section

Since B lies on the circle, we have $y = \sqrt{1 - x^2}$ and so the base of the triangle ABC is $|AB| = 2\sqrt{1 - x^2}$. Since the triangle is equilateral, we see from Figure 13(c) that its height is $\sqrt{3}\, y = \sqrt{3}\sqrt{1 - x^2}$. The cross-sectional area is therefore

$$A(x) = \tfrac{1}{2} \cdot 2\sqrt{1 - x^2} \cdot \sqrt{3}\sqrt{1 - x^2} = \sqrt{3}\,(1 - x^2)$$

and the volume of the solid is

$$V = \int_{-1}^{1} A(x)\,dx = \int_{-1}^{1} \sqrt{3}\,(1 - x^2)\,dx$$

$$= 2\int_{0}^{1} \sqrt{3}\,(1 - x^2)\,dx = 2\sqrt{3}\left[x - \frac{x^3}{3} \right]_{0}^{1} = \frac{4\sqrt{3}}{3}$$

Resources / Module 7
/ Volumes
/ Start of Mystery of the
Topless Pyramid

EXAMPLE 8 Find the volume of a pyramid whose base is a square with side L and whose height is h.

SOLUTION We place the origin O at the vertex of the pyramid and the x-axis along its central axis as in Figure 14. Any plane P_x that passes through x and is perpendicular to the x-axis intersects the pyramid in a square with side of length s, say. We can express s in terms of x by observing from the similar triangles in Figure 15 that

$$\frac{x}{h} = \frac{s/2}{L/2} = \frac{s}{L}$$

and so $s = Lx/h$. [Another method is to observe that the line OP has slope $L/(2h)$ and so its equation is $y = Lx/(2h)$.] Thus, the cross-sectional area is

$$A(x) = s^2 = \frac{L^2}{h^2}x^2$$

FIGURE 14   **FIGURE 15**

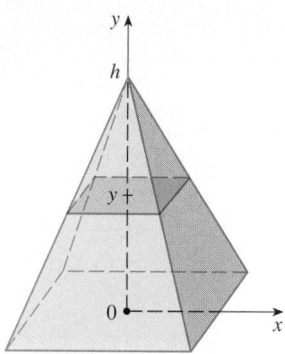

FIGURE 16

The pyramid lies between $x = 0$ and $x = h$, so its volume is

$$V = \int_0^h A(x)\, dx = \int_0^h \frac{L^2}{h^2} x^2 \, dx$$

$$= \frac{L^2}{h^2} \frac{x^3}{3} \Big]_0^h = \frac{L^2 h}{3}$$

NOTE ◦ We didn't need to place the vertex of the pyramid at the origin in Example 8. We did so merely to make the equations simple. If, instead, we had placed the center of the base at the origin and the vertex on the positive y-axis, as in Figure 16, you can verify that we would have obtained the integral

$$V = \int_0^h \frac{L^2}{h^2} (h - y)^2 \, dy = \frac{L^2 h}{3}$$

EXAMPLE 9 A wedge is cut out of a circular cylinder of radius 4 by two planes. One plane is perpendicular to the axis of the cylinder. The other intersects the first at an angle of $30°$ along a diameter of the cylinder. Find the volume of the wedge.

SOLUTION If we place the x-axis along the diameter where the planes meet, then the base of the solid is a semicircle with equation $y = \sqrt{16 - x^2}$, $-4 \leqslant x \leqslant 4$. A cross-section perpendicular to the x-axis at a distance x from the origin is a triangle ABC, as shown in Figure 17, whose base is $y = \sqrt{16 - x^2}$ and whose height is $|BC| = y \tan 30° = \sqrt{16 - x^2}/\sqrt{3}$. Thus, the cross-sectional area is

$$A(x) = \tfrac{1}{2}\sqrt{16 - x^2} \cdot \frac{1}{\sqrt{3}} \sqrt{16 - x^2} = \frac{16 - x^2}{2\sqrt{3}}$$

and the volume is

$$V = \int_{-4}^4 A(x)\, dx = \int_{-4}^4 \frac{16 - x^2}{2\sqrt{3}} \, dx$$

$$= \frac{1}{\sqrt{3}} \int_0^4 (16 - x^2) \, dx = \frac{1}{\sqrt{3}} \left[16x - \frac{x^3}{3} \right]_0^4$$

$$= \frac{128}{3\sqrt{3}}$$

For another method see Exercise 62.

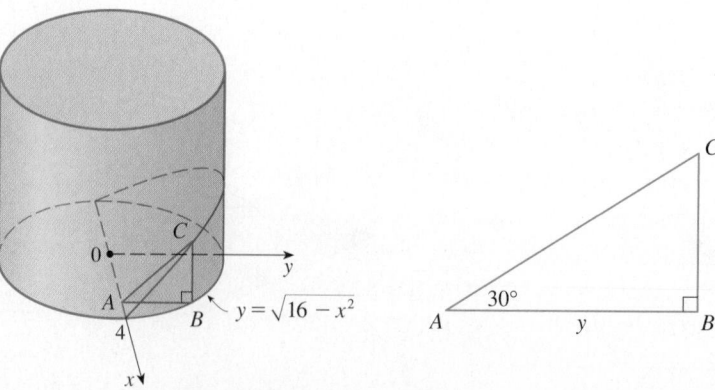

FIGURE 17

6.2 Exercises

1–18 ▓ Find the volume of the solid obtained by rotating the region bounded by the given curves about the specified line. Sketch the region, the solid, and a typical disk or washer.

1. $y = x^2$, $x = 1$, $y = 0$;   about the x-axis

2. $x + 2y = 2$, $x = 0$ $y = 0$;   about the x-axis

3. $y = 1/x$, $x = 1$, $x = 2$, $y = 0$;   about the x-axis

4. $y = \sqrt{x - 1}$, $x = 2$, $x = 5$, $y = 0$;   about the x-axis

5. $y = x^2$, $0 \leqslant x \leqslant 2$, $y = 4$, $x = 0$;   about the y-axis

6. $x = y - y^2$, $x = 0$;   about the y-axis

7. $y = x^2$, $y^2 = x$;   about the x-axis

8. $y = \sec x$, $y = 1$, $x = -1$, $x = 1$;   about the x-axis

9. $y^2 = x$, $x = 2y$;   about the y-axis

10. $y = x^{2/3}$, $x = 1$, $y = 0$;   about the y-axis

11. $y = x$, $y = \sqrt{x}$;   about $y = 1$

12. $y = x^2$, $y = 4$;   about $y = 4$

13. $y = x^4$, $y = 1$;   about $y = 2$

14. $y = 1/x^2$, $y = 0$, $x = 1$, $x = 3$; about $y = -1$

15. $x = y^2$, $x = 1$;   about $x = 1$

16. $y = x$, $y = \sqrt{x}$;   about $x = 2$

17. $y = x^2$, $x = y^2$;   about $x = -1$

18. $y = x$, $y = 0$, $x = 2$, $x = 4$;   about $x = 1$

19–30 ▓ Refer to the figure and find the volume generated by rotating the given region about the specified line.

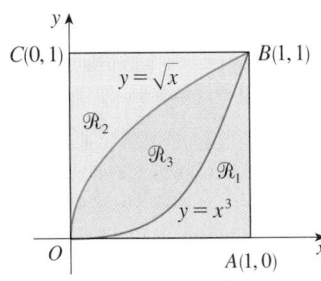

y
$C(0, 1)$ $B(1, 1)$
$y = \sqrt{x}$
$\mathcal{R}_2$
$\mathcal{R}_3$
$\mathcal{R}_1$
$y = x^3$
O $A(1, 0)$ x

19. $\mathcal{R}_1$ about OA

20. $\mathcal{R}_1$ about OC

21. $\mathcal{R}_1$ about AB

22. $\mathcal{R}_1$ about BC

23. $\mathcal{R}_2$ about OA

24. $\mathcal{R}_2$ about OC

25. $\mathcal{R}_2$ about AB

26. $\mathcal{R}_2$ about BC

27. $\mathcal{R}_3$ about OA

28. $\mathcal{R}_3$ about OC

29. $\mathcal{R}_3$ about AB

30. $\mathcal{R}_3$ about BC

31–36 ▓ Set up, but do not evaluate, an integral for the volume of the solid obtained by rotating the region bounded by the given curves about the specified line.

31. $y = \tan^3 x$, $y = 1$, $x = 0$;   about $y = 1$

32. $y = (x - 2)^4$, $8x - y = 16$;   about $x = 10$

33. $y = 0$, $y = \sin x$, $0 \leqslant x \leqslant \pi$;   about $y = 1$

34. $y = 0$, $y = \sin x$, $0 \leqslant x \leqslant \pi$;   about $y = -2$

35. $x^2 - y^2 = 1$, $x = 3$;   about $x = -2$

36. $2x + 3y = 6$, $(y - 1)^2 = 4 - x$;   about $x = -5$

37–38 ▓ Use a graph to find approximate x-coordinates of the points of intersection of the given curves. Then find (approximately) the volume of the solid obtained by rotating about the x-axis the region bounded by these curves.

37. $y = x^2$, $y = \sqrt{x + 1}$ **38.** $y = x^4$, $y = 3x - x^3$

CAS **39–40** ▓ Use a computer algebra system to find the exact volume of the solid obtained by rotating the region bounded by the given curves about the specified line.

39. $y = \sin^2 x$, $y = 0$, $0 \leqslant x \leqslant \pi$;   about $y = -1$

40. $y = x^2 - 2x$, $y = x \cos(\pi x/4)$;   about $y = 2$

41–44 ▓ Each integral represents the volume of a solid. Describe the solid.

41. $\pi \displaystyle\int_0^{\pi/2} \cos^2 x \, dx$ **42.** $\pi \displaystyle\int_2^5 y \, dy$

43. $\pi \displaystyle\int_0^1 (y^4 - y^8) \, dy$

44. $\pi \displaystyle\int_0^{\pi/2} [(1 + \cos x)^2 - 1^2] \, dx$

45. A CAT scan produces equally spaced cross-sectional views of a human organ that provide information about the organ otherwise obtained only by surgery. Suppose that a CAT scan of a human liver shows cross-sections spaced 1.5 cm apart. The liver is 15 cm long and the cross-sectional areas, in square centimeters, are 0, 18, 58, 79, 94, 106, 117, 128, 63, 39, and 0. Use the Midpoint Rule to estimate the volume of the liver.

46. A log 10 m long is cut at 1-meter intervals and its cross-sectional areas A (at a distance x from the end of the log) are listed in the table. Use the Midpoint Rule with $n = 5$ to estimate the volume of the log.

x (m)	A (m^2)	x (m)	A (m^2)
0	0.68	6	0.53
1	0.65	7	0.55
2	0.64	8	0.52
3	0.61	9	0.50
4	0.58	10	0.48
5	0.59		

47–59 |||| Find the volume of the described solid S.

47. A right circular cone with height h and base radius r

48. A frustum of a right circular cone with height h, lower base radius R, and top radius r

49. A cap of a sphere with radius r and height h

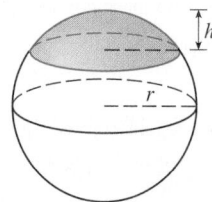

50. A frustum of a pyramid with square base of side b, square top of side a, and height h

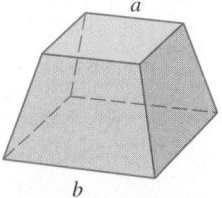

What happens if $a = b$? What happens if $a = 0$?

51. A pyramid with height h and rectangular base with dimensions b and $2b$

52. A pyramid with height h and base an equilateral triangle with side a (a tetrahedron)

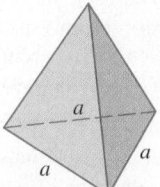

53. A tetrahedron with three mutually perpendicular faces and three mutually perpendicular edges with lengths 3 cm, 4 cm, and 5 cm

54. The base of S is a circular disk with radius r. Parallel cross-sections perpendicular to the base are squares.

55. The base of S is an elliptical region with boundary curve $9x^2 + 4y^2 = 36$. Cross-sections perpendicular to the x-axis are isosceles right triangles with hypotenuse in the base.

56. The base of S is the parabolic region $\{(x, y) \mid x^2 \le y \le 1\}$. Cross-sections perpendicular to the y-axis are equilateral triangles.

57. S has the same base as in Exercise 56, but cross-sections perpendicular to the y-axis are squares.

58. The base of S is the triangular region with vertices $(0, 0)$, $(3, 0)$, and $(0, 2)$. Cross-sections perpendicular to the y-axis are semicircles.

59. S has the same base as in Exercise 58, but cross-sections perpendicular to the y-axis are isosceles triangles with height equal to the base.

60. The base of S is a circular disk with radius r. Parallel cross-sections perpendicular to the base are isosceles triangles with height h and unequal side in the base.
(a) Set up an integral for the volume of S.
(b) By interpreting the integral as an area, find the volume of S.

61. (a) Set up an integral for the volume of a solid *torus* (the donut-shaped solid shown in the figure) with radii r and R.
(b) By interpreting the integral as an area, find the volume of the torus.

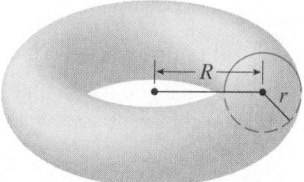

62. Solve Example 9 taking cross-sections to be parallel to the line of intersection of the two planes.

63. (a) Cavalieri's Principle states that if a family of parallel planes gives equal cross-sectional areas for two solids S_1 and S_2, then the volumes of S_1 and S_2 are equal. Prove this principle.
(b) Use Cavalieri's Principle to find the volume of the oblique cylinder shown in the figure.

64. Find the volume common to two circular cylinders, each with radius r, if the axes of the cylinders intersect at right angles.

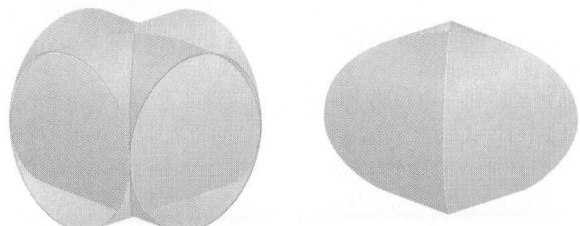

65. Find the volume common to two spheres, each with radius r, if the center of each sphere lies on the surface of the other sphere.

66. A bowl is shaped like a hemisphere with diameter 30 cm. A ball with diameter 10 cm is placed in the bowl and water is poured into the bowl to a depth of h centimeters. Find the volume of water in the bowl.

67. A hole of radius r is bored through a cylinder of radius $R > r$ at right angles to the axis of the cylinder. Set up, but do not evaluate, an integral for the volume cut out.

68. A hole of radius r is bored through the center of a sphere of radius $R > r$. Find the volume of the remaining portion of the sphere.

69. Some of the pioneers of calculus, such as Kepler and Newton, were inspired by the problem of finding the volumes of wine barrels. (In fact Kepler published a book *Stereometria doliorum* in 1715 devoted to methods for finding the volumes of barrels.) They often approximated the shape of the sides by parabolas.
(a) A barrel with height h and maximum radius R is constructed by rotating about the x-axis the parabola $y = R - cx^2$, $-h/2 \leqslant x \leqslant h/2$, where c is a positive constant. Show that the radius of each end of the barrel is $r = R - d$, where $d = ch^2/4$.
(b) Show that the volume enclosed by the barrel is

$$V = \tfrac{1}{3}\pi h \left(2R^2 + r^2 - \tfrac{2}{5}d^2\right)$$

70. Suppose that a region $\mathcal{R}$ has area A and lies above the x-axis. When $\mathcal{R}$ is rotated about the x-axis, it sweeps out a solid with volume V_1. When $\mathcal{R}$ is rotated about the line $y = -k$ (where k is a positive number), it sweeps out a solid with volume V_2. Express V_2 in terms of V_1, k, and A.

|||| 6.3 Volumes by Cylindrical Shells

FIGURE 1

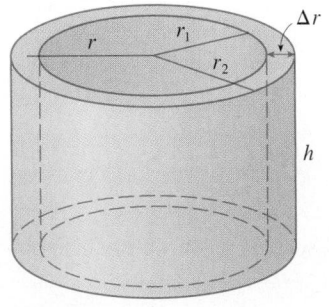

FIGURE 2

Some volume problems are very difficult to handle by the methods of the preceding section. For instance, let's consider the problem of finding the volume of the solid obtained by rotating about the y-axis the region bounded by $y = 2x^2 - x^3$ and $y = 0$. (See Figure 1.) If we slice perpendicular to the y-axis, we get a washer. But to compute the inner radius and the outer radius of the washer, we would have to solve the cubic equation $y = 2x^2 - x^3$ for x in terms of y; that's not easy.

Fortunately, there is a method, called the **method of cylindrical shells**, that is easier to use in such a case. Figure 2 shows a cylindrical shell with inner radius r_1, outer radius r_2, and height h. Its volume V is calculated by subtracting the volume V_1 of the inner cylinder from the volume V_2 of the outer cylinder:

$$V = V_2 - V_1$$
$$= \pi r_2^2 h - \pi r_1^2 h = \pi(r_2^2 - r_1^2)h$$
$$= \pi(r_2 + r_1)(r_2 - r_1)h$$
$$= 2\pi \frac{r_2 + r_1}{2} h(r_2 - r_1)$$

If we let $\Delta r = r_2 - r_1$ (the thickness of the shell) and $r = \tfrac{1}{2}(r_2 + r_1)$ (the average radius of the shell), then this formula for the volume of a cylindrical shell becomes

1

$$V = 2\pi r h\, \Delta r$$

FIGURE 3

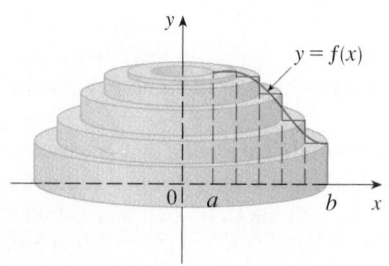

FIGURE 4

and it can be remembered as

$$V = [\text{circumference}][\text{height}][\text{thickness}]$$

Now let S be the solid obtained by rotating about the y-axis the region bounded by $y = f(x)$ [where $f(x) \geq 0$], $y = 0$, $x = a$, and $x = b$, where $b > a \geq 0$. (See Figure 3.) We divide the interval $[a, b]$ into n subintervals $[x_{i-1}, x_i]$ of equal width Δx and let $\bar{x}_i$ be the midpoint of the ith subinterval. If the rectangle with base $[x_{i-1}, x_i]$ and height $f(\bar{x}_i)$ is rotated about the y-axis, then the result is a cylindrical shell with average radius $\bar{x}_i$, height $f(\bar{x}_i)$, and thickness Δx (see Figure 4), so by Formula 1 its volume is

$$V_i = (2\pi\bar{x}_i)[f(\bar{x}_i)]\,\Delta x$$

Therefore, an approximation to the volume V of S is given by the sum of the volumes of these shells:

$$V \approx \sum_{i=1}^{n} V_i = \sum_{i=1}^{n} 2\pi\bar{x}_i f(\bar{x}_i)\,\Delta x$$

This approximation appears to become better as $n \to \infty$. But, from the definition of an integral, we know that

$$\lim_{n\to\infty} \sum_{i=1}^{n} 2\pi\bar{x}_i f(\bar{x}_i)\,\Delta x = \int_a^b 2\pi x f(x)\,dx$$

Thus, the following appears plausible:

---

2   The volume of the solid in Figure 3, obtained by rotating about the y-axis the region under the curve $y = f(x)$ from a to b, is

$$V = \int_a^b 2\pi x f(x)\,dx \qquad \text{where } 0 \leq a < b$$

The argument using cylindrical shells makes Formula 2 seem reasonable, but later we will be able to prove it (see Exercise 65 in Section 8.1).

The best way to remember Formula 2 is to think of a typical shell, cut and flattened as in Figure 5, with radius x, circumference $2\pi x$, height $f(x)$, and thickness Δx or dx:

$$\int_a^b \underbrace{(2\pi x)}_{\text{circumference}} \underbrace{[f(x)]}_{\text{height}}\,dx$$

FIGURE 5

This type of reasoning will be helpful in other situations, such as when we rotate about lines other than the y-axis.

EXAMPLE 1 Find the volume of the solid obtained by rotating about the y-axis the region bounded by $y = 2x^2 - x^3$ and $y = 0$.

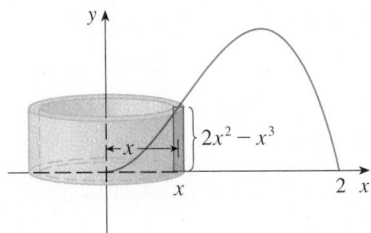

FIGURE 6

SOLUTION From the sketch in Figure 6 we see that a typical shell has radius x, circumference $2\pi x$, and height $f(x) = 2x^2 - x^3$. So, by the shell method, the volume is

$$V = \int_0^2 (2\pi x)(2x^2 - x^3)\, dx = 2\pi \int_0^2 (2x^3 - x^4)\, dx$$

$$= 2\pi \left[\tfrac{1}{2}x^4 - \tfrac{1}{5}x^5 \right]_0^2 = 2\pi \left(8 - \tfrac{32}{5} \right) = \tfrac{16}{5}\pi$$

It can be verified that the shell method gives the same answer as slicing.

▐▐▐▐ Figure 7 shows a computer-generated picture of the solid whose volume we computed in Example 1.

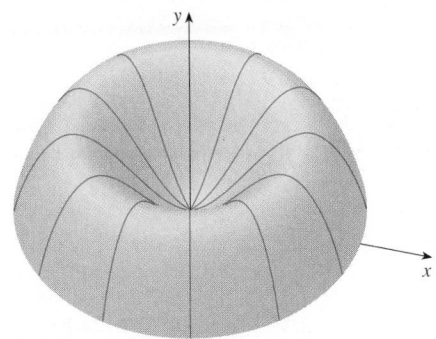

FIGURE 7

NOTE ◦ Comparing the solution of Example 1 with the remarks at the beginning of this section, we see that the method of cylindrical shells is much easier than the washer method for this problem. We did not have to find the coordinates of the local maximum and we did not have to solve the equation of the curve for x in terms of y. However, in other examples the methods of the preceding section may be easier.

EXAMPLE 2 Find the volume of the solid obtained by rotating about the y-axis the region between $y = x$ and $y = x^2$.

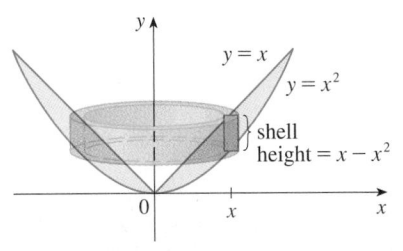

FIGURE 8

SOLUTION The region and a typical shell are shown in Figure 8. We see that the shell has radius x, circumference $2\pi x$, and height $x - x^2$. So the volume is

$$V = \int_0^1 (2\pi x)(x - x^2)\, dx = 2\pi \int_0^1 (x^2 - x^3)\, dx$$

$$= 2\pi \left[\frac{x^3}{3} - \frac{x^4}{4} \right]_0^1 = \frac{\pi}{6}$$

 Module 6.2/6.3 compares shells with disks and washers.

As the following example shows, the shell method works just as well if we rotate about the x-axis. We simply have to draw a diagram to identify the radius and height of a shell.

EXAMPLE 3 Use cylindrical shells to find the volume of the solid obtained by rotating about the x-axis the region under the curve $y = \sqrt{x}$ from 0 to 1.

SOLUTION This problem was solved using disks in Example 2 in Section 6.2. To use shells we relabel the curve $y = \sqrt{x}$ (in the figure in that example) as $x = y^2$ in Figure 9. For rotation about the x-axis we see that a typical shell has radius y, circumference $2\pi y$, and height $1 - y^2$. So the volume is

$$V = \int_0^1 (2\pi y)(1 - y^2)\, dy = 2\pi \int_0^1 (y - y^3)\, dy$$

$$= 2\pi \left[\frac{y^2}{2} - \frac{y^4}{4} \right]_0^1 = \frac{\pi}{2}$$

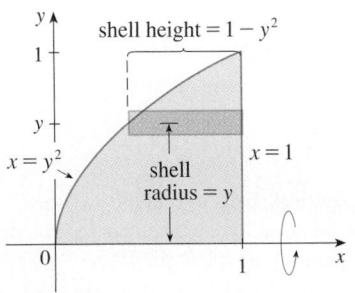

FIGURE 9

In this problem the disk method was simpler.

EXAMPLE 4 Find the volume of the solid obtained by rotating the region bounded by $y = x - x^2$ and $y = 0$ about the line $x = 2$.

SOLUTION Figure 10 shows the region and a cylindrical shell formed by rotation about the line $x = 2$. It has radius $2 - x$, circumference $2\pi(2 - x)$, and height $x - x^2$.

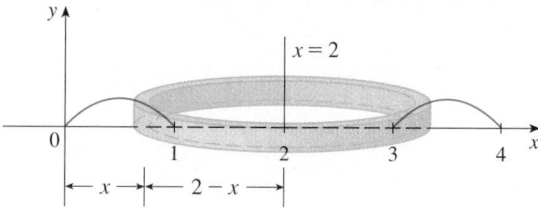

FIGURE 10

The volume of the given solid is

$$V = \int_0^1 2\pi(2 - x)(x - x^2)\,dx = 2\pi \int_0^1 (x^3 - 3x^2 + 2x)\,dx$$

$$= 2\pi \left[\frac{x^4}{4} - x^3 + x^2 \right]_0^1 = \frac{\pi}{2}$$

6.3 Exercises

1. Let S be the solid obtained by rotating the region shown in the figure about the y-axis. Explain why it is awkward to use slicing to find the volume V of S. Sketch a typical approximating shell. What are its circumference and height? Use shells to find V.

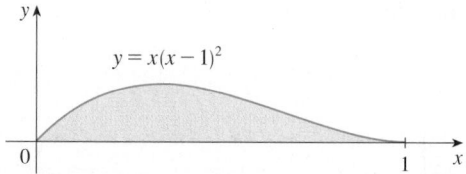

2. Let S be the solid obtained by rotating the region shown in the figure about the y-axis. Sketch a typical cylindrical shell and find its circumference and height. Use shells to find the volume of S. Do you think this method is preferable to slicing? Explain.

3–7 ▏▏▏ Use the method of cylindrical shells to find the volume generated by rotating the region bounded by the given curves about the y-axis. Sketch the region and a typical shell.

3. $y = 1/x$, $y = 0$, $x = 1$, $x = 2$

4. $y = x^2$, $y = 0$, $x = 1$

5. $y = x^2$, $0 \le x \le 2$, $y = 4$, $x = 0$

6. $y = 3 + 2x - x^2$, $x + y = 3$

7. $y = 4(x - 2)^2$, $y = x^2 - 4x + 7$

8. Let V be the volume of the solid obtained by rotating about the y-axis the region bounded by $y = \sqrt{x}$ and $y = x^2$. Find V both by slicing and by cylindrical shells. In both cases draw a diagram to explain your method.

9–14 ▏▏▏ Use the method of cylindrical shells to find the volume of the solid obtained by rotating the region bounded by the given curves about the x-axis. Sketch the region and a typical shell.

9. $x = 1 + y^2$, $x = 0$, $y = 1$, $y = 2$

10. $x = \sqrt{y}$, $x = 0$, $y = 1$

11. $y = x^3$, $y = 8$, $x = 0$

12. $x = 4y^2 - y^3$, $x = 0$

13. $y = 4x^2$, $2x + y = 6$

14. $x + y = 3$, $x = 4 - (y - 1)^2$

15–20 ▏▏▏ Use the method of cylindrical shells to find the volume generated by rotating the region bounded by the given curves about the specified axis. Sketch the region and a typical shell.

15. $y = x^2$, $y = 0$, $x = 1$, $x = 2$; about $x = 1$

16. $y = x^2$, $y = 0$, $x = -2$, $x = -1$; about the y-axis

17. $y = x^2$, $y = 0$, $x = 1$, $x = 2$; about $x = 4$

18. $y = 4x - x^2$, $y = 8x - 2x^2$; about $x = -2$

19. $y = \sqrt{x - 1}$, $y = 0$, $x = 5$; about $y = 3$

20. $y = x^2$, $x = y^2$; about $y = -1$

21–26 |||| Set up, but do not evaluate, an integral for the volume of the solid obtained by rotating the region bounded by the given curves about the specified axis.

21. $y = \sin x$, $y = 0$, $x = 2\pi$, $x = 3\pi$; about the y-axis

22. $y = x$, $y = 4x - x^2$; about $x = 7$

23. $y = x^4$, $y = \sin(\pi x/2)$; about $x = -1$

24. $y = 1/(1 + x^2)$, $y = 0$, $x = 0$, $x = 2$; about $x = 2$

25. $x = \sqrt{\sin y}$, $0 \leqslant y \leqslant \pi$, $x = 0$; about $y = 4$

26. $x^2 - y^2 = 7$, $x = 4$; about $y = 5$

27. Use the Midpoint Rule with $n = 4$ to estimate the volume obtained by rotating about the y-axis the region under the curve $y = \tan x$, $0 \leqslant x \leqslant \pi/4$.

28. If the region shown in the figure is rotated about the y-axis to form a solid, use the Midpoint Rule with $n = 5$ to estimate the volume of the solid.

29–32 |||| Each integral represents the volume of a solid. Describe the solid.

29. $\displaystyle\int_0^3 2\pi x^5 \, dx$

30. $\displaystyle 2\pi \int_0^2 \frac{y}{1 + y^2} \, dy$

31. $\displaystyle\int_0^1 2\pi(3 - y)(1 - y^2) \, dy$

32. $\displaystyle\int_0^{\pi/4} 2\pi(\pi - x)(\cos x - \sin x) \, dx$

33–34 |||| Use a graph to estimate the x-coordinates of the points of intersection of the given curves. Then use this information to estimate the volume of the solid obtained by rotating about the y-axis the region enclosed by these curves.

33. $y = 0$, $y = x + x^2 - x^4$

34. $y = x^4$, $y = 3x - x^3$

[CAS] **35–36** |||| Use a computer algebra system to find the exact volume of the solid obtained by rotating the region bounded by the given curves about the specified line.

35. $y = \sin^2 x$, $y = \sin^4 x$, $0 \leqslant x \leqslant \pi$; about $x = \pi/2$

36. $y = x^3 \sin x$, $y = 0$, $0 \leqslant x \leqslant \pi$; about $x = -1$

37–42 |||| The region bounded by the given curves is rotated about the specified axis. Find the volume of the resulting solid by any method.

37. $y = x^2 + x - 2$, $y = 0$; about the x-axis

38. $y = x^2 - 3x + 2$, $y = 0$; about the y-axis

39. $y = 5$, $y = x^2 - 5x + 9$; about $x = -1$

40. $x = 1 - y^4$, $x = 0$; about $x = 2$

41. $x^2 + (y - 1)^2 = 1$; about the y-axis

42. $x^2 + (y - 1)^2 = 1$; about the x-axis

43–45 |||| Use cylindrical shells to find the volume of the solid.

43. A sphere of radius r

44. The solid torus of Exercise 61 in Section 6.2

45. A right circular cone with height h and base radius r

46. Suppose you make napkin rings by drilling holes with different diameters through two wooden balls (which also have different diameters). You discover that both napkin rings have the same height h, as shown in the figure.
(a) Guess which ring has more wood in it.
(b) Check your guess: Use cylindrical shells to compute the volume of a napkin ring created by drilling a hole with radius r through the center of a sphere of radius R and express the answer in terms of h.

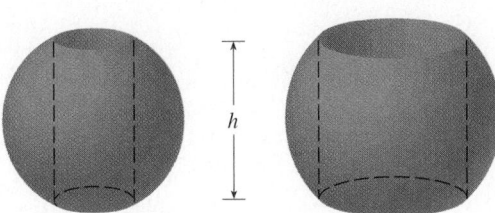

6.4 Work

The term *work* is used in everyday language to mean the total amount of effort required to perform a task. In physics it has a technical meaning that depends on the idea of a *force*. Intuitively, you can think of a force as describing a push or pull on an object—for example, a horizontal push of a book across a table or the downward pull of Earth's gravity on a ball. In general, if an object moves along a straight line with position function $s(t)$, then the **force** F on the object (in the same direction) is defined by Newton's Second Law of Motion as the product of its mass m and its acceleration:

$$\boxed{1} \qquad F = m \frac{d^2 s}{dt^2}$$

In the SI metric system, the mass is measured in kilograms (kg), the displacement in meters (m), the time in seconds (s), and the force in newtons (N = kg·m/s²). Thus, a force of 1 N acting on a mass of 1 kg produces an acceleration of 1 m/s². In the U.S. Customary system the fundamental unit is chosen to be the unit of force, which is the pound.

In the case of constant acceleration, the force F is also constant and the work done is defined to be the product of the force F and the distance d that the object moves:

$$\boxed{2} \qquad W = Fd \qquad \text{work} = \text{force} \times \text{distance}$$

If F is measured in newtons and d in meters, then the unit for W is a newton-meter, which is called a joule (J). If F is measured in pounds and d in feet, then the unit for W is a foot-pound (ft-lb), which is about 1.36 J.

EXAMPLE 1

(a) How much work is done in lifting a 1.2-kg book off the floor to put it on a desk that is 0.7 m high? Use the fact that the acceleration due to gravity is $g = 9.8$ m/s².
(b) How much work is done in lifting a 20-lb weight 6 ft off the ground?

SOLUTION

(a) The force exerted is equal and opposite to that exerted by gravity, so Equation 1 gives

$$F = mg = (1.2)(9.8) = 11.76 \text{ N}$$

and then Equation 2 gives the work done as

$$W = Fd = (11.76)(0.7) \approx 8.2 \text{ J}$$

(b) Here the force is given as $F = 20$ lb, so the work done is

$$W = Fd = 20 \cdot 6 = 120 \text{ ft-lb}$$

Notice that in part (b), unlike part (a), we did not have to multiply by g because we were given the *weight* (which is a force) and not the mass of the object.

Equation 2 defines work as long as the force is constant, but what happens if the force is variable? Let's suppose that the object moves along the x-axis in the positive direction, from $x = a$ to $x = b$, and at each point x between a and b a force $f(x)$ acts on the object, where f is a continuous function. We divide the interval $[a, b]$ into n subintervals with endpoints $x_0, x_1, \ldots, x_n$ and equal width Δx. We choose a sample point x_i^* in the ith subinterval $[x_{i-1}, x_i]$. Then the force at that point is $f(x_i^*)$. If n is large, then Δx is small, and since f is continuous, the values of f don't change very much over the interval $[x_{i-1}, x_i]$. In other words, f is almost constant on the interval and so the work W_i that is done in moving the particle from x_{i-1} to x_i is approximately given by Equation 2:

$$W_i \approx f(x_i^*)\,\Delta x$$

Thus, we can approximate the total work by

3
$$W \approx \sum_{i=1}^{n} f(x_i^*)\,\Delta x$$

It seems that this approximation becomes better as we make n larger. Therefore, we define the **work done in moving the object from a to b** as the limit of this quantity as $n \to \infty$. Since the right side of (3) is a Riemann sum, we recognize its limit as being a definite integral and so

4
$$W = \lim_{n \to \infty} \sum_{i=1}^{n} f(x_i^*)\,\Delta x = \int_a^b f(x)\,dx$$

EXAMPLE 2 When a particle is located a distance x feet from the origin, a force of $x^2 + 2x$ pounds acts on it. How much work is done in moving it from $x = 1$ to $x = 3$?

SOLUTION
$$W = \int_1^3 (x^2 + 2x)\,dx = \frac{x^3}{3} + x^2 \Big]_1^3 = \frac{50}{3}$$

The work done is $16\frac{2}{3}$ ft-lb.

In the next example we use a law from physics: **Hooke's Law** states that the force required to maintain a spring stretched x units beyond its natural length is proportional to x:

$$f(x) = kx$$

where k is a positive constant (called the **spring constant**). Hooke's Law holds provided that x is not too large (see Figure 1).

EXAMPLE 3 A force of 40 N is required to hold a spring that has been stretched from its natural length of 10 cm to a length of 15 cm. How much work is done in stretching the spring from 15 cm to 18 cm?

SOLUTION According to Hooke's Law, the force required to hold the spring stretched x meters beyond its natural length is $f(x) = kx$. When the spring is stretched from 10 cm to 15 cm, the amount stretched is 5 cm $= 0.05$ m. This means that $f(0.05) = 40$, so

$$0.05k = 40 \qquad k = \frac{40}{0.05} = 800$$

Thus, $f(x) = 800x$ and the work done in stretching the spring from 15 cm to 18 cm is

$$W = \int_{0.05}^{0.08} 800x\,dx = 800 \frac{x^2}{2} \Big]_{0.05}^{0.08}$$

$$= 400[(0.08)^2 - (0.05)^2] = 1.56 \text{ J}$$

frictionless 0
surface

(a) Natural position of spring

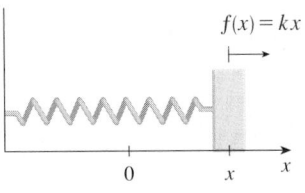

$f(x) = kx$

0   x x

(b) Stretched position of spring

FIGURE 1
Hooke's Law

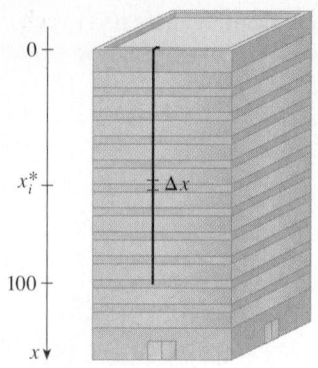

FIGURE 2

▐▐▐ If we had placed the origin at the bottom of the cable and the x-axis upward, we would have gotten

$$W = \int_0^{100} 2(100 - x)\, dx$$

which gives the same answer.

EXAMPLE 4 A 200-lb cable is 100 ft long and hangs vertically from the top of a tall building. How much work is required to lift the cable to the top of the building?

SOLUTION Here we don't have a formula for the force function, but we can use an argument similar to the one that led to Definition 4.

Let's place the origin at the top of the building and the x-axis pointing downward as in Figure 2. We divide the cable into small parts with length Δx. If x_i^* is a point in the ith such interval, then all points in the interval are lifted by approximately the same amount, namely x_i^*. The cable weighs 2 pounds per foot, so the weight of the ith part is $2\Delta x$. Thus, the work done on the ith part, in foot-pounds, is

$$\underbrace{(2\,\Delta x)}_{\text{force}} \quad \underbrace{x_i^*}_{\text{distance}} = 2x_i^*\,\Delta x$$

We get the total work done by adding all these approximations and letting the number of parts become large (so $\Delta x \to 0$):

$$W = \lim_{n \to \infty} \sum_{i=1}^n 2x_i^*\,\Delta x = \int_0^{100} 2x\,dx$$

$$= x^2 \big]_0^{100} = 10{,}000 \text{ ft-lb}$$

EXAMPLE 5 A tank has the shape of an inverted circular cone with height 10 m and base radius 4 m. It is filled with water to a height of 8 m. Find the work required to empty the tank by pumping all of the water to the top of the tank. (The density of water is 1000 kg/m³.)

SOLUTION Let's measure depths from the top of the tank by introducing a vertical coordinate line as in Figure 3. The water extends from a depth of 2 m to a depth of 10 m and so we divide the interval [2, 10] into n subintervals with endpoints $x_0, x_1, \ldots, x_n$ and choose x_i^* in the ith subinterval. This divides the water into n layers. The ith layer is approximated by a circular cylinder with radius r_i and height Δx. We can compute r_i from similar triangles, using Figure 4, as follows:

$$\frac{r_i}{10 - x_i^*} = \frac{4}{10} \qquad r_i = \tfrac{2}{5}(10 - x_i^*)$$

FIGURE 3

FIGURE 4

Thus, an approximation to the volume of the ith layer of water is

$$V_i \approx \pi r_i^2\,\Delta x = \frac{4\pi}{25}(10 - x_i^*)^2\,\Delta x$$

and so its mass is

$$m_i = \text{density} \times \text{volume}$$

$$\approx 1000 \cdot \frac{4\pi}{25}(10 - x_i^*)^2\,\Delta x = 160\pi(10 - x_i^*)^2\,\Delta x$$

The force required to raise this layer must overcome the force of gravity and so

$$F_i = m_i g \approx (9.8)160\pi(10 - x_i^*)^2\,\Delta x$$

$$\approx 1570\pi(10 - x_i^*)^2\,\Delta x$$

Each particle in the layer must travel a distance of approximately x_i^*. The work W_i done to raise this layer to the top is approximately the product of the force F_i and the distance x_i^*:

$$W_i \approx F_i x_i^* \approx 1570\pi x_i^*(10 - x_i^*)^2\,\Delta x$$

To find the total work done in emptying the entire tank, we add the contributions of each of the n layers and then take the limit as $n \to \infty$:

$$W = \lim_{n \to \infty} \sum_{i=1}^{n} 1570\pi x_i^*(10 - x_i^*)^2 \, \Delta x = \int_2^{10} 1570\pi x(10 - x)^2 \, dx$$

$$= 1570\pi \int_2^{10} (100x - 20x^2 + x^3) \, dx = 1570\pi \left[50x^2 - \frac{20x^3}{3} + \frac{x^4}{4} \right]_2^{10}$$

$$= 1570\pi \left(\tfrac{2048}{3} \right) \approx 3.4 \times 10^6 \text{ J}$$

6.4 Exercises

1. Find the work done in pushing a car a distance of 8 m while exerting a constant force of 900 N.

2. How much work is done by a weightlifter in raising a 60-kg barbell from the floor to a height of 2 m?

3. A particle is moved along the x-axis by a force that measures $10/(1 + x)^2$ pounds at a point x feet from the origin. Find the work done in moving the particle from the origin to a distance of 9 ft.

4. When a particle is located a distance x meters from the origin, a force of $\cos(\pi x/3)$ newtons acts on it. How much work is done in moving the particle from $x = 1$ to $x = 2$? Interpret your answer by considering the work done from $x = 1$ to $x = 1.5$ and from $x = 1.5$ to $x = 2$.

5. Shown is the graph of a force function (in newtons) that increases to its maximum value and then remains constant. How much work is done by the force in moving an object a distance of 8 m?

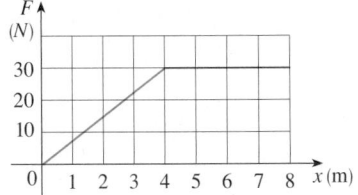

6. The table shows values of a force function $f(x)$, where x is measured in meters and $f(x)$ in newtons. Use the Midpoint Rule to estimate the work done by the force in moving an object from $x = 4$ to $x = 20$.

x	4	6	8	10	12	14	16	18	20
$f(x)$	5	5.8	7.0	8.8	9.6	8.2	6.7	5.2	4.1

7. A force of 10 lb is required to hold a spring stretched 4 in. beyond its natural length. How much work is done in stretching it from its natural length to 6 in. beyond its natural length?

8. A spring has a natural length of 20 cm. If a 25-N force is required to keep it stretched to a length of 30 cm, how much work is required to stretch it from 20 cm to 25 cm?

9. Suppose that 2 J of work is needed to stretch a spring from its natural length of 30 cm to a length of 42 cm. How much work is needed to stretch it from 35 cm to 40 cm?

10. If the work required to stretch a spring 1 ft beyond its natural length is 12 ft-lb, how much work is needed to stretch it 9 in. beyond its natural length?

11. How far beyond its natural length will a force of 30 N keep the spring in Exercise 9 stretched?

12. If 6 J of work is needed to stretch a spring from 10 cm to 12 cm and another 10 J is needed to stretch it from 12 cm to 14 cm, what is the natural length of the spring?

13–20 |||| Show how to approximate the required work by a Riemann sum. Then express the work as an integral and evaluate it.

13. A heavy rope, 50 ft long, weighs 0.5 lb/ft and hangs over the edge of a building 120 ft high.
   (a) How much work is done in pulling the rope to the top of the building?
   (b) How much work is done in pulling half the rope to the top of the building?

14. A chain lying on the ground is 10 m long and its mass is 80 kg. How much work is required to raise one end of the chain to a height of 6 m?

15. A cable that weighs 2 lb/ft is used to lift 800 lb of coal up a mineshaft 500 ft deep. Find the work done.

16. A bucket that weighs 4 lb and a rope of negligible weight are used to draw water from a well that is 80 ft deep. The bucket is filled with 40 lb of water and is pulled up at a rate of 2 ft/s, but water leaks out of a hole in the bucket at a rate of 0.2 lb/s. Find the work done in pulling the bucket to the top of the well.

17. A leaky 10-kg bucket is lifted from the ground to a height of 12 m at a constant speed with a rope that weighs 0.8 kg/m. Initially the bucket contains 36 kg of water, but the water leaks at a constant rate and finishes draining just as the bucket reaches the 12 m level. How much work is done?

18. A 10-ft chain weighs 25 lb and hangs from a ceiling. Find the work done in lifting the lower end of the chain to the ceiling so that it's level with the upper end.

19. An aquarium 2 m long, 1 m wide, and 1 m deep is full of water. Find the work needed to pump half of the water out of the aquarium. (Use the fact that the density of water is 1000 kg/m³.)

20. A circular swimming pool has a diameter of 24 ft, the sides are 5 ft high, and the depth of the water is 4 ft. How much work is required to pump all of the water out over the side? (Use the fact that water weighs 62.5 lb/ft³.)

21–24 ▎▎▎ A tank is full of water. Find the work required to pump the water out of the outlet. In Exercises 23 and 24 use the fact that water weighs 62.5 lb/ft³.

21.

22.

23.

semicircle

24.
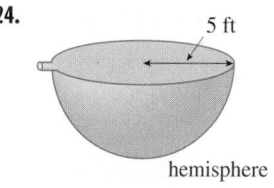
hemisphere

25. Suppose that for the tank in Exercise 21 the pump breaks down after 4.7×10^5 J of work has been done. What is the depth of the water remaining in the tank?

26. Solve Exercise 22 if the tank is half full of oil that has a density of 920 kg/m³.

27. When gas expands in a cylinder with radius r, the pressure at any given time is a function of the volume: $P = P(V)$. The force exerted by the gas on the piston (see the figure) is the product of the pressure and the area: $F = \pi r^2 P$. Show that the work done by the gas when the volume expands from volume V_1 to volume V_2 is

$$W = \int_{V_1}^{V_2} P \, dV$$

piston head

V

x

28. In a steam engine the pressure P and volume V of steam satisfy the equation $PV^{1.4} = k$, where k is a constant. (This is true for adiabatic expansion, that is, expansion in which there is no heat transfer between the cylinder and its surroundings.) Use Exercise 27 to calculate the work done by the engine during a cycle when the steam starts at a pressure of 160 lb/in² and a volume of 100 in³ and expands to a volume of 800 in³.

29. Newton's Law of Gravitation states that two bodies with masses m_1 and m_2 attract each other with a force

$$F = G \frac{m_1 m_2}{r^2}$$

where r is the distance between the bodies and G is the gravitational constant. If one of the bodies is fixed, find the work needed to move the other from $r = a$ to $r = b$.

30. Use Newton's Law of Gravitation to compute the work required to launch a 1000-kg satellite vertically to an orbit 1000 km high. You may assume that Earth's mass is 5.98×10^{24} kg and is concentrated at its center. Take the radius of Earth to be 6.37×10^6 m and $G = 6.67 \times 10^{-11}$ N·m²/kg².

6.5 Average Value of a Function

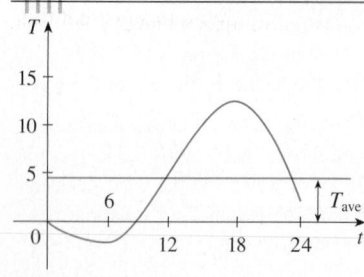

FIGURE 1

It is easy to calculate the average value of finitely many numbers $y_1, y_2, \ldots, y_n$:

$$y_{ave} = \frac{y_1 + y_2 + \cdots + y_n}{n}$$

But how do we compute the average temperature during a day if infinitely many temperature readings are possible? Figure 1 shows the graph of a temperature function $T(t)$, where t is measured in hours and T in °C, and a guess at the average temperature, T_{ave}.

In general, let's try to compute the average value of a function $y = f(x)$, $a \le x \le b$. We start by dividing the interval $[a, b]$ into n equal subintervals, each with length $\Delta x = (b - a)/n$. Then we choose points $x_1^*, \ldots, x_n^*$ in successive subintervals and calculate the average of the numbers $f(x_1^*), \ldots, f(x_n^*)$:

$$\frac{f(x_1^*) + \cdots + f(x_n^*)}{n}$$

(For example, if f represents a temperature function and $n = 24$, this means that we take temperature readings every hour and then average them.) Since $\Delta x = (b - a)/n$, we can write $n = (b - a)/\Delta x$ and the average value becomes

$$\frac{f(x_1^*) + \cdots + f(x_n^*)}{\dfrac{b - a}{\Delta x}} = \frac{1}{b - a}[f(x_1^*)\,\Delta x + \cdots + f(x_n^*)\,\Delta x]$$

$$= \frac{1}{b - a}\sum_{i=1}^{n} f(x_i^*)\,\Delta x$$

If we let n increase, we would be computing the average value of a large number of closely spaced values. (For example, we would be averaging temperature readings taken every minute or even every second.) The limiting value is

$$\lim_{n \to \infty} \frac{1}{b - a}\sum_{i=1}^{n} f(x_i^*)\,\Delta x = \frac{1}{b - a}\int_a^b f(x)\,dx$$

by the definition of a definite integral.

Therefore, we define the **average value of f** on the interval $[a, b]$ as

$$f_{\text{ave}} = \frac{1}{b - a}\int_a^b f(x)\,dx$$

▓ For a positive function, we can think of this definition as saying

$$\frac{\text{area}}{\text{width}} = \text{average height}$$

EXAMPLE 1 Find the average value of the function $f(x) = 1 + x^2$ on the interval $[-1, 2]$.

SOLUTION With $a = -1$ and $b = 2$ we have

$$f_{\text{ave}} = \frac{1}{b - a}\int_a^b f(x)\,dx = \frac{1}{2 - (-1)}\int_{-1}^{2}(1 + x^2)\,dx$$

$$= \frac{1}{3}\left[x + \frac{x^3}{3}\right]_{-1}^{2} = 2$$

If $T(t)$ is the temperature at time t, we might wonder if there is a specific time when the temperature is the same as the average temperature. For the temperature function graphed in Figure 1, we see that there are two such times—just before noon and just before midnight. In general, is there a number c at which the value of a function f is exactly equal to the average value of the function, that is, $f(c) = f_{\text{ave}}$? The following theorem says that this is true for continuous functions.

> **The Mean Value Theorem for Integrals** If f is continuous on $[a, b]$, then there exists a number c in $[a, b]$ such that
>
> $$f(c) = f_{\text{ave}} = \frac{1}{b - a}\int_a^b f(x)\,dx$$
>
> that is, $$\int_a^b f(x)\,dx = f(c)(b - a)$$

The Mean Value Theorem for Integrals is a consequence of the Mean Value Theorem for derivatives and the Fundamental Theorem of Calculus. The proof is outlined in Exercise 23.

The geometric interpretation of the Mean Value Theorem for Integrals is that, for *positive* functions f, there is a number c such that the rectangle with base $[a, b]$ and height $f(c)$ has the same area as the region under the graph of f from a to b. (See Figure 2 and the more picturesque interpretation in the margin note.)

|||| You can always chop off the top of a (two-dimensional) mountain at a certain height and use it to fill in the valleys so that the mountain becomes completely flat.

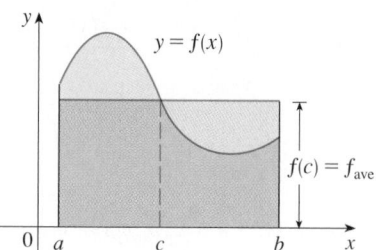

FIGURE 2

EXAMPLE 2 Since $f(x) = 1 + x^2$ is continuous on the interval $[-1, 2]$, the Mean Value Theorem for Integrals says there is a number c in $[-1, 2]$ such that

$$\int_{-1}^{2} (1 + x^2)\, dx = f(c)[2 - (-1)]$$

In this particular case we can find c explicitly. From Example 1 we know that $f_{ave} = 2$, so the value of c satisfies

$$f(c) = f_{ave} = 2$$

Therefore $\qquad\qquad 1 + c^2 = 2 \qquad$ so $\qquad c^2 = 1$

Thus, in this case there happen to be two numbers $c = \pm 1$ in the interval $[-1, 2]$ that work in the Mean Value Theorem for Integrals.

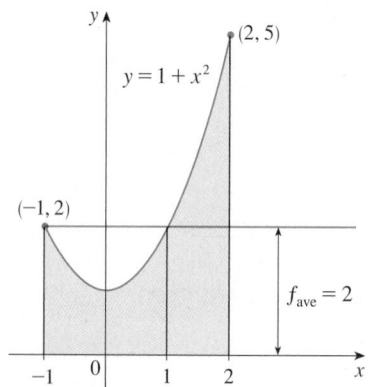

FIGURE 3

Examples 1 and 2 are illustrated by Figure 3.

EXAMPLE 3 Show that the average velocity of a car over a time interval $[t_1, t_2]$ is the same as the average of its velocities during the trip.

SOLUTION If $s(t)$ is the displacement of the car at time t, then, by definition, the average velocity of the car over the interval is

$$\frac{\Delta s}{\Delta t} = \frac{s(t_2) - s(t_1)}{t_2 - t_1}$$

On the other hand, the average value of the velocity function on the interval is

$$v_{ave} = \frac{1}{t_2 - t_1} \int_{t_1}^{t_2} v(t)\, dt = \frac{1}{t_2 - t_1} \int_{t_1}^{t_2} s'(t)\, dt$$

$$= \frac{1}{t_2 - t_1} [s(t_2) - s(t_1)] \qquad \text{(by the Net Change Theorem)}$$

$$= \frac{s(t_2) - s(t_1)}{t_2 - t_1} = \text{average velocity}$$

6.5 Exercises

1–8 ▥ Find the average value of the function on the given interval.

1. $f(x) = x^2$, $[-1, 1]$ **2.** $f(x) = x - x^2$, $[0, 2]$

3. $g(x) = \cos x$, $[0, \pi/2]$ **4.** $g(x) = x^2\sqrt{1 + x^3}$, $[0, 2]$

5. $f(t) = t\sqrt{1 + t^2}$, $[0, 5]$

6. $f(\theta) = \sec\theta\tan\theta$, $[0, \pi/4]$

7. $h(x) = \cos^4 x \sin x$, $[0, \pi]$

8. $h(r) = 3/(1 + r)^2$, $[1, 6]$

9–12 ▥

(a) Find the average value of f on the given interval.
(b) Find c such that $f_{ave} = f(c)$.
(c) Sketch the graph of f and a rectangle whose area is the same as the area under the graph of f.

9. $f(x) = (x - 3)^2$, $[2, 5]$ **10.** $f(x) = \sqrt{x}$, $[0, 4]$

11. $f(x) = 2\sin x - \sin 2x$, $[0, \pi]$

12. $f(x) = 2x/(1 + x^2)^2$, $[0, 2]$

13. If f is continuous and $\int_1^3 f(x)\, dx = 8$, show that f takes on the value 4 at least once on the interval $[1, 3]$.

14. Find the numbers b such that the average value of $f(x) = 2 + 6x - 3x^2$ on the interval $[0, b]$ is equal to 3.

15. The table gives values of a continuous function. Use the Midpoint Rule to estimate the average value of f on $[20, 50]$.

x	20	25	30	35	40	45	50
$f(x)$	42	38	31	29	35	48	60

16. The velocity graph of an accelerating car is shown.
   (a) Estimate the average velocity of the car during the first 12 seconds.
   (b) At what time was the instantaneous velocity equal to the average velocity?

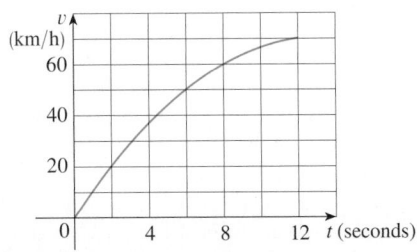

17. In a certain city the temperature (in °F) t hours after 9 A.M. was modeled by the function

$$T(t) = 50 + 14\sin\frac{\pi t}{12}$$

Find the average temperature during the period from 9 A.M. to 9 P.M.

18. The temperature of a metal rod, 5 m long, is $4x$ (in °C) at a distance x meters from one end of the rod. What is the average temperature of the rod?

19. The linear density in a rod 8 m long is $12/\sqrt{x + 1}$ kg/m, where x is measured in meters from one end of the rod. Find the average density of the rod.

20. If a freely falling body starts from rest, then its displacement is given by $s = \frac{1}{2}gt^2$. Let the velocity after a time T be v_T. Show that if we compute the average of the velocities with respect to t we get $v_{ave} = \frac{1}{2}v_T$, but if we compute the average of the velocities with respect to s we get $v_{ave} = \frac{2}{3}v_T$.

21. Use the result of Exercise 59 in Section 5.5 to compute the average volume of inhaled air in the lungs in one respiratory cycle.

22. The velocity v of blood that flows in a blood vessel with radius R and length l at a distance r from the central axis is

$$v(r) = \frac{P}{4\eta l}(R^2 - r^2)$$

where P is the pressure difference between the ends of the vessel and η is the viscosity of the blood (see Example 7 in Section 3.4). Find the average velocity (with respect to r) over the interval $0 \leq r \leq R$. Compare the average velocity with the maximum velocity.

23. Prove the Mean Value Theorem for Integrals by applying the Mean Value Theorem for derivatives (see Section 4.2) to the function $F(x) = \int_a^x f(t)\, dt$.

24. If $f_{ave}[a, b]$ denotes the average value of f on the interval $[a, b]$ and $a < c < b$, show that

$$f_{ave}[a, b] = \frac{c - a}{b - a}\, f_{ave}[a, c] + \frac{b - c}{b - a}\, f_{ave}[c, b]$$

6 Review

1. (a) Draw two typical curves $y = f(x)$ and $y = g(x)$, where $f(x) \geqslant g(x)$ for $a \leqslant x \leqslant b$. Show how to approximate the area between these curves by a Riemann sum and sketch the corresponding approximating rectangles. Then write an expression for the exact area.
   (b) Explain how the situation changes if the curves have equations $x = f(y)$ and $x = g(y)$, where $f(y) \geqslant g(y)$ for $c \leqslant y \leqslant d$.

2. Suppose that Sue runs faster than Kathy throughout a 1500-meter race. What is the physical meaning of the area between their velocity curves for the first minute of the race?

3. (a) Suppose S is a solid with known cross-sectional areas. Explain how to approximate the volume of S by a Riemann sum. Then write an expression for the exact volume.

(b) If S is a solid of revolution, how do you find the cross-sectional areas?

4. (a) What is the volume of a cylindrical shell?
   (b) Explain how to use cylindrical shells to find the volume of a solid of revolution.
   (c) Why might you want to use the shell method instead of slicing?

5. Suppose that you push a book across a 6-meter-long table by exerting a force $f(x)$ at each point from $x = 0$ to $x = 6$. What does $\int_0^6 f(x)\, dx$ represent? If $f(x)$ is measured in newtons, what are the units for the integral?

6. (a) What is the average value of a function f on an interval $[a, b]$?
   (b) What does the Mean Value Theorem for Integrals say? What is its geometric interpretation?

1–6 ‖ Find the area of the region bounded by the given curves.

1. $y = x^2 - x - 6$, $y = 0$

2. $y = 20 - x^2$, $y = x^2 - 12$

3. $y = 1 - x^2$, $y = 1 - \sqrt{x}$

4. $x + y = 0$, $x = y^2 + 3y$

5. $y = \sin(\pi x/2)$, $y = x^2 - 2x$

6. $y = \sqrt{x}$, $y = x^2$, $x = 2$

7–11 ‖ Find the volume of the solid obtained by rotating the region bounded by the given curves about the specified axis.

7. $y = 2x$, $y = x^2$; about the x-axis

8. $x = 1 + y^2$, $y = x - 3$; about the y-axis

9. $x = 0$, $x = 9 - y^2$; about $x = -1$

10. $y = x^2 + 1$, $y = 9 - x^2$; about $y = -1$

11. $x^2 - y^2 = a^2$, $x = a + h$ (where $a > 0$, $h > 0$); about the y-axis

12–14 ‖ Set up, but do not evaluate, an integral for the volume of the solid obtained by rotating the region bounded by the given curves about the specified axis.

12. $y = \cos x$, $y = 0$, $x = 3\pi/2$, $x = 5\pi/2$; about the y-axis

13. $y = x^3$, $y = x^2$; about $y = 1$

14. $y = x^3$, $y = 8$, $x = 0$; about $x = 2$

15. Find the volumes of the solids obtained by rotating the region bounded by the curves $y = x$ and $y = x^2$ about the following lines:
    (a) The x-axis   (b) The y-axis   (c) $y = 2$

16. Let $\mathcal{R}$ be the region in the first quadrant bounded by the curves $y = x^3$ and $y = 2x - x^2$. Calculate the following quantities.
    (a) The area of $\mathcal{R}$
    (b) The volume obtained by rotating $\mathcal{R}$ about the x-axis
    (c) The volume obtained by rotating $\mathcal{R}$ about the y-axis

17. Let $\mathcal{R}$ be the region bounded by the curves $y = \tan(x^2)$, $x = 1$, and $y = 0$. Use the Midpoint Rule with $n = 4$ to estimate the following.
    (a) The area of $\mathcal{R}$
    (b) The volume obtained by rotating $\mathcal{R}$ about the x-axis

18. Let $\mathcal{R}$ be the region bounded by the curves $y = 1 - x^2$ and $y = x^6 - x + 1$. Estimate the following quantities.
    (a) The x-coordinates of the points of intersection of the curves
    (b) The area of $\mathcal{R}$
    (c) The volume generated when $\mathcal{R}$ is rotated about the x-axis
    (d) The volume generated when $\mathcal{R}$ is rotated about the y-axis

19–22 ‖ Each integral represents the volume of a solid. Describe the solid.

19. $\int_0^{\pi/2} 2\pi x \cos x \, dx$

20. $\int_0^{\pi/2} 2\pi \cos^2 x \, dx$

21. $\int_0^2 2\pi y(4 - y^2)\, dy$

22. $\int_0^1 \pi\left[(2 - x^2)^2 - (2 - \sqrt{x})^2\right] dx$

23. The base of a solid is a circular disk with radius 3. Find the volume of the solid if parallel cross-sections perpendicular to the base are isosceles right triangles with hypotenuse lying along the base.

24. The base of a solid is the region bounded by the parabolas $y = x^2$ and $y = 2 - x^2$. Find the volume of the solid if the cross-sections perpendicular to the x-axis are squares with one side lying along the base.

25. The height of a monument is 20 m. A horizontal cross-section at a distance x meters from the top is an equilateral triangle with side $x/4$ meters. Find the volume of the monument.

26. (a) The base of a solid is a square with vertices located at $(1, 0), (0, 1), (-1, 0)$, and $(0, -1)$. Each cross-section perpendicular to the x-axis is a semicircle. Find the volume of the solid.
(b) Show that by cutting the solid of part (a), we can rearrange it to form a cone. Thus compute its volume more simply.

27. A force of 30 N is required to maintain a spring stretched from its natural length of 12 cm to a length of 15 cm. How much work is done in stretching the spring from 12 cm to 20 cm?

28. A 1600-lb elevator is suspended by a 200-ft cable that weighs 10 lb/ft. How much work is required to raise the elevator from the basement to the third floor, a distance of 30 ft?

29. A tank full of water has the shape of a paraboloid of revolution as shown in the figure; that is, its shape is obtained by rotating a parabola about a vertical axis.
(a) If its height is 4 ft and the radius at the top is 4 ft, find the work required to pump the water out of the tank.
(b) After 4000 ft-lb of work has been done, what is the depth of the water remaining in the tank?

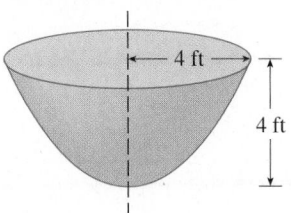

30. Find the average value of the function $f(t) = t \sin(t^2)$ on the interval $[0, 10]$.

31. If f is a continuous function, what is the limit as $h \to 0$ of the average value of f on the interval $[x, x + h]$?

32. Let $\mathcal{R}_1$ be the region bounded by $y = x^2$, $y = 0$, and $x = b$, where $b > 0$. Let $\mathcal{R}_2$ be the region bounded by $y = x^2$, $x = 0$, and $y = b^2$.
(a) Is there a value of b such that $\mathcal{R}_1$ and $\mathcal{R}_2$ have the same area?
(b) Is there a value of b such that $\mathcal{R}_1$ sweeps out the same volume when rotated about the x-axis and the y-axis?
(c) Is there a value of b such that $\mathcal{R}_1$ and $\mathcal{R}_2$ sweep out the same volume when rotated about the x-axis?
(d) Is there a value of b such that $\mathcal{R}_1$ and $\mathcal{R}_2$ sweep out the same volume when rotated about the y-axis?

1. (a) Find a positive continuous function f such that the area under the graph of f from 0 to t is
$A(t) = t^3$ for all $t > 0$.

(b) A solid is generated by rotating about the x-axis the region under the curve $y = f(x)$,
where f is a positive function and $x \geq 0$. The volume generated by the part of the curve
from $x = 0$ to $x = b$ is b^2 for all $b > 0$. Find the function f.

2. There is a line through the origin that divides the region bounded by the parabola $y = x - x^2$
and the x-axis into two regions with equal area. What is the slope of that line?

3. The figure shows a horizontal line $y = c$ intersecting the curve $y = 8x - 27x^3$. Find the number c such that the areas of the shaded regions are equal.

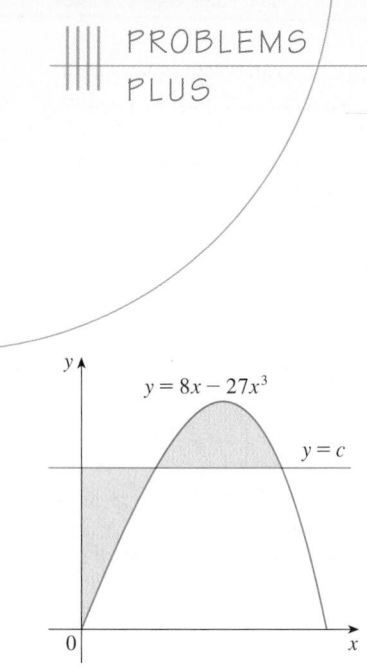

4. A cylindrical glass of radius r and height L is filled with water and then tilted until the water
remaining in the glass exactly covers its base.

(a) Determine a way to "slice" the water into parallel rectangular cross-sections and then
set up a definite integral for the volume of the water in the glass.

(b) Determine a way to "slice" the water into parallel cross-sections that are trapezoids and
then *set up* a definite integral for the volume of the water.

(c) Find the volume of water in the glass by evaluating one of the integrals in part (a) or
part (b).

(d) Find the volume of the water in the glass from purely geometric considerations.

(e) Suppose the glass is tilted until the water exactly covers half the base. In what direction
can you "slice" the water into triangular cross-sections? Rectangular cross-sections?
Cross-sections that are segments of circles? Find the volume of water in the glass.

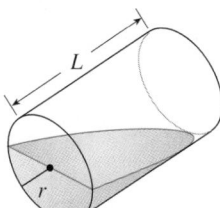

5. (a) Show that the volume of a segment of height h of a sphere of radius r is

$$V = \tfrac{1}{3}\pi h^2(3r - h)$$

(b) Show that if a sphere of radius 1 is sliced by a plane at a distance x from the center in
such a way that the volume of one segment is twice the volume of the other, then x is a
solution of the equation

$$3x^3 - 9x + 2 = 0$$

where $0 < x < 1$. Use Newton's method to find x accurate to four decimal places.

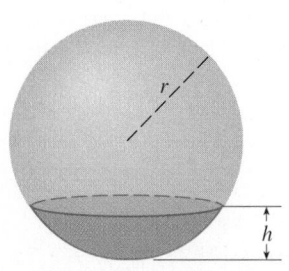

(c) Using the formula for the volume of a segment of a sphere, it can be shown that the depth
x to which a floating sphere of radius r sinks in water is a root of the equation

$$x^3 - 3rx^2 + 4r^3s = 0$$

where s is the specific gravity of the sphere. Suppose a wooden sphere of radius 0.5 m has
specific gravity 0.75. Calculate, to four-decimal-place accuracy, the depth to which the
sphere will sink.

(d) A hemispherical bowl has radius 5 inches and water is running into the bowl at the rate
of 0.2 in³/s.
  (i) How fast is the water level in the bowl rising at the instant the water is 3 inches deep?
  (ii) At a certain instant, the water is 4 inches deep. How long will it take to fill the bowl?

6. Archimedes' Principle states that the buoyant force on an object partially or fully submerged in a fluid is equal to the weight of the fluid that the object displaces. Thus, for an object of density ρ_0 floating partly submerged in a fluid of density ρ_f, the buoyant force is given by $F = \rho_f g \int_{-h}^{0} A(y)\, dy$, where g is the acceleration due to gravity and $A(y)$ is the area of a typical cross-section of the object. The weight of the object is given by

$$W = \rho_0 g \int_{-h}^{L-h} A(y)\, dy$$

(a) Show that the percentage of the volume of the object above the surface of the liquid is

$$100\,\frac{\rho_f - \rho_0}{\rho_f}$$

(b) The density of ice is $917\ \text{kg/m}^3$ and the density of seawater is $1030\ \text{kg/m}^3$. What percentage of the volume of an iceberg is above water?

(c) An ice cube floats in a glass filled to the brim with water. Does the water overflow when the ice melts?

(d) A sphere of radius 0.4 m and having negligible weight is floating in a large freshwater lake. How much work is required to completely submerge the sphere? The density of the water is $1000\ \text{kg/m}^3$.

7. Water in an open bowl evaporates at a rate proportional to the area of the surface of the water. (This means that the rate of decrease of the volume is proportional to the area of the surface.) Show that the depth of the water decreases at a constant rate, regardless of the shape of the bowl.

8. A sphere of radius 1 overlaps a smaller sphere of radius r in such a way that their intersection is a circle of radius r. (In other words, they intersect in a great circle of the small sphere.) Find r so that the volume inside the small sphere and outside the large sphere is as large as possible.

9. The figure shows a curve C with the property that, for every point P on the middle curve $y = 2x^2$, the areas A and B are equal. Find an equation for C.

10. A paper drinking cup filled with water has the shape of a cone with height h and semivertical angle θ (see the figure). A ball is placed carefully in the cup, thereby displacing some of the water and making it overflow. What is the radius of the ball that causes the greatest volume of water to spill out of the cup?

FIGURE FOR PROBLEM 9

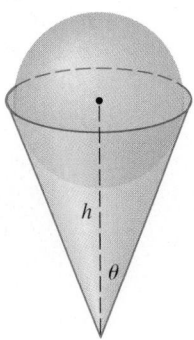

11. A *clepsydra*, or water clock, is a glass container with a small hole in the bottom through which water can flow. The "clock" is calibrated for measuring time by placing markings on the container corresponding to water levels at equally spaced times. Let $x = f(y)$ be continuous on the interval $[0, b]$ and assume that the container is formed by rotating the graph of f about the y-axis. Let V denote the volume of water and h the height of the water level at time t.
(a) Determine V as a function of h.
(b) Show that

$$\frac{dV}{dt} = \pi[f(h)]^2 \frac{dh}{dt}$$

(c) Suppose that A is the area of the hole in the bottom of the container. It follows from Torricelli's Law that the rate of change of the volume of the water is given by

$$\frac{dV}{dt} = kA\sqrt{h}$$

where k is a negative constant. Determine a formula for the function f such that dh/dt is a constant C. What is the advantage in having $dh/dt = C$?

12. A cylindrical container of radius r and height L is partially filled with a liquid whose volume is V. If the container is rotated about its axis of symmetry with constant angular speed ω, then the container will induce a rotational motion in the liquid around the same axis. Eventually, the liquid will be rotating at the same angular speed as the container. The surface of the liquid will be convex, as indicated in the figure, because the centrifugal force on the liquid particles increases with the distance from the axis of the container. It can be shown that the surface of the liquid is a paraboloid of revolution generated by rotating the parabola

$$y = h + \frac{\omega^2 x^2}{2g}$$

about the y-axis, where g is the acceleration due to gravity.
(a) Determine h as a function of ω.
(b) At what angular speed will the surface of the liquid touch the bottom? At what speed will it spill over the top?
(c) Suppose the radius of the container is 2 ft, the height is 7 ft, and the container and liquid are rotating at the same constant angular speed. The surface of the liquid is 5 ft below the top of the tank at the central axis and 4 ft below the top of the tank 1 ft out from the central axis.
   (i) Determine the angular speed of the container and the volume of the fluid.
   (ii) How far below the top of the tank is the liquid at the wall of the container?

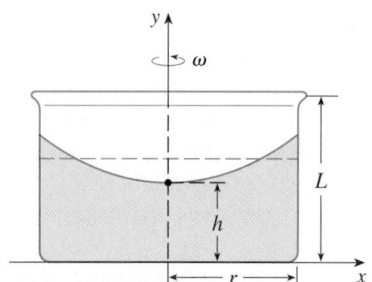

FIGURE FOR PROBLEM 12

13. If the tangent at a point P on the curve $y = x^3$ intersects the curve again at Q, let A be the area of the region bounded by the curve and the line segment PQ. Let B be the area of the region defined in the same way starting with Q instead of P. What is the relationship between A and B?

CAS **14.** Suppose we are planning to make a taco from a round tortilla with diameter 8 inches by bending the tortilla so that it is shaped as if it is partially wrapped around a circular cylinder. We will fill the tortilla to the edge (but no more) with meat, cheese, and other ingredients. Our problem is to decide how to curve the tortilla in order to maximize the volume of food it can hold.

(a) We start by placing a circular cylinder of radius r along a diameter of the tortilla and folding the tortilla around the cylinder. Let x represent the distance from the center of the tortilla to a point P on the diameter (see the figure). Show that the cross-sectional area of the filled taco in the plane through P perpendicular to the axis of the cylinder is

$$A(x) = r\sqrt{16 - x^2} - \tfrac{1}{2}r^2 \sin\left(\frac{2}{r}\sqrt{16 - x^2}\right)$$

and write an expression for the volume of the filled taco.

(b) Determine (approximately) the value of r that maximizes the volume of the taco. (Use a graphical approach with your CAS.)

CHAPTER 7

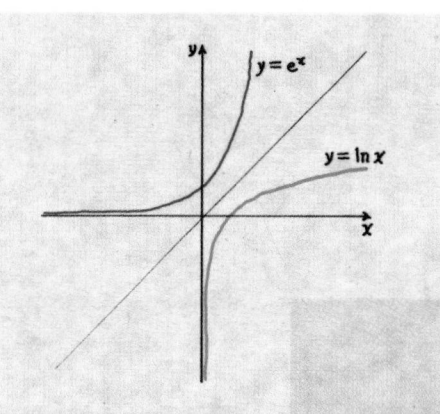

The graphs of the functions of this chapter appear as reflections of each other—the natural exponential and logarithmic functions, the restricted tangent and inverse tangent functions, and the hyperbolic sine function and its inverse.

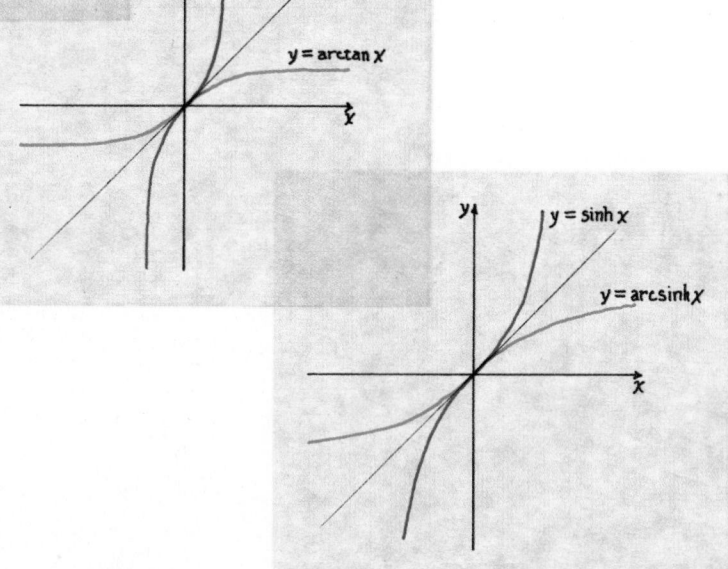

Inverse Functions:
Exponential, Logarithmic, and Inverse Trigonometric Functions

The common theme that links the functions of this chapter is that they occur as pairs of inverse functions. In particular, two of the most important functions that occur in mathematics and its applications are the exponential function $f(x) = a^x$ and its inverse function, the logarithmic function $g(x) = \log_a x$. In this chapter we investigate their properties, compute their derivatives, and use them to describe exponential growth and decay in biology, physics, chemistry, and other sciences. We also study the inverses of trigonometric and hyperbolic functions. Finally, we look at a method (l'Hospital's Rule) for computing difficult limits and apply it to sketching curves.

There are two possible ways of defining the exponential and logarithmic functions and developing their properties and derivatives. One is to start with the exponential function (defined as in algebra or precalculus courses) and then define the logarithm as its inverse. That is the approach taken in Sections 7.2, 7.3, and 7.4 and is probably the most intuitive method. The other way is to start by defining the logarithm as an integral and then define the exponential function as its inverse. This approach is followed in Sections 7.2*, 7.3*, and 7.4* and, although it is less intuitive, many instructors prefer it because it is more rigorous and the properties follow more easily. You need only read one of these two approaches (whichever your instructor recommends).

7.1 Inverse Functions

Table 1 gives data from an experiment in which a bacteria culture started with 100 bacteria in a limited nutrient medium; the size of the bacteria population was recorded at hourly intervals. The number of bacteria N is a function of the time t: $N = f(t)$.

Suppose, however, that the biologist changes her point of view and becomes interested in the time required for the population to reach various levels. In other words, she is thinking of t as a function of N. This function is called the *inverse function* of f, denoted by f^{-1}, and read "f inverse." Thus, $t = f^{-1}(N)$ is the time required for the population level to reach N. The values of f^{-1} can be found by reading Table 1 from right to left or by consulting Table 2. For instance, $f^{-1}(550) = 6$ because $f(6) = 550$.

TABLE 1 N as a function of t

t (hours)	$N = f(t)$ = population at time t
0	100
1	168
2	259
3	358
4	445
5	509
6	550
7	573
8	586

TABLE 2 t as a function of N

N	$t = f^{-1}(N)$ = time to reach N bacteria
100	0
168	1
259	2
358	3
445	4
509	5
550	6
573	7
586	8

Not all functions possess inverses. Let's compare the functions f and g whose arrow diagrams are shown in Figure 1.

 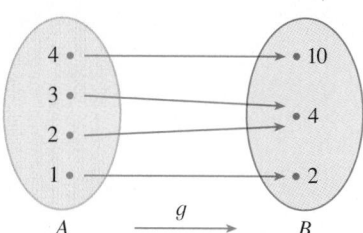

FIGURE 1

Note that f never takes on the same value twice (any two inputs in A have different outputs), whereas g does take on the same value twice (both 2 and 3 have the same output, 4). In symbols,

$$g(2) = g(3)$$

but
$$f(x_1) \neq f(x_2) \qquad \text{whenever } x_1 \neq x_2$$

Functions that have this property are called *one-to-one functions.*

|||| In the language of inputs and outputs, this definition says that f is one-to-one if each output corresponds to only one input.

> **1** **Definition** A function f is called a **one-to-one function** if it never takes on the same value twice; that is,
>
> $$f(x_1) \neq f(x_2) \qquad \text{whenever } x_1 \neq x_2$$

If a horizontal line intersects the graph of f in more than one point, then we see from Figure 2 that there are numbers x_1 and x_2 such that $f(x_1) = f(x_2)$. This means that f is not one-to-one. Therefore, we have the following geometric method for determining whether a function is one-to-one.

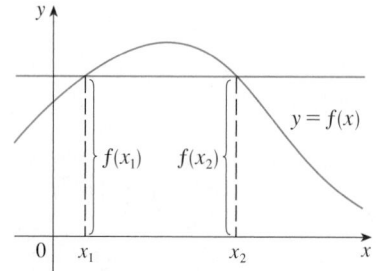

FIGURE 2
This function is not one-to-one because $f(x_1) = f(x_2)$.

> **Horizontal Line Test** A function is one-to-one if and only if no horizontal line intersects its graph more than once.

EXAMPLE 1 Is the function $f(x) = x^3$ one-to-one?

SOLUTION 1 If $x_1 \neq x_2$, then $x_1^3 \neq x_2^3$ (two different numbers can't have the same cube). Therefore, by Definition 1, $f(x) = x^3$ is one-to-one.

SOLUTION 2 From Figure 3 we see that no horizontal line intersects the graph of $f(x) = x^3$ more than once. Therefore, by the Horizontal Line Test, f is one-to-one. ▬

FIGURE 3
$f(x) = x^3$ is one-to-one.

EXAMPLE 2 Is the function $g(x) = x^2$ one-to-one?

SOLUTION 1 This function is not one-to-one because, for instance,

$$g(1) = 1 = g(-1)$$

and so 1 and -1 have the same output.

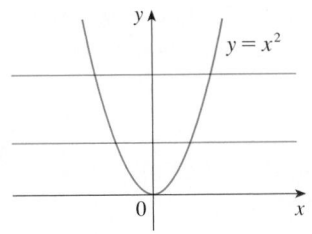

FIGURE 4

$g(x) = x^2$ is not one-to-one.

FIGURE 5

f

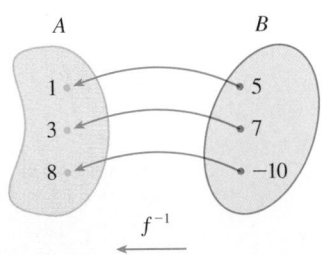

f^{-1}

FIGURE 6

The inverse function reverses
inputs and outputs.

SOLUTION 2 From Figure 4 we see that there are horizontal lines that intersect the graph of g more than once. Therefore, by the Horizontal Line Test, g is not one-to-one. ▬

One-to-one functions are important because they are precisely the functions that possess inverse functions according to the following definition.

> **2** **Definition** Let f be a one-to-one function with domain A and range B. Then its **inverse function** f^{-1} has domain B and range A and is defined by
>
> $$f^{-1}(y) = x \iff f(x) = y$$
>
> for any y in B.

This definition says that if f maps x into y, then f^{-1} maps y back into x. (If f were not one-to-one, then f^{-1} would not be uniquely defined.) The arrow diagram in Figure 5 indicates that f^{-1} reverses the effect of f. Note that

> domain of f^{-1} = range of f
>
> range of f^{-1} = domain of f

For example, the inverse function of $f(x) = x^3$ is $f^{-1}(x) = x^{1/3}$ because if $y = x^3$, then

$$f^{-1}(y) = f^{-1}(x^3) = (x^3)^{1/3} = x$$

⊘ **CAUTION** ▫ Do not mistake the -1 in f^{-1} for an exponent. Thus

$$f^{-1}(x) \quad \text{does } not \text{ mean} \quad \frac{1}{f(x)}$$

The reciprocal $1/f(x)$ could, however, be written as $[f(x)]^{-1}$.

EXAMPLE 3 If $f(1) = 5$, $f(3) = 7$, and $f(8) = -10$, find $f^{-1}(7)$, $f^{-1}(5)$, and $f^{-1}(-10)$.

SOLUTION From the definition of f^{-1} we have

$$f^{-1}(7) = 3 \quad \text{because} \quad f(3) = 7$$

$$f^{-1}(5) = 1 \quad \text{because} \quad f(1) = 5$$

$$f^{-1}(-10) = 8 \quad \text{because} \quad f(8) = -10$$

The diagram in Figure 6 makes it clear how f^{-1} reverses the effect of f in this case. ▬

The letter x is traditionally used as the independent variable, so when we concentrate on f^{-1} rather than on f, we usually reverse the roles of x and y in Definition 2 and write

3
$$f^{-1}(x) = y \iff f(y) = x$$

By substituting for y in Definition 2 and substituting for x in (3), we get the following **cancellation equations**:

4
$$f^{-1}(f(x)) = x \quad \text{for every } x \text{ in } A$$
$$f(f^{-1}(x)) = x \quad \text{for every } x \text{ in } B$$

The first cancellation equation says that if we start with x, apply f, and then apply f^{-1}, we arrive back at x, where we started (see the machine diagram in Figure 7). Thus, f^{-1} undoes what f does. The second equation says that f undoes what f^{-1} does.

FIGURE 7

For example, if $f(x) = x^3$, then $f^{-1}(x) = x^{1/3}$ and the cancellation equations become

$$f^{-1}(f(x)) = (x^3)^{1/3} = x$$
$$f(f^{-1}(x)) = (x^{1/3})^3 = x$$

These equations simply say that the cube function and the cube root function cancel each other when applied in succession.

Now let's see how to compute inverse functions. If we have a function $y = f(x)$ and are able to solve this equation for x in terms of y, then according to Definition 2 we must have $x = f^{-1}(y)$. If we want to call the independent variable x, we then interchange x and y and arrive at the equation $y = f^{-1}(x)$.

---

5 **How to Find the Inverse Function of a One-To-One Function f**

STEP 1 Write $y = f(x)$.

STEP 2 Solve this equation for x in terms of y (if possible).

STEP 3 To express f^{-1} as a function of x, interchange x and y. The resulting equation is $y = f^{-1}(x)$.

EXAMPLE 4 Find the inverse function of $f(x) = x^3 + 2$.

SOLUTION According to (5) we first write

$$y = x^3 + 2$$

Then we solve this equation for x:

$$x^3 = y - 2$$

$$x = \sqrt[3]{y - 2}$$

|||| In Example 4, notice how f^{-1} reverses the effect of f. The function f is the rule "Cube, then add 2"; f^{-1} is the rule "Subtract 2, then take the cube root."

Finally, we interchange x and y:

$$y = \sqrt[3]{x - 2}$$

Therefore, the inverse function is $f^{-1}(x) = \sqrt[3]{x - 2}$.

The principle of interchanging x and y to find the inverse function also gives us the method for obtaining the graph of f^{-1} from the graph of f. Since $f(a) = b$ if and only if $f^{-1}(b) = a$, the point (a, b) is on the graph of f if and only if the point (b, a) is on the graph of f^{-1}. But we get the point (b, a) from (a, b) by reflecting about the line $y = x$. (See Figure 8.)

Therefore, as illustrated by Figure 9:

The graph of f^{-1} is obtained by reflecting the graph of f about the line $y = x$.

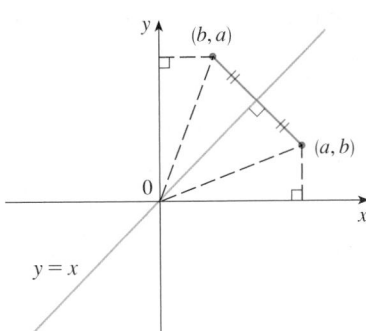

FIGURE 8   **FIGURE 9**

EXAMPLE 5 Sketch the graphs of $f(x) = \sqrt{-1 - x}$ and its inverse function using the same coordinate axes.

SOLUTION First we sketch the curve $y = \sqrt{-1 - x}$ (the top half of the parabola $y^2 = -1 - x$, or $x = -y^2 - 1$) and then we reflect about the line $y = x$ to get the graph of f^{-1}. (See Figure 10.) As a check on our graph, notice that the expression for f^{-1} is $f^{-1}(x) = -x^2 - 1, x \geqslant 0$. So the graph of f^{-1} is the right half of the parabola $y = -x^2 - 1$ and this seems reasonable from Figure 10.

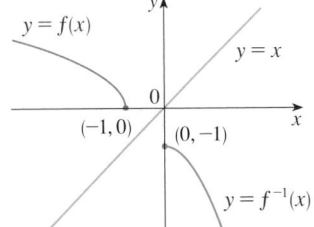

FIGURE 10

|||| **The Calculus of Inverse Functions**

Now let's look at inverse functions from the point of view of calculus. Suppose that f is both one-to-one and continuous. We think of a continuous function as one whose graph has no break in it. (It consists of just one piece.) Since the graph of f^{-1} is obtained from the graph of f by reflecting about the line $y = x$, the graph of f^{-1} has no break in it either (see Figure 9). Thus, we might expect that f^{-1} is also a continuous function.

This geometrical argument does not prove the following theorem but at least it makes the theorem plausible. A proof can be found in Appendix F.

6 Theorem If f is a one-to-one continuous function defined on an interval, then its inverse function f^{-1} is also continuous.

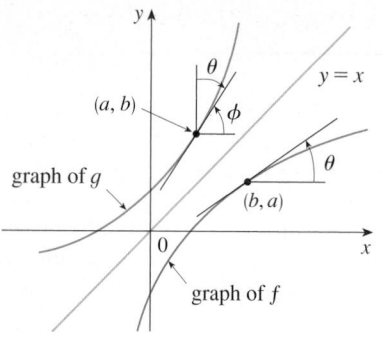

FIGURE 11

Now suppose that f is a one-to-one differentiable function. Geometrically we can think of a differentiable function as one whose graph has no corner or kink in it. We get the graph of f^{-1} by reflecting the graph of f about the line $y = x$, so the graph of f^{-1} has no corner or kink in it either. We therefore expect that f^{-1} is also differentiable (except where its tangents are vertical). In fact, we can predict the value of the derivative of f^{-1} at a given point by a geometric argument. In Figure 11 the graphs of f and its inverse $g = f^{-1}$ are shown. If $f(b) = a$, then $g(a) = f^{-1}(a) = b$ and $g'(a)$ is the slope of the tangent to the graph of g at (a, b), which is $\tan \phi$. Likewise, $f'(b) = \tan \theta$. From Figure 11 we see that $\theta + \phi = \pi/2$, so

$$g'(a) = \tan \phi = \tan\left(\frac{\pi}{2} - \theta\right) = \frac{1}{\tan \theta} = \frac{1}{f'(b)}$$

that is,

$$g'(a) = \frac{1}{f'(g(a))}$$

---

7 **Theorem** If f is a one-to-one differentiable function with inverse function $g = f^{-1}$ and $f'(g(a)) \neq 0$, then the inverse function is differentiable at a and

$$g'(a) = \frac{1}{f'(g(a))}$$

Proof Write the definition of derivative as in Equation 3.1.3:

$$g'(a) = \lim_{x \to a} \frac{g(x) - g(a)}{x - a}$$

By (3) we have

$$g(x) = y \iff f(y) = x$$

and

$$g(a) = b \iff f(b) = a$$

Since f is differentiable, it is continuous, so $g = f^{-1}$ is continuous by Theorem 6. Thus, if $x \to a$, then $g(x) \to g(a)$, that is, $y \to b$. Therefore

$$g'(a) = \lim_{x \to a} \frac{g(x) - g(a)}{x - a} = \lim_{y \to b} \frac{y - b}{f(y) - f(b)}$$

$$= \lim_{y \to b} \frac{1}{\dfrac{f(y) - f(b)}{y - b}} = \frac{1}{\lim\limits_{y \to b} \dfrac{f(y) - f(b)}{y - b}}$$

$$= \frac{1}{f'(b)} = \frac{1}{f'(g(a))}$$

NOTE 1 ▫ Replacing a by the general number x in the formula of Theorem 7, we get

$$\boxed{8} \qquad g'(x) = \frac{1}{f'(g(x))}$$

If we write $y = g(x)$, then $f(y) = x$, so Equation 8, when expressed in Leibniz notation, becomes

$$\frac{dy}{dx} = \frac{1}{\dfrac{dx}{dy}}$$

NOTE 2 ▫ If it is known in advance that f^{-1} is differentiable, then its derivative can be computed more easily than in the proof of Theorem 7 by using implicit differentiation. If $y = f^{-1}(x)$, then $f(y) = x$. Differentiating the equation $f(y) = x$ implicitly with respect to x, remembering that y is a function of x, and using the Chain Rule, we get

$$f'(y)\frac{dy}{dx} = 1$$

Therefore

$$\frac{dy}{dx} = \frac{1}{f'(y)} = \frac{1}{\dfrac{dx}{dy}}$$

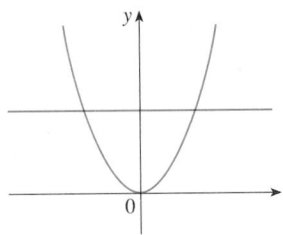

(a) $y = x^2$, $x \in \mathbb{R}$

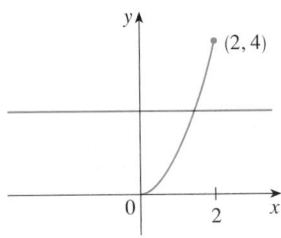

(b) $f(x) = x^2$, $0 \leqslant x \leqslant 2$

FIGURE 12

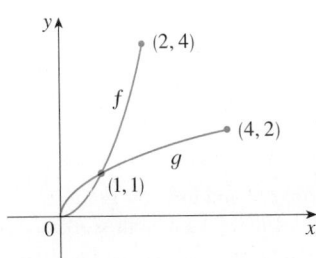

FIGURE 13

EXAMPLE 6 Although the function $y = x^2$, $x \in \mathbb{R}$, is not one-to-one and therefore does not have an inverse function, we can turn it into a one-to-one function by restricting its domain. For instance, the function $f(x) = x^2$, $0 \leqslant x \leqslant 2$, is one-to-one (by the Horizontal Line Test) and has domain $[0, 2]$ and range $[0, 4]$. (See Figure 12.) Thus, f has an inverse function $g = f^{-1}$ with domain $[0, 4]$ and range $[0, 2]$.

Without computing a formula for g' we can still calculate $g'(1)$. Since $f(1) = 1$, we have $g(1) = 1$. Also $f'(x) = 2x$. So by Theorem 7 we have

$$g'(1) = \frac{1}{f'(g(1))} = \frac{1}{f'(1)} = \frac{1}{2}$$

In this case it is easy to find g explicitly. In fact, $g(x) = \sqrt{x}$, $0 \leqslant x \leqslant 4$. [In general, we could use the method given by (5).] Then $g'(x) = 1/(2\sqrt{x})$, so $g'(1) = \frac{1}{2}$, which agrees with the preceding computation. The functions f and g are graphed in Figure 13. ▬

EXAMPLE 7 If $f(x) = 2x + \cos x$, find $(f^{-1})'(1)$.

SOLUTION Notice that f is one-to-one because

$$f'(x) = 2 - \sin x > 0$$

and so f is increasing. To use Theorem 7 we need to know $f^{-1}(1)$ and we can find it by inspection:

$$f(0) = 1 \quad \Rightarrow \quad f^{-1}(1) = 0$$

Therefore

$$(f^{-1})'(1) = \frac{1}{f'(f^{-1}(1))} = \frac{1}{f'(0)} = \frac{1}{2 - \sin 0} = \frac{1}{2}$$

|||| 7.1 Exercises

1. (a) What is a one-to-one function?
(b) How can you tell from the graph of a function whether it is one-to-one?

2. (a) Suppose f is a one-to-one function with domain A and range B. How is the inverse function f^{-1} defined? What is the domain of f^{-1}? What is the range of f^{-1}?
(b) If you are given a formula for f, how do you find a formula for f^{-1}?
(c) If you are given the graph of f, how do you find the graph of f^{-1}?

3–16 |||| A function is given by a table of values, a graph, a formula, or a verbal description. Determine whether it is one-to-one.

3.

x	1	2	3	4	5	6
$f(x)$	1.5	2.0	3.6	5.3	2.8	2.0

4.

x	1	2	3	4	5	6
$f(x)$	1	2	4	8	16	32

5.

6.

7.

8.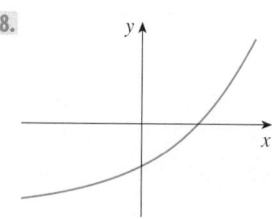

9. $f(x) = \frac{1}{2}(x + 5)$

10. $f(x) = 1 + 4x - x^2$

11. $g(x) = \sqrt{x}$

12. $g(x) = |x|$

13. $h(x) = x^4 + 5$

14. $h(x) = x^4 + 5, \quad 0 \leq x \leq 2$

15. $f(t)$ is the height of a football t seconds after kickoff.

16. $f(t)$ is your height at age t.

17–18 |||| Use a graph to decide whether f is one-to-one.

17. $f(x) = x^3 - x$

18. $f(x) = x^3 + x$

19. If f is a one-to-one function such that $f(2) = 9$, what is $f^{-1}(9)$?

20. If $f(x) = x + \cos x$, find $f^{-1}(1)$.

21. If $h(x) = x + \sqrt{x}$, find $h^{-1}(6)$.

22. The graph of f is given.
(a) Why is f one-to-one?
(b) State the domain and range of f^{-1}.
(c) Estimate the value of $f^{-1}(1)$.

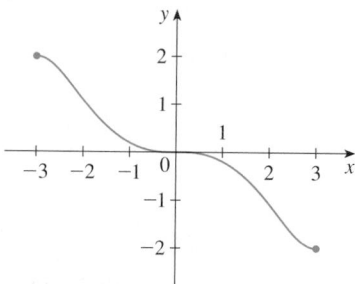

23. The formula $C = \frac{5}{9}(F - 32)$, where $F \geq -459.67$, expresses the Celsius temperature C as a function of the Fahrenheit temperature F. Find a formula for the inverse function and interpret it. What is the domain of the inverse function?

24. In the theory of relativity, the mass of a particle with speed v is

$$m = f(v) = \frac{m_0}{\sqrt{1 - v^2/c^2}}$$

where m_0 is the rest mass of the particle and c is the speed of light in a vacuum. Find the inverse function of f and explain its meaning.

25–30 |||| Find a formula for the inverse of the function.

25. $f(x) = 3 - 2x$

26. $f(x) = \dfrac{4x - 1}{2x + 3}$

27. $f(x) = \sqrt{10 - 3x}$

28. $y = 2x^3 + 3$

29. $y = \dfrac{1 - \sqrt{x}}{1 + \sqrt{x}}$

30. $f(x) = 2x^2 - 8x, \quad x \geq 2$

31–32 |||| Find an explicit formula for f^{-1} and use it to graph f^{-1}, f, and the line $y = x$ on the same screen. To check your work, see whether the graphs of f and f^{-1} are reflections about the line.

31. $f(x) = 1 - 2/x^2, \quad x > 0$

32. $f(x) = \sqrt{x^2 + 2x}, \quad x > 0$

33. Use the given graph of f to sketch the graph of f^{-1}.

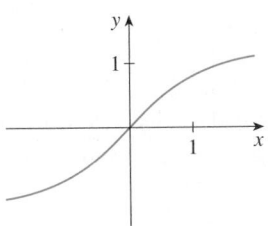

34. Use the given graph of f to sketch the graphs of f^{-1} and $1/f$.

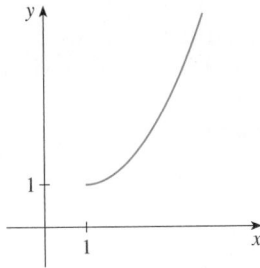

35–38 ▏▏▏▏

(a) Show that f is one-to-one.

(b) Use Theorem 7 to find $g'(a)$, where $g = f^{-1}$.

(c) Calculate $g(x)$ and state the domain and range of g.

(d) Calculate $g'(a)$ from the formula in part (c) and check that it agrees with the result of part (b).

(e) Sketch the graphs of f and g on the same axes.

35. $f(x) = x^3$, $a = 8$

36. $f(x) = \sqrt{x - 2}$, $a = 2$

37. $f(x) = 9 - x^2$, $0 \le x \le 3$, $a = 8$

38. $f(x) = 1/(x - 1)$, $x > 1$, $a = 2$

39–42 ▏▏▏▏ Find $(f^{-1})'(a)$.

39. $f(x) = x^3 + x + 1$, $a = 1$

40. $f(x) = x^5 - x^3 + 2x$, $a = 2$

41. $f(x) = 3 + x^2 + \tan(\pi x/2)$, $-1 < x < 1$, $a = 3$

42. $f(x) = \sqrt{x^3 + x^2 + x + 1}$, $a = 2$

43. Suppose g is the inverse function of f and $f(4) = 5, f'(4) = \frac{2}{3}$. Find $g'(5)$.

44. Suppose g is the inverse function of a differentiable function f and let $G(x) = 1/g(x)$. If $f(3) = 2$ and $f'(3) = \frac{1}{9}$, find $G'(2)$.

CAS **45.** Use a computer algebra system to find an explicit expression for the inverse of the function $f(x) = \sqrt{x^3 + x^2 + x + 1}$. (Your CAS will produce three possible expressions. Explain why two of them are irrelevant in this context.)

46. Show that $h(x) = \sin x, x \in \mathbb{R}$, is not one-to-one, but its restriction $f(x) = \sin x, -\pi/2 \le x \le \pi/2$, is one-to-one. Compute the derivative of $f^{-1} = \sin^{-1}$ by the method of Note 2.

47. (a) If we shift a curve to the left, what happens to its reflection about the line $y = x$? In view of this geometric principle, find an expression for the inverse of $g(x) = f(x + c)$, where f is a one-to-one function.

(b) Find an expression for the inverse of $h(x) = f(cx)$, where $c \ne 0$.

48. (a) If f is a one-to-one, twice differentiable function with inverse function g, show that

$$g''(x) = -\frac{f''(g(x))}{[f'(g(x))]^3}$$

(b) Deduce that if f is increasing and concave upward, then its inverse function is concave downward.

7.2 Exponential Functions and Their Derivatives

▏▏▏▏ If your instructor has assigned Sections 7.2*, 7.3*, and 7.4*, you don't need to read Sections 7.2–7.4 (pp. 421–450).

The function $f(x) = 2^x$ is called an *exponential function* because the variable, x, is the exponent. It should not be confused with the power function $g(x) = x^2$, in which the variable is the base.

In general, an **exponential function** is a function of the form

$$f(x) = a^x$$

where a is a positive constant. Let's recall what this means.

If $x = n$, a positive integer, then

$$a^n = \underbrace{a \cdot a \cdot \cdots \cdot a}_{n \text{ factors}}$$

If $x = 0$, then $a^0 = 1$, and if $x = -n$, where n is a positive integer, then

$$a^{-n} = \frac{1}{a^n}$$

If x is a rational number, $x = p/q$, where p and q are integers and $q > 0$, then

$$a^x = a^{p/q} = \sqrt[q]{a^p} = \left(\sqrt[q]{a}\right)^p$$

But what is the meaning of a^x if x is an irrational number? For instance, what is meant by $2^{\sqrt{3}}$ or 5^π?

To help us answer this question we first look at the graph of the function $y = 2^x$, where x is rational. A representation of this graph is shown in Figure 1. We want to enlarge the domain of $y = 2^x$ to include both rational and irrational numbers.

There are holes in the graph in Figure 1 corresponding to irrational values of x. We want to fill in the holes by defining $f(x) = 2^x$, where $x \in \mathbb{R}$, so that f is an increasing function. In particular, since the irrational number $\sqrt{3}$ satisfies

$$1.7 < \sqrt{3} < 1.8$$

we must have

$$2^{1.7} < 2^{\sqrt{3}} < 2^{1.8}$$

and we know what $2^{1.7}$ and $2^{1.8}$ mean because 1.7 and 1.8 are rational numbers. Similarly, if we use better approximations for $\sqrt{3}$, we obtain better approximations for $2^{\sqrt{3}}$:

$$1.73 < \sqrt{3} < 1.74 \quad \Rightarrow \quad 2^{1.73} < 2^{\sqrt{3}} < 2^{1.74}$$
$$1.732 < \sqrt{3} < 1.733 \quad \Rightarrow \quad 2^{1.732} < 2^{\sqrt{3}} < 2^{1.733}$$
$$1.7320 < \sqrt{3} < 1.7321 \quad \Rightarrow \quad 2^{1.7320} < 2^{\sqrt{3}} < 2^{1.7321}$$
$$1.73205 < \sqrt{3} < 1.73206 \quad \Rightarrow \quad 2^{1.73205} < 2^{\sqrt{3}} < 2^{1.73206}$$

$$\vdots \qquad\qquad \vdots \qquad\qquad\qquad \vdots \qquad\qquad \vdots$$

It can be shown that there is exactly one number that is greater than all of the numbers

$$2^{1.7}, \quad 2^{1.73}, \quad 2^{1.732}, \quad 2^{1.7320}, \quad 2^{1.73205}, \quad \dots$$

and less than all of the numbers

$$2^{1.8}, \quad 2^{1.74}, \quad 2^{1.733}, \quad 2^{1.7321}, \quad 2^{1.73206}, \quad \dots$$

We define $2^{\sqrt{3}}$ to be this number. Using the preceding approximation process we can compute it correct to six decimal places:

$$2^{\sqrt{3}} \approx 3.321997$$

Similarly, we can define 2^x where x is any irrational number. Figure 2 shows how all the holes in Figure 1 have been filled to complete the graph of the function $f(x) = 2^x$, $x \in \mathbb{R}$. In general, if a is any positive number, we define

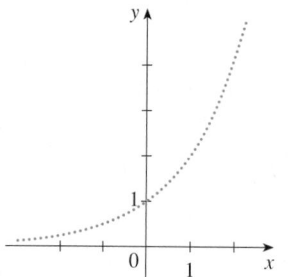

FIGURE 1
Representation of $y = 2^x$, x rational

||| A proof of this fact is given in J. Marsden and A. Weinstein, *Calculus Unlimited* (Menlo Park, CA: Benjamin/Cummings, 1980).

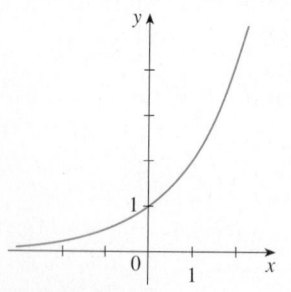

FIGURE 2
$y = 2^x$, x real

$\boxed{1}$

$$a^x = \lim_{r \to x} a^r \qquad r \text{ rational}$$

This definition makes sense because any irrational number can be approximated as closely as we like by a rational number. For instance, because $\sqrt{3}$ has the decimal representation $\sqrt{3} = 1.7320508 \ldots$, Definition 1 says that $2^{\sqrt{3}}$ is the limit of the sequence of numbers

$$2^{1.7}, \quad 2^{1.73}, \quad 2^{1.732}, \quad 2^{1.7320}, \quad 2^{1.73205}, \quad 2^{1.732050}, \quad 2^{1.7320508}, \quad \ldots$$

Similarly, 5^{π} is the limit of the sequence of numbers

$$5^{3.1}, \quad 5^{3.14}, \quad 5^{3.141}, \quad 5^{3.1415}, \quad 5^{3.14159}, \quad 5^{3.141592}, \quad 5^{3.1415926}, \quad \ldots$$

It can be shown that Definition 1 uniquely specifies a^x and makes the function $f(x) = a^x$ continuous.

The graphs of members of the family of functions $y = a^x$ are shown in Figure 3 for various values of the base a. Notice that all of these graphs pass through the same point $(0, 1)$ because $a^0 = 1$ for $a \neq 0$. Notice also that as the base a gets larger, the exponential function grows more rapidly (for $x > 0$).

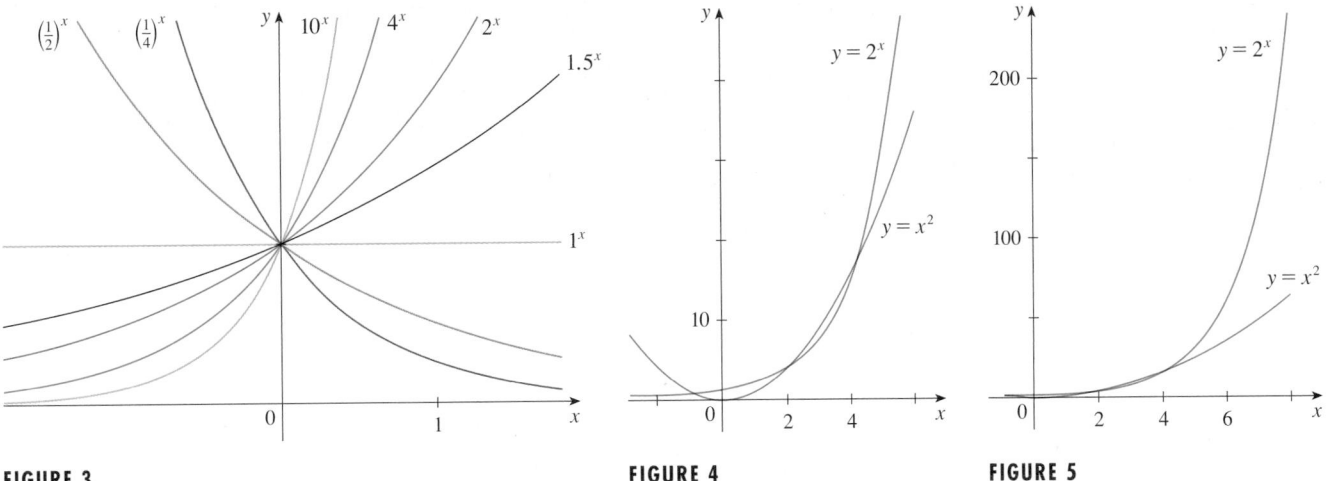

FIGURE 3

Members of the family of exponential functions

FIGURE 4

FIGURE 5

Figure 4 shows how the exponential function $y = 2^x$ compares with the power function $y = x^2$. The graphs intersect three times, but ultimately the exponential curve $y = 2^x$ grows far more rapidly than the parabola $y = x^2$. (See also Figure 5.)

You can see from Figure 3 that there are basically three kinds of exponential functions $y = a^x$. If $0 < a < 1$, the exponential function decreases; if $a = 1$, it is a constant; and if $a > 1$, it increases. These three cases are illustrated in Figure 6. Since $(1/a)^x = 1/a^x = a^{-x}$, the graph of $y = (1/a)^x$ is just the reflection of the graph of $y = a^x$ about the y-axis.

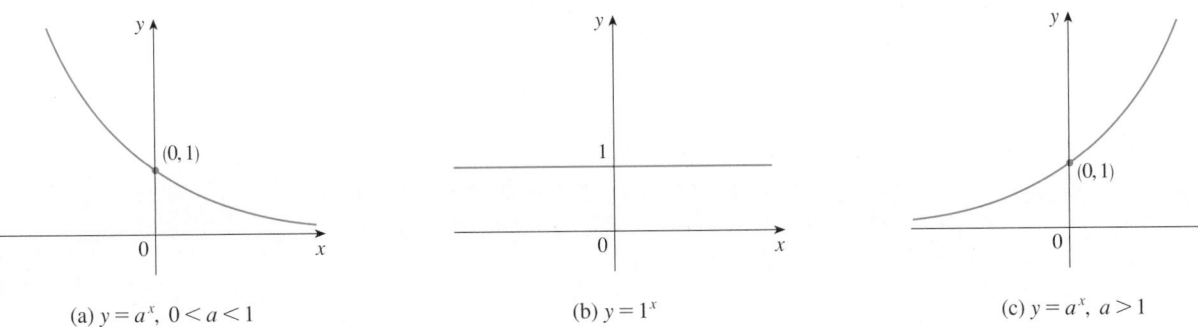

(a) $y = a^x$, $0 < a < 1$

(b) $y = 1^x$

(c) $y = a^x$, $a > 1$

FIGURE 6

The properties of the exponential function are summarized in the following theorem.

> **2** **Theorem** If $a > 0$ and $a \neq 1$, then $f(x) = a^x$ is a continuous function with domain $\mathbb{R}$ and range $(0, \infty)$. In particular, $a^x > 0$ for all x. If $0 < a < 1$, $f(x) = a^x$ is a decreasing function; if $a > 1$, f is an increasing function. If $a, b > 0$ and $x, y \in \mathbb{R}$, then
>
> **1.** $a^{x+y} = a^x a^y$ **2.** $a^{x-y} = \dfrac{a^x}{a^y}$ **3.** $(a^x)^y = a^{xy}$ **4.** $(ab)^x = a^x b^x$

The reason for the importance of the exponential function lies in properties 1–4, which are called the **Laws of Exponents**. If x and y are rational numbers, then these laws are well known from elementary algebra. For arbitrary real numbers x and y these laws can be deduced from the special case where the exponents are rational by using Equation 1.

The following limits can be read from the graphs shown in Figure 6 or proved from the definition of a limit at infinity. (See Exercise 73 in Section 7.3.)

> **3**   If $a > 1$, then $\lim\limits_{x \to \infty} a^x = \infty$ and $\lim\limits_{x \to -\infty} a^x = 0$
>
>   If $0 < a < 1$, then $\lim\limits_{x \to \infty} a^x = 0$ and $\lim\limits_{x \to -\infty} a^x = \infty$

In particular, if $a \neq 1$, then the x-axis is a horizontal asymptote of the graph of the exponential function $y = a^x$.

EXAMPLE 1
(a) Find $\lim_{x \to \infty} (2^{-x} - 1)$.
(b) Sketch the graph of the function $y = 2^{-x} - 1$.

SOLUTION

(a) $\lim\limits_{x \to \infty} (2^{-x} - 1) = \lim\limits_{x \to \infty} \left[\left(\tfrac{1}{2} \right)^x - 1 \right]$

                 $= 0 - 1$ $\left[\text{by (3) with } a = \tfrac{1}{2} < 1 \right]$

                 $= -1$

(b) We write $y = \left(\tfrac{1}{2} \right)^x - 1$ as in part (a). The graph of $y = \left(\tfrac{1}{2} \right)^x$ is shown in Figure 3, so we shift it down one unit to obtain the graph of $y = \left(\tfrac{1}{2} \right)^x - 1$ shown in Figure 7. (For a review of shifting graphs, see Section 1.3.) Part (a) shows that the line $y = -1$ is a horizontal asymptote.

FIGURE 7

‖‖‖ Applications of Exponential Functions

The exponential function occurs very frequently in mathematical models of nature and society. Here we indicate briefly how it arises in the description of population growth and radioactive decay. In Chapter 10 we will pursue these and other applications in greater detail.

In Section 3.4 we considered a bacteria population that doubles every hour and saw that if the initial population is n_0, then the population after t hours is given by the function $f(t) = n_0 2^t$. This population function is a constant multiple of the exponential function $y = 2^t$, so it exhibits the rapid growth that we observed in Figures 2 and 5. Under ideal conditions (unlimited space and nutrition and freedom from disease) this exponential growth is typical of what actually occurs in nature.

What about the human population? Table 1 shows data for the population of the world in the 20th century and Figure 8 shows the corresponding scatter plot.

TABLE 1

Year	Population (millions)
1900	1650
1910	1750
1920	1860
1930	2070
1940	2300
1950	2560
1960	3040
1970	3710
1980	4450
1990	5280
2000	6080

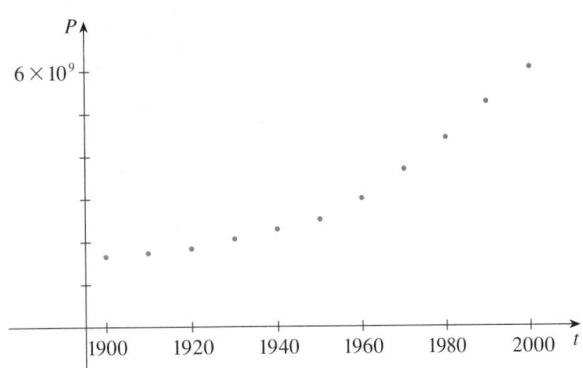

FIGURE 8 Scatter plot for world population growth

The pattern of the data points in Figure 8 suggests exponential growth, so we use a graphing calculator with exponential regression capability to apply the method of least squares and obtain the exponential model

$$P = (0.008079266) \cdot (1.013731)^t$$

Figure 9 shows the graph of this exponential function together with the original data points. We see that the exponential curve fits the data reasonably well. The period of relatively slow population growth is explained by the two world wars and the Great Depression of the 1930s.

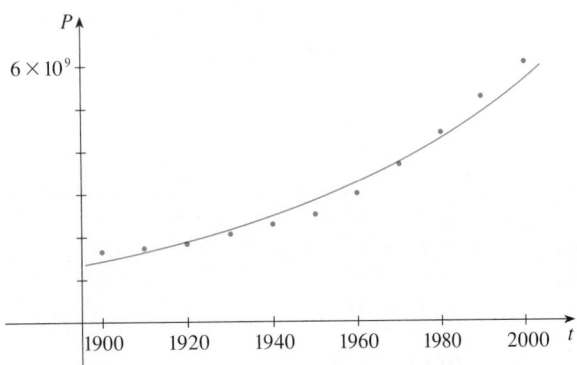

FIGURE 9
Exponential model for
population growth

Exponential functions also occur in the study of the decay of radioactive substances. For instance, when physicists say the *half-life* of strontium-90, ^{90}Sr, is 25 years they mean that half of any given quantity of ^{90}Sr will disintegrate in 25 years. So if the initial mass of a sample of ^{90}Sr is 24 mg and the mass that remains after t years is $m(t)$, then

$$m(25) = \frac{1}{2}(24) \qquad m(50) = \frac{1}{2^2}(24)$$

$$m(75) = \frac{1}{2^3}(24) \qquad m(100) = \frac{1}{2^4}(24)$$

From this pattern, we see that the mass remaining after t years is

$$\boxed{4} \qquad\qquad m(t) = \frac{1}{2^{t/25}}(24) = 24 \cdot 2^{-t/25}$$

This is an exponential function with base $a = 2^{-1/25}$. (See Exercise 55 and Section 10.4.)

||| Derivatives of Exponential Functions

Let's try to compute the derivative of the exponential function $f(x) = a^x$ using the definition of a derivative:

$$f'(x) = \lim_{h \to 0} \frac{f(x+h) - f(x)}{h} = \lim_{h \to 0} \frac{a^{x+h} - a^x}{h}$$

$$= \lim_{h \to 0} \frac{a^x a^h - a^x}{h} = \lim_{h \to 0} \frac{a^x(a^h - 1)}{h}$$

The factor a^x doesn't depend on h, so we can take it in front of the limit:

$$f'(x) = a^x \lim_{h \to 0} \frac{a^h - 1}{h}$$

Notice that the limit is the value of the derivative of f at 0, that is,

$$\lim_{h \to 0} \frac{a^h - 1}{h} = f'(0)$$

Therefore, we have shown that if the exponential function $f(x) = a^x$ is differentiable at 0, then it is differentiable everywhere and

$$\boxed{5} \qquad\qquad f'(x) = f'(0)a^x$$

This equation says that *the rate of change of any exponential function is proportional to the function itself.* (The slope is proportional to the height.)

Numerical evidence for the existence of $f'(0)$ is given in the table at the left for the cases $a = 2$ and $a = 3$. (Values are stated correct to four decimal places. For the case $a = 2$, see also Example 3 in Section 3.1.) It appears that the limits exist and

h	$\dfrac{2^h - 1}{h}$	$\dfrac{3^h - 1}{h}$
0.1	0.7177	1.1612
0.01	0.6956	1.1047
0.001	0.6934	1.0992
0.0001	0.6932	1.0987

$$\text{for } a = 2, \quad f'(0) = \lim_{h \to 0} \frac{2^h - 1}{h} \approx 0.69$$

$$\text{for } a = 3, \quad f'(0) = \lim_{h \to 0} \frac{3^h - 1}{h} \approx 1.10$$

In fact, it can be proved that these limits exist and, correct to six decimal places, the values are

$$\boxed{6} \qquad \frac{d}{dx}(2^x)\bigg|_{x=0} \approx 0.693147 \qquad \frac{d}{dx}(3^x)\bigg|_{x=0} \approx 1.098612$$

Thus, from Equation 5 we have

$$\boxed{7} \qquad \frac{d}{dx}(2^x) \approx (0.69)2^x \qquad \frac{d}{dx}(3^x) \approx (1.10)3^x$$

Of all possible choices for the base a in Equation 5, the simplest differentiation formula occurs when $f'(0) = 1$. In view of the estimates of $f'(0)$ for $a = 2$ and $a = 3$, it seems reasonable that there is a number a between 2 and 3 for which $f'(0) = 1$. It is traditional to denote this value by the letter e. Thus, we have the following definition.

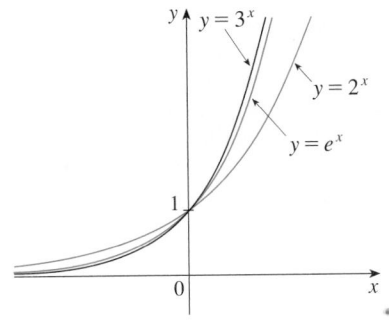

FIGURE 10

> **8 Definition of the Number e**
>
> e is the number such that $\quad \displaystyle\lim_{h \to 0} \frac{e^h - 1}{h} = 1$

Geometrically, this means that of all the possible exponential functions $y = a^x$, the function $f(x) = e^x$ is the one whose tangent line at $(0, 1)$ has a slope $f'(0)$ that is exactly 1 (see Figures 10 and 11).

If we put $a = e$ and, therefore, $f'(0) = 1$ in Equation 5, it becomes the following important differentiation formula.

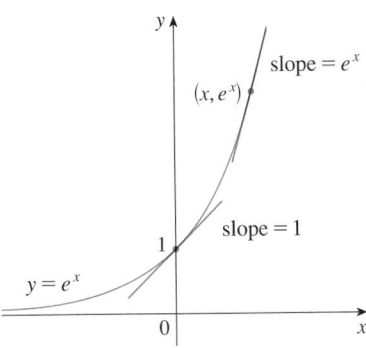

FIGURE 11

> **9 Derivative of the Natural Exponential Function**
>
> $$\frac{d}{dx}(e^x) = e^x$$

Thus, the exponential function $f(x) = e^x$ has the property that it is its own derivative. The geometrical significance of this fact is that the slope of a tangent line to the curve $y = e^x$ at any point is equal to the y-coordinate of the point (see Figure 11).

EXAMPLE 2 Differentiate the function $y = e^{\tan x}$.

SOLUTION To use the Chain Rule, we let $u = \tan x$. Then we have $y = e^u$, so

$$\frac{dy}{dx} = \frac{dy}{du}\frac{du}{dx} = e^u \frac{du}{dx} = e^{\tan x} \sec^2 x$$

In general if we combine Formula 9 with the Chain Rule, as in Example 2, we get

$$\boxed{10} \qquad \frac{d}{dx}(e^u) = e^u \frac{du}{dx}$$

EXAMPLE 3 Find y' if $y = e^{-4x} \sin 5x$.

SOLUTION Using Formula 10 and the Product Rule, we have

$$y' = e^{-4x}(\cos 5x)(5) + (\sin 5x)e^{-4x}(-4) = e^{-4x}(5 \cos 5x - 4 \sin 5x)$$

We have seen that e is a number that lies somewhere between 2 and 3, but we can use Equation 5 to estimate the numerical value of e more accurately. Let $e = 2^c$. Then $e^x = 2^{cx}$. If $f(x) = 2^x$, then from Equation 5 we have $f'(x) = k2^x$, where the value of k is $f'(0) \approx 0.693147$. Thus, by the Chain Rule,

$$e^x = \frac{d}{dx}(e^x) = \frac{d}{dx}(2^{cx}) = k2^{cx}\frac{d}{dx}(cx) = ck2^{cx}$$

Putting $x = 0$, we have $1 = ck$, so $c = 1/k$ and

$$e = 2^{1/k} \approx 2^{1/0.693147} \approx 2.71828$$

It can be shown that the approximate value to 20 decimal places is

$$e \approx 2.71828182845904523536$$

The decimal expansion of e is nonrepeating because e is an irrational number.

EXAMPLE 4 In Example 6 in Section 3.4 we considered a population of bacteria cells in a homogeneous nutrient medium. We showed that if the population doubles every hour, then the population after t hours is

$$n = n_0 2^t$$

where n_0 is the initial population. Now we can use (5) and (6) to compute the growth rate:

‖ The rate of growth is proportional to the size of the population.

$$\frac{dn}{dt} \approx n_0(0.693147)2^t$$

For instance, if the initial population is $n_0 = 1000$ cells, then the growth rate after two hours is

$$\frac{dn}{dt}\bigg|_{t=2} \approx (1000)(0.693147)2^t\big|_{t=2}$$

$$= (4000)(0.693147) \approx 2773 \text{ cells/h}$$

EXAMPLE 5 Find the absolute maximum value of the function $f(x) = xe^{-x}$.

SOLUTION We differentiate to find any critical numbers:

$$f'(x) = xe^{-x}(-1) + e^{-x}(1) = e^{-x}(1 - x)$$

Since exponential functions are always positive, we see that $f'(x) > 0$ when $1 - x > 0$, that is, when $x < 1$. Similarly, $f'(x) < 0$ when $x > 1$. By the First Derivative Test for Absolute Extreme Values, f has an absolute maximum value when $x = 1$ and the value is

$$f(1) = (1)e^{-1} = \frac{1}{e} \approx 0.37$$

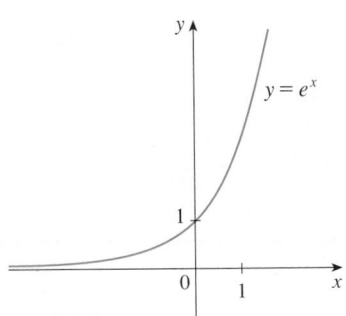

FIGURE 12
The natural exponential function

|||| Exponential Graphs

The exponential function $f(x) = e^x$ is one of the most frequently occurring functions in calculus and its applications, so it is important to be familiar with its graph (Figure 12) and properties. We summarize these properties as follows, using the fact that this function is just a special case of the exponential functions considered in Theorem 2 but with base $a = e > 1$.

---

11 **Properties of the Natural Exponential Function** The exponential function $f(x) = e^x$ is an increasing continuous function with domain $\mathbb{R}$ and range $(0, \infty)$. Thus, $e^x > 0$ for all x. Also

$$\lim_{x \to -\infty} e^x = 0 \qquad \lim_{x \to \infty} e^x = \infty$$

So the x-axis is a horizontal asymptote of $f(x) = e^x$.

EXAMPLE 6 Find $\displaystyle\lim_{x \to \infty} \frac{e^{2x}}{e^{2x} + 1}$.

SOLUTION We divide numerator and denominator by e^{2x}:

$$\lim_{x \to \infty} \frac{e^{2x}}{e^{2x} + 1} = \lim_{x \to \infty} \frac{1}{1 + e^{-2x}} = \frac{1}{1 + \lim_{x \to \infty} e^{-2x}}$$

$$= \frac{1}{1 + 0} = 1$$

We have used the fact that $t = -2x \to -\infty$ as $x \to \infty$ and so

$$\lim_{x \to \infty} e^{-2x} = \lim_{t \to -\infty} e^t = 0$$

EXAMPLE 7 Use the first and second derivatives of $f(x) = e^{1/x}$, together with asymptotes, to sketch its graph.

SOLUTION Notice that the domain of f is $\{x \mid x \neq 0\}$, so we check for vertical asymptotes by computing the left and right limits as $x \to 0$. As $x \to 0^+$, we know that $t = 1/x \to \infty$, so

$$\lim_{x \to 0^+} e^{1/x} = \lim_{t \to \infty} e^t = \infty$$

and this shows that $x = 0$ is a vertical asymptote. As $x \to 0^-$, we have $t = 1/x \to -\infty$, so

$$\lim_{x \to 0^-} e^{1/x} = \lim_{t \to -\infty} e^t = 0$$

As $x \to \pm\infty$, we have $1/x \to 0$ and so

$$\lim_{x \to \pm\infty} e^{1/x} = e^0 = 1$$

This shows that $y = 1$ is a horizontal asymptote.

Now let's compute the derivative. The Chain Rule gives

$$f'(x) = -\frac{e^{1/x}}{x^2}$$

Since $e^{1/x} > 0$ and $x^2 > 0$ for all $x \neq 0$, we have $f'(x) < 0$ for all $x \neq 0$. Thus, f is decreasing on $(-\infty, 0)$ and on $(0, \infty)$. There is no critical number, so the function has no maximum or minimum. The second derivative is

$$f''(x) = -\frac{x^2 e^{1/x}(-1/x^2) - e^{1/x}(2x)}{x^4} = \frac{e^{1/x}(2x + 1)}{x^4}$$

Since $e^{1/x} > 0$ and $x^4 > 0$, we have $f''(x) > 0$ when $x > -\frac{1}{2}$ ($x \neq 0$) and $f''(x) < 0$ when $x < -\frac{1}{2}$. So the curve is concave downward on $\left(-\infty, -\frac{1}{2}\right)$ and concave upward on $\left(-\frac{1}{2}, 0\right)$ and on $(0, \infty)$. The inflection point is $\left(-\frac{1}{2}, e^{-2}\right)$.

To sketch the graph of f we first draw the horizontal asymptote $y = 1$ (as a dashed line), together with the parts of the curve near the asymptotes in a preliminary sketch [Figure 13(a)]. These parts reflect the information concerning limits and the fact that f is decreasing on both $(-\infty, 0)$ and $(0, \infty)$. Notice that we have indicated that $f(x) \to 0$ as $x \to 0^-$ even though $f(0)$ does not exist. In Figure 13(b) we finish the sketch by incorporating the information concerning concavity and the inflection point. In Figure 13(c) we check our work with a graphing device.

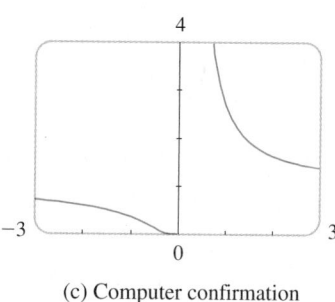

FIGURE 13 (a) Preliminary sketch (b) Finished sketch (c) Computer confirmation

▥ Integration

Because the exponential function $y = e^x$ has a simple derivative, its integral is also simple:

[12]
$$\int e^x \, dx = e^x + C$$

EXAMPLE 8 Evaluate $\int x^2 e^{x^3} \, dx$.

SOLUTION We substitute $u = x^3$. Then $du = 3x^2 \, dx$, so $x^2 \, dx = \frac{1}{3} du$ and

$$\int x^2 e^{x^3} \, dx = \frac{1}{3} \int e^u \, du = \frac{1}{3} e^u + C = \frac{1}{3} e^{x^3} + C$$

EXAMPLE 9 Find the area under the curve $y = e^{-3x}$ from 0 to 1.

SOLUTION The area is

$$A = \int_0^1 e^{-3x} \, dx = -\frac{1}{3} e^{-3x} \Big]_0^1 = \frac{1}{3}(1 - e^{-3})$$

7.2 Exercises

1. (a) Write an equation that defines the exponential function with base $a > 0$.
   (b) What is the domain of this function?
   (c) If $a \neq 1$, what is the range of this function?
   (d) Sketch the general shape of the graph of the exponential function for each of the following cases.
      (i) $a > 1$ (ii) $a = 1$ (iii) $0 < a < 1$

2. (a) How is the number e defined?
   (b) What is an approximate value for e?
   (c) What is the natural exponential function?

3–6 ||| Graph the given functions on a common screen. How are these graphs related?

3. $y = 2^x$, $y = e^x$, $y = 5^x$, $y = 20^x$

4. $y = e^x$, $y = e^{-x}$, $y = 8^x$, $y = 8^{-x}$

5. $y = 3^x$, $y = 10^x$, $y = \left(\frac{1}{3}\right)^x$, $y = \left(\frac{1}{10}\right)^x$

6. $y = 0.9^x$, $y = 0.6^x$, $y = 0.3^x$, $y = 0.1^x$

7–12 ||| Make a rough sketch of the graph of the function. Do not use a calculator. Just use the graphs given in Figures 3 and 12 and, if necessary, the transformations of Section 1.3.

7. $y = 4^x - 3$

8. $y = 4^{x-3}$

9. $y = -2^{-x}$

10. $y = 1 + 2e^x$

11. $y = 3 - e^x$

12. $y = 2 + 5(1 - e^{-x})$

13. Starting with the graph of $y = e^x$, write the equation of the graph that results from
   (a) shifting 2 units downward
   (b) shifting 2 units to the right
   (c) reflecting about the x-axis
   (d) reflecting about the y-axis
   (e) reflecting about the x-axis and then about the y-axis

14. Starting with the graph of $y = e^x$, find the equation of the graph that results from
   (a) reflecting about the line $y = 4$
   (b) reflecting about the line $x = 2$

15–16 ||| Find the domain of each function.

15. (a) $f(x) = \dfrac{1}{1 + e^x}$

   (b) $f(x) = \dfrac{1}{1 - e^x}$

16. (a) $g(t) = \sin(e^{-t})$

   (b) $g(t) = \sqrt{1 - 2^t}$

17–18 ||| Find the exponential function $f(x) = Ca^x$ whose graph is given.

17.

18.
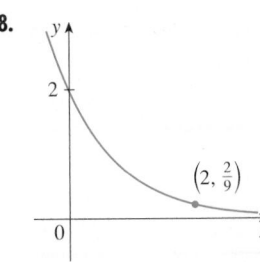

19. Suppose the graphs of $f(x) = x^2$ and $g(x) = 2^x$ are drawn on a coordinate grid where the unit of measurement is 1 inch. Show that, at a distance 2 ft to the right of the origin, the height of the graph of f is 48 ft but the height of the graph of g is about 265 mi.

20. Compare the rates of growth of the functions $f(x) = x^5$ and $g(x) = 5^x$ by graphing both functions in several viewing rectangles. Find all points of intersection of the graphs correct to one decimal place.

21. Compare the functions $f(x) = x^{10}$ and $g(x) = e^x$ by graphing both f and g in several viewing rectangles. When does the graph of g finally surpass the graph of f?

22. Use a graph to estimate the values of x such that $e^x > 1{,}000{,}000{,}000$.

23–28 ||| Find the limit.

23. $\lim\limits_{x \to \infty} (1.001)^x$

24. $\lim\limits_{x \to \infty} e^{-x^2}$

25. $\lim\limits_{x \to \infty} \dfrac{e^{3x} - e^{-3x}}{e^{3x} + e^{-3x}}$

26. $\lim\limits_{x \to (\pi/2)^+} e^{\tan x}$

27. $\lim\limits_{x \to 2^+} e^{3/(2-x)}$

28. $\lim\limits_{x \to 2^-} e^{3/(2-x)}$

29–42 ||| Differentiate the function.

29. $f(x) = x^2 e^x$

30. $y = \dfrac{e^x}{1 + x}$

31. $y = e^{ax^3}$

32. $y = e^u (\cos u + cu)$

33. $f(u) = e^{1/u}$

34. $g(x) = \sqrt{x}\, e^x$

35. $F(t) = e^{t \sin 2t}$

36. $y = e^{k \tan \sqrt{x}}$

37. $y = \sqrt{1 + 2e^{3x}}$

38. $y = \cos(e^{\pi x})$

39. $y = e^{e^x}$

40. $y = \sqrt{1 + xe^{-2x}}$

41. $y = \dfrac{ae^x + b}{ce^x + d}$

42. $y = \dfrac{e^x + e^{-x}}{e^x - e^{-x}}$

43–44 ‖‖‖ Find an equation of the tangent line to the curve at the given point.

43. $y = e^{2x} \cos \pi x$, $(0, 1)$

44. $y = e^x/x$, $(1, e)$

---

45. Find y' if $e^{x^2 y} = x + y$.

46. Find an equation of the tangent line to the curve $xe^y + ye^x = 1$ at the point $(0, 1)$.

47. Show that the function $y = e^x + e^{-x/2}$ satisfies the differential equation $2y'' - y' - y = 0$.

48. Show that the function $y = Ae^{-x} + Bxe^{-x}$ satisfies the differential equation $y'' + 2y' + y = 0$.

49. For what values of r does the function $y = e^{rx}$ satisfy the equation $y'' + 6y' + 8y = 0$?

50. Find the values of λ for which $y = e^{\lambda x}$ satisfies the equation $y + y' = y''$.

51. If $f(x) = e^{2x}$, find a formula for $f^{(n)}(x)$.

52. Find the thousandth derivative of $f(x) = xe^{-x}$.

53. (a) Use the Intermediate Value Theorem to show that there is a root of the equation $e^x + x = 0$.
(b) Use Newton's method to find the root of the equation in part (a) correct to six decimal places.

54. Use a graph to find an initial approximation (to one decimal place) to the root of the equation $e^{-x^2} = x^3 + x - 3$. Then use Newton's method to find the root correct to six decimal places.

55. If the initial mass of a sample of ^{90}Sr is 24 mg, then the mass after t years, from Equation 4, is

$$m(t) = 24 \cdot 2^{-t/25}$$

(a) Find the mass remaining after 40 years.
(b) Use Equation 7 and the Chain Rule to estimate the rate at which the mass decays after 40 years.
(c) Use a graphing device to estimate the time required for the mass to be reduced to 5 mg.

56. For the period from 1980 to 2000, the percentage of households in the United States with at least one VCR has been modeled by the function

$$V(t) = \dfrac{85}{1 + 53e^{-0.5t}}$$

where the time t is measured in years since midyear 1980, so $0 \le t \le 20$. Use a graph to estimate the time at which the number of VCRs was increasing most rapidly. Then use derivatives to give a more accurate estimate.

57. Under certain circumstances a rumor spreads according to the equation

$$p(t) = \dfrac{1}{1 + ae^{-kt}}$$

where $p(t)$ is the proportion of the population that knows the rumor at time t and a and k are positive constants. [In Section 10.5 we will see that this is a reasonable model for $p(t)$.]
(a) Find $\lim_{t \to \infty} p(t)$.
(b) Find the rate of spread of the rumor.
(c) Graph p for the case $a = 10$, $k = 0.5$ with t measured in hours. Use the graph to estimate how long it will take for 80% of the population to hear the rumor.

58. An object is attached to the end of a vibrating spring and its displacement from its equilibrium position is $y = 8e^{-t/2} \sin 4t$, where t is measured in seconds and y is measured in centimeters.
(a) Graph the displacement function together with the functions $y = 8e^{-t/2}$ and $y = -8e^{-t/2}$. How are these graphs related? Can you explain why?
(b) Use the graph to estimate the maximum value of the displacement. Does it occur when the graph touches the graph of $y = 8e^{-t/2}$?
(c) What is the velocity of the object when it first returns to its equilibrium position?
(d) Use the graph to estimate the time after which the displacement is no more than 2 cm from equilibrium.

59. The flash unit on a camera operates by storing charge on a capacitor and releasing it suddenly when the flash is set off. The following data describe the charge Q remaining on the capacitor (measured in microcoulombs, μC) at time t (measured in seconds).

t	0.00	0.02	0.04	0.06	0.08	0.10
Q	100.00	81.87	67.03	54.88	44.93	36.76

(a) Use a graphing calculator or computer to find an exponential model for the charge. (See Section 1.2.)
(b) The derivative $Q'(t)$ represents the electric current (measured in microamperes, μA) flowing from the capacitor to the flash bulb. Use part (a) to estimate the current when $t = 0.04$ s. Compare with the result of Example 2 in Section 2.1.

60. The table gives the U.S. population from 1790 to 1860.

Year	Population	Year	Population
1790	3,929,000	1830	12,861,000
1800	5,308,000	1840	17,063,000
1810	7,240,000	1850	23,192,000
1820	9,639,000	1860	31,443,000

(a) Use a graphing calculator or computer to fit an exponential function to the data. Graph the data points and the exponential model. How good is the fit?

(b) Estimate the rates of population growth in 1800 and 1850 by averaging slopes of secant lines.

(c) Use the exponential model in part (a) to estimate the rates of growth in 1800 and 1850. Compare these estimates with the ones in part (b).

(d) Use the exponential model to predict the population in 1870. Compare with the actual population of 38,558,000. Can you explain the discrepancy?

61. Find the absolute maximum value of the function
$f(x) = x - e^x$.

62. Find the absolute minimum value of the function
$g(x) = e^x/x$, $x > 0$.

63–64   Find (a) the intervals of increase or decrease, (b) the intervals of concavity, and (c) the points of inflection.

63. $f(x) = xe^x$ **64.** $f(x) = x^2 e^x$

65–67   Discuss the curve using the guidelines of Section 4.5.

65. $y = e^{-1/(x+1)}$ **66.** $y = e^{2x} - e^x$

67. $y = e^{3x} + e^{-2x}$

68–69   Draw a graph of f that shows all the important aspects of the curve. Estimate the local maximum and minimum values and then use calculus to find these values exactly. Use a graph of f'' to estimate the inflection points.

68. $f(x) = e^{\cos x}$ **69.** $f(x) = e^{x^3 - x}$

70. The family of bell-shaped curves
$$y = \frac{1}{\sigma\sqrt{2\pi}} e^{-(x-\mu)^2/(2\sigma^2)}$$
occurs in probability and statistics, where it is called the *normal density function*. The constant μ is called the *mean* and the positive constant σ is called the *standard deviation*. For simplicity, let's scale the function so as to remove the factor $1/(\sigma\sqrt{2\pi})$ and let's analyze the special case where $\mu = 0$. So we study the function
$$f(x) = e^{-x^2/(2\sigma^2)}$$
(a) Find the asymptote, maximum value, and inflection points of f.

(b) What role does σ play in the shape of the curve?

(c) Illustrate by graphing four members of this family on the same screen.

71–78   Evaluate the integral.

71. $\int_0^5 e^{-3x}\,dx$ **72.** $\int_0^1 xe^{-x^2}\,dx$

73. $\int e^x\sqrt{1+e^x}\,dx$ **74.** $\int \sec^2 x\, e^{\tan x}\,dx$

75. $\int \dfrac{e^x+1}{e^x}\,dx$ **76.** $\int \dfrac{e^{1/x}}{x^2}\,dx$

77. $\int \dfrac{e^{\sqrt{x}}}{\sqrt{x}}\,dx$ **78.** $\int e^x \sin(e^x)\,dx$

79. Find, correct to three decimal places, the area of the region bounded by the curves $y = e^x$, $y = e^{3x}$, and $x = 1$.

80. Find $f(x)$ if $f''(x) = 3e^x + 5\sin x$, $f(0) = 1$, and $f'(0) = 2$.

81. Find the volume of the solid obtained by rotating about the x-axis the region bounded by the curves $y = e^x$, $y = 0$, $x = 0$, and $x = 1$.

82. Find the volume of the solid obtained by rotating about the y-axis the region bounded by the curves $y = e^{-x^2}$, $y = 0$, $x = 0$, and $x = 1$.

83. If $f(x) = 3 + x + e^x$, find $(f^{-1})'(4)$.

84. Evaluate $\lim\limits_{x\to\pi} \dfrac{e^{\sin x} - 1}{x - \pi}$.

85. (a) Show that $e^x \geq 1 + x$ if $x \geq 0$.
[*Hint:* Show that $f(x) = e^x - (1 + x)$ is increasing for $x > 0$.]
(b) Deduce that $\frac{4}{3} \leq \int_0^1 e^{x^2}\,dx \leq e$.

86. (a) Use the inequality of Exercise 85(a) to show that, for $x \geq 0$,
$$e^x \geq 1 + x + \tfrac{1}{2}x^2$$
(b) Use part (a) to improve the estimate of $\int_0^1 e^{x^2}\,dx$ given in Exercise 85(b).

87. (a) Use mathematical induction to prove that for $x \geq 0$ and any positive integer n,
$$e^x \geq 1 + x + \frac{x^2}{2!} + \cdots + \frac{x^n}{n!}$$
(b) Use part (a) to show that $e > 2.7$.
(c) Use part (a) to show that
$$\lim_{x\to\infty} \frac{e^x}{x^k} = \infty$$
for any positive integer k.

▏▏▏▏ 7.3 Logarithmic Functions

If $a > 0$ and $a \neq 1$, the exponential function $f(x) = a^x$ is either increasing or decreasing and so it is one-to-one. It therefore has an inverse function f^{-1}, which is called the **logarithmic function with base a** and is denoted by $\log_a$. If we use the formulation of an inverse function given by (7.1.3),

$$f^{-1}(x) = y \iff f(y) = x$$

then we have

[1]
$$\log_a x = y \iff a^y = x$$

Thus, if $x > 0$, $\log_a x$ is the exponent to which the base a must be raised to give x.

EXAMPLE 1 Evaluate (a) $\log_3 81$, (b) $\log_{25} 5$, and (c) $\log_{10} 0.001$.

SOLUTION
(a) $\log_3 81 = 4$ because $3^4 = 81$
(b) $\log_{25} 5 = \frac{1}{2}$ because $25^{1/2} = 5$
(c) $\log_{10} 0.001 = -3$ because $10^{-3} = 0.001$

The cancellation equations (7.1.4), when applied to $f(x) = a^x$ and $f^{-1}(x) = \log_a x$, become

[2]
$$\log_a(a^x) = x \quad \text{for every } x \in \mathbb{R}$$
$$a^{\log_a x} = x \quad \text{for every } x > 0$$

The logarithmic function $\log_a$ has domain $(0, \infty)$ and range $\mathbb{R}$ and is continuous since it is the inverse of a continuous function, namely, the exponential function. Its graph is the reflection of the graph of $y = a^x$ about the line $y = x$.

Figure 1 shows the case where $a > 1$. (The most important logarithmic functions have base $a > 1$.) The fact that $y = a^x$ is a very rapidly increasing function for $x > 0$ is reflected in the fact that $y = \log_a x$ is a very slowly increasing function for $x > 1$.

Figure 2 shows the graphs of $y = \log_a x$ with various values of the base a. Since $\log_a 1 = 0$, the graphs of all logarithmic functions pass through the point $(1, 0)$.

The following theorem summarizes the properties of logarithmic functions.

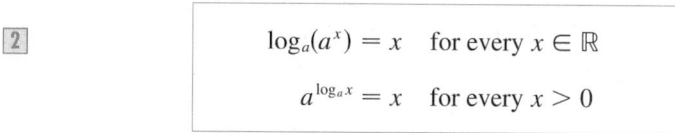

[3] **Theorem** If $a > 1$, the function $f(x) = \log_a x$ is a one-to-one, continuous, increasing function with domain $(0, \infty)$ and range $\mathbb{R}$. If $x, y > 0$ and r is any real number, then

1. $\log_a(xy) = \log_a x + \log_a y$ **2.** $\log_a\left(\dfrac{x}{y}\right) = \log_a x - \log_a y$

3. $\log_a(x^r) = r \log_a x$

FIGURE 1

FIGURE 2

Properties 1, 2, and 3 follow from the corresponding properties of exponential functions given in Section 7.2.

EXAMPLE 2 Use the properties of logarithms in Theorem 3 to evaluate the following.
(a) $\log_4 2 + \log_4 32$ (b) $\log_2 80 - \log_2 5$

SOLUTION
(a) Using Property 1 in Theorem 3, we have

$$\log_4 2 + \log_4 32 = \log_4(2 \cdot 32) = \log_4 64 = 3$$

since $4^3 = 64$.
(b) Using Property 2 we have

$$\log_2 80 - \log_2 5 = \log_2\left(\tfrac{80}{5}\right) = \log_2 16 = 4$$

since $2^4 = 16$.

The limits of exponential functions given in Section 7.2 are reflected in the following limits of logarithmic functions. (Compare with Figure 1.)

> **4** If $a > 1$, then
> $$\lim_{x \to \infty} \log_a x = \infty \quad \text{and} \quad \lim_{x \to 0^+} \log_a x = -\infty$$

In particular, the y-axis is a vertical asymptote of the curve $y = \log_a x$.

EXAMPLE 3 Find $\lim_{x \to 0} \log_{10}(\tan^2 x)$.

SOLUTION As $x \to 0$, we know that $t = \tan^2 x \to \tan^2 0 = 0$ and the values of t are positive. So by (4) with $a = 10 > 1$, we have

$$\lim_{x \to 0} \log_{10}(\tan^2 x) = \lim_{t \to 0^+} \log_{10} t = -\infty$$

▥ Natural Logarithms

Of all possible bases a for logarithms, we will see in the next section that the most convenient choice of a base is the number e, which was defined in Section 7.2. The logarithm with base e is called the **natural logarithm** and has a special notation:

$$\log_e x = \ln x$$

If we put $a = e$ and replace $\log_e$ with "ln" in (1) and (2), then the defining properties of the natural logarithm function become

> **5** $\ln x = y \iff e^y = x$

> **6** $\ln(e^x) = x \quad x \in \mathbb{R}$
> $e^{\ln x} = x \quad x > 0$

In particular, if we set $x = 1$, we get

$$\ln e = 1$$

EXAMPLE 4 Find x if $\ln x = 5$.

SOLUTION 1 From (5) we see that

$$\ln x = 5 \quad \text{means} \quad e^5 = x$$

Therefore, $x = e^5$.

(If you have trouble working with the "ln" notation, just replace it by $\log_e$. Then the equation becomes $\log_e x = 5$; so, by the definition of logarithm, $e^5 = x$.)

SOLUTION 2 Start with the equation

$$\ln x = 5$$

and apply the exponential function to both sides of the equation:

$$e^{\ln x} = e^5$$

But the second cancellation equation in (6) says that $e^{\ln x} = x$. Therefore, $x = e^5$.

EXAMPLE 5 Solve the equation $e^{5-3x} = 10$.

SOLUTION We take natural logarithms of both sides of the equation and use (6):

$$\ln(e^{5-3x}) = \ln 10$$

$$5 - 3x = \ln 10$$

$$3x = 5 - \ln 10$$

$$x = \tfrac{1}{3}(5 - \ln 10)$$

Since the natural logarithm is found on scientific calculators, we can approximate the solution to four decimal places: $x \approx 0.8991$.

EXAMPLE 6 Express $\ln a + \frac{1}{2}\ln b$ as a single logarithm.

SOLUTION Using Properties 3 and 1 of logarithms, we have

$$\ln a + \tfrac{1}{2}\ln b = \ln a + \ln b^{1/2}$$
$$= \ln a + \ln \sqrt{b}$$
$$= \ln(a\sqrt{b})$$

The following formula shows that logarithms with any base can be expressed in terms of the natural logarithm.

7 **Change of Base Formula** For any positive number a $(a \neq 1)$, we have

$$\log_a x = \frac{\ln x}{\ln a}$$

Proof Let $y = \log_a x$. Then, from (1), we have $a^y = x$. Taking natural logarithms of both sides of this equation, we get $y \ln a = \ln x$. Therefore

$$y = \frac{\ln x}{\ln a}$$

Scientific calculators have a key for natural logarithms, so Formula 7 enables us to use a calculator to compute a logarithm with any base (as shown in the next example). Similarly, Formula 7 allows us to graph any logarithmic function on a graphing calculator or computer (see Exercises 20–22).

EXAMPLE 7 Evaluate $\log_8 5$ correct to six decimal places.

SOLUTION Formula 7 gives

$$\log_8 5 = \frac{\ln 5}{\ln 8} \approx 0.773976$$

EXAMPLE 8 In Section 7.2 we showed that the mass of ^{90}Sr that remains from a 24-mg sample after t years is $m = f(t) = 24 \cdot 2^{-t/25}$. Find the inverse of this function and interpret it.

SOLUTION We need to solve the equation $m = 24 \cdot 2^{-t/25}$ for t. We start by taking natural logarithms of both sides:

$$\ln m = \ln(24 \cdot 2^{-t/25}) = \ln 24 + \ln(2^{-t/25})$$

$$\ln m = \ln 24 - \frac{t}{25} \ln 2$$

$$\frac{t}{25} \ln 2 = \ln 24 - \ln m$$

$$t = \frac{25}{\ln 2}(\ln 24 - \ln m)$$

So the inverse function is

$$f^{-1}(m) = \frac{25}{\ln 2}(\ln 24 - \ln m)$$

This function gives the time required for the mass to decay to m milligrams. In particular, the time required for the mass to be reduced to 5 mg is

$$t = f^{-1}(5) = \frac{25}{\ln 2}(\ln 24 - \ln 5) \approx 56.58 \text{ years}$$

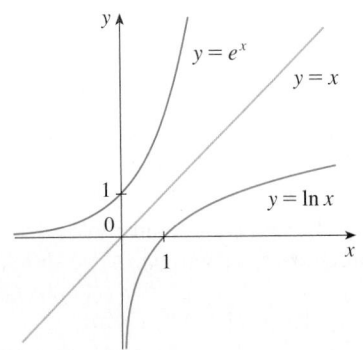

FIGURE 3

The graphs of the exponential function $y = e^x$ and its inverse function, the natural logarithm function, are shown in Figure 3. Because the curve $y = e^x$ crosses the y-axis with a slope of 1, it follows that the reflected curve $y = \ln x$ crosses the x-axis with a slope of 1.

In common with all other logarithmic functions with base greater than 1, the natural logarithm is a continuous, increasing function defined on $(0, \infty)$ and the y-axis is a vertical asymptote.

If we put $a = e$ in (4), then we have the following limits:

$$\boxed{8} \qquad \lim_{x \to \infty} \ln x = \infty \qquad \lim_{x \to 0^+} \ln x = -\infty$$

EXAMPLE 9 Sketch the graph of the function $y = \ln(x - 2) - 1$.

SOLUTION We start with the graph of $y = \ln x$ as given in Figure 3. Using the transformations of Section 1.3, we shift it 2 units to the right to get the graph of $y = \ln(x - 2)$ and then we shift it 1 unit downward to get the graph of $y = \ln(x - 2) - 1$. (See Figure 4.) Notice that the line $x = 2$ is a vertical asymptote since

$$\lim_{x \to 2^+} [\ln(x - 2) - 1] = -\infty$$

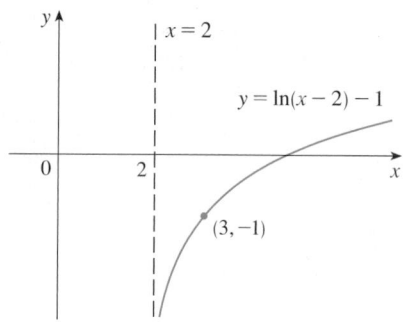

FIGURE 4

We have seen that $\ln x \to \infty$ as $x \to \infty$. But this happens *very* slowly. In fact, $\ln x$ grows more slowly than any positive power of x. To illustrate this fact, we compare approximate values of the functions $y = \ln x$ and $y = x^{1/2} = \sqrt{x}$ in the following table and we graph them in Figures 5 and 6.

x	1	2	5	10	50	100	500	1000	10,000	100,000
$\ln x$	0	0.69	1.61	2.30	3.91	4.6	6.2	6.9	9.2	11.5
$\sqrt{x}$	1	1.41	2.24	3.16	7.07	10.0	22.4	31.6	100	316
$\dfrac{\ln x}{\sqrt{x}}$	0	0.49	0.72	0.73	0.55	0.46	0.28	0.22	0.09	0.04

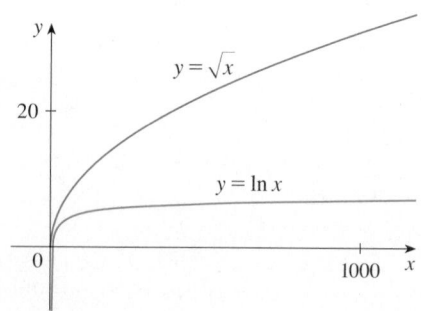

FIGURE 5   **FIGURE 6**

You can see that initially the graphs of $y = \sqrt{x}$ and $y = \ln x$ grow at comparable rates, but eventually the root function far surpasses the logarithm. In fact, we will be able to show in Section 7.7 that

$$\lim_{x \to \infty} \frac{\ln x}{x^p} = 0$$

for any positive power p. So for large x, the values of $\ln x$ are very small compared with x^p. (See Exercise 74.)

7.3 Exercises

1. (a) How is the logarithmic function $y = \log_a x$ defined?
(b) What is the domain of this function?
(c) What is the range of this function?
(d) Sketch the general shape of the graph of the function
$y = \log_a x$ if $a > 1$.

2. (a) What is the natural logarithm?
(b) What is the common logarithm?
(c) Sketch the graphs of the natural logarithm function and the natural exponential function with a common set of axes.

3–8 ▏▏ Find the exact value of each expression.

3. (a) $\log_{10} 1000$ (b) $\log_{16} 4$

4. (a) $\ln e^{-100}$ (b) $\log_3 81$

5. (a) $\log_5 \frac{1}{25}$ (b) $e^{\ln 15}$

6. (a) $\log_{10} 0.1$ (b) $\log_8 320 - \log_8 5$

7. (a) $\log_{12} 3 + \log_{12} 48$ (b) $\log_2 5 - \log_2 90 + 2\log_2 3$

8. (a) $2^{(\log_2 3 + \log_2 5)}$ (b) $e^{3\ln 2}$

9–12 ▏▏ Use the properties of logarithms to expand the quantity.

9. $\log_2 \left(\dfrac{x^3 y}{z^2} \right)$ **10.** $\ln \sqrt{a(b^2 + c^2)}$

11. $\ln(uv)^{10}$ **12.** $\ln \dfrac{3x^2}{(x+1)^5}$

13–18 ▏▏ Express the quantity as a single logarithm.

13. $\log_{10} a - \log_{10} b + \log_{10} c$

14. $\ln(x + y) + \ln(x - y) - 2\ln z$

15. $2\ln 4 - \ln 2$ **16.** $\ln 3 + \frac{1}{3}\ln 8$

17. $\frac{1}{2}\ln x - 5\ln(x^2 + 1)$ **18.** $\ln x + a\ln y - b\ln z$

19. Use Formula 7 to evaluate each logarithm correct to six decimal places.
(a) $\log_{12} e$ (b) $\log_6 13.54$ (c) $\log_2 \pi$

⌁ **20–22** ▏▏ Use Formula 7 to graph the given functions on a common screen. How are these graphs related?

20. $y = \log_2 x, \quad y = \log_4 x, \quad y = \log_6 x, \quad y = \log_8 x$

21. $y = \log_{1.5} x, \quad y = \ln x, \quad y = \log_{10} x, \quad y = \log_{50} x$

22. $y = \ln x, \quad y = \log_{10} x, \quad y = e^x, \quad y = 10^x$

23–28 ▏▏ Make a rough sketch of the graph of each function. Do not use a calculator. Just use the graphs given in Figures 1, 2, and 3 and, if necessary, the transformations of Section 1.3.

23. $y = \log_{10}(x + 5)$ **24.** $y = \log_2(x - 3)$

25. $y = -\ln x$ **26.** $y = \ln(10x)$

27. $y = 5 + \ln(x - 2)$ **28.** $y = \ln|x|$

29–38 ▏▏ Solve each equation for x.

29. (a) $2\ln x = 1$ (b) $e^{-x} = 5$

30. (a) $e^{2x+3} - 7 = 0$ (b) $\ln(5 - 2x) = -3$

31. (a) $5^{x-3} = 10$ (b) $\log_{10}(x + 1) = 4$

32. (a) $e^{3x+1} = k$ (b) $\log_2(mx) = c$

33. $\ln(\ln x) = 1$ **34.** $e^{e^x} = 10$

35. $2\ln x = \ln 2 + \ln(3x - 4)$ **36.** $\ln(2x + 1) = 2 - \ln x$

37. $e^{ax} = Ce^{bx}$, where $a \neq b$ **38.** $7e^x - e^{2x} = 12$

39–42 ▏▏ Find the solution of the equation correct to four decimal places.

39. $e^{2+5x} = 100$ **40.** $\ln(1 + \sqrt{x}) = 2$

41. $\ln(e^x - 2) = 3$ **42.** $3^{1/(x-4)} = 7$

43–44 ▏▏ Solve each inequality for x.

43. (a) $e^x < 10$ (b) $\ln x > -1$

44. (a) $2 < \ln x < 9$ (b) $e^{2-3x} > 4$

45. Suppose that the graph of $y = \log_2 x$ is drawn on a coordinate grid where the unit of measurement is an inch. How many miles to the right of the origin do we have to move before the height of the curve reaches 3 ft?

46. The velocity of a particle that moves in a straight line under the influence of viscous forces is $v(t) = ce^{-kt}$, where c and k are positive constants.
(a) Show that the acceleration is proportional to the velocity.
(b) Explain the significance of the number c.
(c) At what time is the velocity equal to half the initial velocity?

47. The geologist C. F. Richter defined the magnitude of an earthquake to be $\log_{10}(I/S)$, where I is the intensity of the quake (measured by the amplitude of a seismograph 100 km from the epicenter) and S is the intensity of a "standard" earthquake (where the amplitude is only 1 micron $= 10^{-4}$ cm). The 1989 Loma Prieta earthquake that shook San Francisco had a magnitude of 7.1 on the Richter scale. The 1906 San Francisco earthquake was 16 times as intense. What was its magnitude on the Richter scale?

48. A sound so faint that it can just be heard has intensity $I_0 = 10^{-12}$ watt/m² at a frequency of 1000 hertz (Hz). The loudness, in decibels (dB), of a sound with intensity I is then defined to be $L = 10 \log_{10}(I/I_0)$. Amplified rock music is measured at 120 dB, whereas the noise from a motor-driven lawn mower is measured at 106 dB. Find the ratio of the intensity of the rock music to that of the mower.

49. If a bacteria population starts with 100 bacteria and doubles every three hours, then the number of bacteria after t hours is $n = f(t) = 100 \cdot 2^{t/3}$.
(a) Find the inverse of this function and explain its meaning.
(b) When will the population reach 50,000?

50. When a camera flash goes off, the batteries immediately begin to recharge the flash's capacitor, which stores electric charge given by

$$Q(t) = Q_0(1 - e^{-t/a})$$

(The maximum charge capacity is Q_0 and t is measured in seconds.)
(a) Find the inverse of this function and explain its meaning.
(b) How long does it take to recharge the capacitor to 90% of capacity if $a = 2$?

51–56 ||| Find the limit.

51. $\lim\limits_{x \to 2^-} \ln(2 - x)$

52. $\lim\limits_{x \to 3^+} \log_{10}(x^2 - 5x + 6)$

53. $\lim\limits_{x \to 0} \ln(\cos x)$

54. $\lim\limits_{x \to 0^+} \ln(\sin x)$

55. $\lim\limits_{x \to \infty} [\ln(1 + x^2) - \ln(1 + x)]$

56. $\lim\limits_{x \to \infty} [\ln(2 + x) - \ln(1 + x)]$

57–58 ||| Find the domain and range of the function.

57. $f(x) = \log_2(5x - 3)$

58. $G(t) = \ln(e^t - 2)$

59–60 ||| Find (a) the domain of f and (b) f^{-1} and its domain.

59. $f(x) = \sqrt{3 - e^{2x}}$

60. $f(x) = \ln(2 + \ln x)$

61–66 ||| Find the inverse function.

61. $y = \ln(x + 3)$

62. $y = 2^{10^x}$

63. $f(x) = e^{x^3}$

64. $y = (\ln x)^2, \quad x \geq 1$

65. $y = \dfrac{10^x}{10^x + 1}$

66. $y = \dfrac{1 + e^x}{1 - e^x}$

67. On what interval is the function $f(x) = e^{3x} - e^x$ increasing?

68. On what interval is the curve $y = 2e^x - e^{-3x}$ concave downward?

69. (a) Show that the function $f(x) = \ln(x + \sqrt{x^2 + 1})$ is an odd function.
(b) Find the inverse function of f.

70. Find an equation of the tangent to the curve $y = e^{-x}$ that is perpendicular to the line $2x - y = 8$.

71. Show that the equation $x^{1/\ln x} = 2$ has no solution. What can you say about the function $f(x) = x^{1/\ln x}$?

72. Any function of the form $f(x) = [g(x)]^{h(x)}$, where $g(x) > 0$, can be analyzed as a power of e by writing $g(x) = e^{\ln g(x)}$ so that $f(x) = e^{h(x) \ln g(x)}$. Using this device, calculate each limit.
(a) $\lim\limits_{x \to \infty} x^{\ln x}$
(b) $\lim\limits_{x \to 0^+} x^{-\ln x}$
(c) $\lim\limits_{x \to 0^+} x^{1/x}$
(d) $\lim\limits_{x \to \infty} (\ln 2x)^{-\ln x}$

73. Let $a > 1$. Prove, using Definitions 4.4.6 and 4.4.7, that
(a) $\lim\limits_{x \to -\infty} a^x = 0$
(b) $\lim\limits_{x \to \infty} a^x = \infty$

74. (a) Compare the rates of growth of $f(x) = x^{0.1}$ and $g(x) = \ln x$ by graphing both f and g in several viewing rectangles. When does the graph of f finally surpass the graph of g?
(b) Graph the function $h(x) = (\ln x)/x^{0.1}$ in a viewing rectangle that displays the behavior of the function as $x \to \infty$.
(c) Find a number N such that

$$\frac{\ln x}{x^{0.1}} < 0.1 \qquad \text{whenever} \qquad x > N$$

75. Solve the inequality $\ln(x^2 - 2x - 2) \leq 0$.

76. A **prime number** is a positive integer that has no factors other than 1 and itself. The first few primes are 2, 3, 5, 7, 11, 13, 17, ... We denote by $\pi(n)$ the number of primes that are less than or equal to n. For instance, $\pi(15) = 6$ because there are six primes smaller than 15.
(a) Calculate the numbers $\pi(25)$ and $\pi(100)$.
   [*Hint:* To find $\pi(100)$, first compile a list of the primes up to 100 using the *sieve of Eratosthenes:* Write the numbers from 2 to 100 and cross out all multiples of 2. Then cross out all multiples of 3. The next remaining number is 5, so cross out all remaining multiples of it, and so on.]
(b) By inspecting tables of prime numbers and tables of logarithms, the great mathematician K. F. Gauss made the guess in 1792 (when he was 15) that the number of primes up to n is approximately $n/\ln n$ when n is large. More precisely, he conjectured that

$$\lim\limits_{n \to \infty} \frac{\pi(n)}{n/\ln n} = 1$$

This was finally proved, a hundred years later, by Jacques Hadamard and Charles de la Vallée Poussin and is called the **Prime Number Theorem**. Provide evidence for the truth of this theorem by computing the ratio of $\pi(n)$ to $n/\ln n$ for $n = 100, 1000, 10^4, 10^5, 10^6,$ and 10^7. Use the following data: $\pi(1000) = 168$, $\pi(10^4) = 1229$, $\pi(10^5) = 9592$, $\pi(10^6) = 78{,}498$, $\pi(10^7) = 664{,}579$.
(c) Use the Prime Number Theorem to estimate the number of primes up to a billion.

7.4 Derivatives of Logarithmic Functions

In this section we find the derivatives of the logarithmic functions $y = \log_a x$ and the exponential functions $y = a^x$. We start with the natural logarithmic function $y = \ln x$. We know that it is differentiable because it is the inverse of the differentiable function $y = e^x$.

$$\boxed{\quad \frac{d}{dx}(\ln x) = \frac{1}{x} \quad}$$

⨞ 1

Proof Let $y = \ln x$. Then

$$e^y = x$$

Differentiating this equation implicitly with respect to x, we get

$$e^y \frac{dy}{dx} = 1$$

and so

$$\frac{dy}{dx} = \frac{1}{e^y} = \frac{1}{x}$$

EXAMPLE 1 Differentiate $y = \ln(x^3 + 1)$.

SOLUTION To use the Chain Rule we let $u = x^3 + 1$. Then $y = \ln u$, so

$$\frac{dy}{dx} = \frac{dy}{du}\frac{du}{dx} = \frac{1}{u}\frac{du}{dx} = \frac{1}{x^3 + 1}(3x^2) = \frac{3x^2}{x^3 + 1}$$

In general, if we combine Formula 1 with the Chain Rule as in Example 1, we get

⨞ 2

$$\boxed{\quad \frac{d}{dx}(\ln u) = \frac{1}{u}\frac{du}{dx} \quad}$$ or $$\boxed{\quad \frac{d}{dx}[\ln g(x)] = \frac{g'(x)}{g(x)} \quad}$$

EXAMPLE 2 Find $\dfrac{d}{dx} \ln(\sin x)$.

SOLUTION Using (2), we have

$$\frac{d}{dx} \ln(\sin x) = \frac{1}{\sin x}\frac{d}{dx}(\sin x) = \frac{1}{\sin x} \cos x = \cot x$$

EXAMPLE 3 Differentiate $f(x) = \sqrt{\ln x}$.

SOLUTION This time the logarithm is the inner function, so the Chain Rule gives

$$f'(x) = \tfrac{1}{2}(\ln x)^{-1/2} \frac{d}{dx}(\ln x) = \frac{1}{2\sqrt{\ln x}} \cdot \frac{1}{x} = \frac{1}{2x\sqrt{\ln x}}$$

EXAMPLE 4 Find $\dfrac{d}{dx}\ln\dfrac{x+1}{\sqrt{x-2}}$.

SOLUTION 1

$$\frac{d}{dx}\ln\frac{x+1}{\sqrt{x-2}} = \frac{1}{\dfrac{x+1}{\sqrt{x-2}}}\frac{d}{dx}\frac{x+1}{\sqrt{x-2}}$$

$$= \frac{\sqrt{x-2}}{x+1}\;\frac{\sqrt{x-2}\cdot 1 - (x+1)(\tfrac{1}{2})(x-2)^{-1/2}}{x-2}$$

$$= \frac{x-2-\tfrac{1}{2}(x+1)}{(x+1)(x-2)} = \frac{x-5}{2(x+1)(x-2)}$$

SOLUTION 2 If we first simplify the given function using the laws of logarithms, then the differentiation becomes easier:

$$\frac{d}{dx}\ln\frac{x+1}{\sqrt{x-2}} = \frac{d}{dx}\left[\ln(x+1) - \tfrac{1}{2}\ln(x-2)\right]$$

$$= \frac{1}{x+1} - \frac{1}{2}\left(\frac{1}{x-2}\right)$$

(This answer can be left as written, but if we used a common denominator we would see that it gives the same answer as in Solution 1.)

▏▏▎ Figure 1 shows the graph of the function f of Example 4 together with the graph of its derivative. It gives a visual check on our calculation. Notice that $f'(x)$ is large negative when f is rapidly decreasing and $f'(x) = 0$ when f has a minimum.

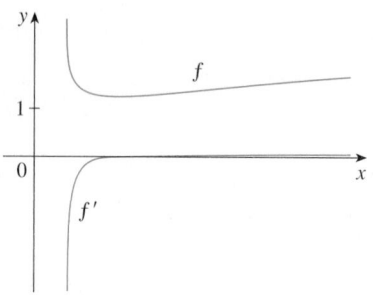

FIGURE 1

EXAMPLE 5 Find the absolute minimum value of $f(x) = x^2 \ln x$.

SOLUTION The domain is $(0, \infty)$ and the Product Rule gives

$$f'(x) = x^2\cdot\frac{1}{x} + 2x\ln x = x(1 + 2\ln x)$$

Therefore, $f'(x) = 0$ when $2\ln x = -1$, that is, $\ln x = -\tfrac{1}{2}$, or $x = e^{-1/2}$. Also, $f'(x) > 0$ when $x > e^{-1/2}$ and $f'(x) < 0$ for $0 < x < e^{-1/2}$. So by the First Derivative Test for Absolute Extreme Values, $f\left(1/\sqrt{e}\right) = -1/(2e)$ is the absolute minimum.

EXAMPLE 6 Discuss the curve $y = \ln(4 - x^2)$ using the guidelines of Section 4.5.

SOLUTION
A. The domain is

$$\{x \mid 4 - x^2 > 0\} = \{x \mid x^2 < 4\} = \{x \mid |x| < 2\} = (-2, 2)$$

B. The y-intercept is $f(0) = \ln 4$. To find the x-intercept we set

$$y = \ln(4 - x^2) = 0$$

We know that $\ln 1 = \log_e 1 = 0$ (since $e^0 = 1$), so we have $4 - x^2 = 1 \Rightarrow x^2 = 3$ and therefore the x-intercepts are $\pm\sqrt{3}$.

C. Since $f(-x) = f(x)$, f is even and the curve is symmetric about the y-axis.

D. We look for vertical asymptotes at the endpoints of the domain. Since $4 - x^2 \to 0^+$ as $x \to 2^-$ and also as $x \to -2^+$, we have

$$\lim_{x\to 2^-}\ln(4 - x^2) = -\infty \qquad \text{and} \qquad \lim_{x\to -2^+}\ln(4 - x^2) = -\infty$$

Thus, the lines $x = 2$ and $x = -2$ are vertical asymptotes.

E.
$$f'(x) = \frac{-2x}{4 - x^2}$$

Since $f'(x) > 0$ when $-2 < x < 0$ and $f'(x) < 0$ when $0 < x < 2$, f is increasing on $(-2, 0)$ and decreasing on $(0, 2)$.

F. The only critical number is $x = 0$. Since f' changes from positive to negative at 0, $f(0) = \ln 4$ is a local maximum by the First Derivative Test.

G.
$$f''(x) = \frac{(4 - x^2)(-2) + 2x(-2x)}{(4 - x^2)^2} = \frac{-8 - 2x^2}{(4 - x^2)^2}$$

Since $f''(x) < 0$ for all x, the curve is concave downward on $(-2, 2)$ and has no inflection point.

H. Using this information, we sketch the curve in Figure 2.

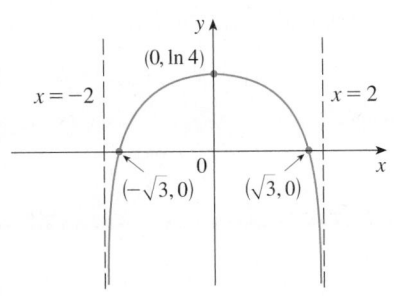

FIGURE 2
$y = \ln(4 - x^2)$

EXAMPLE 7 Find $f'(x)$ if $f(x) = \ln |x|$.

SOLUTION Since

$$f(x) = \begin{cases} \ln x & \text{if } x > 0 \\ \ln(-x) & \text{if } x < 0 \end{cases}$$

it follows that

$$f'(x) = \begin{cases} \dfrac{1}{x} & \text{if } x > 0 \\ \dfrac{1}{-x}(-1) = \dfrac{1}{x} & \text{if } x < 0 \end{cases}$$

Thus, $f'(x) = 1/x$ for all $x \neq 0$.

The result of Example 7 is worth remembering:

⟨3⟩
$$\frac{d}{dx}(\ln |x|) = \frac{1}{x}$$

The corresponding integration formula is

⟨4⟩
$$\int \frac{1}{x}\, dx = \ln |x| + C$$

Notice that this fills the gap in the rule for integrating power functions:

$$\int x^n\, dx = \frac{x^{n+1}}{n + 1} + C \qquad \text{if } n \neq -1$$

The missing case ($n = -1$) is supplied by Formula 4.

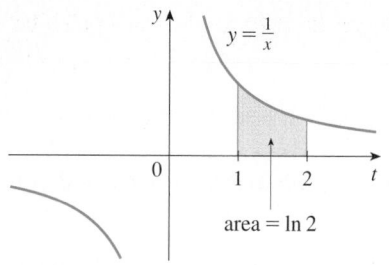

$y = \dfrac{1}{x}$

area = ln 2

FIGURE 3

EXAMPLE 8 Find, correct to three decimal places, the area of the region under the hyperbola $xy = 1$ from $x = 1$ to $x = 2$.

SOLUTION The given region is shown in Figure 3. Using Formula 4 (without the absolute value sign, since $x > 0$), we see that the area is

$$A = \int_1^2 \frac{1}{x}\, dx = \ln x \Big]_1^2$$

$$= \ln 2 - \ln 1 = \ln 2 \approx 0.693$$

EXAMPLE 9 Evaluate $\displaystyle\int \frac{x}{x^2 + 1}\, dx$.

SOLUTION We make the substitution $u = x^2 + 1$ because the differential $du = 2x\, dx$ occurs (except for the constant factor 2). Thus, $x\, dx = \frac{1}{2}\, du$ and

$$\int \frac{x}{x^2 + 1}\, dx = \frac{1}{2}\int \frac{du}{u} = \frac{1}{2}\ln|u| + C$$

$$= \frac{1}{2}\ln|x^2 + 1| + C = \frac{1}{2}\ln(x^2 + 1) + C$$

Notice that we removed the absolute value signs because $x^2 + 1 > 0$ for all x. We could use the properties of logarithms to write the answer as

$$\ln\sqrt{x^2 + 1} + C$$

but this isn't necessary.

▓ Since the function $f(x) = (\ln x)/x$ in Example 10 is positive for $x > 1$, the integral represents the area of the shaded region in Figure 4.

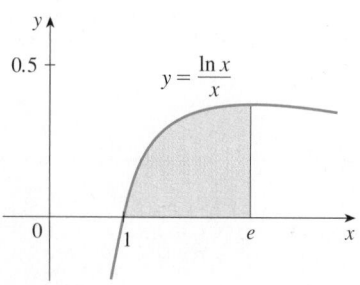

$y = \dfrac{\ln x}{x}$

FIGURE 4

EXAMPLE 10 Calculate $\displaystyle\int_1^e \frac{\ln x}{x}\, dx$.

SOLUTION We let $u = \ln x$ because its differential $du = dx/x$ occurs in the integral. When $x = 1$, $u = \ln 1 = 0$; when $x = e$, $u = \ln e = 1$. Thus

$$\int_1^e \frac{\ln x}{x}\, dx = \int_0^1 u\, du = \frac{u^2}{2}\bigg]_0^1 = \frac{1}{2}$$

EXAMPLE 11 Calculate $\displaystyle\int \tan x\, dx$.

SOLUTION First we write tangent in terms of sine and cosine:

$$\int \tan x\, dx = \int \frac{\sin x}{\cos x}\, dx$$

This suggests that we should substitute $u = \cos x$ since then $du = -\sin x\, dx$ and so $\sin x\, dx = -du$:

$$\int \tan x\, dx = \int \frac{\sin x}{\cos x}\, dx = -\int \frac{du}{u}$$

$$= -\ln|u| + C = -\ln|\cos x| + C$$

Since $-\ln|\cos x| = \ln(1/|\cos x|) = \ln|\sec x|$, the result of Example 11 can also be written as

$$\boxed{5} \qquad \int \tan x\, dx = \ln|\sec x| + C$$

||| General Logarithmic and Exponential Functions

Formula 7 in Section 7.3 expresses a logarithmic function with base a in terms of the natural logarithmic function:

$$\log_a x = \frac{\ln x}{\ln a}$$

Since $\ln a$ is a constant, we can differentiate as follows:

$$\frac{d}{dx}(\log_a x) = \frac{d}{dx}\frac{\ln x}{\ln a} = \frac{1}{\ln a}\frac{d}{dx}(\ln x) = \frac{1}{x \ln a}$$

$$\boxed{6} \qquad \frac{d}{dx}(\log_a x) = \frac{1}{x \ln a}$$

EXAMPLE 12

$$\frac{d}{dx}\log_{10}(2 + \sin x) = \frac{1}{(2 + \sin x)\ln 10}\frac{d}{dx}(2 + \sin x) = \frac{\cos x}{(2 + \sin x)\ln 10}$$

From Formula 6 we see one of the main reasons that natural logarithms (logarithms with base e) are used in calculus: The differentiation formula is simplest when $a = e$ because $\ln e = 1$.

||| **Exponential Functions with Base a** In Section 7.2 we showed that the derivative of the general exponential function $f(x) = a^x$, $a > 0$, is a constant multiple of itself:

$$f'(x) = f'(0)a^x \qquad \text{where} \qquad f'(0) = \lim_{h \to 0}\frac{a^h - 1}{h}$$

We are now in a position to show that the value of the constant is $f'(0) = \ln a$.

$$\boxed{7} \qquad \frac{d}{dx}(a^x) = a^x \ln a$$

Proof We use the fact that $e^{\ln a} = a$:

$$\frac{d}{dx}(a^x) = \frac{d}{dx}(e^{\ln a})^x = \frac{d}{dx}e^{(\ln a)x} = e^{(\ln a)x}\frac{d}{dx}(\ln a)x$$

$$= (e^{\ln a})^x(\ln a) = a^x \ln a$$

In Example 6 in Section 3.4 we considered a population of bacteria cells that doubles every hour and saw that the population after t hours is $n = n_0 2^t$, where n_0 is the initial population. Formula 7 enables us to find the growth rate:

$$\frac{dn}{dt} = n_0 2^t \ln 2$$

EXAMPLE 13 Combining Formula 7 with the Chain Rule, we have

$$\frac{d}{dx}\left(10^{x^2}\right) = 10^{x^2}(\ln 10)\frac{d}{dx}(x^2) = (2\ln 10)x10^{x^2}$$

The integration formula that follows from Formula 7 is

$$\int a^x\, dx = \frac{a^x}{\ln a} + C \qquad a \neq 1$$

EXAMPLE 14

$$\int_0^5 2^x\, dx = \left.\frac{2^x}{\ln 2}\right]_0^5 = \frac{2^5}{\ln 2} - \frac{2^0}{\ln 2} = \frac{31}{\ln 2}$$

|||| **Logarithmic Differentiation**

The calculation of derivatives of complicated functions involving products, quotients, or powers can often be simplified by taking logarithms. The method used in the following example is called **logarithmic differentiation**.

EXAMPLE 15 Differentiate $y = \dfrac{x^{3/4}\sqrt{x^2+1}}{(3x+2)^5}$.

SOLUTION We take logarithms of both sides of the equation and use properties of logarithms to simplify:

$$\ln y = \tfrac{3}{4}\ln x + \tfrac{1}{2}\ln(x^2+1) - 5\ln(3x+2)$$

Differentiating implicitly with respect to x gives

$$\frac{1}{y}\frac{dy}{dx} = \frac{3}{4}\cdot\frac{1}{x} + \frac{1}{2}\cdot\frac{2x}{x^2+1} - 5\cdot\frac{3}{3x+2}$$

Solving for dy/dx, we get

$$\frac{dy}{dx} = y\left(\frac{3}{4x} + \frac{x}{x^2+1} - \frac{15}{3x+2}\right)$$

Because we have an explicit expression for y, we can substitute and write

$$\frac{dy}{dx} = \frac{x^{3/4}\sqrt{x^2+1}}{(3x+2)^5}\left(\frac{3}{4x} + \frac{x}{x^2+1} - \frac{15}{3x+2}\right)$$

|||| If we hadn't used logarithmic differentiation in Example 15, we would have had to use both the Quotient Rule and the Product Rule. The resulting calculation would have been horrendous.

Steps in Logarithmic Differentiation

1. Take logarithms of both sides of an equation $y = f(x)$ and use properties of logarithms to simplify.
2. Differentiate implicitly with respect to x.
3. Solve the resulting equation for y'.

If $f(x) < 0$ for some values of x, then $\ln f(x)$ is not defined, but we can write $|y| = |f(x)|$ and use Equation 3. We illustrate this procedure by proving the general version of the Power Rule, as promised in Section 3.3.

The Power Rule If n is any real number and $f(x) = x^n$, then

$$f'(x) = nx^{n-1}$$

||| If $x = 0$, we can show that $f'(0) = 0$ for $n > 1$ directly from the definition of a derivative.

Proof Let $y = x^n$ and use logarithmic differentiation:

$$\ln|y| = \ln|x|^n = n\ln|x| \qquad x \neq 0$$

Therefore

$$\frac{y'}{y} = \frac{n}{x}$$

Hence

$$y' = n\frac{y}{x} = n\frac{x^n}{x} = nx^{n-1}$$

⊘ You should distinguish carefully between the Power Rule $[(d/dx)\, x^n = nx^{n-1}]$, where the base is variable and the exponent is constant, and the rule for differentiating exponential functions $[(d/dx)\, a^x = a^x \ln a]$, where the base is constant and the exponent is variable. In general there are four cases for exponents and bases:

1. $\dfrac{d}{dx}(a^b) = 0$ (a and b are constants)

2. $\dfrac{d}{dx}[f(x)]^b = b[f(x)]^{b-1}f'(x)$

3. $\dfrac{d}{dx}[a^{g(x)}] = a^{g(x)}(\ln a)g'(x)$

||| Figure 5 illustrates Example 16 by showing the graphs of $f(x) = x^{\sqrt{x}}$ and its derivative.

4. To find $(d/dx)[f(x)]^{g(x)}$, logarithmic differentiation can be used, as in the next example.

EXAMPLE 16 Differentiate $y = x^{\sqrt{x}}$.

SOLUTION 1 Using logarithmic differentiation, we have

$$\ln y = \ln x^{\sqrt{x}} = \sqrt{x}\,\ln x$$

$$\frac{y'}{y} = \sqrt{x}\cdot\frac{1}{x} + (\ln x)\,\frac{1}{2\sqrt{x}}$$

$$y' = y\left(\frac{1}{\sqrt{x}} + \frac{\ln x}{2\sqrt{x}}\right) = x^{\sqrt{x}}\left(\frac{2 + \ln x}{2\sqrt{x}}\right)$$

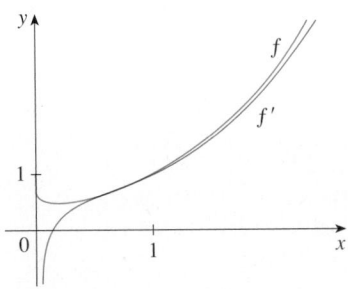

FIGURE 5

SOLUTION 2 Another method is to write $x^{\sqrt{x}} = (e^{\ln x})^{\sqrt{x}}$:

$$\frac{d}{dx}\left(x^{\sqrt{x}}\right) = \frac{d}{dx}\left(e^{\sqrt{x}\ln x}\right) = e^{\sqrt{x}\ln x}\frac{d}{dx}\left(\sqrt{x}\ln x\right)$$

$$= x^{\sqrt{x}}\left(\frac{2 + \ln x}{2\sqrt{x}}\right) \qquad \text{(as in Solution 1)}$$

||| The Number e as a Limit

We have shown that if $f(x) = \ln x$, then $f'(x) = 1/x$. Thus, $f'(1) = 1$. We now use this fact to express the number e as a limit.

From the definition of a derivative as a limit, we have

$$f'(1) = \lim_{h \to 0}\frac{f(1+h) - f(1)}{h} = \lim_{x \to 0}\frac{f(1+x) - f(1)}{x}$$

$$= \lim_{x \to 0}\frac{\ln(1+x) - \ln 1}{x} = \lim_{x \to 0}\frac{1}{x}\ln(1+x)$$

$$= \lim_{x \to 0}\ln(1+x)^{1/x}$$

Because $f'(1) = 1$, we have

$$\lim_{x \to 0}\ln(1+x)^{1/x} = 1$$

Then, by Theorem 2.5.8 and the continuity of the exponential functions, we have

$$e = e^1 = e^{\lim_{x \to 0}\ln(1+x)^{1/x}} = \lim_{x \to 0}e^{\ln(1+x)^{1/x}} = \lim_{x \to 0}(1+x)^{1/x}$$

8

$$e = \lim_{x \to 0}(1+x)^{1/x}$$

Formula 8 is illustrated by the graph of the function $y = (1+x)^{1/x}$ in Figure 6 and a table of values for small values of x.

FIGURE 6

x	$(1+x)^{1/x}$
0.1	2.59374246
0.01	2.70481383
0.001	2.71692393
0.0001	2.71814593
0.00001	2.71826824
0.000001	2.71828047
0.0000001	2.71828169
0.00000001	2.71828181

If we put $n = 1/x$ in Formula 8, then $n \to \infty$ as $x \to 0^+$ and so an alternative expression for e is

$\boxed{9}$

$$e = \lim_{n \to \infty} \left(1 + \frac{1}{n}\right)^n$$

||| 7.4 Exercises

1. Explain why the natural logarithmic function $y = \ln x$ is used much more frequently in calculus than the other logarithmic functions $y = \log_a x$.

2–24 ||| Differentiate the function.

2. $f(x) = \ln(x^2 + 10)$

3. $f(\theta) = \ln(\cos \theta)$

4. $f(x) = \cos(\ln x)$

5. $f(x) = \log_2(1 - 3x)$

6. $f(x) = \log_{10}\left(\dfrac{x}{x - 1}\right)$

7. $f(x) = \sqrt[5]{\ln x}$

8. $f(x) = \ln \sqrt[5]{x}$

9. $f(x) = \sqrt{x} \ln x$

10. $f(t) = \dfrac{1 + \ln t}{1 - \ln t}$

11. $F(t) = \ln \dfrac{(2t + 1)^3}{(3t - 1)^4}$

12. $h(x) = \ln\left(x + \sqrt{x^2 - 1}\right)$

13. $g(x) = \ln \dfrac{a - x}{a + x}$

14. $F(y) = y \ln(1 + e^y)$

15. $f(u) = \dfrac{\ln u}{1 + \ln(2u)}$

16. $y = \ln(x^4 \sin^2 x)$

17. $h(t) = t^3 - 3^t$

18. $y = 10^{\tan \theta}$

19. $y = \ln |2 - x - 5x^2|$

20. $G(u) = \ln \sqrt{\dfrac{3u + 2}{3u - 2}}$

21. $y = \ln(e^{-x} + xe^{-x})$

22. $y = [\ln(1 + e^x)]^2$

23. $y = 5^{-1/x}$

24. $y = 2^{3^{x^2}}$

25–28 ||| Find y' and y''.

25. $y = x \ln x$

26. $y = \dfrac{\ln x}{x^2}$

27. $y = \log_{10} x$

28. $y = \ln(\sec x + \tan x)$

29–32 ||| Differentiate f and find the domain of f.

29. $f(x) = \dfrac{x}{1 - \ln(x - 1)}$

30. $f(x) = \dfrac{1}{1 + \ln x}$

31. $f(x) = x^2 \ln(1 - x^2)$

32. $f(x) = \ln \ln \ln x$

33. If $f(x) = \dfrac{x}{\ln x}$, find $f'(e)$.

34. If $f(x) = x^2 \ln x$, find $f'(1)$.

35–36 ||| Find an equation of the tangent line to the curve at the given point.

35. $y = \ln \ln x$, $\quad (e, 0)$

36. $y = \ln(x^3 - 7)$, $\quad (2, 0)$

37–38 ||| Find $f'(x)$. Check that your answer is reasonable by comparing the graphs of f and f'.

37. $f(x) = \sin x + \ln x$

38. $f(x) = x^{\cos x}$

39–50 ||| Use logarithmic differentiation to find the derivative of the function.

39. $y = (2x + 1)^5(x^4 - 3)^6$

40. $y = \sqrt{x}\, e^{x^2}(x^2 + 1)^{10}$

41. $y = \dfrac{\sin^2 x \, \tan^4 x}{(x^2 + 1)^2}$

42. $y = \sqrt[4]{\dfrac{x^2 + 1}{x^2 - 1}}$

43. $y = x^x$

44. $y = x^{1/x}$

45. $y = x^{\sin x}$

46. $y = (\sin x)^x$

47. $y = (\ln x)^x$

48. $y = x^{\ln x}$

49. $y = x^{e^x}$

50. $y = (\ln x)^{\cos x}$

51. Find y' if $y = \ln(x^2 + y^2)$.

52. Find y' if $x^y = y^x$.

53. Find a formula for $f^{(n)}(x)$ if $f(x) = \ln(x - 1)$.

54. Find $\dfrac{d^9}{dx^9}(x^8 \ln x)$.

55–56 ▏▏▏ Use a graph to estimate the roots of the equation. Then use these estimates as the initial approximations in Newton's method to find the roots correct to six decimal places.

55. $(x - 4)^2 = \ln x$

56. $\ln(4 - x^2) = x$

57. Find the intervals of concavity and the inflection points of the function $f(x) = (\ln x)/\sqrt{x}$.

58. Find the absolute minimum value of the function $f(x) = x \ln x$.

59–62 ▏▏▏ Discuss the curve under the guidelines of Section 4.5.

59. $y = \ln(\sin x)$

60. $y = \ln(\tan^2 x)$

61. $y = \ln(1 + x^2)$

62. $y = \ln(x^2 - 3x + 2)$

CAS **63.** If $f(x) = \ln(2x + x \sin x)$, use the graphs of f, f', and f'' to estimate the intervals of increase and the inflection points of f on the interval $(0, 15]$.

64. Investigate the family of curves $f(x) = \ln(x^2 + c)$. What happens to the inflection points and asymptotes as c changes? Graph several members of the family to illustrate what you discover.

65–76 ▏▏▏ Evaluate the integral.

65. $\displaystyle\int_2^4 \frac{3}{x}\, dx$

66. $\displaystyle\int_1^2 \frac{4 + u^2}{u^3}\, du$

67. $\displaystyle\int_1^2 \frac{dt}{8 - 3t}$

68. $\displaystyle\int_4^9 \left(\sqrt{x} + \frac{1}{\sqrt{x}}\right)^2 dx$

69. $\displaystyle\int_1^e \frac{x^2 + x + 1}{x}\, dx$

70. $\displaystyle\int_e^6 \frac{dx}{x \ln x}$

71. $\displaystyle\int \frac{2 - x^2}{6x - x^3}\, dx$

72. $\displaystyle\int \frac{\cos x}{2 + \sin x}\, dx$

73. $\displaystyle\int \frac{(\ln x)^2}{x}\, dx$

74. $\displaystyle\int \frac{e^x}{e^x + 1}\, dx$

75. $\displaystyle\int_1^2 10^t\, dt$

76. $\displaystyle\int x2^{x^2}\, dx$

77. Show that $\int \cot x \, dx = \ln|\sin x| + C$ by (a) differentiating the right side of the equation and (b) using the method of Example 11.

78. Find, correct to three decimal places, the area of the region above the hyperbola $y = 2/(x - 2)$, below the x-axis, and between the lines $x = -4$ and $x = -1$.

79. Find the volume of the solid obtained by rotating the region under the curve

$$y = \frac{1}{\sqrt{x + 1}}$$

from 0 to 1 about the x-axis.

80. Find the volume of the solid obtained by rotating the region under the curve

$$y = \frac{1}{x^2 + 1}$$

from 0 to 3 about the y-axis.

81. The work done by a gas when it expands from volume V_1 to volume V_2 is $W = \int_{V_1}^{V_2} P\, dV$, where $P = P(V)$ is the pressure as a function of the volume V. (See Exercise 27 in Section 6.4.) Boyle's Law states that when a quantity of gas expands at constant temperature, $PV = C$, where C is a constant. If the initial volume is 600 cm³ and the initial pressure is 150 kPa, find the work done by the gas when it expands at constant temperature to 1000 cm³.

82. Find f if $f''(x) = x^{-2}$, $x > 0$, $f(1) = 0$, and $f(2) = 0$.

83. If g is the inverse function of $f(x) = 2x + \ln x$, find $g'(2)$.

84. If $f(x) = e^x + \ln x$ and $h(x) = f^{-1}(x)$, find $h'(e)$.

85. For what values of m do the line $y = mx$ and the curve $y = x/(x^2 + 1)$ enclose a region? Find the area of the region.

86. (a) Find the linear approximation to $f(x) = \ln x$ near 1.
(b) Illustrate part (a) by graphing f and its linearization.
(c) For what values of x is the linear approximation accurate to within 0.1?

87. Use the definition of derivative to prove that

$$\lim_{x \to 0} \frac{\ln(1 + x)}{x} = 1$$

88. Show that $\displaystyle\lim_{n \to \infty} \left(1 + \frac{x}{n}\right)^n = e^x$ for any $x > 0$.

7.2* The Natural Logarithmic Function

|||| If your instructor has assigned Sections 7.2–7.4, you need not read Sections 7.2*, 7.3*, and 7.4* (pp. 451–476).

In this section we define the natural logarithm as an integral and then show that it obeys the usual laws of logarithms. The Fundamental Theorem makes it easy to differentiate this function.

> **1 Definition** The **natural logarithmic function** is the function defined by
>
> $$\ln x = \int_1^x \frac{1}{t}\, dt \qquad x > 0$$

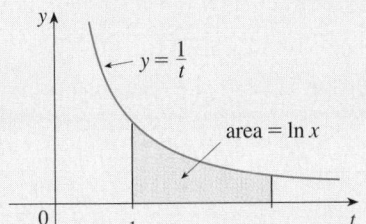

FIGURE 1

The existence of this function depends on the fact that the integral of a continuous function always exists. If $x > 1$, then $\ln x$ can be interpreted geometrically as the area under the hyperbola $y = 1/t$ from $t = 1$ to $t = x$. (See Figure 1.) For $x = 1$, we have

$$\ln 1 = \int_1^1 \frac{1}{t}\, dt = 0$$

For $0 < x < 1$,

$$\ln x = \int_1^x \frac{1}{t}\, dt = -\int_x^1 \frac{1}{t}\, dt < 0$$

and so $\ln x$ is the negative of the area shaded in Figure 2.

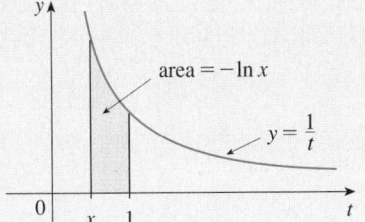

FIGURE 2

EXAMPLE 1
(a) By comparing areas, show that $\frac{1}{2} < \ln 2 < \frac{3}{4}$.
(b) Use the Midpoint Rule with $n = 10$ to estimate the value of $\ln 2$.

SOLUTION
(a) We can interpret $\ln 2$ as the area under the curve $y = 1/t$ from 1 to 2. From Figure 3 we see that this area is larger than the area of rectangle $BCDE$ and smaller than the area of trapezoid $ABCD$. Thus, we have

$$\tfrac{1}{2} \cdot 1 < \ln 2 < 1 \cdot \tfrac{1}{2}\left(1 + \tfrac{1}{2}\right)$$

$$\tfrac{1}{2} < \ln 2 < \tfrac{3}{4}$$

(b) If we use the Midpoint Rule with $f(t) = 1/t$, $n = 10$, and $\Delta t = 0.1$, we get

$$\ln 2 = \int_1^2 \frac{1}{t}\, dt \approx (0.1)[f(1.05) + f(1.15) + \cdots + f(1.95)]$$

$$= (0.1)\left(\frac{1}{1.05} + \frac{1}{1.15} + \cdots + \frac{1}{1.95}\right) \approx 0.693$$

FIGURE 3

Notice that the integral that defines $\ln x$ is exactly the type of integral discussed in Part 1 of the Fundamental Theorem of Calculus (see Section 5.3). In fact, using that theorem, we have

$$\frac{d}{dx} \int_1^x \frac{1}{t}\, dt = \frac{1}{x}$$

and so

$$\boxed{2} \qquad \frac{d}{dx}(\ln x) = \frac{1}{x}$$

We now use this differentiation rule to prove the following properties of the logarithm function.

$\boxed{3}$ **Laws of Logarithms** If x and y are positive numbers and r is a rational number, then

1. $\ln(xy) = \ln x + \ln y$ **2.** $\ln\left(\dfrac{x}{y}\right) = \ln x - \ln y$ **3.** $\ln(x^r) = r \ln x$

Proof

1. Let $f(x) = \ln(ax)$, where a is a positive constant. Then, using Equation 2 and the Chain Rule, we have

$$f'(x) = \frac{1}{ax} \frac{d}{dx}(ax) = \frac{1}{ax} \cdot a = \frac{1}{x}$$

Therefore, $f(x)$ and $\ln x$ have the same derivative and so they must differ by a constant:

$$\ln(ax) = \ln x + C$$

Putting $x = 1$ in this equation, we get $\ln a = \ln 1 + C = 0 + C = C$. Thus

$$\ln(ax) = \ln x + \ln a$$

If we now replace the constant a by any number y, we have

$$\ln(xy) = \ln x + \ln y$$

2. Using Law 1 with $x = 1/y$, we have

$$\ln\frac{1}{y} + \ln y = \ln\left(\frac{1}{y} \cdot y\right) = \ln 1 = 0$$

and so

$$\ln\frac{1}{y} = -\ln y$$

Using Law 1 again, we have

$$\ln\left(\frac{x}{y}\right) = \ln\left(x \cdot \frac{1}{y}\right) = \ln x + \ln\frac{1}{y} = \ln x - \ln y$$

The proof of Law 3 is left as an exercise.

EXAMPLE 2 Expand the expression $\ln\dfrac{(x^2 + 5)^4 \sin x}{x^3 + 1}$.

SOLUTION Using Laws 1, 2, and 3, we get

$$\ln \frac{(x^2 + 5)^4 \sin x}{x^3 + 1} = \ln(x^2 + 5)^4 + \ln \sin x - \ln(x^3 + 1)$$

$$= 4 \ln(x^2 + 5) + \ln \sin x - \ln(x^3 + 1)$$

EXAMPLE 3 Express $\ln a + \frac{1}{2} \ln b$ as a single logarithm.

SOLUTION Using Laws 3 and 1 of logarithms, we have

$$\ln a + \tfrac{1}{2} \ln b = \ln a + \ln b^{1/2}$$

$$= \ln a + \ln \sqrt{b}$$

$$= \ln\left(a\sqrt{b}\right)$$

In order to graph $y = \ln x$, we first determine its limits:

4 (a) $\displaystyle \lim_{x \to \infty} \ln x = \infty$ (b) $\displaystyle \lim_{x \to 0^+} \ln x = -\infty$

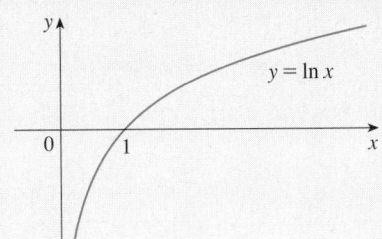

FIGURE 4

Proof
(a) Using Law 3 with $x = 2$ and $r = n$ (where n is any positive integer), we have $\ln(2^n) = n \ln 2$. Now $\ln 2 > 0$, so this shows that $\ln(2^n) \to \infty$ as $n \to \infty$. But $\ln x$ is an increasing function since its derivative $1/x > 0$. Therefore, $\ln x \to \infty$ as $x \to \infty$.
(b) If we let $t = 1/x$, then $t \to \infty$ as $x \to 0^+$. Thus, using (a), we have

$$\lim_{x \to 0^+} \ln x = \lim_{t \to \infty} \ln\left(\frac{1}{t}\right) = \lim_{t \to \infty} (-\ln t) = -\infty$$

If $y = \ln x$, $x > 0$, then

$$\frac{dy}{dx} = \frac{1}{x} > 0 \quad \text{and} \quad \frac{d^2y}{dx^2} = -\frac{1}{x^2} < 0$$

which shows that $\ln x$ is increasing and concave downward on $(0, \infty)$. Putting this information together with (4), we draw the graph of $y = \ln x$ in Figure 4.

Since $\ln 1 = 0$ and $\ln x$ is an increasing continuous function that takes on arbitrarily large values, the Intermediate Value Theorem shows that there is a number where $\ln x$ takes on the value 1 (see Figure 5). This important number is denoted by e.

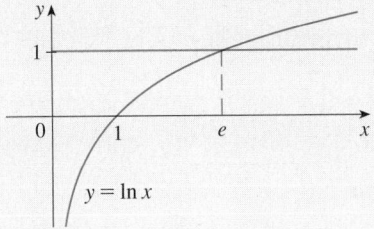

FIGURE 5

5 Definition e is the number such that $\ln e = 1$.

EXAMPLE 4 Use a graphing calculator or computer to estimate the value of e.

SOLUTION According to Definition 5, we estimate the value of e by graphing the curves $y = \ln x$ and $y = 1$ and determining the x-coordinate of the point of intersection. By zooming in repeatedly, as in Figure 6, we find that

$$e \approx 2.718$$

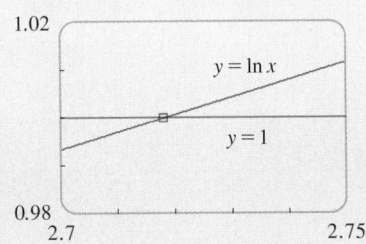

FIGURE 6

With more sophisticated methods, it can be shown that the approximate value of e, to 20 decimal places, is

$$e \approx 2.71828182845904523536$$

The decimal expansion of e is nonrepeating because e is an irrational number.

Now let's use Equation 2 to differentiate functions that involve the natural logarithmic function.

EXAMPLE 5 Differentiate $y = \ln(x^3 + 1)$.

SOLUTION To use the Chain Rule we let $u = x^3 + 1$. Then $y = \ln u$, so

$$\frac{dy}{dx} = \frac{dy}{du}\frac{du}{dx} = \frac{1}{u}\frac{du}{dx} = \frac{1}{x^3 + 1}(3x^2) = \frac{3x^2}{x^3 + 1}$$

In general, if we combine Formula 2 with the Chain Rule as in Example 5, we get

6

$$\frac{d}{dx}(\ln u) = \frac{1}{u}\frac{du}{dx} \qquad \text{or} \qquad \frac{d}{dx}[\ln g(x)] = \frac{g'(x)}{g(x)}$$

EXAMPLE 6 Find $\dfrac{d}{dx}\ln(\sin x)$.

SOLUTION Using (6), we have

$$\frac{d}{dx}\ln(\sin x) = \frac{1}{\sin x}\frac{d}{dx}(\sin x) = \frac{1}{\sin x}\cos x = \cot x$$

EXAMPLE 7 Differentiate $f(x) = \sqrt{\ln x}$.

SOLUTION This time the logarithm is the inner function, so the Chain Rule gives

$$f'(x) = \tfrac{1}{2}(\ln x)^{-1/2}\frac{d}{dx}(\ln x) = \frac{1}{2\sqrt{\ln x}} \cdot \frac{1}{x} = \frac{1}{2x\sqrt{\ln x}}$$

EXAMPLE 8 Find $\dfrac{d}{dx}\ln\dfrac{x+1}{\sqrt{x-2}}$.

SOLUTION 1

$$\frac{d}{dx}\ln\frac{x+1}{\sqrt{x-2}} = \frac{1}{\dfrac{x+1}{\sqrt{x-2}}}\frac{d}{dx}\frac{x+1}{\sqrt{x-2}}$$

$$= \frac{\sqrt{x-2}}{x+1}\frac{\sqrt{x-2}\cdot 1 - (x+1)(\tfrac{1}{2})(x-2)^{-1/2}}{x-2}$$

$$= \frac{x-2-\tfrac{1}{2}(x+1)}{(x+1)(x-2)} = \frac{x-5}{2(x+1)(x-2)}$$

|||| Figure 7 shows the graph of the function f of Example 8 together with the graph of its derivative. It gives a visual check on our calculation. Notice that $f'(x)$ is large negative when f is rapidly decreasing and $f'(x) = 0$ when f has a minimum.

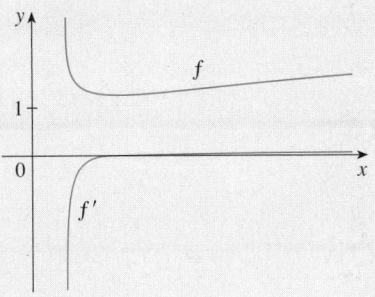

FIGURE 7

SOLUTION 2 If we first simplify the given function using the laws of logarithms, then the differentiation becomes easier:

$$\frac{d}{dx} \ln \frac{x + 1}{\sqrt{x - 2}} = \frac{d}{dx} \left[\ln(x + 1) - \tfrac{1}{2} \ln(x - 2) \right]$$

$$= \frac{1}{x + 1} - \frac{1}{2} \left(\frac{1}{x - 2} \right)$$

(This answer can be left as written, but if we used a common denominator we would see that it gives the same answer as in Solution 1.)

EXAMPLE 9 Discuss the curve $y = \ln(4 - x^2)$ using the guidelines of Section 4.5.

SOLUTION
A. The domain is

$$\{x \mid 4 - x^2 > 0\} = \{x \mid x^2 < 4\} = \{x \mid |x| < 2\} = (-2, 2)$$

B. The y-intercept is $f(0) = \ln 4$. To find the x-intercept we set

$$y = \ln(4 - x^2) = 0$$

We know that $\ln 1 = 0$, so we have $4 - x^2 = 1 \Rightarrow x^2 = 3$ and therefore the x-intercepts are $\pm\sqrt{3}$.
C. Since $f(-x) = f(x)$, f is even and the curve is symmetric about the y-axis.
D. We look for vertical asymptotes at the endpoints of the domain. Since $4 - x^2 \to 0^+$ as $x \to 2^-$ and also as $x \to -2^+$, we have

$$\lim_{x \to 2^-} \ln(4 - x^2) = -\infty \quad \text{and} \quad \lim_{x \to -2^+} \ln(4 - x^2) = -\infty$$

by (4). Thus, the lines $x = 2$ and $x = -2$ are vertical asymptotes.

E.
$$f'(x) = \frac{-2x}{4 - x^2}$$

Since $f'(x) > 0$ when $-2 < x < 0$ and $f'(x) < 0$ when $0 < x < 2$, f is increasing on $(-2, 0)$ and decreasing on $(0, 2)$.
F. The only critical number is $x = 0$. Since f' changes from positive to negative at 0, $f(0) = \ln 4$ is a local maximum by the First Derivative Test.

G.
$$f''(x) = \frac{(4 - x^2)(-2) + 2x(-2x)}{(4 - x^2)^2} = \frac{-8 - 2x^2}{(4 - x^2)^2}$$

Since $f''(x) < 0$ for all x, the curve is concave downward on $(-2, 2)$ and has no inflection point.
H. Using this information, we sketch the curve in Figure 8.

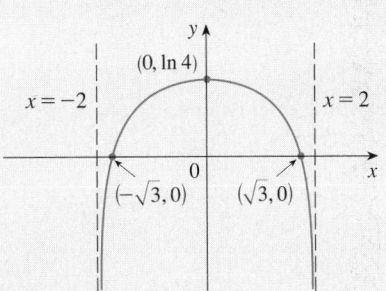

FIGURE 8
$y = \ln(4 - x^2)$

EXAMPLE 10 Find $f'(x)$ if $f(x) = \ln |x|$.

SOLUTION Since

$$f(x) = \begin{cases} \ln x & \text{if } x > 0 \\ \ln(-x) & \text{if } x < 0 \end{cases}$$

it follows that

$$f'(x) = \begin{cases} \dfrac{1}{x} & \text{if } x > 0 \\[2ex] \dfrac{1}{-x}(-1) = \dfrac{1}{x} & \text{if } x < 0 \end{cases}$$

Thus, $f'(x) = 1/x$ for all $x \neq 0$.

The result of Example 10 is worth remembering:

$$\boxed{7} \qquad \boxed{\frac{d}{dx}\left(\ln|x|\right) = \frac{1}{x}}$$

The corresponding integration formula is

$$\boxed{8} \qquad \boxed{\int \frac{1}{x}\,dx = \ln|x| + C}$$

Notice that this fills the gap in the rule for integrating power functions:

$$\int x^n\,dx = \frac{x^{n+1}}{n+1} + C \qquad \text{if } n \neq -1$$

The missing case ($n = -1$) is supplied by Formula 8.

EXAMPLE 11 Evaluate $\displaystyle\int \frac{x}{x^2+1}\,dx$.

SOLUTION We make the substitution $u = x^2 + 1$ because the differential $du = 2x\,dx$ occurs (except for the constant factor 2). Thus, $x\,dx = \frac{1}{2}\,du$ and

$$\int \frac{x}{x^2+1}\,dx = \frac{1}{2}\int \frac{du}{u} = \frac{1}{2}\ln|u| + C$$

$$= \frac{1}{2}\ln|x^2+1| + C = \frac{1}{2}\ln(x^2+1) + C$$

Notice that we removed the absolute value signs because $x^2 + 1 > 0$ for all x. We could use the properties of logarithms to write the answer as

$$\ln\sqrt{x^2+1} + C$$

but this isn't necessary.

EXAMPLE 12 Calculate $\displaystyle\int_1^e \frac{\ln x}{x}\,dx$.

SOLUTION We let $u = \ln x$ because its differential $du = dx/x$ occurs in the integral. When $x = 1$, $u = \ln 1 = 0$; when $x = e$, $u = \ln e = 1$. Thus

$$\int_1^e \frac{\ln x}{x}\,dx = \int_0^1 u\,du = \frac{u^2}{2}\Bigg]_0^1 = \frac{1}{2}$$

‖‖‖ Since the function $f(x) = (\ln x)/x$ in Example 12 is positive for $x > 1$, the integral represents the area of the shaded region in Figure 9.

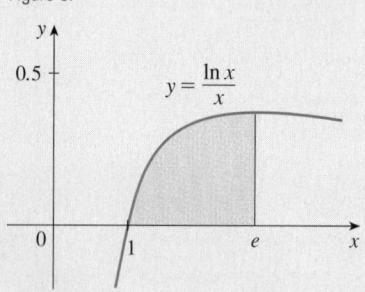

FIGURE 9

EXAMPLE 13 Calculate $\int \tan x \, dx$.

SOLUTION First we write tangent in terms of sine and cosine:

$$\int \tan x \, dx = \int \frac{\sin x}{\cos x} \, dx$$

This suggests that we should substitute $u = \cos x$ since then $du = -\sin x \, dx$ and so $\sin x \, dx = -du$:

$$\int \tan x \, dx = \int \frac{\sin x}{\cos x} \, dx = -\int \frac{du}{u}$$

$$= -\ln|u| + C = -\ln|\cos x| + C$$

Since $-\ln|\cos x| = \ln(1/|\cos x|) = \ln|\sec x|$, the result of Example 13 can also be written as

9

$$\int \tan x \, dx = \ln|\sec x| + C$$

|||| Logarithmic Differentiation

The calculation of derivatives of complicated functions involving products, quotients, or powers can often be simplified by taking logarithms. The method used in the following example is called **logarithmic differentiation**.

EXAMPLE 14 Differentiate

$$y = \frac{x^{3/4} \sqrt{x^2 + 1}}{(3x + 2)^5}$$

SOLUTION We take logarithms of both sides of the equation and use the Laws of Logarithms to simplify:

$$\ln y = \tfrac{3}{4} \ln x + \tfrac{1}{2} \ln(x^2 + 1) - 5 \ln(3x + 2)$$

Differentiating implicitly with respect to x gives

$$\frac{1}{y} \frac{dy}{dx} = \frac{3}{4} \cdot \frac{1}{x} + \frac{1}{2} \cdot \frac{2x}{x^2 + 1} - 5 \cdot \frac{3}{3x + 2}$$

Solving for dy/dx, we get

$$\frac{dy}{dx} = y \left(\frac{3}{4x} + \frac{x}{x^2 + 1} - \frac{15}{3x + 2} \right)$$

Because we have an explicit expression for y, we can substitute and write

|||| If we hadn't used logarithmic differentiation in Example 14, we would have had to use both the Quotient Rule and the Product Rule. The resulting calculation would have been horrendous.

$$\frac{dy}{dx} = \frac{x^{3/4} \sqrt{x^2 + 1}}{(3x + 2)^5} \left(\frac{3}{4x} + \frac{x}{x^2 + 1} - \frac{15}{3x + 2} \right)$$

Steps in Logarithmic Differentiation

1. Take logarithms of both sides of an equation $y = f(x)$ and use the Laws of Logarithms to simplify.

2. Differentiate implicitly with respect to x.

3. Solve the resulting equation for y'.

If $f(x) < 0$ for some values of x, then $\ln f(x)$ is not defined, but we can write $|y| = |f(x)|$ and use Equation 7.

7.2* Exercises

1–4 |||| Use the Laws of Logarithms to expand the quantity.

1. $\ln \dfrac{x^3 y}{z^2}$

2. $\ln \sqrt{a(b^2 + c^2)}$

3. $\ln (uv)^{10}$

4. $\ln \dfrac{3x^2}{(x+1)^5}$

5–8 |||| Express the quantity as a single logarithm.

5. $2 \ln 4 - \ln 2$

6. $\ln 3 + \frac{1}{3} \ln 8$

7. $\frac{1}{2} \ln x - 5 \ln(x^2 + 1)$

8. $\ln x + a \ln y - b \ln z$

9–12 |||| Make a rough sketch of the graph of each function. Do not use a calculator. Just use the graph given in Figure 4 and, if necessary, the transformations of Section 1.3.

9. $y = -\ln x$

10. $y = \ln |x|$

11. $y = \ln(x + 3)$

12. $y = 1 + \ln(x - 2)$

13–30 |||| Differentiate the function.

13. $f(x) = \sqrt{x} \ln x$

14. $f(x) = \ln(x^2 + 10)$

15. $f(\theta) = \ln(\cos \theta)$

16. $f(x) = \cos(\ln x)$

17. $f(x) = \sqrt[5]{\ln x}$

18. $f(x) = \ln \sqrt[5]{x}$

19. $g(x) = \ln \dfrac{a - x}{a + x}$

20. $h(x) = \ln\left(x + \sqrt{x^2 - 1}\right)$

21. $f(u) = \dfrac{\ln u}{1 + \ln(2u)}$

22. $f(t) = \dfrac{1 + \ln t}{1 - \ln t}$

23. $F(t) = \ln \dfrac{(2t+1)^3}{(3t-1)^4}$

24. $y = \ln(x^4 \sin^2 x)$

25. $y = \ln |2 - x - 5x^2|$

26. $G(u) = \ln \sqrt{\dfrac{3u + 2}{3u - 2}}$

27. $y = \ln\left(\dfrac{x+1}{x-1}\right)^{3/5}$

28. $y = (\ln \tan x)^2$

29. $y = \tan[\ln(ax + b)]$

30. $y = \ln |\tan 2x|$

31–32 |||| Find y' and y''.

31. $y = \ln \ln x$

32. $y = \dfrac{\ln x}{x^2}$

33–36 |||| Differentiate f and find the domain of f.

33. $f(x) = \dfrac{x}{1 - \ln(x - 1)}$

34. $f(x) = \dfrac{1}{1 + \ln x}$

35. $f(x) = \sqrt{1 - \ln x}$

36. $f(x) = \ln \ln \ln x$

37. If $f(x) = \dfrac{x}{\ln x}$, find $f'(e)$.

38. If $f(t) = t \ln(4 + 3t)$, find $f'(-1)$.

39–40 |||| Find $f'(x)$. Check that your answer is reasonable by comparing the graphs of f and f'.

39. $f(x) = \sin x + \ln x$

40. $f(x) = \ln(x^2 + x + 1)$

41–42 |||| Find an equation of the tangent line to the curve at the given point.

41. $y = \sin(2 \ln x)$, $(1, 0)$

42. $y = \ln(x^3 - 7)$, $(2, 0)$

43. Find y' if $y = \ln(x^2 + y^2)$.

44. Find y' if $\ln xy = y \sin x$.

45. Find a formula for $f^{(n)}(x)$ if $f(x) = \ln(x - 1)$.

46. Find $\dfrac{d^9}{dx^9}(x^8 \ln x)$.

47–48 ▐▐ Use a graph to estimate the roots of the equation correct to one decimal place. Then use these estimates as the initial approximations in Newton's method to find the roots correct to six decimal places.

47. $(x - 4)^2 = \ln x$

48. $\ln(4 - x^2) = x$

49–52 ▐▐ Discuss the curve under the guidelines of Section 4.5.

49. $y = \ln(\sin x)$

50. $y = \ln(\tan^2 x)$

51. $y = \ln(1 + x^2)$

52. $y = \ln(x^2 - 3x + 2)$

53. If $f(x) = \ln(2x + x \sin x)$, use the graphs of f, f', and f'' to estimate the intervals of increase and the inflection points of f on the interval $(0, 15]$.

54. Investigate the family of curves $f(x) = \ln(x^2 + c)$. What happens to the inflection points and asymptotes as c changes? Graph several members of the family to illustrate what you discover.

55–58 ▐▐ Use logarithmic differentiation to find the derivative of the function.

55. $y = (2x + 1)^5(x^4 - 3)^6$

56. $y = \dfrac{(x^3 + 1)^4 \sin^2 x}{\sqrt[3]{x}}$

57. $y = \dfrac{\sin^2 x \tan^4 x}{(x^2 + 1)^2}$

58. $y = \sqrt[4]{\dfrac{x^2 + 1}{x^2 - 1}}$

59–68 ▐▐ Evaluate the integral.

59. $\int_2^4 \dfrac{3}{x}\, dx$

60. $\int_1^2 \dfrac{4 + u^2}{u^3}\, du$

61. $\int_1^2 \dfrac{dt}{8 - 3t}$

62. $\int_4^9 \left(\sqrt{x} + \dfrac{1}{\sqrt{x}}\right)^2 dx$

63. $\int_1^e \dfrac{x^2 + x + 1}{x}\, dx$

64. $\int_e^6 \dfrac{dx}{x \ln x}$

65. $\int \dfrac{2 - x^2}{6x - x^3}\, dx$

66. $\int \dfrac{\cos x}{2 + \sin x}\, dx$

67. $\int \dfrac{(\ln x)^2}{x}\, dx$

68. $\int \dfrac{(1 + \sqrt{x})^4}{\sqrt{x}}\, dx$

69. Show that $\int \cot x\, dx = \ln|\sin x| + C$ by (a) differentiating the right side of the equation and (b) using the method of Example 13.

70. Find, correct to three decimal places, the area of the region above the hyperbola $y = 2/(x - 2)$, below the x-axis, and between the lines $x = -4$ and $x = -1$.

71. Find the volume of the solid obtained by rotating the region under the curve $y = 1/\sqrt{x + 1}$ from 0 to 1 about the x-axis.

72. Find the volume of the solid obtained by rotating the region under the curve $y = 1/(x^2 + 1)$ from 0 to 3 about the y-axis.

73. The work done by a gas when it expands from volume V_1 to volume V_2 is $W = \int_{V_1}^{V_2} P\, dV$, where $P = P(V)$ is the pressure as a function of the volume V. (See Exercise 27 in Section 6.4.) Boyle's Law states that when a quantity of gas expands at constant temperature, $PV = C$, where C is a constant. If the initial volume is 600 cm³ and the initial pressure is 150 kPa, find the work done by the gas when it expands at constant temperature to 1000 cm³.

74. Find f if $f''(x) = x^{-2}$, $x > 0$, $f(1) = 0$, and $f(2) = 0$.

75. If g is the inverse function of $f(x) = 2x + \ln x$, find $g'(2)$.

76. (a) Find the linear approximation to $f(x) = \ln x$ near 1.
(b) Illustrate part (a) by graphing f and its linearization.
(c) For what values of x is the linear approximation accurate to within 0.1?

77. (a) By comparing areas, show that
$$\tfrac{1}{3} < \ln 1.5 < \tfrac{5}{12}$$
(b) Use the Midpoint Rule with $n = 10$ to estimate $\ln 1.5$.

78. Refer to Example 1.
(a) Find an equation of the tangent line to the curve $y = 1/t$ that is parallel to the secant line AD.
(b) Use part (a) to show that $\ln 2 > 0.66$.

79. By comparing areas, show that
$$\dfrac{1}{2} + \dfrac{1}{3} + \cdots + \dfrac{1}{n} < \ln n < 1 + \dfrac{1}{2} + \dfrac{1}{3} + \cdots + \dfrac{1}{n-1}$$

80. Prove the third law of logarithms. [*Hint:* Start by showing that both sides of the equation have the same derivative.]

81. For what values of m do the line $y = mx$ and the curve $y = x/(x^2 + 1)$ enclose a region? Find the area of the region.

82. Find $\lim_{x \to \infty} [\ln(2 + x) - \ln(1 + x)]$.

83. Use the definition of derivative to prove that
$$\lim_{x \to 0} \dfrac{\ln(1 + x)}{x} = 1$$

84. (a) Compare the rates of growth of $f(x) = x^{0.1}$ and $g(x) = \ln x$ by graphing both f and g in several viewing rectangles. When does the graph of f finally surpass the graph of g?
(b) Graph the function $h(x) = (\ln x)/x^{0.1}$ in a viewing rectangle that displays the behavior of the function as $x \to \infty$.
(c) Find a number N such that
$$\dfrac{\ln x}{x^{0.1}} < 0.1 \quad \text{whenever} \quad x > N$$

7.3* The Natural Exponential Function

Since ln is an increasing function, it is one-to-one and therefore has an inverse function, which we denote by exp. Thus, according to the definition of an inverse function,

$f^{-1}(x) = y \iff f(y) = x$

 1

$$\exp(x) = y \iff \ln y = x$$

and the cancellation equations are

$f^{-1}(f(x)) = x$

$f(f^{-1}(x)) = x$

2

$$\exp(\ln x) = x \quad \text{and} \quad \ln(\exp x) = x$$

In particular, we have

$$\exp(0) = 1 \quad \text{since } \ln 1 = 0$$

$$\exp(1) = e \quad \text{since } \ln e = 1$$

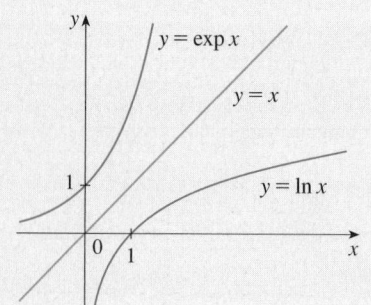

FIGURE 1

We obtain the graph of $y = \exp x$ by reflecting the graph of $y = \ln x$ about the line $y = x$. (See Figure 1.) The domain of exp is the range of ln, that is, $(-\infty, \infty)$; the range of exp is the domain of ln, that is, $(0, \infty)$.

If r is any rational number, then the third law of logarithms gives

$$\ln(e^r) = r \ln e = r$$

Therefore, by (1),

$$\exp(r) = e^r$$

Thus, $\exp(x) = e^x$ whenever x is a rational number. This leads us to define e^x, even for irrational values of x, by the equation

$$e^x = \exp(x)$$

In other words, for the reasons given, we define e^x to be the inverse of the function $\ln x$. In this notation (1) becomes

3

$$e^x = y \iff \ln y = x$$

and the cancellation equations (2) become

4

$$e^{\ln x} = x \quad x > 0$$

5

$$\ln(e^x) = x \quad \text{for all } x$$

EXAMPLE 1 Find x if $\ln x = 5$.

SOLUTION 1 From (3) we see that

$$\ln x = 5 \qquad \text{means} \qquad e^5 = x$$

Therefore, $x = e^5$.

SOLUTION 2 Start with the equation

$$\ln x = 5$$

and apply the exponential function to both sides of the equation:

$$e^{\ln x} = e^5$$

But (4) says that $e^{\ln x} = x$. Therefore, $x = e^5$.

EXAMPLE 2 Solve the equation $e^{5-3x} = 10$.

SOLUTION We take natural logarithms of both sides of the equation and use (5):

$$\ln(e^{5-3x}) = \ln 10$$

$$5 - 3x = \ln 10$$

$$3x = 5 - \ln 10$$

$$x = \tfrac{1}{3}(5 - \ln 10)$$

Since the natural logarithm is found on scientific calculators, we can approximate the solution to four decimal places: $x \approx 0.8991$.

The exponential function $f(x) = e^x$ is one of the most frequently occurring functions in calculus and its applications, so it is important to be familiar with its graph (Figure 2) and its properties (which follow from the fact that it is the inverse of the natural logarithmic function).

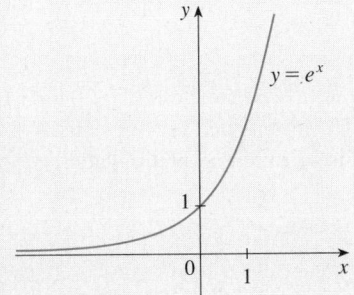

FIGURE 2
The natural exponential function

---

6 **Properties of the Natural Exponential Function** The exponential function $f(x) = e^x$ is an increasing continuous function with domain $\mathbb{R}$ and range $(0, \infty)$. Thus, $e^x > 0$ for all x. Also

$$\lim_{x \to -\infty} e^x = 0 \qquad \lim_{x \to \infty} e^x = \infty$$

So the x-axis is a horizontal asymptote of $f(x) = e^x$.

EXAMPLE 3 Find $\displaystyle \lim_{x \to \infty} \frac{e^{2x}}{e^{2x} + 1}$.

SOLUTION We divide numerator and denominator by e^{2x}:

$$\lim_{x \to \infty} \frac{e^{2x}}{e^{2x} + 1} = \lim_{x \to \infty} \frac{1}{1 + e^{-2x}} = \frac{1}{1 + \lim\limits_{x \to \infty} e^{-2x}}$$

$$= \frac{1}{1 + 0} = 1$$

We have used the fact that $t = -2x \to -\infty$ as $x \to \infty$ and so

$$\lim_{x \to \infty} e^{-2x} = \lim_{t \to -\infty} e^t = 0$$

We now verify that $f(x) = e^x$ has the properties expected of an exponential function.

---

7 **Laws of Exponents** If x and y are real numbers and r is rational, then

1. $e^{x+y} = e^x e^y$ **2.** $e^{x-y} = \dfrac{e^x}{e^y}$ **3.** $(e^x)^r = e^{rx}$

Proof of Law 1 Using the first law of logarithms and Equation 5, we have

$$\ln(e^x e^y) = \ln(e^x) + \ln(e^y) = x + y = \ln(e^{x+y})$$

Since ln is a one-to-one function, it follows that $e^x e^y = e^{x+y}$.

Laws 2 and 3 are proved similarly (see Exercises 85 and 86). As we will see in the next section, Law 3 actually holds when r is any real number.

||| **Differentiation**

The natural exponential function has the remarkable property that *it is its own derivative.*

8
$$\frac{d}{dx}(e^x) = e^x$$

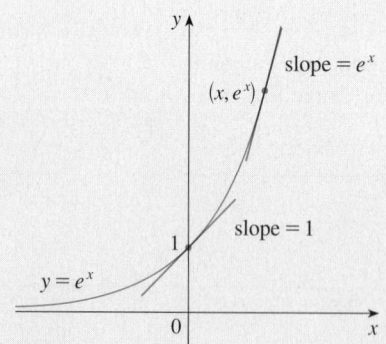

FIGURE 3

Proof The function $y = e^x$ is differentiable because it is the inverse function of $y = \ln x$, which we know is differentiable with nonzero derivative. To find its derivative, we use the inverse function method. Let $y = e^x$. Then $\ln y = x$ and, differentiating this latter equation implicitly with respect to x, we get

$$\frac{1}{y}\frac{dy}{dx} = 1$$

$$\frac{dy}{dx} = y = e^x$$

The geometric interpretation of Formula 8 is that the slope of a tangent line to the curve $y = e^x$ at any point is equal to the y-coordinate of the point (see Figure 3). This property implies that the exponential curve $y = e^x$ grows very rapidly (see Exercise 90).

EXAMPLE 4 Differentiate the function $y = e^{\tan x}$.

SOLUTION To use the Chain Rule, we let $u = \tan x$. Then we have $y = e^u$, so

$$\frac{dy}{dx} = \frac{dy}{du}\frac{du}{dx} = e^u \frac{du}{dx} = e^{\tan x}\sec^2 x$$

In general if we combine Formula 8 with the Chain Rule, as in Example 4, we get

$$9 \qquad \frac{d}{dx}(e^u) = e^u \frac{du}{dx}$$

EXAMPLE 5 Find y' if $y = e^{-4x} \sin 5x$.

SOLUTION Using Formula 9 and the Product Rule, we have

$$y' = e^{-4x}(\cos 5x)(5) + (\sin 5x)e^{-4x}(-4) = e^{-4x}(5 \cos 5x - 4 \sin 5x) \qquad \blacksquare$$

EXAMPLE 6 Find the absolute maximum value of the function $f(x) = xe^{-x}$.

SOLUTION We differentiate to find any critical numbers:

$$f'(x) = xe^{-x}(-1) + e^{-x}(1) = e^{-x}(1 - x)$$

Since exponential functions are always positive, we see that $f'(x) > 0$ when $1 - x > 0$, that is, when $x < 1$. Similarly, $f'(x) < 0$ when $x > 1$. By the First Derivative Test for Absolute Extreme Values, f has an absolute maximum value when $x = 1$ and the value is

$$f(1) = (1)e^{-1} = \frac{1}{e} \approx 0.37 \qquad \blacksquare$$

EXAMPLE 7 Use the first and second derivatives of $f(x) = e^{1/x}$, together with asymptotes, to sketch its graph.

SOLUTION Notice that the domain of f is $\{x \mid x \neq 0\}$, so we check for vertical asymptotes by computing the left and right limits as $x \to 0$. As $x \to 0^+$, we know that $t = 1/x \to \infty$, so

$$\lim_{x \to 0^+} e^{1/x} = \lim_{t \to \infty} e^t = \infty$$

and this shows that $x = 0$ is a vertical asymptote. As $x \to 0^-$, we have $t = 1/x \to -\infty$, so

$$\lim_{x \to 0^-} e^{1/x} = \lim_{t \to -\infty} e^t = 0$$

As $x \to \pm\infty$, we have $1/x \to 0$ and so

$$\lim_{x \to \pm\infty} e^{1/x} = e^0 = 1$$

This shows that $y = 1$ is a horizontal asymptote.

Now let's compute the derivative. The Chain Rule gives

$$f'(x) = -\frac{e^{1/x}}{x^2}$$

Since $e^{1/x} > 0$ and $x^2 > 0$ for all $x \neq 0$, we have $f'(x) < 0$ for all $x \neq 0$. Thus, f is decreasing on $(-\infty, 0)$ and on $(0, \infty)$. There is no critical number, so the function has no maximum or minimum. The second derivative is

$$f''(x) = -\frac{x^2 e^{1/x}(-1/x^2) - e^{1/x}(2x)}{x^4} = \frac{e^{1/x}(2x + 1)}{x^4}$$

Since $e^{1/x} > 0$ and $x^4 > 0$, we have $f''(x) > 0$ when $x > -\frac{1}{2}$ ($x \ne 0$) and $f''(x) < 0$ when $x < -\frac{1}{2}$. So the curve is concave downward on $\left(-\infty, -\frac{1}{2}\right)$ and concave upward on $\left(-\frac{1}{2}, 0\right)$ and on $(0, \infty)$. The inflection point is $\left(-\frac{1}{2}, e^{-2}\right)$.

To sketch the graph of f we first draw the horizontal asymptote $y = 1$ (as a dashed line), together with the parts of the curve near the asymptotes in a preliminary sketch [Figure 4(a)]. These parts reflect the information concerning limits and the fact that f is decreasing on both $(-\infty, 0)$ and $(0, \infty)$. Notice that we have indicated that $f(x) \to 0$ as $x \to 0^-$ even though $f(0)$ does not exist. In Figure 4(b) we finish the sketch by incorporating the information concerning concavity and the inflection point. In Figure 4(c) we check our work with a graphing device.

FIGURE 4 (a) Preliminary sketch   (b) Finished sketch   (c) Computer confirmation

|||| Integration

Because the exponential function $y = e^x$ has a simple derivative, its integral is also simple:

$$\boxed{10} \qquad \int e^x \, dx = e^x + C$$

EXAMPLE 8 Evaluate $\displaystyle\int x^2 e^{x^3} \, dx$.

SOLUTION We substitute $u = x^3$. Then $du = 3x^2 \, dx$, so $x^2 \, dx = \frac{1}{3} \, du$ and

$$\int x^2 e^{x^3} \, dx = \frac{1}{3} \int e^u \, du = \frac{1}{3} e^u + C = \frac{1}{3} e^{x^3} + C$$

EXAMPLE 9 Find the area under the curve $y = e^{-3x}$ from 0 to 1.

SOLUTION The area is

$$A = \int_0^1 e^{-3x} \, dx = -\frac{1}{3} e^{-3x} \Big]_0^1 = \frac{1}{3} (1 - e^{-3})$$

7.3* Exercises

1. (a) How is the number e defined?
(b) What is an approximate value for e?
(c) Sketch, by hand, the graph of the function $f(x) = e^x$ with particular attention to how the graph crosses the y-axis. What fact allows you to do this?

2–4 |||| Simplify each expression.

2. (a) $e^{\ln 6}$ (b) $\ln \sqrt{e}$

3. (a) $\ln e^{\sqrt{2}}$ (b) $e^{3\ln 2}$

4. (a) $\ln e^{\sin x}$ (b) $e^{x + \ln x}$

5–12 |||| Solve each equation for x.

5. (a) $2 \ln x = 1$ (b) $e^{-x} = 5$

6. (a) $e^{2x+3} - 7 = 0$ (b) $\ln(5 - 2x) = -3$

7. $\ln(\ln x) = 1$

8. $e^{e^x} = 10$

9. $2 \ln x = \ln 2 + \ln(3x - 4)$

10. $\ln(2x + 1) = 2 - \ln x$

11. $e^{ax} = Ce^{bx}$, where $a \neq b$

12. $7e^x - e^{2x} = 12$

13–16 |||| Find the solution of the equation correct to four decimal places.

13. $e^{2+5x} = 100$ **14.** $\ln(1 + \sqrt{x}) = 2$

15. $\ln(e^x - 2) = 3$ **16.** $e^{1/(x-4)} = 7$

17–18 |||| Solve each inequality for x.

17. (a) $e^x < 10$ (b) $\ln x > -1$

18. (a) $2 < \ln x < 9$ (b) $e^{2-3x} > 4$

19–22 |||| Make a rough sketch of the graph of each function. Do not use a calculator. Just use the graph given in Figure 2 and, if necessary, the transformations of Section 1.3.

19. $y = e^{-x}$ **20.** $y = 1 + 2e^x$

21. $y = 3 - e^x$ **22.** $y = 2 + 5(1 - e^{-x})$

23. Starting with the graph of $y = e^x$, write the equation of the graph that results from
(a) shifting 2 units downward
(b) shifting 2 units to the right

(c) reflecting about the x-axis
(d) reflecting about the y-axis
(e) reflecting about the x-axis and then about the y-axis

24. Starting with the graph of $y = e^x$, find the equation of the graph that results from
(a) reflecting about the line $y = 4$
(b) reflecting about the line $x = 2$

25–30 |||| Find the limit.

25. $\displaystyle \lim_{x \to \infty} e^{1-x^3}$ **26.** $\displaystyle \lim_{x \to (\pi/2)^+} e^{\tan x}$

27. $\displaystyle \lim_{x \to \infty} \frac{e^{3x} - e^{-3x}}{e^{3x} + e^{-3x}}$ **28.** $\displaystyle \lim_{x \to -\infty} \frac{e^{3x} - e^{-3x}}{e^{3x} + e^{-3x}}$

29. $\displaystyle \lim_{x \to 2^+} e^{3/(2-x)}$ **30.** $\displaystyle \lim_{x \to 2^-} e^{3/(2-x)}$

31–44 |||| Differentiate the function.

31. $f(x) = x^2 e^x$ **32.** $y = \dfrac{e^x}{1 + x}$

33. $y = e^{ax^3}$ **34.** $y = e^u(\cos u + cu)$

35. $f(u) = e^{1/u}$ **36.** $y = e^x \ln x$

37. $F(t) = e^{t \sin 2t}$ **38.** $y = e^{k \tan \sqrt{x}}$

39. $y = \sqrt{1 + 2e^{3x}}$ **40.** $y = \cos(e^{\pi x})$

41. $y = e^{e^x}$ **42.** $y = \sqrt{1 + xe^{-2x}}$

43. $y = \dfrac{ae^x + b}{ce^x + d}$ **44.** $y = \dfrac{e^x + e^{-x}}{e^x - e^{-x}}$

45–46 |||| Find an equation of the tangent line to the curve at the given point.

45. $y = e^{2x} \cos \pi x$, $(0, 1)$ **46.** $y = e^x/x$, $(1, e)$

47. Find y' if $e^{x^2 y} = x + y$.

48. Show that the function $y = Ae^{-x} + Bxe^{-x}$ satisfies the differential equation $y'' + 2y' + y = 0$.

49. For what values of r does the function $y = e^{rx}$ satisfy the equation $y'' + 6y' + 8y = 0$?

50. Find the values of λ for which $y = e^{\lambda x}$ satisfies the equation $y + y' = y''$.

51. If $f(x) = e^{2x}$, find a formula for $f^{(n)}(x)$.

52. Find the thousandth derivative of $f(x) = xe^{-x}$.

53. (a) Use the Intermediate Value Theorem to show that there is a root of the equation $e^x + x = 0$.
(b) Use Newton's method to find the root of the equation in part (a) correct to six decimal places.

54. Use a graph to find an initial approximation (to one decimal place) to the root of the equation

$$e^{-x^2} = x^3 + x - 3$$

Then use Newton's method to find the root correct to six decimal places.

55. If the initial mass of a sample of ^{90}Sr is 24 mg, then the mass after t years is

$$m(t) = 24 \cdot e^{-(\ln 2)t/25}$$

(a) Find the mass remaining after 40 years.
(b) At what rate does the mass decay after 40 years?
(c) How long does it take for the mass to be reduced to 5 mg?

56. For the period from 1980 to 2000, the percentage of households in the United States with at least one VCR has been modeled by the function

$$V(t) = \frac{85}{1 + 53e^{-0.5t}}$$

where the time t is measured in years since midyear 1980, so $0 \le t \le 20$. Use a graph to estimate the time at which the number of VCRs was increasing most rapidly. Then use derivatives to give a more accurate estimate.

57. Under certain circumstances a rumor spreads according to the equation

$$p(t) = \frac{1}{1 + ae^{-kt}}$$

where $p(t)$ is the proportion of the population that knows the rumor at time t and a and k are positive constants. [In Section 10.5 we will see that this is a reasonable model for $p(t)$.]
(a) Find $\lim_{t \to \infty} p(t)$.
(b) Find the rate of spread of the rumor.
(c) Graph p for the case $a = 10$, $k = 0.5$ with t measured in hours. Use the graph to estimate how long it will take for 80% of the population to hear the rumor.

58. An object is attached to the end of a vibrating spring and its displacement from its equilibrium position is $y = 8e^{-t/2} \sin 4t$, where t is measured in seconds and y is measured in centimeters.
(a) Graph the displacement function together with the functions $y = 8e^{-t/2}$ and $y = -8e^{-t/2}$. How are these graphs related? Can you explain why?
(b) Use the graph to estimate the maximum value of the displacement. Does it occur when the graph touches the graph of $y = 8e^{-t/2}$?
(c) What is the velocity of the object when it first returns to its equilibrium position?

(d) Use the graph to estimate the time after which the displacement is no more than 2 cm from equilibrium.

59. Find the absolute maximum value of the function $f(x) = x - e^x$.

60. Find the absolute minimum value of the function $g(x) = e^x/x$, $x > 0$.

61. On what interval is the curve $y = xe^{3x}$ concave upward?

62. On what interval is the function $f(x) = x^2 e^{-x}$ increasing?

63–65 ||| Discuss the curve using the guidelines of Section 4.5.
63. $y = e^{-1/(x+1)}$ **64.** $y = e^{2x} - e^x$
65. $y = e^{3x} + e^{-2x}$

66–67 ||| Draw a graph of f that shows all the important aspects of the curve. Estimate the local maximum and minimum values and then use calculus to find these values exactly. Use a graph of f'' to estimate the inflection points.
66. $f(x) = e^{\cos x}$ **67.** $f(x) = e^{x^3 - x}$

68. The family of bell-shaped curves

$$y = \frac{1}{\sigma\sqrt{2\pi}} e^{-(x-\mu)^2/(2\sigma^2)}$$

occurs in probability and statistics, where it is called the *normal density function*. The constant μ is called the *mean* and the positive constant σ is called the *standard deviation*. For simplicity, let's scale the function so as to remove the factor $1/(\sigma\sqrt{2\pi})$ and let's analyze the special case where $\mu = 0$. So we study the function

$$f(x) = e^{-x^2/(2\sigma^2)}$$

(a) Find the asymptote, maximum value, and inflection points of f.
(b) What role does σ play in the shape of the curve?
(c) Illustrate by graphing four members of this family on the same screen.

69–76 ||| Evaluate the integral.
69. $\int_0^5 e^{-3x}\,dx$ **70.** $\int_0^1 xe^{-x^2}\,dx$

71. $\int e^x\sqrt{1 + e^x}\,dx$ **72.** $\int \sec^2 x\, e^{\tan x}\,dx$

73. $\int \frac{e^x + 1}{e^x}\,dx$ **74.** $\int \frac{e^{1/x}}{x^2}\,dx$

75. $\int \frac{e^{\sqrt{x}}}{\sqrt{x}}\,dx$ **76.** $\int e^x \sin(e^x)\,dx$

77. Find, correct to three decimal places, the area of the region bounded by the curves $y = e^x$, $y = e^{3x}$, and $x = 1$.

78. Find $f(x)$ if $f''(x) = 3e^x + 5 \sin x$, $f(0) = 1$, and $f'(0) = 2$.

79. Find the volume of the solid obtained by rotating about the x-axis the region bounded by the curves $y = e^x$, $y = 0$, $x = 0$, and $x = 1$.

80. Find the volume of the solid obtained by rotating about the y-axis the region bounded by the curves $y = e^{-x^2}$, $y = 0$, $x = 0$, and $x = 1$.

81–82 |||| Find the inverse function of f. Check your answer by graphing both f and f^{-1} on the same screen.

81. $f(x) = \ln(x + 3)$

82. $f(x) = \dfrac{1 + e^x}{1 - e^x}$

83. If $f(x) = 3 + x + e^x$, find $(f^{-1})'(4)$.

84. Evaluate $\displaystyle\lim_{x \to \pi} \frac{e^{\sin x} - 1}{x - \pi}$.

85. Prove the second law of exponents [see (7)].

86. Prove the third law of exponents [see (7)].

87. (a) Show that $e^x \geq 1 + x$ if $x \geq 0$.
   [*Hint:* Show that $f(x) = e^x - (1 + x)$ is increasing for $x > 0$.]
   (b) Deduce that $\frac{4}{3} \leq \int_0^1 e^{x^2}\, dx \leq e$.

88. (a) Use the inequality of Exercise 87(a) to show that, for $x \geq 0$,
$$e^x \geq 1 + x + \tfrac{1}{2}x^2$$
   (b) Use part (a) to improve the estimate of $\int_0^1 e^{x^2}\, dx$ given in Exercise 87(b).

89. (a) Use mathematical induction to prove that for $x \geq 0$ and any positive integer n,
$$e^x \geq 1 + x + \frac{x^2}{2!} + \cdots + \frac{x^n}{n!}$$
   (b) Use part (a) to show that $e > 2.7$.
   (c) Use part (a) to show that
$$\lim_{x \to \infty} \frac{e^x}{x^k} = \infty$$
   for any positive integer k.

90. This exercise illustrates Exercise 89(c) for the case $k = 10$.
   (a) Compare the rates of growth of $f(x) = x^{10}$ and $g(x) = e^x$ by graphing both f and g in several viewing rectangles. When does the graph of g finally surpass the graph of f?
   (b) Find a viewing rectangle that shows how the function $h(x) = e^x/x^{10}$ behaves for large x.
   (c) Find a number N such that
$$\frac{e^x}{x^{10}} > 10^{10} \qquad \text{whenever} \qquad x > N$$

7.4* General Logarithmic and Exponential Functions

In this section we use the natural exponential and logarithmic functions to study exponential and logarithmic functions with base $a > 0$.

General Exponential Functions

If $a > 0$ and r is any rational number, then by (4) and (7) in Section 7.3*,

$$a^r = (e^{\ln a})^r = e^{r \ln a}$$

Therefore, even for irrational numbers x, we *define*

$$a^x = e^{x \ln a}$$

Thus, for instance,

$$2^{\sqrt{3}} = e^{\sqrt{3} \ln 2} \approx e^{1.20} \approx 3.32$$

The function $f(x) = a^x$ is called the **exponential function with base a**. Notice that a^x is positive for all x because e^x is positive for all x.

Definition 1 allows us to extend one of the laws of logarithms. We know that $\ln(a^r) = r \ln a$ when r is rational. But if we now let r be *any* real number we have, from Definition 1,

$$\ln a^r = \ln(e^{r \ln a}) = r \ln a$$

Thus

$$\boxed{2} \qquad\qquad \ln a^r = r \ln a \qquad \text{for any real number } r$$

The general laws of exponents follow from Definition 1 together with the laws of exponents for e^x.

$\boxed{3}$ **Laws of Exponents** If x and y are real numbers and $a, b > 0$, then

1. $a^{x+y} = a^x a^y$ **2.** $a^{x-y} = a^x/a^y$ **3.** $(a^x)^y = a^{xy}$ **4.** $(ab)^x = a^x b^x$

Proof

1. Using Definition 1 and the laws of exponents for e^x, we have

$$a^{x+y} = e^{(x+y)\ln a} = e^{x \ln a + y \ln a}$$
$$= e^{x \ln a} e^{y \ln a} = a^x a^y$$

3. Using Equation 2 we obtain

$$(a^x)^y = e^{y \ln(a^x)} = e^{yx \ln a}$$
$$= e^{xy \ln a} = a^{xy}$$

The remaining proofs are left as exercises.

The differentiation formula for exponential functions is also a consequence of Definition 1:

$$\boxed{4} \qquad\qquad \frac{d}{dx}(a^x) = a^x \ln a$$

Proof
$$\frac{d}{dx}(a^x) = \frac{d}{dx}(e^{x \ln a}) = e^{x \ln a} \frac{d}{dx}(x \ln a)$$
$$= a^x \ln a$$

Notice that if $a = e$, then $\ln e = 1$ and Formula 4 simplifies to a formula that we already know: $(d/dx) e^x = e^x$. In fact, the reason that the natural exponential function is used more often than other exponential functions is that its differentiation formula is simpler.

EXAMPLE 1 In Example 6 in Section 3.4 we considered a population of bacteria cells in a homogeneous nutrient medium. We showed that if the population doubles every hour, then the population after t hours is

$$n = n_0 2^t$$

where n_0 is the initial population. Now we can use (4) to compute the growth rate:

$$\frac{dn}{dt} = n_0 2^t \ln 2$$

For instance, if the initial population is $n_0 = 1000$ cells, then the growth rate after two hours is

$$\frac{dn}{dt}\bigg|_{t=2} = (1000)2^t \ln 2 \,\big|_{t=2}$$

$$= 4000 \ln 2 \approx 2773 \text{ cells/h}$$

EXAMPLE 2 Combining Formula 4 with the Chain Rule, we have

$$\frac{d}{dx}\left(10^{x^2}\right) = 10^{x^2} (\ln 10) \frac{d}{dx}(x^2) = (2 \ln 10)x10^{x^2}$$

|||| Exponential Graphs

If $a > 1$, then $\ln a > 0$, so $(d/dx)\, a^x = a^x \ln a > 0$, which shows that $y = a^x$ is increasing (see Figure 1). If $0 < a < 1$, then $\ln a < 0$ and so $y = a^x$ is decreasing (see Figure 2).

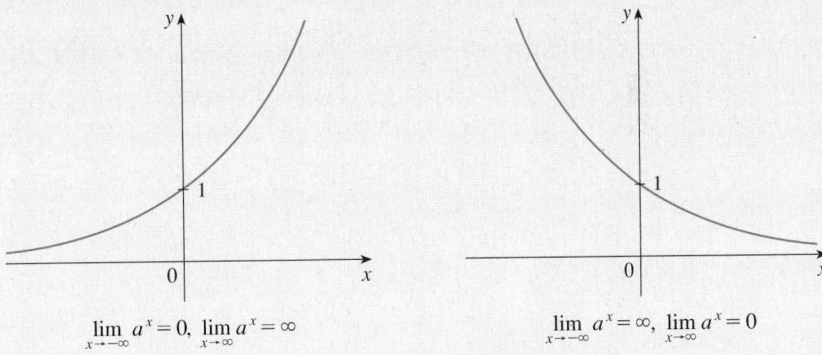

$$\lim_{x \to -\infty} a^x = 0, \ \lim_{x \to \infty} a^x = \infty \qquad\qquad \lim_{x \to -\infty} a^x = \infty, \ \lim_{x \to \infty} a^x = 0$$

FIGURE 1 $y = a^x, \ a > 1$ **FIGURE 2** $y = a^x, \ 0 < a < 1$

Notice from Figure 3 that as the base a gets larger, the exponential function grows more rapidly (for $x > 0$).

Figure 4 shows how the exponential function $y = 2^x$ compares with the power function $y = x^2$. The graphs intersect three times, but ultimately the exponential curve $y = 2^x$ grows far more rapidly than the parabola $y = x^2$. (See also Figure 5.)

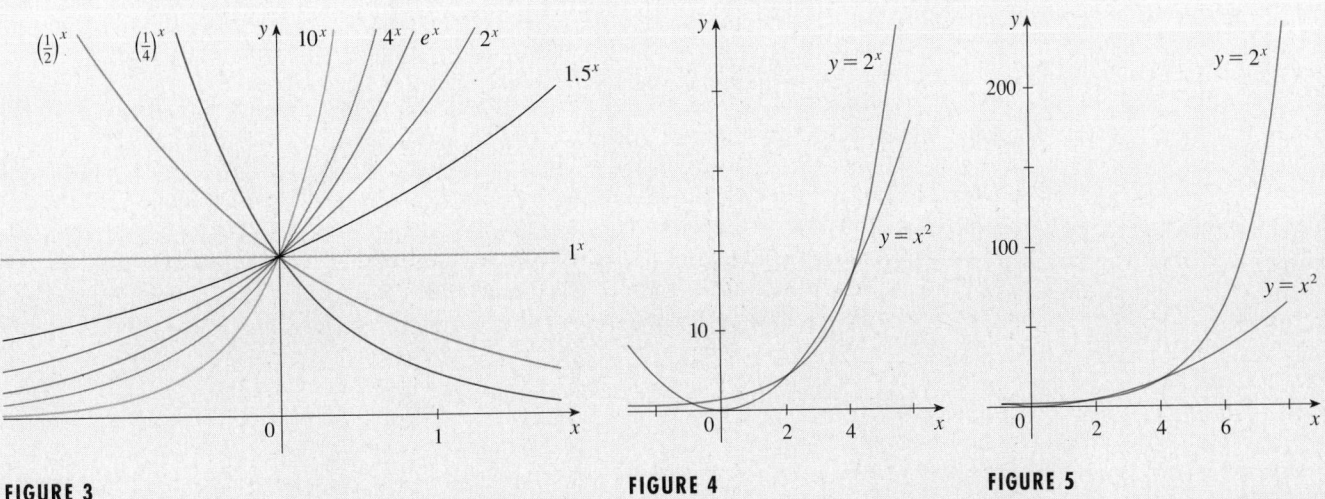

FIGURE 3   **FIGURE 4**   **FIGURE 5**

In Chapter 10 we will show why exponential functions occur in the description of population growth and radioactive decay. Let's look at human population growth. Table 1 shows data for the population of the world in the 20th century and Figure 6 shows the corresponding scatter plot.

TABLE 1

Year	Population (millions)
1900	1650
1910	1750
1920	1860
1930	2070
1940	2300
1950	2560
1960	3040
1970	3710
1980	4450
1990	5280
2000	6080

FIGURE 6 Scatter plot for world population growth

The pattern of the data points in Figure 6 suggests exponential growth, so we use a graphing calculator with exponential regression capability to apply the method of least squares and obtain the exponential model

$$P = (0.008079266) \cdot (1.013731)^t$$

Figure 7 shows the graph of this exponential function together with the original data points. We see that the exponential curve fits the data reasonably well. The period of relatively slow population growth is explained by the two world wars and the Great Depression of the 1930s.

FIGURE 7
Exponential model for
population growth

||| **Exponential Integrals**

The integration formula that follows from Formula 4 is

$$\int a^x \, dx = \frac{a^x}{\ln a} + C \qquad a \neq 1$$

EXAMPLE 3
$$\int_0^5 2^x \, dx = \frac{2^x}{\ln 2}\Big]_0^5 = \frac{2^5}{\ln 2} - \frac{2^0}{\ln 2} = \frac{31}{\ln 2}$$

|||| The Power Rule Versus the Exponential Rule

Now that we have defined arbitrary powers of numbers, we are in a position to prove the general version of the Power Rule, as promised in Section 3.3.

> **The Power Rule** If n is any real number and $f(x) = x^n$, then
> $$f'(x) = nx^{n-1}$$

|||| If $x = 0$, we can show that $f'(0) = 0$ for $n > 1$ directly from the definition of a derivative.

Proof Let $y = x^n$ and use logarithmic differentiation:
$$\ln|y| = \ln|x|^n = n \ln|x| \qquad x \neq 0$$

Therefore
$$\frac{y'}{y} = \frac{n}{x}$$

Hence
$$y' = n\frac{y}{x} = n\frac{x^n}{x} = nx^{n-1}$$

 You should distinguish carefully between the Power Rule $[(d/dx)\, x^n = nx^{n-1}]$, where the base is variable and the exponent is constant, and the rule for differentiating exponential functions $[(d/dx)\, a^x = a^x \ln a]$, where the base is constant and the exponent is variable.

In general there are four cases for exponents and bases:

1. $\dfrac{d}{dx}(a^b) = 0 \qquad (a \text{ and } b \text{ are constants})$

2. $\dfrac{d}{dx}[f(x)]^b = b[f(x)]^{b-1}f'(x)$

3. $\dfrac{d}{dx}[a^{g(x)}] = a^{g(x)}(\ln a)g'(x)$

4. To find $(d/dx)[f(x)]^{g(x)}$, logarithmic differentiation can be used, as in the next example.

|||| Figure 8 illustrates Example 4 by showing the graphs of $f(x) = x^{\sqrt{x}}$ and its derivative.

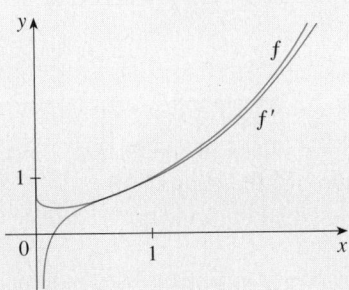

FIGURE 8

EXAMPLE 4 Differentiate $y = x^{\sqrt{x}}$.

SOLUTION 1 Using logarithmic differentiation, we have
$$\ln y = \ln x^{\sqrt{x}} = \sqrt{x} \ln x$$
$$\frac{y'}{y} = \sqrt{x} \cdot \frac{1}{x} + (\ln x)\frac{1}{2\sqrt{x}}$$
$$y' = y\left(\frac{1}{\sqrt{x}} + \frac{\ln x}{2\sqrt{x}}\right) = x^{\sqrt{x}}\left(\frac{2 + \ln x}{2\sqrt{x}}\right)$$

SOLUTION 2 Another method is to write $x^{\sqrt{x}} = (e^{\ln x})^{\sqrt{x}}$:

$$\frac{d}{dx}\left(x^{\sqrt{x}}\right) = \frac{d}{dx}\left(e^{\sqrt{x}\,\ln x}\right)$$

$$= e^{\sqrt{x}\,\ln x}\frac{d}{dx}\left(\sqrt{x}\,\ln x\right)$$

$$= x^{\sqrt{x}}\left(\frac{2 + \ln x}{2\sqrt{x}}\right) \qquad \text{(as in Solution 1)}$$

‖‖‖ **General Logarithmic Functions**

If $a > 0$ and $a \neq 1$, then $f(x) = a^x$ is a one-to-one function. Its inverse function is called the **logarithmic function with base a** and is denoted by $\log_a$. Thus

$\boxed{5}$
$$\log_a x = y \iff a^y = x$$

In particular, we see that

$$\log_e x = \ln x$$

The cancellation equations for the inverse functions $\log_a x$ and a^x are

$$a^{\log_a x} = x \qquad \text{and} \qquad \log_a(a^x) = x$$

Figure 9 shows the case where $a > 1$. (The most important logarithmic functions have base $a > 1$.) The fact that $y = a^x$ is a very rapidly increasing function for $x > 0$ is reflected in the fact that $y = \log_a x$ is a very slowly increasing function for $x > 1$.

FIGURE 9   **FIGURE 10**

Figure 10 shows the graphs of $y = \log_a x$ with various values of the base a. Since $\log_a 1 = 0$, the graphs of all logarithmic functions pass through the point $(1, 0)$.

The laws of logarithms are similar to those for the natural logarithm and can be deduced from the laws of exponents (see Exercise 61).

The following formula shows that logarithms with any base can be expressed in terms of the natural logarithm.

---

6 **Change of Base Formula** For any positive number a $(a \neq 1)$, we have

$$\log_a x = \frac{\ln x}{\ln a}$$

Proof Let $y = \log_a x$. Then, from (1), we have $a^y = x$. Taking natural logarithms of both sides of this equation, we get $y \ln a = \ln x$. Therefore

$$y = \frac{\ln x}{\ln a}$$

Scientific calculators have a key for natural logarithms, so Formula 6 enables us to use a calculator to compute a logarithm with any base (as shown in the next example). Similarly, Formula 6 allows us to graph any logarithmic function on a graphing calculator or computer (see Exercises 14–16).

EXAMPLE 5 Evaluate $\log_8 5$ correct to six decimal places.

SOLUTION Formula 6 gives

$$\log_8 5 = \frac{\ln 5}{\ln 8} \approx 0.773976$$

Formula 6 enables us to differentiate any logarithmic function. Since $\ln a$ is a constant, we can differentiate as follows:

$$\frac{d}{dx}(\log_a x) = \frac{d}{dx}\left(\frac{\ln x}{\ln a}\right)$$

$$= \frac{1}{\ln a}\frac{d}{dx}(\ln x) = \frac{1}{x \ln a}$$

7

$$\frac{d}{dx}(\log_a x) = \frac{1}{x \ln a}$$

||| NOTATION FOR LOGARITHMS

Most textbooks in calculus and the sciences, as well as calculators, use the notation $\ln x$ for the natural logarithm and $\log x$ for the "common logarithm," $\log_{10} x$. In the more advanced mathematical and scientific literature and in computer languages, however, the notation $\log x$ usually denotes the natural logarithm.

EXAMPLE 6

$$\frac{d}{dx}\log_{10}(2 + \sin x) = \frac{1}{(2 + \sin x)\ln 10}\frac{d}{dx}(2 + \sin x)$$

$$= \frac{\cos x}{(2 + \sin x)\ln 10}$$

From Formula 7 we see one of the main reasons that natural logarithms (logarithms with base e) are used in calculus: The differentiation formula is simplest when $a = e$ because $\ln e = 1$.

|||| The Number e as a Limit

We have shown that if $f(x) = \ln x$, then $f'(x) = 1/x$. Thus, $f'(1) = 1$. We now use this fact to express the number e as a limit.

From the definition of a derivative as a limit, we have

$$f'(1) = \lim_{h \to 0} \frac{f(1 + h) - f(1)}{h} = \lim_{x \to 0} \frac{f(1 + x) - f(1)}{x}$$

$$= \lim_{x \to 0} \frac{\ln(1 + x) - \ln 1}{x} = \lim_{x \to 0} \frac{1}{x} \ln(1 + x)$$

$$= \lim_{x \to 0} \ln(1 + x)^{1/x}$$

Because $f'(1) = 1$, we have

$$\lim_{x \to 0} \ln(1 + x)^{1/x} = 1$$

Then, by Theorem 2.5.8 and the continuity of the exponential functions, we have

$$e = e^1 = e^{\lim_{x \to 0} \ln(1+x)^{1/x}} = \lim_{x \to 0} e^{\ln(1+x)^{1/x}} = \lim_{x \to 0} (1 + x)^{1/x}$$

$$\boxed{8} \qquad \boxed{e = \lim_{x \to 0} (1 + x)^{1/x}}$$

Formula 8 is illustrated by the graph of the function $y = (1 + x)^{1/x}$ in Figure 11 and a table of values for small values of x.

x	$(1 + x)^{1/x}$
0.1	2.59374246
0.01	2.70481383
0.001	2.71692393
0.0001	2.71814593
0.00001	2.71826824
0.000001	2.71828047
0.0000001	2.71828169
0.00000001	2.71828181

FIGURE 11

If we put $n = 1/x$ in Formula 8, then $n \to \infty$ as $x \to 0^+$ and so an alternative expression for e is

$$\boxed{9} \qquad \boxed{e = \lim_{n \to \infty} \left(1 + \frac{1}{n}\right)^n}$$

7.4* Exercises

1. (a) Write an equation that defines a^x when a is a positive number and x is a real number.
(b) What is the domain of the function $f(x) = a^x$?
(c) If $a \neq 1$, what is the range of this function?
(d) Sketch the general shape of the graph of the exponential function for each of the following cases.
   (i) $a > 1$ (ii) $a = 1$ (iii) $0 < a < 1$

2. (a) If a is a positive number and $a \neq 1$, how is $\log_a x$ defined?
(b) What is the domain of the function $f(x) = \log_a x$?
(c) What is the range of this function?
(d) If $a > 1$, sketch the general shapes of the graphs of $y = \log_a x$ and $y = a^x$ with a common set of axes.

3–6 ▥ Write the expression as a power of e.

3. $5^{\sqrt{7}}$

4. 10^{x^2}

5. $(\cos x)^x$

6. $x^{\cos x}$

7–10 ▥ Evaluate the expression.

7. (a) $\log_{10} 1000$ (b) $\log_2 \frac{1}{16}$

8. (a) $\log_{10} 0.1$ (b) $\log_8 320 - \log_8 5$

9. (a) $\log_{12} 3 + \log_{12} 48$ (b) $\log_5 5^{\sqrt{2}}$

10. (a) $\log_a \dfrac{1}{a}$ (b) $10^{(\log_{10} 4 + \log_{10} 7)}$

11–12 ▥ Graph the given functions on a common screen. How are these graphs related?

11. $y = 2^x$, $y = e^x$, $y = 5^x$, $y = 20^x$

12. $y = 3^x$, $y = 10^x$, $y = \left(\frac{1}{3}\right)^x$, $y = \left(\frac{1}{10}\right)^x$

13. Use Formula 6 to evaluate each logarithm correct to six decimal places.
(a) $\log_{12} e$ (b) $\log_6 13.54$ (c) $\log_2 \pi$

14–16 ▥ Use Formula 6 to graph the given functions on a common screen. How are these graphs related?

14. $y = \log_2 x$, $y = \log_4 x$, $y = \log_6 x$, $y = \log_8 x$

15. $y = \log_{1.5} x$, $y = \ln x$, $y = \log_{10} x$, $y = \log_{50} x$

16. $y = \ln x$, $y = \log_{10} x$, $y = e^x$, $y = 10^x$

17–18 ▥ Find the exponential function $f(x) = Ca^x$ whose graph is given.

17.

18.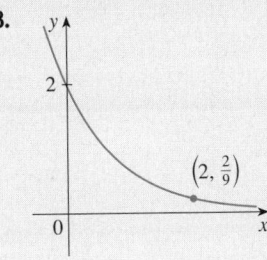

19. (a) Show that if the graphs of $f(x) = x^2$ and $g(x) = 2^x$ are drawn on a coordinate grid where the unit of measurement is 1 inch, then at a distance 2 ft to the right of the origin the height of the graph of f is 48 ft but the height of the graph of g is about 265 mi.
(b) Suppose that the graph of $y = \log_2 x$ is drawn on a coordinate grid where the unit of measurement is an inch. How many miles to the right of the origin do we have to move before the height of the curve reaches 3 ft?

20. Compare the rates of growth of the functions $f(x) = x^5$ and $g(x) = 5^x$ by graphing both functions in several viewing rectangles. Find all points of intersection of the graphs correct to one decimal place.

21–22 ▥ Find the limit.

21. $\lim\limits_{t \to \infty} 2^{-t^2}$

22. $\lim\limits_{x \to 3^+} \log_{10}(x^2 - 5x + 6)$

23–38 ▥ Differentiate the function.

23. $h(t) = t^3 - 3^t$

24. $g(x) = x^4 4^x$

25. $y = 5^{-1/x}$

26. $y = 10^{\tan \theta}$

27. $f(u) = (2^u + 2^{-u})^{10}$

28. $y = 2^{3^{x^2}}$

29. $f(x) = \log_3(x^2 - 4)$

30. $f(x) = \log_{10}\left(\dfrac{x}{x-1}\right)$

31. $y = x^x$

32. $y = x^{1/x}$

33. $y = x^{\sin x}$

34. $y = (\sin x)^x$

35. $y = (\ln x)^x$

36. $y = x^{\ln x}$

37. $y = x^{e^x}$

38. $y = (\ln x)^{\cos x}$

39. Find an equation of the tangent line to the curve $y = 10^x$ at the point $(1, 10)$.

40. If $f(x) = x^{\cos x}$, find $f'(x)$. Check that your answer is reasonable by comparing the graphs of f and f'.

41–46 ║║║ Evaluate the integral.

41. $\displaystyle\int_1^2 10^t \, dt$

42. $\displaystyle\int_0^1 4^{-2u} \, du$

43. $\displaystyle\int \frac{\log_{10} x}{x} \, dx$

44. $\displaystyle\int (x^5 + 5^x) \, dx$

45. $\displaystyle\int 3^{\sin\theta} \cos\theta \, d\theta$

46. $\displaystyle\int \frac{2^x}{2^x + 1} \, dx$

47. Find the area of the region bounded by the curves $y = 2^x$, $y = 5^x$, $x = -1$, and $x = 1$.

48. The region under the curve $y = 10^{-x}$ from $x = 0$ to $x = 1$ is rotated about the x-axis. Find the volume of the resulting solid.

49. Use a graph to find the root of the equation $2^x = 1 + 3^{-x}$ correct to one decimal place. Then use this estimate as the initial approximation in Newton's method to find the root correct to six decimal places.

50. Find y' if $x^y = y^x$.

51. Find the inverse function of $f(x) = 10^x/(10^x + 1)$.

52. Calculate $\lim_{x\to\infty} x^{-\ln x}$.

53. The geologist C. F. Richter defined the magnitude of an earthquake to be $\log_{10}(I/S)$, where I is the intensity of the quake (measured by the amplitude of a seismograph 100 km from the epicenter) and S is the intensity of a "standard" earthquake (where the amplitude is only 1 micron $= 10^{-4}$ cm). The 1989 Loma Prieta earthquake that shook San Francisco had a magnitude of 7.1 on the Richter scale. The 1906 San Francisco earthquake was 16 times as intense. What was its magnitude on the Richter scale?

54. A sound so faint that it can just be heard has intensity $I_0 = 10^{-12}$ watt/m^2 at a frequency of 1000 hertz (Hz). The loudness, in decibels (dB), of a sound with intensity I is then defined to be $L = 10 \log_{10}(I/I_0)$. Amplified rock music is measured at 120 dB, whereas the noise from a motor-driven lawn mower is measured at 106 dB. Find the ratio of the intensity of the rock music to that of the mower.

55. Referring to Exercise 54, find the rate of change of the loudness with respect to the intensity when the sound is measured at 50 dB (the level of ordinary conversation).

56. According to the Beer-Lambert Law, the light intensity at a depth of x meters below the surface of the ocean is $I(x) = I_0 a^x$, where I_0 is the light intensity at the surface and a is a constant such that $0 < a < 1$.
(a) Express the rate of change of $I(x)$ with respect to x in terms of $I(x)$.

(b) If $I_0 = 8$ and $a = 0.38$, find the rate of change of intensity with respect to depth at a depth of 20 m.
(c) Using the values from part (b), find the average light intensity between the surface and a depth of 20 m.

57. The flash unit on a camera operates by storing charge on a capacitor and releasing it suddenly when the flash is set off. The following data describe the charge remaining on the capacitor (measured in microcoulombs, μC) at time t (measured in seconds).

t	Q	t	Q
0.00	100.00	0.06	54.88
0.02	81.87	0.08	44.93
0.04	67.03	0.10	36.76

(a) Use a graphing calculator or computer to find an exponential model for the charge. (See Section 1.2.)
(b) The derivative $Q'(t)$ represents the electric current (measured in microamperes, μA) flowing from the capacitor to the flash bulb. Use part (a) to estimate the current when $t = 0.04$ s. Compare with the result of Example 2 in Section 2.1.

58. The table gives the U.S. population from 1790 to 1860.

Year	Population	Year	Population
1790	3,929,000	1830	12,861,000
1800	5,308,000	1840	17,063,000
1810	7,240,000	1850	23,192,000
1820	9,639,000	1860	31,443,000

(a) Use a graphing calculator or computer to fit an exponential function to the data. Graph the data points and the exponential model. How good is the fit?
(b) Estimate the rates of population growth in 1800 and 1850 by averaging slopes of secant lines.
(c) Use the exponential model in part (a) to estimate the rates of growth in 1800 and 1850. Compare these estimates with the ones in part (b).
(d) Use the exponential model to predict the population in 1870. Compare with the actual population of 38,558,000. Can you explain the discrepancy?

59. Prove the second law of exponents [see (3)].

60. Prove the fourth law of exponents [see (3)].

61. Deduce the following laws of logarithms from (3):
(a) $\log_a(xy) = \log_a x + \log_a y$
(b) $\log_a(x/y) = \log_a x - \log_a y$
(c) $\log_a(x^y) = y \log_a x$

62. Show that $\displaystyle\lim_{n\to\infty} \left(1 + \frac{x}{n}\right)^n = e^x$ for any $x > 0$.

7.5 Inverse Trigonometric Functions

In this section we apply the ideas of Section 7.1 to find the derivatives of the so-called inverse trigonometric functions. We have a slight difficulty in this task: Because the trigonometric functions are not one-to-one, they do not have inverse functions. The difficulty is overcome by restricting the domains of these functions so that they become one-to-one.

You can see from Figure 1 that the sine function $y = \sin x$ is not one-to-one (use the Horizontal Line Test). But the function $f(x) = \sin x$, $-\pi/2 \le x \le \pi/2$ (see Figure 2), *is* one-to-one. The inverse function of this restricted sine function f exists and is denoted by $\sin^{-1}$ or arcsin. It is called the **inverse sine function** or the **arcsine function**.

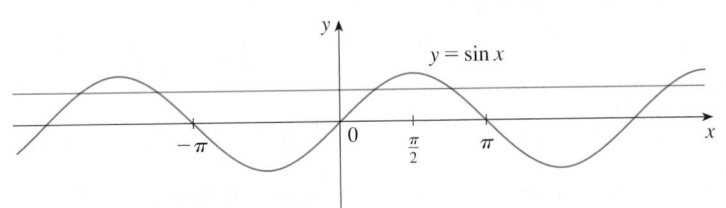

FIGURE 1

FIGURE 2 $\quad y = \sin x, -\frac{\pi}{2} \le x \le \frac{\pi}{2}$

Since the definition of an inverse function says that

$$f^{-1}(x) = y \iff f(y) = x$$

we have

$$\boxed{1} \qquad \sin^{-1}x = y \iff \sin y = x \quad \text{and} \quad -\frac{\pi}{2} \le y \le \frac{\pi}{2}$$

$\oslash \quad \sin^{-1}x \ne \dfrac{1}{\sin x}$

Thus, if $-1 \le x \le 1$, $\sin^{-1}x$ is the number between $-\pi/2$ and $\pi/2$ whose sine is x.

EXAMPLE 1 Evaluate (a) $\sin^{-1}\left(\frac{1}{2}\right)$ and (b) $\tan\left(\arcsin\frac{1}{3}\right)$.

SOLUTION
(a) We have

$$\sin^{-1}\left(\tfrac{1}{2}\right) = \frac{\pi}{6}$$

because $\sin(\pi/6) = \frac{1}{2}$ and $\pi/6$ lies between $-\pi/2$ and $\pi/2$.

(b) Let $\theta = \arcsin\frac{1}{3}$, so $\sin\theta = \frac{1}{3}$. Then we can draw a right triangle with angle θ as in Figure 3 and deduce from the Pythagorean Theorem that the third side has length $\sqrt{9-1} = 2\sqrt{2}$. This enables us to read from the triangle that

$$\tan\left(\arcsin\tfrac{1}{3}\right) = \tan\theta = \frac{1}{2\sqrt{2}}$$

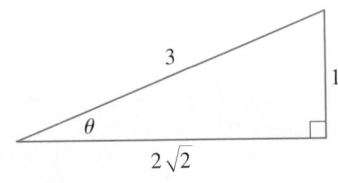

FIGURE 3

The cancellation equations for inverse functions become, in this case,

[2]

$$\sin^{-1}(\sin x) = x \quad \text{for } -\frac{\pi}{2} \le x \le \frac{\pi}{2}$$

$$\sin(\sin^{-1}x) = x \quad \text{for } -1 \le x \le 1$$

⊘   We must be careful when using the first cancellation equation because it is valid only when x lies in the interval $[-\pi/2, \pi/2]$. The following example shows how to proceed when x lies outside this interval.

EXAMPLE 2 Evaluate:

(a) $\sin(\sin^{-1}0.6)$ (b) $\sin^{-1}\left(\sin\dfrac{\pi}{12}\right)$ (c) $\sin^{-1}\left(\sin\dfrac{2\pi}{3}\right)$

SOLUTION

(a) Since 0.6 lies between -1 and 1, the second cancellation equation in (2) gives

$$\sin(\sin^{-1}0.6) = 0.6$$

(b) Since $\pi/12$ lies between $-\pi/2$ and $\pi/2$, the first cancellation equation gives

$$\sin^{-1}\left(\sin\frac{\pi}{12}\right) = \frac{\pi}{12}$$

(c) Since $2\pi/3$ does not lie in the interval $[-\pi/2, \pi/2]$, we can't use the cancellation equation. Instead we note that $\sin(2\pi/3) = \sqrt{3}/2$ and $\sin^{-1}(\sqrt{3}/2) = \pi/3$ because $\pi/3$ lies between $-\pi/2$ and $\pi/2$. Therefore

$$\sin^{-1}\left(\sin\frac{2\pi}{3}\right) = \sin^{-1}\left(\frac{\sqrt{3}}{2}\right) = \frac{\pi}{3}$$

The inverse sine function, $\sin^{-1}$, has domain $[-1, 1]$ and range $[-\pi/2, \pi/2]$, and its graph, shown in Figure 4, is obtained from that of the restricted sine function (Figure 2) by reflection about the line $y = x$.

We know that the sine function f is continuous, so the inverse sine function is also continuous. We also know from Section 3.5 that the sine function is differentiable, so the inverse sine function is also differentiable. We could calculate the derivative of $\sin^{-1}$ by the formula in Theorem 7.1.7, but since we know that $\sin^{-1}$ is differentiable, we can just as easily calculate it by implicit differentiation as follows.

Let $y = \sin^{-1}x$. Then $\sin y = x$ and $-\pi/2 \le y \le \pi/2$. Differentiating $\sin y = x$ implicitly with respect to x, we obtain

$$\cos y \frac{dy}{dx} = 1$$

and

$$\frac{dy}{dx} = \frac{1}{\cos y}$$

Now $\cos y \ge 0$ since $-\pi/2 \le y \le \pi/2$, so

$$\cos y = \sqrt{1 - \sin^2 y} = \sqrt{1 - x^2}$$

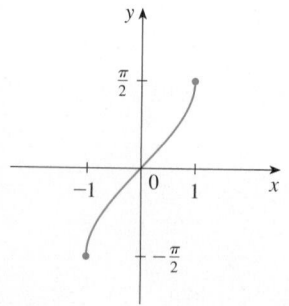

FIGURE 4 $y = \sin^{-1}x = \arcsin x$

Therefore
$$\frac{dy}{dx} = \frac{1}{\cos y} = \frac{1}{\sqrt{1 - x^2}}$$

3
$$\frac{d}{dx}(\sin^{-1}x) = \frac{1}{\sqrt{1 - x^2}} \qquad -1 < x < 1$$

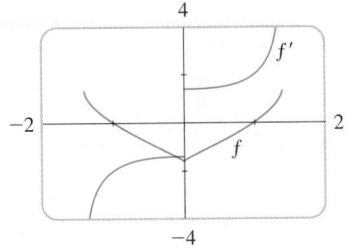

FIGURE 5

‖‖‖ The graphs of the function f of Example 3 and its derivative are shown in Figure 5. Notice that f is not differentiable at 0 and this is consistent with the fact that the graph of f' makes a sudden jump at $x = 0$.

EXAMPLE 3 If $f(x) = \sin^{-1}(x^2 - 1)$, find (a) the domain of f, (b) $f'(x)$, and (c) the domain of f'.

SOLUTION

(a) Since the domain of the inverse sine function is $[-1, 1]$, the domain of f is
$$\{x \mid -1 \leqslant x^2 - 1 \leqslant 1\} = \{x \mid 0 \leqslant x^2 \leqslant 2\}$$
$$= \{x \mid |x| \leqslant \sqrt{2}\} = [-\sqrt{2}, \sqrt{2}]$$

(b) Combining Formula 3 with the Chain Rule, we have
$$f'(x) = \frac{1}{\sqrt{1 - (x^2 - 1)^2}} \frac{d}{dx}(x^2 - 1)$$
$$= \frac{1}{\sqrt{1 - (x^4 - 2x^2 + 1)}} 2x = \frac{2x}{\sqrt{2x^2 - x^4}}$$

(c) The domain of f' is
$$\{x \mid -1 < x^2 - 1 < 1\} = \{x \mid 0 < x^2 < 2\}$$
$$= \{x \mid 0 < |x| < \sqrt{2}\} = (-\sqrt{2}, 0) \cup (0, \sqrt{2})$$

The **inverse cosine function** is handled similarly. The restricted cosine function $f(x) = \cos x$, $0 \leqslant x \leqslant \pi$, is one-to-one (see Figure 6) and so it has an inverse function denoted by $\cos^{-1}$ or arccos.

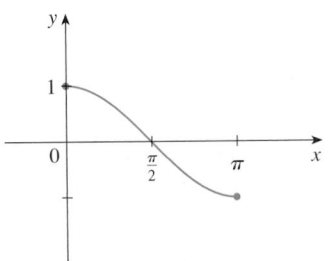

FIGURE 6
$y = \cos x, 0 \leqslant x \leqslant \pi$

4

$$\cos^{-1}x = y \iff \cos y = x \quad \text{and} \quad 0 \leqslant y \leqslant \pi$$

The cancellation equations are

5
$$\cos^{-1}(\cos x) = x \quad \text{for } 0 \leqslant x \leqslant \pi$$
$$\cos(\cos^{-1}x) = x \quad \text{for } -1 \leqslant x \leqslant 1$$

The inverse cosine function, $\cos^{-1}$, has domain $[-1, 1]$ and range $[0, \pi]$ and is a continuous function whose graph is shown in Figure 7. Its derivative is given by

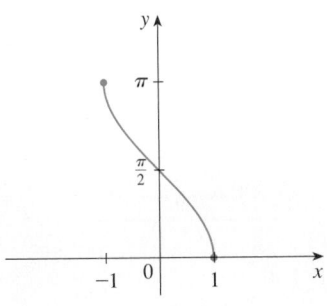

FIGURE 7
$y = \cos^{-1}x = \arccos x$

6

$$\frac{d}{dx}(\cos^{-1}x) = -\frac{1}{\sqrt{1 - x^2}} \qquad -1 < x < 1$$

Formula 6 can be proved by the same method as for Formula 3 and is left as Exercise 17.

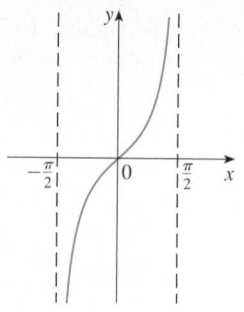

FIGURE 8

$y = \tan x, -\frac{\pi}{2} < x < \frac{\pi}{2}$

The tangent function can be made one-to-one by restricting it to the interval $(-\pi/2, \pi/2)$. Thus, the **inverse tangent function** is defined as the inverse of the function $f(x) = \tan x, -\pi/2 < x < \pi/2$. (See Figure 8.) It is denoted by $\tan^{-1}$ or arctan.

$$\boxed{7} \qquad \tan^{-1}x = y \iff \tan y = x \quad \text{and} \quad -\frac{\pi}{2} < y < \frac{\pi}{2}$$

EXAMPLE 4 Simplify the expression $\cos(\tan^{-1}x)$.

SOLUTION 1 Let $y = \tan^{-1}x$. Then $\tan y = x$ and $-\pi/2 < y < \pi/2$. We want to find $\cos y$ but, since $\tan y$ is known, it is easier to find $\sec y$ first:

$$\sec^2 y = 1 + \tan^2 y = 1 + x^2$$

$$\sec y = \sqrt{1 + x^2} \qquad \text{(since } \sec y > 0 \text{ for } -\pi/2 < y < \pi/2\text{)}$$

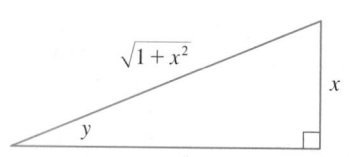

FIGURE 9

Thus $$\cos(\tan^{-1}x) = \cos y = \frac{1}{\sec y} = \frac{1}{\sqrt{1 + x^2}}$$

SOLUTION 2 Instead of using trigonometric identities as in Solution 1, it is perhaps easier to use a diagram. If $y = \tan^{-1}x$, then $\tan y = x$, and we can read from Figure 9 (which illustrates the case $y > 0$) that

$$\cos(\tan^{-1}x) = \cos y = \frac{1}{\sqrt{1 + x^2}}$$

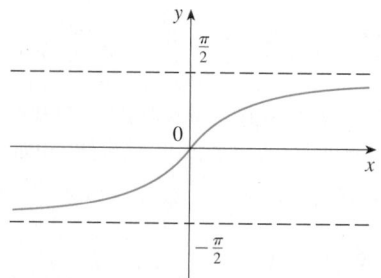

FIGURE 10

$y = \tan^{-1}x = \arctan x$

The inverse tangent function, $\tan^{-1} = \arctan$, has domain $\mathbb{R}$ and range $(-\pi/2, \pi/2)$. Its graph is shown in Figure 10.

We know that

$$\lim_{x \to (\pi/2)^-} \tan x = \infty \qquad \text{and} \qquad \lim_{x \to -(\pi/2)^+} \tan x = -\infty$$

and so the lines $x = \pm\pi/2$ are vertical asymptotes of the graph of tan. Since the graph of $\tan^{-1}$ is obtained by reflecting the graph of the restricted tangent function about the line $y = x$, it follows that the lines $y = \pi/2$ and $y = -\pi/2$ are horizontal asymptotes of the graph of $\tan^{-1}$. This fact is expressed by the following limits:

$$\boxed{8} \qquad \lim_{x \to \infty} \tan^{-1}x = \frac{\pi}{2} \qquad \lim_{x \to -\infty} \tan^{-1}x = -\frac{\pi}{2}$$

EXAMPLE 5 Evaluate $\displaystyle\lim_{x \to 2^+} \arctan\left(\frac{1}{x - 2}\right)$.

SOLUTION Since

$$\frac{1}{x - 2} \to \infty \qquad \text{as } x \to 2^+$$

the first equation in (8) gives

$$\lim_{x \to 2^+} \arctan\left(\frac{1}{x - 2}\right) = \frac{\pi}{2}$$

Since tan is differentiable, $\tan^{-1}$ is also differentiable. To find its derivative, let $y = \tan^{-1}x$. Then $\tan y = x$. Differentiating this latter equation implicitly with respect to x, we have

$$\sec^2 y \, \frac{dy}{dx} = 1$$

and so

$$\frac{dy}{dx} = \frac{1}{\sec^2 y} = \frac{1}{1 + \tan^2 y} = \frac{1}{1 + x^2}$$

$\boxed{9}$

$$\frac{d}{dx}(\tan^{-1}x) = \frac{1}{1 + x^2}$$

The remaining inverse trigonometric functions are not used as frequently and are summarized here.

$\boxed{10}$ $\quad y = \csc^{-1}x \ (|x| \geqslant 1) \iff \csc y = x \quad$ and $\quad y \in (0, \pi/2] \cup (\pi, 3\pi/2]$

$\quad y = \sec^{-1}x \ (|x| \geqslant 1) \iff \sec y = x \quad$ and $\quad y \in [0, \pi/2) \cup [\pi, 3\pi/2)$

$\quad y = \cot^{-1}x \ (x \in \mathbb{R}) \iff \cot y = x \quad$ and $\quad y \in (0, \pi)$

The choice of intervals for y in the definitions of $\csc^{-1}$ and $\sec^{-1}$ is not universally agreed upon. For instance, some authors use $y \in [0, \pi/2) \cup (\pi/2, \pi]$ in the definition of $\sec^{-1}$. [You can see from the graph of the secant function in Figure 11 that both this choice and the one in (10) will work.] The reason for the choice in (10) is that the differentiation formulas are simpler (see Exercise 79).

We collect in Table 11 the differentiation formulas for all of the inverse trigonometric functions. The proofs of the formulas for the derivatives of $\csc^{-1}$, $\sec^{-1}$, and $\cot^{-1}$ are left as Exercises 19–21.

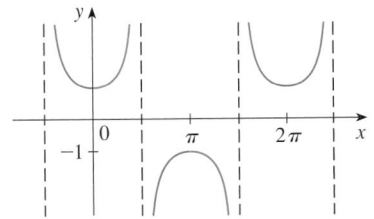

FIGURE 11
$y = \sec x$

$\boxed{11}$ **Table of Derivatives of Inverse Trigonometric Functions**

$$\frac{d}{dx}(\sin^{-1}x) = \frac{1}{\sqrt{1 - x^2}} \qquad\qquad \frac{d}{dx}(\csc^{-1}x) = -\frac{1}{x\sqrt{x^2 - 1}}$$

$$\frac{d}{dx}(\cos^{-1}x) = -\frac{1}{\sqrt{1 - x^2}} \qquad\qquad \frac{d}{dx}(\sec^{-1}x) = \frac{1}{x\sqrt{x^2 - 1}}$$

$$\frac{d}{dx}(\tan^{-1}x) = \frac{1}{1 + x^2} \qquad\qquad \frac{d}{dx}(\cot^{-1}x) = -\frac{1}{1 + x^2}$$

Each of these formulas can be combined with the Chain Rule. For instance, if u is a differentiable function of x, then

$$\frac{d}{dx}(\sin^{-1}u) = \frac{1}{\sqrt{1 - u^2}}\frac{du}{dx} \qquad \text{and} \qquad \frac{d}{dx}(\tan^{-1}u) = \frac{1}{1 + u^2}\frac{du}{dx}$$

EXAMPLE 6 Differentiate (a) $y = \dfrac{1}{\sin^{-1}x}$ and (b) $f(x) = x\tan^{-1}\sqrt{x}$.

SOLUTION

(a)
$$\frac{dy}{dx} = \frac{d}{dx}(\sin^{-1}x)^{-1} = -(\sin^{-1}x)^{-2}\frac{d}{dx}(\sin^{-1}x)$$

$$= -\frac{1}{(\sin^{-1}x)^2\sqrt{1-x^2}}$$

(b)
$$f'(x) = \tan^{-1}\sqrt{x} + x\frac{1}{1+(\sqrt{x})^2}\frac{1}{2}x^{-1/2}$$

$$= \tan^{-1}\sqrt{x} + \frac{\sqrt{x}}{2(1+x)}$$

EXAMPLE 7 Prove the identity $\tan^{-1}x + \cot^{-1}x = \pi/2$.

SOLUTION Although calculus is not needed to prove this identity, the proof using calculus is quite simple. If $f(x) = \tan^{-1}x + \cot^{-1}x$, then

$$f'(x) = \frac{1}{1+x^2} - \frac{1}{1+x^2} = 0$$

for all values of x. Therefore, $f(x) = C$, a constant. To determine the value of C, we put $x = 1$. Then

$$C = f(1) = \tan^{-1}1 + \cot^{-1}1 = \frac{\pi}{4} + \frac{\pi}{4} = \frac{\pi}{2}$$

Thus, $\tan^{-1}x + \cot^{-1}x = \pi/2$.

Each of the formulas in Table 11 gives rise to an integration formula. The two most useful of these are the following:

[12]
$$\int \frac{1}{\sqrt{1-x^2}}\,dx = \sin^{-1}x + C$$

[13]
$$\int \frac{1}{x^2+1}\,dx = \tan^{-1}x + C$$

EXAMPLE 8 Find $\displaystyle\int_0^{1/4}\frac{1}{\sqrt{1-4x^2}}\,dx$.

SOLUTION If we write

$$\int_0^{1/4}\frac{1}{\sqrt{1-4x^2}}\,dx = \int_0^{1/4}\frac{1}{\sqrt{1-(2x)^2}}\,dx$$

then the integral resembles Equation 12 and the substitution $u = 2x$ is suggested. This gives $du = 2\,dx$, so $dx = du/2$. When $x = 0$, $u = 0$; when $x = \frac{1}{4}$, $u = \frac{1}{2}$. So

$$\int_0^{1/4} \frac{1}{\sqrt{1 - 4x^2}}\,dx = \frac{1}{2}\int_0^{1/2} \frac{du}{\sqrt{1 - u^2}} = \frac{1}{2}\sin^{-1}u\Big]_0^{1/2}$$

$$= \frac{1}{2}\big[\sin^{-1}(\tfrac{1}{2}) - \sin^{-1}0\big] = \frac{1}{2}\cdot\frac{\pi}{6} = \frac{\pi}{12}$$

EXAMPLE 9 Evaluate $\displaystyle\int \frac{1}{x^2 + a^2}\,dx$.

SOLUTION To make the given integral more like Equation 13 we write

$$\int \frac{dx}{x^2 + a^2} = \int \frac{dx}{a^2\left(\dfrac{x^2}{a^2} + 1\right)} = \frac{1}{a^2}\int \frac{dx}{\left(\dfrac{x}{a}\right)^2 + 1}$$

This suggests that we substitute $u = x/a$. Then $du = dx/a$, $dx = a\,du$, and

$$\int \frac{dx}{x^2 + a^2} = \frac{1}{a^2}\int \frac{a\,du}{u^2 + 1} = \frac{1}{a}\int \frac{du}{u^2 + 1} = \frac{1}{a}\tan^{-1}u + C$$

Thus, we have the formula

|||| One of the main uses of inverse trigonometric functions is that they often arise when we integrate rational functions.

[14]

$$\int \frac{1}{x^2 + a^2}\,dx = \frac{1}{a}\tan^{-1}\left(\frac{x}{a}\right) + C$$

EXAMPLE 10 Find $\displaystyle\int \frac{x}{x^4 + 9}\,dx$.

SOLUTION We substitute $u = x^2$ because then $du = 2x\,dx$ and we can use Equation 14 with $a = 3$:

$$\int \frac{x}{x^4 + 9}\,dx = \frac{1}{2}\int \frac{du}{u^2 + 9} = \frac{1}{2}\cdot\frac{1}{3}\tan^{-1}\left(\frac{u}{3}\right) + C$$

$$= \frac{1}{6}\tan^{-1}\left(\frac{x^2}{3}\right) + C$$

|||| 7.5 Exercises

1–10 |||| Find the exact value of each expression.

1. (a) $\sin^{-1}(\sqrt{3}/2)$ (b) $\cos^{-1}(-1)$

2. (a) $\arctan(-1)$ (b) $\csc^{-1}2$

3. (a) $\tan^{-1}\sqrt{3}$ (b) $\arcsin(-1/\sqrt{2})$

4. (a) $\sec^{-1}\sqrt{2}$ (b) $\arcsin 1$

5. (a) $\arccos(\cos 2\pi)$ (b) $\tan(\tan^{-1}5)$

6. (a) $\tan^{-1}(\tan 3\pi/4)$ (b) $\cos(\arcsin\tfrac{1}{2})$

7. $\tan\big(\sin^{-1}(\tfrac{2}{3})\big)$

8. $\csc\big(\arccos\tfrac{3}{5}\big)$

9. $\sin\big(2\tan^{-1}\sqrt{2}\big)$

10. $\cos(\tan^{-1}2 + \tan^{-1}3)$

11. Prove that $\cos(\sin^{-1}x) = \sqrt{1 - x^2}$.

12–14 |||| Simplify the expression.

12. $\tan(\sin^{-1}x)$

13. $\sin(\tan^{-1}x)$

14. $\csc(\arctan 2x)$

15–16 ▏▏▏ Graph the given functions on the same screen. How are these graphs related?

15. $y = \sin x$, $-\pi/2 \le x \le \pi/2$; $y = \sin^{-1}x$; $y = x$

16. $y = \tan x$, $-\pi/2 < x < \pi/2$; $y = \tan^{-1}x$; $y = x$

17. Prove Formula 6 for the derivative of $\cos^{-1}$ by the same method as for Formula 3.

18. (a) Prove that $\sin^{-1}x + \cos^{-1}x = \pi/2$.
(b) Use part (a) to prove Formula 6.

19. Prove that $\dfrac{d}{dx}(\cot^{-1}x) = -\dfrac{1}{1 + x^2}$.

20. Prove that $\dfrac{d}{dx}(\sec^{-1}x) = \dfrac{1}{x\sqrt{x^2 - 1}}$.

21. Prove that $\dfrac{d}{dx}(\csc^{-1}x) = -\dfrac{1}{x\sqrt{x^2 - 1}}$.

22–35 ▏▏▏ Find the derivative of the function. Simplify where possible.

22. $y = \sqrt{\tan^{-1}x}$

23. $y = \tan^{-1}\sqrt{x}$ **24.** $h(x) = \sqrt{1 - x^2}\,\arcsin x$

25. $y = \sin^{-1}(2x + 1)$ **26.** $f(x) = x\ln(\arctan x)$

27. $H(x) = (1 + x^2)\arctan x$ **28.** $h(t) = e^{\sec^{-1}t}$

29. $y = \cos^{-1}(e^{2x})$ **30.** $y = x\cos^{-1}x - \sqrt{1 - x^2}$

31. $y = \arctan(\cos\theta)$ **32.** $y = \tan^{-1}\left(x - \sqrt{1 + x^2}\right)$

33. $h(t) = \cot^{-1}(t) + \cot^{-1}(1/t)$

34. $y = \tan^{-1}\left(\dfrac{x}{a}\right) + \ln\sqrt{\dfrac{x - a}{x + a}}$

35. $y = \arccos\left(\dfrac{b + a\cos x}{a + b\cos x}\right)$, $\quad 0 \le x \le \pi$, $a > b > 0$

36–37 ▏▏▏ Find the derivative of the function. Find the domains of the function and its derivative.

36. $f(x) = \arcsin(e^x)$ **37.** $g(x) = \cos^{-1}(3 - 2x)$

38. Find y' if $\tan^{-1}(xy) = 1 + x^2y$.

39. If $g(x) = x\sin^{-1}(x/4) + \sqrt{16 - x^2}$, find $g'(2)$.

40. Find an equation of the tangent line to the curve $y = 3\arccos(x/2)$ at the point $(1, \pi)$.

41–42 ▏▏▏ Find $f'(x)$. Check that your answer is reasonable by comparing the graphs of f and f'.

41. $f(x) = e^{-x}\arctan x$ **42.** $f(x) = x\arcsin(1 - x^2)$

43–46 ▏▏▏ Find the limit.

43. $\displaystyle\lim_{x \to -1^+} \sin^{-1}x$

44. $\displaystyle\lim_{x \to \infty} \arccos\left(\dfrac{1 + x^2}{1 + 2x^2}\right)$

45. $\displaystyle\lim_{x \to \infty} \arctan(e^x)$

46. $\displaystyle\lim_{x \to 0^+} \tan^{-1}(\ln x)$

47. Where should the point P be chosen on the line segment AB so as to maximize the angle θ?

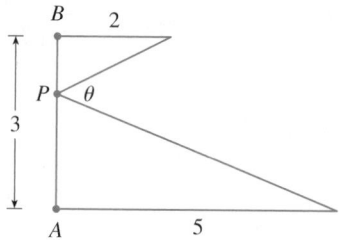

48. A painting in an art gallery has height h and is hung so that its lower edge is a distance d above the eye of an observer (as in the figure). How far from the wall should the observer stand to get the best view? (In other words, where should the observer stand so as to maximize the angle θ subtended at his eye by the painting?)

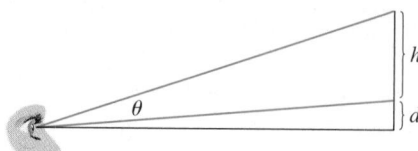

49. A ladder 10 ft long leans against a vertical wall. If the bottom of the ladder slides away from the base of the wall at a speed of 2 ft/s, how fast is the angle between the ladder and the wall changing when the bottom of the ladder is 6 ft from the base of the wall?

50. A lighthouse is located on a small island, 3 km away from the nearest point P on a straight shoreline, and its light makes four revolutions per minute. How fast is the beam of light moving along the shoreline when it is 1 km from P?

51–54 ▏▏▏ Sketch the curve using the guidelines of Section 4.5.

51. $y = \sin^{-1}\left(\dfrac{x}{x + 1}\right)$ **52.** $y = \tan^{-1}\left(\dfrac{x - 1}{x + 1}\right)$

53. $y = x - \tan^{-1}x$ **54.** $y = \tan^{-1}(\ln x)$

CAS 55. If $f(x) = \arctan(\cos(3\arcsin x))$, use the graphs of f, f', and f'' to estimate the x-coordinates of the maximum and minimum points and inflection points of f.

56. Investigate the family of curves given by $f(x) = x - c\sin^{-1}x$. What happens to the number of maxima and minima as c changes? Graph several members of the family to illustrate what you discover.

57. Find the most general antiderivative of the function

$$f(x) = 2x + 5(1 - x^2)^{-1/2}$$

58. Find $f(x)$ if $f'(x) = 4 - 3(1 + x^2)^{-1}$ and $f(\pi/4) = 0$.

59–70 ▌ Evaluate the integral.

59. $\displaystyle\int_{1/2}^{\sqrt{3}/2} \frac{6}{\sqrt{1 - t^2}}\, dt$

60. $\displaystyle\int_0^1 \frac{4}{t^2 + 1}\, dt$

61. $\displaystyle\int_0^{\sqrt{3}/4} \frac{dx}{1 + 16x^2}$

62. $\displaystyle\int \frac{dt}{\sqrt{1 - 4t^2}}$

63. $\displaystyle\int_0^{1/2} \frac{\sin^{-1}x}{\sqrt{1 - x^2}}\, dx$

64. $\displaystyle\int_0^{\pi/2} \frac{\sin x}{1 + \cos^2 x}\, dx$

65. $\displaystyle\int \frac{x + 9}{x^2 + 9}\, dx$

66. $\displaystyle\int \frac{\tan^{-1}x}{1 + x^2}\, dx$

67. $\displaystyle\int \frac{t^2}{\sqrt{1 - t^6}}\, dt$

68. $\displaystyle\int \frac{1}{x\sqrt{x^2 - 4}}\, dx$

69. $\displaystyle\int \frac{dx}{\sqrt{x}(1 + x)}$

70. $\displaystyle\int \frac{e^{2x}}{\sqrt{1 - e^{4x}}}\, dx$

71. Use the method of Example 9 to show that, if $a > 0$,

$$\int \frac{1}{\sqrt{a^2 - x^2}}\, dx = \sin^{-1}\left(\frac{x}{a}\right) + C$$

72. The region under the curve $y = 1/\sqrt{x^2 + 4}$ from $x = 0$ to $x = 2$ is rotated about the x-axis. Find the volume of the resulting solid.

73. Evaluate $\int_0^1 \sin^{-1}x\, dx$ by interpreting it as an area and integrating with respect to y instead of x.

74. Prove that, for $xy \neq 1$,

$$\arctan x + \arctan y = \arctan \frac{x + y}{1 - xy}$$

if the left side lies between $-\pi/2$ and $\pi/2$.

75. Use the result of Exercise 74 to prove the following:
(a) $\arctan\frac{1}{2} + \arctan\frac{1}{3} = \pi/4$
(b) $2\arctan\frac{1}{3} + \arctan\frac{1}{7} = \pi/4$

76. (a) Sketch the graph of the function $f(x) = \sin(\sin^{-1}x)$.
(b) Sketch the graph of the function $g(x) = \sin^{-1}(\sin x)$, $x \in \mathbb{R}$.
(c) Show that $g'(x) = \dfrac{\cos x}{|\cos x|}$.
(d) Sketch the graph of $h(x) = \cos^{-1}(\sin x)$, $x \in \mathbb{R}$, and find its derivative.

77. Use the method of Example 7 to prove the identity

$$2\sin^{-1}x = \cos^{-1}(1 - 2x^2) \qquad x \geq 0$$

78. Prove the identity

$$\arcsin \frac{x - 1}{x + 1} = 2\arctan\sqrt{x} - \frac{\pi}{2}$$

79. Some authors define $y = \sec^{-1}x \iff \sec y = x$ and $y \in [0, \pi/2) \cup (\pi/2, \pi]$. Show that with this definition, we have (instead of the formula given in Exercise 20)

$$\frac{d}{dx}(\sec^{-1}x) = \frac{1}{|x|\sqrt{x^2 - 1}} \qquad |x| > 1$$

80. Let $f(x) = x \arctan(1/x)$ if $x \neq 0$ and $f(0) = 0$.
(a) Is f continuous at 0?
(b) Is f differentiable at 0?

▌▌▌ APPLIED PROJECT

[CAS] **Where to Sit at the Movies**

A movie theater has a screen that is positioned 10 ft off the floor and is 25 ft high. The first row of seats is placed 9 ft from the screen and the rows are set 3 ft apart. The floor of the seating area is inclined at an angle of $\alpha = 20°$ above the horizontal and the distance up the incline that you sit is x. The theater has 21 rows of seats, so $0 \leq x \leq 60$. Suppose you decide that the best place to sit is in the row where the angle θ subtended by the screen at your eyes is a maximum. Let's also suppose that your eyes are 4 ft above the floor, as shown in the figure. (In Exercise 48 in Section 7.5 we looked at a simpler version of this problem, where the floor is horizontal, but this project involves a more complicated situation and requires technology.)

1. Show that

$$\theta = \arccos\left(\frac{a^2 + b^2 - 625}{2ab}\right)$$

where

$$a^2 = (9 + x\cos\alpha)^2 + (31 - x\sin\alpha)^2$$

and

$$b^2 = (9 + x\cos\alpha)^2 + (x\sin\alpha - 6)^2$$

2. Use a graph of θ as a function of x to estimate the value of x that maximizes θ. In which row should you sit? What is the viewing angle θ in this row?

3. Use your computer algebra system to differentiate θ and find a numerical value for the root of the equation $d\theta/dx = 0$. Does this value confirm your result in Problem 2?

4. Use the graph of θ to estimate the average value of θ on the interval $0 \leqslant x \leqslant 60$. Then use your CAS to compute the average value. Compare with the maximum and minimum values of θ.

7.6 Hyperbolic Functions

Certain combinations of the exponential functions e^x and e^{-x} arise so frequently in mathematics and its applications that they deserve to be given special names. In many ways they are analogous to the trigonometric functions, and they have the same relationship to the hyperbola that the trigonometric functions have to the circle. For this reason they are collectively called **hyperbolic functions** and individually called **hyperbolic sine**, **hyperbolic cosine**, and so on.

Definition of the Hyperbolic Functions

$$\sinh x = \frac{e^x - e^{-x}}{2} \qquad\qquad \operatorname{csch} x = \frac{1}{\sinh x}$$

$$\cosh x = \frac{e^x + e^{-x}}{2} \qquad\qquad \operatorname{sech} x = \frac{1}{\cosh x}$$

$$\tanh x = \frac{\sinh x}{\cosh x} \qquad\qquad \coth x = \frac{\cosh x}{\sinh x}$$

The graphs of hyperbolic sine and cosine can be sketched using graphical addition as in Figures 1 and 2.

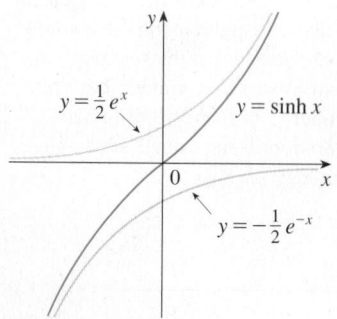

FIGURE 1
$y = \sinh x = \frac{1}{2}e^x - \frac{1}{2}e^{-x}$

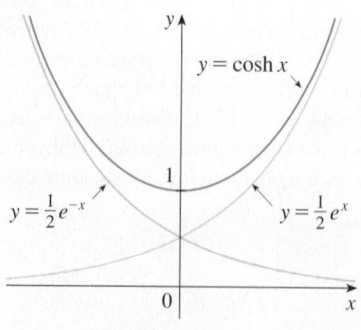

FIGURE 2
$y = \cosh x = \frac{1}{2}e^x + \frac{1}{2}e^{-x}$

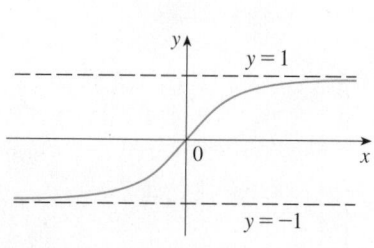

FIGURE 3
$y = \tanh x$

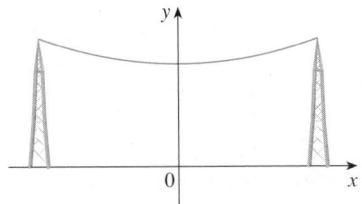

FIGURE 4

A catenary $y = c + a \cosh(x/a)$

Note that sinh has domain $\mathbb{R}$ and range $\mathbb{R}$, while cosh has domain $\mathbb{R}$ and range $[1, \infty)$. The graph of tanh is shown in Figure 3. It has the horizontal asymptotes $y = \pm 1$. (See Exercise 23.)

Some of the mathematical uses of hyperbolic functions will be seen in Chapter 8. Applications to science and engineering occur whenever an entity such as light, velocity, electricity, or radioactivity is gradually absorbed or extinguished, for the decay can be represented by hyperbolic functions. The most famous application is the use of hyperbolic cosine to describe the shape of a hanging wire. It can be proved that if a heavy flexible cable (such as a telephone or power line) is suspended between two points at the same height, then it takes the shape of a curve with equation $y = c + a \cosh(x/a)$ called a *catenary* (see Figure 4). (The Latin word *catena* means "chain.")

The hyperbolic functions satisfy a number of identities that are similar to well-known trigonometric identities. We list some of them here and leave most of the proofs to the exercises.

Hyperbolic Identities

$$\sinh(-x) = -\sinh x \qquad\qquad \cosh(-x) = \cosh x$$

$$\cosh^2 x - \sinh^2 x = 1 \qquad\qquad 1 - \tanh^2 x = \operatorname{sech}^2 x$$

$$\sinh(x + y) = \sinh x \cosh y + \cosh x \sinh y$$

$$\cosh(x + y) = \cosh x \cosh y + \sinh x \sinh y$$

EXAMPLE 1 Prove (a) $\cosh^2 x - \sinh^2 x = 1$ and (b) $1 - \tanh^2 x = \operatorname{sech}^2 x$.

SOLUTION

(a)
$$\cosh^2 x - \sinh^2 x = \left(\frac{e^x + e^{-x}}{2}\right)^2 - \left(\frac{e^x - e^{-x}}{2}\right)^2$$

$$= \frac{e^{2x} + 2 + e^{-2x}}{4} - \frac{e^{2x} - 2 + e^{-2x}}{4}$$

$$= \tfrac{4}{4} = 1$$

(b) We start with the identity proved in part (a):

$$\cosh^2 x - \sinh^2 x = 1$$

If we divide both sides by $\cosh^2 x$, we get

$$1 - \frac{\sinh^2 x}{\cosh^2 x} = \frac{1}{\cosh^2 x}$$

or
$$1 - \tanh^2 x = \operatorname{sech}^2 x$$

The identity proved in Example 1(a) gives a clue to the reason for the name "hyperbolic" functions:

If t is any real number, then the point $P(\cos t, \sin t)$ lies on the unit circle $x^2 + y^2 = 1$ because $\cos^2 t + \sin^2 t = 1$. In fact, t can be interpreted as the radian measure of $\angle POQ$

FIGURE 5

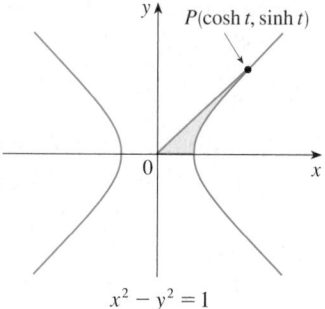

FIGURE 6

in Figure 5. For this reason the trigonometric functions are sometimes called *circular* functions.

Likewise, if t is any real number, then the point $P(\cosh t, \sinh t)$ lies on the right branch of the hyperbola $x^2 - y^2 = 1$ because $\cosh^2 t - \sinh^2 t = 1$ and $\cosh t \geq 1$. This time, t does not represent the measure of an angle. However, it turns out that t represents twice the area of the shaded hyperbolic sector in Figure 6, just as in the trigonometric case t represents twice the area of the shaded circular sector in Figure 5.

The derivatives of the hyperbolic functions are easily computed. For example,

$$\frac{d}{dx}(\sinh x) = \frac{d}{dx}\left(\frac{e^x - e^{-x}}{2}\right) = \frac{e^x + e^{-x}}{2} = \cosh x$$

We list the differentiation formulas for the hyperbolic functions as Table 1. The remaining proofs are left as exercises. Note the analogy with the differentiation formulas for trigonometric functions, but beware that the signs are different in some cases.

---

1 **Derivatives of Hyperbolic Functions**

$$\frac{d}{dx}(\sinh x) = \cosh x \qquad\qquad \frac{d}{dx}(\operatorname{csch} x) = -\operatorname{csch} x \coth x$$

$$\frac{d}{dx}(\cosh x) = \sinh x \qquad\qquad \frac{d}{dx}(\operatorname{sech} x) = -\operatorname{sech} x \tanh x$$

$$\frac{d}{dx}(\tanh x) = \operatorname{sech}^2 x \qquad\qquad \frac{d}{dx}(\coth x) = -\operatorname{csch}^2 x$$

EXAMPLE 2 Any of the differentiation rules in Table 1 can be combined with the Chain Rule. For instance,

$$\frac{d}{dx}\left(\cosh \sqrt{x}\right) = \sinh \sqrt{x} \cdot \frac{d}{dx}\sqrt{x} = \frac{\sinh \sqrt{x}}{2\sqrt{x}}$$

⦚ Inverse Hyperbolic Functions

You can see from Figures 1 and 3 that sinh and tanh are one-to-one functions and so they have inverse functions denoted by $\sinh^{-1}$ and $\tanh^{-1}$. Figure 2 shows that cosh is not one-to-one, but when restricted to the domain $[0, \infty)$ it becomes one-to-one. The inverse hyperbolic cosine function is defined as the inverse of this restricted function.

2

$$y = \sinh^{-1}x \iff \sinh y = x$$

$$y = \cosh^{-1}x \iff \cosh y = x \quad \text{and} \quad y \geq 0$$

$$y = \tanh^{-1}x \iff \tanh y = x$$

The remaining inverse hyperbolic functions are defined similarly (see Exercise 28).

We can sketch the graphs of $\sinh^{-1}$, $\cosh^{-1}$, and $\tanh^{-1}$ in Figures 7, 8, and 9 by using Figures 1, 2, and 3.

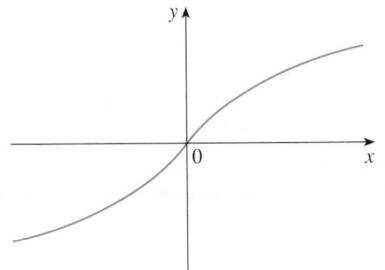

FIGURE 7 $y = \sinh^{-1} x$
domain $= \mathbb{R}$ range $= \mathbb{R}$

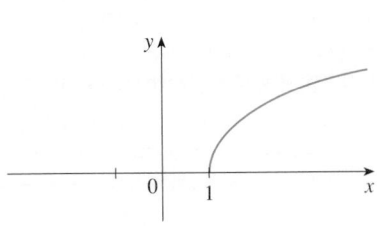

FIGURE 8 $y = \cosh^{-1} x$
domain $= [1, \infty)$ range $= [0, \infty)$

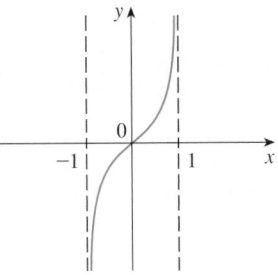

FIGURE 9 $y = \tanh^{-1} x$
domain $= (-1, 1)$ range $= \mathbb{R}$

Since the hyperbolic functions are defined in terms of exponential functions, it's not surprising to learn that the inverse hyperbolic functions can be expressed in terms of logarithms. In particular, we have:

▓▓ Formula 3 is proved in Example 3. The proofs of Formulas 4 and 5 are requested in Exercises 26 and 27.

$$\boxed{3} \qquad \sinh^{-1}x = \ln\left(x + \sqrt{x^2 + 1}\right) \qquad x \in \mathbb{R}$$

$$\boxed{4} \qquad \cosh^{-1}x = \ln\left(x + \sqrt{x^2 - 1}\right) \qquad x \geq 1$$

$$\boxed{5} \qquad \tanh^{-1}x = \tfrac{1}{2} \ln\left(\frac{1 + x}{1 - x}\right) \qquad -1 < x < 1$$

EXAMPLE 3 Show that $\sinh^{-1}x = \ln\left(x + \sqrt{x^2 + 1}\right)$.

SOLUTION Let $y = \sinh^{-1}x$. Then

$$x = \sinh y = \frac{e^y - e^{-y}}{2}$$

so

$$e^y - 2x - e^{-y} = 0$$

or, multiplying by e^y,

$$e^{2y} - 2xe^y - 1 = 0$$

This is really a quadratic equation in e^y:

$$(e^y)^2 - 2x(e^y) - 1 = 0$$

Solving by the quadratic formula, we get

$$e^y = \frac{2x \pm \sqrt{4x^2 + 4}}{2} = x \pm \sqrt{x^2 + 1}$$

Note that $e^y > 0$, but $x - \sqrt{x^2 + 1} < 0$ $\left(\text{because } x < \sqrt{x^2 + 1}\right)$. Thus, the minus sign is inadmissible and we have

$$e^y = x + \sqrt{x^2 + 1}$$

Therefore
$$y = \ln(e^y) = \ln\!\left(x + \sqrt{x^2 + 1}\right)$$

(See Exercise 25 for another method.)

---

6 | **Derivatives of Inverse Hyperbolic Functions**

$$\frac{d}{dx}(\sinh^{-1}x) = \frac{1}{\sqrt{1 + x^2}} \qquad \frac{d}{dx}(\operatorname{csch}^{-1}x) = -\frac{1}{|x|\sqrt{x^2 + 1}}$$

$$\frac{d}{dx}(\cosh^{-1}x) = \frac{1}{\sqrt{x^2 - 1}} \qquad \frac{d}{dx}(\operatorname{sech}^{-1}x) = -\frac{1}{x\sqrt{1 - x^2}}$$

$$\frac{d}{dx}(\tanh^{-1}x) = \frac{1}{1 - x^2} \qquad \frac{d}{dx}(\coth^{-1}x) = \frac{1}{1 - x^2}$$

▐▐ Notice that the formulas for the derivatives of $\tanh^{-1}x$ and $\coth^{-1}x$ appear to be identical. But the domains of these functions have no numbers in common: $\tanh^{-1}x$ is defined for $|x| < 1$, whereas $\coth^{-1}x$ is defined for $|x| > 1$.

The inverse hyperbolic functions are all differentiable because the hyperbolic functions are differentiable. The formulas in Table 6 can be proved either by the method for inverse functions or by differentiating Formulas 3, 4, and 5.

EXAMPLE 4 Prove that $\dfrac{d}{dx}(\sinh^{-1}x) = \dfrac{1}{\sqrt{1 + x^2}}$.

SOLUTION 1 Let $y = \sinh^{-1}x$. Then $\sinh y = x$. If we differentiate this equation implicitly with respect to x, we get

$$\cosh y \,\frac{dy}{dx} = 1$$

Since $\cosh^2 y - \sinh^2 y = 1$ and $\cosh y \geq 0$, we have $\cosh y = \sqrt{1 + \sinh^2 y}$, so

$$\frac{dy}{dx} = \frac{1}{\cosh y} = \frac{1}{\sqrt{1 + \sinh^2 y}} = \frac{1}{\sqrt{1 + x^2}}$$

SOLUTION 2 From Equation 3 (proved in Example 3), we have

$$\frac{d}{dx}(\sinh^{-1}x) = \frac{d}{dx}\ln\!\left(x + \sqrt{x^2 + 1}\right)$$

$$= \frac{1}{x + \sqrt{x^2 + 1}}\frac{d}{dx}\left(x + \sqrt{x^2 + 1}\right)$$

$$= \frac{1}{x + \sqrt{x^2 + 1}}\left(1 + \frac{x}{\sqrt{x^2 + 1}}\right)$$

$$= \frac{\sqrt{x^2 + 1} + x}{\left(x + \sqrt{x^2 + 1}\right)\sqrt{x^2 + 1}}$$

$$= \frac{1}{\sqrt{x^2 + 1}}$$

SECTION 7.6 HYPERBOLIC FUNCTIONS ▬ 491

EXAMPLE 5 Find $\dfrac{d}{dx}[\tanh^{-1}(\sin x)]$.

SOLUTION Using Table 6 and the Chain Rule, we have

$$\frac{d}{dx}[\tanh^{-1}(\sin x)] = \frac{1}{1 - (\sin x)^2}\frac{d}{dx}(\sin x)$$

$$= \frac{1}{1 - \sin^2 x}\cos x = \frac{\cos x}{\cos^2 x} = \sec x$$

EXAMPLE 6 Evaluate $\displaystyle\int_0^1 \frac{dx}{\sqrt{1 + x^2}}$.

SOLUTION Using Table 6 (or Example 4) we know that an antiderivative of $1/\sqrt{1 + x^2}$ is $\sinh^{-1}x$. Therefore

$$\int_0^1 \frac{dx}{\sqrt{1 + x^2}} = \sinh^{-1}x\Big]_0^1$$

$$= \sinh^{-1} 1$$

$$= \ln\left(1 + \sqrt{2}\right) \qquad \text{(from Equation 3)}$$

7.6 Exercises

1–6 ▦ Find the numerical value of each expression.

1. (a) $\sinh 0$ (b) $\cosh 0$

2. (a) $\tanh 0$ (b) $\tanh 1$

3. (a) $\sinh(\ln 2)$ (b) $\sinh 2$

4. (a) $\cosh 3$ (b) $\cosh(\ln 3)$

5. (a) $\operatorname{sech} 0$ (b) $\cosh^{-1} 1$

6. (a) $\sinh 1$ (b) $\sinh^{-1} 1$

7–19 ▦ Prove the identity.

7. $\sinh(-x) = -\sinh x$
(This shows that sinh is an odd function.)

8. $\cosh(-x) = \cosh x$
(This shows that cosh is an even function.)

9. $\cosh x + \sinh x = e^x$

10. $\cosh x - \sinh x = e^{-x}$

11. $\sinh(x + y) = \sinh x \cosh y + \cosh x \sinh y$

12. $\cosh(x + y) = \cosh x \cosh y + \sinh x \sinh y$

13. $\coth^2 x - 1 = \operatorname{csch}^2 x$

14. $\tanh(x + y) = \dfrac{\tanh x + \tanh y}{1 + \tanh x \tanh y}$

15. $\sinh 2x = 2 \sinh x \cosh x$

16. $\cosh 2x = \cosh^2 x + \sinh^2 x$

17. $\tanh(\ln x) = \dfrac{x^2 - 1}{x^2 + 1}$

18. $\dfrac{1 + \tanh x}{1 - \tanh x} = e^{2x}$

19. $(\cosh x + \sinh x)^n = \cosh nx + \sinh nx$
(n any real number)

20. If $\sinh x = \frac{3}{4}$, find the values of the other hyperbolic functions at x.

21. If $\tanh x = \frac{4}{5}$, find the values of the other hyperbolic functions at x.

22. (a) Use the graphs of sinh, cosh, and tanh in Figures 1–3 to draw the graphs of csch, sech, and coth.
(b) Check the graphs that you sketched in part (a) by using a graphing device to produce them.

23. Use the definitions of the hyperbolic functions to find each of the following limits.

(a) $\lim\limits_{x \to \infty} \tanh x$ (b) $\lim\limits_{x \to -\infty} \tanh x$

(c) $\lim\limits_{x \to \infty} \sinh x$ (d) $\lim\limits_{x \to -\infty} \sinh x$

(e) $\lim\limits_{x \to \infty} \operatorname{sech} x$ (f) $\lim\limits_{x \to \infty} \coth x$

(g) $\lim\limits_{x \to 0^+} \coth x$ (h) $\lim\limits_{x \to 0^-} \coth x$

(i) $\lim\limits_{x \to -\infty} \operatorname{csch} x$

24. Prove the formulas given in Table 1 for the derivatives of the functions (a) cosh, (b) tanh, (c) csch, (d) sech, and (e) coth.

25. Give an alternative solution to Example 3 by letting $y = \sinh^{-1}x$ and then using Exercise 9 and Example 1(a) with x replaced by y.

26. Prove Equation 4.

27. Prove Equation 5 using (a) the method of Example 3 and (b) Exercise 18 with x replaced by y.

28. For each of the following functions (i) give a definition like those in (2), (ii) sketch the graph, and (iii) find a formula similar to Equation 3.

(a) csch^{-1} (b) sech^{-1} (c) $\coth^{-1}$

29. Prove the formulas given in Table 6 for the derivatives of the following functions.

(a) $\cosh^{-1}$ (b) $\tanh^{-1}$ (c) csch^{-1}

(d) sech^{-1} (e) $\coth^{-1}$

30–47 ▓ Find the derivative.

30. $f(x) = \tanh 4x$

31. $f(x) = x \cosh x$ **32.** $g(x) = \sinh^2 x$

33. $h(x) = \sinh(x^2)$ **34.** $F(x) = \sinh x \tanh x$

35. $G(x) = \dfrac{1 - \cosh x}{1 + \cosh x}$ **36.** $f(t) = e^t \operatorname{sech} t$

37. $h(t) = \coth \sqrt{1 + t^2}$ **38.** $f(t) = \ln(\sinh t)$

39. $H(t) = \tanh(e^t)$ **40.** $y = \sinh(\cosh x)$

41. $y = e^{\cosh 3x}$ **42.** $y = x^2 \sinh^{-1}(2x)$

43. $y = \tanh^{-1}\sqrt{x}$

44. $y = x \tanh^{-1}x + \ln \sqrt{1 - x^2}$

45. $y = x \sinh^{-1}(x/3) - \sqrt{9 + x^2}$

46. $y = \operatorname{sech}^{-1}\sqrt{1 - x^2}, \quad x > 0$

47. $y = \coth^{-1}\sqrt{x^2 + 1}$

48. A flexible cable always hangs in the shape of a catenary $y = c + a \cosh(x/a)$, where c and a are constants and $a > 0$ (see Figure 4 and Exercise 50). Graph several members of the

family of functions $y = a \cosh(x/a)$. How does the graph change as a varies?

49. A telephone line hangs between two poles 14 m apart in the shape of the catenary $y = 20 \cosh(x/20) - 15$, where x and y are measured in meters.

(a) Find the slope of this curve where it meets the right pole.

(b) Find the angle θ between the line and the pole.

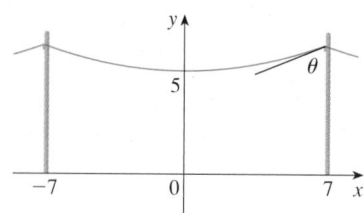

50. Using principles from physics it can be shown that when a cable is hung between two poles, it takes the shape of a curve $y = f(x)$ that satisfies the differential equation

$$\frac{d^2y}{dx^2} = \frac{\rho g}{T}\sqrt{1 + \left(\frac{dy}{dx}\right)^2}$$

where ρ is the linear density of the cable, g is the acceleration due to gravity, and T is the tension in the cable at its lowest point, and the coordinate system is chosen appropriately. Verify that the function

$$y = f(x) = \frac{T}{\rho g} \cosh\left(\frac{\rho g x}{T}\right)$$

is a solution of this differential equation.

51. (a) Show that any function of the form

$$y = A \sinh mx + B \cosh mx$$

satisfies the differential equation $y'' = m^2 y$.

(b) Find $y = y(x)$ such that $y'' = 9y$, $y(0) = -4$, and $y'(0) = 6$.

52. Evaluate $\lim\limits_{x \to \infty} \dfrac{\sinh x}{e^x}$.

53. At what point of the curve $y = \cosh x$ does the tangent have slope 1?

54. If $x = \ln(\sec \theta + \tan \theta)$, show that $\sec \theta = \cosh x$.

55–63 ▓ Evaluate the integral.

55. $\displaystyle\int \sinh x \cosh^2 x \, dx$ **56.** $\displaystyle\int \sinh(1 + 4x) \, dx$

57. $\displaystyle\int \frac{\sinh \sqrt{x}}{\sqrt{x}} \, dx$ **58.** $\displaystyle\int \tanh x \, dx$

59. $\displaystyle\int \frac{\cosh x}{\cosh^2 x - 1} \, dx$ **60.** $\displaystyle\int \frac{\operatorname{sech}^2 x}{2 + \tanh x} \, dx$

61. $\displaystyle\int_4^6 \frac{1}{\sqrt{t^2 - 9}}\, dt$

62. $\displaystyle\int_0^1 \frac{1}{\sqrt{16t^2 + 1}}\, dt$

63. $\displaystyle\int \frac{e^x}{1 - e^{2x}}\, dx$

64. Estimate the value of the number c such that the area under the curve $y = \sinh cx$ between $x = 0$ and $x = 1$ is equal to 1.

65. (a) Use Newton's method or a graphing device to find approximate solutions of the equation $\cosh 2x = 1 + \sinh x$.
(b) Estimate the area of the region bounded by the curves $y = \cosh 2x$ and $y = 1 + \sinh x$.

66. Show that the area of the shaded hyperbolic sector in Figure 6 is $A(t) = \frac{1}{2}t$. [*Hint:* First show that

$$A(t) = \tfrac{1}{2} \sinh t \, \cosh t - \int_1^{\cosh t} \sqrt{x^2 - 1}\, dx$$

and then verify that $A'(t) = \frac{1}{2}$.]

67. Show that if $a \neq 0$ and $b \neq 0$, then there exist numbers α and β such that $ae^x + be^{-x}$ equals either $\alpha \sinh(x + \beta)$ or $\alpha \cosh(x + \beta)$. In other words, almost every function of the form $f(x) = ae^x + be^{-x}$ is a shifted and stretched hyperbolic sine or cosine function.

7.7 Indeterminate Forms and L'Hospital's Rule

Suppose we are trying to analyze the behavior of the function

$$F(x) = \frac{\ln x}{x - 1}$$

Although F is not defined when $x = 1$, we need to know how F behaves *near* 1. In particular, we would like to know the value of the limit

 $\qquad \displaystyle\lim_{x \to 1} \frac{\ln x}{x - 1}$

In computing this limit we can't apply Law 5 of limits (the limit of a quotient is the quotient of the limits, see Section 2.3) because the limit of the denominator is 0. In fact, although the limit in (1) exists, its value is not obvious because both numerator and denominator approach 0 and $\frac{0}{0}$ is not defined.

In general, if we have a limit of the form

$$\lim_{x \to a} \frac{f(x)}{g(x)}$$

where both $f(x) \to 0$ and $g(x) \to 0$ as $x \to a$, then this limit may or may not exist and is called an **indeterminate form of type $\frac{0}{0}$**. We met some limits of this type in Chapter 2. For rational functions, we can cancel common factors:

$$\lim_{x \to 1} \frac{x^2 - x}{x^2 - 1} = \lim_{x \to 1} \frac{x(x - 1)}{(x + 1)(x - 1)} = \lim_{x \to 1} \frac{x}{x + 1} = \frac{1}{2}$$

We used a geometric argument to show that

$$\lim_{x \to 0} \frac{\sin x}{x} = 1$$

But these methods do not work for limits such as (1), so in this section we introduce a systematic method, known as *l'Hospital's Rule,* for the evaluation of indeterminate forms.

Another situation in which a limit is not obvious occurs when we look for a horizontal asymptote of F and need to evaluate the limit

$$\boxed{2} \qquad \lim_{x \to \infty} \frac{\ln x}{x - 1}$$

It isn't obvious how to evaluate this limit because both numerator and denominator become large as $x \to \infty$. There is a struggle between numerator and denominator. If the numerator wins, the limit will be ∞; if the denominator wins, the answer will be 0. Or there may be some compromise, in which case the answer may be some finite positive number. In general, if we have a limit of the form

$$\lim_{x \to a} \frac{f(x)}{g(x)}$$

where both $f(x) \to \infty$ (or $-\infty$) and $g(x) \to \infty$ (or $-\infty$), then the limit may or may not exist and is called an **indeterminate form of type** ∞/∞. We saw in Section 4.4 that this type of limit can be evaluated for certain functions, including rational functions, by dividing numerator and denominator by the highest power of x that occurs in the denominator. For instance,

$$\lim_{x \to \infty} \frac{x^2 - 1}{2x^2 + 1} = \lim_{x \to \infty} \frac{1 - \dfrac{1}{x^2}}{2 + \dfrac{1}{x^2}} = \frac{1 - 0}{2 + 0} = \frac{1}{2}$$

This method does not work for limits such as (2), but l'Hospital's Rule also applies to this type of indeterminate form.

L'Hospital's Rule Suppose f and g are differentiable and $g'(x) \neq 0$ on an open interval I that contains a (except possibly at a). Suppose that

$$\lim_{x \to a} f(x) = 0 \qquad \text{and} \qquad \lim_{x \to a} g(x) = 0$$

or that

$$\lim_{x \to a} f(x) = \pm\infty \qquad \text{and} \qquad \lim_{x \to a} g(x) = \pm\infty$$

(In other words, we have an indeterminate form of type $\frac{0}{0}$ or ∞/∞.) Then

$$\lim_{x \to a} \frac{f(x)}{g(x)} = \lim_{x \to a} \frac{f'(x)}{g'(x)}$$

if the limit on the right side exists (or is ∞ or $-\infty$).

NOTE 1 ◦ L'Hospital's Rule says that the limit of a quotient of functions is equal to the limit of the quotient of their derivatives, provided that the given conditions are satisfied. It is especially important to verify the conditions regarding the limits of f and g before using l'Hospital's Rule.

NOTE 2 ◦ L'Hospital's Rule is also valid for one-sided limits and for limits at infinity or negative infinity; that is, "$x \to a$" can be replaced by any of the symbols $x \to a^+$, $x \to a^-$, $x \to \infty$, or $x \to -\infty$.

NOTE 3 ◦ For the special case in which $f(a) = g(a) = 0$, f' and g' are continuous, and $g'(a) \neq 0$, it is easy to see why l'Hospital's Rule is true. In fact, using the alternative form

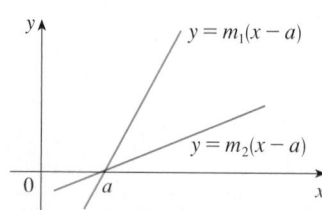

FIGURE 1

||| Figure 1 suggests visually why l'Hospital's Rule might be true. The first graph shows two differentiable functions f and g, each of which approaches 0 as $x \to a$. If we were to zoom in toward the point $(a, 0)$, the graphs would start to look almost linear. But if the functions actually *were* linear, as in the second graph, then their ratio would be

$$\frac{m_1(x - a)}{m_2(x - a)} = \frac{m_1}{m_2}$$

which is the ratio of their derivatives. This suggests that

$$\lim_{x \to a} \frac{f(x)}{g(x)} = \lim_{x \to a} \frac{f'(x)}{g'(x)}$$

IIII L'Hospital's Rule is named after a French nobleman, the Marquis de l'Hospital (1661–1704), but was discovered by a Swiss mathematician, John Bernoulli (1667–1748). See Exercise 78 for the example that the Marquis used to illustrate his rule. See the project on page 504 for further historical details.

of the definition of a derivative, we have

$$\lim_{x \to a} \frac{f'(x)}{g'(x)} = \frac{f'(a)}{g'(a)} = \frac{\displaystyle\lim_{x \to a} \frac{f(x) - f(a)}{x - a}}{\displaystyle\lim_{x \to a} \frac{g(x) - g(a)}{x - a}}$$

$$= \lim_{x \to a} \frac{\dfrac{f(x) - f(a)}{x - a}}{\dfrac{g(x) - g(a)}{x - a}} = \lim_{x \to a} \frac{f(x) - f(a)}{g(x) - g(a)}$$

$$= \lim_{x \to a} \frac{f(x)}{g(x)}$$

The general version of l'Hospital's Rule for the indeterminate form $\frac{0}{0}$ is somewhat more difficult and its proof is deferred to the end of this section. The proof for the indeterminate form ∞/∞ can be found in more advanced books.

EXAMPLE 1 Find $\displaystyle\lim_{x \to 1} \frac{\ln x}{x - 1}$.

SOLUTION Since

$$\lim_{x \to 1} \ln x = \ln 1 = 0 \qquad \text{and} \qquad \lim_{x \to 1} (x - 1) = 0$$

we can apply l'Hospital's Rule:

⊘ Notice that when using l'Hospital's Rule we differentiate the numerator and denominator *separately*. We *do not* use the Quotient Rule.

$$\lim_{x \to 1} \frac{\ln x}{x - 1} = \lim_{x \to 1} \frac{\dfrac{d}{dx}(\ln x)}{\dfrac{d}{dx}(x - 1)} = \lim_{x \to 1} \frac{1/x}{1}$$

$$= \lim_{x \to 1} \frac{1}{x} = 1$$

EXAMPLE 2 Calculate $\displaystyle\lim_{x \to \infty} \frac{e^x}{x^2}$.

IIII The graph of the function of Example 2 is shown in Figure 2. We have noticed previously that exponential functions grow far more rapidly than power functions, so the result of Example 2 is not unexpected. See also Exercise 87.

SOLUTION We have $\lim_{x \to \infty} e^x = \infty$ and $\lim_{x \to \infty} x^2 = \infty$, so l'Hospital's Rule gives

$$\lim_{x \to \infty} \frac{e^x}{x^2} = \lim_{x \to \infty} \frac{\dfrac{d}{dx}(e^x)}{\dfrac{d}{dx}(x^2)} = \lim_{x \to \infty} \frac{e^x}{2x}$$

Since $e^x \to \infty$ and $2x \to \infty$ as $x \to \infty$, the limit on the right side is also indeterminate, but a second application of l'Hospital's Rule gives

$$\lim_{x \to \infty} \frac{e^x}{x^2} = \lim_{x \to \infty} \frac{e^x}{2x} = \lim_{x \to \infty} \frac{e^x}{2} = \infty$$

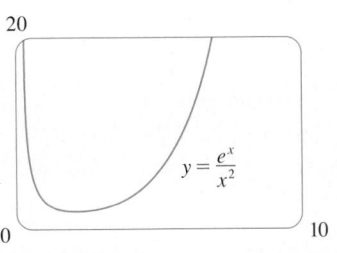

FIGURE 2

║║║ The graph of the function of Example 3 is shown in Figure 3. We have discussed previously the slow growth of logarithms, so it isn't surprising that this ratio approaches 0 as $x \to \infty$. See also Exercise 88.

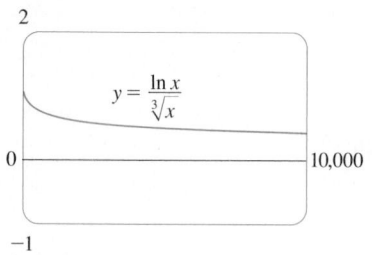

FIGURE 3

EXAMPLE 3 Calculate $\lim\limits_{x \to \infty} \dfrac{\ln x}{\sqrt[3]{x}}$.

SOLUTION Since $\ln x \to \infty$ and $\sqrt[3]{x} \to \infty$ as $x \to \infty$, l'Hospital's Rule applies:

$$\lim_{x \to \infty} \frac{\ln x}{\sqrt[3]{x}} = \lim_{x \to \infty} \frac{1/x}{\frac{1}{3}x^{-2/3}}$$

Notice that the limit on the right side is now indeterminate of type $\frac{0}{0}$. But instead of applying l'Hospital's Rule a second time as we did in Example 2, we simplify the expression and see that a second application is unnecessary:

$$\lim_{x \to \infty} \frac{\ln x}{\sqrt[3]{x}} = \lim_{x \to \infty} \frac{1/x}{\frac{1}{3}x^{-2/3}} = \lim_{x \to \infty} \frac{3}{\sqrt[3]{x}} = 0$$

EXAMPLE 4 Find $\lim\limits_{x \to 0} \dfrac{\tan x - x}{x^3}$. [See Exercise 36(d) in Section 2.2.]

SOLUTION Noting that both $\tan x - x \to 0$ and $x^3 \to 0$ as $x \to 0$, we use l'Hospital's Rule:

$$\lim_{x \to 0} \frac{\tan x - x}{x^3} = \lim_{x \to 0} \frac{\sec^2 x - 1}{3x^2}$$

Since the limit on the right side is still indeterminate of type $\frac{0}{0}$, we apply l'Hospital's Rule again:

$$\lim_{x \to 0} \frac{\sec^2 x - 1}{3x^2} = \lim_{x \to 0} \frac{2\sec^2 x \tan x}{6x}$$

Because $\lim_{x \to 0} \sec^2 x = 1$, we simplify the calculation by writing

$$\lim_{x \to 0} \frac{2\sec^2 x \tan x}{6x} = \frac{1}{3} \lim_{x \to 0} \sec^2 x \lim_{x \to 0} \frac{\tan x}{x} = \frac{1}{3} \lim_{x \to 0} \frac{\tan x}{x}$$

We can evaluate this last limit either by using l'Hospital's Rule a third time or by writing $\tan x$ as $(\sin x)/(\cos x)$ and making use of our knowledge of trigonometric limits. Putting together all the steps, we get

$$\lim_{x \to 0} \frac{\tan x - x}{x^3} = \lim_{x \to 0} \frac{\sec^2 x - 1}{3x^2} = \lim_{x \to 0} \frac{2\sec^2 x \tan x}{6x}$$

$$= \frac{1}{3} \lim_{x \to 0} \frac{\tan x}{x} = \frac{1}{3} \lim_{x \to 0} \frac{\sec^2 x}{1} = \frac{1}{3}$$

║║║ The graph in Figure 4 gives visual confirmation of the result of Example 4. If we were to zoom in too far, however, we would get an inaccurate graph because $\tan x$ is close to x when x is small. See Exercise 36(d) in Section 2.2.

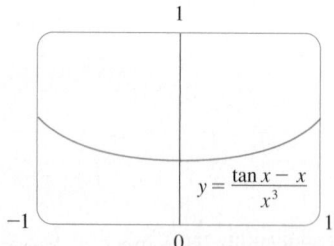

FIGURE 4

EXAMPLE 5 Find $\lim\limits_{x \to \pi^-} \dfrac{\sin x}{1 - \cos x}$.

SOLUTION If we blindly attempted to use l'Hospital's Rule, we would get

$$\lim_{x \to \pi^-} \frac{\sin x}{1 - \cos x} = \lim_{x \to \pi^-} \frac{\cos x}{\sin x} = -\infty$$

This is *wrong*! Although the numerator $\sin x \to 0$ as $x \to \pi^-$, notice that the denominator $(1 - \cos x)$ does not approach 0, so l'Hospital's Rule can't be applied here.

The required limit is, in fact, easy to find because the function is continuous and the denominator is nonzero at π:

$$\lim_{x \to \pi^-} \frac{\sin x}{1 - \cos x} = \frac{\sin \pi}{1 - \cos \pi} = \frac{0}{1 - (-1)} = 0$$

Example 5 shows what can go wrong if you use l'Hospital's Rule without thinking. Other limits *can* be found using l'Hospital's Rule but are more easily found by other methods. (See Examples 3 and 5 in Section 2.3, Example 3 in Section 2.6, and the discussion at the beginning of this section.) So when evaluating any limit, you should consider other methods before using l'Hospital's Rule.

⦀ Indeterminate Products

If $\lim_{x \to a} f(x) = 0$ and $\lim_{x \to a} g(x) = \infty$ (or $-\infty$), then it isn't clear what the value of $\lim_{x \to a} f(x)g(x)$, if any, will be. There is a struggle between f and g. If f wins, the answer will be 0; if g wins, the answer will be ∞ (or $-\infty$). Or there may be a compromise where the answer is a finite nonzero number. This kind of limit is called an **indeterminate form of type $0 \cdot \infty$**. We can deal with it by writing the product fg as a quotient:

$$fg = \frac{f}{1/g} \qquad \text{or} \qquad fg = \frac{g}{1/f}$$

This converts the given limit into an indeterminate form of type $\frac{0}{0}$ or ∞/∞ so that we can use l'Hospital's Rule.

‖‖ Figure 5 shows the graph of the function in Example 6. Notice that the function is undefined at $x = 0$; the graph approaches the origin but never quite reaches it.

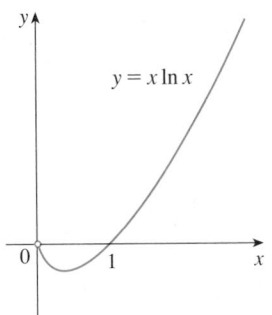

$y = x \ln x$

FIGURE 5

EXAMPLE 6 Evaluate $\lim_{x \to 0^+} x \ln x$.

SOLUTION The given limit is indeterminate because, as $x \to 0^+$, the first factor (x) approaches 0 while the second factor ($\ln x$) approaches $-\infty$. Writing $x = 1/(1/x)$, we have $1/x \to \infty$ as $x \to 0^+$, so l'Hospital's Rule gives

$$\lim_{x \to 0^+} x \ln x = \lim_{x \to 0^+} \frac{\ln x}{1/x} = \lim_{x \to 0^+} \frac{1/x}{-1/x^2} = \lim_{x \to 0^+} (-x) = 0$$

NOTE ∘ In solving Example 6 another possible option would have been to write

$$\lim_{x \to 0^+} x \ln x = \lim_{x \to 0^+} \frac{x}{1/\ln x}$$

This gives an indeterminate form of the type 0/0, but if we apply l'Hospital's Rule we get a more complicated expression than the one we started with. In general, when we rewrite an indeterminate product, we try to choose the option that leads to the simpler limit.

EXAMPLE 7 Use l'Hospital's Rule to help sketch the graph of $f(x) = xe^x$.

SOLUTION Because both x and e^x become large as $x \to \infty$, we have $\lim_{x \to \infty} xe^x = \infty$. As $x \to -\infty$, however, $e^x \to 0$ and so we have an indeterminate product that requires the use of l'Hospital's Rule:

$$\lim_{x \to -\infty} xe^x = \lim_{x \to -\infty} \frac{x}{e^{-x}} = \lim_{x \to -\infty} \frac{1}{-e^{-x}} = \lim_{x \to -\infty} (-e^x) = 0$$

Thus, the x-axis is a horizontal asymptote.

We use the methods of Chapter 4 to gather other information concerning the graph. The derivative is

$$f'(x) = xe^x + e^x = (x + 1)e^x$$

Since e^x is always positive, we see that $f'(x) > 0$ when $x + 1 > 0$, and $f'(x) < 0$ when $x + 1 < 0$. So f is increasing on $(-1, \infty)$ and decreasing on $(-\infty, -1)$. Because $f'(-1) = 0$ and f changes from negative to positive at $x = -1$, $f(-1) = -e^{-1}$ is a local (and absolute) minimum. The second derivative is

$$f''(x) = (x + 1)e^x + e^x = (x + 2)e^x$$

Since $f''(x) > 0$ if $x > -2$ and $f''(x) < 0$ if $x < -2$, f is concave upward on $(-2, \infty)$ and concave downward on $(-\infty, -2)$. The inflection point is $(-2, -2e^{-2})$.

We use this information to sketch the curve in Figure 6.

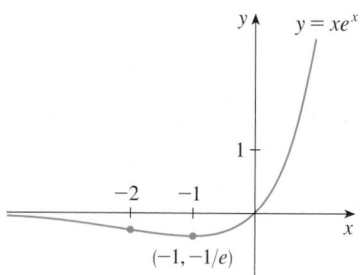

FIGURE 6

||| Indeterminate Differences

If $\lim_{x \to a} f(x) = \infty$ and $\lim_{x \to a} g(x) = \infty$, then the limit

$$\lim_{x \to a} [f(x) - g(x)]$$

is called an **indeterminate form of type** $\infty - \infty$. Again there is a contest between f and g. Will the answer be ∞ (f wins) or will it be $-\infty$ (g wins) or will they compromise on a finite number? To find out, we try to convert the difference into a quotient (for instance, by using a common denominator, or rationalization, or factoring out a common factor) so that we have an indeterminate form of type $\frac{0}{0}$ or ∞/∞.

EXAMPLE 8 Compute $\lim\limits_{x \to (\pi/2)^-} (\sec x - \tan x)$.

SOLUTION First notice that $\sec x \to \infty$ and $\tan x \to \infty$ as $x \to (\pi/2)^-$, so the limit is indeterminate. Here we use a common denominator:

$$\lim_{x \to (\pi/2)^-} (\sec x - \tan x) = \lim_{x \to (\pi/2)^-} \left(\frac{1}{\cos x} - \frac{\sin x}{\cos x} \right)$$

$$= \lim_{x \to (\pi/2)^-} \frac{1 - \sin x}{\cos x} = \lim_{x \to (\pi/2)^-} \frac{-\cos x}{-\sin x} = 0$$

Note that the use of l'Hospital's Rule is justified because $1 - \sin x \to 0$ and $\cos x \to 0$ as $x \to (\pi/2)^-$.

||| Indeterminate Powers

Several indeterminate forms arise from the limit

$$\lim_{x \to a} [f(x)]^{g(x)}$$

1. $\lim\limits_{x \to a} f(x) = 0$ and $\lim\limits_{x \to a} g(x) = 0$ type 0^0

2. $\lim\limits_{x \to a} f(x) = \infty$ and $\lim\limits_{x \to a} g(x) = 0$ type ∞^0

3. $\lim\limits_{x \to a} f(x) = 1$ and $\lim\limits_{x \to a} g(x) = \pm\infty$ type 1^∞

Each of these three cases can be treated either by taking the natural logarithm:

$$\text{let} \quad y = [f(x)]^{g(x)}, \quad \text{then} \quad \ln y = g(x) \ln f(x)$$

or by writing the function as an exponential:

$$[f(x)]^{g(x)} = e^{g(x) \ln f(x)}$$

(Recall that both of these methods were used in differentiating such functions.) In either method we are led to the indeterminate product $g(x) \ln f(x)$, which is of type $0 \cdot \infty$.

EXAMPLE 9 Calculate $\displaystyle\lim_{x \to 0^+} (1 + \sin 4x)^{\cot x}$.

SOLUTION First notice that as $x \to 0^+$, we have $1 + \sin 4x \to 1$ and $\cot x \to \infty$, so the given limit is indeterminate. Let

$$y = (1 + \sin 4x)^{\cot x}$$

Then $$\ln y = \ln[(1 + \sin 4x)^{\cot x}] = \cot x \ln(1 + \sin 4x)$$

so l'Hospital's Rule gives

$$\lim_{x \to 0^+} \ln y = \lim_{x \to 0^+} \frac{\ln(1 + \sin 4x)}{\tan x}$$

$$= \lim_{x \to 0^+} \frac{\dfrac{4 \cos 4x}{1 + \sin 4x}}{\sec^2 x} = 4$$

So far we have computed the limit of $\ln y$, but what we want is the limit of y. To find this we use the fact that $y = e^{\ln y}$:

$$\lim_{x \to 0^+} (1 + \sin 4x)^{\cot x} = \lim_{x \to 0^+} y = \lim_{x \to 0^+} e^{\ln y} = e^4$$

EXAMPLE 10 Find $\displaystyle\lim_{x \to 0^+} x^x$.

SOLUTION Notice that this limit is indeterminate since $0^x = 0$ for any $x > 0$ but $x^0 = 1$ for any $x \neq 0$. We could proceed as in Example 9 or by writing the function as an exponential:

$$x^x = (e^{\ln x})^x = e^{x \ln x}$$

In Example 6 we used l'Hospital's Rule to show that

$$\lim_{x \to 0^+} x \ln x = 0$$

Therefore

$$\lim_{x \to 0^+} x^x = \lim_{x \to 0^+} e^{x \ln x} = e^0 = 1$$

‖‖‖ The graph of the function $y = x^x$, $x > 0$, is shown in Figure 7. Notice that although 0^0 is not defined, the values of the function approach 1 as $x \to 0^+$. This confirms the result of Example 10.

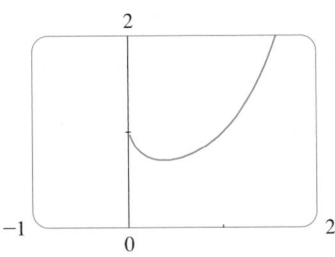

FIGURE 7

In order to give the promised proof of l'Hospital's Rule we first need a generalization of the Mean Value Theorem. The following theorem is named after another French mathematician, Augustin-Louis Cauchy (1789–1857).

‖‖‖ See the biographical sketch of Cauchy on page 97.

3 **Cauchy's Mean Value Theorem** Suppose that the functions f and g are continuous on $[a, b]$ and differentiable on (a, b), and $g'(x) \neq 0$ for all x in (a, b). Then there is a number c in (a, b) such that

$$\frac{f'(c)}{g'(c)} = \frac{f(b) - f(a)}{g(b) - g(a)}$$

Notice that if we take the special case in which $g(x) = x$, then $g'(c) = 1$ and Theorem 3 is just the ordinary Mean Value Theorem. Furthermore, Theorem 3 can be proved in a similar manner. You can verify that all we have to do is change the function h given by Equation 4.2.4 to the function

$$h(x) = f(x) - f(a) - \frac{f(b) - f(a)}{g(b) - g(a)} [g(x) - g(a)]$$

and apply Rolle's Theorem as before.

Proof of L'Hospital's Rule We are assuming that $\lim_{x \to a} f(x) = 0$ and $\lim_{x \to a} g(x) = 0$. Let

$$L = \lim_{x \to a} \frac{f'(x)}{g'(x)}$$

We must show that $\lim_{x \to a} f(x)/g(x) = L$. Define

$$F(x) = \begin{cases} f(x) & \text{if } x \neq a \\ 0 & \text{if } x = a \end{cases} \qquad G(x) = \begin{cases} g(x) & \text{if } x \neq a \\ 0 & \text{if } x = a \end{cases}$$

Then F is continuous on I since f is continuous on $\{x \in I \mid x \neq a\}$ and

$$\lim_{x \to a} F(x) = \lim_{x \to a} f(x) = 0 = F(a)$$

Likewise, G is continuous on I. Let $x \in I$ and $x > a$. Then F and G are continuous on $[a, x]$ and differentiable on (a, x) and $G' \neq 0$ there (since $F' = f'$ and $G' = g'$). Therefore, by Cauchy's Mean Value Theorem there is a number y such that $a < y < x$ and

$$\frac{F'(y)}{G'(y)} = \frac{F(x) - F(a)}{G(x) - G(a)} = \frac{F(x)}{G(x)}$$

Here we have used the fact that, by definition, $F(a) = 0$ and $G(a) = 0$. Now, if we let $x \to a^+$, then $y \to a^+$ (since $a < y < x$), so

$$\lim_{x \to a^+} \frac{f(x)}{g(x)} = \lim_{x \to a^+} \frac{F(x)}{G(x)} = \lim_{y \to a^+} \frac{F'(y)}{G'(y)} = \lim_{y \to a^+} \frac{f'(y)}{g'(y)} = L$$

A similar argument shows that the left-hand limit is also L. Therefore

$$\lim_{x \to a} \frac{f(x)}{g(x)} = L$$

This proves l'Hospital's Rule for the case where a is finite.

If a is infinite, we let $t = 1/x$. Then $t \to 0^+$ as $x \to \infty$, so we have

$$\lim_{x \to \infty} \frac{f(x)}{g(x)} = \lim_{t \to 0^+} \frac{f(1/t)}{g(1/t)}$$

$$= \lim_{t \to 0^+} \frac{f'(1/t)(-1/t^2)}{g'(1/t)(-1/t^2)} \qquad \text{(by l'Hospital's Rule for finite } a\text{)}$$

$$= \lim_{t \to 0^+} \frac{f'(1/t)}{g'(1/t)} = \lim_{x \to \infty} \frac{f'(x)}{g'(x)}$$

7.7 Exercises

1–4 ▐ Given that

$$\lim_{x \to a} f(x) = 0 \qquad \lim_{x \to a} g(x) = 0 \qquad \lim_{x \to a} h(x) = 1$$

$$\lim_{x \to a} p(x) = \infty \qquad \lim_{x \to a} q(x) = \infty$$

which of the following limits are indeterminate forms? For those that are not an indeterminate form, evaluate the limit where possible.

1. (a) $\lim_{x \to a} \dfrac{f(x)}{g(x)}$ (b) $\lim_{x \to a} \dfrac{f(x)}{p(x)}$

(c) $\lim_{x \to a} \dfrac{h(x)}{p(x)}$ (d) $\lim_{x \to a} \dfrac{p(x)}{f(x)}$

(e) $\lim_{x \to a} \dfrac{p(x)}{q(x)}$

2. (a) $\lim_{x \to a} [f(x)p(x)]$ (b) $\lim_{x \to a} [h(x)p(x)]$

(c) $\lim_{x \to a} [p(x)q(x)]$

3. (a) $\lim_{x \to a} [f(x) - p(x)]$ (b) $\lim_{x \to a} [p(x) - q(x)]$

(c) $\lim_{x \to a} [p(x) + q(x)]$

4. (a) $\lim_{x \to a} [f(x)]^{g(x)}$ (b) $\lim_{x \to a} [f(x)]^{p(x)}$ (c) $\lim_{x \to a} [h(x)]^{p(x)}$

(d) $\lim_{x \to a} [p(x)]^{f(x)}$ (e) $\lim_{x \to a} [p(x)]^{q(x)}$ (f) $\lim_{x \to a} \sqrt[q(x)]{p(x)}$

5–62 ▐ Find the limit. Use l'Hospital's Rule where appropriate. If there is a more elementary method, consider using it. If l'Hospital's Rule doesn't apply, explain why.

5. $\lim_{x \to -1} \dfrac{x^2 - 1}{x + 1}$

6. $\lim_{x \to -2} \dfrac{x + 2}{x^2 + 3x + 2}$

7. $\lim_{x \to 1} \dfrac{x^9 - 1}{x^5 - 1}$

8. $\lim_{x \to 1} \dfrac{x^a - 1}{x^b - 1}$

9. $\lim_{x \to (\pi/2)^+} \dfrac{\cos x}{1 - \sin x}$

10. $\lim_{x \to 0} \dfrac{x + \tan x}{\sin x}$

11. $\lim_{t \to 0} \dfrac{e^t - 1}{t^3}$

12. $\lim_{t \to 0} \dfrac{e^{3t} - 1}{t}$

13. $\lim_{x \to 0} \dfrac{\tan px}{\tan qx}$

14. $\lim_{\theta \to \pi/2} \dfrac{1 - \sin \theta}{\csc \theta}$

15. $\lim_{x \to \infty} \dfrac{\ln x}{x}$

16. $\lim_{x \to \infty} \dfrac{e^x}{x}$

17. $\lim_{x \to 0^+} \dfrac{\ln x}{x}$

18. $\lim_{x \to \infty} \dfrac{\ln \ln x}{x}$

19. $\lim_{t \to 0} \dfrac{5^t - 3^t}{t}$

20. $\lim_{x \to 1} \dfrac{\ln x}{\sin \pi x}$

21. $\lim_{x \to 0} \dfrac{e^x - 1 - x}{x^2}$

22. $\lim_{x \to 0} \dfrac{e^x - 1 - x - (x^2/2)}{x^3}$

23. $\lim_{x \to \infty} \dfrac{e^x}{x^3}$

24. $\lim_{x \to 0} \dfrac{\sin x}{\sinh x}$

25. $\lim_{x \to 0} \dfrac{\sin^{-1}x}{x}$

26. $\lim_{x \to 0} \dfrac{\sin x - x}{x^3}$

27. $\lim_{x \to 0} \dfrac{1 - \cos x}{x^2}$

28. $\lim_{x \to \infty} \dfrac{(\ln x)^2}{x}$

29. $\lim_{x \to 0} \dfrac{x + \sin x}{x + \cos x}$

30. $\lim_{x \to 0} \dfrac{\cos mx - \cos nx}{x^2}$

31. $\lim_{x \to \infty} \dfrac{x}{\ln(1 + 2e^x)}$

32. $\lim_{x \to 0} \dfrac{x}{\tan^{-1}(4x)}$

33. $\lim_{x \to 1} \dfrac{1 - x + \ln x}{1 + \cos \pi x}$

34. $\lim_{x \to \infty} \dfrac{\sqrt{x^2 + 2}}{\sqrt{2x^2 + 1}}$

35. $\lim_{x \to 1} \dfrac{x^a - ax + a - 1}{(x - 1)^2}$

36. $\lim_{x \to 0} \dfrac{1 - e^{-2x}}{\sec x}$

37. $\lim_{x \to 0^+} \sqrt{x} \ln x$

38. $\lim_{x \to -\infty} x^2 e^x$

39. $\lim\limits_{x \to 0} \cot 2x \sin 6x$

40. $\lim\limits_{x \to 0^+} \sin x \ln x$

41. $\lim\limits_{x \to \infty} x^3 e^{-x^2}$

42. $\lim\limits_{x \to \pi/4} (1 - \tan x) \sec x$

43. $\lim\limits_{x \to 1^+} \ln x \tan(\pi x/2)$

44. $\lim\limits_{x \to \infty} x \tan(1/x)$

45. $\lim\limits_{x \to 0} \left(\dfrac{1}{x} - \csc x \right)$

46. $\lim\limits_{x \to 0} (\csc x - \cot x)$

47. $\lim\limits_{x \to \infty} \left(\sqrt{x^2 + x} - x \right)$

48. $\lim\limits_{x \to 1} \left(\dfrac{1}{\ln x} - \dfrac{1}{x - 1} \right)$

49. $\lim\limits_{x \to \infty} (x - \ln x)$

50. $\lim\limits_{x \to \infty} (xe^{1/x} - x)$

51. $\lim\limits_{x \to 0^+} x^{x^2}$

52. $\lim\limits_{x \to 0^+} (\tan 2x)^x$

53. $\lim\limits_{x \to 0} (1 - 2x)^{1/x}$

54. $\lim\limits_{x \to \infty} \left(1 + \dfrac{a}{x} \right)^{bx}$

55. $\lim\limits_{x \to \infty} \left(1 + \dfrac{3}{x} + \dfrac{5}{x^2} \right)^x$

56. $\lim\limits_{x \to \infty} x^{(\ln 2)/(1 + \ln x)}$

57. $\lim\limits_{x \to \infty} x^{1/x}$

58. $\lim\limits_{x \to \infty} (e^x + x)^{1/x}$

59. $\lim\limits_{x \to \infty} \left(\dfrac{x}{x + 1} \right)^x$

60. $\lim\limits_{x \to 0} (\cos 3x)^{5/x}$

61. $\lim\limits_{x \to 0^+} (\cos x)^{1/x^2}$

62. $\lim\limits_{x \to \infty} \left(\dfrac{2x - 3}{2x + 5} \right)^{2x+1}$

63–64 ▦ Use a graph to estimate the value of the limit. Then use l'Hospital's Rule to find the exact value.

63. $\lim\limits_{x \to \infty} x \left[\ln(x + 5) - \ln x \right]$

64. $\lim\limits_{x \to \pi/4} (\tan x)^{\tan 2x}$

65–66 ▦ Illustrate l'Hospital's Rule by graphing both $f(x)/g(x)$ and $f'(x)/g'(x)$ near $x = 0$ to see that these ratios have the same limit as $x \to 0$. Also calculate the exact value of the limit.

65. $f(x) = e^x - 1, \quad g(x) = x^3 + 4x$

66. $f(x) = 2x \sin x, \quad g(x) = \sec x - 1$

67–72 Use l'Hospital's Rule to help sketch the curve. Use the guidelines of Section 4.5.

67. $y = xe^{-x}$

68. $y = x(\ln x)^2$

69. $y = xe^{-x^2}$

70. $y = e^x/x$

71. $y = x - \ln(1 + x)$

72. $y = e^x - 3e^{-x} - 4x$

[CAS] **73–75** ▦

(a) Graph the function.
(b) Use l'Hospital's Rule to explain the behavior as $x \to 0^+$ or as $x \to \infty$.
(c) Estimate the maximum and minimum values and then use calculus to find the exact values.
(d) Use a graph of f'' to estimate the x-coordinates of the inflection points.

73. $f(x) = x^{-x}$

74. $f(x) = (\sin x)^{\sin x}$

75. $f(x) = x^{1/x}$

76. Investigate the family of curves given by $f(x) = x^n e^{-x}$, where n is a positive integer. What features do these curves have in common? How do they differ from one another? In particular, what happens to the maximum and minimum points and inflection points as n increases? Illustrate by graphing several members of the family.

77. Investigate the family of curves given by $f(x) = xe^{-cx}$, where c is a real number. Start by computing the limits as $x \to \pm\infty$. Identify any transitional values of c where the basic shape changes. What happens to the maximum or minimum points and inflection points as c changes? Illustrate by graphing several members of the family.

78. The first appearance in print of l'Hospital's Rule was in the book *Analyse des Infiniment Petits* published by the Marquis de l'Hospital in 1696. This was the first calculus *textbook* ever published and the example that the Marquis used in that book to illustrate his rule was to find the limit of the function

$$y = \frac{\sqrt{2a^3x - x^4} - a\sqrt[3]{aax}}{a - \sqrt[4]{ax^3}}$$

as x approaches a, where $a > 0$. (At that time it was common to write aa instead of a^2.) Solve this problem.

79. If an initial amount A_0 of money is invested at an interest rate i compounded n times a year, the value of the investment after t years is

$$A = A_0 \left(1 + \frac{i}{n} \right)^{nt}$$

If we let $n \to \infty$, we refer to the *continuous compounding* of interest. Use l'Hospital's Rule to show that if interest is compounded continuously, then the amount after n years is

$$A = A_0 e^{it}$$

80. If an object with mass m is dropped from rest, one model for its speed v after t seconds, taking air resistance into account, is

$$v = \frac{mg}{c} (1 - e^{-ct/m})$$

where g is the acceleration due to gravity and c is a positive constant. (In Chapter 10 we will be able to deduce this equation from the assumption that the air resistance is proportional to the speed of the object.)

(a) Calculate $\lim_{t\to\infty} v$. What is the meaning of this limit?

(b) For fixed t, use l'Hospital's Rule to calculate $\lim_{m\to\infty} v$. What can you conclude about the speed of a very heavy falling object?

81. In Section 5.3 we investigated the Fresnel function $S(x) = \int_0^x \sin(\frac{1}{2}\pi t^2)\, dt$, which arises in the study of the diffraction of light waves. Evaluate

$$\lim_{x\to 0} \frac{S(x)}{x^3}$$

82. Suppose that the temperature in a long thin rod placed along the x-axis is initially $C/(2a)$ if $|x| \le a$ and 0 if $|x| > a$. It can be shown that if the heat diffusivity of the rod is k, then the temperature of the rod at the point x at time t is

$$T(x, t) = \frac{C}{a\sqrt{4\pi kt}} \int_0^a e^{-(x-u)^2/(4kt)}\, du$$

To find the temperature distribution that results from an initial hot spot concentrated at the origin, we need to compute

$$\lim_{a\to 0} T(x, t)$$

Use l'Hospital's Rule to find this limit.

83. If f' is continuous, $f(2) = 0$, and $f'(2) = 7$, evaluate

$$\lim_{x\to 0} \frac{f(2 + 3x) + f(2 + 5x)}{x}$$

84. For what values of a and b is the following equation true?

$$\lim_{x\to 0} \left(\frac{\sin 2x}{x^3} + a + \frac{b}{x^2} \right) = 0$$

85. If f' is continuous, use l'Hospital's Rule to show that

$$\lim_{h\to 0} \frac{f(x + h) - f(x - h)}{2h} = f'(x)$$

Explain the meaning of this equation with the aid of a diagram.

86. If f'' is continuous, show that

$$\lim_{h\to 0} \frac{f(x + h) - 2f(x) + f(x - h)}{h^2} = f''(x)$$

87. Prove that

$$\lim_{x\to\infty} \frac{e^x}{x^n} = \infty$$

for any positive integer n. This shows that the exponential function approaches infinity faster than any power of x.

88. Prove that

$$\lim_{x\to\infty} \frac{\ln x}{x^p} = 0$$

for any number $p > 0$. This shows that the logarithmic function approaches ∞ more slowly than any power of x.

89. Prove that $\lim_{x\to 0^+} x^\alpha \ln x = 0$ for any $\alpha > 0$.

90. Evaluate $\lim_{x\to 0} \dfrac{1}{x^3} \int_0^x \sin(t^2)\, dt$.

91. The figure shows a sector of a circle with central angle θ. Let $A(\theta)$ be the area of the segment between the chord PR and the arc PR. Let $B(\theta)$ be the area of the triangle PQR. Find $\lim_{\theta\to 0^+} A(\theta)/B(\theta)$.

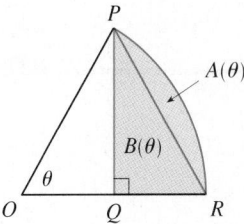

92. The figure shows two regions in the first quadrant: $A(t)$ is the area under the curve $y = \sin(x^2)$ from 0 to t, and $B(t)$ is the area of the triangle with vertices O, P, and $(t, 0)$. Find $\lim_{t\to 0^+} A(t)/B(t)$.

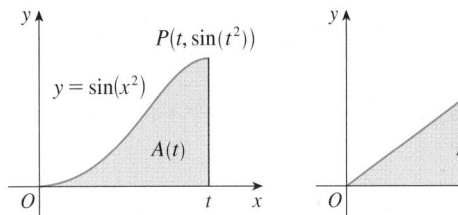

93. Let

$$f(x) = \begin{cases} e^{-1/x^2} & \text{if } x \ne 0 \\ 0 & \text{if } x = 0 \end{cases}$$

(a) Use the definition of derivative to compute $f'(0)$.

(b) Show that f has derivatives of all orders that are defined on $\mathbb{R}$. [*Hint:* First show by induction that there is a polynomial $p_n(x)$ and a nonnegative integer k_n such that $f^{(n)}(x) = p_n(x)f(x)/x^{k_n}$ for $x \ne 0$.]

94. Let

$$f(x) = \begin{cases} |x|^x & \text{if } x \ne 0 \\ 1 & \text{if } x = 0 \end{cases}$$

(a) Show that f is continuous at 0.

(b) Investigate graphically whether f is differentiable at 0 by zooming in several times toward the point $(0, 1)$ on the graph of f.

(c) Show that f is not differentiable at 0. How can you reconcile this fact with the appearance of the graphs in part (b)?

▏▏▏▏ WRITING PROJECT

The Origins of L'Hospital's Rule

▏▏▏▏ The Internet is another source of information for this project. See the web site

www.stewartcalculus.com

and click on *History of Mathematics.*

L'Hospital's Rule was first published in 1696 in the Marquis de l'Hospital's calculus textbook *Analyse des Infiniment Petits,* but the rule was discovered in 1694 by the Swiss mathematician John (Johann) Bernoulli. The explanation is that these two mathematicians had entered into a curious business arrangement whereby the Marquis de l'Hospital bought the rights to Bernoulli's mathematical discoveries. The details, including a translation of l'Hospital's letter to Bernoulli proposing the arrangement, can be found in the book by Eves [1].

Write a report on the historical and mathematical origins of l'Hospital's Rule. Start by providing brief biographical details of both men (the dictionary edited by Gillispie [2] is a good source) and outline the business deal between them. Then give l'Hospital's statement of his rule, which is found in Struik's sourcebook [4] and more briefly in the book of Katz [3]. Notice that l'Hospital and Bernoulli formulated the rule geometrically and gave the answer in terms of differentials. Compare their statement with the version of l'Hospital's Rule given in Section 7.7 and show that the two statements are essentially the same.

1. Howard Eves, *In Mathematical Circles (Volume 2: Quadrants III and IV)* (Boston: Prindle, Weber and Schmidt, 1969), pp. 20–22.

2. C. C. Gillispie, ed., *Dictionary of Scientific Biography* (New York: Scribner's, 1974). See the article on Johann Bernoulli by E. A. Fellmann and J. O. Fleckenstein in Volume II and the article on the Marquis de l'Hospital by Abraham Robinson in Volume VIII.

3. Victor Katz, *A History of Mathematics: An Introduction* (New York: HarperCollins, 1993), p. 484.

4. D. J. Struik, ed., *A Sourcebook in Mathematics, 1200–1800* (Princeton, NJ: Princeton University Press, 1969), pp. 315–316.

▏▏▏▏ **7 Review**

──────── ▫ CONCEPT CHECK ▫ ────────

1. (a) What is a one-to-one function? How can you tell if a function is one-to-one by looking at its graph?
  (b) If f is a one-to-one function, how is its inverse function f^{-1} defined? How do you obtain the graph of f^{-1} from the graph of f?
  (c) Suppose f is a one-to-one function and $g = f^{-1}$. If $f'(g(a)) \neq 0$, write a formula for $g'(a)$.

2. (a) What are the domain and range of the natural exponential function $f(x) = e^x$?
  (b) What are the domain and range of the natural logarithmic function $f(x) = \ln x$?
  (c) How are the graphs of these functions related? Sketch these graphs, by hand, using the same axes.
  (d) If a is a positive number, $a \neq 1$, write an equation that expresses $\log_a x$ in terms of $\ln x$.

3. (a) How is the inverse sine function $f(x) = \sin^{-1}x$ defined? What are its domain and range?
  (b) How is the inverse cosine function $f(x) = \cos^{-1}x$ defined? What are its domain and range?
  (c) How is the inverse tangent function $f(x) = \tan^{-1}x$ defined? What are its domain and range? Sketch its graph.

4. Write the definitions of the hyperbolic functions $\sinh x$, $\cosh x$, and $\tanh x$.

5. State the derivative of each function.
  (a) $y = e^x$
  (b) $y = a^x$
  (c) $y = \ln x$
  (d) $y = \log_a x$
  (e) $y = \sin^{-1}x$
  (f) $y = \cos^{-1}x$
  (g) $y = \tan^{-1}x$
  (h) $y = \sinh x$
  (i) $y = \cosh x$
  (j) $y = \tanh x$
  (k) $y = \sinh^{-1}x$
  (l) $y = \cosh^{-1}x$
  (m) $y = \tanh^{-1}x$

6. (a) How is the number e defined?
  (b) Express e as a limit.
  (c) Why is the natural exponential function $y = e^x$ used more often in calculus than the other exponential functions $y = a^x$?
  (d) Why is the natural logarithmic function $y = \ln x$ used more often in calculus than the other logarithmic functions $y = \log_a x$?

7. (a) What does l'Hospital's Rule say?
  (b) How can you use l'Hospital's Rule if you have a product $f(x)g(x)$ where $f(x) \to 0$ and $g(x) \to \infty$ as $x \to a$?
  (c) How can you use l'Hospital's Rule if you have a difference $f(x) - g(x)$ where $f(x) \to \infty$ and $g(x) \to \infty$ as $x \to a$?
  (d) How can you use l'Hospital's Rule if you have a power $[f(x)]^{g(x)}$ where $f(x) \to 0$ and $g(x) \to 0$ as $x \to a$?

--- ◦ TRUE-FALSE QUIZ ◦ ---

Determine whether the statement is true or false. If it is true, explain why.
If it is false, explain why or give an example that disproves the statement.

1. If f is one-to-one, with domain $\mathbb{R}$, then $f^{-1}(f(6)) = 6$.

2. If f is one-to-one and differentiable, with domain $\mathbb{R}$, then $(f^{-1})'(6) = 1/f'(6)$.

3. The function $f(x) = \cos x$, $-\pi/2 \leq x \leq \pi/2$, is one-to-one.

4. $\tan^{-1}(-1) = 3\pi/4$

5. If $0 < a < b$, then $\ln a < \ln b$.

6. $\pi^{\sqrt{5}} = e^{\sqrt{5}\ln \pi}$

7. You can always divide by e^x.

8. If $a > 0$ and $b > 0$, then $\ln(a + b) = \ln a + \ln b$.

9. If $x > 0$, then $(\ln x)^6 = 6 \ln x$.

10. $\dfrac{d}{dx}(10^x) = x10^{x-1}$

11. $\dfrac{d}{dx}(\ln 10) = \dfrac{1}{10}$

12. The inverse function of $y = e^{3x}$ is $y = \frac{1}{3}\ln x$.

13. $\cos^{-1}x = \dfrac{1}{\cos x}$

14. $\tan^{-1}x = \dfrac{\sin^{-1}x}{\cos^{-1}x}$

15. $\cosh x \geq 1$ for all x

16. $\ln \dfrac{1}{10} = -\displaystyle\int_1^{10}\dfrac{dx}{x}$

17. $\displaystyle\int_2^{16}\dfrac{dx}{x} = 3 \ln 2$

18. $\displaystyle\lim_{x\to\pi^-}\dfrac{\tan x}{1 - \cos x} = \lim_{x\to\pi^-}\dfrac{\sec^2x}{\sin x} = \infty$

--- ◦ EXERCISES ◦ ---

1. The graph of f is shown. Is f one-to-one? Explain.

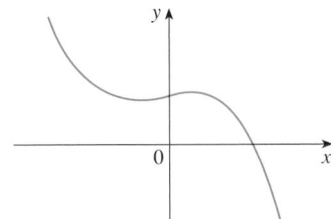

2. The graph of g is given.
(a) Why is g one-to-one?
(b) Estimate the value of $g^{-1}(2)$.
(c) Estimate the domain of g^{-1}.
(d) Sketch the graph of g^{-1}.

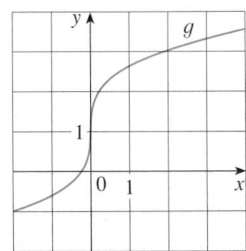

3. Suppose f is one-to-one, $f(7) = 3$, and $f'(7) = 8$. Find
(a) $f^{-1}(3)$ and (b) $(f^{-1})'(3)$.

4. Find the inverse function of $f(x) = \dfrac{x + 1}{2x + 1}$.

5–9 ▦ Sketch a rough graph of the function without using a calculator.

5. $y = 5^x - 1$

6. $y = -e^{-x}$

7. $y = -\ln x$

8. $y = \ln(x - 1)$

9. $y = 2 \arctan x$

10. Let $a > 1$. For large values of x, which of the functions $y = x^a$, $y = a^x$, and $y = \log_a x$ has the largest values and which has the smallest values?

11–12 ▦ Find the exact value of each expression.

11. (a) $e^{2\ln 3}$
(b) $\log_{10}25 + \log_{10}4$

12. (a) $\ln e^\pi$
(b) $\tan(\arcsin \frac{1}{2})$

13–20 ▦ Solve the equation for x.

13. $\ln x = \frac{1}{3}$

14. $e^x = \frac{1}{3}$

15. $e^{e^x} = 17$

16. $\ln(1 + e^{-x}) = 3$

17. $\ln(x + 1) + \ln(x - 1) = 1$

18. $\log_5(c^x) = d$

19. $\tan^{-1}x = 1$

20. $\sin x = 0.3$

21–47 ▦ Differentiate.

21. $f(t) = t^2 \ln t$

22. $g(t) = \dfrac{e^t}{1 + e^t}$

23. $h(\theta) = e^{\tan 2\theta}$

24. $h(u) = 10^{\sqrt{u}}$

25. $y = \ln|\sec 5x + \tan 5x|$

26. $y = e^{-t}(t^2 - 2t + 2)$

27. $y = e^{cx}(c\sin x - \cos x)$

28. $y = \sin^{-1}(e^x)$

29. $y = \ln(\sec^2x)$

30. $y = \ln(x^2 e^x)$

31. $y = xe^{-1/x}$

32. $y = x^r e^{sx}$

33. $y = 2^{-t^2}$

34. $y = e^{\cos x} + \cos(e^x)$

35. $H(v) = v \tan^{-1} v$

36. $F(z) = \log_{10}(1 + z^2)$

37. $y = x \sinh(x^2)$

38. $y = (\cos x)^x$

39. $y = \ln \sin x - \frac{1}{2} \sin^2 x$

40. $y = \arctan(\arcsin \sqrt{x})$

41. $y = \ln\left(\dfrac{1}{x}\right) + \dfrac{1}{\ln x}$

42. $xe^y = y - 1$

43. $y = \ln(\cosh 3x)$

44. $y = \dfrac{(x^2 + 1)^4}{(2x + 1)^3 (3x - 1)^5}$

45. $y = \cosh^{-1}(\sinh x)$

46. $y = x \tanh^{-1}\sqrt{x}$

47. $f(x) = e^{\sin^3(\ln(x^2 + 1))}$

48. Show that

$$\frac{d}{dx}\left(\frac{1}{2}\tan^{-1}x + \frac{1}{4}\ln\frac{(x + 1)^2}{x^2 + 1}\right) = \frac{1}{(1 + x)(1 + x^2)}$$

49–52 ⫿⫿⫿ Find f' in terms of g'.

49. $f(x) = e^{g(x)}$

50. $f(x) = g(e^x)$

51. $f(x) = \ln|g(x)|$

52. $f(x) = g(\ln x)$

53–54 ⫿⫿⫿ Find $f^{(n)}(x)$.

53. $f(x) = 2^x$

54. $f(x) = \ln(2x)$

55. Use mathematical induction to show that if $f(x) = xe^x$, then $f^{(n)}(x) = (x + n)e^x$.

56. Find y' if $y = x + \arctan y$.

57–58 ⫿⫿⫿ Find an equation of the tangent to the curve at the given point.

57. $y = (2 + x)e^{-x}$, $\quad (0, 2)$

58. $y = x \ln x$, $\quad (e, e)$

59. At what point on the curve $y = [\ln(x + 4)]^2$ is the tangent horizontal?

60. If $f(x) = xe^{\sin x}$, find $f'(x)$. Graph f and f' on the same screen and comment.

61. (a) Find an equation of the tangent to the curve $y = e^x$ that is parallel to the line $x - 4y = 1$.
(b) Find an equation of the tangent to the curve $y = e^x$ that passes through the origin.

62. The function $C(t) = K(e^{-at} - e^{-bt})$, where a, b, and K are positive constants and $b > a$, is used to model the concentration at time t of a drug injected into the bloodstream.
(a) Show that $\lim_{t \to \infty} C(t) = 0$.
(b) Find $C'(t)$, the rate at which the drug is cleared from circulation.
(c) When is this rate equal to 0?

63–78 ⫿⫿⫿ Evaluate the limit.

63. $\lim\limits_{x \to \infty} e^{-3x}$

64. $\lim\limits_{x \to 10^-} \ln(100 - x^2)$

65. $\lim\limits_{x \to 3^-} e^{2/(x-3)}$

66. $\lim\limits_{x \to \infty} \arctan(x^3 - x)$

67. $\lim\limits_{x \to 0^+} \ln(\sinh x)$

68. $\lim\limits_{x \to \infty} e^{-x} \sin x$

69. $\lim\limits_{x \to \infty} \dfrac{1 + 2^x}{1 - 2^x}$

70. $\lim\limits_{x \to \infty} \left(1 + \dfrac{4}{x}\right)^x$

71. $\lim\limits_{x \to 0} \dfrac{\tan \pi x}{\ln(1 + x)}$

72. $\lim\limits_{x \to 0} \dfrac{1 - \cos x}{x^2 + x}$

73. $\lim\limits_{x \to 0} \dfrac{e^{4x} - 1 - 4x}{x^2}$

74. $\lim\limits_{x \to \infty} \dfrac{e^{4x} - 1 - 4x}{x^2}$

75. $\lim\limits_{x \to \infty} x^3 e^{-x}$

76. $\lim\limits_{x \to 0^+} x^2 \ln x$

77. $\lim\limits_{x \to 1^+} \left(\dfrac{x}{x - 1} - \dfrac{1}{\ln x}\right)$

78. $\lim\limits_{x \to (\pi/2)^-} (\tan x)^{\cos x}$

79–84 ⫿⫿⫿ Sketch the curve using the guidelines of Section 4.5.

79. $y = \tan^{-1}(1/x)$

80. $y = \sin^{-1}(1/x)$

81. $y = x \ln x$

82. $y = e^{2x - x^2}$

83. $y = e^x + e^{-3x}$

84. $y = \ln(x^2 - 1)$

85. Graph $f(x) = e^{-1/x^2}$ in a viewing rectangle that shows all the main aspects of this function. Estimate the inflection points. Then use calculus to find them exactly.

86. Investigate the family of functions $f(x) = cxe^{-cx^2}$. What happens to the maximum and minimum points and the inflection points as c changes? Illustrate your conclusions by graphing several members of the family.

87. An equation of motion of the form $s = Ae^{-ct}\cos(\omega t + \delta)$ represents damped oscillation of an object. Find the velocity and acceleration of the object.

88. (a) Show that there is exactly one root of the equation $\ln x = 3 - x$ and that it lies between 2 and e.
(b) Find the root of the equation in part (a) correct to four decimal places.

89. The biologist G. F. Gause conducted an experiment in the 1930s with the protozoan *Paramecium* and used the population function

$$P(t) = \frac{64}{1 + 31e^{-0.7944t}}$$

to model his data, where t was measured in days. Use this model to determine when the population was increasing most rapidly.

90–103 ▥ Evaluate the integral.

90. $\displaystyle\int_0^4 \frac{1}{16+t^2}\,dt$

91. $\displaystyle\int_0^1 ye^{-2y^2}\,dy$

92. $\displaystyle\int_2^5 \frac{dr}{1+2r}$

93. $\displaystyle\int_2^4 \frac{1+x-x^2}{x^2}\,dx$

94. $\displaystyle\int_0^{\pi/2} \frac{\cos x}{1+\sin^2 x}\,dx$

95. $\displaystyle\int \frac{e^{\sqrt{x}}}{\sqrt{x}}\,dx$

96. $\displaystyle\int \frac{\cos(\ln x)}{x}\,dx$

97. $\displaystyle\int \frac{x+1}{x^2+2x}\,dx$

98. $\displaystyle\int \frac{e^{-x}}{1+e^{-2x}}\,dx$

99. $\displaystyle\int \tan x \ln(\cos x)\,dx$

100. $\displaystyle\int \frac{x}{\sqrt{1-x^4}}\,dx$

101. $\displaystyle\int 2^{\tan\theta}\sec^2\theta\,d\theta$

102. $\displaystyle\int \sinh au\,du$

103. $\displaystyle\int \frac{\sec\theta\tan\theta}{1+\sec\theta}\,d\theta$

▫ ▫ ▫ ▫ ▫ ▫ ▫ ▫ ▫ ▫ ▫ ▫ ▫ ▫

104–106 ▥ Use properties of integrals to prove the inequality.

104. $\displaystyle\int_0^1 \sqrt{1+e^{2x}}\,dx \geq e-1$

105. $\displaystyle\int_0^1 e^x \cos x\,dx \leq e-1$

106. $\displaystyle\int_0^1 x\sin^{-1}x\,dx \leq \pi/4$

▫ ▫ ▫ ▫ ▫ ▫ ▫ ▫ ▫ ▫ ▫ ▫ ▫ ▫

107–108 ▥ Find $f'(x)$.

107. $\displaystyle f(x) = \int_1^{\sqrt{x}} \frac{e^s}{s}\,ds$

108. $\displaystyle f(x) = \int_{\ln x}^{2x} e^{-t^2}\,dt$

▫ ▫ ▫ ▫ ▫ ▫ ▫ ▫ ▫ ▫ ▫ ▫ ▫ ▫

109. Find the average value of the function $f(x) = 1/x$ on the interval $[1, 4]$.

110. Find the area of the region bounded by the curves $y = e^x$, $y = e^{-x}$, $x = -2$, and $x = 1$.

111. Find the volume of the solid obtained by rotating about the y-axis the region under the curve $y = 1/(1 + x^4)$ from $x = 0$ to $x = 1$.

112. If $f(x) = x + x^2 + e^x$ and $g(x) = f^{-1}(x)$, find $g'(1)$.

113. If g is the inverse function of $f(x) = \ln x + \tan^{-1}x$, find $g'(\pi/4)$.

114. What is the area of the largest rectangle in the first quadrant with two sides on the axes and one vertex on the curve $y = e^{-x}$?

115. What is the area of the largest triangle in the first quadrant with two sides on the axes and the third side tangent to the curve $y = e^{-x}$?

116. Evaluate $\int_0^1 e^x\,dx$ without using the Fundamental Theorem of Calculus. [*Hint:* Use the definition of a definite integral with right endpoints, sum a geometric series, and then use l'Hospital's Rule.]

117. If $F(x) = \int_a^b t^x\,dt$, where $a, b > 0$, then, by the Fundamental Theorem,

$$F(x) = \frac{b^{x+1} - a^{x+1}}{x+1} \qquad x \neq -1$$

$$F(-1) = \ln b - \ln a$$

Use l'Hospital's Rule to show that F is continuous at -1.

118. Show that

$$\cos\{\arctan[\sin(\text{arccot } x)]\} = \sqrt{\frac{x^2+1}{x^2+2}}$$

119. If f is a continuous function such that

$$\int_0^x f(t)\,dt = xe^{2x} + \int_0^x e^{-t}f(t)\,dt$$

for all x, find an explicit formula for $f(x)$.

120. (a) Show that $\ln x < x - 1$ for $x > 0$, $x \neq 1$.
(b) Show that, for $x > 0$, $x \neq 1$,

$$\frac{x-1}{x} < \ln x$$

(c) Deduce *Napier's Inequality:*

$$\frac{1}{b} < \frac{\ln b - \ln a}{b-a} < \frac{1}{a}$$

if $b > a > 0$.

(d) Give a geometric proof of Napier's Inequality by comparing the slopes of the three lines shown in the figure.

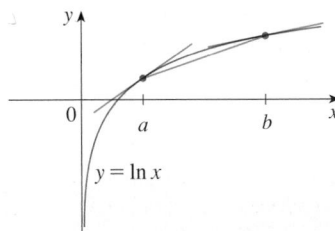

(e) Give another proof of Napier's Inequality by applying Property 8 of integrals (see Section 5.2) to $\int_a^b (1/x)\,dx$.

PROBLEMS PLUS

Cover up the solution to the example and try it yourself.

EXAMPLE For what values of c does the equation $\ln x = cx^2$ have exactly one solution?

SOLUTION One of the most important principles of problem solving is to draw a diagram, even if the problem as stated doesn't explicitly mention a geometric situation. Our present problem can be reformulated geometrically as follows: For what values of c does the curve $y = \ln x$ intersect the curve $y = cx^2$ in exactly one point?

Let's start by graphing $y = \ln x$ and $y = cx^2$ for various values of c. We know that, for $c \neq 0$, $y = cx^2$ is a parabola that opens upward if $c > 0$ and downward if $c < 0$. Figure 1 shows the parabolas $y = cx^2$ for several positive values of c. Most of them don't intersect $y = \ln x$ at all and one intersects twice. We have the feeling that there must be a value of c (somewhere between 0.1 and 0.3) for which the curves intersect exactly once, as in Figure 2.

To find that particular value of c, we let a be the x-coordinate of the single point of intersection. In other words, $\ln a = ca^2$, so a is the unique solution of the given equation. We see from Figure 2 that the curves just touch, so they have a common tangent line when $x = a$. That means the curves $y = \ln x$ and $y = cx^2$ have the same slope when $x = a$. Therefore

$$\frac{1}{a} = 2ca$$

Solving the equations $\ln a = ca^2$ and $1/a = 2ca$, we get

$$\ln a = ca^2 = c \cdot \frac{1}{2c} = \frac{1}{2}$$

Thus, $a = e^{1/2}$ and

$$c = \frac{\ln a}{a^2} = \frac{\ln e^{1/2}}{e} = \frac{1}{2e}$$

For negative values of c we have the situation illustrated in Figure 3: All parabolas $y = cx^2$ with negative values of c intersect $y = \ln x$ exactly once. And let's not forget about $c = 0$: The curve $y = 0x^2 = 0$ is just the x-axis, which intersects $y = \ln x$ exactly once.

FIGURE 1

FIGURE 2

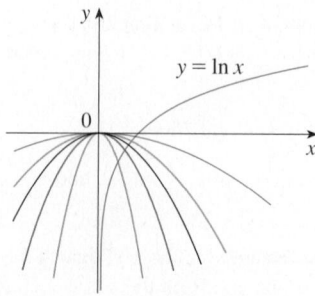

FIGURE 3

To summarize, the required values of c are $c = 1/(2e)$ and $c \leqslant 0$.

1. If a rectangle has its base on the x-axis and two vertices on the curve $y = e^{-x^2}$, show that the rectangle has the largest possible area when the two vertices are at the points of inflection of the curve.

2. Prove that $\log_2 5$ is an irrational number.

3. Show that

$$\frac{d^n}{dx^n}(e^{ax}\sin bx) = r^n e^{ax}\sin(bx + n\theta)$$

where a and b are positive numbers, $r^2 = a^2 + b^2$, and $\theta = \tan^{-1}(b/a)$.

4. Show that $\sin^{-1}(\tanh x) = \tan^{-1}(\sinh x)$.

5. Show that, for $x > 0$,

$$\frac{x}{1 + x^2} < \tan^{-1}x < x$$

6. Suppose f is continuous, $f(0) = 0$, $f(1) = 1$, $f'(x) > 0$, and $\int_0^1 f(x)\,dx = \frac{1}{3}$. Find the value of the integral $\int_0^1 f^{-1}(y)\,dy$.

7. Show that $f(x) = \int_1^x \sqrt{1 + t^3}\,dt$ is one-to-one and find $(f^{-1})'(0)$.

8. If

$$y = \frac{x}{\sqrt{a^2 - 1}} - \frac{2}{\sqrt{a^2 - 1}}\arctan\frac{\sin x}{a + \sqrt{a^2 - 1} + \cos x}$$

show that $y' = \dfrac{1}{a + \cos x}$.

9. For what value of a is the following equation true?

$$\lim_{x\to\infty}\left(\frac{x + a}{x - a}\right)^x = e$$

10. Sketch the set of all points (x, y) such that $|x + y| \leq e^x$.

11. Prove that $\cosh(\sinh x) < \sinh(\cosh x)$ for all x.

12. Show that, for all positive values of x and y,

$$\frac{e^{x+y}}{xy} \geq e^2$$

13. For what value of k does the equation $e^{2x} = k\sqrt{x}$ have exactly one solution?

14. For which positive numbers a is it true that $a^x \geq 1 + x$ for all x?

15. For which positive numbers a does the curve $y = a^x$ intersect the line $y = x$?

CHAPTER 8

The techniques of this chapter enable us to find the height of a rocket a minute after liftoff and to compute the escape velocity of the rocket.

© Ron Lindsey / Phototake

Techniques of Integration

Because of the Fundamental Theorem of Calculus, we can integrate a function if we know an antiderivative, that is, an indefinite integral. We summarize here the most important integrals that we have learned so far.

$$\int x^n \, dx = \frac{x^{n+1}}{n+1} + C \quad (n \neq -1) \qquad \int \frac{1}{x} \, dx = \ln|x| + C$$

$$\int e^x \, dx = e^x + C \qquad \int a^x \, dx = \frac{a^x}{\ln a} + C$$

$$\int \sin x \, dx = -\cos x + C \qquad \int \cos x \, dx = \sin x + C$$

$$\int \sec^2 x \, dx = \tan x + C \qquad \int \csc^2 x \, dx = -\cot x + C$$

$$\int \sec x \tan x \, dx = \sec x + C \qquad \int \csc x \cot x \, dx = -\csc x + C$$

$$\int \sinh x \, dx = \cosh x + C \qquad \int \cosh x \, dx = \sinh x + C$$

$$\int \tan x \, dx = \ln|\sec x| + C \qquad \int \cot x \, dx = \ln|\sin x| + C$$

$$\int \frac{1}{x^2 + a^2} \, dx = \frac{1}{a} \tan^{-1}\left(\frac{x}{a}\right) + C \qquad \int \frac{1}{\sqrt{a^2 - x^2}} \, dx = \sin^{-1}\left(\frac{x}{a}\right) + C$$

In this chapter we develop techniques for using these basic integration formulas to obtain indefinite integrals of more complicated functions. We learned the most important method of integration, the Substitution Rule, in Section 5.5. The other general technique, integration by parts, is presented in Section 8.1. Then we learn methods that are special to particular classes of functions such as trigonometric functions and rational functions.

Integration is not as straightforward as differentiation; there are no rules that absolutely guarantee obtaining an indefinite integral of a function. Therefore, in Section 8.5 we discuss a strategy for integration.

8.1 Integration by Parts

Every differentiation rule has a corresponding integration rule. For instance, the Substitution Rule for integration corresponds to the Chain Rule for differentiation. The rule that corresponds to the Product Rule for differentiation is called the rule for *integration by parts*.

The Product Rule states that if f and g are differentiable functions, then

$$\frac{d}{dx}[f(x)g(x)] = f(x)g'(x) + g(x)f'(x)$$

In the notation for indefinite integrals this equation becomes

$$\int [f(x)g'(x) + g(x)f'(x)] \, dx = f(x)g(x)$$

or

$$\int f(x)g'(x) \, dx + \int g(x)f'(x) \, dx = f(x)g(x)$$

We can rearrange this equation as

$$\boxed{1} \qquad \boxed{\int f(x)g'(x) \, dx = f(x)g(x) - \int g(x)f'(x) \, dx}$$

Formula 1 is called the **formula for integration by parts**. It is perhaps easier to remember in the following notation. Let $u = f(x)$ and $v = g(x)$. Then the differentials are $du = f'(x) \, dx$ and $dv = g'(x) \, dx$, so, by the Substitution Rule, the formula for integration by parts becomes

$$\boxed{2} \qquad \boxed{\int u \, dv = uv - \int v \, du}$$

EXAMPLE 1 Find $\int x \sin x \, dx$.

SOLUTION USING FORMULA 1 Suppose we choose $f(x) = x$ and $g'(x) = \sin x$. Then $f'(x) = 1$ and $g(x) = -\cos x$. (For g we can choose *any* antiderivative of g'.) Thus, using Formula 1, we have

$$\int x \sin x \, dx = f(x)g(x) - \int g(x)f'(x) \, dx$$

$$= x(-\cos x) - \int (-\cos x) \, dx$$

$$= -x \cos x + \int \cos x \, dx$$

$$= -x \cos x + \sin x + C$$

It's wise to check the answer by differentiating it. If we do so, we get $x \sin x$, as expected.

SOLUTION USING FORMULA 2 Let

$$u = x \qquad\qquad dv = \sin x \, dx$$

Then

$$du = dx \qquad\qquad v = -\cos x$$

and so

$$\int x \sin x \, dx = \int \overset{u}{x} \overset{dv}{\overbrace{\sin x \, dx}} = \overset{u}{x} \overset{v}{\overbrace{(-\cos x)}} - \int \overset{v}{\overbrace{(-\cos x)}} \overset{du}{dx}$$

$$= -x \cos x + \int \cos x \, dx$$

$$= -x \cos x + \sin x + C$$

|||| It is helpful to use the pattern:

$$u = \square \qquad dv = \square$$
$$du = \square \qquad v = \square$$

NOTE ▫ Our aim in using integration by parts is to obtain a simpler integral than the one we started with. Thus, in Example 1 we started with $\int x \sin x \, dx$ and expressed it in terms of the simpler integral $\int \cos x \, dx$. If we had chosen $u = \sin x$ and $dv = x \, dx$, then $du = \cos x \, dx$ and $v = x^2/2$, so integration by parts gives

$$\int x \sin x \, dx = (\sin x) \frac{x^2}{2} - \frac{1}{2} \int x^2 \cos x \, dx$$

Although this is true, $\int x^2 \cos x \, dx$ is a more difficult integral than the one we started with. In general, when deciding on a choice for u and dv, we usually try to choose $u = f(x)$ to be a function that becomes simpler when differentiated (or at least not more complicated) as long as $dv = g'(x) \, dx$ can be readily integrated to give v.

EXAMPLE 2 Evaluate $\int \ln x \, dx$.

SOLUTION Here we don't have much choice for u and dv. Let

$$u = \ln x \qquad dv = dx$$

Then

$$du = \frac{1}{x} \, dx \qquad v = x$$

Integrating by parts, we get

$$\int \ln x \, dx = x \ln x - \int x \, \frac{dx}{x}$$

$$= x \ln x - \int dx$$

$$= x \ln x - x + C$$

|||| It's customary to write $\int 1 \, dx$ as $\int dx$.

|||| Check the answer by differentiating it.

Integration by parts is effective in this example because the derivative of the function $f(x) = \ln x$ is simpler than f.

EXAMPLE 3 Find $\int t^2 e^t \, dt$.

SOLUTION Notice that t^2 becomes simpler when differentiated (whereas e^t is unchanged when differentiated or integrated), so we choose

$$u = t^2 \qquad dv = e^t \, dt$$

Then

$$du = 2t \, dt \qquad v = e^t$$

Integration by parts gives

[3] $$\int t^2 e^t \, dt = t^2 e^t - 2 \int t e^t \, dt$$

The integral that we obtained, $\int t e^t \, dt$, is simpler than the original integral but is still not obvious. Therefore, we use integration by parts a second time, this time with $u = t$ and

$dv = e^t \, dt$. Then $du = dt$, $v = e^t$, and

$$\int te^t \, dt = te^t - \int e^t \, dt$$

$$= te^t - e^t + C$$

Putting this in Equation 3, we get

$$\int t^2 e^t \, dt = t^2 e^t - 2 \int te^t \, dt$$

$$= t^2 e^t - 2(te^t - e^t + C)$$

$$= t^2 e^t - 2te^t + 2e^t + C_1 \qquad \text{where } C_1 = -2C$$

EXAMPLE 4 Evaluate $\int e^x \sin x \, dx$.

||| An easier method, using complex numbers, is given in Exercise 48 in Appendix G.

SOLUTION Neither e^x nor $\sin x$ becomes simpler when differentiated, but we try choosing $u = e^x$ and $dv = \sin x \, dx$ anyway. Then $du = e^x \, dx$ and $v = -\cos x$, so integration by parts gives

$$\boxed{4} \qquad \int e^x \sin x \, dx = -e^x \cos x + \int e^x \cos x \, dx$$

The integral that we have obtained, $\int e^x \cos x \, dx$, is no simpler than the original one, but at least it's no more difficult. Having had success in the preceding example integrating by parts twice, we persevere and integrate by parts again. This time we use $u = e^x$ and $dv = \cos x \, dx$. Then $du = e^x \, dx$, $v = \sin x$, and

$$\boxed{5} \qquad \int e^x \cos x \, dx = e^x \sin x - \int e^x \sin x \, dx$$

At first glance, it appears as if we have accomplished nothing because we have arrived at $\int e^x \sin x \, dx$, which is where we started. However, if we put Equation 5 into Equation 4 we get

$$\int e^x \sin x \, dx = -e^x \cos x + e^x \sin x - \int e^x \sin x \, dx$$

This can be regarded as an equation to be solved for the unknown integral. Adding $\int e^x \sin x \, dx$ to both sides, we obtain

$$2 \int e^x \sin x \, dx = -e^x \cos x + e^x \sin x$$

Dividing by 2 and adding the constant of integration, we get

$$\int e^x \sin x \, dx = \tfrac{1}{2} e^x (\sin x - \cos x) + C$$

||| Figure 1 illustrates Example 4 by showing the graphs of $f(x) = e^x \sin x$ and $F(x) = \frac{1}{2} e^x (\sin x - \cos x)$. As a visual check on our work, notice that $f(x) = 0$ when F has a maximum or minimum.

FIGURE 1

If we combine the formula for integration by parts with Part 2 of the Fundamental Theorem of Calculus, we can evaluate definite integrals by parts. Evaluating both sides of Formula 1 between a and b, assuming f' and g' are continuous, and using the Fundamental

Theorem, we obtain

6 $$\int_a^b f(x)g'(x)\,dx = f(x)g(x)\Big]_a^b - \int_a^b g(x)f'(x)\,dx$$

EXAMPLE 5 Calculate $\int_0^1 \tan^{-1}x\,dx$.

SOLUTION Let

$$u = \tan^{-1}x \qquad dv = dx$$

Then

$$du = \frac{dx}{1+x^2} \qquad v = x$$

So Formula 6 gives

$$\int_0^1 \tan^{-1}x\,dx = x\tan^{-1}x\Big]_0^1 - \int_0^1 \frac{x}{1+x^2}\,dx$$

$$= 1\cdot\tan^{-1}1 - 0\cdot\tan^{-1}0 - \int_0^1 \frac{x}{1+x^2}\,dx$$

$$= \frac{\pi}{4} - \int_0^1 \frac{x}{1+x^2}\,dx$$

|||| Since $\tan^{-1}x \geq 0$ for $x \geq 0$, the integral in Example 5 can be interpreted as the area of the region shown in Figure 2.

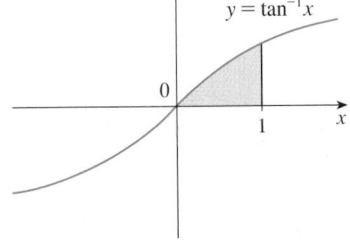

$y = \tan^{-1}x$

FIGURE 2

To evaluate this integral we use the substitution $t = 1 + x^2$ (since u has another meaning in this example). Then $dt = 2x\,dx$, so $x\,dx = dt/2$. When $x = 0$, $t = 1$; when $x = 1$, $t = 2$; so

$$\int_0^1 \frac{x}{1+x^2}\,dx = \tfrac{1}{2}\int_1^2 \frac{dt}{t} = \tfrac{1}{2}\ln|t|\Big]_1^2$$

$$= \tfrac{1}{2}(\ln 2 - \ln 1) = \tfrac{1}{2}\ln 2$$

Therefore

$$\int_0^1 \tan^{-1}x\,dx = \frac{\pi}{4} - \int_0^1 \frac{x}{1+x^2}\,dx = \frac{\pi}{4} - \frac{\ln 2}{2}$$

EXAMPLE 6 Prove the reduction formula

|||| Equation 7 is called a *reduction formula* because the exponent n has been *reduced* to $n-1$ and $n-2$.

7 $$\int \sin^n x\,dx = -\frac{1}{n}\cos x\,\sin^{n-1}x + \frac{n-1}{n}\int \sin^{n-2}x\,dx$$

where $n \geq 2$ is an integer.

SOLUTION Let

$$u = \sin^{n-1}x \qquad dv = \sin x\,dx$$

Then

$$du = (n-1)\sin^{n-2}x\cos x\,dx \qquad v = -\cos x$$

so integration by parts gives

$$\int \sin^n x\,dx = -\cos x\,\sin^{n-1}x + (n-1)\int \sin^{n-2}x\cos^2 x\,dx$$

Since $\cos^2 x = 1 - \sin^2 x$, we have

$$\int \sin^n x \, dx = -\cos x \sin^{n-1} x + (n-1) \int \sin^{n-2} x \, dx - (n-1) \int \sin^n x \, dx$$

As in Example 4, we solve this equation for the desired integral by taking the last term on the right side to the left side. Thus, we have

$$n \int \sin^n x \, dx = -\cos x \sin^{n-1} x + (n-1) \int \sin^{n-2} x \, dx$$

or

$$\int \sin^n x \, dx = -\frac{1}{n} \cos x \sin^{n-1} x + \frac{n-1}{n} \int \sin^{n-2} x \, dx$$

The reduction formula (7) is useful because by using it repeatedly we could eventually express $\int \sin^n x \, dx$ in terms of $\int \sin x \, dx$ (if n is odd) or $\int (\sin x)^0 \, dx = \int dx$ (if n is even).

|||| 8.1 Exercises

1–2 |||| Evaluate the integral using integration by parts with the indicated choices of u and dv.

1. $\int x \ln x \, dx; \quad u = \ln x, \ dv = x \, dx$

2. $\int \theta \sec^2\theta \, d\theta; \quad u = \theta, \ dv = \sec^2\theta \, d\theta$

□ □ □ □ □ □ □ □ □ □ □ □

3–32 |||| Evaluate the integral.

3. $\int x \cos 5x \, dx$

4. $\int xe^{-x} \, dx$

5. $\int re^{r/2} \, dr$

6. $\int t \sin 2t \, dt$

7. $\int x^2 \sin \pi x \, dx$

8. $\int x^2 \cos mx \, dx$

9. $\int \ln(2x + 1) \, dx$

10. $\int \sin^{-1} x \, dx$

11. $\int \arctan 4t \, dt$

12. $\int p^5 \ln p \, dp$

13. $\int (\ln x)^2 \, dx$

14. $\int t^3 e^t \, dt$

15. $\int e^{2\theta} \sin 3\theta \, d\theta$

16. $\int e^{-\theta} \cos 2\theta \, d\theta$

17. $\int y \sinh y \, dy$

18. $\int y \cosh ay \, dy$

19. $\int_0^\pi t \sin 3t \, dt$

20. $\int_0^1 (x^2 + 1)e^{-x} \, dx$

21. $\int_1^2 \frac{\ln x}{x^2} \, dx$

22. $\int_1^4 \sqrt{t} \ln t \, dt$

23. $\int_0^1 \frac{y}{e^{2y}} \, dy$

24. $\int_{\pi/4}^{\pi/2} x \csc^2 x \, dx$

25. $\int_0^{1/2} \cos^{-1} x \, dx$

26. $\int_0^1 x 5^x \, dx$

27. $\int \cos x \ln(\sin x) \, dx$

28. $\int_1^{\sqrt{3}} \arctan(1/x) \, dx$

29. $\int \cos(\ln x) \, dx$

30. $\int_0^1 \frac{r^3}{\sqrt{4 + r^2}} \, dr$

31. $\int_1^2 x^4 (\ln x)^2 \, dx$

32. $\int_0^t e^s \sin(t - s) \, ds$

□ □ □ □ □ □ □ □ □ □ □ □

33–36 |||| First make a substitution and then use integration by parts to evaluate the integral.

33. $\int \sin \sqrt{x} \, dx$

34. $\int_1^4 e^{\sqrt{x}} \, dx$

35. $\int_{\sqrt{\pi/2}}^{\sqrt{\pi}} \theta^3 \cos(\theta^2) \, d\theta$

36. $\int x^5 e^{x^2} \, dx$

□ □ □ □ □ □ □ □ □ □ □ □

37–40 |||| Evaluate the indefinite integral. Illustrate, and check that your answer is reasonable, by graphing both the function and its antiderivative (take $C = 0$).

37. $\int x \cos \pi x \, dx$

38. $\int x^{3/2} \ln x \, dx$

39. $\int (2x + 3)e^x \, dx$

40. $\int x^3 e^{x^2} \, dx$

□ □ □ □ □ □ □ □ □ □ □ □

41. (a) Use the reduction formula in Example 6 to show that

$$\int \sin^2x \, dx = \frac{x}{2} - \frac{\sin 2x}{4} + C$$

(b) Use part (a) and the reduction formula to evaluate $\int \sin^4x \, dx$.

42. (a) Prove the reduction formula

$$\int \cos^nx \, dx = \frac{1}{n}\cos^{n-1}x \sin x + \frac{n-1}{n}\int \cos^{n-2}x \, dx$$

(b) Use part (a) to evaluate $\int \cos^2x \, dx$.
(c) Use parts (a) and (b) to evaluate $\int \cos^4x \, dx$.

43. (a) Use the reduction formula in Example 6 to show that

$$\int_0^{\pi/2} \sin^nx \, dx = \frac{n-1}{n}\int_0^{\pi/2} \sin^{n-2}x \, dx$$

where $n \geq 2$ is an integer.
(b) Use part (a) to evaluate $\int_0^{\pi/2} \sin^3x \, dx$ and $\int_0^{\pi/2} \sin^5x \, dx$.
(c) Use part (a) to show that, for odd powers of sine,

$$\int_0^{\pi/2} \sin^{2n+1}x \, dx = \frac{2 \cdot 4 \cdot 6 \cdot \cdots \cdot 2n}{3 \cdot 5 \cdot 7 \cdot \cdots \cdot (2n+1)}$$

44. Prove that, for even powers of sine,

$$\int_0^{\pi/2} \sin^{2n}x \, dx = \frac{1 \cdot 3 \cdot 5 \cdot \cdots \cdot (2n-1)}{2 \cdot 4 \cdot 6 \cdot \cdots \cdot 2n}\frac{\pi}{2}$$

45–48 ▏▏▏ Use integration by parts to prove the reduction formula.

45. $\int (\ln x)^n \, dx = x(\ln x)^n - n\int (\ln x)^{n-1} \, dx$

46. $\int x^ne^x \, dx = x^ne^x - n\int x^{n-1}e^x \, dx$

47. $\int (x^2 + a^2)^n \, dx$

$$= \frac{x(x^2+a^2)^n}{2n+1} + \frac{2na^2}{2n+1}\int (x^2+a^2)^{n-1} \, dx \quad (n \neq -\tfrac{1}{2})$$

48. $\int \sec^nx \, dx = \frac{\tan x \sec^{n-2}x}{n-1} + \frac{n-2}{n-1}\int \sec^{n-2}x \, dx \quad (n \neq 1)$

49. Use Exercise 45 to find $\int (\ln x)^3 \, dx$.

50. Use Exercise 46 to find $\int x^4e^x \, dx$.

51–52 ▏▏▏ Find the area of the region bounded by the given curves.

51. $y = xe^{-0.4x}, \quad y = 0, \quad x = 5$

52. $y = 5 \ln x, \quad y = x \ln x$

53–54 ▏▏▏ Use a graph to find approximate x-coordinates of the points of intersection of the given curves. Then find (approximately) the area of the region bounded by the curves.

53. $y = x \sin x, \quad y = (x-2)^2$

54. $y = \arctan 3x, \quad y = x/2$

55–58 ▏▏▏ Use the method of cylindrical shells to find the volume generated by rotating the region bounded by the given curves about the specified axis.

55. $y = \cos(\pi x/2), \quad y = 0, \quad 0 \leq x \leq 1$; about the y-axis

56. $y = e^x, \quad y = e^{-x}, \quad x = 1$; about the y-axis

57. $y = e^{-x}, \quad y = 0, \quad x = -1, \quad x = 0$; about $x = 1$

58. $y = e^x, \quad x = 0, \quad y = \pi$; about the x-axis

59. Find the average value of $f(x) = x^2 \ln x$ on the interval $[1, 3]$.

60. A rocket accelerates by burning its onboard fuel, so its mass decreases with time. Suppose the initial mass of the rocket at liftoff (including its fuel) is m, the fuel is consumed at rate r, and the exhaust gases are ejected with constant velocity v_e (relative to the rocket). A model for the velocity of the rocket at time t is given by the equation

$$v(t) = -gt - v_e \ln\frac{m - rt}{m}$$

where g is the acceleration due to gravity and t is not too large. If $g = 9.8 \text{ m/s}^2$, $m = 30,000$ kg, $r = 160$ kg/s, and $v_e = 3000$ m/s, find the height of the rocket one minute after liftoff.

61. A particle that moves along a straight line has velocity $v(t) = t^2e^{-t}$ meters per second after t seconds. How far will it travel during the first t seconds?

62. If $f(0) = g(0) = 0$ and f'' and g'' are continuous, show that

$$\int_0^a f(x)g''(x) \, dx = f(a)g'(a) - f'(a)g(a) + \int_0^a f''(x)g(x) \, dx$$

63. Suppose that $f(1) = 2$, $f(4) = 7$, $f'(1) = 5$, $f'(4) = 3$, and f'' is continuous. Find the value of $\int_1^4 xf''(x) \, dx$.

64. (a) Use integration by parts to show that

$$\int f(x) \, dx = xf(x) - \int xf'(x) \, dx$$

(b) If f and g are inverse functions and f' is continuous, prove that

$$\int_a^b f(x) \, dx = bf(b) - af(a) - \int_{f(a)}^{f(b)} g(y) \, dy$$

[*Hint:* Use part (a) and make the substitution $y = f(x)$.]

(c) In the case where f and g are positive functions and $b > a > 0$, draw a diagram to give a geometric interpretation of part (b).

(d) Use part (b) to evaluate $\int_1^e \ln x \, dx$.

65. We arrived at Formula 6.3.2, $V = \int_a^b 2\pi x f(x) \, dx$, by using cylindrical shells, but now we can use integration by parts to prove it using the slicing method of Section 6.2, at least for the case where f is one-to-one and therefore has an inverse function g. Use the figure to show that

$$V = \pi b^2 d - \pi a^2 c - \int_c^d \pi [g(y)]^2 \, dy$$

Make the substitution $y = f(x)$ and then use integration by parts on the resulting integral to prove that $V = \int_a^b 2\pi x f(x) \, dx$.

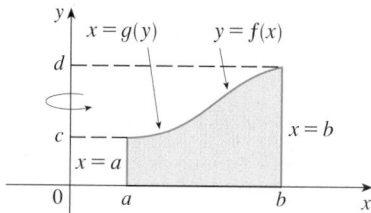

66. Let $I_n = \int_0^{\pi/2} \sin^n x \, dx$.

(a) Show that $I_{2n+2} \leqslant I_{2n+1} \leqslant I_{2n}$.

(b) Use Exercise 44 to show that

$$\frac{I_{2n+2}}{I_{2n}} = \frac{2n + 1}{2n + 2}$$

(c) Use parts (a) and (b) to show that

$$\frac{2n + 1}{2n + 2} \leqslant \frac{I_{2n+1}}{I_{2n}} \leqslant 1$$

and deduce that $\lim_{n \to \infty} I_{2n+1}/I_{2n} = 1$.

(d) Use part (c) and Exercises 43 and 44 to show that

$$\lim_{n \to \infty} \frac{2}{1} \cdot \frac{2}{3} \cdot \frac{4}{3} \cdot \frac{4}{5} \cdot \frac{6}{5} \cdot \frac{6}{7} \cdot \ldots \cdot \frac{2n}{2n - 1} \cdot \frac{2n}{2n + 1} = \frac{\pi}{2}$$

This formula is usually written as an infinite product:

$$\frac{\pi}{2} = \frac{2}{1} \cdot \frac{2}{3} \cdot \frac{4}{3} \cdot \frac{4}{5} \cdot \frac{6}{5} \cdot \frac{6}{7} \cdot \ldots$$

and is called the *Wallis product*.

(e) We construct rectangles as follows. Start with a square of area 1 and attach rectangles of area 1 alternately beside or on top of the previous rectangle (see the figure). Find the limit of the ratios of width to height of these rectangles.

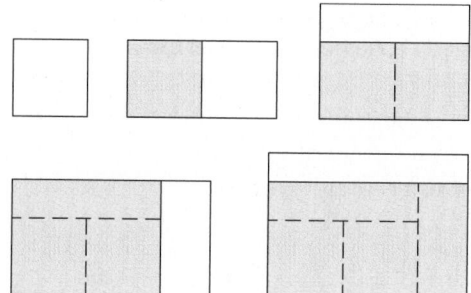

8.2 Trigonometric Integrals

In this section we use trigonometric identities to integrate certain combinations of trigonometric functions. We start with powers of sine and cosine.

EXAMPLE 1 Evaluate $\int \cos^3 x \, dx$.

SOLUTION Simply substituting $u = \cos x$ isn't helpful, since then $du = -\sin x \, dx$. In order to integrate powers of cosine, we would need an extra $\sin x$ factor. Similarly, a power of sine would require an extra $\cos x$ factor. Thus, here we can separate one cosine factor and convert the remaining $\cos^2 x$ factor to an expression involving sine using the identity $\sin^2 x + \cos^2 x = 1$:

$$\cos^3 x = \cos^2 x \cdot \cos x = (1 - \sin^2 x) \cos x$$

We can then evaluate the integral by substituting $u = \sin x$, so $du = \cos x \, dx$ and

$$\int \cos^3 x \, dx = \int \cos^2 x \cdot \cos x \, dx = \int (1 - \sin^2 x) \cos x \, dx$$

$$= \int (1 - u^2) \, du = u - \tfrac{1}{3} u^3 + C$$

$$= \sin x - \tfrac{1}{3} \sin^3 x + C$$

In general, we try to write an integrand involving powers of sine and cosine in a form where we have only one sine factor (and the remainder of the expression in terms of cosine) or only one cosine factor (and the remainder of the expression in terms of sine). The identity $\sin^2 x + \cos^2 x = 1$ enables us to convert back and forth between even powers of sine and cosine.

EXAMPLE 2 Find $\int \sin^5 x \cos^2 x \, dx$

SOLUTION We could convert $\cos^2 x$ to $1 - \sin^2 x$, but we would be left with an expression in terms of $\sin x$ with no extra $\cos x$ factor. Instead, we separate a single sine factor and rewrite the remaining $\sin^4 x$ factor in terms of $\cos x$:

$$\sin^5 x \cos^2 x = (\sin^2 x)^2 \cos^2 x \sin x = (1 - \cos^2 x)^2 \cos^2 x \sin x$$

Substituting $u = \cos x$, we have $du = -\sin x \, dx$ and so

$$\int \sin^5 x \cos^2 x \, dx = \int (\sin^2 x)^2 \cos^2 x \sin x \, dx$$

$$= \int (1 - \cos^2 x)^2 \cos^2 x \sin x \, dx$$

$$= \int (1 - u^2)^2 u^2 (-du) = -\int (u^2 - 2u^4 + u^6) \, du$$

$$= -\left(\frac{u^3}{3} - 2\frac{u^5}{5} + \frac{u^7}{7} \right) + C$$

$$= -\tfrac{1}{3} \cos^3 x + \tfrac{2}{5} \cos^5 x - \tfrac{1}{7} \cos^7 x + C$$

|||| Figure 1 shows the graphs of the integrand $\sin^5 x \cos^2 x$ in Example 2 and its indefinite integral (with $C = 0$). Which is which?

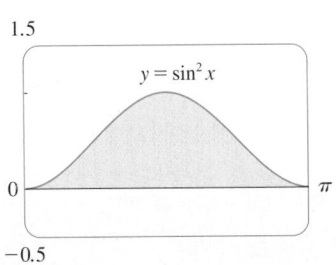

FIGURE 1

In the preceding examples, an odd power of sine or cosine enabled us to separate a single factor and convert the remaining even power. If the integrand contains even powers of both sine and cosine, this strategy fails. In this case, we can take advantage of the following half-angle identities (see Equations 17b and 17a in Appendix D):

$$\sin^2 x = \tfrac{1}{2}(1 - \cos 2x) \qquad \text{and} \qquad \cos^2 x = \tfrac{1}{2}(1 + \cos 2x)$$

|||| Example 3 shows that the area of the region shown in Figure 2 is $\pi/2$.

EXAMPLE 3 Evaluate $\int_0^\pi \sin^2 x \, dx$.

SOLUTION If we write $\sin^2 x = 1 - \cos^2 x$, the integral is no simpler to evaluate. Using the half-angle formula for $\sin^2 x$, however, we have

$$\int_0^\pi \sin^2 x \, dx = \tfrac{1}{2} \int_0^\pi (1 - \cos 2x) \, dx = \left[\tfrac{1}{2}\left(x - \tfrac{1}{2}\sin 2x\right) \right]_0^\pi$$

$$= \tfrac{1}{2}\left(\pi - \tfrac{1}{2}\sin 2\pi\right) - \tfrac{1}{2}\left(0 - \tfrac{1}{2}\sin 0\right) = \tfrac{1}{2}\pi$$

Notice that we mentally made the substitution $u = 2x$ when integrating $\cos 2x$. Another method for evaluating this integral was given in Exercise 41 in Section 8.1.

1.5

$y = \sin^2 x$

0

π

−0.5

FIGURE 2

EXAMPLE 4 Find $\int \sin^4 x \, dx$.

SOLUTION We could evaluate this integral using the reduction formula for $\int \sin^n x \, dx$ (Equation 8.1.7) together with Example 3 (as in Exercise 41 in Section 8.1), but a better method is to write $\sin^4 x = (\sin^2 x)^2$ and use a half-angle formula:

$$\int \sin^4 x \, dx = \int (\sin^2 x)^2 \, dx$$

$$= \int \left(\frac{1 - \cos 2x}{2} \right)^2 dx$$

$$= \tfrac{1}{4} \int (1 - 2 \cos 2x + \cos^2 2x) \, dx$$

Since $\cos^2 2x$ occurs, we must use another half-angle formula

$$\cos^2 2x = \tfrac{1}{2}(1 + \cos 4x)$$

This gives

$$\int \sin^4 x \, dx = \tfrac{1}{4} \int [1 - 2 \cos 2x + \tfrac{1}{2}(1 + \cos 4x)] \, dx$$

$$= \tfrac{1}{4} \int \left(\tfrac{3}{2} - 2 \cos 2x + \tfrac{1}{2} \cos 4x \right) dx$$

$$= \tfrac{1}{4}\left(\tfrac{3}{2}x - \sin 2x + \tfrac{1}{8} \sin 4x \right) + C$$

To summarize, we list guidelines to follow when evaluating integrals of the form $\int \sin^m x \cos^n x \, dx$, where $m \geqslant 0$ and $n \geqslant 0$ are integers.

Strategy for Evaluating $\int \sin^m x \cos^n x \, dx$

(a) If the power of cosine is odd ($n = 2k + 1$), save one cosine factor and use $\cos^2 x = 1 - \sin^2 x$ to express the remaining factors in terms of sine:

$$\int \sin^m x \cos^{2k+1} x \, dx = \int \sin^m x \, (\cos^2 x)^k \cos x \, dx$$

$$= \int \sin^m x \, (1 - \sin^2 x)^k \cos x \, dx$$

Then substitute $u = \sin x$.

(b) If the power of sine is odd ($m = 2k + 1$), save one sine factor and use $\sin^2 x = 1 - \cos^2 x$ to express the remaining factors in terms of cosine:

$$\int \sin^{2k+1} x \cos^n x \, dx = \int (\sin^2 x)^k \cos^n x \sin x \, dx$$

$$= \int (1 - \cos^2 x)^k \cos^n x \sin x \, dx$$

Then substitute $u = \cos x$. [Note that if the powers of both sine and cosine are odd, either (a) or (b) can be used.]

(c) If the powers of both sine and cosine are even, use the half-angle identities

$$\sin^2 x = \tfrac{1}{2}(1 - \cos 2x) \qquad \cos^2 x = \tfrac{1}{2}(1 + \cos 2x)$$

It is sometimes helpful to use the identity

$$\sin x \cos x = \tfrac{1}{2} \sin 2x$$

We can use a similar strategy to evaluate integrals of the form $\int \tan^m x \sec^n x \, dx$. Since $(d/dx) \tan x = \sec^2 x$, we can separate a $\sec^2 x$ factor and convert the remaining (even) power of secant to an expression involving tangent using the identity $\sec^2 x = 1 + \tan^2 x$. Or, since $(d/dx) \sec x = \sec x \tan x$, we can separate a $\sec x \tan x$ factor and convert the remaining (even) power of tangent to secant.

EXAMPLE 5 Evaluate $\int \tan^6 x \sec^4 x \, dx$.

SOLUTION If we separate one $\sec^2 x$ factor, we can express the remaining $\sec^2 x$ factor in terms of tangent using the identity $\sec^2 x = 1 + \tan^2 x$. We can then evaluate the integral by substituting $u = \tan x$ with $du = \sec^2 x \, dx$:

$$\int \tan^6 x \sec^4 x \, dx = \int \tan^6 x \sec^2 x \sec^2 x \, dx$$

$$= \int \tan^6 x \, (1 + \tan^2 x) \sec^2 x \, dx$$

$$= \int u^6 (1 + u^2) \, du = \int (u^6 + u^8) \, du$$

$$= \frac{u^7}{7} + \frac{u^9}{9} + C$$

$$= \tfrac{1}{7} \tan^7 x + \tfrac{1}{9} \tan^9 x + C$$

EXAMPLE 6 Find $\int \tan^5 \theta \sec^7 \theta \, d\theta$.

SOLUTION If we separate a $\sec^2 \theta$ factor, as in the preceding example, we are left with a $\sec^5 \theta$ factor, which isn't easily converted to tangent. However, if we separate a $\sec \theta \tan \theta$ factor, we can convert the remaining power of tangent to an expression involving only secant using the identity $\tan^2 \theta = \sec^2 \theta - 1$. We can then evaluate the integral by substituting $u = \sec \theta$, so $du = \sec \theta \tan \theta \, d\theta$:

$$\int \tan^5 \theta \sec^7 \theta \, d\theta = \int \tan^4 \theta \sec^6 \theta \sec \theta \tan \theta \, d\theta$$

$$= \int (\sec^2 \theta - 1)^2 \sec^6 \theta \sec \theta \tan \theta \, d\theta$$

$$= \int (u^2 - 1)^2 u^6 \, du = \int (u^{10} - 2u^8 + u^6) \, du$$

$$= \frac{u^{11}}{11} - 2 \frac{u^9}{9} + \frac{u^7}{7} + C$$

$$= \tfrac{1}{11} \sec^{11} \theta - \tfrac{2}{9} \sec^9 \theta + \tfrac{1}{7} \sec^7 \theta + C$$

The preceding examples demonstrate strategies for evaluating integrals of the form $\int \tan^m x \sec^n x \, dx$ for two cases, which we summarize here.

Strategy for Evaluating $\int \tan^m x \sec^n x\, dx$

(a) If the power of secant is even ($n = 2k$, $k \geqslant 2$), save a factor of $\sec^2 x$ and use $\sec^2 x = 1 + \tan^2 x$ to express the remaining factors in terms of $\tan x$:

$$\int \tan^m x \sec^{2k} x\, dx = \int \tan^m x\, (\sec^2 x)^{k-1} \sec^2 x\, dx$$

$$= \int \tan^m x\, (1 + \tan^2 x)^{k-1} \sec^2 x\, dx$$

Then substitute $u = \tan x$.

(b) If the power of tangent is odd ($m = 2k + 1$), save a factor of $\sec x \tan x$ and use $\tan^2 x = \sec^2 x - 1$ to express the remaining factors in terms of $\sec x$:

$$\int \tan^{2k+1} x \sec^n x\, dx = \int (\tan^2 x)^k \sec^{n-1} x\, \sec x \tan x\, dx$$

$$= \int (\sec^2 x - 1)^k \sec^{n-1} x\, \sec x \tan x\, dx$$

Then substitute $u = \sec x$.

For other cases, the guidelines are not as clear-cut. We may need to use identities, integration by parts, and occasionally a little ingenuity. We will sometimes need to be able to integrate $\tan x$ by using the formula established in (5.5.5):

$$\int \tan x\, dx = \ln |\sec x| + C$$

We will also need the indefinite integral of secant:

$\boxed{1}$
$$\int \sec x\, dx = \ln |\sec x + \tan x| + C$$

We could verify Formula 1 by differentiating the right side, or as follows. First we multiply numerator and denominator by $\sec x + \tan x$:

$$\int \sec x\, dx = \int \sec x \frac{\sec x + \tan x}{\sec x + \tan x}\, dx$$

$$= \int \frac{\sec^2 x + \sec x \tan x}{\sec x + \tan x}\, dx$$

If we substitute $u = \sec x + \tan x$, then $du = (\sec x \tan x + \sec^2 x)\, dx$, so the integral becomes $\int (1/u)\, du = \ln |u| + C$. Thus, we have

$$\int \sec x\, dx = \ln |\sec x + \tan x| + C$$

EXAMPLE 7 Find $\int \tan^3 x \, dx$.

SOLUTION Here only $\tan x$ occurs, so we use $\tan^2 x = \sec^2 x - 1$ to rewrite a $\tan^2 x$ factor in terms of $\sec^2 x$:

$$\int \tan^3 x \, dx = \int \tan x \tan^2 x \, dx$$

$$= \int \tan x \, (\sec^2 x - 1) \, dx$$

$$= \int \tan x \sec^2 x \, dx - \int \tan x \, dx$$

$$= \frac{\tan^2 x}{2} - \ln|\sec x| + C$$

In the first integral we mentally substituted $u = \tan x$ so that $du = \sec^2 x \, dx$.   ▬

If an even power of tangent appears with an odd power of secant, it is helpful to express the integrand completely in terms of $\sec x$. Powers of $\sec x$ may require integration by parts, as shown in the following example.

EXAMPLE 8 Find $\int \sec^3 x \, dx$.

SOLUTION Here we integrate by parts with

$$u = \sec x \qquad\qquad dv = \sec^2 x \, dx$$

$$du = \sec x \tan x \, dx \qquad\qquad v = \tan x$$

Then

$$\int \sec^3 x \, dx = \sec x \tan x - \int \sec x \tan^2 x \, dx$$

$$= \sec x \tan x - \int \sec x \, (\sec^2 x - 1) \, dx$$

$$= \sec x \tan x - \int \sec^3 x \, dx + \int \sec x \, dx$$

Using Formula 1 and solving for the required integral, we get

$$\int \sec^3 x \, dx = \tfrac{1}{2}\big(\sec x \tan x + \ln|\sec x + \tan x|\big) + C$$ ▬

Integrals such as the one in the preceding example may seem very special but they occur frequently in applications of integration, as we will see in Chapter 9. Integrals of the form $\int \cot^m x \csc^n x \, dx$ can be found by similar methods because of the identity $1 + \cot^2 x = \csc^2 x$.

Finally, we can make use of another set of trigonometric identities:

ⅢⅠ These product identities are discussed in Appendix D.

> **2** To evaluate the integrals (a) $\int \sin mx \cos nx \, dx$, (b) $\int \sin mx \sin nx \, dx$, or (c) $\int \cos mx \cos nx \, dx$, use the corresponding identity:
>
> (a) $\sin A \cos B = \tfrac{1}{2}[\sin(A - B) + \sin(A + B)]$
>
> (b) $\sin A \sin B = \tfrac{1}{2}[\cos(A - B) - \cos(A + B)]$
>
> (c) $\cos A \cos B = \tfrac{1}{2}[\cos(A - B) + \cos(A + B)]$

EXAMPLE 9 Evaluate $\int \sin 4x \cos 5x \, dx$.

SOLUTION This integral could be evaluated using integration by parts, but it's easier to use the identity in Equation 2(a) as follows:

$$\int \sin 4x \cos 5x \, dx = \int \tfrac{1}{2}[\sin(-x) + \sin 9x] \, dx$$

$$= \tfrac{1}{2} \int (-\sin x + \sin 9x) \, dx$$

$$= \tfrac{1}{2}(\cos x - \tfrac{1}{9}\cos 9x) + C$$

‖‖‖ 8.2 Exercises

1–47 ‖‖‖ Evaluate the integral.

1. $\int \sin^3 x \cos^2 x \, dx$

2. $\int \sin^6 x \cos^3 x \, dx$

3. $\int_{\pi/2}^{3\pi/4} \sin^5 x \cos^3 x \, dx$

4. $\int_0^{\pi/2} \cos^5 x \, dx$

5. $\int \cos^5 x \sin^4 x \, dx$

6. $\int \sin^3(mx) \, dx$

7. $\int_0^{\pi/2} \cos^2 \theta \, d\theta$

8. $\int_0^{\pi/2} \sin^2(2\theta) \, d\theta$

9. $\int_0^{\pi} \sin^4(3t) \, dt$

10. $\int_0^{\pi} \cos^6 \theta \, d\theta$

11. $\int (1 + \cos \theta)^2 \, d\theta$

12. $\int x \cos^2 x \, dx$

13. $\int_0^{\pi/4} \sin^4 x \cos^2 x \, dx$

14. $\int_0^{\pi/2} \sin^2 x \cos^2 x \, dx$

15. $\int \sin^3 x \sqrt{\cos x} \, dx$

16. $\int \cos \theta \cos^5(\sin \theta) \, d\theta$

17. $\int \cos^2 x \tan^3 x \, dx$

18. $\int \cot^5 \theta \sin^4 \theta \, d\theta$

19. $\int \dfrac{1 - \sin x}{\cos x} \, dx$

20. $\int \cos^2 x \sin 2x \, dx$

21. $\int \sec^2 x \tan x \, dx$

22. $\int_0^{\pi/2} \sec^4(t/2) \, dt$

23. $\int \tan^2 x \, dx$

24. $\int \tan^4 x \, dx$

25. $\int \sec^6 t \, dt$

26. $\int_0^{\pi/4} \sec^4 \theta \tan^4 \theta \, d\theta$

27. $\int_0^{\pi/3} \tan^5 x \sec^4 x \, dx$

28. $\int \tan^3(2x) \sec^5(2x) \, dx$

29. $\int \tan^3 x \sec x \, dx$

30. $\int_0^{\pi/3} \tan^5 x \sec^6 x \, dx$

31. $\int \tan^5 x \, dx$

32. $\int \tan^6(ay) \, dy$

33. $\int \dfrac{\tan^3 \theta}{\cos^4 \theta} \, d\theta$

34. $\int \tan^2 x \sec x \, dx$

35. $\int_{\pi/6}^{\pi/2} \cot^2 x \, dx$

36. $\int_{\pi/4}^{\pi/2} \cot^3 x \, dx$

37. $\int \cot^3 \alpha \csc^3 \alpha \, d\alpha$

38. $\int \csc^4 x \cot^6 x \, dx$

39. $\int \csc x \, dx$

40. $\int_{\pi/6}^{\pi/3} \csc^3 x \, dx$

41. $\int \sin 5x \sin 2x \, dx$

42. $\int \sin 3x \cos x \, dx$

43. $\int \cos 7\theta \cos 5\theta \, d\theta$

44. $\int \dfrac{\cos x + \sin x}{\sin 2x} \, dx$

45. $\int \dfrac{1 - \tan^2 x}{\sec^2 x} \, dx$

46. $\int \dfrac{dx}{\cos x - 1}$

47. $\int t \sec^2(t^2) \tan^4(t^2) \, dt$

48. If $\int_0^{\pi/4} \tan^6 x \sec x \, dx = I$, express the value of $\int_0^{\pi/4} \tan^8 x \sec x \, dx$ in terms of I.

49–52 ‖‖‖ Evaluate the indefinite integral. Illustrate, and check that your answer is reasonable, by graphing both the integrand and its antiderivative (taking $C = 0$).

49. $\int \sin^5 x \, dx$

50. $\int \sin^4 x \cos^4 x \, dx$

51. $\int \sin 3x \sin 6x \, dx$

52. $\int \sec^4 \dfrac{x}{2} \, dx$

53. Find the average value of the function $f(x) = \sin^2 x \cos^3 x$ on the interval $[-\pi, \pi]$.

54. Evaluate $\int \sin x \cos x \, dx$ by four methods: (a) the substitution $u = \cos x$, (b) the substitution $u = \sin x$, (c) the identity $\sin 2x = 2 \sin x \cos x$, and (d) integration by parts. Explain the different appearances of the answers.

55–56 ||| Find the area of the region bounded by the given curves.

55. $y = \sin x$, $y = \sin^3 x$, $x = 0$, $x = \pi/2$

56. $y = \sin x$, $y = 2 \sin^2 x$, $x = 0$, $x = \pi/2$

57–58 ||| Use a graph of the integrand to guess the value of the integral. Then use the methods of this section to prove that your guess is correct.

57. $\int_0^{2\pi} \cos^3 x \, dx$

58. $\int_0^2 \sin 2\pi x \cos 5\pi x \, dx$

59–62 ||| Find the volume obtained by rotating the region bounded by the given curves about the specified axis.

59. $y = \sin x$, $x = \pi/2$, $x = \pi$, $y = 0$; about the x-axis

60. $y = \tan^2 x$, $y = 0$, $x = 0$, $x = \pi/4$; about the x-axis

61. $y = \cos x$, $y = 0$, $x = 0$, $x = \pi/2$; about $y = -1$

62. $y = \cos x$, $y = 0$, $x = 0$, $x = \pi/2$; about $y = 1$

63. A particle moves on a straight line with velocity function $v(t) = \sin \omega t \cos^2 \omega t$. Find its position function $s = f(t)$ if $f(0) = 0$.

64. Household electricity is supplied in the form of alternating current that varies from 155 V to -155 V with a frequency of 60 cycles per second (Hz). The voltage is thus given by the equation

$$E(t) = 155 \sin(120\pi t)$$

where t is the time in seconds. Voltmeters read the RMS (root-mean-square) voltage, which is the square root of the average value of $[E(t)]^2$ over one cycle.
(a) Calculate the RMS voltage of household current.
(b) Many electric stoves require an RMS voltage of 220 V. Find the corresponding amplitude A needed for the voltage $E(t) = A \sin(120\pi t)$.

65–67 ||| Prove the formula, where m and n are positive integers.

65. $\int_{-\pi}^{\pi} \sin mx \cos nx \, dx = 0$

66. $\int_{-\pi}^{\pi} \sin mx \sin nx \, dx = \begin{cases} 0 & \text{if } m \neq n \\ \pi & \text{if } m = n \end{cases}$

67. $\int_{-\pi}^{\pi} \cos mx \cos nx \, dx = \begin{cases} 0 & \text{if } m \neq n \\ \pi & \text{if } m = n \end{cases}$

68. A *finite Fourier series* is given by the sum

$$f(x) = \sum_{n=1}^{N} a_n \sin nx$$
$$= a_1 \sin x + a_2 \sin 2x + \cdots + a_N \sin Nx$$

Show that the mth coefficient a_m is given by the formula

$$a_m = \frac{1}{\pi} \int_{-\pi}^{\pi} f(x) \sin mx \, dx$$

8.3 Trigonometric Substitution

In finding the area of a circle or an ellipse, an integral of the form $\int \sqrt{a^2 - x^2} \, dx$ arises, where $a > 0$. If it were $\int x\sqrt{a^2 - x^2} \, dx$, the substitution $u = a^2 - x^2$ would be effective but, as it stands, $\int \sqrt{a^2 - x^2} \, dx$ is more difficult. If we change the variable from x to θ by the substitution $x = a \sin \theta$, then the identity $1 - \sin^2\theta = \cos^2\theta$ allows us to get rid of the root sign because

$$\sqrt{a^2 - x^2} = \sqrt{a^2 - a^2 \sin^2\theta} = \sqrt{a^2(1 - \sin^2\theta)} = \sqrt{a^2 \cos^2\theta} = a|\cos \theta|$$

Notice the difference between the substitution $u = a^2 - x^2$ (in which the new variable is a function of the old one) and the substitution $x = a \sin \theta$ (the old variable is a function of the new one).

In general we can make a substitution of the form $x = g(t)$ by using the Substitution Rule in reverse. To make our calculations simpler, we assume that g has an inverse function; that is, g is one-to-one. In this case, if we replace u by x and x by t in the Substitution Rule (Equation 5.5.4), we obtain

$$\int f(x) \, dx = \int f(g(t))g'(t) \, dt$$

This kind of substitution is called *inverse substitution*.

We can make the inverse substitution $x = a \sin \theta$ provided that it defines a one-to-one function. This can be accomplished by restricting θ to lie in the interval $[-\pi/2, \pi/2]$.

In the following table we list trigonometric substitutions that are effective for the given radical expressions because of the specified trigonometric identities. In each case the restriction on θ is imposed to ensure that the function that defines the substitution is one-to-one. (These are the same intervals used in Appendix D in defining the inverse functions.)

Table of Trigonometric Substitutions

Expression	Substitution	Identity
$\sqrt{a^2 - x^2}$	$x = a \sin \theta, \quad -\dfrac{\pi}{2} \leqslant \theta \leqslant \dfrac{\pi}{2}$	$1 - \sin^2\theta = \cos^2\theta$
$\sqrt{a^2 + x^2}$	$x = a \tan \theta, \quad -\dfrac{\pi}{2} < \theta < \dfrac{\pi}{2}$	$1 + \tan^2\theta = \sec^2\theta$
$\sqrt{x^2 - a^2}$	$x = a \sec \theta, \quad 0 \leqslant \theta < \dfrac{\pi}{2}$ or $\pi \leqslant \theta < \dfrac{3\pi}{2}$	$\sec^2\theta - 1 = \tan^2\theta$

EXAMPLE 1 Evaluate $\displaystyle\int \frac{\sqrt{9 - x^2}}{x^2} \, dx$.

SOLUTION Let $x = 3 \sin \theta$, where $-\pi/2 \leqslant \theta \leqslant \pi/2$. Then $dx = 3 \cos \theta \, d\theta$ and

$$\sqrt{9 - x^2} = \sqrt{9 - 9 \sin^2\theta} = \sqrt{9 \cos^2\theta} = 3\,|\cos \theta| = 3 \cos \theta$$

(Note that $\cos \theta \geqslant 0$ because $-\pi/2 \leqslant \theta \leqslant \pi/2$.) Thus, the Inverse Substitution Rule gives

$$\int \frac{\sqrt{9 - x^2}}{x^2} \, dx = \int \frac{3 \cos \theta}{9 \sin^2\theta} \, 3 \cos \theta \, d\theta$$

$$= \int \frac{\cos^2\theta}{\sin^2\theta} \, d\theta = \int \cot^2\theta \, d\theta$$

$$= \int (\csc^2\theta - 1) \, d\theta$$

$$= -\cot \theta - \theta + C$$

FIGURE 1

$\sin \theta = \dfrac{x}{3}$

Since this is an indefinite integral, we must return to the original variable x. This can be done either by using trigonometric identities to express $\cot \theta$ in terms of $\sin \theta = x/3$ or by drawing a diagram, as in Figure 1, where θ is interpreted as an angle of a right triangle. Since $\sin \theta = x/3$, we label the opposite side and the hypotenuse as having lengths x and 3. Then the Pythagorean Theorem gives the length of the adjacent side as $\sqrt{9 - x^2}$, so we can simply read the value of $\cot \theta$ from the figure:

$$\cot \theta = \frac{\sqrt{9 - x^2}}{x}$$

(Although $\theta > 0$ in the diagram, this expression for $\cot \theta$ is valid even when $\theta < 0$.) Since $\sin \theta = x/3$, we have $\theta = \sin^{-1}(x/3)$ and so

$$\int \frac{\sqrt{9 - x^2}}{x^2} \, dx = -\frac{\sqrt{9 - x^2}}{x} - \sin^{-1}\left(\frac{x}{3}\right) + C$$

EXAMPLE 2 Find the area enclosed by the ellipse

$$\frac{x^2}{a^2} + \frac{y^2}{b^2} = 1$$

SOLUTION Solving the equation of the ellipse for y, we get

$$\frac{y^2}{b^2} = 1 - \frac{x^2}{a^2} = \frac{a^2 - x^2}{a^2} \qquad \text{or} \qquad y = \pm\frac{b}{a}\sqrt{a^2 - x^2}$$

Because the ellipse is symmetric with respect to both axes, the total area A is four times the area in the first quadrant (see Figure 2). The part of the ellipse in the first quadrant is given by the function

$$y = \frac{b}{a}\sqrt{a^2 - x^2} \qquad 0 \le x \le a$$

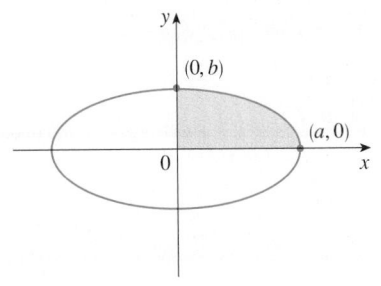

FIGURE 2

$$\frac{x^2}{a^2} + \frac{y^2}{b^2} = 1$$

and so

$$\tfrac{1}{4}A = \int_0^a \frac{b}{a}\sqrt{a^2 - x^2}\, dx$$

To evaluate this integral we substitute $x = a \sin\theta$. Then $dx = a \cos\theta\, d\theta$. To change the limits of integration we note that when $x = 0$, $\sin\theta = 0$, so $\theta = 0$; when $x = a$, $\sin\theta = 1$, so $\theta = \pi/2$. Also

$$\sqrt{a^2 - x^2} = \sqrt{a^2 - a^2\sin^2\theta} = \sqrt{a^2\cos^2\theta} = a|\cos\theta| = a\cos\theta$$

since $0 \le \theta \le \pi/2$. Therefore

$$A = 4\frac{b}{a}\int_0^a \sqrt{a^2 - x^2}\, dx = 4\frac{b}{a}\int_0^{\pi/2} a\cos\theta \cdot a\cos\theta\, d\theta$$

$$= 4ab \int_0^{\pi/2} \cos^2\theta\, d\theta = 4ab \int_0^{\pi/2} \tfrac{1}{2}(1 + \cos 2\theta)\, d\theta$$

$$= 2ab\left[\theta + \tfrac{1}{2}\sin 2\theta\right]_0^{\pi/2} = 2ab\left(\frac{\pi}{2} + 0 - 0\right)$$

$$= \pi ab$$

We have shown that the area of an ellipse with semiaxes a and b is πab. In particular, taking $a = b = r$, we have proved the famous formula that the area of a circle with radius r is πr^2.

NOTE ∘ Since the integral in Example 2 was a definite integral, we changed the limits of integration and did not have to convert back to the original variable x.

EXAMPLE 3 Find $\displaystyle\int \frac{1}{x^2\sqrt{x^2 + 4}}\, dx$.

SOLUTION Let $x = 2\tan\theta$, $-\pi/2 < \theta < \pi/2$. Then $dx = 2\sec^2\theta\, d\theta$ and

$$\sqrt{x^2 + 4} = \sqrt{4(\tan^2\theta + 1)} = \sqrt{4\sec^2\theta} = 2|\sec\theta| = 2\sec\theta$$

Thus, we have

$$\int \frac{dx}{x^2\sqrt{x^2 + 4}} = \int \frac{2\sec^2\theta\, d\theta}{4\tan^2\theta \cdot 2\sec\theta} = \frac{1}{4}\int \frac{\sec\theta}{\tan^2\theta}\, d\theta$$

To evaluate this trigonometric integral we put everything in terms of $\sin\theta$ and $\cos\theta$:

$$\frac{\sec\theta}{\tan^2\theta} = \frac{1}{\cos\theta} \cdot \frac{\cos^2\theta}{\sin^2\theta} = \frac{\cos\theta}{\sin^2\theta}$$

Therefore, making the substitution $u = \sin\theta$, we have

$$\int \frac{dx}{x^2\sqrt{x^2+4}} = \frac{1}{4}\int \frac{\cos\theta}{\sin^2\theta}\,d\theta = \frac{1}{4}\int \frac{du}{u^2}$$

$$= \frac{1}{4}\left(-\frac{1}{u}\right) + C = -\frac{1}{4\sin\theta} + C$$

$$= -\frac{\csc\theta}{4} + C$$

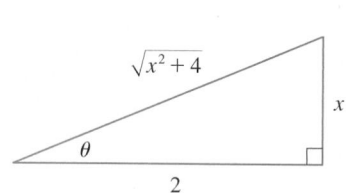

FIGURE 3

$\tan\theta = \dfrac{x}{2}$

We use Figure 3 to determine that $\csc\theta = \sqrt{x^2+4}/x$ and so

$$\int \frac{dx}{x^2\sqrt{x^2+4}} = -\frac{\sqrt{x^2+4}}{4x} + C$$

EXAMPLE 4 Find $\displaystyle\int \frac{x}{\sqrt{x^2+4}}\,dx$.

SOLUTION It would be possible to use the trigonometric substitution $x = 2\tan\theta$ here (as in Example 3). But the direct substitution $u = x^2 + 4$ is simpler, because then $du = 2x\,dx$ and

$$\int \frac{x}{\sqrt{x^2+4}}\,dx = \frac{1}{2}\int \frac{du}{\sqrt{u}} = \sqrt{u} + C = \sqrt{x^2+4} + C$$

NOTE ∘ Example 4 illustrates the fact that even when trigonometric substitutions are possible, they may not give the easiest solution. You should look for a simpler method first.

EXAMPLE 5 Evaluate $\displaystyle\int \frac{dx}{\sqrt{x^2-a^2}}$, where $a > 0$.

SOLUTION 1 We let $x = a\sec\theta$, where $0 < \theta < \pi/2$ or $\pi < \theta < 3\pi/2$. Then $dx = a\sec\theta\tan\theta\,d\theta$ and

$$\sqrt{x^2-a^2} = \sqrt{a^2(\sec^2\theta-1)} = \sqrt{a^2\tan^2\theta} = a|\tan\theta| = a\tan\theta$$

Therefore

$$\int \frac{dx}{\sqrt{x^2-a^2}} = \int \frac{a\sec\theta\tan\theta}{a\tan\theta}\,d\theta$$

$$= \int \sec\theta\,d\theta = \ln|\sec\theta + \tan\theta| + C$$

The triangle in Figure 4 gives $\tan\theta = \sqrt{x^2-a^2}/a$, so we have

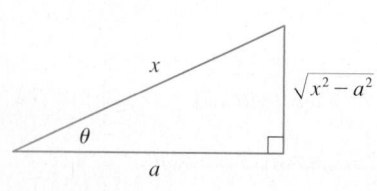

FIGURE 4

$\sec\theta = \dfrac{x}{a}$

$$\int \frac{dx}{\sqrt{x^2-a^2}} = \ln\left|\frac{x}{a} + \frac{\sqrt{x^2-a^2}}{a}\right| + C$$

$$= \ln\left|x + \sqrt{x^2-a^2}\right| - \ln a + C$$

Writing $C_1 = C - \ln a$, we have

$\boxed{1}$
$$\int \frac{dx}{\sqrt{x^2 - a^2}} = \ln\left|x + \sqrt{x^2 - a^2}\right| + C_1$$

SOLUTION 2 For $x > 0$ the hyperbolic substitution $x = a \cosh t$ can also be used. Using the identity $\cosh^2 y - \sinh^2 y = 1$, we have

$$\sqrt{x^2 - a^2} = \sqrt{a^2(\cosh^2 t - 1)} = \sqrt{a^2 \sinh^2 t} = a \sinh t$$

Since $dx = a \sinh t\, dt$, we obtain

$$\int \frac{dx}{\sqrt{x^2 - a^2}} = \int \frac{a \sinh t\, dt}{a \sinh t} = \int dt = t + C$$

Since $\cosh t = x/a$, we have $t = \cosh^{-1}(x/a)$ and

$\boxed{2}$
$$\int \frac{dx}{\sqrt{x^2 - a^2}} = \cosh^{-1}\left(\frac{x}{a}\right) + C$$

Although Formulas 1 and 2 look quite different, they are actually equivalent by Formula 7.6.4.

NOTE ▫ As Example 5 illustrates, hyperbolic substitutions can be used in place of trigonometric substitutions and sometimes they lead to simpler answers. But we usually use trigonometric substitutions because trigonometric identities are more familiar than hyperbolic identities.

EXAMPLE 6 Find $\displaystyle\int_0^{3\sqrt{3}/2} \frac{x^3}{(4x^2 + 9)^{3/2}}\, dx$.

SOLUTION First we note that $(4x^2 + 9)^{3/2} = (\sqrt{4x^2 + 9})^3$ so trigonometric substitution is appropriate. Although $\sqrt{4x^2 + 9}$ is not quite one of the expressions in the table of trigonometric substitutions, it becomes one of them if we make the preliminary substitution $u = 2x$. When we combine this with the tangent substitution, we have $x = \frac{3}{2}\tan\theta$, which gives $dx = \frac{3}{2}\sec^2\theta\, d\theta$ and

$$\sqrt{4x^2 + 9} = \sqrt{9\tan^2\theta + 9} = 3\sec\theta$$

When $x = 0$, $\tan\theta = 0$, so $\theta = 0$; when $x = 3\sqrt{3}/2$, $\tan\theta = \sqrt{3}$, so $\theta = \pi/3$.

$$\int_0^{3\sqrt{3}/2} \frac{x^3}{(4x^2 + 9)^{3/2}}\, dx = \int_0^{\pi/3} \frac{\frac{27}{8}\tan^3\theta}{27\sec^3\theta}\,\frac{3}{2}\sec^2\theta\, d\theta$$

$$= \frac{3}{16}\int_0^{\pi/3} \frac{\tan^3\theta}{\sec\theta}\, d\theta = \frac{3}{16}\int_0^{\pi/3} \frac{\sin^3\theta}{\cos^2\theta}\, d\theta$$

$$= \frac{3}{16}\int_0^{\pi/3} \frac{1 - \cos^2\theta}{\cos^2\theta}\sin\theta\, d\theta$$

Now we substitute $u = \cos\theta$ so that $du = -\sin\theta\, d\theta$. When $\theta = 0$, $u = 1$; when $\theta = \pi/3$, $u = \frac{1}{2}$.

Therefore

$$\int_0^{3\sqrt{3}/2} \frac{x^3}{(4x^2+9)^{3/2}}\,dx = -\tfrac{3}{16}\int_1^{1/2}\frac{1-u^2}{u^2}\,du = \tfrac{3}{16}\int_1^{1/2}(1-u^{-2})\,du$$

$$= \tfrac{3}{16}\left[u+\frac{1}{u}\right]_1^{1/2} = \tfrac{3}{16}\left[\left(\tfrac{1}{2}+2\right)-(1+1)\right] = \tfrac{3}{32}$$

EXAMPLE 7 Evaluate $\displaystyle\int \frac{x}{\sqrt{3-2x-x^2}}\,dx$.

SOLUTION We can transform the integrand into a function for which trigonometric substitution is appropriate by first completing the square under the root sign:

$$3-2x-x^2 = 3-(x^2+2x) = 3+1-(x^2+2x+1)$$

$$= 4-(x+1)^2$$

This suggests that we make the substitution $u = x+1$. Then $du = dx$ and $x = u-1$, so

$$\int \frac{x}{\sqrt{3-2x-x^2}}\,dx = \int \frac{u-1}{\sqrt{4-u^2}}\,du$$

We now substitute $u = 2\sin\theta$, giving $du = 2\cos\theta\,d\theta$ and $\sqrt{4-u^2} = 2\cos\theta$, so

$$\int \frac{x}{\sqrt{3-2x-x^2}}\,dx = \int \frac{2\sin\theta-1}{2\cos\theta}\,2\cos\theta\,d\theta$$

$$= \int (2\sin\theta-1)\,d\theta$$

$$= -2\cos\theta-\theta+C$$

$$= -\sqrt{4-u^2}-\sin^{-1}\!\left(\frac{u}{2}\right)+C$$

$$= -\sqrt{3-2x-x^2}-\sin^{-1}\!\left(\frac{x+1}{2}\right)+C$$

|||| Figure 5 shows the graphs of the integrand in Example 7 and its indefinite integral (with $C = 0$). Which is which?

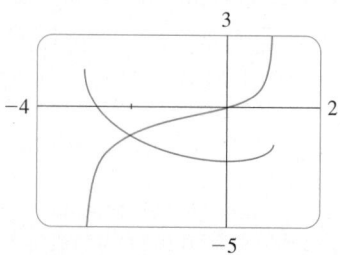

FIGURE 5

8.3 Exercises

1–3 |||| Evaluate the integral using the indicated trigonometric substitution. Sketch and label the associated right triangle.

1. $\displaystyle\int \frac{1}{x^2\sqrt{x^2-9}}\,dx; \quad x = 3\sec\theta$

2. $\displaystyle\int x^3\sqrt{9-x^2}\,dx; \quad x = 3\sin\theta$

3. $\displaystyle\int \frac{x^3}{\sqrt{x^2+9}}\,dx; \quad x = 3\tan\theta$

4–30 |||| Evaluate the integral.

4. $\displaystyle\int_0^{2\sqrt{3}} \frac{x^3}{\sqrt{16-x^2}}\,dx$

5. $\displaystyle\int_{\sqrt{2}}^2 \frac{1}{t^3\sqrt{t^2-1}}\,dt$

6. $\displaystyle\int_0^2 x^3\sqrt{x^2+4}\,dx$

7. $\displaystyle\int \frac{1}{x^2\sqrt{25-x^2}}\,dx$

8. $\displaystyle\int \frac{\sqrt{x^2-a^2}}{x^4}\,dx$

9. $\displaystyle\int \frac{dx}{\sqrt{x^2+16}}$

10. $\displaystyle\int \frac{t^5}{\sqrt{t^2+2}}\,dt$

11. $\int \sqrt{1 - 4x^2}\, dx$

12. $\int_0^1 x\sqrt{x^2 + 4}\, dx$

13. $\int \dfrac{\sqrt{x^2 - 9}}{x^3}\, dx$

14. $\int \dfrac{du}{u\sqrt{5 - u^2}}$

15. $\int \dfrac{x^2}{(a^2 - x^2)^{3/2}}\, dx$

16. $\int \dfrac{dx}{x^2\sqrt{16x^2 - 9}}$

17. $\int \dfrac{x}{\sqrt{x^2 - 7}}\, dx$

18. $\int \dfrac{dx}{[(ax)^2 - b^2]^{3/2}}$

19. $\int \dfrac{\sqrt{1 + x^2}}{x}\, dx$

20. $\int \dfrac{t}{\sqrt{25 - t^2}}\, dt$

21. $\int_0^{2/3} x^3\sqrt{4 - 9x^2}\, dx$

22. $\int_0^1 \sqrt{x^2 + 1}\, dx$

23. $\int \sqrt{5 + 4x - x^2}\, dx$

24. $\int \dfrac{dt}{\sqrt{t^2 - 6t + 13}}$

25. $\int \dfrac{1}{\sqrt{9x^2 + 6x - 8}}\, dx$

26. $\int \dfrac{x^2}{\sqrt{4x - x^2}}\, dx$

27. $\int \dfrac{dx}{(x^2 + 2x + 2)^2}$

28. $\int \dfrac{dx}{(5 - 4x - x^2)^{5/2}}$

29. $\int x\sqrt{1 - x^4}\, dx$

30. $\int_0^{\pi/2} \dfrac{\cos t}{\sqrt{1 + \sin^2 t}}\, dt$

□   □   □   □   □   □   □   □   □   □   □   □

31. (a) Use trigonometric substitution to show that

$$\int \dfrac{dx}{\sqrt{x^2 + a^2}} = \ln\!\left(x + \sqrt{x^2 + a^2}\right) + C$$

(b) Use the hyperbolic substitution $x = a \sinh t$ to show that

$$\int \dfrac{dx}{\sqrt{x^2 + a^2}} = \sinh^{-1}\!\left(\dfrac{x}{a}\right) + C$$

These formulas are connected by Formula 7.6.3.

32. Evaluate

$$\int \dfrac{x^2}{(x^2 + a^2)^{3/2}}\, dx$$

(a) by trigonometric substitution.
(b) by the hyperbolic substitution $x = a \sinh t$.

33. Find the average value of $f(x) = \sqrt{x^2 - 1}/x$, $1 \leq x \leq 7$.

34. Find the area of the region bounded by the hyperbola $9x^2 - 4y^2 = 36$ and the line $x = 3$.

35. Prove the formula $A = \tfrac{1}{2}r^2\theta$ for the area of a sector of a circle with radius r and central angle θ. [*Hint:* Assume $0 < \theta < \pi/2$ and place the center of the circle at the origin so it has the

equation $x^2 + y^2 = r^2$. Then A is the sum of the area of the triangle POQ and the area of the region PQR in the figure.]

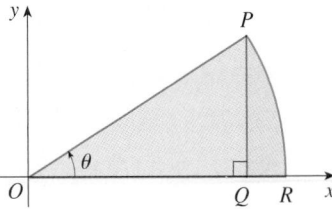

36. Evaluate the integral

$$\int \dfrac{dx}{x^4\sqrt{x^2 - 2}}$$

Graph the integrand and its indefinite integral on the same screen and check that your answer is reasonable.

37. Use a graph to approximate the roots of the equation $x^2\sqrt{4 - x^2} = 2 - x$. Then approximate the area bounded by the curve $y = x^2\sqrt{4 - x^2}$ and the line $y = 2 - x$.

38. A charged rod of length L produces an electric field at point $P(a, b)$ given by

$$E(P) = \int_{-a}^{L-a} \dfrac{\lambda b}{4\pi\varepsilon_0 (x^2 + b^2)^{3/2}}\, dx$$

where λ is the charge density per unit length on the rod and ε_0 is the free space permittivity (see the figure). Evaluate the integral to determine an expression for the electric field $E(P)$.

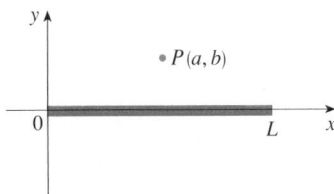

39. Find the area of the crescent-shaped region (called a *lune*) bounded by arcs of circles with radii r and R. (See the figure.)

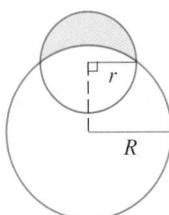

40. A water storage tank has the shape of a cylinder with diameter 10 ft. It is mounted so that the circular cross-sections are vertical. If the depth of the water is 7 ft, what percentage of the total capacity is being used?

41. A torus is generated by rotating the circle $x^2 + (y - R)^2 = r^2$ about the x-axis. Find the volume enclosed by the torus.

8.4 Integration of Rational Functions by Partial Fractions

In this section we show how to integrate any rational function (a ratio of polynomials) by expressing it as a sum of simpler fractions, called *partial fractions,* that we already know how to integrate. To illustrate the method, observe that by taking the fractions $2/(x-1)$ and $1/(x+2)$ to a common denominator we obtain

$$\frac{2}{x-1} - \frac{1}{x+2} = \frac{2(x+2) - (x-1)}{(x-1)(x+2)} = \frac{x+5}{x^2+x-2}$$

If we now reverse the procedure, we see how to integrate the function on the right side of this equation:

$$\int \frac{x+5}{x^2+x-2}\, dx = \int \left(\frac{2}{x-1} - \frac{1}{x+2} \right) dx$$

$$= 2\ln|x-1| - \ln|x+2| + C$$

To see how the method of partial fractions works in general, let's consider a rational function

$$f(x) = \frac{P(x)}{Q(x)}$$

where P and Q are polynomials. It's possible to express f as a sum of simpler fractions provided that the degree of P is less than the degree of Q. Such a rational function is called *proper.* Recall that if

$$P(x) = a_n x^n + a_{n-1}x^{n-1} + \cdots + a_1 x + a_0$$

where $a_n \neq 0$, then the degree of P is n and we write $\deg(P) = n$.

If f is improper, that is, $\deg(P) \geqslant \deg(Q)$, then we must take the preliminary step of dividing Q into P (by long division) until a remainder $R(x)$ is obtained such that $\deg(R) < \deg(Q)$. The division statement is

$$\boxed{1} \qquad\qquad f(x) = \frac{P(x)}{Q(x)} = S(x) + \frac{R(x)}{Q(x)}$$

where S and R are also polynomials.

As the following example illustrates, sometimes this preliminary step is all that is required.

EXAMPLE 1 Find $\displaystyle\int \frac{x^3+x}{x-1}\, dx$.

SOLUTION Since the degree of the numerator is greater than the degree of the denominator, we first perform the long division. This enables us to write

$$\int \frac{x^3+x}{x-1}\, dx = \int \left(x^2 + x + 2 + \frac{2}{x-1} \right) dx$$

$$= \frac{x^3}{3} + \frac{x^2}{2} + 2x + 2\ln|x-1| + C$$

$$
\begin{array}{r}
x^2 + x + 2 \\
x-1\overline{)\,x^3 \qquad\;\; + x\;} \\
\underline{x^3 - x^2} \\
x^2 + x \\
\underline{x^2 - x} \\
2x \\
\underline{2x - 2} \\
2
\end{array}
$$

The next step is to factor the denominator $Q(x)$ as far as possible. It can be shown that any polynomial Q can be factored as a product of linear factors (of the form $ax + b$) and irreducible quadratic factors (of the form $ax^2 + bx + c$, where $b^2 - 4ac < 0$). For instance, if $Q(x) = x^4 - 16$, we could factor it as

$$Q(x) = (x^2 - 4)(x^2 + 4) = (x - 2)(x + 2)(x^2 + 4)$$

The third step is to express the proper rational function $R(x)/Q(x)$ (from Equation 1) as a sum of **partial fractions** of the form

$$\frac{A}{(ax + b)^i} \qquad \text{or} \qquad \frac{Ax + B}{(ax^2 + bx + c)^j}$$

A theorem in algebra guarantees that it is always possible to do this. We explain the details for the four cases that occur.

CASE I ∘ **The denominator $Q(x)$ is a product of distinct linear factors.**
This means that we can write

$$Q(x) = (a_1x + b_1)(a_2x + b_2) \cdots (a_kx + b_k)$$

where no factor is repeated (and no factor is a constant multiple of another). In this case the partial fraction theorem states that there exist constants $A_1, A_2, \ldots, A_k$ such that

$$\boxed{2} \qquad \frac{R(x)}{Q(x)} = \frac{A_1}{a_1x + b_1} + \frac{A_2}{a_2x + b_2} + \cdots + \frac{A_k}{a_kx + b_k}$$

These constants can be determined as in the following example.

EXAMPLE 2 Evaluate $\displaystyle\int \frac{x^2 + 2x - 1}{2x^3 + 3x^2 - 2x}\, dx$.

SOLUTION Since the degree of the numerator is less than the degree of the denominator, we don't need to divide. We factor the denominator as

$$2x^3 + 3x^2 - 2x = x(2x^2 + 3x - 2) = x(2x - 1)(x + 2)$$

Since the denominator has three distinct linear factors, the partial fraction decomposition of the integrand (2) has the form

$$\boxed{3} \qquad \frac{x^2 + 2x - 1}{x(2x - 1)(x + 2)} = \frac{A}{x} + \frac{B}{2x - 1} + \frac{C}{x + 2}$$

‖‖‖ Another method for finding A, B, and C is given in the note after this example.

To determine the values of A, B, and C, we multiply both sides of this equation by the product of the denominators, $x(2x - 1)(x + 2)$, obtaining

$$\boxed{4} \qquad x^2 + 2x - 1 = A(2x - 1)(x + 2) + Bx(x + 2) + Cx(2x - 1)$$

Expanding the right side of Equation 4 and writing it in the standard form for polynomials, we get

$$\boxed{5} \qquad x^2 + 2x - 1 = (2A + B + 2C)x^2 + (3A + 2B - C)x - 2A$$

▕▏▏ Figure 1 shows the graphs of the integrand in Example 2 and its indefinite integral (with $K = 0$). Which is which?

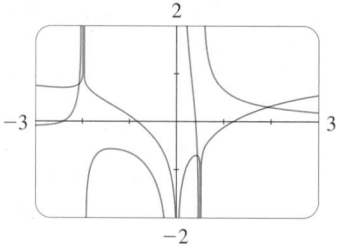

FIGURE 1

The polynomials in Equation 5 are identical, so their coefficients must be equal. The coefficient of x^2 on the right side, $2A + B + 2C$, must equal the coefficient of x^2 on the left side—namely, 1. Likewise, the coefficients of x are equal and the constant terms are equal. This gives the following system of equations for A, B, and C:

$$2A + B + 2C = 1$$
$$3A + 2B - C = 2$$
$$-2A = -1$$

Solving, we get $A = \frac{1}{2}$, $B = \frac{1}{5}$, and $C = -\frac{1}{10}$, and so

$$\int \frac{x^2 + 2x - 1}{2x^3 + 3x^2 - 2x} \, dx = \int \left(\frac{1}{2} \frac{1}{x} + \frac{1}{5} \frac{1}{2x - 1} - \frac{1}{10} \frac{1}{x + 2} \right) dx$$

$$= \tfrac{1}{2} \ln |x| + \tfrac{1}{10} \ln |2x - 1| - \tfrac{1}{10} \ln |x + 2| + K$$

▕▏▏ We could check our work by taking the terms to a common denominator and adding them.

In integrating the middle term we have made the mental substitution $u = 2x - 1$, which gives $du = 2 \, dx$ and $dx = du/2$.

NOTE ◦ We can use an alternative method to find the coefficients A, B, and C in Example 2. Equation 4 is an identity; it is true for every value of x. Let's choose values of x that simplify the equation. If we put $x = 0$ in Equation 4, then the second and third terms on the right side vanish and the equation then becomes $-2A = -1$, or $A = \frac{1}{2}$. Likewise, $x = \frac{1}{2}$ gives $5B/4 = \frac{1}{4}$ and $x = -2$ gives $10C = -1$, so $B = \frac{1}{5}$ and $C = -\frac{1}{10}$. (You may object that Equation 3 is not valid for $x = 0$, $\frac{1}{2}$, or -2, so why should Equation 4 be valid for those values? In fact, Equation 4 is true for all values of x, even $x = 0$, $\frac{1}{2}$, and -2. See Exercise 67 for the reason.)

EXAMPLE 3 Find $\displaystyle\int \frac{dx}{x^2 - a^2}$, where $a \neq 0$.

SOLUTION The method of partial fractions gives

$$\frac{1}{x^2 - a^2} = \frac{1}{(x - a)(x + a)} = \frac{A}{x - a} + \frac{B}{x + a}$$

and therefore

$$A(x + a) + B(x - a) = 1$$

Using the method of the preceding note, we put $x = a$ in this equation and get $A(2a) = 1$, so $A = 1/(2a)$. If we put $x = -a$, we get $B(-2a) = 1$, so $B = -1/(2a)$. Thus

$$\int \frac{dx}{x^2 - a^2} = \frac{1}{2a} \int \left(\frac{1}{x - a} - \frac{1}{x + a} \right) dx$$

$$= \frac{1}{2a} \left(\ln |x - a| - \ln |x + a| \right) + C$$

Since $\ln x - \ln y = \ln(x/y)$, we can write the integral as

$$\boxed{6} \qquad \int \frac{dx}{x^2 - a^2} = \frac{1}{2a} \ln \left| \frac{x-a}{x+a} \right| + C$$

See Exercises 53–54 for ways of using Formula 6.

CASE II ▫ **$Q(x)$ is a product of linear factors, some of which are repeated.**
Suppose the first linear factor $(a_1 x + b_1)$ is repeated r times; that is, $(a_1 x + b_1)^r$ occurs in the factorization of $Q(x)$. Then instead of the single term $A_1/(a_1 x + b_1)$ in Equation 2, we would use

$$\boxed{7} \qquad \frac{A_1}{a_1 x + b_1} + \frac{A_2}{(a_1 x + b_1)^2} + \cdots + \frac{A_r}{(a_1 x + b_1)^r}$$

By way of illustration, we could write

$$\frac{x^3 - x + 1}{x^2(x-1)^3} = \frac{A}{x} + \frac{B}{x^2} + \frac{C}{x-1} + \frac{D}{(x-1)^2} + \frac{E}{(x-1)^3}$$

but we prefer to work out in detail a simpler example.

EXAMPLE 4 Find $\displaystyle \int \frac{x^4 - 2x^2 + 4x + 1}{x^3 - x^2 - x + 1} \, dx$.

SOLUTION The first step is to divide. The result of long division is

$$\frac{x^4 - 2x^2 + 4x + 1}{x^3 - x^2 - x + 1} = x + 1 + \frac{4x}{x^3 - x^2 - x + 1}$$

The second step is to factor the denominator $Q(x) = x^3 - x^2 - x + 1$. Since $Q(1) = 0$, we know that $x - 1$ is a factor and we obtain

$$x^3 - x^2 - x + 1 = (x-1)(x^2 - 1) = (x-1)(x-1)(x+1)$$
$$= (x-1)^2(x+1)$$

Since the linear factor $x - 1$ occurs twice, the partial fraction decomposition is

$$\frac{4x}{(x-1)^2(x+1)} = \frac{A}{x-1} + \frac{B}{(x-1)^2} + \frac{C}{x+1}$$

Multiplying by the least common denominator, $(x-1)^2(x+1)$, we get

$$\boxed{8} \qquad 4x = A(x-1)(x+1) + B(x+1) + C(x-1)^2$$
$$= (A + C)x^2 + (B - 2C)x + (-A + B + C)$$

||| Another method for finding the coefficients:
Put $x = 1$ in (8): $B = 2$.
Put $x = -1$: $C = -1$.
Put $x = 0$: $A = B + C = 1$.

Now we equate coefficients:

$$A \qquad + \ C = 0$$
$$B - 2C = 4$$
$$-A + B + \ C = 0$$

Solving, we obtain $A = 1$, $B = 2$, and $C = -1$, so

$$\int \frac{x^4 - 2x^2 + 4x + 1}{x^3 - x^2 - x + 1}\,dx = \int \left[x + 1 + \frac{1}{x - 1} + \frac{2}{(x - 1)^2} - \frac{1}{x + 1} \right] dx$$

$$= \frac{x^2}{2} + x + \ln|x - 1| - \frac{2}{x - 1} - \ln|x + 1| + K$$

$$= \frac{x^2}{2} + x - \frac{2}{x - 1} + \ln\left|\frac{x - 1}{x + 1}\right| + K \qquad \blacksquare$$

CASE III ▫ $Q(x)$ **contains irreducible quadratic factors, none of which is repeated.**

If $Q(x)$ has the factor $ax^2 + bx + c$, where $b^2 - 4ac < 0$, then, in addition to the partial fractions in Equations 2 and 7, the expression for $R(x)/Q(x)$ will have a term of the form

$\boxed{9}$

$$\frac{Ax + B}{ax^2 + bx + c}$$

where A and B are constants to be determined. For instance, the function given by $f(x) = x/[(x - 2)(x^2 + 1)(x^2 + 4)]$ has a partial fraction decomposition of the form

$$\frac{x}{(x - 2)(x^2 + 1)(x^2 + 4)} = \frac{A}{x - 2} + \frac{Bx + C}{x^2 + 1} + \frac{Dx + E}{x^2 + 4}$$

The term given in (9) can be integrated by completing the square and using the formula

$\boxed{10}$

$$\int \frac{dx}{x^2 + a^2} = \frac{1}{a}\tan^{-1}\left(\frac{x}{a}\right) + C$$

EXAMPLE 5 Evaluate $\displaystyle\int \frac{2x^2 - x + 4}{x^3 + 4x}\,dx$.

SOLUTION Since $x^3 + 4x = x(x^2 + 4)$ can't be factored further, we write

$$\frac{2x^2 - x + 4}{x(x^2 + 4)} = \frac{A}{x} + \frac{Bx + C}{x^2 + 4}$$

Multiplying by $x(x^2 + 4)$, we have

$$2x^2 - x + 4 = A(x^2 + 4) + (Bx + C)x$$

$$= (A + B)x^2 + Cx + 4A$$

Equating coefficients, we obtain

$$A + B = 2 \qquad C = -1 \qquad 4A = 4$$

Thus $A = 1$, $B = 1$, and $C = -1$ and so

$$\int \frac{2x^2 - x + 4}{x^3 + 4x}\,dx = \int \left(\frac{1}{x} + \frac{x - 1}{x^2 + 4} \right) dx$$

In order to integrate the second term we split it into two parts:

$$\int \frac{x-1}{x^2+4}\, dx = \int \frac{x}{x^2+4}\, dx - \int \frac{1}{x^2+4}\, dx$$

We make the substitution $u = x^2 + 4$ in the first of these integrals so that $du = 2x\, dx$. We evaluate the second integral by means of Formula 10 with $a = 2$:

$$\int \frac{2x^2 - x + 4}{x(x^2+4)}\, dx = \int \frac{1}{x}\, dx + \int \frac{x}{x^2+4}\, dx - \int \frac{1}{x^2+4}\, dx$$

$$= \ln|x| + \tfrac{1}{2}\ln(x^2+4) - \tfrac{1}{2}\tan^{-1}(x/2) + K$$

EXAMPLE 6 Evaluate $\displaystyle\int \frac{4x^2 - 3x + 2}{4x^2 - 4x + 3}\, dx.$

SOLUTION Since the degree of the numerator is *not less than* the degree of the denominator, we first divide and obtain

$$\frac{4x^2 - 3x + 2}{4x^2 - 4x + 3} = 1 + \frac{x-1}{4x^2 - 4x + 3}$$

Notice that the quadratic $4x^2 - 4x + 3$ is irreducible because its discriminant is $b^2 - 4ac = -32 < 0$. This means it can't be factored, so we don't need to use the partial fraction technique.

To integrate the given function we complete the square in the denominator:

$$4x^2 - 4x + 3 = (2x - 1)^2 + 2$$

This suggests that we make the substitution $u = 2x - 1$. Then, $du = 2\, dx$ and $x = (u + 1)/2$, so

$$\int \frac{4x^2 - 3x + 2}{4x^2 - 4x + 3}\, dx = \int \left(1 + \frac{x-1}{4x^2 - 4x + 3}\right) dx$$

$$= x + \tfrac{1}{2}\int \frac{\tfrac{1}{2}(u+1) - 1}{u^2 + 2}\, du = x + \tfrac{1}{4}\int \frac{u - 1}{u^2 + 2}\, du$$

$$= x + \tfrac{1}{4}\int \frac{u}{u^2 + 2}\, du - \tfrac{1}{4}\int \frac{1}{u^2 + 2}\, du$$

$$= x + \tfrac{1}{8}\ln(u^2 + 2) - \frac{1}{4}\cdot\frac{1}{\sqrt{2}}\tan^{-1}\left(\frac{u}{\sqrt{2}}\right) + C$$

$$= x + \tfrac{1}{8}\ln(4x^2 - 4x + 3) - \frac{1}{4\sqrt{2}}\tan^{-1}\left(\frac{2x-1}{\sqrt{2}}\right) + C$$

NOTE ▫ Example 6 illustrates the general procedure for integrating a partial fraction of the form

$$\frac{Ax + B}{ax^2 + bx + c} \qquad \text{where } b^2 - 4ac < 0$$

We complete the square in the denominator and then make a substitution that brings the integral into the form

$$\int \frac{Cu + D}{u^2 + a^2}\, du = C \int \frac{u}{u^2 + a^2}\, du + D \int \frac{1}{u^2 + a^2}\, du$$

Then the first integral is a logarithm and the second is expressed in terms of $\tan^{-1}$.

CASE IV ▫ **$Q(x)$ contains a repeated irreducible quadratic factor.**
If $Q(x)$ has the factor $(ax^2 + bx + c)^r$, where $b^2 - 4ac < 0$, then instead of the single partial fraction (9), the sum

$$\boxed{11} \qquad \frac{A_1 x + B_1}{ax^2 + bx + c} + \frac{A_2 x + B_2}{(ax^2 + bx + c)^2} + \cdots + \frac{A_r x + B_r}{(ax^2 + bx + c)^r}$$

occurs in the partial fraction decomposition of $R(x)/Q(x)$. Each of the terms in (11) can be integrated by first completing the square.

▐▐ It would be extremely tedious to work out by hand the numerical values of the coefficients in Example 7. Most computer algebra systems, however, can find the numerical values very quickly. For instance, the Maple command

$$\text{convert(f, parfrac, x)}$$

or the Mathematica command

$$\text{Apart[f]}$$

gives the following values:

$$A = -1, \quad B = \tfrac{1}{8}, \quad C = D = -1,$$
$$E = \tfrac{15}{8}, \quad F = -\tfrac{1}{8}, \quad G = H = \tfrac{3}{4},$$
$$I = -\tfrac{1}{2}, \quad J = \tfrac{1}{2}$$

EXAMPLE 7 Write out the form of the partial fraction decomposition of the function

$$\frac{x^3 + x^2 + 1}{x(x - 1)(x^2 + x + 1)(x^2 + 1)^3}$$

SOLUTION

$$\frac{x^3 + x^2 + 1}{x(x - 1)(x^2 + x + 1)(x^2 + 1)^3}$$

$$= \frac{A}{x} + \frac{B}{x - 1} + \frac{Cx + D}{x^2 + x + 1} + \frac{Ex + F}{x^2 + 1} + \frac{Gx + H}{(x^2 + 1)^2} + \frac{Ix + J}{(x^2 + 1)^3}$$

EXAMPLE 8 Evaluate $\displaystyle \int \frac{1 - x + 2x^2 - x^3}{x(x^2 + 1)^2}\, dx.$

SOLUTION The form of the partial fraction decomposition is

$$\frac{1 - x + 2x^2 - x^3}{x(x^2 + 1)^2} = \frac{A}{x} + \frac{Bx + C}{x^2 + 1} + \frac{Dx + E}{(x^2 + 1)^2}$$

Multiplying by $x(x^2 + 1)^2$, we have

$$-x^3 + 2x^2 - x + 1 = A(x^2 + 1)^2 + (Bx + C)x(x^2 + 1) + (Dx + E)x$$

$$= A(x^4 + 2x^2 + 1) + B(x^4 + x^2) + C(x^3 + x) + Dx^2 + Ex$$

$$= (A + B)x^4 + Cx^3 + (2A + B + D)x^2 + (C + E)x + A$$

If we equate coefficients, we get the system

$$A + B = 0 \qquad C = -1 \qquad 2A + B + D = 2 \qquad C + E = -1 \qquad A = 1$$

which has the solution $A = 1$, $B = -1$, $C = -1$, $D = 1$, and $E = 0$. Thus

$$\int \frac{1 - x + 2x^2 - x^3}{x(x^2 + 1)^2}\, dx = \int \left(\frac{1}{x} - \frac{x+1}{x^2+1} + \frac{x}{(x^2+1)^2} \right) dx$$

$$= \int \frac{dx}{x} - \int \frac{x}{x^2+1}\, dx - \int \frac{dx}{x^2+1} + \int \frac{x\, dx}{(x^2+1)^2}$$

$$= \ln|x| - \tfrac{1}{2}\ln(x^2+1) - \tan^{-1}x - \frac{1}{2(x^2+1)} + K$$

▏▏▏▏ In the second and fourth terms we made the mental substitution $u = x^2 + 1$.

We note that sometimes partial fractions can be avoided when integrating a rational function. For instance, although the integral

$$\int \frac{x^2 + 1}{x(x^2+3)}\, dx$$

could be evaluated by the method of Case III, it's much easier to observe that if $u = x(x^2 + 3) = x^3 + 3x$, then $du = (3x^2 + 3)\, dx$ and so

$$\int \frac{x^2 + 1}{x(x^2+3)}\, dx = \tfrac{1}{3}\ln|x^3 + 3x| + C$$

▏▏▏ **Rationalizing Substitutions**

Some nonrational functions can be changed into rational functions by means of appropriate substitutions. In particular, when an integrand contains an expression of the form $\sqrt[n]{g(x)}$, then the substitution $u = \sqrt[n]{g(x)}$ may be effective. Other instances appear in the exercises.

EXAMPLE 9 Evaluate $\displaystyle\int \frac{\sqrt{x+4}}{x}\, dx$.

SOLUTION Let $u = \sqrt{x+4}$. Then $u^2 = x + 4$, so $x = u^2 - 4$ and $dx = 2u\, du$. Therefore

$$\int \frac{\sqrt{x+4}}{x}\, dx = \int \frac{u}{u^2 - 4}\, 2u\, du = 2\int \frac{u^2}{u^2 - 4}\, du$$

$$= 2\int \left(1 + \frac{4}{u^2 - 4} \right) du$$

We can evaluate this integral either by factoring $u^2 - 4$ as $(u - 2)(u + 2)$ and using partial fractions or by using Formula 6 with $a = 2$:

$$\int \frac{\sqrt{x+4}}{x}\, dx = 2\int du + 8\int \frac{du}{u^2 - 4}$$

$$= 2u + 8 \cdot \frac{1}{2 \cdot 2}\ln\left| \frac{u-2}{u+2} \right| + C$$

$$= 2\sqrt{x+4} + 2\ln\left| \frac{\sqrt{x+4} - 2}{\sqrt{x+4} + 2} \right| + C$$

8.4 Exercises

1–6 ||||| Write out the form of the partial fraction decomposition of the function (as in Example 7). Do not determine the numerical values of the coefficients.

1. (a) $\dfrac{2x}{(x+3)(3x+1)}$ (b) $\dfrac{1}{x^3+2x^2+x}$

2. (a) $\dfrac{x-1}{x^3+x^2}$ (b) $\dfrac{x-1}{x^3+x}$

3. (a) $\dfrac{2}{x^2+3x-4}$ (b) $\dfrac{x^2}{(x-1)(x^2+x+1)}$

4. (a) $\dfrac{x^3}{x^2+4x+3}$ (b) $\dfrac{2x+1}{(x+1)^3(x^2+4)^2}$

5. (a) $\dfrac{x^4}{x^4-1}$ (b) $\dfrac{t^4+t^2+1}{(t^2+1)(t^2+4)^2}$

6. (a) $\dfrac{x^4}{(x^3+x)(x^2-x+3)}$ (b) $\dfrac{1}{x^6-x^3}$

7–38 ||||| Evaluate the integral.

7. $\displaystyle\int \frac{x}{x-6}\,dx$

8. $\displaystyle\int \frac{r^2}{r+4}\,dr$

9. $\displaystyle\int \frac{x-9}{(x+5)(x-2)}\,dx$

10. $\displaystyle\int \frac{1}{(t+4)(t-1)}\,dt$

11. $\displaystyle\int_2^3 \frac{1}{x^2-1}\,dx$

12. $\displaystyle\int_0^1 \frac{x-1}{x^2+3x+2}\,dx$

13. $\displaystyle\int \frac{ax}{x^2-bx}\,dx$

14. $\displaystyle\int \frac{1}{(x+a)(x+b)}\,dx$

15. $\displaystyle\int_0^1 \frac{2x+3}{(x+1)^2}\,dx$

16. $\displaystyle\int_0^1 \frac{x^3-4x-10}{x^2-x-6}\,dx$

17. $\displaystyle\int_1^2 \frac{4y^2-7y-12}{y(y+2)(y-3)}\,dy$

18. $\displaystyle\int \frac{x^2+2x-1}{x^3-x}\,dx$

19. $\displaystyle\int \frac{1}{(x+5)^2(x-1)}\,dx$

20. $\displaystyle\int \frac{x^2}{(x-3)(x+2)^2}\,dx$

21. $\displaystyle\int \frac{5x^2+3x-2}{x^3+2x^2}\,dx$

22. $\displaystyle\int \frac{ds}{s^2(s-1)^2}$

23. $\displaystyle\int \frac{x^2}{(x+1)^3}\,dx$

24. $\displaystyle\int \frac{x^3}{(x+1)^3}\,dx$

25. $\displaystyle\int \frac{10}{(x-1)(x^2+9)}\,dx$

26. $\displaystyle\int \frac{x^2-x+6}{x^3+3x}\,dx$

27. $\displaystyle\int \frac{x^3+x^2+2x+1}{(x^2+1)(x^2+2)}\,dx$

28. $\displaystyle\int \frac{x^2-2x-1}{(x-1)^2(x^2+1)}\,dx$

29. $\displaystyle\int \frac{x+4}{x^2+2x+5}\,dx$

30. $\displaystyle\int \frac{x^3-2x^2+x+1}{x^4+5x^2+4}\,dx$

31. $\displaystyle\int \frac{1}{x^3-1}\,dx$

32. $\displaystyle\int_0^1 \frac{x}{x^2+4x+13}\,dx$

33. $\displaystyle\int_2^5 \frac{x^2+2x}{x^3+3x^2+4}\,dx$

34. $\displaystyle\int \frac{x^3}{x^3+1}\,dx$

35. $\displaystyle\int \frac{dx}{x^4-x^2}$

36. $\displaystyle\int_0^1 \frac{2x^3+5x}{x^4+5x^2+4}\,dx$

37. $\displaystyle\int \frac{x-3}{(x^2+2x+4)^2}\,dx$

38. $\displaystyle\int \frac{x^4+1}{x(x^2+1)^2}\,dx$

39–48 ||||| Make a substitution to express the integrand as a rational function and then evaluate the integral.

39. $\displaystyle\int \frac{1}{x\sqrt{x+1}}\,dx$

40. $\displaystyle\int \frac{1}{x-\sqrt{x+2}}\,dx$

41. $\displaystyle\int_9^{16} \frac{\sqrt{x}}{x-4}\,dx$

42. $\displaystyle\int_0^1 \frac{1}{1+\sqrt[3]{x}}\,dx$

43. $\displaystyle\int \frac{x^3}{\sqrt[3]{x^2+1}}\,dx$

44. $\displaystyle\int_{1/3}^3 \frac{\sqrt{x}}{x^2+x}\,dx$

45. $\displaystyle\int \frac{1}{\sqrt{x}-\sqrt[3]{x}}\,dx$ [*Hint:* Substitute $u=\sqrt[6]{x}$.]

46. $\displaystyle\int \frac{1}{\sqrt[3]{x}+\sqrt[4]{x}}\,dx$ [*Hint:* Substitute $u=\sqrt[12]{x}$.]

47. $\displaystyle\int \frac{e^{2x}}{e^{2x}+3e^x+2}\,dx$

48. $\displaystyle\int \frac{\cos x}{\sin^2 x+\sin x}\,dx$

49–50 ||||| Use integration by parts, together with the techniques of this section, to evaluate the integral.

49. $\displaystyle\int \ln(x^2-x+2)\,dx$

50. $\displaystyle\int x\tan^{-1}x\,dx$

51. Use a graph of $f(x)=1/(x^2-2x-3)$ to decide whether $\int_0^2 f(x)\,dx$ is positive or negative. Use the graph to give a rough estimate of the value of the integral and then use partial fractions to find the exact value.

52. Graph both $y=1/(x^3-2x^2)$ and an antiderivative on the same screen.

53–54 ||||| Evaluate the integral by completing the square and using Formula 6.

53. $\displaystyle\int \frac{dx}{x^2-2x}$

54. $\displaystyle\int \frac{2x+1}{4x^2+12x-7}\,dx$

55. The German mathematician Karl Weierstrass (1815–1897) noticed that the substitution $t=\tan(x/2)$ will convert any rational function of $\sin x$ and $\cos x$ into an ordinary rational function of t.

(a) If $t = \tan(x/2)$, $-\pi < x < \pi$, sketch a right triangle or use trigonometric identities to show that

$$\cos\left(\frac{x}{2}\right) = \frac{1}{\sqrt{1 + t^2}} \quad \text{and} \quad \sin\left(\frac{x}{2}\right) = \frac{t}{\sqrt{1 + t^2}}$$

(b) Show that

$$\cos x = \frac{1 - t^2}{1 + t^2} \quad \text{and} \quad \sin x = \frac{2t}{1 + t^2}$$

(c) Show that

$$dx = \frac{2}{1 + t^2}\, dt$$

56–59 ▮▮▮ Use the substitution in Exercise 55 to transform the integrand into a rational function of t and then evaluate the integral.

56. $\displaystyle\int \frac{dx}{3 - 5\sin x}$

57. $\displaystyle\int \frac{1}{3\sin x - 4\cos x}\, dx$

58. $\displaystyle\int_{\pi/3}^{\pi/2} \frac{1}{1 + \sin x - \cos x}\, dx$

59. $\displaystyle\int \frac{1}{2\sin x + \sin 2x}\, dx$

60–61 ▮▮▮ Find the area of the region under the given curve from a to b.

60. $y = \dfrac{1}{x^2 - 6x + 8}$, $\quad a = 5,\ b = 10$

61. $y = \dfrac{x + 1}{x - 1}$, $\quad a = 2,\ b = 3$

62. Find the volume of the resulting solid if the region under the curve $y = 1/(x^2 + 3x + 2)$ from $x = 0$ to $x = 1$ is rotated about (a) the x-axis and (b) the y-axis.

63. One method of slowing the growth of an insect population without using pesticides is to introduce into the population a number of sterile males that mate with fertile females but produce no offspring. If P represents the number of female insects in a population, S the number of sterile males introduced each generation, and r the population's natural growth rate, then the female population is related to time t by

$$t = \int \frac{P + S}{P[(r - 1)P - S]}\, dP$$

Suppose an insect population with 10,000 females grows at a rate of $r = 0.10$ and 900 sterile males are added. Evaluate the integral to give an equation relating the female population to time. (Note that the resulting equation can't be solved explicitly for P.)

64. Factor $x^4 + 1$ as a difference of squares by first adding and subtracting the same quantity. Use this factorization to evaluate $\int 1/(x^4 + 1)\, dx$.

[CAS] **65.** (a) Use a computer algebra system to find the partial fraction decomposition of the function

$$f(x) = \frac{4x^3 - 27x^2 + 5x - 32}{30x^5 - 13x^4 + 50x^3 - 286x^2 - 299x - 70}$$

(b) Use part (a) to find $\int f(x)\, dx$ (by hand) and compare with the result of using the CAS to integrate f directly. Comment on any discrepancy.

[CAS] **66.** (a) Find the partial fraction decomposition of the function

$$f(x) = \frac{12x^5 - 7x^3 - 13x^2 + 8}{100x^6 - 80x^5 + 116x^4 - 80x^3 + 41x^2 - 20x + 4}$$

(b) Use part (a) to find $\int f(x)\, dx$ and graph f and its indefinite integral on the same screen.

(c) Use the graph of f to discover the main features of the graph of $\int f(x)\, dx$.

67. Suppose that F, G, and Q are polynomials and

$$\frac{F(x)}{Q(x)} = \frac{G(x)}{Q(x)}$$

for all x except when $Q(x) = 0$. Prove that $F(x) = G(x)$ for all x. [*Hint:* Use continuity.]

68. If f is a quadratic function such that $f(0) = 1$ and

$$\int \frac{f(x)}{x^2(x + 1)^3}\, dx$$

is a rational function, find the value of $f'(0)$.

8.5 Strategy for Integration

As we have seen, integration is more challenging than differentiation. In finding the derivative of a function it is obvious which differentiation formula we should apply. But it may not be obvious which technique we should use to integrate a given function.

Until now individual techniques have been applied in each section. For instance, we usually used substitution in Exercises 5.5, integration by parts in Exercises 8.1, and partial fractions in Exercises 8.4. But in this section we present a collection of miscellaneous integrals in random order and the main challenge is to recognize which technique or formula to use. No hard and fast rules can be given as to which method applies in a given situation, but we give some advice on strategy that you may find useful.

A prerequisite for strategy selection is a knowledge of the basic integration formulas. In the following table we have collected the integrals from our previous list together with several additional formulas that we have learned in this chapter. Most of them should be memorized. It is useful to know them all, but the ones marked with an asterisk need not be memorized since they are easily derived. Formula 19 can be avoided by using partial fractions, and trigonometric substitutions can be used in place of Formula 20.

Table of Integration Formulas   Constants of integration have been omitted.

1. $\displaystyle\int x^n \, dx = \frac{x^{n+1}}{n+1}$ $(n \neq -1)$ **2.** $\displaystyle\int \frac{1}{x} \, dx = \ln|x|$

3. $\displaystyle\int e^x \, dx = e^x$ **4.** $\displaystyle\int a^x \, dx = \frac{a^x}{\ln a}$

5. $\displaystyle\int \sin x \, dx = -\cos x$ **6.** $\displaystyle\int \cos x \, dx = \sin x$

7. $\displaystyle\int \sec^2 x \, dx = \tan x$ **8.** $\displaystyle\int \csc^2 x \, dx = -\cot x$

9. $\displaystyle\int \sec x \tan x \, dx = \sec x$ **10.** $\displaystyle\int \csc x \cot x \, dx = -\csc x$

11. $\displaystyle\int \sec x \, dx = \ln|\sec x + \tan x|$ **12.** $\displaystyle\int \csc x \, dx = \ln|\csc x - \cot x|$

13. $\displaystyle\int \tan x \, dx = \ln|\sec x|$ **14.** $\displaystyle\int \cot x \, dx = \ln|\sin x|$

15. $\displaystyle\int \sinh x \, dx = \cosh x$ **16.** $\displaystyle\int \cosh x \, dx = \sinh x$

17. $\displaystyle\int \frac{dx}{x^2 + a^2} = \frac{1}{a} \tan^{-1}\!\left(\frac{x}{a}\right)$ **18.** $\displaystyle\int \frac{dx}{\sqrt{a^2 - x^2}} = \sin^{-1}\!\left(\frac{x}{a}\right)$

*19. $\displaystyle\int \frac{dx}{x^2 - a^2} = \frac{1}{2a} \ln\left|\frac{x-a}{x+a}\right|$ ***20.** $\displaystyle\int \frac{dx}{\sqrt{x^2 \pm a^2}} = \ln\left|x + \sqrt{x^2 \pm a^2}\right|$

Once you are armed with these basic integration formulas, if you don't immediately see how to attack a given integral, you might try the following four-step strategy.

1. Simplify the Integrand if Possible   Sometimes the use of algebraic manipulation or trigonometric identities will simplify the integrand and make the method of integration obvious. Here are some examples:

$$\int \sqrt{x}\left(1 + \sqrt{x}\right) dx = \int \left(\sqrt{x} + x\right) dx$$

$$\int \frac{\tan \theta}{\sec^2 \theta} \, d\theta = \int \frac{\sin \theta}{\cos \theta} \cos^2 \theta \, d\theta$$

$$= \int \sin \theta \cos \theta \, d\theta = \tfrac{1}{2} \int \sin 2\theta \, d\theta$$

$$\int (\sin x + \cos x)^2 \, dx = \int (\sin^2 x + 2 \sin x \cos x + \cos^2 x) \, dx$$

$$= \int (1 + 2 \sin x \cos x) \, dx$$

2. Look for an Obvious Substitution Try to find some function $u = g(x)$ in the integrand whose differential $du = g'(x) \, dx$ also occurs, apart from a constant factor. For instance, in the integral

$$\int \frac{x}{x^2 - 1} \, dx$$

we notice that if $u = x^2 - 1$, then $du = 2x \, dx$. Therefore, we use the substitution $u = x^2 - 1$ instead of the method of partial fractions.

3. Classify the Integrand According to Its Form If Steps 1 and 2 have not led to the solution, then we take a look at the form of the integrand $f(x)$.

(a) *Trigonometric functions.* If $f(x)$ is a product of powers of $\sin x$ and $\cos x$, of $\tan x$ and $\sec x$, or of $\cot x$ and $\csc x$, then we use the substitutions recommended in Section 8.2.

(b) *Rational functions.* If f is a rational function, we use the procedure of Section 8.4 involving partial fractions.

(c) *Integration by parts.* If $f(x)$ is a product of a power of x (or a polynomial) and a transcendental function (such as a trigonometric, exponential, or logarithmic function), then we try integration by parts, choosing u and dv according to the advice given in Section 8.1. If you look at the functions in Exercises 8.1, you will see that most of them are the type just described.

(d) *Radicals.* Particular kinds of substitutions are recommended when certain radicals appear.

(i) If $\sqrt{\pm x^2 \pm a^2}$ occurs, we use a trigonometric substitution according to the table in Section 8.3.

(ii) If $\sqrt[n]{ax + b}$ occurs, we use the rationalizing substitution $u = \sqrt[n]{ax + b}$. More generally, this sometimes works for $\sqrt[n]{g(x)}$.

4. Try Again If the first three steps have not produced the answer, remember that there are basically only two methods of integration: substitution and parts.

(a) *Try substitution.* Even if no substitution is obvious (Step 2), some inspiration or ingenuity (or even desperation) may suggest an appropriate substitution.

(b) *Try parts.* Although integration by parts is used most of the time on products of the form described in Step 3(c), it is sometimes effective on single functions. Looking at Section 8.1, we see that it works on $\tan^{-1}x$, $\sin^{-1}x$, and $\ln x$, and these are all inverse functions.

(c) *Manipulate the integrand.* Algebraic manipulations (perhaps rationalizing the denominator or using trigonometric identities) may be useful in transforming the integral into an easier form. These manipulations may be more substantial than in Step 1 and may involve some ingenuity. Here is an example:

$$\int \frac{dx}{1 - \cos x} = \int \frac{1}{1 - \cos x} \cdot \frac{1 + \cos x}{1 + \cos x} \, dx = \int \frac{1 + \cos x}{1 - \cos^2 x} \, dx$$

$$= \int \frac{1 + \cos x}{\sin^2 x} \, dx = \int \left(\csc^2 x + \frac{\cos x}{\sin^2 x} \right) dx$$

(d) *Relate the problem to previous problems.* When you have built up some experience in integration, you may be able to use a method on a given integral that is similar to a method you have already used on a previous integral. Or you may even be able to express the given integral in terms of a previous one. For instance, $\int \tan^2 x \sec x\, dx$ is a challenging integral, but if we make use of the identity $\tan^2 x = \sec^2 x - 1$, we can write

$$\int \tan^2 x \sec x\, dx = \int \sec^3 x\, dx - \int \sec x\, dx$$

and if $\int \sec^3 x\, dx$ has previously been evaluated (see Example 8 in Section 8.2), then that calculation can be used in the present problem.

(e) *Use several methods.* Sometimes two or three methods are required to evaluate an integral. The evaluation could involve several successive substitutions of different types, or it might combine integration by parts with one or more substitutions.

In the following examples we indicate a method of attack but do not fully work out the integral.

EXAMPLE 1 $\displaystyle\int \frac{\tan^3 x}{\cos^3 x}\, dx$

In Step 1 we rewrite the integral:

$$\int \frac{\tan^3 x}{\cos^3 x}\, dx = \int \tan^3 x \sec^3 x\, dx$$

The integral is now of the form $\int \tan^m x \sec^n x\, dx$ with m odd, so we can use the advice in Section 7.2.

Alternatively, if in Step 1 we had written

$$\int \frac{\tan^3 x}{\cos^3 x}\, dx = \int \frac{\sin^3 x}{\cos^3 x}\frac{1}{\cos^3 x}\, dx = \int \frac{\sin^3 x}{\cos^6 x}\, dx$$

then we could have continued as follows with the substitution $u = \cos x$:

$$\int \frac{\sin^3 x}{\cos^6 x}\, dx = \int \frac{1 - \cos^2 x}{\cos^6 x}\sin x\, dx = \int \frac{1 - u^2}{u^6}(-du)$$

$$= \int \frac{u^2 - 1}{u^6}\, du = \int (u^{-4} - u^{-6})\, du$$

EXAMPLE 2 $\displaystyle\int e^{\sqrt{x}}\, dx$

According to Step 3(d)(ii) we substitute $u = \sqrt{x}$. Then $x = u^2$, so $dx = 2u\, du$ and

$$\int e^{\sqrt{x}}\, dx = 2\int u e^u\, du$$

The integrand is now a product of u and the transcendental function e^u so it can be integrated by parts.

EXAMPLE 3 $\displaystyle\int \frac{x^5 + 1}{x^3 - 3x^2 - 10x}\, dx$

No algebraic simplification or substitution is obvious, so Steps 1 and 2 don't apply here. The integrand is a rational function so we apply the procedure of Section 8.4, remembering that the first step is to divide.

EXAMPLE 4 $\displaystyle\int \frac{dx}{x\sqrt{\ln x}}$

Here Step 2 is all that is needed. We substitute $u = \ln x$ because its differential is $du = dx/x$, which occurs in the integral.

EXAMPLE 5 $\displaystyle\int \sqrt{\frac{1 - x}{1 + x}}\, dx$

Although the rationalizing substitution

$$u = \sqrt{\frac{1 - x}{1 + x}}$$

works here [Step 3(d)(ii)], it leads to a very complicated rational function. An easier method is to do some algebraic manipulation [either as Step 1 or as Step 4(c)]. Multiplying numerator and denominator by $\sqrt{1 - x}$, we have

$$\int \sqrt{\frac{1 - x}{1 + x}}\, dx = \int \frac{1 - x}{\sqrt{1 - x^2}}\, dx$$

$$= \int \frac{1}{\sqrt{1 - x^2}}\, dx - \int \frac{x}{\sqrt{1 - x^2}}\, dx$$

$$= \sin^{-1}x + \sqrt{1 - x^2} + C$$

||||| **Can We Integrate All Continuous Functions?**

The question arises: Will our strategy for integration enable us to find the integral of every continuous function? For example, can we use it to evaluate $\int e^{x^2}\, dx$? The answer is no, at least not in terms of the functions that we are familiar with.

The functions that we have been dealing with in this book are called **elementary functions**. These are the polynomials, rational functions, power functions (x^a), exponential functions (a^x), logarithmic functions, trigonometric and inverse trigonometric functions, hyperbolic and inverse hyperbolic functions, and all functions that can be obtained from these by the five operations of addition, subtraction, multiplication, division, and composition. For instance, the function

$$f(x) = \sqrt{\frac{x^2 - 1}{x^3 + 2x - 1}} + \ln(\cosh x) - xe^{\sin 2x}$$

is an elementary function.

If f is an elementary function, then f' is an elementary function but $\int f(x)\, dx$ need not be an elementary function. Consider $f(x) = e^{x^2}$. Since f is continuous, its integral exists, and if we define the function F by

$$F(x) = \int_0^x e^{t^2}dt$$

then we know from Part 1 of the Fundamental Theorem of Calculus that

$$F'(x) = e^{x^2}$$

Thus, $f(x) = e^{x^2}$ has an antiderivative F, but it has been proved that F is not an elementary function. This means that no matter how hard we try, we will never succeed in evaluating $\int e^{x^2} dx$ in terms of the functions we know. (In Chapter 12, however, we will see how to express $\int e^{x^2} dx$ as an infinite series.) The same can be said of the following integrals:

$$\int \frac{e^x}{x} dx \qquad \int \sin(x^2) dx \qquad \int \cos(e^x) dx$$

$$\int \sqrt{x^3 + 1} \, dx \qquad \int \frac{1}{\ln x} dx \qquad \int \frac{\sin x}{x} dx$$

In fact, the majority of elementary functions don't have elementary antiderivatives. You may be assured, though, that the integrals in the following exercises are all elementary functions.

8.5 Exercises

1–80 ▓ Evaluate the integral.

1. $\int \dfrac{\sin x + \sec x}{\tan x} dx$

2. $\int \tan^3 \theta \, d\theta$

3. $\int_0^2 \dfrac{2t}{(t-3)^2} dt$

4. $\int \dfrac{x}{\sqrt{3-x^4}} dx$

5. $\int_{-1}^1 \dfrac{e^{\arctan y}}{1+y^2} dy$

6. $\int x \csc x \cot x \, dx$

7. $\int_1^3 r^4 \ln r \, dr$

8. $\int_0^4 \dfrac{x-1}{x^2 - 4x - 5} dx$

9. $\int \dfrac{x-1}{x^2 - 4x + 5} dx$

10. $\int \dfrac{x}{x^4 + x^2 + 1} dx$

11. $\int \sin^3 \theta \, \cos^5 \theta \, d\theta$

12. $\int \sin x \cos(\cos x) \, dx$

13. $\int \dfrac{dx}{(1-x^2)^{3/2}}$

14. $\int \dfrac{\sqrt{1 + \ln x}}{x \ln x} dx$

15. $\int_0^{1/2} \dfrac{x}{\sqrt{1-x^2}} dx$

16. $\int_0^{\sqrt{2}/2} \dfrac{x^2}{\sqrt{1-x^2}} dx$

17. $\int x \sin^2 x \, dx$

18. $\int \dfrac{e^{2t}}{1 + e^{4t}} dt$

19. $\int e^{x + e^x} dx$

20. $\int e^{\sqrt[3]{x}} dx$

21. $\int t^3 e^{-2t} dt$

22. $\int x \sin^{-1} x \, dx$

23. $\int_0^1 (1 + \sqrt{x})^8 dx$

24. $\int \ln(x^2 - 1) \, dx$

25. $\int \dfrac{3x^2 - 2}{x^2 - 2x - 8} dx$

26. $\int \dfrac{3x^2 - 2}{x^3 - 2x - 8} dx$

27. $\int \cot x \ln(\sin x) \, dx$

28. $\int \sin \sqrt{at} \, dt$

29. $\int_0^5 \dfrac{3w - 1}{w + 2} dw$

30. $\int_{-2}^2 |x^2 - 4x| \, dx$

31. $\int \sqrt{\dfrac{1+x}{1-x}} \, dx$

32. $\int \dfrac{\sqrt{2x-1}}{2x+3} dx$

33. $\int \sqrt{3 - 2x - x^2} \, dx$

34. $\int_{\pi/4}^{\pi/2} \dfrac{1 + 4 \cot x}{4 - \cot x} dx$

35. $\int_{-1}^1 x^8 \sin x \, dx$

36. $\int \sin 4x \cos 3x \, dx$

37. $\int_0^{\pi/4} \cos^2 \theta \tan^2 \theta \, d\theta$

38. $\int_0^{\pi/4} \tan^5 \theta \, \sec^3 \theta \, d\theta$

39. $\int \dfrac{x}{1 - x^2 + \sqrt{1 - x^2}} dx$

40. $\int \dfrac{1}{\sqrt{4y^2 - 4y - 3}} dy$

41. $\int \theta \tan^2 \theta \, d\theta$

42. $\int x^2 \tan^{-1} x \, dx$

43. $\int e^x \sqrt{1 + e^x} \, dx$

44. $\int \sqrt{1 + e^x} \, dx$

45. $\int x^5 e^{-x^3} dx$

46. $\int \dfrac{1 + e^x}{1 - e^x} dx$

47. $\int \dfrac{x + a}{x^2 + a^2} dx$

48. $\int \dfrac{x}{x^4 - a^4} dx$

49. $\displaystyle\int \frac{1}{x\sqrt{4x+1}}\,dx$

50. $\displaystyle\int \frac{1}{x^2\sqrt{4x+1}}\,dx$

67. $\displaystyle\int_1^3 \frac{\arctan\sqrt{t}}{\sqrt{t}}\,dt$

68. $\displaystyle\int \frac{1}{1+2e^x-e^{-x}}\,dx$

51. $\displaystyle\int \frac{1}{x\sqrt{4x^2+1}}\,dx$

52. $\displaystyle\int \frac{dx}{x(x^4+1)}$

69. $\displaystyle\int \frac{e^{2x}}{1+e^x}\,dx$

70. $\displaystyle\int \frac{\ln(x+1)}{x^2}\,dx$

53. $\displaystyle\int x^2 \sinh mx\,dx$

54. $\displaystyle\int (x+\sin x)^2\,dx$

71. $\displaystyle\int \frac{x}{x^4+4x^2+3}\,dx$

72. $\displaystyle\int \frac{\sqrt{t}}{1+\sqrt[3]{t}}\,dt$

55. $\displaystyle\int \frac{1}{x+4+4\sqrt{x+1}}\,dx$

56. $\displaystyle\int \frac{x\ln x}{\sqrt{x^2-1}}\,dx$

73. $\displaystyle\int \frac{1}{(x-2)(x^2+4)}\,dx$

74. $\displaystyle\int \frac{dx}{e^x-e^{-x}}$

57. $\displaystyle\int x\sqrt[3]{x+c}\,dx$

58. $\displaystyle\int x^2 \ln(1+x)\,dx$

75. $\displaystyle\int \sin x \sin 2x \sin 3x\,dx$

76. $\displaystyle\int (x^2-bx)\sin 2x\,dx$

59. $\displaystyle\int \frac{1}{e^{3x}-e^x}\,dx$

60. $\displaystyle\int \frac{1}{x+\sqrt[3]{x}}\,dx$

77. $\displaystyle\int \frac{\sqrt{x}}{1+x^3}\,dx$

78. $\displaystyle\int \frac{\sec x \cos 2x}{\sin x+\sec x}\,dx$

61. $\displaystyle\int \frac{x^4}{x^{10}+16}\,dx$

62. $\displaystyle\int \frac{x^3}{(x+1)^{10}}\,dx$

79. $\displaystyle\int x\sin^2 x \cos x\,dx$

80. $\displaystyle\int \frac{\sin x \cos x}{\sin^4 x+\cos^4 x}\,dx$

63. $\displaystyle\int \sqrt{x}\,e^{\sqrt{x}}\,dx$

64. $\displaystyle\int_{\pi/4}^{\pi/3} \frac{\ln(\tan x)}{\sin x \cos x}\,dx$

81. The functions $y=e^{x^2}$ and $y=x^2 e^{x^2}$ don't have elementary antiderivatives, but $y=(2x^2+1)e^{x^2}$ does. Evaluate $\int (2x^2+1)e^{x^2}\,dx$.

65. $\displaystyle\int \frac{1}{\sqrt{x+1}+\sqrt{x}}\,dx$

66. $\displaystyle\int_2^3 \frac{u^3+1}{u^3-u^2}\,du$

8.6 Integration Using Tables and Computer Algebra Systems

In this section we describe how to use tables and computer algebra systems to integrate functions that have elementary antiderivatives. You should bear in mind, though, that even the most powerful computer algebra systems can't find explicit formulas for the antiderivatives of functions like e^{x^2} or the other functions described at the end of Section 8.5.

Tables of Integrals

Tables of indefinite integrals are very useful when we are confronted by an integral that is difficult to evaluate by hand and we don't have access to a computer algebra system. A relatively brief table of 120 integrals, categorized by form, is provided on the Reference Pages at the back of the book. More extensive tables are available in *CRC Standard Mathematical Tables and Formulae,* 30th ed. by Daniel Zwillinger (Boca Raton, FL: CRC Press, 1995) (581 entries) or in Gradshteyn and Ryzhik's *Table of Integrals, Series, and Products,* 6e (New York: Academic Press, 2000), which contains hundreds of pages of integrals. It should be remembered, however, that integrals do not often occur in exactly the form listed in a table. Usually we need to use substitution or algebraic manipulation to transform a given integral into one of the forms in the table.

EXAMPLE 1 The region bounded by the curves $y=\arctan x$, $y=0$, and $x=1$ is rotated about the y-axis. Find the volume of the resulting solid.

SOLUTION Using the method of cylindrical shells, we see that the volume is

$$V = \int_0^1 2\pi x \arctan x\,dx$$

|||| The Table of Integrals appears on the Reference Pages at the back of the book.

In the section of the Table of Integrals entitled *Inverse Trigonometric Forms* we locate Formula 92:

$$\int u \tan^{-1}u \, du = \frac{u^2+1}{2}\tan^{-1}u - \frac{u}{2} + C$$

Thus, the volume is

$$V = 2\pi \int_0^1 x \tan^{-1}x \, dx = 2\pi \left[\frac{x^2+1}{2}\tan^{-1}x - \frac{x}{2} \right]_0^1$$

$$= \pi[(x^2+1)\tan^{-1}x - x]_0^1 = \pi(2\tan^{-1}1 - 1)$$

$$= \pi[2(\pi/4) - 1] = \tfrac{1}{2}\pi^2 - \pi$$

EXAMPLE 2 Use the Table of Integrals to find $\int \dfrac{x^2}{\sqrt{5-4x^2}}\, dx$.

SOLUTION If we look at the section of the table entitled *Forms involving* $\sqrt{a^2-u^2}$, we see that the closest entry is number 34:

$$\int \frac{u^2}{\sqrt{a^2-u^2}}\, du = -\frac{u}{2}\sqrt{a^2-u^2} + \frac{a^2}{2}\sin^{-1}\!\left(\frac{u}{a}\right) + C$$

This is not exactly what we have, but we will be able to use it if we first make the substitution $u = 2x$:

$$\int \frac{x^2}{\sqrt{5-4x^2}}\, dx = \int \frac{(u/2)^2}{\sqrt{5-u^2}}\frac{du}{2} = \frac{1}{8}\int \frac{u^2}{\sqrt{5-u^2}}\, du$$

Then we use Formula 34 with $a^2 = 5$ (so $a = \sqrt{5}$):

$$\int \frac{x^2}{\sqrt{5-4x^2}}\, dx = \frac{1}{8}\int \frac{u^2}{\sqrt{5-u^2}}\, du = \frac{1}{8}\left(-\frac{u}{2}\sqrt{5-u^2} + \frac{5}{2}\sin^{-1}\frac{u}{\sqrt{5}} \right) + C$$

$$= -\frac{x}{8}\sqrt{5-4x^2} + \frac{5}{16}\sin^{-1}\!\left(\frac{2x}{\sqrt{5}}\right) + C$$

EXAMPLE 3 Use the Table of Integrals to find $\int x^3 \sin x \, dx$.

SOLUTION If we look in the section called *Trigonometric Forms,* we see that none of the entries explicitly includes a u^3 factor. However, we can use the reduction formula in entry 84 with $n = 3$:

$$\int x^3 \sin x \, dx = -x^3 \cos x + 3\int x^2 \cos x \, dx$$

85. $\displaystyle\int u^n \cos u \, du$
$$= u^n \sin u - n\int u^{n-1}\sin u \, du$$

We now need to evaluate $\int x^2 \cos x \, dx$. We can use the reduction formula in entry 85 with $n = 2$, followed by entry 82:

$$\int x^2 \cos x \, dx = x^2 \sin x - 2\int x \sin x \, dx$$

$$= x^2 \sin x - 2(\sin x - x \cos x) + K$$

Combining these calculations, we get

$$\int x^3 \sin x \, dx = -x^3 \cos x + 3x^2 \sin x + 6x \cos x - 6 \sin x + C$$

where $C = 3K$.

EXAMPLE 4 Use the Table of Integrals to find $\displaystyle\int x\sqrt{x^2 + 2x + 4}\, dx$.

SOLUTION Since the table gives forms involving $\sqrt{a^2 + x^2}$, $\sqrt{a^2 - x^2}$, and $\sqrt{x^2 - a^2}$, but not $\sqrt{ax^2 + bx + c}$, we first complete the square:

$$x^2 + 2x + 4 = (x + 1)^2 + 3$$

If we make the substitution $u = x + 1$ (so $x = u - 1$), the integrand will involve the pattern $\sqrt{a^2 + u^2}$:

$$\int x\sqrt{x^2 + 2x + 4}\, dx = \int (u - 1)\sqrt{u^2 + 3}\, du$$

$$= \int u\sqrt{u^2 + 3}\, du - \int \sqrt{u^2 + 3}\, du$$

The first integral is evaluated using the substitution $t = u^2 + 3$:

$$\int u\sqrt{u^2 + 3}\, du = \tfrac{1}{2}\int \sqrt{t}\, dt = \tfrac{1}{2}\cdot\tfrac{2}{3}t^{3/2} = \tfrac{1}{3}(u^2 + 3)^{3/2}$$

21. $\displaystyle\int \sqrt{a^2 + u^2}\, du = \dfrac{u}{2}\sqrt{a^2 + u^2}$
$$+ \dfrac{a^2}{2}\ln\!\left(u + \sqrt{a^2 + u^2}\right) + C$$

For the second integral we use Formula 21 with $a = \sqrt{3}$:

$$\int \sqrt{u^2 + 3}\, du = \dfrac{u}{2}\sqrt{u^2 + 3} + \tfrac{3}{2}\ln\!\left(u + \sqrt{u^2 + 3}\right)$$

Thus

$$\int x\sqrt{x^2 + 2x + 4}\, dx$$

$$= \tfrac{1}{3}(x^2 + 2x + 4)^{3/2} - \dfrac{x + 1}{2}\sqrt{x^2 + 2x + 4} - \tfrac{3}{2}\ln\!\left(x + 1 + \sqrt{x^2 + 2x + 4}\right) + C$$

Computer Algebra Systems

We have seen that the use of tables involves matching the form of the given integrand with the forms of the integrands in the tables. Computers are particularly good at matching patterns. And just as we used substitutions in conjunction with tables, a CAS can perform substitutions that transform a given integral into one that occurs in its stored formulas. So it isn't surprising that computer algebra systems excel at integration. That doesn't mean that integration by hand is an obsolete skill. We will see that a hand computation sometimes produces an indefinite integral in a form that is more convenient than a machine answer.

To begin, let's see what happens when we ask a machine to integrate the relatively simple function $y = 1/(3x - 2)$. Using the substitution $u = 3x - 2$, an easy calculation by hand gives

$$\int \dfrac{1}{3x - 2}\, dx = \tfrac{1}{3}\ln |3x - 2| + C$$

whereas Derive, Mathematica, and Maple all return the answer

$$\tfrac{1}{3}\ln(3x - 2)$$

The first thing to notice is that computer algebra systems omit the constant of integration. In other words, they produce a *particular* antiderivative, not the most general one. Therefore, when making use of a machine integration, we might have to add a constant. Second, the absolute value signs are omitted in the machine answer. That is fine if our problem is concerned only with values of x greater than $\tfrac{2}{3}$. But if we are interested in other values of x, then we need to insert the absolute value symbol.

In the next example we reconsider the integral of Example 4, but this time we ask a machine for the answer.

EXAMPLE 5 Use a computer algebra system to find $\displaystyle\int x\sqrt{x^2 + 2x + 4}\,dx$.

SOLUTION Maple responds with the answer

$$\tfrac{1}{3}(x^2 + 2x + 4)^{3/2} - \tfrac{1}{4}(2x + 2)\sqrt{x^2 + 2x + 4} - \frac{3}{2}\operatorname{arcsinh}\frac{\sqrt{3}}{3}(1 + x)$$

This looks different from the answer we found in Example 4, but it is equivalent because the third term can be rewritten using the identity

▓▓▓▓ This is Equation 7.6.3.

$$\operatorname{arcsinh} x = \ln\!\left(x + \sqrt{x^2 + 1}\right)$$

Thus

$$\operatorname{arcsinh}\frac{\sqrt{3}}{3}(1 + x) = \ln\!\left[\frac{\sqrt{3}}{3}(1 + x) + \sqrt{\tfrac{1}{3}(1 + x)^2 + 1}\right]$$

$$= \ln\frac{1}{\sqrt{3}}\left[1 + x + \sqrt{(1 + x)^2 + 3}\right]$$

$$= \ln\frac{1}{\sqrt{3}} + \ln\!\left(x + 1 + \sqrt{x^2 + 2x + 4}\right)$$

The resulting extra term $-\tfrac{3}{2}\ln\!\left(1/\sqrt{3}\right)$ can be absorbed into the constant of integration.

Mathematica gives the answer

$$\left(\frac{5}{6} + \frac{x}{6} + \frac{x^2}{3}\right)\sqrt{x^2 + 2x + 4} - \frac{3}{2}\operatorname{arcsinh}\!\left(\frac{1 + x}{\sqrt{3}}\right)$$

Mathematica combined the first two terms of Example 4 (and the Maple result) into a single term by factoring.

Derive gives the answer

$$\tfrac{1}{6}\sqrt{x^2 + 2x + 4}\,(2x^2 + x + 5) - \tfrac{3}{2}\ln\!\left(\sqrt{x^2 + 2x + 4} + x + 1\right)$$

The first term is like the first term in the Mathematica answer, and the second term is identical to the last term in Example 4.

EXAMPLE 6 Use a CAS to evaluate $\displaystyle\int x(x^2 + 5)^8\,dx$.

SOLUTION Maple and Mathematica give the same answer:

$$\tfrac{1}{18}x^{18} + \tfrac{5}{2}x^{16} + 50x^{14} + \tfrac{1750}{3}x^{12} + 4375x^{10} + 21875x^8 + \tfrac{218750}{3}x^6 + 156250x^4 + \tfrac{390625}{2}x^2$$

It's clear that both systems must have expanded $(x^2 + 5)^8$ by the Binomial Theorem and then integrated each term.

If we integrate by hand instead, using the substitution $u = x^2 + 5$, we get

$$\int x(x^2 + 5)^8 \, dx = \tfrac{1}{18}(x^2 + 5)^9 + C$$

▓ Derive and the TI-89/92 also give this answer.

For most purposes, this is a more convenient form of the answer.

EXAMPLE 7 Use a CAS to find $\int \sin^5 x \cos^2 x \, dx$.

SOLUTION In Example 2 in Section 8.2 we found that

$$\boxed{1} \qquad \int \sin^5 x \cos^2 x \, dx = -\tfrac{1}{3}\cos^3 x + \tfrac{2}{5}\cos^5 x - \tfrac{1}{7}\cos^7 x + C$$

Derive and Maple report the answer

$$-\tfrac{1}{7}\sin^4 x \cos^3 x - \tfrac{4}{35}\sin^2 x \cos^3 x - \tfrac{8}{105}\cos^3 x$$

whereas Mathematica produces

$$-\tfrac{5}{64}\cos x - \tfrac{1}{192}\cos 3x + \tfrac{3}{320}\cos 5x - \tfrac{1}{448}\cos 7x$$

We suspect that there are trigonometric identities which show these three answers are equivalent. Indeed, if we ask Derive, Maple, and Mathematica to simplify their expressions using trigonometric identities, they ultimately produce the same form of the answer as in Equation 1.

FIGURE 1

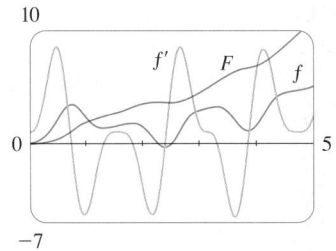

FIGURE 2

EXAMPLE 8 If $f(x) = x + 60 \sin^4 x \cos^5 x$, find the antiderivative F of f such that $F(0) = 0$. Graph F for $0 \le x \le 5$. Where does F have extreme values and inflection points?

SOLUTION The antiderivative of f produced by Maple is

$$F(x) = \tfrac{1}{2}x^2 - \tfrac{20}{3}\sin^3 x \cos^6 x - \tfrac{20}{7}\sin x \cos^6 x + \tfrac{4}{7}\cos^4 x \sin x + \tfrac{16}{21}\cos^2 x \sin x + \tfrac{32}{21}\sin x$$

and we note that $F(0) = 0$. This expression could probably be simplified, but there's no need to do so because a computer algebra system can graph this version of F as easily as any other version. A graph of F is shown in Figure 1. To locate the extreme values of F, we graph its derivative $F' = f$ in Figure 2 and observe that F has a local maximum when $x \approx 2.3$ and a local minimum when $x \approx 2.5$. The graph of $F'' = f'$ in Figure 2 shows that F has inflection points when $x \approx 0.7$, 1.3, 1.8, 2.4, 3.3, and 3.9.

8.6 Exercises

1–4 ▓ Use the indicated entry in the Table of Integrals on the Reference Pages to evaluate the integral.

1. $\displaystyle\int \frac{\sqrt{7 - 2x^2}}{x^2} \, dx$; entry 33

2. $\displaystyle\int \frac{3x}{\sqrt{3 - 2x}} \, dx$; entry 55

3. $\displaystyle\int \sec^3(\pi x) \, dx$; entry 71

4. $\displaystyle\int e^{2\theta} \sin 3\theta \, d\theta$; entry 98

5–30 ║║║ Use the Table of Integrals on the Reference Pages to evaluate the integral.

5. $\int_0^1 2x \cos^{-1}x \, dx$

6. $\int_2^3 \frac{1}{x^2\sqrt{4x^2 - 7}} \, dx$

7. $\int e^{-3x}\cos 4x \, dx$

8. $\int \csc^3(x/2) \, dx$

9. $\int \frac{dx}{x^2\sqrt{4x^2 + 9}}$

10. $\int \frac{\sqrt{2y^2 - 3}}{y^2} \, dy$

11. $\int_{-1}^0 t^2 e^{-t} \, dt$

12. $\int_0^\pi x^2\cos 3x \, dx$

13. $\int \frac{\tan^3(1/z)}{z^2} \, dz$

14. $\int \sin^{-1}\sqrt{x} \, dx$

15. $\int e^x \operatorname{sech}(e^x) \, dx$

16. $\int x\sin(x^2)\cos(3x^2) \, dx$

17. $\int y\sqrt{6 + 4y - 4y^2} \, dy$

18. $\int \frac{x^5}{x^2 + \sqrt{2}} \, dx$

19. $\int \sin^2 x \cos x \ln(\sin x) \, dx$

20. $\int \frac{dx}{e^x(1 + 2e^x)}$

21. $\int \frac{e^x}{3 - e^{2x}} \, dx$

22. $\int_0^2 x^3\sqrt{4x^2 - x^4} \, dx$

23. $\int \sec^5 x \, dx$

24. $\int \sin^6 2x \, dx$

25. $\int \frac{\sqrt{4 + (\ln x)^2}}{x} \, dx$

26. $\int_0^1 x^4 e^{-x} \, dx$

27. $\int \sqrt{e^{2x} - 1} \, dx$

28. $\int e^t\sin(\alpha t - 3) \, dt$

29. $\int \frac{x^4 \, dx}{\sqrt{x^{10} - 2}}$

30. $\int \frac{\sec^2\theta \, \tan^2\theta}{\sqrt{9 - \tan^2\theta}} \, d\theta$

31. Find the volume of the solid obtained when the region under the curve $y = x\sqrt{4 - x^2}$, $0 \le x \le 2$, is rotated about the y-axis.

32. The region under the curve $y = \tan^2 x$ from 0 to $\pi/4$ is rotated about the x-axis. Find the volume of the resulting solid.

33. Verify Formula 53 in the Table of Integrals (a) by differentiation and (b) by using the substitution $t = a + bu$.

34. Verify Formula 31 (a) by differentiation and (b) by substituting $u = a\sin\theta$.

CAS **35–42** ║║║ Use a computer algebra system to evaluate the integral. Compare the answer with the result of using tables. If the answers are not the same, show that they are equivalent.

35. $\int x^2\sqrt{5 - x^2} \, dx$

36. $\int x^2(1 + x^3)^4 \, dx$

37. $\int \sin^3 x \, \cos^2 x \, dx$

38. $\int \tan^2 x \, \sec^4 x \, dx$

39. $\int x\sqrt{1 + 2x} \, dx$

40. $\int \sin^4 x \, dx$

41. $\int \tan^5 x \, dx$

42. $\int x^5\sqrt{x^2 + 1} \, dx$

CAS **43.** Computer algebra systems sometimes need a helping hand from human beings. Ask your CAS to evaluate

$$\int 2^x \sqrt{4^x - 1} \, dx$$

If it doesn't return an answer, ask it to try

$$\int 2^x \sqrt{2^{2x} - 1} \, dx$$

instead. Why do you think it was successful with this form of the integrand?

CAS **44.** Try to evaluate

$$\int (1 + \ln x) \sqrt{1 + (x\ln x)^2} \, dx$$

with a computer algebra system. If it doesn't return an answer, make a substitution that changes the integral into one that the CAS *can* evaluate.

CAS **45–48** ║║║ Use a CAS to find an antiderivative F of f such that $F(0) = 0$. Graph f and F and locate approximately the x-coordinates of the extreme points and inflection points of F.

45. $f(x) = \dfrac{x^2 - 1}{x^4 + x^2 + 1}$

46. $f(x) = xe^{-x}\sin x$, $\quad -5 \le x \le 5$

47. $f(x) = \sin^4 x \, \cos^6 x$, $\quad 0 \le x \le \pi$

48. $f(x) = \dfrac{x^3 - x}{x^6 + 1}$

DISCOVERY PROJECT

CAS **Patterns in Integrals**

In this project a computer algebra system is used to investigate indefinite integrals of families of functions. By observing the patterns that occur in the integrals of several members of the family, you will first guess, and then prove, a general formula for the integral of any member of the family.

1. (a) Use a computer algebra system to evaluate the following integrals.

(i) $\displaystyle\int \frac{1}{(x+2)(x+3)}\,dx$ $\qquad$ (ii) $\displaystyle\int \frac{1}{(x+1)(x+5)}\,dx$

(iii) $\displaystyle\int \frac{1}{(x+2)(x-5)}\,dx$ $\qquad$ (iv) $\displaystyle\int \frac{1}{(x+2)^2}\,dx$

(b) Based on the pattern of your responses in part (a), guess the value of the integral

$$\int \frac{1}{(x+a)(x+b)}\,dx$$

if $a \neq b$. What if $a = b$?

(c) Check your guess by asking your CAS to evaluate the integral in part (b). Then prove it using partial fractions.

2. (a) Use a computer algebra system to evaluate the following integrals.

(i) $\displaystyle\int \sin x \cos 2x\,dx$ $\qquad$ (ii) $\displaystyle\int \sin 3x \cos 7x\,dx$ $\qquad$ (iii) $\displaystyle\int \sin 8x \cos 3x\,dx$

(b) Based on the pattern of your responses in part (a), guess the value of the integral

$$\int \sin ax \cos bx\,dx$$

(c) Check your guess with a CAS. Then prove it using the techniques of Section 7.2. For what values of a and b is it valid?

3. (a) Use a computer algebra system to evaluate the following integrals.

(i) $\displaystyle\int \ln x\,dx$ $\qquad$ (ii) $\displaystyle\int x \ln x\,dx$ $\qquad$ (iii) $\displaystyle\int x^2 \ln x\,dx$

(iv) $\displaystyle\int x^3 \ln x\,dx$ $\qquad$ (v) $\displaystyle\int x^7 \ln x\,dx$

(b) Based on the pattern of your responses in part (a), guess the value of

$$\int x^n \ln x\,dx$$

(c) Use integration by parts to prove the conjecture that you made in part (b). For what values of n is it valid?

4. (a) Use a computer algebra system to evaluate the following integrals.

(i) $\displaystyle\int xe^x\,dx$ $\qquad$ (ii) $\displaystyle\int x^2 e^x\,dx$ $\qquad$ (iii) $\displaystyle\int x^3 e^x\,dx$

(iv) $\displaystyle\int x^4 e^x\,dx$ $\qquad$ (v) $\displaystyle\int x^5 e^x\,dx$

(b) Based on the pattern of your responses in part (a), guess the value of $\int x^6 e^x\,dx$. Then use your CAS to check your guess.

(c) Based on the patterns in parts (a) and (b), make a conjecture as to the value of the integral

$$\int x^n e^x\,dx$$

when n is a positive integer.

(d) Use mathematical induction to prove the conjecture you made in part (c).

8.7 Approximate Integration

There are two situations in which it is impossible to find the exact value of a definite integral.

The first situation arises from the fact that in order to evaluate $\int_a^b f(x)\, dx$ using the Fundamental Theorem of Calculus we need to know an antiderivative of f. Sometimes, however, it is difficult, or even impossible, to find an antiderivative (see Section 8.5). For example, it is impossible to evaluate the following integrals exactly:

$$\int_0^1 e^{x^2}\, dx \qquad \int_{-1}^1 \sqrt{1 + x^3}\, dx$$

The second situation arises when the function is determined from a scientific experiment through instrument readings or collected data. There may be no formula for the function (see Example 5).

In both cases we need to find approximate values of definite integrals. We already know one such method. Recall that the definite integral is defined as a limit of Riemann sums, so any Riemann sum could be used as an approximation to the integral: If we divide $[a, b]$ into n subintervals of equal length $\Delta x = (b - a)/n$, then we have

$$\int_a^b f(x)\, dx \approx \sum_{i=1}^n f(x_i^*)\, \Delta x$$

where x_i^* is any point in the ith subinterval $[x_{i-1}, x_i]$. If x_i^* is chosen to be the left endpoint of the interval, then $x_i^* = x_{i-1}$ and we have

(a) Left endpoint approximation

$$\boxed{1} \qquad \int_a^b f(x)\, dx \approx L_n = \sum_{i=1}^n f(x_{i-1})\, \Delta x$$

If $f(x) \geq 0$, then the integral represents an area and (1) represents an approximation of this area by the rectangles shown in Figure 1(a). If we choose x_i^* to be the right endpoint, then $x_i^* = x_i$ and we have

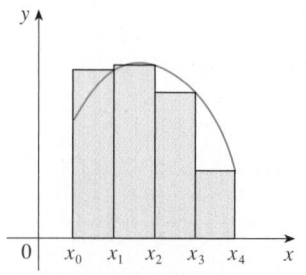

(b) Right endpoint approximation

$$\boxed{2} \qquad \int_a^b f(x)\, dx \approx R_n = \sum_{i=1}^n f(x_i)\, \Delta x$$

[See Figure 1(b).] The approximations L_n and R_n defined by Equations 1 and 2 are called the **left endpoint approximation** and **right endpoint approximation**, respectively.

In Section 5.2 we also considered the case where x_i^* is chosen to be the midpoint $\bar{x}_i$ of the subinterval $[x_{i-1}, x_i]$. Figure 1(c) shows the midpoint approximation M_n, which appears to be better than either L_n or R_n.

(c) Midpoint approximation

FIGURE 1

Midpoint Rule

$$\int_a^b f(x)\, dx \approx M_n = \Delta x\left[f(\bar{x}_1) + f(\bar{x}_2) + \cdots + f(\bar{x}_n) \right]$$

where

$$\Delta x = \frac{b - a}{n}$$

and

$$\bar{x}_i = \tfrac{1}{2}(x_{i-1} + x_i) = \text{midpoint of } [x_{i-1}, x_i]$$

Another approximation, called the Trapezoidal Rule, results from averaging the approximations in Equations 1 and 2:

$$\int_a^b f(x)\, dx \approx \frac{1}{2}\left[\sum_{i=1}^{n} f(x_{i-1})\,\Delta x + \sum_{i=1}^{n} f(x_i)\,\Delta x\right] = \frac{\Delta x}{2}\left[\sum_{i=1}^{n}\left(f(x_{i-1}) + f(x_i)\right)\right]$$

$$= \frac{\Delta x}{2}\left[(f(x_0) + f(x_1)) + (f(x_1) + f(x_2)) + \cdots + (f(x_{n-1}) + f(x_n))\right]$$

$$= \frac{\Delta x}{2}\left[f(x_0) + 2f(x_1) + 2f(x_2) + \cdots + 2f(x_{n-1}) + f(x_n)\right]$$

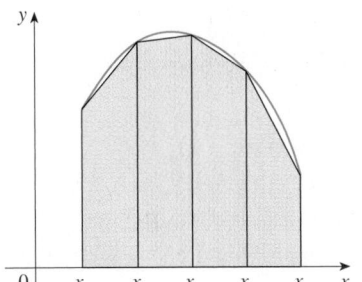

FIGURE 2

Trapezoidal approximation

Trapezoidal Rule

$$\int_a^b f(x)\, dx \approx T_n = \frac{\Delta x}{2}\left[f(x_0) + 2f(x_1) + 2f(x_2) + \cdots + 2f(x_{n-1}) + f(x_n)\right]$$

where $\Delta x = (b - a)/n$ and $x_i = a + i\,\Delta x$.

The reason for the name Trapezoidal Rule can be seen from Figure 2, which illustrates the case $f(x) \geq 0$. The area of the trapezoid that lies above the ith subinterval is

$$\Delta x\left(\frac{f(x_{i-1}) + f(x_i)}{2}\right) = \frac{\Delta x}{2}\left[f(x_{i-1}) + f(x_i)\right]$$

and if we add the areas of all these trapezoids, we get the right side of the Trapezoidal Rule.

EXAMPLE 1 Use (a) the Trapezoidal Rule and (b) the Midpoint Rule with $n = 5$ to approximate the integral $\int_1^2 (1/x)\, dx$.

SOLUTION

(a) With $n = 5$, $a = 1$, and $b = 2$, we have $\Delta x = (2 - 1)/5 = 0.2$, and so the Trapezoidal Rule gives

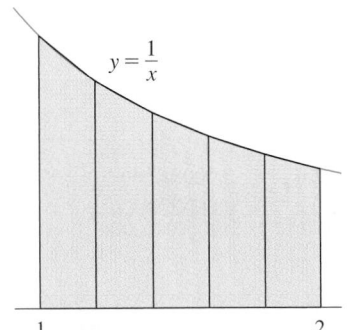

FIGURE 3

$$\int_1^2 \frac{1}{x}\, dx \approx T_5 = \frac{0.2}{2}\left[f(1) + 2f(1.2) + 2f(1.4) + 2f(1.6) + 2f(1.8) + f(2)\right]$$

$$= 0.1\left(\frac{1}{1} + \frac{2}{1.2} + \frac{2}{1.4} + \frac{2}{1.6} + \frac{2}{1.8} + \frac{1}{2}\right)$$

$$\approx 0.695635$$

This approximation is illustrated in Figure 3.

(b) The midpoints of the five subintervals are 1.1, 1.3, 1.5, 1.7, and 1.9, so the Midpoint Rule gives

$$\int_1^2 \frac{1}{x}\, dx \approx \Delta x\left[f(1.1) + f(1.3) + f(1.5) + f(1.7) + f(1.9)\right]$$

$$= \frac{1}{5}\left(\frac{1}{1.1} + \frac{1}{1.3} + \frac{1}{1.5} + \frac{1}{1.7} + \frac{1}{1.9}\right)$$

$$\approx 0.691908$$

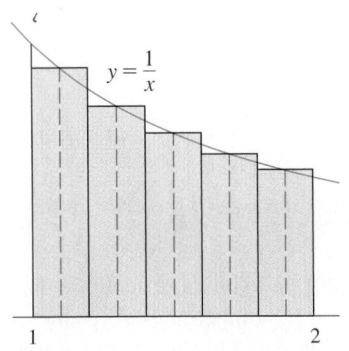

FIGURE 4

This approximation is illustrated in Figure 4.

In Example 1 we deliberately chose an integral whose value can be computed explicitly so that we can see how accurate the Trapezoidal and Midpoint Rules are. By the Fundamental Theorem of Calculus,

$$\int_1^2 \frac{1}{x}\, dx = \ln x]_1^2 = \ln 2 = 0.693147\ldots$$

$\int_a^b f(x)\, dx = \text{approximation} + \text{error}$

The **error** in using an approximation is defined to be the amount that needs to be added to the approximation to make it exact. From the values in Example 1 we see that the errors in the Trapezoidal and Midpoint Rule approximations for $n = 5$ are

$$E_T \approx -0.002488 \qquad \text{and} \qquad E_M \approx 0.001239$$

In general, we have

$$E_T = \int_a^b f(x)\, dx - T_n \qquad \text{and} \qquad E_M = \int_a^b f(x)\, dx - M_n$$

Module 5.1/5.2/8.7 allows you to compare approximation methods.

The following tables show the results of calculations similar to those in Example 1, but for $n = 5$, 10, and 20 and for the left and right endpoint approximations as well as the Trapezoidal and Midpoint Rules.

Approximations to $\int_1^2 \frac{1}{x}\, dx$

n	L_n	R_n	T_n	M_n
5	0.745635	0.645635	0.695635	0.691908
10	0.718771	0.668771	0.693771	0.692835
20	0.705803	0.680803	0.693303	0.693069

Corresponding errors

n	E_L	E_R	E_T	E_M
5	−0.052488	0.047512	−0.002488	0.001239
10	−0.025624	0.024376	−0.000624	0.000312
20	−0.012656	0.012344	−0.000156	0.000078

We can make several observations from these tables:

1. In all of the methods we get more accurate approximations when we increase the value of n. (But very large values of n result in so many arithmetic operations that we have to beware of accumulated round-off error.)

2. The errors in the left and right endpoint approximations are opposite in sign and appear to decrease by a factor of about 2 when we double the value of n.

▥ It turns out that these observations are true in most cases.

3. The Trapezoidal and Midpoint Rules are much more accurate than the endpoint approximations.

4. The errors in the Trapezoidal and Midpoint Rules are opposite in sign and appear to decrease by a factor of about 4 when we double the value of n.

5. The size of the error in the Midpoint Rule is about half the size of the error in the Trapezoidal Rule.

Figure 5 shows why we can usually expect the Midpoint Rule to be more accurate than the Trapezoidal Rule. The area of a typical rectangle in the Midpoint Rule is the same as the trapezoid *ABCD* whose upper side is tangent to the graph at *P*. The area of this trapezoid is closer to the area under the graph than is the area of the trapezoid *AQRD* used in

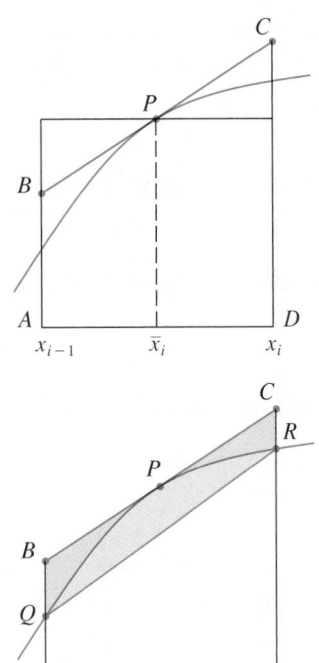

FIGURE 5

|||| K can be any number larger than all the values of $|f''(x)|$, but smaller values of K give better error bounds.

the Trapezoidal Rule. [The midpoint error (shaded red) is smaller than the trapezoidal error (shaded blue).]

These observations are corroborated in the following error estimates, which are proved in books on numerical analysis. Notice that Observation 4 corresponds to the n^2 in each denominator because $(2n)^2 = 4n^2$. The fact that the estimates depend on the size of the second derivative is not surprising if you look at Figure 5, because $f''(x)$ measures how much the graph is curved. [Recall that $f''(x)$ measures how fast the slope of $y = f(x)$ changes.]

> **3 Error Bounds** Suppose $|f''(x)| \leq K$ for $a \leq x \leq b$. If E_T and E_M are the errors in the Trapezoidal and Midpoint Rules, then
>
> $$|E_T| \leq \frac{K(b-a)^3}{12n^2} \qquad \text{and} \qquad |E_M| \leq \frac{K(b-a)^3}{24n^2}$$

Let's apply this error estimate to the Trapezoidal Rule approximation in Example 1. If $f(x) = 1/x$, then $f'(x) = -1/x^2$ and $f''(x) = 2/x^3$. Since $1 \leq x \leq 2$, we have $1/x \leq 1$, so

$$|f''(x)| = \left|\frac{2}{x^3}\right| \leq \frac{2}{1^3} = 2$$

Therefore, taking $K = 2$, $a = 1$, $b = 2$, and $n = 5$ in the error estimate (3), we see that

$$|E_T| \leq \frac{2(2-1)^3}{12(5)^2} = \frac{1}{150} \approx 0.006667$$

Comparing this error estimate of 0.006667 with the actual error of about 0.002488, we see that it can happen that the actual error is substantially less than the upper bound for the error given by (3).

EXAMPLE 2 How large should we take n in order to guarantee that the Trapezoidal and Midpoint Rule approximations for $\int_1^2 (1/x)\, dx$ are accurate to within 0.0001?

SOLUTION We saw in the preceding calculation that $|f''(x)| \leq 2$ for $1 \leq x \leq 2$, so we can take $K = 2$, $a = 1$, and $b = 2$ in (3). Accuracy to within 0.0001 means that the size of the error should be less than 0.0001. Therefore, we choose n so that

$$\frac{2(1)^3}{12n^2} < 0.0001$$

Solving the inequality for n, we get

$$n^2 > \frac{2}{12(0.0001)}$$

|||| It's quite possible that a lower value for n would suffice, but 41 is the smallest value for which the error bound formula can *guarantee* us accuracy to within 0.0001.

or

$$n > \frac{1}{\sqrt{0.0006}} \approx 40.8$$

Thus, $n = 41$ will ensure the desired accuracy.

To simplify our calculations, we first consider the case where $x_0 = -h$, $x_1 = 0$, and $x_2 = h$. (See Figure 8.) We know that the equation of the parabola through P_0, P_1, and P_2 is of the form $y = Ax^2 + Bx + C$ and so the area under the parabola from $x = -h$ to $x = h$ is

▏▏▏▏ Here we have used Theorem 5.5.6. Notice that $Ax^2 + C$ is even and Bx is odd.

$$\int_{-h}^{h} (Ax^2 + Bx + C)\, dx = 2 \int_{0}^{h} (Ax^2 + C)\, dx$$

$$= 2\left[A\frac{x^3}{3} + Cx \right]_{0}^{h}$$

$$= 2\left(A\frac{h^3}{3} + Ch \right) = \frac{h}{3}(2Ah^2 + 6C)$$

But, since the parabola passes through $P_0(-h, y_0)$, $P_1(0, y_1)$, and $P_2(h, y_2)$, we have

$$y_0 = A(-h)^2 + B(-h) + C = Ah^2 - Bh + C$$

$$y_1 = C$$

$$y_2 = Ah^2 + Bh + C$$

and therefore

$$y_0 + 4y_1 + y_2 = 2Ah^2 + 6C$$

Thus, we can rewrite the area under the parabola as

$$\frac{h}{3}(y_0 + 4y_1 + y_2)$$

Now, by shifting this parabola horizontally we do not change the area under it. This means that the area under the parabola through P_0, P_1, and P_2 from $x = x_0$ to $x = x_2$ in Figure 7 is still

$$\frac{h}{3}(y_0 + 4y_1 + y_2)$$

Similarly, the area under the parabola through P_2, P_3, and P_4 from $x = x_2$ to $x = x_4$ is

$$\frac{h}{3}(y_2 + 4y_3 + y_4)$$

If we compute the areas under all the parabolas in this manner and add the results, we get

$$\int_{a}^{b} f(x)\, dx \approx \frac{h}{3}(y_0 + 4y_1 + y_2) + \frac{h}{3}(y_2 + 4y_3 + y_4) + \cdots + \frac{h}{3}(y_{n-2} + 4y_{n-1} + y_n)$$

$$= \frac{h}{3}(y_0 + 4y_1 + 2y_2 + 4y_3 + 2y_4 + \cdots + 2y_{n-2} + 4y_{n-1} + y_n)$$

Although we have derived this approximation for the case in which $f(x) \geqslant 0$, it is a reasonable approximation for any continuous function f and is called Simpson's Rule after the English mathematician Thomas Simpson (1710–1761). Note the pattern of coefficients: $1, 4, 2, 4, 2, 4, 2, \ldots, 4, 2, 4, 1$.

|||| Thomas Simpson was a weaver who taught himself mathematics and went on to become one of the best English mathematicians of the 18th century. What we call Simpson's Rule was actually known to Cavalieri and Gregory in the 17th century, but Simpson popularized it in his best-selling calculus textbook, entitled *A New Treatise of Fluxions*.

Simpson's Rule

$$\int_a^b f(x)\,dx \approx S_n = \frac{\Delta x}{3}[f(x_0) + 4f(x_1) + 2f(x_2) + 4f(x_3) + \cdots$$

$$+ 2f(x_{n-2}) + 4f(x_{n-1}) + f(x_n)]$$

where n is even and $\Delta x = (b - a)/n$.

EXAMPLE 4 Use Simpson's Rule with $n = 10$ to approximate $\int_1^2 (1/x)\,dx$.

SOLUTION Putting $f(x) = 1/x$, $n = 10$, and $\Delta x = 0.1$ in Simpson's Rule, we obtain

$$\int_1^2 \frac{1}{x}\,dx \approx S_{10}$$

$$= \frac{\Delta x}{3}[f(1) + 4f(1.1) + 2f(1.2) + 4f(1.3) + \cdots + 2f(1.8) + 4f(1.9) + f(2)]$$

$$= \frac{0.1}{3}\left(\frac{1}{1} + \frac{4}{1.1} + \frac{2}{1.2} + \frac{4}{1.3} + \frac{2}{1.4} + \frac{4}{1.5} + \frac{2}{1.6} + \frac{4}{1.7} + \frac{2}{1.8} + \frac{4}{1.9} + \frac{1}{2}\right)$$

$$\approx 0.693150$$

Notice that, in Example 4, Simpson's Rule gives us a *much* better approximation ($S_{10} \approx 0.693150$) to the true value of the integral ($\ln 2 \approx 0.693147\ldots$) than does the Trapezoidal Rule ($T_{10} \approx 0.693771$) or the Midpoint Rule ($M_{10} \approx 0.692835$). It turns out (see Exercise 48) that the approximations in Simpson's Rule are weighted averages of those in the Trapezoidal and Midpoint Rules:

$$S_{2n} = \tfrac{1}{3}T_n + \tfrac{2}{3}M_n$$

(Recall that E_T and E_M usually have opposite signs and $|E_M|$ is about half the size of $|E_T|$.)

In many applications of calculus we need to evaluate an integral even if no explicit formula is known for y as a function of x. A function may be given graphically or as a table of values of collected data. If there is evidence that the values are not changing rapidly, then the Trapezoidal Rule or Simpson's Rule can still be used to find an approximate value for $\int_a^b y\,dx$, the integral of y with respect to x.

EXAMPLE 5 Figure 9 shows data traffic on the link from the United States to SWITCH, the Swiss academic and research network, on February 10, 1998. $D(t)$ is the data throughput, measured in megabits per second (Mb/s). Use Simpson's Rule to estimate the total amount of data transmitted on the link up to noon on that day.

FIGURE 9

SOLUTION Because we want the units to be consistent and $D(t)$ is measured in megabits per second, we convert the units for t from hours to seconds. If we let $A(t)$ be the amount of data (in megabits) transmitted by time t, where t is measured in seconds, then $A'(t) = D(t)$. So, by the Net Change Theorem (see Section 5.4), the total amount of data transmitted by noon (when $t = 12 \times 60^2 = 43{,}200$) is

$$A(43{,}200) = \int_0^{43{,}200} D(t)\, dt$$

We estimate the values of $D(t)$ at hourly intervals from the graph and compile them in the table.

t (hours)	t (seconds)	$D(t)$	t (hours)	t (seconds)	$D(t)$
0	0	3.2	7	25,200	1.3
1	3,600	2.7	8	28,800	2.8
2	7,200	1.9	9	32,400	5.7
3	10,800	1.7	10	36,000	7.1
4	14,400	1.3	11	39,600	7.7
5	18,000	1.0	12	43,200	7.9
6	21,600	1.1			

Then we use Simpson's Rule with $n = 12$ and $\Delta t = 3600$ to estimate the integral:

$$\int_0^{43{,}200} A(t)\, dt \approx \frac{\Delta t}{3}[D(0) + 4D(3600) + 2D(7200) + \cdots + 4D(39{,}600) + D(43{,}200)]$$

$$\approx \frac{3600}{3}[3.2 + 4(2.7) + 2(1.9) + 4(1.7) + 2(1.3) + 4(1.0)$$

$$+ 2(1.1) + 4(1.3) + 2(2.8) + 4(5.7) + 2(7.1) + 4(7.7) + 7.9]$$

$$= 143{,}880$$

Thus, the total amount of data transmitted up to noon is about 144,000 megabits, or 144 gigabits.

In Exercises 27 and 28 you are asked to demonstrate, in particular cases, that the error in Simpson's Rule decreases by a factor of about 16 when n is doubled. That is consistent with the appearance of n^4 in the denominator of the following error estimate for Simpson's Rule. It is similar to the estimates given in (3) for the Trapezoidal and Midpoint Rules, but it uses the fourth derivative of f.

> **4 Error Bound for Simpson's Rule** Suppose that $|f^{(4)}(x)| \leq K$ for $a \leq x \leq b$. If E_S is the error involved in using Simpson's Rule, then
>
> $$|E_S| \leq \frac{K(b-a)^5}{180n^4}$$

EXAMPLE 6 How large should we take n in order to guarantee that the Simpson's Rule approximation for $\int_1^2 (1/x) \, dx$ is accurate to within 0.0001?

SOLUTION If $f(x) = 1/x$, then $f^{(4)}(x) = 24/x^5$. Since $x \geqslant 1$, we have $1/x \leqslant 1$ and so

$$\left| f^{(4)}(x) \right| = \left| \frac{24}{x^5} \right| \leqslant 24$$

|||| Many calculators and computer algebra systems have a built-in algorithm that computes an approximation of a definite integral. Some of these machines use Simpson's Rule; others use more sophisticated techniques such as *adaptive* numerical integration. This means that if a function fluctuates much more on a certain part of the interval than it does elsewhere, then that part gets divided into more subintervals. This strategy reduces the number of calculations required to achieve a prescribed accuracy.

Therefore, we can take $K = 24$ in (4). Thus, for an error less than 0.0001 we should choose n so that

$$\frac{24(1)^5}{180n^4} < 0.0001$$

This gives

$$n^4 > \frac{24}{180(0.0001)}$$

or

$$n > \frac{1}{\sqrt[4]{0.00075}} \approx 6.04$$

Therefore, $n = 8$ (n must be even) gives the desired accuracy. (Compare this with Example 2, where we obtained $n = 41$ for the Trapezoidal Rule and $n = 29$ for the Midpoint Rule.)

EXAMPLE 7
(a) Use Simpson's Rule with $n = 10$ to approximate the integral $\int_0^1 e^{x^2} \, dx$.
(b) Estimate the error involved in this approximation.

SOLUTION
(a) If $n = 10$, then $\Delta x = 0.1$ and Simpson's Rule gives

$$\int_0^1 e^{x^2} dx \approx \frac{\Delta x}{3} [f(0) + 4f(0.1) + 2f(0.2) + \cdots + 2f(0.8) + 4f(0.9) + f(1)]$$

$$= \frac{0.1}{3} [e^0 + 4e^{0.01} + 2e^{0.04} + 4e^{0.09} + 2e^{0.16} + 4e^{0.25} + 2e^{0.36}$$

$$+ 4e^{0.49} + 2e^{0.64} + 4e^{0.81} + e^1]$$

$$\approx 1.462681$$

|||| Figure 10 illustrates the calculation in Example 7. Notice that the parabolic arcs are so close to the graph of $y = e^{x^2}$ that they are practically indistinguishable from it.

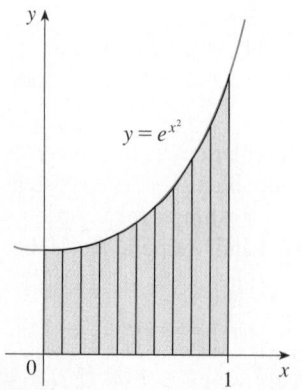

FIGURE 10

(b) The fourth derivative of $f(x) = e^{x^2}$ is

$$f^{(4)}(x) = (12 + 48x^2 + 16x^4)e^{x^2}$$

and so, since $0 \leqslant x \leqslant 1$, we have

$$0 \leqslant f^{(4)}(x) \leqslant (12 + 48 + 16)e^1 = 76e$$

Therefore, putting $K = 76e$, $a = 0$, $b = 1$, and $n = 10$ in (4), we see that the error is at most

$$\frac{76e(1)^5}{180(10)^4} \approx 0.000115$$

(Compare this with Example 3.) Thus, correct to three decimal places, we have

$$\int_0^1 e^{x^2} dx \approx 1.463$$

8.7 Exercises

1. Let $I = \int_0^4 f(x)\,dx$, where f is the function whose graph is shown.
(a) Use the graph to find L_2, R_2, and M_2.
(b) Are these underestimates or overestimates of I?
(c) Use the graph to find T_2. How does it compare with I?
(d) For any value of n, list the numbers L_n, R_n, M_n, T_n, and I in increasing order.

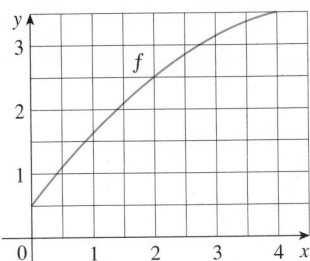

2. The left, right, Trapezoidal, and Midpoint Rule approximations were used to estimate $\int_0^2 f(x)\,dx$, where f is the function whose graph is shown. The estimates were 0.7811, 0.8675, 0.8632, and 0.9540, and the same number of subintervals were used in each case.
(a) Which rule produced which estimate?
(b) Between which two approximations does the true value of $\int_0^2 f(x)\,dx$ lie?

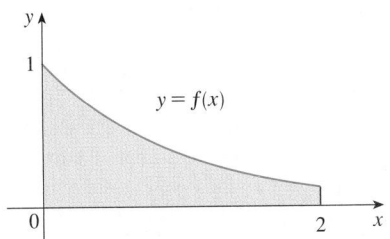

3. Estimate $\int_0^1 \cos(x^2)\,dx$ using (a) the Trapezoidal Rule and (b) the Midpoint Rule, each with $n = 4$. From a graph of the integrand, decide whether your answers are underestimates or overestimates. What can you conclude about the true value of the integral?

4. Draw the graph of $f(x) = \sin(x^2/2)$ in the viewing rectangle $[0, 1]$ by $[0, 0.5]$ and let $I = \int_0^1 f(x)\,dx$.
(a) Use the graph to decide whether L_2, R_2, M_2, and T_2 underestimate or overestimate I.
(b) For any value of n, list the numbers L_n, R_n, M_n, T_n, and I in increasing order.
(c) Compute L_5, R_5, M_5, and T_5. From the graph, which do you think gives the best estimate of I?

5–6 ▒ Use (a) the Midpoint Rule and (b) Simpson's Rule to approximate the given integral with the specified value of n.

(Round your answers to six decimal places.) Compare your results to the actual value to determine the error in each approximation.

5. $\int_0^{\pi} x^2 \sin x\,dx$, $\quad n = 8$

6. $\int_0^1 e^{-\sqrt{x}}\,dx$, $\quad n = 6$

7–18 ▒ Use (a) the Trapezoidal Rule, (b) the Midpoint Rule, and (c) Simpson's Rule to approximate the given integral with the specified value of n. (Round your answers to six decimal places.)

7. $\int_0^2 \sqrt[4]{1 + x^2}\,dx$, $\quad n = 8$

8. $\int_0^{1/2} \sin(x^2)\,dx$, $\quad n = 4$

9. $\int_1^2 \dfrac{\ln x}{1 + x}\,dx$, $\quad n = 10$

10. $\int_0^3 \dfrac{dt}{1 + t^2 + t^4}$, $\quad n = 6$

11. $\int_0^{1/2} \sin(e^{t/2})\,dt$, $\quad n = 8$

12. $\int_0^4 \sqrt{1 + \sqrt{x}}\,dx$, $\quad n = 8$

13. $\int_1^2 e^{1/x}\,dx$, $\quad n = 4$

14. $\int_0^4 \sqrt{x} \sin x\,dx$, $\quad n = 8$

15. $\int_1^5 \dfrac{\cos x}{x}\,dx$, $\quad n = 8$

16. $\int_4^6 \ln(x^3 + 2)\,dx$, $\quad n = 10$

17. $\int_0^3 \dfrac{1}{1 + y^5}\,dy$, $\quad n = 6$

18. $\int_2^4 \dfrac{e^x}{x}\,dx$, $\quad n = 10$

19. (a) Find the approximations T_{10} and M_{10} for the integral $\int_0^2 e^{-x^2}\,dx$.
(b) Estimate the errors in the approximations of part (a).
(c) How large do we have to choose n so that the approximations T_n and M_n to the integral in part (a) are accurate to within 0.00001?

20. (a) Find the approximations T_8 and M_8 for $\int_0^1 \cos(x^2)\,dx$.
(b) Estimate the errors involved in the approximations of part (a).
(c) How large do we have to choose n so that the approximations T_n and M_n to the integral in part (a) are accurate to within 0.00001?

21. (a) Find the approximations T_{10} and S_{10} for $\int_0^1 e^x\,dx$ and the corresponding errors E_T and E_S.
(b) Compare the actual errors in part (a) with the error estimates given by (3) and (4).
(c) How large do we have to choose n so that the approximations T_n, M_n, and S_n to the integral in part (a) are accurate to within 0.00001?

22. How large should n be to guarantee that the Simpson's Rule approximation to $\int_0^1 e^{x^2}\,dx$ is accurate to within 0.00001?

23. The trouble with the error estimates is that it is often very difficult to compute four derivatives and obtain a good upper bound K for $|f^{(4)}(x)|$ by hand. But computer algebra systems have no problem computing $f^{(4)}$ and graphing it, so we can easily find a value for K from a machine graph. This exercise deals with approximations to the integral $I = \int_0^{2\pi} f(x)\,dx$, where $f(x) = e^{\cos x}$.

(a) Use a graph to get a good upper bound for $|f''(x)|$.
(b) Use M_{10} to approximate I.
(c) Use part (a) to estimate the error in part (b).
(d) Use the built-in numerical integration capability of your CAS to approximate I.
(e) How does the actual error compare with the error estimate in part (c)?
(f) Use a graph to get a good upper bound for $|f^{(4)}(x)|$.
(g) Use S_{10} to approximate I.
(h) Use part (f) to estimate the error in part (g).
(i) How does the actual error compare with the error estimate in part (h)?
(j) How large should n be to guarantee that the size of the error in using S_n is less than 0.0001?

[CAS] **24.** Repeat Exercise 23 for the integral $\int_{-1}^{1} \sqrt{4 - x^3}\,dx$.

25–26 ▓ Find the approximations L_n, R_n, T_n, and M_n for $n = 4, 8$, and 16. Then compute the corresponding errors E_L, E_R, E_T, and E_M. (Round your answers to six decimal places. You may wish to use the sum command on a computer algebra system.) What observations can you make? In particular, what happens to the errors when n is doubled?

25. $\int_0^1 x^3\,dx$ **26.** $\int_0^2 e^x\,dx$

27–28 ▓ Find the approximations T_n, M_n, and S_n for $n = 6$ and 12. Then compute the corresponding errors E_T, E_M, and E_S. (Round your answers to six decimal places. You may wish to use the sum command on a computer algebra system.) What observations can you make? In particular, what happens to the errors when n is doubled?

27. $\int_1^4 \sqrt{x}\,dx$ **28.** $\int_{-1}^2 xe^x\,dx$

29. Estimate the area under the graph in the figure by using (a) the Trapezoidal Rule, (b) the Midpoint Rule, and (c) Simpson's Rule, each with $n = 4$.

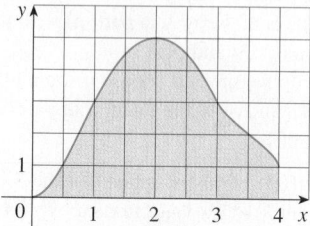

30. The widths (in meters) of a kidney-shaped swimming pool were measured at 2-meter intervals as indicated in the figure.

Use Simpson's Rule to estimate the area of the pool.

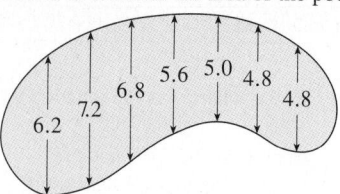

31. (a) Use the Midpoint Rule and the given data to estimate the value of the integral $\int_0^{3.2} f(x)\,dx$.

x	$f(x)$	x	$f(x)$
0.0	6.8	2.0	7.6
0.4	6.5	2.4	8.4
0.8	6.3	2.8	8.8
1.2	6.4	3.2	9.0
1.6	6.9		

(b) If it is known that $-4 \leqslant f''(x) \leqslant 1$ for all x, estimate the error involved in the approximation in part (a).

32. A radar gun was used to record the speed of a runner during the first 5 seconds of a race (see the table). Use Simpson's Rule to estimate the distance the runner covered during those 5 seconds.

t (s)	v (m/s)	t (s)	v (m/s)
0	0	3.0	10.51
0.5	4.67	3.5	10.67
1.0	7.34	4.0	10.76
1.5	8.86	4.5	10.81
2.0	9.73	5.0	10.81
2.5	10.22		

33. The graph of the acceleration $a(t)$ of a car measured in ft/s^2 is shown. Use Simpson's Rule to estimate the increase in the velocity of the car during the 6-second time interval.

34. Water leaked from a tank at a rate of $r(t)$ liters per hour, where the graph of r is as shown. Use Simpson's Rule to estimate the total amount of water that leaked out during the first six hours.

35. The table (supplied by San Diego Gas and Electric) gives the power consumption in megawatts in San Diego County from midnight to 6:00 A.M. on December 8, 1999. Use Simpson's Rule to estimate the energy used during that time period. (Use the fact that power is the derivative of energy.)

t	P	t	P
0:00	1814	3:30	1611
0:30	1735	4:00	1621
1:00	1686	4:30	1666
1:30	1646	5:00	1745
2:00	1637	5:30	1886
2:30	1609	6:00	2052
3:00	1604		

36. Shown is the graph of traffic on an Internet service provider's T1 data line from midnight to 8:00 A.M. D is the data throughput, measured in megabits per second. Use Simpson's Rule to estimate the total amount of data transmitted during that time period.

37. If the region shown in the figure is rotated about the y-axis to form a solid, use Simpson's Rule with $n = 8$ to estimate the volume of the solid.

38. The table shows values of a force function $f(x)$ where x is measured in meters and $f(x)$ in newtons. Use Simpson's Rule to estimate the work done by the force in moving an object a distance of 18 m.

x	0	3	6	9	12	15	18
$f(x)$	9.8	9.1	8.5	8.0	7.7	7.5	7.4

39. The region bounded by the curves $y = \sqrt[3]{1 + x^3}$, $y = 0$, $x = 0$, and $x = 2$ is rotated about the x-axis. Use Simpson's Rule with $n = 10$ to estimate the volume of the resulting solid.

[CAS] **40.** The figure shows a pendulum with length L that makes a maximum angle θ_0 with the vertical. Using Newton's Second Law it can be shown that the period T (the time for one complete swing) is given by

$$T = 4\sqrt{\frac{L}{g}} \int_0^{\pi/2} \frac{dx}{\sqrt{1 - k^2 \sin^2 x}}$$

where $k = \sin\left(\frac{1}{2}\theta_0\right)$ and g is the acceleration due to gravity. If $L = 1$ m and $\theta_0 = 42°$, use Simpson's Rule with $n = 10$ to find the period.

41. The intensity of light with wavelength λ traveling through a diffraction grating with N slits at an angle θ is given by $I(\theta) = N^2 \sin^2 k / k^2$, where $k = (\pi N d \sin \theta)/\lambda$ and d is the distance between adjacent slits. A helium-neon laser with wavelength $\lambda = 632.8 \times 10^{-9}$ m is emitting a narrow band of light, given by $-10^{-6} < \theta < 10^{-6}$, through a grating with 10,000 slits spaced 10^{-4} m apart. Use the Midpoint Rule with $n = 10$ to estimate the total light intensity $\int_{-10^{-6}}^{10^{-6}} I(\theta)\, d\theta$ emerging from the grating.

42. Use the Trapezoidal Rule with $n = 10$ to approximate $\int_0^{20} \cos(\pi x)\, dx$. Compare your result to the actual value. Can you explain the discrepancy?

43. Sketch the graph of a continuous function on $[0, 2]$ for which the Trapezoidal Rule with $n = 2$ is more accurate than the Midpoint Rule.

44. Sketch the graph of a continuous function on $[0, 2]$ for which the right endpoint approximation with $n = 2$ is more accurate than Simpson's Rule.

45. If f is a positive function and $f''(x) < 0$ for $a \le x \le b$, show that

$$T_n < \int_a^b f(x)\, dx < M_n$$

46. Show that if f is a polynomial of degree 3 or lower, then Simpson's Rule gives the exact value of $\int_a^b f(x)\, dx$.

47. Show that $\frac{1}{2}(T_n + M_n) = T_{2n}$.

48. Show that $\frac{1}{3}T_n + \frac{2}{3}M_n = S_{2n}$.

|||| 8.8 Improper Integrals

In defining a definite integral $\int_a^b f(x)\,dx$ we dealt with a function f defined on a finite interval $[a, b]$ and we assumed that f does not have an infinite discontinuity (see Section 5.2). In this section we extend the concept of a definite integral to the case where the interval is infinite and also to the case where f has an infinite discontinuity in $[a, b]$. In either case the integral is called an *improper* integral. One of the most important applications of this idea, probability distributions, will be studied in Section 9.5.

|||| Type I: Infinite Intervals

Try painting a fence that never ends.
Resources / Module 6
JTC / How To Calculate
/ Start of Improper Integrals

Consider the infinite region S that lies under the curve $y = 1/x^2$, above the x-axis, and to the right of the line $x = 1$. You might think that, since S is infinite in extent, its area must be infinite, but let's take a closer look. The area of the part of S that lies to the left of the line $x = t$ (shaded in Figure 1) is

$$A(t) = \int_1^t \frac{1}{x^2}\,dx = -\frac{1}{x}\bigg]_1^t = 1 - \frac{1}{t}$$

Notice that $A(t) < 1$ no matter how large t is chosen.

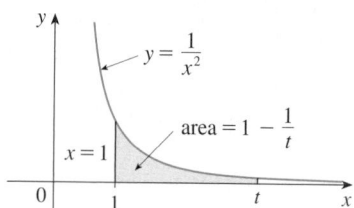

FIGURE 1

We also observe that

$$\lim_{t \to \infty} A(t) = \lim_{t \to \infty}\left(1 - \frac{1}{t}\right) = 1$$

The area of the shaded region approaches 1 as $t \to \infty$ (see Figure 2), so we say that the area of the infinite region S is equal to 1 and we write

$$\int_1^\infty \frac{1}{x^2}\,dx = \lim_{t \to \infty}\int_1^t \frac{1}{x^2}\,dx = 1$$

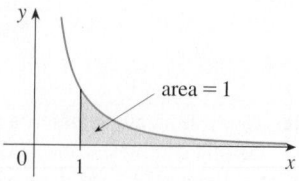

FIGURE 2

Using this example as a guide, we define the integral of f (not necessarily a positive function) over an infinite interval as the limit of integrals over finite intervals.

---

1 | **Definition of an Improper Integral of Type 1**

(a) If $\int_a^t f(x)\, dx$ exists for every number $t \geqslant a$, then

$$\int_a^\infty f(x)\, dx = \lim_{t \to \infty} \int_a^t f(x)\, dx$$

provided this limit exists (as a finite number).

(b) If $\int_t^b f(x)\, dx$ exists for every number $t \leqslant b$, then

$$\int_{-\infty}^b f(x)\, dx = \lim_{t \to -\infty} \int_t^b f(x)\, dx$$

provided this limit exists (as a finite number).

The improper integrals $\int_a^\infty f(x)\, dx$ and $\int_{-\infty}^b f(x)\, dx$ are called **convergent** if the corresponding limit exists and **divergent** if the limit does not exist.

(c) If both $\int_a^\infty f(x)\, dx$ and $\int_{-\infty}^a f(x)\, dx$ are convergent, then we define

$$\int_{-\infty}^\infty f(x)\, dx = \int_{-\infty}^a f(x)\, dx + \int_a^\infty f(x)\, dx$$

In part (c) any real number a can be used (see Exercise 74).

Any of the improper integrals in Definition 1 can be interpreted as an area provided that f is a positive function. For instance, in case (a) if $f(x) \geqslant 0$ and the integral $\int_a^\infty f(x)\, dx$ is convergent, then we define the area of the region $S = \{(x, y) \mid x \geqslant a, 0 \leqslant y \leqslant f(x)\}$ in Figure 3 to be

$$A(S) = \int_a^\infty f(x)\, dx$$

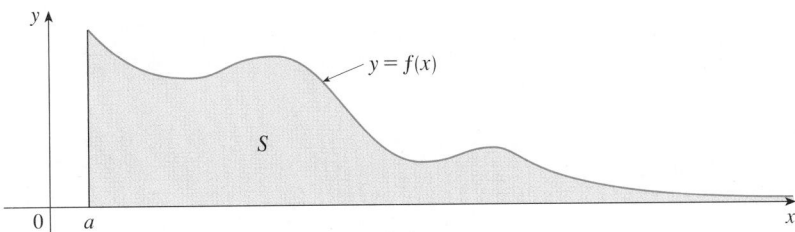

FIGURE 3

This is appropriate because $\int_a^\infty f(x)\, dx$ is the limit as $t \to \infty$ of the area under the graph of f from a to t.

EXAMPLE 1 Determine whether the integral $\int_1^\infty (1/x)\, dx$ is convergent or divergent.

SOLUTION According to part (a) of Definition 1, we have

$$\int_1^\infty \frac{1}{x}\, dx = \lim_{t \to \infty} \int_1^t \frac{1}{x}\, dx = \lim_{t \to \infty} \ln |x|\big]_1^t$$

$$= \lim_{t \to \infty} (\ln t - \ln 1) = \lim_{t \to \infty} \ln t = \infty$$

The limit does not exist as a finite number and so the improper integral $\int_1^\infty (1/x)\, dx$ is divergent.

FIGURE 4

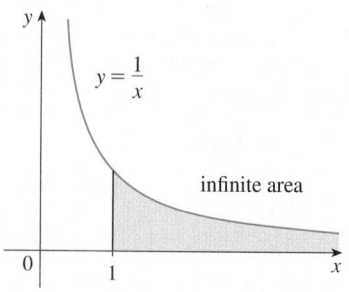

FIGURE 5

Let's compare the result of Example 1 with the example given at the beginning of this section:

$$\int_1^\infty \frac{1}{x^2}\, dx \text{ converges} \qquad \int_1^\infty \frac{1}{x}\, dx \text{ diverges}$$

Geometrically, this says that although the curves $y = 1/x^2$ and $y = 1/x$ look very similar for $x > 0$, the region under $y = 1/x^2$ to the right of $x = 1$ (the shaded region in Figure 4) has finite area whereas the corresponding region under $y = 1/x$ (in Figure 5) has infinite area. Note that both $1/x^2$ and $1/x$ approach 0 as $x \to \infty$ but $1/x^2$ approaches 0 faster than $1/x$. The values of $1/x$ don't decrease fast enough for its integral to have a finite value.

EXAMPLE 2 Evaluate $\int_{-\infty}^0 xe^x\, dx$.

SOLUTION Using part (b) of Definition 1, we have

$$\int_{-\infty}^0 xe^x\, dx = \lim_{t \to -\infty} \int_t^0 xe^x\, dx$$

We integrate by parts with $u = x$, $dv = e^x\, dx$ so that $du = dx$, $v = e^x$:

$$\int_t^0 xe^x\, dx = xe^x \Big]_t^0 - \int_t^0 e^x\, dx$$

$$= -te^t - 1 + e^t$$

We know that $e^t \to 0$ as $t \to -\infty$, and by l'Hospital's Rule we have

$$\lim_{t \to -\infty} te^t = \lim_{t \to -\infty} \frac{t}{e^{-t}} = \lim_{t \to -\infty} \frac{1}{-e^{-t}}$$

$$= \lim_{t \to -\infty} (-e^t) = 0$$

Therefore

$$\int_{-\infty}^0 xe^x\, dx = \lim_{t \to -\infty} (-te^t - 1 + e^t)$$

$$= -0 - 1 + 0 = -1$$

EXAMPLE 3 Evaluate $\int_{-\infty}^\infty \frac{1}{1 + x^2}\, dx$.

SOLUTION It's convenient to choose $a = 0$ in Definition 1(c):

$$\int_{-\infty}^\infty \frac{1}{1 + x^2}\, dx = \int_{-\infty}^0 \frac{1}{1 + x^2}\, dx + \int_0^\infty \frac{1}{1 + x^2}\, dx$$

We must now evaluate the integrals on the right side separately:

$$\int_0^\infty \frac{1}{1 + x^2}\, dx = \lim_{t \to \infty} \int_0^t \frac{dx}{1 + x^2} = \lim_{t \to \infty} \tan^{-1}x \Big]_0^t$$

$$= \lim_{t \to \infty} (\tan^{-1}t - \tan^{-1}0) = \lim_{t \to \infty} \tan^{-1}t = \frac{\pi}{2}$$

$$\int_{-\infty}^{0} \frac{1}{1+x^2}\, dx = \lim_{t \to -\infty} \int_{t}^{0} \frac{dx}{1+x^2} = \lim_{t \to -\infty} \tan^{-1}x \Big]_{t}^{0}$$

$$= \lim_{t \to -\infty} (\tan^{-1}0 - \tan^{-1}t)$$

$$= 0 - \left(-\frac{\pi}{2}\right) = \frac{\pi}{2}$$

Since both of these integrals are convergent, the given integral is convergent and

$$\int_{-\infty}^{\infty} \frac{1}{1+x^2}\, dx = \frac{\pi}{2} + \frac{\pi}{2} = \pi$$

Since $1/(1+x^2) > 0$, the given improper integral can be interpreted as the area of the infinite region that lies under the curve $y = 1/(1+x^2)$ and above the x-axis (see Figure 6).

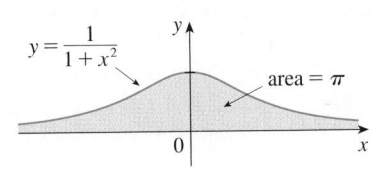

$y = \dfrac{1}{1+x^2}$ area $= \pi$

FIGURE 6

EXAMPLE 4 For what values of p is the integral

$$\int_{1}^{\infty} \frac{1}{x^p}\, dx$$

convergent?

SOLUTION We know from Example 1 that if $p = 1$, then the integral is divergent, so let's assume that $p \neq 1$. Then

$$\int_{1}^{\infty} \frac{1}{x^p}\, dx = \lim_{t \to \infty} \int_{1}^{t} x^{-p}\, dx$$

$$= \lim_{t \to \infty} \frac{x^{-p+1}}{-p+1} \bigg]_{x=1}^{x=t}$$

$$= \lim_{t \to \infty} \frac{1}{1-p} \left[\frac{1}{t^{p-1}} - 1\right]$$

If $p > 1$, then $p - 1 > 0$, so as $t \to \infty$, $t^{p-1} \to \infty$ and $1/t^{p-1} \to 0$. Therefore

$$\int_{1}^{\infty} \frac{1}{x^p}\, dx = \frac{1}{p-1} \qquad \text{if } p > 1$$

and so the integral converges. But if $p < 1$, then $p - 1 < 0$ and so

$$\frac{1}{t^{p-1}} = t^{1-p} \to \infty \qquad \text{as } t \to \infty$$

and the integral diverges.

We summarize the result of Example 4 for future reference:

$$\boxed{2} \qquad \int_{1}^{\infty} \frac{1}{x^p}\, dx \quad \text{is convergent if } p > 1 \text{ and divergent if } p \leq 1.$$

▌▌▌ **Type 2: Discontinuous Integrands**

Suppose that f is a positive continuous function defined on a finite interval $[a, b)$ but has a vertical asymptote at b. Let S be the unbounded region under the graph of f and above the x-axis between a and b. (For Type 1 integrals, the regions extended indefinitely in a

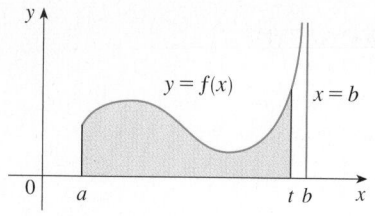

FIGURE 7

horizontal direction. Here the region is infinite in a vertical direction.) The area of the part of S between a and t (the shaded region in Figure 7) is

$$A(t) = \int_a^t f(x)\,dx$$

If it happens that $A(t)$ approaches a definite number A as $t \to b^-$, then we say that the area of the region S is A and we write

$$\int_a^b f(x)\,dx = \lim_{t\to b^-} \int_a^t f(x)\,dx$$

We use this equation to define an improper integral of Type 2 even when f is not a positive function, no matter what type of discontinuity f has at b.

	Definition of an Improper Integral of Type 2

③ Definition of an Improper Integral of Type 2

(a) If f is continuous on $[a, b)$ and is discontinuous at b, then

$$\int_a^b f(x)\,dx = \lim_{t\to b^-} \int_a^t f(x)\,dx$$

if this limit exists (as a finite number).

(b) If f is continuous on $(a, b]$ and is discontinuous at a, then

$$\int_a^b f(x)\,dx = \lim_{t\to a^+} \int_t^b f(x)\,dx$$

if this limit exists (as a finite number).

The improper integral $\int_a^b f(x)\,dx$ is called **convergent** if the corresponding limit exists and **divergent** if the limit does not exist.

(c) If f has a discontinuity at c, where $a < c < b$, and both $\int_a^c f(x)\,dx$ and $\int_c^b f(x)\,dx$ are convergent, then we define

$$\int_a^b f(x)\,dx = \int_a^c f(x)\,dx + \int_c^b f(x)\,dx$$

▌▌▌▌ Parts (b) and (c) of Definition 3 are illustrated in Figures 8 and 9 for the case where $f(x) \geq 0$ and f has vertical asymptotes at a and c, respectively.

FIGURE 8

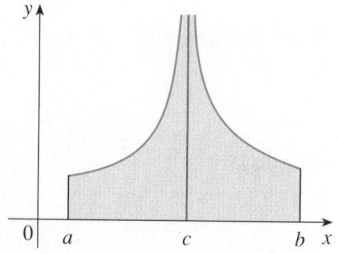

FIGURE 9

EXAMPLE 5 Find $\displaystyle\int_2^5 \frac{1}{\sqrt{x-2}}\,dx$.

SOLUTION We note first that the given integral is improper because $f(x) = 1/\sqrt{x-2}$ has the vertical asymptote $x = 2$. Since the infinite discontinuity occurs at the left endpoint of $[2, 5]$, we use part (b) of Definition 3:

$$\int_2^5 \frac{dx}{\sqrt{x-2}} = \lim_{t\to 2^+} \int_t^5 \frac{dx}{\sqrt{x-2}}$$
$$= \lim_{t\to 2^+} 2\sqrt{x-2}\,\Big]_t^5$$
$$= \lim_{t\to 2^+} 2\left(\sqrt{3} - \sqrt{t-2}\right)$$
$$= 2\sqrt{3}$$

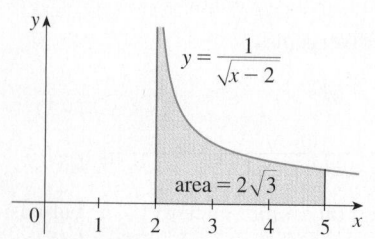

$$y = \frac{1}{\sqrt{x-2}}$$

area $= 2\sqrt{3}$

FIGURE 10

Thus, the given improper integral is convergent and, since the integrand is positive, we can interpret the value of the integral as the area of the shaded region in Figure 10. ▬

EXAMPLE 6 Determine whether $\int_0^{\pi/2} \sec x \, dx$ converges or diverges.

SOLUTION Note that the given integral is improper because $\lim_{x \to (\pi/2)^-} \sec x = \infty$. Using part (a) of Definition 3 and Formula 14 from the Table of Integrals, we have

$$\int_0^{\pi/2} \sec x \, dx = \lim_{t \to (\pi/2)^-} \int_0^t \sec x \, dx$$

$$= \lim_{t \to (\pi/2)^-} \ln \left| \sec x + \tan x \right| \Big]_0^t$$

$$= \lim_{t \to (\pi/2)^-} [\ln(\sec t + \tan t) - \ln 1]$$

$$= \infty$$

because $\sec t \to \infty$ and $\tan t \to \infty$ as $t \to (\pi/2)^-$. Thus, the given improper integral is divergent.

EXAMPLE 7 Evaluate $\int_0^3 \dfrac{dx}{x-1}$ if possible.

SOLUTION Observe that the line $x = 1$ is a vertical asymptote of the integrand. Since it occurs in the middle of the interval $[0, 3]$, we must use part (c) of Definition 3 with $c = 1$:

$$\int_0^3 \frac{dx}{x-1} = \int_0^1 \frac{dx}{x-1} + \int_1^3 \frac{dx}{x-1}$$

where

$$\int_0^1 \frac{dx}{x-1} = \lim_{t \to 1^-} \int_0^t \frac{dx}{x-1} = \lim_{t \to 1^-} \ln |x - 1| \Big]_0^t$$

$$= \lim_{t \to 1^-} \left(\ln |t - 1| - \ln |-1| \right)$$

$$= \lim_{t \to 1^-} \ln(1 - t) = -\infty$$

because $1 - t \to 0^+$ as $t \to 1^-$. Thus, $\int_0^1 dx/(x - 1)$ is divergent. This implies that $\int_0^3 dx/(x - 1)$ is divergent. [We do not need to evaluate $\int_1^3 dx/(x - 1)$.]

⊘   **WARNING** ◦ If we had not noticed the asymptote $x = 1$ in Example 7 and had instead confused the integral with an ordinary integral, then we might have made the following erroneous calculation:

$$\int_0^3 \frac{dx}{x-1} = \ln |x - 1| \Big]_0^3 = \ln 2 - \ln 1 = \ln 2$$

This is wrong because the integral is improper and must be calculated in terms of limits.

From now on, whenever you meet the symbol $\int_a^b f(x) \, dx$ you must decide, by looking at the function f on $[a, b]$, whether it is an ordinary definite integral or an improper integral.

EXAMPLE 8 Evaluate $\int_0^1 \ln x \, dx$.

SOLUTION We know that the function $f(x) = \ln x$ has a vertical asymptote at 0 since $\lim_{x \to 0^+} \ln x = -\infty$. Thus, the given integral is improper and we have

$$\int_0^1 \ln x \, dx = \lim_{t \to 0^+} \int_t^1 \ln x \, dx$$

Now we integrate by parts with $u = \ln x$, $dv = dx$, $du = dx/x$, and $v = x$:

$$\int_t^1 \ln x \, dx = x \ln x \Big]_t^1 - \int_t^1 dx$$

$$= 1 \ln 1 - t \ln t - (1 - t)$$

$$= -t \ln t - 1 + t$$

To find the limit of the first term we use l'Hospital's Rule:

$$\lim_{t \to 0^+} t \ln t = \lim_{t \to 0^+} \frac{\ln t}{1/t}$$

$$= \lim_{t \to 0^+} \frac{1/t}{-1/t^2}$$

$$= \lim_{t \to 0^+} (-t) = 0$$

Therefore
$$\int_0^1 \ln x \, dx = \lim_{t \to 0^+} (-t \ln t - 1 + t)$$

$$= -0 - 1 + 0 = -1$$

Figure 11 shows the geometric interpretation of this result. The area of the shaded region above $y = \ln x$ and below the x-axis is 1.

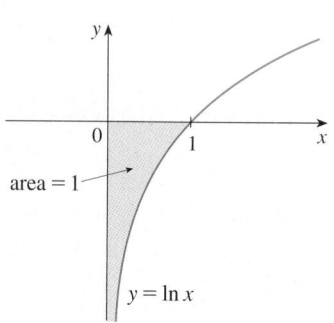

area = 1

$y = \ln x$

FIGURE 11

||||| A Comparison Test for Improper Integrals

Sometimes it is impossible to find the exact value of an improper integral and yet it is important to know whether it is convergent or divergent. In such cases the following theorem is useful. Although we state it for Type 1 integrals, a similar theorem is true for Type 2 integrals.

> **Comparison Theorem** Suppose that f and g are continuous functions with $f(x) \geq g(x) \geq 0$ for $x \geq a$.
>
> (a) If $\int_a^\infty f(x) \, dx$ is convergent, then $\int_a^\infty g(x) \, dx$ is convergent.
>
> (b) If $\int_a^\infty g(x) \, dx$ is divergent, then $\int_a^\infty f(x) \, dx$ is divergent.

We omit the proof of the Comparison Theorem, but Figure 12 makes it seem plausible. If the area under the top curve $y = f(x)$ is finite, then so is the area under the bottom curve $y = g(x)$. And if the area under $y = g(x)$ is infinite, then so is the area under $y = f(x)$. [Note that the reverse is not necessarily true: If $\int_a^\infty g(x) \, dx$ is convergent, $\int_a^\infty f(x) \, dx$ may or may not be convergent, and if $\int_a^\infty f(x) \, dx$ is divergent, $\int_a^\infty g(x) \, dx$ may or may not be divergent.]

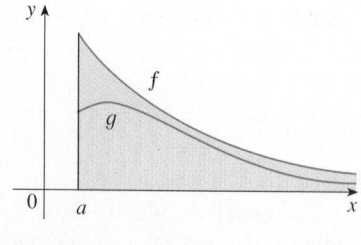

f

g

a

FIGURE 12

EXAMPLE 9 Show that $\int_0^\infty e^{-x^2} \, dx$ is convergent.

SOLUTION We can't evaluate the integral directly because the antiderivative of e^{-x^2} is not an elementary function (as explained in Section 8.5). We write

$$\int_0^\infty e^{-x^2} dx = \int_0^1 e^{-x^2} dx + \int_1^\infty e^{-x^2} dx$$

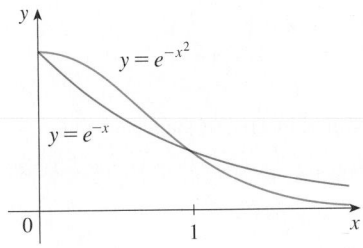

FIGURE 13

and observe that the first integral on the right-hand side is just an ordinary definite integral. In the second integral we use the fact that for $x \geq 1$ we have $x^2 \geq x$, so $-x^2 \leq -x$ and therefore $e^{-x^2} \leq e^{-x}$. (See Figure 13.) The integral of e^{-x} is easy to evaluate:

$$\int_1^\infty e^{-x}\, dx = \lim_{t \to \infty} \int_1^t e^{-x}\, dx$$

$$= \lim_{t \to \infty} (e^{-1} - e^{-t}) = e^{-1}$$

Thus, taking $f(x) = e^{-x}$ and $g(x) = e^{-x^2}$ in the Comparison Theorem, we see that $\int_1^\infty e^{-x^2}\, dx$ is convergent. It follows that $\int_0^\infty e^{-x^2}\, dx$ is convergent.

In Example 9 we showed that $\int_0^\infty e^{-x^2}\, dx$ is convergent without computing its value. In Exercise 70 we indicate how to show that its value is approximately 0.8862. In probability theory it is important to know the exact value of this improper integral, as we will see in Section 9.5; using the methods of multivariable calculus it can be shown that the exact value is $\sqrt{\pi}/2$. Table 1 illustrates the definition of an improper integral by showing how the (computer-generated) values of $\int_0^t e^{-x^2}\, dx$ approach $\sqrt{\pi}/2$ as t becomes large. In fact, these values converge quite quickly because $e^{-x^2} \to 0$ very rapidly as $x \to \infty$.

TABLE 1

t	$\int_0^t e^{-x^2}\, dx$
1	0.7468241328
2	0.8820813908
3	0.8862073483
4	0.8862269118
5	0.8862269255
6	0.8862269255

EXAMPLE 10 The integral $\displaystyle\int_1^\infty \frac{1 + e^{-x}}{x}\, dx$ is divergent by the Comparison Theorem because

$$\frac{1 + e^{-x}}{x} > \frac{1}{x}$$

and $\int_1^\infty (1/x)\, dx$ is divergent by Example 1 [or by (2) with $p = 1$].

Table 2 illustrates the divergence of the integral in Example 10. It appears that the values are not approaching any fixed number.

TABLE 2

t	$\int_1^t [(1 + e^{-x})/x]\, dx$
2	0.8636306042
5	1.8276735512
10	2.5219648704
100	4.8245541204
1000	7.1271392134
10000	9.4297243064

8.8 Exercises

1. Explain why each of the following integrals is improper.

(a) $\displaystyle\int_1^\infty x^4 e^{-x^4}\, dx$

(b) $\displaystyle\int_0^{\pi/2} \sec x\, dx$

(c) $\displaystyle\int_0^2 \frac{x}{x^2 - 5x + 6}\, dx$

(d) $\displaystyle\int_{-\infty}^0 \frac{1}{x^2 + 5}\, dx$

2. Which of the following integrals are improper? Why?

(a) $\displaystyle\int_1^2 \frac{1}{2x - 1}\, dx$

(b) $\displaystyle\int_0^1 \frac{1}{2x - 1}\, dx$

(c) $\displaystyle\int_{-\infty}^\infty \frac{\sin x}{1 + x^2}\, dx$

(d) $\displaystyle\int_1^2 \ln(x - 1)\, dx$

3. Find the area under the curve $y = 1/x^3$ from $x = 1$ to $x = t$ and evaluate it for $t = 10$, 100, and 1000. Then find the total area under this curve for $x \geqslant 1$.

4. (a) Graph the functions $f(x) = 1/x^{1.1}$ and $g(x) = 1/x^{0.9}$ in the viewing rectangles [0, 10] by [0, 1] and [0, 100] by [0, 1].
(b) Find the areas under the graphs of f and g from $x = 1$ to $x = t$ and evaluate for $t = 10$, 100, 10^4, 10^6, 10^{10}, and 10^{20}.
(c) Find the total area under each curve for $x \geqslant 1$, if it exists.

5–40 ▓ Determine whether each integral is convergent or divergent. Evaluate those that are convergent.

5. $\displaystyle\int_1^\infty \frac{1}{(3x+1)^2}\,dx$

6. $\displaystyle\int_{-\infty}^0 \frac{1}{2x-5}\,dx$

7. $\displaystyle\int_{-\infty}^{-1} \frac{1}{\sqrt{2-w}}\,dw$

8. $\displaystyle\int_0^\infty \frac{x}{(x^2+2)^2}\,dx$

9. $\displaystyle\int_4^\infty e^{-y/2}\,dy$

10. $\displaystyle\int_{-\infty}^{-1} e^{-2t}\,dt$

11. $\displaystyle\int_{-\infty}^\infty \frac{x}{1+x^2}\,dx$

12. $\displaystyle\int_{-\infty}^\infty (2-v^4)\,dv$

13. $\displaystyle\int_{-\infty}^\infty xe^{-x^2}\,dx$

14. $\displaystyle\int_{-\infty}^\infty x^2 e^{-x^3}\,dx$

15. $\displaystyle\int_{2\pi}^\infty \sin\theta\,d\theta$

16. $\displaystyle\int_0^\infty \cos^2\alpha\,d\alpha$

17. $\displaystyle\int_1^\infty \frac{x+1}{x^2+2x}\,dx$

18. $\displaystyle\int_0^\infty \frac{dz}{z^2+3z+2}$

19. $\displaystyle\int_0^\infty se^{-5s}\,ds$

20. $\displaystyle\int_{-\infty}^6 re^{r/3}\,dr$

21. $\displaystyle\int_1^\infty \frac{\ln x}{x}\,dx$

22. $\displaystyle\int_{-\infty}^\infty e^{-|x|}\,dx$

23. $\displaystyle\int_{-\infty}^\infty \frac{x^2}{9+x^6}\,dx$

24. $\displaystyle\int_1^\infty \frac{\ln x}{x^3}\,dx$

25. $\displaystyle\int_1^\infty \frac{\ln x}{x^2}\,dx$

26. $\displaystyle\int_0^\infty \frac{x\arctan x}{(1+x^2)^2}\,dx$

27. $\displaystyle\int_0^3 \frac{1}{\sqrt{x}}\,dx$

28. $\displaystyle\int_0^3 \frac{1}{x\sqrt{x}}\,dx$

29. $\displaystyle\int_{-1}^0 \frac{1}{x^2}\,dx$

30. $\displaystyle\int_1^9 \frac{1}{\sqrt[3]{x-9}}\,dx$

31. $\displaystyle\int_{-2}^3 \frac{1}{x^4}\,dx$

32. $\displaystyle\int_0^1 \frac{dx}{\sqrt{1-x^2}}$

33. $\displaystyle\int_0^{33} (x-1)^{-1/5}\,dx$

34. $\displaystyle\int_0^1 \frac{1}{4y-1}\,dy$

35. $\displaystyle\int_0^\pi \sec x\,dx$

36. $\displaystyle\int_0^4 \frac{1}{x^2+x-6}\,dx$

37. $\displaystyle\int_{-1}^1 \frac{e^x}{e^x-1}\,dx$

38. $\displaystyle\int_0^2 \frac{x-3}{2x-3}\,dx$

39. $\displaystyle\int_0^2 z^2 \ln z\,dz$

40. $\displaystyle\int_0^1 \frac{\ln x}{\sqrt{x}}\,dx$

41–46 ▓ Sketch the region and find its area (if the area is finite).

41. $S = \{(x,y) \mid x \leqslant 1,\ 0 \leqslant y \leqslant e^x\}$

42. $S = \{(x,y) \mid x \geqslant -2,\ 0 \leqslant y \leqslant e^{-x/2}\}$

43. $S = \{(x,y) \mid 0 \leqslant y \leqslant 2/(x^2+9)\}$

44. $S = \{(x,y) \mid x \geqslant 0,\ 0 \leqslant y \leqslant x/(x^2+9)\}$

45. $S = \{(x,y) \mid 0 \leqslant x < \pi/2,\ 0 \leqslant y \leqslant \sec^2 x\}$

46. $S = \{(x,y) \mid -2 < x \leqslant 0,\ 0 \leqslant y \leqslant 1/\sqrt{x+2}\}$

47. (a) If $g(x) = (\sin^2 x)/x^2$, use your calculator or computer to make a table of approximate values of $\int_1^t g(x)\,dx$ for $t = 2$, 5, 10, 100, 1000, and 10,000. Does it appear that $\int_1^\infty g(x)\,dx$ is convergent?
(b) Use the Comparison Theorem with $f(x) = 1/x^2$ to show that $\int_1^\infty g(x)\,dx$ is convergent.
(c) Illustrate part (b) by graphing f and g on the same screen for $1 \leqslant x \leqslant 10$. Use your graph to explain intuitively why $\int_1^\infty g(x)\,dx$ is convergent.

48. (a) If $g(x) = 1/(\sqrt{x}-1)$, use your calculator or computer to make a table of approximate values of $\int_2^t g(x)\,dx$ for $t = 5$, 10, 100, 1000, and 10,000. Does it appear that $\int_2^\infty g(x)\,dx$ is convergent or divergent?
(b) Use the Comparison Theorem with $f(x) = 1/\sqrt{x}$ to show that $\int_2^\infty g(x)\,dx$ is divergent.
(c) Illustrate part (b) by graphing f and g on the same screen for $2 \leqslant x \leqslant 20$. Use your graph to explain intuitively why $\int_2^\infty g(x)\,dx$ is divergent.

49–54 ▓ Use the Comparison Theorem to determine whether the integral is convergent or divergent.

49. $\displaystyle\int_1^\infty \frac{\cos^2 x}{1+x^2}\,dx$

50. $\displaystyle\int_1^\infty \frac{2+e^{-x}}{x}\,dx$

51. $\displaystyle\int_1^\infty \frac{dx}{x+e^{2x}}$

52. $\displaystyle\int_1^\infty \frac{x}{\sqrt{1+x^6}}\,dx$

53. $\displaystyle\int_0^{\pi/2} \frac{dx}{x\sin x}$

54. $\displaystyle\int_0^1 \frac{e^{-x}}{\sqrt{x}}\,dx$

55. The integral

$$\int_0^\infty \frac{1}{\sqrt{x}\,(1+x)}\,dx$$

is improper for two reasons: The interval $[0, \infty)$ is infinite and the integrand has an infinite discontinuity at 0. Evaluate it by expressing it as a sum of improper integrals of Type 2 and Type 1 as follows:

$$\int_0^\infty \frac{1}{\sqrt{x}\,(1+x)}\,dx = \int_0^1 \frac{1}{\sqrt{x}\,(1+x)}\,dx + \int_1^\infty \frac{1}{\sqrt{x}\,(1+x)}\,dx$$

56. Evaluate

$$\int_{2}^{\infty} \frac{1}{x\sqrt{x^2 - 4}}\, dx$$

by the same method as in Exercise 55.

57–59 ▐ Find the values of p for which the integral converges and evaluate the integral for those values of p.

57. $\int_{0}^{1} \frac{1}{x^p}\, dx$

58. $\int_{e}^{\infty} \frac{1}{x(\ln x)^p}\, dx$

59. $\int_{0}^{1} x^p \ln x\, dx$

60. (a) Evaluate the integral $\int_{0}^{\infty} x^n e^{-x}\, dx$ for $n = 0, 1, 2,$ and 3.
 (b) Guess the value of $\int_{0}^{\infty} x^n e^{-x}\, dx$ when n is an arbitrary positive integer.
 (c) Prove your guess using mathematical induction.

61. (a) Show that $\int_{-\infty}^{\infty} x\, dx$ is divergent.
 (b) Show that

$$\lim_{t \to \infty} \int_{-t}^{t} x\, dx = 0$$

This shows that we can't define

$$\int_{-\infty}^{\infty} f(x)\, dx = \lim_{t \to \infty} \int_{-t}^{t} f(x)\, dx$$

62. The *average speed* of molecules in an ideal gas is

$$\bar{v} = \frac{4}{\sqrt{\pi}} \left(\frac{M}{2RT} \right)^{3/2} \int_{0}^{\infty} v^3 e^{-Mv^2/(2RT)}\, dv$$

where M is the molecular weight of the gas, R is the gas constant, T is the gas temperature, and v is the molecular speed. Show that

$$\bar{v} = \sqrt{\frac{8RT}{\pi M}}$$

63. We know from Example 1 that the region $\mathcal{R} = \{(x, y) \mid x \geq 1,\ 0 \leq y \leq 1/x\}$ has infinite area. Show that by rotating $\mathcal{R}$ about the x-axis we obtain a solid with finite volume.

64. Use the information and data in Exercises 29 and 30 of Section 6.4 to find the work required to propel a 1000-kg satellite out of Earth's gravitational field.

65. Find the *escape velocity* v_0 that is needed to propel a rocket of mass m out of the gravitational field of a planet with mass M and radius R. Use Newton's Law of Gravitation (see Exercise 29 in Section 6.4) and the fact that the initial kinetic energy of $\frac{1}{2}mv_0^2$ supplies the needed work.

66. Astronomers use a technique called *stellar stereography* to determine the density of stars in a star cluster from the observed (two-dimensional) density that can be analyzed from a photograph. Suppose that in a spherical cluster of radius R the density of stars depends only on the distance r from the center of the cluster. If the perceived star density is given by $y(s)$, where s is the observed planar distance from the center of the cluster, and $x(r)$ is the actual density, it can be shown that

$$y(s) = \int_{s}^{R} \frac{2r}{\sqrt{r^2 - s^2}}\, x(r)\, dr$$

If the actual density of stars in a cluster is $x(r) = \frac{1}{2}(R - r)^2$, find the perceived density $y(s)$.

67. A manufacturer of lightbulbs wants to produce bulbs that last about 700 hours but, of course, some bulbs burn out faster than others. Let $F(t)$ be the fraction of the company's bulbs that burn out before t hours, so $F(t)$ always lies between 0 and 1.
 (a) Make a rough sketch of what you think the graph of F might look like.
 (b) What is the meaning of the derivative $r(t) = F'(t)$?
 (c) What is the value of $\int_{0}^{\infty} r(t)\, dt$? Why?

68. As we will see in Section 10.4, a radioactive substance decays exponentially: The mass at time t is $m(t) = m(0)e^{kt}$, where $m(0)$ is the initial mass and k is a negative constant. The *mean life* M of an atom in the substance is

$$M = -k \int_{0}^{\infty} t e^{kt}\, dt$$

For the radioactive carbon isotope, ^{14}C, used in radiocarbon dating, the value of k is -0.000121. Find the mean life of a ^{14}C atom.

69. Determine how large the number a has to be so that

$$\int_{a}^{\infty} \frac{1}{x^2 + 1}\, dx < 0.001$$

70. Estimate the numerical value of $\int_{0}^{\infty} e^{-x^2}\, dx$ by writing it as the sum of $\int_{0}^{4} e^{-x^2}\, dx$ and $\int_{4}^{\infty} e^{-x^2}\, dx$. Approximate the first integral by using Simpson's Rule with $n = 8$ and show that the second integral is smaller than $\int_{4}^{\infty} e^{-4x}\, dx$, which is less than 0.0000001.

71. If $f(t)$ is continuous for $t \geq 0$, the *Laplace transform* of f is the function F defined by

$$F(s) = \int_{0}^{\infty} f(t)e^{-st}\, dt$$

and the domain of F is the set consisting of all numbers s for which the integral converges. Find the Laplace transforms of the following functions.
 (a) $f(t) = 1$ (b) $f(t) = e^t$ (c) $f(t) = t$

72. Show that if $0 \leq f(t) \leq Me^{at}$ for $t \geq 0$, where M and a are constants, then the Laplace transform $F(s)$ exists for $s > a$.

73. Suppose that $0 \leq f(t) \leq Me^{at}$ and $0 \leq f'(t) \leq Ke^{at}$ for $t \geq 0$, where f' is continuous. If the Laplace transform of $f(t)$ is $F(s)$

and the Laplace transform of $f'(t)$ is $G(s)$, show that

$$G(s) = sF(s) - f(0) \qquad s > a$$

74. If $\int_{-\infty}^{\infty} f(x)\, dx$ is convergent and a and b are real numbers, show that

$$\int_{-\infty}^{a} f(x)\, dx + \int_{a}^{\infty} f(x)\, dx = \int_{-\infty}^{b} f(x)\, dx + \int_{b}^{\infty} f(x)\, dx$$

75. Show that $\int_{0}^{\infty} x^2 e^{-x^2}\, dx = \frac{1}{2} \int_{0}^{\infty} e^{-x^2}\, dx$.

76. Show that $\int_{0}^{\infty} e^{-x^2}\, dx = \int_{0}^{1} \sqrt{-\ln y}\, dy$ by interpreting the integrals as areas.

77. Find the value of the constant C for which the integral

$$\int_{0}^{\infty} \left(\frac{1}{\sqrt{x^2 + 4}} - \frac{C}{x + 2} \right) dx$$

converges. Evaluate the integral for this value of C.

78. Find the value of the constant C for which the integral

$$\int_{0}^{\infty} \left(\frac{x}{x^2 + 1} - \frac{C}{3x + 1} \right) dx$$

converges. Evaluate the integral for this value of C.

▏▏▏▏ 8 Review

---------------------------------- ◦ CONCEPT CHECK ◦ ----------------------------------

1. State the rule for integration by parts. In practice, how do you use it?

2. How do you evaluate $\int \sin^m x \cos^n x\, dx$ if m is odd? What if n is odd? What if m and n are both even?

3. If the expression $\sqrt{a^2 - x^2}$ occurs in an integral, what substitution might you try? What if $\sqrt{a^2 + x^2}$ occurs? What if $\sqrt{x^2 - a^2}$ occurs?

4. What is the form of the partial fraction expansion of a rational function $P(x)/Q(x)$ if the degree of P is less than the degree of Q and $Q(x)$ has only distinct linear factors? What if a linear factor is repeated? What if $Q(x)$ has an irreducible quadratic factor (not repeated)? What if the quadratic factor is repeated?

5. State the rules for approximating the definite integral $\int_{a}^{b} f(x)\, dx$ with the Midpoint Rule, the Trapezoidal Rule, and Simpson's Rule. Which would you expect to give the best estimate? How do you approximate the error for each rule?

6. Define the following improper integrals.

(a) $\int_{a}^{\infty} f(x)\, dx$ (b) $\int_{-\infty}^{b} f(x)\, dx$ (c) $\int_{-\infty}^{\infty} f(x)\, dx$

7. Define the improper integral $\int_{a}^{b} f(x)\, dx$ for each of the following cases.

(a) f has an infinite discontinuity at a.
(b) f has an infinite discontinuity at b.
(c) f has an infinite discontinuity at c, where $a < c < b$.

8. State the Comparison Theorem for improper integrals.

---------------------------------- ◦ TRUE-FALSE QUIZ ◦ ----------------------------------

Determine whether the statement is true or false. If it is true, explain why. If it is false, explain why or give an example that disproves the statement.

1. $\dfrac{x(x^2 + 4)}{x^2 - 4}$ can be put in the form $\dfrac{A}{x + 2} + \dfrac{B}{x - 2}$.

2. $\dfrac{x^2 + 4}{x(x^2 - 4)}$ can be put in the form $\dfrac{A}{x} + \dfrac{B}{x + 2} + \dfrac{C}{x - 2}$.

3. $\dfrac{x^2 + 4}{x^2(x - 4)}$ can be put in the form $\dfrac{A}{x^2} + \dfrac{B}{x - 4}$.

4. $\dfrac{x^2 - 4}{x(x^2 + 4)}$ can be put in the form $\dfrac{A}{x} + \dfrac{B}{x^2 + 4}$.

5. $\int_{0}^{4} \dfrac{x}{x^2 - 1}\, dx = \frac{1}{2} \ln 15$

6. $\int_{1}^{\infty} \dfrac{1}{x^{\sqrt{2}}}\, dx$ is convergent.

7. If f is continuous, then $\int_{-\infty}^{\infty} f(x)\, dx = \lim_{t \to \infty} \int_{-t}^{t} f(x)\, dx$.

8. The Midpoint Rule is always more accurate than the Trapezoidal Rule.

9. (a) Every elementary function has an elementary derivative.
(b) Every elementary function has an elementary antiderivative.

10. If f is continuous on $[0, \infty)$ and $\int_{1}^{\infty} f(x)\, dx$ is convergent, then $\int_{0}^{\infty} f(x)\, dx$ is convergent.

11. If f is a continuous, decreasing function on $[1, \infty)$ and $\lim_{x \to \infty} f(x) = 0$, then $\int_{1}^{\infty} f(x)\, dx$ is convergent.

12. If $\int_{a}^{\infty} f(x)\, dx$ and $\int_{a}^{\infty} g(x)\, dx$ are both convergent, then $\int_{a}^{\infty} [f(x) + g(x)]\, dx$ is convergent.

13. If $\int_{a}^{\infty} f(x)\, dx$ and $\int_{a}^{\infty} g(x)\, dx$ are both divergent, then $\int_{a}^{\infty} [f(x) + g(x)]\, dx$ is divergent.

14. If $f(x) \leq g(x)$ and $\int_{0}^{\infty} g(x)\, dx$ diverges, then $\int_{0}^{\infty} f(x)\, dx$ also diverges.

- EXERCISES -

Note: Additional practice in techniques of integration is provided in Exercises 7.5.

1–40 ▮ Evaluate the integral.

1. $\int_0^5 \dfrac{x}{x+10}\, dx$

2. $\int_0^5 ye^{-0.6y}\, dy$

3. $\int_0^{\pi/2} \dfrac{\cos\theta}{1+\sin\theta}\, d\theta$

4. $\int_1^4 \dfrac{dt}{(2t+1)^3}$

5. $\int \tan^7 x \sec^3 x\, dx$

6. $\int \dfrac{1}{y^2-4y-12}\, dy$

7. $\int \dfrac{\sin(\ln t)}{t}\, dt$

8. $\int \dfrac{dx}{x^2\sqrt{1+x^2}}$

9. $\int_1^4 x^{3/2}\ln x\, dx$

10. $\int_0^1 \dfrac{\sqrt{\arctan x}}{1+x^2}\, dx$

11. $\int_1^2 \dfrac{\sqrt{x^2-1}}{x}\, dx$

12. $\int_{-1}^1 \dfrac{\sin x}{1+x^2}\, dx$

13. $\int \dfrac{dx}{x^3+x}$

14. $\int \dfrac{x^2+2}{x+2}\, dx$

15. $\int \sin^2\theta\,\cos^5\theta\, d\theta$

16. $\int \dfrac{\sec^6\theta}{\tan^2\theta}\, d\theta$

17. $\int x\sec x\tan x\, dx$

18. $\int \dfrac{x^2+8x-3}{x^3+3x^2}\, dx$

19. $\int \dfrac{x+1}{9x^2+6x+5}\, dx$

20. $\int \dfrac{dt}{\sin^2 t+\cos 2t}$

21. $\int \dfrac{dx}{\sqrt{x^2-4x}}$

22. $\int \dfrac{x^3}{(x+1)^{10}}\, dx$

23. $\int \csc^4 4x\, dx$

24. $\int e^x\cos x\, dx$

25. $\int \dfrac{3x^3-x^2+6x-4}{(x^2+1)(x^2+2)}\, dx$

26. $\int \dfrac{dx}{1+e^x}$

27. $\int_0^{\pi/2} \cos^3 x\sin 2x\, dx$

28. $\int \dfrac{\sqrt[3]{x}+1}{\sqrt[3]{x}-1}\, dx$

29. $\int_{-1}^1 x^5\sec x\, dx$

30. $\int \dfrac{dx}{e^x\sqrt{1-e^{-2x}}}$

31. $\int_0^{\ln 10} \dfrac{e^x\sqrt{e^x-1}}{e^x+8}\, dx$

32. $\int_0^{\pi/4} \dfrac{x\sin x}{\cos^3 x}\, dx$

33. $\int \dfrac{x^2}{(4-x^2)^{3/2}}\, dx$

34. $\int (\arcsin x)^2\, dx$

35. $\int \dfrac{1}{\sqrt{x+x^{3/2}}}\, dx$

36. $\int \dfrac{1-\tan\theta}{1+\tan\theta}\, d\theta$

37. $\int (\cos x+\sin x)^2\cos 2x\, dx$

38. $\int x(\tan^{-1}x)^2\, dx$

39. $\int_0^{1/2} \dfrac{xe^{2x}}{(1+2x)^2}\, dx$

40. $\int_{\pi/4}^{\pi/3} \dfrac{\sqrt{\tan\theta}}{\sin 2\theta}\, d\theta$

41–50 ▮ Evaluate the integral or show that it is divergent.

41. $\int_1^\infty \dfrac{1}{(2x+1)^3}\, dx$

42. $\int_0^1 \dfrac{t^2+1}{t^2-1}\, dt$

43. $\int_2^\infty \dfrac{dx}{x\ln x}$

44. $\int_2^6 \dfrac{y}{\sqrt{y-2}}\, dy$

45. $\int_0^4 \dfrac{\ln x}{\sqrt{x}}\, dx$

46. $\int_0^1 \dfrac{1}{2-3x}\, dx$

47. $\int_0^3 \dfrac{dx}{x^2-x-2}$

48. $\int_{-1}^1 \dfrac{x+1}{\sqrt[3]{x^4}}\, dx$

49. $\int_{-\infty}^\infty \dfrac{dx}{4x^2+4x+5}$

50. $\int_1^\infty \dfrac{\tan^{-1}x}{x^2}\, dx$

51–52 ▮ Evaluate the indefinite integral. Illustrate and check that your answer is reasonable by graphing both the function and its antiderivative (take $C=0$).

51. $\int \ln(x^2+2x+2)\, dx$

52. $\int \dfrac{x^3}{\sqrt{x^2+1}}\, dx$

53. Graph the function $f(x)=\cos^2 x\,\sin^3 x$ and use the graph to guess the value of the integral $\int_0^{2\pi} f(x)\, dx$. Then evaluate the integral to confirm your guess.

CAS 54. (a) How would you evaluate $\int x^5 e^{-2x}\, dx$ by hand? (Don't actually carry out the integration.)
(b) How would you evaluate $\int x^5 e^{-2x}\, dx$ using tables? (Don't actually do it.)
(c) Use a CAS to evaluate $\int x^5 e^{-2x}\, dx$.
(d) Graph the integrand and the indefinite integral on the same screen.

55–58 ▮ Use the Table of Integrals on the Reference Pages to evaluate the integral.

55. $\int e^x\sqrt{1-e^{2x}}\, dx$

56. $\int \csc^5 t\, dt$

57. $\int \sqrt{x^2+x+1}\, dx$

58. $\int \dfrac{\cot x}{\sqrt{1+2\sin x}}\, dx$

59. Verify Formula 33 in the Table of Integrals (a) by differentiation and (b) by using a trigonometric substitution.

60. Verify Formula 62 in the Table of Integrals.

61. Is it possible to find a number n such that $\int_0^\infty x^n\, dx$ is convergent?

62. For what values of a is $\int_0^\infty e^{ax} \cos x \, dx$ convergent? Evaluate the integral for those values of a.

63–64 ▒ Use (a) the Trapezoidal Rule, (b) the Midpoint Rule, and (c) Simpson's Rule with $n = 10$ to approximate the given integral. Round your answers to six decimal places.

63. $\int_0^1 \sqrt{1 + x^4} \, dx$

64. $\int_0^{\pi/2} \sqrt{\sin x} \, dx$

▫ ▫ ▫ ▫ ▫ ▫ ▫ ▫ ▫ ▫ ▫ ▫

65. Estimate the errors involved in Exercise 63, parts (a) and (b). How large should n be in each case to guarantee an error of less than 0.00001?

66. Use Simpson's Rule with $n = 6$ to estimate the area under the curve $y = e^x/x$ from $x = 1$ to $x = 4$.

67. The speedometer reading (v) on a car was observed at 1-minute intervals and recorded in the chart. Use Simpson's Rule to estimate the distance traveled by the car.

t (min)	v (mi/h)	t (min)	v (mi/h)
0	40	6	56
1	42	7	57
2	45	8	57
3	49	9	55
4	52	10	56
5	54		

68. A population of honeybees increased at a rate of $r(t)$ bees per week, where the graph of r is as shown. Use Simpson's Rule with six subintervals to estimate the increase in the bee population during the first 24 weeks.

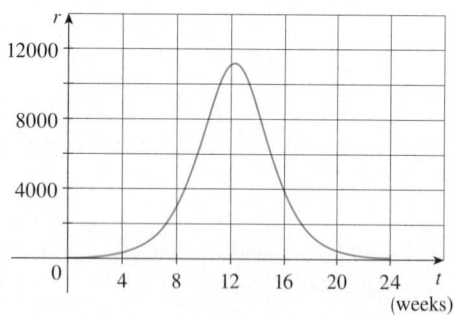

CAS **69.** (a) If $f(x) = \sin(\sin x)$, use a graph to find an upper bound for $|f^{(4)}(x)|$.
(b) Use Simpson's Rule with $n = 10$ to approximate $\int_0^\pi f(x) \, dx$ and use part (a) to estimate the error.
(c) How large should n be to guarantee that the size of the error in using S_n is less than 0.00001?

70. Suppose you are asked to estimate the volume of a football. You measure and find that a football is 28 cm long. You use a piece of string and measure the circumference at its widest

point to be 53 cm. The circumference 7 cm from each end is 45 cm. Use Simpson's Rule to make your estimate.

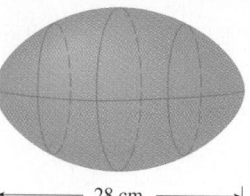

|← 28 cm →|

71. Use the Comparison Theorem to determine whether the integral
$$\int_1^\infty \frac{x^3}{x^5 + 2} \, dx$$
is convergent or divergent.

72. Find the area of the region bounded by the hyperbola $y^2 - x^2 = 1$ and the line $y = 3$.

73. Find the area bounded by the curves $y = \cos x$ and $y = \cos^2 x$ between $x = 0$ and $x = \pi$.

74. Find the area of the region bounded by the curves $y = 1/(2 + \sqrt{x})$, $y = 1/(2 - \sqrt{x})$, and $x = 1$.

75. The region under the curve $y = \cos^2 x$, $0 \le x \le \pi/2$, is rotated about the x-axis. Find the volume of the resulting solid.

76. The region in Exercise 75 is rotated about the y-axis. Find the volume of the resulting solid.

77. If f' is continuous on $[0, \infty)$ and $\lim_{x \to \infty} f(x) = 0$, show that
$$\int_0^\infty f'(x) \, dx = -f(0)$$

78. We can extend our definition of average value of a continuous function to an infinite interval by defining the average value of f on the interval $[a, \infty)$ to be
$$\lim_{t \to \infty} \frac{1}{t - a} \int_a^t f(x) \, dx$$
(a) Find the average value of $y = \tan^{-1} x$ on the interval $[0, \infty)$.
(b) If $f(x) \ge 0$ and $\int_a^\infty f(x) \, dx$ is divergent, show that the average value of f on the interval $[a, \infty)$ is $\lim_{x \to \infty} f(x)$, if this limit exists.
(c) If $\int_a^\infty f(x) \, dx$ is convergent, what is the average value of f on the interval $[a, \infty)$?
(d) Find the average value of $y = \sin x$ on the interval $[0, \infty)$.

79. Use the substitution $u = 1/x$ to show that
$$\int_0^\infty \frac{\ln x}{1 + x^2} \, dx = 0$$

80. The magnitude of the repulsive force between two point charges with the same sign, one of size 1 and the other of size q, is
$$F = \frac{q}{4\pi\varepsilon_0 r^2}$$
where r is the distance between the charges and ε_0 is a constant. The *potential* V at a point P due to the charge q is defined to be the work expended in bringing a unit charge to P from infinity along the straight line that joins q and P. Find a formula for V.

PROBLEMS
PLUS

Cover up the solution to the example and try it yourself first.

EXAMPLE
(a) Prove that if f is a continuous function, then

$$\int_0^a f(x)\, dx = \int_0^a f(a - x)\, dx$$

(b) Use part (a) to show that

$$\int_0^{\pi/2} \frac{\sin^n x}{\sin^n x + \cos^n x}\, dx = \frac{\pi}{4}$$

for all positive numbers n.

||| The principles of problem solving are discussed on page 58.

SOLUTION
(a) At first sight, the given equation may appear somewhat baffling. How is it possible to connect the left side to the right side? Connections can often be made through one of the principles of problem solving: *introduce something extra*. Here the extra ingredient is a new variable. We often think of introducing a new variable when we use the Substitution Rule to integrate a specific function. But that technique is still useful in the present circumstance in which we have a general function f.

Once we think of making a substitution, the form of the right side suggests that it should be $u = a - x$. Then $du = -dx$. When $x = 0$, $u = a$; when $x = a$, $u = 0$. So

$$\int_0^a f(a - x)\, dx = -\int_a^0 f(u)\, du = \int_0^a f(u)\, du$$

But this integral on the right side is just another way of writing $\int_0^a f(x)\, dx$. So the given equation is proved.

(b) If we let the given integral be I and apply part (a) with $a = \pi/2$, we get

$$I = \int_0^{\pi/2} \frac{\sin^n x}{\sin^n x + \cos^n x}\, dx = \int_0^{\pi/2} \frac{\sin^n(\pi/2 - x)}{\sin^n(\pi/2 - x) + \cos^n(\pi/2 - x)}\, dx$$

||| The computer graphs in Figure 1 make it seem plausible that all of the integrals in the example have the same value. The graph of each integrand is labeled with the corresponding value of n.

A well-known trigonometric identity tells us that $\sin(\pi/2 - x) = \cos x$ and $\cos(\pi/2 - x) = \sin x$, so we get

$$I = \int_0^{\pi/2} \frac{\cos^n x}{\cos^n x + \sin^n x}\, dx$$

Notice that the two expressions for I are very similar. In fact, the integrands have the same denominator. This suggests that we should add the two expressions. If we do so, we get

$$2I = \int_0^{\pi/2} \frac{\sin^n x + \cos^n x}{\sin^n x + \cos^n x}\, dx = \int_0^{\pi/2} 1\, dx = \frac{\pi}{2}$$

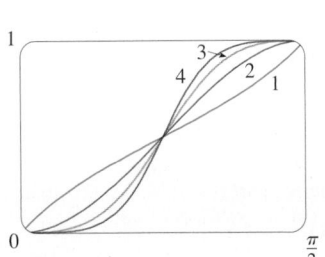

FIGURE 1

Therefore, $I = \pi/4$.

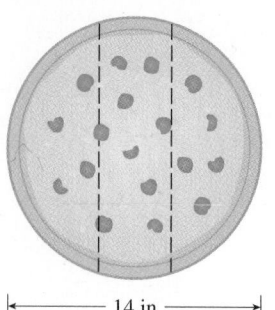

|← —— 14 in —— →|

FIGURE FOR PROBLEM 1

FIGURE FOR PROBLEM 4

 1. Three mathematics students have ordered a 14-inch pizza. Instead of slicing it in the traditional way, they decide to slice it by parallel cuts, as shown in the figure. Being mathematics majors, they are able to determine where to slice so that each gets the same amount of pizza. Where are the cuts made?

2. Evaluate $\int \dfrac{1}{x^7 - x}\,dx$.

The straightforward approach would be to start with partial fractions, but that would be brutal. Try a substitution.

3. Evaluate $\int_0^1 \left(\sqrt[3]{1 - x^7} - \sqrt[7]{1 - x^3} \right) dx$.

4. A man initially standing at the point O walks along a pier pulling a rowboat by a rope of length L. The man keeps the rope straight and taut. The path followed by the boat is a curve called a *tractrix* and it has the property that the rope is always tangent to the curve (see the figure).

(a) Show that if the path followed by the boat is the graph of the function $y = f(x)$, then

$$ f'(x) = \frac{dy}{dx} = \frac{-\sqrt{L^2 - x^2}}{x} $$

(b) Determine the function $y = f(x)$.

5. A function f is defined by

$$ f(x) = \int_0^\pi \cos t \, \cos(x - t)\,dt \qquad 0 \le x \le 2\pi $$

Find the minimum value of f.

6. If n is a positive integer, prove that

$$ \int_0^1 (\ln x)^n\,dx = (-1)^n n! $$

7. Show that

$$ \int_0^1 (1 - x^2)^n\,dx = \frac{2^{2n}(n!)^2}{(2n + 1)!} $$

Hint: Start by showing that if I_n denotes the integral, then

$$ I_{k+1} = \frac{2k + 2}{2k + 3}\,I_k $$

 8. Suppose that f is a positive function such that f' is continuous.

(a) How is the graph of $y = f(x) \sin nx$ related to the graph of $y = f(x)$? What happens as $n \to \infty$?

(b) Make a guess as to the value of the limit

$$ \lim_{n \to \infty} \int_0^1 f(x) \sin nx \, dx $$

based on graphs of the integrand.

(c) Using integration by parts, confirm the guess that you made in part (b). [Use the fact that, since f' is continuous, there is a constant M such that $|f'(x)| \le M$ for $0 \le x \le 1$.]

9. If $0 < a < b$, find $\displaystyle \lim_{t \to 0} \left\{ \int_0^1 [bx + a(1 - x)]^t\,dx \right\}^{1/t}$.

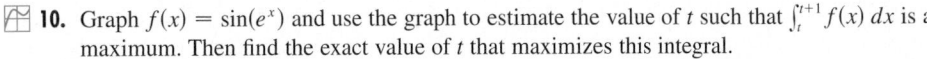

10. Graph $f(x) = \sin(e^x)$ and use the graph to estimate the value of t such that $\int_t^{t+1} f(x)\, dx$ is a maximum. Then find the exact value of t that maximizes this integral.

11. The circle with radius 1 shown in the figure touches the curve $y = |2x|$ twice. Find the area of the region that lies between the two curves.

12. A rocket is fired straight up, burning fuel at the constant rate of b kilograms per second. Let $v = v(t)$ be the velocity of the rocket at time t and suppose that the velocity u of the exhaust gas is constant. Let $M = M(t)$ be the mass of the rocket at time t and note that M decreases as the fuel burns. If we neglect air resistance, it follows from Newton's Second Law that

$$F = M\frac{dv}{dt} - ub$$

where the force $F = -Mg$. Thus

$$\boxed{1} \qquad\qquad M\frac{dv}{dt} - ub = -Mg$$

Let M_1 be the mass of the rocket without fuel, M_2 the initial mass of the fuel, and $M_0 = M_1 + M_2$. Then, until the fuel runs out at time $t = M_2 b$, the mass is $M = M_0 - bt$.

(a) Substitute $M = M_0 - bt$ into Equation 1 and solve the resulting equation for v. Use the initial condition $v(0) = 0$ to evaluate the constant.
(b) Determine the velocity of the rocket at time $t = M_2/b$. This is called the *burnout velocity*.
(c) Determine the height of the rocket $y = y(t)$ at the burnout time.
(d) Find the height of the rocket at any time t.

13. Use integration by parts to show that, for all $x > 0$,

$$0 < \int_0^\infty \frac{\sin t}{\ln(1 + x + t)}\, dt < \frac{2}{\ln(1 + x)}$$

14. The **Chebyshev polynomials** T_n are defined by

$$T_n(x) = \cos(n \arccos x) \qquad n = 0, 1, 2, 3, \ldots$$

(a) What are the domain and range of these functions?
(b) We know that $T_0(x) = 1$ and $T_1(x) = x$. Express T_2 explicitly as a quadratic polynomial and T_3 as a cubic polynomial.
(c) Show that, for $n \geqslant 1$,

$$T_{n+1}(x) = 2x T_n(x) - T_{n-1}(x)$$

(d) Use part (c) to show that T_n is a polynomial of degree n.
(e) Use parts (b) and (c) to express T_4, T_5, T_6, and T_7 explicitly as polynomials.
(f) What are the zeros of T_n? At what numbers does T_n have local maximum and minimum values?
(g) Graph T_2, T_3, T_4, and T_5 on a common screen.
(h) Graph T_5, T_6, and T_7 on a common screen.
(i) Based on your observations from parts (g) and (h), how are the zeros of T_n related to the zeros of T_{n+1}? What about the x-coordinates of the maximum and minimum values?
(j) Based on your graphs in parts (g) and (h), what can you say about $\int_{-1}^1 T_n(x)\, dx$ when n is odd and when n is even?
(k) Use the substitution $u = \arccos x$ to evaluate the integral in part (j).
(l) The family of functions $f(x) = \cos(c \arccos x)$ are defined even when c is not an integer (but then f is not a polynomial). Describe how the graph of f changes as c increases.

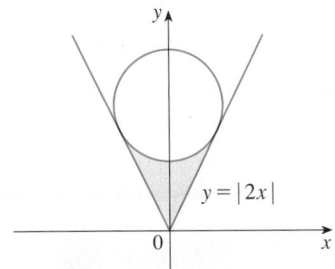

FIGURE FOR PROBLEM 11

CHAPTER 9

Integration enables us to
calculate the force exerted
by water on a dam.

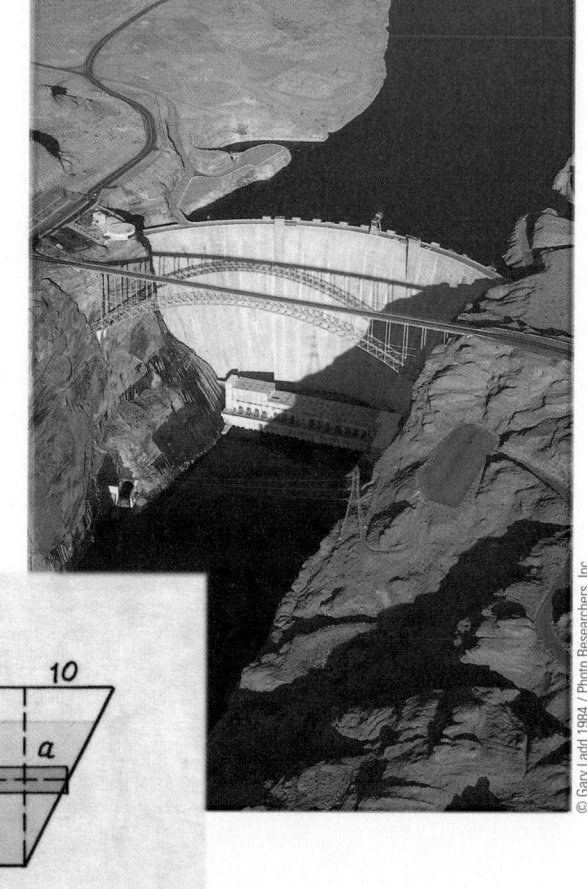

© Gary Ladd 1984 / Photo Researchers, Inc.

Further Applications of Integration

We looked at some applications of integrals in Chapter 6: areas, volumes, work, and average values. Here we explore some of the many other geometric applications of integration—the length of a curve, the area of a surface— as well as quantities of interest in physics, engineering, biology, economics, and statistics. For instance, we will investigate the center of gravity of a plate, the force exerted by water pressure on a dam, the flow of blood from the human heart, and the average time spent on hold during a telephone call.

9.1 Arc Length

FIGURE 1

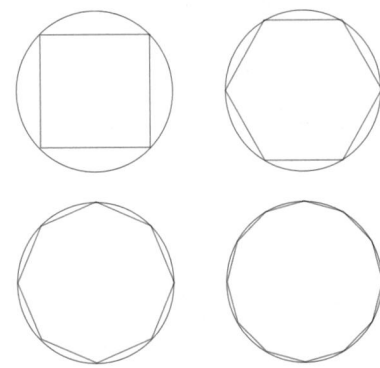

FIGURE 2

What do we mean by the length of a curve? We might think of fitting a piece of string to the curve in Figure 1 and then measuring the string against a ruler. But that might be difficult to do with much accuracy if we have a complicated curve. We need a precise definition for the length of an arc of a curve, in the same spirit as the definitions we developed for the concepts of area and volume.

If the curve is a polygon, we can easily find its length; we just add the lengths of the line segments that form the polygon. (We can use the distance formula to find the distance between the endpoints of each segment.) We are going to define the length of a general curve by first approximating it by a polygon and then taking a limit as the number of segments of the polygon is increased. This process is familiar for the case of a circle, where the circumference is the limit of lengths of inscribed polygons (see Figure 2).

Now suppose that a curve C is defined by the equation $y = f(x)$, where f is continuous and $a \leq x \leq b$. We obtain a polygonal approximation to C by dividing the interval $[a, b]$ into n subintervals with endpoints $x_0, x_1, \ldots, x_n$ and equal width Δx. If $y_i = f(x_i)$, then the point $P_i(x_i, y_i)$ lies on C and the polygon with vertices $P_0, P_1, \ldots, P_n$, illustrated in Figure 3, is an approximation to C. The length L of C is approximately the length of this polygon and the approximation gets better as we let n increase. (See Figure 4, where the arc of the curve between P_{i-1} and P_i has been magnified and approximations with successively smaller values of Δx are shown.) Therefore, we define the **length L** of the curve C

FIGURE 3

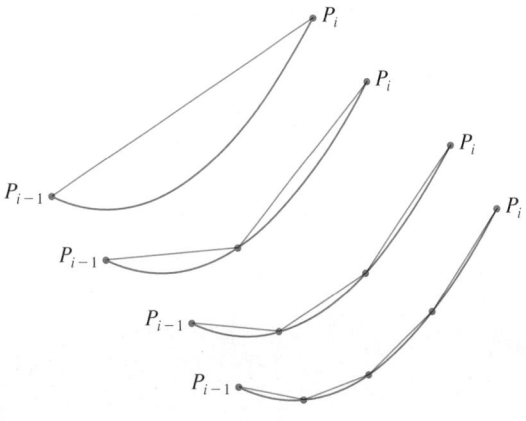

FIGURE 4

with equation $y = f(x)$, $a \leqslant x \leqslant b$, as the limit of the lengths of these inscribed polygons (if the limit exists):

$$\boxed{1} \qquad L = \lim_{n \to \infty} \sum_{i=1}^{n} |P_{i-1}P_i|$$

Notice that the procedure for defining arc length is very similar to the procedure we used for defining area and volume: We divided the curve into a large number of small parts. We then found the approximate lengths of the small parts and added them. Finally, we took the limit as $n \to \infty$.

The definition of arc length given by Equation 1 is not very convenient for computational purposes, but we can derive an integral formula for L in the case where f has a continuous derivative. [Such a function f is called **smooth** because a small change in x produces a small change in $f'(x)$.]

If we let $\Delta y_i = y_i - y_{i-1}$, then

$$|P_{i-1}P_i| = \sqrt{(x_i - x_{i-1})^2 + (y_i - y_{i-1})^2} = \sqrt{(\Delta x)^2 + (\Delta y_i)^2}$$

By applying the Mean Value Theorem to f on the interval $[x_{i-1}, x_i]$, we find that there is a number x_i^* between x_{i-1} and x_i such that

$$f(x_i) - f(x_{i-1}) = f'(x_i^*)(x_i - x_{i-1})$$

that is, $\qquad\qquad\qquad\qquad \Delta y_i = f'(x_i^*)\,\Delta x$

Thus, we have

$$|P_{i-1}P_i| = \sqrt{(\Delta x)^2 + (\Delta y_i)^2}$$
$$= \sqrt{(\Delta x)^2 + [f'(x_i^*)\,\Delta x]^2}$$
$$= \sqrt{1 + [f'(x_i^*)]^2}\,\sqrt{(\Delta x)^2}$$
$$= \sqrt{1 + [f'(x_i^*)]^2}\,\Delta x \qquad \text{(since } \Delta x > 0\text{)}$$

Therefore, by Definition 1,

$$L = \lim_{n \to \infty} \sum_{i=1}^{n} |P_{i-1}P_i| = \lim_{n \to \infty} \sum_{i=1}^{n} \sqrt{1 + [f'(x_i^*)]^2}\,\Delta x$$

We recognize this expression as being equal to

$$\int_a^b \sqrt{1 + [f'(x)]^2}\,dx$$

by the definition of a definite integral. This integral exists because the function $g(x) = \sqrt{1 + [f'(x)]^2}$ is continuous. Thus, we have proved the following theorem:

$\boxed{2}$ **The Arc Length Formula** If f' is continuous on $[a, b]$, then the length of the curve $y = f(x)$, $a \leqslant x \leqslant b$, is

$$L = \int_a^b \sqrt{1 + [f'(x)]^2}\,dx$$

If we use Leibniz notation for derivatives, we can write the arc length formula as follows:

$$\boxed{3} \qquad L = \int_a^b \sqrt{1 + \left(\frac{dy}{dx}\right)^2}\, dx$$

EXAMPLE 1 Find the length of the arc of the semicubical parabola $y^2 = x^3$ between the points $(1, 1)$ and $(4, 8)$. (See Figure 5.)

SOLUTION For the top half of the curve we have

$$y = x^{3/2} \qquad\qquad \frac{dy}{dx} = \tfrac{3}{2}x^{1/2}$$

and so the arc length formula gives

$$L = \int_1^4 \sqrt{1 + \left(\frac{dy}{dx}\right)^2}\, dx = \int_1^4 \sqrt{1 + \tfrac{9}{4}x}\, dx$$

If we substitute $u = 1 + 9x/4$, then $du = 9\, dx/4$. When $x = 1$, $u = \frac{13}{4}$; when $x = 4$, $u = 10$. Therefore

$$L = \tfrac{4}{9}\int_{13/4}^{10} \sqrt{u}\, du = \tfrac{4}{9} \cdot \tfrac{2}{3}u^{3/2}\Big]_{13/4}^{10}$$

$$= \tfrac{8}{27}\left[10^{3/2} - \left(\tfrac{13}{4}\right)^{3/2}\right]$$

$$= \tfrac{1}{27}\left(80\sqrt{10} - 13\sqrt{13}\right)$$

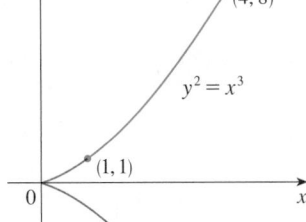

y² = x³

(4, 8)

(1, 1)

FIGURE 5

▮▮▮▮ As a check on our answer to Example 1, notice from Figure 5 that it ought to be slightly larger than the distance from $(1, 1)$ to $(4, 8)$, which is

$$\sqrt{58} \approx 7.615773$$

According to our calculation in Example 1, we have

$$L = \tfrac{1}{27}\left(80\sqrt{10} - 13\sqrt{13}\right) \approx 7.633705$$

Sure enough, this is a bit greater than the length of the line segment.

If a curve has the equation $x = g(y)$, $c \le y \le d$, and $g'(y)$ is continuous, then by interchanging the roles of x and y in Formula 2 or Equation 3, we obtain the following formula for its length:

$$\boxed{4} \qquad L = \int_c^d \sqrt{1 + [g'(y)]^2}\, dy = \int_c^d \sqrt{1 + \left(\frac{dx}{dy}\right)^2}\, dy$$

EXAMPLE 2 Find the length of the arc of the parabola $y^2 = x$ from $(0, 0)$ to $(1, 1)$.

SOLUTION Since $x = y^2$, we have $dx/dy = 2y$, and Formula 4 gives

$$L = \int_0^1 \sqrt{1 + \left(\frac{dx}{dy}\right)^2}\, dy = \int_0^1 \sqrt{1 + 4y^2}\, dy$$

We make the trigonometric substitution $y = \tfrac{1}{2}\tan\theta$, which gives $dy = \tfrac{1}{2}\sec^2\theta\, d\theta$ and $\sqrt{1 + 4y^2} = \sqrt{1 + \tan^2\theta} = \sec\theta$. When $y = 0$, $\tan\theta = 0$, so $\theta = 0$; when $y = 1$, $\tan\theta = 2$, so $\theta = \tan^{-1}2 = \alpha$, say. Thus

$$L = \int_0^\alpha \sec\theta \cdot \tfrac{1}{2}\sec^2\theta\, d\theta = \tfrac{1}{2}\int_0^\alpha \sec^3\theta\, d\theta$$

$$= \tfrac{1}{2} \cdot \tfrac{1}{2}\left[\sec\theta\tan\theta + \ln|\sec\theta + \tan\theta|\right]_0^\alpha \qquad \text{(from Example 8 in Section 8.2)}$$

$$= \tfrac{1}{4}\left(\sec\alpha\tan\alpha + \ln|\sec\alpha + \tan\alpha|\right)$$

(We could have used Formula 21 in the Table of Integrals.) Since $\tan \alpha = 2$, we have $\sec^2\alpha = 1 + \tan^2\alpha = 5$, so $\sec \alpha = \sqrt{5}$ and

$$L = \frac{\sqrt{5}}{2} + \frac{\ln(\sqrt{5} + 2)}{4}$$

|||| Figure 6 shows the arc of the parabola whose length is computed in Example 2, together with polygonal approximations having $n = 1$ and $n = 2$ line segments, respectively. For $n = 1$ the approximate length is $L_1 = \sqrt{2}$, the diagonal of a square. The table shows the approximations L_n that we get by dividing $[0, 1]$ into n equal subintervals. Notice that each time we double the number of sides of the polygon, we get closer to the exact length, which is

$$L = \frac{\sqrt{5}}{2} + \frac{\ln(\sqrt{5} + 2)}{4} \approx 1.478943$$

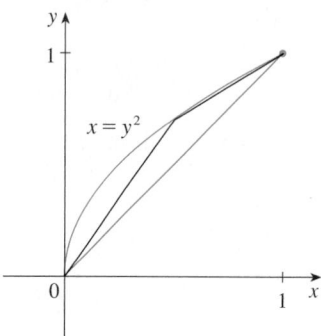

n	L_n
1	1.414
2	1.445
4	1.464
8	1.472
16	1.476
32	1.478
64	1.479

FIGURE 6

Because of the presence of the square root sign in Formulas 2 and 4, the calculation of an arc length often leads to an integral that is very difficult or even impossible to evaluate explicitly. Thus, we sometimes have to be content with finding an approximation to the length of a curve as in the following example.

EXAMPLE 3
(a) Set up an integral for the length of the arc of the hyperbola $xy = 1$ from the point $(1, 1)$ to the point $\left(2, \frac{1}{2}\right)$.
(b) Use Simpson's Rule with $n = 10$ to estimate the arc length.

SOLUTION
(a) We have

$$y = \frac{1}{x} \qquad \frac{dy}{dx} = -\frac{1}{x^2}$$

and so the arc length is

$$L = \int_1^2 \sqrt{1 + \left(\frac{dy}{dx}\right)^2}\, dx = \int_1^2 \sqrt{1 + \frac{1}{x^4}}\, dx = \int_1^2 \frac{\sqrt{x^4 + 1}}{x^2}\, dx$$

(b) Using Simpson's Rule (see Section 8.7) with $a = 1$, $b = 2$, $n = 10$, $\Delta x = 0.1$, and $f(x) = \sqrt{1 + 1/x^4}$, we have

$$L = \int_1^2 \sqrt{1 + \frac{1}{x^4}}\, dx$$

|||| Checking the value of the definite integral with a more accurate approximation produced by a computer algebra system, we see that the approximation using Simpson's Rule is accurate to four decimal places.

$$\approx \frac{\Delta x}{3}[f(1) + 4f(1.1) + 2f(1.2) + 4f(1.3) + \cdots + 2f(1.8) + 4f(1.9) + f(2)]$$

$$\approx 1.1321$$

||| ### The Arc Length Function

We will find it useful to have a function that measures the arc length of a curve from a particular starting point to any other point on the curve. Thus, if a smooth curve C has the equation $y = f(x)$, $a \leqslant x \leqslant b$, let $s(x)$ be the distance along C from the initial point $P_0(a, f(a))$ to the point $Q(x, f(x))$. Then s is a function, called the **arc length function**, and, by Formula 2,

$$\boxed{5} \qquad s(x) = \int_a^x \sqrt{1 + [f'(t)]^2}\, dt$$

(We have replaced the variable of integration by t so that x does not have two meanings.) We can use Part 1 of the Fundamental Theorem of Calculus to differentiate Equation 5 (since the integrand is continuous):

$$\boxed{6} \qquad \frac{ds}{dx} = \sqrt{1 + [f'(x)]^2} = \sqrt{1 + \left(\frac{dy}{dx}\right)^2}$$

Equation 6 shows that the rate of change of s with respect to x is always at least 1 and is equal to 1 when $f'(x)$, the slope of the curve, is 0. The differential of arc length is

$$\boxed{7} \qquad ds = \sqrt{1 + \left(\frac{dy}{dx}\right)^2}\, dx$$

and this equation is sometimes written in the symmetric form

$$\boxed{8} \qquad (ds)^2 = (dx)^2 + (dy)^2$$

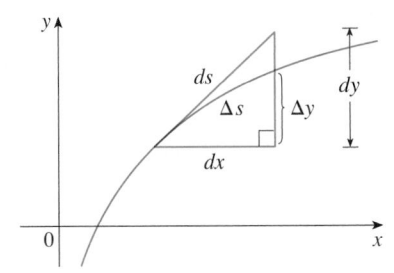

FIGURE 7

The geometric interpretation of Equation 8 is shown in Figure 7. It can be used as a mnemonic device for remembering both of the Formulas 3 and 4. If we write $L = \int ds$, then from Equation 8 either we can solve to get (7), which gives (3), or we can solve to get

$$ds = \sqrt{1 + \left(\frac{dx}{dy}\right)^2}\, dy$$

which gives (4).

EXAMPLE 4 Find the arc length function for the curve $y = x^2 - \frac{1}{8}\ln x$ taking $P_0(1, 1)$ as the starting point.

SOLUTION If $f(x) = x^2 - \frac{1}{8}\ln x$, then

$$f'(x) = 2x - \frac{1}{8x}$$

$$1 + [f'(x)]^2 = 1 + \left(2x - \frac{1}{8x}\right)^2 = 1 + 4x^2 - \frac{1}{2} + \frac{1}{64x^2}$$

$$= 4x^2 + \frac{1}{2} + \frac{1}{64x^2} = \left(2x + \frac{1}{8x}\right)^2$$

$$\sqrt{1 + [f'(x)]^2} = 2x + \frac{1}{8x}$$

Thus, the arc length function is given by

$$s(x) = \int_1^x \sqrt{1 + [f'(t)]^2}\, dt$$

$$= \int_1^x \left(2t - \frac{1}{8t}\right) dt = t^2 + \tfrac{1}{8}\ln t \Big]_1^x$$

$$= x^2 + \tfrac{1}{8}\ln x - 1$$

For instance, the arc length along the curve from $(1, 1)$ to $(3, f(3))$ is

$$s(3) = 3^2 + \tfrac{1}{8}\ln 3 - 1 = 8 + \frac{\ln 3}{8} \approx 8.1373$$

|||| Figure 8 shows the interpretation of the arc length function in Example 4. Figure 9 shows the graph of this arc length function. Why is $s(x)$ negative when x is less than 1?

FIGURE 8

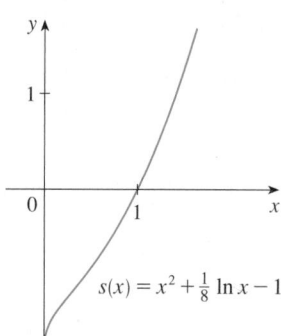

FIGURE 9

9.1 Exercises

1. Use the arc length formula (3) to find the length of the curve $y = 2 - 3x$, $-2 \leqslant x \leqslant 1$. Check your answer by noting that the curve is a line segment and calculating its length by the distance formula.

2. Use the arc length formula to find the length of the curve $y = \sqrt{4 - x^2}$, $0 \leqslant x \leqslant 2$. Check your answer by noting that the curve is a quarter-circle.

3–4 |||| Graph the curve and visually estimate its length. Then find its exact length.

3. $y = \tfrac{2}{3}(x^2 - 1)^{3/2}$, $1 \leqslant x \leqslant 3$

4. $y = \dfrac{x^3}{6} + \dfrac{1}{2x}$, $\tfrac{1}{2} \leqslant x \leqslant 1$

□   □   □   □   □   □   □   □   □   □   □

5–16 |||| Find the length of the curve.

5. $y = 1 + 6x^{3/2}$, $0 \leqslant x \leqslant 1$

6. $y^2 = 4(x + 4)^3$, $0 \leqslant x \leqslant 2$, $y > 0$

7. $y = \dfrac{x^5}{6} + \dfrac{1}{10x^3}$, $1 \leqslant x \leqslant 2$

8. $y = \dfrac{x^2}{2} - \dfrac{\ln x}{4}$, $2 \leqslant x \leqslant 4$

9. $x = \tfrac{1}{3}\sqrt{y}\,(y - 3)$, $1 \leqslant y \leqslant 9$

10. $y = \ln(\cos x)$, $0 \leqslant x \leqslant \pi/3$

11. $y = \ln(\sec x)$, $0 \leqslant x \leqslant \pi/4$

12. $y = \ln x$, $1 \leqslant x \leqslant \sqrt{3}$

13. $y = \cosh x$, $0 \leqslant x \leqslant 1$

14. $y^2 = 4x$, $0 \leqslant y \leqslant 2$

15. $y = e^x$, $0 \leqslant x \leqslant 1$

16. $y = \ln\left(\dfrac{e^x + 1}{e^x - 1}\right)$, $a \leqslant x \leqslant b$, $a > 0$

□   □   □   □   □   □   □   □   □   □   □

17–20 |||| Set up, but do not evaluate, an integral for the length of the curve.

17. $y = \cos x$, $0 \leqslant x \leqslant 2\pi$

18. $y = 2^x$, $0 \leqslant x \leqslant 3$

19. $x = y + y^3, \quad 1 \leq y \leq 4$ **20.** $\dfrac{x^2}{a^2} + \dfrac{y^2}{b^2} = 1$

□   □   □   □   □   □   □   □   □   □

21–24 ||| Use Simpson's Rule with $n = 10$ to estimate the arc length of the curve. Compare your answer with the value of the integral produced by your calculator.

21. $y = xe^{-x}, \quad 0 \leq x \leq 5$ **22.** $x = y + \sqrt{y}, \quad 1 \leq y \leq 2$

23. $y = \sec x, \quad 0 \leq x \leq \pi/3$ **24.** $y = x \ln x, \quad 1 \leq x \leq 3$

□   □   □   □   □   □   □   □   □   □

 25. (a) Graph the curve $y = x\sqrt[3]{4 - x}$, $0 \leq x \leq 4$.
    (b) Compute the lengths of inscribed polygons with $n = 1, 2$, and 4 sides. (Divide the interval into equal subintervals.) Illustrate by sketching these polygons (as in Figure 6).
    (c) Set up an integral for the length of the curve.
    (d) Use your calculator to find the length of the curve to four decimal places. Compare with the approximations in part (b).

26. Repeat Exercise 25 for the curve

$$y = x + \sin x \qquad 0 \leq x \leq 2\pi$$

CAS **27.** Use either a computer algebra system or a table of integrals to find the *exact* length of the arc of the curve $x = \ln(1 - y^2)$ that lies between the points $(0, 0)$ and $\left(\ln \frac{3}{4}, \frac{1}{2}\right)$.

CAS **28.** Use either a computer algebra system or a table of integrals to find the *exact* length of the arc of the curve $y = x^{4/3}$ that lies between the points $(0, 0)$ and $(1, 1)$. If your CAS has trouble evaluating the integral, make a substitution that changes the integral into one that the CAS can evaluate.

29. Sketch the curve with equation $x^{2/3} + y^{2/3} = 1$ and use symmetry to find its length.

30. (a) Sketch the curve $y^3 = x^2$.
    (b) Use Formulas 3 and 4 to set up two integrals for the arc length from $(0, 0)$ to $(1, 1)$. Observe that one of these is an improper integral and evaluate both of them.
    (c) Find the length of the arc of this curve from $(-1, 1)$ to $(8, 4)$.

31. Find the arc length function for the curve $y = 2x^{3/2}$ with starting point $P_0(1, 2)$.

 32. (a) Graph the curve $y = \frac{1}{3}x^3 + 1/(4x)$, $x > 0$.
    (b) Find the arc length function for this curve with starting point $P_0\left(1, \frac{7}{12}\right)$.
    (c) Graph the arc length function.

33. A hawk flying at 15 m/s at an altitude of 180 m accidentally drops its prey. The parabolic trajectory of the falling prey is described by the equation

$$y = 180 - \frac{x^2}{45}$$

until it hits the ground, where y is its height above the ground and x is the horizontal distance traveled in meters. Calculate the distance traveled by the prey from the time it is dropped until the time it hits the ground. Express your answer correct to the nearest tenth of a meter.

34. A steady wind blows a kite due west. The kite's height above ground from horizontal position $x = 0$ to $x = 80$ ft is given by

$$y = 150 - \tfrac{1}{40}(x - 50)^2$$

Find the distance traveled by the kite.

35. A manufacturer of corrugated metal roofing wants to produce panels that are 28 in. wide and 2 in. thick by processing flat sheets of metal as shown in the figure. The profile of the roofing takes the shape of a sine wave. Verify that the sine curve has equation $y = \sin(\pi x/7)$ and find the width w of a flat metal sheet that is needed to make a 28-inch panel. (Use your calculator to evaluate the integral correct to four significant digits.)

36. (a) The figure shows a telephone wire hanging between two poles at $x = -b$ and $x = b$. It takes the shape of a catenary with equation $y = c + a \cosh(x/a)$. Find the length of the wire.
    (b) Suppose two telephone poles are 50 ft apart and the length of the wire between the poles is 51 ft. If the lowest point of the wire must be 20 ft above the ground, how high up on each pole should the wire be attached?

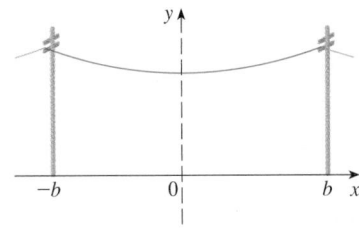

37. Find the length of the curve $y = \int_1^x \sqrt{t^3 - 1}\, dt$, $1 \leq x \leq 4$.

 38. The curves with equations $x^n + y^n = 1$, $n = 4, 6, 8, \dots$, are called **fat circles**. Graph the curves with $n = 2, 4, 6, 8$, and 10 to see why. Set up an integral for the length L_{2k} of the fat circle with $n = 2k$. Without attempting to evaluate this integral, state the value of

$$\lim_{k \to \infty} L_{2k}$$

||| DISCOVERY PROJECT

Arc Length Contest

The curves shown are all examples of graphs of continuous functions f that have the following properties.

1. $f(0) = 0$ and $f(1) = 0$

2. $f(x) \geq 0$ for $0 \leq x \leq 1$

3. The area under the graph of f from 0 to 1 is equal to 1.

The lengths L of these curves, however, are different.

$L \approx 3.249$

$L \approx 2.919$

$L \approx 3.152$

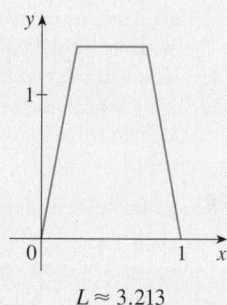

$L \approx 3.213$

Try to discover formulas for two functions that satisfy the given conditions 1, 2, and 3. (Your graphs might be similar to the ones shown or could look quite different.) Then calculate the arc length of each graph. The winning entry will be the one with the smallest arc length.

||| 9.2 Area of a Surface of Revolution

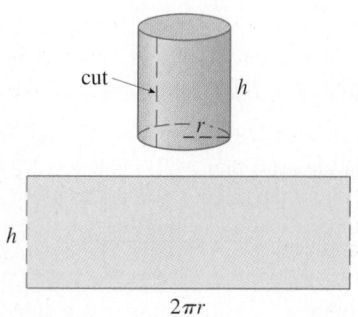

FIGURE 1

A surface of revolution is formed when a curve is rotated about a line. Such a surface is the lateral boundary of a solid of revolution of the type discussed in Sections 6.2 and 6.3.

We want to define the area of a surface of revolution in such a way that it corresponds to our intuition. If the surface area is A, we can imagine that painting the surface would require the same amount of paint as does a flat region with area A.

Let's start with some simple surfaces. The lateral surface area of a circular cylinder with radius r and height h is taken to be $A = 2\pi rh$ because we can imagine cutting the cylinder and unrolling it (as in Figure 1) to obtain a rectangle with dimensions $2\pi r$ and h.

Likewise, we can take a circular cone with base radius r and slant height l, cut it along the dashed line in Figure 2, and flatten it to form a sector of a circle with radius l and central angle $\theta = 2\pi r/l$. We know that, in general, the area of a sector of a circle with radius l and angle θ is $\frac{1}{2}l^2\theta$ (see Exercise 35 in Section 8.3) and so in this case it is

$$A = \tfrac{1}{2}l^2\theta = \tfrac{1}{2}l^2\left(\frac{2\pi r}{l}\right) = \pi rl$$

Therefore, we define the lateral surface area of a cone to be $A = \pi rl$.

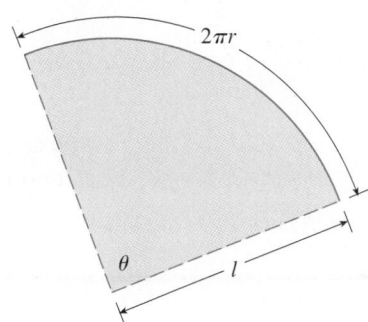

FIGURE 2

What about more complicated surfaces of revolution? If we follow the strategy we used with arc length, we can approximate the original curve by a polygon. When this polygon is rotated about an axis, it creates a simpler surface whose surface area approximates the actual surface area. By taking a limit, we can determine the exact surface area.

The approximating surface, then, consists of a number of *bands,* each formed by rotating a line segment about an axis. To find the surface area, each of these bands can be considered a portion of a circular cone, as shown in Figure 3. The area of the band (or frustum of a cone) with slant height l and upper and lower radii r_1 and r_2 is found by subtracting the areas of two cones:

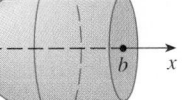

FIGURE 3

$$\boxed{1} \qquad A = \pi r_2(l_1 + l) - \pi r_1 l_1 = \pi[(r_2 - r_1)l_1 + r_2 l]$$

From similar triangles we have

$$\frac{l_1}{r_1} = \frac{l_1 + l}{r_2}$$

which gives

$$r_2 l_1 = r_1 l_1 + r_1 l \qquad \text{or} \qquad (r_2 - r_1)l_1 = r_1 l$$

Putting this in Equation 1, we get

$$A = \pi(r_1 l + r_2 l)$$

or

$$\boxed{2} \qquad \boxed{A = 2\pi r l}$$

where $r = \frac{1}{2}(r_1 + r_2)$ is the average radius of the band.

Now we apply this formula to our strategy. Consider the surface shown in Figure 4, which is obtained by rotating the curve $y = f(x)$, $a \leq x \leq b$, about the x-axis, where f is positive and has a continuous derivative. In order to define its surface area, we divide the interval $[a, b]$ into n subintervals with endpoints $x_0, x_1, \ldots, x_n$ and equal width Δx, as we did in determining arc length. If $y_i = f(x_i)$, then the point $P_i(x_i, y_i)$ lies on the curve. The part of the surface between x_{i-1} and x_i is approximated by taking the line segment $P_{i-1}P_i$ and rotating it about the x-axis. The result is a band with slant height $l = |P_{i-1}P_i|$ and average radius $r = \frac{1}{2}(y_{i-1} + y_i)$ so, by Formula 2, its surface area is

$$2\pi \frac{y_{i-1} + y_i}{2} |P_{i-1}P_i|$$

(a) Surface of revolution

(b) Approximating band

FIGURE 4

As in the proof of Theorem 9.1.2, we have

$$|P_{i-1}P_i| = \sqrt{1 + [f'(x_i^*)]^2}\,\Delta x$$

where x_i^* is some number in $[x_{i-1}, x_i]$. When Δx is small, we have $y_i = f(x_i) \approx f(x_i^*)$ and also $y_{i-1} = f(x_{i-1}) \approx f(x_i^*)$, since f is continuous. Therefore

$$2\pi \frac{y_{i-1} + y_i}{2} |P_{i-1}P_i| \approx 2\pi f(x_i^*)\sqrt{1 + [f'(x_i^*)]^2}\,\Delta x$$

and so an approximation to what we think of as the area of the complete surface of revolution is

3

$$\sum_{i=1}^{n} 2\pi f(x_i^*)\sqrt{1 + [f'(x_i^*)]^2}\,\Delta x$$

This approximation appears to become better as $n \to \infty$ and, recognizing (3) as a Riemann sum for the function $g(x) = 2\pi f(x)\sqrt{1 + [f'(x)]^2}$, we have

$$\lim_{n \to \infty} \sum_{i=1}^{n} 2\pi f(x_i^*)\sqrt{1 + [f'(x_i^*)]^2}\,\Delta x = \int_a^b 2\pi f(x)\sqrt{1 + [f'(x)]^2}\,dx$$

Therefore, in the case where f is positive and has a continuous derivative, we define the **surface area** of the surface obtained by rotating the curve $y = f(x)$, $a \leqslant x \leqslant b$, about the x-axis as

4

$$S = \int_a^b 2\pi f(x)\sqrt{1 + [f'(x)]^2}\,dx$$

With the Leibniz notation for derivatives, this formula becomes

5

$$S = \int_a^b 2\pi y\sqrt{1 + \left(\frac{dy}{dx}\right)^2}\,dx$$

If the curve is described as $x = g(y)$, $c \leqslant y \leqslant d$, then the formula for surface area becomes

6

$$S = \int_c^d 2\pi y\sqrt{1 + \left(\frac{dx}{dy}\right)^2}\,dy$$

and both Formulas 5 and 6 can be summarized symbolically, using the notation for arc length given in Section 9.1, as

7

$$S = \int 2\pi y\,ds$$

For rotation about the y-axis, the surface area formula becomes

8

$$S = \int 2\pi x \, ds$$

where, as before, we can use either

$$ds = \sqrt{1 + \left(\frac{dy}{dx}\right)^2} \, dx \quad \text{or} \quad ds = \sqrt{1 + \left(\frac{dx}{dy}\right)^2} \, dy$$

These formulas can be remembered by thinking of $2\pi y$ or $2\pi x$ as the circumference of a circle traced out by the point (x, y) on the curve as it is rotated about the x-axis or y-axis, respectively (see Figure 5).

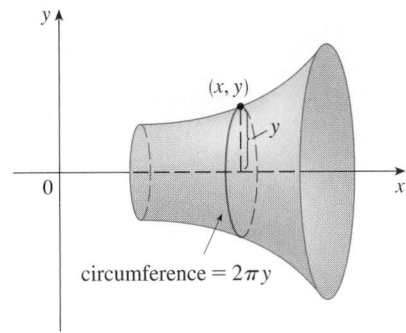

FIGURE 5   (a) Rotation about x-axis: $S = \int 2\pi y \, ds$ (b) Rotation about y-axis: $S = \int 2\pi x \, ds$

EXAMPLE 1 The curve $y = \sqrt{4 - x^2}$, $-1 \le x \le 1$, is an arc of the circle $x^2 + y^2 = 4$. Find the area of the surface obtained by rotating this arc about the x-axis. (The surface is a portion of a sphere of radius 2. See Figure 6.)

SOLUTION We have

$$\frac{dy}{dx} = \tfrac{1}{2}(4 - x^2)^{-1/2}(-2x) = \frac{-x}{\sqrt{4 - x^2}}$$

and so, by Formula 5, the surface area is

$$S = \int_{-1}^{1} 2\pi y \sqrt{1 + \left(\frac{dy}{dx}\right)^2} \, dx$$

$$= 2\pi \int_{-1}^{1} \sqrt{4 - x^2} \sqrt{1 + \frac{x^2}{4 - x^2}} \, dx$$

$$= 2\pi \int_{-1}^{1} \sqrt{4 - x^2} \, \frac{2}{\sqrt{4 - x^2}} \, dx$$

$$= 4\pi \int_{-1}^{1} 1 \, dx = 4\pi(2) = 8\pi$$

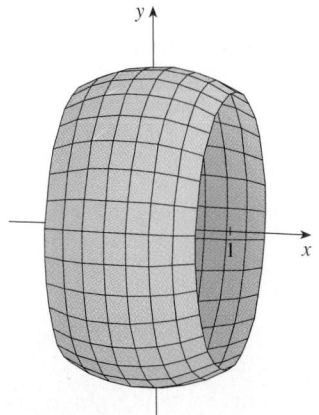

FIGURE 6

▏▎▎▎ Figure 6 shows the portion of the sphere whose surface area is computed in Example 1.

|||| Figure 7 shows the surface of revolution whose area is computed in Example 2.

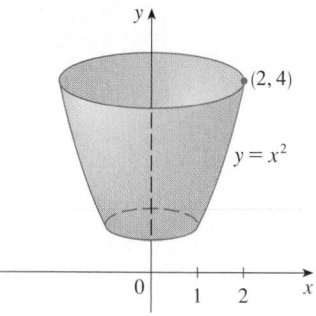

FIGURE 7

EXAMPLE 2 The arc of the parabola $y = x^2$ from $(1, 1)$ to $(2, 4)$ is rotated about the y-axis. Find the area of the resulting surface.

SOLUTION 1 Using

$$y = x^2 \qquad \text{and} \qquad \frac{dy}{dx} = 2x$$

we have, from Formula 8,

$$S = \int 2\pi x \, ds$$

$$= \int_1^2 2\pi x \sqrt{1 + \left(\frac{dy}{dx}\right)^2} \, dx$$

$$= 2\pi \int_1^2 x \sqrt{1 + 4x^2} \, dx$$

Substituting $u = 1 + 4x^2$, we have $du = 8x \, dx$. Remembering to change the limits of integration, we have

$$S = \frac{\pi}{4} \int_5^{17} \sqrt{u} \, du = \frac{\pi}{4} \left[\tfrac{2}{3} u^{3/2}\right]_5^{17}$$

$$= \frac{\pi}{6} \left(17\sqrt{17} - 5\sqrt{5}\right)$$

|||| As a check on our answer to Example 2, notice from Figure 7 that the surface area should be close to that of a circular cylinder with the same height and radius halfway between the upper and lower radius of the surface: $2\pi(1.5)(3) \approx 28.27$. We computed that the surface area was

$$\frac{\pi}{6} \left(17\sqrt{17} - 5\sqrt{5}\right) \approx 30.85$$

which seems reasonable. Alternatively, the surface area should be slightly larger than the area of a frustum of a cone with the same top and bottom edges. From Equation 2, this is $2\pi(1.5)(\sqrt{10}) \approx 29.80$.

SOLUTION 2 Using

$$x = \sqrt{y} \qquad \text{and} \qquad \frac{dx}{dy} = \frac{1}{2\sqrt{y}}$$

we have

$$S = \int 2\pi x \, ds = \int_1^4 2\pi x \sqrt{1 + \left(\frac{dx}{dy}\right)^2} \, dy$$

$$= 2\pi \int_1^4 \sqrt{y} \sqrt{1 + \frac{1}{4y}} \, dy = \pi \int_1^4 \sqrt{4y + 1} \, dy$$

$$= \frac{\pi}{4} \int_5^{17} \sqrt{u} \, du \qquad \text{(where } u = 1 + 4y)$$

$$= \frac{\pi}{6} \left(17\sqrt{17} - 5\sqrt{5}\right) \qquad \text{(as in Solution 1)}$$

EXAMPLE 3 Find the area of the surface generated by rotating the curve $y = e^x$, $0 \le x \le 1$, about the x-axis.

|||| Another method: Use Formula 6 with $x = \ln y$.

SOLUTION Using Formula 5 with

$$y = e^x \qquad \text{and} \qquad \frac{dy}{dx} = e^x$$

we have

$$S = \int_0^1 2\pi y \sqrt{1 + \left(\frac{dy}{dx}\right)^2}\, dx = 2\pi \int_0^1 e^x \sqrt{1 + e^{2x}}\, dx$$

$$= 2\pi \int_1^e \sqrt{1 + u^2}\, du \qquad \text{(where } u = e^x\text{)}$$

$$= 2\pi \int_{\pi/4}^{\alpha} \sec^3\theta\, d\theta \qquad \text{(where } u = \tan\theta \text{ and } \alpha = \tan^{-1}e\text{)}$$

▦ Or use Formula 21 in the Table of Integrals.

$$= 2\pi \cdot \tfrac{1}{2}\big[\sec\theta \tan\theta + \ln|\sec\theta + \tan\theta|\big]_{\pi/4}^{\alpha} \qquad \text{(by Example 8 in Section 8.2)}$$

$$= \pi\big[\sec\alpha \tan\alpha + \ln(\sec\alpha + \tan\alpha) - \sqrt{2} - \ln(\sqrt{2} + 1)\big]$$

Since $\tan\alpha = e$, we have $\sec^2\alpha = 1 + \tan^2\alpha = 1 + e^2$ and

$$S = \pi\big[e\sqrt{1 + e^2} + \ln(e + \sqrt{1 + e^2}) - \sqrt{2} - \ln(\sqrt{2} + 1)\big]$$

9.2 Exercises

1–4 ▦ Set up, but do not evaluate, an integral for the area of the surface obtained by rotating the curve about the given axis.

1. $y = \ln x$, $1 \le x \le 3$; x-axis

2. $y = \sin^2 x$, $0 \le x \le \pi/2$; x-axis

3. $y = \sec x$, $0 \le x \le \pi/4$; y-axis

4. $y = e^x$, $1 \le y \le 2$; y-axis

5–12 ▦ Find the area of the surface obtained by rotating the curve about the x-axis.

5. $y = x^3$, $0 \le x \le 2$

6. $9x = y^2 + 18$, $2 \le x \le 6$

7. $y = \sqrt{x}$, $4 \le x \le 9$

8. $y = \cos 2x$, $0 \le x \le \pi/6$

9. $y = \cosh x$, $0 \le x \le 1$

10. $y = \dfrac{x^3}{6} + \dfrac{1}{2x}$, $\tfrac{1}{2} \le x \le 1$

11. $x = \tfrac{1}{3}(y^2 + 2)^{3/2}$, $1 \le y \le 2$

12. $x = 1 + 2y^2$, $1 \le y \le 2$

13–16 ▦ The given curve is rotated about the y-axis. Find the area of the resulting surface.

13. $y = \sqrt[3]{x}$, $1 \le y \le 2$

14. $y = 1 - x^2$, $0 \le x \le 1$

15. $x = \sqrt{a^2 - y^2}$, $0 \le y \le a/2$

16. $x = a\cosh(y/a)$, $-a \le y \le a$

17–20 ▦ Use Simpson's Rule with $n = 10$ to approximate the area of the surface obtained by rotating the curve about the x-axis. Compare your answer with the value of the integral produced by your calculator.

17. $y = \ln x$, $1 \le x \le 3$

18. $y = x + \sqrt{x}$, $1 \le x \le 2$

19. $y = \sec x$, $0 \le x \le \pi/3$

20. $y = \sqrt{1 + e^x}$, $0 \le x \le 1$

[CAS] **21–22** ▦ Use either a CAS or a table of integrals to find the exact area of the surface obtained by rotating the given curve about the x-axis.

21. $y = 1/x$, $1 \le x \le 2$

22. $y = \sqrt{x^2 + 1}$, $0 \le x \le 3$

[CAS] **23–24** ▦ Use a CAS to find the exact area of the surface obtained by rotating the curve about the y-axis. If your CAS has trouble evaluating the integral, express the surface area as an integral in the other variable.

23. $y = x^3$, $0 \le y \le 1$

24. $y = \ln(x + 1)$, $0 \le x \le 1$

25. If the region $\mathcal{R} = \{(x, y) \mid x \ge 1, 0 \le y \le 1/x\}$ is rotated about the x-axis, the volume of the resulting solid is finite (see Exercise 63 in Section 8.8). Show that the surface area is infinite. (The surface is shown in the figure and is known as **Gabriel's horn**.)

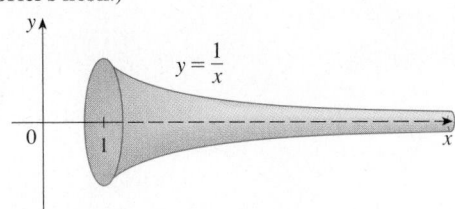

26. If the infinite curve $y = e^{-x}$, $x \geq 0$, is rotated about the x-axis, find the area of the resulting surface.

27. (a) If $a > 0$, find the area of the surface generated by rotating the loop of the curve $3ay^2 = x(a - x)^2$ about the x-axis.
  (b) Find the surface area if the loop is rotated about the y-axis.

28. A group of engineers is building a parabolic satellite dish whose shape will be formed by rotating the curve $y = ax^2$ about the y-axis. If the dish is to have a 10-ft diameter and a maximum depth of 2 ft, find the value of a and the surface area of the dish.

29. The ellipse

$$\frac{x^2}{a^2} + \frac{y^2}{b^2} = 1 \qquad a > b$$

is rotated about the x-axis to form a surface called an *ellipsoid*. Find the surface area of this ellipsoid.

30. Find the surface area of the torus in Exercise 61 in Section 6.2.

31. If the curve $y = f(x)$, $a \leq x \leq b$, is rotated about the horizontal line $y = c$, where $f(x) \leq c$, find a formula for the area of the resulting surface.

[CAS] 32. Use the result of Exercise 31 to set up an integral to find the area of the surface generated by rotating the curve $y = \sqrt{x}$, $0 \leq x \leq 4$, about the line $y = 4$. Then use a CAS to evaluate the integral.

33. Find the area of the surface obtained by rotating the circle $x^2 + y^2 = r^2$ about the line $y = r$.

34. Show that the surface area of a zone of a sphere that lies between two parallel planes is $S = \pi dh$, where d is the diameter of the sphere and h is the distance between the planes. (Notice that S depends only on the distance between the planes and not on their location, provided that both planes intersect the sphere.)

35. Formula 4 is valid only when $f(x) \geq 0$. Show that when $f(x)$ is not necessarily positive, the formula for surface area becomes

$$S = \int_a^b 2\pi |f(x)| \sqrt{1 + [f'(x)]^2} \, dx$$

36. Let L be the length of the curve $y = f(x)$, $a \leq x \leq b$, where f is positive and has a continuous derivative. Let S_f be the surface area generated by rotating the curve about the x-axis. If c is a positive constant, define $g(x) = f(x) + c$ and let S_g be the corresponding surface area generated by the curve $y = g(x)$, $a \leq x \leq b$. Express S_g in terms of S_f and L.

|||| DISCOVERY PROJECT

Rotating on a Slant

We know how to find the volume of a solid of revolution obtained by rotating a region about a horizontal or vertical line (see Section 6.2). We also know how to find the surface area of a surface of revolution if we rotate a curve about a horizontal or vertical line (see Section 9.2). But what if we rotate about a slanted line, that is, a line that is neither horizontal nor vertical? In this project you are asked to discover formulas for the volume of a solid of revolution and for the area of a surface of revolution when the axis of rotation is a slanted line.

Let C be the arc of the curve $y = f(x)$ between the points $P(p, f(p))$ and $Q(q, f(q))$ and let $\mathcal{R}$ be the region bounded by C, by the line $y = mx + b$ (which lies entirely below C), and by the perpendiculars to the line from P and Q.

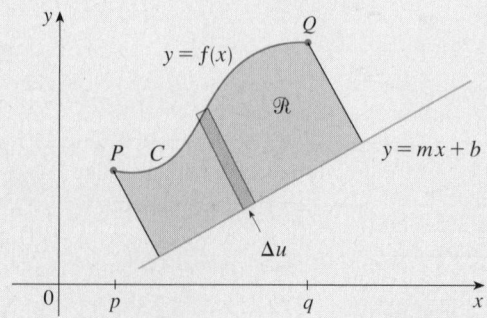

1. Show that the area of $\mathcal{R}$ is

$$\frac{1}{1 + m^2} \int_p^q [f(x) - mx - b][1 + mf'(x)] \, dx$$

[*Hint:* This formula can be verified by subtracting areas, but it will be helpful throughout the project to derive it by first approximating the area using rectangles perpendicular to the line, as shown in the figure. Use the figure to help express Δu in terms of Δx.]

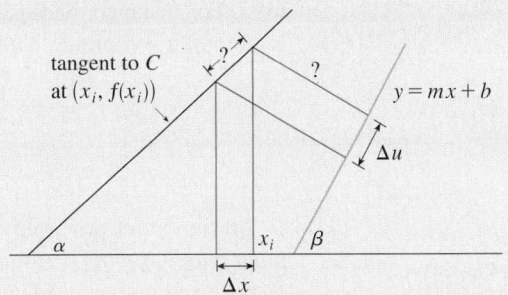

2. Find the area of the region shown in the figure at the left.

3. Find a formula similar to the one in Problem 1 for the volume of the solid obtained by rotating $\mathcal{R}$ about the line $y = mx + b$.

4. Find the volume of the solid obtained by rotating the region of Problem 2 about the line $y = x - 2$.

5. Find a formula for the area of the surface obtained by rotating C about the line $y = mx + b$.

[CAS] 6. Use a computer algebra system to find the exact area of the surface obtained by rotating the curve $y = \sqrt{x}$, $0 \leqslant x \leqslant 4$, about the line $y = \frac{1}{2}x$. Then approximate your result to three decimal places.

FIGURE FOR PROBLEM 2

9.3 Applications to Physics and Engineering

Among the many applications of integral calculus to physics and engineering, we consider two here: force due to water pressure and centers of mass. As with our previous applications to geometry (areas, volumes, and lengths) and to work, our strategy is to break up the physical quantity into a large number of small parts, approximate each small part, add the results, take the limit, and then evaluate the resulting integral.

Hydrostatic Pressure and Force

Deep-sea divers realize that water pressure increases as they dive deeper. This is because the weight of the water above them increases.

In general, suppose that a thin horizontal plate with area A square meters is submerged in a fluid of density ρ kilograms per cubic meter at a depth d meters below the surface of the fluid as in Figure 1. The fluid directly above the plate has volume $V = Ad$, so its mass is $m = \rho V = \rho Ad$. The force exerted by the fluid on the plate is therefore

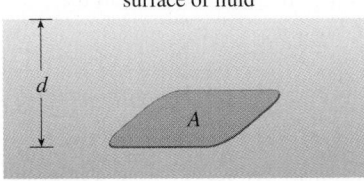

FIGURE 1

$$F = mg = \rho g Ad$$

where g is the acceleration due to gravity. The **pressure** P on the plate is defined to be the force per unit area:

$$P = \frac{F}{A} = \rho g d$$

IIII When using U.S. Customary units, we write $P = \rho g d = \delta d$, where $\delta = \rho g$ is the weight density (as opposed to ρ, which is the mass density). For instance, the weight density of water is $\delta = 62.5 \text{ lb/ft}^3$.

The SI unit for measuring pressure is newtons per square meter, which is called a pascal (abbreviation: $1 \text{ N/m}^2 = 1 \text{ Pa}$). Since this is a small unit, the kilopascal (kPa) is often used. For instance, because the density of water is $\rho = 1000 \text{ kg/m}^3$, the pressure at the bottom of a swimming pool 2 m deep is

$$P = \rho g d = 1000 \text{ kg/m}^3 \times 9.8 \text{ m/s}^2 \times 2 \text{ m}$$

$$= 19{,}600 \text{ Pa} = 19.6 \text{ kPa}$$

An important principle of fluid pressure is the experimentally verified fact that at *any point in a liquid the pressure is the same in all directions.* (A diver feels the same pressure on nose and both ears.) Thus, the pressure in *any* direction at a depth d in a fluid with mass density ρ is given by

1   $$P = \rho g d = \delta d$$

This helps us determine the hydrostatic force against a *vertical* plate or wall or dam in a fluid. This is not a straightforward problem because the pressure is not constant but increases as the depth increases.

EXAMPLE 1 A dam has the shape of the trapezoid shown in Figure 2. The height is 20 m, and the width is 50 m at the top and 30 m at the bottom. Find the force on the dam due to hydrostatic pressure if the water level is 4 m from the top of the dam.

SOLUTION We choose a vertical x-axis with origin at the surface of the water as in Figure 3(a). The depth of the water is 16 m, so we divide the interval $[0, 16]$ into subintervals of equal length with endpoints x_i and we choose $x_i^* \in [x_{i-1}, x_i]$. The ith horizontal strip of the dam is approximated by a rectangle with height Δx and width w_i, where, from similar triangles in Figure 3(b),

$$\frac{a}{16 - x_i^*} = \frac{10}{20} \quad \text{or} \quad a = \frac{16 - x_i^*}{2} = 8 - \frac{x_i^*}{2}$$

and so

$$w_i = 2(15 + a) = 2\left(15 + 8 - \tfrac{1}{2}x_i^*\right) = 46 - x_i^*$$

If A_i is the area of the ith strip, then

$$A_i \approx w_i \, \Delta x = (46 - x_i^*) \, \Delta x$$

If Δx is small, then the pressure P_i on the ith strip is almost constant and we can use Equation 1 to write

$$P_i \approx 1000 g x_i^*$$

The hydrostatic force F_i acting on the ith strip is the product of the pressure and the area:

$$F_i = P_i A_i \approx 1000 g x_i^*(46 - x_i^*) \, \Delta x$$

FIGURE 2

(a)

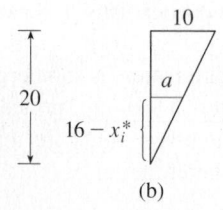

(b)

FIGURE 3

Adding these forces and taking the limit as $n \to \infty$, we obtain the total hydrostatic force on the dam:

$$F = \lim_{n \to \infty} \sum_{i=1}^{n} 1000gx_i^*(46 - x_i^*)\,\Delta x$$

$$= \int_0^{16} 1000gx(46 - x)\,dx$$

$$= 1000(9.8) \int_0^{16} (46x - x^2)\,dx$$

$$= 9800 \left[23x^2 - \frac{x^3}{3} \right]_0^{16}$$

$$\approx 4.43 \times 10^7 \text{ N}$$

EXAMPLE 2 Find the hydrostatic force on one end of a cylindrical drum with radius 3 ft if the drum is submerged in water 10 ft deep.

SOLUTION In this example it is convenient to choose the axes as in Figure 4 so that the origin is placed at the center of the drum. Then the circle has a simple equation, $x^2 + y^2 = 9$. As in Example 1 we divide the circular region into horizontal strips of equal width. From the equation of the circle, we see that the length of the ith strip is $2\sqrt{9 - (y_i^*)^2}$ and so its area is

$$A_i = 2\sqrt{9 - (y_i^*)^2}\,\Delta y$$

The pressure on this strip is approximately

$$\delta d_i = 62.5(7 - y_i^*)$$

and so the force on the strip is approximately

$$\delta d_i A_i = 62.5(7 - y_i^*)2\sqrt{9 - (y_i^*)^2}\,\Delta y$$

The total force is obtained by adding the forces on all the strips and taking the limit:

$$F = \lim_{n \to \infty} \sum_{i=1}^{n} 62.5(7 - y_i^*)2\sqrt{9 - (y_i^*)^2}\,\Delta y$$

$$= 125 \int_{-3}^{3} (7 - y)\sqrt{9 - y^2}\,dy$$

$$= 125 \cdot 7 \int_{-3}^{3} \sqrt{9 - y^2}\,dy - 125 \int_{-3}^{3} y\sqrt{9 - y^2}\,dy$$

The second integral is 0 because the integrand is an odd function (see Theorem 5.5.6). The first integral can be evaluated using the trigonometric substitution $y = 3 \sin \theta$, but it's simpler to observe that it is the area of a semicircular disk with radius 3. Thus

$$F = 875 \int_{-3}^{3} \sqrt{9 - y^2}\,dy = 875 \cdot \tfrac{1}{2}\pi(3)^2$$

$$= \frac{7875\pi}{2} \approx 12{,}370 \text{ lb}$$

FIGURE 4

FIGURE 5

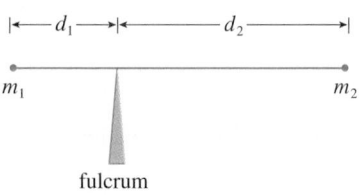

fulcrum

FIGURE 6

▐▐▐ Moments and Centers of Mass

Our main objective here is to find the point P on which a thin plate of any given shape balances horizontally as in Figure 5. This point is called the **center of mass** (or center of gravity) of the plate.

We first consider the simpler situation illustrated in Figure 6, where two masses m_1 and m_2 are attached to a rod of negligible mass on opposite sides of a fulcrum and at distances d_1 and d_2 from the fulcrum. The rod will balance if

$$\boxed{2} \qquad m_1 d_1 = m_2 d_2$$

This is an experimental fact discovered by Archimedes and called the Law of the Lever. (Think of a lighter person balancing a heavier one on a seesaw by sitting farther away from the center.)

Now suppose that the rod lies along the x-axis with m_1 at x_1 and m_2 at x_2 and the center of mass at $\bar{x}$. If we compare Figures 6 and 7, we see that $d_1 = \bar{x} - x_1$ and $d_2 = x_2 - \bar{x}$ and so Equation 2 gives

$$m_1(\bar{x} - x_1) = m_2(x_2 - \bar{x})$$

$$m_1\bar{x} + m_2\bar{x} = m_1 x_1 + m_2 x_2$$

$$\boxed{3} \qquad \bar{x} = \frac{m_1 x_1 + m_2 x_2}{m_1 + m_2}$$

The numbers $m_1 x_1$ and $m_2 x_2$ are called the **moments** of the masses m_1 and m_2 (with respect to the origin), and Equation 3 says that the center of mass $\bar{x}$ is obtained by adding the moments of the masses and dividing by the total mass $m = m_1 + m_2$.

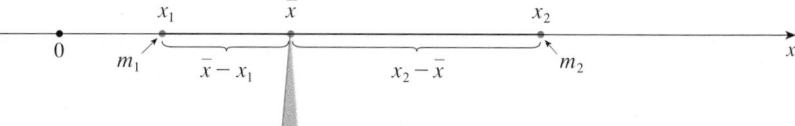

FIGURE 7

In general, if we have a system of n particles with masses $m_1, m_2, \ldots, m_n$ located at the points $x_1, x_2, \ldots, x_n$ on the x-axis, it can be shown similarly that the center of mass of the system is located at

$$\boxed{4} \qquad \bar{x} = \frac{\displaystyle\sum_{i=1}^{n} m_i x_i}{\displaystyle\sum_{i=1}^{n} m_i} = \frac{\displaystyle\sum_{i=1}^{n} m_i x_i}{m}$$

where $m = \Sigma\, m_i$ is the total mass of the system, and the sum of the individual moments

$$M = \sum_{i=1}^{n} m_i x_i$$

is called the **moment of the system about the origin.** Then Equation 4 could be rewritten as $m\bar{x} = M$, which says that if the total mass were considered as being concentrated at the center of mass $\bar{x}$, then its moment would be the same as the moment of the system.

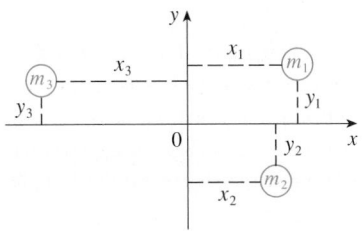

FIGURE 8

Now we consider a system of n particles with masses $m_1, m_2, \ldots, m_n$ located at the points $(x_1, y_1), (x_2, y_2), \ldots, (x_n, y_n)$ in the xy-plane as shown in Figure 8. By analogy with the one-dimensional case, we define the **moment of the system about the y-axis** to be

$$\boxed{5} \qquad\qquad M_y = \sum_{i=1}^{n} m_i x_i$$

and the **moment of the system about the x-axis** as

$$\boxed{6} \qquad\qquad M_x = \sum_{i=1}^{n} m_i y_i$$

Then M_y measures the tendency of the system to rotate about the y-axis and M_x measures the tendency to rotate about the x-axis.

As in the one-dimensional case, the coordinates $(\bar{x}, \bar{y})$ of the center of mass are given in terms of the moments by the formulas

$$\boxed{7} \qquad\qquad \bar{x} = \frac{M_y}{m} \qquad\qquad \bar{y} = \frac{M_x}{m}$$

where $m = \Sigma \, m_i$ is the total mass. Since $m\bar{x} = M_y$ and $m\bar{y} = M_x$, the center of mass $(\bar{x}, \bar{y})$ is the point where a single particle of mass m would have the same moments as the system.

EXAMPLE 3 Find the moments and center of mass of the system of objects that have masses 3, 4, and 8 at the points $(-1, 1)$, $(2, -1)$, and $(3, 2)$.

SOLUTION We use Equations 5 and 6 to compute the moments:

$$M_y = 3(-1) + 4(2) + 8(3) = 29$$

$$M_x = 3(1) + 4(-1) + 8(2) = 15$$

Since $m = 3 + 4 + 8 = 15$, we use Equations 7 to obtain

$$\bar{x} = \frac{M_y}{m} = \frac{29}{15} \qquad\qquad \bar{y} = \frac{M_x}{m} = \frac{15}{15} = 1$$

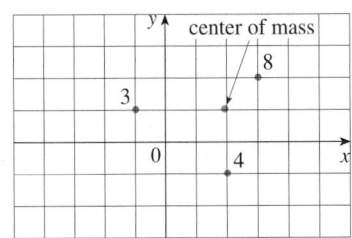

FIGURE 9

Thus, the center of mass is $\left(1\tfrac{14}{15}, 1\right)$. (See Figure 9.)

Next we consider a flat plate (called a *lamina*) with uniform density ρ that occupies a region $\mathcal{R}$ of the plane. We wish to locate the center of mass of the plate, which is called the **centroid** of $\mathcal{R}$. In doing so we use the following physical principles: The **symmetry principle** says that if $\mathcal{R}$ is symmetric about a line l, then the centroid of $\mathcal{R}$ lies on l. (If $\mathcal{R}$ is reflected about l, then $\mathcal{R}$ remains the same so its centroid remains fixed. But the only fixed points lie on l.) Thus, the centroid of a rectangle is its center. Moments should be defined so that if the entire mass of a region is concentrated at the center of mass, then its moments remain unchanged. Also, the moment of the union of two nonoverlapping regions should be the sum of the moments of the individual regions.

(a)

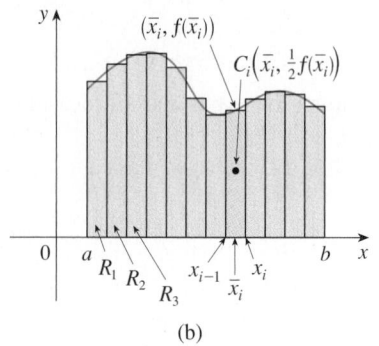

(b)

FIGURE 10

Suppose that the region $\mathcal{R}$ is of the type shown in Figure 10(a); that is, $\mathcal{R}$ lies between the lines $x = a$ and $x = b$, above the x-axis, and beneath the graph of f, where f is a continuous function. We divide the interval $[a, b]$ into n subintervals with endpoints $x_0, x_1, \ldots, x_n$ and equal width Δx. We choose the sample point x_i^* to be the midpoint $\bar{x}_i$ of the ith subinterval, that is, $\bar{x}_i = (x_{i-1} + x_i)/2$. This determines the polygonal approximation to $\mathcal{R}$ shown in Figure 10(b). The centroid of the ith approximating rectangle R_i is its center $C_i(\bar{x}_i, \frac{1}{2}f(\bar{x}_i))$. Its area is $f(\bar{x}_i)\,\Delta x$, so its mass is

$$\rho f(\bar{x}_i)\,\Delta x$$

The moment of R_i about the y-axis is the product of its mass and the distance from C_i to the y-axis, which is $\bar{x}_i$. Thus

$$M_y(R_i) = [\rho f(\bar{x}_i)\,\Delta x]\,\bar{x}_i = \rho\bar{x}_i f(\bar{x}_i)\,\Delta x$$

Adding these moments, we obtain the moment of the polygonal approximation to $\mathcal{R}$, and then by taking the limit as $n \to \infty$ we obtain the moment of $\mathcal{R}$ itself about the y-axis:

$$M_y = \lim_{n \to \infty} \sum_{i=1}^{n} \rho\bar{x}_i f(\bar{x}_i)\,\Delta x = \rho \int_a^b x f(x)\,dx$$

In a similar fashion we compute the moment of R_i about the x-axis as the product of its mass and the distance from C_i to the x-axis:

$$M_x(R_i) = [\rho f(\bar{x}_i)\,\Delta x]\tfrac{1}{2}f(\bar{x}_i) = \rho \cdot \tfrac{1}{2}[f(\bar{x}_i)]^2\,\Delta x$$

Again we add these moments and take the limit to obtain the moment of $\mathcal{R}$ about the x-axis:

$$M_x = \lim_{n \to \infty} \sum_{i=1}^{n} \rho \cdot \tfrac{1}{2}[f(\bar{x}_i)]^2\,\Delta x = \rho \int_a^b \tfrac{1}{2}[f(x)]^2\,dx$$

Just as for systems of particles, the center of mass of the plate is defined so that $m\bar{x} = M_y$ and $m\bar{y} = M_x$. But the mass of the plate is the product of its density and its area:

$$m = \rho A = \rho \int_a^b f(x)\,dx$$

and so

$$\bar{x} = \frac{M_y}{m} = \frac{\rho \int_a^b x f(x)\,dx}{\rho \int_a^b f(x)\,dx} = \frac{\int_a^b x f(x)\,dx}{\int_a^b f(x)\,dx}$$

$$\bar{y} = \frac{M_x}{m} = \frac{\rho \int_a^b \tfrac{1}{2}[f(x)]^2\,dx}{\rho \int_a^b f(x)\,dx} = \frac{\int_a^b \tfrac{1}{2}[f(x)]^2\,dx}{\int_a^b f(x)\,dx}$$

Notice the cancellation of the ρ's. The location of the center of mass is independent of the density.

In summary, the center of mass of the plate (or the centroid of $\mathcal{R}$) is located at the point $(\bar{x}, \bar{y})$, where

8
$$\bar{x} = \frac{1}{A} \int_a^b x f(x)\, dx \qquad \bar{y} = \frac{1}{A} \int_a^b \tfrac{1}{2}[f(x)]^2\, dx$$

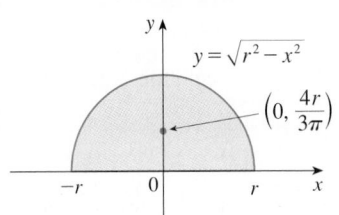

$$y = \sqrt{r^2 - x^2}$$

$$\left(0, \frac{4r}{3\pi}\right)$$

FIGURE 11

EXAMPLE 4 Find the center of mass of a semicircular plate of radius r.

SOLUTION In order to use (8) we place the semicircle as in Figure 11 so that $f(x) = \sqrt{r^2 - x^2}$ and $a = -r$, $b = r$. Here there is no need to use the formula to calculate $\bar{x}$ because, by the symmetry principle, the center of mass must lie on the y-axis, so $\bar{x} = 0$. The area of the semicircle is $A = \pi r^2/2$, so

$$\bar{y} = \frac{1}{A} \int_{-r}^r \tfrac{1}{2}[f(x)]^2\, dx$$

$$= \frac{1}{\pi r^2/2} \cdot \tfrac{1}{2} \int_{-r}^r \left(\sqrt{r^2 - x^2}\right)^2 dx$$

$$= \frac{2}{\pi r^2} \int_0^r (r^2 - x^2)\, dx = \frac{2}{\pi r^2}\left[r^2 x - \frac{x^3}{3}\right]_0^r$$

$$= \frac{2}{\pi r^2}\frac{2r^3}{3} = \frac{4r}{3\pi}$$

The center of mass is located at the point $(0, 4r/(3\pi))$.

EXAMPLE 5 Find the centroid of the region bounded by the curves $y = \cos x$, $y = 0$, $x = 0$, and $x = \pi/2$.

SOLUTION The area of the region is

$$A = \int_0^{\pi/2} \cos x\, dx = \sin x \Big]_0^{\pi/2} = 1$$

so Formulas 8 give

$$\bar{x} = \frac{1}{A} \int_0^{\pi/2} x f(x)\, dx = \int_0^{\pi/2} x \cos x\, dx$$

$$= x \sin x \Big]_0^{\pi/2} - \int_0^{\pi/2} \sin x\, dx \qquad \text{(by integration by parts)}$$

$$= \frac{\pi}{2} - 1$$

$$\bar{y} = \frac{1}{A} \int_0^{\pi/2} \tfrac{1}{2}[f(x)]^2\, dx = \tfrac{1}{2} \int_0^{\pi/2} \cos^2 x\, dx$$

$$= \tfrac{1}{4} \int_0^{\pi/2} (1 + \cos 2x)\, dx = \tfrac{1}{4}\left[x + \tfrac{1}{2}\sin 2x\right]_0^{\pi/2}$$

$$= \frac{\pi}{8}$$

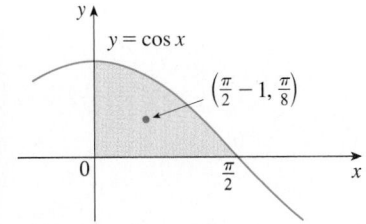

$$y = \cos x$$

$$\left(\frac{\pi}{2} - 1, \frac{\pi}{8}\right)$$

FIGURE 12

The centroid is $((\pi/2) - 1, \pi/8)$ and is shown in Figure 12.

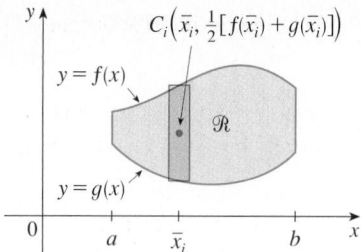

FIGURE 13

If the region $\mathcal{R}$ lies between two curves $y = f(x)$ and $y = g(x)$, where $f(x) \geqslant g(x)$, as illustrated in Figure 13, then the same sort of argument that led to Formulas 8 can be used to show that the centroid of $\mathcal{R}$ is $(\bar{x}, \bar{y})$, where

$$\boxed{9} \qquad \bar{x} = \frac{1}{A} \int_a^b x[f(x) - g(x)]\, dx \qquad \bar{y} = \frac{1}{A} \int_a^b \tfrac{1}{2}\{[f(x)]^2 - [g(x)]^2\}\, dx$$

(See Exercise 43.)

EXAMPLE 6 Find the centroid of the region bounded by the line $y = x$ and the parabola $y = x^2$.

SOLUTION The region is sketched in Figure 14. We take $f(x) = x$, $g(x) = x^2$, $a = 0$, and $b = 1$ in Formulas 9. First we note that the area of the region is

$$A = \int_0^1 (x - x^2)\, dx = \frac{x^2}{2} - \frac{x^3}{3}\Big]_0^1 = \frac{1}{6}$$

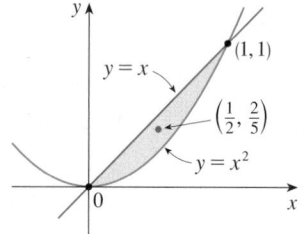

FIGURE 14

Therefore

$$\bar{x} = \frac{1}{A} \int_0^1 x[f(x) - g(x)]\, dx = \frac{1}{\frac{1}{6}} \int_0^1 x(x - x^2)\, dx$$

$$= 6 \int_0^1 (x^2 - x^3)\, dx = 6\left[\frac{x^3}{3} - \frac{x^4}{4}\right]_0^1 = \frac{1}{2}$$

$$\bar{y} = \frac{1}{A} \int_0^1 \tfrac{1}{2}\{[f(x)]^2 - [g(x)]^2\}\, dx = \frac{1}{\frac{1}{6}} \int_0^1 \tfrac{1}{2}(x^2 - x^4)\, dx$$

$$= 3\left[\frac{x^3}{3} - \frac{x^5}{5}\right]_0^1 = \frac{2}{5}$$

The centroid is $\left(\frac{1}{2}, \frac{2}{5}\right)$.

We end this section by showing a surprising connection between centroids and volumes of revolution.

‖‖‖ This theorem is named after the Greek mathematician Pappus of Alexandria, who lived in the fourth century A.D.

> **Theorem of Pappus** Let $\mathcal{R}$ be a plane region that lies entirely on one side of a line l in the plane. If $\mathcal{R}$ is rotated about l, then the volume of the resulting solid is the product of the area A of $\mathcal{R}$ and the distance d traveled by the centroid of $\mathcal{R}$.

Proof We give the proof for the special case in which the region lies between $y = f(x)$ and $y = g(x)$ as in Figure 13 and the line l is the y-axis. Using the method of cylindrical shells (see Section 6.3), we have

$$V = \int_a^b 2\pi x[f(x) - g(x)]\, dx$$

$$= 2\pi \int_a^b x[f(x) - g(x)]\, dx$$

$$= 2\pi(\bar{x}A) \qquad \text{(by Formulas 9)}$$

$$= (2\pi\bar{x})A = Ad$$

where $d = 2\pi\bar{x}$ is the distance traveled by the centroid during one rotation about the y-axis.

EXAMPLE 7 A torus is formed by rotating a circle of radius r about a line in the plane of the circle that is a distance R ($> r$) from the center of the circle. Find the volume of the torus.

SOLUTION The circle has area $A = \pi r^2$. By the symmetry principle, its centroid is its center and so the distance traveled by the centroid during a rotation is $d = 2\pi R$. Therefore, by the Theorem of Pappus, the volume of the torus is

$$V = Ad = (2\pi R)(\pi r^2) = 2\pi^2 r^2 R$$

The method of Example 7 should be compared with the method of Exercise 61 in Section 6.2.

9.3 Exercises

1. An aquarium 5 ft long, 2 ft wide, and 3 ft deep is full of water. Find (a) the hydrostatic pressure on the bottom of the aquarium, (b) the hydrostatic force on the bottom, and (c) the hydrostatic force on one end of the aquarium.

2. A swimming pool 5 m wide, 10 m long, and 3 m deep is filled with seawater of density 1030 kg/m³ to a depth of 2.5 m. Find (a) the hydrostatic pressure at the bottom of the pool, (b) the hydrostatic force on the bottom, and (c) the hydrostatic force on one end of the pool.

3–9 ▓ A vertical plate is submerged in water and has the indicated shape. Explain how to approximate the hydrostatic force against one side of the plate by a Riemann sum. Then express the force as an integral and evaluate it.

3.

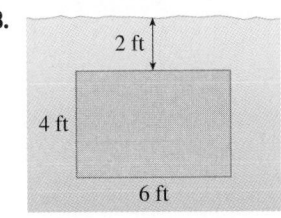
2 ft
4 ft
6 ft

4.

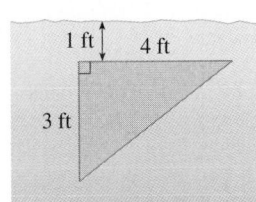
1 ft   4 ft
3 ft

5.

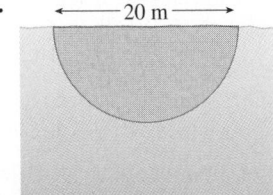
←——— 20 m ———→

6.

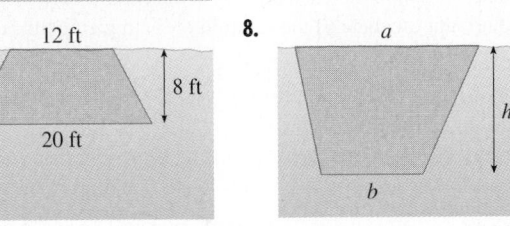
5 m
4 m

7.

12 ft
8 ft
20 ft

8.

a
h
b

9.

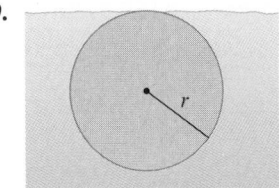
r

10. A large tank is designed with ends in the shape of the region between the curves $y = x^2/2$ and $y = 12$, measured in feet. Find the hydrostatic force on one end of the tank if it is filled to a depth of 8 ft with gasoline. (Assume the gasoline's density is 42.0 lb/ft³.)

11. A trough is filled with a liquid of density 840 kg/m³. The ends of the trough are equilateral triangles with sides 8 m long and vertex at the bottom. Find the hydrostatic force on one end of the trough.

12. A vertical dam has a semicircular gate as shown in the figure. Find the hydrostatic force against the gate.

2 m
water level
12 m
4 m

13. A cube with 20-cm-long sides is sitting on the bottom of an aquarium in which the water is one meter deep. Find the hydrostatic force on (a) the top of the cube and (b) one of the sides of the cube.

14. A dam is inclined at an angle of 30° from the vertical and has the shape of an isosceles trapezoid 100 ft wide at the top and

50 ft wide at the bottom and with a slant height of 70 ft. Find the hydrostatic force on the dam when it is full of water.

15. A swimming pool is 20 ft wide and 40 ft long and its bottom is an inclined plane, the shallow end having a depth of 3 ft and the deep end, 9 ft. If the pool is full of water, find the hydrostatic force on (a) the shallow end, (b) the deep end, (c) one of the sides, and (d) the bottom of the pool.

16. Suppose that a plate is immersed vertically in a fluid with density ρ and the width of the plate is $w(x)$ at a depth of x meters beneath the surface of the fluid. If the top of the plate is at depth a and the bottom is at depth b, show that the hydrostatic force on one side of the plate is

$$F = \int_a^b \rho g x w(x)\, dx$$

17. A vertical, irregularly shaped plate is submerged in water. The table shows measurements of its width, taken at the indicated depths. Use Simpson's Rule to estimate the force of the water against the plate.

Depth (m)	2.0	2.5	3.0	3.5	4.0	4.5	5.0
Plate width (m)	0	0.8	1.7	2.4	2.9	3.3	3.6

18. (a) Use the formula of Exercise 16 to show that

$$F = (\rho g \bar{x})A$$

where $\bar{x}$ is the x-coordinate of the centroid of the plate and A is its area. This equation shows that the hydrostatic force against a vertical plane region is the same as if the region were horizontal at the depth of the centroid of the region.

(b) Use the result of part (a) to give another solution to Exercise 9.

19–20 |||| Point-masses m_i are located on the x-axis as shown. Find the moment M of the system about the origin and the center of mass $\bar{x}$.

19.
$m_1 = 40 \quad m_2 = 30$
$0 \quad 2 \quad\quad 5 \quad\quad x$

20.
$m_1 = 25 \quad\quad m_2 = 20 \quad\quad m_3 = 10$
$-2 \quad 0 \quad\quad 3 \quad\quad 7 \quad x$

21–22 |||| The masses m_i are located at the points P_i. Find the moments M_x and M_y and the center of mass of the system.

21. $m_1 = 6,\ m_2 = 5,\ m_3 = 10;$
$P_1(1, 5),\ P_2(3, -2),\ P_3(-2, -1)$

22. $m_1 = 6,\ m_2 = 5,\ m_3 = 1,\ m_4 = 4;$
$P_1(1, -2),\ P_2(3, 4),\ P_3(-3, -7),\ P_4(6, -1)$

23–26 |||| Sketch the region bounded by the curves, and visually estimate the location of the centroid. Then find the exact coordinates of the centroid.

23. $y = 4 - x^2,\quad y = 0$

24. $3x + 2y = 6,\quad y = 0,\quad x = 0$

25. $y = e^x,\quad y = 0,\quad x = 0,\quad x = 1$

26. $y = 1/x,\quad y = 0,\quad x = 1,\quad x = 2$

27–31 |||| Find the centroid of the region bounded by the given curves.

27. $y = \sqrt{x},\quad y = x$

28. $y = x + 2,\quad y = x^2$

29. $y = \sin x,\quad y = \cos x,\quad x = 0,\quad x = \pi/4$

30. $y = x,\quad y = 0,\quad y = 1/x,\quad x = 2$

31. $x = 5 - y^2,\quad x = 0$

32–34 |||| Calculate the moments M_x and M_y and the center of mass of a lamina with the given density and shape.

32. $\rho = 5$

33. $\rho = 1$

34. $\rho = 2$

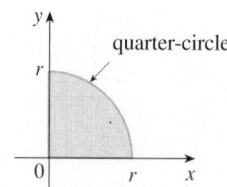

35. Find the centroid of the region bounded by the curves $y = 2^x$ and $y = x^2, 0 \leq x \leq 2$, to three decimal places. Sketch the region and plot the centroid to see if your answer is reasonable.

36. Use a graph to find approximate x-coordinates of the points of intersection of the curves $y = x + \ln x$ and $y = x^3 - x$. Then find (approximately) the centroid of the region bounded by these curves.

37. Prove that the centroid of any triangle is located at the point of intersection of the medians. [*Hints:* Place the axes so that the vertices are $(a, 0)$, $(0, b)$, and $(c, 0)$. Recall that a median is a line segment from a vertex to the midpoint of the opposite side. Recall also that the medians intersect at a point two-thirds of the way from each vertex (along the median) to the opposite side.]

38–39 |||| Find the centroid of the region shown, not by integration, but by locating the centroids of the rectangles and triangles (from Exercise 37) and using additivity of moments.

38. **39.**

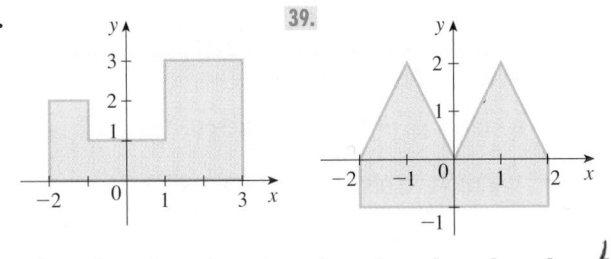

40–42 |||| Use the Theorem of Pappus to find the volume of the given solid.

40. A sphere of radius r (Use Example 4.)

41. A cone with height h and base radius r

42. The solid obtained by rotating the triangle with vertices $(2, 3)$, $(2, 5)$, and $(5, 4)$ about the x-axis

43. Prove Formulas 9.

44. Let $\mathcal{R}$ be the region that lies between the curves $y = x^m$ and $y = x^n$, $0 \le x \le 1$, where m and n are integers with $0 \le n < m$.
(a) Sketch the region $\mathcal{R}$.
(b) Find the coordinates of the centroid of $\mathcal{R}$.
(c) Try to find values of m and n such that the centroid lies *outside* $\mathcal{R}$.

9.4 Applications to Economics and Biology

In this section we consider some applications of integration to economics (consumer surplus) and biology (blood flow, cardiac output). Others are described in the exercises.

Consumer Surplus

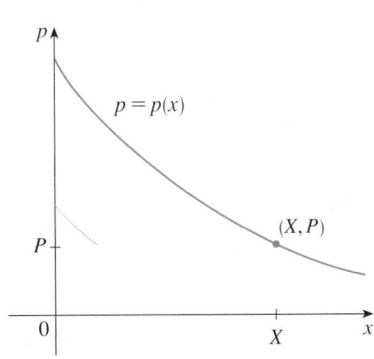

FIGURE 1
A typical demand curve

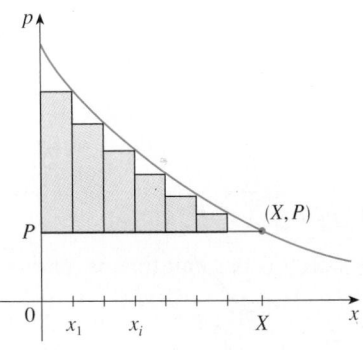

FIGURE 2

Recall from Section 4.8 that the demand function $p(x)$ is the price that a company has to charge in order to sell x units of a commodity. Usually, selling larger quantities requires lowering prices, so the demand function is a decreasing function. The graph of a typical demand function, called a **demand curve**, is shown in Figure 1. If X is the amount of the commodity that is currently available, then $P = p(X)$ is the current selling price.

We divide the interval $[0, X]$ into n subintervals, each of length $\Delta x = X/n$, and let $x_i^* = x_i$ be the right endpoint of the ith subinterval, as in Figure 2. If, after the first x_{i-1} units were sold, a total of only x_i units had been available and the price per unit had been set at $p(x_i)$ dollars, then the additional Δx units could have been sold (but no more). The consumers who would have paid $p(x_i)$ dollars placed a high value on the product; they would have paid what it was worth to them. So, in paying only P dollars they have saved an amount of

$$(\text{savings per unit})(\text{number of units}) = [p(x_i) - P]\Delta x$$

Considering similar groups of willing consumers for each of the subintervals and adding the savings, we get the total savings:

$$\sum_{i=1}^{n} [p(x_i) - P]\Delta x$$

(This sum corresponds to the area enclosed by the rectangles in Figure 2.) If we let $n \to \infty$, this Riemann sum approaches the integral

$$\boxed{1} \qquad \int_0^X [p(x) - P]\, dx$$

which economists call the **consumer surplus** for the commodity.

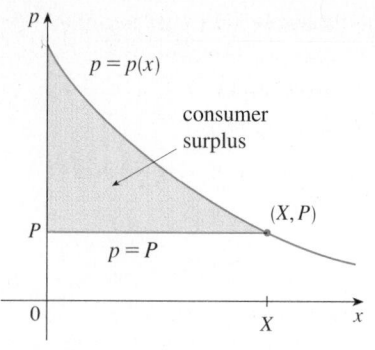

FIGURE 3

The consumer surplus represents the amount of money saved by consumers in purchasing the commodity at price P, corresponding to an amount demanded of X. Figure 3 shows the interpretation of the consumer surplus as the area under the demand curve and above the line $p = P$.

EXAMPLE 1 The demand for a product, in dollars, is

$$p = 1200 - 0.2x - 0.0001x^2$$

Find the consumer surplus when the sales level is 500.

SOLUTION Since the number of products sold is $X = 500$, the corresponding price is

$$P = 1200 - (0.2)(500) - (0.0001)(500)^2 = 1075$$

Therefore, from Definition 1, the consumer surplus is

$$\int_0^{500} [p(x) - P]\, dx = \int_0^{500} (1200 - 0.2x - 0.0001x^2 - 1075)\, dx$$

$$= \int_0^{500} (125 - 0.2x - 0.0001x^2)\, dx$$

$$= 125x - 0.1x^2 - (0.0001)\left(\frac{x^3}{3}\right)\Bigg]_0^{500}$$

$$= (125)(500) - (0.1)(500)^2 - \frac{(0.0001)(500)^3}{3}$$

$$= \$33{,}333.33$$

||||| Blood Flow

In Example 7 in Section 3.4 we discussed the law of laminar flow:

$$v(r) = \frac{P}{4\eta l}(R^2 - r^2)$$

which gives the velocity v of blood that flows along a blood vessel with radius R and length l at a distance r from the central axis, where P is the pressure difference between the ends of the vessel and η is the viscosity of the blood. Now, in order to compute the rate of blood flow, or *flux* (volume per unit time), we consider smaller, equally spaced radii $r_1, r_2, \ldots$. The approximate area of the ring (or washer) with inner radius r_{i-1} and outer radius r_i is

$$2\pi r_i\, \Delta r \qquad \text{where} \quad \Delta r = r_i - r_{i-1}$$

(See Figure 4.) If Δr is small, then the velocity is almost constant throughout this ring and can be approximated by $v(r_i)$. Thus, the volume of blood per unit time that flows across the ring is approximately

$$(2\pi r_i\, \Delta r)v(r_i) = 2\pi r_i v(r_i)\, \Delta r$$

and the total volume of blood that flows across a cross-section per unit time is approximately

$$\sum_{i=1}^{n} 2\pi r_i v(r_i)\, \Delta r$$

FIGURE 4

FIGURE 5

This approximation is illustrated in Figure 5. Notice that the velocity (and hence the volume per unit time) increases toward the center of the blood vessel. The approximation gets better as n increases. When we take the limit we get the exact value of the **flux** (or *discharge*), which is the volume of blood that passes a cross-section per unit time:

$$F = \lim_{n \to \infty} \sum_{i=1}^{n} 2\pi r_i v(r_i)\, \Delta r = \int_0^R 2\pi r v(r)\, dr$$

$$= \int_0^R 2\pi r \frac{P}{4\eta l}\,(R^2 - r^2)\, dr$$

$$= \frac{\pi P}{2\eta l} \int_0^R (R^2 r - r^3)\, dr = \frac{\pi P}{2\eta l} \left[R^2 \frac{r^2}{2} - \frac{r^4}{4} \right]_{r=0}^{r=R}$$

$$= \frac{\pi P}{2\eta l} \left[\frac{R^4}{2} - \frac{R^4}{4} \right] = \frac{\pi P R^4}{8\eta l}$$

The resulting equation

$$\boxed{2} \qquad\qquad F = \frac{\pi P R^4}{8\eta l}$$

is called **Poiseuille's Law**; it shows that the flux is proportional to the fourth power of the radius of the blood vessel.

‖‖‖‖ Cardiac Output

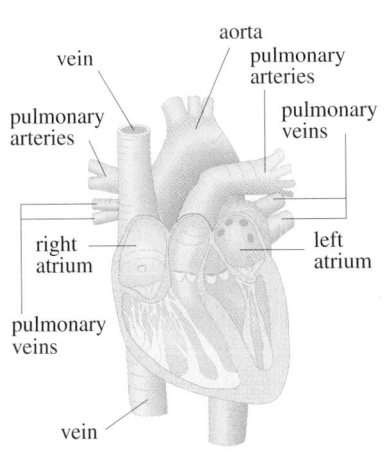

FIGURE 6

Figure 6 shows the human cardiovascular system. Blood returns from the body through the veins, enters the right atrium of the heart, and is pumped to the lungs through the pulmonary arteries for oxygenation. It then flows back into the left atrium through the pulmonary veins and then out to the rest of the body through the aorta. The **cardiac output** of the heart is the volume of blood pumped by the heart per unit time, that is, the rate of flow into the aorta.

The *dye dilution method* is used to measure the cardiac output. Dye is injected into the right atrium and flows through the heart into the aorta. A probe inserted into the aorta measures the concentration of the dye leaving the heart at equally spaced times over a time interval $[0, T]$ until the dye has cleared. Let $c(t)$ be the concentration of the dye at time t. If we divide $[0, T]$ into subintervals of equal length Δt, then the amount of dye that flows past the measuring point during the subinterval from $t = t_{i-1}$ to $t = t_i$ is approximately

$$(\text{concentration})(\text{volume}) = c(t_i)(F\,\Delta t)$$

where F is the rate of flow that we are trying to determine. Thus, the total amount of dye is approximately

$$\sum_{i=1}^{n} c(t_i) F\, \Delta t = F \sum_{i=1}^{n} c(t_i)\, \Delta t$$

and, letting $n \to \infty$, we find that the amount of dye is

$$A = F \int_0^T c(t)\, dt$$

Thus, the cardiac output is given by

$$\boxed{3} \qquad F = \frac{A}{\displaystyle\int_0^T c(t)\, dt}$$

where the amount of dye A is known and the integral can be approximated from the concentration readings.

EXAMPLE 2 A 5-mg bolus of dye is injected into a right atrium. The concentration of the dye (in milligrams per liter) is measured in the aorta at one-second intervals as shown in the chart. Estimate the cardiac output.

SOLUTION Here $A = 5$, $\Delta t = 1$, and $T = 10$. We use Simpson's Rule to approximate the integral of the concentration:

t	$c(t)$	t	$c(t)$
0	0	6	6.1
1	0.4	7	4.0
2	2.8	8	2.3
3	6.5	9	1.1
4	9.8	10	0
5	8.9		

$$\int_0^{10} c(t)\, dt \approx \tfrac{1}{3}[0 + 4(0.4) + 2(2.8) + 4(6.5) + 2(9.8) + 4(8.9)$$

$$+ 2(6.1) + 4(4.0) + 2(2.3) + 4(1.1) + 0]$$

$$\approx 41.87$$

Thus, Formula 3 gives the cardiac output to be

$$F = \frac{A}{\displaystyle\int_0^{10} c(t)\, dt} \approx \frac{5}{41.87}$$

$$\approx 0.12 \text{ L/s} = 7.2 \text{ L/min}$$

9.4 Exercises

1. The marginal cost function $C'(x)$ was defined to be the derivative of the cost function. (See Sections 3.4 and 4.8.) If the marginal cost of maufacturing x meters of a fabric is $C'(x) = 5 - 0.008x + 0.000009x^2$ (measured in dollars per meter) and the fixed start-up cost is $C(0) = \$20,000$, use the Net Change Theorem to find the cost of producing the first 2000 units.

2. The marginal revenue from the sale of x units of a product is $12 - 0.0004x$. If the revenue from the sale of the first 1000 units is \$12,400, find the revenue from the sale of the first 5000 units.

3. The marginal cost of producing x units of a certain product is $74 + 1.1x - 0.002x^2 + 0.00004x^3$ (in dollars per unit). Find the increase in cost if the production level is raised from 1200 units to 1600 units.

4. The demand function for a certain commodity is $p = 5 - x/10$. Find the consumer surplus when the sales level is 30. Illustrate by drawing the demand curve and identifying the consumer surplus as an area.

5. A demand curve is given by $p = 450/(x + 8)$. Find the consumer surplus when the selling price is \$10.

6. The **supply function** $p_S(x)$ for a commodity gives the relation between the selling price and the number of units that manufacturers will produce at that price. For a higher price, manufacturers will produce more units, so p_S is an increasing function of x. Let X be the amount of the commodity currently produced and let $P = p_S(X)$ be the current price. Some producers would be willing to make and sell the commodity for a lower selling price and are therefore receiving more than their minimal price. The excess is called the **producer surplus**. An argument similar to that for consumer surplus shows that the surplus is given by the integral

$$\int_0^X [P - p_S(x)]\, dx$$

Calculate the producer surplus for the supply function $p_S(x) = 3 + 0.01x^2$ at the sales level $X = 10$. Illustrate by drawing the supply curve and identifying the producer surplus as an area.

7. If a supply curve is modeled by the equation $p = 200 + 0.2x^{3/2}$, find the producer surplus when the selling price is \$400.

8. For a given commodity and pure competition, the number of units produced and the price per unit are determined as the coordinates of the point of intersection of the supply and demand curves. Given the demand curve $p = 50 - x/20$ and the supply curve $p = 20 + x/10$, find the consumer surplus and the producer surplus. Illustrate by sketching the supply and demand curves and identifying the surpluses as areas.

9. A company modeled the demand curve for its product (in dollars) by

$$p = \frac{800,000e^{-x/5000}}{x + 20,000}$$

Use a graph to estimate the sales level when the selling price is $16. Then find (approximately) the consumer surplus for this sales level.

10. A movie theater has been charging $7.50 per person and selling about 400 tickets on a typical weeknight. After surveying their customers, the theater estimates that for every 50 cents that they lower the price, the number of moviegoers will increase by 35 per night. Find the demand function and calculate the consumer surplus when the tickets are priced at $6.00.

11. If the amount of capital that a company has at time t is $f(t)$, then the derivative, $f'(t)$, is called the *net investment flow*. Suppose that the net investment flow is $\sqrt{t}$ million dollars per year (where t is measured in years). Find the increase in capital (the *capital formation*) from the fourth year to the eighth year.

12. A hot, wet summer is causing a mosquito population explosion in a lake resort area. The number of mosquitos is increasing at an estimated rate of $2200 + 10e^{0.8t}$ per week (where t is measured in weeks). By how much does the mosquito population increase between the fifth and ninth weeks of summer?

13. Use Poiseuille's Law to calculate the rate of flow in a small human artery where we can take $\eta = 0.027$, $R = 0.008$ cm, $l = 2$ cm, and $P = 4000$ dynes/cm^2.

14. High blood pressure results from constriction of the arteries. To maintain a normal flow rate (flux), the heart has to pump harder, thus increasing the blood pressure. Use Poiseuille's Law to show that if R_0 and P_0 are normal values of the radius and pressure in an artery and the constricted values are R and P, then for the flux to remain constant, P and R are related by the equation

$$\frac{P}{P_0} = \left(\frac{R_0}{R}\right)^4$$

Deduce that if the radius of an artery is reduced to three-fourths of its former value, then the pressure is more than tripled.

15. The dye dilution method is used to measure cardiac output with 8 mg of dye. The dye concentrations, in mg/L, are modeled by $c(t) = \frac{1}{4}t(12 - t)$, $0 \leqslant t \leqslant 12$, where t is measured in seconds. Find the cardiac output.

16. After an 8-mg injection of dye, the readings of dye concentration at two-second intervals are as shown in the table. Use Simpson's Rule to estimate the cardiac output.

t	$c(t)$	t	$c(t)$
0	0	12	3.9
2	2.4	14	2.3
4	5.1	16	1.6
6	7.8	18	0.7
8	7.6	20	0
10	5.4		

||||| 9.5 Probability

Calculus plays a role in the analysis of random behavior. Suppose we consider the cholesterol level of a person chosen at random from a certain age group, or the height of an adult female chosen at random, or the lifetime of a randomly chosen battery of a certain type. Such quantities are called **continuous random variables** because their values actually range over an interval of real numbers, although they might be measured or recorded only to the nearest integer. We might want to know the probability that a blood cholesterol level is greater than 250, or the probability that the height of an adult female is between 60 and 70 inches, or the probability that the battery we are buying lasts between 100 and 200 hours. If X represents the lifetime of that type of battery, we denote this last probability as follows:

$$P(100 \leqslant X \leqslant 200)$$

According to the frequency interpretation of probability, this number is the long-run proportion of all batteries of the specified type whose lifetimes are between 100 and 200 hours. Since it represents a proportion, the probability naturally falls between 0 and 1.

Every continuous random variable X has a **probability density function** f. This means that the probability that X lies between a and b is found by integrating f from a to b:

$$\boxed{1} \qquad P(a \leqslant X \leqslant b) = \int_a^b f(x)\,dx$$

For example, Figure 1 shows the graph of a model of the probability density function f for a random variable X defined to be the height in inches of an adult female in the United States (according to data from the National Health Survey). The probability that the height of a woman chosen at random from this population is between 60 and 70 inches is equal to the area under the graph of f from 60 to 70.

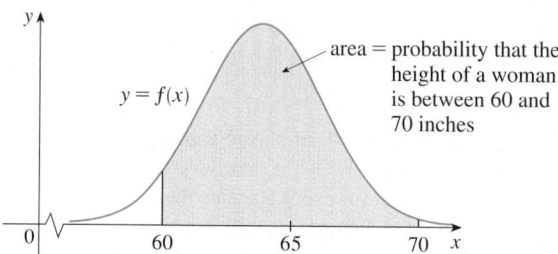

FIGURE 1

Probability density function
for the height of an adult female

In general, the probability density function f of a random variable X satisfies the condition $f(x) \geqslant 0$ for all x. Because probabilities are measured on a scale from 0 to 1, it follows that

$$\boxed{2} \qquad \int_{-\infty}^{\infty} f(x)\,dx = 1$$

EXAMPLE 1 Let $f(x) = 0.006x(10 - x)$ for $0 \leqslant x \leqslant 10$ and $f(x) = 0$ for all other values of x.
(a) Verify that f is a probability density function.
(b) Find $P(4 \leqslant X \leqslant 8)$.

SOLUTION
(a) For $0 \leqslant x \leqslant 10$ we have $0.006x(10 - x) \geqslant 0$, so $f(x) \geqslant 0$ for all x. We also need to check that Equation 2 is satisfied:

$$\int_{-\infty}^{\infty} f(x)\,dx = \int_0^{10} 0.006x(10 - x)\,dx = 0.006 \int_0^{10} (10x - x^2)\,dx$$

$$= 0.006 \left[5x^2 - \tfrac{1}{3}x^3\right]_0^{10} = 0.006\left(500 - \tfrac{1000}{3}\right) = 1$$

Therefore, f is a probability density function.

(b) The probability that X lies between 4 and 8 is

$$P(4 \leqslant X \leqslant 8) = \int_4^8 f(x)\,dx = 0.006 \int_4^8 (10x - x^2)\,dx$$

$$= 0.006\left[5x^2 - \tfrac{1}{3}x^3\right]_4^8 = 0.544$$

EXAMPLE 2 Phenomena such as waiting times and equipment failure times are commonly modeled by exponentially decreasing probability density functions. Find the exact form of such a function.

SOLUTION Think of the random variable as being the time you wait on hold before an agent of a company you're telephoning answers your call. So instead of x, let's use t to represent time, in minutes. If f is the probability density function and you call at time $t = 0$, then, from Definition 1, $\int_0^2 f(t)\,dt$ represents the probability that an agent answers within the first two minutes and $\int_4^5 f(t)\,dt$ is the probability that your call is answered during the fifth minute.

It's clear that $f(t) = 0$ for $t < 0$ (the agent can't answer before you place the call). For $t > 0$ we are told to use an exponentially decreasing function, that is, a function of the form $f(t) = Ae^{-ct}$, where A and c are positive constants. Thus

$$f(t) = \begin{cases} 0 & \text{if } t < 0 \\ Ae^{-ct} & \text{if } t \geq 0 \end{cases}$$

We use condition 2 to determine the value of A:

$$1 = \int_{-\infty}^{\infty} f(t)\,dt = \int_{-\infty}^{0} f(t)\,dt + \int_0^{\infty} f(t)\,dt$$

$$= \int_0^{\infty} Ae^{-ct}\,dt = \lim_{x \to \infty} \int_0^x Ae^{-ct}\,dt$$

$$= \lim_{x \to \infty} \left[-\frac{A}{c} e^{-ct} \right]_0^x = \lim_{x \to \infty} \frac{A}{c}(1 - e^{-cx})$$

$$= \frac{A}{c}$$

Therefore, $A/c = 1$ and so $A = c$. Thus, every exponential density function has the form

$$f(t) = \begin{cases} 0 & \text{if } t < 0 \\ ce^{-ct} & \text{if } t \geq 0 \end{cases}$$

A typical graph is shown in Figure 2.

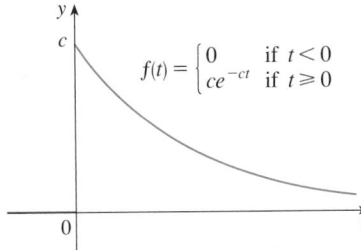

$$f(t) = \begin{cases} 0 & \text{if } t < 0 \\ ce^{-ct} & \text{if } t \geq 0 \end{cases}$$

FIGURE 2

An exponential density function

Average Values

Suppose you're waiting for a company to answer your phone call and you wonder how long, on average, you can expect to wait. Let $f(t)$ be the corresponding density function, where t is measured in minutes, and think of a sample of N people who have called this company. Most likely, none of them had to wait more than an hour, so let's restrict our attention to the interval $0 \leq t \leq 60$. Let's divide that interval into n intervals of length Δt and endpoints $0, t_1, t_2, \ldots$ (Think of Δt as lasting a minute, or half a minute, or 10 seconds, or even a second.) The probability that somebody's call gets answered during the time period from t_{i-1} to t_i is the area under the curve $y = f(t)$ from t_{i-1} to t_i, which is approximately equal to $f(\bar{t}_i)\,\Delta t$. (This is the area of the approximating rectangle in Figure 3, where $\bar{t}_i$ is the midpoint of the interval.)

Since the long-run proportion of calls that get answered in the time period from t_{i-1} to t_i is $f(\bar{t}_i)\,\Delta t$, we expect that, out of our sample of N callers, the number whose call was answered in that time period is approximately $Nf(\bar{t}_i)\,\Delta t$ and the time that each waited is about $\bar{t}_i$. Therefore, the total time they waited is the product of these numbers: approximately $\bar{t}_i[Nf(\bar{t}_i)\,\Delta t]$. Adding over all such intervals, we get the approximate total of everybody's waiting times:

$$\sum_{i=1}^{n} N\bar{t}_i f(\bar{t}_i)\,\Delta t$$

$y = f(t)$

FIGURE 3

If we now divide by the number of callers N, we get the approximate *average* waiting time:

$$\sum_{i=1}^{n} \bar{t}_i f(\bar{t}_i)\,\Delta t$$

We recognize this as a Riemann sum for the function $tf(t)$. As the time interval shrinks (that is, $\Delta t \to 0$ and $n \to \infty$), this Riemann sum approaches the integral

$$\int_0^{60} tf(t)\,dt$$

This integral is called the *mean waiting time*.

In general, the **mean** of any probability density function f is defined to be

$$\mu = \int_{-\infty}^{\infty} xf(x)\,dx$$

|||| It is traditional to denote the mean by the Greek letter μ (mu).

The mean can be interpreted as the long-run average value of the random variable X. It can also be interpreted as a measure of centrality of the probability density function.

The expression for the mean resembles an integral we have seen before. If $\mathcal{R}$ is the region that lies under the graph of f, we know from Formula 9.3.8 that the x-coordinate of the centroid of $\mathcal{R}$ is

$$\bar{x} = \frac{\displaystyle\int_{-\infty}^{\infty} xf(x)\,dx}{\displaystyle\int_{-\infty}^{\infty} f(x)\,dx} = \int_{-\infty}^{\infty} xf(x)\,dx = \mu$$

because of Equation 2. So a thin plate in the shape of $\mathcal{R}$ balances at a point on the vertical line $x = \mu$. (See Figure 4.)

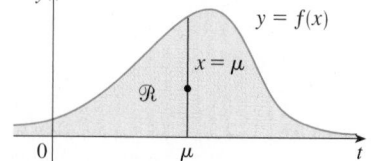

FIGURE 4
$\mathcal{R}$ balances at a point on the line $x = \mu$

EXAMPLE 3 Find the mean of the exponential distribution of Example 2:

$$f(t) = \begin{cases} 0 & \text{if } t < 0 \\ ce^{-ct} & \text{if } t \geq 0 \end{cases}$$

SOLUTION According to the definition of a mean, we have

$$\mu = \int_{-\infty}^{\infty} tf(t)\,dt = \int_0^{\infty} tce^{-ct}\,dt$$

To evaluate this integral we use integration by parts, with $u = t$ and $dv = ce^{-ct}\,dt$:

$$\int_0^{\infty} tce^{-ct}\,dt = \lim_{x \to \infty} \int_0^x tce^{-ct}\,dt = \lim_{x \to \infty}\left(-te^{-ct}\Big]_0^x + \int_0^x e^{-ct}\,dt \right)$$

|||| The limit of the first term is 0 by l'Hospital's Rule.

$$= \lim_{x \to \infty}\left(-xe^{-cx} + \frac{1}{c} - \frac{e^{-cx}}{c} \right)$$

$$= \frac{1}{c}$$

The mean is $\mu = 1/c$, so we can rewrite the probability density function as

$$f(t) = \begin{cases} 0 & \text{if } t < 0 \\ \mu^{-1}e^{-t/\mu} & \text{if } t \geq 0 \end{cases}$$

EXAMPLE 4 Suppose the average waiting time for a customer's call to be answered by a company representative is five minutes.
(a) Find the probability that a call is answered during the first minute.
(b) Find the probability that a customer waits more than five minutes to be answered.

SOLUTION
(a) We are given that the mean of the exponential distribution is $\mu = 5$ min and so, from the result of Example 3, we know that the probability density function is

$$f(t) = \begin{cases} 0 & \text{if } t < 0 \\ 0.2e^{-t/5} & \text{if } t \geqslant 0 \end{cases}$$

Thus, the probability that a call is answered during the first minute is

$$P(0 \leqslant T \leqslant 1) = \int_0^1 f(t)\, dt$$

$$= \int_0^1 0.2e^{-t/5}\, dt$$

$$= 0.2(-5)e^{-t/5}\Big]_0^1$$

$$= 1 - e^{-1/5} \approx 0.1813$$

So about 18% of customers' calls are answered during the first minute.

(b) The probability that a customer waits more than five minutes is

$$P(T > 5) = \int_5^\infty f(t)\, dt = \int_5^\infty 0.2e^{-t/5}\, dt$$

$$= \lim_{x \to \infty} \int_5^x 0.2e^{-t/5}\, dt = \lim_{x \to \infty} (e^{-1} - e^{-x/5})$$

$$= \frac{1}{e} \approx 0.368$$

About 37% of customers wait more than five minutes before their calls are answered.

Notice the result of Example 4(b): Even though the mean waiting time is 5 minutes, only 37% of callers wait more than 5 minutes. The reason is that some callers have to wait much longer (maybe 10 or 15 minutes), and this brings up the average.

Another measure of centrality of a probability density function is the *median*. That is a number m such that half the callers have a waiting time less than m and the other callers have a waiting time longer than m. In general, the **median** of a probability density function is the number m such that

$$\int_m^\infty f(x)\, dx = \tfrac{1}{2}$$

This means that half the area under the graph of f lies to the right of m. In Exercise 7 you are asked to show that the median waiting time for the company described in Example 4 is approximately 3.5 minutes.

|||| Normal Distributions

Many important random phenomena—such as test scores on aptitude tests, heights and weights of individuals from a homogeneous population, annual rainfall in a given location—are modeled by a **normal distribution**. This means that the probability density function of the random variable X is a member of the family of functions

$$\boxed{3} \qquad f(x) = \frac{1}{\sigma\sqrt{2\pi}}\, e^{-(x-\mu)^2/(2\sigma^2)}$$

|||| The standard deviation is denoted by the lowercase Greek letter σ (sigma).

You can verify that the mean for this function is μ. The positive constant σ is called the **standard deviation**; it measures how spread out the values of X are. From the bell-shaped graphs of members of the family in Figure 5, we see that for small values of σ the values of X are clustered about the mean, whereas for larger values of σ the values of X are more spread out. Statisticians have methods for using sets of data to estimate μ and σ.

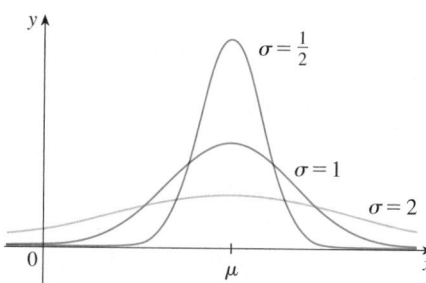

FIGURE 5

Normal distributions

The factor $1/(\sigma\sqrt{2\pi})$ is needed to make f a probability density function. In fact, it can be verified using the methods of multivariable calculus that

$$\int_{-\infty}^{\infty} \frac{1}{\sigma\sqrt{2\pi}}\, e^{-(x-\mu)^2/(2\sigma^2)}\, dx = 1$$

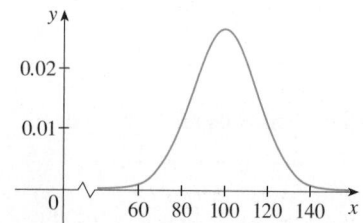

FIGURE 6

Distribution of IQ scores

EXAMPLE 5 Intelligence Quotient (IQ) scores are distributed normally with mean 100 and standard deviation 15. (Figure 6 shows the corresponding probability density function.)
(a) What percentage of the population has an IQ score between 85 and 115?
(b) What percentage of the population has an IQ above 140?

SOLUTION
(a) Since IQ scores are normally distributed, we use the probability density function given by Equation 3 with $\mu = 100$ and $\sigma = 15$:

$$P(85 \leqslant X \leqslant 115) = \int_{85}^{115} \frac{1}{15\sqrt{2\pi}}\, e^{-(x-100)^2/(2\cdot 15^2)}\, dx$$

Recall from Section 8.5 that the function $y = e^{-x^2}$ doesn't have an elementary antiderivative, so we can't evaluate the integral exactly. But we can use the numerical integration capability of a calculator or computer (or the Midpoint Rule or Simpson's Rule) to estimate the integral. Doing so, we find that

$$P(85 \leqslant X \leqslant 115) \approx 0.68$$

So about 68% of the population has an IQ between 85 and 115, that is, within one standard deviation of the mean.

(b) The probability that the IQ score of a person chosen at random is more than 140 is

$$P(X > 140) = \int_{140}^{\infty} \frac{1}{15\sqrt{2\pi}} e^{-(x-100)^2/450} \, dx$$

To avoid the improper integral we could approximate it by the integral from 140 to 200. (It's quite safe to say that people with an IQ over 200 are extremely rare.) Then

$$P(X > 140) \approx \int_{140}^{200} \frac{1}{15\sqrt{2\pi}} e^{-(x-100)^2/450} \, dx \approx 0.0038$$

Therefore, about 0.4% of the population has an IQ over 140.

9.5 Exercises

1. Let $f(x)$ be the probability density function for the lifetime of a manufacturer's highest quality car tire, where x is measured in miles. Explain the meaning of each integral.

(a) $\int_{30,000}^{40,000} f(x) \, dx$ (b) $\int_{25,000}^{\infty} f(x) \, dx$

2. Let $f(t)$ be the probability density function for the time it takes you to drive to school in the morning, where t is measured in minutes. Express the following probabilities as integrals.
(a) The probability that you drive to school in less than 15 minutes
(b) The probability that it takes you more than half an hour to get to school

3. Let $f(x) = \frac{3}{64} x \sqrt{16 - x^2}$ for $0 \leq x \leq 4$ and $f(x) = 0$ for all other values of x.
(a) Verify that f is a probability density function.
(b) Find $P(X < 2)$.

4. Let $f(x) = kx^2(1 - x)$ if $0 \leq x \leq 1$ and $f(x) = 0$ if $x < 0$ or $x > 1$.
(a) For what value of k is f a probability density function?
(b) For that value of k, find $P\left(X \geq \frac{1}{2}\right)$.
(c) Find the mean.

5. A spinner from a board game randomly indicates a real number between 0 and 10. The spinner is fair in the sense that it indicates a number in a given interval with the same probability as it indicates a number in any other interval of the same length.
(a) Explain why the function

$$f(x) = \begin{cases} 0.1 & \text{if } 0 \leq x \leq 10 \\ 0 & \text{if } x < 0 \text{ or } x > 10 \end{cases}$$

is a probability density function for the spinner's values.
(b) What does your intuition tell you about the value of the mean? Check your guess by evaluating an integral.

6. (a) Explain why the function whose graph is shown is a probability density function.

(b) Use the graph to find the following probabilities:
(i) $P(X < 3)$ (ii) $P(3 \leq X \leq 8)$
(c) Calculate the mean.

7. Show that the median waiting time for a phone call to the company described in Example 4 is about 3.5 minutes.

8. (a) A type of lightbulb is labeled as having an average lifetime of 1000 hours. It's reasonable to model the probability of failure of these bulbs by an exponential density function with mean $\mu = 1000$. Use this model to find the probability that a bulb
(i) fails within the first 200 hours,
(ii) burns for more than 800 hours.
(b) What is the median lifetime of these lightbulbs?

9. The manager of a fast-food restaurant determines that the average time that her customers wait for service is 2.5 minutes.
(a) Find the probability that a customer has to wait for more than 4 minutes.
(b) Find the probability that a customer is served within the first 2 minutes.
(c) The manager wants to advertise that anybody who isn't served within a certain number of minutes gets a free hamburger. But she doesn't want to give away free hamburgers to more than 2% of her customers. What should the advertisement say?

10. According to the National Health Survey, the heights of adult males in the United States are normally distributed with mean 69.0 inches and standard deviation 2.8 inches.
(a) What is the probability that an adult male chosen at random is between 65 inches and 73 inches tall?

(b) What percentage of the adult male population is more than 6 feet tall?

11. The "Garbage Project" at the University of Arizona reports that the amount of paper discarded by households per week is normally distributed with mean 9.4 lb and standard deviation 4.2 lb. What percentage of households throw out at least 10 lb of paper a week?

12. Boxes are labeled as containing 500 g of cereal. The machine filling the boxes produces weights that are normally distributed with standard deviation 12 g.
(a) If the target weight is 500 g, what is the probability that the machine produces a box with less than 480 g of cereal?
(b) Suppose a law states that no more than 5% of a manufacturer's cereal boxes can contain less than the stated weight of 500 g. At what target weight should the manufacturer set its filling machine?

13. For any normal distribution, find the probability that the random variable lies within two standard deviations of the mean.

14. The standard deviation for a random variable with probability density function f and mean μ is defined by

$$\sigma = \left[\int_{-\infty}^{\infty} (x - \mu)^2 f(x)\, dx \right]^{1/2}$$

Find the standard deviation for an exponential density function with mean μ.

15. The hydrogen atom is composed of one proton in the nucleus and one electron, which moves about the nucleus. In the quantum theory of atomic structure, it is assumed that the electron does not move in a well-defined orbit. Instead, it occupies a state known as an *orbital*, which may be thought of as a "cloud" of negative charge surrounding the nucleus. At the state of lowest energy, called the *ground state*, or *1s-orbital*, the shape of this cloud is assumed to be a sphere centered at the nucleus. This sphere is described in terms of the probability density function

$$p(r) = \frac{4}{a_0^3}\, r^2 e^{-2r/a_0} \qquad r \geq 0$$

where a_0 is the *Bohr radius* ($a_0 \approx 5.59 \times 10^{-11}$ m). The integral

$$P(r) = \int_0^r \frac{4}{a_0^3}\, s^2 e^{-2s/a_0}\, ds$$

gives the probability that the electron will be found within the sphere of radius r meters centered at the nucleus.
(a) Verify that $p(r)$ is a probability density function.
(b) Find $\lim_{r \to \infty} p(r)$. For what value of r does $p(r)$ have its maximum value?
(c) Graph the density function.
(d) Find the probability that the electron will be within the sphere of radius $4a_0$ centered at the nucleus.
(e) Calculate the mean distance of the electron from the nucleus in the ground state of the hydrogen atom.

---

9 Review

───── ▫ CONCEPT CHECH ▫ ─────

1. (a) How is the length of a curve defined?
(b) Write an expression for the length of a smooth curve given by $y = f(x)$, $a \leq x \leq b$.
(c) What if x is given as a function of y?

2. (a) Write an expression for the surface area of the surface obtained by rotating the curve $y = f(x)$, $a \leq x \leq b$, about the x-axis.
(b) What if x is given as a function of y?
(c) What if the curve is rotated about the y-axis?

3. Describe how we can find the hydrostatic force against a vertical wall submersed in a fluid.

4. (a) What is the physical significance of the center of mass of a thin plate?
(b) If the plate lies between $y = f(x)$ and $y = 0$, where $a \leq x \leq b$, write expressions for the coordinates of the center of mass.

5. What does the Theorem of Pappus say?

6. Given a demand function $p(x)$, explain what is meant by the consumer surplus when the amount of a commodity currently available is X and the current selling price is P. Illustrate with a sketch.

7. (a) What is the cardiac output of the heart?
(b) Explain how the cardiac output can be measured by the dye dilution method.

8. What is a probability density function? What properties does such a function have?

9. Suppose $f(x)$ is the probability density function for the weight of a female college student, where x is measured in pounds.
(a) What is the meaning of the integral $\int_0^{100} f(x)\, dx$?
(b) Write an expression for the mean of this density function.
(c) How can we find the median of this density function?

10. What is a normal distribution? What is the significance of the standard deviation?

· EXERCISES ·

1–2 ▥ Find the length of the curve.

1. $y = \frac{1}{6}(x^2 + 4)^{3/2}, \quad 0 \le x \le 3$

2. $y = 2 \ln \sin(\frac{1}{2}x), \quad \pi/3 \le x \le \pi$

3. (a) Find the length of the curve

$$y = \frac{x^4}{16} + \frac{1}{2x^2} \qquad 1 \le x \le 2$$

(b) Find the area of the surface obtained by rotating the curve in part (a) about the y-axis.

4. (a) The curve $y = x^2, 0 \le x \le 1$, is rotated about the y-axis. Find the area of the resulting surface.

(b) Find the area of the surface obtained by rotating the curve in part (a) about the x-axis.

5. Use Simpson's Rule with $n = 6$ to estimate the length of the curve $y = e^{-x^2}, 0 \le x \le 3$.

6. Use Simpson's Rule with $n = 6$ to estimate the area of the surface obtained by rotating the curve in Exercise 5 about the x-axis.

7. Find the length of the curve

$$y = \int_1^x \sqrt{\sqrt{t} - 1} \, dt \qquad 1 \le x \le 16$$

8. Find the area of the surface obtained by rotating the curve in Exercise 7 about the y-axis.

9. A gate in an irrigation canal is constructed in the form of a trapezoid 3 ft wide at the bottom, 5 ft wide at the top, and 2 ft high. It is placed vertically in the canal, with the water extending to its top. Find the hydrostatic force on one side of the gate.

10. A trough is filled with water and its vertical ends have the shape of the parabolic region in the figure. Find the hydrostatic force on one end of the trough.

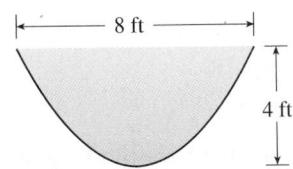

11–12 ▥ Find the centroid of the region bounded by the given curves.

11. $y = 4 - x^2, \quad y = x + 2$

12. $y = \sin x, \quad y = 0, \quad x = \pi/4, \quad x = 3\pi/4$

13–14 ▥ Find the centroid of the region shown.

13.

14.

15. Find the volume obtained when the circle of radius 1 with center $(1, 0)$ is rotated about the y-axis.

16. Use the Theorem of Pappus and the fact that the volume of a sphere of radius r is $\frac{4}{3}\pi r^3$ to find the centroid of the semicircular region bounded by the curve $y = \sqrt{r^2 - x^2}$ and the x-axis.

17. The demand function for a commodity is given by $p = 2000 - 0.1x - 0.01x^2$. Find the consumer surplus when the sales level is 100.

18. After a 6-mg injection of dye into a heart, the readings of dye concentration at two-second intervals are as shown in the table. Use Simpson's Rule to estimate the cardiac output.

t	$c(t)$	t	$c(t)$
0	0	14	4.7
2	1.9	16	3.3
4	3.3	18	2.1
6	5.1	20	1.1
8	7.6	22	0.5
10	7.1	24	0
12	5.8		

19. (a) Explain why the function

$$f(x) = \begin{cases} \frac{\pi}{20} \sin\left(\frac{\pi x}{10}\right) & \text{if } 0 \le x \le 10 \\ 0 & \text{if } x < 0 \text{ or } x > 10 \end{cases}$$

is a probability density function.

(b) Find $P(X < 4)$.

(c) Calculate the mean. Is the value what you would expect?

20. Lengths of human pregnancies are normally distributed with mean 268 days and standard deviation 15 days. What percentage of pregnancies last between 250 days and 280 days?

21. The length of time spent waiting in line at a certain bank is modeled by an exponential density function with mean 8 minutes.

(a) What is the probability that a customer is served in the first 3 minutes?

(b) What is the probability that a customer has to wait more than 10 minutes?

(c) What is the median waiting time?

1. Find the area of the region $S = \{(x, y) \mid x \geqslant 0,\ y \leqslant 1,\ x^2 + y^2 \leqslant 4y\}$.

2. Find the centroid of the region enclosed by the loop of the curve $y^2 = x^3 - x^4$.

3. If a sphere of radius r is sliced by a plane whose distance from the center of the sphere is d, then the sphere is divided into two pieces called *segments of one base*. The corresponding surfaces are called *spherical zones of one base*.
   (a) Determine the surface areas of the two spherical zones indicated in the figure.
   (b) Determine the approximate area of the Arctic Ocean by assuming that it is approximately circular in shape, with center at the North Pole and "circumference" at 75° north latitude. Use $r = 3960$ mi for the radius of Earth.
   (c) A sphere of radius r is inscribed in a right circular cylinder of radius r. Two planes perpendicular to the central axis of the cylinder and a distance h apart cut off a *spherical zone of two bases* on the sphere. Show that the surface area of the spherical zone equals the surface area of the region that the two planes cut off on the cylinder.
   (d) The *Torrid Zone* is the region on the surface of Earth that is between the Tropic of Cancer (23.45° north latitude) and the Tropic of Capricorn (23.45° south latitude). What is the area of the Torrid Zone?

 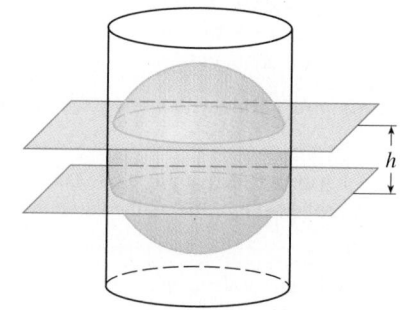

4. (a) Show that an observer at height H above the north pole of a sphere of radius r can see a part of the sphere that has area

$$\frac{2\pi r^2 H}{r + H}$$

   (b) Two spheres with radii r and R are placed so that the distance between their centers is d, where $d > r + R$. Where should a light be placed on the line joining the centers of the spheres in order to illuminate the largest total surface?

5. Suppose that the density of seawater, $\rho = \rho(z)$, varies with the depth z below the surface.
   (a) Show that the hydrostatic pressure is governed by the differential equation

$$\frac{dP}{dz} = \rho(z)g$$

   where g is the acceleration due to gravity. Let P_0 and ρ_0 be the pressure and density at $z = 0$. Express the pressure at depth z as an integral.
   (b) Suppose the density of seawater at depth z is given by $\rho = \rho_0 e^{z/H}$, where H is a positive constant. Find the total force, expressed as an integral, exerted on a vertical circular porthole of radius r whose center is located at a distance $L > r$ below the surface.

6. The figure shows a semicircle with radius 1, horizontal diameter PQ, and tangent lines at P and Q. At what height above the diameter should the horizontal line be placed so as to minimize the shaded area?

7. Let P be a pyramid with a square base of side $2b$ and suppose that S is a sphere with its center on the base of P and is tangent to all eight edges of P. Find the height of P. Then find the volume of the intersection of S and P.

P Q

FIGURE FOR PROBLEM 6

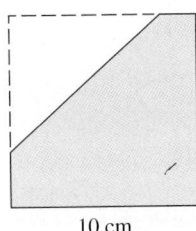

10 cm

FIGURE FOR PROBLEM 10

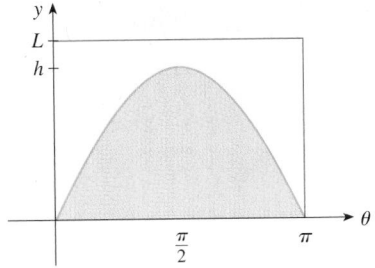

FIGURE FOR PROBLEM 11

8. Consider a flat metal plate to be placed vertically under water with its top 2 m below the surface of the water. Determine a shape for the plate so that if the plate is divided into any number of horizontal strips of equal height, the hydrostatic force on each strip is the same.

9. A uniform disk with radius 1 m is to be cut by a line so that the center of mass of the smaller piece lies halfway along a radius. How close to the center of the disk should the cut be made? (Express your answer correct to two decimal places.)

10. A triangle with area 30 cm^2 is cut from a corner of a square with side 10 cm, as shown in the figure. If the centroid of the remaining region is 4 cm from the right side of the square, how far is it from the bottom of the square?

11. In a famous 18th-century problem, known as *Buffon's needle problem*, a needle of length h is dropped onto a flat surface (for example, a table) on which parallel lines L units apart, $L \geq h$, have been drawn. The problem is to determine the probability that the needle will come to rest intersecting one of the lines. Assume that the lines run east-west, parallel to the x-axis in a rectangular coordinate system (as in the figure). Let y be the distance from the "southern" end of the needle to the nearest line to the north. (If the needle's southern end lies on a line, let $y = 0$. If the needle happens to lie east-west, let the "western" end be the "southern" end.) Let θ be the angle that the needle makes with a ray extending eastward from the "southern" end. Then $0 \leq y \leq L$ and $0 \leq \theta \leq \pi$. Note that the needle intersects one of the lines only when $y < h \sin \theta$. Now, the total set of possibilities for the needle can be identified with the rectangular region $0 \leq y \leq L$, $0 \leq \theta \leq \pi$, and the proportion of times that the needle intersects a line is the ratio

$$\frac{\text{area under } y = h \sin \theta}{\text{area of rectangle}}$$

This ratio is the probability that the needle intersects a line. Find the probability that the needle will intersect a line if $h = L$. What if $h = L/2$?

12. If the needle in Problem 11 has length $h > L$, it's possible for the needle to intersect more than one line.
    (a) If $L = 4$, find the probability that a needle of length 7 will intersect at least one line. [*Hint:* Proceed as in Problem 11. Define y as before; then the total set of possibilities for the needle can be identified with the same rectangular region $0 \leq y \leq L$, $0 \leq \theta \leq \pi$. What portion of the rectangle corresponds to the needle intersecting a line?]
    (b) If $L = 4$, find the probability that a needle of length 7 will intersect *two* lines.
    (c) If $2L < h \leq 3L$, find a general formula for the probability that the needle intersects three lines.

CHAPTER 10

By analyzing pairs of differential equations we gain insight into population cycles of predators and prey, such as the Canada lynx and snowshoe hare.

© Jeff Lepore / Photo Researchers, Inc.

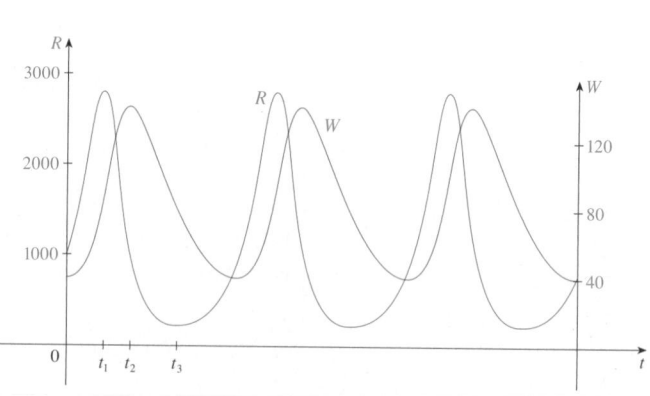

Differential Equations

Perhaps the most important of all the applications of calculus is to differential equations. When physical scientists or social scientists use calculus, more often than not it is to analyze a differential equation that has arisen in the process of modeling some phenomenon that they are studying.

Although it is often impossible to find an explicit formula for the solution of a differential equation, we will see that graphical and numerical approaches provide the needed information.

10.1 Modeling with Differential Equations

|||| Now is a good time to read (or reread) the discussion of mathematical modeling on page 25.

In describing the process of modeling in Section 1.2, we talked about formulating a mathematical model of a real-world problem either through intuitive reasoning about the phenomenon or from a physical law based on evidence from experiments. The mathematical model often takes the form of a *differential equation,* that is, an equation that contains an unknown function and some of its derivatives. This is not surprising because in a real-world problem we often notice that changes occur and we want to predict future behavior on the basis of how current values change. Let's begin by examining several examples of how differential equations arise when we model physical phenomena.

|||| Models of Population Growth

One model for the growth of a population is based on the assumption that the population grows at a rate proportional to the size of the population. That is a reasonable assumption for a population of bacteria or animals under ideal conditions (unlimited environment, adequate nutrition, absence of predators, immunity from disease).

Let's identify and name the variables in this model:

t = time   (the independent variable)

P = the number of individuals in the population   (the dependent variable)

The rate of growth of the population is the derivative dP/dt. So our assumption that the rate of growth of the population is proportional to the population size is written as the equation

$$\boxed{1} \qquad \frac{dP}{dt} = kP$$

where k is the proportionality constant. Equation 1 is our first model for population growth; it is a differential equation because it contains an unknown function P and its derivative dP/dt.

Having formulated a model, let's look at its consequences. If we rule out a population of 0, then $P(t) > 0$ for all t. So, if $k > 0$, then Equation 1 shows that $P'(t) > 0$ for all t. This means that the population is always increasing. In fact, as $P(t)$ increases, Equation 1 shows that dP/dt becomes larger. In other words, the growth rate increases as the population increases.

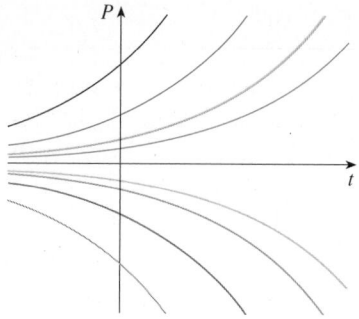

FIGURE 1

The family of solutions of $dP/dt = kP$

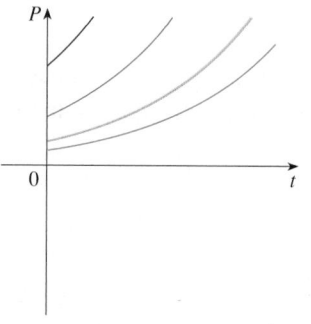

FIGURE 2

The family of solutions $P(t) = Ce^{kt}$
with $C > 0$ and $t \geqslant 0$

Let's try to think of a solution of Equation 1. This equation asks us to find a function whose derivative is a constant multiple of itself. We know that exponential functions have that property. In fact, if we let $P(t) = Ce^{kt}$, then

$$P'(t) = C(ke^{kt}) = k(Ce^{kt}) = kP(t)$$

Thus, any exponential function of the form $P(t) = Ce^{kt}$ is a solution of Equation 1. When we study this equation in detail in Section 10.4, we will see that there is no other solution.

Allowing C to vary through all the real numbers, we get the *family* of solutions $P(t) = Ce^{kt}$ whose graphs are shown in Figure 1. But populations have only positive values and so we are interested only in the solutions with $C > 0$. And we are probably concerned only with values of t greater than the initial time $t = 0$. Figure 2 shows the physically meaningful solutions. Putting $t = 0$, we get $P(0) = Ce^{k(0)} = C$, so the constant C turns out to be the initial population, $P(0)$.

Equation 1 is appropriate for modeling population growth under ideal conditions, but we have to recognize that a more realistic model must reflect the fact that a given environment has limited resources. Many populations start by increasing in an exponential manner, but the population levels off when it approaches its *carrying capacity K* (or decreases toward K if it ever exceeds K). For a model to take into account both trends, we make two assumptions:

- $\dfrac{dP}{dt} \approx kP$ if P is small   (Initially, the growth rate is proportional to P.)

- $\dfrac{dP}{dt} < 0$ if $P > K$ (P decreases if it ever exceeds K.)

A simple expression that incorporates both assumptions is given by the equation

$$\boxed{2} \qquad \frac{dP}{dt} = kP\left(1 - \frac{P}{K}\right)$$

Notice that if P is small compared with K, then P/K is close to 0 and so $dP/dt \approx kP$. If $P > K$, then $1 - P/K$ is negative and so $dP/dt < 0$.

Equation 2 is called the *logistic differential equation* and was proposed by the Dutch mathematical biologist Pierre-François Verhulst in the 1840s as a model for world population growth. We will develop techniques that enable us to find explicit solutions of the logistic equation in Section 10.5, but for now we can deduce qualitative characteristics of the solutions directly from Equation 2. We first observe that the constant functions $P(t) = 0$ and $P(t) = K$ are solutions because, in either case, one of the factors on the right side of Equation 2 is zero. (This certainly makes physical sense: If the population is ever either 0 or at the carrying capacity, it stays that way.) These two constant solutions are called *equilibrium solutions*.

If the initial population $P(0)$ lies between 0 and K, then the right side of Equation 2 is positive, so $dP/dt > 0$ and the population increases. But if the population exceeds the carrying capacity $(P > K)$, then $1 - P/K$ is negative, so $dP/dt < 0$ and the population decreases. Notice that, in either case, if the population approaches the carrying capacity $(P \rightarrow K)$, then $dP/dt \rightarrow 0$, which means the population levels off. So we expect that the solutions of the logistic differential equation have graphs that look something like the ones in Figure 3. Notice that the graphs move away from the equilibrium solution $P = 0$ and move toward the equilibrium solution $P = K$.

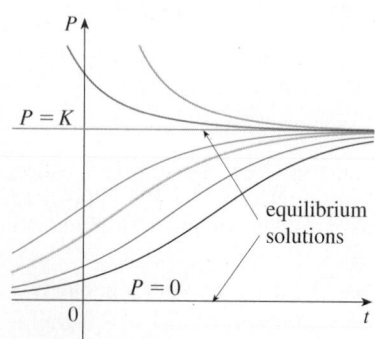

FIGURE 3

Solutions of the logistic equation

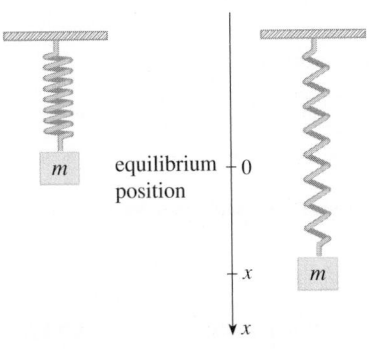

FIGURE 4

‖‖ A Model for the Motion of a Spring

Let's now look at an example of a model from the physical sciences. We consider the motion of an object with mass m at the end of a vertical spring (as in Figure 4). In Section 6.4 we discussed Hooke's Law, which says that if the spring is stretched (or compressed) x units from its natural length, then it exerts a force that is proportional to x:

$$\text{restoring force} = -kx$$

where k is a positive constant (called the *spring constant*). If we ignore any external resisting forces (due to air resistance or friction) then, by Newton's Second Law (force equals mass times acceleration), we have

$$\boxed{3} \qquad m\frac{d^2x}{dt^2} = -kx$$

This is an example of what is called a *second-order differential equation* because it involves second derivatives. Let's see what we can guess about the form of the solution directly from the equation. We can rewrite Equation 3 in the form

$$\frac{d^2x}{dt^2} = -\frac{k}{m}x$$

which says that the second derivative of x is proportional to x but has the opposite sign. We know two functions with this property, the sine and cosine functions. In fact, it turns out that all solutions of Equation 3 can be written as combinations of certain sine and cosine functions (see Exercise 3). This is not surprising; we expect the spring to oscillate about its equilibrium position and so it is natural to think that trigonometric functions are involved.

‖‖ General Differential Equations

In general, a **differential equation** is an equation that contains an unknown function and one or more of its derivatives. The **order** of a differential equation is the order of the highest derivative that occurs in the equation. Thus, Equations 1 and 2 are first-order equations and Equation 3 is a second-order equation. In all three of those equations the independent variable is called t and represents time, but in general the independent variable doesn't have to represent time. For example, when we consider the differential equation

$$\boxed{4} \qquad y' = xy$$

it is understood that y is an unknown function of x.

A function f is called a **solution** of a differential equation if the equation is satisfied when $y = f(x)$ and its derivatives are substituted into the equation. Thus, f is a solution of Equation 4 if

$$f'(x) = xf(x)$$

for all values of x in some interval.

When we are asked to *solve* a differential equation we are expected to find all possible solutions of the equation. We have already solved some particularly simple differential equations, namely, those of the form

$$y' = f(x)$$

For instance, we know that the general solution of the differential equation

$$y' = x^3$$

is given by

$$y = \frac{x^4}{4} + C$$

where C is an arbitrary constant.

But, in general, solving a differential equation is not an easy matter. There is no systematic technique that enables us to solve all differential equations. In Section 10.2, however, we will see how to draw rough graphs of solutions even when we have no explicit formula. We will also learn how to find numerical approximations to solutions.

EXAMPLE 1 Show that every member of the family of functions

$$y = \frac{1 + ce^t}{1 - ce^t}$$

is a solution of the differential equation $y' = \frac{1}{2}(y^2 - 1)$.

SOLUTION We use the Quotient Rule to differentiate the expression for y:

$$y' = \frac{(1 - ce^t)(ce^t) - (1 + ce^t)(-ce^t)}{(1 - ce^t)^2}$$

$$= \frac{ce^t - c^2e^{2t} + ce^t + c^2e^{2t}}{(1 - ce^t)^2} = \frac{2ce^t}{(1 - ce^t)^2}$$

The right side of the differential equation becomes

$$\tfrac{1}{2}(y^2 - 1) = \frac{1}{2}\left[\left(\frac{1 + ce^t}{1 - ce^t}\right)^2 - 1\right] = \frac{1}{2}\left[\frac{(1 + ce^t)^2 - (1 - ce^t)^2}{(1 - ce^t)^2}\right]$$

$$= \frac{1}{2}\frac{4ce^t}{(1 - ce^t)^2} = \frac{2ce^t}{(1 - ce^t)^2}$$

Therefore, for every value of c, the given function is a solution of the differential equation.

|||| Figure 5 shows graphs of seven members of the family in Example 1. The differential equation shows that if $y \approx \pm 1$, then $y' \approx 0$. That is borne out by the flatness of the graphs near $y = 1$ and $y = -1$.

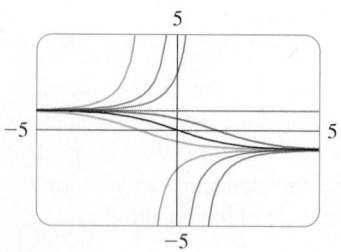

FIGURE 5

When applying differential equations, we are usually not as interested in finding a family of solutions (the *general solution*) as we are in finding a solution that satisfies some additional requirement. In many physical problems we need to find the particular solution that satisfies a condition of the form $y(t_0) = y_0$. This is called an **initial condition**, and the problem of finding a solution of the differential equation that satisfies the initial condition is called an **initial-value problem**.

Geometrically, when we impose an initial condition, we look at the family of solution curves and pick the one that passes through the point (t_0, y_0). Physically, this corresponds to measuring the state of a system at time t_0 and using the solution of the initial-value problem to predict the future behavior of the system.

EXAMPLE 2 Find a solution of the differential equation $y' = \frac{1}{2}(y^2 - 1)$ that satisfies the initial condition $y(0) = 2$.

SOLUTION Substituting the values $t = 0$ and $y = 2$ into the formula

$$y = \frac{1 + ce^t}{1 - ce^t}$$

from Example 1, we get

$$2 = \frac{1 + ce^0}{1 - ce^0} = \frac{1 + c}{1 - c}$$

Solving this equation for c, we get $2 - 2c = 1 + c$, which gives $c = \frac{1}{3}$. So the solution of the initial-value problem is

$$y = \frac{1 + \frac{1}{3}e^t}{1 - \frac{1}{3}e^t} = \frac{3 + e^t}{3 - e^t}$$

▓ 10.1 Exercises

1. Show that $y = x - x^{-1}$ is a solution of the differential equation $xy' + y = 2x$.

2. Verify that $y = \sin x \cos x - \cos x$ is a solution of the initial-value problem

$$y' + (\tan x)y = \cos^2 x \qquad y(0) = -1$$

on the interval $-\pi/2 < x < \pi/2$.

3. (a) For what nonzero values of k does the function $y = \sin kt$ satisfy the differential equation $y'' + 9y = 0$?
(b) For those values of k, verify that every member of the family of functions

$$y = A \sin kt + B \cos kt$$

is also a solution.

4. For what values of r does the function $y = e^{rt}$ satisfy the differential equation $y'' + y' - 6y = 0$?

5. Which of the following functions are solutions of the differential equation $y'' + 2y' + y = 0$?
(a) $y = e^t$ (b) $y = e^{-t}$
(c) $y = te^{-t}$ (d) $y = t^2 e^{-t}$

6. (a) Show that every member of the family of functions $y = Ce^{x^2/2}$ is a solution of the differential equation $y' = xy$.
(b) Illustrate part (a) by graphing several members of the family of solutions on a common screen.
(c) Find a solution of the differential equation $y' = xy$ that satisfies the initial condition $y(0) = 5$.

(d) Find a solution of the differential equation $y' = xy$ that satisfies the initial condition $y(1) = 2$.

7. (a) What can you say about a solution of the equation $y' = -y^2$ just by looking at the differential equation?
(b) Verify that all members of the family $y = 1/(x + C)$ are solutions of the equation in part (a).
(c) Can you think of a solution of the differential equation $y' = -y^2$ that is not a member of the family in part (b)?
(d) Find a solution of the initial-value problem

$$y' = -y^2 \qquad y(0) = 0.5$$

8. (a) What can you say about the graph of a solution of the equation $y' = xy^3$ when x is close to 0? What if x is large?
(b) Verify that all members of the family $y = (c - x^2)^{-1/2}$ are solutions of the differential equation $y' = xy^3$.
(c) Graph several members of the family of solutions on a common screen. Do the graphs confirm what you predicted in part (a)?
(d) Find a solution of the initial-value problem

$$y' = xy^3 \qquad y(0) = 2$$

9. A population is modeled by the differential equation

$$\frac{dP}{dt} = 1.2P\left(1 - \frac{P}{4200}\right)$$

(a) For what values of P is the population increasing?
(b) For what values of P is the population decreasing?
(c) What are the equilibrium solutions?

10. A function $y(t)$ satisfies the differential equation

$$\frac{dy}{dt} = y^4 - 6y^3 + 5y^2$$

(a) What are the constant solutions of the equation?
(b) For what values of y is y increasing?
(c) For what values of y is y decreasing?

11. Explain why the functions with the given graphs *can't* be solutions of the differential equation

$$\frac{dy}{dt} = e^t(y - 1)^2$$

(a)

(b)
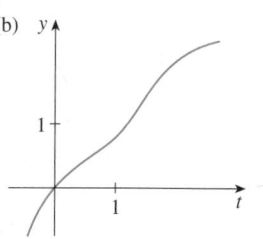

12. The function with the given graph is a solution of one of the following differential equations. Decide which is the correct equation and justify your answer.

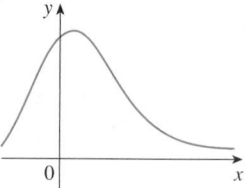

A. $y' = 1 + xy$ B. $y' = -2xy$ C. $y' = 1 - 2xy$

13. Psychologists interested in learning theory study **learning curves**. A learning curve is the graph of a function $P(t)$, the performance of someone learning a skill as a function of the training time t. The derivative dP/dt represents the rate at which performance improves.
(a) When do you think P increases most rapidly? What happens to dP/dt as t increases? Explain.
(b) If M is the maximum level of performance of which the learner is capable, explain why the differential equation

$$\frac{dP}{dt} = k(M - P) \qquad k \text{ a positive constant}$$

is a reasonable model for learning.
(c) Make a rough sketch of a possible solution of this differential equation.

14. Suppose you have just poured a cup of freshly brewed coffee with temperature 95°C in a room where the temperature is 20°C.
(a) When do you think the coffee cools most quickly? What happens to the rate of cooling as time goes by? Explain.
(b) **Newton's Law of Cooling** states that the rate of cooling of an object is proportional to the temperature difference between the object and its surroundings, provided that this difference is not too large. Write a differential equation that expresses Newton's Law of Cooling for this particular situation. What is the initial condition? In view of your answer to part (a), do you think this differential equation is an appropriate model for cooling?
(c) Make a rough sketch of the graph of the solution of the initial-value problem in part (b).

|||| 10.2 Direction Fields and Euler's Method

Unfortunately, it's impossible to solve most differential equations in the sense of obtaining an explicit formula for the solution. In this section we show that, despite the absence of an explicit solution, we can still learn a lot about the solution through a graphical approach (direction fields) or a numerical approach (Euler's method).

|||| Direction Fields

Suppose we are asked to sketch the graph of the solution of the initial-value problem

$$y' = x + y \qquad y(0) = 1$$

We don't know a formula for the solution, so how can we possibly sketch its graph? Let's think about what the differential equation means. The equation $y' = x + y$ tells us that the slope at any point (x, y) on the graph (called the *solution curve*) is equal to the sum of the

x- and y-coordinates of the point (see Figure 1). In particular, because the curve passes through the point $(0, 1)$, its slope there must be $0 + 1 = 1$. So a small portion of the solution curve near the point $(0, 1)$ looks like a short line segment through $(0, 1)$ with slope 1 (see Figure 2).

FIGURE 1

A solution of $y' = x + y$

FIGURE 2

Beginning of the solution curve through $(0, 1)$

As a guide to sketching the rest of the curve, let's draw short line segments at a number of points (x, y) with slope $x + y$. The result is called a *direction field* and is shown in Figure 3. For instance, the line segment at the point $(1, 2)$ has slope $1 + 2 = 3$. The direction field allows us to visualize the general shape of the solution curves by indicating the direction in which the curves proceed at each point.

FIGURE 3

Direction field for $y' = x + y$

FIGURE 4

The solution curve through $(0, 1)$

Now we can sketch the solution curve through the point $(0, 1)$ by following the direction field as in Figure 4. Notice that we have drawn the curve so that it is parallel to nearby line segments.

In general, suppose we have a first-order differential equation of the form

$$y' = F(x, y)$$

where $F(x, y)$ is some expression in x and y. The differential equation says that the slope of a solution curve at a point (x, y) on the curve is $F(x, y)$. If we draw short line segments with slope $F(x, y)$ at several points (x, y), the result is called a **direction field** (or **slope field**). These line segments indicate the direction in which a solution curve is heading, so the direction field helps us visualize the general shape of these curves.

FIGURE 5

FIGURE 6

Module 10.2A shows direction fields and solution curves for a variety of differential equations.

EXAMPLE 1

(a) Sketch the direction field for the differential equation $y' = x^2 + y^2 - 1$.

(b) Use part (a) to sketch the solution curve that passes through the origin.

SOLUTION

(a) We start by computing the slope at several points in the following chart:

x	-2	-1	0	1	2	-2	-1	0	1	2	$\dots$
y	0	0	0	0	0	1	1	1	1	1	$\dots$
$y' = x^2 + y^2 - 1$	3	0	-1	0	3	4	1	0	1	4	$\dots$

Now we draw short line segments with these slopes at these points. The result is the direction field shown in Figure 5.

(b) We start at the origin and move to the right in the direction of the line segment (which has slope -1). We continue to draw the solution curve so that it moves parallel to the nearby line segments. The resulting solution curve is shown in Figure 6. Returning to the origin, we draw the solution curve to the left as well.

The more line segments we draw in a direction field, the clearer the picture becomes. Of course, it's tedious to compute slopes and draw line segments for a huge number of points by hand, but computers are well suited for this task. Figure 7 shows a more detailed, computer-drawn direction field for the differential equation in Example 1. It enables us to draw, with reasonable accuracy, the solution curves shown in Figure 8 with y-intercepts $-2, -1, 0, 1,$ and 2.

FIGURE 7

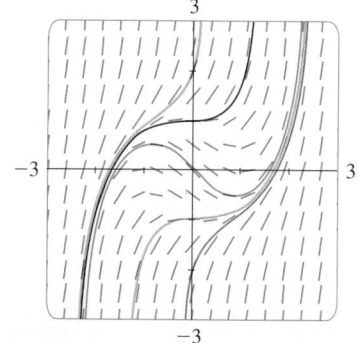

FIGURE 8

Now let's see how direction fields give insight into physical situations. The simple electric circuit shown in Figure 9 contains an electromotive force (usually a battery or generator) that produces a voltage of $E(t)$ volts (V) and a current of $I(t)$ amperes (A) at time t. The circuit also contains a resistor with a resistance of R ohms (Ω) and an inductor with an inductance of L henries (H).

Ohm's Law gives the drop in voltage due to the resistor as RI. The voltage drop due to the inductor is $L(dI/dt)$. One of Kirchhoff's laws says that the sum of the voltage drops is equal to the supplied voltage $E(t)$. Thus, we have

FIGURE 9

$$\boxed{1} \qquad L\frac{dI}{dt} + RI = E(t)$$

which is a first-order differential equation that models the current I at time t.

EXAMPLE 2 Suppose that in the simple circuit of Figure 9 the resistance is 12 Ω, the inductance is 4 H, and a battery gives a constant voltage of 60 V.

(a) Draw a direction field for Equation 1 with these values.

(b) What can you say about the limiting value of the current?

(c) Identify any equilibrium solutions.

(d) If the switch is closed when $t = 0$ so the current starts with $I(0) = 0$, use the direction field to sketch the solution curve.

SOLUTION

(a) If we put $L = 4$, $R = 12$, and $E(t) = 60$ in Equation 1, we get

$$4\frac{dI}{dt} + 12I = 60 \qquad \text{or} \qquad \frac{dI}{dt} = 15 - 3I$$

The direction field for this differential equation is shown in Figure 10.

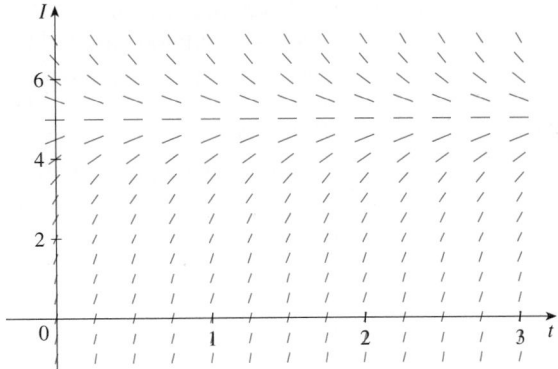

FIGURE 10

(b) It appears from the direction field that all solutions approach the value 5 A, that is,

$$\lim_{t \to \infty} I(t) = 5$$

$\frac{dI}{dt} = 15 - 3I$

(c) It appears that the constant function $I(t) = 5$ is an equilibrium solution. Indeed, we can verify this directly from the differential equation. If $I(t) = 5$, then the left side is $dI/dt = 0$ and the right side is $15 - 3(5) = 0$.

(d) We use the direction field to sketch the solution curve that passes through $(0, 0)$, as shown in red in Figure 11.

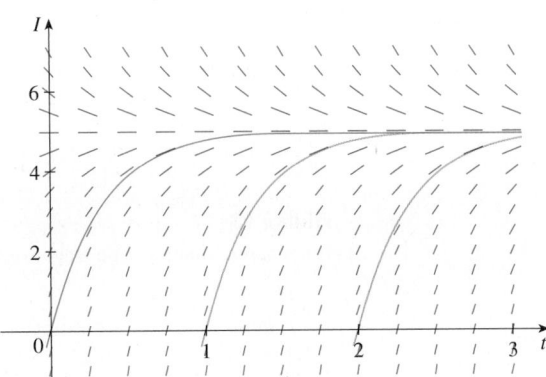

FIGURE 11

Notice from Figure 10 that the line segments along any horizontal line are parallel. That is because the independent variable t does not occur on the right side of the equation $I' = 15 - 3I$. In general, a differential equation of the form

$$y' = f(y)$$

in which the independent variable is missing from the right side, is called **autonomous**. For such an equation, the slopes corresponding to two different points with the same y-coordinate must be equal. This means that if we know one solution to an autonomous differential equation, then we can obtain infinitely many others just by shifting the graph of the known solution to the right or left. In Figure 11 we have shown the solutions that result from shifting the solution curve of Example 2 one and two time units (namely, seconds) to the right. They correspond to closing the switch when $t = 1$ or $t = 2$.

|||| **Euler's Method**

The basic idea behind direction fields can be used to find numerical approximations to solutions of differential equations. We illustrate the method on the initial-value problem that we used to introduce direction fields:

$$y' = x + y \qquad y(0) = 1$$

The differential equation tells us that $y'(0) = 0 + 1 = 1$, so the solution curve has slope 1 at the point $(0, 1)$. As a first approximation to the solution we could use the linear approximation $L(x) = x + 1$. In other words, we could use the tangent line at $(0, 1)$ as a rough approximation to the solution curve (see Figure 12).

Euler's idea was to improve on this approximation by proceeding only a short distance along this tangent line and then making a midcourse correction by changing direction as indicated by the direction field. Figure 13 shows what happens if we start out along the tangent line but stop when $x = 0.5$. (This horizontal distance traveled is called the *step size*.) Since $L(0.5) = 1.5$, we have $y(0.5) \approx 1.5$ and we take $(0.5, 1.5)$ as the starting point for a new line segment. The differential equation tells us that $y'(0.5) = 0.5 + 1.5 = 2$, so we use the linear function

$$y = 1.5 + 2(x - 0.5) = 2x + 0.5$$

as an approximation to the solution for $x > 0.5$ (the orange segment in Figure 13). If we decrease the step size from 0.5 to 0.25, we get the better Euler approximation shown in Figure 14.

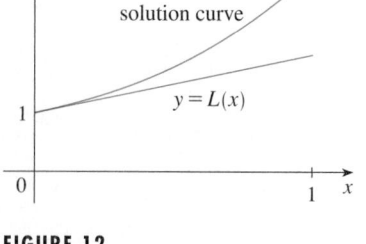

FIGURE 12

First Euler approximation

FIGURE 13

Euler approximation with step size 0.5

FIGURE 14

Euler approximation with step size 0.25

In general, Euler's method says to start at the point given by the initial value and proceed in the direction indicated by the direction field. Stop after a short time, look at the slope at the new location, and proceed in that direction. Keep stopping and changing direction according to the direction field. Euler's method does not produce the exact solution to an initial-value problem—it gives approximations. But by decreasing the step size (and therefore increasing the number of midcourse corrections), we obtain successively better approximations to the exact solution. (Compare Figures 12, 13, and 14.)

For the general first-order initial-value problem $y' = F(x, y)$, $y(x_0) = y_0$, our aim is to find approximate values for the solution at equally spaced numbers x_0, $x_1 = x_0 + h$, $x_2 = x_1 + h, \ldots$, where h is the step size. The differential equation tells us that the slope at (x_0, y_0) is $y' = F(x_0, y_0)$, so Figure 15 shows that the approximate value of the solution when $x = x_1$ is

$$y_1 = y_0 + hF(x_0, y_0)$$

Similarly,

$$y_2 = y_1 + hF(x_1, y_1)$$

In general,

$$y_n = y_{n-1} + hF(x_{n-1}, y_{n-1})$$

FIGURE 15

EXAMPLE 3 Use Euler's method with step size 0.1 to construct a table of approximate values for the solution of the initial-value problem

$$y' = x + y \qquad y(0) = 1$$

SOLUTION We are given that $h = 0.1$, $x_0 = 0$, $y_0 = 1$, and $F(x, y) = x + y$. So we have

$$y_1 = y_0 + hF(x_0, y_0) = 1 + 0.1(0 + 1) = 1.1$$

$$y_2 = y_1 + hF(x_1, y_1) = 1.1 + 0.1(0.1 + 1.1) = 1.22$$

$$y_3 = y_2 + hF(x_2, y_2) = 1.22 + 0.1(0.2 + 1.22) = 1.362$$

This means that if $y(x)$ is the exact solution, then $y(0.3) \approx 1.362$.

 Module 10.2B shows how Euler's method works numerically and visually for a variety of differential equations and step sizes.

Proceeding with similar calculations, we get the values in the table:

n	x_n	y_n	n	x_n	y_n
1	0.1	1.100000	6	0.6	1.943122
2	0.2	1.220000	7	0.7	2.197434
3	0.3	1.362000	8	0.8	2.487178
4	0.4	1.528200	9	0.9	2.815895
5	0.5	1.721020	10	1.0	3.187485

For a more accurate table of values in Example 3 we could decrease the step size. But for a large number of small steps the amount of computation is considerable and so we need to program a calculator or computer to carry out these calculations. The following table shows the results of applying Euler's method with decreasing step size to the initial-value problem of Example 3.

ⅢⅢ Computer software packages that produce numerical approximations to solutions of differential equations use methods that are refinements of Euler's method. Although Euler's method is simple and not as accurate, it is the basic idea on which the more accurate methods are based.

Step size	Euler estimate of $y(0.5)$	Euler estimate of $y(1)$
0.500	1.500000	2.500000
0.250	1.625000	2.882813
0.100	1.721020	3.187485
0.050	1.757789	3.306595
0.020	1.781212	3.383176
0.010	1.789264	3.409628
0.005	1.793337	3.423034
0.001	1.796619	3.433848

Notice that the Euler estimates in the table seem to be approaching limits, namely, the true values of $y(0.5)$ and $y(1)$. Figure 16 shows graphs of the Euler approximations with step sizes 0.5, 0.25, 0.1, 0.05, 0.02, 0.01, and 0.005. They are approaching the exact solution curve as the step size h approaches 0.

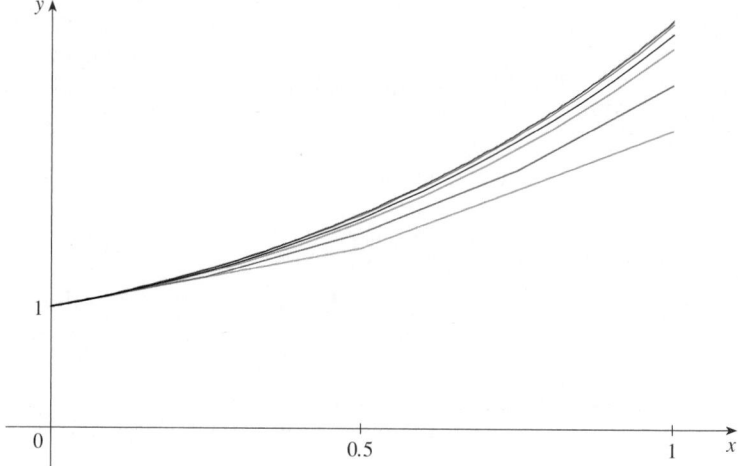

FIGURE 16

Euler approximations
approaching the exact solution

EXAMPLE 4 In Example 2 we discussed a simple electric circuit with resistance 12 Ω, inductance 4 H, and a battery with voltage 60 V. If the switch is closed when $t = 0$, we modeled the current I at time t by the initial-value problem

$$\frac{dI}{dt} = 15 - 3I \qquad I(0) = 0$$

Estimate the current in the circuit half a second after the switch is closed.

SOLUTION We use Euler's method with $F(t, I) = 15 - 3I$, $t_0 = 0$, $I_0 = 0$, and step size $h = 0.1$ second:

$$I_1 = 0 + 0.1(15 - 3 \cdot 0) = 1.5$$

$$I_2 = 1.5 + 0.1(15 - 3 \cdot 1.5) = 2.55$$

$$I_3 = 2.55 + 0.1(15 - 3 \cdot 2.55) = 3.285$$

$$I_4 = 3.285 + 0.1(15 - 3 \cdot 3.285) = 3.7995$$

$$I_5 = 3.7995 + 0.1(15 - 3 \cdot 3.7995) = 4.15965$$

So the current after 0.5 s is

$$I(0.5) \approx 4.16 \text{ A}$$

10.2 Exercises

1. A direction field for the differential equation $y' = y\left(1 - \frac{1}{4}y^2\right)$ is shown.
(a) Sketch the graphs of the solutions that satisfy the given initial conditions.
  (i) $y(0) = 1$ (ii) $y(0) = -1$
  (iii) $y(0) = -3$ (iv) $y(0) = 3$
(b) Find all the equilibrium solutions.

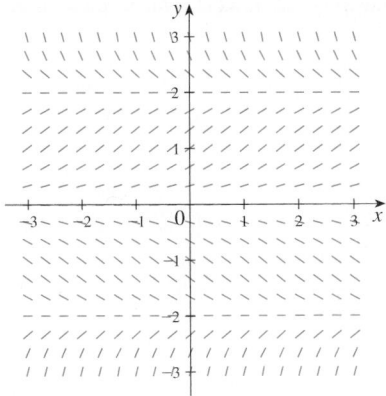

2. A direction field for the differential equation $y' = x \sin y$ is shown.
(a) Sketch the graphs of the solutions that satisfy the given initial conditions.
  (i) $y(0) = 1$ (ii) $y(0) = 2$ (iii) $y(0) = \pi$
  (iv) $y(0) = 4$ (v) $y(0) = 5$
(b) Find all the equilibrium solutions.

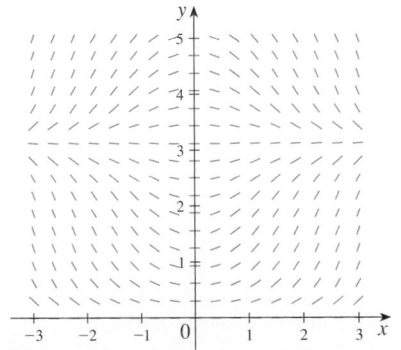

3–6 |||| Match the differential equation with its direction field (labeled I–IV). Give reasons for your answer.

3. $y' = y - 1$ **4.** $y' = y - x$

5. $y' = y^2 - x^2$ **6.** $y' = y^3 - x^3$

I

II

III

IV
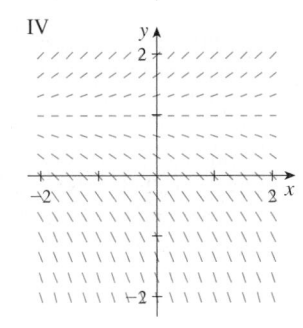

7. Use the direction field labeled I (for Exercises 3–6) to sketch the graphs of the solutions that satisfy the given initial conditions.
  (a) $y(0) = 1$ (b) $y(0) = 0$ (c) $y(0) = -1$

8. Repeat Exercise 7 for the direction field labeled III.

9–10 |||| Sketch a direction field for the differential equation. Then use it to sketch three solution curves.

9. $y' = 1 + y$ **10.** $y' = x^2 - y^2$

11–14 |||| Sketch the direction field of the differential equation. Then use it to sketch a solution curve that passes through the given point.

11. $y' = y - 2x$, $(1, 0)$ **12.** $y' = 1 - xy$, $(0, 0)$

13. $y' = y + xy$, $(0, 1)$ **14.** $y' = x - xy$, $(1, 0)$

CAS **15–16** |||| Use a computer algebra system to draw a direction field for the given differential equation. Get a printout and sketch on it the solution curve that passes through $(0, 1)$. Then use the CAS to draw the solution curve and compare it with your sketch.

15. $y' = y \sin 2x$ **16.** $y' = \sin(x + y)$

CAS **17.** Use a computer algebra system to draw a direction field for the differential equation $y' = y^3 - 4y$. Get a printout and sketch on it solutions that satisfy the initial condition $y(0) = c$ for various values of c. For what values of c does $\lim_{t \to \infty} y(t)$ exist? What are the possible values for this limit?

18. Make a rough sketch of a direction field for the autonomous differential equation $y' = f(y)$, where the graph of f is as shown. How does the limiting behavior of solutions depend on the value of $y(0)$?

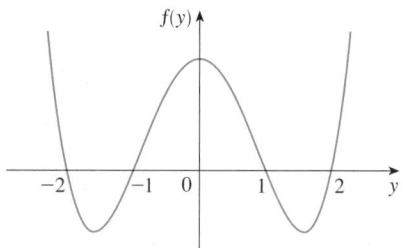

19. (a) Use Euler's method with each of the following step sizes to estimate the value of $y(0.4)$, where y is the solution of the initial-value problem $y' = y$, $y(0) = 1$.
    (i) $h = 0.4$ (ii) $h = 0.2$ (iii) $h = 0.1$
(b) We know that the exact solution of the initial-value problem in part (a) is $y = e^x$. Draw, as accurately as you can, the graph of $y = e^x$, $0 \le x \le 0.4$, together with the Euler approximations using the step sizes in part (a). (Your sketches should resemble Figures 12, 13, and 14.) Use your sketches to decide whether your estimates in part (a) are underestimates or overestimates.
(c) The error in Euler's method is the difference between the exact value and the approximate value. Find the errors made in part (a) in using Euler's method to estimate the true value of $y(0.4)$, namely $e^{0.4}$. What happens to the error each time the step size is halved?

20. A direction field for a differential equation is shown. Draw, with a ruler, the graphs of the Euler approximations to the solution curve that passes through the origin. Use step sizes $h = 1$ and $h = 0.5$. Will the Euler estimates be underestimates or overestimates? Explain.

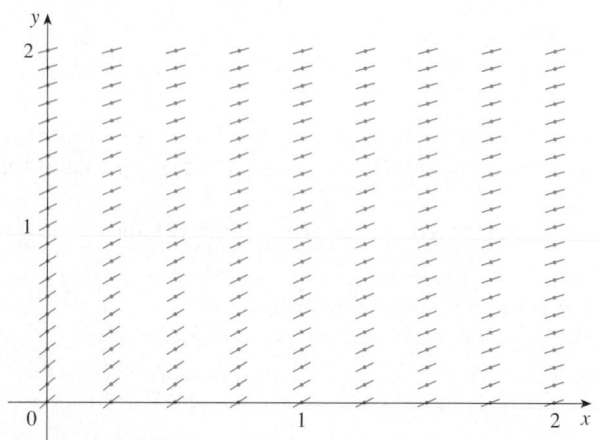

21. Use Euler's method with step size 0.5 to compute the approximate y-values y_1, y_2, y_3, and y_4 of the solution of the initial-value problem $y' = y - 2x$, $y(1) = 0$.

22. Use Euler's method with step size 0.2 to estimate $y(1)$, where $y(x)$ is the solution of the initial-value problem $y' = 1 - xy$, $y(0) = 0$.

23. Use Euler's method with step size 0.1 to estimate $y(0.5)$, where $y(x)$ is the solution of the initial-value problem $y' = y + xy$, $y(0) = 1$.

24. (a) Use Euler's method with step size 0.2 to estimate $y(1.4)$, where $y(x)$ is the solution of the initial-value problem $y' = x - xy$, $y(1) = 0$.
(b) Repeat part (a) with step size 0.1.

25. (a) Program a calculator or computer to use Euler's method to compute $y(1)$, where $y(x)$ is the solution of the initial-value problem

$$\frac{dy}{dx} + 3x^2 y = 6x^2 \qquad y(0) = 3$$

    (i) $h = 1$ (ii) $h = 0.1$
    (iii) $h = 0.01$ (iv) $h = 0.001$
(b) Verify that $y = 2 + e^{-x^3}$ is the exact solution of the differential equation.
(c) Find the errors in using Euler's method to compute $y(1)$ with the step sizes in part (a). What happens to the error when the step size is divided by 10?

26. (a) Program your computer algebra system, using Euler's method with step size 0.01, to calculate $y(2)$, where y is the solution of the initial-value problem

$$y' = x^3 - y^3 \qquad y(0) = 1$$

(b) Check your work by using the CAS to draw the solution curve.

27. The figure shows a circuit containing an electromotive force, a capacitor with a capacitance of C farads (F), and a resistor with a resistance of R ohms (Ω). The voltage drop across the capacitor is Q/C, where Q is the charge (in coulombs), so in this case Kirchhoff's Law gives

$$RI + \frac{Q}{C} = E(t)$$

But $I = dQ/dt$, so we have

$$R \frac{dQ}{dt} + \frac{1}{C} Q = E(t)$$

Suppose the resistance is 5 Ω, the capacitance is 0.05 F, and a battery gives a constant voltage of 60 V.
(a) Draw a direction field for this differential equation.
(b) What is the limiting value of the charge?

(c) Is there an equilibrium solution?

(d) If the initial charge is $Q(0) = 0$ C, use the direction field to sketch the solution curve.

(e) If the initial charge is $Q(0) = 0$ C, use Euler's method with step size 0.1 to estimate the charge after half a second.

28. In Exercise 14 in Section 10.1 we considered a 95°C cup of coffee in a 20°C room. Suppose it is known that the coffee cools

at a rate of 1°C per minute when its temperature is 70°C.

(a) What does the differential equation become in this case?

(b) Sketch a direction field and use it to sketch the solution curve for the initial-value problem. What is the limiting value of the temperature?

(c) Use Euler's method with step size $h = 2$ minutes to estimate the temperature of the coffee after 10 minutes.

10.3 Separable Equations

We have looked at first-order differential equations from a geometric point of view (direction fields) and from a numerical point of view (Euler's method). What about the symbolic point of view? It would be nice to have an explicit formula for a solution of a differential equation. Unfortunately, that is not always possible. But in this section we examine a certain type of differential equation that *can* be solved explicitly.

A **separable equation** is a first-order differential equation in which the expression for dy/dx can be factored as a function of x times a function of y. In other words, it can be written in the form

$$\frac{dy}{dx} = g(x)f(y)$$

The name *separable* comes from the fact that the expression on the right side can be "separated" into a function of x and a function of y. Equivalently, if $f(y) \neq 0$, we could write

$$\boxed{1} \qquad \frac{dy}{dx} = \frac{g(x)}{h(y)}$$

where $h(y) = 1/f(y)$. To solve this equation we rewrite it in the differential form

$$h(y)\, dy = g(x)\, dx$$

so that all y's are on one side of the equation and all x's are on the other side. Then we integrate both sides of the equation:

▓ The technique for solving separable differential equations was first used by James Bernoulli (in 1690) in solving a problem about pendulums and by Leibniz (in a letter to Huygens in 1691). John Bernoulli explained the general method in a paper published in 1694.

$$\boxed{2} \qquad \int h(y)\, dy = \int g(x)\, dx$$

Equation 2 defines y implicitly as a function of x. In some cases we may be able to solve for y in terms of x.

We use the Chain Rule to justify this procedure: If h and g satisfy (2), then

$$\frac{d}{dx}\left(\int h(y)\, dy \right) = \frac{d}{dx}\left(\int g(x)\, dx \right)$$

so

$$\frac{d}{dy}\left(\int h(y)\, dy \right)\frac{dy}{dx} = g(x)$$

and

$$h(y)\frac{dy}{dx} = g(x)$$

Thus, Equation 1 is satisfied.

EXAMPLE 1

(a) Solve the differential equation $\dfrac{dy}{dx} = \dfrac{x^2}{y^2}$.

(b) Find the solution of this equation that satisfies the initial condition $y(0) = 2$.

SOLUTION

(a) We write the equation in terms of differentials and integrate both sides:

$$y^2\,dy = x^2\,dx$$

$$\int y^2\,dy = \int x^2\,dx$$

$$\tfrac{1}{3}y^3 = \tfrac{1}{3}x^3 + C$$

|||| Figure 1 shows graphs of several members of the family of solutions of the differential equation in Example 1. The solution of the initial-value problem in part (b) is shown in red.

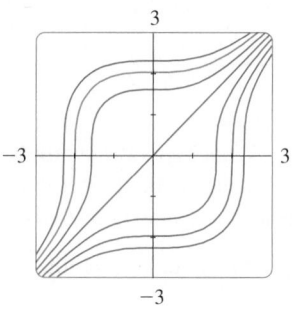

FIGURE 1

where C is an arbitrary constant. (We could have used a constant C_1 on the left side and another constant C_2 on the right side. But then we could combine these constants by writing $C = C_2 - C_1$.)

Solving for y, we get

$$y = \sqrt[3]{x^3 + 3C}$$

We could leave the solution like this or we could write it in the form

$$y = \sqrt[3]{x^3 + K}$$

where $K = 3C$. (Since C is an arbitrary constant, so is K.)

(b) If we put $x = 0$ in the general solution in part (a), we get $y(0) = \sqrt[3]{K}$. To satisfy the initial condition $y(0) = 2$, we must have $\sqrt[3]{K} = 2$ and so $K = 8$.

Thus, the solution of the initial-value problem is

$$y = \sqrt[3]{x^3 + 8}$$

|||| Some computer algebra systems can plot curves defined by implicit equations. Figure 2 shows the graphs of several members of the family of solutions of the differential equation in Example 2. As we look at the curves from left to right, the values of C are 3, 2, 1, 0, -1, -2, and -3.

FIGURE 2

EXAMPLE 2 Solve the differential equation $\dfrac{dy}{dx} = \dfrac{6x^2}{2y + \cos y}$.

SOLUTION Writing the equation in differential form and integrating both sides, we have

$$(2y + \cos y)\,dy = 6x^2\,dx$$

$$\int (2y + \cos y)\,dy = \int 6x^2\,dx$$

3. $$y^2 + \sin y = 2x^3 + C$$

where C is a constant. Equation 3 gives the general solution implicitly. In this case it's impossible to solve the equation to express y explicitly as a function of x.

EXAMPLE 3 Solve the equation $y' = x^2 y$.

SOLUTION First we rewrite the equation using Leibniz notation:

$$\frac{dy}{dx} = x^2 y$$

|||| If a solution y is a function that satisfies $y(x) \neq 0$ for some x, it follows from a uniqueness theorem for solutions of differential equations that $y(x) \neq 0$ for all x.

If $y \neq 0$, we can rewrite it in differential notation and integrate:

$$\frac{dy}{y} = x^2\,dx \qquad y \neq 0$$

$$\int \frac{dy}{y} = \int x^2\,dx$$

$$\ln|y| = \frac{x^3}{3} + C$$

This equation defines y implicitly as a function of x. But in this case we can solve explicitly for y as follows:

$$|y| = e^{\ln|y|} = e^{(x^3/3)+C} = e^C e^{x^3/3}$$

so

$$y = \pm e^C e^{x^3/3}$$

We can easily verify that the function $y = 0$ is also a solution of the given differential equation. So we can write the general solution in the form

$$y = A e^{x^3/3}$$

where A is an arbitrary constant ($A = e^C$, or $A = -e^C$, or $A = 0$).

|||| Figure 3 shows a direction field for the differential equation in Example 3. Compare it with Figure 4, in which we use the equation $y = A e^{x^3/3}$ to graph solutions for several values of A. If you use the direction field to sketch solution curves with y-intercepts 5, 2, 1, -1, and -2, they will resemble the curves in Figure 4.

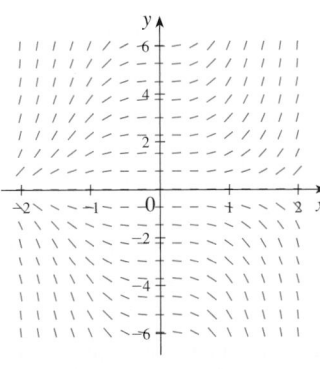

FIGURE 3

FIGURE 4

EXAMPLE 4 In Section 10.2 we modeled the current $I(t)$ in the electric circuit shown in Figure 5 by the differential equation

$$L\frac{dI}{dt} + RI = E(t)$$

Find an expression for the current in a circuit where the resistance is 12 Ω, the inductance is 4 H, a battery gives a constant voltage of 60 V, and the switch is turned on when $t = 0$. What is the limiting value of the current?

SOLUTION With $L = 4$, $R = 12$, and $E(t) = 60$, the equation becomes

$$4\frac{dI}{dt} + 12I = 60$$

FIGURE 5

or
$$\frac{dI}{dt} = 15 - 3I$$

and the initial-value problem is

$$\frac{dI}{dt} = 15 - 3I \qquad I(0) = 0$$

We recognize this equation as being separable, and we solve it as follows:

$$\int \frac{dI}{15 - 3I} = \int dt \qquad (15 - 3I \neq 0)$$

$$-\tfrac{1}{3} \ln |15 - 3I| = t + C$$

$$|15 - 3I| = e^{-3(t+C)}$$

$$15 - 3I = \pm e^{-3C} e^{-3t} = A e^{-3t}$$

$$I = 5 - \tfrac{1}{3} A e^{-3t}$$

Since $I(0) = 0$, we have $5 - \tfrac{1}{3}A = 0$, so $A = 15$ and the solution is

$$I(t) = 5 - 5e^{-3t}$$

The limiting current, in amperes, is

$$\lim_{t \to \infty} I(t) = \lim_{t \to \infty} (5 - 5e^{-3t}) = 5 - 5 \lim_{t \to \infty} e^{-3t}$$

$$= 5 - 0 = 5$$

▍ Figure 6 shows how the solution in Example 4 (the current) approaches its limiting value. Comparison with Figure 11 in Section 10.2 shows that we were able to draw a fairly accurate solution curve from the direction field.

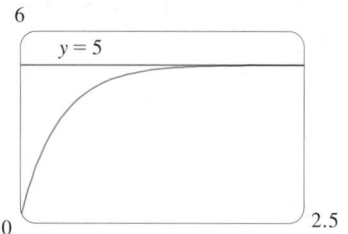

FIGURE 6

▍ Orthogonal Trajectories

An **orthogonal trajectory** of a family of curves is a curve that intersects each curve of the family orthogonally, that is, at right angles (see Figure 7). For instance, each member of the family $y = mx$ of straight lines through the origin is an orthogonal trajectory of the family $x^2 + y^2 = r^2$ of concentric circles with center the origin (see Figure 8). We say that the two families are orthogonal trajectories of each other.

orthogonal
trajectory

FIGURE 7

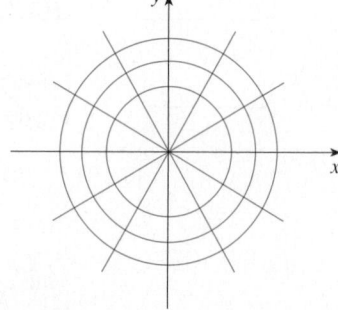

FIGURE 8

EXAMPLE 5 Find the orthogonal trajectories of the family of curves $x = ky^2$, where k is an arbitrary constant.

SOLUTION The curves $x = ky^2$ form a family of parabolas whose axis of symmetry is the x-axis. The first step is to find a single differential equation that is satisfied by all members of the family. If we differentiate $x = ky^2$, we get

$$1 = 2ky \frac{dy}{dx} \quad \text{or} \quad \frac{dy}{dx} = \frac{1}{2ky}$$

This differential equation depends on k, but we need an equation that is valid for all values of k simultaneously. To eliminate k we note that, from the equation of the given general parabola $x = ky^2$, we have $k = x/y^2$ and so the differential equation can be written as

$$\frac{dy}{dx} = \frac{1}{2ky} = \frac{1}{2 \dfrac{x}{y^2} y}$$

or

$$\frac{dy}{dx} = \frac{y}{2x}$$

This means that the slope of the tangent line at any point (x, y) on one of the parabolas is $y' = y/(2x)$. On an orthogonal trajectory the slope of the tangent line must be the negative reciprocal of this slope. Therefore, the orthogonal trajectories must satisfy the differential equation

$$\frac{dy}{dx} = -\frac{2x}{y}$$

This differential equation is separable, and we solve it as follows:

$$\int y \, dy = -\int 2x \, dx$$

$$\frac{y^2}{2} = -x^2 + C$$

4    $$x^2 + \frac{y^2}{2} = C$$

where C is an arbitrary positive constant. Thus, the orthogonal trajectories are the family of ellipses given by Equation 4 and sketched in Figure 9.

Orthogonal trajectories occur in various branches of physics. For example, in an electrostatic field the lines of force are orthogonal to the lines of constant potential. Also, the streamlines in aerodynamics are orthogonal trajectories of the velocity-equipotential curves.

FIGURE 9

||| **Mixing Problems**

A typical mixing problem involves a tank of fixed capacity filled with a thoroughly mixed solution of some substance, such as salt. A solution of a given concentration enters the tank at a fixed rate and the mixture, thoroughly stirred, leaves at a fixed rate, which may differ from the entering rate. If $y(t)$ denotes the amount of substance in the tank at time t, then $y'(t)$ is the rate at which the substance is being added minus the rate at which it is being removed. The mathematical description of this situation often leads to a first-order separable differential equation. We can use the same type of reasoning to model a variety of phenomena: chemical reactions, discharge of pollutants into a lake, injection of a drug into the bloodstream.

EXAMPLE 6 A tank contains 20 kg of salt dissolved in 5000 L of water. Brine that contains 0.03 kg of salt per liter of water enters the tank at a rate of 25 L/min. The solution is kept thoroughly mixed and drains from the tank at the same rate. How much salt remains in the tank after half an hour?

SOLUTION Let $y(t)$ be the amount of salt (in kilograms) after t minutes. We are given that $y(0) = 20$ and we want to find $y(30)$. We do this by finding a differential equation satisfied by $y(t)$. Note that dy/dt is the rate of change of the amount of salt, so

$$\boxed{5} \qquad \frac{dy}{dt} = (\text{rate in}) - (\text{rate out})$$

where (rate in) is the rate at which salt enters the tank and (rate out) is the rate at which salt leaves the tank. We have

$$\text{rate in} = \left(0.03\,\frac{\text{kg}}{\text{L}}\right)\left(25\,\frac{\text{L}}{\text{min}}\right) = 0.75\,\frac{\text{kg}}{\text{min}}$$

The tank always contains 5000 L of liquid, so the concentration at time t is $y(t)/5000$ (measured in kilograms per liter). Since the brine flows out at a rate of 25 L/min, we have

$$\text{rate out} = \left(\frac{y(t)}{5000}\,\frac{\text{kg}}{\text{L}}\right)\left(25\,\frac{\text{L}}{\text{min}}\right) = \frac{y(t)}{200}\,\frac{\text{kg}}{\text{min}}$$

Thus, from Equation 5 we get

$$\frac{dy}{dt} = 0.75 - \frac{y(t)}{200} = \frac{150 - y(t)}{200}$$

Solving this separable differential equation, we obtain

$$\int \frac{dy}{150 - y} = \int \frac{dt}{200}$$

$$-\ln|150 - y| = \frac{t}{200} + C$$

Since $y(0) = 20$, we have $-\ln 130 = C$, so

$$-\ln|150 - y| = \frac{t}{200} - \ln 130$$

Therefore $\qquad |150 - y| = 130e^{-t/200}$

Since $y(t)$ is continuous and $y(0) = 20$ and the right side is never 0, we deduce that $150 - y(t)$ is always positive. Thus, $|150 - y| = 150 - y$ and so

$$y(t) = 150 - 130e^{-t/200}$$

The amount of salt after 30 min is

$$y(30) = 150 - 130e^{-30/200} \approx 38.1 \text{ kg}$$

‖‖ Figure 10 shows the graph of the function $y(t)$ of Example 6. Notice that, as time goes by, the amount of salt approaches 150 kg.

FIGURE 10

10.3 Exercises

1–10 ‖ Solve the differential equation.

1. $\dfrac{dy}{dx} = \dfrac{y}{x}$

2. $\dfrac{dy}{dx} = \dfrac{e^{2x}}{4y^3}$

3. $(x^2 + 1)y' = xy$

4. $y' = y^2 \sin x$

5. $(1 + \tan y)y' = x^2 + 1$

6. $\dfrac{du}{dr} = \dfrac{1 + \sqrt{r}}{1 + \sqrt{u}}$

7. $\dfrac{dy}{dt} = \dfrac{te^t}{y\sqrt{1 + y^2}}$

8. $y' = \dfrac{xy}{2 \ln y}$

9. $\dfrac{du}{dt} = 2 + 2u + t + tu$

10. $\dfrac{dz}{dt} + e^{t+z} = 0$

11–18 ‖ Find the solution of the differential equation that satisfies the given initial condition.

11. $\dfrac{dy}{dx} = y^2 + 1, \quad y(1) = 0$

12. $\dfrac{dy}{dx} = \dfrac{y \cos x}{1 + y^2}, \quad y(0) = 1$

13. $x \cos x = (2y + e^{3y})y', \quad y(0) = 0$

14. $\dfrac{dP}{dt} = \sqrt{Pt}, \quad P(1) = 2$

15. $\dfrac{du}{dt} = \dfrac{2t + \sec^2 t}{2u}, \quad u(0) = -5$

16. $\dfrac{dy}{dt} = te^y, \quad y(1) = 0$

17. $y' \tan x = a + y, \quad y(\pi/3) = a, \quad 0 < x < \pi/2$

18. $xy' + y = y^2, \quad y(1) = -1$

19. Find an equation of the curve that satisfies $dy/dx = 4x^3y$ and whose y-intercept is 7.

20. Find an equation of the curve that passes through the point $(1, 1)$ and whose slope at (x, y) is y^2/x^3.

21. (a) Solve the differential equation $y' = 2x\sqrt{1 - y^2}$.
(b) Solve the initial-value problem $y' = 2x\sqrt{1 - y^2}, y(0) = 0$, and graph the solution.
(c) Does the initial-value problem $y' = 2x\sqrt{1 - y^2}, y(0) = 2$, have a solution? Explain.

22. Solve the equation $e^{-y}y' + \cos x = 0$ and graph several members of the family of solutions. How does the solution curve change as the constant C varies?

CAS **23.** Solve the initial-value problem $y' = (\sin x)/\sin y, y(0) = \pi/2$, and graph the solution (if your CAS does implicit plots).

CAS **24.** Solve the equation $y' = x\sqrt{x^2 + 1}/(ye^y)$ and graph several members of the family of solutions (if your CAS does implicit plots). How does the solution curve change as the constant C varies?

CAS **25–26** ‖

(a) Use a computer algebra system to draw a direction field for the differential equation. Get a printout and use it to sketch some solution curves without solving the differential equation.
(b) Solve the differential equation.
(c) Use the CAS to draw several members of the family of solutions obtained in part (b). Compare with the curves from part (a).

25. $y' = 1/y$

26. $y' = x^2/y$

27–30 ‖ Find the orthogonal trajectories of the family of curves. Use a graphing device to draw several members of each family on a common screen.

27. $y = kx^2$

28. $x^2 - y^2 = k$

29. $y = (x + k)^{-1}$

30. $y = ke^{-x}$

31. Solve the initial-value problem in Exercise 27 in Section 10.2 to find an expression for the charge at time t. Find the limiting value of the charge.

32. In Exercise 28 in Section 10.2 we discussed a differential equation that models the temperature of a 95°C cup of coffee in a 20°C room. Solve the differential equation to find an expression for the temperature of the coffee at time t.

33. In Exercise 13 in Section 10.1 we formulated a model for learning in the form of the differential equation

$$\frac{dP}{dt} = k(M - P)$$

where $P(t)$ measures the performance of someone learning a skill after a training time t, M is the maximum level of performance, and k is a positive constant. Solve this differential equation to find an expression for $P(t)$. What is the limit of this expression?

34. In an elementary chemical reaction, single molecules of two reactants A and B form a molecule of the product C: A + B → C. The law of mass action states that the rate of reaction is proportional to the product of the concentrations of A and B:

$$\frac{d[C]}{dt} = k[A][B]$$

(See Example 4 in Section 3.4.) Thus, if the initial concentrations are $[A] = a$ moles/L and $[B] = b$ moles/L and we write

$x = [C]$, then we have

$$\frac{dx}{dt} = k(a - x)(b - x)$$

`CAS`
(a) Assuming that $a \neq b$, find x as a function of t. Use the fact that the initial concentration of C is 0.
(b) Find $x(t)$ assuming that $a = b$. How does this expression for $x(t)$ simplify if it is known that $[C] = a/2$ after 20 seconds?

35. In contrast to the situation of Exercise 34, experiments show that the reaction $H_2 + Br_2 \rightarrow 2HBr$ satisfies the rate law

$$\frac{d[HBr]}{dt} = k[H_2][Br_2]^{1/2}$$

and so for this reaction the differential equation becomes

$$\frac{dx}{dt} = k(a - x)(b - x)^{1/2}$$

where $x = [HBr]$ and a and b are the initial concentrations of hydrogen and bromine.
(a) Find x as a function of t in the case where $a = b$. Use the fact that $x(0) = 0$.
(b) If $a > b$, find t as a function of x. $\left[\textit{Hint:} \text{ In performing the integration, make the substitution } u = \sqrt{b - x}. \right]$

36. A sphere with radius 1 m has temperature 15°C. It lies inside a concentric sphere with radius 2 m and temperature 25°C. The temperature $T(r)$ at a distance r from the common center of the spheres satisfies the differential equation

$$\frac{d^2 T}{dr^2} + \frac{2}{r} \frac{dT}{dr} = 0$$

If we let $S = dT/dr$, then S satisfies a first-order differential equation. Solve it to find an expression for the temperature $T(r)$ between the spheres.

37. A glucose solution is administered intravenously into the bloodstream at a constant rate r. As the glucose is added, it is converted into other substances and removed from the bloodstream at a rate that is proportional to the concentration at that time. Thus, a model for the concentration $C = C(t)$ of the glucose solution in the bloodstream is

$$\frac{dC}{dt} = r - kC$$

where k is a positive constant.
(a) Suppose that the concentration at time $t = 0$ is C_0. Determine the concentration at any time t by solving the differential equation.
(b) Assuming that $C_0 < r/k$, find $\lim_{t \to \infty} C(t)$ and interpret your answer.

38. A certain small country has $10 billion in paper currency in circulation, and each day $50 million comes into the country's banks. The government decides to introduce new currency by having the banks replace old bills with new ones whenever old

currency comes into the banks. Let $x = x(t)$ denote the amount of new currency in circulation at time t, with $x(0) = 0$.
(a) Formulate a mathematical model in the form of an initial-value problem that represents the "flow" of the new currency into circulation.
(b) Solve the initial-value problem found in part (a).
(c) How long will it take for the new bills to account for 90% of the currency in circulation?

39. A tank contains 1000 L of brine with 15 kg of dissolved salt. Pure water enters the tank at a rate of 10 L/min. The solution is kept thoroughly mixed and drains from the tank at the same rate. How much salt is in the tank (a) after t minutes and (b) after 20 minutes?

40. A tank contains 1000 L of pure water. Brine that contains 0.05 kg of salt per liter of water enters the tank at a rate of 5 L/min. Brine that contains 0.04 kg of salt per liter of water enters the tank at a rate of 10 L/min. The solution is kept thoroughly mixed and drains from the tank at a rate of 15 L/min. How much salt is in the tank (a) after t minutes and (b) after one hour?

41. When a raindrop falls, it increases in size and so its mass at time t is a function of t, $m(t)$. The rate of growth of the mass is $km(t)$ for some positive constant k. When we apply Newton's Law of Motion to the raindrop, we get $(mv)' = gm$, where v is the velocity of the raindrop (directed downward) and g is the acceleration due to gravity. The *terminal velocity* of the raindrop is $\lim_{t \to \infty} v(t)$. Find an expression for the terminal velocity in terms of g and k.

42. An object of mass m is moving horizontally through a medium which resists the motion with a force that is a function of the velocity; that is,

$$m \frac{d^2 s}{dt^2} = m \frac{dv}{dt} = f(v)$$

where $v = v(t)$ and $s = s(t)$ represent the velocity and position of the object at time t, respectively. For example, think of a boat moving through the water.
(a) Suppose that the resisting force is proportional to the velocity, that is, $f(v) = -kv$, k a positive constant. (This model is appropriate for small values of v.) Let $v(0) = v_0$ and $s(0) = s_0$ be the initial values of v and s. Determine v and s at any time t. What is the total distance that the object travels from time $t = 0$?
(b) For larger values of v a better model is obtained by supposing that the resisting force is proportional to the square of the velocity, that is, $f(v) = -kv^2$, $k > 0$. (This model was first proposed by Newton.) Let v_0 and s_0 be the initial values of v and s. Determine v and s at any time t. What is the total distance that the object travels in this case?

43. Let $A(t)$ be the area of a tissue culture at time t and let M be the final area of the tissue when growth is complete. Most cell divisions occur on the periphery of the tissue and the number of cells on the periphery is proportional to $\sqrt{A(t)}$. So a reasonable model for the growth of tissue is obtained by assuming that the rate of growth of the area is jointly proportional to $\sqrt{A(t)}$ and $M - A(t)$.

(a) Formulate a differential equation and use it to show that the tissue grows fastest when $A(t) = M/3$.

(b) Solve the differential equation to find an expression for $A(t)$. Use a computer algebra system to perform the integration.

44. According to Newton's Law of Universal Gravitation, the gravitational force on an object of mass m that has been projected vertically upward from Earth's surface is

$$F = \frac{mgR^2}{(x + R)^2}$$

where $x = x(t)$ is the object's distance above the surface at time t, R is Earth's radius, and g is the acceleration due to gravity. Also, by Newton's Second Law, $F = ma = m(dv/dt)$

and so

$$m\frac{dv}{dt} = -\frac{mgR^2}{(x + R)^2}$$

(a) Suppose a rocket is fired vertically upward with an initial velocity v_0. Let h be the maximum height above the surface reached by the object. Show that

$$v_0 = \sqrt{\frac{2gRh}{R + h}}$$

[*Hint:* By the Chain Rule, $m(dv/dt) = mv(dv/dx)$.]

(b) Calculate $v_e = \lim_{h \to \infty} v_0$. This limit is called the *escape velocity* for Earth.

(c) Use $R = 3960$ mi and $g = 32$ ft/s^2 to calculate v_e in feet per second and in miles per second.

APPLIED PROJECT

How Fast Does a Tank Drain?

If water (or other liquid) drains from a tank, we expect that the flow will be greatest at first (when the water depth is greatest) and will gradually decrease as the water level decreases. But we need a more precise mathematical description of how the flow decreases in order to answer the kinds of questions that engineers ask: How long does it take for a tank to drain completely? How much water should a tank hold in order to guarantee a certain minimum water pressure for a sprinkler system?

Let $h(t)$ and $V(t)$ be the height and volume of water in a tank at time t. If water leaks through a hole with area a at the bottom of the tank, then Torricelli's Law says that

$$\boxed{1} \qquad \frac{dV}{dt} = -a\sqrt{2gh}$$

where g is the acceleration due to gravity. So the rate at which water flows from the tank is proportional to the square root of the water height.

1. (a) Suppose the tank is cylindrical with height 6 ft and radius 2 ft and the hole is circular with radius 1 in. If we take $g = 32$ ft/s^2, show that y satisfies the differential equation

$$\frac{dh}{dt} = -\frac{1}{72}\sqrt{h}$$

(b) Solve this equation to find the height of the water at time t, assuming the tank is full at time $t = 0$.

(c) How long will it take for the water to drain completely?

2. Because of the rotation and viscosity of the liquid, the theoretical model given by Equation 1 isn't quite accurate. Instead, the model

$$\boxed{2} \qquad \frac{dh}{dt} = k\sqrt{h}$$

is often used and the constant k (which depends on the physical properties of the liquid) is determined from data concerning the draining of the tank.

(a) Suppose that a hole is drilled in the side of a cylindrical bottle and the height h of the water (above the hole) decreases from 10 cm to 3 cm in 68 seconds. Use Equation 2 to find an expression for $h(t)$. Evaluate $h(t)$ for $t = 10, 20, 30, 40, 50, 60$.

▐▐▐ This part of the project is best done as a classroom demonstration or as a group project with three students in each group: a timekeeper to call out seconds, a bottle keeper to estimate the height every 10 seconds, and a record keeper to record these values.

(b) Drill a 4-mm hole near the bottom of the cylindrical part of a two-liter plastic soft-drink bottle. Attach a strip of masking tape marked in centimeters from 0 to 10, with 0 corresponding to the top of the hole. With one finger over the hole, fill the bottle with water to the 10-cm mark. Then take your finger off the hole and record the values of $h(t)$ for $t = 10, 20, 30, 40, 50, 60$ seconds. (You will probably find that it takes 68 seconds for the level to decrease to $h = 3$ cm.) Compare your data with the values of $h(t)$ from part (a). How well did the model predict the actual values?

3. In many parts of the world, the water for sprinkler systems in large hotels and hospitals is supplied by gravity from cylindrical tanks on or near the roofs of the buildings. Suppose such a tank has radius 10 ft and the diameter of the outlet is 2.5 inches. An engineer has to guarantee that the water pressure will be at least 2160 lb/ft^2 for a period of 10 minutes. (When a fire happens, the electrical system might fail and it could take up to 10 minutes for the emergency generator and fire pump to be activated.) What height should the engineer specify for the tank in order to make such a guarantee? (Use the fact that the water pressure at a depth of d feet is $P = 62.5d$. See Section 9.3.)

4. Not all water tanks are shaped like cylinders. Suppose a tank has cross-sectional area $A(h)$ at height h. Then the volume of water up to height h is $V = \int_0^h A(u)\,du$ and so the Fundamental Theorem of Calculus gives $dV/dh = A(h)$. It follows that

$$\frac{dV}{dt} = \frac{dV}{dh}\frac{dh}{dt} = A(h)\frac{dh}{dt}$$

and so Torricelli's Law becomes

$$A(h)\frac{dh}{dt} = -a\sqrt{2gh}$$

(a) Suppose the tank has the shape of a sphere with radius 2 m and is initially half full of water. If the radius of the circular hole is 1 cm and we take $g = 10$ m/s^2, show that h satisfies the differential equation

$$(4h - h^2)\frac{dh}{dt} = -0.0001\sqrt{20h}$$

(b) How long will it take for the water to drain completely?

▐▐▐▐ APPLIED PROJECT

Which Is Faster, Going Up or Coming Down?

Suppose you throw a ball into the air. Do you think it takes longer to reach its maximum height or to fall back to Earth from its maximum height? We will solve the problem in this project but, before getting started, think about that situation and make a guess based on your physical intuition.

1. A ball with mass m is projected vertically upward from Earth's surface with a positive initial velocity v_0. We assume the forces acting on the ball are the force of gravity and a retarding force of air resistance with direction opposite to the direction of motion and with magnitude $p\,|v(t)|$, where p is a positive constant and $v(t)$ is the velocity of the ball at time t. In both

|||| In modeling force due to air resistance, various functions have been used, depending on the physical characteristics and speed of the ball. Here we use a linear model, $-pv$, but a quadratic model ($-pv^2$ on the way up and pv^2 on the way down) is another possibility for higher speeds (see Exercise 42 in Section 10.3). For a golf ball, experiments have shown that a good model is $-pv^{1.3}$ going up and $p|v|^{1.3}$ coming down. But no matter which force function $-f(v)$ is used [where $f(v) > 0$ for $v > 0$ and $f(v) < 0$ for $v < 0$], the answer to the question remains the same. See F. Brauer, "What Goes Up Must Come Down, Eventually," *Amer. Math. Monthly* 108 (2001), pp. 437–440.

the ascent and the descent, the total force acting on the ball is $-pv - mg$. [During ascent, $v(t)$ is positive and the resistance acts downward; during descent, $v(t)$ is negative and the resistance acts upward.] So, by Newton's Second Law, the equation of motion is

$$mv' = -pv - mg$$

Solve this differential equation to show that the velocity is

$$v(t) = \left(v_0 + \frac{mg}{p}\right)e^{-pt/m} - \frac{mg}{p}$$

2. Show that the height of the ball, until it hits the ground, is

$$y(t) = \left(v_0 + \frac{mg}{p}\right)\frac{m}{p}(1 - e^{-pt/m}) - \frac{mgt}{p}$$

3. Let t_1 be the time that the ball takes to reach its maximum height. Show that

$$t_1 = \frac{m}{p}\ln\left(\frac{mg + pv_0}{mg}\right)$$

Find this time for a ball with mass 1 kg and initial velocity 20 m/s. Assume the air resistance is $\frac{1}{10}$ of the speed.

4. Let t_2 be the time at which the ball falls back to Earth. For the particular ball in Problem 3, estimate t_2 by using a graph of the height function $y(t)$. Which is faster, going up or coming down?

al, it's not easy to find t_2 because it's impossible to solve the equation $y(t) = 0$ ly. We can, however, use an indirect method to determine whether ascent or descent r; we determine whether $y(2t_1)$ is positive or negative. Show that

$$y(2t_1) = \frac{m^2 g}{p^2}\left(x - \frac{1}{x} - 2\ln x\right)$$

where $x = e^{pt_1/m}$. Then show that $x > 1$ and the function

$$f(x) = x - \frac{1}{x} - 2\ln x$$

is increasing for $x > 1$. Use this result to decide whether $y(2t_1)$ is positive or negative. What can you conclude? Is ascent or descent faster?

10.4 Exponential Growth and Decay

One of the models for population growth that we considered in Section 10.1 was based on the assumption that the population grows at a rate proportional to the size of the population:

$$\frac{dP}{dt} = kP$$

Is that a reasonable assumption? Suppose we have a population (of bacteria, for instance) with size $P = 1000$ and at a certain time it is growing at a rate of $P' = 300$ bacteria per hour. Now let's take another 1000 bacteria of the same type and put them with the first population. Each half of the new population was growing at a rate of 300 bacteria per hour. We would expect the total population of 2000 to increase at a rate of 600 bacteria per hour initially (provided there's enough room and nutrition). So if we double the size, we double the growth rate. In general, it seems reasonable that the growth rate should be proportional to the size.

The same assumption applies in other situations as well. In nuclear physics, the mass of a radioactive substance decays at a rate proportional to the mass. In chemistry, the rate of a unimolecular first-order reaction is proportional to the concentration of the substance. In finance, the value of a savings account with continuously compounded interest increases at a rate proportional to that value.

In general, if $y(t)$ is the value of a quantity y at time t and if the rate of change of y with respect to t is proportional to its size $y(t)$ at any time, then

$$\boxed{1} \qquad \frac{dy}{dt} = ky$$

where k is a constant. Equation 1 is sometimes called the **law of natural growth** (if $k > 0$) or the **law of natural decay** (if $k < 0$). Because it is a separable differential equation we can solve it by the methods of Section 10.3:

$$\int \frac{dy}{y} = \int k \, dt$$

$$\ln|y| = kt + C$$

$$|y| = e^{kt+C} = e^C e^{kt}$$

$$y = Ae^{kt}$$

where A ($= \pm e^C$ or 0) is an arbitrary constant. To see the significance of the constant A, we observe that

$$y(0) = Ae^{k \cdot 0} = A$$

Therefore, A is the initial value of the function.

Because Equation 1 occurs so frequently in nature, we summarize what we have just proved for future use.

$\boxed{2}$ The solution of the initial-value problem

$$\frac{dy}{dt} = ky \qquad y(0) = y_0$$

is

$$y(t) = y_0 e^{kt}$$

|||| Population Growth

What is the significance of the proportionality constant k? In the context of population growth, we can write

$$\boxed{3} \qquad \frac{dP}{dt} = kP \qquad \text{or} \qquad \frac{1}{P}\frac{dP}{dt} = k$$

The quantity

$$\frac{1}{P}\frac{dP}{dt}$$

is the growth rate divided by the population size; it is called the **relative growth rate**. According to (3), instead of saying "the growth rate is proportional to population size" we could say "the relative growth rate is constant." Then (2) says that a population with constant relative growth rate must grow exponentially. Notice that the relative growth rate k appears as the coefficient of t in the exponential function $y_0 e^{kt}$. For instance, if

$$\frac{dP}{dt} = 0.02P$$

and t is measured in years, then the relative growth rate is $k = 0.02$ and the population grows at a relative rate of 2% per year. If the population at time 0 is P_0, then the expression for the population is

$$P(t) = P_0 e^{0.02t}$$

TABLE 1

Year	Population (millions)
1900	1650
1910	1750
1920	1860
1930	2070
1940	2300
1950	2560
1960	3040
1970	3710
1980	4450
1990	5280
2000	6080

EXAMPLE 1 Assuming that the growth rate is proportional to population size, use the data in Table 1 to model the population of the world in the 20th century. What is the relative growth rate? How well does the model fit the data?

SOLUTION We measure the time t in years and let $t = 0$ in the year 1900. We measure the population $P(t)$ in millions of people. Then the initial condition is $P(0) = 1650$. We are assuming that the growth rate is proportional to population size, so the initial-value problem is

$$\frac{dP}{dt} = kP \qquad P(0) = 1650$$

From (2) we know that the solution is

$$P(t) = 1650 e^{kt}$$

One way to estimate the relative growth rate k is to use the fact that the population in 1910 was 1750 million. Therefore

$$P(10) = 1650 e^{k(10)} = 1750$$

We solve this equation for k:

$$e^{10k} = \frac{1750}{1650}$$

$$k = \frac{1}{10}\ln\frac{1750}{1650} \approx 0.005884$$

Thus, the relative growth rate is about 0.6% per year and the model becomes

$$P(t) = 1650 e^{0.005884t}$$

Table 2 and Figure 1 allow us to compare the predictions of this model with the actual data. You can see that the predictions become quite inaccurate after about 30 years and they underestimate by a factor of more than 2 in 2000.

TABLE 2

Year	Model	Population
1900	1650	1650
1910	1750	1750
1920	1856	1860
1930	1969	2070
1940	2088	2300
1950	2214	2560
1960	2349	3040
1970	2491	3710
1980	2642	4450
1990	2802	5280
2000	2972	6080

FIGURE 1 A possible model for world population growth

Another possibility for estimating k would be to use the given population for 1950, for instance, instead of 1910. Then

$$P(50) = 1650e^{50k} = 2560$$

$$k = \frac{1}{50} \ln \frac{2560}{1650} \approx 0.0087846$$

The estimate for the relative growth rate is now 0.88% per year and the model is

$$P(t) = 1650e^{0.0087846t}$$

The predictions with this second model are shown in Table 3 and Figure 2. This exponential model is more accurate over a longer period of time, but it too lags behind reality in recent years.

|||| In Sections 7.2 and 7.4* we modeled the same data with an exponential function, but there we used the method of least squares.

TABLE 3

Year	Model	Population
1900	1650	1650
1910	1802	1750
1920	1967	1860
1930	2148	2070
1940	2345	2300
1950	2560	2560
1960	2795	3040
1970	3052	3710
1980	3332	4450
1990	3638	5280
2000	3972	6080

FIGURE 2 Another model for world population growth

EXAMPLE 2 Use the data in Table 1 to model the population of the world in the second half of the 20th century. Use the model to estimate the population in 1993 and to predict the population in the year 2010.

SOLUTION Here we let $t = 0$ in the year 1950. Then the initial-value problem is

$$\frac{dP}{dt} = kP \qquad P(0) = 2560$$

and the solution is

$$P(t) = 2560e^{kt}$$

Let's estimate k by using the population in 1960:

$$P(10) = 2560e^{10k} = 3040$$

$$k = \frac{1}{10} \ln \frac{3040}{2560} \approx 0.017185$$

he relative growth rate is about 1.7% per year and the model is

$$P(t) = 2560e^{0.017185t}$$

We estimate that the world population in 1993 was

$$P(43) = 2560e^{0.017185(43)} \approx 5360 \text{ million}$$

The model predicts that the population in 2010 will be

$$P(60) = 2560e^{0.017185(60)} \approx 7179 \text{ million}$$

The graph in Figure 3 shows that the model is fairly accurate to date, so the estimate for 1993 is quite reliable. But the prediction for 2010 is riskier.

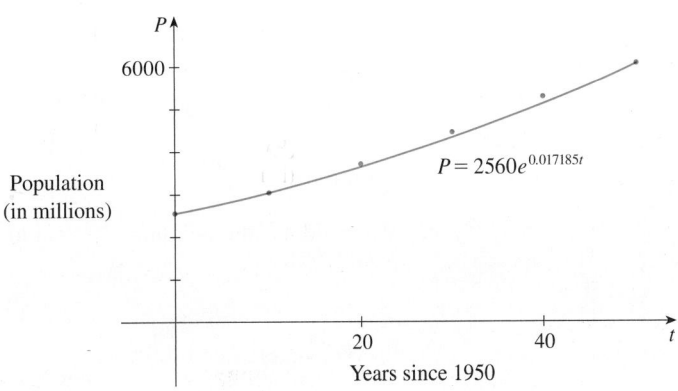

Population
(in millions)

$P = 2560e^{0.017185t}$

Years since 1950

FIGURE 3
A model for world population growth
in the second half of the 20th century

▌▌▌ <u>Radioactive Decay</u>

Radioactive substances decay by spontaneously emitting radiation. If $m(t)$ is the mass remaining from an initial mass m_0 of the substance after time t, then the relative decay rate

$$-\frac{1}{m}\frac{dm}{dt}$$

has been found experimentally to be constant. (Since dm/dt is negative, the relative decay rate is positive.) It follows that

$$\frac{dm}{dt} = km$$

where k is a negative constant. In other words, radioactive substances decay at a rate proportional to the remaining mass. This means that we can use (2) to show that the mass decays exponentially:

$$m(t) = m_0 e^{kt}$$

Physicists express the rate of decay in terms of **half-life**, the time required for half of any given quantity to decay.

EXAMPLE 3 The half-life of radium-226 ($^{226}_{88}$Ra) is 1590 years.
(a) A sample of radium-226 has a mass of 100 mg. Find a formula for the mass of $^{226}_{88}$Ra that remains after t years.
(b) Find the mass after 1000 years correct to the nearest milligram.
(c) When will the mass be reduced to 30 mg?

SOLUTION
(a) Let $m(t)$ be the mass of radium-226 (in milligrams) that remains after t years. Then $dm/dt = km$ and $y(0) = 100$, so (2) gives

$$m(t) = m(0)e^{kt} = 100e^{kt}$$

In order to determine the value of k, we use the fact that $y(1590) = \frac{1}{2}(100)$. Thus

$$100e^{1590k} = 50 \qquad \text{so} \qquad e^{1590k} = \tfrac{1}{2}$$

and

$$1590k = \ln\tfrac{1}{2} = -\ln 2$$

$$k = -\frac{\ln 2}{1590}$$

Therefore $$m(t) = 100e^{-(\ln 2/1590)t}$$

We could use the fact that $e^{\ln 2} = 2$ to write the expression for $m(t)$ in the alternative form

$$m(t) = 100 \times 2^{-t/1590}$$

(b) The mass after 1000 years is

$$m(1000) = 100e^{-(\ln 2/1590)1000} \approx 65 \text{ mg}$$

(c) We want to find the value of t such that $m(t) = 30$, that is,

$$100e^{-(\ln 2/1590)t} = 30 \qquad \text{or} \qquad e^{-(\ln 2/1590)t} = 0.3$$

We solve this equation for t by taking the natural logarithm of both sides:

$$-\frac{\ln 2}{1590}t = \ln 0.3$$

Thus

$$t = -1590\frac{\ln 0.3}{\ln 2} \approx 2762 \text{ years}$$

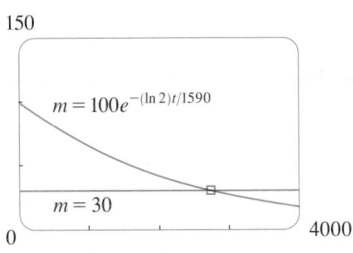

150

$m = 100e^{-(\ln 2)t/1590}$

$m = 30$

0   4000

FIGURE 4

As a check on our work in Example 3, we use a graphing device to draw the graph of $m(t)$ in Figure 4 together with the horizontal line $m = 30$. These curves intersect when $t \approx 2800$, and this agrees with the answer to part (c).

ⅲ Newton's Law of Cooling

Newton's Law of Cooling states that the rate of cooling of an object is proportional to the temperature difference between the object and its surroundings, provided that this difference is not too large. (This law also applies to warming.) If we let $T(t)$ be the temperature of the object at time t and T_s be the temperature of the surroundings, then we can formulate Newton's Law of Cooling as a differential equation:

$$\frac{dT}{dt} = k(T - T_s)$$

where k is a constant. We could solve this equation as a separable differential equation by the method of Section 10.3, but an easier method is to make the change of variable $y(t) = T(t) - T_s$. Because T_s is constant, we have $y'(t) = T'(t)$ and so the equation becomes

$$\frac{dy}{dt} = ky$$

We can then use (2) to find an expression for y, from which we can find T.

EXAMPLE 4 A bottle of soda pop at room temperature (72°F) is placed in a refrigerator where the temperature is 44°F. After half an hour the soda pop has cooled to 61°F.
(a) What is the temperature of the soda pop after another half hour?
(b) How long does it take for the soda pop to cool to 50°F?

SOLUTION
(a) Let $T(t)$ be the temperature of the soda after t minutes. The surrounding temperature is $T_s = 44°F$, so Newton's Law of Cooling states that

$$\frac{dT}{dt} = k(T - 44)$$

If we let $y = T - 44$, then $y(0) = T(0) - 44 = 72 - 44 = 28$, so y is a solution of the initial-value problem

$$\frac{dy}{dt} = ky \qquad y(0) = 28$$

and by (2) we have

$$y(t) = y(0)e^{kt} = 28e^{kt}$$

We are given that $T(30) = 61$, so $y(30) = 61 - 44 = 17$ and

$$28e^{30k} = 17 \qquad e^{30k} = \tfrac{17}{28}$$

Taking logarithms, we have

$$k = \frac{\ln\left(\tfrac{17}{28}\right)}{30} \approx -0.01663$$

Thus

$$y(t) = 28e^{-0.01663t}$$

$$T(t) = 44 + 28e^{-0.01663t}$$

$$T(60) = 44 + 28e^{-0.01663(60)} \approx 54.3$$

So after another half hour the pop has cooled to about 54°F.

(b) We have $T(t) = 50$ when

$$44 + 28e^{-0.01663t} = 50$$

$$e^{-0.01663t} = \tfrac{6}{28}$$

$$t = \frac{\ln\left(\tfrac{6}{28}\right)}{-0.01663} \approx 92.6$$

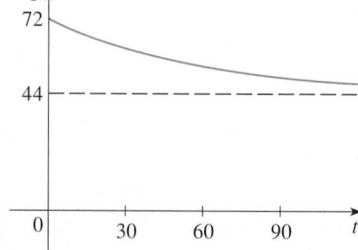

FIGURE 5

The pop cools to 50°F after about 1 hour 33 minutes.

Notice that in Example 4, we have

$$\lim_{t \to \infty} T(t) = \lim_{t \to \infty} (44 + 28e^{-0.01663t}) = 44 + 28 \cdot 0 = 44$$

which is to be expected. The graph of the temperature function is shown in Figure 5.

‖‖‖ **Continuously Compounded Interest**

EXAMPLE 5 If $1000 is invested at 6% interest, compounded annually, then after 1 year the investment is worth $1000(1.06) = $1060, after 2 years it's worth $[1000(1.06)]1.06 = $1123.60, and after t years it's worth $1000(1.06)^t$. In general, if an amount A_0 is invested at an interest rate r ($r = 0.06$ in this example), then after t years it's worth $A_0(1 + r)^t$. Usually, however, interest is compounded more frequently, say, n times a year. Then in each compounding period the interest rate is r/n and there are nt compounding periods in t years, so the value of the investment is

$$A_0\left(1 + \frac{r}{n}\right)^{nt}$$

For instance, after 3 years at 6% interest a $1000 investment will be worth

$$\$1000(1.06)^3 = \$1191.02 \quad \text{with annual compounding}$$

$$\$1000(1.03)^6 = \$1194.05 \quad \text{with semiannual compounding}$$

$$\$1000(1.015)^{12} = \$1195.62 \quad \text{with quarterly compounding}$$

$$\$1000(1.005)^{36} = \$1196.68 \quad \text{with monthly compounding}$$

$$\$1000\left(1 + \frac{0.06}{365}\right)^{365 \cdot 3} = \$1197.20 \quad \text{with daily compounding}$$

You can see that the interest paid increases as the number of compounding periods (n) increases. If we let $n \to \infty$, then we will be compounding the interest **continuously** and the value of the investment will be

$$A(t) = \lim_{n \to \infty} A_0\left(1 + \frac{r}{n}\right)^{nt} = \lim_{n \to \infty} A_0\left[\left(1 + \frac{r}{n}\right)^{n/r}\right]^{rt}$$

$$= A_0\left[\lim_{n \to \infty}\left(1 + \frac{r}{n}\right)^{n/r}\right]^{rt}$$

$$= A_0\left[\lim_{m \to \infty}\left(1 + \frac{1}{m}\right)^{m}\right]^{rt} \qquad \text{(where } m = n/r\text{)}$$

But the limit in this expression is equal to the number e (see Equation 7.4.9 or 7.4*.9). So with continuous compounding of interest at interest rate r, the amount after t years is

$$A(t) = A_0 e^{rt}$$

If we differentiate this equation, we get

$$\frac{dA}{dt} = rA_0 e^{rt} = rA(t)$$

which says that, with continuous compounding of interest, the rate of increase of an investment is proportional to its size.

Returning to the example of $1000 invested for 3 years at 6% interest, we see that with continuous compounding of interest the value of the investment will be

$$A(3) = \$1000 e^{(0.06)3}$$

$$= \$1000 e^{0.18} = \$1197.22$$

Notice how close this is to the amount we calculated for daily compounding, $1197.20. But the amount is easier to compute if we use continuous compounding.

10.4 Exercises

1. A population of protozoa develops with a constant relative growth rate of 0.7944 per member per day. On day zero the population consists of two members. Find the population size after six days.

2. A common inhabitant of human intestines is the bacterium *Escherichia coli*. A cell of this bacterium in a nutrient-broth medium divides into two cells every 20 minutes. The initial population of a culture is 60 cells.
(a) Find the relative growth rate.
(b) Find an expression for the number of cells after t hours.
(c) Find the number of cells after 8 hours.
(d) Find the rate of growth after 8 hours.
(e) When will the population reach 20,000 cells?

3. A bacteria culture starts with 500 bacteria and grows at a rate proportional to its size. After 3 hours there are 8000 bacteria.
(a) Find an expression for the number of bacteria after t hours.
(b) Find the number of bacteria after 4 hours.
(c) Find the rate of growth after 4 hours.
(d) When will the population reach 30,000?

4. A bacteria culture grows with constant relative growth rate. After 2 hours there are 600 bacteria and after 8 hours the count is 75,000.
(a) Find the initial population.
(b) Find an expression for the population after t hours.
(c) Find the number of cells after 5 hours.
(d) Find the rate of growth after 5 hours.
(e) When will the population reach 200,000?

5. The table gives estimates of the world population, in millions, from 1750 to 2000:

Year	Population	Year	Population
1750	790	1900	1650
1800	980	1950	2560
1850	1260	2000	6080

(a) Use the exponential model and the population figures for 1750 and 1800 to predict the world population in 1900 and 1950. Compare with the actual figures.
(b) Use the exponential model and the population figures for 1850 and 1900 to predict the world population in 1950. Compare with the actual population.
(c) Use the exponential model and the population figures for 1900 and 1950 to predict the world population in 2000. Compare with the actual population and try to explain the discrepancy.

6. The table gives the population of the United States, in millions, for the years 1900–2000.

Year	Population	Year	Population
1900	76	1960	179
1910	92	1970	203
1920	106	1980	227
1930	123	1990	250
1940	131	2000	275
1950	150		

(a) Use the exponential model and the census figures for 1900 and 1910 to predict the population in 2000. Compare with the actual figure and try to explain the discrepancy.
(b) Use the exponential model and the census figures for 1980 and 1990 to predict the population in 2000. Compare with the actual population. Then use this model to predict the population in the years 2010 and 2020.
(c) Graph both of the exponential functions in parts (a) and (b) together with a plot of the actual population. Are these models reasonable ones?

7. Experiments show that if the chemical reaction

$$N_2O_5 \rightarrow 2NO_2 + \tfrac{1}{2}O_2$$

takes place at 45°C, the rate of reaction of dinitrogen pentoxide is proportional to its concentration as follows:

$$-\frac{d[N_2O_5]}{dt} = 0.0005[N_2O_5]$$

(See Example 4 in Section 3.4.)
(a) Find an expression for the concentration $[N_2O_5]$ after t seconds if the initial concentration is C.
(b) How long will the reaction take to reduce the concentration of N_2O_5 to 90% of its original value?

8. Bismuth-210 has a half-life of 5.0 days.
(a) A sample originally has a mass of 800 mg. Find a formula for the mass remaining after t days.
(b) Find the mass remaining after 30 days.
(c) When is the mass reduced to 1 mg?
(d) Sketch the graph of the mass function.

9. The half-life of cesium-137 is 30 years. Suppose we have a 100-mg sample.
(a) Find the mass that remains after t years.
(b) How much of the sample remains after 100 years?
(c) After how long will only 1 mg remain?

10. After 3 days a sample of radon-222 decayed to 58% of its original amount.
(a) What is the half-life of radon-222?
(b) How long would it take the sample to decay to 10% of its original amount?

11. Scientists can determine the age of ancient objects by a method called *radiocarbon dating*. The bombardment of the upper atmosphere by cosmic rays converts nitrogen to a radioactive isotope of carbon, ^{14}C, with a half-life of about 5730 years. Vegetation absorbs carbon dioxide through the atmosphere and animal life assimilates ^{14}C through food chains. When a plant or animal dies, it stops replacing its carbon and the amount of ^{14}C begins to decrease through radioactive decay. Therefore, the level of radioactivity must also decay exponentially. A parchment fragment was discovered that had about 74% as much ^{14}C radioactivity as does plant material on Earth today. Estimate the age of the parchment.

12. A curve passes through the point $(0, 5)$ and has the property that the slope of the curve at every point P is twice the y-coordinate of P. What is the equation of the curve?

13. A roast turkey is taken from an oven when its temperature has reached 185°F and is placed on a table in a room where the temperature is 75°F.
   (a) If the temperature of the turkey is 150°F after half an hour, what is the temperature after 45 min?
   (b) When will the turkey have cooled to 100°F?

14. A thermometer is taken from a room where the temperature is 20°C to the outdoors, where the temperature is 5°C. After one minute the thermometer reads 12°C.
   (a) What will the reading on the thermometer be after one more minute?
   (b) When will the thermometer read 6°C?

15. When a cold drink is taken from a refrigerator, its temperature is 5°C. After 25 minutes in a 20°C room its temperature has increased to 10°C.
   (a) What is the temperature of the drink after 50 minutes?
   (b) When will its temperature be 15°C?

16. A freshly brewed cup of coffee has temperature 95°C in a 20°C room. When its temperature is 70°C, it is cooling at a rate of 1°C per minute. When does this occur?

17. The rate of change of atmospheric pressure P with respect to altitude h is proportional to P, provided that the temperature is constant. At 15°C the pressure is 101.3 kPa at sea level and 87.14 kPa at $h = 1000$ m.
   (a) What is the pressure at an altitude of 3000 m?
   (b) What is the pressure at the top of Mount McKinley, at an altitude of 6187 m?

18. (a) If $500 is borrowed at 14% interest, find the amounts due at the end of 2 years if the interest is compounded (i) annually, (ii) quarterly, (iii) monthly, (iv) daily, (v) hourly, and (vi) continuously.

   (b) Suppose $500 is borrowed and the interest is compounded continuously. If $A(t)$ is the amount due after t years, where $0 \le t \le 2$, graph $A(t)$ for each of the interest rates 14%, 10%, and 6% on a common screen.

19. (a) If $3000 is invested at 5% interest, find the value of the investment at the end of 5 years if the interest is compounded (i) annually, (ii) semiannually, (iii) monthly, (iv) weekly, (v) daily, and (vi) continuously.
   (b) If $A(t)$ is the amount of the investment at time t for the case of continuous compounding, write a differential equation and an initial condition satisfied by $A(t)$.

20. (a) How long will it take an investment to double in value if the interest rate is 6% compounded continuously?
   (b) What is the equivalent annual interest rate?

21. Consider a population $P = P(t)$ with constant relative birth and death rates α and β, respectively, and a constant emigration rate m, where α, β, and m are positive constants. Assume that $\alpha > \beta$. Then the rate of change of the population at time t is modeled by the differential equation

$$\frac{dP}{dt} = kP - m \qquad \text{where } k = \alpha - \beta$$

   (a) Find the solution of this equation that satisfies the initial condition $P(0) = P_0$.
   (b) What condition on m will lead to an exponential expansion of the population?
   (c) What condition on m will result in a constant population? A population decline?
   (d) In 1847, the population of Ireland was about 8 million and the difference between the relative birth and death rates was 1.6% of the population. Because of the potato famine in the 1840s and 1850s, about 210,000 inhabitants per year emigrated from Ireland. Was the population expanding or declining at that time?

22. Let c be a positive number. A differential equation of the form

$$\frac{dy}{dt} = ky^{1+c}$$

where k is a positive constant, is called a *doomsday equation* because the exponent in the expression ky^{1+c} is larger than that for natural growth (that is, ky).
   (a) Determine the solution that satisfies the initial condition $y(0) = y_0$.
   (b) Show that there is a finite time $t = T$ (doomsday) such that $\lim_{t \to T^-} y(t) = \infty$.
   (c) An especially prolific breed of rabbits has the growth term $ky^{1.01}$. If 2 such rabbits breed initially and the warren has 16 rabbits after three months, then when is doomsday?

APPLIED PROJECT

Calculus and Baseball

In this project we explore three of the many applications of calculus to baseball. The physical interactions of the game, especially the collision of ball and bat, are quite complex and their models are discussed in detail in a book by Robert Adair, *The Physics of Baseball*, 3d ed. (New York: HarperPerennial, 2002).

Batter's box

An overhead view of the position of a baseball bat, shown every fiftieth of a second during a typical swing. (Adapted from *The Physics of Baseball*)

1. It may surprise you to learn that the collision of baseball and bat lasts only about a thousandth of a second. Here we calculate the average force on the bat during this collision by first computing the change in the ball's momentum.

   The *momentum* p of an object is the product of its mass m and its velocity v, that is, $p = mv$. Suppose an object, moving along a straight line, is acted on by a force $F = F(t)$ that is a continuous function of time.

   (a) Show that the change in momentum over a time interval $[t_0, t_1]$ is equal to the integral of F from t_0 to t_1; that is, show that

   $$p(t_1) - p(t_0) = \int_{t_0}^{t_1} F(t)\, dt$$

   This integral is called the *impulse* of the force over the time interval.

   (b) A pitcher throws a 90-mi/h fastball to a batter, who hits a line drive directly back to the pitcher. The ball is in contact with the bat for 0.001 s and leaves the bat with velocity 110 mi/h. A baseball weighs 5 oz and, in U.S. Customary units, its mass is measured in slugs: $m = w/g$ where $g = 32$ ft/s^2.

   (i) Find the change in the ball's momentum.

   (ii) Find the average force on the bat.

2. In this problem we calculate the work required for a pitcher to throw a 90-mi/h fastball by first considering kinetic energy.

   The *kinetic energy* K of an object of mass m and velocity v is given by $K = \frac{1}{2}mv^2$. Suppose an object of mass m, moving in a straight line, is acted on by a force $F = F(s)$ that depends on its position s. According to Newton's Second Law

   $$F(s) = ma = m\frac{dv}{dt}$$

   where a and v denote the acceleration and velocity of the object.

   (a) Show that the work done in moving the object from a position s_0 to a position s_1 is equal to the change in the object's kinetic energy; that is, show that

   $$W = \int_{s_0}^{s_1} F(s)\, ds = \tfrac{1}{2}mv_1^2 - \tfrac{1}{2}mv_0^2$$

   where $v_0 = v(s_0)$ and $v_1 = v(s_1)$ are the velocities of the object at the positions s_0 and s_1. *Hint:* By the Chain Rule,

   $$m\frac{dv}{dt} = m\frac{dv}{ds}\frac{ds}{dt} = mv\frac{dv}{ds}$$

   (b) How many foot-pounds of work does it take to throw a baseball at a speed of 90 mi/h?

3. (a) An outfielder fields a baseball 280 ft away from home plate and throws it directly to the catcher with an initial velocity of 100 ft/s. Assume that the velocity $v(t)$ of the ball after t seconds satisfies the differential equation $dv/dt = -v/10$ because of air resistance. How long does it take for the ball to reach home plate? (Ignore any vertical motion of the ball.)

   (b) The manager of the team wonders whether the ball will reach home plate sooner if it is relayed by an infielder. The shortstop can position himself directly between the outfielder and home plate, catch the ball thrown by the outfielder, turn, and throw the ball to the catcher with an initial velocity of 105 ft/s. The manager clocks the relay time of the shortstop (catching, turning, throwing) at half a second. How far from home plate should the shortstop position himself to minimize the total time for the ball to reach the plate? Should the manager encourage a direct throw or a relayed throw? What if the shortstop can throw at 115 ft/s?

(c) For what throwing velocity of the shortstop does a relayed throw take the same time as a direct throw?

10.5 The Logistic Equation

In this section we discuss in detail a model for population growth, the logistic model, that is more sophisticated than exponential growth. In doing so we use all the tools at our disposal—direction fields and Euler's method from Section 10.2 and the explicit solution of separable differential equations from Section 10.3. In the exercises we investigate other possible models for population growth, some of which take into account harvesting and seasonal growth.

The Logistic Model

As we discussed in Section 10.1, a population often increases exponentially in its early stages but levels off eventually and approaches its carrying capacity because of limited resources. If $P(t)$ is the size of the population at time t, we assume that

$$\frac{dP}{dt} \approx kP \qquad \text{if } P \text{ is small}$$

This says that the growth rate is initially close to being proportional to size. In other words, the relative growth rate is almost constant when the population is small. But we also want to reflect the fact that the relative growth rate decreases as the population P increases and becomes negative if P ever exceeds its **carrying capacity** K, the maximum population that the environment is capable of sustaining in the long run. The simplest expression for the relative growth rate that incorporates these assumptions is

$$\frac{1}{P} \frac{dP}{dt} = k\left(1 - \frac{P}{K}\right)$$

Multiplying by P, we obtain the model for population growth known as the **logistic differential equation**:

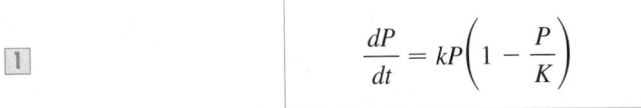

$$\boxed{1} \qquad \frac{dP}{dt} = kP\left(1 - \frac{P}{K}\right)$$

Notice from Equation 1 that if P is small compared with K, then P/K is close to 0 and so $dP/dt \approx kP$. However, if $P \to K$ (the population approaches its carrying capacity), then $P/K \to 1$, so $dP/dt \to 0$. We can deduce information about whether solutions increase or decrease directly from Equation 1. If the population P lies between 0 and K, then the right side of the equation is positive, so $dP/dt > 0$ and the population increases. But if the population exceeds the carrying capacity ($P > K$), then $1 - P/K$ is negative, so $dP/dt < 0$ and the population decreases.

‖‖ Direction Fields

Let's start our more detailed analysis of the logistic differential equation by looking at a direction field.

EXAMPLE 1 Draw a direction field for the logistic equation with $k = 0.08$ and carrying capacity $K = 1000$. What can you deduce about the solutions?

SOLUTION In this case the logistic differential equation is

$$\frac{dP}{dt} = 0.08P\left(1 - \frac{P}{1000}\right)$$

A direction field for this equation is shown in Figure 1. We show only the first quadrant because negative populations aren't meaningful and we are interested only in what happens after $t = 0$.

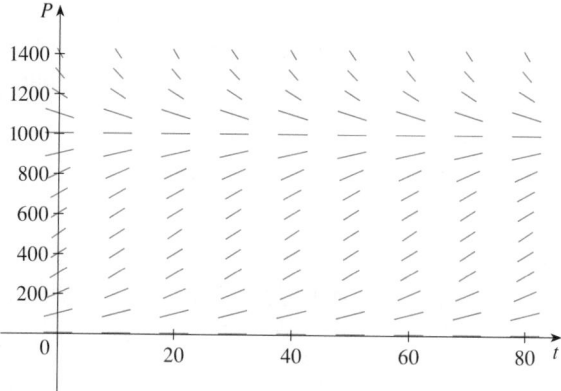

FIGURE 1

Direction field for the logistic equation in Example 1

The logistic equation is autonomous (dP/dt depends only on P, not on t), so the slopes are the same along any horizontal line. As expected, the slopes are positive for $0 < P < 1000$ and negative for $P > 1000$.

The slopes are small when P is close to 0 or 1000 (the carrying capacity). Notice that the solutions move away from the equilibrium solution $P = 0$ and move toward the equilibrium solution $P = 1000$.

In Figure 2 we use the direction field to sketch solution curves with initial populations $P(0) = 100$, $P(0) = 400$, and $P(0) = 1300$. Notice that solution curves that start below $P = 1000$ are increasing and those that start above $P = 1000$ are decreasing. The slopes are greatest when $P \approx 500$ and, therefore, the solution curves that start below $P = 1000$ have inflection points when $P \approx 500$. In fact we can prove that all solution curves that start below $P = 500$ have an inflection point when P is exactly 500 (see Exercise 9).

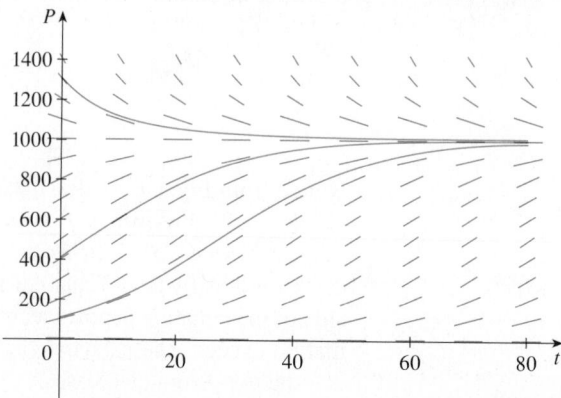

FIGURE 2

Solution curves for the logistic equation in Example 1

||| Euler's Method

Next let's use Euler's method to obtain numerical estimates for solutions of the logistic differential equation at specific times.

EXAMPLE 2 Use Euler's method with step sizes 20, 10, 5, 1, and 0.1 to estimate the population sizes $P(40)$ and $P(80)$, where P is the solution of the initial-value problem

$$\frac{dP}{dt} = 0.08P\left(1 - \frac{P}{1000}\right) \qquad P(0) = 100$$

SOLUTION With step size $h = 20$, $t_0 = 0$, $P_0 = 100$, and

$$F(t, P) = 0.08P\left(1 - \frac{P}{1000}\right)$$

we get, using the notation of Section 10.2,

$$P_1 = 100 + 20F(0, 100) = 244$$
$$P_2 = 244 + 20F(20, 244) \approx 539.14$$
$$P_3 = 539.14 + 20F(40, 539.14) \approx 936.69$$
$$P_4 = 936.69 + 20F(60, 936.69) \approx 1031.57$$

Thus, our estimates for the population sizes at times $t = 40$ and $t = 80$ are

$$P(40) \approx 539 \qquad P(80) \approx 1032$$

For smaller step sizes we need to program a calculator or computer. The table gives the results.

Step size	Euler estimate of $P(40)$	Euler estimate of $P(80)$
20	539	1032
10	647	997
5	695	991
1	725	986
0.1	731	985

Figure 3 shows a graph of the Euler approximations with step sizes $h = 10$ and $h = 1$. We see that the Euler approximation with $h = 1$ looks very much like the lower solution curve that we drew using a direction field in Figure 2.

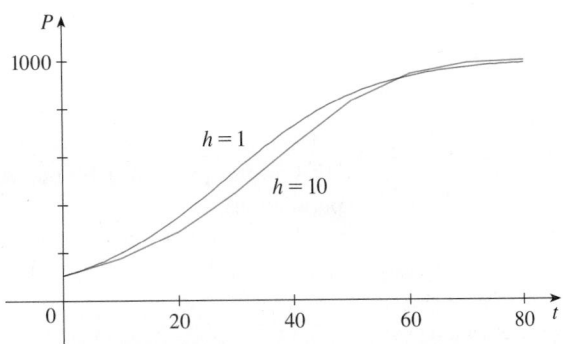

FIGURE 3
Euler approximations of the solution curve in Example 2

||| **The Analytic Solution**

The logistic equation (1) is separable and so we can solve it explicitly using the method of Section 10.3. Since

$$\frac{dP}{dt} = kP\left(1 - \frac{P}{K}\right)$$

we have

$$\boxed{2} \qquad \int \frac{dP}{P(1 - P/K)} = \int k \, dt$$

To evaluate the integral on the left side, we write

$$\frac{1}{P(1 - P/K)} = \frac{K}{P(K - P)}$$

Using partial fractions (see Section 8.4), we get

$$\frac{K}{P(K - P)} = \frac{1}{P} + \frac{1}{K - P}$$

This enables us to rewrite Equation 2:

$$\int \left(\frac{1}{P} + \frac{1}{K - P}\right) dP = \int k \, dt$$

$$\ln |P| - \ln |K - P| = kt + C$$

$$\ln \left|\frac{K - P}{P}\right| = -kt - C$$

$$\left|\frac{K - P}{P}\right| = e^{-kt-C} = e^{-C}e^{-kt}$$

$$\boxed{3} \qquad \frac{K - P}{P} = Ae^{-kt}$$

where $A = \pm e^{-C}$. Solving Equation 3 for P, we get

$$\frac{K}{P} - 1 = Ae^{-kt} \qquad \Rightarrow \qquad \frac{P}{K} = \frac{1}{1 + Ae^{-kt}}$$

so

$$P = \frac{K}{1 + Ae^{-kt}}$$

We find the value of A by putting $t = 0$ in Equation 3. If $t = 0$, then $P = P_0$ (the initial population), so

$$\frac{K - P_0}{P_0} = Ae^0 = A$$

Thus, the solution to the logistic equation is

$$\boxed{4} \qquad P(t) = \frac{K}{1 + Ae^{-kt}} \qquad \text{where } A = \frac{K - P_0}{P_0}$$

Using the expression for $P(t)$ in Equation 4, we see that

$$\lim_{t \to \infty} P(t) = K$$

which is to be expected.

EXAMPLE 3 Write the solution of the initial-value problem

$$\frac{dP}{dt} = 0.08P\left(1 - \frac{P}{1000}\right) \qquad P(0) = 100$$

find the population sizes $P(40)$ and $P(80)$. At what time does the population

differential equation is a logistic equation with $k = 0.08$, carrying capac-
and initial population $P_0 = 100$. So Equation 4 gives the population at
time t a

$$P(t) = \frac{1000}{1 + Ae^{-0.08t}} \qquad \text{where } A = \frac{1000 - 100}{100} = 9$$

Thus $$P(t) = \frac{1000}{1 + 9e^{-0.08t}}$$

So the population sizes when $t = 40$ and 80 are

$$P(40) = \frac{1000}{1 + 9e^{-3.2}} \approx 731.6 \qquad P(80) = \frac{1000}{1 + 9e^{-6.4}} \approx 985.3$$

||| Compare these values with the Euler
estimates from Example 2:
$$P(40) \approx 731 \qquad P(80) \approx 985$$

The population reaches 900 when

$$\frac{1000}{1 + 9e^{-0.08t}} = 900$$

Solving this equation for t, we get

$$1 + 9e^{-0.08t} = \tfrac{10}{9}$$

$$e^{-0.08t} = \tfrac{1}{81}$$

$$-0.08t = \ln \tfrac{1}{81} = -\ln 81$$

$$t = \frac{\ln 81}{0.08} \approx 54.9$$

||| Compare the solution curve in Figure 4 with
the lowest solution curve we drew from the
direction field in Figure 2.

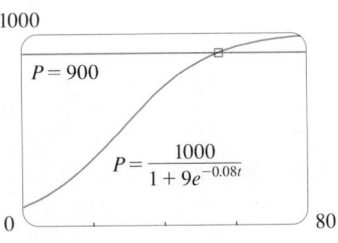

FIGURE 4

So the population reaches 900 when t is approximately 55. As a check on our work, we
graph the population curve in Figure 4 and observe where it intersects the line $P = 900$.
The cursor indicates that $t \approx 55$.

|||| **Comparison of the Natural Growth and Logistic Models**

In the 1930s the biologist G. F. Gause conducted an experiment with the protozoan *Paramecium* and used a logistic equation to model his data. The table gives his daily count of the population of protozoa. He estimated the initial relative growth rate to be 0.7944 and the carrying capacity to be 64.

t (days)	0	1	2	3	4	5	6	7	8	9	10	11	12	13	14	15	16
P (observed)	2	3	22	16	39	52	54	47	50	76	69	51	57	70	53	59	57

EXAMPLE 4 Find the exponential and logistic models for Gause's data. Compare the predicted values with the observed values and comment on the fit.

SOLUTION Given the relative growth rate $k = 0.7944$ and the initial population $P_0 = 2$, the exponential model is

$$P(t) = P_0 e^{kt} = 2e^{0.7944t}$$

Gause used the same value of k for his logistic model. [This is reasonable because $P_0 = 2$ is small compared with the carrying capacity ($K = 64$). The equation

$$\frac{1}{P_0}\frac{dP}{dt}\bigg|_{t=0} = k\left(1 - \frac{2}{64}\right) \approx k$$

shows that the value of k for the logistic model is very close to the value for the exponential model.]

Then the solution of the logistic equation in Equation 4 gives

$$P(t) = \frac{K}{1 + Ae^{-kt}} = \frac{64}{1 + Ae^{-0.7944t}}$$

where

$$A = \frac{K - P_0}{P_0} = \frac{64 - 2}{2} = 31$$

So

$$P(t) = \frac{64}{1 + 31e^{-0.7944t}}$$

We use these equations to calculate the predicted values (rounded to the nearest integer) and compare them in the table.

t (days)	0	1	2	3	4	5	6	7	8	9	10	11	12	13	14	15	16
P (observed)	2	3	22	16	39	52	54	47	50	76	69	51	57	70	53	59	57
P (logistic model)	2	4	9	17	28	40	51	57	61	62	63	64	64	64	64	64	64
P (exponential model)	2	4	10	22	48	106	...										

We notice from the table and from the graph in Figure 5 that for the first three or four days the exponential model gives results comparable to those of the more sophisticated logistic model. For $t \geqslant 5$, however, the exponential model is hopelessly inaccurate, but the logistic model fits the observations reasonably well.

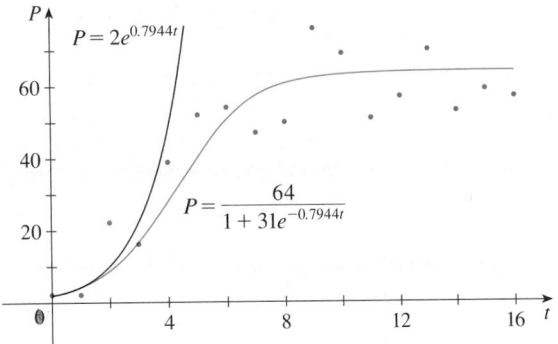

FIGURE 5

The exponential and logistic
models for the *Paramecium* data

||| **Other Models for Population Growth**

The Law of Natural Growth and the logistic differential equation are not the only equations that have been proposed to model population growth. In Exercise 14 we look at the Gompertz growth function and in Exercises 15 and 16 we investigate seasonal-growth models.

Two of the other models are modifications of the logistic model. The differential equation

$$\frac{dP}{dt} = kP\left(1 - \frac{P}{K}\right) - c$$

has been used to model populations that are subject to "harvesting" of one sort or another. (Think of a population of fish being caught at a constant rate). This equation is explored in Exercises 11 and 12.

For some species there is a minimum population level m below which the species tends to become extinct. (Adults may not be able to find suitable mates.) Such populations have been modeled by the differential equation

$$\frac{dP}{dt} = kP\left(1 - \frac{P}{K}\right)\left(1 - \frac{m}{P}\right)$$

where the extra factor, $1 - m/P$, takes into account the consequences of a sparse population (see Exercise 13).

||| **10.5 Exercises**

1. Suppose that a population develops according to the logistic equation

$$\frac{dP}{dt} = 0.05P - 0.0005P^2$$

where t is measured in weeks.
(a) What is the carrying capacity? What is the value of k?
(b) A direction field for this equation is shown at the right. Where are the slopes close to 0? Where are they largest? Which solutions are increasing? Which solutions are decreasing?
(c) Use the direction field to sketch solutions for initial populations of 20, 40, 60, 80, 120, and 140. What do these

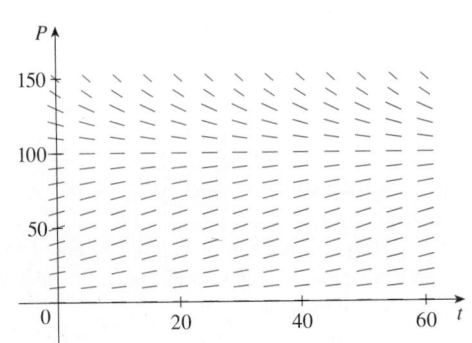

solutions have in common? How do they differ? Which solutions have inflection points? At what population levels do they occur?

(d) What are the equilibrium solutions? How are the other solutions related to these solutions?

2. Suppose that a population grows according to a logistic model with carrying capacity 6000 and $k = 0.0015$ per year.
  (a) Write the logistic differential equation for these data.
  (b) Draw a direction field (either by hand or with a computer algebra system). What does it tell you about the solution curves?
  (c) Use the direction field to sketch the solution curves for initial populations of 1000, 2000, 4000, and 8000. What can you say about the concavity of these curves? What is the significance of the inflection points?
  (d) Program a calculator or computer to use Euler's method with step size $h = 1$ to estimate the population after 50 years if the initial population is 1000.
  (e) If the initial population is 1000, write a formula for the population after t years. Use it to find the population after 50 years and compare with your estimate in part (d).
  (f) Graph the solution in part (e) and compare with the solution curve you sketched in part (c).

3. The Pacific halibut fishery has been modeled by the differential equation

$$\frac{dy}{dt} = ky\left(1 - \frac{y}{K}\right)$$

where $y(t)$ is the biomass (the total mass of the members of the population) in kilograms at time t (measured in years), the carrying capacity is estimated to be $K = 8 \times 10^7$ kg, and $k = 0.71$ per year.
  (a) If $y(0) = 2 \times 10^7$ kg, find the biomass a year later.
  (b) How long will it take for the biomass to reach 4×10^7 kg?

4. The table gives the number of yeast cells in a new laboratory culture.

Time (hours)	Yeast cells	Time (hours)	Yeast cells
0	18	10	509
2	39	12	597
4	80	14	640
6	171	16	664
8	336	18	672

  (a) Plot the data and use the plot to estimate the carrying capacity for the yeast population.
  (b) Use the data to estimate the initial relative growth rate.
  (c) Find both an exponential model and a logistic model for these data.
  (d) Compare the predicted values with the observed values, both in a table and with graphs. Comment on how well your models fit the data.
  (e) Use your logistic model to estimate the number of yeast cells after 7 hours.

5. The population of the world was about 5.3 billion in 1990. Birth rates in the 1990s ranged from 35 to 40 million per year and death rates ranged from 15 to 20 million per year. Let's assume that the carrying capacity for world population is 100 billion.
  (a) Write the logistic differential equation for these data. (Because the initial population is small compared to the carrying capacity, you can take k to be an estimate of the initial relative growth rate.)
  (b) Use the logistic model to estimate the world population in the year 2000 and compare with the actual population of 6.1 billion.
  (c) Use the logistic model to predict the world population in the years 2100 and 2500.
  (d) What are your predictions if the carrying capacity is 50 billion?

6. (a) Make a guess as to the carrying capacity for the U.S. population. Use it and the fact that the population was 250 million in 1990 to formulate a logistic model for the U.S. population.
  (b) Determine the value of k in your model by using the fact that the population in 2000 was 275 million.
  (c) Use your model to predict the U.S. population in the years 2100 and 2200.
  (d) Use your model to predict the year in which the U.S. population will exceed 300 million.

7. One model for the spread of a rumor is that the rate of spread is proportional to the product of the fraction y of the population who have heard the rumor and the fraction who have not heard the rumor.
  (a) Write a differential equation that is satisfied by y.
  (b) Solve the differential equation.
  (c) A small town has 1000 inhabitants. At 8 A.M., 80 people have heard a rumor. By noon half the town has heard it. At what time will 90% of the population have heard the rumor?

8. Biologists stocked a lake with 400 fish and estimated the carrying capacity (the maximal population for the fish of that species in that lake) to be 10,000. The number of fish tripled in the first year.
  (a) Assuming that the size of the fish population satisfies the logistic equation, find an expression for the size of the population after t years.
  (b) How long will it take for the population to increase to 5000?

9. (a) Show that if P satisfies the logistic equation (1), then

$$\frac{d^2P}{dt^2} = k^2P\left(1 - \frac{P}{K}\right)\left(1 - \frac{2P}{K}\right)$$

  (b) Deduce that a population grows fastest when it reaches half its carrying capacity.

10. For a fixed value of K (say $K = 10$), the family of logistic functions given by Equation 4 depends on the initial value P_0 and the proportionality constant k. Graph several members of this family. How does the graph change when P_0 varies? How does it change when k varies?

11. Let's modify the logistic differential equation of Example 1 as follows:

$$\frac{dP}{dt} = 0.08P\left(1 - \frac{P}{1000}\right) - 15$$

(a) Suppose $P(t)$ represents a fish population at time t, where t is measured in weeks. Explain the meaning of the term -15.
(b) Draw a direction field for this differential equation.
(c) What are the equilibrium solutions?
(d) Use the direction field to sketch several solution curves. Describe what happens to the fish population for various initial populations.
(e) Solve this differential equation explicitly, either by using partial fractions or with a computer algebra system. Use the initial populations 200 and 300. Graph the solutions and compare with your sketches in part (d). [CAS]

[CAS] **12.** Consider the differential equation

$$\frac{dP}{dt} = 0.08P\left(1 - \frac{P}{1000}\right) - c$$

as a model for a fish population, where t is measured in weeks and c is a constant.
(a) Use a CAS to draw direction fields for various values of c.
(b) From your direction fields in part (a), determine the values of c for which there is at least one equilibrium solution. For what values of c does the fish population always die out?
(c) Use the differential equation to prove what you discovered graphically in part (b).
(d) What would you recommend for a limit to the weekly catch of this fish population?

13. There is considerable evidence to support the theory that for some species there is a minimum population m such that the species will become extinct if the size of the population falls below m. This condition can be incorporated into the logistic equation by introducing the factor $(1 - m/P)$. Thus, the modified logistic model is given by the differential equation

$$\frac{dP}{dt} = kP\left(1 - \frac{P}{K}\right)\left(1 - \frac{m}{P}\right)$$

(a) Use the differential equation to show that any solution is increasing if $m < P < K$ and decreasing if $0 < P < m$.
(b) For the case where $k = 0.08$, $K = 1000$, and $m = 200$, draw a direction field and use it to sketch several solution curves. Describe what happens to the population for various initial populations. What are the equilibrium solutions?
(c) Solve the differential equation explicitly, either by using partial fractions or with a computer algebra system. Use the initial population P_0.

(d) Use the solution in part (c) to show that if $P_0 < m$, then the species will become extinct. [*Hint:* Show that the numerator in your expression for $P(t)$ is 0 for some value of t.]

14. Another model for a growth function for a limited population is given by the **Gompertz function**, which is a solution of the differential equation

$$\frac{dP}{dt} = c \ln\left(\frac{K}{P}\right)P$$

where c is a constant and K is the carrying capacity.
(a) Solve this differential equation.
(b) Compute $\lim_{t\to\infty} P(t)$.
(c) Graph the Gompertz growth function for $K = 1000$, $P_0 = 100$, and $c = 0.05$, and compare it with the logistic function in Example 3. What are the similarities? What are the differences?
(d) We know from Exercise 9 that the logistic function grows fastest when $P = K/2$. Use the Gompertz differential equation to show that the Gompertz function grows fastest when $P = K/e$.

15. In a **seasonal-growth model**, a periodic function of time is introduced to account for seasonal variations in the rate of growth. Such variations could, for example, be caused by seasonal changes in the availability of food.
(a) Find the solution of the seasonal-growth model

$$\frac{dP}{dt} = kP \cos(rt - \phi) \qquad P(0) = P_0$$

where k, r, and ϕ are positive constants.
(b) By graphing the solution for several values of k, r, and ϕ, explain how the values of k, r, and ϕ affect the solution. What can you say about $\lim_{t\to\infty} P(t)$?

16. Suppose we alter the differential equation in Exercise 15 as follows:

$$\frac{dP}{dt} = kP \cos^2(rt - \phi) \qquad P(0) = P_0$$

(a) Solve this differential equation with the help of a table of integrals or a CAS.
(b) Graph the solution for several values of k, r, and ϕ. How do the values of k, r, and ϕ affect the solution? What can you say about $\lim_{t\to\infty} P(t)$ in this case?

17. Graphs of logistic functions (Figures 2 and 4) look suspiciously similar to the graph of the hyperbolic tangent function (Figure 3 in Section 7.6). Explain the similarity by showing that the logistic function given by Equation 4 can be written as

$$P(t) = \tfrac{1}{2}K\left[1 + \tanh\left(\tfrac{1}{2}k(t - c)\right)\right]$$

where $c = (\ln A)/k$. Thus, the logistic function is really just a shifted hyperbolic tangent.

10.6 Linear Equations

A first-order **linear** differential equation is one that can be put into the form

$$\boxed{1} \qquad \frac{dy}{dx} + P(x)y = Q(x)$$

where P and Q are continuous functions on a given interval. This type of equation occurs frequently in various sciences, as we will see.

An example of a linear equation is $xy' + y = 2x$ because, for $x \neq 0$, it can be written in the form

$$\boxed{2} \qquad y' + \frac{1}{x}y = 2$$

Notice that this differential equation is not separable because it's impossible to factor the expression for y' as a function of x times a function of y. But we can still solve the equation by noticing, by the Product Rule, that

$$xy' + y = (xy)'$$

and so we can rewrite the equation as

$$(xy)' = 2x$$

If we now integrate both sides of this equation, we get

$$xy = x^2 + C \qquad \text{or} \qquad y = x + \frac{C}{x}$$

If we had been given the differential equation in the form of Equation 2, we would have had to take the preliminary step of multiplying each side of the equation by x.

It turns out that every first-order linear differential equation can be solved in a similar fashion by multiplying both sides of Equation 1 by a suitable function $I(x)$ called an *integrating factor.* We try to find I so that the left side of Equation 1, when multiplied by $I(x)$, becomes the derivative of the product $I(x)y$:

$$\boxed{3} \qquad I(x)(y' + P(x)y) = (I(x)y)'$$

If we can find such a function I, then Equation 1 becomes

$$(I(x)y)' = I(x)Q(x)$$

Integrating both sides, we would have

$$I(x)y = \int I(x)Q(x)\,dx + C$$

so the solution would be

$$\boxed{4} \qquad y(x) = \frac{1}{I(x)}\left[\int I(x)Q(x)\,dx + C\right]$$

To find such an I, we expand Equation 3 and cancel terms:

$$I(x)y' + I(x)P(x)y = (I(x)y)' = I'(x)y + I(x)y'$$

$$I(x)P(x) = I'(x)$$

This is a separable differential equation for I, which we solve as follows:

$$\int \frac{dI}{I} = \int P(x)\,dx$$

$$\ln|I| = \int P(x)\,dx$$

$$I = Ae^{\int P(x)\,dx}$$

where $A = \pm e^{C}$. We are looking for a particular integrating factor, not the most general one, so we take $A = 1$ and use

$$\boxed{5} \qquad\qquad I(x) = e^{\int P(x)\,dx}$$

Thus, a formula for the general solution to Equation 1 is provided by Equation 4, where I is given by Equation 5. Instead of memorizing this formula, however, we just remember the form of the integrating factor.

> To solve the linear differential equation $y' + P(x)y = Q(x)$, multiply both sides by the **integrating factor** $I(x) = e^{\int P(x)\,dx}$ and integrate both sides.

EXAMPLE 1 Solve the differential equation $\dfrac{dy}{dx} + 3x^2 y = 6x^2$.

SOLUTION The given equation is linear since it has the form of Equation 1 with $P(x) = 3x^2$ and $Q(x) = 6x^2$. An integrating factor is

$$I(x) = e^{\int 3x^2\,dx} = e^{x^3}$$

Multiplying both sides of the differential equation by e^{x^3}, we get

$$e^{x^3}\frac{dy}{dx} + 3x^2 e^{x^3} y = 6x^2 e^{x^3}$$

or

$$\frac{d}{dx}\left(e^{x^3}y\right) = 6x^2 e^{x^3}$$

Integrating both sides, we have

$$e^{x^3}y = \int 6x^2 e^{x^3}\,dx = 2e^{x^3} + C$$

$$y = 2 + Ce^{-x^3}$$

‖‖‖‖ Figure 1 shows the graphs of several members of the family of solutions in Example 1. Notice that they all approach 2 as $x \to \infty$.

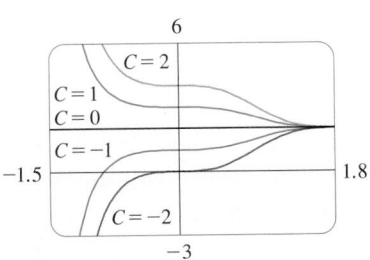

FIGURE 1

EXAMPLE 2 Find the solution of the initial-value problem

$$x^2 y' + xy = 1 \qquad x > 0 \qquad y(1) = 2$$

SOLUTION We must first divide both sides by the coefficient of y' to put the differential equation into standard form:

$$\boxed{6} \qquad y' + \frac{1}{x}y = \frac{1}{x^2} \qquad x > 0$$

The integrating factor is

$$I(x) = e^{\int (1/x)\,dx} = e^{\ln x} = x$$

Multiplication of Equation 6 by x gives

$$xy' + y = \frac{1}{x} \qquad \text{or} \qquad (xy)' = \frac{1}{x}$$

Then

$$xy = \int \frac{1}{x}\,dx = \ln x + C$$

and so

$$y = \frac{\ln x + C}{x}$$

Since $y(1) = 2$, we have

$$2 = \frac{\ln 1 + C}{1} = C$$

Therefore, the solution to the initial-value problem is

$$y = \frac{\ln x + 2}{x}$$

|||| The solution of the initial-value problem in Example 2 is shown in Figure 2.

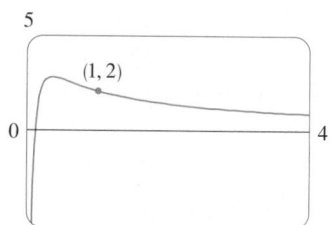

FIGURE 2

EXAMPLE 3 Solve $y' + 2xy = 1$.

SOLUTION The given equation is in the standard form for a linear equation. Multiplying by the integrating factor

$$e^{\int 2x\,dx} = e^{x^2}$$

we get

$$e^{x^2}y' + 2xe^{x^2}y = e^{x^2}$$

or

$$(e^{x^2}y)' = e^{x^2}$$

Therefore

$$e^{x^2}y = \int e^{x^2}\,dx + C$$

|||| Even though the solutions of the differential equation in Example 3 are expressed in terms of an integral, they can still be graphed by a computer algebra system (Figure 3).

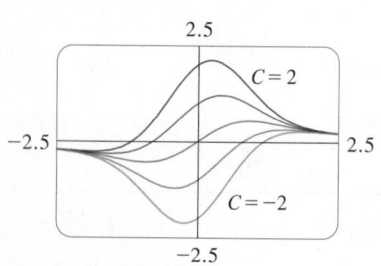

FIGURE 3

Recall from Section 8.5 that $\int e^{x^2}\,dx$ can't be expressed in terms of elementary functions. Nonetheless, it's a perfectly good function and we can leave the answer as

$$y = e^{-x^2}\int e^{x^2}\,dx + Ce^{-x^2}$$

Another way of writing the solution is

$$y = e^{-x^2} \int_0^x e^{t^2} \, dt + Ce^{-x^2}$$

(Any number can be chosen for the lower limit of integration.)

‖‖ Application to Electric Circuits

In Section 10.2 we considered the simple electric circuit shown in Figure 4: An electromotive force (usually a battery or generator) produces a voltage of $E(t)$ volts (V) and a current of $I(t)$ amperes (A) at time t. The circuit also contains a resistor with a resistance of R ohms (Ω) and an inductor with an inductance of L henries (H).

Ohm's Law gives the drop in voltage due to the resistor as RI. The voltage drop due to the inductor is $L(dI/dt)$. One of Kirchhoff's laws says that the sum of the voltage drops is equal to the supplied voltage $E(t)$. Thus, we have

FIGURE 4

$$\boxed{7} \qquad L\frac{dI}{dt} + RI = E(t)$$

which is a first-order linear differential equation. The solution gives the current I at time t.

EXAMPLE 4 Suppose that in the simple circuit of Figure 4 the resistance is 12 Ω and the inductance is 4 H. If a battery gives a constant voltage of 60 V and the switch is closed when $t = 0$ so the current starts with $I(0) = 0$, find (a) $I(t)$, (b) the current after 1 s, and (c) the limiting value of the current.

SOLUTION

(a) If we put $L = 4$, $R = 12$, and $E(t) = 60$ in Equation 7, we obtain the initial-value problem

‖‖ The differential equation in Example 4 is both linear and separable, so an alternative method is to solve it as a separable equation (Example 4 in Section 10.3). If we replace the battery by a generator, however, we get an equation that is linear but not separable (Example 5).

$$4\frac{dI}{dt} + 12I = 60 \qquad I(0) = 0$$

or

$$\frac{dI}{dt} + 3I = 15 \qquad I(0) = 0$$

Multiplying by the integrating factor $e^{\int 3 \, dt} = e^{3t}$, we get

$$e^{3t}\frac{dI}{dt} + 3e^{3t}I = 15e^{3t}$$

$$\frac{d}{dt}(e^{3t}I) = 15e^{3t}$$

$$e^{3t}I = \int 15e^{3t} \, dt = 5e^{3t} + C$$

$$I(t) = 5 + Ce^{-3t}$$

Since $I(0) = 0$, we have $5 + C = 0$, so $C = -5$ and

$$I(t) = 5(1 - e^{-3t})$$

▥ Figure 5 shows how the current in Example 4 approaches its limiting value.

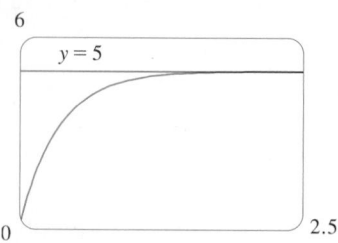

FIGURE 5

(b) After 1 second the current is

$$I(1) = 5(1 - e^{-3}) \approx 4.75 \text{ A}$$

(c)

$$\lim_{t \to \infty} I(t) = \lim_{t \to \infty} 5(1 - e^{-3t})$$

$$= 5 - 5 \lim_{t \to \infty} e^{-3t}$$

$$= 5 - 0 = 5$$

EXAMPLE 5 Suppose that the resistance and inductance remain as in Example 4 but, instead of the battery, we use a generator that produces a variable voltage of $E(t) = 60 \sin 30t$ volts. Find $I(t)$.

SOLUTION This time the differential equation becomes

$$4 \frac{dI}{dt} + 12I = 60 \sin 30t \quad \text{or} \quad \frac{dI}{dt} + 3I = 15 \sin 30t$$

The same integrating factor e^{3t} gives

$$\frac{d}{dt} (e^{3t}I) = e^{3t} \frac{dI}{dt} + 3e^{3t}I = 15e^{3t} \sin 30t$$

▥ Figure 6 shows the graph of the current when the battery is replaced by a generator.

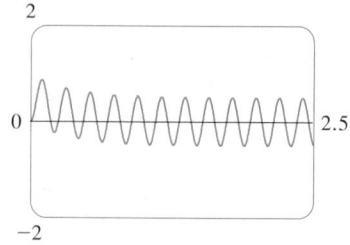

FIGURE 6

Using Formula 98 in the Table of Integrals, we have

$$e^{3t}I = \int 15e^{3t} \sin 30t \, dt = 15 \frac{e^{3t}}{909} (3 \sin 30t - 30 \cos 30t) + C$$

$$I = \tfrac{5}{101} (\sin 30t - 10 \cos 30t) + Ce^{-3t}$$

Since $I(0) = 0$, we get

$$-\tfrac{50}{101} + C = 0$$

so

$$I(t) = \tfrac{5}{101}(\sin 30t - 10 \cos 30t) + \tfrac{50}{101}e^{-3t}$$

▥▥ 10.6 Exercises

1–4 ▥ Determine whether the differential equation is linear.

1. $y' + e^x y = x^2 y^2$

2. $y + \sin x = x^3 y'$

3. $xy' + \ln x - x^2 y = 0$

4. $y' + \cos y = \tan x$

◻ ◻ ◻ ◻ ◻ ◻ ◻ ◻ ◻ ◻ ◻ ◻

5–14 ▥ Solve the differential equation.

5. $y' + 2y = 2e^x$

6. $y' = x + 5y$

7. $xy' - 2y = x^2$

8. $x^2 y' + 2xy = \cos^2 x$

9. $xy' + y = \sqrt{x}$

10. $1 + xy = xy'$

11. $\dfrac{dy}{dx} + 2xy = x^2$

12. $\dfrac{dy}{dx} = x \sin 2x + y \tan x, \quad -\pi/2 < x < \pi/2$

13. $(1 + t) \dfrac{du}{dt} + u = 1 + t, \quad t > 0$

14. $t \ln t \dfrac{dr}{dt} + r = te^t$

◻ ◻ ◻ ◻ ◻ ◻ ◻ ◻ ◻ ◻ ◻

15–20 ▥ Solve the initial-value problem.

15. $y' = x + y, \quad y(0) = 2$

16. $t \dfrac{dy}{dt} + 2y = t^3, \quad t > 0, \quad y(1) = 0$

17. $\dfrac{dv}{dt} - 2tv = 3t^2 e^{t^2}, \quad v(0) = 5$

18. $2xy' + y = 6x$, $x > 0$, $y(4) = 20$

19. $xy' = y + x^2 \sin x$, $y(\pi) = 0$

20. $x \dfrac{dy}{dx} - \dfrac{y}{x + 1} = x$, $y(1) = 0$, $x > 0$

21–22 ⦀ Solve the differential equation and use a graphing calculator or computer to graph several members of the family of solutions. How does the solution curve change as C varies?

21. $xy' + y = x \cos x$, $x > 0$

22. $y' + (\cos x)y = \cos x$

23. A **Bernoulli differential equation** (named after James Bernoulli) is of the form

$$\frac{dy}{dx} + P(x)y = Q(x)y^n$$

Observe that, if $n = 0$ or 1, the Bernoulli equation is linear. For other values of n, show that the substitution $u = y^{1-n}$ transforms the Bernoulli equation into the linear equation

$$\frac{du}{dx} + (1 - n)P(x)u = (1 - n)Q(x)$$

24–26 ⦀ Use the method of Exercise 23 to solve the differential equation.

24. $xy' + y = -xy^2$

25. $y' + \dfrac{2}{x}y = \dfrac{y^3}{x^2}$

26. $y' + y = xy^3$

27. In the circuit shown in Figure 4, a battery supplies a constant voltage of 40 V, the inductance is 2 H, the resistance is 10 Ω, and $I(0) = 0$.
(a) Find $I(t)$.
(b) Find the current after 0.1 s.

28. In the circuit shown in Figure 4, a generator supplies a voltage of $E(t) = 40 \sin 60t$ volts, the inductance is 1 H, the resistance is 20 Ω, and $I(0) = 1$ A.
(a) Find $I(t)$.
(b) Find the current after 0.1 s.
(c) Use a graphing device to draw the graph of the current function.

29. The figure shows a circuit containing an electromotive force, a capacitor with a capacitance of C farads (F), and a resistor with a resistance of R ohms (Ω). The voltage drop across the

capacitor is Q/C, where Q is the charge (in coulombs), so in this case Kirchhoff's Law gives

$$RI + \frac{Q}{C} = E(t)$$

But $I = dQ/dt$ (see Example 3 in Section 3.4), so we have

$$R\frac{dQ}{dt} + \frac{1}{C}Q = E(t)$$

Suppose the resistance is 5 Ω, the capacitance is 0.05 F, a battery gives a constant voltage of 60 V, and the initial charge is $Q(0) = 0$ C. Find the charge and the current at time t.

30. In the circuit of Exercise 29, $R = 2\ \Omega$, $C = 0.01$ F, $Q(0) = 0$, and $E(t) = 10 \sin 60t$. Find the charge and the current at time t.

31. Let $P(t)$ be the performance level of someone learning a skill as a function of the training time t. The graph of P is called a *learning curve*. In Exercise 13 in Section 10.1 we proposed the differential equation

$$\frac{dP}{dt} = k[M - P(t)]$$

as a reasonable model for learning, where k is a positive constant. Solve it as a linear differential equation and use your solution to graph the learning curve.

32. Two new workers were hired for an assembly line. Jim processed 25 units during the first hour and 45 units during the second hour. Mark processed 35 units during the first hour and 50 units the second hour. Using the model of Exercise 31 and assuming that $P(0) = 0$, estimate the maximum number of units per hour that each worker is capable of processing.

33. In Section 10.3 we looked at mixing problems in which the volume of fluid remained constant and saw that such problems give rise to separable equations. (See Example 6 in that section.) If the rates of flow into and out of the system are different, then the volume is not constant and the resulting differential equation is linear but not separable.

A tank contains 100 L of water. A solution with a salt concentration of 0.4 kg/L is added at a rate of 5 L/min. The solution is kept mixed and is drained from the tank at a rate of 3 L/min. If $y(t)$ is the amount of salt (in kilograms) after t minutes, show that y satisfies the differential equation

$$\frac{dy}{dt} = 2 - \frac{3y}{100 + 2t}$$

Solve this equation and find the concentration after 20 minutes.

34. A tank with a capacity of 400 L is full of a mixture of water and chlorine with a concentration of 0.05 g of chlorine per liter. In order to reduce the concentration of chlorine, fresh water is pumped into the tank at a rate of 4 L/s. The mixture is kept stirred and is pumped out at a rate of 10 L/s. Find the amount of chlorine in the tank as a function of time.

35. An object with mass m is dropped from rest and we assume that the air resistance is proportional to the speed of the object. If $s(t)$ is the distance dropped after t seconds, then the speed is $v = s'(t)$ and the acceleration is $a = v'(t)$. If g is the acceleration due to gravity, then the downward force on the object is $mg - cv$, where c is a positive constant, and Newton's Second Law gives

$$m\frac{dv}{dt} = mg - cv$$

(a) Solve this as a linear equation to show that

$$v = \frac{mg}{c}\left(1 - e^{-ct/m}\right)$$

(b) What is the limiting velocity?
(c) Find the distance the object has fallen after t seconds.

36. If we ignore air resistance, we can conclude that heavier objects fall no faster than lighter objects. But if we take air resistance into account, our conclusion changes. Use the expression for the velocity of a falling object in Exercise 35(a) to find dv/dm and show that heavier objects *do* fall faster than lighter ones.

10.7 Predator-Prey Systems

We have looked at a variety of models for the growth of a single species that lives alone in an environment. In this section we consider more realistic models that take into account the interaction of two species in the same habitat. We will see that these models take the form of a pair of linked differential equations.

We first consider the situation in which one species, called the *prey,* has an ample food supply and the second species, called the *predators,* feeds on the prey. Examples of prey and predators include rabbits and wolves in an isolated forest, food fish and sharks, aphids and ladybugs, and bacteria and amoebas. Our model will have two dependent variables and both are functions of time. We let $R(t)$ be the number of prey (using R for rabbits) and $W(t)$ be the number of predators (with W for wolves) at time t.

In the absence of predators, the ample food supply would support exponential growth of the prey, that is,

$$\frac{dR}{dt} = kR \qquad \text{where } k \text{ is a positive constant}$$

In the absence of prey, we assume that the predator population would decline at a rate proportional to itself, that is,

$$\frac{dW}{dt} = -rW \qquad \text{where } r \text{ is a positive constant}$$

With both species present, however, we assume that the principal cause of death among the prey is being eaten by a predator, and the birth and survival rates of the predators depend on their available food supply, namely, the prey. We also assume that the two species encounter each other at a rate that is proportional to both populations and is therefore proportional to the product RW. (The more there are of either population, the more encounters there are likely to be.) A system of two differential equations that incorporates these assumptions is as follows:

W represents the predator.

R represents the prey.

$$\boxed{1} \qquad \frac{dR}{dt} = kR - aRW \qquad\qquad \frac{dW}{dt} = -rW + bRW$$

where k, r, a, and b are positive constants. Notice that the term $-aRW$ decreases the natural growth rate of the prey and the term bRW increases the natural growth rate of the predators.

IIII The Lotka-Volterra equations were proposed as a model to explain the variations in the shark and food-fish populations in the Adriatic Sea by the Italian mathematician Vito Volterra (1860–1940).

The equations in (1) are known as the **predator-prey equations**, or the **Lotka-Volterra equations**. A **solution** of this system of equations is a pair of functions $R(t)$ and $W(t)$ that describe the populations of prey and predator as functions of time. Because the system is coupled (R and W occur in both equations), we can't solve one equation and then the other; we have to solve them simultaneously. Unfortunately, it is usually impossible to find explicit formulas for R and W as functions of t. We can, however, use graphical methods to analyze the equations.

EXAMPLE 1 Suppose that populations of rabbits and wolves are described by the Lotka-Volterra equations (1) with $k = 0.08$, $a = 0.001$, $r = 0.02$, and $b = 0.00002$. The time t is measured in months.
(a) Find the constant solutions (called the **equilibrium solutions**) and interpret the answer.
(b) Use the system of differential equations to find an expression for dW/dR.
(c) Draw a direction field for the resulting differential equation in the RW-plane. Then use that direction field to sketch some solution curves.
(d) Suppose that, at some point in time, there are 1000 rabbits and 40 wolves. Draw the corresponding solution curve and use it to describe the changes in both population levels.
(e) Use part (d) to make sketches of R and W as functions of t.

SOLUTION
(a) With the given values of k, a, r, and b, the Lotka-Volterra equations become

$$\frac{dR}{dt} = 0.08R - 0.001RW$$

$$\frac{dW}{dt} = -0.02W + 0.00002RW$$

Both R and W will be constant if both derivatives are 0, that is,

$$R' = R(0.08 - 0.001W) = 0$$

$$W' = W(-0.02 + 0.00002R) = 0$$

One solution is given by $R = 0$ and $W = 0$. (This makes sense: If there are no rabbits or wolves, the populations are certainly not going to increase.) The other constant solution is

$$W = \frac{0.08}{0.001} = 80 \qquad R = \frac{0.02}{0.00002} = 1000$$

So the equilibrium populations consist of 80 wolves and 1000 rabbits. This means that 1000 rabbits are just enough to support a constant wolf population of 80. There are neither too many wolves (which would result in fewer rabbits) nor too few wolves (which would result in more rabbits).

(b) We use the Chain Rule to eliminate t:

$$\frac{dW}{dt} = \frac{dW}{dR}\frac{dR}{dt}$$

so

$$\frac{dW}{dR} = \frac{\dfrac{dW}{dt}}{\dfrac{dR}{dt}} = \frac{-0.02W + 0.00002RW}{0.08R - 0.001RW}$$

(c) If we think of W as a function of R, we have the differential equation

$$\frac{dW}{dR} = \frac{-0.02W + 0.00002RW}{0.08R - 0.001RW}$$

We draw the direction field for this differential equation in Figure 1 and we use it to sketch several solution curves in Figure 2. If we move along a solution curve, we observe how the relationship between R and W changes as time passes. Notice that the curves appear to be closed in the sense that if we travel along a curve, we always return to the same point. Notice also that the point $(1000, 80)$ is inside all the solution curves. That point is called an *equilibrium point* because it corresponds to the equilibrium solution $R = 1000$, $W = 80$.

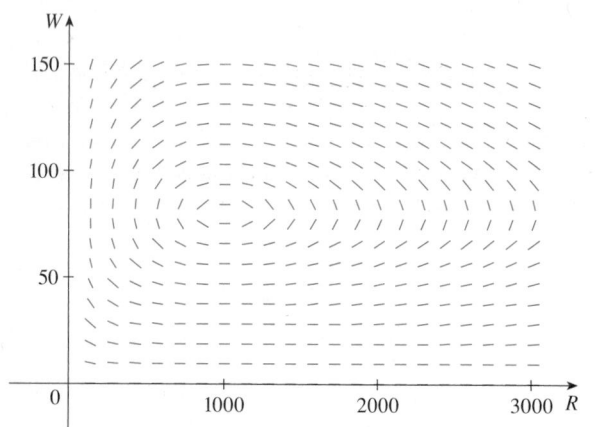

FIGURE 1 Direction field for the predator-prey system

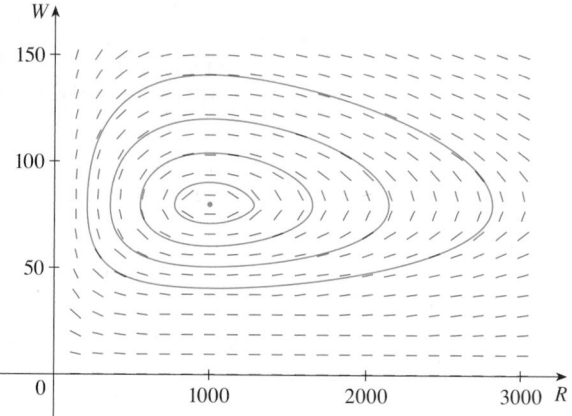

FIGURE 2 Phase portrait of the system

When we represent solutions of a system of differential equations as in Figure 2, we refer to the RW-plane as the **phase plane**, and we call the solution curves **phase trajectories**. So a phase trajectory is a path traced out by solutions (R, W) as time goes by. A **phase portrait** consists of equilibrium points and typical phase trajectories, as shown in Figure 2.

(d) Starting with 1000 rabbits and 40 wolves corresponds to drawing the solution curve through the point $P_0(1000, 40)$. Figure 3 shows this phase trajectory with the direction field removed. Starting at the point P_0 at time $t = 0$ and letting t increase, do we move clockwise or counterclockwise around the phase trajectory? If we put $R = 1000$ and

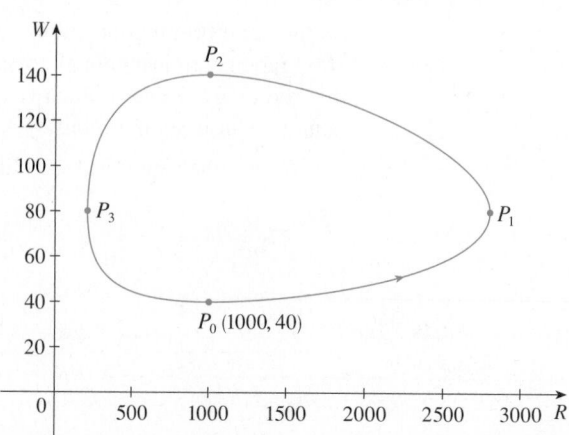

FIGURE 3
Phase trajectory through $(1000, 40)$

$W = 40$ in the first differential equation, we get

$$\frac{dR}{dt} = 0.08(1000) - 0.001(1000)(40) = 80 - 40 = 40$$

Since $dR/dt > 0$, we conclude that R is increasing at P_0 and so we move counter-clockwise around the phase trajectory.

We see that at P_0 there aren't enough wolves to maintain a balance between the populations, so the rabbit population increases. That results in more wolves and eventually there are so many wolves that the rabbits have a hard time avoiding them. So the number of rabbits begins to decline (at P_1, where we estimate that R reaches its maximum population of about 2800). This means that at some later time the wolf population starts to fall (at P_2, where $R = 1000$ and $W \approx 140$). But this benefits the rabbits, so their population later starts to increase (at P_3, where $W = 80$ and $R \approx 210$). As a consequence, the wolf population eventually starts to increase as well. This happens when the populations return to their initial values of $R = 1000$ and $W = 40$, and the entire cycle begins again.

(e) From the description in part (d) of how the rabbit and wolf populations rise and fall, we can sketch the graphs of $R(t)$ and $W(t)$. Suppose the points P_1, P_2, and P_3 in Figure 3 are reached at times t_1, t_2, and t_3. Then we can sketch graphs of R and W as in Figure 4.

 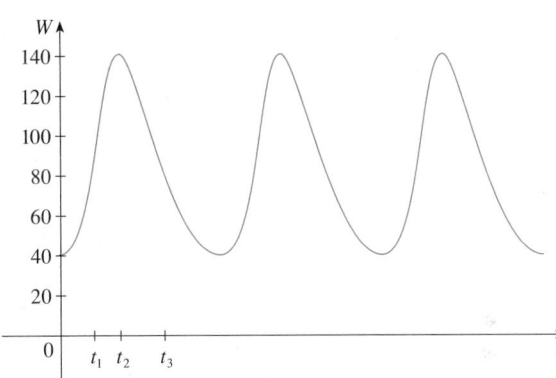

FIGURE 4

Graphs of the rabbit and wolf populations as functions of time

To make the graphs easier to compare, we draw the graphs on the same axes but with different scales for R and W, as in Figure 5. Notice that the rabbits reach their maximum populations about a quarter of a cycle before the wolves.

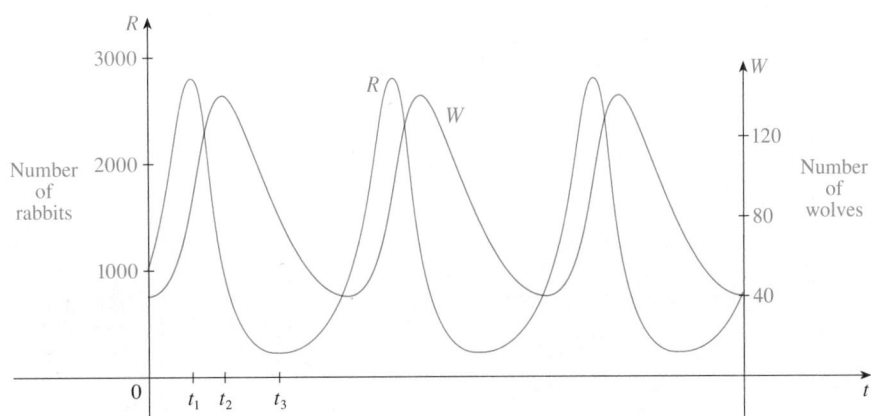

FIGURE 5

Comparison of the rabbit and wolf populations

An important part of the modeling process, as we discussed in Section 1.2, is to interpret our mathematical conclusions as real-world predictions and to test the predictions against real data. The Hudson's Bay Company, which started trading in animal furs in Canada in 1670, has kept records that date back to the 1840s. Figure 6 shows graphs of the number of pelts of the snowshoe hare and its predator, the Canada lynx, traded by the company over a 90-year period. You can see that the coupled oscillations in the hare and lynx populations predicted by the Lotka-Volterra model do actually occur and the period of these cycles is roughly 10 years.

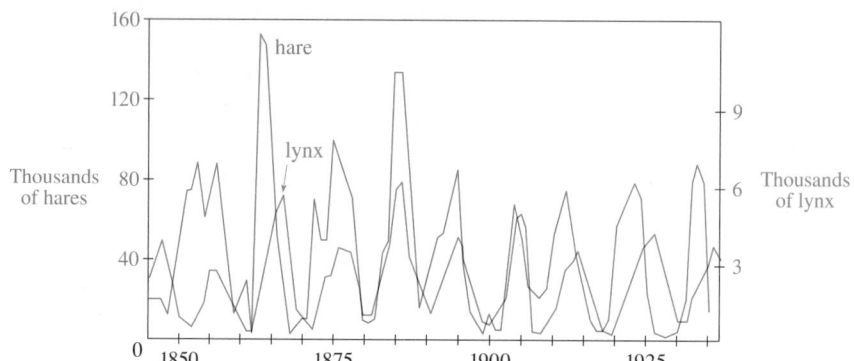

FIGURE 6

Relative abundance of hare and lynx from Hudson's Bay Company records

Although the relatively simple Lotka-Volterra model has had some success in explaining and predicting coupled populations, more sophisticated models have also been proposed. One way to modify the Lotka-Volterra equations is to assume that, in the absence of predators, the prey grow according to a logistic model with carrying capacity K. Then the Lotka-Volterra equations (1) are replaced by the system of differential equations

$$\frac{dR}{dt} = kR\left(1 - \frac{R}{K}\right) - aRW \qquad \frac{dW}{dt} = -rW + bRW$$

This model is investigated in Exercises 9 and 10.

Models have also been proposed to describe and predict population levels of two species that compete for the same resources or cooperate for mutual benefit. Such models are explored in Exercise 2.

10.7 Exercises

1. For each predator-prey system, determine which of the variables, x or y, represents the prey population and which represents the predator population. Is the growth of the prey restricted just by the predators or by other factors as well? Do the predators feed only on the prey or do they have additional food sources? Explain.

(a) $\dfrac{dx}{dt} = -0.05x + 0.0001xy$

  $\dfrac{dy}{dt} = 0.1y - 0.005xy$

(b) $\dfrac{dx}{dt} = 0.2x - 0.0002x^2 - 0.006xy$

  $\dfrac{dy}{dt} = -0.015y + 0.00008xy$

2. Each system of differential equations is a model for two species that either compete for the same resources or cooperate for mutual benefit (flowering plants and insect pollinators, for instance). Decide whether each system describes competition or cooperation and explain why it is a reasonable model. (Ask yourself what effect an increase in one species has on the growth rate of the other.)

(a) $\dfrac{dx}{dt} = 0.12x - 0.0006x^2 + 0.00001xy$

  $\dfrac{dy}{dt} = 0.08x + 0.00004xy$

(b) $\dfrac{dx}{dt} = 0.15x - 0.0002x^2 - 0.0006xy$

  $\dfrac{dy}{dt} = 0.2y - 0.00008y^2 - 0.0002xy$

3–4 ▦ A phase trajectory is shown for populations of rabbits (R) and foxes (F).

(a) Describe how each population changes as time goes by.

(b) Use your description to make a rough sketch of the graphs of R and F as functions of time.

3.

4.

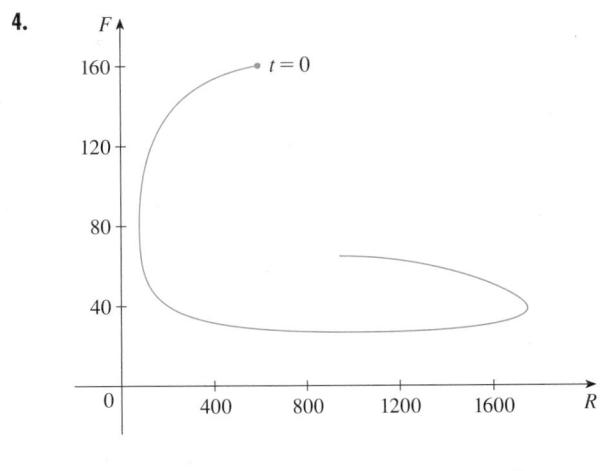

5–6 ▦ Graphs of populations of two species are shown. Use them to sketch the corresponding phase trajectory.

5.

6.

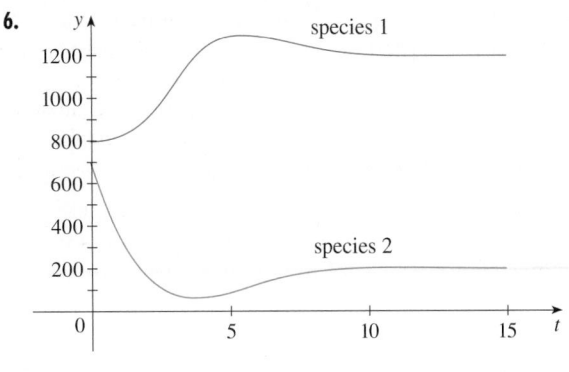

7. In Example 1(b) we showed that the rabbit and wolf populations satisfy the differential equation

$$\frac{dW}{dR} = \frac{-0.02W + 0.00002RW}{0.08R - 0.001RW}$$

By solving this separable differential equation, show that

$$\frac{R^{0.02}W^{0.08}}{e^{0.00002R}e^{0.001W}} = C$$

where C is a constant.

It is impossible to solve this equation for W as an explicit function of R (or vice versa). If you have a computer algebra system that graphs implicitly defined curves, use this equation and your CAS to draw the solution curve that passes through the point $(1000, 40)$ and compare with Figure 3.

8. Populations of aphids and ladybugs are modeled by the equations

$$\frac{dA}{dt} = 2A - 0.01AL$$

$$\frac{dL}{dt} = -0.5L + 0.0001AL$$

(a) Find the equilibrium solutions and explain their significance.

(b) Find an expression for dL/dA.

(c) The direction field for the differential equation in part (b) is shown. Use it to sketch a phase portrait. What do the phase trajectories have in common?

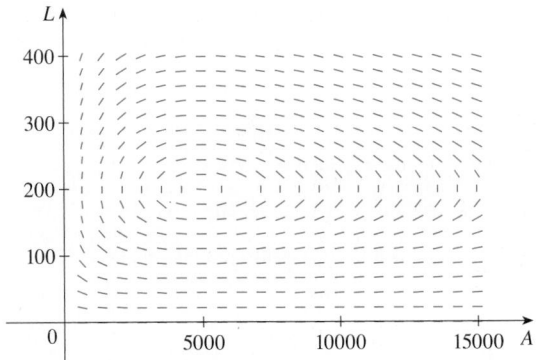

(d) Suppose that at time $t = 0$ there are 1000 aphids and 200 ladybugs. Draw the corresponding phase trajectory and use it to describe how both populations change.

(e) Use part (d) to make rough sketches of the aphid and ladybug populations as functions of t. How are the graphs related to each other?

9. In Example 1 we used Lotka-Volterra equations to model populations of rabbits and wolves. Let's modify those equations as follows:

$$\frac{dR}{dt} = 0.08R(1 - 0.0002R) - 0.001RW$$

$$\frac{dW}{dt} = -0.02W + 0.00002RW$$

(a) According to these equations, what happens to the rabbit population in the absence of wolves?

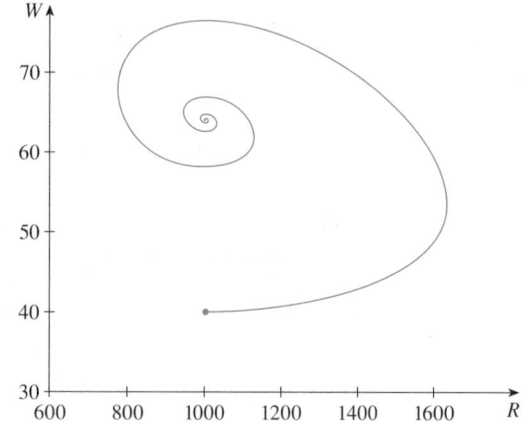

(b) Find all the equilibrium solutions and explain their significance.

(c) The figure shows the phase trajectory that starts at the point (1000, 40). Describe what eventually happens to the rabbit and wolf populations.

(d) Sketch graphs of the rabbit and wolf populations as functions of time.

[CAS] **10.** In Exercise 8 we modeled populations of aphids and ladybugs with a Lotka-Volterra system. Suppose we modify those equations as follows:

$$\frac{dA}{dt} = 2A(1 - 0.0001A) - 0.01AL$$

$$\frac{dL}{dt} = -0.5L + 0.0001AL$$

(a) In the absence of ladybugs, what does the model predict about the aphids?

(b) Find the equilibrium solutions.

(c) Find an expression for dL/dA.

(d) Use a computer algebra system to draw a direction field for the differential equation in part (c). Then use the direction field to sketch a phase portrait. What do the phase trajectories have in common?

(e) Suppose that at time $t = 0$ there are 1000 aphids and 200 ladybugs. Draw the corresponding phase trajectory and use it to describe how both populations change.

(f) Use part (e) to make rough sketches of the aphid and ladybug populations as functions of t. How are the graphs related to each other?

10 Review

∘ CONCEPT CHECK ∘

1. (a) What is a differential equation?
(b) What is the order of a differential equation?
(c) What is an initial condition?

2. What can you say about the solutions of the equation $y' = x^2 + y^2$ just by looking at the differential equation?

3. What is a direction field for the differential equation $y' = F(x, y)$?

4. Explain how Euler's method works.

5. What is a separable differential equation? How do you solve it?

6. What is a first-order linear differential equation? How do you solve it?

7. (a) Write a differential equation that expresses the law of natural growth. What does it say in terms of relative growth rate?
(b) Under what circumstances is this an appropriate model for population growth?
(c) What are the solutions of this equation?

8. (a) Write the logistic equation.
(b) Under what circumstances is this an appropriate model for population growth?

9. (a) Write Lotka-Volterra equations to model populations of food fish (F) and sharks (S).
(b) What do these equations say about each population in the absence of the other?

--------------------- ◦ TRUE-FALSE QUIZ ◦ ---------------------

Determine whether the statement is true or false. If it is true, explain why.
If it is false, explain why or give an example that disproves the statement.

1. All solutions of the differential equation $y' = -1 - y^4$ are decreasing functions.

2. The function $f(x) = (\ln x)/x$ is a solution of the differential equation $x^2 y' + xy = 1$.

3. The equation $y' = x + y$ is separable.

4. The equation $y' = 3y - 2x + 6xy - 1$ is separable.

5. The equation $e^x y' = y$ is linear.

6. The equation $y' + xy = e^y$ is linear.

7. If y is the solution of the initial-value problem

$$\frac{dy}{dt} = 2y\left(1 - \frac{y}{5}\right) \qquad y(0) = 1$$

then $\lim_{t \to \infty} y = 5$.

--------------------- ◦ EXERCISES ◦ ---------------------

1. (a) A direction field for the differential equation
$y' = y(y - 2)(y - 4)$ is shown. Sketch the graphs of the solutions that satisfy the given initial conditions.

  (i) $y(0) = -0.3$ (ii) $y(0) = 1$
  (iii) $y(0) = 3$ (iv) $y(0) = 4.3$

(b) If the initial condition is $y(0) = c$, for what values of c is $\lim_{t \to \infty} y(t)$ finite? What are the equilibrium solutions?

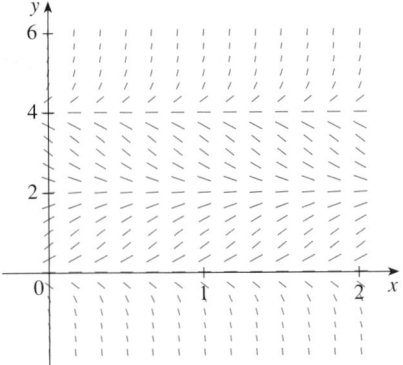

2. (a) Sketch a direction field for the differential equation
$y' = x/y$. Then use it to sketch the four solutions that satisfy the initial conditions $y(0) = 1$, $y(0) = -1$, $y(2) = 1$, and $y(-2) = 1$.

(b) Check your work in part (a) by solving the differential equation explicitly. What type of curve is each solution curve?

3. (a) A direction field for the differential equation $y' = x^2 - y^2$ is shown. Sketch the solution of the initial-value problem

$$y' = x^2 - y^2 \qquad y(0) = 1$$

Use your graph to estimate the value of $y(0.3)$.

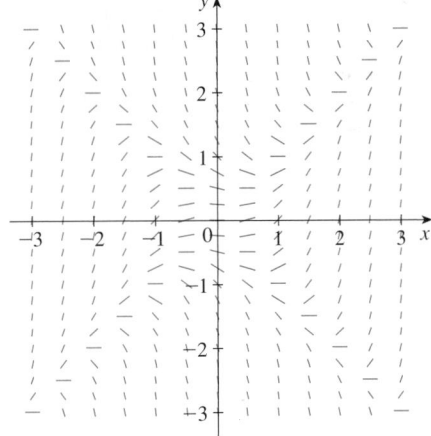

(b) Use Euler's method with step size 0.1 to estimate $y(0.3)$ where $y(x)$ is the solution of the initial-value problem in part (a). Compare with your estimate from part (a).

(c) On what lines are the centers of the horizontal line segments of the direction field in part (a) located? What happens when a solution curve crosses these lines?

4. (a) Use Euler's method with step size 0.2 to estimate $y(0.4)$, where $y(x)$ is the solution of the initial-value problem

$$y' = 2xy^2 \qquad y(0) = 1$$

(b) Repeat part (a) with step size 0.1.

(c) Find the exact solution of the differential equation and compare the value at 0.4 with the approximations in parts (a) and (b).

5–8 ⫼ Solve the differential equation.

5. $y' = xe^{-\sin x} - y \cos x$ **6.** $\dfrac{dx}{dt} = 1 - t + x - tx$

7. $(3y^2 + 2y)y' = x \cos x$ **8.** $x^2 y' - y = 2x^3 e^{-1/x}$

9–11 ▏▎ Solve the initial-value problem.

9. $xyy' = \ln x$, $\quad y(1) = 2$

10. $1 + x = 2xyy'$, $\quad x > 0$, $\quad y(1) = -2$

11. $y' + y = \sqrt{x}e^{-x}$, $\quad y(0) = 3$

▫ ▫ ▫ ▫ ▫ ▫ ▫ ▫ ▫ ▫ ▫

12. Solve the initial-value problem $2yy' = xe^x$, $y(0) = 1$, and graph the solution.

13–14 ▏▎ Find the orthogonal trajectories of the family of curves.

13. $kx^2 + y^2 = 1$ $\qquad\qquad$ **14.** $y = \dfrac{k}{1 + x^2}$

▫ ▫ ▫ ▫ ▫ ▫ ▫ ▫ ▫ ▫ ▫

15. A bacteria culture starts with 1000 bacteria and the growth rate is proportional to the number of bacteria. After 2 hours the population is 9000.
   (a) Find an expression for the number of bacteria after t hours.
   (b) Find the number of bacteria after 3 h.
   (c) Find the rate of growth after 3 h.
   (d) How long does it take for the number of bacteria to double?

16. An isotope of strontium, ^{90}Sr, has a half-life of 25 years.
   (a) Find the mass of ^{90}Sr that remains from a sample of 18 mg after t years.
   (b) How long would it take for the mass to decay to 2 mg?

17. Let $C(t)$ be the concentration of a drug in the bloodstream. As the body eliminates the drug, $C(t)$ decreases at a rate that is proportional to the amount of the drug that is present at the time. Thus, $C'(t) = -kC(t)$, where k is a positive number called the *elimination constant* of the drug.
   (a) If C_0 is the concentration at time $t = 0$, find the concentration at time t.
   (b) If the body eliminates half the drug in 30 h, how long does it take to eliminate 90% of the drug?

18. (a) The population of the world was 5.28 billion in 1990 and 6.07 billion in 2000. Find an exponential model for these data and use the model to predict the world population in the year 2020.
   (b) According to the model in part (a), when will the world population exceed 10 billion?
   (c) Use the data in part (a) to find a logistic model for the population. Assume a carrying capacity of 100 billion. Then use the logistic model to predict the population in 2020. Compare with your prediction from the exponential model.
   (d) According to the logistic model, when will the world population exceed 10 billion? Compare with your prediction in part (b).

19. The von Bertalanffy growth model is used to predict the length $L(t)$ of a fish over a period of time. If L_∞ is the largest length for a species, then the hypothesis is that the rate of growth in length is proportional to $L_\infty - L$, the length yet to be achieved.
   (a) Formulate and solve a differential equation to find an expression for $L(t)$.
   (b) For the North Sea haddock it has been determined that $L_\infty = 53$ cm, $L(0) = 10$ cm, and the constant of proportionality is 0.2. What does the expression for $L(t)$ become with these data?

20. A tank contains 100 L of pure water. Brine that contains 0.1 kg of salt per liter enters the tank at a rate of 10 L/min. The solution is kept thoroughly mixed and drains from the tank at the same rate. How much salt is in the tank after 6 minutes?

21. One model for the spread of an epidemic is that the rate of spread is jointly proportional to the number of infected people and the number of uninfected people. In an isolated town of 5000 inhabitants, 160 people have a disease at the beginning of the week and 1200 have it at the end of the week. How long does it take for 80% of the population to become infected?

22. The Brentano-Stevens Law in psychology models the way that a subject reacts to a stimulus. It states that if R represents the reaction to an amount S of stimulus, then the relative rates of increase are proportional:

$$\frac{1}{R}\frac{dR}{dt} = \frac{k}{S}\frac{dS}{dt}$$

where k is a positive constant. Find R as a function of S.

23. The transport of a substance across a capillary wall in lung physiology has been modeled by the differential equation

$$\frac{dh}{dt} = -\frac{R}{V}\left(\frac{h}{k + h}\right)$$

where h is the hormone concentration in the bloodstream, t is time, R is the maximum transport rate, V is the volume of the capillary, and k is a positive constant that measures the affinity between the hormones and the enzymes that assist the process. Solve this differential equation to find a relationship between h and t.

24. Populations of birds and insects are modeled by the equations

$$\frac{dx}{dt} = 0.4x - 0.002xy$$

$$\frac{dy}{dt} = -0.2y + 0.000008xy$$

   (a) Which of the variables, x or y, represents the bird population and which represents the insect population? Explain.

(b) Find the equilibrium solutions and explain their significance.

(c) Find an expression for dy/dx.

(d) The direction field for the differential equation in part (c) is shown. Use it to sketch the phase trajectory corresponding to initial populations of 100 birds and 40,000 insects. Then use the phase trajectory to describe how both populations change.

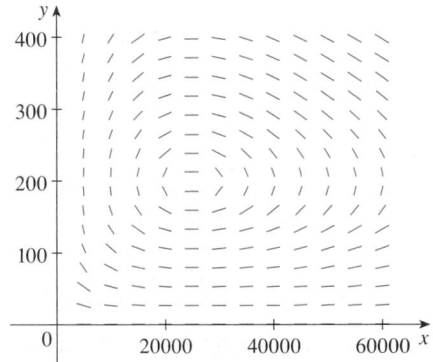

(e) Use part (d) to make rough sketches of the bird and insect populations as functions of time. How are these graphs related to each other?

25. Suppose the model of Exercise 24 is replaced by the equations

$$\frac{dx}{dt} = 0.4x(1 - 0.000005x) - 0.002xy$$

$$\frac{dy}{dt} = -0.2y + 0.000008xy$$

(a) According to these equations, what happens to the insect population in the absence of birds?

(b) Find the equilibrium solutions and explain their significance.

(c) The figure shows the phase trajectory that starts with 100 birds and 40,000 insects. Describe what eventually happens to the bird and insect populations.

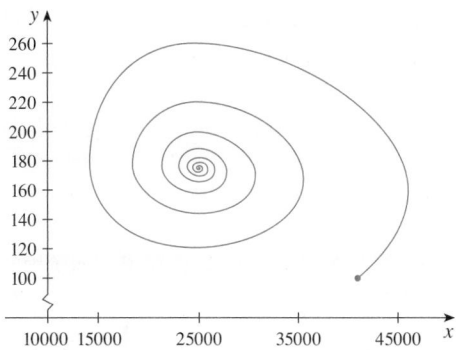

(d) Sketch graphs of the bird and insect populations as functions of time.

26. Barbara weighs 60 kg and is on a diet of 1600 calories per day, of which 850 are used automatically by basal metabolism. She spends about 15 cal/kg/day times her weight doing exercise. If 1 kg of fat contains 10,000 cal and we assume that the storage of calories in the form of fat is 100% efficient, formulate a differential equation and solve it to find her weight as a function of time. Does her weight ultimately approach an equilibrium weight?

27. When a flexible cable of uniform density is suspended between two fixed points and hangs of its own weight, the shape $y = f(x)$ of the cable must satisfy a differential equation of the form

$$\frac{d^2y}{dx^2} = k\sqrt{1 + \left(\frac{dy}{dx}\right)^2}$$

where k is a positive constant. Consider the cable shown in the figure.

(a) Let $z = dy/dx$ in the differential equation. Solve the resulting first-order differential equation (in z), and then integrate to find y.

(b) Determine the length of the cable.

1. Find all functions f such that f' is continuous and

$$[f(x)]^2 = 100 + \int_0^x \{[f(t)]^2 + [f'(t)]^2\}\, dt \qquad \text{for all real } x$$

2. A student forgot the Product Rule for differentiation and made the mistake of thinking that $(fg)' = f'g'$. However, he was lucky and got the correct answer. The function f that he used was $f(x) = e^{x^2}$ and the domain of his problem was the interval $(\frac{1}{2}, \infty)$. What was the function g?

3. Let f be a function with the property that $f(0) = 1$, $f'(0) = 1$, and $f(a + b) = f(a)f(b)$ for all real numbers a and b. Show that $f'(x) = f(x)$ for all x and deduce that $f(x) = e^x$.

4. Find all functions f that satisfy the equation

$$\left(\int f(x)\, dx\right)\left(\int \frac{1}{f(x)}\, dx\right) = -1$$

5. A peach pie is taken out of the oven at 5:00 P.M. At that time it is piping hot: 100°C. At 5:10 P.M. its temperature is 80°C; at 5:20 P.M. it is 65°C. What is the temperature of the room?

6. Snow began to fall during the morning of February 2 and continued steadily into the afternoon. At noon a snowplow began removing snow from a road at a constant rate. The plow traveled 6 km from noon to 1 P.M. but only 3 km from 1 P.M. to 2 P.M. When did the snow begin to fall? [*Hints:* To get started, let t be the time measured in hours after noon; let $x(t)$ be the distance traveled by the plow at time t; then the speed of the plow is dx/dt. Let b be the number of hours before noon that it began to snow. Find an expression for the height of the snow at time t. Then use the given information that the rate of removal R (in m³/h) is constant.]

7. A dog sees a rabbit running in a straight line across an open field and gives chase. In a rectangular coordinate system (as shown in the figure), assume:

  (i) The rabbit is at the origin and the dog is at the point $(L, 0)$ at the instant the dog first sees the rabbit.

  (ii) The rabbit runs up the y-axis and the dog always runs straight for the rabbit.

  (iii) The dog runs at the same speed as the rabbit.

  (a) Show that the dog's path is the graph of the function $y = f(x)$, where y satisfies the differential equation

$$x\frac{d^2y}{dx^2} = \sqrt{1 + \left(\frac{dy}{dx}\right)^2}$$

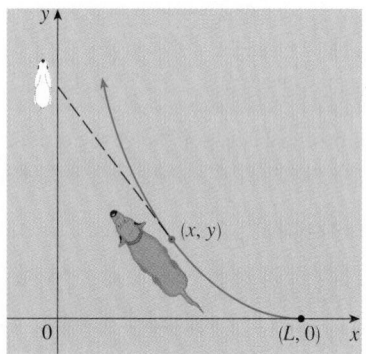

FIGURE FOR PROBLEM 7

  (b) Determine the solution of the equation in part (a) that satisfies the initial conditions $y = y' = 0$ when $x = L$. [*Hint:* Let $z = dy/dx$ in the differential equation and solve the resulting first-order equation to find z; then integrate z to find y.]

  (c) Does the dog ever catch the rabbit?

8. (a) Suppose that the dog in Problem 7 runs twice as fast as the rabbit. Find a differential equation for the path of the dog. Then solve it to find the point where the dog catches the rabbit.

  (b) Suppose the dog runs half as fast as the rabbit. How close does the dog get to the rabbit? What are their positions when they are closest?

9. A planning engineer for a new alum plant must present some estimates to his company regarding the capacity of a silo designed to contain bauxite ore until it is processed into alum. The ore resembles pink talcum powder and is poured from a conveyor at the top of the silo. The silo is a cylinder 100 ft high with a radius of 200 ft. The conveyor carries $60{,}000\pi$ ft^3/h and the ore maintains a conical shape whose radius is 1.5 times its height.

(a) If, at a certain time t, the pile is 60 ft high, how long will it take for the pile to reach the top of the silo?

(b) Management wants to know how much room will be left in the floor area of the silo when the pile is 60 ft high. How fast is the floor area of the pile growing at that height?

(c) Suppose a loader starts removing the ore at the rate of $20{,}000\pi$ ft^3/h when the height of the pile reaches 90 ft. Suppose, also, that the pile continues to maintain its shape. How long will it take for the pile to reach the top of the silo under these conditions?

10. Find the curve that passes through the point $(3, 2)$ and has the property that if the tangent line is drawn at any point P on the curve, then the part of the tangent line that lies in the first quadrant is bisected at P.

11. Recall that the normal line to a curve at a point P on the curve is the line that passes through P and is perpendicular to the tangent line at P. Find the curve that passes through the point $(3, 2)$ and has the property that if the normal line is drawn at any point on the curve, then the y-intercept of the normal line is always 6.

12. Find all curves with the property that if the normal line is drawn at any point P on the curve, then the part of the normal line between P and the x-axis is bisected by the y-axis.

CHAPTER 11

Parametric curves are used to
represent letters and other symbols on laser printers. See the
Laboratory Project on page 705.

Parametric Equations and
Polar Coordinates

So far we have described plane curves by giving y as a function of x [$y = f(x)$] or x as a function of y [$x = g(y)$] or by giving a relation between x and y that defines y implicitly as a function of x [$f(x, y) = 0$]. In this chapter we discuss two new methods for describing curves.

Some curves, such as the cycloid, are best handled when both x and y are given in terms of a third variable t called a parameter [$x = f(t)$, $y = g(t)$]. Other curves, such as the cardioid, have their most convenient description when we use a new coordinate system, called the polar coordinate system.

11.1 Curves Defined by Parametric Equations

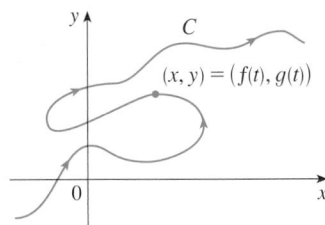

FIGURE 1

Imagine that a particle moves along the curve C shown in Figure 1. It is impossible to describe C by an equation of the form $y = f(x)$ because C fails the Vertical Line Test. But the x- and y-coordinates of the particle are functions of time and so we can write $x = f(t)$ and $y = g(t)$. Such a pair of equations is often a convenient way of describing a curve and gives rise to the following definition.

Suppose that x and y are both given as functions of a third variable t (called a **parameter**) by the equations

$$x = f(t) \qquad y = g(t)$$

(called **parametric equations**). Each value of t determines a point (x, y), which we can plot in a coordinate plane. As t varies, the point $(x, y) = (f(t), g(t))$ varies and traces out a curve C, which we call a **parametric curve**. The parameter t does not necessarily represent time and, in fact, we could use a letter other than t for the parameter. But in many applications of parametric curves, t does denote time and therefore we can interpret $(x, y) = (f(t), g(t))$ as the position of a particle at time t.

EXAMPLE 1 Sketch and identify the curve defined by the parametric equations

$$x = t^2 - 2t \qquad y = t + 1$$

SOLUTION Each value of t gives a point on the curve, as shown in the table. For instance, if $t = 0$, then $x = 0$, $y = 1$ and so the corresponding point is $(0, 1)$. In Figure 2 we plot the points (x, y) determined by several values of the parameter and we join them to produce a curve.

t	x	y
-2	8	-1
-1	3	0
0	0	1
1	-1	2
2	0	3
3	3	4
4	8	5

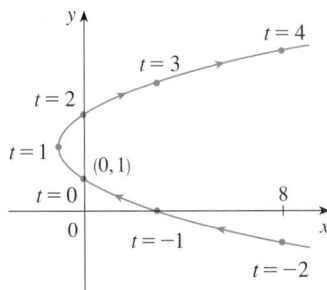

FIGURE 2

A particle whose position is given by the parametric equations moves along the curve in the direction of the arrows as t increases. Notice that the consecutive points marked on the curve appear at equal time intervals but not at equal distances. That is because the particle slows down and then speeds up as t increases.

It appears from Figure 2 that the curve traced out by the particle may be a parabola. This can be confirmed by eliminating the parameter t as follows. We obtain $t = y - 1$ from the second equation and substitute into the first equation. This gives

$$x = t^2 - 2t = (y - 1)^2 - 2(y - 1) = y^2 - 4y + 3$$

and so the curve represented by the given parametric equations is the parabola $x = y^2 - 4y + 3$.

No restriction was placed on the parameter t in Example 1, so we assumed that t could be any real number. But sometimes we restrict t to lie in a finite interval. For instance, the parametric curve

$$x = t^2 - 2t \qquad y = t + 1 \qquad 0 \leqslant t \leqslant 4$$

shown in Figure 3 is the part of the parabola in Example 1 that starts at the point $(0, 1)$ and ends at the point $(8, 5)$. The arrowhead indicates the direction in which the curve is traced as t increases from 0 to 4.

In general, the curve with parametric equations

$$x = f(t) \qquad y = g(t) \qquad a \leqslant t \leqslant b$$

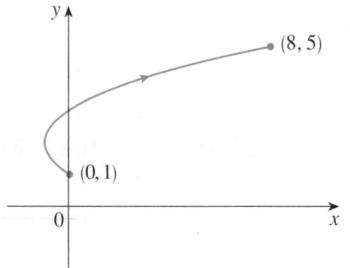

FIGURE 3

has **initial point** $(f(a), g(a))$ and **terminal point** $(f(b), g(b))$.

EXAMPLE 2 What curve is represented by the parametric equations $x = \cos t$, $y = \sin t$, $0 \leqslant t \leqslant 2\pi$?

SOLUTION If we plot points, it appears that the curve is a circle. We can confirm this impression by eliminating t. Observe that

$$x^2 + y^2 = \cos^2 t + \sin^2 t = 1$$

Thus, the point (x, y) moves on the unit circle $x^2 + y^2 = 1$. Notice that in this example the parameter t can be interpreted as the angle (in radians) shown in Figure 4. As t increases from 0 to 2π, the point $(x, y) = (\cos t, \sin t)$ moves once around the circle in the counterclockwise direction starting from the point $(1, 0)$.

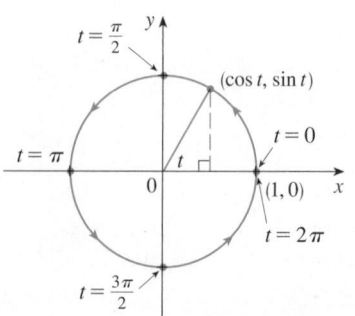

FIGURE 4

EXAMPLE 3 What curve is represented by the parametric equations $x = \sin 2t$, $y = \cos 2t$, $0 \leqslant t \leqslant 2\pi$?

SOLUTION Again we have

$$x^2 + y^2 = \sin^2 2t + \cos^2 2t = 1$$

so the parametric equations again represent the unit circle $x^2 + y^2 = 1$. But as t increases from 0 to 2π, the point $(x, y) = (\sin 2t, \cos 2t)$ starts at $(0, 1)$ and moves *twice* around the circle in the clockwise direction as indicated in Figure 5.

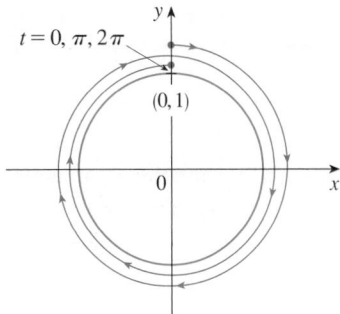

FIGURE 5

Examples 2 and 3 show that different sets of parametric equations can represent the same curve. Thus, we distinguish between a *curve,* which is a set of points, and a *parametric curve,* in which the points are traced in a particular way.

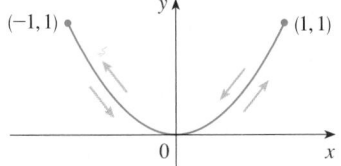

FIGURE 6

EXAMPLE 4 Sketch the curve with parametric equations $x = \sin t$, $y = \sin^2 t$.

SOLUTION Observe that $y = (\sin t)^2 = x^2$ and so the point (x, y) moves on the parabola $y = x^2$. But note also that, since $-1 \leqslant \sin t \leqslant 1$, we have $-1 \leqslant x \leqslant 1$, so the parametric equations represent only the part of the parabola for which $-1 \leqslant x \leqslant 1$. Since $\sin t$ is periodic, the point $(x, y) = (\sin t, \sin^2 t)$ moves back and forth infinitely often along the parabola from $(-1, 1)$ to $(1, 1)$. (See Figure 6.)

Module 11.1A gives an animation of the relationship between motion along a parametric curve $x = f(t)$, $y = g(t)$ and motion along the graphs of f and g as functions of t. Clicking on TRIG gives you the family of parametric curves

$$x = a \cos bt \qquad y = c \sin dt$$

If you choose $a = b = c = d = 1$ and click START, you will see how the graphs of $x = \cos t$ and $y = \sin t$ relate to the circle in Example 2. If you choose $a = b = c = 1, d = 2$, you will see graphs as in Figure 7. By clicking on PAUSE and then repeatedly on STEP, you can see from the color coding how motion along the graphs of $x = \cos t$ and $y = \sin 2t$ corresponds to motion along the parametric curve, which is called a **Lissajous figure.**

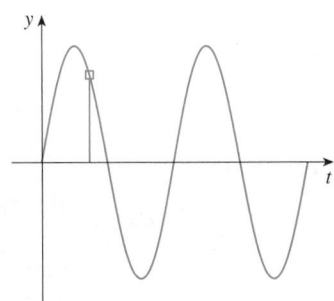

FIGURE 7 $\qquad x = \cos t \quad y = \sin 2t \qquad\qquad\qquad y = \sin 2t$

|||| Graphing Devices

Most graphing calculators and computer graphing programs can be used to graph curves defined by parametric equations. In fact, it's instructive to watch a parametric curve being drawn by a graphing calculator because the points are plotted in order as the corresponding parameter values increase.

EXAMPLE 5 Use a graphing device to graph the curve $x = y^4 - 3y^2$.

SOLUTION If we let the parameter be $t = y$, then we have the equations

$$x = t^4 - 3t^2 \qquad y = t$$

Using these parametric equations to graph the curve, we obtain Figure 8. It would be possible to solve the given equation ($x = y^4 - 3y^2$) for y as four functions of x and graph them individually, but the parametric equations provide a much easier method.

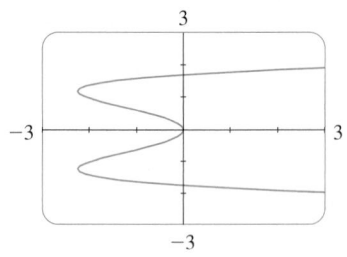

FIGURE 8

In general, if we need to graph an equation of the form $x = g(y)$, we can use the parametric equations

$$x = g(t) \qquad y = t$$

Notice also that curves with equations $y = f(x)$ (the ones we are most familiar with—graphs of functions) can also be regarded as curves with parametric equations

$$x = t \qquad y = f(t)$$

Graphing devices are particularly useful when sketching complicated curves. For instance, the curves shown in Figures 9 and 10 would be virtually impossible to produce by hand.

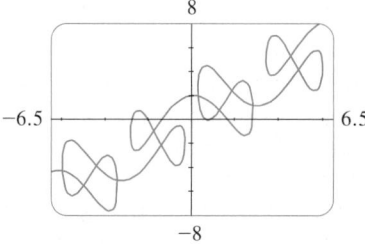

FIGURE 9
$x = t + 2 \sin 2t, \ y = t + 2 \cos 5t,$
$-2\pi \leqslant t \leqslant 2\pi$

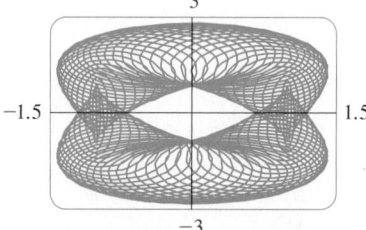

FIGURE 10
$x = \cos t - \cos 80t \sin t,$
$y = 2 \sin t - \sin 80t, \ 0 \leqslant t \leqslant 2\pi$

One of the most important uses of parametric curves is in computer-aided design (CAD). In the Laboratory Project after Section 11.2 we will investigate special parametric curves, called **Bézier curves**, that are used extensively in manufacturing, especially in the automotive industry. These curves are also employed in specifying the shapes of letters and other symbols in laser printers.

|||| The Cycloid

An animation in Module 11.1B shows how the cycloid is formed as the circle moves.

EXAMPLE 6 The curve traced out by a point P on the circumference of a circle as the circle rolls along a straight line is called a **cycloid** (see Figure 11). If the circle has radius r and rolls along the x-axis and if one position of P is the origin, find parametric equations for the cycloid.

FIGURE 11

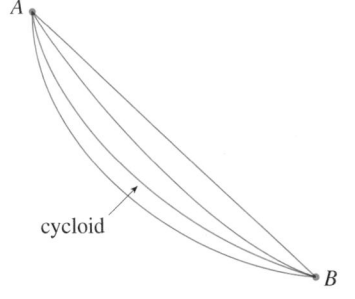

FIGURE 12

SOLUTION We choose as parameter the angle of rotation θ of the circle ($\theta = 0$ when P is at the origin). Suppose the circle has rotated through θ radians. Because the circle has been in contact with the line, we see from Figure 12 that the distance it has rolled from the origin is

$$|OT| = \text{arc } PT = r\theta$$

Therefore, the center of the circle is $C(r\theta, r)$. Let the coordinates of P be (x, y). Then from Figure 12 we see that

$$x = |OT| - |PQ| = r\theta - r\sin\theta = r(\theta - \sin\theta)$$

$$y = |TC| - |QC| = r - r\cos\theta = r(1 - \cos\theta)$$

Therefore, parametric equations of the cycloid are

$$\boxed{1} \qquad x = r(\theta - \sin\theta) \qquad y = r(1 - \cos\theta) \qquad \theta \in \mathbb{R}$$

One arch of the cycloid comes from one rotation of the circle and so is described by $0 \le \theta \le 2\pi$. Although Equations 1 were derived from Figure 12, which illustrates the case where $0 < \theta < \pi/2$, it can be seen that these equations are still valid for other values of θ (see Exercise 37).

Although it is possible to eliminate the parameter θ from Equations 1, the resulting Cartesian equation in x and y is very complicated and not as convenient to work with as the parametric equations.

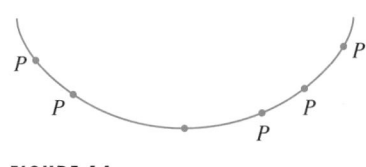

FIGURE 13

One of the first people to study the cycloid was Galileo, who proposed that bridges be built in the shape of cycloids and who tried to find the area under one arch of a cycloid. Later this curve arose in connection with the *brachistochrone problem:* Find the curve along which a particle will slide in the shortest time (under the influence of gravity) from a point A to a lower point B not directly beneath A. The Swiss mathematician John Bernoulli, who posed this problem in 1696, showed that among all possible curves that join A to B, as in Figure 13, the particle will take the least time sliding from A to B if the curve is part of an inverted arch of a cycloid.

The Dutch physicist Huygens had already shown that the cycloid is also the solution to the *tautochrone problem;* that is, no matter where a particle P is placed on an inverted cycloid, it takes the same time to slide to the bottom (see Figure 14). Huygens proposed that pendulum clocks (which he invented) swing in cycloidal arcs because then the pendulum takes the same time to make a complete oscillation whether it swings through a wide or a small arc.

FIGURE 14

║║ **Families of Parametric Curves**

EXAMPLE 7 Investigate the family of curves with parametric equations

$$x = a + \cos t \qquad y = a\tan t + \sin t$$

What do these curves have in common? How does the shape change as a increases?

SOLUTION We use a graphing device to produce the graphs for the cases $a = -2, -1,$ $-0.5, -0.2, 0, 0.5, 1,$ and 2 shown in Figure 15. Notice that all of these curves (except the case $a = 0$) have two branches, and both branches approach the vertical asymptote $x = a$ as x approaches a from the left or right.

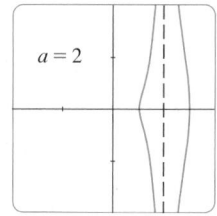

FIGURE 15 Members of the family $x = a + \cos t$, $y = a \tan t + \sin t$, all graphed in the viewing rectangle $[-4, 4]$ by $[-4, 4]$

When $a < -1$, both branches are smooth; but when a reaches -1, the right branch acquires a sharp point, called a *cusp*. For a between -1 and 0 the cusp turns into a loop, which becomes larger as a approaches 0. When $a = 0$, both branches come together and form a circle (see Example 2). For a between 0 and 1, the left branch has a loop, which shrinks to become a cusp when $a = 1$. For $a > 1$, the branches become smooth again, and as a increases further, they become less curved. Notice that the curves with a positive are reflections about the y-axis of the corresponding curves with a negative.

These curves are called **conchoids of Nicomedes** after the ancient Greek scholar Nicomedes. He called them conchoids because the shape of their outer branches resembles that of a conch shell or mussel shell.

‖‖‖ **11.1** Exercises

1–4 ‖‖‖ Sketch the curve by using the parametric equations to plot points. Indicate with an arrow the direction in which the curve is traced as t increases.

1. $x = 1 + \sqrt{t}$, $y = t^2 - 4t$, $0 \leqslant t \leqslant 5$

2. $x = 2 \cos t$, $y = t - \cos t$, $0 \leqslant t \leqslant 2\pi$

3. $x = 5 \sin t$, $y = t^2$, $-\pi \leqslant t \leqslant \pi$

4. $x = e^{-t} + t$, $y = e^t - t$, $-2 \leqslant t \leqslant 2$

5–10 ‖‖‖
(a) Sketch the curve by using the parametric equations to plot points. Indicate with an arrow the direction in which the curve is traced as t increases.
(b) Eliminate the parameter to find a Cartesian equation of the curve.

5. $x = 3t - 5$, $y = 2t + 1$

6. $x = 1 + t$, $y = 5 - 2t$, $-2 \leqslant t \leqslant 3$

7. $x = t^2 - 2$, $y = 5 - 2t$, $-3 \leqslant t \leqslant 4$

8. $x = 1 + 3t$, $y = 2 - t^2$

9. $x = \sqrt{t}$, $y = 1 - t$

10. $x = t^2$, $y = t^3$

11–18 ‖‖‖
(a) Eliminate the parameter to find a Cartesian equation of the curve.
(b) Sketch the curve and indicate with an arrow the direction in which the curve is traced as the parameter increases.

11. $x = \sin \theta$, $y = \cos \theta$, $0 \leqslant \theta \leqslant \pi$

12. $x = 4 \cos \theta$, $y = 5 \sin \theta$, $-\pi/2 \leqslant \theta \leqslant \pi/2$

13. $x = \sin^2\theta$, $y = \cos^2\theta$

14. $x = \sec \theta$, $y = \tan \theta$, $-\pi/2 < \theta < \pi/2$

15. $x = e^t$, $y = e^{-t}$

16. $x = \ln t$, $y = \sqrt{t}$, $t \geqslant 1$

17. $x = \cosh t, \quad y = \sinh t$

18. $x = 1 + \cos \theta, \quad y = 2 \cos \theta - 1$

□ □ □ □ □ □ □ □ □ □

19–22 ▓ Describe the motion of a particle with position (x, y) as t varies in the given interval.

19. $x = \cos \pi t, \quad y = \sin \pi t, \quad 1 \leqslant t \leqslant 2$

20. $x = 2 + \cos t, \quad y = 3 + \sin t, \quad 0 \leqslant t \leqslant 2\pi$

21. $x = 2 \sin t, \quad y = 3 \cos t, \quad 0 \leqslant t \leqslant 2\pi$

22. $x = \cos^2 t, \quad y = \cos t, \quad 0 \leqslant t \leqslant 4\pi$

□ □ □ □ □ □ □ □ □ □

23. Suppose a curve is given by the parametric equations $x = f(t)$, $y = g(t)$, where the range of f is $[1, 4]$ and the range of g is $[2, 3]$. What can you say about the curve?

24. Match the graphs of the parametric equations $x = f(t)$ and $y = g(t)$ in (a)–(d) with the parametric curves labeled I–IV. Give reasons for your choices.

(a)

I

(b)

II

(c)

III

(d)

IV
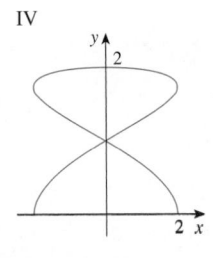

25–27 ▓ Use the graphs of $x = f(t)$ and $y = g(t)$ to sketch the parametric curve $x = f(t)$, $y = g(t)$. Indicate with arrows the direction in which the curve is traced as t increases.

25.

26.

27.
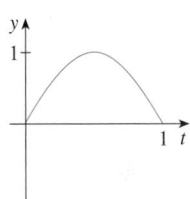

□ □ □ □ □ □ □ □ □ □

28. Match the parametric equations with the graphs labeled I–VI. Give reasons for your choices. (Do not use a graphing device.)

(a) $x = t^3 - 2t, \quad y = t^2 - t$

(b) $x = t^3 - 1, \quad y = 2 - t^2$

(c) $x = \sin 3t, \quad y = \sin 4t$

(d) $x = t + \sin 2t, \quad y = t + \sin 3t$

(e) $x = \sin(t + \sin t), \quad y = \cos(t + \cos t)$

(f) $x = \cos t, \quad y = \sin(t + \sin 5t)$

I

II

III

IV

V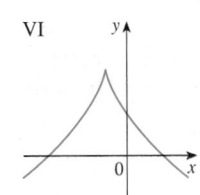

VI

29. Graph the curve $x = y - 3y^3 + y^5$.

30. Graph the curves $y = x^5$ and $x = y(y - 1)^2$ and find their points of intersection correct to one decimal place.

31. (a) Show that the parametric equations

$$x = x_1 + (x_2 - x_1)t \qquad y = y_1 + (y_2 - y_1)t$$

where $0 \le t \le 1$, describe the line segment that joins the points $P_1(x_1, y_1)$ and $P_2(x_2, y_2)$.

(b) Find parametric equations to represent the line segment from $(-2, 7)$ to $(3, -1)$.

32. Use a graphing device and the result of Exercise 31(a) to draw the triangle with vertices $A(1, 1)$, $B(4, 2)$, and $C(1, 5)$.

33. Find parametric equations for the path of a particle that moves along the circle $x^2 + (y - 1)^2 = 4$ in the manner described.

(a) Once around clockwise, starting at $(2, 1)$

(b) Three times around counterclockwise, starting at $(2, 1)$

(c) Halfway around counterclockwise, starting at $(0, 3)$

34. Graph the semicircle traced by the particle in Exercise 33(c).

35. (a) Find parametric equations for the ellipse $x^2/a^2 + y^2/b^2 = 1$. [*Hint:* Modify the equations of a circle in Example 2.]

(b) Use these parametric equations to graph the ellipse when $a = 3$ and $b = 1, 2, 4,$ and 8.

(c) How does the shape of the ellipse change as b varies?

36. Find three different sets of parametric equations to represent the curve $y = x^3$, $x \in \mathbb{R}$.

37. Derive Equations 1 for the case $\pi/2 < \theta < \pi$.

38. Let P be a point at a distance d from the center of a circle of radius r. The curve traced out by P as the circle rolls along a straight line is called a **trochoid.** (Think of the motion of a point on a spoke of a bicycle wheel.) The cycloid is the special case of a trochoid with $d = r$. Using the same parameter θ as for the cycloid and assuming the line is the x-axis and $\theta = 0$ when P is at one of its lowest points, show that parametric equations of the trochoid are

$$x = r\theta - d \sin \theta \qquad y = r - d \cos \theta$$

Sketch the trochoid for the cases $d < r$ and $d > r$.

39. If a and b are fixed numbers, find parametric equations for the curve that consists of all possible positions of the point P in the

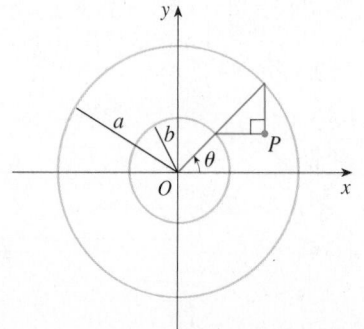

figure, using the angle θ as the parameter. Then eliminate the parameter and identify the curve.

40. If a and b are fixed numbers, find parametric equations for the curve that consists of all possible positions of the point P in the figure, using the angle θ as the parameter. The line segment AB is tangent to the larger circle.

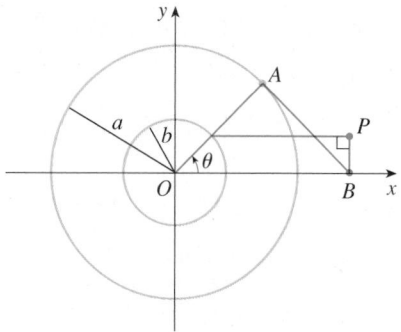

41. A curve, called a **witch of Maria Agnesi,** consists of all possible positions of the point P in the figure. Show that parametric equations for this curve can be written as

$$x = 2a \cot \theta \qquad y = 2a \sin^2\theta$$

Sketch the curve.

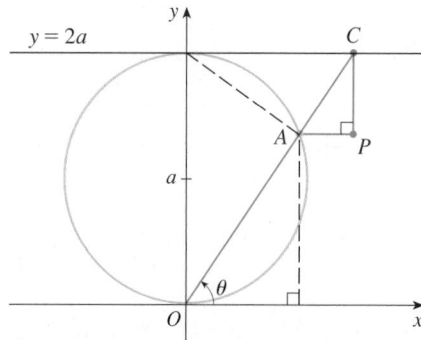

42. Find parametric equations for the curve that consists of all possible positions of the point P in the figure, where $|OP| = |AB|$. Sketch the curve. (This curve is called the **cissoid of Diocles** after the Greek scholar Diocles, who introduced the cissoid as a graphical method for constructing the edge of a cube whose volume is twice that of a given cube.)

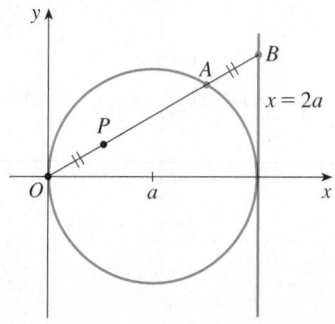

43. Suppose that the position of one particle at time t is given by

$$x_1 = 3 \sin t \qquad y_1 = 2 \cos t \qquad 0 \le t \le 2\pi$$

and the position of a second particle is given by

$$x_2 = -3 + \cos t \qquad y_2 = 1 + \sin t \qquad 0 \le t \le 2\pi$$

(a) Graph the paths of both particles. How many points of intersection are there?

(b) Are any of these points of intersection *collision points*? In other words, are the particles ever at the same place at the same time? If so, find the collision points.

(c) Describe what happens if the path of the second particle is given by

$$x_2 = 3 + \cos t \qquad y_2 = 1 + \sin t \qquad 0 \le t \le 2\pi$$

44. If a projectile is fired with an initial velocity of v_0 meters per second at an angle α above the horizontal and air resistance is assumed to be negligible, then its position after t seconds is given by the parametric equations

$$x = (v_0 \cos \alpha)t \qquad y = (v_0 \sin \alpha)t - \tfrac{1}{2}gt^2$$

where g is the acceleration due to gravity (9.8 m/s^2).

(a) If a gun is fired with $\alpha = 30°$ and $v_0 = 500$ m/s, when will the bullet hit the ground? How far from the gun will it hit the ground? What is the maximum height reached by the bullet?

(b) Use a graphing device to check your answers to part (a). Then graph the path of the projectile for several other values of the angle α to see where it hits the ground. Summarize your findings.

(c) Show that the path is parabolic by eliminating the parameter.

45. Investigate the family of curves defined by the parametric equations $x = t^2$, $y = t^3 - ct$. How does the shape change as c increases? Illustrate by graphing several members of the family.

46. The **swallowtail catastrophe curves** are defined by the parametric equations $x = 2ct - 4t^3$, $y = -ct^2 + 3t^4$. Graph several of these curves. What features do the curves have in common? How do they change when c increases?

47. The curves with equations $x = a \sin nt$, $y = b \cos t$ are called **Lissajous figures**. Investigate how these curves vary when a, b, and n vary. (Take n to be a positive integer.)

48. Investigate the family of curves defined by the parametric equations

$$x = \sin t \, (c - \sin t) \qquad y = \cos t \, (c - \sin t)$$

How does the shape change as c changes? In particular, you should identify the transitional values of c for which the basic shape of the curve changes.

LABORATORY PROJECT

⊞ Running Circles around Circles

In this project we investigate families of curves, called *hypocycloids* and *epicycloids,* that are generated by the motion of a point on a circle that rolls inside or outside another circle.

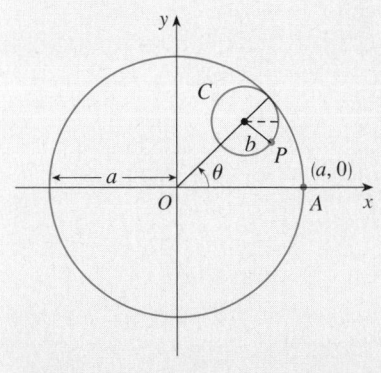

1. A **hypocycloid** is a curve traced out by a fixed point P on a circle C of radius b as C rolls on the inside of a circle with center O and radius a. Show that if the initial position of P is $(a, 0)$ and the parameter θ is chosen as in the figure, then parametric equations of the hypocycloid are

$$x = (a - b) \cos \theta + b \cos\!\left(\frac{a - b}{b}\theta\right) \qquad y = (a - b) \sin \theta - b \sin\!\left(\frac{a - b}{b}\theta\right)$$

2. Use a graphing device (or the interactive graphic in TEC Module 11.1B) to draw the graphs of hypocycloids with a a positive integer and $b = 1$. How does the value of a affect the graph? Show that if we take $a = 4$, then the parametric equations of the hypocycloid reduce to

$$x = 4 \cos^3\theta \qquad y = 4 \sin^3\theta$$

This curve is called a **hypocycloid of four cusps**, or an **astroid**.

Look at Module 11.1B to see how hypocycloids and epicycloids are formed by the motion of rolling circles.

3. Now try $b = 1$ and $a = n/d$, a fraction where n and d have no common factor. First let $n = 1$ and try to determine graphically the effect of the denominator d on the shape of the graph. Then let n vary while keeping d constant. What happens when $n = d + 1$?

4. What happens if $b = 1$ and a is irrational? Experiment with an irrational number like $\sqrt{2}$ or $e - 2$. Take larger and larger values for θ and speculate on what would happen if we were to graph the hypocycloid for all real values of θ.

5. If the circle C rolls on the *outside* of the fixed circle, the curve traced out by P is called an **epicycloid**. Find parametric equations for the epicycloid.

6. Investigate the possible shapes for epicycloids. Use methods similar to Problems 2–4.

|||| 11.2 Calculus with Parametric Curves

Having seen how to represent curves by parametric equations, we now apply the methods of calculus to these parametric curves. In particular, we solve problems involving tangents, area, arc length, and surface area.

|||| Tangents

In the preceding section we saw that some curves defined by parametric equations $x = f(t)$ and $y = g(t)$ can also be expressed, by eliminating the parameter, in the form $y = F(x)$. (See Exercise 67 for general conditions under which this is possible.) If we substitute $x = f(t)$ and $y = g(t)$ in the equation $y = F(x)$, we get

$$g(t) = F(f(t))$$

and so, if g, F, and f are differentiable, the Chain Rule gives

$$g'(t) = F'(f(t))f'(t) = F'(x)f'(t)$$

If $f'(t) \neq 0$, we can solve for $F'(x)$:

[1]

$$F'(x) = \frac{g'(t)}{f'(t)}$$

Since the slope of the tangent to the curve $y = F(x)$ at $(x, F(x))$ is $F'(x)$, Equation 1 enables us to find tangents to parametric curves without having to eliminate the parameter. Using Leibniz notation, we can rewrite Equation 1 in an easily remembered form:

|||| If we think of a parametric curve as being traced out by a moving particle, then dy/dt and dx/dt are the vertical and horizontal velocities of the particle and Formula 2 says that the slope of the tangent is the ratio of these velocities.

[2]

$$\frac{dy}{dx} = \frac{\dfrac{dy}{dt}}{\dfrac{dx}{dt}} \quad \text{if} \quad \frac{dx}{dt} \neq 0$$

It can be seen from Equation 2 that the curve has a horizontal tangent when $dy/dt = 0$ (provided that $dx/dt \neq 0$) and it has a vertical tangent when $dx/dt = 0$ (provided that $dy/dt \neq 0$). This information is useful for sketching parametric curves.

As we know from Chapter 4, it is also useful to consider d^2y/dx^2. This can be found by replacing y by dy/dx in Equation 2:

⊘ Note that $\dfrac{d^2y}{dx^2} \neq \dfrac{\dfrac{d^2y}{dt^2}}{\dfrac{d^2x}{dt^2}}$

$$\frac{d^2y}{dx^2} = \frac{d}{dx}\left(\frac{dy}{dx}\right) = \frac{\dfrac{d}{dt}\left(\dfrac{dy}{dx}\right)}{\dfrac{dx}{dt}}$$

EXAMPLE 1

A curve C is defined by the parametric equations $x = t^2$, $y = t^3 - 3t$.
(a) Show that C has two tangents at the point $(3, 0)$ and find their equations.
(b) Find the points on C where the tangent is horizontal or vertical.
(c) Determine where the curve is concave upward or downward.
(d) Sketch the curve.

SOLUTION

(a) Notice that $y = t^3 - 3t = t(t^2 - 3) = 0$ when $t = 0$ or $t = \pm\sqrt{3}$. Therefore, the point $(3, 0)$ on C arises from two values of the parameter, $t = \sqrt{3}$ and $t = -\sqrt{3}$. This indicates that C crosses itself at $(3, 0)$. Since

$$\frac{dy}{dx} = \frac{dy/dt}{dx/dt} = \frac{3t^2 - 3}{2t} = \frac{3}{2}\left(t - \frac{1}{t}\right)$$

the slope of the tangent when $t = \pm\sqrt{3}$ is $dy/dx = \pm 6/(2\sqrt{3}) = \pm\sqrt{3}$, so the equations of the tangents at $(3, 0)$ are

$$y = \sqrt{3}\,(x - 3) \qquad \text{and} \qquad y = -\sqrt{3}\,(x - 3)$$

(b) C has a horizontal tangent when $dy/dx = 0$, that is, when $dy/dt = 0$ and $dx/dt \neq 0$. Since $dy/dt = 3t^2 - 3$, this happens when $t^2 = 1$, that is, $t = \pm 1$. The corresponding points on C are $(1, -2)$ and $(1, 2)$. C has a vertical tangent when $dx/dt = 2t = 0$, that is, $t = 0$. (Note that $dy/dt \neq 0$ there.) The corresponding point on C is $(0, 0)$.

(c) To determine concavity we calculate the second derivative:

$$\frac{d^2y}{dx^2} = \frac{\dfrac{d}{dt}\left(\dfrac{dy}{dx}\right)}{\dfrac{dx}{dt}} = \frac{\dfrac{3}{2}\left(1 + \dfrac{1}{t^2}\right)}{2t} = \frac{3(t^2 + 1)}{4t^3}$$

Thus, the curve is concave upward when $t > 0$ and concave downward when $t < 0$.

(d) Using the information from parts (b) and (c), we sketch C in Figure 1.

FIGURE 1

EXAMPLE 2

(a) Find the tangent to the cycloid $x = r(\theta - \sin\theta)$, $y = r(1 - \cos\theta)$ at the point where $\theta = \pi/3$. (See Example 6 in Section 11.1.)
(b) At what points is the tangent horizontal? When is it vertical?

SOLUTION

(a) The slope of the tangent line is

$$\frac{dy}{dx} = \frac{dy/d\theta}{dx/d\theta} = \frac{r\sin\theta}{r(1 - \cos\theta)} = \frac{\sin\theta}{1 - \cos\theta}$$

When $\theta = \pi/3$, we have

$$x = r\left(\frac{\pi}{3} - \sin\frac{\pi}{3}\right) = r\left(\frac{\pi}{3} - \frac{\sqrt{3}}{2}\right) \qquad y = r\left(1 - \cos\frac{\pi}{3}\right) = \frac{r}{2}$$

and

$$\frac{dy}{dx} = \frac{\sin(\pi/3)}{1 - \cos(\pi/3)} = \frac{\sqrt{3}/2}{1 - \frac{1}{2}} = \sqrt{3}$$

Therefore, the slope of the tangent is $\sqrt{3}$ and its equation is

$$y - \frac{r}{2} = \sqrt{3}\left(x - \frac{r\pi}{3} + \frac{r\sqrt{3}}{2}\right) \qquad \text{or} \qquad \sqrt{3}\,x - y = r\left(\frac{\pi}{\sqrt{3}} - 2\right)$$

The tangent is sketched in Figure 2.

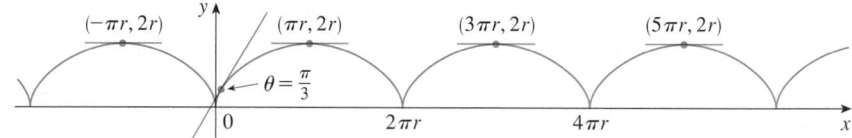

FIGURE 2

(b) The tangent is horizontal when $dy/dx = 0$, which occurs when $\sin\theta = 0$ and $1 - \cos\theta \neq 0$, that is, $\theta = (2n - 1)\pi$, n an integer. The corresponding point on the cycloid is $((2n - 1)\pi r, 2r)$.

When $\theta = 2n\pi$, both $dx/d\theta$ and $dy/d\theta$ are 0. It appears from the graph that there are vertical tangents at those points. We can verify this by using l'Hospital's Rule as follows:

$$\lim_{\theta \to 2n\pi^+} \frac{dy}{dx} = \lim_{\theta \to 2n\pi^+} \frac{\sin\theta}{1 - \cos\theta} = \lim_{\theta \to 2n\pi^+} \frac{\cos\theta}{\sin\theta} = \infty$$

A similar computation shows that $dy/dx \to -\infty$ as $\theta \to 2n\pi^-$, so indeed there are vertical tangents when $\theta = 2n\pi$, that is, when $x = 2n\pi r$.

||| Areas

We know that the area under a curve $y = F(x)$ from a to b is $A = \int_a^b F(x)\,dx$, where $F(x) \geq 0$. If the curve is given by parametric equations $x = f(t)$, $y = g(t)$ and is traversed once as t increases from α to β, then we can adapt the earlier formula by using the Substitution Rule for Definite Integrals as follows:

$$A = \int_a^b y\,dx = \int_\alpha^\beta g(t)f'(t)\,dt$$

$$\left[\text{or} \quad \int_\beta^\alpha g(t)f'(t)\,dt \quad \text{if } (f(\beta), g(\beta)) \text{ is the leftmost endpoint}\right]$$

EXAMPLE 3 Find the area under one arch of the cycloid $x = r(\theta - \sin\theta)$, $y = r(1 - \cos\theta)$. (See Figure 3.)

FIGURE 3

▐▐▐ The result of Example 3 says that the area under one arch of the cycloid is three times the area of the rolling circle that generates the cycloid (see Example 6 in Section 11.1). Galileo guessed this result but it was first proved by the French mathematician Roberval and the Italian mathematician Torricelli.

SOLUTION One arch of the cycloid is given by $0 \le \theta \le 2\pi$. Using the Substitution Rule with $y = r(1 - \cos\theta)$ and $dx = r(1 - \cos\theta)\,d\theta$, we have

$$A = \int_0^{2\pi r} y\, dx = \int_0^{2\pi} r(1 - \cos\theta)\, r(1 - \cos\theta)\, d\theta$$

$$= r^2 \int_0^{2\pi} (1 - \cos\theta)^2\, d\theta = r^2 \int_0^{2\pi} (1 - 2\cos\theta + \cos^2\theta)\, d\theta$$

$$= r^2 \int_0^{2\pi} \left[1 - 2\cos\theta + \tfrac{1}{2}(1 + \cos 2\theta)\right] d\theta$$

$$= r^2 \left[\tfrac{3}{2}\theta - 2\sin\theta + \tfrac{1}{4}\sin 2\theta\right]_0^{2\pi}$$

$$= r^2\left(\tfrac{3}{2} \cdot 2\pi\right) = 3\pi r^2$$

▐▐▐ Arc Length

We already know how to find the length L of a curve C given in the form $y = F(x)$, $a \le x \le b$. Formula 9.1.3 says that if F' is continuous, then

$$\boxed{3} \qquad L = \int_a^b \sqrt{1 + \left(\frac{dy}{dx}\right)^2}\, dx$$

Suppose that C can also be described by the parametric equations $x = f(t)$ and $y = g(t)$, $\alpha \le t \le \beta$, where $dx/dt = f'(t) > 0$. This means that C is traversed once, from left to right, as t increases from α to β and $f(\alpha) = a$, $f(\beta) = b$. Putting Formula 2 into Formula 3 and using the Substitution Rule, we obtain

$$L = \int_a^b \sqrt{1 + \left(\frac{dy}{dx}\right)^2}\, dx = \int_\alpha^\beta \sqrt{1 + \left(\frac{dy/dt}{dx/dt}\right)^2}\, \frac{dx}{dt}\, dt$$

Since $dx/dt > 0$, we have

$$\boxed{4} \qquad L = \int_\alpha^\beta \sqrt{\left(\frac{dx}{dt}\right)^2 + \left(\frac{dy}{dt}\right)^2}\, dt$$

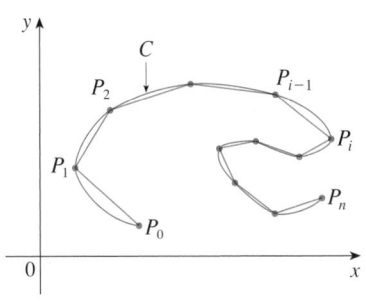

FIGURE 4

Even if C can't be expressed in the form $y = F(x)$, Formula 4 is still valid but we obtain it by polygonal approximations. We divide the parameter interval $[\alpha, \beta]$ into n subintervals of equal width Δt. If $t_0, t_1, t_2, \ldots, t_n$ are the endpoints of these subintervals, then $x_i = f(t_i)$ and $y_i = g(t_i)$ are the coordinates of points $P_i(x_i, y_i)$ that lie on C and the polygon with vertices $P_0, P_1, \ldots, P_n$ approximates C (see Figure 4).

As in Section 9.1, we define the length L of C to be the limit of the lengths of these approximating polygons as $n \to \infty$:

$$L = \lim_{n\to\infty} \sum_{i=1}^n |P_{i-1}P_i|$$

The Mean Value Theorem, when applied to f on the interval $[t_{i-1}, t_i]$, gives a number t_i^* in (t_{i-1}, t_i) such that

$$f(t_i) - f(t_{i-1}) = f'(t_i^*)(t_i - t_{i-1})$$

If we let $\Delta x_i = x_i - x_{i-1}$ and $\Delta y_i = y_i - y_{i-1}$, this equation becomes

$$\Delta x_i = f'(t_i^*)\, \Delta t$$

Similarly, when applied to g, the Mean Value Theorem gives a number t_i^{**} in (t_{i-1}, t_i) such that

$$\Delta y_i = g'(t_i^{**})\, \Delta t$$

Therefore

$$
\begin{aligned}
|P_{i-1}P_i| &= \sqrt{(\Delta x_i)^2 + (\Delta y_i)^2} \\
&= \sqrt{[f'(t_i^*)\Delta t]^2 + [g'(t_i^{**})\Delta t]^2} \\
&= \sqrt{[f'(t_i^*)]^2 + [g'(t_i^{**})]^2}\; \Delta t
\end{aligned}
$$

and so

$$\boxed{5} \qquad L = \lim_{n \to \infty} \sum_{i=1}^{n} \sqrt{[f'(t_i^*)]^2 + [g'(t_i^{**})]^2}\; \Delta t$$

The sum in (5) resembles a Riemann sum for the function $\sqrt{[f'(t)]^2 + [g'(t)]^2}$ but it is not exactly a Riemann sum because $t_i^* \neq t_i^{**}$ in general. Nevertheless, if f' and g' are continuous, it can be shown that the limit in (5) is the same as if t_i^* and t_i^{**} were equal, namely,

$$L = \int_{\alpha}^{\beta} \sqrt{[f'(t)]^2 + [g'(t)]^2}\; dt$$

Thus, using Leibniz notation, we have the following result, which has the same form as (4).

---

6 Theorem If a curve C is described by the parametric equations $x = f(t)$, $y = g(t)$, $\alpha \leqslant t \leqslant \beta$, where f' and g' are continuous on $[\alpha, \beta]$ and C is traversed exactly once as t increases from α to β, then the length of C is

$$L = \int_{\alpha}^{\beta} \sqrt{\left(\frac{dx}{dt}\right)^2 + \left(\frac{dy}{dt}\right)^2}\; dt$$

Notice that the formula in Theorem 6 is consistent with the general formulas $L = \int ds$ and $(ds)^2 = (dx)^2 + (dy)^2$ of Section 9.1.

EXAMPLE 4 If we use the representation of the unit circle given in Example 2 in Section 11.1,

$$x = \cos t \qquad y = \sin t \qquad 0 \leqslant t \leqslant 2\pi$$

then $dx/dt = -\sin t$ and $dy/dt = \cos t$, so Theorem 6 gives

$$
L = \int_{0}^{2\pi} \sqrt{\left(\frac{dx}{dt}\right)^2 + \left(\frac{dy}{dt}\right)^2}\; dt = \int_{0}^{2\pi} \sqrt{\sin^2 t + \cos^2 t}\; dt
$$

$$= \int_{0}^{2\pi} dt = 2\pi$$

as expected. If, on the other hand, we use the representation given in Example 3 in Section 11.1,

$$x = \sin 2t \qquad y = \cos 2t \qquad 0 \leqslant t \leqslant 2\pi$$

then $dx/dt = 2 \cos 2t$, $dy/dt = -2 \sin 2t$, and the integral in Theorem 6 gives

$$\int_0^{2\pi} \sqrt{\left(\frac{dx}{dt}\right)^2 + \left(\frac{dy}{dt}\right)^2}\, dt = \int_0^{2\pi} \sqrt{4 \cos^2 2t + 4 \sin^2 2t}\, dt = \int_0^{2\pi} 2\, dt = 4\pi$$

⊘ Notice that the integral gives twice the arc length of the circle because as t increases from 0 to 2π, the point $(\sin 2t, \cos 2t)$ traverses the circle twice. In general, when finding the length of a curve C from a parametric representation, we have to be careful to ensure that C is traversed only once as t increases from α to β.

EXAMPLE 5 Find the length of one arch of the cycloid $x = r(\theta - \sin \theta)$, $y = r(1 - \cos \theta)$.

SOLUTION From Example 3 we see that one arch is described by the parameter interval $0 \le \theta \le 2\pi$. Since

$$\frac{dx}{d\theta} = r(1 - \cos \theta) \qquad \text{and} \qquad \frac{dy}{d\theta} = r \sin \theta$$

we have

$$L = \int_0^{2\pi} \sqrt{\left(\frac{dx}{d\theta}\right)^2 + \left(\frac{dy}{d\theta}\right)^2}\, d\theta = \int_0^{2\pi} \sqrt{r^2(1 - \cos \theta)^2 + r^2 \sin^2\theta}\, d\theta$$

$$= \int_0^{2\pi} \sqrt{r^2(1 - 2\cos \theta + \cos^2\theta + \sin^2\theta)}\, d\theta = r\int_0^{2\pi} \sqrt{2(1 - \cos \theta)}\, d\theta$$

||| The result of Example 5 says that the length of one arch of a cycloid is eight times the radius of the generating circle (see Figure 5). This was first proved in 1658 by Sir Christopher Wren, who later became the architect of St. Paul's Cathedral in London.

To evaluate this integral we use the identity $\sin^2 x = \frac{1}{2}(1 - \cos 2x)$ with $\theta = 2x$, which gives $1 - \cos \theta = 2 \sin^2(\theta/2)$. Since $0 \le \theta \le 2\pi$, we have $0 \le \theta/2 \le \pi$ and so $\sin(\theta/2) \ge 0$. Therefore

$$\sqrt{2(1 - \cos \theta)} = \sqrt{4 \sin^2(\theta/2)} = 2|\sin(\theta/2)| = 2 \sin(\theta/2)$$

and so

$$L = 2r\int_0^{2\pi} \sin(\theta/2)\, d\theta = 2r\left[-2 \cos(\theta/2)\right]_0^{2\pi}$$

$$= 2r[2 + 2] = 8r$$

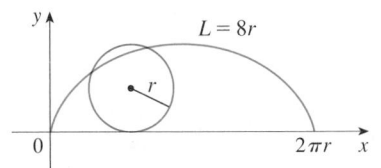

$L = 8r$

FIGURE 5

Surface Area

In the same way as for arc length, we can adapt Formula 9.2.5 to obtain a formula for surface area. If the curve given by the parametric equations $x = f(t)$, $y = g(t)$, $\alpha \le t \le \beta$, is rotated about the x-axis, where f', g' are continuous and $g(t) \ge 0$, then the area of the resulting surface is given by

$$\boxed{7} \qquad S = \int_\alpha^\beta 2\pi y \sqrt{\left(\frac{dx}{dt}\right)^2 + \left(\frac{dy}{dt}\right)^2}\, dt$$

The general symbolic formulas $S = \int 2\pi y\, ds$ and $S = \int 2\pi x\, ds$ (Formulas 9.2.7 and 9.2.8) are still valid, but for parametric curves we use

$$ds = \sqrt{\left(\frac{dx}{dt}\right)^2 + \left(\frac{dy}{dt}\right)^2}\, dt$$

EXAMPLE 6 Show that the surface area of a sphere of radius r is $4\pi r^2$.

SOLUTION The sphere is obtained by rotating the semicircle

$$x = r\cos t \qquad y = r\sin t \qquad 0 \le t \le \pi$$

about the x-axis. Therefore, from Formula 7, we get

$$S = \int_0^\pi 2\pi r \sin t \sqrt{(-r\sin t)^2 + (r\cos t)^2}\, dt$$

$$= 2\pi \int_0^\pi r\sin t \sqrt{r^2(\sin^2 t + \cos^2 t)}\, dt$$

$$= 2\pi \int_0^\pi r\sin t \cdot r\, dt = 2\pi r^2 \int_0^\pi \sin t\, dt$$

$$= 2\pi r^2 (-\cos t)\Big]_0^\pi = 4\pi r^2$$

11.2 Exercises

1–2 ▏▎▍ Find dy/dx.

1. $x = t - t^3, \quad y = 2 - 5t$ **2.** $x = te^t, \quad y = t + e^t$

3–6 ▏▎▍ Find an equation of the tangent to the curve at the point corresponding to the given value of the parameter.

3. $x = t^4 + 1, \quad y = t^3 + t; \quad t = -1$

4. $x = 2t^2 + 1, \quad y = \frac{1}{3}t^3 - t; \quad t = 3$

5. $x = e^{\sqrt{t}}, \quad y = t - \ln t^2; \quad t = 1$

6. $x = \cos\theta + \sin 2\theta, \quad y = \sin\theta + \cos 2\theta; \quad \theta = 0$

7–8 ▏▎▍ Find an equation of the tangent to the curve at the given point by two methods: (a) without eliminating the parameter and (b) by first eliminating the parameter.

7. $x = e^t, \quad y = (t - 1)^2; \quad (1, 1)$

8. $x = \tan\theta, \quad y = \sec\theta; \quad (1, \sqrt{2})$

9–10 ▏▎▍ Find an equation of the tangent(s) to the curve at the given point. Then graph the curve and the tangent(s).

9. $x = 2\sin 2t, \quad y = 2\sin t; \quad (\sqrt{3}, 1)$

10. $x = \sin t, \quad y = \sin(t + \sin t); \quad (0, 0)$

11–16 ▏▎▍ Find dy/dx and d^2y/dx^2. For which values of t is the curve concave upward?

11. $x = 4 + t^2, \quad y = t^2 + t^3$ **12.** $x = t^3 - 12t, \quad y = t^2 - 1$

13. $x = t - e^t, \quad y = t + e^{-t}$ **14.** $x = t + \ln t, \quad y = t - \ln t$

15. $x = 2\sin t, \quad y = 3\cos t, \quad 0 < t < 2\pi$

16. $x = \cos 2t, \quad y = \cos t, \quad 0 < t < \pi$

17–20 ▏▎▍ Find the points on the curve where the tangent is horizontal or vertical. If you have a graphing device, graph the curve to check your work.

17. $x = 10 - t^2, \quad y = t^3 - 12t$

18. $x = 2t^3 + 3t^2 - 12t, \quad y = 2t^3 + 3t^2 + 1$

19. $x = 2\cos\theta, \quad y = \sin 2\theta$

20. $x = \cos 3\theta, \quad y = 2\sin\theta$

21. Use a graph to estimate the coordinates of the leftmost point on the curve $x = t^4 - t^2$, $y = t + \ln t$. Then use calculus to find the exact coordinates.

22. Try to estimate the coordinates of the highest point and the leftmost point on the curve $x = te^t$, $y = te^{-t}$. Then find the exact coordinates. What are the asymptotes of this curve?

23–24 ▏▎▍ Graph the curve in a viewing rectangle that displays all the important aspects of the curve.

23. $x = t^4 - 2t^3 - 2t^2, \quad y = t^3 - t$

24. $x = t^4 + 4t^3 - 8t^2, \quad y = 2t^2 - t$

25. Show that the curve $x = \cos t$, $y = \sin t \cos t$ has two tangents at $(0, 0)$ and find their equations. Sketch the curve.

26. At what point does the curve $x = 1 - 2\cos^2 t$, $y = (\tan t)(1 - 2\cos^2 t)$ cross itself? Find the equations of both tangents at that point.

27. (a) Find the slope of the tangent line to the trochoid $x = r\theta - d\sin\theta$, $y = r - d\cos\theta$ in terms of θ. (See Exercise 38 in Section 11.1.)
  (b) Show that if $d < r$, then the trochoid does not have a vertical tangent.

28. (a) Find the slope of the tangent to the astroid $x = a\cos^3\theta$, $y = a\sin^3\theta$ in terms of θ. (Astroids are explored in the Laboratory Project on page 695.)

(b) At what points is the tangent horizontal or vertical?

(c) At what points does the tangent have slope 1 or -1?

29. At what points on the curve $x = t^3 + 4t$, $y = 6t^2$ is the tangent parallel to the line with equations $x = -7t$, $y = 12t - 5$?

30. Find equations of the tangents to the curve $x = 3t^2 + 1$, $y = 2t^3 + 1$ that pass through the point $(4, 3)$.

31. Use the parametric equations of an ellipse, $x = a \cos \theta$, $y = b \sin \theta$, $0 \le \theta \le 2\pi$, to find the area that it encloses.

32. Find the area bounded by the curve $x = t - 1/t$, $y = t + 1/t$ and the line $y = 2.5$.

33. Find the area bounded by the curve $x = \cos t$, $y = e^t$, $0 \le t \le \pi/2$, and the lines $y = 1$ and $x = 0$.

34. Find the area of the region enclosed by the astroid $x = a \cos^3\theta$, $y = a \sin^3\theta$. (Astroids are explored in the Laboratory Project on page 695.)

35. Find the area under one arch of the trochoid of Exercise 38 in Section 11.1 for the case $d < r$.

36. Let $\mathcal{R}$ be the region enclosed by the loop of the curve in Example 1.

(a) Find the area of $\mathcal{R}$.

(b) If $\mathcal{R}$ is rotated about the x-axis, find the volume of the resulting solid.

(c) Find the centroid of $\mathcal{R}$.

37–40 Set up, but do not evaluate, an integral that represents the length of the curve.

37. $x = t - t^2$, $y = \frac{4}{3}t^{3/2}$, $1 \le t \le 2$

38. $x = 1 + e^t$, $y = t^2$, $-3 \le t \le 3$

39. $x = t + \cos t$, $y = t - \sin t$, $0 \le t \le 2\pi$

40. $x = \ln t$, $y = \sqrt{t + 1}$, $1 \le t \le 5$

41–44 Find the length of the curve.

41. $x = 1 + 3t^2$, $y = 4 + 2t^3$, $0 \le t \le 1$

42. $x = a(\cos \theta + \theta \sin \theta)$, $y = a(\sin \theta - \theta \cos \theta)$, $0 \le \theta \le \pi$

43. $x = \dfrac{t}{1 + t}$, $y = \ln(1 + t)$, $0 \le t \le 2$

44. $x = e^t + e^{-t}$, $y = 5 - 2t$, $0 \le t \le 3$

45–47 Graph the curve and find its length.

45. $x = e^t \cos t$, $y = e^t \sin t$, $0 \le t \le \pi$

46. $x = \cos t + \ln(\tan \frac{1}{2}t)$, $y = \sin t$, $\pi/4 \le t \le 3\pi/4$

47. $x = e^t - t$, $y = 4e^{t/2}$, $-8 \le t \le 3$

48. Find the length of the loop of the curve $x = 3t - t^3$, $y = 3t^2$.

49. Use Simpson's Rule with $n = 6$ to estimate the length of the curve $x = t - e^t$, $y = t + e^t$, $-6 \le t \le 6$.

50. In Exercise 41 in Section 11.1 you were asked to derive the parametric equations $x = 2a \cot \theta$, $y = 2a \sin^2\theta$ for the curve called the witch of Maria Agnesi. Use Simpson's Rule with $n = 4$ to estimate the length of the arc of this curve given by $\pi/4 \le \theta \le \pi/2$.

51–52 Find the distance traveled by a particle with position (x, y) as t varies in the given time interval. Compare with the length of the curve.

51. $x = \sin^2 t$, $y = \cos^2 t$, $0 \le t \le 3\pi$

52. $x = \cos^2 t$, $y = \cos t$, $0 \le t \le 4\pi$

53. Show that the total length of the ellipse $x = a \sin \theta$, $y = b \cos \theta$, $a > b > 0$, is

$$L = 4a \int_0^{\pi/2} \sqrt{1 - e^2 \sin^2\theta}\, d\theta$$

where e is the eccentricity of the ellipse $\left(e = c/a\right.$, where $c = \sqrt{a^2 - b^2}\,\big)$.

54. Find the total length of the astroid $x = a \cos^3\theta$, $y = a \sin^3\theta$, where $a > 0$.

[CAS] **55.** (a) Graph the **epitrochoid** with equations

$$x = 11 \cos t - 4 \cos(11t/2)$$
$$y = 11 \sin t - 4 \sin(11t/2)$$

What parameter interval gives the complete curve?

(b) Use your CAS to find the approximate length of this curve.

[CAS] **56.** A curve called **Cornu's spiral** is defined by the parametric equations

$$x = C(t) = \int_0^t \cos(\pi u^2/2)\, du$$
$$y = S(t) = \int_0^t \sin(\pi u^2/2)\, du$$

where C and S are the Fresnel functions that were introduced in Chapter 5.

(a) Graph this curve. What happens as $t \to \infty$ and as $t \to -\infty$?

(b) Find the length of Cornu's spiral from the origin to the point with parameter value t.

57–58 Set up, but do not evaluate, an integral that represents the area of the surface obtained by rotating the given curve about the x-axis.

57. $x = t - t^2$, $y = \frac{4}{3}t^{3/2}$, $1 \le t \le 2$

58. $x = \sin^2 t$, $y = \sin 3t$, $0 \le t \le \pi/3$

59–61 ‖‖‖ Find the area of the surface obtained by rotating the given curve about the *x*-axis.

59. $x = t^3$, $y = t^2$, $0 \le t \le 1$

60. $x = 3t - t^3$, $y = 3t^2$, $0 \le t \le 1$

61. $x = a \cos^3\theta$, $y = a \sin^3\theta$, $0 \le \theta \le \pi/2$

62. Graph the curve

$$x = 2 \cos\theta - \cos 2\theta \qquad y = 2 \sin\theta - \sin 2\theta$$

If this curve is rotated about the *x*-axis, find the area of the resulting surface. (Use your graph to help find the correct parameter interval.)

63. If the curve

$$x = t + t^3 \qquad y = t - \frac{1}{t^2} \qquad 1 \le t \le 2$$

is rotated about the *x*-axis, use your calculator to estimate the area of the resulting surface to three decimal places.

64. If the arc of the curve in Exercise 50 is rotated about the *x*-axis, estimate the area of the resulting surface using Simpson's Rule with $n = 4$.

65–66 ‖‖‖ Find the surface area generated by rotating the given curve about the *y*-axis.

65. $x = 3t^2$, $y = 2t^3$, $0 \le t \le 5$

66. $x = e^t - t$, $y = 4e^{t/2}$, $0 \le t \le 1$

67. If f' is continuous and $f'(t) \ne 0$ for $a \le t \le b$, show that the parametric curve $x = f(t)$, $y = g(t)$, $a \le t \le b$, can be put in the form $y = F(x)$. [*Hint:* Show that f^{-1} exists.]

68. Use Formula 2 to derive Formula 7 from Formula 9.2.5 for the case in which the curve can be represented in the form $y = F(x)$, $a \le x \le b$.

69. The **curvature** at a point P of a curve is defined as

$$\kappa = \left| \frac{d\phi}{ds} \right|$$

where ϕ is the angle of inclination of the tangent line at P, as shown in the figure. Thus, the curvature is the absolute value of the rate of change of ϕ with respect to arc length. It can be regarded as a measure of the rate of change of direction of the curve at P and will be studied in greater detail in Chapter 14.

(a) For a parametric curve $x = x(t)$, $y = y(t)$, derive the formula

$$\kappa = \frac{|\dot{x}\ddot{y} - \ddot{x}\dot{y}|}{[\dot{x}^2 + \dot{y}^2]^{3/2}}$$

where the dots indicate derivatives with respect to t, so $\dot{x} = dx/dt$. [*Hint:* Use $\phi = \tan^{-1}(dy/dx)$ and Equation 2 to find $d\phi/dt$. Then use the Chain Rule to find $d\phi/ds$.]

(b) By regarding a curve $y = f(x)$ as the parametric curve $x = x$, $y = f(x)$, with parameter x, show that the formula in part (a) becomes

$$\kappa = \frac{|d^2y/dx^2|}{[1 + (dy/dx)^2]^{3/2}}$$

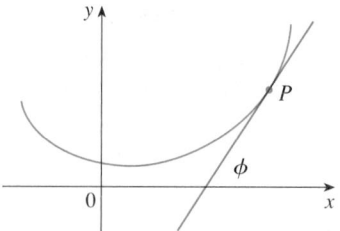

70. (a) Use the formula in Exercise 69(b) to find the curvature of the parabola $y = x^2$ at the point $(1, 1)$.
(b) At what point does this parabola have maximum curvature?

71. Use the formula in Exercise 69(a) to find the curvature of the cycloid $x = \theta - \sin\theta$, $y = 1 - \cos\theta$ at the top of one of its arches.

72. (a) Show that the curvature at each point of a straight line is $\kappa = 0$.
(b) Show that the curvature at each point of a circle of radius r is $\kappa = 1/r$.

73. A string is wound around a circle and then unwound while being held taut. The curve traced by the point P at the end of the string is called the **involute** of the circle. If the circle has radius r and center O and the initial position of P is $(r, 0)$, and if the parameter θ is chosen as in the figure, show that parametric equations of the involute are

$$x = r(\cos\theta + \theta \sin\theta) \qquad y = r(\sin\theta - \theta \cos\theta)$$

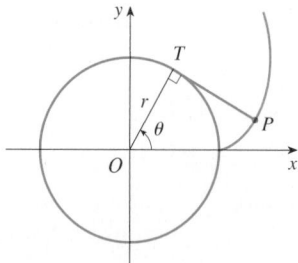

74. A cow is tied to a silo with radius r by a rope just long enough to reach the opposite side of the silo. Find the area available for grazing by the cow.

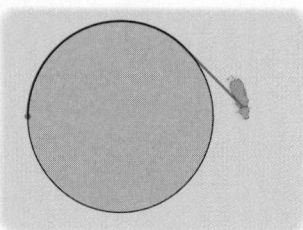

LABORATORY PROJECT

Bézier Curves

The **Bézier curves** are used in computer-aided design and are named after the French mathematician Pierre Bézier (1910–1999), who worked in the automotive industry. A cubic Bézier curve is determined by four **control points**, $P_0(x_0, y_0)$, $P_1(x_1, y_1)$, $P_2(x_2, y_2)$, and $P_3(x_3, y_3)$, and is defined by the parametric equations

$$x = x_0(1 - t)^3 + 3x_1t(1 - t)^2 + 3x_2t^2(1 - t) + x_3t^3$$

$$y = y_0(1 - t)^3 + 3y_1t(1 - t)^2 + 3y_2t^2(1 - t) + y_3t^3$$

where $0 \leq t \leq 1$. Notice that when $t = 0$ we have $(x, y) = (x_0, y_0)$ and when $t = 1$ we have $(x, y) = (x_3, y_3)$, so the curve starts at P_0 and ends at P_3.

1. Graph the Bézier curve with control points $P_0(4, 1)$, $P_1(28, 48)$, $P_2(50, 42)$, and $P_3(40, 5)$. Then, on the same screen, graph the line segments P_0P_1, P_1P_2, and P_2P_3. (Exercise 31 in Section 11.1 shows how to do this.) Notice that the middle control points P_1 and P_2 don't lie on the curve; the curve starts at P_0, heads toward P_1 and P_2 without reaching them, and ends at P_3.

2. From the graph in Problem 1 it appears that the tangent at P_0 passes through P_1 and the tangent at P_3 passes through P_2. Prove it.

3. Try to produce a Bézier curve with a loop by changing the second control point in Problem 1.

4. Some laser printers use Bézier curves to represent letters and other symbols. Experiment with control points until you find a Bézier curve that gives a reasonable representation of the letter C.

5. More complicated shapes can be represented by piecing together two or more Bézier curves. Suppose the first Bézier curve has control points P_0, P_1, P_2, P_3 and the second one has control points P_3, P_4, P_5, P_6. If we want these two pieces to join together smoothly, then the tangents at P_3 should match and so the points P_2, P_3, and P_4 all have to lie on this common tangent line. Using this principle, find control points for a pair of Bézier curves that represent the letter S.

11.3 Polar Coordinates

A coordinate system represents a point in the plane by an ordered pair of numbers called coordinates. Usually we use Cartesian coordinates, which are directed distances from two perpendicular axes. Here we describe a coordinate system introduced by Newton, called the **polar coordinate system**, which is more convenient for many purposes.

We choose a point in the plane that is called the **pole** (or origin) and is labeled O. Then we draw a ray (half-line) starting at O called the **polar axis**. This axis is usually drawn horizontally to the right and corresponds to the positive x-axis in Cartesian coordinates.

If P is any other point in the plane, let r be the distance from O to P and let θ be the angle (usually measured in radians) between the polar axis and the line OP as in Figure 1. Then the point P is represented by the ordered pair (r, θ) and r, θ are called **polar coordinates** of P. We use the convention that an angle is positive if measured in the counterclockwise direction from the polar axis and negative in the clockwise direction. If $P = O$, then $r = 0$ and we agree that $(0, \theta)$ represents the pole for any value of θ.

FIGURE 1

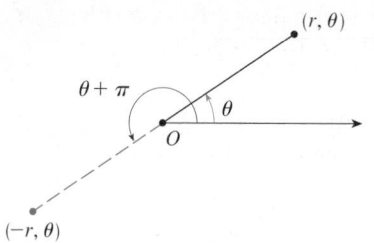

FIGURE 2

We extend the meaning of polar coordinates (r, θ) to the case in which r is negative by agreeing that, as in Figure 2, the points $(-r, \theta)$ and (r, θ) lie on the same line through O and at the same distance $|r|$ from O, but on opposite sides of O. If $r > 0$, the point (r, θ) lies in the same quadrant as θ; if $r < 0$, it lies in the quadrant on the opposite side of the pole. Notice that $(-r, \theta)$ represents the same point as $(r, \theta + \pi)$.

EXAMPLE 1 Plot the points whose polar coordinates are given.
(a) $(1, 5\pi/4)$ (b) $(2, 3\pi)$ (c) $(2, -2\pi/3)$ (d) $(-3, 3\pi/4)$

SOLUTION The points are plotted in Figure 3. In part (d) the point $(-3, 3\pi/4)$ is located three units from the pole in the fourth quadrant because the angle $3\pi/4$ is in the second quadrant and $r = -3$ is negative.

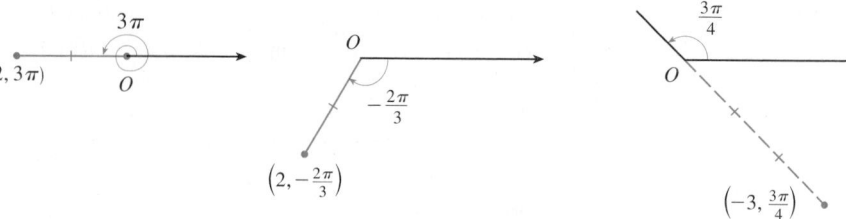

FIGURE 3

In the Cartesian coordinate system every point has only one representation, but in the polar coordinate system each point has many representations. For instance, the point $(1, 5\pi/4)$ in Example 1(a) could be written as $(1, -3\pi/4)$ or $(1, 13\pi/4)$ or $(-1, \pi/4)$. (See Figure 4.)

FIGURE 4

In fact, since a complete counterclockwise rotation is given by an angle 2π, the point represented by polar coordinates (r, θ) is also represented by

$$(r, \theta + 2n\pi) \qquad \text{and} \qquad (-r, \theta + (2n + 1)\pi)$$

where n is any integer.

The connection between polar and Cartesian coordinates can be seen from Figure 5, in which the pole corresponds to the origin and the polar axis coincides with the positive x-axis. If the point P has Cartesian coordinates (x, y) and polar coordinates (r, θ), then, from the figure, we have

$$\cos \theta = \frac{x}{r} \qquad \sin \theta = \frac{y}{r}$$

and so

FIGURE 5

$$x = r \cos \theta \qquad y = r \sin \theta$$

Although Equations 1 were deduced from Figure 5, which illustrates the case where $r > 0$ and $0 < \theta < \pi/2$, these equations are valid for all values of r and θ. (See the general definition of $\sin \theta$ and $\cos \theta$ in Appendix D.)

Equations 1 allow us to find the Cartesian coordinates of a point when the polar coordinates are known. To find r and θ when x and y are known, we use the equations

$$\boxed{\;r^2 = x^2 + y^2 \qquad \tan\theta = \frac{y}{x}\;}$$

2

which can be deduced from Equations 1 or simply read from Figure 5.

EXAMPLE 2 Convert the point $(2, \pi/3)$ from polar to Cartesian coordinates.

SOLUTION Since $r = 2$ and $\theta = \pi/3$, Equations 1 give

$$x = r\cos\theta = 2\cos\frac{\pi}{3} = 2 \cdot \frac{1}{2} = 1$$

$$y = r\sin\theta = 2\sin\frac{\pi}{3} = 2 \cdot \frac{\sqrt{3}}{2} = \sqrt{3}$$

Therefore, the point is $\left(1, \sqrt{3}\right)$ in Cartesian coordinates.

EXAMPLE 3 Represent the point with Cartesian coordinates $(1, -1)$ in terms of polar coordinates.

SOLUTION If we choose r to be positive, then Equations 2 give

$$r = \sqrt{x^2 + y^2} = \sqrt{1^2 + (-1)^2} = \sqrt{2}$$

$$\tan\theta = \frac{y}{x} = -1$$

Since the point $(1, -1)$ lies in the fourth quadrant, we can choose $\theta = -\pi/4$ or $\theta = 7\pi/4$. Thus, one possible answer is $\left(\sqrt{2}, -\pi/4\right)$; another is $\left(\sqrt{2}, 7\pi/4\right)$.

NOTE ∘ Equations 2 do not uniquely determine θ when x and y are given because, as θ increases through the interval $0 \leq \theta < 2\pi$, each value of $\tan\theta$ occurs twice. Therefore, in converting from Cartesian to polar coordinates, it's not good enough just to find r and θ that satisfy Equations 2. As in Example 3, we must choose θ so that the point (r, θ) lies in the correct quadrant.

‖‖‖ **Polar Curves**

The **graph of a polar equation** $r = f(\theta)$, or more generally $F(r, \theta) = 0$, consists of all points P that have at least one polar representation (r, θ) whose coordinates satisfy the equation.

EXAMPLE 4 What curve is represented by the polar equation $r = 2$?

SOLUTION The curve consists of all points (r, θ) with $r = 2$. Since r represents the distance from the point to the pole, the curve $r = 2$ represents the circle with center O and radius 2. In general, the equation $r = a$ represents a circle with center O and radius $|a|$. (See Figure 6.)

FIGURE 6

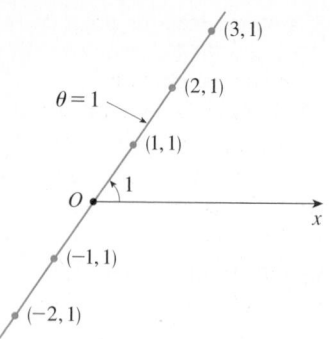

FIGURE 7

EXAMPLE 5 Sketch the polar curve $\theta = 1$.

SOLUTION This curve consists of all points (r, θ) such that the polar angle θ is 1 radian. It is the straight line that passes through O and makes an angle of 1 radian with the polar axis (see Figure 7). Notice that the points $(r, 1)$ on the line with $r > 0$ are in the first quadrant, whereas those with $r < 0$ are in the third quadrant.

EXAMPLE 6
(a) Sketch the curve with polar equation $r = 2 \cos \theta$.
(b) Find a Cartesian equation for this curve.

SOLUTION
(a) In Figure 8 we find the values of r for some convenient values of θ and plot the corresponding points (r, θ). Then we join these points to sketch the curve, which appears to be a circle. We have used only values of θ between 0 and π, since if we let θ increase beyond π, we obtain the same points again.

FIGURE 8

Table of values and graph of $r = 2 \cos \theta$

θ	$r = 2 \cos \theta$
0	2
$\pi/6$	$\sqrt{3}$
$\pi/4$	$\sqrt{2}$
$\pi/3$	1
$\pi/2$	0
$2\pi/3$	-1
$3\pi/4$	$-\sqrt{2}$
$5\pi/6$	$-\sqrt{3}$
π	-2

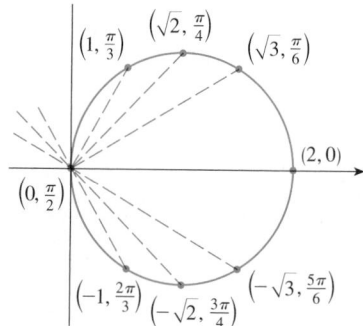

(b) To convert the given equation into a Cartesian equation we use Equations 1 and 2. From $x = r \cos \theta$ we have $\cos \theta = x/r$, so the equation $r = 2 \cos \theta$ becomes $r = 2x/r$, which gives

$$2x = r^2 = x^2 + y^2 \quad \text{or} \quad x^2 + y^2 - 2x = 0$$

Completing the square, we obtain

$$(x - 1)^2 + y^2 = 1$$

which is an equation of a circle with center $(1, 0)$ and radius 1.

||| Figure 9 shows a geometrical illustration that the circle in Example 6 has the equation $r = 2 \cos \theta$. The angle OPQ is a right angle (Why?) and so $r/2 = \cos \theta$.

FIGURE 9

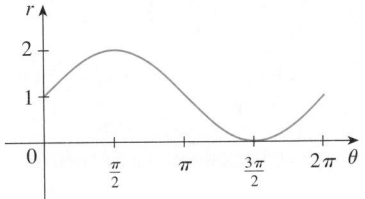

FIGURE 10

$r = 1 + \sin\theta$ in Cartesian coordinates,
$0 \le \theta \le 2\pi$

EXAMPLE 7 Sketch the curve $r = 1 + \sin\theta$.

SOLUTION Instead of plotting points as in Example 6, we first sketch the graph of $r = 1 + \sin\theta$ in *Cartesian* coordinates in Figure 10 by shifting the sine curve up one unit. This enables us to read at a glance the values of r that correspond to increasing values of θ. For instance, we see that as θ increases from 0 to $\pi/2$, r (the distance from O) increases from 1 to 2, so we sketch the corresponding part of the polar curve in Figure 11(a). As θ increases from $\pi/2$ to π, Figure 10 shows that r decreases from 2 to 1, so we sketch the next part of the curve as in Figure 11(b). As θ increases from π to $3\pi/2$, r decreases from 1 to 0 as shown in part (c). Finally, as θ increases from $3\pi/2$ to 2π, r increases from 0 to 1 as shown in part (d). If we let θ increase beyond 2π or decrease beyond 0, we would simply retrace our path. Putting together the parts of the curve from Figure 11(a)–(d), we sketch the complete curve in part (e). It is called a **cardioid** because it's shaped like a heart.

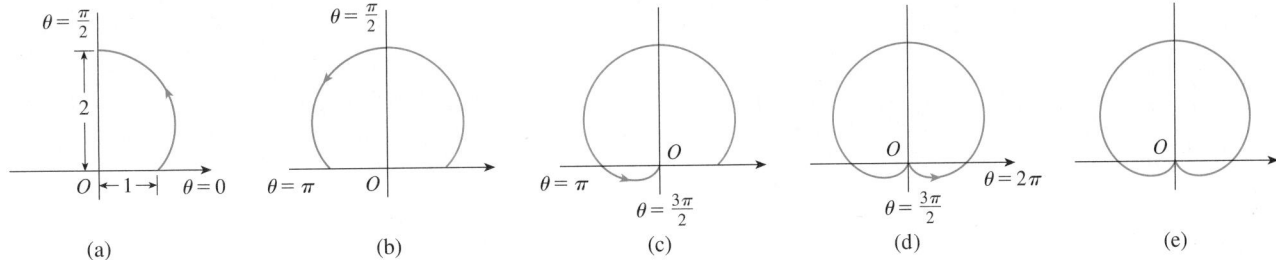

(a)   (b)   (c)   (d)   (e)

FIGURE 11

Stages in sketching the cardioid $r = 1 + \sin\theta$

TEC Module 11.3 helps you see how polar curves are traced out by showing animations similar to Figures 10–13. Tangents to these polar curves can also be visualized as in Figure 15 (see page 712).

EXAMPLE 8 Sketch the curve $r = \cos 2\theta$.

SOLUTION As in Example 7, we first sketch $r = \cos 2\theta$, $0 \le \theta \le 2\pi$, in Cartesian coordinates in Figure 12. As θ increases from 0 to $\pi/4$, Figure 12 shows that r decreases from 1 to 0 and so we draw the corresponding portion of the polar curve in Figure 13 (indicated by ①). As θ increases from $\pi/4$ to $\pi/2$, r goes from 0 to -1. This means that the distance from O increases from 0 to 1, but instead of being in the first quadrant this portion of the polar curve (indicated by ②) lies on the opposite side of the pole in the third quadrant. The remainder of the curve is drawn in a similar fashion, with the arrows and numbers indicating the order in which the portions are traced out. The resulting curve has four loops and is called a **four-leaved rose**.

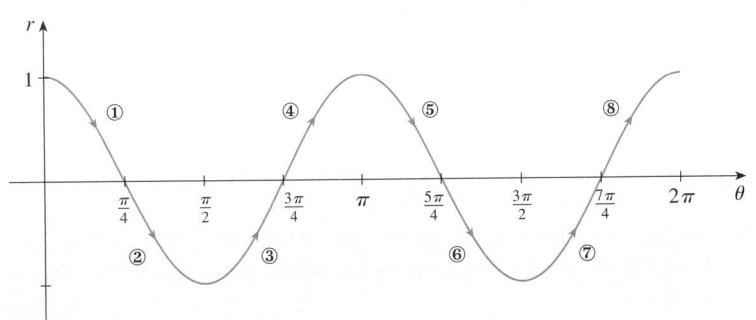

FIGURE 12

$r = \cos 2\theta$ in Cartesian coordinates

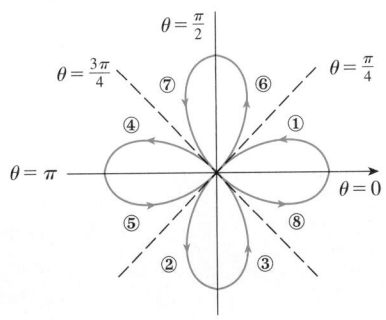

FIGURE 13

Four-leaved rose $r = \cos 2\theta$

|||| **Symmetry**

When we sketch polar curves it is sometimes helpful to take advantage of symmetry. The following three rules are explained by Figure 14.

(a) If a polar equation is unchanged when θ is replaced by $-\theta$, the curve is symmetric about the polar axis.

(b) If the equation is unchanged when r is replaced by $-r$, or when θ is replaced by $\theta + \pi$, the curve is symmetric about the pole. (This means that the curve remains unchanged if we rotate it through $180°$ about the origin.)

(c) If the equation is unchanged when θ is replaced by $\pi - \theta$, the curve is symmetric about the vertical line $\theta = \pi/2$.

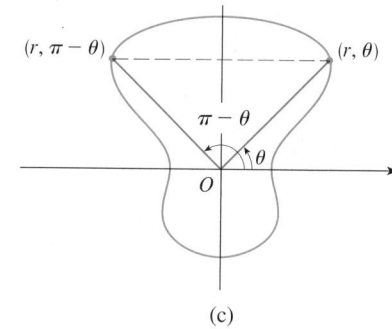

(a)

(b)

(c)

FIGURE 14

The curves sketched in Examples 6 and 8 are symmetric about the polar axis, since $\cos(-\theta) = \cos\theta$. The curves in Examples 7 and 8 are symmetric about $\theta = \pi/2$ because $\sin(\pi - \theta) = \sin\theta$ and $\cos 2(\pi - \theta) = \cos 2\theta$. The four-leaved rose is also symmetric about the pole. These symmetry properties could have been used in sketching the curves. For instance, in Example 6 we need only have plotted points for $0 \leq \theta \leq \pi/2$ and then reflected about the polar axis to obtain the complete circle.

|||| **Tangents to Polar Curves**

To find a tangent line to a polar curve $r = f(\theta)$ we regard θ as a parameter and write its parametric equations as

$$x = r\cos\theta = f(\theta)\cos\theta \qquad y = r\sin\theta = f(\theta)\sin\theta$$

Then, using the method for finding slopes of parametric curves (Equation 11.2.2) and the Product Rule, we have

$$\boxed{3} \qquad \frac{dy}{dx} = \frac{\dfrac{dy}{d\theta}}{\dfrac{dx}{d\theta}} = \frac{\dfrac{dr}{d\theta}\sin\theta + r\cos\theta}{\dfrac{dr}{d\theta}\cos\theta - r\sin\theta}$$

We locate horizontal tangents by finding the points where $dy/d\theta = 0$ (provided that $dx/d\theta \neq 0$). Likewise, we locate vertical tangents at the points where $dx/d\theta = 0$ (provided that $dy/d\theta \neq 0$).

Notice that if we are looking for tangent lines at the pole, then $r = 0$ and Equation 3 simplifies to

$$\frac{dy}{dx} = \tan\theta \qquad \text{if} \quad \frac{dr}{d\theta} \neq 0$$

For instance, in Example 8 we found that $r = \cos 2\theta = 0$ when $\theta = \pi/4$ or $3\pi/4$. This means that the lines $\theta = \pi/4$ and $\theta = 3\pi/4$ (or $y = x$ and $y = -x$) are tangent lines to $r = \cos 2\theta$ at the origin.

EXAMPLE 9

(a) For the cardioid $r = 1 + \sin\theta$ of Example 7, find the slope of the tangent line when $\theta = \pi/3$.

(b) Find the points on the cardioid where the tangent line is horizontal or vertical.

SOLUTION Using Equation 3 with $r = 1 + \sin\theta$, we have

$$\frac{dy}{dx} = \frac{\dfrac{dr}{d\theta}\sin\theta + r\cos\theta}{\dfrac{dr}{d\theta}\cos\theta - r\sin\theta} = \frac{\cos\theta\sin\theta + (1 + \sin\theta)\cos\theta}{\cos\theta\cos\theta - (1 + \sin\theta)\sin\theta}$$

$$= \frac{\cos\theta(1 + 2\sin\theta)}{1 - 2\sin^2\theta - \sin\theta} = \frac{\cos\theta(1 + 2\sin\theta)}{(1 + \sin\theta)(1 - 2\sin\theta)}$$

(a) The slope of the tangent at the point where $\theta = \pi/3$ is

$$\left.\frac{dy}{dx}\right|_{\theta=\pi/3} = \frac{\cos(\pi/3)(1 + 2\sin(\pi/3))}{(1 + \sin(\pi/3))(1 - 2\sin(\pi/3))}$$

$$= \frac{\frac{1}{2}(1 + \sqrt{3})}{(1 + \sqrt{3}/2)(1 - \sqrt{3})} = \frac{1 + \sqrt{3}}{(2 + \sqrt{3})(1 - \sqrt{3})}$$

$$= \frac{1 + \sqrt{3}}{-1 - \sqrt{3}} = -1$$

(b) Observe that

$$\frac{dy}{d\theta} = \cos\theta(1 + 2\sin\theta) = 0 \qquad \text{when } \theta = \frac{\pi}{2}, \frac{3\pi}{2}, \frac{7\pi}{6}, \frac{11\pi}{6}$$

$$\frac{dx}{d\theta} = (1 + \sin\theta)(1 - 2\sin\theta) = 0 \qquad \text{when } \theta = \frac{3\pi}{2}, \frac{\pi}{6}, \frac{5\pi}{6}$$

Therefore, there are horizontal tangents at the points $(2, \pi/2)$, $(\frac{1}{2}, 7\pi/6)$, $(\frac{1}{2}, 11\pi/6)$ and vertical tangents at $(\frac{3}{2}, \pi/6)$ and $(\frac{3}{2}, 5\pi/6)$. When $\theta = 3\pi/2$, both $dy/d\theta$ and $dx/d\theta$ are 0, so we must be careful. Using l'Hospital's Rule, we have

$$\lim_{\theta\to(3\pi/2)^-}\frac{dy}{dx} = \left(\lim_{\theta\to(3\pi/2)^-}\frac{1 + 2\sin\theta}{1 - 2\sin\theta}\right)\left(\lim_{\theta\to(3\pi/2)^-}\frac{\cos\theta}{1 + \sin\theta}\right)$$

$$= -\frac{1}{3}\lim_{\theta\to(3\pi/2)^-}\frac{\cos\theta}{1 + \sin\theta}$$

$$= -\frac{1}{3}\lim_{\theta\to(3\pi/2)^-}\frac{-\sin\theta}{\cos\theta} = \infty$$

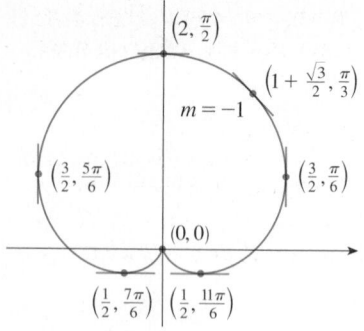

FIGURE 15

Tangent lines for $r = 1 + \sin \theta$

By symmetry,

$$\lim_{\theta \to (3\pi/2)^+} \frac{dy}{dx} = -\infty$$

Thus, there is a vertical tangent line at the pole (see Figure 15).

NOTE ▫ Instead of having to remember Equation 3, we could employ the method used to derive it. For instance, in Example 9 we could have written

$$x = r \cos \theta = (1 + \sin \theta) \cos \theta = \cos \theta + \tfrac{1}{2} \sin 2\theta$$

$$y = r \sin \theta = (1 + \sin \theta) \sin \theta = \sin \theta + \sin^2 \theta$$

Then we have

$$\frac{dy}{dx} = \frac{dy/d\theta}{dx/d\theta} = \frac{\cos \theta + 2 \sin \theta \, \cos \theta}{-\sin \theta + \cos 2\theta} = \frac{\cos \theta + \sin 2\theta}{-\sin \theta + \cos 2\theta}$$

which is equivalent to our previous expression.

||||| Graphing Polar Curves with Graphing Devices

Although it's useful to be able to sketch simple polar curves by hand, we need to use a graphing calculator or computer when we are faced with a curve as complicated as the one shown in Figure 16.

Some graphing devices have commands that enable us to graph polar curves directly. With other machines we need to convert to parametric equations first. In this case we take the polar equation $r = f(\theta)$ and write its parametric equations as

$$x = r \cos \theta = f(\theta) \cos \theta \qquad y = r \sin \theta = f(\theta) \sin \theta$$

Some machines require that the parameter be called t rather than θ.

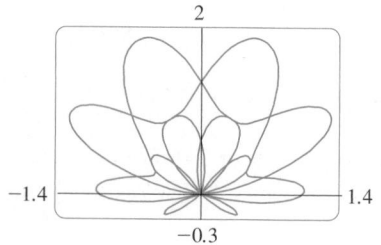

FIGURE 16

$r = \sin \theta + \sin^3(5\theta/2)$

EXAMPLE 10 Graph the curve $r = \sin(8\theta/5)$.

SOLUTION Let's assume that our graphing device doesn't have a built-in polar graphing command. In this case we need to work with the corresponding parametric equations, which are

$$x = r \cos \theta = \sin(8\theta/5) \cos \theta \qquad y = r \sin \theta = \sin(8\theta/5) \sin \theta$$

In any case we need to determine the domain for θ. So we ask ourselves: How many complete rotations are required until the curve starts to repeat itself? If the answer is n, then

$$\sin \frac{8(\theta + 2n\pi)}{5} = \sin \left(\frac{8\theta}{5} + \frac{16n\pi}{5} \right) = \sin \frac{8\theta}{5}$$

and so we require that $16n\pi/5$ be an even multiple of π. This will first occur when $n = 5$. Therefore, we will graph the entire curve if we specify that $0 \le \theta \le 10\pi$. Switching from θ to t, we have the equations

$$x = \sin(8t/5) \cos t \qquad y = \sin(8t/5) \sin t \qquad 0 \le t \le 10\pi$$

and Figure 17 shows the resulting curve. Notice that this rose has 16 loops.

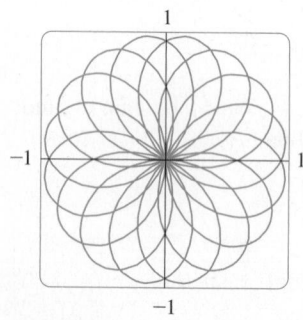

FIGURE 17

$r = \sin(8\theta/5)$

EXAMPLE 11 Investigate the family of polar curves given by $r = 1 + c \sin \theta$. How does the shape change as c changes? (These curves are called **limaçons**, after a French word for snail, because of the shape of the curves for certain values of c.)

SOLUTION Figure 18 shows computer-drawn graphs for various values of c. For $c > 1$ there is a loop that decreases in size as c decreases. When $c = 1$ the loop disappears and the curve becomes the cardioid that we sketched in Example 7. For c between 1 and $\frac{1}{2}$ the cardioid's cusp is smoothed out and becomes a "dimple." When c decreases from $\frac{1}{2}$ to 0, the limaçon is shaped like an oval. This oval becomes more circular as $c \to 0$, and when $c = 0$ the curve is just the circle $r = 1$.

▓ In Exercise 53 you are asked to prove analytically what we have discovered from the graphs in Figure 18.

     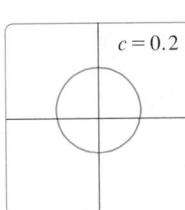

$c = 2.5$ $c = 1.7$ $c = 1$ $c = 0.7$ $c = 0.5$ $c = 0.2$

     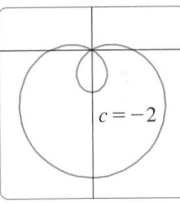

$c = 0$ $c = -0.2$ $c = -0.5$ $c = -0.8$ $c = -1$ $c = -2$

FIGURE 18
Members of the family of limaçons $r = 1 + c \sin \theta$

The remaining parts of Figure 18 show that as c becomes negative, the shapes change in reverse order. In fact, these curves are reflections about the horizontal axis of the corresponding curves with positive c.

11.3 Exercises

1–2 ▓ Plot the point whose polar coordinates are given. Then find two other pairs of polar coordinates of this point, one with $r > 0$ and one with $r < 0$.

1. (a) $(1, \pi/2)$ (b) $(-2, \pi/4)$ (c) $(3, 2)$

2. (a) $(3, 0)$ (b) $(2, -\pi/7)$ (c) $(-1, -\pi/2)$

3–4 ▓ Plot the point whose polar coordinates are given. Then find the Cartesian coordinates of the point.

3. (a) $(3, \pi/2)$ (b) $(2\sqrt{2}, 3\pi/4)$ (c) $(-1, \pi/3)$

4. (a) $(2, 2\pi/3)$ (b) $(4, 3\pi)$ (c) $(-2, -5\pi/6)$

5–6 ▓ The Cartesian coordinates of a point are given.
(i) Find polar coordinates (r, θ) of the point, where $r > 0$ and $0 \le \theta < 2\pi$.
(ii) Find polar coordinates (r, θ) of the point, where $r < 0$ and $0 \le \theta < 2\pi$.

5. (a) $(1, 1)$ (b) $(2\sqrt{3}, -2)$

6. (a) $\left(-1, -\sqrt{3}\right)$ (b) $(-2, 3)$

7–12 ▓ Sketch the region in the plane consisting of points whose polar coordinates satisfy the given conditions.

7. $1 \le r \le 2$

8. $r \ge 0, \quad \pi/3 \le \theta \le 2\pi/3$

9. $0 \le r < 4, \quad -\pi/2 \le \theta < \pi/6$

10. $2 < r \le 5, \quad 3\pi/4 < \theta < 5\pi/4$

11. $2 < r < 3, \quad 5\pi/3 \le \theta \le 7\pi/3$

12. $-1 \le r \le 1, \quad \pi/4 \le \theta \le 3\pi/4$

13. Find the distance between the points with polar coordinates $(1, \pi/6)$ and $(3, 3\pi/4)$.

14. Find a formula for the distance between the points with polar coordinates (r_1, θ_1) and (r_2, θ_2).

15–20 ||| Identify the curve by finding a Cartesian equation for the curve.

15. $r = 2$

16. $r \cos \theta = 1$

17. $r = 3 \sin \theta$

18. $r = 2 \sin \theta + 2 \cos \theta$

19. $r = \csc \theta$

20. $r = \tan \theta \sec \theta$

21–26 ||| Find a polar equation for the curve represented by the given Cartesian equation.

21. $x = 3$

22. $x^2 + y^2 = 9$

23. $x = -y^2$

24. $x + y = 9$

25. $x^2 + y^2 = 2cx$

26. $x^2 - y^2 = 1$

27–28 ||| For each of the described curves, decide if the curve would be more easily given by a polar equation or a Cartesian equation. Then write an equation for the curve.

27. (a) A line through the origin that makes an angle of $\pi/6$ with the positive x-axis
(b) A vertical line through the point $(3, 3)$

28. (a) A circle with radius 5 and center $(2, 3)$
(b) A circle centered at the origin with radius 4

29–46 ||| Sketch the curve with the given polar equation.

29. $\theta = -\pi/6$

30. $r^2 - 3r + 2 = 0$

31. $r = \sin \theta$

32. $r = -3 \cos \theta$

33. $r = 2(1 - \sin \theta)$

34. $r = 1 - 3 \cos \theta$

35. $r = \theta, \quad \theta \geq 0$

36. $r = \ln \theta, \quad \theta \geq 1$

37. $r = \sin 2\theta$

38. $r = 2 \cos 3\theta$

39. $r = 2 \cos 4\theta$

40. $r = \sin 5\theta$

41. $r^2 = 4 \cos 2\theta$

42. $r^2 = \sin 2\theta$

43. $r = 2 \cos(3\theta/2)$

44. $r^2 \theta = 1$

45. $r = 1 + 2 \cos 2\theta$

46. $r = 1 + 2 \cos(\theta/2)$

47–48 ||| The figure shows the graph of r as a function of θ in Cartesian coordinates. Use it to sketch the corresponding polar curve.

47.

48.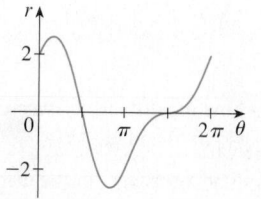

49. Show that the polar curve $r = 4 + 2 \sec \theta$ (called a **conchoid**) has the line $x = 2$ as a vertical asymptote by showing that $\lim_{r \to \pm\infty} x = 2$. Use this fact to help sketch the conchoid.

50. Show that the curve $r = 2 - \csc \theta$ (also a conchoid) has the line $y = -1$ as a horizontal asymptote by showing that $\lim_{r \to \pm\infty} y = -1$. Use this fact to help sketch the conchoid.

51. Show that the curve $r = \sin \theta \tan \theta$ (called a **cissoid of Diocles**) has the line $x = 1$ as a vertical asymptote. Show also that the curve lies entirely within the vertical strip $0 \leq x < 1$. Use these facts to help sketch the cissoid.

52. Sketch the curve $(x^2 + y^2)^3 = 4x^2y^2$.

53. (a) In Example 11 the graphs suggest that the limaçon $r = 1 + c \sin \theta$ has an inner loop when $|c| > 1$. Prove that this is true, and find the values of θ that correspond to the inner loop.
(b) From Figure 18 it appears that the limaçon loses its dimple when $c = \frac{1}{2}$. Prove this.

54. Match the polar equations with the graphs labeled I–VI. Give reasons for your choices. (Don't use a graphing device.)
(a) $r = \sin(\theta/2)$
(b) $r = \sin(\theta/4)$
(c) $r = \sec(3\theta)$
(d) $r = \theta \sin \theta$
(e) $r = 1 + 4 \cos 5\theta$
(f) $r = 1/\sqrt{\theta}$

I   II   III

IV   V   VI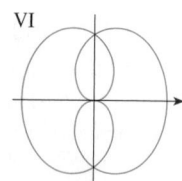

55–60 ||| Find the slope of the tangent line to the given polar curve at the point specified by the value of θ.

55. $r = 2 \sin \theta, \quad \theta = \pi/6$

56. $r = 2 - \sin \theta, \quad \theta = \pi/3$

57. $r = 1/\theta, \quad \theta = \pi$

58. $r = \ln \theta, \quad \theta = e$

59. $r = 1 + \cos \theta, \quad \theta = \pi/6$

60. $r = \sin 3\theta, \quad \theta = \pi/6$

61–66 ||| Find the points on the given curve where the tangent line is horizontal or vertical.

61. $r = 3 \cos \theta$

62. $r = \cos \theta + \sin \theta$

63. $r = 1 + \cos \theta$

64. $r = e^\theta$

65. $r = \cos 2\theta$

66. $r^2 = \sin 2\theta$

67. Show that the polar equation $r = a \sin\theta + b \cos\theta$, where $ab \neq 0$, represents a circle, and find its center and radius.

68. Show that the curves $r = a \sin\theta$ and $r = a \cos\theta$ intersect at right angles.

69–74 ▐▐▐▐ Use a graphing device to graph the polar curve. Choose the parameter interval to make sure that you produce the entire curve.

69. $r = 1 + 2\sin(\theta/2)$ (nephroid of Freeth)

70. $r = \sqrt{1 - 0.8\sin^2\theta}$ (hippopede)

71. $r = e^{\sin\theta} - 2\cos(4\theta)$ (butterfly curve)

72. $r = \sin^2(4\theta) + \cos(4\theta)$

73. $r = 2 - 5\sin(\theta/6)$

74. $r = \cos(\theta/2) + \cos(\theta/3)$

75. How are the graphs of $r = 1 + \sin(\theta - \pi/6)$ and $r = 1 + \sin(\theta - \pi/3)$ related to the graph of $r = 1 + \sin\theta$? In general, how is the graph of $r = f(\theta - \alpha)$ related to the graph of $r = f(\theta)$?

76. Use a graph to estimate the y-coordinate of the highest points on the curve $r = \sin 2\theta$. Then use calculus to find the exact value.

77. (a) Investigate the family of curves defined by the polar equations $r = \sin n\theta$, where n is a positive integer. How is the number of loops related to n?
(b) What happens if the equation in part (a) is replaced by $r = |\sin n\theta|$?

78. A family of curves is given by the equations $r = 1 + c \sin n\theta$, where c is a real number and n is a positive integer. How does the graph change as n increases? How does it change as c changes? Illustrate by graphing enough members of the family to support your conclusions.

79. A family of curves has polar equations

$$r = \frac{1 - a\cos\theta}{1 + a\cos\theta}$$

Investigate how the graph changes as the number a changes. In particular, you should identify the transitional values of a for which the basic shape of the curve changes.

80. The astronomer Giovanni Cassini (1625–1712) studied the family of curves with polar equations

$$r^4 - 2c^2 r^2 \cos 2\theta + c^4 - a^4 = 0$$

where a and c are positive real numbers. These curves are called the **ovals of Cassini** even though they are oval shaped only for certain values of a and c. (Cassini thought that these curves might represent planetary orbits better than Kepler's ellipses.) Investigate the variety of shapes that these curves may have. In particular, how are a and c related to each other when the curve splits into two parts?

81. Let P be any point (except the origin) on the curve $r = f(\theta)$. If ψ is the angle between the tangent line at P and the radial line OP, show that

$$\tan\psi = \frac{r}{dr/d\theta}$$

[*Hint:* Observe that $\psi = \phi - \theta$ in the figure.]

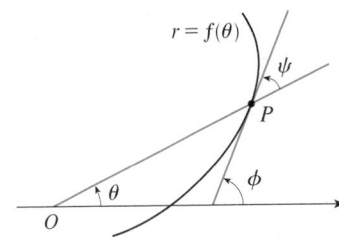

82. (a) Use Exercise 81 to show that the angle between the tangent line and the radial line is $\psi = \pi/4$ at every point on the curve $r = e^\theta$.
(b) Illustrate part (a) by graphing the curve and the tangent lines at the points where $\theta = 0$ and $\pi/2$.
(c) Prove that any polar curve $r = f(\theta)$ with the property that the angle ψ between the radial line and the tangent line is a constant must be of the form $r = Ce^{k\theta}$, where C and k are constants.

11.4 Areas and Lengths in Polar Coordinates

In this section we develop the formula for the area of a region whose boundary is given by a polar equation. We need to use the formula for the area of a sector of a circle

$$\boxed{1} \qquad A = \tfrac{1}{2}r^2\theta$$

where, as in Figure 1, r is the radius and θ is the radian measure of the central angle. Formula 1 follows from the fact that the area of a sector is proportional to its central angle: $A = (\theta/2\pi)\pi r^2 = \tfrac{1}{2}r^2\theta$. (See also Exercise 35 in Section 8.3.)

FIGURE 1

FIGURE 2

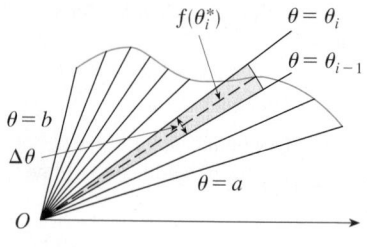

FIGURE 3

Let $\mathcal{R}$ be the region, illustrated in Figure 2, bounded by the polar curve $r = f(\theta)$ and by the rays $\theta = a$ and $\theta = b$, where f is a positive continuous function and where $0 < b - a \le 2\pi$. We divide the interval $[a, b]$ into subintervals with endpoints θ_0, θ_1, $\theta_2, \ldots, \theta_n$ and equal width $\Delta\theta$. The rays $\theta = \theta_i$ then divide $\mathcal{R}$ into n smaller regions with central angle $\Delta\theta = \theta_i - \theta_{i-1}$. If we choose θ_i^* in the ith subinterval $[\theta_{i-1}, \theta_i]$, then the area ΔA_i of the ith region is approximated by the area of the sector of a circle with central angle $\Delta\theta$ and radius $f(\theta_i^*)$. (See Figure 3.)

Thus, from Formula 1 we have

$$\Delta A_i \approx \tfrac{1}{2}[f(\theta_i^*)]^2 \Delta\theta$$

and so an approximation to the total area A of $\mathcal{R}$ is

$$\boxed{2} \qquad A \approx \sum_{i=1}^{n} \tfrac{1}{2}[f(\theta_i^*)]^2 \Delta\theta$$

It appears from Figure 3 that the approximation in (2) improves as $n \to \infty$. But the sums in (2) are Riemann sums for the function $g(\theta) = \tfrac{1}{2}[f(\theta)]^2$, so

$$\lim_{n \to \infty} \sum_{i=1}^{n} \tfrac{1}{2}[f(\theta_i^*)]^2 \Delta\theta = \int_a^b \tfrac{1}{2}[f(\theta)]^2 \, d\theta$$

It therefore appears plausible (and can in fact be proved) that the formula for the area A of the polar region $\mathcal{R}$ is

$$\boxed{3} \qquad A = \int_a^b \tfrac{1}{2}[f(\theta)]^2 \, d\theta$$

Formula 3 is often written as

$$\boxed{4} \qquad A = \int_a^b \tfrac{1}{2} r^2 \, d\theta$$

with the understanding that $r = f(\theta)$. Note the similarity between Formulas 1 and 4.

When we apply Formula 3 or 4 it is helpful to think of the area as being swept out by a rotating ray through O that starts with angle a and ends with angle b.

EXAMPLE 1 Find the area enclosed by one loop of the four-leaved rose $r = \cos 2\theta$.

SOLUTION The curve $r = \cos 2\theta$ was sketched in Example 8 in Section 11.3. Notice from Figure 4 that the region enclosed by the right loop is swept out by a ray that rotates from $\theta = -\pi/4$ to $\theta = \pi/4$. Therefore, Formula 4 gives

$$A = \int_{-\pi/4}^{\pi/4} \tfrac{1}{2} r^2 \, d\theta = \tfrac{1}{2} \int_{-\pi/4}^{\pi/4} \cos^2 2\theta \, d\theta$$

$$= \int_0^{\pi/4} \cos^2 2\theta \, d\theta = \int_0^{\pi/4} \tfrac{1}{2}(1 + \cos 4\theta) \, d\theta$$

$$= \tfrac{1}{2}\left[\theta + \tfrac{1}{4}\sin 4\theta\right]_0^{\pi/4} = \frac{\pi}{8}$$

FIGURE 4

EXAMPLE 2 Find the area of the region that lies inside the circle $r = 3 \sin \theta$ and outside the cardioid $r = 1 + \sin \theta$.

SOLUTION The cardioid (see Example 7 in Section 11.3) and the circle are sketched in Figure 5 and the desired region is shaded. The values of a and b in Formula 4 are determined by finding the points of intersection of the two curves. They intersect when $3 \sin \theta = 1 + \sin \theta$, which gives $\sin \theta = \frac{1}{2}$, so $\theta = \pi/6, 5\pi/6$. The desired area can be found by subtracting the area inside the cardioid between $\theta = \pi/6$ and $\theta = 5\pi/6$ from the area inside the circle from $\pi/6$ to $5\pi/6$. Thus

$$A = \tfrac{1}{2} \int_{\pi/6}^{5\pi/6} (3 \sin \theta)^2 \, d\theta - \tfrac{1}{2} \int_{\pi/6}^{5\pi/6} (1 + \sin \theta)^2 \, d\theta$$

Since the region is symmetric about the vertical axis $\theta = \pi/2$, we can write

$$A = 2 \left[\tfrac{1}{2} \int_{\pi/6}^{\pi/2} 9 \sin^2\theta \, d\theta - \tfrac{1}{2} \int_{\pi/6}^{\pi/2} (1 + 2 \sin \theta + \sin^2\theta) \, d\theta \right]$$

$$= \int_{\pi/6}^{\pi/2} (8 \sin^2\theta - 1 - 2 \sin \theta) \, d\theta$$

$$= \int_{\pi/6}^{\pi/2} (3 - 4 \cos 2\theta - 2 \sin \theta) \, d\theta \qquad \left[\text{because } \sin^2\theta = \tfrac{1}{2}(1 - \cos 2\theta) \right]$$

$$= 3\theta - 2 \sin 2\theta + 2 \cos \theta \Big]_{\pi/6}^{\pi/2} = \pi$$

Example 2 illustrates the procedure for finding the area of the region bounded by two polar curves. In general, let $\mathcal{R}$ be a region, as illustrated in Figure 6, that is bounded by curves with polar equations $r = f(\theta)$, $r = g(\theta)$, $\theta = a$, and $\theta = b$, where $f(\theta) \geq g(\theta) \geq 0$ and $0 < b - a \leq 2\pi$. The area A of $\mathcal{R}$ is found by subtracting the area inside $r = g(\theta)$ from the area inside $r = f(\theta)$, so using Formula 3 we have

$$A = \int_a^b \tfrac{1}{2} [f(\theta)]^2 \, d\theta - \int_a^b \tfrac{1}{2} [g(\theta)]^2 \, d\theta$$

$$= \tfrac{1}{2} \int_a^b ([f(\theta)]^2 - [g(\theta)]^2) \, d\theta$$

⊘ **CAUTION** ▫ The fact that a single point has many representations in polar coordinates sometimes makes it difficult to find all the points of intersection of two polar curves. For instance, it is obvious from Figure 5 that the circle and the cardioid have three points of intersection; however, in Example 2 we solved the equations $r = 3 \sin \theta$ and $r = 1 + \sin \theta$ and found only two such points, $\left(\frac{3}{2}, \pi/6 \right)$ and $\left(\frac{3}{2}, 5\pi/6 \right)$. The origin is also a point of intersection, but we can't find it by solving the equations of the curves because the origin has no single representation in polar coordinates that satisfies both equations. Notice that, when represented as $(0, 0)$ or $(0, \pi)$, the origin satisfies $r = 3 \sin \theta$ and so it lies on the circle; when represented as $(0, 3\pi/2)$, it satisfies $r = 1 + \sin \theta$ and so it lies on the cardioid. Think of two points moving along the curves as the parameter value θ increases from 0 to 2π. On one curve the origin is reached at $\theta = 0$ and $\theta = \pi$; on the other curve it is reached at $\theta = 3\pi/2$. The points don't collide at the origin because they reach the origin at different times, but the curves intersect there nonetheless.

Thus, to find *all* points of intersection of two polar curves, it is recommended that you draw the graphs of both curves. It is especially convenient to use a graphing calculator or computer to help with this task.

FIGURE 5

FIGURE 6

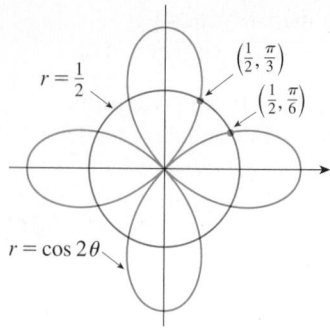

$r = \frac{1}{2}$

$\left(\frac{1}{2}, \frac{\pi}{3}\right)$

$\left(\frac{1}{2}, \frac{\pi}{6}\right)$

$r = \cos 2\theta$

FIGURE 7

EXAMPLE 3 Find all points of intersection of the curves $r = \cos 2\theta$ and $r = \frac{1}{2}$.

SOLUTION If we solve the equations $r = \cos 2\theta$ and $r = \frac{1}{2}$, we get $\cos 2\theta = \frac{1}{2}$ and, therefore, $2\theta = \pi/3, 5\pi/3, 7\pi/3, 11\pi/3$. Thus, the values of θ between 0 and 2π that satisfy both equations are $\theta = \pi/6, 5\pi/6, 7\pi/6, 11\pi/6$. We have found four points of intersection: $\left(\frac{1}{2}, \pi/6\right)$, $\left(\frac{1}{2}, 5\pi/6\right)$, $\left(\frac{1}{2}, 7\pi/6\right)$, and $\left(\frac{1}{2}, 11\pi/6\right)$.

However, you can see from Figure 7 that the curves have four other points of intersection—namely, $\left(\frac{1}{2}, \pi/3\right)$, $\left(\frac{1}{2}, 2\pi/3\right)$, $\left(\frac{1}{2}, 4\pi/3\right)$, and $\left(\frac{1}{2}, 5\pi/3\right)$. These can be found using symmetry or by noticing that another equation of the circle is $r = -\frac{1}{2}$ and then solving the equations $r = \cos 2\theta$ and $r = -\frac{1}{2}$.

▏▏▏▏ Arc Length

To find the length of a polar curve $r = f(\theta)$, $a \le \theta \le b$, we regard θ as a parameter and write the parametric equations of the curve as

$$x = r \cos \theta = f(\theta) \cos \theta \qquad y = r \sin \theta = f(\theta) \sin \theta$$

Using the Product Rule and differentiating with respect to θ, we obtain

$$\frac{dx}{d\theta} = \frac{dr}{d\theta} \cos \theta - r \sin \theta \qquad \frac{dy}{d\theta} = \frac{dr}{d\theta} \sin \theta + r \cos \theta$$

so, using $\cos^2\theta + \sin^2\theta = 1$, we have

$$\left(\frac{dx}{d\theta}\right)^2 + \left(\frac{dy}{d\theta}\right)^2 = \left(\frac{dr}{d\theta}\right)^2 \cos^2\theta - 2r \frac{dr}{d\theta} \cos \theta \sin \theta + r^2 \sin^2\theta$$

$$+ \left(\frac{dr}{d\theta}\right)^2 \sin^2\theta + 2r \frac{dr}{d\theta} \sin \theta \cos \theta + r^2 \cos^2\theta$$

$$= \left(\frac{dr}{d\theta}\right)^2 + r^2$$

Assuming that f' is continuous, we can use Theorem 11.2.6 to write the arc length as

$$L = \int_a^b \sqrt{\left(\frac{dx}{d\theta}\right)^2 + \left(\frac{dy}{d\theta}\right)^2} \, d\theta$$

Therefore, the length of a curve with polar equation $r = f(\theta)$, $a \le \theta \le b$, is

$$\boxed{5 \qquad L = \int_a^b \sqrt{r^2 + \left(\frac{dr}{d\theta}\right)^2} \, d\theta}$$

EXAMPLE 4 Find the length of the cardioid $r = 1 + \sin \theta$.

SOLUTION The cardioid is shown in Figure 8. (We sketched it in Example 7 in Section 11.3.) Its full length is given by the parameter interval $0 \le \theta \le 2\pi$, so Formula 5 gives

$$L = \int_0^{2\pi} \sqrt{r^2 + \left(\frac{dr}{d\theta}\right)^2} \, d\theta = \int_0^{2\pi} \sqrt{(1 + \sin \theta)^2 + \cos^2\theta} \, d\theta$$

$$= \int_0^{2\pi} \sqrt{2 + 2 \sin \theta} \, d\theta$$

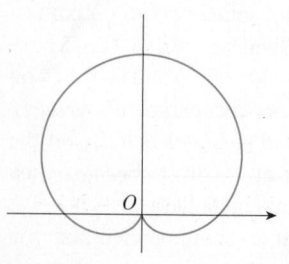

O

FIGURE 8

$r = 1 + \sin \theta$

We could evaluate this integral by multiplying and dividing the integrand by $\sqrt{2 - 2\sin\theta}$, or we could use a computer algebra system. In any event, we find that the length of the cardioid is $L = 8$.

11.4 Exercises

1–4 ||| Find the area of the region that is bounded by the given curve and lies in the specified sector.

1. $r = \sqrt{\theta}, \quad 0 \leqslant \theta \leqslant \pi/4$

2. $r = e^{\theta/2}, \quad \pi \leqslant \theta \leqslant 2\pi$

3. $r = \sin\theta, \quad \pi/3 \leqslant \theta \leqslant 2\pi/3$

4. $r = \sqrt{\sin\theta}, \quad 0 \leqslant \theta \leqslant \pi$

5–8 ||| Find the area of the shaded region.

5.

$r = \theta$

6.

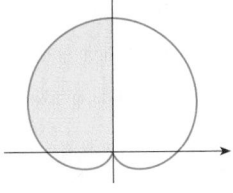

$r = 1 + \sin\theta$

7.

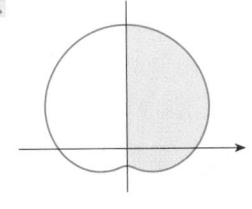

$r = 4 + 3\sin\theta$

8.

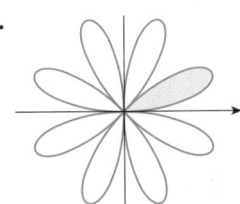

$r = \sin 4\theta$

9–14 ||| Sketch the curve and find the area that it encloses.

9. $r = 3\cos\theta$

10. $r = 3(1 + \cos\theta)$

11. $r^2 = 4\cos 2\theta$

12. $r^2 = \sin 2\theta$

13. $r = 2\cos 3\theta$

14. $r = 2 + \cos 2\theta$

15–16 ||| Graph the curve and find the area that it encloses.

15. $r = 1 + 2\sin 6\theta$

16. $r = 2\sin\theta + 3\sin 9\theta$

17–21 ||| Find the area of the region enclosed by one loop of the curve.

17. $r = \sin 2\theta$

18. $r = 4\sin 3\theta$

19. $r = 3\cos 5\theta$

20. $r = 2\cos 4\theta$

21. $r = 1 + 2\sin\theta$ (inner loop)

22. Find the area enclosed by the loop of the **strophoid** $r = 2\cos\theta - \sec\theta$.

23–28 ||| Find the area of the region that lies inside the first curve and outside the second curve.

23. $r = 4\sin\theta, \quad r = 2$

24. $r = 1 - \sin\theta, \quad r = 1$

25. $r^2 = 8\cos 2\theta, \quad r = 2$

26. $r = 2 + \sin\theta, \quad r = 3\sin\theta$

27. $r = 3\cos\theta, \quad r = 1 + \cos\theta$

28. $r = 1 + \cos\theta, \quad r = 3\cos\theta$

29–34 ||| Find the area of the region that lies inside both curves.

29. $r = \sin\theta, \quad r = \cos\theta$

30. $r = \sin 2\theta, \quad r = \sin\theta$

31. $r = \sin 2\theta, \quad r = \cos 2\theta$

32. $r^2 = 2\sin 2\theta, \quad r = 1$

33. $r = 3 + 2\sin\theta, \quad r = 2$

34. $r = a\sin\theta, \quad r = b\cos\theta, \quad a > 0, \ b > 0$

35. Find the area inside the larger loop and outside the smaller loop of the limaçon $r = \frac{1}{2} + \cos\theta$.

36. Find the area between a large loop and the enclosed small loop of the curve $r = 1 + 2\cos 3\theta$.

37–42 ||| Find all points of intersection of the given curves.

37. $r = \sin\theta, \quad r = \cos\theta$

38. $r = 2, \quad r = 2\cos 2\theta$

39. $r = \cos\theta, \quad r = 1 - \cos\theta$

40. $r = \cos 3\theta, \quad r = \sin 3\theta$

41. $r = \sin\theta, \quad r = \sin 2\theta$

42. $r^2 = \sin 2\theta, \quad r^2 = \cos 2\theta$

43. The points of intersection of the cardioid $r = 1 + \sin\theta$ and the spiral loop $r = 2\theta$, $-\pi/2 \leqslant \theta \leqslant \pi/2$, can't be found exactly. Use a graphing device to find the approximate values of θ at which they intersect. Then use these values to estimate the area that lies inside both curves.

44. Use a graph to estimate the values of θ for which the curves $r = 3 + \sin 5\theta$ and $r = 6\sin\theta$ intersect. Then estimate the area that lies inside both curves.

45–48 ▏▏▏▏ Find the exact length of the polar curve.

45. $r = 3 \sin \theta$, $\quad 0 \le \theta \le \pi/3$ **46.** $r = e^{2\theta}$, $\quad 0 \le \theta \le 2\pi$

47. $r = \theta^2$, $\quad 0 \le \theta \le 2\pi$ **48.** $r = \theta$, $\quad 0 \le \theta \le 2\pi$

49–52 ▏▏▏▏ Use a calculator to find the length of the curve correct to four decimal places.

49. $r = 3 \sin 2\theta$ **50.** $r = 4 \sin 3\theta$

51. $r = \sin(\theta/2)$ **52.** $r = 1 + \cos(\theta/3)$

53–54 ▏▏▏▏ Graph the curve and find its length.

53. $r = \cos^4(\theta/4)$ **54.** $r = \cos^2(\theta/2)$

55. (a) Use Formula 11.2.7 to show that the area of the surface generated by rotating the polar curve

$$r = f(\theta) \qquad a \le \theta \le b$$

(where f' is continuous and $0 \le a < b \le \pi$) about the polar axis is

$$S = \int_a^b 2\pi r \sin \theta \sqrt{r^2 + \left(\frac{dr}{d\theta}\right)^2}\, d\theta$$

(b) Use the formula in part (a) to find the surface area generated by rotating the lemniscate $r^2 = \cos 2\theta$ about the polar axis.

56. (a) Find a formula for the area of the surface generated by rotating the polar curve $r = f(\theta)$, $a \le \theta \le b$ (where f' is continuous and $0 \le a < b \le \pi$), about the line $\theta = \pi/2$.

(b) Find the surface area generated by rotating the lemniscate $r^2 = \cos 2\theta$ about the line $\theta = \pi/2$.

▏▏▏▏ 11.5 Conic Sections

In this section we give geometric definitions of parabolas, ellipses, and hyperbolas and derive their standard equations. They are called **conic sections**, or **conics**, because they result from intersecting a cone with a plane as shown in Figure 1.

ellipse

parabola

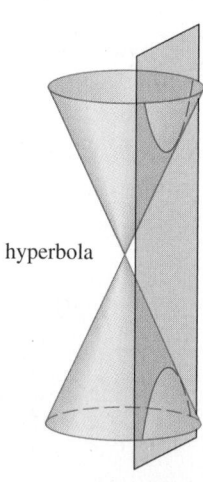
hyperbola

FIGURE 1
Conics

▏▏▏▏ Parabolas

A **parabola** is the set of points in a plane that are equidistant from a fixed point F (called the **focus**) and a fixed line (called the **directrix**). This definition is illustrated by Figure 2. Notice that the point halfway between the focus and the directrix lies on the parabola; it is called the **vertex**. The line through the focus perpendicular to the directrix is called the **axis** of the parabola.

In the 16th century Galileo showed that the path of a projectile that is shot into the air at an angle to the ground is a parabola. Since then, parabolic shapes have been used in designing automobile headlights, reflecting telescopes, and suspension bridges.

FIGURE 2

(See Problem 14 on page 220 for the reflection property of parabolas that makes them so useful.)

We obtain a particularly simple equation for a parabola if we place its vertex at the origin O and its directrix parallel to the x-axis as in Figure 3. If the focus is the point $(0, p)$, then the directrix has the equation $y = -p$. If $P(x, y)$ is any point on the parabola, then the distance from P to the focus is

$$|PF| = \sqrt{x^2 + (y - p)^2}$$

and the distance from P to the directrix is $|y + p|$. (Figure 3 illustrates the case where $p > 0$.) The defining property of a parabola is that these distances are equal:

$$\sqrt{x^2 + (y - p)^2} = |y + p|$$

[We get an] equivalent equation by squaring and simplifying:

$$x^2 + (y - p)^2 = |y + p|^2 = (y + p)^2$$
$$x^2 + y^2 - 2py + p^2 = y^2 + 2py + p^2$$
$$x^2 = 4py$$

[An] equation of the parabola with focus $(0, p)$ and directrix $y = -p$ is

$$x^2 = 4py$$

[If a] $= 1/(4p)$, then the standard equation of a parabola (1) becomes $y = ax^2$. [It opens upward] if $p > 0$ and downward if $p < 0$ [see Figure 4, parts (a) and (b)]. The [parabola is symmet]ric with respect to the y-axis because (1) is unchanged when x is replaced by $-x$.

FIGURE 3

[Handwritten annotation:] I have huge tits would you like to feel them? - girl directly to your right

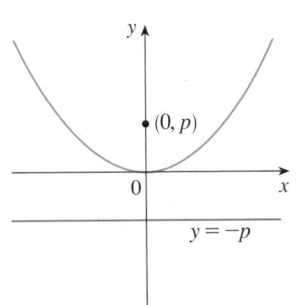

(a) $x^2 = 4py$, $p > 0$

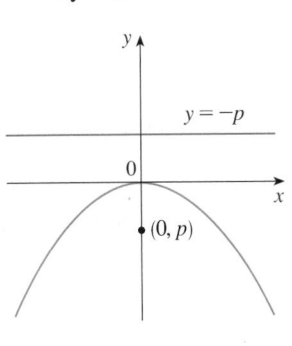

(b) $x^2 = 4py$, $p < 0$

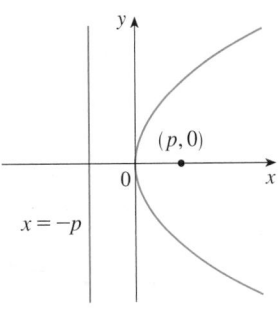

(c) $y^2 = 4px$, $p > 0$

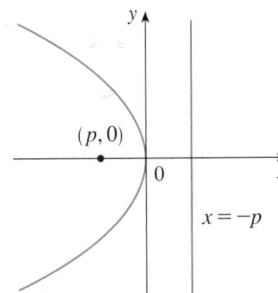

(d) $y^2 = 4px$, $p < 0$

FIGURE 4

If we interchange x and y in (1), we obtain

$$\boxed{2} \qquad \boxed{y^2 = 4px}$$

which is an equation of the parabola with focus $(p, 0)$ and directrix $x = -p$. (Interchanging x and y amounts to reflecting about the diagonal line $y = x$.) The parabola opens to the right if $p > 0$ and to the left if $p < 0$ [see Figure 4, parts (c) and (d)]. In both cases the graph is symmetric with respect to the x-axis, which is the axis of the parabola.

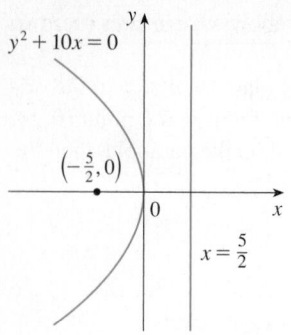

$y^2 + 10x = 0$

$(-\frac{5}{2}, 0)$

$x = \frac{5}{2}$

FIGURE 5

EXAMPLE 1 Find the focus and directrix of the parabola $y^2 + 10x = 0$ and sketch the graph.

SOLUTION If we write the equation as $y^2 = -10x$ and compare it with Equation 2, we see that $4p = -10$, so $p = -\frac{5}{2}$. Thus, the focus is $(p, 0) = (-\frac{5}{2}, 0)$ and the directrix is $x = \frac{5}{2}$. The sketch is shown in Figure 5.

|||| Ellipses

An **ellipse** is the set of points in a plane the sum of whose distances from two fixed points F_1 and F_2 is a constant (see Figure 6). These two fixed points are called the **foci** (plural of **focus**). One of Kepler's laws is that the orbits of the planets in the solar system are ellipses with the Sun at one focus.

P

F_1 F_2

FIGURE 6

In order to obtain the simplest equation for an ellipse, we place the foci on the x-axis at the points $(-c, 0)$ and $(c, 0)$ as in Figure 7 so that the origin is halfway between the foci. Let the sum of the distances from a point on the ellipse to the foci be $2a > 0$. Then $P(x, y)$ is a point on the ellipse when

$$|PF_1| + |PF_2| = 2a$$

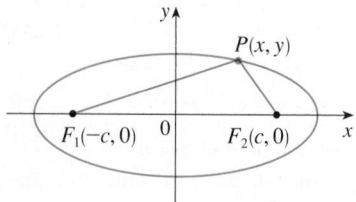

$P(x, y)$

$F_1(-c, 0)$ 0 $F_2(c, 0)$

FIGURE 7

that is,

$$\sqrt{(x + c)^2 + y^2} + \sqrt{(x - c)^2 + y^2} = 2a$$

or

$$\sqrt{(x - c)^2 + y^2} = 2a - \sqrt{(x + c)^2 + y^2}$$

Squaring both sides, we have

$$x^2 - 2cx + c^2 + y^2 = 4a^2 - 4a\sqrt{(x + c)^2 + y^2} + x^2 + 2cx + c^2 + y^2$$

which simplifies to

$$a\sqrt{(x + c)^2 + y^2} = a^2 + cx$$

We square again:

$$a^2(x^2 + 2cx + c^2 + y^2) = a^4 + 2a^2cx + c^2x^2$$

which becomes

$$(a^2 - c^2)x^2 + a^2y^2 = a^2(a^2 - c^2)$$

From triangle F_1F_2P in Figure 7 we see that $2c < 2a$, so $c < a$ and, therefore, $a^2 - c^2 > 0$. For convenience, let $b^2 = a^2 - c^2$. Then the equation of the ellipse becomes $b^2x^2 + a^2y^2 = a^2b^2$ or, if both sides are divided by a^2b^2,

$$\boxed{3} \qquad \frac{x^2}{a^2} + \frac{y^2}{b^2} = 1$$

Since $b^2 = a^2 - c^2 < a^2$, it follows that $b < a$. The x-intercepts are found by setting $y = 0$. Then $x^2/a^2 = 1$, or $x^2 = a^2$, so $x = \pm a$. The corresponding points $(a, 0)$ and $(-a, 0)$ are called the **vertices** of the ellipse and the line segment joining the vertices is called the **major axis**. To find the y-intercepts we set $x = 0$ and obtain $y^2 = b^2$, so $y = \pm b$. Equation 3 is unchanged if x is replaced by $-x$ or y is replaced by $-y$, so the ellipse is symmetric about both axes. Notice that if the foci coincide, then $c = 0$, so $a = b$ and the ellipse becomes a circle with radius $r = a = b$.

We summarize this discussion as follows (see also Figure 8).

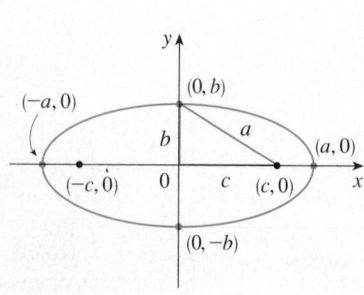

$(-a, 0)$

$(0, b)$

b a

$(a, 0)$

$(-c, 0)$ 0 c $(c, 0)$

$(0, -b)$

FIGURE 8

$\frac{x^2}{a^2} + \frac{y^2}{b^2} = 1$

$\boxed{4}$ The ellipse

$$\frac{x^2}{a^2} + \frac{y^2}{b^2} = 1 \qquad a \geq b > 0$$

has foci $(\pm c, 0)$, where $c^2 = a^2 - b^2$, and vertices $(\pm a, 0)$.

If the foci of an ellipse are located on the y-axis at $(0, \pm c)$, then we can find its equation by interchanging x and y in (4). (See Figure 9.)

---

5   The ellipse

$$\frac{x^2}{b^2} + \frac{y^2}{a^2} = 1 \qquad a \ge b > 0$$

has foci $(0, \pm c)$, where $c^2 = a^2 - b^2$, and vertices $(0, \pm a)$.

EXAMPLE 2   Sketch the graph of $9x^2 + 16y^2 = 144$ and locate the foci.

SOLUTION   Divide both sides of the equation by 144:

$$\frac{x^2}{16} + \frac{y^2}{9} = 1$$

The equation is now in the standard form for an ellipse, so we have $a^2 = 16$, $b^2 = 9$, $a = 4$, and $b = 3$. The x-intercepts are ± 4 and the y-intercepts are ± 3. Also, $c^2 = a^2 - b^2 = 7$, so $c = \sqrt{7}$ and the foci are $(\pm\sqrt{7}, 0)$. The graph is sketched in Figure 10.

EXAMPLE 3   Find an equation of the ellipse with foci $(0, \pm 2)$ and vertices $(0, \pm 3)$.

SOLUTION   Using the notation of (5), we have $c = 2$ and $a = 3$. Then we obtain $b^2 = a^2 - c^2 = 9 - 4 = 5$, so an equation of the ellipse is

$$\frac{x^2}{5} + \frac{y^2}{9} = 1$$

Another way of writing the equation is $9x^2 + 5y^2 = 45$.

Like parabolas, ellipses have an interesting reflection property that has practical consequences. If a source of light or sound is placed at one focus of a surface with elliptical cross-sections, then all the light or sound is reflected off the surface to the other focus (see Exercise 59). This principle is used in *lithotripsy*, a treatment for kidney stones. A reflector with elliptical cross-section is placed in such a way that the kidney stone is at one focus. High-intensity sound waves generated at the other focus are reflected to the stone and destroy it without damaging surrounding tissue. The patient is spared the trauma of surgery and recovers within a few days.

‖‖ Hyperbolas

A **hyperbola** is the set of all points in a plane the difference of whose distances from two fixed points F_1 and F_2 (the foci) is a constant. This definition is illustrated in Figure 11.

Hyperbolas occur frequently as graphs of equations in chemistry, physics, biology, and economics (Boyle's Law, Ohm's Law, supply and demand curves). A particularly significant application of hyperbolas is found in the navigation systems developed in World Wars I and II (see Exercise 51).

Notice that the definition of a hyperbola is similar to that of an ellipse; the only change is that the sum of distances has become a difference of distances. In fact, the derivation of the equation of a hyperbola is also similar to the one given earlier for an ellipse. It is left

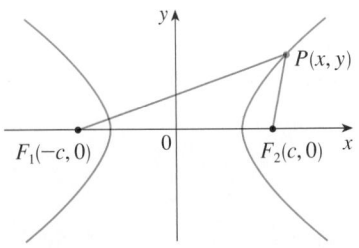

FIGURE 10

$9x^2 + 16y^2 = 144$

FIGURE 11

P is on the hyperbola when

$|PF_1| - |PF_2| = \pm 2a$

as Exercise 52 to show that when the foci are on the x-axis at $(\pm c, 0)$ and the difference of distances is $|PF_1| - |PF_2| = \pm 2a$, then the equation of the hyperbola is

$$\boxed{6} \qquad \frac{x^2}{a^2} - \frac{y^2}{b^2} = 1$$

where $c^2 = a^2 + b^2$. Notice that the x-intercepts are again $\pm a$ and the points $(a, 0)$ and $(-a, 0)$ are the **vertices** of the hyperbola. But if we put $x = 0$ in Equation 6 we get $y^2 = -b^2$, which is impossible, so there is no y-intercept. The hyperbola is symmetric with respect to both axes.

To analyze the hyperbola further, we look at Equation 6 and obtain

$$\frac{x^2}{a^2} = 1 + \frac{y^2}{b^2} \geq 1$$

This shows that $x^2 \geq a^2$, so $|x| = \sqrt{x^2} \geq a$. Therefore, we have $x \geq a$ or $x \leq -a$. This means that the hyperbola consists of two parts, called its *branches*.

When we draw a hyperbola it is useful to first draw its **asymptotes**, which are the dashed lines $y = (b/a)x$ and $y = -(b/a)x$ shown in Figure 12. Both branches of the hyperbola approach the asymptotes; that is, they come arbitrarily close to the asymptotes. [See Exercise 55 in Section 4.5, where $y = (b/a)x$ is shown to be a slant asymptote.]

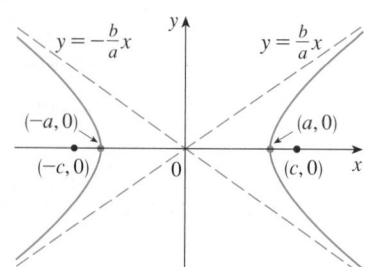

FIGURE 12
$\dfrac{x^2}{a^2} - \dfrac{y^2}{b^2} = 1$

$\boxed{7}$ The hyperbola

$$\frac{x^2}{a^2} - \frac{y^2}{b^2} = 1$$

has foci $(\pm c, 0)$, where $c^2 = a^2 + b^2$, vertices $(\pm a, 0)$, and asymptotes $y = \pm(b/a)x$.

If the foci of a hyperbola are on the y-axis, then by reversing the roles of x and y we obtain the following information, which is illustrated in Figure 13.

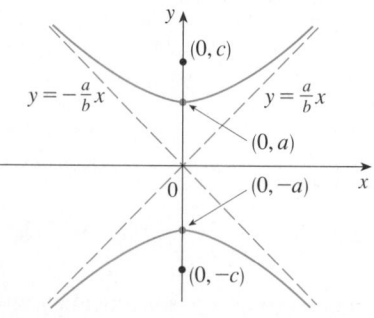

FIGURE 13
$\dfrac{y^2}{a^2} - \dfrac{x^2}{b^2} = 1$

$\boxed{8}$ The hyperbola

$$\frac{y^2}{a^2} - \frac{x^2}{b^2} = 1$$

has foci $(0, \pm c)$, where $c^2 = a^2 + b^2$, vertices $(0, \pm a)$, and asymptotes $y = \pm(a/b)x$.

EXAMPLE 4 Find the foci and asymptotes of the hyperbola $9x^2 - 16y^2 = 144$ and sketch its graph.

SOLUTION If we divide both sides of the equation by 144, it becomes

$$\frac{x^2}{16} - \frac{y^2}{9} = 1$$

which is of the form given in (7) with $a = 4$ and $b = 3$. Since $c^2 = 16 + 9 = 25$, the foci are $(\pm 5, 0)$. The asymptotes are the lines $y = \frac{3}{4}x$ and $y = -\frac{3}{4}x$. The graph is shown in Figure 14.

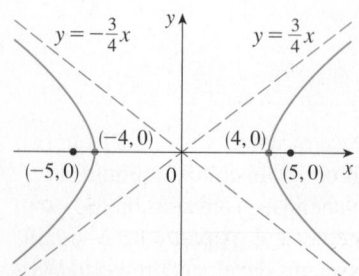

FIGURE 14
$9x^2 - 16y^2 = 144$

EXAMPLE 5 Find the foci and equation of the hyperbola with vertices $(0, \pm1)$ and asymptote $y = 2x$.

SOLUTION From (8) and the given information, we see that $a = 1$ and $a/b = 2$. Thus, $b = a/2 = \frac{1}{2}$ and $c^2 = a^2 + b^2 = \frac{5}{4}$. The foci are $\left(0, \pm\sqrt{5}/2\right)$ and the equation of the hyperbola is

$$y^2 - 4x^2 = 1$$

▥ Shifted Conics

As discussed in Appendix C, we shift conics by taking the standard equations (1), (2), (4), (5), (7), and (8) and replacing x and y by $x - h$ and $y - k$.

EXAMPLE 6 Find an equation of the ellipse with foci $(2, -2)$, $(4, -2)$ and vertices $(1, -2)$, $(5, -2)$.

SOLUTION The major axis is the line segment that joins the vertices $(1, -2)$, $(5, -2)$ and has length 4, so $a = 2$. The distance between the foci is 2, so $c = 1$. Thus, $b^2 = a^2 - c^2 = 3$. Since the center of the ellipse is $(3, -2)$, we replace x and y in (4) by $x - 3$ and $y + 2$ to obtain

$$\frac{(x - 3)^2}{4} + \frac{(y + 2)^2}{3} = 1$$

as the equation of the ellipse.

EXAMPLE 7 Sketch the conic

$$9x^2 - 4y^2 - 72x + 8y + 176 = 0$$

and find its foci.

SOLUTION We complete the squares as follows:

$$4(y^2 - 2y) - 9(x^2 - 8x) = 176$$

$$4(y^2 - 2y + 1) - 9(x^2 - 8x + 16) = 176 + 4 - 144$$

$$4(y - 1)^2 - 9(x - 4)^2 = 36$$

$$\frac{(y - 1)^2}{9} - \frac{(x - 4)^2}{4} = 1$$

This is in the form (8) except that x and y are replaced by $x - 4$ and $y - 1$. Thus, $a^2 = 9$, $b^2 = 4$, and $c^2 = 13$. The hyperbola is shifted four units to the right and one unit upward. The foci are $\left(4, 1 + \sqrt{13}\right)$ and $\left(4, 1 - \sqrt{13}\right)$ and the vertices are $(4, 4)$ and $(4, -2)$. The asymptotes are $y - 1 = \pm\frac{3}{2}(x - 4)$. The hyperbola is sketched in Figure 15.

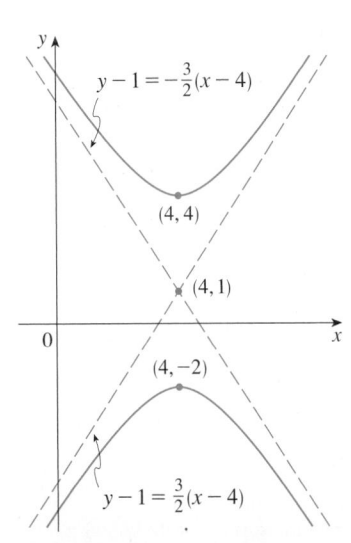

FIGURE 15
$9x^2 - 4y^2 - 72x + 8y + 176 = 0$

11.5 Exercises

1–8 ||| Find the vertex, focus, and directrix of the parabola and sketch its graph.

1. $x = 2y^2$

2. $4y + x^2 = 0$

3. $4x^2 = -y$

4. $y^2 = 12x$

5. $(x + 2)^2 = 8(y - 3)$

6. $x - 1 = (y + 5)^2$

7. $y^2 + 2y + 12x + 25 = 0$

8. $y + 12x - 2x^2 = 16$

9–10 ||| Find an equation of the parabola. Then find the focus and directrix.

9.

10.
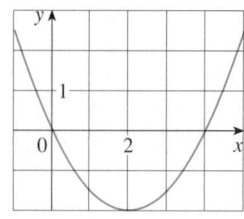

11–16 ||| Find the vertices and foci of the ellipse and sketch its graph.

11. $\dfrac{x^2}{9} + \dfrac{y^2}{5} = 1$

12. $\dfrac{x^2}{64} + \dfrac{y^2}{100} = 1$

13. $4x^2 + y^2 = 16$

14. $4x^2 + 25y^2 = 25$

15. $9x^2 - 18x + 4y^2 = 27$

16. $x^2 + 2y^2 - 6x + 4y + 7 = 0$

17–18 ||| Find an equation of the ellipse. Then find its foci.

17.

18.
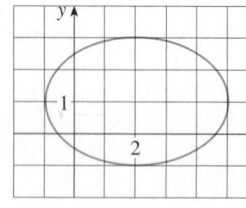

19–24 ||| Find the vertices, foci, and asymptotes of the hyperbola and sketch its graph.

19. $\dfrac{x^2}{144} - \dfrac{y^2}{25} = 1$

20. $\dfrac{y^2}{16} - \dfrac{x^2}{36} = 1$

21. $y^2 - x^2 = 4$

22. $9x^2 - 4y^2 = 36$

23. $2y^2 - 3x^2 - 4y + 12x + 8 = 0$

24. $16x^2 - 9y^2 + 64x - 90y = 305$

25–30 ||| Identify the type of conic section whose equation is given and find the vertices and foci.

25. $x^2 = y + 1$

26. $x^2 = y^2 + 1$

27. $x^2 = 4y - 2y^2$

28. $y^2 - 8y = 6x - 16$

29. $y^2 + 2y = 4x^2 + 3$

30. $4x^2 + 4x + y^2 = 0$

31–48 ||| Find an equation for the conic that satisfies the given conditions.

31. Parabola, vertex $(0, 0)$, focus $(0, -2)$

32. Parabola, vertex $(1, 0)$, directrix $x = -5$

33. Parabola, focus $(-4, 0)$, directrix $x = 2$

34. Parabola, focus $(3, 6)$, vertex $(3, 2)$

35. Parabola, vertex $(0, 0)$, axis the x-axis, passing through $(1, -4)$

36. Parabola, vertical axis, passing through $(-2, 3)$, $(0, 3)$, and $(1, 9)$

37. Ellipse, foci $(\pm 2, 0)$, vertices $(\pm 5, 0)$

38. Ellipse, foci $(0, \pm 5)$, vertices $(0, \pm 13)$

39. Ellipse, foci $(0, 2)$, $(0, 6)$ vertices $(0, 0)$, $(0, 8)$

40. Ellipse, foci $(0, -1)$, $(8, -1)$, vertex $(9, -1)$

41. Ellipse, center $(2, 2)$, focus $(0, 2)$, vertex $(5, 2)$

42. Ellipse, foci $(\pm 2, 0)$, passing through $(2, 1)$

43. Hyperbola, foci $(0, \pm 3)$, vertices $(0, \pm 1)$

44. Hyperbola, foci $(\pm 6, 0)$, vertices $(\pm 4, 0)$

45. Hyperbola, foci $(1, 3)$ and $(7, 3)$, vertices $(2, 3)$ and $(6, 3)$

46. Hyperbola, foci $(2, -2)$ and $(2, 8)$, vertices $(2, 0)$ and $(2, 6)$

47. Hyperbola, vertices $(\pm 3, 0)$, asymptotes $y = \pm 2x$

48. Hyperbola, foci $(2, 2)$ and $(6, 2)$, asymptotes $y = x - 2$ and $y = 6 - x$

49. The point in a lunar orbit nearest the surface of the moon is called *perilune* and the point farthest from the surface is called *apolune*. The *Apollo 11* spacecraft was placed in an elliptical lunar orbit with perilune altitude 110 km and apolune altitude 314 km (above the moon). Find an equation of this ellipse if the radius of the moon is 1728 km and the center of the moon is at one focus.

50. A cross-section of a parabolic reflector is shown in the figure. The bulb is located at the focus and the opening at the focus is 10 cm.
   (a) Find an equation of the parabola.
   (b) Find the diameter of the opening $|CD|$, 11 cm from the vertex.

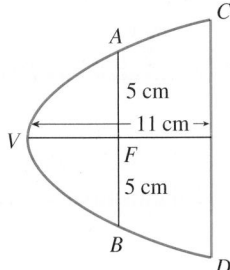

51. In the LORAN (LOng RAnge Navigation) radio navigation system, two radio stations located at A and B transmit simultaneous signals to a ship or an aircraft located at P. The onboard computer converts the time difference in receiving these signals into a distance difference $|PA| - |PB|$, and this, according to the definition of a hyperbola, locates the ship or aircraft on one branch of a hyperbola (see the figure). Suppose that station B is located 400 mi due east of station A on a coastline. A ship received the signal from B 1200 microseconds (μs) before it received the signal from A.
   (a) Assuming that radio signals travel at a speed of 980 ft/μs, find an equation of the hyperbola on which the ship lies.
   (b) If the ship is due north of B, how far off the coastline is the ship?

52. Use the definition of a hyperbola to derive Equation 6 for a hyperbola with foci $(\pm c, 0)$ and vertices $(\pm a, 0)$.

53. Show that the function defined by the upper branch of the hyperbola $y^2/a^2 - x^2/b^2 = 1$ is concave upward.

54. Find an equation for the ellipse with foci $(1, 1)$ and $(-1, -1)$ and major axis of length 4.

55. Determine the type of curve represented by the equation

$$\frac{x^2}{k} + \frac{y^2}{k - 16} = 1$$

in each of the following cases: (a) $k > 16$, (b) $0 < k < 16$, and (c) $k < 0$.
   (d) Show that all the curves in parts (a) and (b) have the same foci, no matter what the value of k is.

56. (a) Show that the equation of the tangent line to the parabola $y^2 = 4px$ at the point (x_0, y_0) can be written as

$$y_0 y = 2p(x + x_0)$$

   (b) What is the x-intercept of this tangent line? Use this fact to draw the tangent line.

57. Use Simpson's Rule with $n = 10$ to estimate the length of the ellipse $x^2 + 4y^2 = 4$.

58. The planet Pluto travels in an elliptical orbit around the Sun (at one focus). The length of the major axis is 1.18×10^{10} km and the length of the minor axis is 1.14×10^{10} km. Use Simpson's Rule with $n = 10$ to estimate the distance traveled by the planet during one complete orbit around the Sun.

59. Let $P(x_1, y_1)$ be a point on the ellipse $x^2/a^2 + y^2/b^2 = 1$ with foci F_1 and F_2 and let α and β be the angles between the lines PF_1, PF_2 and the ellipse as in the figure. Prove that $\alpha = \beta$. This explains how whispering galleries and lithotripsy work. Sound coming from one focus is reflected and passes through the other focus. [*Hint:* Use the formula in Problem 13 on page 220 to show that $\tan \alpha = \tan \beta$.]

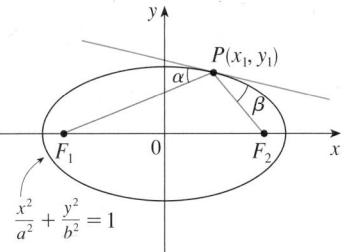

60. Let $P(x_1, y_1)$ be a point on the hyperbola $x^2/a^2 - y^2/b^2 = 1$ with foci F_1 and F_2 and let α and β be the angles between the lines PF_1, PF_2 and the hyperbola as shown in the figure. Prove that $\alpha = \beta$. (This is the reflection property of the hyperbola. It shows that light aimed at a focus F_2 of a hyperbolic mirror is reflected toward the other focus F_1.)

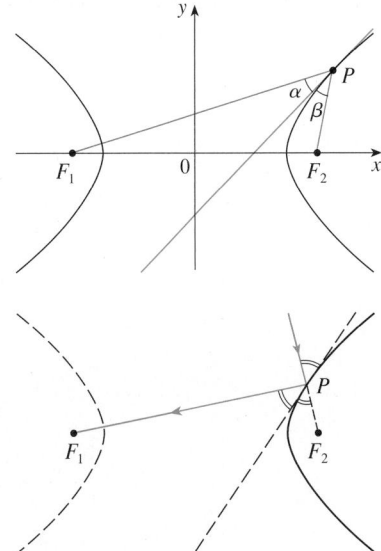

11.6 Conic Sections in Polar Coordinates

In the preceding section we defined the parabola in terms of a focus and directrix, but we defined the ellipse and hyperbola in terms of two foci. In this section we give a more unified treatment of all three types of conic sections in terms of a focus and directrix. Furthermore, if we place the focus at the origin, then a conic section has a simple polar equation. In Chapter 14 we will use the polar equation of an ellipse to derive Kepler's laws of planetary motion.

---

1   Theorem   Let F be a fixed point (called the **focus**) and l be a fixed line (called the **directrix**) in a plane. Let e be a fixed positive number (called the **eccentricity**). The set of all points P in the plane such that

$$\frac{|PF|}{|Pl|} = e \qquad \text{(The ratio of the distance from } F \text{ to the distance from } l \text{ is the constant } e.)}$$

is a conic section. The conic is

         (a) an ellipse if $e < 1$

         (b) a parabola if $e = 1$

         (c) a hyperbola if $e > 1$

Proof   Notice that if the eccentricity is $e = 1$, then $|PF| = |Pl|$ and so the given condition simply becomes the definition of a parabola as given in Section 11.5.

Let us place the focus F at the origin and the directrix parallel to the y-axis and d units to the right. Thus, the directrix has equation $x = d$ and is perpendicular to the polar axis. If the point P has polar coordinates (r, θ), we see from Figure 1 that

$$|PF| = r \qquad |Pl| = d - r\cos\theta$$

Thus, the condition $|PF|/|Pl| = e$, or $|PF| = e|Pl|$, becomes

2 $$r = e(d - r\cos\theta)$$

If we square both sides of this polar equation and convert to rectangular coordinates, we get

$$x^2 + y^2 = e^2(d - x)^2 = e^2(d^2 - 2dx + x^2)$$

or $$(1 - e^2)x^2 + 2de^2x + y^2 = e^2d^2$$

After completing the square, we have

3 $$\left(x + \frac{e^2d}{1 - e^2}\right)^2 + \frac{y^2}{1 - e^2} = \frac{e^2d^2}{(1 - e^2)^2}$$

If $e < 1$, we recognize Equation 3 as the equation of an ellipse. In fact, it is of the form

$$\frac{(x - h)^2}{a^2} + \frac{y^2}{b^2} = 1$$

FIGURE 1

where

  $\boxed{4}$ $$h = -\frac{e^2 d}{1 - e^2} \quad , \quad a^2 = \frac{e^2 d^2}{(1 - e^2)^2} \quad b^2 = \frac{e^2 d^2}{1 - e^2}$$

In Section 11.5 we found that the foci of an ellipse are at a distance c from the center, where

$\boxed{5}$ $$c^2 = a^2 - b^2 = \frac{e^4 d^2}{(1 - e^2)^2}$$

This shows that

$$c = \frac{e^2 d}{1 - e^2} = -h$$

and confirms that the focus as defined in Theorem 1 means the same as the focus defined in Section 11.5. It also follows from Equations 4 and 5 that the eccentricity is given by

$$e = \frac{c}{a}$$

If $e > 1$, then $1 - e^2 < 0$ and we see that Equation 3 represents a hyperbola. Just as we did before, we could rewrite Equation 3 in the form

$$\frac{(x - h)^2}{a^2} - \frac{y^2}{b^2} = 1$$

and see that

$$e = \frac{c}{a} \quad \text{where} \quad c^2 = a^2 + b^2$$

By solving Equation 2 for r, we see that the polar equation of the conic shown in Figure 1 can be written as

$$r = \frac{ed}{1 + e \cos \theta}$$

If the directrix is chosen to be to the left of the focus as $x = -d$, or if the directrix is chosen to be parallel to the polar axis as $y = \pm d$, then the polar equation of the conic is given by the following theorem, which is illustrated by Figure 2. (See Exercises 21–23.)

$\boxed{6}$ **Theorem** A polar equation of the form

$$r = \frac{ed}{1 \pm e \cos \theta} \qquad \text{or} \qquad r = \frac{ed}{1 \pm e \sin \theta}$$

represents a conic section with eccentricity e. The conic is an ellipse if $e < 1$, a parabola if $e = 1$, or a hyperbola if $e > 1$.

EXAMPLE 1 Find a polar equation for a parabola that has its focus at the origin and whose directrix is the line $y = -6$.

SOLUTION Using Theorem 6 with $e = 1$ and $d = 6$, and using part (d) of Figure 2, we see that the equation of the parabola is

$$r = \frac{6}{1 - \sin \theta}$$

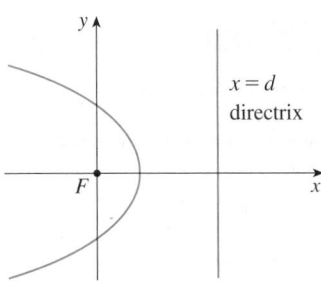

(a) $r = \dfrac{ed}{1 + e \cos \theta}$

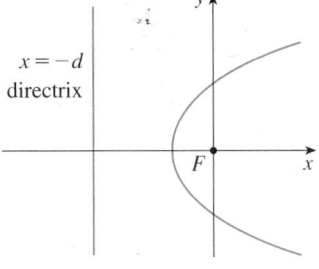

(b) $r = \dfrac{ed}{1 - e \cos \theta}$

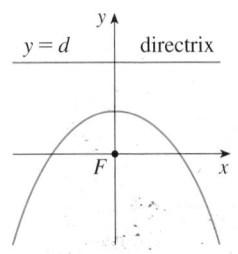

(c) $r = \dfrac{ed}{1 + e \sin \theta}$

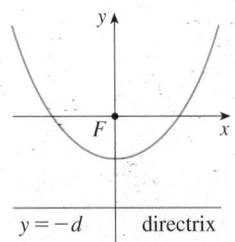

(d) $r = \dfrac{ed}{1 - e \sin \theta}$

FIGURE 2

Polar equations of conics

EXAMPLE 2 A conic is given by the polar equation

$$r = \frac{10}{3 - 2\cos\theta}$$

Find the eccentricity, identify the conic, locate the directrix, and sketch the conic.

SOLUTION Dividing numerator and denominator by 3, we write the equation as

$$r = \frac{\frac{10}{3}}{1 - \frac{2}{3}\cos\theta}$$

From Theorem 6 we see that this represents an ellipse with $e = \frac{2}{3}$. Since $ed = \frac{10}{3}$, we have

$$d = \frac{\frac{10}{3}}{e} = \frac{\frac{10}{3}}{\frac{2}{3}} = 5$$

so the directrix has Cartesian equation $x = -5$. When $\theta = 0$, $r = 10$; when $\theta = \pi$, $r = 2$. So the vertices have polar coordinates $(10, 0)$ and $(2, \pi)$. The ellipse is sketched in Figure 3.

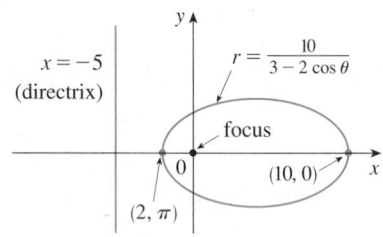

FIGURE 3

EXAMPLE 3 Sketch the conic $r = \dfrac{12}{2 + 4\sin\theta}$.

SOLUTION Writing the equation in the form

$$r = \frac{6}{1 + 2\sin\theta}$$

we see that the eccentricity is $e = 2$ and the equation therefore represents a hyperbola. Since $ed = 6$, $d = 3$ and the directrix has equation $y = 3$. The vertices occur when $\theta = \pi/2$ and $3\pi/2$, so they are $(2, \pi/2)$ and $(-6, 3\pi/2) = (6, \pi/2)$. It is also useful to plot the x-intercepts. These occur when $\theta = 0, \pi$; in both cases $r = 6$. For additional accuracy we could draw the asymptotes. Note that $r \to \pm\infty$ when $2 + 4\sin\theta \to 0^+$ or 0^- and $2 + 4\sin\theta = 0$ when $\sin\theta = -\frac{1}{2}$. Thus, the asymptotes are parallel to the rays $\theta = 7\pi/6$ and $\theta = 11\pi/6$. The hyperbola is sketched in Figure 4.

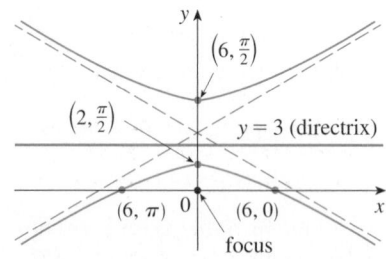

FIGURE 4
$$r = \frac{12}{2 + 4\sin\theta}$$

When rotating conic sections, we find it much more convenient to use polar equations than Cartesian equations. We just use the fact (see Exercise 75 in Section 11.3) that the graph of $r = f(\theta - \alpha)$ is the graph of $r = f(\theta)$ rotated counterclockwise about the origin through an angle α.

EXAMPLE 4 If the ellipse of Example 2 is rotated through an angle $\pi/4$ about the origin, find a polar equation and graph the resulting ellipse.

SOLUTION We get the equation of the rotated ellipse by replacing θ with $\theta - \pi/4$ in the equation given in Example 2. So the new equation is

$$r = \frac{10}{3 - 2\cos(\theta - \pi/4)}$$

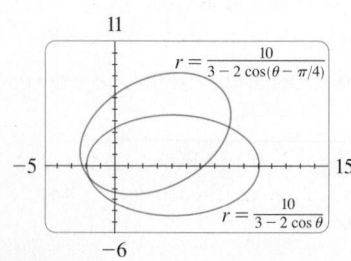

FIGURE 5

We use this equation to graph the rotated ellipse in Figure 5. Notice that the ellipse has been rotated about its left focus.

In Figure 6 we use a computer to sketch a number of conics to demonstrate the effect of varying the eccentricity e. Notice that when e is close to 0 the ellipse is nearly circular, whereas it becomes more elongated as $e \to 1^-$. When $e = 1$, of course, the conic is a parabola.

$e = 0.1$ $e = 0.5$ $e = 0.68$ $e = 0.86$ $e = 0.96$

$e = 1$ $e = 1.1$ $e = 1.4$ $e = 4$

FIGURE 6

11.6 Exercises

1–8 Write a polar equation of a conic with the focus at the origin and the given data.

1. Hyperbola,   eccentricity $\frac{7}{4}$,   directrix $y = 6$

2. Parabola,   directrix $x = 4$

3. Ellipse,   eccentricity $\frac{3}{4}$,   directrix $x = -5$

4. Hyperbola,   eccentricity 2,   directrix $y = -2$

5. Parabola,   vertex $(4, 3\pi/2)$

6. Ellipse,   eccentricity 0.8,   vertex $(1, \pi/2)$

7. Ellipse,   eccentricity $\frac{1}{2}$,   directrix $r = 4 \sec \theta$

8. Hyperbola,   eccentricity 3,   directrix $r = -6 \csc \theta$

9–16 (a) Find the eccentricity, (b) identify the conic, (c) give an equation of the directrix, and (d) sketch the conic.

9. $r = \dfrac{1}{1 + \sin \theta}$ **10.** $r = \dfrac{6}{3 + 2 \sin \theta}$

11. $r = \dfrac{12}{4 - \sin \theta}$ **12.** $r = \dfrac{4}{2 - 3 \cos \theta}$

13. $r = \dfrac{9}{6 + 2 \cos \theta}$ **14.** $r = \dfrac{5}{2 - 2 \sin \theta}$

15. $r = \dfrac{3}{4 - 8 \cos \theta}$ **16.** $r = \dfrac{4}{2 + \cos \theta}$

17. (a) Find the eccentricity and directrix of the conic $r = 1/(4 - 3 \cos \theta)$ and graph the conic and its directrix.
(b) If this conic is rotated counterclockwise about the origin through an angle $\pi/3$, write the resulting equation and graph its curve.

18. Graph the parabola $r = 5/(2 + 2 \sin \theta)$ and its directrix. Also graph the curve obtained by rotating this parabola about its focus through an angle $\pi/6$.

19. Graph the conics $r = e/(1 - e \cos \theta)$ with $e = 0.4, 0.6, 0.8$, and 1.0 on a common screen. How does the value of e affect the shape of the curve?

20. (a) Graph the conics $r = ed/(1 + e \sin \theta)$ for $e = 1$ and various values of d. How does the value of d affect the shape of the conic?
(b) Graph these conics for $d = 1$ and various values of e. How does the value of e affect the shape of the conic?

21. Show that a conic with focus at the origin, eccentricity e, and directrix $x = -d$ has polar equation
$$r = \frac{ed}{1 - e \cos \theta}$$

22. Show that a conic with focus at the origin, eccentricity e, and directrix $y = d$ has polar equation
$$r = \frac{ed}{1 + e \sin \theta}$$

23. Show that a conic with focus at the origin, eccentricity e, and directrix $y = -d$ has polar equation

$$r = \frac{ed}{1 - e \sin \theta}$$

24. Show that the parabolas $r = c/(1 + \cos \theta)$ and $r = d/(1 - \cos \theta)$ intersect at right angles.

25. (a) Show that the polar equation of an ellipse with directrix $x = -d$ can be written in the form

$$r = \frac{a(1 - e^2)}{1 - e \cos \theta}$$

(b) Find an approximate polar equation for the elliptical orbit of Earth around the Sun (at one focus) given that the eccentricity is about 0.017 and the length of the major axis is about 2.99×10^8 km.

26. (a) The planets move around the Sun in elliptical orbits with the Sun at one focus. The positions of a planet that are closest to and farthest from the Sun are called its *perihelion* and

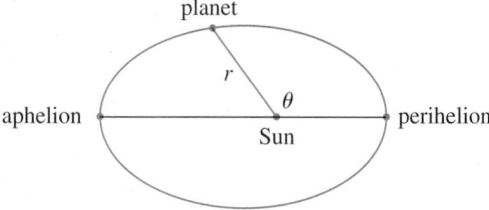

planet

r

θ

aphelion

Sun

perihelion

aphelion, respectively. Use Exercise 25(a) to show that the perihelion distance from a planet to the Sun is $a(1 - e)$ and the aphelion distance is $a(1 + e)$.

(b) Use the data of Exercise 25(b) to find the distances from Earth to the Sun at perihelion and at aphelion.

27. The orbit of Halley's comet, last seen in 1986 and due to return in 2062, is an ellipse with eccentricity 0.97 and one focus at the Sun. The length of its major axis is 36.18 AU. [An astronomical unit (AU) is the mean distance between Earth and the Sun, about 93 million miles.] Find a polar equation for the orbit of Halley's comet. What is the maximum distance from the comet to the Sun?

28. The Hale-Bopp comet, discovered in 1995, has an elliptical orbit with eccentricity 0.9951 and the length of the major axis is 356.5 AU. Find a polar equation for the orbit of this comet. How close to the Sun does it come?

29. The planet Mercury travels in an elliptical orbit with eccentricity 0.206. Its minimum distance from the Sun is 4.6×10^7 km. Use the results of Exercise 26(a) to find its maximum distance from the Sun.

30. The distance from the planet Pluto to the Sun is 4.43×10^9 km at perihelion and 7.37×10^9 km at aphelion. Use Exercise 26 to find the eccentricity of Pluto's orbit.

31. Using the data from Exercise 29, find the distance traveled by the planet Mercury during one complete orbit around the Sun. (If your calculator or computer algebra system evaluates definite integrals, use it. Otherwise, use Simpson's Rule.)

---

11 Review
---------------------------- ○ CONCEPT CHECK ○ ----------------------------

1. (a) What is a parametric curve?
(b) How do you sketch a parametric curve?

2. (a) How do you find the slope of a tangent to a parametric curve?
(b) How do you find the area under a parametric curve?

3. Write an expression for each of the following:
(a) The length of a parametric curve
(b) The area of the surface obtained by rotating a parametric curve about the x-axis

4. (a) Use a diagram to explain the meaning of the polar coordinates (r, θ) of a point.
(b) Write equations that express the Cartesian coordinates (x, y) of a point in terms of the polar coordinates.
(c) What equations would you use to find the polar coordinates of a point if you knew the Cartesian coordinates?

5. (a) How do you find the slope of a tangent line to a polar curve?
(b) How do you find the area of a region bounded by a polar curve?

(c) How do you find the length of a polar curve?

6. (a) Give a geometric definition of a parabola.
(b) Write an equation of a parabola with focus $(0, p)$ and directrix $y = -p$. What if the focus is $(p, 0)$ and the directrix is $x = -p$?

7. (a) Give a definition of an ellipse in terms of foci.
(b) Write an equation for the ellipse with foci $(\pm c, 0)$ and vertices $(\pm a, 0)$.

8. (a) Give a definition of a hyperbola in terms of foci.
(b) Write an equation for the hyperbola with foci $(\pm c, 0)$ and vertices $(\pm a, 0)$.
(c) Write equations for the asymptotes of the hyperbola in part (b).

9. (a) What is the eccentricity of a conic section?
(b) What can you say about the eccentricity if the conic section is an ellipse? A hyperbola? A parabola?
(c) Write a polar equation for a conic section with eccentricity e and directrix $x = d$. What if the directrix is $x = -d$? $y = d$? $y = -d$?

━━━━━━━━━━━━━━━ ∘ TRUE-FALSE QUIZ ∘ ━━━━━━━━━━━━━━━

Determine whether the statement is true or false. If it is true, explain why.
If it is false, explain why or give an example that disproves the statement.

1. If the parametric curve $x = f(t)$, $y = g(t)$ satisfies $g'(1) = 0$,
then it has a horizontal tangent when $t = 1$.

2. If $x = f(t)$ and $y = g(t)$ are twice differentiable, then
$d^2y/dx^2 = (d^2y/dt^2)/(d^2x/dt^2)$.

3. The length of the curve $x = f(t)$, $y = g(t)$, $a \leq t \leq b$, is
$\int_a^b \sqrt{[f'(t)]^2 + [g'(t)]^2}\, dt$.

sented by (x, y) in Cartesian coordinates
ᵃ) in polar coordinates, then

5. The polar curves $r = 1 - \sin 2\theta$ and $r = \sin 2\theta - 1$ have the
same graph.

6. The equations $r = 2$, $x^2 + y^2 = 4$, and $x = 2 \sin 3t$,
$y = 2 \cos 3t$ $(0 \leq t \leq 2\pi)$ all have the same graph.

7. The parametric equations $x = t^2$, $y = t^4$ have the same graph
as $x = t^3$, $y = t^6$.

8. The graph of $y^2 = 2y + 3x$ is a parabola.

9. A tangent line to a parabola intersects the parabola only once.

10. A hyperbola never intersects its directrix.

━━━━━━━━━━━━━━━ ∘ EXERCISES ∘ ━━━━━━━━━━━━━━━

c curve and eliminate the parameter to
of the curve.

t, $-4 \leq t \leq 1$

θ

$1 + \sin \theta$

⸱⸱ Write t⸱⸱ ⸱ferent sets of parametric equations for the
curve $y = \sqrt{x}$.

6. Use the graphs of $x = f(t)$ and $y = g(t)$ to sketch the parametric curve $x = f(t)$, $y = g(t)$. Indicate with arrows the
direction in which the curve is traced as t increases.

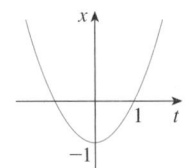

7–14 ▒ Sketch the polar curve.

7. $r = 1 - \cos \theta$ **8.** $r = \sin 4\theta$

9. $r = 1 + \cos 2\theta$ **10.** $r = 3 + \cos 3\theta$

11. $r^2 = \sec 2\theta$ **12.** $r = 2 \cos(\theta/2)$

13. $r = \dfrac{1}{1 + \cos \theta}$ **14.** $r = \dfrac{8}{4 + 3 \sin \theta}$

15–16 ▒ Find a polar equation for the curve represented by the
given Cartesian equation.

15. $x + y = 2$ **16.** $x^2 + y^2 = 2$

17. The curve with polar equation $r = (\sin \theta)/\theta$ is called a
cochleoid. Use a graph of r as a function of θ in Cartesian
coordinates to sketch the cochleoid by hand. Then graph it with
a machine to check your sketch.

18. Graph the ellipse $r = 2/(4 - 3 \cos \theta)$ and its directrix. Also
graph the ellipse obtained by rotation about the origin through
an angle $2\pi/3$.

19–22 ▒ Find the slope of the tangent line to the given curve at the
point corresponding to the specified value of the parameter.

19. $x = \ln t$, $y = 1 + t^2$; $t = 1$

20. $x = t^3 + 6t + 1$, $y = 2t - t^2$; $t = -1$

21. $r = e^{-\theta}$; $\theta = \pi$

22. $r = 3 + \cos 3\theta$; $\theta = \pi/2$

23–24 ▒ Find dy/dx and d^2y/dx^2.

23. $x = t \cos t$, $y = t \sin t$

24. $x = 1 + t^2$, $y = t - t^3$

25. Use a graph to estimate the coordinates of the lowest point on
the curve $x = t^3 - 3t$, $y = t^2 + t + 1$. Then use calculus to
find the exact coordinates.

26. Find the area enclosed by the loop of the curve in Exercise 25.

27. At what points does the curve

$$x = 2a \cos t - a \cos 2t \qquad y = 2a \sin t - a \sin 2t$$

have vertical or horizontal tangents? Use this information to help sketch the curve.

28. Find the area enclosed by the curve in Exercise 27.

29. Find the area enclosed by the curve $r^2 = 9 \cos 5\theta$.

30. Find the area enclosed by the inner loop of the curve $r = 1 - 3 \sin \theta$.

31. Find the points of intersection of the curves $r = 2$ and $r = 4 \cos \theta$.

32. Find the points of intersection of the curves $r = \cot \theta$ and $r = 2 \cos \theta$.

33. Find the area of the region that lies inside both of the circles $r = 2 \sin \theta$ and $r = \sin \theta + \cos \theta$.

34. Find the area of the region that lies inside the curve $r = 2 + \cos 2\theta$ but outside the curve $r = 2 + \sin \theta$.

35–38 ‖‖ Find the length of the curve.

35. $x = 3t^2, \quad y = 2t^3, \quad 0 \le t \le 2$

36. $x = 2 + 3t, \quad y = \cosh 3t, \quad 0 \le t \le 1$

37. $r = 1/\theta, \quad \pi \le \theta \le 2\pi$

38. $r = \sin^3(\theta/3), \quad 0 \le \theta \le \pi$

39–40 ‖‖ Find the area of the surface obtained by rotating the given curve about the x-axis.

39. $x = 4\sqrt{t}, \quad y = \dfrac{t^3}{3} + \dfrac{1}{2t^2}, \quad 1 \le t \le 4$

40. $x = 2 + 3t, \quad y = \cosh 3t, \quad 0 \le t \le 1$

41. The curves defined by the parametric equations

$$x = \frac{t^2 - c}{t^2 + 1} \qquad y = \frac{t(t^2 - c)}{t^2 + 1}$$

are called **strophoids** (from a Greek word meaning "to turn or twist"). Investigate how these curves vary as c varies.

42. A family of curves has polar equations $r^a = |\sin 2\theta|$ where a is a positive number. Investigate how the curves change as a changes.

43–46 ‖‖ Find the foci and vertices and sketch the graph.

43. $\dfrac{x^2}{9} + \dfrac{y^2}{8} = 1$

44. $4x^2 - y^2 = 16$

45. $6y^2 + x - 36y + 55 = 0$

46. $25x^2 + 4y^2 + 50x - 16y = 59$

47. Find an equation of the parabola with focus $(0, 6)$ and directrix $y = 2$.

48. Find an equation of the hyperbola with foci $(0, \pm5)$ and vertices $(0, \pm2)$.

49. Find an equation of the hyperbola with foci $(\pm3, 0)$ and asymptotes $2y = \pm x$.

50. Find an equation of the ellipse with foci $(3, \pm2)$ and major axis with length 8.

51. Find an equation for the ellipse that shares a vertex and a focus with the parabola $x^2 + y = 100$ and that has its other focus at the origin.

52. Show that if m is any real number, then there are exactly two lines of slope m that are tangent to the ellipse $x^2/a^2 + y^2/b^2 = 1$ and their equations are $y = mx \pm \sqrt{a^2m^2 + b^2}$.

53. Find a polar equation for the ellipse with focus at the origin, eccentricity $\frac{1}{3}$, and directrix with equation $r = 4 \sec \theta$.

54. Show that the angles between the polar axis and the asymptotes of the hyperbola $r = ed/(1 - e \cos \theta)$, $e > 1$, are given by $\cos^{-1}(\pm1/e)$.

55. In the figure the circle of radius a is stationary, and for every θ, the point P is the midpoint of the segment QR. The curve traced out by P for $0 < \theta < \pi$ is called the **longbow curve**. Find parametric equations for this curve.

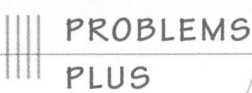

PROBLEMS PLUS

1. A curve is defined by the parametric equations

$$x = \int_1^t \frac{\cos u}{u}\, du \qquad y = \int_1^t \frac{\sin u}{u}\, du$$

Find the length of the arc of the curve from the origin to the nearest point where there is a vertical tangent line.

2. (a) Find the highest and lowest points on the curve $x^4 + y^4 = x^2 + y^2$.
   (b) Sketch the curve. (Notice that it is symmetric with respect to both axes and both of the lines $y = \pm x$, so it suffices to consider $y \geq x \geq 0$ initially.)

   CAS (c) Use polar coordinates and a computer algebra system to find the area enclosed by the curve.

3. What is the smallest viewing rectangle that contains every member of the family of polar curves $r = 1 + c\sin\theta$, where $0 \leq c \leq 1$? Illustrate your answer by graphing several members of the family in this viewing rectangle.

4. Four bugs are placed at the four corners of a square with side length a. The bugs crawl counterclockwise at the same speed and each bug crawls directly toward the next bug at all times. They approach the center of the square along spiral paths.
   (a) Find the polar equation of a bug's path assuming the pole is at the center of the square. (Use the fact that the line joining one bug to the next is tangent to the bug's path.)
   (b) Find the distance traveled by a bug by the time it meets the other bugs at the center.

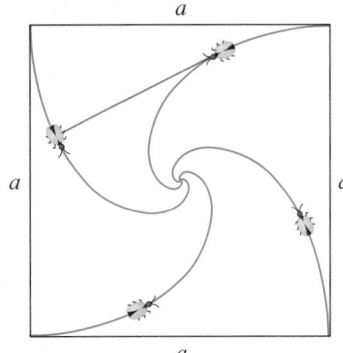

5. A curve called the **folium of Descartes** is defined by the parametric equations

$$x = \frac{3t}{1 + t^3} \qquad y = \frac{3t^2}{1 + t^3}$$

   (a) Show that if (a, b) lies on the curve, then so does (b, a); that is, the curve is symmetric with respect to the line $y = x$. Where does the curve intersect this line?
   (b) Find the points on the curve where the tangent lines are horizontal or vertical.
   (c) Show that the line $y = -x - 1$ is a slant asymptote.
   (d) Sketch the curve.
   (e) Show that a Cartesian equation of this curve is $x^3 + y^3 = 3xy$.
   (f) Show that the polar equation can be written in the form

$$r = \frac{3\sec\theta\tan\theta}{1 + \tan^3\theta}$$

   (g) Find the area enclosed by the loop of this curve.

   CAS (h) Show that the area of the loop is the same as the area that lies between the asymptote and the infinite branches of the curve. (Use a computer algebra system to evaluate the integral.)

CHAPTER 12

Bessel functions, which are
used to model the vibra-
tions of drumheads and
cymbals, are defined as
sums of infinite series in
Section 12.8. Notice how
closely the computer-
generated models (which
involve Bessel functions
and cosine functions)
match the photographs of a
vibrating rubber membrane.

National Film Board of Canada

Infinite Sequences and Series

Infinite sequences and series were introduced briefly in *A Preview of Calculus* in connection with Zeno's paradoxes and the decimal representation of numbers. Their importance in calculus stems from Newton's idea of representing functions as sums of infinite series. For instance, in finding areas he often integrated a function by first expressing it as a series and then integrating each term of the series. We will pursue his idea in Section 12.10 in order to integrate such functions as e^{-x^2}. (Recall that we have previously been unable to do this.) Many of the functions that arise in mathematical physics and chemistry, such as Bessel functions, are defined as sums of series, so it is important to be familiar with the basic concepts of convergence of infinite sequences and series.

Physicists also use series in another way, as we will see in Section 11.12. In studying fields as diverse as optics, special relativity, and electromagnetism, they analyze phenomena by replacing a function with the first few terms in the series that represents it.

A **sequence** can be thought of as a list of numbers written in a definite order:

$$a_1, \ a_2, \ a_3, \ a_4, \ \ldots, \ a_n, \ldots$$

The number a_1 is called the *first term*, a_2 is the *second term*, and in general a_n is the *nth term*. We will deal exclusively with infinite sequences and so each term a_n will have a successor a_{n+1}.

Notice that for every positive integer n there is a corresponding number a_n and so a sequence can be defined as a function whose domain is the set of positive integers. But we usually write a_n instead of the function notation $f(n)$ for the value of the function at the number n.

NOTATION ∘ The sequence $\{a_1, a_2, a_3, \ldots\}$ is also denoted by

$$\{a_n\} \qquad \text{or} \qquad \{a_n\}_{n=1}^{\infty}$$

EXAMPLE 1 Some sequences can be defined by giving a formula for the *n*th term. In the following examples we give three descriptions of the sequence: one by using the preceding notation, another by using the defining formula, and a third by writing out the terms of the sequence. Notice that *n* doesn't have to start at 1.

(a) $\left\{\dfrac{n}{n+1}\right\}_{n=1}^{\infty}$ $\qquad a_n = \dfrac{n}{n+1}$ $\qquad \left\{\dfrac{1}{2}, \dfrac{2}{3}, \dfrac{3}{4}, \dfrac{4}{5}, \ldots, \dfrac{n}{n+1}, \ldots\right\}$

(b) $\left\{\dfrac{(-1)^n(n+1)}{3^n}\right\}$ $\qquad a_n = \dfrac{(-1)^n(n+1)}{3^n}$ $\qquad \left\{-\dfrac{2}{3}, \dfrac{3}{9}, -\dfrac{4}{27}, \dfrac{5}{81}, \ldots, \dfrac{(-1)^n(n+1)}{3^n}, \ldots\right\}$

(c) $\left\{\sqrt{n-3}\right\}_{n=3}^{\infty}$ $\qquad$ $a_n = \sqrt{n-3}, \; n \geq 3$ $\qquad$ $\left\{0, 1, \sqrt{2}, \sqrt{3}, \ldots, \sqrt{n-3}, \ldots\right\}$

(d) $\left\{\cos\dfrac{n\pi}{6}\right\}_{n=0}^{\infty}$ $\qquad$ $a_n = \cos\dfrac{n\pi}{6}, \; n \geq 0$ $\qquad$ $\left\{1, \dfrac{\sqrt{3}}{2}, \dfrac{1}{2}, 0, \ldots, \cos\dfrac{n\pi}{6}, \ldots\right\}$

EXAMPLE 2 Find a formula for the general term a_n of the sequence

$$\left\{\frac{3}{5}, -\frac{4}{25}, \frac{5}{125}, -\frac{6}{625}, \frac{7}{3125}, \ldots\right\}$$

assuming that the pattern of the first few terms continues.

SOLUTION We are given that

$$a_1 = \frac{3}{5} \qquad a_2 = -\frac{4}{25} \qquad a_3 = \frac{5}{125} \qquad a_4 = -\frac{6}{625} \qquad a_5 = \frac{7}{3125}$$

Notice that the numerators of these fractions start with 3 and increase by 1 whenever we go to the next term. The second term has numerator 4, the third term has numerator 5; in general, the nth term will have numerator $n + 2$. The denominators are the powers of 5, so a_n has denominator 5^n. The signs of the terms are alternately positive and negative, so we need to multiply by a power of -1. In Example 1(b) the factor $(-1)^n$ meant we started with a negative term. Here we want to start with a positive term and so we use $(-1)^{n-1}$ or $(-1)^{n+1}$. Therefore,

$$a_n = (-1)^{n-1}\frac{n+2}{5^n}$$

EXAMPLE 3 Here are some sequences that don't have a simple defining equation.

(a) The sequence $\{p_n\}$, where p_n is the population of the world as of January 1 in the year n.

(b) If we let a_n be the digit in the nth decimal place of the number e, then $\{a_n\}$ is a well-defined sequence whose first few terms are

$$\{7, 1, 8, 2, 8, 1, 8, 2, 8, 4, 5, \ldots\}$$

(c) The **Fibonacci sequence** $\{f_n\}$ is defined recursively by the conditions

$$f_1 = 1 \qquad f_2 = 1 \qquad f_n = f_{n-1} + f_{n-2} \qquad n \geq 3$$

Each term is the sum of the two preceding terms. The first few terms are

$$\{1, 1, 2, 3, 5, 8, 13, 21, \ldots\}$$

This sequence arose when the 13th-century Italian mathematician known as Fibonacci solved a problem concerning the breeding of rabbits (see Exercise 65).

A sequence such as the one in Example 1(a), $a_n = n/(n + 1)$, can be pictured either by plotting its terms on a number line as in Figure 1 or by plotting its graph as in Figure 2. Note that, since a sequence is a function whose domain is the set of positive integers, its graph consists of isolated points with coordinates

$$(1, a_1) \qquad (2, a_2) \qquad (3, a_3) \qquad \ldots \qquad (n, a_n) \qquad \ldots$$

FIGURE 1

FIGURE 2

From Figure 1 or 2 it appears that the terms of the sequence $a_n = n/(n + 1)$ are approaching 1 as n becomes large. In fact, the difference

$$1 - \frac{n}{n + 1} = \frac{1}{n + 1}$$

can be made as small as we like by taking n sufficiently large. We indicate this by writing

$$\lim_{n \to \infty} \frac{n}{n + 1} = 1$$

In general, the notation

$$\lim_{n \to \infty} a_n = L$$

means that the terms of the sequence $\{a_n\}$ approach L as n becomes large. Notice that the following definition of the limit of a sequence is very similar to the definition of a limit of a function at infinity given in Section 4.4.

> **1 Definition** A sequence $\{a_n\}$ has the **limit** L and we write
>
> $$\lim_{n \to \infty} a_n = L \qquad \text{or} \qquad a_n \to L \text{ as } n \to \infty$$
>
> if we can make the terms a_n as close to L as we like by taking n sufficiently large. If $\lim_{n \to \infty} a_n$ exists, we say the sequence **converges** (or is **convergent**). Otherwise, we say the sequence **diverges** (or is **divergent**).

Figure 3 illustrates Definition 1 by showing the graphs of two sequences that have the limit L.

FIGURE 3
Graphs of two
sequences with
$\lim_{n \to \infty} a_n = L$

A more precise version of Definition 1 is as follows.

|||| Compare this definition with Definition 4.4.5.

> **2 Definition** A sequence $\{a_n\}$ has the **limit** L and we write
>
> $$\lim_{n \to \infty} a_n = L \qquad \text{or} \qquad a_n \to L \text{ as } n \to \infty$$
>
> if for every $\varepsilon > 0$ there is a corresponding integer N such that
>
> $$|a_n - L| < \varepsilon \qquad \text{whenever } n > N$$

Definition 2 is illustrated by Figure 4, in which the terms $a_1, a_2, a_3, \ldots$ are plotted on a number line. No matter how small an interval $(L - \varepsilon, L + \varepsilon)$ is chosen, there exists an N such that all terms of the sequence from a_{N+1} onward must lie in that interval.

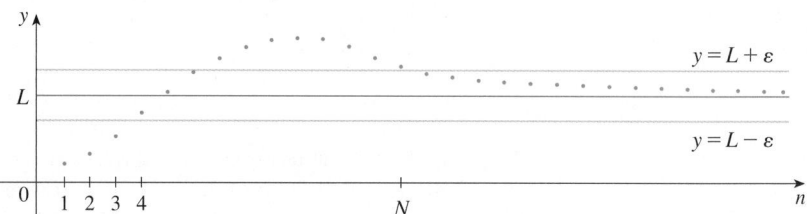

FIGURE 4

Another illustration of Definition 2 is given in Figure 5. The points on the graph of $\{a_n\}$ must lie between the horizontal lines $y = L + \varepsilon$ and $y = L - \varepsilon$ if $n > N$. This picture must be valid no matter how small ε is chosen, but usually a smaller ε requires a larger N.

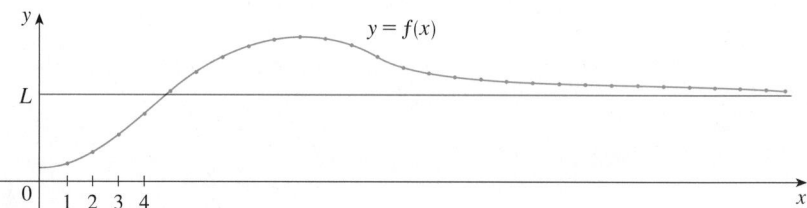

FIGURE 5

Comparison of Definition 2 and Definition 4.4.5 shows that the only difference between $\lim_{n\to\infty} a_n = L$ and $\lim_{x\to\infty} f(x) = L$ is that n is required to be an integer. Thus, we have the following theorem, which is illustrated by Figure 6.

> **3** **Theorem** If $\lim_{x\to\infty} f(x) = L$ and $f(n) = a_n$ when n is an integer, then $\lim_{n\to\infty} a_n = L$.

FIGURE 6

In particular, since we know that $\lim_{x\to\infty} (1/x^r) = 0$ when $r > 0$ (Theorem 4.4.4), we have

4
$$\lim_{n\to\infty} \frac{1}{n^r} = 0 \quad \text{if } r > 0$$

If a_n becomes large as n becomes large, we use the notation $\lim_{n\to\infty} a_n = \infty$. The following precise definition is similar to Definition 4.4.7.

> **5** **Definition** $\lim_{n\to\infty} a_n = \infty$ means that for every positive number M there is an integer N such that
> $$a_n > M \quad \text{whenever } n > N$$

If $\lim_{n\to\infty} a_n = \infty$, then the sequence $\{a_n\}$ is divergent but in a special way. We say that $\{a_n\}$ diverges to ∞.

The Limit Laws given in Section 2.3 also hold for the limits of sequences and their proofs are similar.

Limit Laws for Sequences

If $\{a_n\}$ and $\{b_n\}$ are convergent sequences and c is a constant, then

$$\lim_{n \to \infty} (a_n + b_n) = \lim_{n \to \infty} a_n + \lim_{n \to \infty} b_n$$

$$\lim_{n \to \infty} (a_n - b_n) = \lim_{n \to \infty} a_n - \lim_{n \to \infty} b_n$$

$$\lim_{n \to \infty} c a_n = c \lim_{n \to \infty} a_n \qquad\qquad \lim_{n \to \infty} c = c$$

$$\lim_{n \to \infty} (a_n b_n) = \lim_{n \to \infty} a_n \cdot \lim_{n \to \infty} b_n$$

$$\lim_{n \to \infty} \frac{a_n}{b_n} = \frac{\displaystyle\lim_{n \to \infty} a_n}{\displaystyle\lim_{n \to \infty} b_n} \quad \text{if } \lim_{n \to \infty} b_n \neq 0$$

$$\lim_{n \to \infty} a_n^p = \left[\lim_{n \to \infty} a_n \right]^p \quad \text{if } p > 0 \text{ and } a_n > 0$$

The Squeeze Theorem can also be adapted for sequences as follows (see Figure 7).

Squeeze Theorem for Sequences

If $a_n \leq b_n \leq c_n$ for $n \geq n_0$ and $\lim_{n \to \infty} a_n = \lim_{n \to \infty} c_n = L$, then $\lim_{n \to \infty} b_n = L$.

Another useful fact about limits of sequences is given by the following theorem, whose proof is left as Exercise 69.

6 **Theorem** If $\lim_{n \to \infty} |a_n| = 0$, then $\lim_{n \to \infty} a_n = 0$.

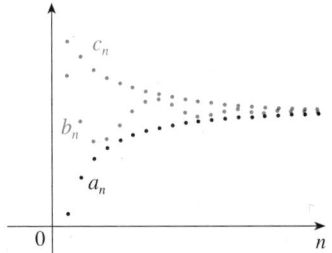

FIGURE 7
The sequence $\{b_n\}$ is squeezed between the sequences $\{a_n\}$ and $\{c_n\}$.

EXAMPLE 4 Find $\lim_{n \to \infty} \dfrac{n}{n + 1}$.

SOLUTION The method is similar to the one we used in Section 4.4: Divide numerator and denominator by the highest power of n and then use the Limit Laws.

$$\lim_{n \to \infty} \frac{n}{n + 1} = \lim_{n \to \infty} \frac{1}{1 + \dfrac{1}{n}} = \frac{\displaystyle\lim_{n \to \infty} 1}{\displaystyle\lim_{n \to \infty} 1 + \lim_{n \to \infty} \dfrac{1}{n}}$$

$$= \frac{1}{1 + 0} = 1$$

|||| This shows that the guess we made earlier from Figures 1 and 2 was correct.

Here we used Equation 4 with $r = 1$.

EXAMPLE 5 Calculate $\lim\limits_{n\to\infty} \dfrac{\ln n}{n}$.

SOLUTION Notice that both numerator and denominator approach infinity as $n \to \infty$. We can't apply l'Hospital's Rule directly because it applies not to sequences but to functions of a real variable. However, we can apply l'Hospital's Rule to the related function $f(x) = (\ln x)/x$ and obtain

$$\lim_{x\to\infty} \frac{\ln x}{x} = \lim_{x\to\infty} \frac{1/x}{1} = 0$$

Therefore, by Theorem 3 we have

$$\lim_{n\to\infty} \frac{\ln n}{n} = 0$$

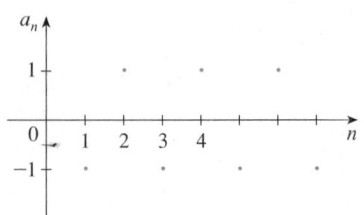

FIGURE 8

EXAMPLE 6 Determine whether the sequence $a_n = (-1)^n$ is convergent or divergent.

SOLUTION If we write out the terms of the sequence, we obtain

$$\{-1, 1, -1, 1, -1, 1, -1, \ldots\}$$

The graph of this sequence is shown in Figure 8. Since the terms oscillate between 1 and -1 infinitely often, a_n does not approach any number. Thus, $\lim_{n\to\infty} (-1)^n$ does not exist; that is, the sequence $\{(-1)^n\}$ is divergent.

‖‖‖ The graph of the sequence in Example 7 is shown in Figure 9 and supports the answer.

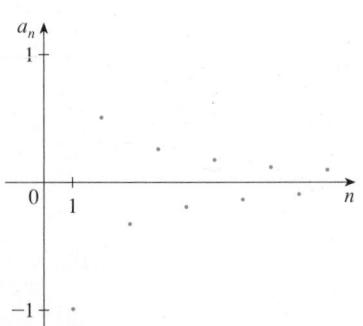

FIGURE 9

EXAMPLE 7 Evaluate $\lim\limits_{n\to\infty} \dfrac{(-1)^n}{n}$ if it exists.

SOLUTION

$$\lim_{n\to\infty} \left| \frac{(-1)^n}{n} \right| = \lim_{n\to\infty} \frac{1}{n} = 0$$

Therefore, by Theorem 6,

$$\lim_{n\to\infty} \frac{(-1)^n}{n} = 0$$

EXAMPLE 8 Discuss the convergence of the sequence $a_n = n!/n^n$, where $n! = 1 \cdot 2 \cdot 3 \cdot \cdots \cdot n$.

SOLUTION Both numerator and denominator approach infinity as $n \to \infty$ but here we have no corresponding function for use with l'Hospital's Rule ($x!$ is not defined when x is not an integer). Let's write out a few terms to get a feeling for what happens to a_n as n gets large:

$$a_1 = 1 \qquad a_2 = \frac{1 \cdot 2}{2 \cdot 2} \qquad a_3 = \frac{1 \cdot 2 \cdot 3}{3 \cdot 3 \cdot 3}$$

$$\boxed{7} \qquad a_n = \frac{1 \cdot 2 \cdot 3 \cdot \cdots \cdot n}{n \cdot n \cdot n \cdot \cdots \cdot n}$$

It appears from these expressions and the graph in Figure 10 that the terms are decreas-

IIII CREATING GRAPHS OF SEQUENCES

Some computer algebra systems have special commands that enable us to create sequences and graph them directly. With most graphing calculators, however, sequences can be graphed by using parametric equations. For instance, the sequence in Example 8 can be graphed by entering the parametric equations

$$x = t \qquad y = t!/t^t$$

and graphing in dot mode starting with $t = 1$, setting the t-step equal to 1. The result is shown in Figure 10.

FIGURE 10

ing and perhaps approach 0. To confirm this, observe from Equation 7 that

$$a_n = \frac{1}{n}\left(\frac{2 \cdot 3 \cdot \cdots \cdot n}{n \cdot n \cdot \cdots \cdot n}\right)$$

Notice that the expression in parentheses is at most 1 because the numerator is less than (or equal to) the denominator. So

$$0 < a_n \le \frac{1}{n}$$

We know that $1/n \to 0$ as $n \to \infty$. Therefore, $a_n \to 0$ as $n \to \infty$ by the Squeeze Theorem.

EXAMPLE 9 For what values of r is the sequence $\{r^n\}$ convergent?

SOLUTION We know from Section 4.4 and the graphs of the exponential functions in Section 7.2 (or Section 7.4*) that $\lim_{x\to\infty} a^x = \infty$ for $a > 1$ and $\lim_{x\to\infty} a^x = 0$ for $0 < a < 1$. Therefore, putting $a = r$ and using Theorem 2, we have

$$\lim_{n\to\infty} r^n = \begin{cases} \infty & \text{if } r > 1 \\ 0 & \text{if } 0 < r < 1 \end{cases}$$

It is obvious that

$$\lim_{n\to\infty} 1^n = 1 \qquad \text{and} \qquad \lim_{n\to\infty} 0^n = 0$$

If $-1 < r < 0$, then $0 < |r| < 1$, so

$$\lim_{n\to\infty} |r^n| = \lim_{n\to\infty} |r|^n = 0$$

and therefore $\lim_{n\to\infty} r^n = 0$ by Theorem 6. If $r \le -1$, then $\{r^n\}$ diverges as in Example 6. Figure 11 shows the graphs for various values of r. (The case $r = -1$ is shown in Figure 8.)

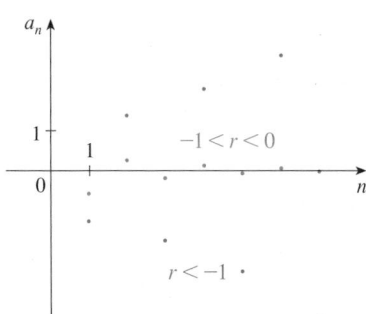

FIGURE 11
The sequence $a_n = r^n$

The results of Example 9 are summarized for future use as follows.

---

8 The sequence $\{r^n\}$ is convergent if $-1 < r \le 1$ and divergent for all other values of r.

$$\lim_{n\to\infty} r^n = \begin{cases} 0 & \text{if } -1 < r < 1 \\ 1 & \text{if } r = 1 \end{cases}$$

---

⁹ Definition A sequence $\{a_n\}$ is called **increasing** if $a_n < a_{n+1}$ for all $n \geq 1$, that is, $a_1 < a_2 < a_3 < \cdots$. It is called **decreasing** if $a_n > a_{n+1}$ for all $n \geq 1$. It is called **monotonic** if it is either increasing or decreasing.

EXAMPLE 10 The sequence $\left\{\dfrac{3}{n+5}\right\}$ is decreasing because

$$\frac{3}{n+5} > \frac{3}{(n+1)+5} = \frac{3}{n+6}$$

for all $n \geq 1$. (The right side is smaller because it has a larger denominator.)

EXAMPLE 11 Show that the sequence $a_n = \dfrac{n}{n^2+1}$ is decreasing.

SOLUTION 1 We must show that $a_{n+1} < a_n$, that is,

$$\frac{n+1}{(n+1)^2+1} < \frac{n}{n^2+1}$$

This inequality is equivalent to the one we get by cross-multiplication:

$$\frac{n+1}{(n+1)^2+1} < \frac{n}{n^2+1} \iff (n+1)(n^2+1) < n[(n+1)^2+1]$$

$$\iff n^3+n^2+n+1 < n^3+2n^2+2n$$

$$\iff 1 < n^2+n$$

Since $n \geq 1$, we know that the inequality $n^2+n > 1$ is true. Therefore, $a_{n+1} < a_n$ and so $\{a_n\}$ is decreasing.

SOLUTION 2 Consider the function $f(x) = \dfrac{x}{x^2+1}$:

$$f'(x) = \frac{x^2+1-2x^2}{(x^2+1)^2} = \frac{1-x^2}{(x^2+1)^2} < 0 \qquad \text{whenever } x^2 > 1$$

Thus, f is decreasing on $(1, \infty)$ and so $f(n) > f(n+1)$. Therefore, $\{a_n\}$ is decreasing.

¹⁰ Definition A sequence $\{a_n\}$ is **bounded above** if there is a number M such that

$$a_n \leq M \qquad \text{for all } n \geq 1$$

It is **bounded below** if there is a number m such that

$$m \leq a_n \qquad \text{for all } n \geq 1$$

If it is bounded above and below, then $\{a_n\}$ is a **bounded sequence**.

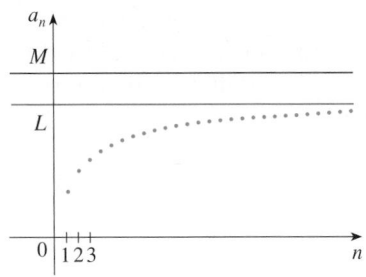

FIGURE 12

For instance, the sequence $a_n = n$ is bounded below ($a_n > 0$) but not above. The sequence $a_n = n/(n + 1)$ is bounded because $0 < a_n < 1$ for all n.

We know that not every bounded sequence is convergent [for instance, the sequence $a_n = (-1)^n$ satisfies $-1 \leq a_n \leq 1$ but is divergent from Example 6] and not every monotonic sequence is convergent ($a_n = n \rightarrow \infty$). But if a sequence is both bounded *and* monotonic, then it must be convergent. This fact is proved as Theorem 11, but intuitively you can understand why it is true by looking at Figure 12. If $\{a_n\}$ is increasing and $a_n \leq M$ for all n, then the terms are forced to crowd together and approach some number L.

The proof of Theorem 11 is based on the **Completeness Axiom** for the set $\mathbb{R}$ of real numbers, which says that if S is a nonempty set of real numbers that has an upper bound M ($x \leq M$ for all x in S), then S has a **least upper bound** b. (This means that b is an upper bound for S, but if M is any other upper bound, then $b \leq M$.) The Completeness Axiom is an expression of the fact that there is no gap or hole in the real number line.

> **11 Monotonic Sequence Theorem** Every bounded, monotonic sequence is convergent.

Proof Suppose $\{a_n\}$ is an increasing sequence. Since $\{a_n\}$ is bounded, the set $S = \{a_n \mid n \geq 1\}$ has an upper bound. By the Completeness Axiom it has a least upper bound L. Given $\varepsilon > 0$, $L - \varepsilon$ is *not* an upper bound for S (since L is the *least* upper bound). Therefore

$$a_N > L - \varepsilon \qquad \text{for some integer } N$$

But the sequence is increasing so $a_n \geq a_N$ for every $n > N$. Thus, if $n > N$ we have

$$a_n > L - \varepsilon$$

so

$$0 \leq L - a_n < \varepsilon$$

since $a_n \leq L$. Thus

$$|L - a_n| < \varepsilon \qquad \text{whenever } n > N$$

so $\lim_{n \to \infty} a_n = L$.

A similar proof (using the greatest lower bound) works if $\{a_n\}$ is decreasing. ▬

The proof of Theorem 11 shows that a sequence that is increasing and bounded above is convergent. (Likewise, a decreasing sequence that is bounded below is convergent.) This fact is used many times in dealing with infinite series.

EXAMPLE 12 Investigate the sequence $\{a_n\}$ defined by the recurrence relation

$$a_1 = 2 \qquad a_{n+1} = \tfrac{1}{2}(a_n + 6) \qquad \text{for } n = 1, 2, 3, \ldots$$

SOLUTION We begin by computing the first several terms:

$$a_1 = 2 \qquad\qquad a_2 = \tfrac{1}{2}(2 + 6) = 4 \qquad a_3 = \tfrac{1}{2}(4 + 6) = 5$$

$$a_4 = \tfrac{1}{2}(5 + 6) = 5.5 \qquad a_5 = 5.75 \qquad\qquad a_6 = 5.875$$

$$a_7 = 5.9375 \qquad\qquad a_8 = 5.96875 \qquad a_9 = 5.984375$$

||| Mathematical induction is often used in dealing with recursive sequences. See page 59 for a discussion of the Principle of Mathematical Induction.

These initial terms suggest that the sequence is increasing and the terms are approaching 6. To confirm that the sequence is increasing we use mathematical induction to show that $a_{n+1} > a_n$ for all $n \geq 1$. This is true for $n = 1$ because $a_2 = 4 > a_1$. If we assume that it is true for $n = k$, then we have

$$a_{k+1} > a_k$$

so

$$a_{k+1} + 6 > a_k + 6$$

and

$$\tfrac{1}{2}(a_{k+1} + 6) > \tfrac{1}{2}(a_k + 6)$$

Thus

$$a_{k+2} > a_{k+1}$$

We have deduced that $a_{n+1} > a_n$ is true for $n = k + 1$. Therefore, the inequality is true for all n by induction.

Next we verify that $\{a_n\}$ is bounded by showing that $a_n < 6$ for all n. (Since the sequence is increasing, we already know that it has a lower bound: $a_n \geq a_1 = 2$ for all n.) We know that $a_1 < 6$, so the assertion is true for $n = 1$. Suppose it is true for $n = k$. Then

$$a_k < 6$$

so

$$a_k + 6 < 12$$

$$\tfrac{1}{2}(a_k + 6) < \tfrac{1}{2}(12) = 6$$

Thus

$$a_{k+1} < 6$$

This shows, by mathematical induction, that $a_n < 6$ for all n.

Since the sequence $\{a_n\}$ is increasing and bounded, Theorem 11 guarantees that it has a limit. The theorem doesn't tell us what the value of the limit is. But now that we know $L = \lim_{n \to \infty} a_n$ exists, we can use the recurrence relation to write

$$\lim_{n \to \infty} a_{n+1} = \lim_{n \to \infty} \tfrac{1}{2}(a_n + 6) = \tfrac{1}{2}\left(\lim_{n \to \infty} a_n + 6\right) = \tfrac{1}{2}(L + 6)$$

||| A proof of this fact is requested in Exercise 52.

Since $a_n \to L$, it follows that $a_{n+1} \to L$, too (as $n \to \infty$, $n + 1 \to \infty$, too). So we have

$$L = \tfrac{1}{2}(L + 6)$$

Solving this equation for L, we get $L = 6$, as predicted. ▬

||| **12.1** Exercises

1. (a) What is a sequence?
  (b) What does it mean to say that $\lim_{n \to \infty} a_n = 8$?
  (c) What does it mean to say that $\lim_{n \to \infty} a_n = \infty$?

2. (a) What is a convergent sequence? Give two examples.
  (b) What is a divergent sequence? Give two examples.

3–8 ||| List the first five terms of the sequence.

3. $a_n = 1 - (0.2)^n$

4. $a_n = \dfrac{n + 1}{3n - 1}$

5. $a_n = \dfrac{3(-1)^n}{n!}$

6. $\{2 \cdot 4 \cdot 6 \cdot \cdots \cdot (2n)\}$

7. $a_1 = 3$, $\quad a_{n+1} = 2a_n - 1$ **8.** $a_1 = 4$, $\quad a_{n+1} = \dfrac{a_n}{a_n - 1}$

9–14 ▥ Find a formula for the general term a_n of the sequence, assuming that the pattern of the first few terms continues.

9. $\left\{ \frac{1}{2}, \frac{1}{4}, \frac{1}{8}, \frac{1}{16}, \ldots \right\}$

10. $\left\{ \frac{1}{2}, \frac{1}{4}, \frac{1}{6}, \frac{1}{8}, \ldots \right\}$

11. $\{2, 7, 12, 17, \ldots\}$

12. $\left\{ -\frac{1}{4}, \frac{2}{9}, -\frac{3}{16}, \frac{4}{25}, \ldots \right\}$

13. $\left\{ 1, -\frac{2}{3}, \frac{4}{9}, -\frac{8}{27}, \ldots \right\}$

14. $\{5, 1, 5, 1, 5, 1, \ldots\}$

15–40 ▥ Determine whether the sequence converges or diverges. If it converges, find the limit.

15. $a_n = n(n - 1)$

16. $a_n = \dfrac{n + 1}{3n - 1}$

17. $a_n = \dfrac{3 + 5n^2}{n + n^2}$

18. $a_n = \dfrac{\sqrt{n}}{1 + \sqrt{n}}$

19. $a_n = \dfrac{2^n}{3^{n+1}}$

20. $a_n = \dfrac{n}{1 + \sqrt{n}}$

21. $a_n = \dfrac{(-1)^{n-1} n}{n^2 + 1}$

22. $a_n = \dfrac{(-1)^n n^3}{n^3 + 2n^2 + 1}$

23. $a_n = \cos(n/2)$

24. $a_n = \cos(2/n)$

25. $\left\{ \dfrac{(2n - 1)!}{(2n + 1)!} \right\}$

26. $\{\arctan 2n\}$

27. $\left\{ \dfrac{e^n + e^{-n}}{e^{2n} - 1} \right\}$

28. $\left\{ \dfrac{\ln n}{\ln 2n} \right\}$

29. $\{n^2 e^{-n}\}$

30. $\{n \cos n\pi\}$

31. $a_n = \dfrac{\cos^2 n}{2^n}$

32. $a_n = \ln(n + 1) - \ln n$

33. $a_n = n \sin(1/n)$

34. $a_n = \sqrt{n} - \sqrt{n^2 - 1}$

35. $a_n = \left(1 + \dfrac{2}{n} \right)^{1/n}$

36. $a_n = \dfrac{\sin 2n}{1 + \sqrt{n}}$

37. $\{0, 1, 0, 0, 1, 0, 0, 0, 1, \ldots\}$

38. $\left\{ \frac{1}{1}, \frac{1}{3}, \frac{1}{2}, \frac{1}{4}, \frac{1}{3}, \frac{1}{5}, \frac{1}{4}, \frac{1}{6}, \ldots \right\}$

39. $a_n = \dfrac{n!}{2^n}$

40. $a_n = \dfrac{(-3)^n}{n!}$

▦ **41–48** ▥ Use a graph of the sequence to decide whether the sequence is convergent or divergent. If the sequence is convergent, guess the value of the limit from the graph and then prove your guess. (See the margin note on page 743 for advice on graphing sequences.)

41. $a_n = (-1)^n \dfrac{n + 1}{n}$

42. $a_n = 2 + (-2/\pi)^n$

43. $\left\{ \arctan\left(\dfrac{2n}{2n + 1} \right) \right\}$

44. $\left\{ \dfrac{\sin n}{\sqrt{n}} \right\}$

45. $a_n = \dfrac{n^3}{n!}$

46. $a_n = \sqrt[n]{3^n + 5^n}$

47. $a_n = \dfrac{1 \cdot 3 \cdot 5 \cdot \cdots \cdot (2n - 1)}{(2n)^n}$

48. $a_n = \dfrac{1 \cdot 3 \cdot 5 \cdot \cdots \cdot (2n - 1)}{n!}$

49. If \$1000 is invested at 6% interest, compounded annually, then after n years the investment is worth $a_n = 1000(1.06)^n$ dollars.
(a) Find the first five terms of the sequence $\{a_n\}$.
(b) Is the sequence convergent or divergent? Explain.

50. Find the first 40 terms of the sequence defined by

$$a_{n+1} = \begin{cases} \frac{1}{2} a_n & \text{if } a_n \text{ is an even number} \\ 3a_n + 1 & \text{if } a_n \text{ is an odd number} \end{cases}$$

and $a_1 = 11$. Do the same if $a_1 = 25$. Make a conjecture about this type of sequence.

51. For what values of r is the sequence $\{nr^n\}$ convergent?

52. (a) If $\{a_n\}$ is convergent, show that

$$\lim_{n \to \infty} a_{n+1} = \lim_{n \to \infty} a_n$$

(b) A sequence $\{a_n\}$ is defined by $a_1 = 1$ and $a_{n+1} = 1/(1 + a_n)$ for $n \geq 1$. Assuming that $\{a_n\}$ is convergent, find its limit.

53. Suppose you know that $\{a_n\}$ is a decreasing sequence and all its terms lie between the numbers 5 and 8. Explain why the sequence has a limit. What can you say about the value of the limit?

54–60 ▥ Determine whether the sequence is increasing, decreasing, or not monotonic. Is the sequence bounded?

54. $a_n = \dfrac{1}{5^n}$

55. $a_n = \dfrac{1}{2n + 3}$

56. $a_n = \dfrac{2n - 3}{3n + 4}$

57. $a_n = \cos(n\pi/2)$

58. $a_n = ne^{-n}$

59. $a_n = \dfrac{n}{n^2 + 1}$

60. $a_n = n + \dfrac{1}{n}$

61. Find the limit of the sequence

$$\left\{ \sqrt{2}, \sqrt{2\sqrt{2}}, \sqrt{2\sqrt{2\sqrt{2}}}, \ldots \right\}$$

62. A sequence $\{a_n\}$ is given by $a_1 = \sqrt{2}$, $a_{n+1} = \sqrt{2 + a_n}$.
(a) By induction or otherwise, show that $\{a_n\}$ is increasing and bounded above by 3. Apply Theorem 11 to show that $\lim_{n \to \infty} a_n$ exists.
(b) Find $\lim_{n \to \infty} a_n$.

63. Show that the sequence defined by $a_1 = 1$, $a_{n+1} = 3 - 1/a_n$ is increasing and $a_n < 3$ for all n. Deduce that $\{a_n\}$ is convergent and find its limit.

64. Show that the sequence defined by

$$a_1 = 2 \qquad a_{n+1} = \frac{1}{3 - a_n}$$

satisfies $0 < a_n \le 2$ and is decreasing. Deduce that the sequence is convergent and find its limit.

65. (a) Fibonacci posed the following problem: Suppose that rabbits live forever and that every month each pair produces a new pair which becomes productive at age 2 months. If we start with one newborn pair, how many pairs of rabbits will we have in the nth month? Show that the answer is f_n, where $\{f_n\}$ is the Fibonacci sequence defined in Example 3(c).
(b) Let $a_n = f_{n+1}/f_n$ and show that $a_{n-1} = 1 + 1/a_{n-2}$. Assuming that $\{a_n\}$ is convergent, find its limit.

66. (a) Let $a_1 = a$, $a_2 = f(a)$, $a_3 = f(a_2) = f(f(a))$, ..., $a_{n+1} = f(a_n)$, where f is a continuous function. If $\lim_{n \to \infty} a_n = L$, show that $f(L) = L$.
(b) Illustrate part (a) by taking $f(x) = \cos x$, $a = 1$, and estimating the value of L to five decimal places.

67. (a) Use a graph to guess the value of the limit

$$\lim_{n \to \infty} \frac{n^5}{n!}$$

(b) Use a graph of the sequence in part (a) to find the smallest values of N that correspond to $\varepsilon = 0.1$ and $\varepsilon = 0.001$ in Definition 2.

68. Use Definition 2 directly to prove that $\lim_{n \to \infty} r^n = 0$ when $|r| < 1$.

69. Prove Theorem 6.
[*Hint:* Use either Definition 2 or the Squeeze Theorem.]

70. Let $a_n = \left(1 + \dfrac{1}{n}\right)^n$.
(a) Show that if $0 \le a < b$, then

$$\frac{b^{n+1} - a^{n+1}}{b - a} < (n + 1)b^n$$

(b) Deduce that $b^n[(n + 1)a - nb] < a^{n+1}$.
(c) Use $a = 1 + 1/(n + 1)$ and $b = 1 + 1/n$ in part (b) to show that $\{a_n\}$ is increasing.
(d) Use $a = 1$ and $b = 1 + 1/(2n)$ in part (b) to show that $a_{2n} < 4$.
(e) Use parts (c) and (d) to show that $a_n < 4$ for all n.

(f) Use Theorem 11 to show that $\lim_{n \to \infty} (1 + 1/n)^n$ exists. (The limit is e. See Equation 7.4.9.)

71. Let a and b be positive numbers with $a > b$. Let a_1 be their arithmetic mean and b_1 their geometric mean:

$$a_1 = \frac{a + b}{2} \qquad b_1 = \sqrt{ab}$$

Repeat this process so that, in general,

$$a_{n+1} = \frac{a_n + b_n}{2} \qquad b_{n+1} = \sqrt{a_n b_n}$$

(a) Use mathematical induction to show that

$$a_n > a_{n+1} > b_{n+1} > b_n$$

(b) Deduce that both $\{a_n\}$ and $\{b_n\}$ are convergent.
(c) Show that $\lim_{n \to \infty} a_n = \lim_{n \to \infty} b_n$. Gauss called the common value of these limits the **arithmetic-geometric mean** of the numbers a and b.

72. (a) Show that if $\lim_{n \to \infty} a_{2n} = L$ and $\lim_{n \to \infty} a_{2n+1} = L$, then $\{a_n\}$ is convergent and $\lim_{n \to \infty} a_n = L$.
(b) If $a_1 = 1$ and

$$a_{n+1} = 1 + \frac{1}{1 + a_n}$$

find the first eight terms of the sequence $\{a_n\}$. Then use part (a) to show that $\lim_{n \to \infty} a_n = \sqrt{2}$. This gives the **continued fraction expansion**

$$\sqrt{2} = 1 + \cfrac{1}{2 + \cfrac{1}{2 + \cdots}}$$

73. The size of an undisturbed fish population has been modeled by the formula

$$p_{n+1} = \frac{bp_n}{a + p_n}$$

where p_n is the fish population after n years and a and b are positive constants that depend on the species and its environment. Suppose that the population in year 0 is $p_0 > 0$.
(a) Show that if $\{p_n\}$ is convergent, then the only possible values for its limit are 0 and $b - a$.
(b) Show that $p_{n+1} < (b/a)p_n$.
(c) Use part (b) to show that if $a > b$, then $\lim_{n \to \infty} p_n = 0$; in other words, the population dies out.
(d) Now assume that $a < b$. Show that if $p_0 < b - a$, then $\{p_n\}$ is increasing and $0 < p_n < b - a$. Show also that if $p_0 > b - a$, then $\{p_n\}$ is decreasing and $p_n > b - a$. Deduce that if $a < b$, then $\lim_{n \to \infty} p_n = b - a$.

LABORATORY PROJECT

[CAS] **Logistic Sequences**

A sequence that arises in ecology as a model for population growth is defined by the **logistic difference equation**

$$p_{n+1} = kp_n(1 - p_n)$$

where p_n measures the size of the population of the nth generation of a single species. To keep the numbers manageable, p_n is a fraction of the maximal size of the population, so $0 \leqslant p_n \leqslant 1$. Notice that the form of this equation is similar to the logistic differential equation in Section 10.5. The discrete model—with sequences instead of continuous functions—is preferable for modeling insect populations, where mating and death occur in a periodic fashion.

An ecologist is interested in predicting the size of the population as time goes on, and asks these questions: Will it stabilize at a limiting value? Will it change in a cyclical fashion? Or will it exhibit random behavior?

Write a program to compute the first n terms of this sequence starting with an initial population p_0, where $0 < p_0 < 1$. Use this program to do the following.

1. Calculate 20 or 30 terms of the sequence for $p_0 = \frac{1}{2}$ and for two values of k such that $1 < k < 3$. Graph the sequences. Do they appear to converge? Repeat for a different value of p_0 between 0 and 1. Does the limit depend on the choice of p_0? Does it depend on the choice of k?

2. Calculate terms of the sequence for a value of k between 3 and 3.4 and plot them. What do you notice about the behavior of the terms?

3. Experiment with values of k between 3.4 and 3.5. What happens to the terms?

4. For values of k between 3.6 and 4, compute and plot at least 100 terms and comment on the behavior of the sequence. What happens if you change p_0 by 0.001? This type of behavior is called *chaotic* and is exhibited by insect populations under certain conditions.

12.2 Series

If we try to add the terms of an infinite sequence $\{a_n\}_{n=1}^{\infty}$ we get an expression of the form

[1] $$a_1 + a_2 + a_3 + \cdots + a_n + \cdots$$

which is called an **infinite series** (or just a **series**) and is denoted, for short, by the symbol

$$\sum_{n=1}^{\infty} a_n \qquad \text{or} \qquad \sum a_n$$

But does it make sense to talk about the sum of infinitely many terms?

It would be impossible to find a finite sum for the series

$$1 + 2 + 3 + 4 + 5 + \cdots + n + \cdots$$

because if we start adding the terms we get the cumulative sums $1, 3, 6, 10, 15, 21, \ldots$ and, after the nth term, we get $n(n + 1)/2$, which becomes very large as n increases.

However, if we start to add the terms of the series

$$\frac{1}{2} + \frac{1}{4} + \frac{1}{8} + \frac{1}{16} + \frac{1}{32} + \frac{1}{64} + \cdots + \frac{1}{2^n} + \cdots$$

n	Sum of first n terms
1	0.50000000
2	0.75000000
3	0.87500000
4	0.93750000
5	0.96875000
6	0.98437500
7	0.99218750
10	0.99902344
15	0.99996948
20	0.99999905
25	0.99999997

we get $\frac{1}{2}, \frac{3}{4}, \frac{7}{8}, \frac{15}{16}, \frac{31}{32}, \frac{63}{64}, \ldots, 1 - 1/2^n, \ldots$. The table shows that as we add more and more terms, these *partial sums* become closer and closer to 1. (See also Figure 11 in *A Preview of Calculus*, page 7.) In fact, by adding sufficiently many terms of the series we can make the partial sums as close as we like to 1. So it seems reasonable to say that the sum of this infinite series is 1 and to write

$$\sum_{n=1}^{\infty} \frac{1}{2^n} = \frac{1}{2} + \frac{1}{4} + \frac{1}{8} + \frac{1}{16} + \cdots + \frac{1}{2^n} + \cdots = 1$$

We use a similar idea to determine whether or not a general series (1) has a sum. We consider the **partial sums**

$$s_1 = a_1$$

$$s_2 = a_1 + a_2$$

$$s_3 = a_1 + a_2 + a_3$$

$$s_4 = a_1 + a_2 + a_3 + a_4$$

and, in general,

$$s_n = a_1 + a_2 + a_3 + \cdots + a_n = \sum_{i=1}^{n} a_i$$

These partial sums form a new sequence $\{s_n\}$, which may or may not have a limit. If $\lim_{n\to\infty} s_n = s$ exists (as a finite number), then, as in the preceding example, we call it the sum of the infinite series Σa_n.

---

2 Definition Given a series $\sum_{n=1}^{\infty} a_n = a_1 + a_2 + a_3 + \cdots$, let s_n denote its nth partial sum:

$$s_n = \sum_{i=1}^{n} a_i = a_1 + a_2 + \cdots + a_n$$

If the sequence $\{s_n\}$ is convergent and $\lim_{n\to\infty} s_n = s$ exists as a real number, then the series Σa_n is called **convergent** and we write

$$a_1 + a_2 + \cdots + a_n + \cdots = s \qquad \text{or} \qquad \sum_{n=1}^{\infty} a_n = s$$

The number s is called the **sum** of the series. Otherwise, the series is called **divergent**.

Thus, when we write $\sum_{n=1}^{\infty} a_n = s$ we mean that by adding sufficiently many terms of the series we can get as close as we like to the number s. Notice that

$$\sum_{n=1}^{\infty} a_n = \lim_{n\to\infty} \sum_{i=1}^{n} a_i$$

|||| Compare with the improper integral

$$\int_1^{\infty} f(x)\, dx = \lim_{t\to\infty} \int_1^{t} f(x)\, dx$$

To find this integral we integrate from 1 to t and then let $t \to \infty$. For a series, we sum from 1 to n and then let $n \to \infty$.

EXAMPLE 1 An important example of an infinite series is the **geometric series**

$$a + ar + ar^2 + ar^3 + \cdots + ar^{n-1} + \cdots = \sum_{n=1}^{\infty} ar^{n-1} \qquad a \neq 0$$

Each term is obtained from the preceding one by multiplying it by the common ratio r. (We have already considered the special case where $a = \frac{1}{2}$ and $r = \frac{1}{2}$ on page 749.)

If $r = 1$, then $s_n = a + a + \cdots + a = na \to \pm\infty$. Since $\lim_{n\to\infty} s_n$ doesn't exist, the geometric series diverges in this case.

If $r \neq 1$, we have

$$s_n = a + ar + ar^2 + \cdots + ar^{n-1}$$

and

$$rs_n = \qquad ar + ar^2 + \cdots + ar^{n-1} + ar^n$$

Subtracting these equations, we get

$$s_n - rs_n = a - ar^n$$

3
$$s_n = \frac{a(1 - r^n)}{1 - r}$$

If $-1 < r < 1$, we know from (12.1.8) that $r^n \to 0$ as $n \to \infty$, so

$$\lim_{n\to\infty} s_n = \lim_{n\to\infty} \frac{a(1 - r^n)}{1 - r} = \frac{a}{1 - r} - \frac{a}{1 - r} \lim_{n\to\infty} r^n = \frac{a}{1 - r}$$

Thus, when $|r| < 1$ the geometric series is convergent and its sum is $a/(1 - r)$.

If $r \le -1$ or $r > 1$, the sequence $\{r^n\}$ is divergent by (12.1.8) and so, by Equation 3, $\lim_{n\to\infty} s_n$ does not exist. Therefore, the geometric series diverges in those cases.

We summarize the results of Example 1 as follows.

---

4 The geometric series

$$\sum_{n=1}^{\infty} ar^{n-1} = a + ar + ar^2 + \cdots$$

is convergent if $|r| < 1$ and its sum is

$$\sum_{n=1}^{\infty} ar^{n-1} = \frac{a}{1 - r} \qquad |r| < 1$$

If $|r| \ge 1$, the geometric series is divergent.

EXAMPLE 2 Find the sum of the geometric series

$$5 - \frac{10}{3} + \frac{20}{9} - \frac{40}{27} + \cdots$$

SOLUTION The first term is $a = 5$ and the common ratio is $r = -\frac{2}{3}$. Since $|r| = \frac{2}{3} < 1$, the series is convergent by (4) and its sum is

$$5 - \frac{10}{3} + \frac{20}{9} - \frac{40}{27} + \cdots = \frac{5}{1 - \left(-\frac{2}{3}\right)} = \frac{5}{\frac{5}{3}} = 3$$

▐▐▐ Figure 1 provides a geometric demonstration of the result in Example 1. If the triangles are constructed as shown and s is the sum of the series, then, by similar triangles,

$$\frac{s}{a} = \frac{a}{a - ar} \qquad \text{so} \qquad s = \frac{a}{1 - r}$$

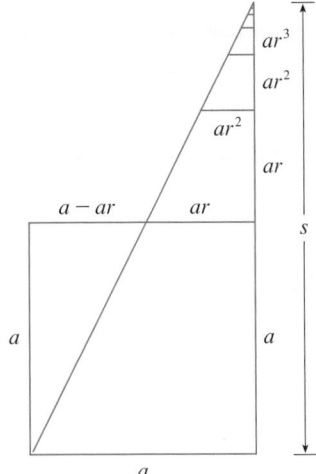

FIGURE 1

▐▐▐ In words: The sum of a convergent geometric series is

$$\frac{\text{first term}}{1 - \text{common ratio}}$$

|||| What do we really mean when we say that the sum of the series in Example 2 is 3? Of course, we can't literally add an infinite number of terms, one by one. But, according to Definition 2, the total sum is the limit of the sequence of partial sums. So, by taking the sum of sufficiently many terms, we can get as close as we like to the number 3. The table shows the first ten partial sums s_n and the graph in Figure 2 shows how the sequence of partial sums approaches 3.

n	s_n
1	5.000000
2	1.666667
3	3.888889
4	2.407407
5	3.395062
6	2.736626
7	3.175583
8	2.882945
9	3.078037
10	2.947975

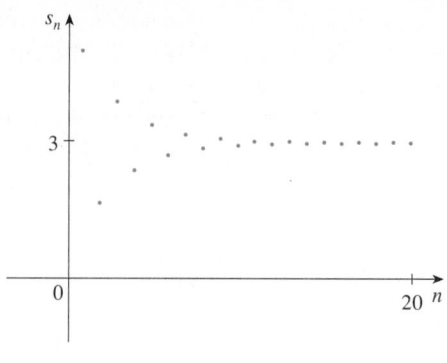

FIGURE 2

EXAMPLE 3 Is the series $\sum_{n=1}^{\infty} 2^{2n}3^{1-n}$ convergent or divergent?

SOLUTION Let's rewrite the nth term of the series in the form ar^{n-1}:

$$\sum_{n=1}^{\infty} 2^{2n}3^{1-n} = \sum_{n=1}^{\infty} \frac{4^n}{3^{n-1}} = \sum_{n=1}^{\infty} 4\left(\tfrac{4}{3}\right)^{n-1}$$

|||| Another way to identify a and r is to write out the first few terms:

$$4 + \tfrac{16}{3} + \tfrac{64}{9} + \cdots$$

We recognize this series as a geometric series with $a = 4$ and $r = \tfrac{4}{3}$. Since $r > 1$, the series diverges by (4).

EXAMPLE 4 Write the number $2.3\overline{17} = 2.3171717\ldots$ as a ratio of integers.

SOLUTION

$$2.3171717\ldots = 2.3 + \frac{17}{10^3} + \frac{17}{10^5} + \frac{17}{10^7} + \cdots$$

After the first term we have a geometric series with $a = 17/10^3$ and $r = 1/10^2$. Therefore

$$2.3\overline{17} = 2.3 + \frac{\dfrac{17}{10^3}}{1 - \dfrac{1}{10^2}} = 2.3 + \frac{\dfrac{17}{1000}}{\dfrac{99}{100}}$$

$$= \frac{23}{10} + \frac{17}{990} = \frac{1147}{495}$$

EXAMPLE 5 Find the sum of the series $\sum_{n=0}^{\infty} x^n$, where $|x| < 1$.

SOLUTION Notice that this series starts with $n = 0$ and so the first term is $x^0 = 1$. (With series, we adopt the convention that $x^0 = 1$ even when $x = 0$.) Thus

$$\sum_{n=0}^{\infty} x^n = 1 + x + x^2 + x^3 + x^4 + \cdots$$

 Module 12.2 explores a series that depends on an angle θ in a triangle and enables you to see how rapidly the series converges when θ varies.

This is a geometric series with $a = 1$ and $r = x$. Since $|r| = |x| < 1$, it converges and (4) gives

[5]

$$\sum_{n=0}^{\infty} x^n = \frac{1}{1 - x}$$

EXAMPLE 6 Show that the series $\displaystyle\sum_{n=1}^{\infty} \frac{1}{n(n+1)}$ is convergent, and find its sum.

SOLUTION This is not a geometric series, so we go back to the definition of a convergent series and compute the partial sums.

$$s_n = \sum_{i=1}^{n} \frac{1}{i(i+1)} = \frac{1}{1 \cdot 2} + \frac{1}{2 \cdot 3} + \frac{1}{3 \cdot 4} + \cdots + \frac{1}{n(n+1)}$$

We can simplify this expression if we use the partial fraction decomposition

$$\frac{1}{i(i+1)} = \frac{1}{i} - \frac{1}{i+1}$$

(see Section 8.4). Thus, we have

$$
\begin{aligned}
s_n &= \sum_{i=1}^{n} \frac{1}{i(i+1)} = \sum_{i=1}^{n} \left(\frac{1}{i} - \frac{1}{i+1} \right) \\
&= \left(1 - \frac{1}{2} \right) + \left(\frac{1}{2} - \frac{1}{3} \right) + \left(\frac{1}{3} - \frac{1}{4} \right) + \cdots + \left(\frac{1}{n} - \frac{1}{n+1} \right) \\
&= 1 - \frac{1}{n+1}
\end{aligned}
$$

|||| Notice that the terms cancel in pairs. This is an example of a **telescoping sum**: Because of all the cancellations, the sum collapses (like an old-fashioned collapsing telescope) into just two terms.

and so

$$\lim_{n \to \infty} s_n = \lim_{n \to \infty} \left(1 - \frac{1}{n+1} \right) = 1 - 0 = 1$$

Therefore, the given series is convergent and

$$\sum_{n=1}^{\infty} \frac{1}{n(n+1)} = 1$$

|||| Figure 3 illustrates Example 6 by showing the graphs of the sequence of terms $a_n = 1/[n(n+1)]$ and the sequence $\{s_n\}$ of partial sums. Notice that $a_n \to 0$ and $s_n \to 1$. See Exercises 54 and 55 for two geometric interpretations of Example 6.

EXAMPLE 7 Show that the **harmonic series**

$$\sum_{n=1}^{\infty} \frac{1}{n} = 1 + \frac{1}{2} + \frac{1}{3} + \frac{1}{4} + \cdots$$

is divergent.

SOLUTION

$$s_1 = 1$$

$$s_2 = 1 + \frac{1}{2}$$

$$s_4 = 1 + \frac{1}{2} + \left(\frac{1}{3} + \frac{1}{4} \right) > 1 + \frac{1}{2} + \left(\frac{1}{4} + \frac{1}{4} \right) = 1 + \frac{2}{2}$$

$$
\begin{aligned}
s_8 &= 1 + \frac{1}{2} + \left(\frac{1}{3} + \frac{1}{4} \right) + \left(\frac{1}{5} + \frac{1}{6} + \frac{1}{7} + \frac{1}{8} \right) \\
&> 1 + \frac{1}{2} + \left(\frac{1}{4} + \frac{1}{4} \right) + \left(\frac{1}{8} + \frac{1}{8} + \frac{1}{8} + \frac{1}{8} \right) \\
&= 1 + \frac{1}{2} + \frac{1}{2} + \frac{1}{2} = 1 + \frac{3}{2}
\end{aligned}
$$

$$
\begin{aligned}
s_{16} &= 1 + \frac{1}{2} + \left(\frac{1}{3} + \frac{1}{4} \right) + \left(\frac{1}{5} + \cdots + \frac{1}{8} \right) + \left(\frac{1}{9} + \cdots + \frac{1}{16} \right) \\
&> 1 + \frac{1}{2} + \left(\frac{1}{4} + \frac{1}{4} \right) + \left(\frac{1}{8} + \cdots + \frac{1}{8} \right) + \left(\frac{1}{16} + \cdots + \frac{1}{16} \right) \\
&= 1 + \frac{1}{2} + \frac{1}{2} + \frac{1}{2} + \frac{1}{2} = 1 + \frac{4}{2}
\end{aligned}
$$

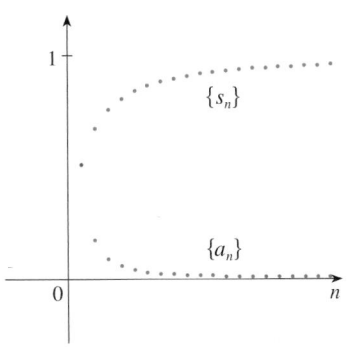

FIGURE 3

Similarly, $s_{32} > 1 + \frac{5}{2}$, $s_{64} > 1 + \frac{6}{2}$, and in general

$$s_{2^n} > 1 + \frac{n}{2}$$

|||| The method used in Example 7 for showing that the harmonic series diverges is due to the French scholar Nicole Oresme (1323–1382).

This shows that $s_{2^n} \to \infty$ as $n \to \infty$ and so $\{s_n\}$ is divergent. Therefore, the harmonic series diverges.

---

6 **Theorem** If the series $\sum\limits_{n=1}^{\infty} a_n$ is convergent, then $\lim\limits_{n \to \infty} a_n = 0$.

Proof Let $s_n = a_1 + a_2 + \cdots + a_n$. Then $a_n = s_n - s_{n-1}$. Since $\sum a_n$ is convergent, the sequence $\{s_n\}$ is convergent. Let $\lim_{n \to \infty} s_n = s$. Since $n - 1 \to \infty$ as $n \to \infty$, we also have $\lim_{n \to \infty} s_{n-1} = s$. Therefore

$$\lim_{n \to \infty} a_n = \lim_{n \to \infty} (s_n - s_{n-1}) = \lim_{n \to \infty} s_n - \lim_{n \to \infty} s_{n-1}$$
$$= s - s = 0$$

NOTE 1 ▫ With any *series* $\sum a_n$ we associate two *sequences:* the sequence $\{s_n\}$ of its partial sums and the sequence $\{a_n\}$ of its terms. If $\sum a_n$ is convergent, then the limit of the sequence $\{s_n\}$ is s (the sum of the series) and, as Theorem 6 asserts, the limit of the sequence $\{a_n\}$ is 0.

NOTE 2 ▫ The converse of Theorem 6 is not true in general. If $\lim_{n \to \infty} a_n = 0$, we cannot conclude that $\sum a_n$ is convergent. Observe that for the harmonic series $\sum 1/n$ we have $a_n = 1/n \to 0$ as $n \to \infty$, but we showed in Example 7 that $\sum 1/n$ is divergent.

---

7 **The Test for Divergence** If $\lim\limits_{n \to \infty} a_n$ does not exist or if $\lim\limits_{n \to \infty} a_n \neq 0$, then the series $\sum\limits_{n=1}^{\infty} a_n$ is divergent.

The Test for Divergence follows from Theorem 6 because, if the series is not divergent, then it is convergent, and so $\lim_{n \to \infty} a_n = 0$.

EXAMPLE 8 Show that the series $\sum\limits_{n=1}^{\infty} \dfrac{n^2}{5n^2 + 4}$ diverges.

SOLUTION

$$\lim_{n \to \infty} a_n = \lim_{n \to \infty} \frac{n^2}{5n^2 + 4} = \lim_{n \to \infty} \frac{1}{5 + 4/n^2} = \frac{1}{5} \neq 0$$

So the series diverges by the Test for Divergence.

NOTE 3 ▫ If we find that $\lim_{n \to \infty} a_n \neq 0$, we know that $\sum a_n$ is divergent. If we find that $\lim_{n \to \infty} a_n = 0$, we know *nothing* about the convergence or divergence of $\sum a_n$. Remember the warning in Note 2: If $\lim_{n \to \infty} a_n = 0$, the series $\sum a_n$ might converge or it might diverge.

8 Theorem If $\Sigma\, a_n$ and $\Sigma\, b_n$ are convergent series, then so are the series $\Sigma\, ca_n$ (where c is a constant), $\Sigma\,(a_n + b_n)$, and $\Sigma\,(a_n - b_n)$, and

(i) $\displaystyle\sum_{n=1}^{\infty} ca_n = c \sum_{n=1}^{\infty} a_n$

(ii) $\displaystyle\sum_{n=1}^{\infty} (a_n + b_n) = \sum_{n=1}^{\infty} a_n + \sum_{n=1}^{\infty} b_n$

(iii) $\displaystyle\sum_{n=1}^{\infty} (a_n - b_n) = \sum_{n=1}^{\infty} a_n - \sum_{n=1}^{\infty} b_n$

These properties of convergent series follow from the corresponding Limit Laws for Sequences in Section 11.1. For instance, here is how part (ii) of Theorem 8 is proved:
Let

$$s_n = \sum_{i=1}^{n} a_i \qquad s = \sum_{n=1}^{\infty} a_n \qquad t_n = \sum_{i=1}^{n} b_i \qquad t = \sum_{n=1}^{\infty} b_n$$

The nth partial sum for the series $\Sigma\,(a_n + b_n)$ is

$$u_n = \sum_{i=1}^{n} (a_i + b_i)$$

and, using Equation 5.2.9, we have

$$\lim_{n\to\infty} u_n = \lim_{n\to\infty} \sum_{i=1}^{n} (a_i + b_i) = \lim_{n\to\infty} \left(\sum_{i=1}^{n} a_i + \sum_{i=1}^{n} b_i \right)$$

$$= \lim_{n\to\infty} \sum_{i=1}^{n} a_i + \lim_{n\to\infty} \sum_{i=1}^{n} b_i$$

$$= \lim_{n\to\infty} s_n + \lim_{n\to\infty} t_n = s + t$$

Therefore, $\Sigma\,(a_n + b_n)$ is convergent and its sum is

$$\sum_{n=1}^{\infty} (a_n + b_n) = s + t = \sum_{n=1}^{\infty} a_n + \sum_{n=1}^{\infty} b_n$$

EXAMPLE 9 Find the sum of the series $\displaystyle\sum_{n=1}^{\infty} \left(\frac{3}{n(n+1)} + \frac{1}{2^n} \right)$.

SOLUTION The series $\Sigma\, 1/2^n$ is a geometric series with $a = \frac{1}{2}$ and $r = \frac{1}{2}$, so

$$\sum_{n=1}^{\infty} \frac{1}{2^n} = \frac{\frac{1}{2}}{1 - \frac{1}{2}} = 1$$

In Example 6 we found that

$$\sum_{n=1}^{\infty} \frac{1}{n(n+1)} = 1$$

So, by Theorem 8, the given series is convergent and

$$\sum_{n=1}^{\infty} \left(\frac{3}{n(n+1)} + \frac{1}{2^n} \right) = 3 \sum_{n=1}^{\infty} \frac{1}{n(n+1)} + \sum_{n=1}^{\infty} \frac{1}{2^n}$$

$$= 3 \cdot 1 + 1 = 4$$

NOTE 4 ∘ A finite number of terms doesn't affect the convergence or divergence of a series. For instance, suppose that we were able to show that the series

$$\sum_{n=4}^{\infty} \frac{n}{n^3 + 1}$$

is convergent. Since

$$\sum_{n=1}^{\infty} \frac{n}{n^3 + 1} = \frac{1}{2} + \frac{2}{9} + \frac{3}{28} + \sum_{n=4}^{\infty} \frac{n}{n^3 + 1}$$

it follows that the entire series $\sum_{n=1}^{\infty} n/(n^3 + 1)$ is convergent. Similarly, if it is known that the series $\sum_{n=N+1}^{\infty} a_n$ converges, then the full series

$$\sum_{n=1}^{\infty} a_n = \sum_{n=1}^{N} a_n + \sum_{n=N+1}^{\infty} a_n$$

is also convergent.

|||| 12.2 Exercises

1. (a) What is the difference between a sequence and a series?
(b) What is a convergent series? What is a divergent series?

2. Explain what it means to say that $\sum_{n=1}^{\infty} a_n = 5$.

3–8 |||| Find at least 10 partial sums of the series. Graph both the sequence of terms and the sequence of partial sums on the same screen. Does it appear that the series is convergent or divergent? If it is convergent, find the sum. If it is divergent, explain why.

3. $\displaystyle\sum_{n=1}^{\infty} \frac{12}{(-5)^n}$

4. $\displaystyle\sum_{n=1}^{\infty} \frac{2n^2 - 1}{n^2 + 1}$

5. $\displaystyle\sum_{n=1}^{\infty} \tan n$

6. $\displaystyle\sum_{n=1}^{\infty} (0.6)^{n-1}$

7. $\displaystyle\sum_{n=1}^{\infty} \left(\frac{1}{n^{1.5}} - \frac{1}{(n+1)^{1.5}} \right)$

8. $\displaystyle\sum_{n=2}^{\infty} \frac{1}{n(n-1)}$

9. Let $a_n = \dfrac{2n}{3n + 1}$.
(a) Determine whether $\{a_n\}$ is convergent.
(b) Determine whether $\sum_{n=1}^{\infty} a_n$ is convergent.

10. (a) Explain the difference between

$$\sum_{i=1}^{n} a_i \quad \text{and} \quad \sum_{j=1}^{n} a_j$$

(b) Explain the difference between

$$\sum_{i=1}^{n} a_i \quad \text{and} \quad \sum_{j=1}^{n} a_j$$

11–34 |||| Determine whether the series is convergent or divergent. If it is convergent, find its sum.

11. $3 + 2 + \frac{4}{3} + \frac{8}{9} + \cdots$

12. $\frac{1}{8} - \frac{1}{4} + \frac{1}{2} - 1 + \cdots$

13. $-2 + \frac{5}{2} - \frac{25}{8} + \frac{125}{32} - \cdots$

14. $1 + 0.4 + 0.16 + 0.064 + \cdots$

15. $\displaystyle\sum_{n=1}^{\infty} 5\left(\frac{2}{3}\right)^{n-1}$

16. $\displaystyle\sum_{n=1}^{\infty} \frac{(-6)^{n-1}}{5^{n-1}}$

17. $\displaystyle\sum_{n=1}^{\infty} \frac{(-3)^{n-1}}{4^n}$

18. $\displaystyle\sum_{n=0}^{\infty} \frac{1}{(\sqrt{2})^n}$

19. $\displaystyle\sum_{n=0}^{\infty} \frac{\pi^n}{3^{n+1}}$

20. $\displaystyle\sum_{n=1}^{\infty} \frac{e^n}{3^{n-1}}$

21. $\displaystyle\sum_{n=1}^{\infty} \frac{n}{n + 5}$

22. $\displaystyle\sum_{n=1}^{\infty} \frac{3}{n}$

23. $\displaystyle\sum_{n=2}^{\infty} \frac{2}{n^2 - 1}$

24. $\displaystyle\sum_{n=1}^{\infty} \frac{(n + 1)^2}{n(n + 2)}$

25. $\displaystyle\sum_{k=2}^{\infty} \frac{k^2}{k^2 - 1}$

26. $\displaystyle\sum_{n=1}^{\infty} \frac{2}{n^2 + 4n + 3}$

27. $\displaystyle\sum_{n=1}^{\infty} \frac{3^n + 2^n}{6^n}$

28. $\displaystyle\sum_{n=1}^{\infty} [(0.8)^{n-1} - (0.3)^n]$

29. $\displaystyle\sum_{n=1}^{\infty} \sqrt[n]{2}$

30. $\displaystyle\sum_{n=1}^{\infty} \ln\left(\frac{n}{2n + 5}\right)$

31. $\displaystyle\sum_{n=1}^{\infty} \arctan n$

32. $\displaystyle\sum_{k=1}^{\infty} (\cos 1)^k$

33. $\displaystyle\sum_{n=1}^{\infty} \left(\frac{3}{n(n + 3)} + \frac{5}{4^n} \right)$

34. $\displaystyle\sum_{n=1}^{\infty} \left(\frac{3}{5^n} + \frac{2}{n} \right)$

35–40 |||| Express the number as a ratio of integers.

35. $0.\overline{2} = 0.2222\ldots$

36. $0.\overline{73} = 0.73737373\ldots$

37. $3.\overline{417} = 3.417417417\ldots$

38. $6.2\overline{54}$

39. $0.123\overline{456}$

40. $5.6\overline{021}$

41–45 ▏▏▏ Find the values of x for which the series converges. Find the sum of the series for those values of x.

41. $\displaystyle\sum_{n=1}^{\infty} \frac{x^n}{3^n}$

42. $\displaystyle\sum_{n=1}^{\infty} (x - 4)^n$

43. $\displaystyle\sum_{n=0}^{\infty} 4^n x^n$

44. $\displaystyle\sum_{n=0}^{\infty} \frac{(x + 3)^n}{2^n}$

45. $\displaystyle\sum_{n=0}^{\infty} \frac{\cos^n x}{2^n}$

46. We have seen that the harmonic series is a divergent series whose terms approach 0. Show that

$$\sum_{n=1}^{\infty} \ln\left(1 + \frac{1}{n}\right)$$

is another series with this property.

[CAS] **47–48** ▏▏▏ Use the partial fraction command on your CAS to find a convenient expression for the partial sum, and then use this expression to find the sum of the series. Check your answer by using the CAS to sum the series directly.

47. $\displaystyle\sum_{n=1}^{\infty} \frac{1}{(4n + 1)(4n - 3)}$

48. $\displaystyle\sum_{n=1}^{\infty} \frac{n^2 + 3n + 1}{(n^2 + n)^2}$

49. If the nth partial sum of a series $\sum_{n=1}^{\infty} a_n$ is

$$s_n = \frac{n - 1}{n + 1}$$

find a_n and $\sum_{n=1}^{\infty} a_n$.

50. If the nth partial sum of a series $\sum_{n=1}^{\infty} a_n$ is $s_n = 3 - n2^{-n}$, find a_n and $\sum_{n=1}^{\infty} a_n$.

51. When money is spent on goods and services, those that receive the money also spend some of it. The people receiving some of the twice-spent money will spend some of that, and so on. Economists call this chain reaction the *multiplier effect*. In a hypothetical isolated community, the local government begins the process by spending D dollars. Suppose that each recipient of spent money spends $100c\%$ and saves $100s\%$ of the money that he or she receives. The values c and s are called the *marginal propensity to consume* and the *marginal propensity to save* and, of course, $c + s = 1$.
(a) Let S_n be the total spending that has been generated after n transactions. Find an equation for S_n.
(b) Show that $\lim_{n \to \infty} S_n = kD$, where $k = 1/s$. The number k is called the *multiplier*. What is the multiplier if the marginal propensity to consume is 80%?

Note: The federal government uses this principle to justify deficit spending. Banks use this principle to justify lending a large percentage of the money that they receive in deposits.

52. A certain ball has the property that each time it falls from a height h onto a hard, level surface, it rebounds to a height rh, where $0 < r < 1$. Suppose that the ball is dropped from an initial height of H meters.

(a) Assuming that the ball continues to bounce indefinitely, find the total distance that it travels. (Use the fact that the ball falls $\frac{1}{2}gt^2$ meters in t seconds.)
(b) Calculate the total time that the ball travels.
(c) Suppose that each time the ball strikes the surface with velocity v it rebounds with velocity $-kv$, where $0 < k < 1$. How long will it take for the ball to come to rest?

53. What is the value of c if $\displaystyle\sum_{n=2}^{\infty} (1 + c)^{-n} = 2$?

54. Graph the curves $y = x^n$, $0 \leqslant x \leqslant 1$, for $n = 0, 1, 2, 3, 4, \ldots$ on a common screen. By finding the areas between successive curves, give a geometric demonstration of the fact, shown in Example 6, that

$$\sum_{n=1}^{\infty} \frac{1}{n(n + 1)} = 1$$

55. The figure shows two circles C and D of radius 1 that touch at P. T is a common tangent line; C_1 is the circle that touches C, D, and T; C_2 is the circle that touches C, D, and C_1; C_3 is the circle that touches C, D, and C_2. This procedure can be continued indefinitely and produces an infinite sequence of circles $\{C_n\}$. Find an expression for the diameter of C_n and thus provide another geometric demonstration of Example 6.

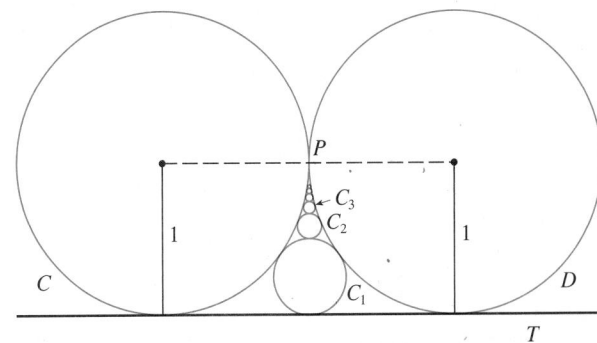

56. A right triangle ABC is given with $\angle A = \theta$ and $|AC| = b$. CD is drawn perpendicular to AB, DE is drawn perpendicular to BC, $EF \perp AB$, and this process is continued indefinitely as shown in the figure. Find the total length of all the perpendiculars

$$|CD| + |DE| + |EF| + |FG| + \cdots$$

in terms of b and θ.

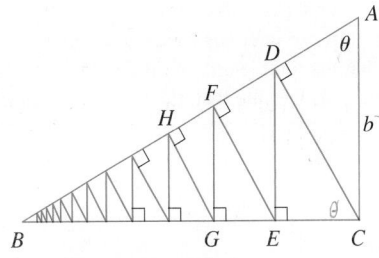

57. What is wrong with the following calculation?

$$0 = 0 + 0 + 0 + \cdots$$
$$= (1 - 1) + (1 - 1) + (1 - 1) + \cdots$$
$$= 1 - 1 + 1 - 1 + 1 - 1 + \cdots$$
$$= 1 + (-1 + 1) + (-1 + 1) + (-1 + 1) + \cdots$$
$$= 1 + 0 + 0 + 0 + \cdots = 1$$

(Guido Ubaldus thought that this proved the existence of God because "something has been created out of nothing.")

58. Suppose that $\sum_{n=1}^{\infty} a_n \ (a_n \neq 0)$ is known to be a convergent series. Prove that $\sum_{n=1}^{\infty} 1/a_n$ is a divergent series.

59. Prove part (i) of Theorem 8.

60. If $\Sigma\, a_n$ is divergent and $c \neq 0$, show that $\Sigma\, ca_n$ is divergent.

61. If $\Sigma\, a_n$ is convergent and $\Sigma\, b_n$ is divergent, show that the series $\Sigma\, (a_n + b_n)$ is divergent. [*Hint:* Argue by contradiction.]

62. If $\Sigma\, a_n$ and $\Sigma\, b_n$ are both divergent, is $\Sigma\, (a_n + b_n)$ necessarily divergent?

63. Suppose that a series $\Sigma\, a_n$ has positive terms and its partial sums s_n satisfy the inequality $s_n \leq 1000$ for all n. Explain why $\Sigma\, a_n$ must be convergent.

64. The Fibonacci sequence was defined in Section 12.1 by the equations

$$f_1 = 1, \quad f_2 = 1, \quad f_n = f_{n-1} + f_{n-2} \quad n \geq 3$$

Show that each of the following statements is true.

(a) $\dfrac{1}{f_{n-1} f_{n+1}} = \dfrac{1}{f_{n-1} f_n} - \dfrac{1}{f_n f_{n+1}}$

(b) $\displaystyle\sum_{n=2}^{\infty} \frac{1}{f_{n-1} f_{n+1}} = 1$

(c) $\displaystyle\sum_{n=2}^{\infty} \frac{f_n}{f_{n-1} f_{n+1}} = 2$

65. The **Cantor set**, named after the German mathematician Georg Cantor (1845–1918), is constructed as follows. We start with the closed interval [0, 1] and remove the open interval $\left(\frac{1}{3}, \frac{2}{3}\right)$. That leaves the two intervals $\left[0, \frac{1}{3}\right]$ and $\left[\frac{2}{3}, 1\right]$ and we remove the open middle third of each. Four intervals remain and again we remove the open middle third of each of them. We continue this procedure indefinitely, at each step removing the open middle third of every interval that remains from the preceding step. The Cantor set consists of the numbers that remain in [0, 1] after all those intervals have been removed.

(a) Show that the total length of all the intervals that are removed is 1. Despite that, the Cantor set contains infi-

nitely many numbers. Give examples of some numbers in the Cantor set.

(b) The **Sierpinski carpet** is a two-dimensional counterpart of the Cantor set. It is constructed by removing the center one-ninth of a square of side 1, then removing the centers of the eight smaller remaining squares, and so on. (The figure shows the first three steps of the construction.) Show that the sum of the areas of the removed squares is 1. This implies that the Sierpinski carpet has area 0.

66. (a) A sequence $\{a_n\}$ is defined recursively by the equation $a_n = \frac{1}{2}(a_{n-1} + a_{n-2})$ for $n \geq 3$, where a_1 and a_2 can be any real numbers. Experiment with various values of a_1 and a_2 and use your calculator to guess the limit of the sequence.

(b) Find $\lim_{n \to \infty} a_n$ in terms of a_1 and a_2 by expressing $a_{n+1} - a_n$ in terms of $a_2 - a_1$ and summing a series.

67. Consider the series

$$\sum_{n=1}^{\infty} \frac{n}{(n+1)!}$$

(a) Find the partial sums $s_1, s_2, s_3,$ and s_4. Do you recognize the denominators? Use the pattern to guess a formula for s_n.

(b) Use mathematical induction to prove your guess.

(c) Show that the given infinite series is convergent, and find its sum.

68. In the figure there are infinitely many circles approaching the vertices of an equilateral triangle, each circle touching other circles and sides of the triangle. If the triangle has sides of length 1, find the total area occupied by the circles.

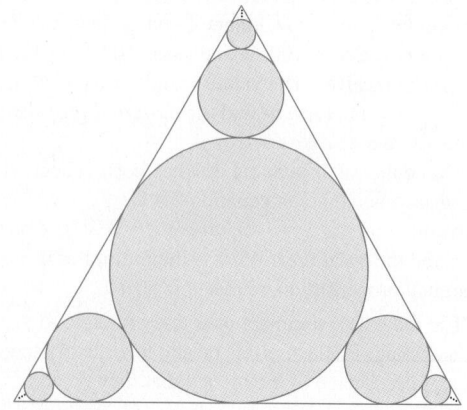

12.3 The Integral Test and Estimates of Sums

In general, it is difficult to find the exact sum of a series. We were able to accomplish this for geometric series and the series $\sum 1/[n(n+1)]$ because in each of those cases we could find a simple formula for the nth partial sum s_n. But usually it isn't easy to compute $\lim_{n \to \infty} s_n$. Therefore, in the next few sections we develop several tests that enable us to determine whether a series is convergent or divergent without explicitly finding its sum. (In some cases, however, our methods will enable us to find good estimates of the sum.) Our first test involves improper integrals.

We begin by investigating the series whose terms are the reciprocals of the squares of the positive integers:

$$\sum_{n=1}^{\infty} \frac{1}{n^2} = \frac{1}{1^2} + \frac{1}{2^2} + \frac{1}{3^2} + \frac{1}{4^2} + \frac{1}{5^2} + \cdots$$

n	$s_n = \sum\limits_{i=1}^{n} \dfrac{1}{i^2}$
5	1.4636
10	1.5498
50	1.6251
100	1.6350
500	1.6429
1000	1.6439
5000	1.6447

There's no simple formula for the sum s_n of the first n terms, but the computer-generated table of values given in the margin suggests that the partial sums are approaching a number near 1.64 as $n \to \infty$ and so it looks as if the series is convergent.

We can confirm this impression with a geometric argument. Figure 1 shows the curve $y = 1/x^2$ and rectangles that lie below the curve. The base of each rectangle is an interval of length 1; the height is equal to the value of the function $y = 1/x^2$ at the right endpoint of the interval. So the sum of the areas of the rectangles is

$$\frac{1}{1^2} + \frac{1}{2^2} + \frac{1}{3^2} + \frac{1}{4^2} + \frac{1}{5^2} + \cdots = \sum_{n=1}^{\infty} \frac{1}{n^2}$$

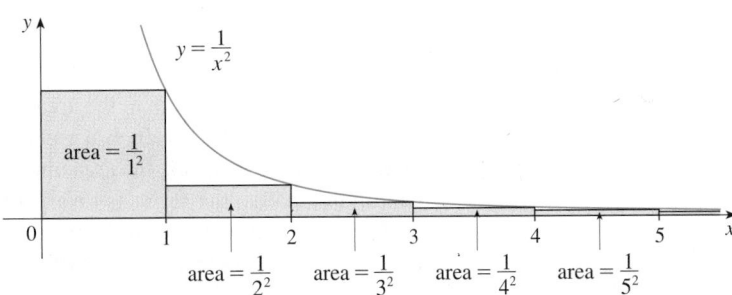

FIGURE 1

If we exclude the first rectangle, the total area of the remaining rectangles is smaller than the area under the curve $y = 1/x^2$ for $x \geqslant 1$, which is the value of the integral $\int_1^{\infty} (1/x^2) \, dx$. In Section 8.8 we discovered that this improper integral is convergent and has value 1. So the picture shows that all the partial sums are less than

$$\frac{1}{1^2} + \int_1^{\infty} \frac{1}{x^2} \, dx = 2$$

Thus, the partial sums are bounded. We also know that the partial sums are increasing (because all the terms are positive). Therefore, the partial sums converge (by the Monotonic Sequence Theorem) and so the series is convergent. The sum of the series (the limit of the partial sums) is also less than 2:

$$\sum_{n=1}^{\infty} \frac{1}{n^2} = \frac{1}{1^2} + \frac{1}{2^2} + \frac{1}{3^2} + \frac{1}{4^2} + \cdots < 2$$

[The exact sum of this series was found by the Swiss mathematician Leonhard Euler (1707–1783) to be $\pi^2/6$, but the proof of this fact is quite difficult. (See Problem 6 in the Problems Plus following Chapter 16.)]

Now let's look at the series

n	$s_n = \sum\limits_{i=1}^{n} \dfrac{1}{\sqrt{i}}$
5	3.2317
10	5.0210
50	12.7524
100	18.5896
500	43.2834
1000	61.8010
5000	139.9681

$$\sum_{n=1}^{\infty} \frac{1}{\sqrt{n}} = \frac{1}{\sqrt{1}} + \frac{1}{\sqrt{2}} + \frac{1}{\sqrt{3}} + \frac{1}{\sqrt{4}} + \frac{1}{\sqrt{5}} + \cdots$$

The table of values of s_n suggests that the partial sums aren't approaching a finite number, so we suspect that the given series may be divergent. Again we use a picture for confirmation. Figure 2 shows the curve $y = 1/\sqrt{x}$, but this time we use rectangles whose tops lie *above* the curve.

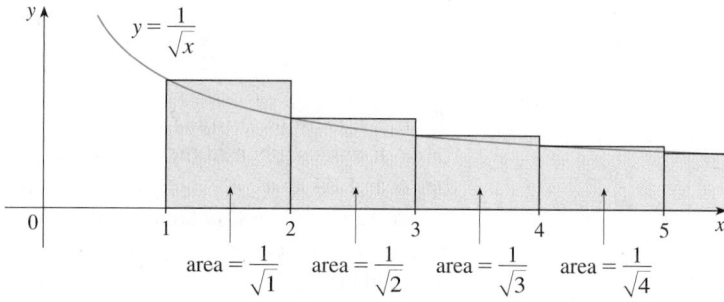

FIGURE 2

The base of each rectangle is an interval of length 1. The height is equal to the value of the function $y = 1/\sqrt{x}$ at the *left* endpoint of the interval. So the sum of the areas of all the rectangles is

$$\frac{1}{\sqrt{1}} + \frac{1}{\sqrt{2}} + \frac{1}{\sqrt{3}} + \frac{1}{\sqrt{4}} + \frac{1}{\sqrt{5}} + \cdots = \sum_{n=1}^{\infty} \frac{1}{\sqrt{n}}$$

This total area is greater than the area under the curve $y = 1/\sqrt{x}$ for $x \geqslant 1$, which is equal to the integral $\int_1^\infty (1/\sqrt{x})\, dx$. But we know from Section 8.8 that this improper integral is divergent. In other words, the area under the curve is infinite. So the sum of the series must be infinite; that is, the series is divergent.

The same sort of geometric reasoning that we used for these two series can be used to prove the following test. (The proof is given at the end of this section.)

The Integral Test Suppose f is a continuous, positive, decreasing function on $[1, \infty)$ and let $a_n = f(n)$. Then the series $\sum_{n=1}^{\infty} a_n$ is convergent if and only if the improper integral $\int_1^\infty f(x)\, dx$ is convergent. In other words:

(i) If $\int_1^\infty f(x)\, dx$ is convergent, then $\sum\limits_{n=1}^{\infty} a_n$ is convergent.

(ii) If $\int_1^\infty f(x)\, dx$ is divergent, then $\sum\limits_{n=1}^{\infty} a_n$ is divergent.

NOTE ▫ When we use the Integral Test it is not necessary to start the series or the integral at $n = 1$. For instance, in testing the series

$$\sum_{n=4}^{\infty} \frac{1}{(n-3)^2} \qquad \text{we use} \qquad \int_4^\infty \frac{1}{(x-3)^2}\, dx$$

Also, it is not necessary that f be always decreasing. What is important is that f be *ultimately* decreasing, that is, decreasing for x larger than some number N. Then $\sum_{n=N}^{\infty} a_n$ is convergent, so $\sum_{n=1}^{\infty} a_n$ is convergent by Note 4 of Section 12.2.

EXAMPLE 1 Test the series $\displaystyle\sum_{n=1}^{\infty} \frac{1}{n^2 + 1}$ for convergence or divergence.

SOLUTION The function $f(x) = 1/(x^2 + 1)$ is continuous, positive, and decreasing on $[1, \infty)$ so we use the Integral Test:

$$\int_1^{\infty} \frac{1}{x^2 + 1}\, dx = \lim_{t \to \infty} \int_1^t \frac{1}{x^2 + 1}\, dx = \lim_{t \to \infty} \tan^{-1}x \Big]_1^t$$

$$= \lim_{t \to \infty} \left(\tan^{-1}t - \frac{\pi}{4} \right) = \frac{\pi}{2} - \frac{\pi}{4} = \frac{\pi}{4}$$

Thus, $\int_1^{\infty} 1/(x^2 + 1)\, dx$ is a convergent integral and so, by the Integral Test, the series $\Sigma\, 1/(n^2 + 1)$ is convergent.

EXAMPLE 2 For what values of p is the series $\displaystyle\sum_{n=1}^{\infty} \frac{1}{n^p}$ convergent?

SOLUTION If $p < 0$, then $\lim_{n \to \infty} (1/n^p) = \infty$. If $p = 0$, then $\lim_{n \to \infty} (1/n^p) = 1$. In either case $\lim_{n \to \infty} (1/n^p) \neq 0$, so the given series diverges by the Test for Divergence (12.2.7).

If $p > 0$, then the function $f(x) = 1/x^p$ is clearly continuous, positive, and decreasing on $[1, \infty)$. We found in Chapter 8 [see (8.8.2)] that

$$\int_1^{\infty} \frac{1}{x^p}\, dx \text{ converges if } p > 1 \text{ and diverges if } p \leq 1$$

It follows from the Integral Test that the series $\Sigma\, 1/n^p$ converges if $p > 1$ and diverges if $0 < p \leq 1$. (For $p = 1$, this series is the harmonic series discussed in Example 7 in Section 12.2.)

The series in Example 2 is called the **p-series**. It is important in the rest of this chapter, so we summarize the results of Example 2 for future reference as follows.

---

1 The *p*-series $\displaystyle\sum_{n=1}^{\infty} \frac{1}{n^p}$ is convergent if $p > 1$ and divergent if $p \leq 1$.

EXAMPLE 3
(a) The series

$$\sum_{n=1}^{\infty} \frac{1}{n^3} = \frac{1}{1^3} + \frac{1}{2^3} + \frac{1}{3^3} + \frac{1}{4^3} + \cdots$$

is convergent because it is a *p*-series with $p = 3 > 1$.
(b) The series

$$\sum_{n=1}^{\infty} \frac{1}{n^{1/3}} = \sum_{n=1}^{\infty} \frac{1}{\sqrt[3]{n}} = 1 + \frac{1}{\sqrt[3]{2}} + \frac{1}{\sqrt[3]{3}} + \frac{1}{\sqrt[3]{4}} + \cdots$$

is divergent because it is a *p*-series with $p = \frac{1}{3} < 1$.

NOTE ▫ We should *not* infer from the Integral Test that the sum of the series is equal to the value of the integral. In fact,

$$\sum_{n=1}^{\infty} \frac{1}{n^2} = \frac{\pi^2}{6} \qquad \text{whereas} \qquad \int_1^{\infty} \frac{1}{x^2}\,dx = 1$$

Therefore, in general,

$$\sum_{n=1}^{\infty} a_n \neq \int_1^{\infty} f(x)\,dx$$

EXAMPLE 4 Determine whether the series $\displaystyle\sum_{n=1}^{\infty} \frac{\ln n}{n}$ converges or diverges.

SOLUTION The function $f(x) = (\ln x)/x$ is positive and continuous for $x > 1$ because the logarithm function is continuous. But it is not obvious whether or not f is decreasing, so we compute its derivative:

$$f'(x) = \frac{(1/x)x - \ln x}{x^2} = \frac{1 - \ln x}{x^2}$$

Thus, $f'(x) < 0$ when $\ln x > 1$, that is, $x > e$. It follows that f is decreasing when $x > e$ and so we can apply the Integral Test:

$$\int_1^{\infty} \frac{\ln x}{x}\,dx = \lim_{t \to \infty} \int_1^t \frac{\ln x}{x}\,dx = \lim_{t \to \infty} \left. \frac{(\ln x)^2}{2} \right]_1^t$$

$$= \lim_{t \to \infty} \frac{(\ln t)^2}{2} = \infty$$

Since this improper integral is divergent, the series $\Sigma\, (\ln n)/n$ is also divergent by the Integral Test.

║║║ Estimating the Sum of a Series

Suppose we have been able to use the Integral Test to show that a series $\Sigma\, a_n$ is convergent and we now want to find an approximation to the sum s of the series. Of course, any partial sum s_n is an approximation to s because $\lim_{n \to \infty} s_n = s$. But how good is such an approximation? To find out, we need to estimate the size of the **remainder**

$$R_n = s - s_n = a_{n+1} + a_{n+2} + a_{n+3} + \cdots$$

The remainder R_n is the error made when s_n, the sum of the first n terms, is used as an approximation to the total sum.

We use the same notation and ideas as in the Integral Test, assuming that f is decreasing on $[n, \infty)$. Comparing the areas of the rectangles with the area under $y = f(x)$ for $x > n$ in Figure 3, we see that

$$R_n = a_{n+1} + a_{n+2} + \cdots \leq \int_n^{\infty} f(x)\,dx$$

Similarly, we see from Figure 4 that

$$R_n = a_{n+1} + a_{n+2} + \cdots \geq \int_{n+1}^{\infty} f(x)\,dx$$

FIGURE 3

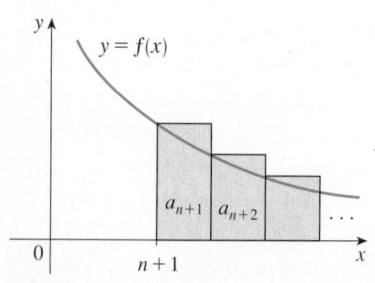

FIGURE 4

So we have proved the following error estimate.

> **2** **Remainder Estimate for the Integral Test** Suppose $f(k) = a_k$, where f is a continuous, positive, decreasing function for $x \geq n$ and Σa_n is convergent. If $R_n = s - s_n$, then
>
> $$\int_{n+1}^{\infty} f(x)\, dx \leq R_n \leq \int_{n}^{\infty} f(x)\, dx$$

EXAMPLE 5
(a) Approximate the sum of the series $\Sigma\, 1/n^3$ by using the sum of the first 10 terms. Estimate the error involved in this approximation.
(b) How many terms are required to ensure that the sum is accurate to within 0.0005?

SOLUTION In both parts (a) and (b) we need to know $\int_{n}^{\infty} f(x)\, dx$. With $f(x) = 1/x^3$, we have

$$\int_{n}^{\infty} \frac{1}{x^3}\, dx = \lim_{t \to \infty} \left[-\frac{1}{2x^2} \right]_{n}^{t} = \lim_{t \to \infty} \left(-\frac{1}{2t^2} + \frac{1}{2n^2} \right) = \frac{1}{2n^2}$$

(a)

$$\sum_{n=1}^{\infty} \frac{1}{n^3} \approx s_{10} = \frac{1}{1^3} + \frac{1}{2^3} + \frac{1}{3^3} + \cdots + \frac{1}{10^3} \approx 1.1975$$

According to the remainder estimate in (2), we have

$$R_{10} \leq \int_{10}^{\infty} \frac{1}{x^3}\, dx = \frac{1}{2(10)^2} = \frac{1}{200}$$

So the size of the error is at most 0.005.

(b) Accuracy to within 0.0005 means that we have to find a value of n such that $R_n \leq 0.0005$. Since

$$R_n \leq \int_{n}^{\infty} \frac{1}{x^3}\, dx = \frac{1}{2n^2}$$

we want

$$\frac{1}{2n^2} < 0.0005$$

Solving this inequality, we get

$$n^2 > \frac{1}{0.001} = 1000 \quad \text{or} \quad n > \sqrt{1000} \approx 31.6$$

We need 32 terms to ensure accuracy to within 0.0005.

If we add s_n to each side of the inequalities in (2), we get

> **3**
>
> $$s_n + \int_{n+1}^{\infty} f(x)\, dx \leq s \leq s_n + \int_{n}^{\infty} f(x)\, dx$$

because $s_n + R_n = s$. The inequalities in (3) give a lower bound and an upper bound for s. They provide a more accurate approximation to the sum of the series than the partial sum s_n does.

EXAMPLE 6 Use (3) with $n = 10$ to estimate the sum of the series $\sum_{n=1}^{\infty} \dfrac{1}{n^3}$.

SOLUTION The inequalities in (3) become

$$s_{10} + \int_{11}^{\infty} \frac{1}{x^3}\, dx \leqslant s \leqslant s_{10} + \int_{10}^{\infty} \frac{1}{x^3}\, dx$$

From Example 5 we know that

$$\int_{n}^{\infty} \frac{1}{x^3}\, dx = \frac{1}{2n^2}$$

so

$$s_{10} + \frac{1}{2(11)^2} \leqslant s \leqslant s_{10} + \frac{1}{2(10)^2}$$

Using $s_{10} \approx 1.197532$, we get

$$1.201664 \leqslant s \leqslant 1.202532$$

If we approximate s by the midpoint of this interval, then the error is at most half the length of the interval. So

$$\sum_{n=1}^{\infty} \frac{1}{n^3} \approx 1.2021 \qquad \text{with error} < 0.0005$$

If we compare Example 6 with Example 5, we see that the improved estimate in (3) can be much better than the estimate $s \approx s_n$. To make the error smaller than 0.0005 we had to use 32 terms in Example 5 but only 10 terms in Example 6.

||| Proof of the Integral Test

We have already seen the basic idea behind the proof of the Integral Test in Figures 1 and 2 for the series $\Sigma\, 1/n^2$ and $\Sigma\, 1/\sqrt{n}$. For the general series $\Sigma\, a_n$ look at Figures 5 and 6. The area of the first shaded rectangle in Figure 5 is the value of f at the right endpoint of $[1, 2]$, that is, $f(2) = a_2$. So, comparing the areas of the shaded rectangles with the area under $y = f(x)$ from 1 to n, we see that

$$\boxed{4} \qquad a_2 + a_3 + \cdots + a_n \leqslant \int_{1}^{n} f(x)\, dx$$

(Notice that this inequality depends on the fact that f is decreasing.) Likewise, Figure 6 shows that

$$\boxed{5} \qquad \int_{1}^{n} f(x)\, dx \leqslant a_1 + a_2 + \cdots + a_{n-1}$$

FIGURE 5

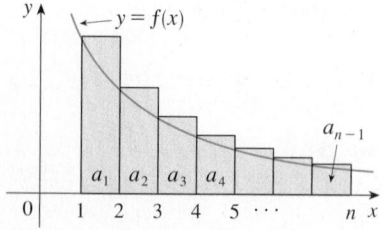

FIGURE 6

(i) If $\int_1^\infty f(x)\,dx$ is convergent, then (4) gives

$$\sum_{i=2}^{n} a_i \le \int_1^n f(x)\,dx \le \int_1^\infty f(x)\,dx$$

since $f(x) \ge 0$. Therefore

$$s_n = a_1 + \sum_{i=2}^{n} a_i \le a_1 + \int_1^\infty f(x)\,dx = M,\text{ say}$$

Since $s_n \le M$ for all n, the sequence $\{s_n\}$ is bounded above. Also

$$s_{n+1} = s_n + a_{n+1} \ge s_n$$

since $a_{n+1} = f(n+1) \ge 0$. Thus, $\{s_n\}$ is an increasing bounded sequence and so it is convergent by the Monotonic Sequence Theorem (12.1.11). This means that $\sum a_n$ is convergent.

(ii) If $\int_1^\infty f(x)\,dx$ is divergent, then $\int_1^n f(x)\,dx \to \infty$ as $n \to \infty$ because $f(x) \ge 0$. But (5) gives

$$\int_1^n f(x)\,dx \le \sum_{i=1}^{n-1} a_i = s_{n-1}$$

and so $s_{n-1} \to \infty$. This implies that $s_n \to \infty$ and so $\sum a_n$ diverges.

12.3 Exercises

1. Draw a picture to show that

$$\sum_{n=2}^{\infty} \frac{1}{n^{1.3}} < \int_1^\infty \frac{1}{x^{1.3}}\,dx$$

What can you conclude about the series?

2. Suppose f is a continuous positive decreasing function for $x \ge 1$ and $a_n = f(n)$. By drawing a picture, rank the following three quantities in increasing order:

$$\int_1^6 f(x)\,dx \qquad \sum_{i=1}^{5} a_i \qquad \sum_{i=2}^{6} a_i$$

3–8 ▯ Use the Integral Test to determine whether the series is convergent or divergent.

3. $\sum_{n=1}^{\infty} \frac{1}{n^4}$ **4.** $\sum_{n=1}^{\infty} \frac{1}{\sqrt[4]{n}}$ **5.** $\sum_{n=1}^{\infty} \frac{1}{3n+1}$

6. $\sum_{n=1}^{\infty} e^{-n}$ **7.** $\sum_{n=1}^{\infty} ne^{-n}$ **8.** $\sum_{n=1}^{\infty} \frac{n+2}{n+1}$

9–24 ▯ Determine whether the series is convergent or divergent.

9. $\sum_{n=1}^{\infty} \frac{2}{n^{0.85}}$ **10.** $\sum_{n=1}^{\infty} (n^{-1.4} + 3n^{-1.2})$

11. $1 + \frac{1}{8} + \frac{1}{27} + \frac{1}{64} + \frac{1}{125} + \cdots$

12. $1 + \frac{1}{2\sqrt{2}} + \frac{1}{3\sqrt{3}} + \frac{1}{4\sqrt{4}} + \frac{1}{5\sqrt{5}} + \cdots$

13. $\sum_{n=1}^{\infty} \frac{5 - 2\sqrt{n}}{n^3}$ **14.** $\sum_{n=3}^{\infty} \frac{5}{n-2}$

15. $\sum_{n=1}^{\infty} \frac{1}{n^2+4}$ **16.** $\sum_{n=1}^{\infty} \frac{3n+2}{n(n+1)}$

17. $\sum_{n=1}^{\infty} \frac{n}{n^2+1}$ **18.** $\sum_{n=1}^{\infty} \frac{1}{n^2-4n+5}$

19. $\sum_{n=1}^{\infty} ne^{-n^2}$ **20.** $\sum_{n=1}^{\infty} \frac{\ln n}{n^2}$

21. $\sum_{n=2}^{\infty} \frac{1}{n \ln n}$ **22.** $\sum_{n=1}^{\infty} \frac{n}{n^4+1}$

23. $\sum_{n=1}^{\infty} \frac{1}{n^3+n}$ **24.** $\sum_{n=3}^{\infty} \frac{1}{n \ln n \ln(\ln n)}$

25–28 ▯ Find the values of p for which the series is convergent.

25. $\sum_{n=2}^{\infty} \frac{1}{n(\ln n)^p}$ **26.** $\sum_{n=3}^{\infty} \frac{1}{n \ln n \,[\ln(\ln n)]^p}$

27. $\displaystyle\sum_{n=1}^{\infty} n(1 + n^2)^p$

28. $\displaystyle\sum_{n=1}^{\infty} \dfrac{\ln n}{n^p}$

▢ ▢ ▢ ▢ ▢ ▢ ▢ ▢ ▢ ▢ ▢ ▢ ▢

29. The Riemann zeta-function ζ is defined by

$$\zeta(x) = \sum_{n=1}^{\infty} \frac{1}{n^x}$$

and is used in number theory to study the distribution of prime numbers. What is the domain of ζ?

30. (a) Find the partial sum s_{10} of the series $\sum_{n=1}^{\infty} 1/n^4$. Estimate the error in using s_{10} as an approximation to the sum of the series.
(b) Use (3) with $n = 10$ to give an improved estimate of the sum.
(c) Find a value of n so that s_n is within 0.00001 of the sum.

31. (a) Use the sum of the first 10 terms to estimate the sum of the series $\sum_{n=1}^{\infty} 1/n^2$. How good is this estimate?
(b) Improve this estimate using (3) with $n = 10$.
(c) Find a value of n that will ensure that the error in the approximation $s \approx s_n$ is less than 0.001.

32. Find the sum of the series $\sum_{n=1}^{\infty} 1/n^5$ correct to three decimal places.

33. Estimate $\sum_{n=1}^{\infty} n^{-3/2}$ to within 0.01.

34. How many terms of the series $\sum_{n=2}^{\infty} 1/[n(\ln n)^2]$ would you need to add to find its sum to within 0.01?

35. Show that if we want to approximate the sum of the series $\sum_{n=1}^{\infty} n^{-1.001}$ so that the error is less than 5 in the ninth decimal place, then we need to add more than $10^{11,301}$ terms!

CAS **36.** (a) Show that the series $\sum_{n=1}^{\infty} (\ln n)^2/n^2$ is convergent.
(b) Find an upper bound for the error in the approximation $s \approx s_n$.
(c) What is the smallest value of n such that this upper bound is less than 0.05?
(d) Find s_n for this value of n.

37. (a) Use (4) to show that if s_n is the nth partial sum of the harmonic series, then

$$s_n \leqslant 1 + \ln n$$

(b) The harmonic series diverges, but very slowly. Use part (a) to show that the sum of the first million terms is less than 15 and the sum of the first billion terms is less than 22.

38. Use the following steps to show that the sequence

$$t_n = 1 + \frac{1}{2} + \frac{1}{3} + \cdots + \frac{1}{n} - \ln n$$

has a limit. (The value of the limit is denoted by γ and is called Euler's constant.)
(a) Draw a picture like Figure 6 with $f(x) = 1/x$ and interpret t_n as an area [or use (5)] to show that $t_n > 0$ for all n.
(b) Interpret

$$t_n - t_{n+1} = [\ln(n + 1) - \ln n] - \frac{1}{n + 1}$$

as a difference of areas to show that $t_n - t_{n+1} > 0$. Therefore, $\{t_n\}$ is a decreasing sequence.
(c) Use the Monotonic Sequence Theorem to show that $\{t_n\}$ is convergent.

39. Find all positive values of b for which the series $\sum_{n=1}^{\infty} b^{\ln n}$ converges.

12.4 The Comparison Tests

In the comparison tests the idea is to compare a given series with a series that is known to be convergent or divergent. For instance, the series

$$\sum_{n=1}^{\infty} \frac{1}{2^n + 1}$$

reminds us of the series $\sum_{n=1}^{\infty} 1/2^n$, which is a geometric series with $a = \frac{1}{2}$ and $r = \frac{1}{2}$ and is therefore convergent. Because the series (1) is so similar to a convergent series, we have the feeling that it too must be convergent. Indeed, it is. The inequality

$$\frac{1}{2^n + 1} < \frac{1}{2^n}$$

shows that our given series (1) has smaller terms than those of the geometric series and therefore all its partial sums are also smaller than 1 (the sum of the geometric series). This means that its partial sums form a bounded increasing sequence, which is convergent. It also follows that the sum of the series is less than the sum of the geometric series:

$$\sum_{n=1}^{\infty} \frac{1}{2^n + 1} < 1$$

Similar reasoning can be used to prove the following test, which applies only to series whose terms are positive. The first part says that if we have a series whose terms are *smaller* than those of a known *convergent* series, then our series is also convergent. The second part says that if we start with a series whose terms are *larger* than those of a known *divergent* series, then it too is divergent.

The Comparison Test Suppose that $\Sigma\, a_n$ and $\Sigma\, b_n$ are series with positive terms.

(i) If $\Sigma\, b_n$ is convergent and $a_n \le b_n$ for all n, then $\Sigma\, a_n$ is also convergent.

(ii) If $\Sigma\, b_n$ is divergent and $a_n \ge b_n$ for all n, then $\Sigma\, a_n$ is also divergent.

‖‖ It is important to keep in mind the distinction between a sequence and a series. A sequence is a list of numbers, whereas a series is a sum. With every series $\Sigma\, a_n$ there are associated two sequences: the sequence $\{a_n\}$ of terms and the sequence $\{s_n\}$ of partial sums.

Proof

(i) Let

$$s_n = \sum_{i=1}^{n} a_i \qquad t_n = \sum_{i=1}^{n} b_i \qquad t = \sum_{n=1}^{\infty} b_n$$

Since both series have positive terms, the sequences $\{s_n\}$ and $\{t_n\}$ are increasing $(s_{n+1} = s_n + a_{n+1} \ge s_n)$. Also $t_n \to t$, so $t_n \le t$ for all n. Since $a_i \le b_i$, we have $s_n \le t_n$. Thus, $s_n \le t$ for all n. This means that $\{s_n\}$ is increasing and bounded above and therefore converges by the Monotonic Sequence Theorem. Thus, $\Sigma\, a_n$ converges.

(ii) If $\Sigma\, b_n$ is divergent, then $t_n \to \infty$ (since $\{t_n\}$ is increasing). But $a_i \ge b_i$ so $s_n \ge t_n$. Thus, $s_n \to \infty$. Therefore, $\Sigma\, a_n$ diverges.

Standard Series for Use with the Comparison Test

In using the Comparison Test we must, of course, have some known series $\Sigma\, b_n$ for the purpose of comparison. Most of the time we use either a *p*-series $\left[\Sigma\, 1/n^p \text{ converges if } p > 1 \text{ and diverges if } p \le 1; \text{ see } (12.3.1)\right]$ or a geometric series $\left[\Sigma\, ar^{n-1} \text{ converges if } |r| < 1 \text{ and diverges if } |r| \ge 1; \text{ see } (12.2.4)\right]$.

EXAMPLE 1 Determine whether the series $\displaystyle\sum_{n=1}^{\infty} \frac{5}{2n^2 + 4n + 3}$ converges or diverges.

SOLUTION For large n the dominant term in the denominator is $2n^2$ so we compare the given series with the series $\Sigma\, 5/(2n^2)$. Observe that

$$\frac{5}{2n^2 + 4n + 3} < \frac{5}{2n^2}$$

because the left side has a bigger denominator. (In the notation of the Comparison Test, a_n is the left side and b_n is the right side.) We know that

$$\sum_{n=1}^{\infty} \frac{5}{2n^2} = \frac{5}{2} \sum_{n=1}^{\infty} \frac{1}{n^2}$$

is convergent because it's a constant times a *p*-series with $p = 2 > 1$. Therefore

$$\sum_{n=1}^{\infty} \frac{5}{2n^2 + 4n + 3}$$

is convergent by part (i) of the Comparison Test.

NOTE 1 ◦ Although the condition $a_n \leq b_n$ or $a_n \geq b_n$ in the Comparison Test is given for all n, we need verify only that it holds for $n \geq N$, where N is some fixed integer, because the convergence of a series is not affected by a finite number of terms. This is illustrated in the next example.

EXAMPLE 2 Test the series $\sum_{n=1}^{\infty} \dfrac{\ln n}{n}$ for convergence or divergence.

SOLUTION This series was tested (using the Integral Test) in Example 4 in Section 12.3, but it is also possible to test it by comparing it with the harmonic series. Observe that $\ln n > 1$ for $n \geq 3$ and so

$$\frac{\ln n}{n} > \frac{1}{n} \qquad n \geq 3$$

We know that $\sum 1/n$ is divergent (p-series with $p = 1$). Thus, the given series is divergent by the Comparison Test.

NOTE 2 ◦ The terms of the series being tested must be smaller than those of a convergent series or larger than those of a divergent series. If the terms are larger than the terms of a convergent series or smaller than those of a divergent series, then the Comparison Test doesn't apply. Consider, for instance, the series

$$\sum_{n=1}^{\infty} \frac{1}{2^n - 1}$$

The inequality

$$\frac{1}{2^n - 1} > \frac{1}{2^n}$$

is useless as far as the Comparison Test is concerned because $\sum b_n = \sum \left(\frac{1}{2}\right)^n$ is convergent and $a_n > b_n$. Nonetheless, we have the feeling that $\sum 1/(2^n - 1)$ ought to be convergent because it is very similar to the convergent geometric series $\sum \left(\frac{1}{2}\right)^n$. In such cases the following test can be used.

> **The Limit Comparison Test** Suppose that $\sum a_n$ and $\sum b_n$ are series with positive terms. If
>
> $$\lim_{n \to \infty} \frac{a_n}{b_n} = c$$
>
> where c is a finite number and $c > 0$, then either both series converge or both diverge.

▐▐ Exercises 40 and 41 deal with the cases $c = 0$ and $c = \infty$.

Proof Let m and M be positive numbers such that $m < c < M$. Because a_n/b_n is close to c for large n, there is an integer N such that

$$m < \frac{a_n}{b_n} < M \qquad \text{when } n > N$$

and so $\qquad\qquad mb_n < a_n < Mb_n \qquad \text{when } n > N$

If $\Sigma \, b_n$ converges, so does $\Sigma \, Mb_n$. Thus, $\Sigma \, a_n$ converges by part (i) of the Comparison Test. If $\Sigma \, b_n$ diverges, so does $\Sigma \, mb_n$ and part (ii) of the Comparison Test shows that $\Sigma \, a_n$ diverges.

EXAMPLE 3 Test the series $\displaystyle\sum_{n=1}^{\infty} \frac{1}{2^n - 1}$ for convergence or divergence.

SOLUTION We use the Limit Comparison Test with

$$a_n = \frac{1}{2^n - 1} \qquad b_n = \frac{1}{2^n}$$

and obtain

$$\lim_{n \to \infty} \frac{a_n}{b_n} = \lim_{n \to \infty} \frac{1/(2^n - 1)}{1/2^n} = \lim_{n \to \infty} \frac{2^n}{2^n - 1} = \lim_{n \to \infty} \frac{1}{1 - 1/2^n} = 1 > 0$$

Since this limit exists and $\Sigma \, 1/2^n$ is a convergent geometric series, the given series converges by the Limit Comparison Test.

EXAMPLE 4 Determine whether the series $\displaystyle\sum_{n=1}^{\infty} \frac{2n^2 + 3n}{\sqrt{5 + n^5}}$ converges or diverges.

SOLUTION The dominant part of the numerator is $2n^2$ and the dominant part of the denominator is $\sqrt{n^5} = n^{5/2}$. This suggests taking

$$a_n = \frac{2n^2 + 3n}{\sqrt{5 + n^5}} \qquad b_n = \frac{2n^2}{n^{5/2}} = \frac{2}{n^{1/2}}$$

$$\lim_{n \to \infty} \frac{a_n}{b_n} = \lim_{n \to \infty} \frac{2n^2 + 3n}{\sqrt{5 + n^5}} \cdot \frac{n^{1/2}}{2} = \lim_{n \to \infty} \frac{2n^{5/2} + 3n^{3/2}}{2\sqrt{5 + n^5}}$$

$$= \lim_{n \to \infty} \frac{2 + \dfrac{3}{n}}{2\sqrt{\dfrac{5}{n^5} + 1}} = \frac{2 + 0}{2\sqrt{0 + 1}} = 1$$

Since $\Sigma \, b_n = 2 \, \Sigma \, 1/n^{1/2}$ is divergent $\left(p\text{-series with } p = \frac{1}{2} < 1\right)$, the given series diverges by the Limit Comparison Test.

Notice that in testing many series we find a suitable comparison series $\Sigma \, b_n$ by keeping only the highest powers in the numerator and denominator.

||| **Estimating Sums**

If we have used the Comparison Test to show that a series $\Sigma \, a_n$ converges by comparison with a series $\Sigma \, b_n$, then we may be able to estimate the sum $\Sigma \, a_n$ by comparing remainders. As in Section 12.3, we consider the remainder

$$R_n = s - s_n = a_{n+1} + a_{n+2} + \cdots$$

For the comparison series $\Sigma \, b_n$ we consider the corresponding remainder

$$T_n = t - t_n = b_{n+1} + b_{n+2} + \cdots$$

Since $a_n \leq b_n$ for all n, we have $R_n \leq T_n$. If $\Sigma\, b_n$ is a p-series, we can estimate its remainder T_n as in Section 12.3. If $\Sigma\, b_n$ is a geometric series, then T_n is the sum of a geometric series and we can sum it exactly (see Exercises 35 and 36). In either case we know that R_n is smaller than T_n.

EXAMPLE 5 Use the sum of the first 100 terms to approximate the sum of the series $\Sigma\, 1/(n^3 + 1)$. Estimate the error involved in this approximation.

SOLUTION Since

$$\frac{1}{n^3 + 1} < \frac{1}{n^3}$$

the given series is convergent by the Comparison Test. The remainder T_n for the comparison series $\Sigma\, 1/n^3$ was estimated in Example 5 in Section 12.3 using the Remainder Estimate for the Integral Test. There we found that

$$T_n \leq \int_n^\infty \frac{1}{x^3}\, dx = \frac{1}{2n^2}$$

Therefore, the remainder R_n for the given series satisfies

$$R_n \leq T_n \leq \frac{1}{2n^2}$$

With $n = 100$ we have

$$R_{100} \leq \frac{1}{2(100)^2} = 0.00005$$

Using a programmable calculator or a computer, we find that

$$\sum_{n=1}^{\infty} \frac{1}{n^3 + 1} \approx \sum_{n=1}^{100} \frac{1}{n^3 + 1} \approx 0.6864538$$

with error less than 0.00005.

12.4 Exercises

1. Suppose $\Sigma\, a_n$ and $\Sigma\, b_n$ are series with positive terms and $\Sigma\, b_n$ is known to be convergent.
   (a) If $a_n > b_n$ for all n, what can you say about $\Sigma\, a_n$? Why?
   (b) If $a_n < b_n$ for all n, what can you say about $\Sigma\, a_n$? Why?

2. Suppose $\Sigma\, a_n$ and $\Sigma\, b_n$ are series with positive terms and $\Sigma\, b_n$ is known to be divergent.
   (a) If $a_n > b_n$ for all n, what can you say about $\Sigma\, a_n$? Why?
   (b) If $a_n < b_n$ for all n, what can you say about $\Sigma\, a_n$? Why?

3–32 ||||| Determine whether the series converges or diverges.

3. $\sum_{n=1}^{\infty} \dfrac{1}{n^2 + n + 1}$

4. $\sum_{n=1}^{\infty} \dfrac{2}{n^3 + 4}$

5. $\sum_{n=1}^{\infty} \dfrac{5}{2 + 3^n}$

6. $\sum_{n=2}^{\infty} \dfrac{1}{n - \sqrt{n}}$

7. $\sum_{n=1}^{\infty} \dfrac{n + 1}{n^2}$

8. $\sum_{n=1}^{\infty} \dfrac{4 + 3^n}{2^n}$

9. $\sum_{n=1}^{\infty} \dfrac{\cos^2 n}{n^2 + 1}$

10. $\sum_{n=1}^{\infty} \dfrac{n^2 - 1}{3n^4 + 1}$

11. $\sum_{n=2}^{\infty} \dfrac{n^2 + 1}{n^3 - 1}$

12. $\sum_{n=0}^{\infty} \dfrac{1 + \sin n}{10^n}$

13. $\sum_{n=1}^{\infty} \dfrac{n - 1}{n4^n}$

14. $\sum_{n=2}^{\infty} \dfrac{\sqrt{n}}{n - 1}$

15. $\sum_{n=1}^{\infty} \dfrac{2 + (-1)^n}{n\sqrt{n}}$

16. $\sum_{n=1}^{\infty} \dfrac{1}{\sqrt{n^3 + 1}}$

17. $\sum_{n=1}^{\infty} \dfrac{1}{\sqrt{n^2 + 1}}$

18. $\sum_{n=1}^{\infty} \dfrac{1}{2n + 3}$

19. $\displaystyle\sum_{n=1}^{\infty} \frac{2^n}{1+3^n}$

20. $\displaystyle\sum_{n=1}^{\infty} \frac{1+2^n}{1+3^n}$

21. $\displaystyle\sum_{n=1}^{\infty} \frac{1}{1+\sqrt{n}}$

22. $\displaystyle\sum_{n=3}^{\infty} \frac{n+2}{(n+1)^3}$

23. $\displaystyle\sum_{n=1}^{\infty} \frac{5+2n}{(1+n^2)^2}$

24. $\displaystyle\sum_{n=1}^{\infty} \frac{n^2-5n}{n^3+n+1}$

25. $\displaystyle\sum_{n=1}^{\infty} \frac{1+n+n^2}{\sqrt{1+n^2+n^6}}$

26. $\displaystyle\sum_{n=1}^{\infty} \frac{n+5}{\sqrt[3]{n^7+n^2}}$

27. $\displaystyle\sum_{n=1}^{\infty} \left(1+\frac{1}{n}\right)^2 e^{-n}$

28. $\displaystyle\sum_{n=1}^{\infty} \frac{2n^2+7n}{3^n(n^2+5n-1)}$

29. $\displaystyle\sum_{n=1}^{\infty} \frac{1}{n!}$

30. $\displaystyle\sum_{n=1}^{\infty} \frac{n!}{n^n}$

31. $\displaystyle\sum_{n=1}^{\infty} \sin\left(\frac{1}{n}\right)$

32. $\displaystyle\sum_{n=1}^{\infty} \frac{1}{n^{1+1/n}}$

33–36 ‖ Use the sum of the first 10 terms to approximate the sum of the series. Estimate the error.

33. $\displaystyle\sum_{n=1}^{\infty} \frac{1}{n^4+n^2}$

34. $\displaystyle\sum_{n=1}^{\infty} \frac{1+\cos n}{n^5}$

35. $\displaystyle\sum_{n=1}^{\infty} \frac{1}{1+2^n}$

36. $\displaystyle\sum_{n=1}^{\infty} \frac{n}{(n+1)3^n}$

37. The meaning of the decimal representation of a number $0.d_1d_2d_3\ldots$ (where the digit d_i is one of the numbers 0, 1, 2, …, 9) is that

$$0.d_1d_2d_3d_4\ldots = \frac{d_1}{10} + \frac{d_2}{10^2} + \frac{d_3}{10^3} + \frac{d_4}{10^4} + \cdots$$

Show that this series always converges.

38. For what values of p does the series $\sum_{n=2}^{\infty} 1/(n^p \ln n)$ converge?

39. Prove that if $a_n \geqslant 0$ and Σa_n converges, then Σa_n^2 also converges.

40. (a) Suppose that Σa_n and Σb_n are series with positive terms and Σb_n is convergent. Prove that if

$$\lim_{n\to\infty} \frac{a_n}{b_n} = 0$$

then Σa_n is also convergent.
(b) Use part (a) to show that the series converges.
 (i) $\displaystyle\sum_{n=1}^{\infty} \frac{\ln n}{n^3}$
 (ii) $\displaystyle\sum_{n=1}^{\infty} \frac{\ln n}{\sqrt{n}e^n}$

41. (a) Suppose that Σa_n and Σb_n are series with positive terms and Σb_n is divergent. Prove that if

$$\lim_{n\to\infty} \frac{a_n}{b_n} = \infty$$

then Σa_n is also divergent.
(b) Use part (a) to show that the series diverges.
 (i) $\displaystyle\sum_{n=2}^{\infty} \frac{1}{\ln n}$
 (ii) $\displaystyle\sum_{n=1}^{\infty} \frac{\ln n}{n}$

42. Give an example of a pair of series Σa_n and Σb_n with positive terms where $\lim_{n\to\infty}(a_n/b_n)=0$ and Σb_n diverges, but Σa_n converges. [Compare with Exercise 40.]

43. Show that if $a_n > 0$ and $\lim_{n\to\infty} na_n \neq 0$, then Σa_n is divergent.

44. Show that if $a_n > 0$ and Σa_n is convergent, then $\Sigma \ln(1+a_n)$ is convergent.

45. If Σa_n is a convergent series with positive terms, is it true that $\Sigma \sin(a_n)$ is also convergent?

46. If Σa_n and Σb_n are both convergent series with positive terms, is it true that $\Sigma a_n b_n$ is also convergent?

12.5 Alternating Series

The convergence tests that we have looked at so far apply only to series with positive terms. In this section and the next we learn how to deal with series whose terms are not necessarily positive. Of particular importance are *alternating series,* whose terms alternate in sign.

An **alternating series** is a series whose terms are alternately positive and negative. Here are two examples:

$$1 - \frac{1}{2} + \frac{1}{3} - \frac{1}{4} + \frac{1}{5} - \frac{1}{6} + \cdots = \sum_{n=1}^{\infty} \frac{(-1)^{n-1}}{n}$$

$$-\frac{1}{2} + \frac{2}{3} - \frac{3}{4} + \frac{4}{5} - \frac{5}{6} + \frac{6}{7} - \cdots = \sum_{n=1}^{\infty} (-1)^n \frac{n}{n+1}$$

We see from these examples that the nth term of an alternating series is of the form

$$a_n = (-1)^{n-1}b_n \qquad \text{or} \qquad a_n = (-1)^n b_n$$

where b_n is a positive number. $\left(\text{In fact, } b_n = |a_n|.\right)$

The following test says that if the terms of an alternating series decrease toward 0 in absolute value, then the series converges.

The Alternating Series Test   If the alternating series

$$\sum_{n=1}^{\infty} (-1)^{n-1}b_n = b_1 - b_2 + b_3 - b_4 + b_5 - b_6 + \cdots \qquad (b_n > 0)$$

satisfies

(i) $b_{n+1} \leqslant b_n$ for all n

(ii) $\lim_{n \to \infty} b_n = 0$

then the series is convergent.

Before giving the proof let's look at Figure 1, which gives a picture of the idea behind the proof. We first plot $s_1 = b_1$ on a number line. To find s_2 we subtract b_2, so s_2 is to the left of s_1. Then to find s_3 we add b_3, so s_3 is to the right of s_2. But, since $b_3 < b_2$, s_3 is to the left of s_1. Continuing in this manner, we see that the partial sums oscillate back and forth. Since $b_n \to 0$, the successive steps are becoming smaller and smaller. The even partial sums $s_2, s_4, s_6, \ldots$ are increasing and the odd partial sums $s_1, s_3, s_5, \ldots$ are decreasing. Thus, it seems plausible that both are converging to some number s, which is the sum of the series. Therefore, in the following proof we consider the even and odd partial sums separately.

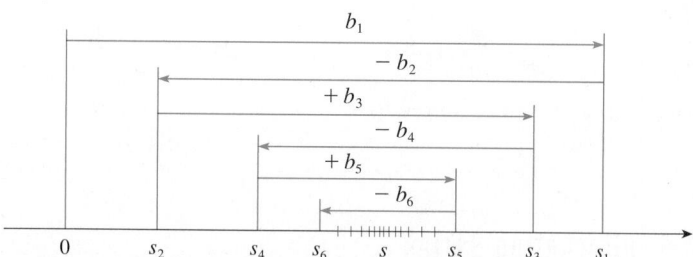

FIGURE 1

Proof of the Alternating Series Test   We first consider the even partial sums:

$$s_2 = b_1 - b_2 \geqslant 0 \qquad\qquad \text{since } b_2 \leqslant b_1$$

$$s_4 = s_2 + (b_3 - b_4) \geqslant s_2 \qquad \text{since } b_4 \leqslant b_3$$

In general $s_{2n} = s_{2n-2} + (b_{2n-1} - b_{2n}) \geqslant s_{2n-2}$ since $b_{2n} \leqslant b_{2n-1}$

Thus $0 \leqslant s_2 \leqslant s_4 \leqslant s_6 \leqslant \cdots \leqslant s_{2n} \leqslant \cdots$

But we can also write

$$s_{2n} = b_1 - (b_2 - b_3) - (b_4 - b_5) - \cdots - (b_{2n-2} - b_{2n-1}) - b_{2n}$$

Every term in brackets is positive, so $s_{2n} \leq b_1$ for all n. Therefore, the sequence $\{s_{2n}\}$ of even partial sums is increasing and bounded above. It is therefore convergent by the Monotonic Sequence Theorem. Let's call its limit s, that is,

$$\lim_{n \to \infty} s_{2n} = s$$

Now we compute the limit of the odd partial sums:

$$\lim_{n \to \infty} s_{2n+1} = \lim_{n \to \infty} (s_{2n} + b_{2n+1})$$

$$= \lim_{n \to \infty} s_{2n} + \lim_{n \to \infty} b_{2n+1}$$

$$= s + 0 \qquad\qquad \text{[by condition (ii)]}$$

$$= s$$

Since both the even and odd partial sums converge to s, we have $\lim_{n \to \infty} s_n = s$ (see Exercise 72 in Section 12.1) and so the series is convergent.

|||| Figure 2 illustrates Example 1 by showing the graphs of the terms $a_n = (-1)^{n-1}/n$ and the partial sums s_n. Notice how the values of s_n zigzag across the limiting value, which appears to be about 0.7. In fact, the exact sum of the series is $\ln 2 \approx 0.693$ (see Exercise 36).

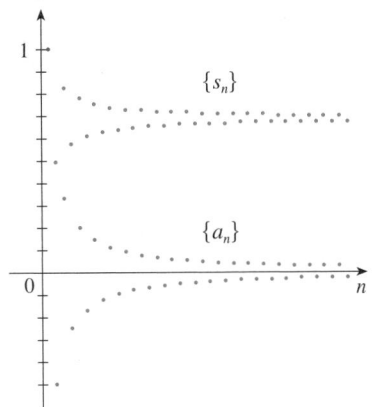

FIGURE 2

EXAMPLE 1 The alternating harmonic series

$$1 - \frac{1}{2} + \frac{1}{3} - \frac{1}{4} + \cdots = \sum_{n=1}^{\infty} \frac{(-1)^{n-1}}{n}$$

satisfies

(i) $b_{n+1} < b_n$ because $\dfrac{1}{n+1} < \dfrac{1}{n}$

(ii) $\lim\limits_{n \to \infty} b_n = \lim\limits_{n \to \infty} \dfrac{1}{n} = 0$

so the series is convergent by the Alternating Series Test.

EXAMPLE 2 The series $\displaystyle\sum_{n=1}^{\infty} \frac{(-1)^n 3n}{4n-1}$ is alternating but

$$\lim_{n \to \infty} b_n = \lim_{n \to \infty} \frac{3n}{4n-1} = \lim_{n \to \infty} \frac{3}{4 - \dfrac{1}{n}} = \frac{3}{4}$$

so condition (ii) is not satisfied. Instead, we look at the limit of the nth term of the series:

$$\lim_{n \to \infty} a_n = \lim_{n \to \infty} \frac{(-1)^n 3n}{4n-1}$$

This limit does not exist, so the series diverges by the Test for Divergence.

EXAMPLE 3 Test the series $\displaystyle\sum_{n=1}^{\infty} (-1)^{n+1} \frac{n^2}{n^3+1}$ for convergence or divergence.

SOLUTION The given series is alternating so we try to verify conditions (i) and (ii) of the Alternating Series Test.

Unlike the situation in Example 1, it is not obvious that the sequence given by $b_n = n^2/(n^3+1)$ is decreasing. However, if we consider the related function

$f(x) = x^2/(x^3 + 1)$, we find that

$$f'(x) = \frac{x(2 - x^3)}{(x^3 + 1)^2}$$

Since we are considering only positive x, we see that $f'(x) < 0$ if $2 - x^3 < 0$, that is, $x > \sqrt[3]{2}$. Thus, f is decreasing on the interval $(\sqrt[3]{2}, \infty)$. This means that $f(n + 1) < f(n)$ and therefore $b_{n+1} < b_n$ when $n \geq 2$. (The inequality $b_2 < b_1$ can be verified directly but all that really matters is that the sequence $\{b_n\}$ is eventually decreasing.)

Condition (ii) is readily verified:

$$\lim_{n \to \infty} b_n = \lim_{n \to \infty} \frac{n^2}{n^3 + 1} = \lim_{n \to \infty} \frac{\dfrac{1}{n}}{1 + \dfrac{1}{n^3}} = 0$$

❚❚❚ Instead of verifying condition (i) of the Alternating Series Test by computing a derivative, we could verify that $b_{n+1} < b_n$ directly by using the technique of Solution 1 of Example 11 in Section 12.1.

Thus, the given series is convergent by the Alternating Series Test. ▬

❚❚❚❚❚ Estimating Sums

A partial sum s_n of any convergent series can be used as an approximation to the total sum s, but this is not of much use unless we can estimate the accuracy of the approximation. The error involved in using $s \approx s_n$ is the remainder $R_n = s - s_n$. The next theorem says that for series that satisfy the conditions of the Alternating Series Test, the size of the error is smaller than b_{n+1}, which is the absolute value of the first neglected term.

❚❚❚ You can see geometrically why the Alternating Series Estimation Theorem is true by looking at Figure 1 (on page 772). Notice that $s - s_4 < b_5$, $|s - s_5| < b_6$, and so on. Notice also that s lies between any two consecutive partial sums.

Alternating Series Estimation Theorem If $s = \Sigma (-1)^{n-1}b_n$ is the sum of an alternating series that satisfies

(i) $0 \leq b_{n+1} \leq b_n$ and   (ii) $\lim_{n \to \infty} b_n = 0$

then

$$|R_n| = |s - s_n| \leq b_{n+1}$$

Proof We know from the proof of the Alternating Series Test that s lies between any two consecutive partial sums s_n and s_{n+1}. It follows that

$$|s - s_n| \leq |s_{n+1} - s_n| = b_{n+1}$$ ▬

EXAMPLE 4 Find the sum of the series $\displaystyle\sum_{n=0}^{\infty} \frac{(-1)^n}{n!}$ correct to three decimal places. (By definition, $0! = 1$.)

SOLUTION We first observe that the series is convergent by the Alternating Series Test because

(i) $\dfrac{1}{(n + 1)!} = \dfrac{1}{n!(n + 1)} < \dfrac{1}{n!}$

(ii) $0 < \dfrac{1}{n!} < \dfrac{1}{n} \to 0$ so $\dfrac{1}{n!} \to 0$ as $n \to \infty$

To get a feel for how many terms we need to use in our approximation, let's write out the first few terms of the series:

$$s = \frac{1}{0!} - \frac{1}{1!} + \frac{1}{2!} - \frac{1}{3!} + \frac{1}{4!} - \frac{1}{5!} + \frac{1}{6!} - \frac{1}{7!} + \cdots$$

$$= 1 - 1 + \tfrac{1}{2} - \tfrac{1}{6} + \tfrac{1}{24} - \tfrac{1}{120} + \tfrac{1}{720} - \tfrac{1}{5040} + \cdots$$

Notice that

$$b_7 = \tfrac{1}{5040} < \tfrac{1}{5000} = 0.0002$$

and

$$s_6 = 1 - 1 + \tfrac{1}{2} - \tfrac{1}{6} + \tfrac{1}{24} - \tfrac{1}{120} + \tfrac{1}{720} \approx 0.368056$$

By the Alternating Series Estimation Theorem we know that

$$|s - s_6| \leq b_7 < 0.0002$$

This error of less than 0.0002 does not affect the third decimal place, so we have

$$s \approx 0.368$$

correct to three decimal places.

|||| In Section 12.10 we will prove that $e^x = \sum_{n=0}^{\infty} x^n/n!$ for all x, so what we have obtained in Example 4 is actually an approximation to the number e^{-1}.

⊘ **NOTE** ∘ The rule that the error (in using s_n to approximate s) is smaller than the first neglected term is, in general, valid only for alternating series that satisfy the conditions of the Alternating Series Estimation Theorem. The rule does not apply to other types of series.

12.5 Exercises

1. (a) What is an alternating series?
  (b) Under what conditions does an alternating series converge?
  (c) If these conditions are satisfied, what can you say about the remainder after n terms?

2–20 |||| Test the series for convergence or divergence.

2. $-\frac{1}{3} + \frac{2}{4} - \frac{3}{5} + \frac{4}{6} - \frac{5}{7} + \cdots$

3. $\frac{4}{7} - \frac{4}{8} + \frac{4}{9} - \frac{4}{10} + \frac{4}{11} - \cdots$

4. $\frac{1}{\ln 2} - \frac{1}{\ln 3} + \frac{1}{\ln 4} - \frac{1}{\ln 5} + \frac{1}{\ln 6} - \cdots$

5. $\sum_{n=1}^{\infty} \frac{(-1)^{n-1}}{\sqrt{n}}$

6. $\sum_{n=1}^{\infty} \frac{(-1)^{n-1}}{3n-1}$

7. $\sum_{n=1}^{\infty} (-1)^n \frac{3n-1}{2n+1}$

8. $\sum_{n=1}^{\infty} (-1)^n \frac{2n}{4n^2+1}$

9. $\sum_{n=1}^{\infty} \frac{(-1)^{n+1}}{4n^2+1}$

10. $\sum_{n=1}^{\infty} (-1)^n \frac{\sqrt{n}}{1+2\sqrt{n}}$

11. $\sum_{n=1}^{\infty} (-1)^{n+1} \frac{n^2}{n^3+4}$

12. $\sum_{n=1}^{\infty} (-1)^{n-1} \frac{e^{1/n}}{n}$

13. $\sum_{n=2}^{\infty} (-1)^n \frac{n}{\ln n}$

14. $\sum_{n=1}^{\infty} (-1)^{n-1} \frac{\ln n}{n}$

15. $\sum_{n=1}^{\infty} \frac{\cos n\pi}{n^{3/4}}$

16. $\sum_{n=1}^{\infty} \frac{\sin(n\pi/2)}{n!}$

17. $\sum_{n=1}^{\infty} (-1)^n \sin\left(\frac{\pi}{n}\right)$

18. $\sum_{n=1}^{\infty} (-1)^n \cos\left(\frac{\pi}{n}\right)$

19. $\sum_{n=1}^{\infty} (-1)^n \frac{n^n}{n!}$

20. $\sum_{n=1}^{\infty} \left(-\frac{n}{5}\right)^n$

 21–22 |||| Calculate the first 10 partial sums of the series and graph both the sequence of terms and the sequence of partial sums on the same screen. Estimate the error in using the 10th partial sum to approximate the total sum.

21. $\sum_{n=1}^{\infty} \frac{(-1)^{n-1}}{n^{3/2}}$

22. $\sum_{n=1}^{\infty} \frac{(-1)^{n-1}}{n^3}$

23–26 |||| How many terms of the series do we need to add in order to find the sum to the indicated accuracy?

23. $\sum_{n=1}^{\infty} \frac{(-1)^{n-1}}{n^2}$ ($|\text{error}| < 0.01$)

24. $\sum_{n=1}^{\infty} \frac{(-1)^{n+1}}{n^4}$ ($|\text{error}| < 0.001$)

25. $\displaystyle\sum_{n=1}^{\infty} \frac{(-2)^n}{n!}$ ($|\text{error}| < 0.01$)

26. $\displaystyle\sum_{n=1}^{\infty} \frac{(-1)^n n}{4^n}$ ($|\text{error}| < 0.002$)

27–30 ||||| Approximate the sum of the series correct to four decimal places.

27. $\displaystyle\sum_{n=1}^{\infty} \frac{(-1)^{n+1}}{n^5}$

28. $\displaystyle\sum_{n=1}^{\infty} \frac{(-1)^n n}{8^n}$

29. $\displaystyle\sum_{n=1}^{\infty} \frac{(-1)^{n-1} n^2}{10^n}$

30. $\displaystyle\sum_{n=1}^{\infty} \frac{(-1)^n}{3^n n!}$

31. Is the 50th partial sum s_{50} of the alternating series $\sum_{n=1}^{\infty} (-1)^{n-1}/n$ an overestimate or an underestimate of the total sum? Explain.

32–34 ||||| For what values of p is each series convergent?

32. $\displaystyle\sum_{n=1}^{\infty} \frac{(-1)^{n-1}}{n^p}$

33. $\displaystyle\sum_{n=1}^{\infty} \frac{(-1)^n}{n+p}$

34. $\displaystyle\sum_{n=2}^{\infty} (-1)^{n-1} \frac{(\ln n)^p}{n}$

35. Show that the series $\sum (-1)^{n-1} b_n$, where $b_n = 1/n$ if n is odd and $b_n = 1/n^2$ if n is even, is divergent. Why does the Alternating Series Test not apply?

36. Use the following steps to show that

$$\sum_{n=1}^{\infty} \frac{(-1)^{n-1}}{n} = \ln 2$$

Let h_n and s_n be the partial sums of the harmonic and alternating harmonic series.
(a) Show that $s_{2n} = h_{2n} - h_n$.
(b) From Exercise 38 in Section 12.3 we have

$$h_n - \ln n \to \gamma \qquad \text{as } n \to \infty$$

and therefore

$$h_{2n} - \ln(2n) \to \gamma \qquad \text{as } n \to \infty$$

Use these facts together with part (a) to show that $s_{2n} \to \ln 2$ as $n \to \infty$.

|||||| 12.6 Absolute Convergence and the Ratio and Root Tests

Given any series $\sum a_n$, we can consider the corresponding series

$$\sum_{n=1}^{\infty} |a_n| = |a_1| + |a_2| + |a_3| + \cdots$$

whose terms are the absolute values of the terms of the original series.

||||| We have convergence tests for series with positive terms and for alternating series. But what if the signs of the terms switch back and forth irregularly? We will see in Example 3 that the idea of absolute convergence sometimes helps in such cases.

> **1   Definition**   A series $\sum a_n$ is called **absolutely convergent** if the series of absolute values $\sum |a_n|$ is convergent.

Notice that if $\sum a_n$ is a series with positive terms, then $|a_n| = a_n$ and so absolute convergence is the same as convergence in this case.

EXAMPLE 1   The series

$$\sum_{n=1}^{\infty} \frac{(-1)^{n-1}}{n^2} = 1 - \frac{1}{2^2} + \frac{1}{3^2} - \frac{1}{4^2} + \cdots$$

is absolutely convergent because

$$\sum_{n=1}^{\infty} \left| \frac{(-1)^{n-1}}{n^2} \right| = \sum_{n=1}^{\infty} \frac{1}{n^2} = 1 + \frac{1}{2^2} + \frac{1}{3^2} + \frac{1}{4^2} + \cdots$$

is a convergent p-series ($p = 2$).

EXAMPLE 2 We know that the alternating harmonic series

$$\sum_{n=1}^{\infty} \frac{(-1)^{n-1}}{n} = 1 - \frac{1}{2} + \frac{1}{3} - \frac{1}{4} + \cdots$$

is convergent (see Example 1 in Section 12.5), but it is not absolutely convergent because the corresponding series of absolute values is

$$\sum_{n=1}^{\infty} \left| \frac{(-1)^{n-1}}{n} \right| = \sum_{n=1}^{\infty} \frac{1}{n} = 1 + \frac{1}{2} + \frac{1}{3} + \frac{1}{4} + \cdots$$

which is the harmonic series (p-series with $p = 1$) and is therefore divergent.

---

2 Definition A series $\sum a_n$ is called **conditionally convergent** if it is convergent but not absolutely convergent.

Example 2 shows that the alternating harmonic series is conditionally convergent. Thus, it is possible for a series to be convergent but not absolutely convergent. However, the next theorem shows that absolute convergence implies convergence.

---

3 Theorem If a series $\sum a_n$ is absolutely convergent, then it is convergent.

Proof Observe that the inequality

$$0 \leq a_n + |a_n| \leq 2|a_n|$$

is true because $|a_n|$ is either a_n or $-a_n$. If $\sum a_n$ is absolutely convergent, then $\sum |a_n|$ is convergent, so $\sum 2|a_n|$ is convergent. Therefore, by the Comparison Test, $\sum (a_n + |a_n|)$ is convergent. Then

$$\sum a_n = \sum (a_n + |a_n|) - \sum |a_n|$$

is the difference of two convergent series and is therefore convergent.

|||| Figure 1 shows the graphs of the terms a_n and partial sums s_n of the series in Example 3. Notice that the series is not alternating but has positive and negative terms.

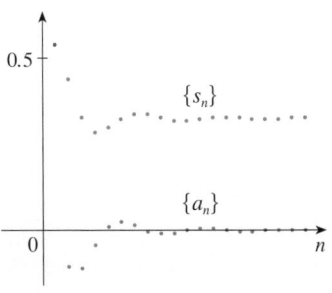

FIGURE 1

EXAMPLE 3 Determine whether the series

$$\sum_{n=1}^{\infty} \frac{\cos n}{n^2} = \frac{\cos 1}{1^2} + \frac{\cos 2}{2^2} + \frac{\cos 3}{3^2} + \cdots$$

is convergent or divergent.

SOLUTION This series has both positive and negative terms, but it is not alternating. (The first term is positive, the next three are negative, and the following three are positive. The signs change irregularly.) We can apply the Comparison Test to the series of absolute values

$$\sum_{n=1}^{\infty} \left| \frac{\cos n}{n^2} \right| = \sum_{n=1}^{\infty} \frac{|\cos n|}{n^2}$$

Since $|\cos n| \leq 1$ for all n, we have

$$\frac{|\cos n|}{n^2} \leq \frac{1}{n^2}$$

We know that $\Sigma\, 1/n^2$ is convergent (p-series with $p = 2$) and therefore $\Sigma\, |\cos n|/n^2$ is convergent by the Comparison Test. Thus, the given series $\Sigma\, (\cos n)/n^2$ is absolutely convergent and therefore convergent by Theorem 3.

The following test is very useful in determining whether a given series is absolutely convergent.

The Ratio Test

(i) If $\displaystyle\lim_{n\to\infty} \left|\frac{a_{n+1}}{a_n}\right| = L < 1$, then the series $\displaystyle\sum_{n=1}^{\infty} a_n$ is absolutely convergent
(and therefore convergent).

(ii) If $\displaystyle\lim_{n\to\infty} \left|\frac{a_{n+1}}{a_n}\right| = L > 1$ or $\displaystyle\lim_{n\to\infty} \left|\frac{a_{n+1}}{a_n}\right| = \infty$, then the series $\displaystyle\sum_{n=1}^{\infty} a_n$
is divergent.

(iii) If $\displaystyle\lim_{n\to\infty} \left|\frac{a_{n+1}}{a_n}\right| = 1$, the Ratio Test is inconclusive; that is, no conclusion can
be drawn about the convergence or divergence of $\Sigma\, a_n$.

Proof

(i) The idea is to compare the given series with a convergent geometric series. Since $L < 1$, we can choose a number r such that $L < r < 1$. Since

$$\lim_{n\to\infty} \left|\frac{a_{n+1}}{a_n}\right| = L \quad \text{and} \quad L < r$$

the ratio $|a_{n+1}/a_n|$ will eventually be less than r; that is, there exists an integer N such that

$$\left|\frac{a_{n+1}}{a_n}\right| < r \quad \text{whenever } n \geq N$$

or, equivalently,

4 $$|a_{n+1}| < |a_n|r \quad \text{whenever } n \geq N$$

Putting n successively equal to $N, N + 1, N + 2, \ldots$ in (4), we obtain

$$|a_{N+1}| < |a_N|r$$

$$|a_{N+2}| < |a_{N+1}|r < |a_N|r^2$$

$$|a_{N+3}| < |a_{N+2}|r < |a_N|r^3$$

and, in general,

5 $$|a_{N+k}| < |a_N|r^k \quad \text{for all } k \geq 1$$

Now the series

$$\sum_{k=1}^{\infty} |a_N|r^k = |a_N|r + |a_N|r^2 + |a_N|r^3 + \cdots$$

is convergent because it is a geometric series with $0 < r < 1$. So the inequality (5), together with the Comparison Test, shows that the series

$$\sum_{n=N+1}^{\infty} |a_n| = \sum_{k=1}^{\infty} |a_{N+k}| = |a_{N+1}| + |a_{N+2}| + |a_{N+3}| + \cdots$$

is also convergent. It follows that the series $\sum_{n=1}^{\infty} |a_n|$ is convergent. (Recall that a finite number of terms doesn't affect convergence.) Therefore, $\sum a_n$ is absolutely convergent.

(ii) If $|a_{n+1}/a_n| \to L > 1$ or $|a_{n+1}/a_n| \to \infty$, then the ratio $|a_{n+1}/a_n|$ will eventually be greater than 1; that is, there exists an integer N such that

$$\left| \frac{a_{n+1}}{a_n} \right| > 1 \qquad \text{whenever } n \geq N$$

This means that $|a_{n+1}| > |a_n|$ whenever $n \geq N$ and so

$$\lim_{n \to \infty} a_n \neq 0$$

Therefore, $\sum a_n$ diverges by the Test for Divergence.

NOTE ◦ Part (iii) of the Ratio Test says that if $\lim_{n \to \infty} |a_{n+1}/a_n| = 1$, the test gives no information. For instance, for the convergent series $\sum 1/n^2$ we have

$$\left| \frac{a_{n+1}}{a_n} \right| = \frac{\dfrac{1}{(n+1)^2}}{\dfrac{1}{n^2}} = \frac{n^2}{(n+1)^2} = \frac{1}{\left(1 + \dfrac{1}{n}\right)^2} \to 1 \qquad \text{as } n \to \infty$$

whereas for the divergent series $\sum 1/n$ we have

$$\left| \frac{a_{n+1}}{a_n} \right| = \frac{\dfrac{1}{n+1}}{\dfrac{1}{n}} = \frac{n}{n+1} = \frac{1}{1 + \dfrac{1}{n}} \to 1 \qquad \text{as } n \to \infty$$

Therefore, if $\lim_{n \to \infty} |a_{n+1}/a_n| = 1$, the series $\sum a_n$ might converge or it might diverge. In this case the Ratio Test fails and we must use some other test.

EXAMPLE 4 Test the series $\displaystyle\sum_{n=1}^{\infty} (-1)^n \frac{n^3}{3^n}$ for absolute convergence.

|||| ESTIMATING SUMS

In the last three sections we used various methods for estimating the sum of a series—the method depended on which test was used to prove convergence. What about series for which the Ratio Test works? There are two possibilities: If the series happens to be an alternating series, as in Example 4, then it is best to use the methods of Section 12.5. If the terms are all positive, then use the special methods explained in Exercise 34.

SOLUTION We use the Ratio Test with $a_n = (-1)^n n^3/3^n$:

$$\left| \frac{a_{n+1}}{a_n} \right| = \left| \frac{\dfrac{(-1)^{n+1}(n+1)^3}{3^{n+1}}}{\dfrac{(-1)^n n^3}{3^n}} \right| = \frac{(n+1)^3}{3^{n+1}} \cdot \frac{3^n}{n^3}$$

$$= \frac{1}{3} \left(\frac{n+1}{n} \right)^3 = \frac{1}{3} \left(1 + \frac{1}{n} \right)^3 \to \frac{1}{3} < 1$$

Thus, by the Ratio Test, the given series is absolutely convergent and therefore convergent.

EXAMPLE 5 Test the convergence of the series $\displaystyle\sum_{n=1}^{\infty} \frac{n^n}{n!}$.

SOLUTION Since the terms $a_n = n^n/n!$ are positive, we don't need the absolute value signs.

$$\frac{a_{n+1}}{a_n} = \frac{(n+1)^{n+1}}{(n+1)!} \cdot \frac{n!}{n^n} = \frac{(n+1)(n+1)^n}{(n+1)n!} \cdot \frac{n!}{n^n}$$

$$= \left(\frac{n+1}{n}\right)^n = \left(1 + \frac{1}{n}\right)^n \to e \qquad \text{as } n \to \infty$$

(See Equation 7.4.9 or 7.4*.9.) Since $e > 1$, the given series is divergent by the Ratio Test.

NOTE ∘ Although the Ratio Test works in Example 5, an easier method is to use the Test for Divergence. Since

$$a_n = \frac{n^n}{n!} = \frac{n \cdot n \cdot n \cdot \cdots \cdot n}{1 \cdot 2 \cdot 3 \cdot \cdots \cdot n} \geq n$$

it follows that a_n does not approach 0 as $n \to \infty$. Therefore, the given series is divergent by the Test for Divergence.

The following test is convenient to apply when nth powers occur. Its proof is similar to the proof of the Ratio Test and is left as Exercise 38.

The Root Test

(i) If $\displaystyle\lim_{n \to \infty} \sqrt[n]{|a_n|} = L < 1$, then the series $\displaystyle\sum_{n=1}^{\infty} a_n$ is absolutely convergent (and therefore convergent).

(ii) If $\displaystyle\lim_{n \to \infty} \sqrt[n]{|a_n|} = L > 1$ or $\displaystyle\lim_{n \to \infty} \sqrt[n]{|a_n|} = \infty$, then the series $\displaystyle\sum_{n=1}^{\infty} a_n$ is divergent.

(iii) If $\displaystyle\lim_{n \to \infty} \sqrt[n]{|a_n|} = 1$, the Root Test is inconclusive.

If $\lim_{n \to \infty} \sqrt[n]{|a_n|} = 1$, then part (iii) of the Root Test says that the test gives no information. The series $\Sigma\, a_n$ could converge or diverge. (If $L = 1$ in the Ratio Test, don't try the Root Test because L will again be 1.)

EXAMPLE 6 Test the convergence of the series $\displaystyle\sum_{n=1}^{\infty} \left(\frac{2n+3}{3n+2}\right)^n$.

SOLUTION

$$a_n = \left(\frac{2n+3}{3n+2}\right)^n$$

$$\sqrt[n]{|a_n|} = \frac{2n+3}{3n+2} = \frac{2 + \dfrac{3}{n}}{3 + \dfrac{2}{n}} \to \frac{2}{3} < 1$$

Thus, the given series converges by the Root Test.

||| **Rearrangements**

The question of whether a given convergent series is absolutely convergent or conditionally convergent has a bearing on the question of whether infinite sums behave like finite sums.

If we rearrange the order of the terms in a finite sum, then of course the value of the sum remains unchanged. But this is not always the case for an infinite series. By a **rearrangement** of an infinite series $\Sigma \, a_n$ we mean a series obtained by simply changing the order of the terms. For instance, a rearrangement of $\Sigma \, a_n$ could start as follows:

$$a_1 + a_2 + a_5 + a_3 + a_4 + a_{15} + a_6 + a_7 + a_{20} + \cdots$$

It turns out that

if $\Sigma \, a_n$ is an absolutely convergent series with sum s,
then any rearrangement of $\Sigma \, a_n$ has the same sum s.

However, any conditionally convergent series can be rearranged to give a different sum. To illustrate this fact let's consider the alternating harmonic series

$$\boxed{6} \qquad 1 - \tfrac{1}{2} + \tfrac{1}{3} - \tfrac{1}{4} + \tfrac{1}{5} - \tfrac{1}{6} + \tfrac{1}{7} - \tfrac{1}{8} + \cdots = \ln 2$$

(See Exercise 36 in Section 12.5.) If we multiply this series by $\tfrac{1}{2}$, we get

$$\tfrac{1}{2} - \tfrac{1}{4} + \tfrac{1}{6} - \tfrac{1}{8} + \cdots = \tfrac{1}{2}\ln 2$$

Inserting zeros between the terms of this series, we have

||| Adding these zeros does not affect the sum of the series; each term in the sequence of partial sums is repeated, but the limit is the same.

$$\boxed{7} \qquad 0 + \tfrac{1}{2} + 0 - \tfrac{1}{4} + 0 + \tfrac{1}{6} + 0 - \tfrac{1}{8} + \cdots = \tfrac{1}{2}\ln 2$$

Now we add the series in Equations 6 and 7 using Theorem 12.2.8:

$$\boxed{8} \qquad 1 + \tfrac{1}{3} - \tfrac{1}{2} + \tfrac{1}{5} + \tfrac{1}{7} - \tfrac{1}{4} + \cdots = \tfrac{3}{2}\ln 2$$

Notice that the series in (8) contains the same terms as in (6), but rearranged so that one negative term occurs after each pair of positive terms. The sums of these series, however, are different. In fact, Riemann proved that

if $\Sigma \, a_n$ is a conditionally convergent series and r is any real number whatsoever, then there is a rearrangement of $\Sigma \, a_n$ that has a sum equal to r.

A proof of this fact is outlined in Exercise 40.

||||| **12.6 Exercises**

1. What can you say about the series $\Sigma \, a_n$ in each of the following cases?

(a) $\displaystyle \lim_{n \to \infty} \left| \frac{a_{n+1}}{a_n} \right| = 8$ (b) $\displaystyle \lim_{n \to \infty} \left| \frac{a_{n+1}}{a_n} \right| = 0.8$

(c) $\displaystyle \lim_{n \to \infty} \left| \frac{a_{n+1}}{a_n} \right| = 1$

2–28 ||| Determine whether the series is absolutely convergent, conditionally convergent, or divergent.

2. $\displaystyle \sum_{n=1}^{\infty} \frac{n^2}{2^n}$

3. $\displaystyle \sum_{n=0}^{\infty} \frac{(-10)^n}{n!}$

4. $\displaystyle \sum_{n=1}^{\infty} (-1)^{n-1} \frac{2^n}{n^4}$

5. $\displaystyle \sum_{n=1}^{\infty} \frac{(-1)^{n+1}}{\sqrt[4]{n}}$

6. $\displaystyle \sum_{n=1}^{\infty} \frac{(-1)^n}{n^4}$

7. $\displaystyle \sum_{n=1}^{\infty} (-1)^n \frac{n}{5+n}$

8. $\displaystyle \sum_{n=1}^{\infty} (-1)^{n-1} \frac{n}{n^2+1}$

9. $\displaystyle \sum_{n=1}^{\infty} \frac{1}{(2n)!}$

10. $\displaystyle \sum_{n=1}^{\infty} e^{-n} n!$

11. $\displaystyle \sum_{n=1}^{\infty} \frac{(-1)^n e^{1/n}}{n^3}$

12. $\displaystyle \sum_{n=1}^{\infty} \frac{\sin 4n}{4^n}$

13. $\displaystyle\sum_{n=1}^{\infty} \frac{n(-3)^n}{4^{n-1}}$

14. $\displaystyle\sum_{n=1}^{\infty} (-1)^{n+1} \frac{n^2 2^n}{n!}$

15. $\displaystyle\sum_{n=1}^{\infty} \frac{10^n}{(n+1)4^{2n+1}}$

16. $\displaystyle\sum_{n=1}^{\infty} \frac{3 - \cos n}{n^{2/3} - 2}$

17. $\displaystyle\sum_{n=2}^{\infty} \frac{(-1)^n}{\ln n}$

18. $\displaystyle\sum_{n=1}^{\infty} \frac{n!}{n^n}$

19. $\displaystyle\sum_{n=1}^{\infty} \frac{\cos(n\pi/3)}{n!}$

20. $\displaystyle\sum_{n=2}^{\infty} \frac{(-1)^n}{(\ln n)^n}$

21. $\displaystyle\sum_{n=1}^{\infty} \frac{n^n}{3^{1+3n}}$

22. $\displaystyle\sum_{n=2}^{\infty} \frac{(-1)^n}{n \ln n}$

23. $\displaystyle\sum_{n=1}^{\infty} \left(\frac{n^2+1}{2n^2+1}\right)^n$

24. $\displaystyle\sum_{n=1}^{\infty} \frac{(-1)^n}{(\arctan n)^n}$

25. $1 - \dfrac{1 \cdot 3}{3!} + \dfrac{1 \cdot 3 \cdot 5}{5!} - \dfrac{1 \cdot 3 \cdot 5 \cdot 7}{7!} + \cdots$

$\quad + (-1)^{n-1} \dfrac{1 \cdot 3 \cdot 5 \cdot \,\cdots\, \cdot (2n-1)}{(2n-1)!} + \cdots$

26. $\dfrac{2}{5} + \dfrac{2 \cdot 6}{5 \cdot 8} + \dfrac{2 \cdot 6 \cdot 10}{5 \cdot 8 \cdot 11} + \dfrac{2 \cdot 6 \cdot 10 \cdot 14}{5 \cdot 8 \cdot 11 \cdot 14} + \cdots$

27. $\displaystyle\sum_{n=1}^{\infty} \frac{2 \cdot 4 \cdot 6 \cdot \,\cdots\, \cdot (2n)}{n!}$

28. $\displaystyle\sum_{n=1}^{\infty} (-1)^n \frac{2^n n!}{5 \cdot 8 \cdot 11 \cdot \,\cdots\, \cdot (3n+2)}$

---

29. The terms of a series are defined recursively by the equations

$$a_1 = 2 \qquad a_{n+1} = \frac{5n+1}{4n+3} a_n$$

Determine whether $\Sigma\, a_n$ converges or diverges.

30. A series $\Sigma\, a_n$ is defined by the equations

$$a_1 = 1 \qquad a_{n+1} = \frac{2 + \cos n}{\sqrt{n}} a_n$$

Determine whether $\Sigma\, a_n$ converges or diverges.

31. For which of the following series is the Ratio Test inconclusive (that is, it fails to give a definite answer)?

(a) $\displaystyle\sum_{n=1}^{\infty} \frac{1}{n^3}$

(b) $\displaystyle\sum_{n=1}^{\infty} \frac{n}{2^n}$

(c) $\displaystyle\sum_{n=1}^{\infty} \frac{(-3)^{n-1}}{\sqrt{n}}$

(d) $\displaystyle\sum_{n=1}^{\infty} \frac{\sqrt{n}}{1+n^2}$

32. For which positive integers k is the following series convergent?

$$\sum_{n=1}^{\infty} \frac{(n!)^2}{(kn)!}$$

33. (a) Show that $\sum_{n=0}^{\infty} x^n/n!$ converges for all x.
(b) Deduce that $\lim_{n \to \infty} x^n/n! = 0$ for all x.

34. Let $\Sigma\, a_n$ be a series with positive terms and let $r_n = a_{n+1}/a_n$. Suppose that $\lim_{n \to \infty} r_n = L < 1$, so $\Sigma\, a_n$ converges by the Ratio Test. As usual, we let R_n be the remainder after n terms, that is,

$$R_n = a_{n+1} + a_{n+2} + a_{n+3} + \cdots$$

(a) If $\{r_n\}$ is a decreasing sequence and $r_{n+1} < 1$, show, by summing a geometric series, that

$$R_n \le \frac{a_{n+1}}{1 - r_{n+1}}$$

(b) If $\{r_n\}$ is an increasing sequence, show that

$$R_n \le \frac{a_{n+1}}{1 - L}$$

35. (a) Find the partial sum s_5 of the series $\sum_{n=1}^{\infty} 1/n2^n$. Use Exercise 34 to estimate the error in using s_5 as an approximation to the sum of the series.
(b) Find a value of n so that s_n is within 0.00005 of the sum. Use this value of n to approximate the sum of the series.

36. Use the sum of the first 10 terms to approximate the sum of the series

$$\sum_{n=1}^{\infty} \frac{n}{2^n}$$

Use Exercise 34 to estimate the error.

37. Prove that if $\Sigma\, a_n$ is absolutely convergent, then

$$\left| \sum_{n=1}^{\infty} a_n \right| \le \sum_{n=1}^{\infty} |a_n|$$

38. Prove the Root Test. *[Hint for part (i):* Take any number r such that $L < r < 1$ and use the fact that there is an integer N such that $\sqrt[n]{|a_n|} < r$ whenever $n \ge N$.]

39. Given any series $\Sigma\, a_n$ we define a series $\Sigma\, a_n^+$ whose terms are all the positive terms of $\Sigma\, a_n$ and a series $\Sigma\, a_n^-$ whose terms are all the negative terms of $\Sigma\, a_n$. To be specific, we let

$$a_n^+ = \frac{a_n + |a_n|}{2} \qquad a_n^- = \frac{a_n - |a_n|}{2}$$

Notice that if $a_n > 0$, then $a_n^+ = a_n$ and $a_n^- = 0$, whereas if $a_n < 0$, then $a_n^- = a_n$ and $a_n^+ = 0$.
(a) If $\Sigma\, a_n$ is absolutely convergent, show that both of the series $\Sigma\, a_n^+$ and $\Sigma\, a_n^-$ are convergent.
(b) If $\Sigma\, a_n$ is conditionally convergent, show that both of the series $\Sigma\, a_n^+$ and $\Sigma\, a_n^-$ are divergent.

40. Prove that if $\Sigma\, a_n$ is a conditionally convergent series and r is any real number, then there is a rearrangement of $\Sigma\, a_n$ whose sum is r. *[Hints:* Use the notation of Exercise 39. Take just enough positive terms a_n^+ so that their sum is greater than r. Then add just enough negative terms a_n^- so that the cumulative sum is less than r. Continue in this manner and use Theorem 12.2.6.]

12.7 Strategy for Testing Series

We now have several ways of testing a series for convergence or divergence; the problem is to decide which test to use on which series. In this respect testing series is similar to integrating functions. Again there are no hard and fast rules about which test to apply to a given series, but you may find the following advice of some use.

It is not wise to apply a list of the tests in a specific order until one finally works. That would be a waste of time and effort. Instead, as with integration, the main strategy is to classify the series according to its *form*.

1. If the series is of the form $\Sigma \, 1/n^p$, it is a *p*-series, which we know to be convergent if $p > 1$ and divergent if $p \leq 1$.

2. If the series has the form $\Sigma \, ar^{n-1}$ or $\Sigma \, ar^n$, it is a geometric series, which converges if $|r| < 1$ and diverges if $|r| \geq 1$. Some preliminary algebraic manipulation may be required to bring the series into this form.

3. If the series has a form that is similar to a *p*-series or a geometric series, then one of the comparison tests should be considered. In particular, if a_n is a rational function or algebraic function of *n* (involving roots of polynomials), then the series should be compared with a *p*-series. Notice that most of the series in Exercises 12.4 have this form. (The value of *p* should be chosen as in Section 12.4 by keeping only the highest powers of *n* in the numerator and denominator.) The comparison tests apply only to series with positive terms, but if $\Sigma \, a_n$ has some negative terms, then we can apply the Comparison Test to $\Sigma \, |a_n|$ and test for absolute convergence.

4. If you can see at a glance that $\lim_{n \to \infty} a_n \neq 0$, then the Test for Divergence should be used.

5. If the series is of the form $\Sigma \, (-1)^{n-1} b_n$ or $\Sigma \, (-1)^n b_n$, then the Alternating Series Test is an obvious possibility.

6. Series that involve factorials or other products (including a constant raised to the *n*th power) are often conveniently tested using the Ratio Test. Bear in mind that $|a_{n+1}/a_n| \to 1$ as $n \to \infty$ for all *p*-series and therefore all rational or algebraic functions of *n*. Thus, the Ratio Test should not be used for such series.

7. If a_n is of the form $(b_n)^n$, then the Root Test may be useful.

8. If $a_n = f(n)$, where $\int_1^{\infty} f(x) \, dx$ is easily evaluated, then the Integral Test is effective (assuming the hypotheses of this test are satisfied).

In the following examples we don't work out all the details but simply indicate which tests should be used.

EXAMPLE 1 $\displaystyle\sum_{n=1}^{\infty} \frac{n-1}{2n+1}$

Since $a_n \to \frac{1}{2} \neq 0$ as $n \to \infty$, we should use the Test for Divergence.

EXAMPLE 2 $\displaystyle\sum_{n=1}^{\infty} \frac{\sqrt{n^3+1}}{3n^3+4n^2+2}$

Since a_n is an algebraic function of *n*, we compare the given series with a *p*-series.

The comparison series for the Limit Comparison Test is $\Sigma\, b_n$, where

$$b_n = \frac{\sqrt{n^3}}{3n^3} = \frac{n^{3/2}}{3n^3} = \frac{1}{3n^{3/2}}$$

EXAMPLE 3 $\displaystyle\sum_{n=1}^{\infty} ne^{-n^2}$

Since the integral $\int_1^{\infty} xe^{-x^2}\,dx$ is easily evaluated, we use the Integral Test. The Ratio Test also works.

EXAMPLE 4 $\displaystyle\sum_{n=1}^{\infty} (-1)^n \frac{n^3}{n^4 + 1}$

Since the series is alternating, we use the Alternating Series Test.

EXAMPLE 5 $\displaystyle\sum_{k=1}^{\infty} \frac{2^k}{k!}$

Since the series involves $k!$, we use the Ratio Test.

EXAMPLE 6 $\displaystyle\sum_{n=1}^{\infty} \frac{1}{2 + 3^n}$

Since the series is closely related to the geometric series $\Sigma\, 1/3^n$, we use the Comparison Test.

12.7 Exercises

1–38 ▐▐ Test the series for convergence or divergence.

1. $\displaystyle\sum_{n=1}^{\infty} \frac{n^2 - 1}{n^2 + n}$

2. $\displaystyle\sum_{n=1}^{\infty} \frac{n - 1}{n^2 + n}$

3. $\displaystyle\sum_{n=1}^{\infty} \frac{1}{n^2 + n}$

4. $\displaystyle\sum_{n=1}^{\infty} (-1)^{n-1} \frac{n - 1}{n^2 + n}$

5. $\displaystyle\sum_{n=1}^{\infty} \frac{(-3)^{n+1}}{2^{3n}}$

6. $\displaystyle\sum_{n=1}^{\infty} \left(\frac{3n}{1 + 8n}\right)^n$

7. $\displaystyle\sum_{n=2}^{\infty} \frac{1}{n\sqrt{\ln n}}$

8. $\displaystyle\sum_{k=1}^{\infty} \frac{2^k k!}{(k + 2)!}$

9. $\displaystyle\sum_{k=1}^{\infty} k^2 e^{-k}$

10. $\displaystyle\sum_{n=1}^{\infty} n^2 e^{-n^3}$

11. $\displaystyle\sum_{n=2}^{\infty} \frac{(-1)^{n+1}}{n \ln n}$

12. $\displaystyle\sum_{n=1}^{\infty} (-1)^n \frac{n}{n^2 + 25}$

13. $\displaystyle\sum_{n=1}^{\infty} \frac{3^n n^2}{n!}$

14. $\displaystyle\sum_{n=1}^{\infty} \sin n$

15. $\displaystyle\sum_{n=0}^{\infty} \frac{n!}{2 \cdot 5 \cdot 8 \cdots (3n + 2)}$

16. $\displaystyle\sum_{n=1}^{\infty} \frac{n^2 + 1}{n^3 + 1}$

17. $\displaystyle\sum_{n=1}^{\infty} (-1)^n 2^{1/n}$

18. $\displaystyle\sum_{n=2}^{\infty} \frac{(-1)^{n-1}}{\sqrt{n} - 1}$

19. $\displaystyle\sum_{n=1}^{\infty} (-1)^n \frac{\ln n}{\sqrt{n}}$

20. $\displaystyle\sum_{k=1}^{\infty} \frac{k + 5}{5^k}$

21. $\displaystyle\sum_{n=1}^{\infty} \frac{(-2)^{2n}}{n^n}$

22. $\displaystyle\sum_{n=1}^{\infty} \frac{\sqrt{n^2 - 1}}{n^3 + 2n^2 + 5}$

23. $\displaystyle\sum_{n=1}^{\infty} \tan(1/n)$

24. $\displaystyle\sum_{n=1}^{\infty} \frac{\cos(n/2)}{n^2 + 4n}$

25. $\displaystyle\sum_{n=1}^{\infty} \frac{n!}{e^{n^2}}$

26. $\displaystyle\sum_{n=1}^{\infty} \frac{n^2 + 1}{5^n}$

27. $\displaystyle\sum_{k=1}^{\infty} \frac{k \ln k}{(k + 1)^3}$

28. $\displaystyle\sum_{n=1}^{\infty} \frac{e^{1/n}}{n^2}$

29. $\displaystyle\sum_{n=1}^{\infty} \frac{\tan^{-1}n}{n\sqrt{n}}$

30. $\displaystyle\sum_{j=1}^{\infty} (-1)^j \frac{\sqrt{j}}{j + 5}$

31. $\displaystyle\sum_{k=1}^{\infty} \frac{5^k}{3^k + 4^k}$

32. $\displaystyle\sum_{n=1}^{\infty} \frac{(2n)^n}{n^{2n}}$

33. $\displaystyle\sum_{n=1}^{\infty} \frac{\sin(1/n)}{\sqrt{n}}$

34. $\displaystyle\sum_{n=1}^{\infty} \frac{1}{n + n \cos^2 n}$

35. $\displaystyle\sum_{n=1}^{\infty} \left(\frac{n}{n + 1}\right)^{n^2}$

36. $\displaystyle\sum_{n=2}^{\infty} \frac{1}{(\ln n)^{\ln n}}$

37. $\displaystyle\sum_{n=1}^{\infty} (\sqrt[n]{2} - 1)^n$

38. $\displaystyle\sum_{n=1}^{\infty} (\sqrt[n]{2} - 1)$

12.8 Power Series

A **power series** is a series of the form

$$\boxed{1} \qquad \sum_{n=0}^{\infty} c_n x^n = c_0 + c_1 x + c_2 x^2 + c_3 x^3 + \cdots$$

where x is a variable and the c_n's are constants called the **coefficients** of the series. For each fixed x, the series (1) is a series of constants that we can test for convergence or divergence. A power series may converge for some values of x and diverge for other values of x. The sum of the series is a function

$$f(x) = c_0 + c_1 x + c_2 x^2 + \cdots + c_n x^n + \cdots$$

whose domain is the set of all x for which the series converges. Notice that f resembles a polynomial. The only difference is that f has infinitely many terms.

For instance, if we take $c_n = 1$ for all n, the power series becomes the geometric series

$$\sum_{n=0}^{\infty} x^n = 1 + x + x^2 + \cdots + x^n + \cdots$$

which converges when $-1 < x < 1$ and diverges when $|x| \geqslant 1$ (see Equation 12.2.5).

More generally, a series of the form

$$\boxed{2} \qquad \sum_{n=0}^{\infty} c_n (x - a)^n = c_0 + c_1(x - a) + c_2(x - a)^2 + \cdots$$

is called a **power series in $(x - a)$** or a **power series centered at a** or a **power series about a**. Notice that in writing out the term corresponding to $n = 0$ in Equations 1 and 2 we have adopted the convention that $(x - a)^0 = 1$ even when $x = a$. Notice also that when $x = a$ all of the terms are 0 for $n \geqslant 1$ and so the power series (2) always converges when $x = a$.

EXAMPLE 1 For what values of x is the series $\displaystyle\sum_{n=0}^{\infty} n! x^n$ convergent?

SOLUTION We use the Ratio Test. If we let a_n, as usual, denote the nth term of the series, then $a_n = n! x^n$. If $x \neq 0$, we have

$$\lim_{n \to \infty} \left| \frac{a_{n+1}}{a_n} \right| = \lim_{n \to \infty} \left| \frac{(n + 1)! x^{n+1}}{n! x^n} \right| = \lim_{n \to \infty} (n + 1)|x| = \infty$$

By the Ratio Test, the series diverges when $x \neq 0$. Thus, the given series converges only when $x = 0$.

EXAMPLE 2 For what values of x does the series $\displaystyle\sum_{n=1}^{\infty} \frac{(x - 3)^n}{n}$ converge?

SOLUTION Let $a_n = (x - 3)^n / n$. Then

$$\left| \frac{a_{n+1}}{a_n} \right| = \left| \frac{(x - 3)^{n+1}}{n + 1} \cdot \frac{n}{(x - 3)^n} \right|$$

$$= \frac{1}{1 + \dfrac{1}{n}} |x - 3| \to |x - 3| \qquad \text{as } n \to \infty$$

|||| TRIGONOMETRIC SERIES

A power series is a series in which each term is a power function. A **trigonometric series**

$$\sum_{n=0}^{\infty} (a_n \cos nx + b_n \sin nx)$$

is a series whose terms are trigonometric functions. This type of series is discussed on the web site

www.stewartcalculus.com

Click on *Additional Topics* and then on *Fourier Series*.

By the Ratio Test, the given series is absolutely convergent, and therefore convergent, when $|x - 3| < 1$ and divergent when $|x - 3| > 1$. Now

$$|x - 3| < 1 \quad \Longleftrightarrow \quad -1 < x - 3 < 1 \quad \Longleftrightarrow \quad 2 < x < 4$$

so the series converges when $2 < x < 4$ and diverges when $x < 2$ or $x > 4$.

The Ratio Test gives no information when $|x - 3| = 1$ so we must consider $x = 2$ and $x = 4$ separately. If we put $x = 4$ in the series, it becomes $\Sigma\, 1/n$, the harmonic series, which is divergent. If $x = 2$, the series is $\Sigma\, (-1)^n/n$, which converges by the Alternating Series Test. Thus, the given power series converges for $2 \leqslant x < 4$.

We will see that the main use of a power series is that it provides a way to represent some of the most important functions that arise in mathematics, physics, and chemistry. In particular, the sum of the power series in the next example is called a **Bessel function**, after the German astronomer Friedrich Bessel (1784–1846), and the function given in Exercise 33 is another example of a Bessel function. In fact, these functions first arose when Bessel solved Kepler's equation for describing planetary motion. Since that time, these functions have been applied in many different physical situations, including the temperature distribution in a circular plate and the shape of a vibrating drumhead (see the photographs on page 736).

EXAMPLE 3 Find the domain of the Bessel function of order 0 defined by

$$J_0(x) = \sum_{n=0}^{\infty} \frac{(-1)^n x^{2n}}{2^{2n}(n!)^2}$$

SOLUTION Let $a_n = (-1)^n x^{2n}/[2^{2n}(n!)^2]$. Then

$$\left| \frac{a_{n+1}}{a_n} \right| = \left| \frac{(-1)^{n+1} x^{2(n+1)}}{2^{2(n+1)}[(n+1)!]^2} \cdot \frac{2^{2n}(n!)^2}{(-1)^n x^{2n}} \right|$$

$$= \frac{x^{2n+2}}{2^{2n+2}(n+1)^2(n!)^2} \cdot \frac{2^{2n}(n!)^2}{x^{2n}}$$

$$= \frac{x^2}{4(n+1)^2} \to 0 < 1 \qquad \text{for all } x$$

Thus, by the Ratio Test, the given series converges for all values of x. In other words, the domain of the Bessel function J_0 is $(-\infty, \infty) = \mathbb{R}$.

Recall that the sum of a series is equal to the limit of the sequence of partial sums. So when we define the Bessel function in Example 3 as the sum of a series we mean that, for every real number x,

$$J_0(x) = \lim_{n \to \infty} s_n(x) \qquad \text{where} \qquad s_n(x) = \sum_{i=0}^{n} \frac{(-1)^i x^{2i}}{2^{2i}(i!)^2}$$

The first few partial sums are

$$s_0(x) = 1 \qquad s_1(x) = 1 - \frac{x^2}{4} \qquad s_2(x) = 1 - \frac{x^2}{4} + \frac{x^4}{64}$$

$$s_3(x) = 1 - \frac{x^2}{4} + \frac{x^4}{64} - \frac{x^6}{2304} \qquad s_4(x) = 1 - \frac{x^2}{4} + \frac{x^4}{64} - \frac{x^6}{2304} + \frac{x^8}{147{,}456}$$

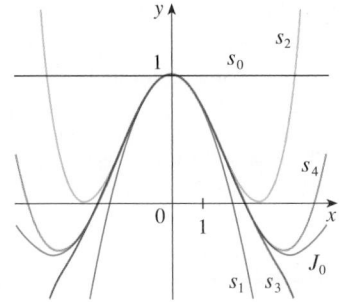

FIGURE 1
Partial sums of the Bessel function J_0

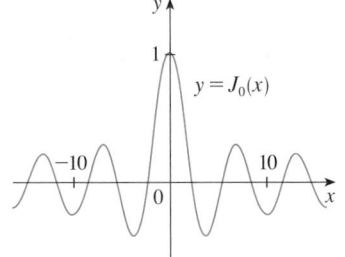

FIGURE 2

Figure 1 shows the graphs of these partial sums, which are polynomials. They are all approximations to the function J_0, but notice that the approximations become better when more terms are included. Figure 2 shows a more complete graph of the Bessel function.

For the power series that we have looked at so far, the set of values of x for which the series is convergent has always turned out to be an interval [a finite interval for the geometric series and the series in Example 2, the infinite interval $(-\infty, \infty)$ in Example 3, and a collapsed interval $[0, 0] = \{0\}$ in Example 1]. The following theorem, proved in Appendix F, says that this is true in general.

---

3 Theorem For a given power series $\sum_{n=0}^{\infty} c_n(x - a)^n$ there are only three possibilities:

(i) The series converges only when $x = a$.

(ii) The series converges for all x.

(iii) There is a positive number R such that the series converges if $|x - a| < R$ and diverges if $|x - a| > R$.

The number R in case (iii) is called the **radius of convergence** of the power series. By convention, the radius of convergence is $R = 0$ in case (i) and $R = \infty$ in case (ii). The **interval of convergence** of a power series is the interval that consists of all values of x for which the series converges. In case (i) the interval consists of just a single point a. In case (ii) the interval is $(-\infty, \infty)$. In case (iii) note that the inequality $|x - a| < R$ can be rewritten as $a - R < x < a + R$. When x is an *endpoint* of the interval, that is, $x = a \pm R$, anything can happen—the series might converge at one or both endpoints or it might diverge at both endpoints. Thus, in case (iii) there are four possibilities for the interval of convergence:

$$(a - R, a + R) \qquad (a - R, a + R] \qquad [a - R, a + R) \qquad [a - R, a + R]$$

The situation is illustrated in Figure 3.

FIGURE 3

We summarize here the radius and interval of convergence for each of the examples already considered in this section.

	Series	Radius of convergence	Interval of convergence
Geometric series	$\sum_{n=0}^{\infty} x^n$	$R = 1$	$(-1, 1)$
Example 1	$\sum_{n=0}^{\infty} n!\, x^n$	$R = 0$	$\{0\}$
Example 2	$\sum_{n=1}^{\infty} \dfrac{(x - 3)^n}{n}$	$R = 1$	$[2, 4)$
Example 3	$\sum_{n=0}^{\infty} \dfrac{(-1)^n x^{2n}}{2^{2n}(n!)^2}$	$R = \infty$	$(-\infty, \infty)$

In general, the Ratio Test (or sometimes the Root Test) should be used to determine the radius of convergence R. The Ratio and Root Tests always fail when x is an endpoint of the interval of convergence, so the endpoints must be checked with some other test.

EXAMPLE 4 Find the radius of convergence and interval of convergence of the series

$$\sum_{n=0}^{\infty} \frac{(-3)^n x^n}{\sqrt{n+1}}$$

SOLUTION Let $a_n = (-3)^n x^n / \sqrt{n+1}$. Then

$$\left| \frac{a_{n+1}}{a_n} \right| = \left| \frac{(-3)^{n+1} x^{n+1}}{\sqrt{n+2}} \cdot \frac{\sqrt{n+1}}{(-3)^n x^n} \right| = \left| -3x \sqrt{\frac{n+1}{n+2}} \right|$$

$$= 3 \sqrt{\frac{1+(1/n)}{1+(2/n)}} \, |x| \; \rightarrow \; 3|x| \qquad \text{as } n \to \infty$$

By the Ratio Test, the given series converges if $3|x| < 1$ and diverges if $3|x| > 1$. Thus, it converges if $|x| < \frac{1}{3}$ and diverges if $|x| > \frac{1}{3}$. This means that the radius of convergence is $R = \frac{1}{3}$.

We know the series converges in the interval $\left(-\frac{1}{3}, \frac{1}{3} \right)$, but we must now test for convergence at the endpoints of this interval. If $x = -\frac{1}{3}$, the series becomes

$$\sum_{n=0}^{\infty} \frac{(-3)^n \left(-\frac{1}{3} \right)^n}{\sqrt{n+1}} = \sum_{n=0}^{\infty} \frac{1}{\sqrt{n+1}} = \frac{1}{\sqrt{1}} + \frac{1}{\sqrt{2}} + \frac{1}{\sqrt{3}} + \frac{1}{\sqrt{4}} + \cdots$$

which diverges. (Use the Integral Test or simply observe that it is a p-series with $p = \frac{1}{2} < 1$.) If $x = \frac{1}{3}$, the series is

$$\sum_{n=0}^{\infty} \frac{(-3)^n \left(\frac{1}{3} \right)^n}{\sqrt{n+1}} = \sum_{n=0}^{\infty} \frac{(-1)^n}{\sqrt{n+1}}$$

which converges by the Alternating Series Test. Therefore, the given power series converges when $-\frac{1}{3} < x \leq \frac{1}{3}$, so the interval of convergence is $\left(-\frac{1}{3}, \frac{1}{3} \right]$.

EXAMPLE 5 Find the radius of convergence and interval of convergence of the series

$$\sum_{n=0}^{\infty} \frac{n(x+2)^n}{3^{n+1}}$$

SOLUTION If $a_n = n(x+2)^n / 3^{n+1}$, then

$$\left| \frac{a_{n+1}}{a_n} \right| = \left| \frac{(n+1)(x+2)^{n+1}}{3^{n+2}} \cdot \frac{3^{n+1}}{n(x+2)^n} \right|$$

$$= \left(1 + \frac{1}{n} \right) \frac{|x+2|}{3} \; \rightarrow \; \frac{|x+2|}{3} \qquad \text{as } n \to \infty$$

Using the Ratio Test, we see that the series converges if $|x+2|/3 < 1$ and it diverges if $|x+2|/3 > 1$. So it converges if $|x+2| < 3$ and diverges if $|x+2| > 3$. Thus, the radius of convergence is $R = 3$.

The inequality $|x + 2| < 3$ can be written as $-5 < x < 1$, so we test the series at the endpoints -5 and 1. When $x = -5$, the series is

$$\sum_{n=0}^{\infty} \frac{n(-3)^n}{3^{n+1}} = \tfrac{1}{3} \sum_{n=0}^{\infty} (-1)^n n$$

which diverges by the Test for Divergence [$(-1)^n n$ doesn't converge to 0]. When $x = 1$, the series is

$$\sum_{n=0}^{\infty} \frac{n(3)^n}{3^{n+1}} = \tfrac{1}{3} \sum_{n=0}^{\infty} n$$

which also diverges by the Test for Divergence. Thus, the series converges only when $-5 < x < 1$, so the interval of convergence is $(-5, 1)$.

12.8 Exercises

1. What is a power series?

2. (a) What is the radius of convergence of a power series? How do you find it?
(b) What is the interval of convergence of a power series? How do you find it?

3–28 ▥ Find the radius of convergence and interval of convergence of the series.

3. $\displaystyle\sum_{n=1}^{\infty} \frac{x^n}{\sqrt{n}}$

4. $\displaystyle\sum_{n=0}^{\infty} \frac{(-1)^n x^n}{n + 1}$

5. $\displaystyle\sum_{n=1}^{\infty} \frac{(-1)^{n-1} x^n}{n^3}$

6. $\displaystyle\sum_{n=1}^{\infty} \sqrt{n}\, x^n$

7. $\displaystyle\sum_{n=0}^{\infty} \frac{x^n}{n!}$

8. $\displaystyle\sum_{n=1}^{\infty} n^n x^n$

9. $\displaystyle\sum_{n=1}^{\infty} (-1)^n n 4^n x^n$

10. $\displaystyle\sum_{n=1}^{\infty} \frac{x^n}{n3^n}$

11. $\displaystyle\sum_{n=1}^{\infty} \frac{(-2)^n x^n}{\sqrt[4]{n}}$

12. $\displaystyle\sum_{n=1}^{\infty} \frac{x^n}{5^n n^5}$

13. $\displaystyle\sum_{n=2}^{\infty} (-1)^n \frac{x^n}{4^n \ln n}$

14. $\displaystyle\sum_{n=0}^{\infty} (-1)^n \frac{x^{2n}}{(2n)!}$

15. $\displaystyle\sum_{n=0}^{\infty} \sqrt{n}\, (x - 1)^n$

16. $\displaystyle\sum_{n=0}^{\infty} n^3 (x - 5)^n$

17. $\displaystyle\sum_{n=1}^{\infty} (-1)^n \frac{(x + 2)^n}{n2^n}$

18. $\displaystyle\sum_{n=1}^{\infty} \frac{(-2)^n}{\sqrt{n}} (x + 3)^n$

19. $\displaystyle\sum_{n=1}^{\infty} \frac{(x - 2)^n}{n^n}$

20. $\displaystyle\sum_{n=1}^{\infty} \frac{(3x - 2)^n}{n3^n}$

21. $\displaystyle\sum_{n=1}^{\infty} \frac{n}{b^n} (x - a)^n, \quad b > 0$

22. $\displaystyle\sum_{n=1}^{\infty} \frac{n(x - 4)^n}{n^3 + 1}$

23. $\displaystyle\sum_{n=1}^{\infty} n!(2x - 1)^n$

24. $\displaystyle\sum_{n=1}^{\infty} \frac{n^2 x^n}{2 \cdot 4 \cdot 6 \cdot\,\cdots\,\cdot (2n)}$

25. $\displaystyle\sum_{n=1}^{\infty} \frac{(4x + 1)^n}{n^2}$

26. $\displaystyle\sum_{n=2}^{\infty} (-1)^n \frac{(2x + 3)^n}{n \ln n}$

27. $\displaystyle\sum_{n=2}^{\infty} \frac{x^n}{(\ln n)^n}$

28. $\displaystyle\sum_{n=1}^{\infty} \frac{2 \cdot 4 \cdot 6 \cdot\,\cdots\,\cdot (2n)}{1 \cdot 3 \cdot 5 \cdot\,\cdots\,\cdot (2n - 1)} x^n$

29. If $\sum_{n=0}^{\infty} c_n 4^n$ is convergent, does it follow that the following series are convergent?

(a) $\displaystyle\sum_{n=0}^{\infty} c_n(-2)^n$

(b) $\displaystyle\sum_{n=0}^{\infty} c_n(-4)^n$

30. Suppose that $\sum_{n=0}^{\infty} c_n x^n$ converges when $x = -4$ and diverges when $x = 6$. What can be said about the convergence or divergence of the following series?

(a) $\displaystyle\sum_{n=0}^{\infty} c_n$

(b) $\displaystyle\sum_{n=0}^{\infty} c_n 8^n$

(c) $\displaystyle\sum_{n=0}^{\infty} c_n(-3)^n$

(d) $\displaystyle\sum_{n=0}^{\infty} (-1)^n c_n 9^n$

31. If k is a positive integer, find the radius of convergence of the series

$$\sum_{n=0}^{\infty} \frac{(n!)^k}{(kn)!} x^n$$

32. Graph the first several partial sums $s_n(x)$ of the series $\sum_{n=0}^{\infty} x^n$, together with the sum function $f(x) = 1/(1 - x)$, on a common screen. On what interval do these partial sums appear to be converging to $f(x)$?

33. The function J_1 defined by

$$J_1(x) = \sum_{n=0}^{\infty} \frac{(-1)^n x^{2n+1}}{n!(n + 1)!2^{2n+1}}$$

is called the *Bessel function of order 1*.
(a) Find its domain.
(b) Graph the first several partial sums on a common screen.

CAS (c) If your CAS has built-in Bessel functions, graph J_1 on the same screen as the partial sums in part (b) and observe how the partial sums approximate J_1.

34. The function A defined by

$$A(x) = 1 + \frac{x^3}{2 \cdot 3} + \frac{x^6}{2 \cdot 3 \cdot 5 \cdot 6} + \frac{x^9}{2 \cdot 3 \cdot 5 \cdot 6 \cdot 8 \cdot 9} + \cdots$$

is called the *Airy function* after the English mathematician and astronomer Sir George Airy (1801–1892).
(a) Find the domain of the Airy function.
(b) Graph the first several partial sums $s_n(x)$ on a common screen.

CAS (c) If your CAS has built-in Airy functions, graph A on the same screen as the partial sums in part (b) and observe how the partial sums approximate A.

35. A function f is defined by

$$f(x) = 1 + 2x + x^2 + 2x^3 + x^4 + \cdots$$

that is, its coefficients are $c_{2n} = 1$ and $c_{2n+1} = 2$ for all $n \geqslant 0$. Find the interval of convergence of the series and find an explicit formula for $f(x)$.

36. If $f(x) = \sum_{n=0}^{\infty} c_n x^n$, where $c_{n+4} = c_n$ for all $n \geqslant 0$, find the interval of convergence of the series and a formula for $f(x)$.

37. Show that if $\lim_{n \to \infty} \sqrt[n]{|c_n|} = c$, where $c \neq 0$, then the radius of convergence of the power series $\Sigma\, c_n x^n$ is $R = 1/c$.

38. Suppose that the power series $\Sigma\, c_n (x - a)^n$ satisfies $c_n \neq 0$ for all n. Show that if $\lim_{n \to \infty} |c_n/c_{n+1}|$ exists, then it is equal to the radius of convergence of the power series.

39. Suppose the series $\Sigma\, c_n x^n$ has radius of convergence 2 and the series $\Sigma\, d_n x^n$ has radius of convergence 3. What is the radius of convergence of the series $\Sigma\, (c_n + d_n) x^n$?

40. Suppose that the radius of convergence of the power series $\Sigma\, c_n x^n$ is R. What is the radius of convergence of the power series $\Sigma\, c_n x^{2n}$?

12.9 Representations of Functions as Power Series

In this section we learn how to represent certain types of functions as sums of power series by manipulating geometric series or by differentiating or integrating such a series. You might wonder why we would ever want to express a known function as a sum of infinitely many terms. We will see later that this strategy is useful for integrating functions that don't have elementary antiderivatives, for solving differential equations, and for approximating functions by polynomials. (Scientists do this to simplify the expressions they deal with; computer scientists do this to represent functions on calculators and computers.)

We start with an equation that we have seen before:

▍▍▍ A geometric illustration of Equation 1 is shown in Figure 1. Because the sum of a series is the limit of the sequence of partial sums, we have

$$\frac{1}{1-x} = \lim_{n \to \infty} s_n(x)$$

where

$$s_n(x) = 1 + x + x^2 + \cdots + x^n$$

is the nth partial sum. Notice that as n increases, $s_n(x)$ becomes a better approximation to $f(x)$ for $-1 < x < 1$.

$$\boxed{1} \qquad \frac{1}{1-x} = 1 + x + x^2 + x^3 + \cdots = \sum_{n=0}^{\infty} x^n \qquad |x| < 1$$

We first encountered this equation in Example 5 in Section 12.2, where we obtained it by observing that it is a geometric series with $a = 1$ and $r = x$. But here our point of view is different. We now regard Equation 1 as expressing the function $f(x) = 1/(1 - x)$ as a sum of a power series.

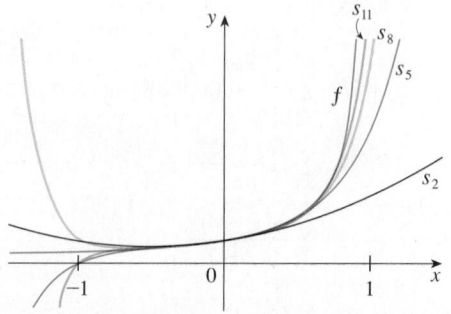

FIGURE 1

$f(x) = \dfrac{1}{1-x}$ and some partial sums

EXAMPLE 1 Express $1/(1 + x^2)$ as the sum of a power series and find the interval of convergence.

SOLUTION Replacing x by $-x^2$ in Equation 1, we have

$$\frac{1}{1 + x^2} = \frac{1}{1 - (-x^2)} = \sum_{n=0}^{\infty} (-x^2)^n$$

$$= \sum_{n=0}^{\infty} (-1)^n x^{2n} = 1 - x^2 + x^4 - x^6 + x^8 - \cdots$$

Because this is a geometric series, it converges when $|-x^2| < 1$, that is, $x^2 < 1$, or $|x| < 1$. Therefore, the interval of convergence is $(-1, 1)$. (Of course, we could have determined the radius of convergence by applying the Ratio Test, but that much work is unnecessary here.)

EXAMPLE 2 Find a power series representation for $1/(x + 2)$.

SOLUTION In order to put this function in the form of the left side of Equation 1 we first factor a 2 from the denominator:

$$\frac{1}{2 + x} = \frac{1}{2\left(1 + \dfrac{x}{2}\right)} = \frac{1}{2\left[1 - \left(-\dfrac{x}{2}\right)\right]}$$

$$= \frac{1}{2} \sum_{n=0}^{\infty} \left(-\frac{x}{2}\right)^n = \sum_{n=0}^{\infty} \frac{(-1)^n}{2^{n+1}} x^n$$

This series converges when $|-x/2| < 1$, that is, $|x| < 2$. So the interval of convergence is $(-2, 2)$.

EXAMPLE 3 Find a power series representation of $x^3/(x + 2)$.

SOLUTION Since this function is just x^3 times the function in Example 2, all we have to do is to multiply that series by x^3:

|||| It's legitimate to move x^3 across the sigma sign because it doesn't depend on n. [Use Theorem 12.2.8(i) with $c = x^3$.]

$$\frac{x^3}{x + 2} = x^3 \cdot \frac{1}{x + 2} = x^3 \sum_{n=0}^{\infty} \frac{(-1)^n}{2^{n+1}} x^n = \sum_{n=0}^{\infty} \frac{(-1)^n}{2^{n+1}} x^{n+3}$$

$$= \tfrac{1}{2}x^3 - \tfrac{1}{4}x^4 + \tfrac{1}{8}x^5 - \tfrac{1}{16}x^6 + \cdots$$

Another way of writing this series is as follows:

$$\frac{x^3}{x + 2} = \sum_{n=3}^{\infty} \frac{(-1)^{n-1}}{2^{n-2}} x^n$$

As in Example 2, the interval of convergence is $(-2, 2)$.

|||| **Differentiation and Integration of Power Series**

The sum of a power series is a function $f(x) = \sum_{n=0}^{\infty} c_n(x - a)^n$ whose domain is the interval of convergence of the series. We would like to be able to differentiate and integrate such functions, and the following theorem (which we won't prove) says that we can do so by differentiating or integrating each individual term in the series, just as we would for a polynomial. This is called **term-by-term differentiation and integration**.

---

2 Theorem If the power series $\sum c_n(x - a)^n$ has radius of convergence $R > 0$, then the function f defined by

$$f(x) = c_0 + c_1(x - a) + c_2(x - a)^2 + \cdots = \sum_{n=0}^{\infty} c_n(x - a)^n$$

is differentiable (and therefore continuous) on the interval $(a - R, a + R)$ and

(i) $f'(x) = c_1 + 2c_2(x - a) + 3c_3(x - a)^2 + \cdots = \sum_{n=1}^{\infty} nc_n(x - a)^{n-1}$

(ii) $\int f(x)\, dx = C + c_0(x - a) + c_1 \dfrac{(x - a)^2}{2} + c_2 \dfrac{(x - a)^3}{3} + \cdots$

$$= C + \sum_{n=0}^{\infty} c_n \frac{(x - a)^{n+1}}{n + 1}$$

The radii of convergence of the power series in Equations (i) and (ii) are both R.

||| In part (ii), $\int c_0\, dx = c_0 x + C_1$ is written as $c_0(x - a) + C$, where $C = C_1 + ac_0$, so all the terms of the series have the same form.

NOTE 1 ◦ Equations (i) and (ii) in Theorem 2 can be rewritten in the form

(iii) $\dfrac{d}{dx}\left[\displaystyle\sum_{n=0}^{\infty} c_n(x - a)^n \right] = \displaystyle\sum_{n=0}^{\infty} \dfrac{d}{dx}\left[c_n(x - a)^n \right]$

(iv) $\displaystyle\int \left[\sum_{n=0}^{\infty} c_n(x - a)^n \right] dx = \sum_{n=0}^{\infty} \int c_n(x - a)^n\, dx$

We know that, for finite sums, the derivative of a sum is the sum of the derivatives and the integral of a sum is the sum of the integrals. Equations (iii) and (iv) assert that the same is true for infinite sums, provided we are dealing with *power series*. (For other types of series of functions the situation is not as simple; see Exercise 36.)

NOTE 2 ◦ Although Theorem 2 says that the radius of convergence remains the same when a power series is differentiated or integrated, this does not mean that the *interval* of convergence remains the same. It may happen that the original series converges at an endpoint, whereas the differentiated series diverges there. (See Exercise 37.)

NOTE 3 ◦ The idea of differentiating a power series term by term is the basis for a powerful method for solving differential equations. We will discuss this method in Chapter 18.

EXAMPLE 4 In Example 3 in Section 12.8 we saw that the Bessel function

$$J_0(x) = \sum_{n=0}^{\infty} \frac{(-1)^n x^{2n}}{2^{2n}(n!)^2}$$

is defined for all x. Thus, by Theorem 2, J_0 is differentiable for all x and its derivative is found by term-by-term differentiation as follows:

$$J_0'(x) = \sum_{n=0}^{\infty} \frac{d}{dx} \frac{(-1)^n x^{2n}}{2^{2n}(n!)^2} = \sum_{n=1}^{\infty} \frac{(-1)^n 2n x^{2n-1}}{2^{2n}(n!)^2}$$

EXAMPLE 5 Express $1/(1 - x)^2$ as a power series by differentiating Equation 1. What is the radius of convergence?

SOLUTION Differentiating each side of the equation

$$\frac{1}{1 - x} = 1 + x + x^2 + x^3 + \cdots = \sum_{n=0}^{\infty} x^n$$

we get

$$\frac{1}{(1 - x)^2} = 1 + 2x + 3x^2 + \cdots = \sum_{n=1}^{\infty} nx^{n-1}$$

If we wish, we can replace n by $n + 1$ and write the answer as

$$\frac{1}{(1 - x)^2} = \sum_{n=0}^{\infty} (n + 1)x^n$$

According to Theorem 2, the radius of convergence of the differentiated series is the same as the radius of convergence of the original series, namely, $R = 1$.

EXAMPLE 6 Find a power series representation for $\ln(1 - x)$ and its radius of convergence.

SOLUTION We notice that, except for a factor of -1, the derivative of this function is $1/(1 - x)$. So we integrate both sides of Equation 1:

$$-\ln(1 - x) = \int \frac{1}{1 - x} \, dx = \int (1 + x + x^2 + \cdots) \, dx$$

$$= x + \frac{x^2}{2} + \frac{x^3}{3} + \cdots + C = \sum_{n=0}^{\infty} \frac{x^{n+1}}{n + 1} + C$$

$$= \sum_{n=1}^{\infty} \frac{x^n}{n} + C \qquad |x| < 1$$

To determine the value of C we put $x = 0$ in this equation and obtain $-\ln(1 - 0) = C$. Thus, $C = 0$ and

$$\ln(1 - x) = -x - \frac{x^2}{2} - \frac{x^3}{3} - \cdots = -\sum_{n=1}^{\infty} \frac{x^n}{n} \qquad |x| < 1$$

The radius of convergence is the same as for the original series: $R = 1$.

Notice what happens if we put $x = \frac{1}{2}$ in the result of Example 6. Since $\ln \frac{1}{2} = -\ln 2$, we see that

$$\ln 2 = \frac{1}{2} + \frac{1}{8} + \frac{1}{24} + \frac{1}{64} + \cdots = \sum_{n=1}^{\infty} \frac{1}{n2^n}$$

EXAMPLE 7 Find a power series representation for $f(x) = \tan^{-1}x$.

SOLUTION We observe that $f'(x) = 1/(1 + x^2)$ and find the required series by integrating the power series for $1/(1 + x^2)$ found in Example 1.

$$\tan^{-1}x = \int \frac{1}{1 + x^2} \, dx = \int (1 - x^2 + x^4 - x^6 + \cdots) \, dx$$

$$= C + x - \frac{x^3}{3} + \frac{x^5}{5} - \frac{x^7}{7} + \cdots$$

|||| The power series for $\tan^{-1}x$ obtained in Example 7 is called *Gregory's series* after the Scottish mathematician James Gregory (1638–1675), who had anticipated some of Newton's discoveries. We have shown that Gregory's series is valid when $-1 < x < 1$, but it turns out (although it isn't easy to prove) that it is also valid when $x = \pm 1$. Notice that when $x = 1$ the series becomes

$$\frac{\pi}{4} = 1 - \frac{1}{3} + \frac{1}{5} - \frac{1}{7} + \cdots$$

This beautiful result is known as the Leibniz formula for π.

To find C we put $x = 0$ and obtain $C = \tan^{-1}0 = 0$. Therefore

$$\tan^{-1}x = x - \frac{x^3}{3} + \frac{x^5}{5} - \frac{x^7}{7} + \cdots = \sum_{n=0}^{\infty} (-1)^n \frac{x^{2n+1}}{2n+1}$$

Since the radius of convergence of the series for $1/(1 + x^2)$ is 1, the radius of convergence of this series for $\tan^{-1}x$ is also 1.

EXAMPLE 8

(a) Evaluate $\int [1/(1 + x^7)]\,dx$ as a power series.

(b) Use part (a) to approximate $\int_0^{0.5} [1/(1 + x^7)]\,dx$ correct to within 10^{-7}.

SOLUTION

(a) The first step is to express the integrand, $1/(1 + x^7)$, as the sum of a power series. As in Example 1, we start with Equation 1 and replace x by $-x^7$:

$$\frac{1}{1 + x^7} = \frac{1}{1 - (-x^7)} = \sum_{n=0}^{\infty} (-x^7)^n$$

$$= \sum_{n=0}^{\infty} (-1)^n x^{7n} = 1 - x^7 + x^{14} - \cdots$$

|||| This example demonstrates one way in which power series representations are useful. Integrating $1/(1 + x^7)$ by hand is incredibly difficult. Different computer algebra systems return different forms of the answer, but they are all extremely complicated. (If you have a CAS, try it yourself.) The infinite series answer that we obtain in Example 8(a) is actually much easier to deal with than the finite answer provided by a CAS.

Now we integrate term by term:

$$\int \frac{1}{1 + x^7}\,dx = \int \sum_{n=0}^{\infty} (-1)^n x^{7n}\,dx = C + \sum_{n=0}^{\infty} (-1)^n \frac{x^{7n+1}}{7n+1}$$

$$= C + x - \frac{x^8}{8} + \frac{x^{15}}{15} - \frac{x^{22}}{22} + \cdots$$

This series converges for $|-x^7| < 1$, that is, for $|x| < 1$.

(b) In applying the Fundamental Theorem of Calculus it doesn't matter which antiderivative we use, so let's use the antiderivative from part (a) with $C = 0$:

$$\int_0^{0.5} \frac{1}{1 + x^7}\,dx = \left[x - \frac{x^8}{8} + \frac{x^{15}}{15} - \frac{x^{22}}{22} + \cdots \right]_0^{1/2}$$

$$= \frac{1}{2} - \frac{1}{8 \cdot 2^8} + \frac{1}{15 \cdot 2^{15}} - \frac{1}{22 \cdot 2^{22}} + \cdots + \frac{(-1)^n}{(7n+1)2^{7n+1}} + \cdots$$

This infinite series is the exact value of the definite integral, but since it is an alternating series, we can approximate the sum using the Alternating Series Estimation Theorem. If we stop adding after the term with $n = 3$, the error is smaller than the term with $n = 4$:

$$\frac{1}{29 \cdot 2^{29}} \approx 6.4 \times 10^{-11}$$

So we have

$$\int_0^{0.5} \frac{1}{1 + x^7}\,dx \approx \frac{1}{2} - \frac{1}{8 \cdot 2^8} + \frac{1}{15 \cdot 2^{15}} - \frac{1}{22 \cdot 2^{22}} \approx 0.49951374$$

12.9 Exercises

1. If the radius of convergence of the power series $\sum_{n=0}^{\infty} c_n x^n$ is 10, what is the radius of convergence of the series $\sum_{n=1}^{\infty} n c_n x^{n-1}$? Why?

2. Suppose you know that the series $\sum_{n=0}^{\infty} b_n x^n$ converges for $|x| < 2$. What can you say about the following series? Why?

$$\sum_{n=0}^{\infty} \frac{b_n}{n+1} x^{n+1}$$

3–10 ▮▮▮▮ Find a power series representation for the function and determine the interval of convergence.

3. $f(x) = \dfrac{1}{1+x}$

4. $f(x) = \dfrac{3}{1-x^4}$

5. $f(x) = \dfrac{1}{1-x^3}$

6. $f(x) = \dfrac{1}{1+9x^2}$

7. $f(x) = \dfrac{1}{x-5}$

8. $f(x) = \dfrac{x}{4x+1}$

9. $f(x) = \dfrac{x}{9+x^2}$

10. $f(x) = \dfrac{x^2}{a^3-x^3}$

11–12 ▮▮▮▮ Express the function as the sum of a power series by first using partial fractions. Find the interval of convergence.

11. $f(x) = \dfrac{3}{x^2+x-2}$

12. $f(x) = \dfrac{7x-1}{3x^2+2x-1}$

13. (a) Use differentiation to find a power series representation for

$$f(x) = \frac{1}{(1+x)^2}$$

What is the radius of convergence?

(b) Use part (a) to find a power series for

$$f(x) = \frac{1}{(1+x)^3}$$

(c) Use part (b) to find a power series for

$$f(x) = \frac{x^2}{(1+x)^3}$$

14. (a) Find a power series representation for $f(x) = \ln(1+x)$. What is the radius of convergence?

(b) Use part (a) to find a power series for $f(x) = x \ln(1+x)$.

(c) Use part (a) to find a power series for $f(x) = \ln(x^2+1)$.

15–18 ▮▮▮▮ Find a power series representation for the function and determine the radius of convergence.

15. $f(x) = \ln(5-x)$

16. $f(x) = \dfrac{x^2}{(1-2x)^2}$

17. $f(x) = \dfrac{x^3}{(x-2)^2}$

18. $f(x) = \arctan(x/3)$

19–22 ▮▮▮▮ Find a power series representation for f, and graph f and several partial sums $s_n(x)$ on the same screen. What happens as n increases?

19. $f(x) = \ln(3+x)$

20. $f(x) = \dfrac{1}{x^2+25}$

21. $f(x) = \ln\left(\dfrac{1+x}{1-x}\right)$

22. $f(x) = \tan^{-1}(2x)$

23–26 ▮▮▮▮ Evaluate the indefinite integral as a power series. What is the radius of convergence?

23. $\displaystyle\int \frac{t}{1-t^8}\, dt$

24. $\displaystyle\int \frac{\ln(1-t)}{t}\, dt$

25. $\displaystyle\int \frac{x-\tan^{-1}x}{x^3}\, dx$

26. $\displaystyle\int \tan^{-1}(x^2)\, dx$

27–30 ▮▮▮▮ Use a power series to approximate the definite integral to six decimal places.

27. $\displaystyle\int_0^{0.2} \frac{1}{1+x^5}\, dx$

28. $\displaystyle\int_0^{0.4} \ln(1+x^4)\, dx$

29. $\displaystyle\int_0^{1/3} x^2 \tan^{-1}(x^4)\, dx$

30. $\displaystyle\int_0^{0.5} \frac{dx}{1+x^6}$

31. Use the result of Example 6 to compute $\ln 1.1$ correct to five decimal places.

32. Show that the function

$$f(x) = \sum_{n=0}^{\infty} \frac{(-1)^n x^{2n}}{(2n)!}$$

is a solution of the differential equation

$$f''(x) + f(x) = 0$$

33. (a) Show that J_0 (the Bessel function of order 0 given in Example 4) satisfies the differential equation

$$x^2 J_0''(x) + x J_0'(x) + x^2 J_0(x) = 0$$

(b) Evaluate $\int_0^1 J_0(x)\, dx$ correct to three decimal places.

34. The Bessel function of order 1 is defined by

$$J_1(x) = \sum_{n=0}^{\infty} \frac{(-1)^n x^{2n+1}}{n!(n+1)!2^{2n+1}}$$

(a) Show that J_1 satisfies the differential equation

$$x^2 J_1''(x) + x J_1'(x) + (x^2 - 1)J_1(x) = 0$$

(b) Show that $J_0'(x) = -J_1(x)$.

35. (a) Show that the function

$$f(x) = \sum_{n=0}^{\infty} \frac{x^n}{n!}$$

is a solution of the differential equation

$$f'(x) = f(x)$$

(b) Show that $f(x) = e^x$.

36. Let $f_n(x) = (\sin nx)/n^2$. Show that the series $\Sigma f_n(x)$ converges for all values of x but the series of derivatives $\Sigma f_n'(x)$ diverges when $x = 2n\pi$, n an integer. For what values of x does the series $\Sigma f_n''(x)$ converge?

37. Let

$$f(x) = \sum_{n=1}^{\infty} \frac{x^n}{n^2}$$

Find the intervals of convergence for f, f', and f''.

38. (a) Starting with the geometric series $\Sigma_{n=0}^{\infty} x^n$, find the sum of the series

$$\sum_{n=1}^{\infty} nx^{n-1} \qquad |x| < 1$$

(b) Find the sum of each of the following series.

(i) $\displaystyle\sum_{n=1}^{\infty} nx^n, \quad |x| < 1$ (ii) $\displaystyle\sum_{n=1}^{\infty} \frac{n}{2^n}$

(c) Find the sum of each of the following series.

(i) $\displaystyle\sum_{n=2}^{\infty} n(n-1)x^n, \quad |x| < 1$

(ii) $\displaystyle\sum_{n=2}^{\infty} \frac{n^2 - n}{2^n}$ (iii) $\displaystyle\sum_{n=1}^{\infty} \frac{n^2}{2^n}$

39. Use the power series for $\tan^{-1} x$ to prove the following expression for π as the sum of an infinite series:

$$\pi = 2\sqrt{3} \sum_{n=0}^{\infty} \frac{(-1)^n}{(2n+1)3^n}$$

40. (a) By completing the square, show that

$$\int_0^{1/2} \frac{dx}{x^2 - x + 1} = \frac{\pi}{3\sqrt{3}}$$

(b) By factoring $x^3 + 1$ as a sum of cubes, rewrite the integral in part (a). Then express $1/(x^3 + 1)$ as the sum of a power series and use it to prove the following formula for π:

$$\pi = \frac{3\sqrt{3}}{4} \sum_{n=0}^{\infty} \frac{(-1)^n}{8^n} \left(\frac{2}{3n+1} + \frac{1}{3n+2} \right)$$

12.10 Taylor and Maclaurin Series

In the preceding section we were able to find power series representations for a certain restricted class of functions. Here we investigate more general problems: Which functions have power series representations? How can we find such representations?

We start by supposing that f is any function that can be represented by a power series

$$\boxed{1} \quad f(x) = c_0 + c_1(x - a) + c_2(x - a)^2 + c_3(x - a)^3 + c_4(x - a)^4 + \cdots \qquad |x - a| < R$$

Let's try to determine what the coefficients c_n must be in terms of f. To begin, notice that if we put $x = a$ in Equation 1, then all terms after the first one are 0 and we get

$$f(a) = c_0$$

By Theorem 12.9.2, we can differentiate the series in Equation 1 term by term:

$$\boxed{2} \quad f'(x) = c_1 + 2c_2(x - a) + 3c_3(x - a)^2 + 4c_4(x - a)^3 + \cdots \qquad |x - a| < R$$

and substitution of $x = a$ in Equation 2 gives

$$f'(a) = c_1$$

Now we differentiate both sides of Equation 2 and obtain

$$\boxed{3} \quad f''(x) = 2c_2 + 2 \cdot 3c_3(x - a) + 3 \cdot 4c_4(x - a)^2 + \cdots \qquad |x - a| < R$$

Again we put $x = a$ in Equation 3. The result is

$$f''(a) = 2c_2$$

Let's apply the procedure one more time. Differentiation of the series in Equation 3 gives

$$\boxed{4} \quad f'''(x) = 2 \cdot 3c_3 + 2 \cdot 3 \cdot 4c_4(x - a) + 3 \cdot 4 \cdot 5c_5(x - a)^2 + \cdots \qquad |x - a| < R$$

and substitution of $x = a$ in Equation 4 gives

$$f'''(a) = 2 \cdot 3c_3 = 3!c_3$$

By now you can see the pattern. If we continue to differentiate and substitute $x = a$, we obtain

$$f^{(n)}(a) = 2 \cdot 3 \cdot 4 \cdot \cdots \cdot nc_n = n!c_n$$

Solving this equation for the nth coefficient c_n, we get

$$c_n = \frac{f^{(n)}(a)}{n!}$$

This formula remains valid even for $n = 0$ if we adopt the conventions that $0! = 1$ and $f^{(0)} = f$. Thus, we have proved the following theorem.

$\boxed{5}$ **Theorem** If f has a power series representation (expansion) at a, that is, if

$$f(x) = \sum_{n=0}^{\infty} c_n(x - a)^n \qquad |x - a| < R$$

then its coefficients are given by the formula

$$c_n = \frac{f^{(n)}(a)}{n!}$$

Substituting this formula for c_n back into the series, we see that *if f has a power series expansion at a, then it must be of the following form.*

$$\boxed{6} \quad f(x) = \sum_{n=0}^{\infty} \frac{f^{(n)}(a)}{n!} (x - a)^n$$

$$= f(a) + \frac{f'(a)}{1!}(x - a) + \frac{f''(a)}{2!}(x - a)^2 + \frac{f'''(a)}{3!}(x - a)^3 + \cdots$$

|||| The Taylor series is named after the English mathematician Brook Taylor (1685–1731) and the Maclaurin series is named in honor of the Scottish mathematician Colin Maclaurin (1698–1746) despite the fact that the Maclaurin series is really just a special case of the Taylor series. But the idea of representing particular functions as sums of power series goes back to Newton, and the general Taylor series was known to the Scottish mathematician James Gregory in 1668 and to the Swiss mathematician John Bernoulli in the 1690s. Taylor was apparently unaware of the work of Gregory and Bernoulli when he published his discoveries on series in 1715 in his book *Methodus incrementorum directa et inversa.* Maclaurin series are named after Colin Maclaurin because he popularized them in his calculus textbook *Treatise of Fluxions* published in 1742.

The series in Equation 6 is called the **Taylor series of the function f at a** (or **about a** or **centered at a**). For the special case $a = 0$ the Taylor series becomes

$$\boxed{7} \qquad f(x) = \sum_{n=0}^{\infty} \frac{f^{(n)}(0)}{n!} x^n = f(0) + \frac{f'(0)}{1!} x + \frac{f''(0)}{2!} x^2 + \cdots$$

This case arises frequently enough that it is given the special name **Maclaurin series**.

NOTE ▫ We have shown that *if f can be represented as a power series about a, then f is equal to the sum of its Taylor series.* But there exist functions that are not equal to the sum of their Taylor series. An example of such a function is given in Exercise 62.

EXAMPLE 1 Find the Maclaurin series of the function $f(x) = e^x$ and its radius of convergence.

SOLUTION If $f(x) = e^x$, then $f^{(n)}(x) = e^x$, so $f^{(n)}(0) = e^0 = 1$ for all n. Therefore, the Taylor series for f at 0 (that is, the Maclaurin series) is

$$\sum_{n=0}^{\infty} \frac{f^{(n)}(0)}{n!} x^n = \sum_{n=0}^{\infty} \frac{x^n}{n!} = 1 + \frac{x}{1!} + \frac{x^2}{2!} + \frac{x^3}{3!} + \cdots$$

To find the radius of convergence we let $a_n = x^n/n!$. Then

$$\left| \frac{a_{n+1}}{a_n} \right| = \left| \frac{x^{n+1}}{(n+1)!} \cdot \frac{n!}{x^n} \right| = \frac{|x|}{n+1} \to 0 < 1$$

so, by the Ratio Test, the series converges for all x and the radius of convergence is $R = \infty$.

The conclusion we can draw from Theorem 5 and Example 1 is that *if e^x has a power series expansion at 0,* then

$$e^x = \sum_{n=0}^{\infty} \frac{x^n}{n!}$$

So how can we determine whether e^x *does* have a power series representation?

Let's investigate the more general question: Under what circumstances is a function equal to the sum of its Taylor series? In other words, if f has derivatives of all orders, when is it true that

$$f(x) = \sum_{n=0}^{\infty} \frac{f^{(n)}(a)}{n!} (x - a)^n$$

As with any convergent series, this means that $f(x)$ is the limit of the sequence of partial sums. In the case of the Taylor series, the partial sums are

$$T_n(x) = \sum_{i=0}^{n} \frac{f^{(i)}(a)}{i!} (x - a)^i$$

$$= f(a) + \frac{f'(a)}{1!} (x - a) + \frac{f''(a)}{2!} (x - a)^2 + \cdots + \frac{f^{(n)}(a)}{n!} (x - a)^n$$

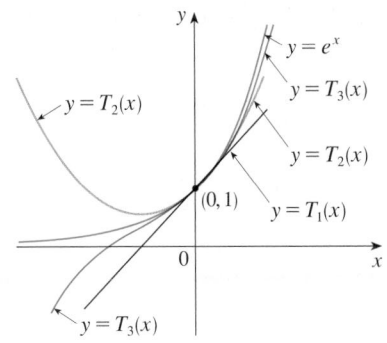

FIGURE 1

|||| As n increases, $T_n(x)$ appears to approach e^x in Figure 1. This suggests that e^x is equal to the sum of its Taylor series.

Notice that T_n is a polynomial of degree n called the **nth-degree Taylor polynomial of f at a**. For instance, for the exponential function $f(x) = e^x$, the result of Example 1 shows that the Taylor polynomials at 0 (or Maclaurin polynomials) with $n = 1, 2,$ and 3 are

$$T_1(x) = 1 + x \qquad T_2(x) = 1 + x + \frac{x^2}{2!} \qquad T_3(x) = 1 + x + \frac{x^2}{2!} + \frac{x^3}{3!}$$

The graphs of the exponential function and these three Taylor polynomials are drawn in Figure 1.

In general, $f(x)$ is the sum of its Taylor series if

$$f(x) = \lim_{n \to \infty} T_n(x)$$

If we let

$$R_n(x) = f(x) - T_n(x) \qquad \text{so that} \qquad f(x) = T_n(x) + R_n(x)$$

then $R_n(x)$ is called the **remainder** of the Taylor series. If we can somehow show that $\lim_{n \to \infty} R_n(x) = 0$, then it follows that

$$\lim_{n \to \infty} T_n(x) = \lim_{n \to \infty} [f(x) - R_n(x)] = f(x) - \lim_{n \to \infty} R_n(x) = f(x)$$

We have therefore proved the following.

> **8 Theorem** If $f(x) = T_n(x) + R_n(x)$, where T_n is the nth-degree Taylor polynomial of f at a and
>
> $$\lim_{n \to \infty} R_n(x) = 0$$
>
> for $|x - a| < R$, then f is equal to the sum of its Taylor series on the interval $|x - a| < R$.

In trying to show that $\lim_{n \to \infty} R_n(x) = 0$ for a specific function f, we usually use the following fact.

> **9 Taylor's Inequality** If $|f^{(n+1)}(x)| \le M$ for $|x - a| \le d$, then the remainder $R_n(x)$ of the Taylor series satisfies the inequality
>
> $$|R_n(x)| \le \frac{M}{(n+1)!} |x - a|^{n+1} \qquad \text{for } |x - a| \le d$$

To see why this is true for $n = 1$, we assume that $|f''(x)| \le M$. In particular, we have $f''(x) \le M$, so for $a \le x \le a + d$ we have

$$\int_a^x f''(t)\, dt \le \int_a^x M\, dt$$

An antiderivative of f'' is f', so by Part 2 of the Fundamental Theorem of Calculus, we have

$$f'(x) - f'(a) \le M(x - a) \qquad \text{or} \qquad f'(x) \le f'(a) + M(x - a)$$

‖‖‖ As alternatives to Taylor's Inequality, we have the following formulas for the remainder term. If $f^{(n+1)}$ is continuous on an interval I and $x \in I$, then

$$R_n(x) = \frac{1}{n!} \int_a^x (x-t)^n f^{(n+1)}(t)\, dt$$

This is called the *integral form of the remainder term*. Another formula, called *Lagrange's form of the remainder term*, states that there is a number z between x and a such that

$$R_n(x) = \frac{f^{(n+1)}(z)}{(n+1)!} (x-a)^{n+1}$$

This version is an extension of the Mean Value Theorem (which is the case $n = 0$).

Proofs of these formulas, together with discussions of how to use them to solve the examples of Sections 12.10 and 12.12, are given on the web site

www.stewartcalculus.com

Click on *Additional Topics* and then on *Formulas for the Remainder Term in Taylor Series.*

Thus
$$\int_a^x f'(t)\, dt \le \int_a^x [f'(a) + M(t-a)]\, dt$$

$$f(x) - f(a) \le f'(a)(x-a) + M\frac{(x-a)^2}{2}$$

$$f(x) - f(a) - f'(a)(x-a) \le \frac{M}{2}(x-a)^2$$

But $R_1(x) = f(x) - T_1(x) = f(x) - f(a) - f'(a)(x-a)$. So

$$R_1(x) \le \frac{M}{2}(x-a)^2$$

A similar argument, using $f''(x) \ge -M$, shows that

$$R_1(x) \ge -\frac{M}{2}(x-a)^2$$

So
$$|R_1(x)| \le \frac{M}{2}|x-a|^2$$

Although we have assumed that $x > a$, similar calculations show that this inequality is also true for $x < a$.

This proves Taylor's Inequality for the case where $n = 1$. The result for any n is proved in a similar way by integrating $n + 1$ times. (See Exercise 61 for the case $n = 2$.)

NOTE ▫ In Section 12.12 we will explore the use of Taylor's Inequality in approximating functions. Our immediate use of it is in conjunction with Theorem 8.

In applying Theorems 8 and 9 it is often helpful to make use of the following fact.

[10]
$$\lim_{n\to\infty} \frac{x^n}{n!} = 0 \qquad \text{for every real number } x$$

This is true because we know from Example 1 that the series $\Sigma\, x^n/n!$ converges for all x and so its nth term approaches 0.

EXAMPLE 2 Prove that e^x is equal to the sum of its Maclaurin series.

SOLUTION If $f(x) = e^x$, then $f^{(n+1)}(x) = e^x$ for all n. If d is any positive number and $|x| \le d$, then $|f^{(n+1)}(x)| = e^x \le e^d$. So Taylor's Inequality, with $a = 0$ and $M = e^d$, says that

$$|R_n(x)| \le \frac{e^d}{(n+1)!}|x|^{n+1} \qquad \text{for } |x| \le d$$

Notice that the same constant $M = e^d$ works for every value of n. But, from Equation 10, we have

$$\lim_{n\to\infty} \frac{e^d}{(n+1)!}|x|^{n+1} = e^d \lim_{n\to\infty} \frac{|x|^{n+1}}{(n+1)!} = 0$$

It follows from the Squeeze Theorem that $\lim_{n \to \infty} |R_n(x)| = 0$ and therefore $\lim_{n \to \infty} R_n(x) = 0$ for all values of x. By Theorem 8, e^x is equal to the sum of its Maclaurin series, that is,

$$\boxed{11} \qquad e^x = \sum_{n=0}^{\infty} \frac{x^n}{n!} \qquad \text{for all } x$$

IIII In 1748 Leonard Euler used Equation 12 to find the value of e correct to 23 digits. In 2000 Xavier Gourdon and S. Kondo, again using the series in (12), computed e to more than twelve billion decimal places. The special techniques they employed to speed up the computation are explained on the web page

www.numbers.computation.free.fr

In particular, if we put $x = 1$ in Equation 11, we obtain the following expression for the number e as a sum of an infinite series:

$$\boxed{12} \qquad e = \sum_{n=0}^{\infty} \frac{1}{n!} = 1 + \frac{1}{1!} + \frac{1}{2!} + \frac{1}{3!} + \cdots$$

EXAMPLE 3 Find the Taylor series for $f(x) = e^x$ at $a = 2$.

SOLUTION We have $f^{(n)}(2) = e^2$ and so, putting $a = 2$ in the definition of a Taylor series (6), we get

$$\sum_{n=0}^{\infty} \frac{f^{(n)}(2)}{n!} (x - 2)^n = \sum_{n=0}^{\infty} \frac{e^2}{n!} (x - 2)^n$$

Again it can be verified, as in Example 1, that the radius of convergence is $R = \infty$. As in Example 2 we can verify that $\lim_{n \to \infty} R_n(x) = 0$, so

$$\boxed{13} \qquad e^x = \sum_{n=0}^{\infty} \frac{e^2}{n!} (x - 2)^n \qquad \text{for all } x$$

We have two power series expansions for e^x, the Maclaurin series in Equation 11 and the Taylor series in Equation 13. The first is better if we are interested in values of x near 0 and the second is better if x is near 2.

EXAMPLE 4 Find the Maclaurin series for $\sin x$ and prove that it represents $\sin x$ for all x.

SOLUTION We arrange our computation in two columns as follows:

$$f(x) = \sin x \qquad\qquad f(0) = 0$$
$$f'(x) = \cos x \qquad\qquad f'(0) = 1$$
$$f''(x) = -\sin x \qquad\qquad f''(0) = 0$$
$$f'''(x) = -\cos x \qquad\qquad f'''(0) = -1$$
$$f^{(4)}(x) = \sin x \qquad\qquad f^{(4)}(0) = 0$$

Since the derivatives repeat in a cycle of four, we can write the Maclaurin series as follows:

$$f(0) + \frac{f'(0)}{1!} x + \frac{f''(0)}{2!} x^2 + \frac{f'''(0)}{3!} x^3 + \cdots$$

$$= x - \frac{x^3}{3!} + \frac{x^5}{5!} - \frac{x^7}{7!} + \cdots = \sum_{n=0}^{\infty} (-1)^n \frac{x^{2n+1}}{(2n+1)!}$$

▮▮▮▮ Figure 2 shows the graph of sin x together with its Taylor (or Maclaurin) polynomials

$$T_1(x) = x$$

$$T_3(x) = x - \frac{x^3}{3!}$$

$$T_5(x) = x - \frac{x^3}{3!} + \frac{x^5}{5!}$$

Notice that, as n increases, $T_n(x)$ becomes a better approximation to sin x.

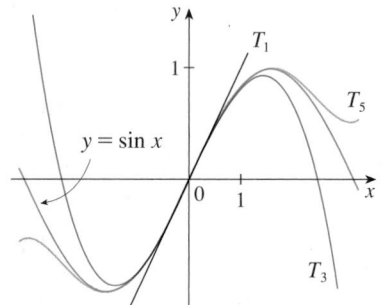

FIGURE 2

Since $f^{(n+1)}(x)$ is $\pm\sin x$ or $\pm\cos x$, we know that $|f^{(n+1)}(x)| \le 1$ for all x. So we can take $M = 1$ in Taylor's Inequality:

$$\boxed{14} \qquad |R_n(x)| \le \frac{M}{(n+1)!}|x^{n+1}| = \frac{|x|^{n+1}}{(n+1)!}$$

By Equation 10 the right side of this inequality approaches 0 as $n \to \infty$, so $|R_n(x)| \to 0$ by the Squeeze Theorem. It follows that $R_n(x) \to 0$ as $n \to \infty$, so sin x is equal to the sum of its Maclaurin series by Theorem 8.

We state the result of Example 4 for future reference.

$$\boxed{15} \qquad \sin x = x - \frac{x^3}{3!} + \frac{x^5}{5!} - \frac{x^7}{7!} + \cdots$$

$$= \sum_{n=0}^{\infty} (-1)^n \frac{x^{2n+1}}{(2n+1)!} \qquad \text{for all } x$$

EXAMPLE 5 Find the Maclaurin series for cos x.

SOLUTION We could proceed directly as in Example 4 but it's easier to differentiate the Maclaurin series for sin x given by Equation 15:

$$\cos x = \frac{d}{dx}(\sin x) = \frac{d}{dx}\left(x - \frac{x^3}{3!} + \frac{x^5}{5!} - \frac{x^7}{7!} + \cdots\right)$$

$$= 1 - \frac{3x^2}{3!} + \frac{5x^4}{5!} - \frac{7x^6}{7!} + \cdots = 1 - \frac{x^2}{2!} + \frac{x^4}{4!} - \frac{x^6}{6!} + \cdots$$

▮▮▮▮ The Maclaurin series for e^x, sin x, and cos x that we found in Examples 2, 4, and 5 were discovered, using different methods, by Newton. (There is evidence that the series for sin x and cos x were known to Indian astronomers more than a century before Newton, but this knowledge didn't spread to the rest of the world.)

These equations are remarkable because they say we know everything about each of these functions if we know all its derivatives at the single number 0.

Since the Maclaurin series for sin x converges for all x, Theorem 2 in Section 12.9 tells us that the differentiated series for cos x also converges for all x. Thus

$$\boxed{16} \qquad \cos x = 1 - \frac{x^2}{2!} + \frac{x^4}{4!} - \frac{x^6}{6!} + \cdots$$

$$= \sum_{n=0}^{\infty} (-1)^n \frac{x^{2n}}{(2n)!} \qquad \text{for all } x$$

EXAMPLE 6 Find the Maclaurin series for the function $f(x) = x \cos x$.

SOLUTION Instead of computing derivatives and substituting in Equation 7, it's easier to multiply the series for cos x (Equation 16) by x:

$$x \cos x = x \sum_{n=0}^{\infty} (-1)^n \frac{x^{2n}}{(2n)!} = \sum_{n=0}^{\infty} (-1)^n \frac{x^{2n+1}}{(2n)!}$$

EXAMPLE 7 Represent $f(x) = \sin x$ as the sum of its Taylor series centered at $\pi/3$.

SOLUTION Arranging our work in columns, we have

$$f(x) = \sin x \qquad\qquad f\left(\frac{\pi}{3}\right) = \frac{\sqrt{3}}{2}$$

$$f'(x) = \cos x \qquad\qquad f'\left(\frac{\pi}{3}\right) = \frac{1}{2}$$

$$f''(x) = -\sin x \qquad\qquad f''\left(\frac{\pi}{3}\right) = -\frac{\sqrt{3}}{2}$$

$$f'''(x) = -\cos x \qquad\qquad f'''\left(\frac{\pi}{3}\right) = -\frac{1}{2}$$

▐▐▐▐ We have obtained two different series representations for sin x, the Maclaurin series in Example 4 and the Taylor series in Example 7. It is best to use the Maclaurin series for values of x near 0 and the Taylor series for x near $\pi/3$. Notice that the third Taylor polynomial T_3 in Figure 3 is a good approximation to sin x near $\pi/3$ but not as good near 0. Compare it with the third Maclaurin polynomial T_3 in Figure 2, where the opposite is true.

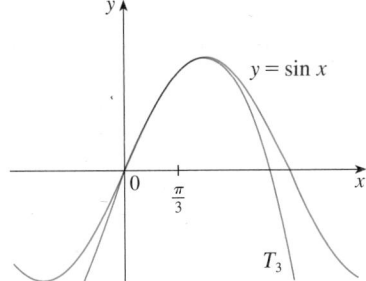

$y = \sin x$

T_3

FIGURE 3

and this pattern repeats indefinitely. Therefore, the Taylor series at $\pi/3$ is

$$f\left(\frac{\pi}{3}\right) + \frac{f'\left(\frac{\pi}{3}\right)}{1!}\left(x - \frac{\pi}{3}\right) + \frac{f''\left(\frac{\pi}{3}\right)}{2!}\left(x - \frac{\pi}{3}\right)^2 + \frac{f'''\left(\frac{\pi}{3}\right)}{3!}\left(x - \frac{\pi}{3}\right)^3 + \cdots$$

$$= \frac{\sqrt{3}}{2} + \frac{1}{2 \cdot 1!}\left(x - \frac{\pi}{3}\right) - \frac{\sqrt{3}}{2 \cdot 2!}\left(x - \frac{\pi}{3}\right)^2 - \frac{1}{2 \cdot 3!}\left(x - \frac{\pi}{3}\right)^3 + \cdots$$

The proof that this series represents sin x for all x is very similar to that in Example 4. [Just replace x by $x - \pi/3$ in (14).] We can write the series in sigma notation if we separate the terms that contain $\sqrt{3}$:

$$\sin x = \sum_{n=0}^{\infty} \frac{(-1)^n \sqrt{3}}{2(2n)!}\left(x - \frac{\pi}{3}\right)^{2n} + \sum_{n=0}^{\infty} \frac{(-1)^n}{2(2n+1)!}\left(x - \frac{\pi}{3}\right)^{2n+1}$$

The power series that we obtained by indirect methods in Examples 5 and 6 and in Section 12.9 are indeed the Taylor or Maclaurin series of the given functions because Theorem 5 asserts that, no matter how a power series representation $f(x) = \Sigma\, c_n(x - a)^n$ is obtained, it is always true that $c_n = f^{(n)}(a)/n!$. In other words, the coefficients are uniquely determined.

We collect in the following table, for future reference, some important Maclaurin series that we have derived in this section and the preceding one.

Important Maclaurin series and their intervals of convergence

$$\frac{1}{1-x} = \sum_{n=0}^{\infty} x^n = 1 + x + x^2 + x^3 + \cdots \qquad\qquad (-1, 1)$$

$$e^x = \sum_{n=0}^{\infty} \frac{x^n}{n!} = 1 + \frac{x}{1!} + \frac{x^2}{2!} + \frac{x^3}{3!} + \cdots \qquad\qquad (-\infty, \infty)$$

$$\sin x = \sum_{n=0}^{\infty} (-1)^n \frac{x^{2n+1}}{(2n+1)!} = x - \frac{x^3}{3!} + \frac{x^5}{5!} - \frac{x^7}{7!} + \cdots \qquad (-\infty, \infty)$$

$$\cos x = \sum_{n=0}^{\infty} (-1)^n \frac{x^{2n}}{(2n)!} = 1 - \frac{x^2}{2!} + \frac{x^4}{4!} - \frac{x^6}{6!} + \cdots \qquad (-\infty, \infty)$$

$$\tan^{-1} x = \sum_{n=0}^{\infty} (-1)^n \frac{x^{2n+1}}{2n+1} = x - \frac{x^3}{3} + \frac{x^5}{5} - \frac{x^7}{7} + \cdots \qquad [-1, 1]$$

Module 12.10/12.12 enables you to see how successive Taylor polynomials approach the original function.

One reason that Taylor series are important is that they enable us to integrate functions that we couldn't previously handle. In fact, in the introduction to this chapter we mentioned that Newton often integrated functions by first expressing them as power series and then integrating the series term by term. The function $f(x) = e^{-x^2}$ can't be integrated by techniques discussed so far because its antiderivative is not an elementary function (see Section 8.5). In the following example we use Newton's idea to integrate this function.

EXAMPLE 8

(a) Evaluate $\int e^{-x^2}\, dx$ as an infinite series.

(b) Evaluate $\int_0^1 e^{-x^2}\, dx$ correct to within an error of 0.001.

SOLUTION

(a) First we find the Maclaurin series for $f(x) = e^{-x^2}$. Although it's possible to use the direct method, let's find it simply by replacing x with $-x^2$ in the series for e^x given in the table of Maclaurin series. Thus, for all values of x,

$$e^{-x^2} = \sum_{n=0}^{\infty} \frac{(-x^2)^n}{n!} = \sum_{n=0}^{\infty} (-1)^n \frac{x^{2n}}{n!} = 1 - \frac{x^2}{1!} + \frac{x^4}{2!} - \frac{x^6}{3!} + \cdots$$

Now we integrate term by term:

$$\int e^{-x^2}\, dx = \int \left(1 - \frac{x^2}{1!} + \frac{x^4}{2!} - \frac{x^6}{3!} + \cdots + (-1)^n \frac{x^{2n}}{n!} + \cdots\right) dx$$

$$= C + x - \frac{x^3}{3 \cdot 1!} + \frac{x^5}{5 \cdot 2!} - \frac{x^7}{7 \cdot 3!} + \cdots + (-1)^n \frac{x^{2n+1}}{(2n+1)n!} + \cdots$$

This series converges for all x because the original series for e^{-x^2} converges for all x.

(b) The Evaluation Theorem gives

|||| We can take $C = 0$ in the antiderivative in part (a).

$$\int_0^1 e^{-x^2}\, dx = \left[x - \frac{x^3}{3 \cdot 1!} + \frac{x^5}{5 \cdot 2!} - \frac{x^7}{7 \cdot 3!} + \frac{x^9}{9 \cdot 4!} - \cdots \right]_0^1$$

$$= 1 - \tfrac{1}{3} + \tfrac{1}{10} - \tfrac{1}{42} + \tfrac{1}{216} - \cdots$$

$$\approx 1 - \tfrac{1}{3} + \tfrac{1}{10} - \tfrac{1}{42} + \tfrac{1}{216} \approx 0.7475$$

The Alternating Series Estimation Theorem shows that the error involved in this approximation is less than

$$\frac{1}{11 \cdot 5!} = \frac{1}{1320} < 0.001$$

Another use of Taylor series is illustrated in the next example. The limit could be found with l'Hospital's Rule, but instead we use a series.

EXAMPLE 9 Evaluate $\displaystyle\lim_{x \to 0} \frac{e^x - 1 - x}{x^2}$.

SOLUTION Using the Maclaurin series for e^x, we have

||| Some computer algebra systems compute
limits in this way.

$$\lim_{x \to 0} \frac{e^x - 1 - x}{x^2} = \lim_{x \to 0} \frac{\left(1 + \dfrac{x}{1!} + \dfrac{x^2}{2!} + \dfrac{x^3}{3!} + \cdots\right) - 1 - x}{x^2}$$

$$= \lim_{x \to 0} \frac{\dfrac{x^2}{2!} + \dfrac{x^3}{3!} + \dfrac{x^4}{4!} + \cdots}{x^2}$$

$$= \lim_{x \to 0} \left(\frac{1}{2} + \frac{x}{3!} + \frac{x^2}{4!} + \frac{x^3}{5!} + \cdots\right)$$

$$= \frac{1}{2}$$

because power series are continuous functions.

||| Multiplication and Division of Power Series

If power series are added or subtracted, they behave like polynomials (Theorem 12.2.8 shows this). In fact, as the following example illustrates, they can also be multiplied and divided like polynomials. We find only the first few terms because the calculations for the later terms become tedious and the initial terms are the most important ones.

EXAMPLE 10 Find the first three nonzero terms in the Maclaurin series for (a) $e^x \sin x$ and (b) $\tan x$.

SOLUTION

(a) Using the Maclaurin series for e^x and $\sin x$ in the table on page 803, we have

$$e^x \sin x = \left(1 + \frac{x}{1!} + \frac{x^2}{2!} + \frac{x^3}{3!} + \cdots\right)\left(x - \frac{x^3}{3!} + \cdots\right)$$

We multiply these expressions, collecting like terms just as for polynomials:

$$\begin{array}{r}
1 + x + \frac{1}{2}x^2 + \frac{1}{6}x^3 + \cdots \\
x \qquad\qquad - \frac{1}{6}x^3 + \cdots \\
\hline
x + x^2 + \frac{1}{2}x^3 + \frac{1}{6}x^4 + \cdots \\
- \frac{1}{6}x^3 - \frac{1}{6}x^4 - \cdots \\
\hline
x + x^2 + \frac{1}{3}x^3 + \cdots
\end{array}$$

Thus

$$e^x \sin x = x + x^2 + \frac{1}{3}x^3 + \cdots$$

(b) Using the Maclaurin series in the table, we have

$$\tan x = \frac{\sin x}{\cos x} = \frac{x - \dfrac{x^3}{3!} + \dfrac{x^5}{5!} - \cdots}{1 - \dfrac{x^2}{2!} + \dfrac{x^4}{4!} - \cdots}$$

We use a procedure like long division:

$$
\begin{array}{r}
x + \frac{1}{3}x^3 + \frac{2}{15}x^5 + \cdots \\
1 - \frac{1}{2}x^2 + \frac{1}{24}x^4 - \cdots \overline{\smash{\big)}\, x - \frac{1}{6}x^3 + \frac{1}{120}x^5 - \cdots} \\
x - \frac{1}{2}x^3 + \frac{1}{24}x^5 - \cdots \\
\hline
\frac{1}{3}x^3 - \frac{1}{30}x^5 + \cdots \\
\frac{1}{3}x^3 - \frac{1}{6}x^5 + \cdots \\
\hline
\frac{2}{15}x^5 + \cdots
\end{array}
$$

Thus $\qquad \tan x = x + \frac{1}{3}x^3 + \frac{2}{15}x^5 + \cdots$

Although we have not attempted to justify the formal manipulations used in Example 10, they are legitimate. There is a theorem which states that if both $f(x) = \Sigma\, c_n x^n$ and $g(x) = \Sigma\, b_n x^n$ converge for $|x| < R$ and the series are multiplied as if they were polynomials, then the resulting series also converges for $|x| < R$ and represents $f(x)g(x)$. For division we require $b_0 \neq 0$; the resulting series converges for sufficiently small $|x|$.

12.10 Exercises

1. If $f(x) = \Sigma_{n=0}^{\infty} b_n(x - 5)^n$ for all x, write a formula for b_8.

2. (a) The graph of f is shown. Explain why the series

$$1.6 - 0.8(x - 1) + 0.4(x - 1)^2 - 0.1(x - 1)^3 + \cdots$$

is *not* the Taylor series of f centered at 1.

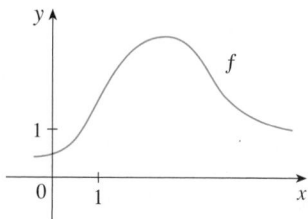

(b) Explain why the series

$$2.8 + 0.5(x - 2) + 1.5(x - 2)^2 - 0.1(x - 2)^3 + \cdots$$

is *not* the Taylor series of f centered at 2.

3–10 |||| Find the Maclaurin series for $f(x)$ using the definition of a Maclaurin series. [Assume that f has a power series expansion. Do not show that $R_n(x) \to 0$.] Also find the associated radius of convergence.

3. $f(x) = \cos x$ **4.** $f(x) = \sin 2x$

5. $f(x) = (1 + x)^{-3}$ **6.** $f(x) = \ln(1 + x)$

7. $f(x) = e^{5x}$ **8.** $f(x) = xe^x$

9. $f(x) = \sinh x$ **10.** $f(x) = \cosh x$

11–18 |||| Find the Taylor series for $f(x)$ centered at the given value of a. [Assume that f has a power series expansion. Do not show that $R_n(x) \to 0$.]

11. $f(x) = 1 + x + x^2$, $a = 2$

12. $f(x) = x^3$, $a = -1$

13. $f(x) = e^x$, $a = 3$

14. $f(x) = \ln x$, $a = 2$

15. $f(x) = \cos x$, $a = \pi$

16. $f(x) = \sin x$, $a = \pi/2$

17. $f(x) = 1/\sqrt{x}$, $a = 9$

18. $f(x) = x^{-2}$, $a = 1$

19. Prove that the series obtained in Exercise 3 represents $\cos x$ for all x.

20. Prove that the series obtained in Exercise 16 represents $\sin x$ for all x.

21. Prove that the series obtained in Exercise 9 represents $\sinh x$ for all x.

22. Prove that the series obtained in Exercise 10 represents $\cosh x$ for all x.

23–32 |||| Use a Maclaurin series derived in this section to obtain the Maclaurin series for the given function.

23. $f(x) = \cos \pi x$ **24.** $f(x) = e^{-x/2}$

25. $f(x) = x \tan^{-1} x$ **26.** $f(x) = \sin(x^4)$

27. $f(x) = x^2 e^{-x}$ **28.** $f(x) = x \cos 2x$

29. $f(x) = \sin^2 x$ [*Hint:* Use $\sin^2 x = \frac{1}{2}(1 - \cos 2x)$.]

30. $f(x) = \cos^2 x$

31. $f(x) = \begin{cases} \dfrac{\sin x}{x} & \text{if } x \neq 0 \\ 1 & \text{if } x = 0 \end{cases}$

32. $f(x) = \begin{cases} \dfrac{x - \sin x}{x^3} & \text{if } x \neq 0 \\ \frac{1}{6} & \text{if } x = 0 \end{cases}$

33–36 ▓ Find the Maclaurin series of f (by any method) and its radius of convergence. Graph f and its first few Taylor polynomials on the same screen. What do you notice about the relationship between these polynomials and f?

33. $f(x) = \sqrt{1 + x}$ **34.** $f(x) = e^{-x^2} + \cos x$

35. $f(x) = \cos(x^2)$ **36.** $f(x) = 2^x$

37. Use the Maclaurin series for e^x to calculate $e^{-0.2}$ correct to five decimal places.

38. Use the Maclaurin series for $\sin x$ to compute $\sin 3°$ correct to five decimal places.

39–42 ▓ Evaluate the indefinite integral as an infinite series.

39. $\displaystyle\int x \cos(x^3)\, dx$ **40.** $\displaystyle\int \frac{\sin x}{x}\, dx$

41. $\displaystyle\int \sqrt{x^3 + 1}\, dx$ **42.** $\displaystyle\int \frac{e^x - 1}{x}\, dx$

43–46 ▓ Use series to approximate the definite integral to within the indicated accuracy.

43. $\displaystyle\int_0^1 x \cos(x^3)\, dx$ (three decimal places)

44. $\displaystyle\int_0^{0.2} [\tan^{-1}(x^3) + \sin(x^3)]\, dx$ (five decimal places)

45. $\displaystyle\int_0^{0.1} \frac{dx}{\sqrt{1 + x^3}}$ ($|\text{error}| < 10^{-8}$)

46. $\displaystyle\int_0^{0.5} x^2 e^{-x^2}\, dx$ ($|\text{error}| < 0.001$)

47–49 ▓ Use series to evaluate the limit.

47. $\displaystyle\lim_{x \to 0} \frac{x - \tan^{-1} x}{x^3}$ **48.** $\displaystyle\lim_{x \to 0} \frac{1 - \cos x}{1 + x - e^x}$

49. $\displaystyle\lim_{x \to 0} \frac{\sin x - x + \frac{1}{6}x^3}{x^5}$

50. Use the series in Example 10(b) to evaluate

$$\lim_{x \to 0} \frac{\tan x - x}{x^3}$$

We found this limit in Example 4 in Section 7.7 using l'Hospital's Rule three times. Which method do you prefer?

51–54 ▓ Use multiplication or division of power series to find the first three nonzero terms in the Maclaurin series for each function.

51. $y = e^{-x^2} \cos x$ **52.** $y = \sec x$

53. $y = \dfrac{x}{\sin x}$ **54.** $y = e^x \ln(1 - x)$

55–60 ▓ Find the sum of the series.

55. $\displaystyle\sum_{n=0}^{\infty} (-1)^n \frac{x^{4n}}{n!}$ **56.** $\displaystyle\sum_{n=0}^{\infty} \frac{(-1)^n \pi^{2n}}{6^{2n}(2n)!}$

57. $\displaystyle\sum_{n=0}^{\infty} \frac{(-1)^n \pi^{2n+1}}{4^{2n+1}(2n+1)!}$ **58.** $\displaystyle\sum_{n=0}^{\infty} \frac{3^n}{5^n n!}$

59. $3 + \dfrac{9}{2!} + \dfrac{27}{3!} + \dfrac{81}{4!} + \cdots$

60. $1 - \ln 2 + \dfrac{(\ln 2)^2}{2!} - \dfrac{(\ln 2)^3}{3!} + \cdots$

61. Prove Taylor's Inequality for $n = 2$, that is, prove that if $|f'''(x)| \leq M$ for $|x - a| \leq d$, then

$$|R_2(x)| \leq \frac{M}{6}|x - a|^3 \qquad \text{for } |x - a| \leq d$$

62. (a) Show that the function defined by

$$f(x) = \begin{cases} e^{-1/x^2} & \text{if } x \neq 0 \\ 0 & \text{if } x = 0 \end{cases}$$

is not equal to its Maclaurin series.

(b) Graph the function in part (a) and comment on its behavior near the origin.

‖ LABORATORY PROJECT

[CAS] **An Elusive Limit**

This project deals with the function

$$f(x) = \frac{\sin(\tan x) - \tan(\sin x)}{\arcsin(\arctan x) - \arctan(\arcsin x)}$$

1. Use your computer algebra system to evaluate $f(x)$ for $x = 1, 0.1, 0.01, 0.001,$ and 0.0001. Does it appear that f has a limit as $x \to 0$?

2. Use the CAS to graph f near $x = 0$. Does it appear that f has a limit as $x \to 0$?

3. Try to evaluate $\lim_{x\to 0} f(x)$ with l'Hospital's Rule, using the CAS to find derivatives of the numerator and denominator. What do you discover? How many applications of l'Hospital's Rule are required?

4. Evaluate $\lim_{x\to 0} f(x)$ by using the CAS to find sufficiently many terms in the Taylor series of the numerator and denominator. (Use the command `taylor` in Maple or `Series` in Mathematica.)

5. Use the limit command on your CAS to find $\lim_{x\to 0} f(x)$ directly. (Most computer algebra systems use the method of Problem 4 to compute limits.)

6. In view of the answers to Problems 4 and 5, how do you explain the results of Problems 1 and 2?

‖ **12.11 The Binomial Series**

You may be acquainted with the Binomial Theorem, which states that if a and b are any real numbers and k is a positive integer, then

$$(a + b)^k = a^k + ka^{k-1}b + \frac{k(k-1)}{2!}a^{k-2}b^2 + \frac{k(k-1)(k-2)}{3!}a^{k-3}b^3$$

$$+ \cdots + \frac{k(k-1)(k-2)\cdots(k-n+1)}{n!}a^{k-n}b^n$$

$$+ \cdots + kab^{k-1} + b^k$$

The traditional notation for the binomial coefficients is

$$\binom{k}{0} = 1 \qquad \binom{k}{n} = \frac{k(k-1)(k-2)\cdots(k-n+1)}{n!} \qquad n = 1, 2, \ldots, k$$

which enables us to write the Binomial Theorem in the abbreviated form

$$(a + b)^k = \sum_{n=0}^{k} \binom{k}{n} a^{k-n}b^n$$

In particular, if we put $a = 1$ and $b = x$, we get

$$\boxed{1} \qquad (1 + x)^k = \sum_{n=0}^{k} \binom{k}{n} x^n$$

One of Newton's accomplishments was to extend the Binomial Theorem (Equation 1) to the case in which k is no longer a positive integer. (See the Writing Project on page 812.) In this case the expression for $(1 + x)^k$ is no longer a finite sum; it becomes an infinite series. To find this series we compute the Maclaurin series of $(1 + x)^k$ in the usual way:

$$f(x) = (1 + x)^k \qquad\qquad\qquad f(0) = 1$$

$$f'(x) = k(1 + x)^{k-1} \qquad\qquad\qquad f'(0) = k$$

$$f''(x) = k(k - 1)(1 + x)^{k-2} \qquad\qquad f''(0) = k(k - 1)$$

$$f'''(x) = k(k - 1)(k - 2)(1 + x)^{k-3} \qquad f'''(0) = k(k - 1)(k - 2)$$

$$\vdots \qquad\qquad\qquad\qquad\qquad\qquad\qquad \vdots$$

$$f^{(n)}(x) = k(k - 1) \cdots (k - n + 1)(1 + x)^{k-n} \qquad f^{(n)}(0) = k(k - 1) \cdots (k - n + 1)$$

Therefore, the Maclaurin series of $f(x) = (1 + x)^k$ is

$$\sum_{n=0}^{\infty} \frac{f^{(n)}(0)}{n!} x^n = \sum_{n=0}^{\infty} \frac{k(k - 1) \cdots (k - n + 1)}{n!} x^n$$

This series is called the **binomial series**. If its nth term is a_n, then

$$\left| \frac{a_{n+1}}{a_n} \right| = \left| \frac{k(k - 1) \cdots (k - n + 1)(k - n)x^{n+1}}{(n + 1)!} \cdot \frac{n!}{k(k - 1) \cdots (k - n + 1)x^n} \right|$$

$$= \frac{|k - n|}{n + 1} |x| = \frac{\left| 1 - \dfrac{k}{n} \right|}{1 + \dfrac{1}{n}} |x| \to |x| \qquad \text{as } n \to \infty$$

Thus, by the Ratio Test, the binomial series converges if $|x| < 1$ and diverges if $|x| > 1$.

The following theorem states that $(1 + x)^k$ is equal to the sum of its Maclaurin series. It is possible to prove this by showing that the remainder term $R_n(x)$ approaches 0, but that turns out to be quite difficult. The proof outlined in Exercise 19 is much easier.

---

2   The Binomial Series   If k is any real number and $|x| < 1$, then

$$(1 + x)^k = 1 + kx + \frac{k(k - 1)}{2!} x^2 + \frac{k(k - 1)(k - 2)}{3!} x^3 + \cdots$$

$$= \sum_{n=0}^{\infty} \binom{k}{n} x^n$$

where $\quad \dbinom{k}{n} = \dfrac{k(k - 1) \cdots (k - n + 1)}{n!} \quad (n \geqslant 1) \quad$ and $\quad \dbinom{k}{0} = 1$

Although the binomial series always converges when $|x| < 1$, the question of whether or not it converges at the endpoints, ± 1, depends on the value of k. It turns out that the series converges at 1 if $-1 < k \leq 0$ and at both endpoints if $k \geq 0$. Notice that if k is a positive integer and $n > k$, then the expression for $\binom{k}{n}$ contains a factor $(k - k)$, so $\binom{k}{n} = 0$ for $n > k$. This means that the series terminates and reduces to the ordinary Binomial Theorem (Equation 1) when k is a positive integer.

As we have seen, the binomial series is just a special case of the Maclaurin series; it occurs so frequently that it is worth remembering.

EXAMPLE 1 Expand $\dfrac{1}{(1 + x)^2}$ as a power series.

SOLUTION We use the binomial series with $k = -2$. The binomial coefficient is

$$\binom{-2}{n} = \frac{(-2)(-3)(-4) \cdots (-2 - n + 1)}{n!}$$

$$= \frac{(-1)^n 2 \cdot 3 \cdot 4 \cdot \cdots \cdot n(n + 1)}{n!} = (-1)^n (n + 1)$$

and so, when $|x| < 1$,

$$\frac{1}{(1 + x)^2} = (1 + x)^{-2} = \sum_{n=0}^{\infty} \binom{-2}{n} x^n$$

$$= \sum_{n=0}^{\infty} (-1)^n (n + 1) x^n = 1 - 2x + 3x^2 - 4x^3 + \cdots$$

EXAMPLE 2 Find the Maclaurin series for the function $f(x) = \dfrac{1}{\sqrt{4 - x}}$ and its radius of convergence.

SOLUTION As given, $f(x)$ is not quite of the form $(1 + x)^k$ so we rewrite it as follows:

$$\frac{1}{\sqrt{4 - x}} = \frac{1}{\sqrt{4\left(1 - \dfrac{x}{4}\right)}} = \frac{1}{2\sqrt{1 - \dfrac{x}{4}}} = \frac{1}{2}\left(1 - \frac{x}{4}\right)^{-1/2}$$

Using the binomial series with $k = -\frac{1}{2}$ and with x replaced by $-x/4$, we have

$$\frac{1}{\sqrt{4 - x}} = \frac{1}{2}\left(1 - \frac{x}{4}\right)^{-1/2} = \frac{1}{2}\sum_{n=0}^{\infty} \binom{-\frac{1}{2}}{n}\left(-\frac{x}{4}\right)^n$$

$$= \frac{1}{2}\left[1 + \left(-\frac{1}{2}\right)\left(-\frac{x}{4}\right) + \frac{\left(-\frac{1}{2}\right)\left(-\frac{3}{2}\right)}{2!}\left(-\frac{x}{4}\right)^2 + \frac{\left(-\frac{1}{2}\right)\left(-\frac{3}{2}\right)\left(-\frac{5}{2}\right)}{3!}\left(-\frac{x}{4}\right)^3 \right.$$

$$\left. + \cdots + \frac{\left(-\frac{1}{2}\right)\left(-\frac{3}{2}\right)\left(-\frac{5}{2}\right) \cdots \left(-\frac{1}{2} - n + 1\right)}{n!}\left(-\frac{x}{4}\right)^n + \cdots \right]$$

$$= \frac{1}{2}\left[1 + \frac{1}{8}x + \frac{1 \cdot 3}{2!8^2}x^2 + \frac{1 \cdot 3 \cdot 5}{3!8^3}x^3 + \cdots + \frac{1 \cdot 3 \cdot 5 \cdot \cdots \cdot (2n - 1)}{n!8^n}x^n + \cdots \right]$$

We know from (2) that this series converges when $|-x/4| < 1$, that is, $|x| < 4$, so the radius of convergence is $R = 4$.

▐▐ A binomial series is a special case of a Taylor series. Figure 1 shows the graphs of the first three Taylor polynomials computed from the answer to Example 2.

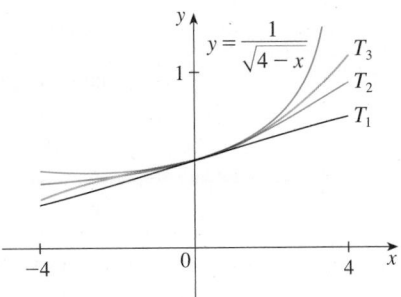

FIGURE 1

12.11 Exercises

1–8 ▓ Use the binomial series to expand the function as a power series. State the radius of convergence.

1. $\sqrt{1 + x}$

2. $\dfrac{1}{(1 + x)^4}$

3. $\dfrac{1}{(2 + x)^3}$

4. $(1 - x)^{2/3}$

5. $\sqrt[4]{1 - 8x}$

6. $\dfrac{1}{\sqrt[5]{32 - x}}$

7. $\dfrac{x}{\sqrt{4 + x^2}}$

8. $\dfrac{x^2}{\sqrt{2 + x}}$

□   □   □   □   □   □   □   □   □   ◻

9–10 ▓ Use the binomial series to expand the function as a Maclaurin series and to find the first three Taylor polynomials T_1, T_2, and T_3. Graph the function and these Taylor polynomials in the interval of convergence.

9. $(1 + 2x)^{3/4}$

10. $\sqrt[3]{1 + 4x}$

□   □   □   □   □   □   □   □   □   □   □   □

11. (a) Use the binomial series to expand $1/\sqrt{1 - x^2}$.
(b) Use part (a) to find the Maclaurin series for $\sin^{-1}x$.

12. (a) Use the binomial series to expand $1/\sqrt{1 + x^2}$.
(b) Use part (a) to find the Maclaurin series for $\sinh^{-1}x$.

13. (a) Expand $\sqrt[3]{1 + x}$ as a power series.
(b) Use part (a) to estimate $\sqrt[3]{1.01}$ correct to four decimal places.

14. (a) Expand $1/\sqrt[4]{1 + x}$ as a power series.
(b) Use part (a) to estimate $1/\sqrt[4]{1.1}$ correct to three decimal places.

15. (a) Expand $f(x) = x/(1 - x)^2$ as a power series.
(b) Use part (a) to find the sum of the series
$$\sum_{n=1}^{\infty} \frac{n}{2^n}$$

16. (a) Expand $f(x) = (x + x^2)/(1 - x)^3$ as a power series.
(b) Use part (a) to find the sum of the series
$$\sum_{n=1}^{\infty} \frac{n^2}{2^n}$$

17. (a) Use the binomial series to find the Maclaurin series of $f(x) = \sqrt{1 + x^2}$.
(b) Use part (a) to evaluate $f^{(10)}(0)$.

18. (a) Use the binomial series to find the Maclaurin series of $f(x) = 1/\sqrt{1 + x^3}$.
(b) Use part (a) to evaluate $f^{(9)}(0)$.

19. Use the following steps to prove (2).
(a) Let $g(x) = \sum_{n=0}^{\infty} \binom{k}{n}x^n$. Differentiate this series to show that
$$g'(x) = \frac{kg(x)}{1 + x} \qquad -1 < x < 1$$
(b) Let $h(x) = (1 + x)^{-k}g(x)$ and show that $h'(x) = 0$.
(c) Deduce that $g(x) = (1 + x)^k$.

20. In Exercise 53 in Section 11.2 it was shown that the length of the ellipse $x = a \sin \theta$, $y = b \cos \theta$, where $a > b > 0$, is
$$L = 4a \int_0^{\pi/2} \sqrt{1 - e^2 \sin^2 \theta} \; d\theta$$
where $e = \sqrt{a^2 - b^2}/a$ is the eccentricity of the ellipse. Expand the integrand as a binomial series and use the result of Exercise 44 in Section 8.1 to express L as a series in powers of the eccentricity up to the term in e^6.

|||| WRITING PROJECT

How Newton Discovered the Binomial Series

The Binomial Theorem, which gives the expansion of $(a + b)^k$, was known to Chinese mathematicians many centuries before the time of Newton for the case where the exponent k is a positive integer. In 1665, when he was 22, Newton was the first to discover the infinite series expansion of $(a + b)^k$ when k is a fractional exponent (positive or negative). He didn't publish his discovery, but he stated it and gave examples of how to use it in a letter (now called the *epistola prior*) dated June 13, 1676, that he sent to Henry Oldenburg, secretary of the Royal Society of London, to transmit to Leibniz. When Leibniz replied, he asked how Newton had discovered the binomial series. Newton wrote a second letter, the *epistola posterior* of October 24, 1676, in which he explained in great detail how he arrived at his discovery by a very indirect route. He was investigating the areas under the curves $y = (1 - x^2)^{n/2}$ from 0 to x for $n = 0, 1, 2, 3, 4, \ldots$. These are easy to calculate if n is even. By observing patterns and interpolating, Newton was able to guess the answers for odd values of n. Then he realized he could get the same answers by expressing $(1 - x^2)^{n/2}$ as an infinite series.

Write a report on Newton's discovery of the binomial series. Start by giving the statement of the binomial series in Newton's notation (see the *epistola prior* on page 285 of [4] or page 402 of [2]). Explain why Newton's version is equivalent to Theorem 2 on page 809. Then read Newton's *epistola posterior* (page 287 in [4] or page 404 in [2]) and explain the patterns that Newton discovered in the areas under the curves $y = (1 - x^2)^{n/2}$. Show how he was able to guess the areas under the remaining curves and how he verified his answers. Finally, explain how these discoveries led to the binomial series. The books by Edwards [1] and Katz [3] contain commentaries on Newton's letters.

1. C. H. Edwards, *The Historical Development of the Calculus* (New York: Springer-Verlag, 1979), pp. 178–187.

2. John Fauvel and Jeremy Gray, eds., *The History of Mathematics: A Reader* (London: MacMillan Press, 1987).

3. Victor Katz, *A History of Mathematics: An Introduction* (New York: HarperCollins, 1993), pp. 463–466.

4. D. J. Struik, ed., *A Sourcebook in Mathematics, 1200–1800* (Princeton, N.J.: Princeton University Press, 1969).

|||| 12.12 Applications of Taylor Polynomials

In this section we explore two types of applications of Taylor polynomials. First we look at how they are used to approximate functions—computer scientists like them because polynomials are the simplest of functions. Then we investigate how physicists and engineers use them in such fields as relativity, optics, blackbody radiation, electric dipoles, the velocity of water waves, and building highways across a desert.

|||| Approximating Functions by Polynomials

Suppose that $f(x)$ is equal to the sum of its Taylor series at a:

$$f(x) = \sum_{n=0}^{\infty} \frac{f^{(n)}(a)}{n!} (x - a)^n$$

In Section 12.10 we introduced the notation $T_n(x)$ for the nth partial sum of this series and called it the nth-degree Taylor polynomial of f at a. Thus

$$T_n(x) = \sum_{i=0}^{n} \frac{f^{(i)}(a)}{i!} (x - a)^i$$

$$= f(a) + \frac{f'(a)}{1!} (x - a) + \frac{f''(a)}{2!} (x - a)^2 + \cdots + \frac{f^{(n)}(a)}{n!} (x - a)^n$$

Since f is the sum of its Taylor series, we know that $T_n(x) \to f(x)$ as $n \to \infty$ and so T_n can be used as an approximation to f: $f(x) \approx T_n(x)$.

Notice that the first-degree Taylor polynomial

$$T_1(x) = f(a) + f'(a)(x - a)$$

is the same as the linearization of f at a that we discussed in Section 3.10. Notice also that T_1 and its derivative have the same values at a that f and f' have. In general, it can be shown that the derivatives of T_n at a agree with those of f up to and including derivatives of order n (see Exercise 36).

To illustrate these ideas let's take another look at the graphs of $y = e^x$ and its first few Taylor polynomials, as shown in Figure 1. The graph of T_1 is the tangent line to $y = e^x$ at $(0, 1)$; this tangent line is the best linear approximation to e^x near $(0, 1)$. The graph of T_2 is the parabola $y = 1 + x + x^2/2$, and the graph of T_3 is the cubic curve $y = 1 + x + x^2/2 + x^3/6$, which is a closer fit to the exponential curve $y = e^x$ than T_2. The next Taylor polynomial T_4 would be an even better approximation, and so on.

The values in the table give a numerical demonstration of the convergence of the Taylor polynomials $T_n(x)$ to the function $y = e^x$. We see that when $x = 0.2$ the convergence is very rapid, but when $x = 3$ it is somewhat slower. In fact, the farther x is from 0, the more slowly $T_n(x)$ converges to e^x.

When using a Taylor polynomial T_n to approximate a function f, we have to ask the questions: How good an approximation is it? How large should we take n to be in order to achieve a desired accuracy? To answer these questions we need to look at the absolute value of the remainder:

$$|R_n(x)| = |f(x) - T_n(x)|$$

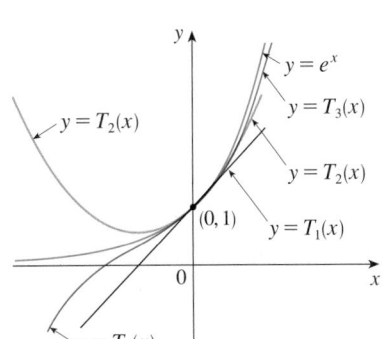

FIGURE 1

	$x = 0.2$	$x = 3.0$
$T_2(x)$	1.220000	8.500000
$T_4(x)$	1.221400	16.375000
$T_6(x)$	1.221403	19.412500
$T_8(x)$	1.221403	20.009152
$T_{10}(x)$	1.221403	20.079665
e^x	1.221403	20.085537

There are three possible methods for estimating the size of the error:

1. If a graphing device is available, we can use it to graph $|R_n(x)|$ and thereby estimate the error.

2. If the series happens to be an alternating series, we can use the Alternating Series Estimation Theorem.

3. In all cases we can use Taylor's Inequality (Theorem 12.10.9), which says that if $|f^{(n+1)}(x)| \leq M$, then

$$|R_n(x)| \leq \frac{M}{(n + 1)!} |x - a|^{n+1}$$

EXAMPLE 1
(a) Approximate the function $f(x) = \sqrt[3]{x}$ by a Taylor polynomial of degree 2 at $a = 8$.
(b) How accurate is this approximation when $7 \leq x \leq 9$?

SOLUTION

(a)
$$f(x) = \sqrt[3]{x} = x^{1/3} \qquad f(8) = 2$$
$$f'(x) = \tfrac{1}{3}x^{-2/3} \qquad f'(8) = \tfrac{1}{12}$$
$$f''(x) = -\tfrac{2}{9}x^{-5/3} \qquad f''(8) = -\tfrac{1}{144}$$
$$f'''(x) = \tfrac{10}{27}x^{-8/3}$$

Thus, the second-degree Taylor polynomial is

$$T_2(x) = f(8) + \frac{f'(8)}{1!}(x - 8) + \frac{f''(8)}{2!}(x - 8)^2$$
$$= 2 + \tfrac{1}{12}(x - 8) - \tfrac{1}{288}(x - 8)^2$$

The desired approximation is

$$\sqrt[3]{x} \approx T_2(x) = 2 + \tfrac{1}{12}(x - 8) - \tfrac{1}{288}(x - 8)^2$$

(b) The Taylor series is not alternating when $x < 8$, so we can't use the Alternating Series Estimation Theorem in this example. But we can use Taylor's Inequality with $n = 2$ and $a = 8$:

$$|R_2(x)| \le \frac{M}{3!}|x - 8|^3$$

where $|f'''(x)| \le M$. Because $x \ge 7$, we have $x^{8/3} \ge 7^{8/3}$ and so

$$f'''(x) = \frac{10}{27} \cdot \frac{1}{x^{8/3}} \le \frac{10}{27} \cdot \frac{1}{7^{8/3}} < 0.0021$$

Therefore, we can take $M = 0.0021$. Also $7 \le x \le 9$, so $-1 \le x - 8 \le 1$ and $|x - 8| \le 1$. Then Taylor's Inequality gives

$$|R_2(x)| \le \frac{0.0021}{3!} \cdot 1^3 = \frac{0.0021}{6} < 0.0004$$

Thus, if $7 \le x \le 9$, the approximation in part (a) is accurate to within 0.0004. ▬

Let's use a graphing device to check the calculation in Example 1. Figure 2 shows that the graphs of $y = \sqrt[3]{x}$ and $y = T_2(x)$ are very close to each other when x is near 8. Figure 3 shows the graph of $|R_2(x)|$ computed from the expression

$$|R_2(x)| = |\sqrt[3]{x} - T_2(x)|$$

We see from the graph that

$$|R_2(x)| < 0.0003$$

when $7 \le x \le 9$. Thus, the error estimate from graphical methods is slightly better than the error estimate from Taylor's Inequality in this case.

FIGURE 2

FIGURE 3

EXAMPLE 2

(a) What is the maximum error possible in using the approximation

$$\sin x \approx x - \frac{x^3}{3!} + \frac{x^5}{5!}$$

when $-0.3 \leqslant x \leqslant 0.3$? Use this approximation to find $\sin 12°$ correct to six decimal places.

(b) For what values of x is this approximation accurate to within 0.00005?

SOLUTION

(a) Notice that the Maclaurin series

$$\sin x = x - \frac{x^3}{3!} + \frac{x^5}{5!} - \frac{x^7}{7!} + \cdots$$

is alternating for all nonzero values of x, and the successive terms decrease in size because $|x| < 1$, so we can use the Alternating Series Estimation Theorem. The error in approximating $\sin x$ by the first three terms of its Maclaurin series is at most

$$\left| \frac{x^7}{7!} \right| = \frac{|x|^7}{5040}$$

If $-0.3 \leqslant x \leqslant 0.3$, then $|x| \leqslant 0.3$, so the error is smaller than

$$\frac{(0.3)^7}{5040} \approx 4.3 \times 10^{-8}$$

To find $\sin 12°$ we first convert to radian measure.

$$\sin 12° = \sin\left(\frac{12\pi}{180}\right) = \sin\left(\frac{\pi}{15}\right)$$

$$\approx \frac{\pi}{15} - \left(\frac{\pi}{15}\right)^3 \frac{1}{3!} + \left(\frac{\pi}{15}\right)^5 \frac{1}{5!}$$

$$\approx 0.20791169$$

Thus, correct to six decimal places, $\sin 12° \approx 0.207912$.

(b) The error will be smaller than 0.00005 if

$$\frac{|x|^7}{5040} < 0.00005$$

Solving this inequality for x, we get

$$|x|^7 < 0.252 \qquad \text{or} \qquad |x| < (0.252)^{1/7} \approx 0.821$$

So the given approximation is accurate to within 0.00005 when $|x| < 0.82$. ▬

Module 12.10/12.12 graphically shows the remainders in Taylor polynomial approximations.

What if we use Taylor's Inequality to solve Example 2? Since $f^{(7)}(x) = -\cos x$, we have $|f^{(7)}(x)| \leqslant 1$ and so

$$|R_6(x)| \leqslant \frac{1}{7!} |x|^7$$

So we get the same estimates as with the Alternating Series Estimation Theorem.

FIGURE 4

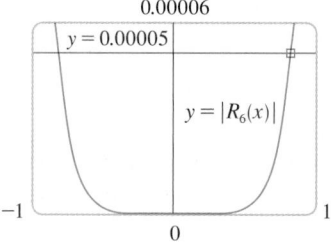

FIGURE 5

What about graphical methods? Figure 4 shows the graph of

$$|R_6(x)| = |\sin x - (x - \tfrac{1}{6}x^3 + \tfrac{1}{120}x^5)|$$

and we see from it that $|R_6(x)| < 4.3 \times 10^{-8}$ when $|x| \leqslant 0.3$. This is the same estimate that we obtained in Example 2. For part (b) we want $|R_6(x)| < 0.00005$, so we graph both $y = |R_6(x)|$ and $y = 0.00005$ in Figure 5. By placing the cursor on the right intersection point we find that the inequality is satisfied when $|x| < 0.82$. Again this is the same estimate that we obtained in the solution to Example 2.

If we had been asked to approximate $\sin 72°$ instead of $\sin 12°$ in Example 2, it would have been wise to use the Taylor polynomials at $a = \pi/3$ (instead of $a = 0$) because they are better approximations to $\sin x$ for values of x close to $\pi/3$. Notice that $72°$ is close to $60°$ (or $\pi/3$ radians) and the derivatives of $\sin x$ are easy to compute at $\pi/3$.

Figure 6 shows the graphs of the Maclaurin polynomial approximations

$$T_1(x) = x \qquad\qquad T_3(x) = x - \frac{x^3}{3!}$$

$$T_5(x) = x - \frac{x^3}{3!} + \frac{x^5}{5!} \qquad T_7(x) = x - \frac{x^3}{3!} + \frac{x^5}{5!} - \frac{x^7}{7!}$$

to the sine curve. You can see that as n increases, $T_n(x)$ is a good approximation to $\sin x$ on a larger and larger interval.

FIGURE 6

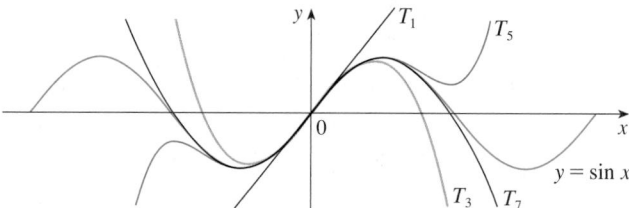

One use of the type of calculation done in Examples 1 and 2 occurs in calculators and computers. For instance, when you press the sin or e^x key on your calculator, or when a computer programmer uses a subroutine for a trigonometric or exponential or Bessel function, in many machines a polynomial approximation is calculated. The polynomial is often a Taylor polynomial that has been modified so that the error is spread more evenly throughout an interval.

▓ Applications to Physics

Taylor polynomials are also used frequently in physics. In order to gain insight into an equation, a physicist often simplifies a function by considering only the first two or three terms in its Taylor series. In other words, the physicist uses a Taylor polynomial as an approximation to the function. Taylor's Inequality can then be used to gauge the accuracy of the approximation. The following example shows one way in which this idea is used in special relativity.

EXAMPLE 3 In Einstein's theory of special relativity the mass of an object moving with velocity v is

$$m = \frac{m_0}{\sqrt{1 - v^2/c^2}}$$

where m_0 is the mass of the object when at rest and c is the speed of light. The kinetic energy of the object is the difference between its total energy and its energy at rest:

$$K = mc^2 - m_0c^2$$

(a) Show that when v is very small compared with c, this expression for K agrees with classical Newtonian physics: $K = \frac{1}{2}m_0v^2$.

(b) Use Taylor's Inequality to estimate the difference in these expressions for K when $|v| \leq 100$ m/s.

SOLUTION

(a) Using the expressions given for K and m, we get

$$K = mc^2 - m_0c^2 = \frac{m_0c^2}{\sqrt{1 - v^2/c^2}} - m_0c^2$$

$$= m_0c^2\left[\left(1 - \frac{v^2}{c^2}\right)^{-1/2} - 1\right]$$

|||| The upper curve in Figure 7 is the graph of the expression for the kinetic energy K of an object with velocity v in special relativity. The lower curve shows the function used for K in classical Newtonian physics. When v is much smaller than the speed of light, the curves are practically identical.

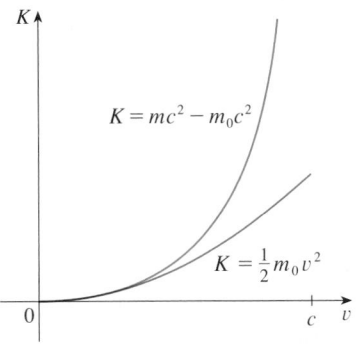

FIGURE 7

With $x = -v^2/c^2$, the Maclaurin series for $(1 + x)^{-1/2}$ is most easily computed as a binomial series with $k = -\frac{1}{2}$. (Notice that $|x| < 1$ because $v < c$.) Therefore, we have

$$(1 + x)^{-1/2} = 1 - \frac{1}{2}x + \frac{\left(-\frac{1}{2}\right)\left(-\frac{3}{2}\right)}{2!}x^2 + \frac{\left(-\frac{1}{2}\right)\left(-\frac{3}{2}\right)\left(-\frac{5}{2}\right)}{3!}x^3 + \cdots$$

$$= 1 - \frac{1}{2}x + \frac{3}{8}x^2 - \frac{5}{16}x^3 + \cdots$$

and

$$K = m_0c^2\left[\left(1 + \frac{1}{2}\frac{v^2}{c^2} + \frac{3}{8}\frac{v^4}{c^4} + \frac{5}{16}\frac{v^6}{c^6} + \cdots\right) - 1\right]$$

$$= m_0c^2\left(\frac{1}{2}\frac{v^2}{c^2} + \frac{3}{8}\frac{v^4}{c^4} + \frac{5}{16}\frac{v^6}{c^6} + \cdots\right)$$

If v is much smaller than c, then all terms after the first are very small when compared with the first term. If we omit them, we get

$$K \approx m_0c^2\left(\frac{1}{2}\frac{v^2}{c^2}\right) = \frac{1}{2}m_0v^2$$

(b) If $x = -v^2/c^2$, $f(x) = m_0c^2[(1 + x)^{-1/2} - 1]$, and M is a number such that $|f''(x)| \leq M$, then we can use Taylor's Inequality to write

$$|R_1(x)| \leq \frac{M}{2!}x^2$$

We have $f''(x) = \frac{3}{4}m_0c^2(1 + x)^{-5/2}$ and we are given that $|v| \leq 100$ m/s, so

$$|f''(x)| = \frac{3m_0c^2}{4(1 - v^2/c^2)^{5/2}} \leq \frac{3m_0c^2}{4(1 - 100^2/c^2)^{5/2}} \quad (= M)$$

Thus, with $c = 3 \times 10^8$ m/s,

$$|R_1(x)| \leq \frac{1}{2} \cdot \frac{3m_0c^2}{4(1 - 100^2/c^2)^{5/2}} \cdot \frac{100^4}{c^4} < (4.17 \times 10^{-10})m_0$$

So when $|v| \leq 100$ m/s, the magnitude of the error in using the Newtonian expression for kinetic energy is at most $(4.2 \times 10^{-10})m_0$.

Another application to physics occurs in optics. Figure 8 is adapted from *Optics,* 4th ed., by Eugene Hecht (San Francisco: Addison-Wesley, 2002), page 153. It depicts a wave from the point source S meeting a spherical interface of radius R centered at C. The ray SA is refracted toward P.

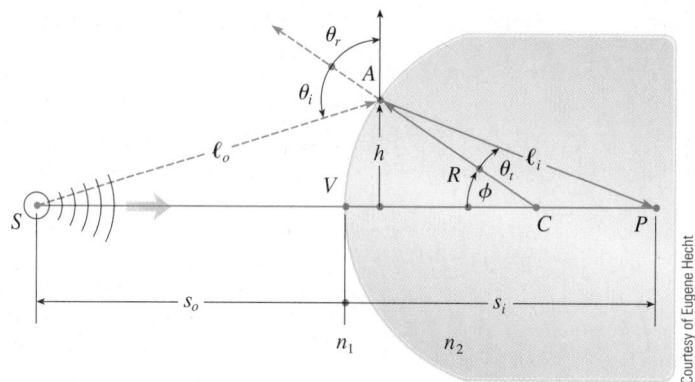

FIGURE 8

Refraction at a spherical interface

Using Fermat's principle that light travels so as to minimize the time taken, Hecht derives the equation

$$\boxed{1} \qquad \frac{n_1}{\ell_o} + \frac{n_2}{\ell_i} = \frac{1}{R}\left(\frac{n_2 s_i}{\ell_i} - \frac{n_1 s_o}{\ell_o}\right)$$

where n_1 and n_2 are indexes of refraction and ℓ_o, ℓ_i, s_o, and s_i are the distances indicated in Figure 8. By the Law of Cosines, applied to triangles ACS and ACP, we have

▏▎ Here we use the identity

$$\cos(\pi - \phi) = -\cos\phi$$

$$\boxed{2} \qquad \ell_o = \sqrt{R^2 + (s_o + R)^2 - 2R(s_o + R)\cos\phi}$$

$$\ell_i = \sqrt{R^2 + (s_i - R)^2 + 2R(s_i - R)\cos\phi}$$

Because Equation 1 is cumbersome to work with, Gauss, in 1841, simplified it by using the linear approximation $\cos\phi \approx 1$ for small values of ϕ. (This amounts to using the Taylor polynomial of degree 1.) Then Equation 1 becomes the following simpler equation [as you are asked to show in Exercise 32(a)]:

$$\boxed{3} \qquad \frac{n_1}{s_o} + \frac{n_2}{s_i} = \frac{n_2 - n_1}{R}$$

The resulting optical theory is known as *Gaussian optics,* or *first-order optics,* and has become the basic theoretical tool used to design lenses.

A more accurate theory is obtained by approximating $\cos\phi$ by its Taylor polynomial of degree 3 (which is the same as the Taylor polynomial of degree 2). This takes into account rays for which ϕ is not so small, that is, rays that strike the surface at greater distances h above the axis. In Exercise 32(b) you are asked to use this approximation to derive the more accurate equation

$$\boxed{4} \qquad \frac{n_1}{s_o} + \frac{n_2}{s_i} = \frac{n_2 - n_1}{R} + h^2\left[\frac{n_1}{2s_o}\left(\frac{1}{s_o} + \frac{1}{R}\right)^2 + \frac{n_2}{2s_i}\left(\frac{1}{R} - \frac{1}{s_i}\right)^2\right]$$

The resulting optical theory is known as *third-order optics.*

Other applications of Taylor polynomials to physics and engineering are explored in Exercises 30, 31, 33, 34, and 35 and in the Applied Project on page 821.

‖ **12.12** Exercises

1. (a) Find the Taylor polynomials up to degree 6 for
$f(x) = \cos x$ centered at $a = 0$. Graph f and these polynomials on a common screen.
(b) Evaluate f and these polynomials at $x = \pi/4$, $\pi/2$, and π.
(c) Comment on how the Taylor polynomials converge to $f(x)$.

2. (a) Find the Taylor polynomials up to degree 3 for $f(x) = 1/x$
centered at $a = 1$. Graph f and these polynomials on a
common screen.
(b) Evaluate f and these polynomials at $x = 0.9$ and 1.3.
(c) Comment on how the Taylor polynomials converge to $f(x)$.

3–10 ‖‖ Find the Taylor polynomial $T_n(x)$ for the function f at the
number a. Graph f and T_n on the same screen.

3. $f(x) = \ln x$, $a = 1$, $n = 4$

4. $f(x) = e^x$, $a = 2$, $n = 3$

5. $f(x) = \sin x$, $a = \pi/6$, $n = 3$

6. $f(x) = \cos x$, $a = 2\pi/3$, $n = 4$

7. $f(x) = \arcsin x$, $a = 0$, $n = 3$

8. $f(x) = \dfrac{\ln x}{x}$, $a = 1$, $n = 3$

9. $f(x) = xe^{-2x}$, $a = 0$, $n = 3$

10. $f(x) = \sqrt{3 + x^2}$, $a = 1$, $n = 2$

CAS **11–12** ‖‖ Use a computer algebra system to find the Taylor polynomials T_n at $a = 0$ for the given values of n. Then graph these
polynomials and f on the same screen.

11. $f(x) = \sec x$, $n = 2, 4, 6, 8$

12. $f(x) = \tan x$, $n = 1, 3, 5, 7, 9$

13–22 ‖‖‖
(a) Approximate f by a Taylor polynomial with degree n at the
number a.
(b) Use Taylor's Inequality to estimate the accuracy of the approximation $f(x) \approx T_n(x)$ when x lies in the given interval.
(c) Check your result in part (b) by graphing $|R_n(x)|$.

13. $f(x) = \sqrt{x}$, $a = 4$, $n = 2$, $4 \le x \le 4.2$

14. $f(x) = x^{-2}$, $a = 1$, $n = 2$, $0.9 \le x \le 1.1$

15. $f(x) = x^{2/3}$, $a = 1$, $n = 3$, $0.8 \le x \le 1.2$

16. $f(x) = \cos x$, $a = \pi/3$, $n = 4$, $0 \le x \le 2\pi/3$

17. $f(x) = \tan x$, $a = 0$, $n = 3$, $0 \le x \le \pi/6$

18. $f(x) = \ln(1 + 2x)$, $a = 1$, $n = 3$, $0.5 \le x \le 1.5$

19. $f(x) = e^{x^2}$, $a = 0$, $n = 3$, $0 \le x \le 0.1$

20. $f(x) = x \ln x$, $a = 1$, $n = 3$, $0.5 \le x \le 1.5$

21. $f(x) = x \sin x$, $a = 0$, $n = 4$, $-1 \le x \le 1$

22. $f(x) = \sinh 2x$, $a = 0$, $n = 5$, $-1 \le x \le 1$

23. Use the information from Exercise 5 to estimate $\sin 35°$
correct to five decimal places.

24. Use the information from Exercise 16 to estimate $\cos 69°$
correct to five decimal places.

25. Use Taylor's Inequality to determine the number of terms of
the Maclaurin series for e^x that should be used to estimate $e^{0.1}$
to within 0.00001.

26. How many terms of the Maclaurin series for $\ln(1 + x)$ do you
need to use to estimate $\ln 1.4$ to within 0.001?

27–28 ‖‖ Use the Alternating Series Estimation Theorem or
Taylor's Inequality to estimate the range of values of x for which
the given approximation is accurate to within the stated error.
Check your answer graphically.

27. $\sin x \approx x - \dfrac{x^3}{6}$ $\quad (|\,\text{error}\,| < 0.01)$

28. $\cos x \approx 1 - \dfrac{x^2}{2} + \dfrac{x^4}{24}$ $\quad (|\,\text{error}\,| < 0.005)$

29. A car is moving with speed 20 m/s and acceleration 2 m/s²
at a given instant. Using a second-degree Taylor polynomial,
estimate how far the car moves in the next second. Would it
be reasonable to use this polynomial to estimate the distance
traveled during the next minute?

30. The resistivity ρ of a conducting wire is the reciprocal of the
conductivity and is measured in units of ohm-meters (Ω-m).
The resistivity of a given metal depends on the temperature
according to the equation

$$\rho(t) = \rho_{20} e^{\alpha(t-20)}$$

where t is the temperature in °C. There are tables that list the
values of α (called the temperature coefficient) and ρ_{20} (the
resistivity at 20°C) for various metals. Except at very low temperatures, the resistivity varies almost linearly with temperature
and so it is common to approximate the expression for $\rho(t)$ by
its first- or second-degree Taylor polynomial at $t = 20$.
(a) Find expressions for these linear and quadratic
approximations.
(b) For copper, the tables give $\alpha = 0.0039/°C$ and
$\rho_{20} = 1.7 \times 10^{-8}$ Ω-m. Graph the resistivity of copper
and the linear and quadratic approximations for
$-250°C \le t \le 1000°C$.

(c) For what values of t does the linear approximation agree with the exponential expression to within one percent?

31. An electric dipole consists of two electric charges of equal magnitude and opposite signs. If the charges are q and $-q$ and are located at a distance d from each other, then the electric field E at the point P in the figure is

$$E = \frac{q}{D^2} - \frac{q}{(D + d)^2}$$

By expanding this expression for E as a series in powers of d/D, show that E is approximately proportional to $1/D^3$ when P is far away from the dipole.

32. (a) Derive Equation 3 for Gaussian optics from Equation 1 by approximating $\cos \phi$ in Equation 2 by its first-degree Taylor polynomial.
(b) Show that if $\cos \phi$ is replaced by its third-degree Taylor polynomial in Equation 2, then Equation 1 becomes Equation 4 for third-order optics. [*Hint:* Use the first two terms in the binomial series for ℓ_o^{-1} and ℓ_i^{-1}. Also, use $\phi \approx \sin \phi$.]

33. If a water wave with length L moves with velocity v across a body of water with depth d, as in the figure, then

$$v^2 = \frac{gL}{2\pi} \tanh \frac{2\pi d}{L}$$

(a) If the water is deep, show that $v \approx \sqrt{gL/(2\pi)}$.
(b) If the water is shallow, use the Maclaurin series for tanh to show that $v \approx \sqrt{gd}$. (Thus, in shallow water the velocity of a wave tends to be independent of the length of the wave.)
(c) Use the Alternating Series Estimation Theorem to show that if $L > 10d$, then the estimate $v^2 \approx gd$ is accurate to within $0.014gL$.

34. The period of a pendulum with length L that makes a maximum angle θ_0 with the vertical is

$$T = 4\sqrt{\frac{L}{g}} \int_0^{\pi/2} \frac{dx}{\sqrt{1 - k^2 \sin^2 x}}$$

where $k = \sin\left(\frac{1}{2}\theta_0\right)$ and g is the acceleration due to gravity. (In Exercise 40 in Section 8.7 we approximated this integral using Simpson's Rule.)
(a) Expand the integrand as a binomial series and use the result of Exercise 44 in Section 8.1 to show that

$$T = 2\pi\sqrt{\frac{L}{g}}\left[1 + \frac{1^2}{2^2}k^2 + \frac{1^2 3^2}{2^2 4^2}k^4 + \frac{1^2 3^2 5^2}{2^2 4^2 6^2}k^6 + \cdots\right]$$

If θ_0 is not too large, the approximation $T \approx 2\pi\sqrt{L/g}$, obtained by using only the first term in the series, is often used. A better approximation is obtained by using two terms:

$$T \approx 2\pi\sqrt{\frac{L}{g}}\left(1 + \tfrac{1}{4}k^2\right)$$

(b) Notice that all the terms in the series after the first one have coefficients that are at most $\frac{1}{4}$. Use this fact to compare this series with a geometric series and show that

$$2\pi\sqrt{\frac{L}{g}}\left(1 + \tfrac{1}{4}k^2\right) \leq T \leq 2\pi\sqrt{\frac{L}{g}}\frac{4 - 3k^2}{4 - 4k^2}$$

(c) Use the inequalities in part (b) to estimate the period of a pendulum with $L = 1$ meter and $\theta_0 = 10°$. How does it compare with the estimate $T \approx 2\pi\sqrt{L/g}$? What if $\theta_0 = 42°$?

35. If a surveyor measures differences in elevation when making plans for a highway across a desert, corrections must be made for the curvature of the Earth.
(a) If R is the radius of the Earth and L is the length of the highway, show that the correction is

$$C = R \sec(L/R) - R$$

(b) Use a Taylor polynomial to show that

$$C \approx \frac{L^2}{2R} + \frac{5L^4}{24R^3}$$

(c) Compare the corrections given by the formulas in parts (a) and (b) for a highway that is 100 km long. (Take the radius of Earth to be 6370 km.)

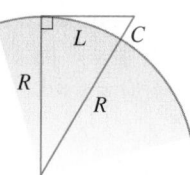

36. Show that T_n and f have the same derivatives at a up to order n.

37. In Section 4.9 we considered Newton's method for approximating a root r of the equation $f(x) = 0$, and from an initial approximation x_1 we obtained successive approximations $x_2, x_3, \ldots$, where

$$x_{n+1} = x_n - \frac{f(x_n)}{f'(x_n)}$$

Use Taylor's Inequality with $n = 1$, $a = x_n$, and $x = r$ to show that if $f''(x)$ exists on an interval I containing r, x_n, and x_{n+1}, and $|f''(x)| \leq M$, $|f'(x)| \geq K$ for all $x \in I$, then

$$|x_{n+1} - r| \leq \frac{M}{2K}|x_n - r|^2$$

[This means that if x_n is accurate to d decimal places, then x_{n+1} is accurate to about $2d$ decimal places. More precisely, if the error at stage n is at most 10^{-m}, then the error at stage $n + 1$ is at most $(M/2K)10^{-2m}$.]

Radiation from the Stars

Any object emits radiation when heated. A *blackbody* is a system that absorbs all the radiation that falls on it. For instance, a matte black surface or a large cavity with a small hole in its wall (like a blastfurnace) is a blackbody and emits blackbody radiation. Even the radiation from the Sun is close to being blackbody radiation.

Proposed in the late 19th century, the Rayleigh-Jeans Law expresses the energy density of blackbody radiation of wavelength λ as

$$f(\lambda) = \frac{8\pi kT}{\lambda^4}$$

where λ is measured in meters, T is the temperature in kelvins (K), and k is Boltzmann's constant. The Rayleigh-Jeans Law agrees with experimental measurements for long wavelengths but disagrees drastically for short wavelengths. [The law predicts that $f(\lambda) \to \infty$ as $\lambda \to 0^+$ but experiments have shown that $f(\lambda) \to 0$.] This fact is known as the *ultraviolet catastrophe*.

In 1900 Max Planck found a better model (known now as Planck's Law) for blackbody radiation:

$$f(\lambda) = \frac{8\pi hc\lambda^{-5}}{e^{hc/(\lambda kT)} - 1}$$

where λ is measured in meters, T is the temperature (in kelvins), and

$$h = \text{Planck's constant} = 6.6262 \times 10^{-34} \text{ J·s}$$

$$c = \text{speed of light} = 2.997925 \times 10^8 \text{ m/s}$$

$$k = \text{Boltzmann's constant} = 1.3807 \times 10^{-23} \text{ J/K}$$

1. Use l'Hospital's Rule to show that

    $$\lim_{\lambda \to 0^+} f(\lambda) = 0 \qquad \text{and} \qquad \lim_{\lambda \to \infty} f(\lambda) = 0$$

    for Planck's Law. So this law models blackbody radiation better than the Rayleigh-Jeans Law for short wavelengths.

2. Use a Taylor polynomial to show that, for large wavelengths, Planck's Law gives approximately the same values as the Rayleigh-Jeans Law.

3. Graph f as given by both laws on the same screen and comment on the similarities and differences. Use $T = 5700$ K (the temperature of the Sun). (You may want to change from meters to the more convenient unit of micrometers: $1 \ \mu\text{m} = 10^{-6}$ m.)

4. Use your graph in Problem 3 to estimate the value of λ for which $f(\lambda)$ is a maximum under Planck's Law.

5. Investigate how the graph of f changes as T varies. (Use Planck's Law.) In particular, graph f for the stars Betelgeuse ($T = 3400$ K), Procyon ($T = 6400$ K), and Sirius ($T = 9200$ K) as well as the Sun. How does the total radiation emitted (the area under the curve) vary with T? Use the graph to comment on why Sirius is known as a blue star and Betelgeuse as a red star.

12 Review

1. (a) What is a convergent sequence?
   (b) What is a convergent series?
   (c) What does $\lim_{n \to \infty} a_n = 3$ mean?
   (d) What does $\sum_{n=1}^{\infty} a_n = 3$ mean?

2. (a) What is a bounded sequence?
   (b) What is a monotonic sequence?
   (c) What can you say about a bounded monotonic sequence?

3. (a) What is a geometric series? Under what circumstances is it convergent? What is its sum?
   (b) What is a p-series? Under what circumstances is it convergent?

4. Suppose $\Sigma\, a_n = 3$ and s_n is the nth partial sum of the series. What is $\lim_{n \to \infty} a_n$? What is $\lim_{n \to \infty} s_n$?

5. State the following.
   (a) The Test for Divergence
   (b) The Integral Test
   (c) The Comparison Test
   (d) The Limit Comparison Test
   (e) The Alternating Series Test
   (f) The Ratio Test
   (g) The Root Test

6. (a) What is an absolutely convergent series?
   (b) What can you say about such a series?
   (c) What is a conditionally convergent series?

7. (a) If a series is convergent by the Integral Test, how do you estimate its sum?
   (b) If a series is convergent by the Comparison Test, how do you estimate its sum?

(c) If a series is convergent by the Alternating Series Test, how do you estimate its sum?

8. (a) Write the general form of a power series.
   (b) What is the radius of convergence of a power series?
   (c) What is the interval of convergence of a power series?

9. Suppose $f(x)$ is the sum of a power series with radius of convergence R.
   (a) How do you differentiate f? What is the radius of convergence of the series for f'?
   (b) How do you integrate f? What is the radius of convergence of the series for $\int f(x)\, dx$?

10. (a) Write an expression for the nth-degree Taylor polynomial of f centered at a.
   (b) Write an expression for the Taylor series of f centered at a.
   (c) Write an expression for the Maclaurin series of f.
   (d) How do you show that $f(x)$ is equal to the sum of its Taylor series?
   (e) State Taylor's Inequality.

11. Write the Maclaurin series and the interval of convergence for each of the following functions.
   (a) $1/(1-x)$ (b) e^x
   (c) $\sin x$ (d) $\cos x$
   (e) $\tan^{-1} x$

12. Write the binomial series expansion of $(1+x)^k$. What is the radius of convergence of this series?

Determine whether the statement is true or false. If it is true, explain why. If it is false, explain why or give an example that disproves the statement.

1. If $\lim_{n \to \infty} a_n = 0$, then $\Sigma\, a_n$ is convergent.

2. The series $\sum_{n=1}^{\infty} n^{-\sin 1}$ is convergent.

3. If $\lim_{n \to \infty} a_n = L$, then $\lim_{n \to \infty} a_{2n+1} = L$.

4. If $\Sigma\, c_n 6^n$ is convergent, then $\Sigma\, c_n(-2)^n$ is convergent.

5. If $\Sigma\, c_n 6^n$ is convergent, then $\Sigma\, c_n(-6)^n$ is convergent.

6. If $\Sigma\, c_n x^n$ diverges when $x = 6$, then it diverges when $x = 10$.

7. The Ratio Test can be used to determine whether $\Sigma\, 1/n^3$ converges.

8. The Ratio Test can be used to determine whether $\Sigma\, 1/n!$ converges.

9. If $0 \le a_n \le b_n$ and $\Sigma\, b_n$ diverges, then $\Sigma\, a_n$ diverges.

10. $\displaystyle\sum_{n=0}^{\infty} \frac{(-1)^n}{n!} = \frac{1}{e}$

11. If $-1 < \alpha < 1$, then $\lim_{n \to \infty} \alpha^n = 0$.

12. If $\Sigma\, a_n$ is divergent, then $\Sigma\, |a_n|$ is divergent.

13. If $f(x) = 2x - x^2 + \frac{1}{3}x^3 - \cdots$ converges for all x, then $f'''(0) = 2$.

14. If $\{a_n\}$ and $\{b_n\}$ are divergent, then $\{a_n + b_n\}$ is divergent.

15. If $\{a_n\}$ and $\{b_n\}$ are divergent, then $\{a_n b_n\}$ is divergent.

16. If $\{a_n\}$ is decreasing and $a_n > 0$ for all n, then $\{a_n\}$ is convergent.

17. If $a_n > 0$ and $\Sigma\, a_n$ converges, then $\Sigma\, (-1)^n a_n$ converges.

18. If $a_n > 0$ and $\lim_{n \to \infty} (a_{n+1}/a_n) < 1$, then $\lim_{n \to \infty} a_n = 0$.

◦ EXERCISES ◦

1–8 ⫿ Determine whether the sequence is convergent or divergent. If it is convergent, find its limit.

1. $a_n = \dfrac{2 + n^3}{1 + 2n^3}$

2. $a_n = \dfrac{9^{n+1}}{10^n}$

3. $a_n = \dfrac{n^3}{1 + n^2}$

4. $a_n = \cos(n\pi/2)$

5. $a_n = \dfrac{n \sin n}{n^2 + 1}$

6. $a_n = \dfrac{\ln n}{\sqrt{n}}$

7. $\{(1 + 3/n)^{4n}\}$

8. $\{(-10)^n/n!\}$

9. A sequence is defined recursively by the equations $a_1 = 1$, $a_{n+1} = \frac{1}{3}(a_n + 4)$. Show that $\{a_n\}$ is increasing and $a_n < 2$ for all n. Deduce that $\{a_n\}$ is convergent and find its limit.

10. Show that $\lim_{n\to\infty} n^4 e^{-n} = 0$ and use a graph to find the smallest value of N that corresponds to $\varepsilon = 0.1$ in the precise definition of a limit.

11–22 ⫿ Determine whether the series is convergent or divergent.

11. $\displaystyle\sum_{n=1}^{\infty} \frac{n}{n^3 + 1}$

12. $\displaystyle\sum_{n=1}^{\infty} \frac{n^2 + 1}{n^3 + 1}$

13. $\displaystyle\sum_{n=1}^{\infty} \frac{n^3}{5^n}$

14. $\displaystyle\sum_{n=1}^{\infty} \frac{(-1)^n}{\sqrt{n + 1}}$

15. $\displaystyle\sum_{n=2}^{\infty} \frac{1}{n\sqrt{\ln n}}$

16. $\displaystyle\sum_{n=1}^{\infty} \ln\!\left(\frac{n}{3n + 1}\right)$

17. $\displaystyle\sum_{n=1}^{\infty} \frac{\cos 3n}{1 + (1.2)^n}$

18. $\displaystyle\sum_{n=1}^{\infty} \frac{n^{2n}}{(1 + 2n^2)^n}$

19. $\displaystyle\sum_{n=1}^{\infty} \frac{1 \cdot 3 \cdot 5 \cdot \,\cdots\, \cdot (2n - 1)}{5^n n!}$

20. $\displaystyle\sum_{n=1}^{\infty} \frac{(-5)^{2n}}{n^2 9^n}$

21. $\displaystyle\sum_{n=1}^{\infty} (-1)^{n-1} \frac{\sqrt{n}}{n + 1}$

22. $\displaystyle\sum_{n=1}^{\infty} \frac{\sqrt{n + 1} - \sqrt{n - 1}}{n}$

23–26 ⫿ Determine whether the series is conditionally convergent, absolutely convergent, or divergent.

23. $\displaystyle\sum_{n=1}^{\infty} (-1)^{n-1} n^{-1/3}$

24. $\displaystyle\sum_{n=1}^{\infty} (-1)^{n-1} n^{-3}$

25. $\displaystyle\sum_{n=1}^{\infty} \frac{(-1)^n (n + 1) 3^n}{2^{2n+1}}$

26. $\displaystyle\sum_{n=2}^{\infty} \frac{(-1)^n \sqrt{n}}{\ln n}$

27–31 ⫿ Find the sum of the series.

27. $\displaystyle\sum_{n=1}^{\infty} \frac{2^{2n+1}}{5^n}$

28. $\displaystyle\sum_{n=1}^{\infty} \frac{1}{n(n + 3)}$

29. $\displaystyle\sum_{n=1}^{\infty} [\tan^{-1}(n + 1) - \tan^{-1} n]$

30. $\displaystyle\sum_{n=0}^{\infty} \frac{(-1)^n \pi^n}{3^{2n}(2n)!}$

31. $1 - e + \dfrac{e^2}{2!} - \dfrac{e^3}{3!} + \dfrac{e^4}{4!} - \cdots$

32. Express the repeating decimal $4.17326326326\ldots$ as a fraction.

33. Show that $\cosh x \geqslant 1 + \frac{1}{2}x^2$ for all x.

34. For what values of x does the series $\sum_{n=1}^{\infty} (\ln x)^n$ converge?

35. Find the sum of the series $\displaystyle\sum_{n=1}^{\infty} \frac{(-1)^{n+1}}{n^5}$ correct to four decimal places.

36. (a) Find the partial sum s_5 of the series $\sum_{n=1}^{\infty} 1/n^6$ and estimate the error in using it as an approximation to the sum of the series.
(b) Find the sum of this series correct to five decimal places.

37. Use the sum of the first eight terms to approximate the sum of the series $\sum_{n=1}^{\infty} (2 + 5^n)^{-1}$. Estimate the error involved in this approximation.

38. (a) Show that the series $\displaystyle\sum_{n=1}^{\infty} \frac{n^n}{(2n)!}$ is convergent.

(b) Deduce that $\displaystyle\lim_{n\to\infty} \frac{n^n}{(2n)!} = 0$.

39. Prove that if the series $\sum_{n=1}^{\infty} a_n$ is absolutely convergent, then the series

$$\sum_{n=1}^{\infty} \left(\frac{n + 1}{n}\right) a_n$$

is also absolutely convergent.

40–43 ⫿ Find the radius of convergence and interval of convergence of the series.

40. $\displaystyle\sum_{n=1}^{\infty} (-1)^n \frac{x^n}{n^2 5^n}$

41. $\displaystyle\sum_{n=1}^{\infty} \frac{(x + 2)^n}{n 4^n}$

42. $\displaystyle\sum_{n=1}^{\infty} \frac{2^n (x - 2)^n}{(n + 2)!}$

43. $\displaystyle\sum_{n=0}^{\infty} \frac{2^n (x - 3)^n}{\sqrt{n + 3}}$

44. Find the radius of convergence of the series

$$\sum_{n=1}^{\infty} \frac{(2n)!}{(n!)^2} x^n$$

45. Find the Taylor series of $f(x) = \sin x$ at $a = \pi/6$.

46. Find the Taylor series of $f(x) = \cos x$ at $a = \pi/3$.

47–54 ▓ Find the Maclaurin series for f and its radius of convergence. You may use either the direct method (definition of a Maclaurin series) or known series such as geometric series, binomial series, or the Maclaurin series for e^x, $\sin x$, and $\tan^{-1}x$.

47. $f(x) = \dfrac{x^2}{1 + x}$ **48.** $f(x) = \tan^{-1}(x^2)$

49. $f(x) = \ln(1 - x)$ **50.** $f(x) = xe^{2x}$

51. $f(x) = \sin(x^4)$ **52.** $f(x) = 10^x$

53. $f(x) = 1/\sqrt[4]{16 - x}$ **54.** $f(x) = (1 - 3x)^{-5}$

55. Evaluate $\displaystyle\int \frac{e^x}{x}\,dx$ as an infinite series.

56. Use series to approximate $\int_0^1 \sqrt{1 + x^4}\,dx$ correct to two decimal places.

57–58 ▓
(a) Approximate f by a Taylor polynomial with degree n at the number a.
(b) Graph f and T_n on a common screen.
(c) Use Taylor's Inequality to estimate the accuracy of the approximation $f(x) \approx T_n(x)$ when x lies in the given interval.
(d) Check your result in part (c) by graphing $|R_n(x)|$.

57. $f(x) = \sqrt{x}$, $a = 1$, $n = 3$, $0.9 \leqslant x \leqslant 1.1$

58. $f(x) = \sec x$, $a = 0$, $n = 2$, $0 \leqslant x \leqslant \pi/6$

59. Use series to evaluate the following limit.

$$\lim_{x \to 0} \frac{\sin x - x}{x^3}$$

60. The force due to gravity on an object with mass m at a height h above the surface of the Earth is

$$F = \frac{mgR^2}{(R + h)^2}$$

where R is the radius of the Earth and g is the acceleration due to gravity.
(a) Express F as a series in powers of h/R.
(b) Observe that if we approximate F by the first term in the series, we get the expression $F \approx mg$ that is usually used when h is much smaller than R. Use the Alternating Series Estimation Theorem to estimate the range of values of h for which the approximation $F \approx mg$ is accurate to within 1%. (Use $R = 6400$ km.)

61. Suppose that $f(x) = \sum_{n=0}^{\infty} c_n x^n$ for all x.
(a) If f is an odd function, show that

$$c_0 = c_2 = c_4 = \cdots = 0$$

(b) If f is an even function, show that

$$c_1 = c_3 = c_5 = \cdots = 0$$

62. If $f(x) = e^{x^2}$, show that $f^{(2n)}(0) = \dfrac{(2n)!}{n!}$.

1. If $f(x) = \sin(x^3)$, find $f^{(15)}(0)$.

2. A function f is defined by

$$f(x) = \lim_{n \to \infty} \frac{x^{2n} - 1}{x^{2n} + 1}$$

   Where is f continuous?

3. (a) Show that $\tan \frac{1}{2}x = \cot \frac{1}{2}x - 2 \cot x$.

   (b) Find the sum of the series

$$\sum_{n=1}^{\infty} \frac{1}{2^n} \tan \frac{x}{2^n}$$

4. Let $\{P_n\}$ be a sequence of points determined as in the figure. Thus $|AP_1| = 1$, $|P_n P_{n+1}| = 2^{n-1}$, and angle $AP_n P_{n+1}$ is a right angle. Find $\lim_{n \to \infty} \angle P_n A P_{n+1}$.

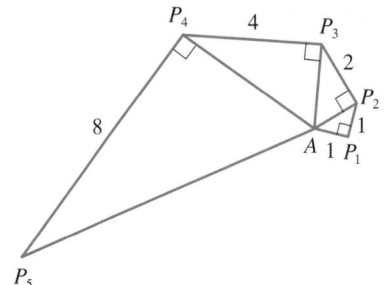

FIGURE FOR PROBLEM 4

5. To construct the **snowflake curve**, start with an equilateral triangle with sides of length 1. Step 1 in the construction is to divide each side into three equal parts, construct an equilateral triangle on the middle part, and then delete the middle part (see the figure). Step 2 is to repeat Step 1 for each side of the resulting polygon. This process is repeated at each succeeding step. The snowflake curve is the curve that results from repeating this process indefinitely.

   (a) Let s_n, l_n, and p_n represent the number of sides, the length of a side, and the total length of the nth approximating curve (the curve obtained after Step n of the construction), respectively. Find formulas for s_n, l_n, and p_n.

   (b) Show that $p_n \to \infty$ as $n \to \infty$.

   (c) Sum an infinite series to find the area enclosed by the snowflake curve.

   Parts (b) and (c) show that the snowflake curve is infinitely long but encloses only a finite area.

   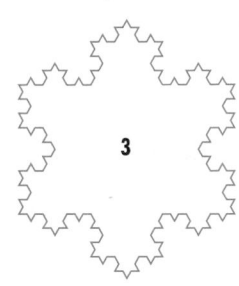

6. Find the sum of the series

$$1 + \frac{1}{2} + \frac{1}{3} + \frac{1}{4} + \frac{1}{6} + \frac{1}{8} + \frac{1}{9} + \frac{1}{12} + \cdots$$

   where the terms are the reciprocals of the positive integers whose only prime factors are 2s and 3s.

7. (a) Show that for $xy \neq -1$,

$$\arctan x - \arctan y = \arctan \frac{x - y}{1 + xy}$$

   if the left side lies between $-\pi/2$ and $\pi/2$.

   (b) Show that

$$\arctan \frac{120}{119} - \arctan \frac{1}{239} = \frac{\pi}{4}$$

   (c) Deduce the following formula of John Machin (1680–1751):

$$4 \arctan \frac{1}{5} - \arctan \frac{1}{239} = \frac{\pi}{4}$$

(d) Use the Maclaurin series for arctan to show that

$$0.197395560 < \arctan\tfrac{1}{5} < 0.197395562$$

(e) Show that

$$0.004184075 < \arctan\tfrac{1}{239} < 0.004184077$$

(f) Deduce that, correct to seven decimal places,

$$\pi \approx 3.1415927$$

Machin used this method in 1706 to find π correct to 100 decimal places. Recently, with the aid of computers, the value of π has been computed to increasingly greater accuracy. In 1999, Takahashi and Kanada, using methods of Borwein and Brent/Salamin, calculated the value of π to 206,158,430,000 decimal places!

8. (a) Prove a formula similar to the one in Problem 7(a) but involving arccot instead of arctan.
(b) Find the sum of the series

$$\sum_{n=0}^{\infty} \operatorname{arccot}(n^2 + n + 1)$$

9. Find the interval of convergence of $\sum_{n=1}^{\infty} n^3 x^n$ and find its sum.

10. If $a_0 + a_1 + a_2 + \cdots + a_k = 0$, show that

$$\lim_{n\to\infty} \left(a_0 \sqrt{n} + a_1 \sqrt{n+1} + a_2 \sqrt{n+2} + \cdots + a_k \sqrt{n+k}\right) = 0$$

If you don't see how to prove this, try the problem-solving strategy of *using analogy* (see page 58). Try the special cases $k = 1$ and $k = 2$ first. If you can see how to prove the assertion for these cases, then you will probably see how to prove it in general.

11. Find the sum of the series $\displaystyle\sum_{n=2}^{\infty} \ln\left(1 - \frac{1}{n^2}\right)$.

12. Suppose you have a large supply of books, all the same size, and you stack them at the edge of a table, with each book extending farther beyond the edge of the table than the one beneath it. Show that it is possible to do this so that the top book extends entirely beyond the table. In fact, show that the top book can extend any distance at all beyond the edge of the table if the stack is high enough. Use the following method of stacking: The top book extends half its length beyond the second book. The second book extends a quarter of its length beyond the third. The third extends one-sixth of its length beyond the fourth, and so on. (Try it yourself with a deck of cards.) Consider centers of mass.

FIGURE FOR PROBLEM 12

13. Let

$$u = 1 + \frac{x^3}{3!} + \frac{x^6}{6!} + \frac{x^9}{9!} + \cdots$$

$$v = x + \frac{x^4}{4!} + \frac{x^7}{7!} + \frac{x^{10}}{10!} + \cdots$$

$$w = \frac{x^2}{2!} + \frac{x^5}{5!} + \frac{x^8}{8!} + \cdots$$

Show that $u^3 + v^3 + w^3 - 3uvw = 1$.

14. If $p > 1$, evaluate the expression

$$\frac{1 + \dfrac{1}{2^p} + \dfrac{1}{3^p} + \dfrac{1}{4^p} + \cdots}{1 - \dfrac{1}{2^p} + \dfrac{1}{3^p} - \dfrac{1}{4^p} + \cdots}$$

FIGURE FOR PROBLEM 15

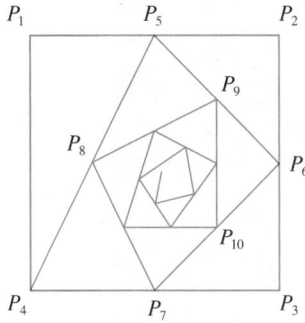

FIGURE FOR PROBLEM 18

15. Suppose that circles of equal diameter are packed tightly in n rows inside an equilateral triangle. (The figure illustrates the case $n = 4$.) If A is the area of the triangle and A_n is the total area occupied by the n rows of circles, show that

$$\lim_{n \to \infty} \frac{A_n}{A} = \frac{\pi}{2\sqrt{3}}$$

16. A sequence $\{a_n\}$ is defined recursively by the equations

$$a_0 = a_1 = 1 \qquad n(n-1)a_n = (n-1)(n-2)a_{n-1} - (n-3)a_{n-2}$$

Find the sum of the series $\sum_{n=0}^{\infty} a_n$.

17. Taking the value of x^x at 0 to be 1 and integrating a series term-by-term, show that

$$\int_0^1 x^x \, dx = \sum_{n=1}^{\infty} \frac{(-1)^{n-1}}{n^n}$$

18. Starting with the vertices $P_1(0, 1)$, $P_2(1, 1)$, $P_3(1, 0)$, $P_4(0, 0)$ of a square, we construct further points as shown in the figure: P_5 is the midpoint of P_1P_2, P_6 is the midpoint of P_2P_3, P_7 is the midpoint of P_3P_4, and so on. The polygonal spiral path $P_1P_2P_3P_4P_5P_6P_7 \ldots$ approaches a point P inside the square.

(a) If the coordinates of P_n are (x_n, y_n), show that $\frac{1}{2}x_n + x_{n+1} + x_{n+2} + x_{n+3} = 2$ and find a similar equation for the y-coordinates.

(b) Find the coordinates of P.

19. If $f(x) = \sum_{m=0}^{\infty} c_m x^m$ has positive radius of convergence and $e^{f(x)} = \sum_{n=0}^{\infty} d_n x^n$, show that

$$nd_n = \sum_{i=1}^{n} i c_i d_{n-i} \qquad n \geq 1$$

20. Right-angled triangles are constructed as in the figure. Each triangle has height 1 and its base is the hypotenuse of the preceding triangle. Show that this sequence of triangles makes indefinitely many turns around P by showing that $\sum \theta_n$ is a divergent series.

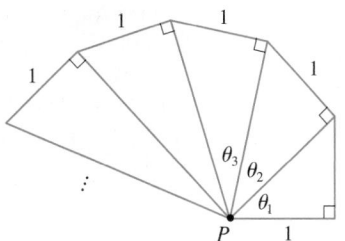

21. Consider the series whose terms are the reciprocals of the positive integers that can be written in base 10 notation without using the digit 0. Show that this series is convergent and the sum is less than 90.

22. (a) Show that the Maclaurin series of the function

$$f(x) = \frac{x}{1 - x - x^2} \qquad \text{is} \qquad \sum_{n=1}^{\infty} f_n x^n$$

where f_n is the nth Fibonacci number, that is, $f_1 = 1$, $f_2 = 1$, and $f_n = f_{n-1} + f_{n-2}$ for $n \geq 3$. [*Hint:* Write $x/(1 - x - x^2) = c_0 + c_1 x + c_2 x^2 + \cdots$ and multiply both sides of this equation by $1 - x - x^2$.]

(b) By writing $f(x)$ as a sum of partial fractions and thereby obtaining the Maclaurin series in a different way, find an explicit formula for the nth Fibonacci number.

CHAPTER 13

Wind velocity is a vector because it has both magnitude and direction. Pictured are velocity vectors indicating the wind pattern over San Francisco Bay at 12:00 P.M. on June 11, 2002.

Vectors and the Geometry of Space

In this chapter we introduce vectors and coordinate systems for three-dimensional space. This will be the setting for our study of the calculus of functions of two variables in Chapter 15 because the graph of such a function is a surface in space. In this chapter we will see that vectors provide particularly simple descriptions of lines and planes in space.

13.1 Three-Dimensional Coordinate Systems

FIGURE 1
Coordinate axes

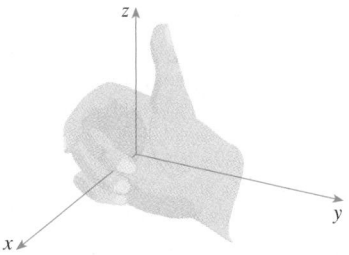

FIGURE 2
Right-hand rule

To locate a point in a plane, two numbers are necessary. We know that any point in the plane can be represented as an ordered pair (a, b) of real numbers, where a is the x-coordinate and b is the y-coordinate. For this reason, a plane is called two-dimensional. To locate a point in space, three numbers are required. We represent any point in space by an ordered triple (a, b, c) of real numbers.

In order to represent points in space, we first choose a fixed point O (the origin) and three directed lines through O that are perpendicular to each other, called the **coordinate axes** and labeled the x-axis, y-axis, and z-axis. Usually we think of the x- and y-axes as being horizontal and the z-axis as being vertical, and we draw the orientation of the axes as in Figure 1. The direction of the z-axis is determined by the **right-hand rule** as illustrated in Figure 2: If you curl the fingers of your right hand around the z-axis in the direction of a 90° counterclockwise rotation from the positive x-axis to the positive y-axis, then your thumb points in the positive direction of the z-axis.

The three coordinate axes determine the three **coordinate planes** illustrated in Figure 3(a). The xy-plane is the plane that contains the x- and y-axes; the yz-plane contains the y- and z-axes; the xz-plane contains the x- and z-axes. These three coordinate planes divide space into eight parts, called **octants**. The **first octant**, in the foreground, is determined by the positive axes.

FIGURE 3

(a) Coordinate planes

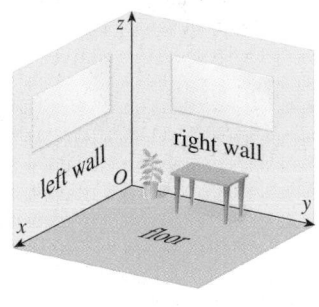

(b)

Because many people have some difficulty visualizing diagrams of three-dimensional figures, you may find it helpful to do the following [see Figure 3(b)]. Look at any bottom corner of a room and call the corner the origin. The wall on your left is in the xz-plane, the wall on your right is in the yz-plane, and the floor is in the xy-plane. The x-axis runs along the intersection of the floor and the left wall. The y-axis runs along the intersection of the floor and the right wall. The z-axis runs up from the floor toward the ceiling along the intersection of the two walls. You are situated in the first octant, and you can now imagine seven other rooms situated in the other seven octants (three on the same floor and four on the floor below), all connected by the common corner point O.

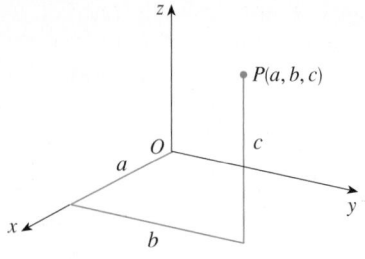

FIGURE 4

Now if P is any point in space, let a be the (directed) distance from the yz-plane to P, let b be the distance from the xz-plane to P, and let c be the distance from the xy-plane to P. We represent the point P by the ordered triple (a, b, c) of real numbers and we call a, b, and c the **coordinates** of P; a is the x-coordinate, b is the y-coordinate, and c is the z-coordinate. Thus, to locate the point (a, b, c) we can start at the origin O and move a units along the x-axis, then b units parallel to the y-axis, and then c units parallel to the z-axis as in Figure 4.

The point $P(a, b, c)$ determines a rectangular box as in Figure 5. If we drop a perpendicular from P to the xy-plane, we get a point Q with coordinates $(a, b, 0)$ called the **projection** of P on the xy-plane. Similarly, $R(0, b, c)$ and $S(a, 0, c)$ are the projections of P on the yz-plane and xz-plane, respectively.

As numerical illustrations, the points $(-4, 3, -5)$ and $(3, -2, -6)$ are plotted in Figure 6.

FIGURE 5

FIGURE 6

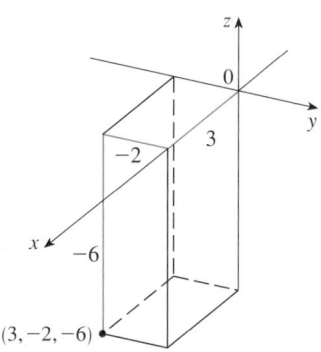

The Cartesian product $\mathbb{R} \times \mathbb{R} \times \mathbb{R} = \{(x, y, z) \mid x, y, z \in \mathbb{R}\}$ is the set of all ordered triples of real numbers and is denoted by $\mathbb{R}^3$. We have given a one-to-one correspondence between points P in space and ordered triples (a, b, c) in $\mathbb{R}^3$. It is called a **three-dimensional rectangular coordinate system**. Notice that, in terms of coordinates, the first octant can be described as the set of points whose coordinates are all positive.

In two-dimensional analytic geometry, the graph of an equation involving x and y is a curve in $\mathbb{R}^2$. In three-dimensional analytic geometry, an equation in x, y, and z represents a *surface* in $\mathbb{R}^3$.

EXAMPLE 1 What surfaces in $\mathbb{R}^3$ are represented by the following equations?
(a) $z = 3$ (b) $y = 5$

SOLUTION
(a) The equation $z = 3$ represents the set $\{(x, y, z) \mid z = 3\}$, which is the set of all points in $\mathbb{R}^3$ whose z-coordinate is 3. This is the horizontal plane that is parallel to the xy-plane and three units above it as in Figure 7(a).

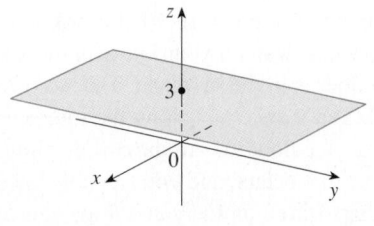

FIGURE 7   (a) $z = 3$, a plane in $\mathbb{R}^3$

(b) $y = 5$, a plane in $\mathbb{R}^3$

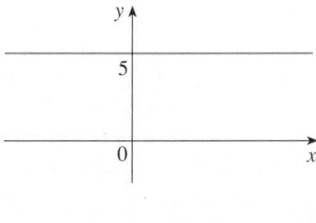

(c) $y = 5$, a line in $\mathbb{R}^2$

(b) The equation $y = 5$ represents the set of all points in $\mathbb{R}^3$ whose y-coordinate is 5. This is the vertical plane that is parallel to the xz-plane and five units to the right of it as in Figure 7(b). ▬

NOTE ▫ When an equation is given, we must understand from the context whether it represents a curve in $\mathbb{R}^2$ or a surface in $\mathbb{R}^3$. In Example 1, $y = 5$ represents a plane in $\mathbb{R}^3$, but of course $y = 5$ can also represent a line in $\mathbb{R}^2$ if we are dealing with two-dimensional analytic geometry. See Figure 7(b) and (c).

In general, if k is a constant, then $x = k$ represents a plane parallel to the yz-plane, $y = k$ is a plane parallel to the xz-plane, and $z = k$ is a plane parallel to the xy-plane. In Figure 5, the faces of the rectangular box are formed by the three coordinate planes $x = 0$ (the yz-plane), $y = 0$ (the xz-plane), and $z = 0$ (the xy-plane), and the planes $x = a$, $y = b$, and $z = c$.

EXAMPLE 2 Describe and sketch the surface in $\mathbb{R}^3$ represented by the equation $y = x$.

SOLUTION The equation represents the set of all points in $\mathbb{R}^3$ whose x- and y-coordinates are equal, that is, $\{(x, x, z) \mid x \in \mathbb{R}, z \in \mathbb{R}\}$. This is a vertical plane that intersects the xy-plane in the line $y = x$, $z = 0$. The portion of this plane that lies in the first octant is sketched in Figure 8. ▬

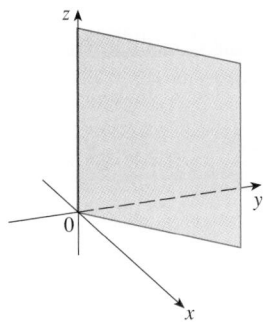

FIGURE 8
The plane $y = x$

The familiar formula for the distance between two points in a plane is easily extended to the following three-dimensional formula.

> **Distance Formula in Three Dimensions** The distance $|P_1P_2|$ between the points $P_1(x_1, y_1, z_1)$ and $P_2(x_2, y_2, z_2)$ is
>
> $$|P_1P_2| = \sqrt{(x_2 - x_1)^2 + (y_2 - y_1)^2 + (z_2 - z_1)^2}$$

To see why this formula is true, we construct a rectangular box as in Figure 9, where P_1 and P_2 are opposite vertices and the faces of the box are parallel to the coordinate planes. If $A(x_2, y_1, z_1)$ and $B(x_2, y_2, z_1)$ are the vertices of the box indicated in the figure, then

$$|P_1A| = |x_2 - x_1| \qquad |AB| = |y_2 - y_1| \qquad |BP_2| = |z_2 - z_1|$$

Because triangles P_1BP_2 and P_1AB are both right-angled, two applications of the Pythagorean Theorem give

$$|P_1P_2|^2 = |P_1B|^2 + |BP_2|^2$$

and

$$|P_1B|^2 = |P_1A|^2 + |AB|^2$$

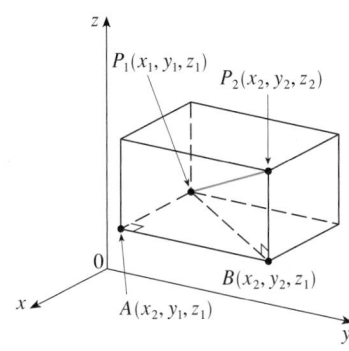

FIGURE 9

Combining these equations, we get

$$\begin{aligned}
|P_1P_2|^2 &= |P_1A|^2 + |AB|^2 + |BP_2|^2 \\
&= |x_2 - x_1|^2 + |y_2 - y_1|^2 + |z_2 - z_1|^2 \\
&= (x_2 - x_1)^2 + (y_2 - y_1)^2 + (z_2 - z_1)^2
\end{aligned}$$

Therefore $\qquad |P_1P_2| = \sqrt{(x_2 - x_1)^2 + (y_2 - y_1)^2 + (z_2 - z_1)^2}$

EXAMPLE 3 The distance from the point $P(2, -1, 7)$ to the point $Q(1, -3, 5)$ is

$$|PQ| = \sqrt{(1 - 2)^2 + (-3 + 1)^2 + (5 - 7)^2}$$
$$= \sqrt{1 + 4 + 4} = 3$$

EXAMPLE 4 Find an equation of a sphere with radius r and center $C(h, k, l)$.

SOLUTION By definition, a sphere is the set of all points $P(x, y, z)$ whose distance from C is r. (See Figure 10.) Thus, P is on the sphere if and only if $|PC| = r$. Squaring both sides, we have $|PC|^2 = r^2$ or

$$(x - h)^2 + (y - k)^2 + (z - l)^2 = r^2$$

The result of Example 4 is worth remembering.

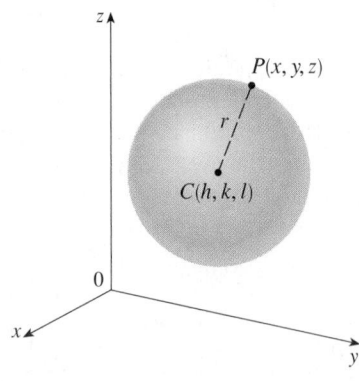

FIGURE 10

Equation of a Sphere An equation of a sphere with center $C(h, k, l)$ and radius r is

$$(x - h)^2 + (y - k)^2 + (z - l)^2 = r^2$$

In particular, if the center is the origin O, then an equation of the sphere is

$$x^2 + y^2 + z^2 = r^2$$

EXAMPLE 5 Show that $x^2 + y^2 + z^2 + 4x - 6y + 2z + 6 = 0$ is the equation of a sphere, and find its center and radius.

SOLUTION We can rewrite the given equation in the form of an equation of a sphere if we complete squares:

$$(x^2 + 4x + 4) + (y^2 - 6y + 9) + (z^2 + 2z + 1) = -6 + 4 + 9 + 1$$
$$(x + 2)^2 + (y - 3)^2 + (z + 1)^2 = 8$$

Comparing this equation with the standard form, we see that it is the equation of a sphere with center $(-2, 3, -1)$ and radius $\sqrt{8} = 2\sqrt{2}$.

EXAMPLE 6 What region in $\mathbb{R}^3$ is represented by the following inequalities?

$$1 \le x^2 + y^2 + z^2 \le 4 \qquad z \le 0$$

SOLUTION The inequalities

$$1 \le x^2 + y^2 + z^2 \le 4$$

can be rewritten as

$$1 \le \sqrt{x^2 + y^2 + z^2} \le 2$$

so they represent the points (x, y, z) whose distance from the origin is at least 1 and at most 2. But we are also given that $z \le 0$, so the points lie on or below the xy-plane. Thus, the given inequalities represent the region that lies between (or on) the spheres $x^2 + y^2 + z^2 = 1$ and $x^2 + y^2 + z^2 = 4$ and beneath (or on) the xy-plane. It is sketched in Figure 11.

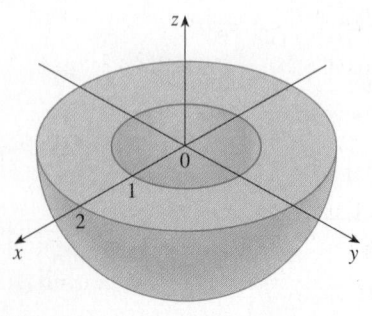

FIGURE 11

13.1 Exercises

1. Suppose you start at the origin, move along the x-axis a distance of 4 units in the positive direction, and then move downward a distance of 3 units. What are the coordinates of your position?

2. Sketch the points $(0, 5, 2)$, $(4, 0, -1)$, $(2, 4, 6)$, and $(1, -1, 2)$ on a single set of coordinate axes.

3. Which of the points $P(6, 2, 3)$, $Q(-5, -1, 4)$, and $R(0, 3, 8)$ is closest to the xz-plane? Which point lies in the yz-plane?

4. What are the projections of the point $(2, 3, 5)$ on the xy-, yz-, and xz-planes? Draw a rectangular box with the origin and $(2, 3, 5)$ as opposite vertices and with its faces parallel to the coordinate planes. Label all vertices of the box. Find the length of the diagonal of the box.

5. Describe and sketch the surface in $\mathbb{R}^3$ represented by the equation $x + y = 2$.

6. (a) What does the equation $x = 4$ represent in $\mathbb{R}^2$? What does it represent in $\mathbb{R}^3$? Illustrate with sketches.
   (b) What does the equation $y = 3$ represent in $\mathbb{R}^3$? What does $z = 5$ represent? What does the pair of equations $y = 3$, $z = 5$ represent? In other words, describe the set of points (x, y, z) such that $y = 3$ and $z = 5$. Illustrate with a sketch.

7. Show that the triangle with vertices $P(-2, 4, 0)$, $Q(1, 2, -1)$, and $R(-1, 1, 2)$ is an equilateral triangle.

8. Find the lengths of the sides of the triangle with vertices $A(1, 2, -3)$, $B(3, 4, -2)$, and $C(3, -2, 1)$. Is ABC a right triangle? Is it an isosceles triangle?

9. Determine whether the points lie on a straight line.
   (a) $A(5, 1, 3)$, $B(7, 9, -1)$, $C(1, -15, 11)$
   (b) $K(0, 3, -4)$, $L(1, 2, -2)$, $M(3, 0, 1)$

10. Find the distance from $(3, 7, -5)$ to each of the following.
    (a) The xy-plane   (b) The yz-plane
    (c) The xz-plane   (d) The x-axis
    (e) The y-axis   (f) The z-axis

11. Find an equation of the sphere with center $(1, -4, 3)$ and radius 5. What is the intersection of this sphere with the xz-plane?

12. Find an equation of the sphere with center $(6, 5, -2)$ and radius $\sqrt{7}$. Describe its intersection with each of the coordinate planes.

13. Find an equation of the sphere that passes through the point $(4, 3, -1)$ and has center $(3, 8, 1)$.

14. Find an equation of the sphere that passes through the origin and whose center is $(1, 2, 3)$.

15–18 ▐▐ Show that the equation represents a sphere, and find its center and radius.

15. $x^2 + y^2 + z^2 - 6x + 4y - 2z = 11$

16. $x^2 + y^2 + z^2 = 4x - 2y$

17. $x^2 + y^2 + z^2 = x + y + z$

18. $4x^2 + 4y^2 + 4z^2 - 8x + 16y = 1$

19. (a) Prove that the midpoint of the line segment from $P_1(x_1, y_1, z_1)$ to $P_2(x_2, y_2, z_2)$ is
$$\left(\frac{x_1 + x_2}{2}, \frac{y_1 + y_2}{2}, \frac{z_1 + z_2}{2} \right)$$
    (b) Find the lengths of the medians of the triangle with vertices $A(1, 2, 3)$, $B(-2, 0, 5)$, and $C(4, 1, 5)$.

20. Find an equation of a sphere if one of its diameters has endpoints $(2, 1, 4)$ and $(4, 3, 10)$.

21. Find equations of the spheres with center $(2, -3, 6)$ that touch (a) the xy-plane, (b) the yz-plane, (c) the xz-plane.

22. Find an equation of the largest sphere with center $(5, 4, 9)$ that is contained in the first octant.

23–34 ▐▐ Describe in words the region of $\mathbb{R}^3$ represented by the equation or inequality.

23. $y = -4$ 24. $x = 10$

25. $x > 3$ 26. $y \geqslant 0$

27. $0 \leqslant z \leqslant 6$ 28. $y = z$

29. $x^2 + y^2 + z^2 > 1$

30. $1 \leqslant x^2 + y^2 + z^2 \leqslant 25$

31. $x^2 + y^2 + z^2 - 2z < 3$ 32. $x^2 + y^2 = 1$

33. $x^2 + z^2 \leqslant 9$ 34. $xyz = 0$

35–38 ▐▐ Write inequalities to describe the region.

35. The half-space consisting of all points to the left of the xz-plane

36. The solid rectangular box in the first octant bounded by the planes $x = 1$, $y = 2$, and $z = 3$

37. The region consisting of all points between (but not on) the spheres of radius r and R centered at the origin, where $r < R$

38. The solid upper hemisphere of the sphere of radius 2 centered at the origin

39. The figure shows a line L_1 in space and a second line L_2, which is the projection of L_1 on the xy-plane. (In other words,

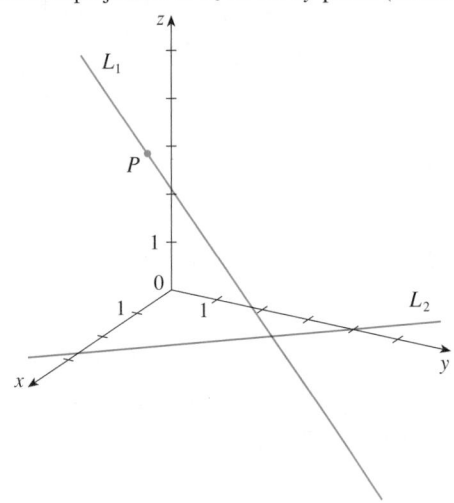

the points on L_2 are directly beneath, or above, the points on L_1.)

(a) Find the coordinates of the point P on the line L_1.

(b) Locate on the diagram the points A, B, and C, where the line L_1 intersects the xy-plane, the yz-plane, and the xz-plane, respectively.

40. Consider the points P such that the distance from P to $A(-1, 5, 3)$ is twice the distance from P to $B(6, 2, -2)$. Show that the set of all such points is a sphere, and find its center and radius.

41. Find an equation of the set of all points equidistant from the points $A(-1, 5, 3)$ and $B(6, 2, -2)$. Describe the set.

42. Find the volume of the solid that lies inside both of the spheres

$$x^2 + y^2 + z^2 + 4x - 2y + 4z + 5 = 0$$

and

$$x^2 + y^2 + z^2 = 4$$

13.2 Vectors

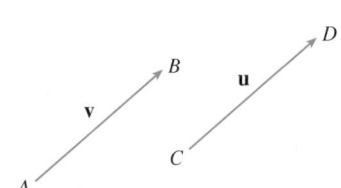

FIGURE 1
Equivalent vectors

The term **vector** is used by scientists to indicate a quantity (such as displacement or velocity or force) that has both magnitude and direction. A vector is often represented by an arrow or a directed line segment. The length of the arrow represents the magnitude of the vector and the arrow points in the direction of the vector. We denote a vector by printing a letter in boldface (**v**) or by putting an arrow above the letter ($\vec{v}$).

For instance, suppose a particle moves along a line segment from point A to point B. The corresponding **displacement vector v**, shown in Figure 1, has **initial point** A (the tail) and **terminal point** B (the tip) and we indicate this by writing $\mathbf{v} = \overrightarrow{AB}$. Notice that the vector $\mathbf{u} = \overrightarrow{CD}$ has the same length and the same direction as **v** even though it is in a different position. We say that **u** and **v** are **equivalent** (or **equal**) and we write $\mathbf{u} = \mathbf{v}$. The **zero vector**, denoted by **0**, has length 0. It is the only vector with no specific direction.

Combining Vectors

FIGURE 2

Suppose a particle moves from A to B, so its displacement vector is $\overrightarrow{AB}$. Then the particle changes direction and moves from B to C, with displacement vector $\overrightarrow{BC}$ as in Figure 2. The combined effect of these displacements is that the particle has moved from A to C. The resulting displacement vector $\overrightarrow{AC}$ is called the *sum* of $\overrightarrow{AB}$ and $\overrightarrow{BC}$ and we write

$$\overrightarrow{AC} = \overrightarrow{AB} + \overrightarrow{BC}$$

In general, if we start with vectors **u** and **v**, we first move **v** so that its tail coincides with the tip of **u** and define the sum of **u** and **v** as follows.

> **Definition of Vector Addition** If **u** and **v** are vectors positioned so the initial point of **v** is at the terminal point of **u**, then the **sum u + v** is the vector from the initial point of **u** to the terminal point of **v**.

The definition of vector addition is illustrated in Figure 3. You can see why this definition is sometimes called the **Triangle Law**.

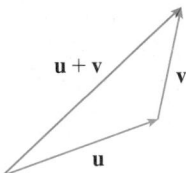

FIGURE 3 The Triangle Law

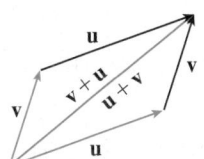

FIGURE 4 The Parallelogram Law

In Figure 4 we start with the same vectors **u** and **v** as in Figure 3 and draw another copy of **v** with the same initial point as **u**. Completing the parallelogram, we see that **u** + **v** = **v** + **u**. This also gives another way to construct the sum: If we place **u** and **v** so they start at the same point, then **u** + **v** lies along the diagonal of the parallelogram with **u** and **v** as sides. (This is called the **Parallelogram Law**.)

EXAMPLE 1 Draw the sum of the vectors **a** and **b** shown in Figure 5.

SOLUTION First we translate **b** and place its tail at the tip of **a**, being careful to draw a copy of **b** that has the same length and direction. Then we draw the vector **a** + **b** [see Figure 6(a)] starting at the initial point of **a** and ending at the terminal point of the copy of **b**.

Alternatively, we could place **b** so it starts where **a** starts and construct **a** + **b** by the Parallelogram Law as in Figure 6(b).

FIGURE 5

Visual 13.2 shows how the Triangle and Parallelogram Laws work for various vectors **u** and **v**.

(a)

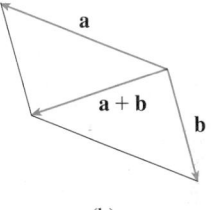

(b)

FIGURE 6

It is possible to multiply a vector by a real number c. (In this context we call the real number c a **scalar** to distinguish it from a vector.) For instance, we want $2\mathbf{v}$ to be the same vector as $\mathbf{v} + \mathbf{v}$, which has the same direction as **v** but is twice as long. In general, we multiply a vector by a scalar as follows.

Definition of Scalar Multiplication If c is a scalar and **v** is a vector, then the **scalar multiple** $c\mathbf{v}$ is the vector whose length is $|c|$ times the length of **v** and whose direction is the same as **v** if $c > 0$ and is opposite to **v** if $c < 0$. If $c = 0$ or $\mathbf{v} = \mathbf{0}$, then $c\mathbf{v} = \mathbf{0}$.

This definition is illustrated in Figure 7. We see that real numbers work like scaling factors here; that's why we call them scalars. Notice that two nonzero vectors are **parallel** if they are scalar multiples of one another. In particular, the vector $-\mathbf{v} = (-1)\mathbf{v}$ has the same length as **v** but points in the opposite direction. We call it the **negative** of **v**.

By the **difference** $\mathbf{u} - \mathbf{v}$ of two vectors we mean

$$\mathbf{u} - \mathbf{v} = \mathbf{u} + (-\mathbf{v})$$

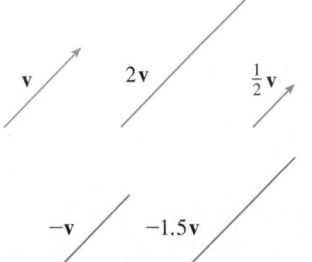

FIGURE 7
Scalar multiples of **v**

So we can construct $\mathbf{u} - \mathbf{v}$ by first drawing the negative of $\mathbf{v}$, $-\mathbf{v}$, and then adding it to $\mathbf{u}$ by the Parallelogram Law as in Figure 8(a). Alternatively, since $\mathbf{v} + (\mathbf{u} - \mathbf{v}) = \mathbf{u}$, the vector $\mathbf{u} - \mathbf{v}$, when added to $\mathbf{v}$, gives $\mathbf{u}$. So we could construct $\mathbf{u} - \mathbf{v}$ as in Figure 8(b) by means of the Triangle Law.

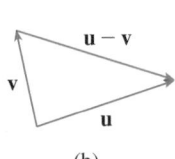

(a) (b)

FIGURE 8
Drawing $\mathbf{u} - \mathbf{v}$

EXAMPLE 2 If $\mathbf{a}$ and $\mathbf{b}$ are the vectors shown in Figure 9, draw $\mathbf{a} - 2\mathbf{b}$.

SOLUTION We first draw the vector $-2\mathbf{b}$ pointing in the direction opposite to $\mathbf{b}$ and twice as long. We place it with its tail at the tip of $\mathbf{a}$ and then use the Triangle Law to draw $\mathbf{a} + (-2\mathbf{b})$ as in Figure 10.

FIGURE 9   **FIGURE 10**

|||| ## Components

For some purposes it's best to introduce a coordinate system and treat vectors algebraically. If we place the initial point of a vector $\mathbf{a}$ at the origin of a rectangular coordinate system, then the terminal point of $\mathbf{a}$ has coordinates of the form (a_1, a_2) or (a_1, a_2, a_3), depending on whether our coordinate system is two- or three-dimensional (see Figure 11). These coordinates are called the **components** of $\mathbf{a}$ and we write

$$\mathbf{a} = \langle a_1, a_2 \rangle \qquad \text{or} \qquad \mathbf{a} = \langle a_1, a_2, a_3 \rangle$$

We use the notation $\langle a_1, a_2 \rangle$ for the ordered pair that refers to a vector so as not to confuse it with the ordered pair (a_1, a_2) that refers to a point in the plane.

For instance, the vectors shown in Figure 12 are all equivalent to the vector $\overrightarrow{OP} = \langle 3, 2 \rangle$ whose terminal point is $P(3, 2)$. What they have in common is that the terminal point is reached from the initial point by a displacement of three units to the right and two upward. We can think of all these geometric vectors as **representations** of the

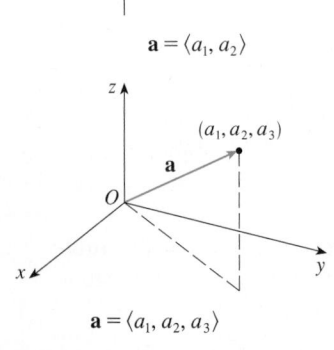

$$\mathbf{a} = \langle a_1, a_2 \rangle$$

$$\mathbf{a} = \langle a_1, a_2, a_3 \rangle$$

FIGURE 11

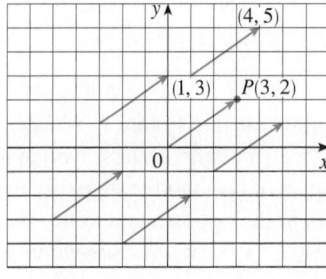

FIGURE 12
Representations of the vector $\mathbf{a} = \langle 3, 2 \rangle$

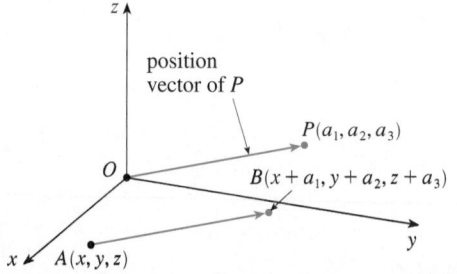

FIGURE 13
Representations of $\mathbf{a} = \langle a_1, a_2, a_3 \rangle$

algebraic vector $\mathbf{a} = \langle 3, 2 \rangle$. The particular representation $\overrightarrow{OP}$ from the origin to the point $P(3, 2)$ is called the **position vector** of the point P.

In three dimensions, the vector $\mathbf{a} = \overrightarrow{OP} = \langle a_1, a_2, a_3 \rangle$ is the **position vector** of the point $P(a_1, a_2, a_3)$. (See Figure 13.) Let's consider any other representation $\overrightarrow{AB}$ of $\mathbf{a}$, where the initial point is $A(x_1, y_1, z_1)$ and the terminal point is $B(x_2, y_2, z_2)$. Then we must have $x_1 + a_1 = x_2$, $y_1 + a_2 = y_2$, and $z_1 + a_3 = z_2$ and so $a_1 = x_2 - x_1$, $a_2 = y_2 - y_1$, and $a_3 = z_2 - z_1$. Thus, we have the following result.

> **1** Given the points $A(x_1, y_1, z_1)$ and $B(x_2, y_2, z_2)$, the vector $\mathbf{a}$ with representation $\overrightarrow{AB}$ is
> $$\mathbf{a} = \langle x_2 - x_1, y_2 - y_1, z_2 - z_1 \rangle$$

EXAMPLE 3 Find the vector represented by the directed line segment with initial point $A(2, -3, 4)$ and terminal point $B(-2, 1, 1)$.

SOLUTION By (1), the vector corresponding to $\overrightarrow{AB}$ is
$$\mathbf{a} = \langle -2 - 2, 1 - (-3), 1 - 4 \rangle = \langle -4, 4, -3 \rangle$$

The **magnitude** or **length** of the vector $\mathbf{v}$ is the length of any of its representations and is denoted by the symbol $|\mathbf{v}|$ or $\|\mathbf{v}\|$. By using the distance formula to compute the length of a segment OP, we obtain the following formulas.

> The length of the two-dimensional vector $\mathbf{a} = \langle a_1, a_2 \rangle$ is
> $$|\mathbf{a}| = \sqrt{a_1^2 + a_2^2}$$
> The length of the three-dimensional vector $\mathbf{a} = \langle a_1, a_2, a_3 \rangle$ is
> $$|\mathbf{a}| = \sqrt{a_1^2 + a_2^2 + a_3^2}$$

How do we add vectors algebraically? Figure 14 shows that if $\mathbf{a} = \langle a_1, a_2 \rangle$ and $\mathbf{b} = \langle b_1, b_2 \rangle$, then the sum is $\mathbf{a} + \mathbf{b} = \langle a_1 + b_1, a_2 + b_2 \rangle$, at least for the case where the components are positive. In other words, *to add algebraic vectors we add their components*. Similarly, *to subtract vectors we subtract components*. From the similar triangles in Figure 15 we see that the components of $c\mathbf{a}$ are ca_1 and ca_2. So *to multiply a vector by a scalar we multiply each component by that scalar*.

> If $\mathbf{a} = \langle a_1, a_2 \rangle$ and $\mathbf{b} = \langle b_1, b_2 \rangle$, then
> $$\mathbf{a} + \mathbf{b} = \langle a_1 + b_1, a_2 + b_2 \rangle \qquad \mathbf{a} - \mathbf{b} = \langle a_1 - b_1, a_2 - b_2 \rangle$$
> $$c\mathbf{a} = \langle ca_1, ca_2 \rangle$$
> Similarly, for three-dimensional vectors,
> $$\langle a_1, a_2, a_3 \rangle + \langle b_1, b_2, b_3 \rangle = \langle a_1 + b_1, a_2 + b_2, a_3 + b_3 \rangle$$
> $$\langle a_1, a_2, a_3 \rangle - \langle b_1, b_2, b_3 \rangle = \langle a_1 - b_1, a_2 - b_2, a_3 - b_3 \rangle$$
> $$c\langle a_1, a_2, a_3 \rangle = \langle ca_1, ca_2, ca_3 \rangle$$

FIGURE 14

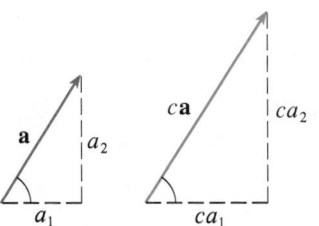

FIGURE 15

EXAMPLE 4 If $\mathbf{a} = \langle 4, 0, 3 \rangle$ and $\mathbf{b} = \langle -2, 1, 5 \rangle$, find $|\mathbf{a}|$ and the vectors $\mathbf{a} + \mathbf{b}$, $\mathbf{a} - \mathbf{b}$, $3\mathbf{b}$, and $2\mathbf{a} + 5\mathbf{b}$.

SOLUTION
$$|\mathbf{a}| = \sqrt{4^2 + 0^2 + 3^2} = \sqrt{25} = 5$$

$$\mathbf{a} + \mathbf{b} = \langle 4, 0, 3 \rangle + \langle -2, 1, 5 \rangle$$
$$= \langle 4 - 2, 0 + 1, 3 + 5 \rangle = \langle 2, 1, 8 \rangle$$

$$\mathbf{a} - \mathbf{b} = \langle 4, 0, 3 \rangle - \langle -2, 1, 5 \rangle$$
$$= \langle 4 - (-2), 0 - 1, 3 - 5 \rangle = \langle 6, -1, -2 \rangle$$

$$3\mathbf{b} = 3\langle -2, 1, 5 \rangle = \langle 3(-2), 3(1), 3(5) \rangle = \langle -6, 3, 15 \rangle$$

$$2\mathbf{a} + 5\mathbf{b} = 2\langle 4, 0, 3 \rangle + 5\langle -2, 1, 5 \rangle$$
$$= \langle 8, 0, 6 \rangle + \langle -10, 5, 25 \rangle = \langle -2, 5, 31 \rangle$$

We denote by V_2 the set of all two-dimensional vectors and by V_3 the set of all three-dimensional vectors. More generally, we will later need to consider the set V_n of all n-dimensional vectors. An n-dimensional vector is an ordered n-tuple:

$$\mathbf{a} = \langle a_1, a_2, \ldots, a_n \rangle$$

where $a_1, a_2, \ldots, a_n$ are real numbers that are called the components of $\mathbf{a}$. Addition and scalar multiplication are defined in terms of components just as for the cases $n = 2$ and $n = 3$.

|||| Vectors in n dimensions are used to list various quantities in an organized way. For instance, the components of a six-dimensional vector

$$\mathbf{p} = \langle p_1, p_2, p_3, p_4, p_5, p_6 \rangle$$

might represent the prices of six different ingredients required to make a particular product. Four-dimensional vectors $\langle x, y, z, t \rangle$ are used in relativity theory, where the first three components specify a position in space and the fourth represents time.

Properties of Vectors If $\mathbf{a}$, $\mathbf{b}$, and $\mathbf{c}$ are vectors in V_n and c and d are scalars, then

1. $\mathbf{a} + \mathbf{b} = \mathbf{b} + \mathbf{a}$

2. $\mathbf{a} + (\mathbf{b} + \mathbf{c}) = (\mathbf{a} + \mathbf{b}) + \mathbf{c}$

3. $\mathbf{a} + \mathbf{0} = \mathbf{a}$

4. $\mathbf{a} + (-\mathbf{a}) = \mathbf{0}$

5. $c(\mathbf{a} + \mathbf{b}) = c\mathbf{a} + c\mathbf{b}$

6. $(c + d)\mathbf{a} = c\mathbf{a} + d\mathbf{a}$

7. $(cd)\mathbf{a} = c(d\mathbf{a})$

8. $1\mathbf{a} = \mathbf{a}$

These eight properties of vectors can be readily verified either geometrically or algebraically. For instance, Property 1 can be seen from Figure 4 (it's equivalent to the Parallelogram Law) or as follows for the case $n = 2$:

$$\mathbf{a} + \mathbf{b} = \langle a_1, a_2 \rangle + \langle b_1, b_2 \rangle = \langle a_1 + b_1, a_2 + b_2 \rangle$$
$$= \langle b_1 + a_1, b_2 + a_2 \rangle = \langle b_1, b_2 \rangle + \langle a_1, a_2 \rangle$$
$$= \mathbf{b} + \mathbf{a}$$

We can see why Property 2 (the associative law) is true by looking at Figure 16 and applying the Triangle Law several times: The vector $\overrightarrow{PQ}$ is obtained either by first constructing $\mathbf{a} + \mathbf{b}$ and then adding $\mathbf{c}$ or by adding $\mathbf{a}$ to the vector $\mathbf{b} + \mathbf{c}$.

Three vectors in V_3 play a special role. Let

$$\mathbf{i} = \langle 1, 0, 0 \rangle \qquad \mathbf{j} = \langle 0, 1, 0 \rangle \qquad \mathbf{k} = \langle 0, 0, 1 \rangle$$

FIGURE 16

Then $\mathbf{i}$, $\mathbf{j}$, and $\mathbf{k}$ are vectors that have length 1 and point in the directions of the positive x-, y-, and z-axes. Similarly, in two dimensions we define $\mathbf{i} = \langle 1, 0 \rangle$ and $\mathbf{j} = \langle 0, 1 \rangle$. (See Figure 17.)

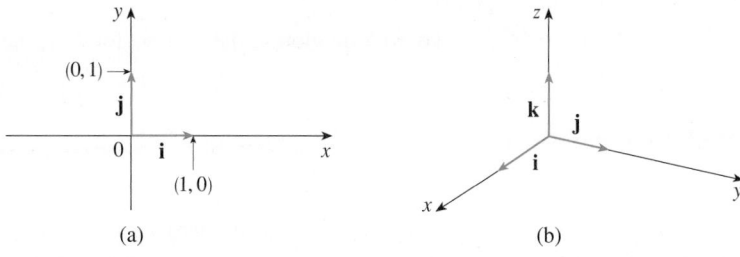

FIGURE 17

Standard basis vectors in V_2 and V_3

(a)   (b)

If $\mathbf{a} = \langle a_1, a_2, a_3 \rangle$, then we can write

$$\mathbf{a} = \langle a_1, a_2, a_3 \rangle = \langle a_1, 0, 0 \rangle + \langle 0, a_2, 0 \rangle + \langle 0, 0, a_3 \rangle$$

$$= a_1 \langle 1, 0, 0 \rangle + a_2 \langle 0, 1, 0 \rangle + a_3 \langle 0, 0, 1 \rangle$$

$\boxed{2}$ $$\mathbf{a} = a_1 \mathbf{i} + a_2 \mathbf{j} + a_3 \mathbf{k}$$

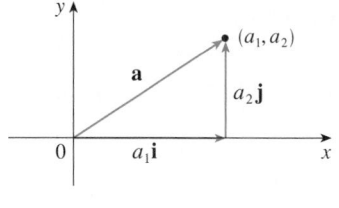

(a) $\mathbf{a} = a_1\mathbf{i} + a_2\mathbf{j}$

Thus, any vector in V_3 can be expressed in terms of the **standard basis vectors $\mathbf{i}$, $\mathbf{j}$, and $\mathbf{k}$.** For instance,

$$\langle 1, -2, 6 \rangle = \mathbf{i} - 2\mathbf{j} + 6\mathbf{k}$$

Similarly, in two dimensions, we can write

$\boxed{3}$ $$\mathbf{a} = \langle a_1, a_2 \rangle = a_1 \mathbf{i} + a_2 \mathbf{j}$$

See Figure 18 for the geometric interpretation of Equations 3 and 2 and compare with Figure 17.

EXAMPLE 5 If $\mathbf{a} = \mathbf{i} + 2\mathbf{j} - 3\mathbf{k}$ and $\mathbf{b} = 4\mathbf{i} + 7\mathbf{k}$, express the vector $2\mathbf{a} + 3\mathbf{b}$ in terms of $\mathbf{i}$, $\mathbf{j}$, and $\mathbf{k}$.

SOLUTION Using Properties 1, 2, 5, 6, and 7 of vectors, we have

$$2\mathbf{a} + 3\mathbf{b} = 2(\mathbf{i} + 2\mathbf{j} - 3\mathbf{k}) + 3(4\mathbf{i} + 7\mathbf{k})$$

$$= 2\mathbf{i} + 4\mathbf{j} - 6\mathbf{k} + 12\mathbf{i} + 21\mathbf{k} = 14\mathbf{i} + 4\mathbf{j} + 15\mathbf{k}$$

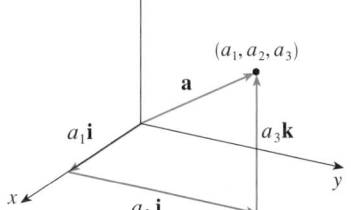

(b) $\mathbf{a} = a_1\mathbf{i} + a_2\mathbf{j} + a_3\mathbf{k}$

FIGURE 18

A **unit vector** is a vector whose length is 1. For instance, $\mathbf{i}$, $\mathbf{j}$, and $\mathbf{k}$ are all unit vectors. In general, if $\mathbf{a} \neq \mathbf{0}$, then the unit vector that has the same direction as $\mathbf{a}$ is

$\boxed{4}$ $$\mathbf{u} = \frac{1}{|\mathbf{a}|}\mathbf{a} = \frac{\mathbf{a}}{|\mathbf{a}|}$$

In order to verify this, we let $c = 1/|\mathbf{a}|$. Then $\mathbf{u} = c\mathbf{a}$ and c is a positive scalar, so $\mathbf{u}$ has the same direction as $\mathbf{a}$. Also

$$|\mathbf{u}| = |c\mathbf{a}| = |c||\mathbf{a}| = \frac{1}{|\mathbf{a}|}|\mathbf{a}| = 1$$

EXAMPLE 6 Find the unit vector in the direction of the vector $2\mathbf{i} - \mathbf{j} - 2\mathbf{k}$.

SOLUTION The given vector has length

$$|2\mathbf{i} - \mathbf{j} - 2\mathbf{k}| = \sqrt{2^2 + (-1)^2 + (-2)^2} = \sqrt{9} = 3$$

so, by Equation 4, the unit vector with the same direction is

$$\tfrac{1}{3}(2\mathbf{i} - \mathbf{j} - 2\mathbf{k}) = \tfrac{2}{3}\mathbf{i} - \tfrac{1}{3}\mathbf{j} - \tfrac{2}{3}\mathbf{k}$$

||||| Applications

Vectors are useful in many aspects of physics and engineering. In Chapter 14 we will see how they describe the velocity and acceleration of objects moving in space. Here we look at forces.

A force is represented by a vector because it has both a magnitude (measured in pounds or newtons) and a direction. If several forces are acting on an object, the **resultant force** experienced by the object is the vector sum of these forces.

EXAMPLE 7 A 100-lb weight hangs from two wires as shown in Figure 19. Find the tensions (forces) $\mathbf{T}_1$ and $\mathbf{T}_2$ in both wires and their magnitudes.

SOLUTION We first express $\mathbf{T}_1$ and $\mathbf{T}_2$ in terms of their horizontal and vertical components. From Figure 20 we see that

$$\mathbf{T}_1 = -|\mathbf{T}_1|\cos 50°\,\mathbf{i} + |\mathbf{T}_1|\sin 50°\,\mathbf{j}$$

$$\mathbf{T}_2 = |\mathbf{T}_2|\cos 32°\,\mathbf{i} + |\mathbf{T}_2|\sin 32°\,\mathbf{j}$$

The resultant $\mathbf{T}_1 + \mathbf{T}_2$ of the tensions counterbalances the weight $\mathbf{w}$ and so we must have

$$\mathbf{T}_1 + \mathbf{T}_2 = -\mathbf{w} = 100\mathbf{j}$$

Thus

$$\left(-|\mathbf{T}_1|\cos 50° + |\mathbf{T}_2|\cos 32°\right)\mathbf{i} + \left(|\mathbf{T}_1|\sin 50° + |\mathbf{T}_2|\sin 32°\right)\mathbf{j} = 100\mathbf{j}$$

Equating components, we get

$$-|\mathbf{T}_1|\cos 50° + |\mathbf{T}_2|\cos 32° = 0$$

$$|\mathbf{T}_1|\sin 50° + |\mathbf{T}_2|\sin 32° = 100$$

Solving the first of these equations for $|\mathbf{T}_2|$ and substituting into the second, we get

$$|\mathbf{T}_1|\sin 50° + \frac{|\mathbf{T}_1|\cos 50°}{\cos 32°}\sin 32° = 100$$

So the magnitudes of the tensions are

$$|\mathbf{T}_1| = \frac{100}{\sin 50° + \tan 32° \cos 50°} \approx 85.64 \text{ lb}$$

and

$$|\mathbf{T}_2| = \frac{|\mathbf{T}_1|\cos 50°}{\cos 32°} \approx 64.91 \text{ lb}$$

Substituting these values in (5) and (6), we obtain the tension vectors

$$\mathbf{T}_1 \approx -55.05\,\mathbf{i} + 65.60\,\mathbf{j} \qquad \mathbf{T}_2 \approx 55.05\,\mathbf{i} + 34.40\,\mathbf{j}$$

FIGURE 19

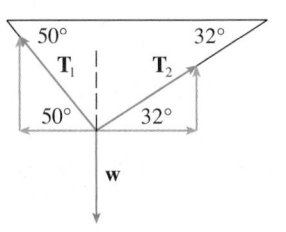

FIGURE 20

13.2 Exercises

1. Are the following quantities vectors or scalars? Explain.
(a) The cost of a theater ticket
(b) The current in a river
(c) The initial flight path from Houston to Dallas
(d) The population of the world

2. What is the relationship between the point (4, 7) and the vector $\langle 4, 7 \rangle$? Illustrate with a sketch.

3. Name all the equal vectors in the parallelogram shown.

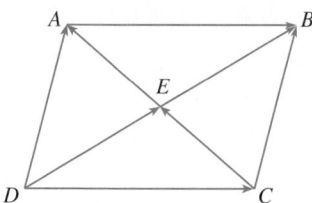

4. Write each combination of vectors as a single vector.
(a) $\overrightarrow{PQ} + \overrightarrow{QR}$ (b) $\overrightarrow{RP} + \overrightarrow{PS}$
(c) $\overrightarrow{QS} - \overrightarrow{PS}$ (d) $\overrightarrow{RS} + \overrightarrow{SP} + \overrightarrow{PQ}$

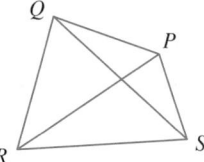

5. Copy the vectors in the figure and use them to draw the following vectors.
(a) $\mathbf{u} + \mathbf{v}$ (b) $\mathbf{u} - \mathbf{v}$
(c) $\mathbf{v} + \mathbf{w}$ (d) $\mathbf{w} + \mathbf{v} + \mathbf{u}$

6. Copy the vectors in the figure and use them to draw the following vectors.
(a) $\mathbf{a} + \mathbf{b}$ (b) $\mathbf{a} - \mathbf{b}$
(c) $2\mathbf{a}$ (d) $-\frac{1}{2}\mathbf{b}$
(e) $2\mathbf{a} + \mathbf{b}$ (f) $\mathbf{b} - 3\mathbf{a}$

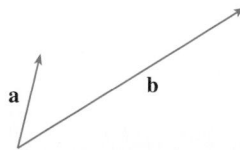

7–12 ▓ Find a vector $\mathbf{a}$ with representation given by the directed line segment $\overrightarrow{AB}$. Draw $\overrightarrow{AB}$ and the equivalent representation starting at the origin.

7. $A(2, 3)$, $B(-2, 1)$ **8.** $A(-2, -2)$, $B(5, 3)$

9. $A(-1, -1)$, $B(-3, 4)$ **10.** $A(-2, 2)$, $B(3, 0)$

11. $A(0, 3, 1)$, $B(2, 3, -1)$ **12.** $A(4, 0, -2)$, $B(4, 2, 1)$

13–16 ▓ Find the sum of the given vectors and illustrate geometrically.

13. $\langle 3, -1 \rangle$, $\langle -2, 4 \rangle$ **14.** $\langle -2, -1 \rangle$, $\langle 5, 7 \rangle$

15. $\langle 0, 1, 2 \rangle$, $\langle 0, 0, -3 \rangle$ **16.** $\langle -1, 0, 2 \rangle$, $\langle 0, 4, 0 \rangle$

17–22 ▓ Find $|\mathbf{a}|$, $\mathbf{a} + \mathbf{b}$, $\mathbf{a} - \mathbf{b}$, $2\mathbf{a}$, and $3\mathbf{a} + 4\mathbf{b}$.

17. $\mathbf{a} = \langle -4, 3 \rangle$, $\mathbf{b} = \langle 6, 2 \rangle$

18. $\mathbf{a} = 2\mathbf{i} - 3\mathbf{j}$, $\mathbf{b} = \mathbf{i} + 5\mathbf{j}$

19. $\mathbf{a} = \langle 6, 2, 3 \rangle$, $\mathbf{b} = \langle -1, 5, -2 \rangle$

20. $\mathbf{a} = \langle -3, -4, -1 \rangle$, $\mathbf{b} = \langle 6, 2, -3 \rangle$

21. $\mathbf{a} = \mathbf{i} - 2\mathbf{j} + \mathbf{k}$, $\mathbf{b} = \mathbf{j} + 2\mathbf{k}$

22. $\mathbf{a} = 3\mathbf{i} - 2\mathbf{k}$, $\mathbf{b} = \mathbf{i} - \mathbf{j} + \mathbf{k}$

23–25 ▓ Find a unit vector that has the same direction as the given vector.

23. $\langle 9, -5 \rangle$ **24.** $12\mathbf{i} - 5\mathbf{j}$

25. $8\mathbf{i} - \mathbf{j} + 4\mathbf{k}$

26. Find a vector that has the same direction as $\langle -2, 4, 2 \rangle$ but has length 6.

27. If $\mathbf{v}$ lies in the first quadrant and makes an angle $\pi/3$ with the positive x-axis and $|\mathbf{v}| = 4$, find $\mathbf{v}$ in component form.

28. If a child pulls a sled through the snow with a force of 50 N exerted at an angle of 38° above the horizontal, find the horizontal and vertical components of the force.

29. Two forces $\mathbf{F}_1$ and $\mathbf{F}_2$ with magnitudes 10 lb and 12 lb act on an object at a point P as shown in the figure. Find the resultant force $\mathbf{F}$ acting at P as well as its magnitude and its direction. (Indicate the direction by finding the angle θ shown in the figure.)

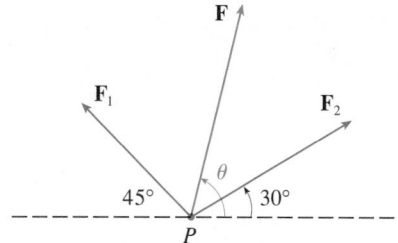

30. Velocities have both direction and magnitude and thus are vectors. The magnitude of a velocity vector is called *speed*. Suppose that a wind is blowing from the direction N45°W at a speed of 50 km/h. (This means that the direction from which the wind blows is 45° west of the northerly direction.) A pilot is steering a plane in the direction N60°E at an airspeed (speed in still air) of 250 km/h. The *true course*, or *track*, of the plane is the direction of the resultant of the velocity vectors of the plane and the wind. The *ground speed* of the plane is the magnitude of the resultant. Find the true course and the ground speed of the plane.

31. A woman walks due west on the deck of a ship at 3 mi/h. The ship is moving north at a speed of 22 mi/h. Find the speed and direction of the woman relative to the surface of the water.

32. Ropes 3 m and 5 m in length are fastened to a holiday decoration that is suspended over a town square. The decoration has a mass of 5 kg. The ropes, fastened at different heights, make angles of 52° and 40° with the horizontal. Find the tension in each wire and the magnitude of each tension.

33. A clothesline is tied between two poles, 8 m apart. The line is quite taut and has negligible sag. When a wet shirt with a mass of 0.8 kg is hung at the middle of the line, the midpoint is pulled down 8 cm. Find the tension in each half of the clothesline.

34. The tension **T** at each end of the chain has magnitude 25 N. What is the weight of the chain?

35. If A, B, and C are the vertices of a triangle, find $\overrightarrow{AB} + \overrightarrow{BC} + \overrightarrow{CA}$.

36. Let C be the point on the line segment AB that is twice as far from B as it is from A. If $\mathbf{a} = \overrightarrow{OA}$, $\mathbf{b} = \overrightarrow{OB}$, and $\mathbf{c} = \overrightarrow{OC}$, show that $\mathbf{c} = \frac{2}{3}\mathbf{a} + \frac{1}{3}\mathbf{b}$.

37. (a) Draw the vectors $\mathbf{a} = \langle 3, 2 \rangle$, $\mathbf{b} = \langle 2, -1 \rangle$, and $\mathbf{c} = \langle 7, 1 \rangle$.
(b) Show, by means of a sketch, that there are scalars s and t such that $\mathbf{c} = s\mathbf{a} + t\mathbf{b}$.
(c) Use the sketch to estimate the values of s and t.
(d) Find the exact values of s and t.

38. Suppose that **a** and **b** are nonzero vectors that are not parallel and **c** is any vector in the plane determined by **a** and **b**. Give a geometric argument to show that **c** can be written as $\mathbf{c} = s\mathbf{a} + t\mathbf{b}$ for suitable scalars s and t. Then give an argument using components.

39. If $\mathbf{r} = \langle x, y, z \rangle$ and $\mathbf{r}_0 = \langle x_0, y_0, z_0 \rangle$, describe the set of all points (x, y, z) such that $|\mathbf{r} - \mathbf{r}_0| = 1$.

40. If $\mathbf{r} = \langle x, y \rangle$, $\mathbf{r}_1 = \langle x_1, y_1 \rangle$, and $\mathbf{r}_2 = \langle x_2, y_2 \rangle$, describe the set of all points (x, y) such that $|\mathbf{r} - \mathbf{r}_1| + |\mathbf{r} - \mathbf{r}_2| = k$, where $k > |\mathbf{r}_1 - \mathbf{r}_2|$.

41. Figure 16 gives a geometric demonstration of Property 2 of vectors. Use components to give an algebraic proof of this fact for the case $n = 2$.

42. Prove Property 5 of vectors algebraically for the case $n = 3$. Then use similar triangles to give a geometric proof.

43. Use vectors to prove that the line joining the midpoints of two sides of a triangle is parallel to the third side and half its length.

44. Suppose the three coordinate planes are all mirrored and a light ray given by the vector $\mathbf{a} = \langle a_1, a_2, a_3 \rangle$ first strikes the xz-plane, as shown in the figure. Use the fact that the angle of incidence equals the angle of reflection to show that the direction of the reflected ray is given by $\mathbf{b} = \langle a_1, -a_2, a_3 \rangle$. Deduce that, after being reflected by all three mutually perpendicular mirrors, the resulting ray is parallel to the initial ray. (American space scientists used this principle, together with laser beams and an array of corner mirrors on the Moon, to calculate very precisely the distance from the Earth to the Moon.)

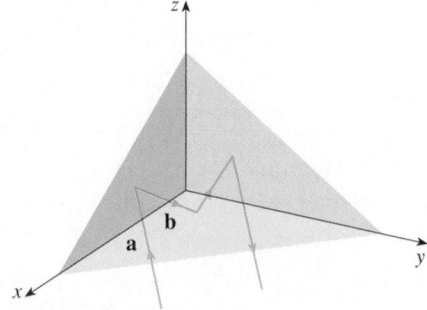

13.3 The Dot Product

So far we have added two vectors and multiplied a vector by a scalar. The question arises: Is it possible to multiply two vectors so that their product is a useful quantity? One such product is the dot product, whose definition follows. Another is the cross product, which is discussed in the next section.

---

1 **Definition** If $\mathbf{a} = \langle a_1, a_2, a_3 \rangle$ and $\mathbf{b} = \langle b_1, b_2, b_3 \rangle$, then the **dot product** of $\mathbf{a}$ and $\mathbf{b}$ is the number $\mathbf{a} \cdot \mathbf{b}$ given by

$$\mathbf{a} \cdot \mathbf{b} = a_1 b_1 + a_2 b_2 + a_3 b_3$$

Thus, to find the dot product of $\mathbf{a}$ and $\mathbf{b}$ we multiply corresponding components and add. The result is not a vector. It is a real number, that is, a scalar. For this reason, the dot product is sometimes called the **scalar product** (or **inner product**). Although Definition 1 is given for three-dimensional vectors, the dot product of two-dimensional vectors is defined in a similar fashion:

$$\langle a_1, a_2 \rangle \cdot \langle b_1, b_2 \rangle = a_1 b_1 + a_2 b_2$$

EXAMPLE 1

$$\langle 2, 4 \rangle \cdot \langle 3, -1 \rangle = 2(3) + 4(-1) = 2$$

$$\langle -1, 7, 4 \rangle \cdot \left\langle 6, 2, -\tfrac{1}{2} \right\rangle = (-1)(6) + 7(2) + 4\left(-\tfrac{1}{2}\right) = 6$$

$$(\mathbf{i} + 2\mathbf{j} - 3\mathbf{k}) \cdot (2\mathbf{j} - \mathbf{k}) = 1(0) + 2(2) + (-3)(-1) = 7$$

The dot product obeys many of the laws that hold for ordinary products of real numbers. These are stated in the following theorem.

---

2 **Properties of the Dot Product** If $\mathbf{a}$, $\mathbf{b}$, and $\mathbf{c}$ are vectors in V_3 and c is a scalar, then

1. $\mathbf{a} \cdot \mathbf{a} = |\mathbf{a}|^2$ 2. $\mathbf{a} \cdot \mathbf{b} = \mathbf{b} \cdot \mathbf{a}$

3. $\mathbf{a} \cdot (\mathbf{b} + \mathbf{c}) = \mathbf{a} \cdot \mathbf{b} + \mathbf{a} \cdot \mathbf{c}$ 4. $(c\mathbf{a}) \cdot \mathbf{b} = c(\mathbf{a} \cdot \mathbf{b}) = \mathbf{a} \cdot (c\mathbf{b})$

5. $\mathbf{0} \cdot \mathbf{a} = 0$

These properties are easily proved using Definition 1. For instance, here are the proofs of Properties 1 and 3:

1. $\mathbf{a} \cdot \mathbf{a} = a_1^2 + a_2^2 + a_3^2 = |\mathbf{a}|^2$

3. $\mathbf{a} \cdot (\mathbf{b} + \mathbf{c}) = \langle a_1, a_2, a_3 \rangle \cdot \langle b_1 + c_1, b_2 + c_2, b_3 + c_3 \rangle$

$$= a_1(b_1 + c_1) + a_2(b_2 + c_2) + a_3(b_3 + c_3)$$

$$= a_1 b_1 + a_1 c_1 + a_2 b_2 + a_2 c_2 + a_3 b_3 + a_3 c_3$$

$$= (a_1 b_1 + a_2 b_2 + a_3 b_3) + (a_1 c_1 + a_2 c_2 + a_3 c_3)$$

$$= \mathbf{a} \cdot \mathbf{b} + \mathbf{a} \cdot \mathbf{c}$$

The proofs of the remaining properties are left as exercises.

The dot product $\mathbf{a} \cdot \mathbf{b}$ can be given a geometric interpretation in terms of the **angle** θ **between a and b**, which is defined to be the angle between the representations of $\mathbf{a}$ and $\mathbf{b}$ that start at the origin, where $0 \leqslant \theta \leqslant \pi$. In other words, θ is the angle between the

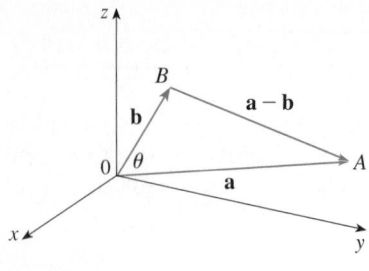

FIGURE 1

line segments $\overrightarrow{OA}$ and $\overrightarrow{OB}$ in Figure 1. Note that if **a** and **b** are parallel vectors, then $\theta = 0$ or $\theta = \pi$.

The formula in the following theorem is used by physicists as the *definition* of the dot product.

> **3 Theorem** If θ is the angle between the vectors **a** and **b**, then
> $$\mathbf{a} \cdot \mathbf{b} = |\mathbf{a}||\mathbf{b}| \cos \theta$$

Proof If we apply the Law of Cosines to triangle OAB in Figure 1, we get

$$\boxed{4} \qquad |AB|^2 = |OA|^2 + |OB|^2 - 2|OA||OB| \cos \theta$$

(Observe that the Law of Cosines still applies in the limiting cases when $\theta = 0$ or π, or $\mathbf{a} = \mathbf{0}$ or $\mathbf{b} = \mathbf{0}$.) But $|OA| = |\mathbf{a}|$, $|OB| = |\mathbf{b}|$, and $|AB| = |\mathbf{a} - \mathbf{b}|$, so Equation 4 becomes

$$\boxed{5} \qquad |\mathbf{a} - \mathbf{b}|^2 = |\mathbf{a}|^2 + |\mathbf{b}|^2 - 2|\mathbf{a}||\mathbf{b}| \cos \theta$$

Using Properties 1, 2, and 3 of the dot product, we can rewrite the left side of this equation as follows:

$$|\mathbf{a} - \mathbf{b}|^2 = (\mathbf{a} - \mathbf{b}) \cdot (\mathbf{a} - \mathbf{b})$$
$$= \mathbf{a} \cdot \mathbf{a} - \mathbf{a} \cdot \mathbf{b} - \mathbf{b} \cdot \mathbf{a} + \mathbf{b} \cdot \mathbf{b}$$
$$= |\mathbf{a}|^2 - 2\mathbf{a} \cdot \mathbf{b} + |\mathbf{b}|^2$$

Therefore, Equation 5 gives

$$|\mathbf{a}|^2 - 2\mathbf{a} \cdot \mathbf{b} + |\mathbf{b}|^2 = |\mathbf{a}|^2 + |\mathbf{b}|^2 - 2|\mathbf{a}||\mathbf{b}| \cos \theta$$

Thus
$$-2\mathbf{a} \cdot \mathbf{b} = -2|\mathbf{a}||\mathbf{b}| \cos \theta$$

or
$$\mathbf{a} \cdot \mathbf{b} = |\mathbf{a}||\mathbf{b}| \cos \theta$$

EXAMPLE 2 If the vectors **a** and **b** have lengths 4 and 6, and the angle between them is $\pi/3$, find $\mathbf{a} \cdot \mathbf{b}$.

SOLUTION Using Theorem 3, we have

$$\mathbf{a} \cdot \mathbf{b} = |\mathbf{a}||\mathbf{b}| \cos(\pi/3) = 4 \cdot 6 \cdot \tfrac{1}{2} = 12$$

The formula in Theorem 3 also enables us to find the angle between two vectors.

> **6 Corollary** If θ is the angle between the nonzero vectors **a** and **b**, then
> $$\cos \theta = \frac{\mathbf{a} \cdot \mathbf{b}}{|\mathbf{a}||\mathbf{b}|}$$

EXAMPLE 3 Find the angle between the vectors $\mathbf{a} = \langle 2, 2, -1 \rangle$ and $\mathbf{b} = \langle 5, -3, 2 \rangle$.

SOLUTION Since

$$|\mathbf{a}| = \sqrt{2^2 + 2^2 + (-1)^2} = 3 \quad \text{and} \quad |\mathbf{b}| = \sqrt{5^2 + (-3)^2 + 2^2} = \sqrt{38}$$

and since

$$\mathbf{a} \cdot \mathbf{b} = 2(5) + 2(-3) + (-1)(2) = 2$$

we have, from Corollary 6,

$$\cos \theta = \frac{\mathbf{a} \cdot \mathbf{b}}{|\mathbf{a}||\mathbf{b}|} = \frac{2}{3\sqrt{38}}$$

So the angle between **a** and **b** is

$$\theta = \cos^{-1}\left(\frac{2}{3\sqrt{38}}\right) \approx 1.46 \quad (\text{or } 84°)$$

Two nonzero vectors **a** and **b** are called **perpendicular** or **orthogonal** if the angle between them is $\theta = \pi/2$. Then Theorem 3 gives

$$\mathbf{a} \cdot \mathbf{b} = |\mathbf{a}||\mathbf{b}| \cos(\pi/2) = 0$$

and conversely if $\mathbf{a} \cdot \mathbf{b} = 0$, then $\cos \theta = 0$, so $\theta = \pi/2$. The zero vector **0** is considered to be perpendicular to all vectors. Therefore, we have the following method for determining whether two vectors are orthogonal.

> [7]   Two vectors **a** and **b** are orthogonal if and only if $\mathbf{a} \cdot \mathbf{b} = 0$.

EXAMPLE 4 Show that $2\mathbf{i} + 2\mathbf{j} - \mathbf{k}$ is perpendicular to $5\mathbf{i} - 4\mathbf{j} + 2\mathbf{k}$.

SOLUTION Since

$$(2\mathbf{i} + 2\mathbf{j} - \mathbf{k}) \cdot (5\mathbf{i} - 4\mathbf{j} + 2\mathbf{k}) = 2(5) + 2(-4) + (-1)(2) = 0$$

these vectors are perpendicular by (7).

Because $\cos \theta > 0$ if $0 \leq \theta < \pi/2$ and $\cos \theta < 0$ if $\pi/2 < \theta \leq \pi$, we see that $\mathbf{a} \cdot \mathbf{b}$ is positive for $\theta < \pi/2$ and negative for $\theta > \pi/2$. We can think of $\mathbf{a} \cdot \mathbf{b}$ as measuring the extent to which **a** and **b** point in the same direction. The dot product $\mathbf{a} \cdot \mathbf{b}$ is positive if **a** and **b** point in the same general direction, 0 if they are perpendicular, and negative if they point in generally opposite directions (see Figure 2). In the extreme case where **a** and **b** point in exactly the same direction, we have $\theta = 0$, so $\cos \theta = 1$ and

$$\mathbf{a} \cdot \mathbf{b} = |\mathbf{a}||\mathbf{b}|$$

If **a** and **b** point in exactly opposite directions, then $\theta = \pi$ and so $\cos \theta = -1$ and $\mathbf{a} \cdot \mathbf{b} = -|\mathbf{a}||\mathbf{b}|$.

FIGURE 2

Visual 13.3A shows an animation of Figure 2.

|||| Direction Angles and Direction Cosines

The **direction angles** of a nonzero vector **a** are the angles α, β, and γ (in the interval $[0, \pi]$) that **a** makes with the positive x-, y-, and z-axes (see Figure 3 on page 846).

The cosines of these direction angles, $\cos \alpha$, $\cos \beta$, and $\cos \gamma$, are called the **direction cosines** of the vector **a**. Using Corollary 6 with **b** replaced by **i**, we obtain

$$[8] \qquad \cos \alpha = \frac{\mathbf{a} \cdot \mathbf{i}}{|\mathbf{a}||\mathbf{i}|} = \frac{a_1}{|\mathbf{a}|}$$

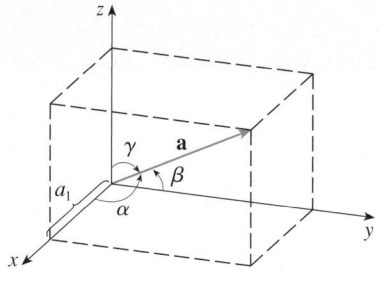

FIGURE 3

(This can also be seen directly from Figure 3.) Similarly, we also have

[9]

$$\cos \beta = \frac{a_2}{|\mathbf{a}|} \qquad \cos \gamma = \frac{a_3}{|\mathbf{a}|}$$

By squaring the expressions in Equations 8 and 9 and adding, we see that

[10]

$$\cos^2\alpha + \cos^2\beta + \cos^2\gamma = 1$$

We can also use Equations 8 and 9 to write

$$\mathbf{a} = \langle a_1, a_2, a_3 \rangle = \langle |\mathbf{a}| \cos \alpha, |\mathbf{a}| \cos \beta, |\mathbf{a}| \cos \gamma \rangle$$

$$= |\mathbf{a}| \langle \cos \alpha, \cos \beta, \cos \gamma \rangle$$

Therefore

[11]

$$\frac{1}{|\mathbf{a}|} \mathbf{a} = \langle \cos \alpha, \cos \beta, \cos \gamma \rangle$$

which says that the direction cosines of $\mathbf{a}$ are the components of the unit vector in the direction of $\mathbf{a}$.

EXAMPLE 5 Find the direction angles of the vector $\mathbf{a} = \langle 1, 2, 3 \rangle$.

SOLUTION Since $|\mathbf{a}| = \sqrt{1^2 + 2^2 + 3^2} = \sqrt{14}$, Equations 8 and 9 give

$$\cos \alpha = \frac{1}{\sqrt{14}} \qquad \cos \beta = \frac{2}{\sqrt{14}} \qquad \cos \gamma = \frac{3}{\sqrt{14}}$$

and so

$$\alpha = \cos^{-1}\left(\frac{1}{\sqrt{14}}\right) \approx 74° \qquad \beta = \cos^{-1}\left(\frac{2}{\sqrt{14}}\right) \approx 58° \qquad \gamma = \cos^{-1}\left(\frac{3}{\sqrt{14}}\right) \approx 37°$$

|||| **Projections**

Figure 4 shows representations $\overrightarrow{PQ}$ and $\overrightarrow{PR}$ of two vectors $\mathbf{a}$ and $\mathbf{b}$ with the same initial point P. If S is the foot of the perpendicular from R to the line containing $\overrightarrow{PQ}$, then the vector with representation $\overrightarrow{PS}$ is called the **vector projection** of $\mathbf{b}$ onto $\mathbf{a}$ and is denoted by $\text{proj}_{\mathbf{a}} \mathbf{b}$.

 Visual 13.3B shows how Figure 4 changes when we vary $\mathbf{a}$ and $\mathbf{b}$.

 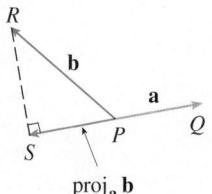

FIGURE 4

Vector projections

The **scalar projection** of $\mathbf{b}$ onto $\mathbf{a}$ (also called the **component of b along a**) is defined to be the magnitude of the vector projection, which is the number $|\mathbf{b}| \cos \theta$, where θ is the

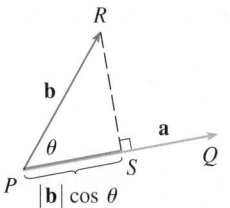

FIGURE 5

Scalar projection

angle between **a** and **b**. (See Figure 5; you can think of the scalar projection of **b** as being the length of a shadow of **b**.) This is denoted by comp$_a$ **b**. Observe that it is negative if $\pi/2 < \theta \le \pi$. The equation

$$\mathbf{a} \cdot \mathbf{b} = |\mathbf{a}||\mathbf{b}| \cos \theta = |\mathbf{a}|(|\mathbf{b}| \cos \theta)$$

shows that the dot product of **a** and **b** can be interpreted as the length of **a** times the scalar projection of **b** onto **a**. Since

$$|\mathbf{b}| \cos \theta = \frac{\mathbf{a} \cdot \mathbf{b}}{|\mathbf{a}|} = \frac{\mathbf{a}}{|\mathbf{a}|} \cdot \mathbf{b}$$

the component of **b** along **a** can be computed by taking the dot product of **b** with the unit vector in the direction of **a**. We summarize these ideas as follows.

Scalar projection of **b** onto **a**: $\displaystyle \text{comp}_a \, \mathbf{b} = \frac{\mathbf{a} \cdot \mathbf{b}}{|\mathbf{a}|}$

Vector projection of **b** onto **a**: $\displaystyle \text{proj}_a \, \mathbf{b} = \left(\frac{\mathbf{a} \cdot \mathbf{b}}{|\mathbf{a}|}\right) \frac{\mathbf{a}}{|\mathbf{a}|} = \frac{\mathbf{a} \cdot \mathbf{b}}{|\mathbf{a}|^2} \, \mathbf{a}$

Notice that the vector projection is the scalar projection times the unit vector in the direction of **a**.

EXAMPLE 6 Find the scalar projection and vector projection of $\mathbf{b} = \langle 1, 1, 2 \rangle$ onto $\mathbf{a} = \langle -2, 3, 1 \rangle$.

SOLUTION Since $|\mathbf{a}| = \sqrt{(-2)^2 + 3^2 + 1^2} = \sqrt{14}$, the scalar projection of **b** onto **a** is

$$\text{comp}_a \, \mathbf{b} = \frac{\mathbf{a} \cdot \mathbf{b}}{|\mathbf{a}|} = \frac{(-2)(1) + 3(1) + 1(2)}{\sqrt{14}} = \frac{3}{\sqrt{14}}$$

The vector projection is this scalar projection times the unit vector in the direction of **a**:

$$\text{proj}_a \, \mathbf{b} = \frac{3}{\sqrt{14}} \frac{\mathbf{a}}{|\mathbf{a}|} = \frac{3}{14} \mathbf{a} = \left\langle -\frac{3}{7}, \frac{9}{14}, \frac{3}{14} \right\rangle$$

One use of projections occurs in physics in calculating work. In Section 6.4 we defined the work done by a constant force F in moving an object through a distance d as $W = Fd$, but this applies only when the force is directed along the line of motion of the object. Suppose, however, that the constant force is a vector $\mathbf{F} = \overrightarrow{PR}$ pointing in some other direction as in Figure 6. If the force moves the object from P to Q, then the **displacement vector** is $\mathbf{D} = \overrightarrow{PQ}$. The **work** done by this force is defined to be the product of the component of the force along **D** and the distance moved:

$$W = \big(|\mathbf{F}| \cos \theta\big)|\mathbf{D}|$$

But then, from Theorem 3, we have

$$\boxed{12} \qquad\qquad W = |\mathbf{F}||\mathbf{D}| \cos \theta = \mathbf{F} \cdot \mathbf{D}$$

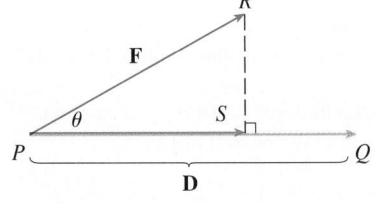

FIGURE 6

Thus, the work done by a constant force $\mathbf{F}$ is the dot product $\mathbf{F} \cdot \mathbf{D}$, where $\mathbf{D}$ is the displacement vector.

EXAMPLE 7 A crate is hauled 8 m up a ramp under a constant force of 200 N applied at an angle of $25°$ to the ramp. Find the work done.

SOLUTION If $\mathbf{F}$ and $\mathbf{D}$ are the force and displacement vectors, as pictured in Figure 7, then the work done is

$$W = \mathbf{F} \cdot \mathbf{D} = |\mathbf{F}||\mathbf{D}| \cos 25°$$

$$= (200)(8) \cos 25° \approx 1450 \text{ N·m} = 1450 \text{ J}$$

FIGURE 7

EXAMPLE 8 A force is given by a vector $\mathbf{F} = 3\mathbf{i} + 4\mathbf{j} + 5\mathbf{k}$ and moves a particle from the point $P(2, 1, 0)$ to the point $Q(4, 6, 2)$. Find the work done.

SOLUTION The displacement vector is $\mathbf{D} = \overrightarrow{PQ} = \langle 2, 5, 2 \rangle$, so by Equation 12, the work done is

$$W = \mathbf{F} \cdot \mathbf{D} = \langle 3, 4, 5 \rangle \cdot \langle 2, 5, 2 \rangle$$

$$= 6 + 20 + 10 = 36$$

If the unit of length is meters and the magnitude of the force is measured in newtons, then the work done is 36 joules.

13.3 Exercises

1. Which of the following expressions are meaningful? Which are meaningless? Explain.
   (a) $(\mathbf{a} \cdot \mathbf{b}) \cdot \mathbf{c}$ (b) $(\mathbf{a} \cdot \mathbf{b})\mathbf{c}$
   (c) $|\mathbf{a}|(\mathbf{b} \cdot \mathbf{c})$ (d) $\mathbf{a} \cdot (\mathbf{b} + \mathbf{c})$
   (e) $\mathbf{a} \cdot \mathbf{b} + \mathbf{c}$ (f) $|\mathbf{a}| \cdot (\mathbf{b} + \mathbf{c})$

2. Find the dot product of two vectors if their lengths are 6 and $\frac{1}{3}$ and the angle between them is $\pi/4$.

3–10 IIII Find $\mathbf{a} \cdot \mathbf{b}$.

3. $\mathbf{a} = \langle 4, -1 \rangle$, $\mathbf{b} = \langle 3, 6 \rangle$

4. $\mathbf{a} = \langle \frac{1}{2}, 4 \rangle$, $\mathbf{b} = \langle -8, -3 \rangle$

5. $\mathbf{a} = \langle 5, 0, -2 \rangle$, $\mathbf{b} = \langle 3, -1, 10 \rangle$

6. $\mathbf{a} = \langle s, 2s, 3s \rangle$, $\mathbf{b} = \langle t, -t, 5t \rangle$

7. $\mathbf{a} = \mathbf{i} - 2\mathbf{j} + 3\mathbf{k}$, $\mathbf{b} = 5\mathbf{i} + 9\mathbf{k}$

8. $\mathbf{a} = 4\mathbf{j} - 3\mathbf{k}$, $\mathbf{b} = 2\mathbf{i} + 4\mathbf{j} + 6\mathbf{k}$

9. $|\mathbf{a}| = 12$, $|\mathbf{b}| = 15$,   the angle between $\mathbf{a}$ and $\mathbf{b}$ is $\pi/6$

10. $|\mathbf{a}| = 4$, $|\mathbf{b}| = 10$,   the angle between $\mathbf{a}$ and $\mathbf{b}$ is $120°$

11–12 IIII If $\mathbf{u}$ is a unit vector, find $\mathbf{u} \cdot \mathbf{v}$ and $\mathbf{u} \cdot \mathbf{w}$.

11.

12.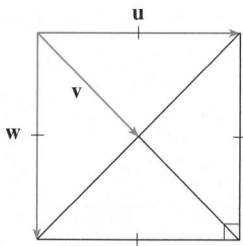

13. (a) Show that $\mathbf{i} \cdot \mathbf{j} = \mathbf{j} \cdot \mathbf{k} = \mathbf{k} \cdot \mathbf{i} = 0$.
   (b) Show that $\mathbf{i} \cdot \mathbf{i} = \mathbf{j} \cdot \mathbf{j} = \mathbf{k} \cdot \mathbf{k} = 1$.

14. A street vendor sells a hamburgers, b hot dogs, and c soft drinks on a given day. He charges $2 for a hamburger, $1.50 for a hot dog, and $1 for a soft drink. If $\mathbf{A} = \langle a, b, c \rangle$ and $\mathbf{P} = \langle 2, 1.5, 1 \rangle$, what is the meaning of the dot product $\mathbf{A} \cdot \mathbf{P}$?

15–20 IIII Find the angle between the vectors. (First find an exact expression and then approximate to the nearest degree.)

15. $\mathbf{a} = \langle 3, 4 \rangle$, $\mathbf{b} = \langle 5, 12 \rangle$

16. $\mathbf{a} = \langle \sqrt{3}, 1 \rangle$, $\mathbf{b} = \langle 0, 5 \rangle$

17. $\mathbf{a} = \langle 1, 2, 3 \rangle$, $\quad \mathbf{b} = \langle 4, 0, -1 \rangle$

18. $\mathbf{a} = \langle 6, -3, 2 \rangle$, $\quad \mathbf{b} = \langle 2, 1, -2 \rangle$

19. $\mathbf{a} = \mathbf{j} + \mathbf{k}$, $\quad \mathbf{b} = \mathbf{i} + 2\mathbf{j} - 3\mathbf{k}$

20. $\mathbf{a} = 2\mathbf{i} - \mathbf{j} + \mathbf{k}$, $\quad \mathbf{b} = 3\mathbf{i} + 2\mathbf{j} - \mathbf{k}$

21–22 ▓ Find, correct to the nearest degree, the three angles of the triangle with the given vertices.

21. $A(1, 0)$, $\quad B(3, 6)$, $\quad C(-1, 4)$

22. $D(0, 1, 1)$, $\quad E(-2, 4, 3)$, $\quad F(1, 2, -1)$

23–24 ▓ Determine whether the given vectors are orthogonal, parallel, or neither.

23. (a) $\mathbf{a} = \langle -5, 3, 7 \rangle$, $\quad \mathbf{b} = \langle 6, -8, 2 \rangle$
(b) $\mathbf{a} = \langle 4, 6 \rangle$, $\quad \mathbf{b} = \langle -3, 2 \rangle$
(c) $\mathbf{a} = -\mathbf{i} + 2\mathbf{j} + 5\mathbf{k}$, $\quad \mathbf{b} = 3\mathbf{i} + 4\mathbf{j} - \mathbf{k}$
(d) $\mathbf{a} = 2\mathbf{i} + 6\mathbf{j} - 4\mathbf{k}$, $\quad \mathbf{b} = -3\mathbf{i} - 9\mathbf{j} + 6\mathbf{k}$

24. (a) $\mathbf{u} = \langle -3, 9, 6 \rangle$, $\quad \mathbf{v} = \langle 4, -12, -8 \rangle$
(b) $\mathbf{u} = \mathbf{i} - \mathbf{j} + 2\mathbf{k}$, $\quad \mathbf{v} = 2\mathbf{i} - \mathbf{j} + \mathbf{k}$
(c) $\mathbf{u} = \langle a, b, c \rangle$, $\quad \mathbf{v} = \langle -b, a, 0 \rangle$

---

25. Use vectors to decide whether the triangle with vertices $P(1, -3, -2)$, $Q(2, 0, -4)$, and $R(6, -2, -5)$ is right-angled.

26. For what values of b are the vectors $\langle -6, b, 2 \rangle$ and $\langle b, b^2, b \rangle$ orthogonal?

27. Find a unit vector that is orthogonal to both $\mathbf{i} + \mathbf{j}$ and $\mathbf{i} + \mathbf{k}$.

28. Find two unit vectors that make an angle of $60°$ with $\mathbf{v} = \langle 3, 4 \rangle$.

29–33 ▓ Find the direction cosines and direction angles of the vector. (Give the direction angles correct to the nearest degree.)

29. $\langle 3, 4, 5 \rangle$

30. $\langle 1, -2, -1 \rangle$

31. $2\mathbf{i} + 3\mathbf{j} - 6\mathbf{k}$

32. $2\mathbf{i} - \mathbf{j} + 2\mathbf{k}$

33. $\langle c, c, c \rangle$, $\quad$ where $c > 0$

---

34. If a vector has direction angles $\alpha = \pi/4$ and $\beta = \pi/3$, find the third direction angle γ.

35–40 ▓ Find the scalar and vector projections of $\mathbf{b}$ onto $\mathbf{a}$.

35. $\mathbf{a} = \langle 3, -4 \rangle$, $\quad \mathbf{b} = \langle 5, 0 \rangle$

36. $\mathbf{a} = \langle 1, 2 \rangle$, $\quad \mathbf{b} = \langle -4, 1 \rangle$

37. $\mathbf{a} = \langle 4, 2, 0 \rangle$, $\quad \mathbf{b} = \langle 1, 1, 1 \rangle$

38. $\mathbf{a} = \langle -1, -2, 2 \rangle$, $\quad \mathbf{b} = \langle 3, 3, 4 \rangle$

39. $\mathbf{a} = \mathbf{i} + \mathbf{k}$, $\quad \mathbf{b} = \mathbf{i} - \mathbf{j}$

40. $\mathbf{a} = 2\mathbf{i} - 3\mathbf{j} + \mathbf{k}$, $\quad \mathbf{b} = \mathbf{i} + 6\mathbf{j} - 2\mathbf{k}$

---

41. Show that the vector $\operatorname{orth}_a \mathbf{b} = \mathbf{b} - \operatorname{proj}_a \mathbf{b}$ is orthogonal to $\mathbf{a}$. (It is called an **orthogonal projection** of $\mathbf{b}$.)

42. For the vectors in Exercise 36, find $\operatorname{orth}_a \mathbf{b}$ and illustrate by drawing the vectors $\mathbf{a}$, $\mathbf{b}$, $\operatorname{proj}_a \mathbf{b}$, and $\operatorname{orth}_a \mathbf{b}$.

43. If $\mathbf{a} = \langle 3, 0, -1 \rangle$, find a vector $\mathbf{b}$ such that $\operatorname{comp}_a \mathbf{b} = 2$.

44. Suppose that $\mathbf{a}$ and $\mathbf{b}$ are nonzero vectors.
(a) Under what circumstances is $\operatorname{comp}_a \mathbf{b} = \operatorname{comp}_b \mathbf{a}$?
(b) Under what circumstances is $\operatorname{proj}_a \mathbf{b} = \operatorname{proj}_b \mathbf{a}$?

45. A constant force with vector representation $\mathbf{F} = 10\mathbf{i} + 18\mathbf{j} - 6\mathbf{k}$ moves an object along a straight line from the point $(2, 3, 0)$ to the point $(4, 9, 15)$. Find the work done if the distance is measured in meters and the magnitude of the force is measured in newtons.

46. Find the work done by a force of 20 lb acting in the direction N50°W in moving an object 4 ft due west.

47. A woman exerts a horizontal force of 25 lb on a crate as she pushes it up a ramp that is 10 ft long and inclined at an angle of 20° above the horizontal. Find the work done on the box.

48. A wagon is pulled a distance of 100 m along a horizontal path by a constant force of 50 N. The handle of the wagon is held at an angle of 30° above the horizontal. How much work is done?

49. Use a scalar projection to show that the distance from a point $P_1(x_1, y_1)$ to the line $ax + by + c = 0$ is

$$\frac{|ax_1 + by_1 + c|}{\sqrt{a^2 + b^2}}$$

Use this formula to find the distance from the point $(-2, 3)$ to the line $3x - 4y + 5 = 0$.

50. If $\mathbf{r} = \langle x, y, z \rangle$, $\mathbf{a} = \langle a_1, a_2, a_3 \rangle$, and $\mathbf{b} = \langle b_1, b_2, b_3 \rangle$, show that the vector equation $(\mathbf{r} - \mathbf{a}) \cdot (\mathbf{r} - \mathbf{b}) = 0$ represents a sphere, and find its center and radius.

51. Find the angle between a diagonal of a cube and one of its edges.

52. Find the angle between a diagonal of a cube and a diagonal of one of its faces.

53. A molecule of methane, CH_4, is structured with the four hydrogen atoms at the vertices of a regular tetrahedron and the carbon atom at the centroid. The *bond angle* is the angle formed by the H—C—H combination; it is the angle between the lines that join the carbon atom to two of the hydrogen atoms. Show that the bond angle is about 109.5°. [*Hint:* Take the vertices of the tetrahedron to be the points $(1, 0, 0)$, $(0, 1, 0)$,

(0, 0, 1), and (1, 1, 1) as shown in the figure. Then the centroid is $\left(\frac{1}{2}, \frac{1}{2}, \frac{1}{2}\right)$.]

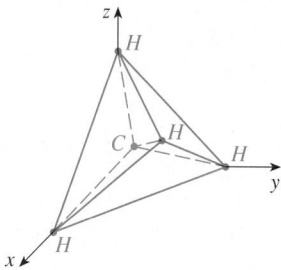

54. If $\mathbf{c} = |\mathbf{a}|\mathbf{b} + |\mathbf{b}|\mathbf{a}$, where $\mathbf{a}$, $\mathbf{b}$, and $\mathbf{c}$ are all nonzero vectors, show that $\mathbf{c}$ bisects the angle between $\mathbf{a}$ and $\mathbf{b}$.

55. Prove Properties 2, 4, and 5 of the dot product (Theorem 2).

56. Suppose that all sides of a quadrilateral are equal in length and opposite sides are parallel. Use vector methods to show that the diagonals are perpendicular.

57. Use Theorem 3 to prove the *Cauchy-Schwarz Inequality:*

$$|\mathbf{a} \cdot \mathbf{b}| \leq |\mathbf{a}|\,|\mathbf{b}|$$

58. The *Triangle Inequality for vectors* is

$$|\mathbf{a} + \mathbf{b}| \leq |\mathbf{a}| + |\mathbf{b}|$$

(a) Give a geometric interpretation of the Triangle Inequality.
(b) Use the Cauchy-Schwarz Inequality from Exercise 57 to prove the Triangle Inequality. [*Hint:* Use the fact that $|\mathbf{a} + \mathbf{b}|^2 = (\mathbf{a} + \mathbf{b}) \cdot (\mathbf{a} + \mathbf{b})$ and use Property 3 of the dot product.]

59. The Parallelogram Law states that

$$|\mathbf{a} + \mathbf{b}|^2 + |\mathbf{a} - \mathbf{b}|^2 = 2|\mathbf{a}|^2 + 2|\mathbf{b}|^2$$

(a) Give a geometric interpretation of the Parallelogram Law.
(b) Prove the Parallelogram Law. (See the hint in Exercise 58.)

13.4 The Cross Product

The **cross product** $\mathbf{a} \times \mathbf{b}$ of two vectors $\mathbf{a}$ and $\mathbf{b}$, unlike the dot product, is a vector. For this reason it is also called the **vector product**. Note that $\mathbf{a} \times \mathbf{b}$ is defined only when $\mathbf{a}$ and $\mathbf{b}$ are *three-dimensional* vectors.

> **1 Definition** If $\mathbf{a} = \langle a_1, a_2, a_3 \rangle$ and $\mathbf{b} = \langle b_1, b_2, b_3 \rangle$, then the **cross product** of $\mathbf{a}$ and $\mathbf{b}$ is the vector
>
> $$\mathbf{a} \times \mathbf{b} = \langle a_2 b_3 - a_3 b_2, \, a_3 b_1 - a_1 b_3, \, a_1 b_2 - a_2 b_1 \rangle$$

This may seem like a strange way of defining a product. The reason for the particular form of Definition 1 is that the cross product defined in this way has many useful properties, as we will soon see. In particular, we will show that the vector $\mathbf{a} \times \mathbf{b}$ is perpendicular to both $\mathbf{a}$ and $\mathbf{b}$.

In order to make Definition 1 easier to remember, we use the notation of determinants. A **determinant of order 2** is defined by

$$\begin{vmatrix} a & b \\ c & d \end{vmatrix} = ad - bc$$

For example,

$$\begin{vmatrix} 2 & 1 \\ -6 & 4 \end{vmatrix} = 2(4) - 1(-6) = 14$$

A **determinant of order 3** can be defined in terms of second-order determinants as follows:

$$\boxed{2} \qquad \begin{vmatrix} a_1 & a_2 & a_3 \\ b_1 & b_2 & b_3 \\ c_1 & c_2 & c_3 \end{vmatrix} = a_1 \begin{vmatrix} b_2 & b_3 \\ c_2 & c_3 \end{vmatrix} - a_2 \begin{vmatrix} b_1 & b_3 \\ c_1 & c_3 \end{vmatrix} + a_3 \begin{vmatrix} b_1 & b_2 \\ c_1 & c_2 \end{vmatrix}$$

Observe that each term on the right side of Equation 2 involves a number a_i in the first row of the determinant, and a_i is multiplied by the second-order determinant obtained from the left side by deleting the row and column in which a_i appears. Notice also the minus sign in the second term. For example,

$$\begin{vmatrix} 1 & 2 & -1 \\ 3 & 0 & 1 \\ -5 & 4 & 2 \end{vmatrix} = 1\begin{vmatrix} 0 & 1 \\ 4 & 2 \end{vmatrix} - 2\begin{vmatrix} 3 & 1 \\ -5 & 2 \end{vmatrix} + (-1)\begin{vmatrix} 3 & 0 \\ -5 & 4 \end{vmatrix}$$

$$= 1(0 - 4) - 2(6 + 5) + (-1)(12 - 0) = -38$$

If we now rewrite Definition 1 using second-order determinants and the standard basis vectors $\mathbf{i}$, $\mathbf{j}$, and $\mathbf{k}$, we see that the cross product of the vectors $\mathbf{a} = a_1\mathbf{i} + a_2\mathbf{j} + a_3\mathbf{k}$ and $\mathbf{b} = b_1\mathbf{i} + b_2\mathbf{j} + b_3\mathbf{k}$ is

$$\boxed{3} \qquad \mathbf{a} \times \mathbf{b} = \begin{vmatrix} a_2 & a_3 \\ b_2 & b_3 \end{vmatrix}\mathbf{i} - \begin{vmatrix} a_1 & a_3 \\ b_1 & b_3 \end{vmatrix}\mathbf{j} + \begin{vmatrix} a_1 & a_2 \\ b_1 & b_2 \end{vmatrix}\mathbf{k}$$

In view of the similarity between Equations 2 and 3, we often write

$$\boxed{4} \qquad \mathbf{a} \times \mathbf{b} = \begin{vmatrix} \mathbf{i} & \mathbf{j} & \mathbf{k} \\ a_1 & a_2 & a_3 \\ b_1 & b_2 & b_3 \end{vmatrix}$$

Although the first row of the symbolic determinant in Equation 4 consists of vectors, if we expand it as if it were an ordinary determinant using the rule in Equation 2, we obtain Equation 3. The symbolic formula in Equation 4 is probably the easiest way of remembering and computing cross products.

EXAMPLE 1 If $\mathbf{a} = \langle 1, 3, 4 \rangle$ and $\mathbf{b} = \langle 2, 7, -5 \rangle$, then

$$\mathbf{a} \times \mathbf{b} = \begin{vmatrix} \mathbf{i} & \mathbf{j} & \mathbf{k} \\ 1 & 3 & 4 \\ 2 & 7 & -5 \end{vmatrix}$$

$$= \begin{vmatrix} 3 & 4 \\ 7 & -5 \end{vmatrix}\mathbf{i} - \begin{vmatrix} 1 & 4 \\ 2 & -5 \end{vmatrix}\mathbf{j} + \begin{vmatrix} 1 & 3 \\ 2 & 7 \end{vmatrix}\mathbf{k}$$

$$= (-15 - 28)\mathbf{i} - (-5 - 8)\mathbf{j} + (7 - 6)\mathbf{k} = -43\mathbf{i} + 13\mathbf{j} + \mathbf{k} \qquad ▬$$

EXAMPLE 2 Show that $\mathbf{a} \times \mathbf{a} = \mathbf{0}$ for any vector $\mathbf{a}$ in V_3.

SOLUTION If $\mathbf{a} = \langle a_1, a_2, a_3 \rangle$, then

$$\mathbf{a} \times \mathbf{a} = \begin{vmatrix} \mathbf{i} & \mathbf{j} & \mathbf{k} \\ a_1 & a_2 & a_3 \\ a_1 & a_2 & a_3 \end{vmatrix}$$

$$= (a_2 a_3 - a_3 a_2)\mathbf{i} - (a_1 a_3 - a_3 a_1)\mathbf{j} + (a_1 a_2 - a_2 a_1)\mathbf{k}$$

$$= 0\mathbf{i} - 0\mathbf{j} + 0\mathbf{k} = \mathbf{0} \qquad ▬$$

One of the most important properties of the cross product is given by the following theorem.

> **5** **Theorem** The vector $\mathbf{a} \times \mathbf{b}$ is orthogonal to both $\mathbf{a}$ and $\mathbf{b}$.

Proof In order to show that $\mathbf{a} \times \mathbf{b}$ is orthogonal to $\mathbf{a}$, we compute their dot product as follows:

$$(\mathbf{a} \times \mathbf{b}) \cdot \mathbf{a} = \begin{vmatrix} a_2 & a_3 \\ b_2 & b_3 \end{vmatrix} a_1 - \begin{vmatrix} a_1 & a_3 \\ b_1 & b_3 \end{vmatrix} a_2 + \begin{vmatrix} a_1 & a_2 \\ b_1 & b_2 \end{vmatrix} a_3$$

$$= a_1(a_2b_3 - a_3b_2) - a_2(a_1b_3 - a_3b_1) + a_3(a_1b_2 - a_2b_1)$$

$$= a_1a_2b_3 - a_1b_2a_3 - a_1a_2b_3 + b_1a_2a_3 + a_1b_2a_3 - b_1a_2a_3$$

$$= 0$$

A similar computation shows that $(\mathbf{a} \times \mathbf{b}) \cdot \mathbf{b} = 0$. Therefore, $\mathbf{a} \times \mathbf{b}$ is orthogonal to both $\mathbf{a}$ and $\mathbf{b}$.

If $\mathbf{a}$ and $\mathbf{b}$ are represented by directed line segments with the same initial point (as in Figure 1), then Theorem 5 says that the cross product $\mathbf{a} \times \mathbf{b}$ points in a direction perpendicular to the plane through $\mathbf{a}$ and $\mathbf{b}$. It turns out that the direction of $\mathbf{a} \times \mathbf{b}$ is given by the *right-hand rule:* If the fingers of your right hand curl in the direction of a rotation (through an angle less than 180°) from $\mathbf{a}$ to $\mathbf{b}$, then your thumb points in the direction of $\mathbf{a} \times \mathbf{b}$.

Now that we know the direction of the vector $\mathbf{a} \times \mathbf{b}$, the remaining thing we need to complete its geometric description is its length $|\mathbf{a} \times \mathbf{b}|$. This is given by the following theorem.

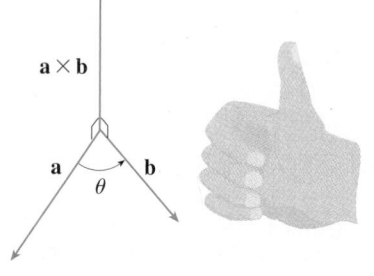

FIGURE 1

Visual 13.4 shows how $\mathbf{a} \times \mathbf{b}$ changes as $\mathbf{b}$ changes.

> **6** **Theorem** If θ is the angle between $\mathbf{a}$ and $\mathbf{b}$ (so $0 \leq \theta \leq \pi$), then
>
> $$|\mathbf{a} \times \mathbf{b}| = |\mathbf{a}||\mathbf{b}| \sin \theta$$

Proof From the definitions of the cross product and length of a vector, we have

$$|\mathbf{a} \times \mathbf{b}|^2 = (a_2b_3 - a_3b_2)^2 + (a_3b_1 - a_1b_3)^2 + (a_1b_2 - a_2b_1)^2$$

$$= a_2^2b_3^2 - 2a_2a_3b_2b_3 + a_3^2b_2^2 + a_3^2b_1^2 - 2a_1a_3b_1b_3 + a_1^2b_3^2$$

$$+ a_1^2b_2^2 - 2a_1a_2b_1b_2 + a_2^2b_1^2$$

$$= (a_1^2 + a_2^2 + a_3^2)(b_1^2 + b_2^2 + b_3^2) - (a_1b_1 + a_2b_2 + a_3b_3)^2$$

$$= |\mathbf{a}|^2|\mathbf{b}|^2 - (\mathbf{a} \cdot \mathbf{b})^2$$

$$= |\mathbf{a}|^2|\mathbf{b}|^2 - |\mathbf{a}|^2|\mathbf{b}|^2 \cos^2\theta \qquad \text{(by Theorem 13.3.3)}$$

$$= |\mathbf{a}|^2|\mathbf{b}|^2(1 - \cos^2\theta)$$

$$= |\mathbf{a}|^2|\mathbf{b}|^2 \sin^2\theta$$

Taking square roots and observing that $\sqrt{\sin^2\theta} = \sin \theta$ because $\sin \theta \geq 0$ when $0 \leq \theta \leq \pi$, we have

$$|\mathbf{a} \times \mathbf{b}| = |\mathbf{a}||\mathbf{b}| \sin \theta$$

Geometric characterization of $\mathbf{a} \times \mathbf{b}$

Since a vector is completely determined by its magnitude and direction, we can now say that $\mathbf{a} \times \mathbf{b}$ is the vector that is perpendicular to both $\mathbf{a}$ and $\mathbf{b}$, whose orientation is determined by the right-hand rule, and whose length is $|\mathbf{a}||\mathbf{b}|\sin\theta$. In fact, that is exactly how physicists *define* $\mathbf{a}\times\mathbf{b}$.

> **7 Corollary** Two nonzero vectors $\mathbf{a}$ and $\mathbf{b}$ are parallel if and only if
>
> $$\mathbf{a}\times\mathbf{b}=\mathbf{0}$$

Proof Two nonzero vectors $\mathbf{a}$ and $\mathbf{b}$ are parallel if and only if $\theta=0$ or π. In either case $\sin\theta=0$, so $|\mathbf{a}\times\mathbf{b}|=0$ and therefore $\mathbf{a}\times\mathbf{b}=\mathbf{0}$. ▬

The geometric interpretation of Theorem 6 can be seen by looking at Figure 2. If $\mathbf{a}$ and $\mathbf{b}$ are represented by directed line segments with the same initial point, then they determine a parallelogram with base $|\mathbf{a}|$, altitude $|\mathbf{b}|\sin\theta$, and area

$$A=|\mathbf{a}|(|\mathbf{b}|\sin\theta)=|\mathbf{a}\times\mathbf{b}|$$

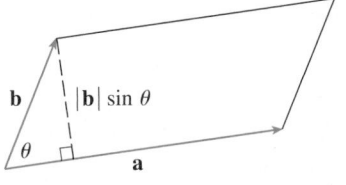

$|\mathbf{b}|\sin\theta$

FIGURE 2

Thus, we have the following way of interpreting the magnitude of a cross product.

> The length of the cross product $\mathbf{a}\times\mathbf{b}$ is equal to the area of the parallelogram determined by $\mathbf{a}$ and $\mathbf{b}$.

EXAMPLE 3 Find a vector perpendicular to the plane that passes through the points $P(1,4,6)$, $Q(-2,5,-1)$, and $R(1,-1,1)$.

SOLUTION The vector $\overrightarrow{PQ}\times\overrightarrow{PR}$ is perpendicular to both $\overrightarrow{PQ}$ and $\overrightarrow{PR}$ and is therefore perpendicular to the plane through P, Q, and R. We know from (13.2.1) that

$$\overrightarrow{PQ}=(-2-1)\mathbf{i}+(5-4)\mathbf{j}+(-1-6)\mathbf{k}=-3\mathbf{i}+\mathbf{j}-7\mathbf{k}$$
$$\overrightarrow{PR}=(1-1)\mathbf{i}+(-1-4)\mathbf{j}+(1-6)\mathbf{k}=-5\mathbf{j}-5\mathbf{k}$$

We compute the cross product of these vectors:

$$\overrightarrow{PQ}\times\overrightarrow{PR}=\begin{vmatrix} \mathbf{i} & \mathbf{j} & \mathbf{k} \\ -3 & 1 & -7 \\ 0 & -5 & -5 \end{vmatrix}$$

$$=(-5-35)\mathbf{i}-(15-0)\mathbf{j}+(15-0)\mathbf{k}=-40\mathbf{i}-15\mathbf{j}+15\mathbf{k}$$

So the vector $\langle-40,-15,15\rangle$ is perpendicular to the given plane. Any nonzero scalar multiple of this vector, such as $\langle-8,-3,3\rangle$, is also perpendicular to the plane. ▬

EXAMPLE 4 Find the area of the triangle with vertices $P(1,4,6)$, $Q(-2,5,-1)$, and $R(1,-1,1)$.

SOLUTION In Example 3 we computed that $\overrightarrow{PQ}\times\overrightarrow{PR}=\langle-40,-15,15\rangle$. The area of the parallelogram with adjacent sides PQ and PR is the length of this cross product:

$$|\overrightarrow{PQ}\times\overrightarrow{PR}|=\sqrt{(-40)^2+(-15)^2+15^2}=5\sqrt{82}$$

The area A of the triangle PQR is half the area of this parallelogram, that is, $\frac{5}{2}\sqrt{82}$. ▬

If we apply Theorems 5 and 6 to the standard basis vectors $\mathbf{i}$, $\mathbf{j}$, and $\mathbf{k}$ using $\theta = \pi/2$, we obtain

$$\mathbf{i} \times \mathbf{j} = \mathbf{k} \qquad \mathbf{j} \times \mathbf{k} = \mathbf{i} \qquad \mathbf{k} \times \mathbf{i} = \mathbf{j}$$

$$\mathbf{j} \times \mathbf{i} = -\mathbf{k} \qquad \mathbf{k} \times \mathbf{j} = -\mathbf{i} \qquad \mathbf{i} \times \mathbf{k} = -\mathbf{j}$$

Observe that

$$\mathbf{i} \times \mathbf{j} \neq \mathbf{j} \times \mathbf{i}$$

Thus, the cross product is not commutative. Also

$$\mathbf{i} \times (\mathbf{i} \times \mathbf{j}) = \mathbf{i} \times \mathbf{k} = -\mathbf{j}$$

whereas

$$(\mathbf{i} \times \mathbf{i}) \times \mathbf{j} = \mathbf{0} \times \mathbf{j} = \mathbf{0}$$

So the associative law for multiplication does not usually hold; that is, in general,

$$(\mathbf{a} \times \mathbf{b}) \times \mathbf{c} \neq \mathbf{a} \times (\mathbf{b} \times \mathbf{c})$$

However, some of the usual laws of algebra *do* hold for cross products. The following theorem summarizes the properties of vector products.

---

8 **Theorem** If $\mathbf{a}$, $\mathbf{b}$, and $\mathbf{c}$ are vectors and c is a scalar, then

1. $\mathbf{a} \times \mathbf{b} = -\mathbf{b} \times \mathbf{a}$
2. $(c\mathbf{a}) \times \mathbf{b} = c(\mathbf{a} \times \mathbf{b}) = \mathbf{a} \times (c\mathbf{b})$
3. $\mathbf{a} \times (\mathbf{b} + \mathbf{c}) = \mathbf{a} \times \mathbf{b} + \mathbf{a} \times \mathbf{c}$
4. $(\mathbf{a} + \mathbf{b}) \times \mathbf{c} = \mathbf{a} \times \mathbf{c} + \mathbf{b} \times \mathbf{c}$
5. $\mathbf{a} \cdot (\mathbf{b} \times \mathbf{c}) = (\mathbf{a} \times \mathbf{b}) \cdot \mathbf{c}$
6. $\mathbf{a} \times (\mathbf{b} \times \mathbf{c}) = (\mathbf{a} \cdot \mathbf{c})\mathbf{b} - (\mathbf{a} \cdot \mathbf{b})\mathbf{c}$

These properties can be proved by writing the vectors in terms of their components and using the definition of a cross product. We give the proof of Property 5 and leave the remaining proofs as exercises.

Proof of Property 5 If $\mathbf{a} = \langle a_1, a_2, a_3 \rangle$, $\mathbf{b} = \langle b_1, b_2, b_3 \rangle$, and $\mathbf{c} = \langle c_1, c_2, c_3 \rangle$, then

$$
\begin{aligned}
\boxed{9} \quad \mathbf{a} \cdot (\mathbf{b} \times \mathbf{c}) &= a_1(b_2c_3 - b_3c_2) + a_2(b_3c_1 - b_1c_3) + a_3(b_1c_2 - b_2c_1) \\
&= a_1b_2c_3 - a_1b_3c_2 + a_2b_3c_1 - a_2b_1c_3 + a_3b_1c_2 - a_3b_2c_1 \\
&= (a_2b_3 - a_3b_2)c_1 + (a_3b_1 - a_1b_3)c_2 + (a_1b_2 - a_2b_1)c_3 \\
&= (\mathbf{a} \times \mathbf{b}) \cdot \mathbf{c}
\end{aligned}
$$

The product $\mathbf{a} \cdot (\mathbf{b} \times \mathbf{c})$ that occurs in Property 5 is called the **scalar triple product** of the vectors $\mathbf{a}$, $\mathbf{b}$, and $\mathbf{c}$. Notice from Equation 9 that we can write the scalar triple product as a determinant:

$$
\boxed{10} \qquad \mathbf{a} \cdot (\mathbf{b} \times \mathbf{c}) = \begin{vmatrix} a_1 & a_2 & a_3 \\ b_1 & b_2 & b_3 \\ c_1 & c_2 & c_3 \end{vmatrix}
$$

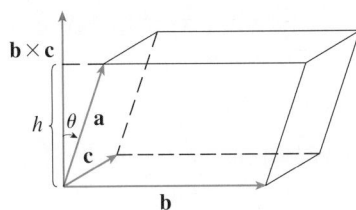

FIGURE 3

The geometric significance of the scalar triple product can be seen by considering the parallelepiped determined by the vectors **a**, **b**, and **c** (Figure 3). The area of the base parallelogram is $A = |\mathbf{b} \times \mathbf{c}|$. If θ is the angle between **a** and $\mathbf{b} \times \mathbf{c}$, then the height h of the parallelepiped is $h = |\mathbf{a}||\cos\theta|$. (We must use $|\cos\theta|$ instead of $\cos\theta$ in case $\theta > \pi/2$.) Therefore, the volume of the parallelepiped is

$$V = Ah = |\mathbf{b} \times \mathbf{c}||\mathbf{a}||\cos\theta| = |\mathbf{a} \cdot (\mathbf{b} \times \mathbf{c})|$$

Thus, we have proved the following formula.

> **11** The volume of the parallelepiped determined by the vectors **a**, **b**, and **c** is the magnitude of their scalar triple product:
>
> $$V = |\mathbf{a} \cdot (\mathbf{b} \times \mathbf{c})|$$

If we use the formula in (11) and discover that the volume of the parallelepiped determined by **a**, **b**, and **c** is 0, then the vectors must lie in the same plane; that is, they are **coplanar**.

EXAMPLE 5 Use the scalar triple product to show that the vectors $\mathbf{a} = \langle 1, 4, -7 \rangle$, $\mathbf{b} = \langle 2, -1, 4 \rangle$, and $\mathbf{c} = \langle 0, -9, 18 \rangle$ are coplanar.

SOLUTION We use Equation 10 to compute their scalar triple product:

$$\mathbf{a} \cdot (\mathbf{b} \times \mathbf{c}) = \begin{vmatrix} 1 & 4 & -7 \\ 2 & -1 & 4 \\ 0 & -9 & 18 \end{vmatrix}$$

$$= 1 \begin{vmatrix} -1 & 4 \\ -9 & 18 \end{vmatrix} - 4 \begin{vmatrix} 2 & 4 \\ 0 & 18 \end{vmatrix} - 7 \begin{vmatrix} 2 & -1 \\ 0 & -9 \end{vmatrix}$$

$$= 1(18) - 4(36) - 7(-18) = 0$$

Therefore, by (11) the volume of the parallelepiped determined by **a**, **b**, and **c** is 0. This means that **a**, **b**, and **c** are coplanar.

The idea of a cross product occurs often in physics. In particular, we consider a force **F** acting on a rigid body at a point given by a position vector **r**. (For instance, if we tighten a bolt by applying a force to a wrench as in Figure 4, we produce a turning effect.) The **torque** $\boldsymbol{\tau}$ (relative to the origin) is defined to be the cross product of the position and force vectors

$$\boldsymbol{\tau} = \mathbf{r} \times \mathbf{F}$$

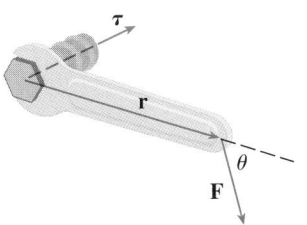

FIGURE 4

and measures the tendency of the body to rotate about the origin. The direction of the torque vector indicates the axis of rotation. According to Theorem 6, the magnitude of the torque vector is

$$|\boldsymbol{\tau}| = |\mathbf{r} \times \mathbf{F}| = |\mathbf{r}||\mathbf{F}|\sin\theta$$

where θ is the angle between the position and force vectors. Observe that the only component of **F** that can cause a rotation is the one perpendicular to **r**, that is, $|\mathbf{F}|\sin\theta$. The magnitude of the torque is equal to the area of the parallelogram determined by **r** and **F**.

FIGURE 5

EXAMPLE 6 A bolt is tightened by applying a 40-N force to a 0.25-m wrench as shown in Figure 5. Find the magnitude of the torque about the center of the bolt.

SOLUTION The magnitude of the torque vector is

$$|\boldsymbol{\tau}| = |\mathbf{r} \times \mathbf{F}| = |\mathbf{r}||\mathbf{F}| \sin 75° = (0.25)(40) \sin 75°$$
$$= 10 \sin 75° \approx 9.66 \text{ N·m}$$

If the bolt is right-threaded, then the torque vector itself is

$$\boldsymbol{\tau} = |\boldsymbol{\tau}|\, \mathbf{n} \approx 9.66\, \mathbf{n}$$

where $\mathbf{n}$ is a unit vector directed down into the page.

13.4 Exercises

1–7 ▓ Find the cross product $\mathbf{a} \times \mathbf{b}$ and verify that it is orthogonal to both $\mathbf{a}$ and $\mathbf{b}$.

1. $\mathbf{a} = \langle 1, 2, 0 \rangle$, $\mathbf{b} = \langle 0, 3, 1 \rangle$

2. $\mathbf{a} = \langle 5, 1, 4 \rangle$, $\mathbf{b} = \langle -1, 0, 2 \rangle$

3. $\mathbf{a} = 2\mathbf{i} + \mathbf{j} - \mathbf{k}$, $\mathbf{b} = \mathbf{j} + 2\mathbf{k}$

4. $\mathbf{a} = \mathbf{i} - \mathbf{j} + \mathbf{k}$, $\mathbf{b} = \mathbf{i} + \mathbf{j} + \mathbf{k}$

5. $\mathbf{a} = 3\mathbf{i} + 2\mathbf{j} + 4\mathbf{k}$, $\mathbf{b} = \mathbf{i} - 2\mathbf{j} - 3\mathbf{k}$

6. $\mathbf{a} = \mathbf{i} + e^t\mathbf{j} + e^{-t}\mathbf{k}$, $\mathbf{b} = 2\mathbf{i} + e^t\mathbf{j} - e^{-t}\mathbf{k}$

7. $\mathbf{a} = \langle t, t^2, t^3 \rangle$, $\mathbf{b} = \langle 1, 2t, 3t^2 \rangle$

8. If $\mathbf{a} = \mathbf{i} - 2\mathbf{k}$ and $\mathbf{b} = \mathbf{j} + \mathbf{k}$, find $\mathbf{a} \times \mathbf{b}$. Sketch $\mathbf{a}$, $\mathbf{b}$, and $\mathbf{a} \times \mathbf{b}$ as vectors starting at the origin.

9. State whether each expression is meaningful. If not, explain why. If so, state whether it is a vector or a scalar.
(a) $\mathbf{a} \cdot (\mathbf{b} \times \mathbf{c})$ (b) $\mathbf{a} \times (\mathbf{b} \cdot \mathbf{c})$
(c) $\mathbf{a} \times (\mathbf{b} \times \mathbf{c})$ (d) $(\mathbf{a} \cdot \mathbf{b}) \times \mathbf{c}$
(e) $(\mathbf{a} \cdot \mathbf{b}) \times (\mathbf{c} \cdot \mathbf{d})$ (f) $(\mathbf{a} \times \mathbf{b}) \cdot (\mathbf{c} \times \mathbf{d})$

10–11 ▓ Find $|\mathbf{u} \times \mathbf{v}|$ and determine whether $\mathbf{u} \times \mathbf{v}$ is directed into the page or out of the page.

10.

11.

12. The figure shows a vector $\mathbf{a}$ in the xy-plane and a vector $\mathbf{b}$ in the direction of $\mathbf{k}$. Their lengths are $|\mathbf{a}| = 3$ and $|\mathbf{b}| = 2$.
(a) Find $|\mathbf{a} \times \mathbf{b}|$.

(b) Use the right-hand rule to decide whether the components of $\mathbf{a} \times \mathbf{b}$ are positive, negative, or 0.

13. If $\mathbf{a} = \langle 1, 2, 1 \rangle$ and $\mathbf{b} = \langle 0, 1, 3 \rangle$, find $\mathbf{a} \times \mathbf{b}$ and $\mathbf{b} \times \mathbf{a}$.

14. If $\mathbf{a} = \langle 3, 1, 2 \rangle$, $\mathbf{b} = \langle -1, 1, 0 \rangle$, and $\mathbf{c} = \langle 0, 0, -4 \rangle$, show that $\mathbf{a} \times (\mathbf{b} \times \mathbf{c}) \neq (\mathbf{a} \times \mathbf{b}) \times \mathbf{c}$.

15. Find two unit vectors orthogonal to both $\langle 1, -1, 1 \rangle$ and $\langle 0, 4, 4 \rangle$.

16. Find two unit vectors orthogonal to both $\mathbf{i} + \mathbf{j} + \mathbf{k}$ and $2\mathbf{i} + \mathbf{k}$.

17. Show that $\mathbf{0} \times \mathbf{a} = \mathbf{0} = \mathbf{a} \times \mathbf{0}$ for any vector $\mathbf{a}$ in V_3.

18. Show that $(\mathbf{a} \times \mathbf{b}) \cdot \mathbf{b} = 0$ for all vectors $\mathbf{a}$ and $\mathbf{b}$ in V_3.

19. Prove Property 1 of Theorem 8.

20. Prove Property 2 of Theorem 8.

21. Prove Property 3 of Theorem 8.

22. Prove Property 4 of Theorem 8.

23. Find the area of the parallelogram with vertices $A(-2, 1)$, $B(0, 4)$, $C(4, 2)$, and $D(2, -1)$.

24. Find the area of the parallelogram with vertices $K(1, 2, 3)$, $L(1, 3, 6)$, $M(3, 8, 6)$, and $N(3, 7, 3)$.

25–28 ▓ (a) Find a vector orthogonal to the plane through the points P, Q, and R, and (b) find the area of triangle PQR.

25. $P(1, 0, 0)$, $Q(0, 2, 0)$, $R(0, 0, 3)$

26. $P(2, 1, 5)$, $Q(-1, 3, 4)$, $R(3, 0, 6)$

27. $P(0, -2, 0)$, $Q(4, 1, -2)$, $R(5, 3, 1)$

28. $P(2, 0, -3)$, $Q(3, 1, 0)$, $R(5, 2, 2)$

29–30 ▦ Find the volume of the parallelepiped determined by the vectors **a**, **b**, and **c**.

29. $\mathbf{a} = \langle 6, 3, -1 \rangle$, $\mathbf{b} = \langle 0, 1, 2 \rangle$, $\mathbf{c} = \langle 4, -2, 5 \rangle$

30. $\mathbf{a} = \mathbf{i} + \mathbf{j} - \mathbf{k}$, $\mathbf{b} = \mathbf{i} - \mathbf{j} + \mathbf{k}$, $\mathbf{c} = -\mathbf{i} + \mathbf{j} + \mathbf{k}$

31–32 ▦ Find the volume of the parallelepiped with adjacent edges PQ, PR, and PS.

31. $P(2, 0, -1)$, $Q(4, 1, 0)$, $R(3, -1, 1)$, $S(2, -2, 2)$

32. $P(0, 1, 2)$, $Q(2, 4, 5)$, $R(-1, 0, 1)$, $S(6, -1, 4)$

33. Use the scalar triple product to verify that the vectors $\mathbf{a} = 2\mathbf{i} + 3\mathbf{j} + \mathbf{k}$, $\mathbf{b} = \mathbf{i} - \mathbf{j}$, and $\mathbf{c} = 7\mathbf{i} + 3\mathbf{j} + 2\mathbf{k}$ are coplanar.

34. Use the scalar triple product to determine whether the points $P(1, 0, 1)$, $Q(2, 4, 6)$, $R(3, -1, 2)$, and $S(6, 2, 8)$ lie in the same plane.

35. A bicycle pedal is pushed by a foot with a 60-N force as shown. The shaft of the pedal is 18 cm long. Find the magnitude of the torque about P.

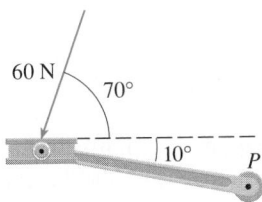

36. Find the magnitude of the torque about P if a 36-lb force is applied as shown.

37. A wrench 30 cm long lies along the positive y-axis and grips a bolt at the origin. A force is applied in the direction $\langle 0, 3, -4 \rangle$ at the end of the wrench. Find the magnitude of the force needed to supply 100 J of torque to the bolt.

38. Let $\mathbf{v} = 5\mathbf{j}$ and let $\mathbf{u}$ be a vector with length 3 that starts at the origin and rotates in the xy-plane. Find the maximum and

minimum values of the length of the vector $\mathbf{u} \times \mathbf{v}$. In what direction does $\mathbf{u} \times \mathbf{v}$ point?

39. (a) Let P be a point not on the line L that passes through the points Q and R. Show that the distance d from the point P to the line L is
$$d = \frac{|\mathbf{a} \times \mathbf{b}|}{|\mathbf{a}|}$$
where $\mathbf{a} = \overrightarrow{QR}$ and $\mathbf{b} = \overrightarrow{QP}$.

(b) Use the formula in part (a) to find the distance from the point $P(1, 1, 1)$ to the line through $Q(0, 6, 8)$ and $R(-1, 4, 7)$.

40. (a) Let P be a point not on the plane that passes through the points Q, R, and S. Show that the distance d from P to the plane is
$$d = \frac{|(\mathbf{a} \times \mathbf{b}) \cdot \mathbf{c}|}{|\mathbf{a} \times \mathbf{b}|}$$
where $\mathbf{a} = \overrightarrow{QR}$, $\mathbf{b} = \overrightarrow{QS}$, and $\mathbf{c} = \overrightarrow{QP}$.

(b) Use the formula in part (a) to find the distance from the point $P(2, 1, 4)$ to the plane through the points $Q(1, 0, 0)$, $R(0, 2, 0)$, and $S(0, 0, 3)$.

41. Prove that $(\mathbf{a} - \mathbf{b}) \times (\mathbf{a} + \mathbf{b}) = 2(\mathbf{a} \times \mathbf{b})$.

42. Prove part 6 of Theorem 8, that is,
$$\mathbf{a} \times (\mathbf{b} \times \mathbf{c}) = (\mathbf{a} \cdot \mathbf{c})\mathbf{b} - (\mathbf{a} \cdot \mathbf{b})\mathbf{c}$$

43. Use Exercise 42 to prove that
$$\mathbf{a} \times (\mathbf{b} \times \mathbf{c}) + \mathbf{b} \times (\mathbf{c} \times \mathbf{a}) + \mathbf{c} \times (\mathbf{a} \times \mathbf{b}) = \mathbf{0}$$

44. Prove that
$$(\mathbf{a} \times \mathbf{b}) \cdot (\mathbf{c} \times \mathbf{d}) = \begin{vmatrix} \mathbf{a} \cdot \mathbf{c} & \mathbf{b} \cdot \mathbf{c} \\ \mathbf{a} \cdot \mathbf{d} & \mathbf{b} \cdot \mathbf{d} \end{vmatrix}$$

45. Suppose that $\mathbf{a} \neq \mathbf{0}$.
(a) If $\mathbf{a} \cdot \mathbf{b} = \mathbf{a} \cdot \mathbf{c}$, does it follow that $\mathbf{b} = \mathbf{c}$?
(b) If $\mathbf{a} \times \mathbf{b} = \mathbf{a} \times \mathbf{c}$, does it follow that $\mathbf{b} = \mathbf{c}$?
(c) If $\mathbf{a} \cdot \mathbf{b} = \mathbf{a} \cdot \mathbf{c}$ and $\mathbf{a} \times \mathbf{b} = \mathbf{a} \times \mathbf{c}$, does it follow that $\mathbf{b} = \mathbf{c}$?

46. If $\mathbf{v}_1$, $\mathbf{v}_2$, and $\mathbf{v}_3$ are noncoplanar vectors, let
$$\mathbf{k}_1 = \frac{\mathbf{v}_2 \times \mathbf{v}_3}{\mathbf{v}_1 \cdot (\mathbf{v}_2 \times \mathbf{v}_3)} \qquad \mathbf{k}_2 = \frac{\mathbf{v}_3 \times \mathbf{v}_1}{\mathbf{v}_1 \cdot (\mathbf{v}_2 \times \mathbf{v}_3)}$$
$$\mathbf{k}_3 = \frac{\mathbf{v}_1 \times \mathbf{v}_2}{\mathbf{v}_1 \cdot (\mathbf{v}_2 \times \mathbf{v}_3)}$$

(These vectors occur in the study of crystallography. Vectors of the form $n_1\mathbf{v}_1 + n_2\mathbf{v}_2 + n_3\mathbf{v}_3$, where each n_i is an integer, form a *lattice* for a crystal. Vectors written similarly in terms of $\mathbf{k}_1$, $\mathbf{k}_2$, and $\mathbf{k}_3$ form the *reciprocal lattice*.)
(a) Show that $\mathbf{k}_i$ is perpendicular to $\mathbf{v}_j$ if $i \neq j$.
(b) Show that $\mathbf{k}_i \cdot \mathbf{v}_i = 1$ for $i = 1, 2, 3$.
(c) Show that $\mathbf{k}_1 \cdot (\mathbf{k}_2 \times \mathbf{k}_3) = \dfrac{1}{\mathbf{v}_1 \cdot (\mathbf{v}_2 \times \mathbf{v}_3)}$.

DISCOVERY PROJECT

The Geometry of a Tetrahedron

A tetrahedron is a solid with four vertices, P, Q, R, and S, and four triangular faces as shown in the figure.

1. Let $\mathbf{v}_1$, $\mathbf{v}_2$, $\mathbf{v}_3$, and $\mathbf{v}_4$ be vectors with lengths equal to the areas of the faces opposite the vertices P, Q, R, and S, respectively, and directions perpendicular to the respective faces and pointing outward. Show that

$$\mathbf{v}_1 + \mathbf{v}_2 + \mathbf{v}_3 + \mathbf{v}_4 = \mathbf{0}$$

2. The volume V of a tetrahedron is one-third the distance from a vertex to the opposite face, times the area of that face.
   (a) Find a formula for the volume of a tetrahedron in terms of the coordinates of its vertices P, Q, R, and S.
   (b) Find the volume of the tetrahedron whose vertices are $P(1, 1, 1)$, $Q(1, 2, 3)$, $R(1, 1, 2)$, and $S(3, -1, 2)$.

3. Suppose the tetrahedron in the figure has a trirectangular vertex S. (This means that the three angles at S are all right angles.) Let A, B, and C be the areas of the three faces that meet at S, and let D be the area of the opposite face PQR. Using the result of Problem 1, or otherwise, show that

$$D^2 = A^2 + B^2 + C^2$$

(This is a three-dimensional version of the Pythagorean Theorem.)

13.5 Equations of Lines and Planes

A line in the xy-plane is determined when a point on the line and the direction of the line (its slope or angle of inclination) are given. The equation of the line can then be written using the point-slope form.

Likewise, a line L in three-dimensional space is determined when we know a point $P_0(x_0, y_0, z_0)$ on L and the direction of L. In three dimensions the direction of a line is conveniently described by a vector, so we let $\mathbf{v}$ be a vector parallel to L. Let $P(x, y, z)$ be an arbitrary point on L and let $\mathbf{r}_0$ and $\mathbf{r}$ be the position vectors of P_0 and P (that is, they have representations $\overrightarrow{OP_0}$ and $\overrightarrow{OP}$). If $\mathbf{a}$ is the vector with representation $\overrightarrow{P_0P}$, as in Figure 1, then the Triangle Law for vector addition gives $\mathbf{r} = \mathbf{r}_0 + \mathbf{a}$. But, since $\mathbf{a}$ and $\mathbf{v}$ are parallel vectors, there is a scalar t such that $\mathbf{a} = t\mathbf{v}$. Thus

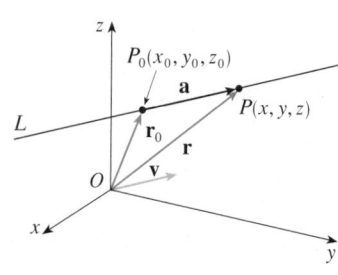

FIGURE 1

$$\boxed{1} \qquad \boxed{\mathbf{r} = \mathbf{r}_0 + t\mathbf{v}}$$

which is a **vector equation** of L. Each value of the **parameter** t gives the position vector $\mathbf{r}$ of a point on L. In other words, as t varies, the line is traced out by the tip of the vector $\mathbf{r}$. As Figure 2 indicates, positive values of t correspond to points on L that lie on one side of P_0, whereas negative values of t correspond to points that lie on the other side of P_0.

If the vector $\mathbf{v}$ that gives the direction of the line L is written in component form as $\mathbf{v} = \langle a, b, c \rangle$, then we have $t\mathbf{v} = \langle ta, tb, tc \rangle$. We can also write $\mathbf{r} = \langle x, y, z \rangle$ and $\mathbf{r}_0 = \langle x_0, y_0, z_0 \rangle$, so the vector equation (1) becomes

$$\langle x, y, z \rangle = \langle x_0 + ta, y_0 + tb, z_0 + tc \rangle$$

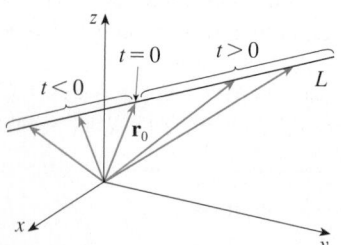

FIGURE 2

Two vectors are equal if and only if corresponding components are equal. Therefore, we have the three scalar equations:

2

$$x = x_0 + at \qquad y = y_0 + bt \qquad z = z_0 + ct$$

where $t \in \mathbb{R}$. These equations are called **parametric equations** of the line L through the point $P_0(x_0, y_0, z_0)$ and parallel to the vector $\mathbf{v} = \langle a, b, c \rangle$. Each value of the parameter t gives a point (x, y, z) on L.

⦙⦙⦙ Figure 3 shows the line L in Example 1 and its relation to the given point and to the vector that gives its direction.

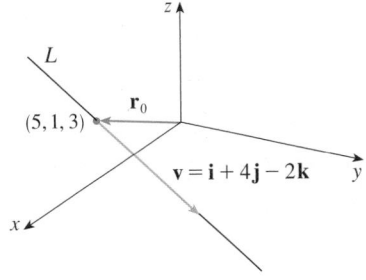

FIGURE 3

EXAMPLE 1

(a) Find a vector equation and parametric equations for the line that passes through the point $(5, 1, 3)$ and is parallel to the vector $\mathbf{i} + 4\mathbf{j} - 2\mathbf{k}$.
(b) Find two other points on the line.

SOLUTION

(a) Here $\mathbf{r}_0 = \langle 5, 1, 3 \rangle = 5\mathbf{i} + \mathbf{j} + 3\mathbf{k}$ and $\mathbf{v} = \mathbf{i} + 4\mathbf{j} - 2\mathbf{k}$, so the vector equation (1) becomes

$$\mathbf{r} = (5\mathbf{i} + \mathbf{j} + 3\mathbf{k}) + t(\mathbf{i} + 4\mathbf{j} - 2\mathbf{k})$$

or

$$\mathbf{r} = (5 + t)\mathbf{i} + (1 + 4t)\mathbf{j} + (3 - 2t)\mathbf{k}$$

Parametric equations are

$$x = 5 + t \qquad y = 1 + 4t \qquad z = 3 - 2t$$

(b) Choosing the parameter value $t = 1$ gives $x = 6$, $y = 5$, and $z = 1$, so $(6, 5, 1)$ is a point on the line. Similarly, $t = -1$ gives the point $(4, -3, 5)$. ◼

The vector equation and parametric equations of a line are not unique. If we change the point or the parameter or choose a different parallel vector, then the equations change. For instance, if, instead of $(5, 1, 3)$, we choose the point $(6, 5, 1)$ in Example 1, then the parametric equations of the line become

$$x = 6 + t \qquad y = 5 + 4t \qquad z = 1 - 2t$$

Or, if we stay with the point $(5, 1, 3)$ but choose the parallel vector $2\mathbf{i} + 8\mathbf{j} - 4\mathbf{k}$, we arrive at the equations

$$x = 5 + 2t \qquad y = 1 + 8t \qquad z = 3 - 4t$$

In general, if a vector $\mathbf{v} = \langle a, b, c \rangle$ is used to describe the direction of a line L, then the numbers a, b, and c are called **direction numbers** of L. Since any vector parallel to $\mathbf{v}$ could also be used, we see that any three numbers proportional to a, b, and c could also be used as a set of direction numbers for L.

Another way of describing a line L is to eliminate the parameter t from Equations 2. If none of a, b, or c is 0, we can solve each of these equations for t, equate the results, and obtain

3

$$\frac{x - x_0}{a} = \frac{y - y_0}{b} = \frac{z - z_0}{c}$$

These equations are called **symmetric equations** of L. Notice that the numbers a, b, and c that appear in the denominators of Equations 3 are direction numbers of L, that is, components of a vector parallel to L. If one of a, b, or c is 0, we can still eliminate t. For instance, if $a = 0$, we could write the equations of L as

$$x = x_0 \qquad \frac{y - y_0}{b} = \frac{z - z_0}{c}$$

This means that L lies in the vertical plane $x = x_0$.

|||| Figure 4 shows the line L in Example 2 and the point P where it intersects the xy-plane.

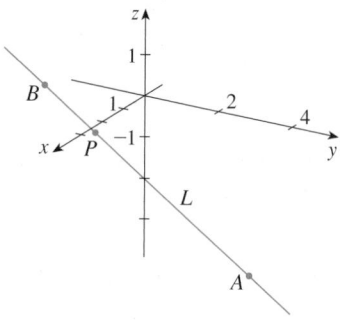

FIGURE 4

EXAMPLE 2
(a) Find parametric equations and symmetric equations of the line that passes through the points $A(2, 4, -3)$ and $B(3, -1, 1)$.
(b) At what point does this line intersect the xy-plane?

SOLUTION
(a) We are not explicitly given a vector parallel to the line, but observe that the vector $\mathbf{v}$ with representation $\overrightarrow{AB}$ is parallel to the line and

$$\mathbf{v} = \langle 3 - 2, -1 - 4, 1 - (-3) \rangle = \langle 1, -5, 4 \rangle$$

Thus, direction numbers are $a = 1$, $b = -5$, and $c = 4$. Taking the point $(2, 4, -3)$ as P_0, we see that parametric equations (2) are

$$x = 2 + t \qquad y = 4 - 5t \qquad z = -3 + 4t$$

and symmetric equations (3) are

$$\frac{x - 2}{1} = \frac{y - 4}{-5} = \frac{z + 3}{4}$$

(b) The line intersects the xy-plane when $z = 0$, so we put $z = 0$ in the symmetric equations and obtain

$$\frac{x - 2}{1} = \frac{y - 4}{-5} = \frac{3}{4}$$

This gives $x = \frac{11}{4}$ and $y = \frac{1}{4}$, so the line intersects the xy-plane at the point $\left(\frac{11}{4}, \frac{1}{4}, 0\right)$. ▬

In general, the procedure of Example 2 shows that direction numbers of the line L through the points $P_0(x_0, y_0, z_0)$ and $P_1(x_1, y_1, z_1)$ are $x_1 - x_0$, $y_1 - y_0$, and $z_1 - z_0$ and so symmetric equations of L are

$$\frac{x - x_0}{x_1 - x_0} = \frac{y - y_0}{y_1 - y_0} = \frac{z - z_0}{z_1 - z_0}$$

Often, we need a description, not of an entire line, but of just a line segment. How, for instance, could we describe the line segment AB in Example 2? If we put $t = 0$ in the parametric equations in Example 2(a), we get the point $(2, 4, -3)$ and if we put $t = 1$ we get $(3, -1, 1)$. So the line segment AB is described by the parametric equations

$$x = 2 + t \qquad y = 4 - 5t \qquad z = -3 + 4t \qquad 0 \le t \le 1$$

or by the corresponding vector equation

$$\mathbf{r}(t) = \langle 2 + t, 4 - 5t, -3 + 4t \rangle \qquad 0 \le t \le 1$$

In general, we know from Equation 1 that the vector equation of a line through the (tip of the) vector $\mathbf{r}_0$ in the direction of a vector $\mathbf{v}$ is $\mathbf{r} = \mathbf{r}_0 + t\mathbf{v}$. If the line also passes through (the tip of) $\mathbf{r}_1$, then we can take $\mathbf{v} = \mathbf{r}_1 - \mathbf{r}_0$ and so its vector equation is

$$\mathbf{r} = \mathbf{r}_0 + t(\mathbf{r}_1 - \mathbf{r}_0) = (1 - t)\mathbf{r}_0 + t\mathbf{r}_1$$

The line segment from $\mathbf{r}_0$ to $\mathbf{r}_1$ is given by the parameter interval $0 \leqslant t \leqslant 1$.

> **4** The line segment from $\mathbf{r}_0$ to $\mathbf{r}_1$ is given by the vector equation
>
> $$\mathbf{r}(t) = (1 - t)\mathbf{r}_0 + t\mathbf{r}_1 \qquad 0 \leqslant t \leqslant 1$$

||| The lines L_1 and L_2 in Example 3, shown in Figure 5, are skew lines.

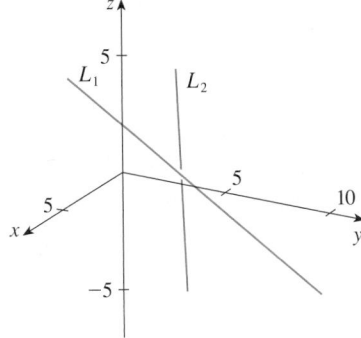

FIGURE 5

EXAMPLE 3 Show that the lines L_1 and L_2 with parametric equations

$$x = 1 + t \qquad y = -2 + 3t \qquad z = 4 - t$$

$$x = 2s \qquad y = 3 + s \qquad z = -3 + 4s$$

are **skew lines**; that is, they do not intersect and are not parallel (and therefore do not lie in the same plane).

SOLUTION The lines are not parallel because the corresponding vectors $\langle 1, 3, -1 \rangle$ and $\langle 2, 1, 4 \rangle$ are not parallel. (Their components are not proportional.) If L_1 and L_2 had a point of intersection, there would be values of t and s such that

$$1 + \quad t = 2s$$

$$-2 + 3t = 3 + s$$

$$4 - \quad t = -3 + 4s$$

But if we solve the first two equations, we get $t = \frac{11}{5}$ and $s = \frac{8}{5}$, and these values don't satisfy the third equation. Therefore, there are no values of t and s that satisfy the three equations. Thus, L_1 and L_2 do not intersect. Hence, L_1 and L_2 are skew lines.

||| **Planes**

Although a line in space is determined by a point and a direction, a plane in space is more difficult to describe. A single vector parallel to a plane is not enough to convey the "direction" of the plane, but a vector perpendicular to the plane does completely specify its direction. Thus, a plane in space is determined by a point $P_0(x_0, y_0, z_0)$ in the plane and a vector $\mathbf{n}$ that is orthogonal to the plane. This orthogonal vector $\mathbf{n}$ is called a **normal vector**. Let $P(x, y, z)$ be an arbitrary point in the plane, and let $\mathbf{r}_0$ and $\mathbf{r}$ be the position vectors of P_0 and P. Then the vector $\mathbf{r} - \mathbf{r}_0$ is represented by $\overrightarrow{P_0P}$. (See Figure 6.) The normal vector $\mathbf{n}$ is orthogonal to every vector in the given plane. In particular, $\mathbf{n}$ is orthogonal to $\mathbf{r} - \mathbf{r}_0$ and so we have

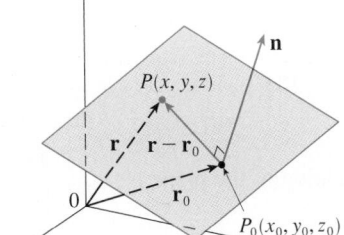

FIGURE 6

5

$$\mathbf{n} \cdot (\mathbf{r} - \mathbf{r}_0) = 0$$

which can be rewritten as

6

$$\mathbf{n} \cdot \mathbf{r} = \mathbf{n} \cdot \mathbf{r}_0$$

Either Equation 5 or Equation 6 is called a **vector equation of the plane**.

To obtain a scalar equation for the plane, we write $\mathbf{n} = \langle a, b, c \rangle$, $\mathbf{r} = \langle x, y, z \rangle$, and $\mathbf{r}_0 = \langle x_0, y_0, z_0 \rangle$. Then the vector equation (5) becomes

$$\langle a, b, c \rangle \cdot \langle x - x_0, y - y_0, z - z_0 \rangle = 0$$

or

$$\boxed{7} \qquad a(x - x_0) + b(y - y_0) + c(z - z_0) = 0$$

Equation 7 is the **scalar equation of the plane through** $P_0(x_0, y_0, z_0)$ **with normal vector** $\mathbf{n} = \langle a, b, c \rangle$.

EXAMPLE 4 Find an equation of the plane through the point $(2, 4, -1)$ with normal vector $\mathbf{n} = \langle 2, 3, 4 \rangle$. Find the intercepts and sketch the plane.

SOLUTION Putting $a = 2$, $b = 3$, $c = 4$, $x_0 = 2$, $y_0 = 4$, and $z_0 = -1$ in Equation 7, we see that an equation of the plane is

$$2(x - 2) + 3(y - 4) + 4(z + 1) = 0$$

or

$$2x + 3y + 4z = 12$$

To find the x-intercept we set $y = z = 0$ in this equation and obtain $x = 6$. Similarly, the y-intercept is 4 and the z-intercept is 3. This enables us to sketch the portion of the plane that lies in the first octant (see Figure 7).

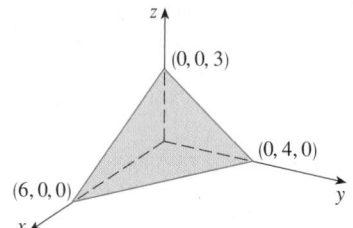

FIGURE 7

By collecting terms in Equation 7 as we did in Example 4, we can rewrite the equation of a plane as

$$\boxed{8} \qquad ax + by + cz + d = 0$$

where $d = -(ax_0 + by_0 + cz_0)$. Equation 8 is called a **linear equation** in x, y, and z. Conversely, it can be shown that if a, b, and c are not all 0, then the linear equation (8) represents a plane with normal vector $\langle a, b, c \rangle$. (See Exercise 73.)

|||| Figure 8 shows the portion of the plane in Example 5 that is enclosed by triangle PQR.

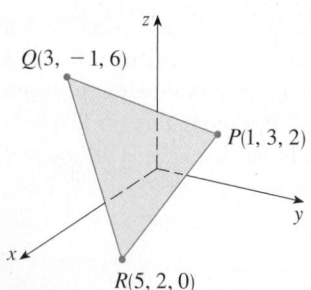

FIGURE 8

EXAMPLE 5 Find an equation of the plane that passes through the points $P(1, 3, 2)$, $Q(3, -1, 6)$, and $R(5, 2, 0)$.

SOLUTION The vectors $\mathbf{a}$ and $\mathbf{b}$ corresponding to $\overrightarrow{PQ}$ and $\overrightarrow{PR}$ are

$$\mathbf{a} = \langle 2, -4, 4 \rangle \qquad \mathbf{b} = \langle 4, -1, -2 \rangle$$

Since both $\mathbf{a}$ and $\mathbf{b}$ lie in the plane, their cross product $\mathbf{a} \times \mathbf{b}$ is orthogonal to the plane and can be taken as the normal vector. Thus

$$\mathbf{n} = \mathbf{a} \times \mathbf{b} = \begin{vmatrix} \mathbf{i} & \mathbf{j} & \mathbf{k} \\ 2 & -4 & 4 \\ 4 & -1 & -2 \end{vmatrix} = 12\mathbf{i} + 20\mathbf{j} + 14\mathbf{k}$$

With the point $P(1, 3, 2)$ and the normal vector $\mathbf{n}$, an equation of the plane is

$$12(x - 1) + 20(y - 3) + 14(z - 2) = 0$$

or

$$6x + 10y + 7z = 50$$

EXAMPLE 6 Find the point at which the line with parametric equations $x = 2 + 3t$, $y = -4t$, $z = 5 + t$ intersects the plane $4x + 5y - 2z = 18$.

SOLUTION We substitute the expressions for x, y, and z from the parametric equations into the equation of the plane:

$$4(2 + 3t) + 5(-4t) - 2(5 + t) = 18$$

This simplifies to $-10t = 20$, so $t = -2$. Therefore, the point of intersection occurs when the parameter value is $t = -2$. Then $x = 2 + 3(-2) = -4$, $y = -4(-2) = 8$, $z = 5 - 2 = 3$ and so the point of intersection is $(-4, 8, 3)$.

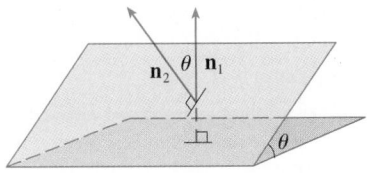

FIGURE 9

Two planes are **parallel** if their normal vectors are parallel. For instance, the planes $x + 2y - 3z = 4$ and $2x + 4y - 6z = 3$ are parallel because their normal vectors are $\mathbf{n}_1 = \langle 1, 2, -3 \rangle$ and $\mathbf{n}_2 = \langle 2, 4, -6 \rangle$ and $\mathbf{n}_2 = 2\mathbf{n}_1$. If two planes are not parallel, then they intersect in a straight line and the angle between the two planes is defined as the acute angle between their normal vectors (see angle θ in Figure 9).

EXAMPLE 7

(a) Find the angle between the planes $x + y + z = 1$ and $x - 2y + 3z = 1$.
(b) Find symmetric equations for the line of intersection L of these two planes.

|||| Figure 10 shows the planes in Example 7 and their line of intersection L.

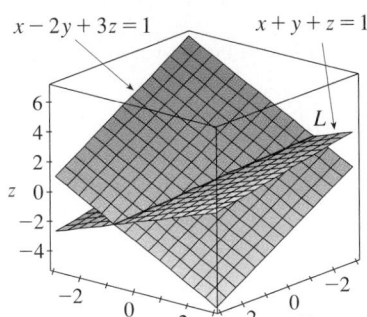

FIGURE 10

SOLUTION
(a) The normal vectors of these planes are

$$\mathbf{n}_1 = \langle 1, 1, 1 \rangle \qquad \mathbf{n}_2 = \langle 1, -2, 3 \rangle$$

and so, if θ is the angle between the planes, Corollary 13.3.6 gives

$$\cos \theta = \frac{\mathbf{n}_1 \cdot \mathbf{n}_2}{|\mathbf{n}_1| |\mathbf{n}_2|} = \frac{1(1) + 1(-2) + 1(3)}{\sqrt{1 + 1 + 1}\sqrt{1 + 4 + 9}} = \frac{2}{\sqrt{42}}$$

$$\theta = \cos^{-1}\left(\frac{2}{\sqrt{42}}\right) \approx 72°$$

(b) We first need to find a point on L. For instance, we can find the point where the line intersects the xy-plane by setting $z = 0$ in the equations of both planes. This gives the equations $x + y = 1$ and $x - 2y = 1$, whose solution is $x = 1$, $y = 0$. So the point $(1, 0, 0)$ lies on L.

Now we observe that, since L lies in both planes, it is perpendicular to both of the normal vectors. Thus, a vector $\mathbf{v}$ parallel to L is given by the cross product

|||| Another way to find the line of intersection is to solve the equations of the planes for two of the variables in terms of the third, which can be taken as the parameter.

$$\mathbf{v} = \mathbf{n}_1 \times \mathbf{n}_2 = \begin{vmatrix} \mathbf{i} & \mathbf{j} & \mathbf{k} \\ 1 & 1 & 1 \\ 1 & -2 & 3 \end{vmatrix} = 5\mathbf{i} - 2\mathbf{j} - 3\mathbf{k}$$

and so the symmetric equations of L can be written as

$$\frac{x - 1}{5} = \frac{y}{-2} = \frac{z}{-3}$$

NOTE ▫ Since a linear equation in x, y, and z represents a plane and two nonparallel planes intersect in a line, it follows that two linear equations can represent a line. The points (x, y, z) that satisfy both $a_1 x + b_1 y + c_1 z + d_1 = 0$ and $a_2 x + b_2 y + c_2 z + d_2 = 0$

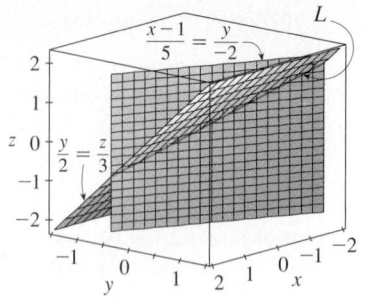

FIGURE 11

▌▌▌▌ Figure 11 shows how the line L in Example 7 can also be regarded as the line of intersection of planes derived from its symmetric equations.

lie on both of these planes, and so the pair of linear equations represents the line of intersection of the planes (if they are not parallel). For instance, in Example 7 the line L was given as the line of intersection of the planes $x + y + z = 1$ and $x - 2y + 3z = 1$. The symmetric equations that we found for L could be written as

$$\frac{x - 1}{5} = \frac{y}{-2} \quad \text{and} \quad \frac{y}{-2} = \frac{z}{-3}$$

which is again a pair of linear equations. They exhibit L as the line of intersection of the planes $(x - 1)/5 = y/(-2)$ and $y/(-2) = z/(-3)$. (See Figure 11.)

In general, when we write the equations of a line in the symmetric form

$$\frac{x - x_0}{a} = \frac{y - y_0}{b} = \frac{z - z_0}{c}$$

we can regard the line as the line of intersection of the two planes

$$\frac{x - x_0}{a} = \frac{y - y_0}{b} \quad \text{and} \quad \frac{y - y_0}{b} = \frac{z - z_0}{c}$$

EXAMPLE 8 Find a formula for the distance D from a point $P_1(x_1, y_1, z_1)$ to the plane $ax + by + cz + d = 0$.

SOLUTION Let $P_0(x_0, y_0, z_0)$ be any point in the given plane and let $\mathbf{b}$ be the vector corresponding to $\overrightarrow{P_0P_1}$. Then

$$\mathbf{b} = \langle x_1 - x_0, y_1 - y_0, z_1 - z_0 \rangle$$

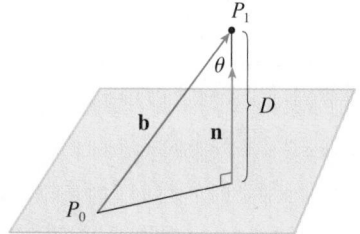

FIGURE 12

From Figure 12 you can see that the distance D from P_1 to the plane is equal to the absolute value of the scalar projection of $\mathbf{b}$ onto the normal vector $\mathbf{n} = \langle a, b, c \rangle$. (See Section 13.3.) Thus

$$D = |\text{comp}_\mathbf{n}\, \mathbf{b}| = \frac{|\mathbf{n} \cdot \mathbf{b}|}{|\mathbf{n}|}$$

$$= \frac{|a(x_1 - x_0) + b(y_1 - y_0) + c(z_1 - z_0)|}{\sqrt{a^2 + b^2 + c^2}}$$

$$= \frac{|(ax_1 + by_1 + cz_1) - (ax_0 + by_0 + cz_0)|}{\sqrt{a^2 + b^2 + c^2}}$$

Since P_0 lies in the plane, its coordinates satisfy the equation of the plane and so we have $ax_0 + by_0 + cz_0 + d = 0$. Thus, the formula for D can be written as

$$\boxed{\; D = \frac{|ax_1 + by_1 + cz_1 + d|}{\sqrt{a^2 + b^2 + c^2}} \;}$$

$\boxed{9}$

EXAMPLE 9 Find the distance between the parallel planes $10x + 2y - 2z = 5$ and $5x + y - z = 1$.

SOLUTION First we note that the planes are parallel because their normal vectors $\langle 10, 2, -2 \rangle$ and $\langle 5, 1, -1 \rangle$ are parallel. To find the distance D between the planes, we choose any point on one plane and calculate its distance to the other plane. In particular, if we put $y = z = 0$ in the equation of the first plane, we get $10x = 5$ and so

$\left(\frac{1}{2}, 0, 0\right)$ is a point in this plane. By Formula 9, the distance between $\left(\frac{1}{2}, 0, 0\right)$ and the plane $5x + y - z - 1 = 0$ is

$$D = \frac{\left|5\left(\frac{1}{2}\right) + 1(0) - 1(0) - 1\right|}{\sqrt{5^2 + 1^2 + (-1)^2}} = \frac{\frac{3}{2}}{3\sqrt{3}} = \frac{\sqrt{3}}{6}$$

So the distance between the planes is $\sqrt{3}/6$.

EXAMPLE 10 In Example 3 we showed that the lines

$$L_1: \quad x = 1 + t \quad y = -2 + 3t \quad z = 4 - t$$

$$L_2: \quad x = 2s \quad\quad y = 3 + s \quad\quad z = -3 + 4s$$

are skew. Find the distance between them.

SOLUTION Since the two lines L_1 and L_2 are skew, they can be viewed as lying on two parallel planes P_1 and P_2. The distance between L_1 and L_2 is the same as the distance between P_1 and P_2, which can be computed as in Example 9. The common normal vector to both planes must be orthogonal to both $\mathbf{v}_1 = \langle 1, 3, -1 \rangle$ (the direction of L_1) and $\mathbf{v}_2 = \langle 2, 1, 4 \rangle$ (the direction of L_2). So a normal vector is

$$\mathbf{n} = \mathbf{v}_1 \times \mathbf{v}_2 = \begin{vmatrix} \mathbf{i} & \mathbf{j} & \mathbf{k} \\ 1 & 3 & -1 \\ 2 & 1 & 4 \end{vmatrix} = 13\mathbf{i} - 6\mathbf{j} - 5\mathbf{k}$$

If we put $s = 0$ in the equations of L_2, we get the point $(0, 3, -3)$ on L_2 and so an equation for P_2 is

$$13(x - 0) - 6(y - 3) - 5(z + 3) = 0 \quad \text{or} \quad 13x - 6y - 5z + 3 = 0$$

If we now set $t = 0$ in the equations for L_1, we get the point $(1, -2, 4)$ on P_1. So the distance between L_1 and L_2 is the same as the distance from $(1, -2, 4)$ to $13x - 6y - 5z + 3 = 0$. By Formula 9, this distance is

$$D = \frac{|13(1) - 6(-2) - 5(4) + 3|}{\sqrt{13^2 + (-6)^2 + (-5)^2}} = \frac{8}{\sqrt{230}} \approx 0.53$$

13.5 Exercises

1. Determine whether each statement is true or false.
 (a) Two lines parallel to a third line are parallel.
 (b) Two lines perpendicular to a third line are parallel.
 (c) Two planes parallel to a third plane are parallel.
 (d) Two planes perpendicular to a third plane are parallel.
 (e) Two lines parallel to a plane are parallel.
 (f) Two lines perpendicular to a plane are parallel.
 (g) Two planes parallel to a line are parallel.
 (h) Two planes perpendicular to a line are parallel.
 (i) Two planes either intersect or are parallel.
 (j) Two lines either intersect or are parallel.
 (k) A plane and a line either intersect or are parallel.

2–5 ‖‖‖ Find a vector equation and parametric equations for the line.

2. The line through the point $(1, 0, -3)$ and parallel to the vector $2\mathbf{i} - 4\mathbf{j} + 5\mathbf{k}$

3. The line through the point $(-2, 4, 10)$ and parallel to the vector $\langle 3, 1, -8 \rangle$

4. The line through the origin and parallel to the line $x = 2t$, $y = 1 - t, z = 4 + 3t$

5. The line through the point $(1, 0, 6)$ and perpendicular to the plane $x + 3y + z = 5$

6–12 ‖‖ Find parametric equations and symmetric equations for the line.

6. The line through the origin and the point $(1, 2, 3)$

7. The line through the points $(1, 3, 2)$ and $(-4, 3, 0)$

8. The line through the points $(6, 1, -3)$ and $(2, 4, 5)$

9. The line through the points $(0, \frac{1}{2}, 1)$ and $(2, 1, -3)$

10. The line through $(2, 1, 0)$ and perpendicular to both $\mathbf{i} + \mathbf{j}$ and $\mathbf{j} + \mathbf{k}$

11. The line through $(1, -1, 1)$ and parallel to the line $x + 2 = \frac{1}{2}y = z - 3$

12. The line of intersection of the planes $x + y + z = 1$ and $x + z = 0$

13. Is the line through $(-4, -6, 1)$ and $(-2, 0 -3)$ parallel to the line through $(10, 18, 4)$ and $(5, 3, 14)$?

14. Is the line through $(4, 1, -1)$ and $(2, 5, 3)$ perpendicular to the line through $(-3, 2, 0)$ and $(5, 1, 4)$?

15. (a) Find symmetric equations for the line that passes through the point $(0, 2, -1)$ and is parallel to the line with parametric equations $x = 1 + 2t$, $y = 3t$, $z = 5 - 7t$.
   (b) Find the points in which the required line in part (a) intersects the coordinate planes.

16. (a) Find parametric equations for the line through $(5, 1, 0)$ that is perpendicular to the plane $2x - y + z = 1.$
   (b) In what points does this line intersect the coordinate planes?

17. Find a vector equation for the line segment from $(2, -1, 4)$ to $(4, 6, 1)$.

18. Find parametric equations for the line segment from $(10, 3, 1)$ to $(5, 6, -3)$.

19–22 ‖‖ Determine whether the lines L_1 and L_2 are parallel, skew, or intersecting. If they intersect, find the point of intersection.

19. L_1: $x = -6t$, $\quad y = 1 + 9t$, $\quad z = -3t$
   L_2: $x = 1 + 2s$, $\quad y = 4 - 3s$, $\quad z = s$

20. L_1: $x = 1 + 2t$, $\quad y = 3t$, $\quad z = 2 - t$
   L_2: $x = -1 + s$, $\quad y = 4 + s$, $\quad z = 1 + 3s$

21. L_1: $\dfrac{x}{1} = \dfrac{y - 1}{2} = \dfrac{z - 2}{3}$, $\quad L_2$: $\dfrac{x - 3}{-4} = \dfrac{y - 2}{-3} = \dfrac{z - 1}{2}$

22. L_1: $\dfrac{x - 1}{2} = \dfrac{y - 3}{2} = \dfrac{z - 2}{-1}$

   L_2: $\dfrac{x - 2}{1} = \dfrac{y - 6}{-1} = \dfrac{z + 2}{3}$

23–38 ‖‖ Find an equation of the plane.

23. The plane through the point $(6, 3, 2)$ and perpendicular to the vector $\langle -2, 1, 5 \rangle$

24. The plane through the point $(4, 0, -3)$ and with normal vector $\mathbf{j} + 2\mathbf{k}$

25. The plane through the point $(1, -1, 1)$ and with normal vector $\mathbf{i} + \mathbf{j} - \mathbf{k}$

26. The plane through the point $(-2, 8, 10)$ and perpendicular to the line $x = 1 + t$, $y = 2t$, $z = 4 - 3t$

27. The plane through the origin and parallel to the plane $2x - y + 3z = 1$

28. The plane through the point $(-1, 6, -5)$ and parallel to the plane $x + y + z + 2 = 0$

29. The plane through the point $(4, -2, 3)$ and parallel to the plane $3x - 7z = 12$

30. The plane that contains the line $x = 3 + 2t$, $y = t$, $z = 8 - t$ and is parallel to the plane $2x + 4y + 8z = 17$

31. The plane through the points $(0, 1, 1)$, $(1, 0, 1)$, and $(1, 1, 0)$

32. The plane through the origin and the points $(2, -4, 6)$ and $(5, 1, 3)$

33. The plane through the points $(3, -1, 2)$, $(8, 2, 4)$, and $(-1, -2, -3)$

34. The plane that passes through the point $(1, 2, 3)$ and contains the line $x = 3t$, $y = 1 + t$, $z = 2 - t$

35. The plane that passes through the point $(6, 0, -2)$ and contains the line $x = 4 - 2t$, $y = 3 + 5t$, $z = 7 + 4t$

36. The plane that passes through the point $(1, -1, 1)$ and contains the line with symmetric equations $x = 2y = 3z$

37. The plane that passes through the point $(-1, 2, 1)$ and contains the line of intersection of the planes $x + y - z = 2$ and $2x - y + 3z = 1$

38. The plane that passes through the line of intersection of the planes $x - z = 1$ and $y + 2z = 3$ and is perpendicular to the plane $x + y - 2z = 1$

39–41 ‖‖ Find the point at which the line intersects the given plane.

39. $x = 3 - t$, $y = 2 + t$, $z = 5t$; $\quad x - y + 2z = 9$

40. $x = 1 + 2t$, $y = 4t$, $z = 2 - 3t$; $\quad x + 2y - z + 1 = 0$

41. $x = y - 1 = 2z$; $\quad 4x - y + 3z = 8$

42. Where does the line through $(1, 0, 1)$ and $(4, -2, 2)$ intersect the plane $x + y + z = 6$?

43. Find direction numbers for the line of intersection of the planes $x + y + z = 1$ and $x + z = 0$.

44. Find the cosine of the angle between the planes $x + y + z = 0$ and $x + 2y + 3z = 1$.

45–50 |||| Determine whether the planes are parallel, perpendicular, or neither. If neither, find the angle between them.

45. $x + 4y - 3z = 1$, $\quad -3x + 6y + 7z = 0$

46. $2z = 4y - x$, $\quad 3x - 12y + 6z = 1$

47. $x + y + z = 1$, $\quad x - y + z = 1$

48. $2x - 3y + 4z = 5$, $\quad x + 6y + 4z = 3$

49. $x = 4y - 2z$, $\quad 8y = 1 + 2x + 4z$

50. $x + 2y + 2z = 1$, $\quad 2x - y + 2z = 1$

51–52 |||| (a) Find symmetric equations for the line of intersection of the planes and (b) find the angle between the planes.

51. $x + y - z = 2$, $\quad 3x - 4y + 5z = 6$

52. $x - 2y + z = 1$, $\quad 2x + y + z = 1$

53–54 |||| Find parametric equations for the line of intersection of the planes.

53. $z = x + y$, $\quad 2x - 5y - z = 1$

54. $2x + 5z + 3 = 0$, $\quad x - 3y + z + 2 = 0$

55. Find an equation for the plane consisting of all points that are equidistant from the points $(1, 1, 0)$ and $(0, 1, 1)$.

56. Find an equation for the plane consisting of all points that are equidistant from the points $(-4, 2, 1)$ and $(2, -4, 3)$.

57. Find an equation of the plane with x-intercept a, y-intercept b, and z-intercept c.

58. (a) Find the point at which the given lines intersect:
$$\mathbf{r} = \langle 1, 1, 0 \rangle + t\langle 1, -1, 2 \rangle$$
and $\quad \mathbf{r} = \langle 2, 0, 2 \rangle + s\langle -1, 1, 0 \rangle$
(b) Find an equation of the plane that contains these lines.

59. Find parametric equations for the line through the point $(0, 1, 2)$ that is parallel to the plane $x + y + z = 2$ and perpendicular to the line $x = 1 + t, y = 1 - t, z = 2t$.

60. Find parametric equations for the line through the point $(0, 1, 2)$ that is perpendicular to the line $x = 1 + t$, $y = 1 - t, z = 2t$ and intersects this line.

61. Which of the following four planes are parallel? Are any of them identical?
$$P_1: 4x - 2y + 6z = 3 \qquad P_2: 4x - 2y - 2z = 6$$
$$P_3: -6x + 3y - 9z = 5 \qquad P_4: z = 2x - y - 3$$

62. Which of the following four lines are parallel? Are any of them identical?
$$L_1: x = 1 + t, \quad y = t, \quad z = 2 - 5t$$
$$L_2: x + 1 = y - 2 = 1 - z$$
$$L_3: x = 1 + t, \quad y = 4 + t, \quad z = 1 - t$$
$$L_4: \mathbf{r} = \langle 2, 1, -3 \rangle + t\langle 2, 2, -10 \rangle$$

63–64 |||| Use the formula in Exercise 39 in Section 13.4 to find the distance from the point to the given line.

63. $(1, 2, 3)$; $\quad x = 2 + t, \quad y = 2 - 3t, \quad z = 5t$

64. $(1, 0, -1)$; $\quad x = 5 - t, \quad y = 3t, \quad z = 1 + 2t$

65–66 |||| Find the distance from the point to the given plane.

65. $(2, 8, 5)$, $\quad x - 2y - 2z = 1$

66. $(3, -2, 7)$, $\quad 4x - 6y + z = 5$

67–68 |||| Find the distance between the given parallel planes.

67. $z = x + 2y + 1$, $\quad 3x + 6y - 3z = 4$

68. $3x + 6y - 9z = 4$, $\quad x + 2y - 3z = 1$

69. Show that the distance between the parallel planes $ax + by + cz + d_1 = 0$ and $ax + by + cz + d_2 = 0$ is
$$D = \frac{|d_1 - d_2|}{\sqrt{a^2 + b^2 + c^2}}$$

70. Find equations of the planes that are parallel to the plane $x + 2y - 2z = 1$ and two units away from it.

71. Show that the lines with symmetric equations $x = y = z$ and $x + 1 = y/2 = z/3$ are skew, and find the distance between these lines.

72. Find the distance between the skew lines with parametric equations $x = 1 + t, y = 1 + 6t, z = 2t$, and $x = 1 + 2s$, $y = 5 + 15s, z = -2 + 6s$.

73. If a, b, and c are not all 0, show that the equation $ax + by + cz + d = 0$ represents a plane and $\langle a, b, c \rangle$ is a normal vector to the plane.
  Hint: Suppose $a \neq 0$ and rewrite the equation in the form
$$a\left(x + \frac{d}{a}\right) + b(y - 0) + c(z - 0) = 0$$

74. Give a geometric description of each family of planes.
(a) $x + y + z = c$
(b) $x + y + cz = 1$
(c) $y \cos \theta + z \sin \theta = 1$

LABORATORY PROJECT

Putting 3D in Perspective

Computer graphics programmers face the same challenge as the great painters of the past: how to represent a three-dimensional scene as a flat image on a two-dimensional plane (a screen or a canvas). To create the illusion of perspective, in which closer objects appear larger than those farther away, three-dimensional objects in the computer's memory are projected onto a rectangular screen window from a viewpoint where the eye, or camera, is located. The viewing volume—the portion of space that will be visible—is the region contained by the four planes that pass through the viewpoint and an edge of the screen window. If objects in the scene extend beyond these four planes, they must be truncated before pixel data are sent to the screen. These planes are therefore called *clipping planes*.

1. Suppose the screen is represented by a rectangle in the yz-plane with vertices $(0, \pm 400, 0)$ and $(0, \pm 400, 600)$, and the camera is placed at $(1000, 0, 0)$. A line L in the scene passes through the points $(230, -285, 102)$ and $(860, 105, 264)$. At what points should L be clipped by the clipping planes?

2. If the clipped line segment is projected on the screen window, identify the resulting line segment.

3. Use parametric equations to plot the edges of the screen window, the clipped line segment, and its projection on the screen window. Then add sight lines connecting the viewpoint to each end of the clipped segments to verify that the projection is correct.

4. A rectangle with vertices $(621, -147, 206)$, $(563, 31, 242)$, $(657, -111, 86)$, and $(599, 67, 122)$ is added to the scene. The line L intersects this rectangle. To make the rectangle appear opaque, a programmer can use *hidden line rendering*, which removes portions of objects that are behind other objects. Identify the portion of L that should be removed.

|||| 13.6 Cylinders and Quadric Surfaces

We have already looked at two special types of surfaces—planes (in Section 13.5) and spheres (in Section 13.1). Here we investigate two other types of surfaces—cylinders and quadric surfaces.

In order to sketch the graph of a surface, it is useful to determine the curves of intersection of the surface with planes parallel to the coordinate planes. These curves are called **traces** (or cross-sections) of the surface.

|||| Cylinders

A **cylinder** is a surface that consists of all lines (called **rulings**) that are parallel to a given line and pass through a given plane curve.

EXAMPLE 1 Sketch the graph of the surface $z = x^2$.

SOLUTION Notice that the equation of the graph, $z = x^2$, doesn't involve y. This means that any vertical plane with equation $y = k$ (parallel to the xz-plane) intersects the graph in a curve with equation $z = x^2$. So these vertical traces are parabolas. Figure 1 shows how the graph is formed by taking the parabola $z = x^2$ in the xz-plane and moving it in the direction of the y-axis. The graph is a surface, called a **parabolic cylinder**, made up of infinitely many shifted copies of the same parabola. Here the rulings of the cylinder are parallel to the y-axis.

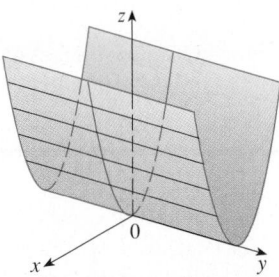

FIGURE 1

The surface $z = x^2$ is a parabolic cylinder.

We noticed that the variable y is missing from the equation of the cylinder in Example 1. This is typical of a surface whose rulings are parallel to one of the coordinate axes. If one of the variables x, y, or z is missing from the equation of a surface, then the surface is a cylinder.

EXAMPLE 2 Identify and sketch the surfaces.

(a) $x^2 + y^2 = 1$ (b) $y^2 + z^2 = 1$

SOLUTION

(a) Since z is missing and the equations $x^2 + y^2 = 1$, $z = k$ represent a circle with radius 1 in the plane $z = k$, the surface $x^2 + y^2 = 1$ is a circular cylinder whose axis is the z-axis (see Figure 2). Here the rulings are vertical lines.

(b) In this case x is missing and the surface is a circular cylinder whose axis is the x-axis (see Figure 3). It is obtained by taking the circle $y^2 + z^2 = 1$, $x = 0$ in the yz-plane and moving it parallel to the x-axis.

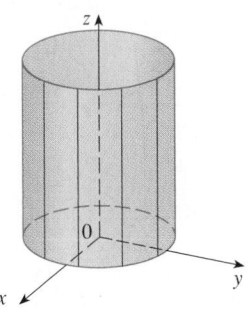

FIGURE 2 $x^2 + y^2 = 1$

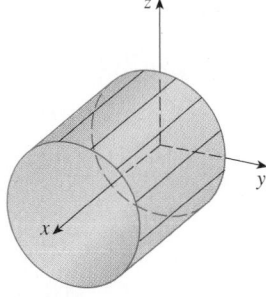

FIGURE 3 $y^2 + z^2 = 1$

NOTE ▫ When you are dealing with surfaces, it is important to recognize that an equation like $x^2 + y^2 = 1$ represents a cylinder and not a circle. The trace of the cylinder $x^2 + y^2 = 1$ in the xy-plane is the circle with equations $x^2 + y^2 = 1$, $z = 0$.

‖‖ Quadric Surfaces

A **quadric surface** is the graph of a second-degree equation in three variables x, y, and z. The most general such equation is

$$Ax^2 + By^2 + Cz^2 + Dxy + Eyz + Fxz + Gx + Hy + Iz + J = 0$$

where $A, B, C, \ldots, J$ are constants, but by translation and rotation it can be brought into one of the two standard forms

$$Ax^2 + By^2 + Cz^2 + J = 0 \qquad \text{or} \qquad Ax^2 + By^2 + Iz = 0$$

Quadric surfaces are the counterparts in three dimensions of the conic sections in the plane. (See Section 11.5 for a review of conic sections.)

EXAMPLE 3 Use traces to sketch the quadric surface with equation

$$x^2 + \frac{y^2}{9} + \frac{z^2}{4} = 1$$

SOLUTION By substituting $z = 0$, we find that the trace in the xy-plane is $x^2 + y^2/9 = 1$, which we recognize as an equation of an ellipse. In general, the horizontal trace in the plane $z = k$ is

$$x^2 + \frac{y^2}{9} = 1 - \frac{k^2}{4} \qquad z = k$$

which is an ellipse, provided that $k^2 < 4$, that is, $-2 < k < 2$.

Similarly, the vertical traces are also ellipses:

$$\frac{y^2}{9} + \frac{z^2}{4} = 1 - k^2 \qquad x = k \qquad (\text{if } -1 < k < 1)$$

$$x^2 + \frac{z^2}{4} = 1 - \frac{k^2}{9} \qquad y = k \qquad (\text{if } -3 < k < 3)$$

Figure 4 shows how drawing some traces indicates the shape of the surface. It's called an **ellipsoid** because all of its traces are ellipses. Notice that it is symmetric with respect to each coordinate plane; this is a reflection of the fact that its equation involves only even powers of x, y, and z.

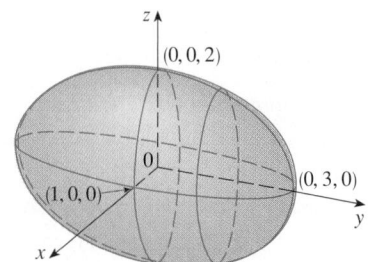

FIGURE 4

The ellipsoid $x^2 + \dfrac{y^2}{9} + \dfrac{z^2}{4} = 1$

EXAMPLE 4 Use traces to sketch the surface $z = 4x^2 + y^2$.

SOLUTION If we put $x = 0$, we get $z = y^2$, so the yz-plane intersects the surface in a parabola. If we put $x = k$ (a constant), we get $z = y^2 + 4k^2$. This means that if we slice the graph with any plane parallel to the yz-plane, we obtain a parabola that opens upward. Similarly, if $y = k$, the trace is $z = 4x^2 + k^2$, which is again a parabola that opens upward. If we put $z = k$, we get the horizontal traces $4x^2 + y^2 = k$, which we recognize as a family of ellipses. Knowing the shapes of the traces, we can sketch the graph in Figure 5. Because of the elliptical and parabolic traces, the quadric surface $z = 4x^2 + y^2$ is called an **elliptic paraboloid**.

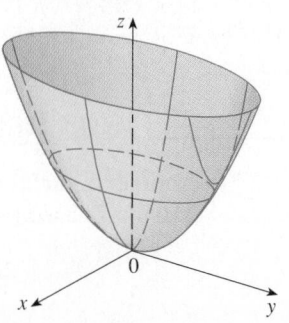

FIGURE 5

The surface $z = 4x^2 + y^2$ is an elliptic paraboloid. Horizontal traces are ellipses; vertical traces are parabolas.

EXAMPLE 5 Sketch the surface $z = y^2 - x^2$.

SOLUTION The traces in the vertical planes $x = k$ are the parabolas $z = y^2 - k^2$, which open upward. The traces in $y = k$ are the parabolas $z = -x^2 + k^2$, which open downward. The horizontal traces are $y^2 - x^2 = k$, a family of hyperbolas. We draw the families of traces in Figure 6, and we show how the traces appear when placed in their correct planes in Figure 7.

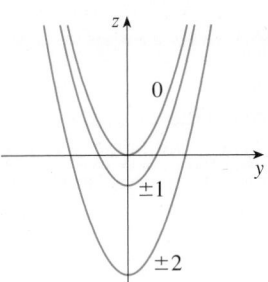
Traces in $x = k$ are $z = y^2 - k^2$

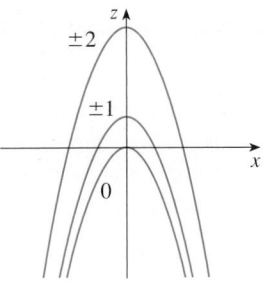
Traces in $y = k$ are $z = -x^2 + k^2$

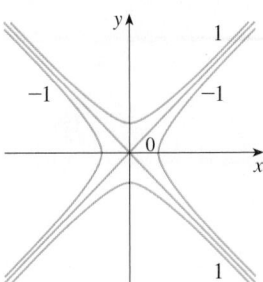
Traces in $z = k$ are $y^2 - x^2 = k$

FIGURE 6
Vertical traces are parabolas; horizontal traces are hyperbolas. All traces are labeled with the value of k.

Traces in $x = k$

Traces in $y = k$

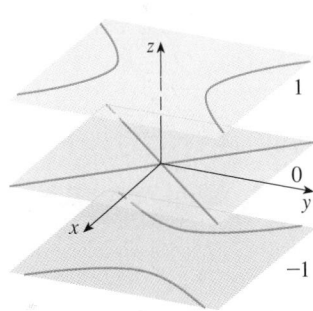
Traces in $z = k$

FIGURE 7
Traces moved to their correct planes

In Module 13.6A you can investigate how traces determine the shape of a surface.

In Figure 8 we fit together the traces from Figure 7 to form the surface $z = y^2 - x^2$, a **hyperbolic paraboloid**. Notice that the shape of the surface near the origin resembles that of a saddle. This surface will be investigated further in Section 15.7 when we discuss saddle points.

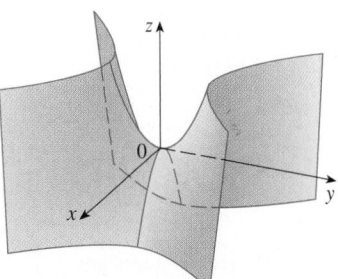

FIGURE 8
The surface $z = y^2 - x^2$ is a hyperbolic paraboloid.

EXAMPLE 6 Sketch the surface $\dfrac{x^2}{4} + y^2 - \dfrac{z^2}{4} = 1$.

SOLUTION The trace in any horizontal plane $z = k$ is the ellipse

$$\frac{x^2}{4} + y^2 = 1 + \frac{k^2}{4} \qquad z = k$$

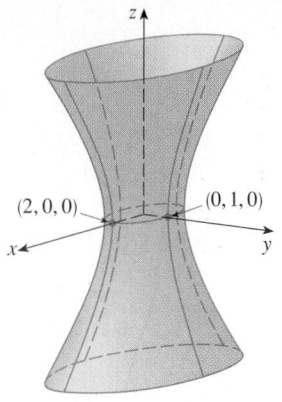

$(2,0,0)$ $(0,1,0)$

FIGURE 9

but the traces in the xz- and yz-planes are the hyperbolas

$$\frac{x^2}{4} - \frac{z^2}{4} = 1 \qquad y = 0 \qquad \text{and} \qquad y^2 - \frac{z^2}{4} = 1 \qquad x = 0$$

This surface is called a **hyperboloid of one sheet** and is sketched in Figure 9.

The idea of using traces to draw a surface is employed in three-dimensional graphing software for computers. In most such software, traces in the vertical planes $x = k$ and $y = k$ are drawn for equally spaced values of k, and parts of the graph are eliminated using hidden line removal. Table 1 shows computer-drawn graphs of the six basic types of quadric surfaces in standard form. All surfaces are symmetric with respect to the z-axis. If a quadric surface is symmetric about a different axis, its equation changes accordingly.

TABLE 1 Graphs of quadric surfaces

Surface	Equation	Surface	Equation
Ellipsoid	$\dfrac{x^2}{a^2} + \dfrac{y^2}{b^2} + \dfrac{z^2}{c^2} = 1$ All traces are ellipses. If $a = b = c$, the ellipsoid is a sphere.	Cone	$\dfrac{z^2}{c^2} = \dfrac{x^2}{a^2} + \dfrac{y^2}{b^2}$ Horizontal traces are ellipses. Vertical traces in the planes $x = k$ and $y = k$ are hyperbolas if $k \neq 0$ but are pairs of lines if $k = 0$.
Elliptic Paraboloid	$\dfrac{z}{c} = \dfrac{x^2}{a^2} + \dfrac{y^2}{b^2}$ Horizontal traces are ellipses. Vertical traces are parabolas. The variable raised to the first power indicates the axis of the paraboloid.	Hyperboloid of One Sheet	$\dfrac{x^2}{a^2} + \dfrac{y^2}{b^2} - \dfrac{z^2}{c^2} = 1$ Horizontal traces are ellipses. Vertical traces are hyperbolas. The axis of symmetry corresponds to the variable whose coefficient is negative.
Hyperbolic Paraboloid	$\dfrac{z}{c} = \dfrac{x^2}{a^2} - \dfrac{y^2}{b^2}$ Horizontal traces are hyperbolas. Vertical traces are parabolas. The case where $c < 0$ is illustrated.	Hyperboloid of Two Sheets	$-\dfrac{x^2}{a^2} - \dfrac{y^2}{b^2} + \dfrac{z^2}{c^2} = 1$ Horizontal traces in $z = k$ are ellipses if $k > c$ or $k < -c$. Vertical traces are hyperbolas. The two minus signs indicate two sheets.

In Module 13.6B you can see how changing a, b, and c in Table 1 affects the shape of the quadric surface.

EXAMPLE 7 Identify and sketch the surface $4x^2 - y^2 + 2z^2 + 4 = 0$.

SOLUTION Dividing by -4, we first put the equation in standard form:

$$-x^2 + \frac{y^2}{4} - \frac{z^2}{2} = 1$$

Comparing this equation with Table 1, we see that it represents a hyperboloid of two sheets, the only difference being that in this case the axis of the hyperboloid is the y-axis. The traces in the xy- and yz-planes are the hyperbolas

$$-x^2 + \frac{y^2}{4} = 1 \quad z = 0 \quad \text{and} \quad \frac{y^2}{4} - \frac{z^2}{2} = 1 \quad x = 0$$

The surface has no trace in the xz-plane, but traces in the vertical planes $y = k$ for $|k| > 2$ are the ellipses

$$x^2 + \frac{z^2}{2} = \frac{k^2}{4} - 1 \quad y = k$$

which can be written as

$$\frac{x^2}{\frac{k^2}{4} - 1} + \frac{z^2}{2\left(\frac{k^2}{4} - 1\right)} = 1 \quad y = k$$

These traces are used to make the sketch in Figure 10.

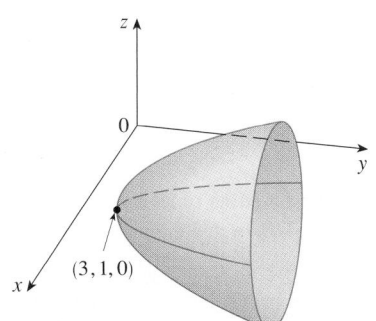

FIGURE 10
$4x^2 - y^2 + 2z^2 + 4 = 0$

EXAMPLE 8 Classify the quadric surface $x^2 + 2z^2 - 6x - y + 10 = 0$.

SOLUTION By completing the square we rewrite the equation as

$$y - 1 = (x - 3)^2 + 2z^2$$

Comparing this equation with Table 1, we see that it represents an elliptic paraboloid. Here, however, the axis of the paraboloid is parallel to the y-axis, and it has been shifted so that its vertex is the point $(3, 1, 0)$. The traces in the plane $y = k$ ($k > 1$) are the ellipses

$$(x - 3)^2 + 2z^2 = k - 1 \quad y = k$$

The trace in the xy-plane is the parabola with equation $y = 1 + (x - 3)^2$, $z = 0$. The paraboloid is sketched in Figure 11.

FIGURE 11
$x^2 + 2z^2 - 6x - y + 10 = 0$

13.6 Exercises

1. (a) What does the equation $y = x^2$ represent as a curve in $\mathbb{R}^2$?
(b) What does it represent as a surface in $\mathbb{R}^3$?
(c) What does the equation $z = y^2$ represent?

2. (a) Sketch the graph of $y = e^x$ as a curve in $\mathbb{R}^2$.
(b) Sketch the graph of $y = e^x$ as a surface in $\mathbb{R}^3$.
(c) Describe and sketch the surface $z = e^y$.

3–8 |||| Describe and sketch the surface.

3. $y^2 + 4z^2 = 4$

4. $z = 4 - x^2$

5. $x - y^2 = 0$

6. $yz = 4$

7. $z = \cos x$

8. $x^2 - y^2 = 1$

9. (a) Find and identify the traces of the quadric surface $x^2 + y^2 - z^2 = 1$ and explain why the graph looks like the graph of the hyperboloid of one sheet in Table 1.
(b) If we change the equation in part (a) to $x^2 - y^2 + z^2 = 1$, how is the graph affected?
(c) What if we change the equation in part (a) to $x^2 + y^2 + 2y - z^2 = 0$?

10. (a) Find and identify the traces of the quadric surface
$-x^2 - y^2 + z^2 = 1$ and explain why the graph looks like
the graph of the hyperboloid of two sheets in Table 1.
(b) If the equation in part (a) is changed to $x^2 - y^2 - z^2 = 1$,
what happens to the graph? Sketch the new graph.

11–20 |||| Find the traces of the given surface in the planes $x = k$,
$y = k$, $z = k$. Then identify the surface and sketch it.

11. $4x^2 + 9y^2 + 36z^2 = 36$ **12.** $4y = x^2 + z^2$

13. $y^2 = x^2 + z^2$ **14.** $z = x^2 - y^2$

15. $-x^2 + 4y^2 - z^2 = 4$ **16.** $25y^2 + z^2 = 100 + 4x^2$

17. $x^2 + 4z^2 - y = 0$ **18.** $x^2 + 4y^2 + z^2 = 4$

19. $y = z^2 - x^2$ **20.** $16x^2 = y^2 + 4z^2$

21–28 |||| Match the equation with its graph (labeled I–VIII). Give
reasons for your choices.

21. $x^2 + 4y^2 + 9z^2 = 1$ **22.** $9x^2 + 4y^2 + z^2 = 1$

23. $x^2 - y^2 + z^2 = 1$ **24.** $-x^2 + y^2 - z^2 = 1$

25. $y = 2x^2 + z^2$ **26.** $y^2 = x^2 + 2z^2$

27. $x^2 + 2z^2 = 1$ **28.** $y = x^2 - z^2$

29–36 |||| Reduce the equation to one of the standard forms,
classify the surface, and sketch it.

29. $z^2 = 4x^2 + 9y^2 + 36$ **30.** $x^2 = 2y^2 + 3z^2$

31. $x = 2y^2 + 3z^2$ **32.** $4x - y^2 + 4z^2 = 0$

33. $4x^2 + y^2 + 4z^2 - 4y - 24z + 36 = 0$

34. $4y^2 + z^2 - x - 16y - 4z + 20 = 0$

35. $x^2 - y^2 + z^2 - 4x - 2y - 2z + 4 = 0$

36. $x^2 - y^2 + z^2 - 2x + 2y + 4z + 2 = 0$

37–40 |||| Use a computer with three-dimensional graphing soft-
ware to graph the surface. Experiment with viewpoints and with
domains for the variables until you get a good view of the surface.

37. $z = 3x^2 - 5y^2$ **38.** $8x^2 + 15y^2 + 5z^2 = 100$

39. $z^2 = x^2 + 4y^2$ **40.** $z = y^2 + xy$

41. Sketch the region bounded by the surfaces $z = \sqrt{x^2 + y^2}$
and $x^2 + y^2 = 1$ for $1 \le z \le 2$.

42. Sketch the region bounded by the paraboloids $z = x^2 + y^2$
and $z = 2 - x^2 - y^2$.

43. Find an equation for the surface obtained by rotating the
parabola $y = x^2$ about the y-axis.

44. Find an equation for the surface obtained by rotating the line
$x = 3y$ about the x-axis.

45. Find an equation for the surface consisting of all points that
are equidistant from the point $(-1, 0, 0)$ and the plane $x = 1$.
Identify the surface.

46. Find an equation for the surface consisting of all points P for
which the distance from P to the x-axis is twice the distance
from P to the yz-plane. Identify the surface.

47. Show that if the point (a, b, c) lies on the hyperbolic paraboloid $z = y^2 - x^2$, then the lines with parametric equations
$x = a + t$, $y = b + t$, $z = c + 2(b - a)t$ and $x = a + t$,
$y = b - t$, $z = c - 2(b + a)t$ both lie entirely on this paraboloid. (This shows that the hyperbolic paraboloid is what is
called a **ruled surface**; that is, it can be generated by the
motion of a straight line. In fact, this exercise shows that
through each point on the hyperbolic paraboloid there are two
generating lines. The only other quadric surfaces that are ruled
surfaces are cylinders, cones, and hyperboloids of one sheet.)

48. Show that the curve of intersection of the surfaces
$x^2 + 2y^2 - z^2 + 3x = 1$ and $2x^2 + 4y^2 - 2z^2 - 5y = 0$
lies in a plane.

49. Graph the surfaces $z = x^2 + y^2$ and $z = 1 - y^2$ on a common
screen using the domain $|x| \le 1.2$, $|y| \le 1.2$ and observe the
curve of intersection of these surfaces. Show that the projection
of this curve onto the xy-plane is an ellipse.

I

II

III

IV

V

VI

VII

VIII
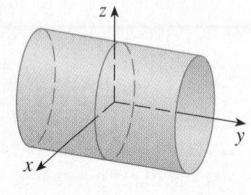

|||| 13.7 Cylindrical and Spherical Coordinates

Recall that in plane geometry we introduced the polar coordinate system in order to give a convenient description of certain curves and regions. (See Section 11.3.) In three dimensions there are two coordinate systems that are similar to polar coordinates and give convenient descriptions of some commonly occurring surfaces and solids. They will be especially useful in Chapter 16 when we compute volumes and triple integrals.

|||| Cylindrical Coordinates

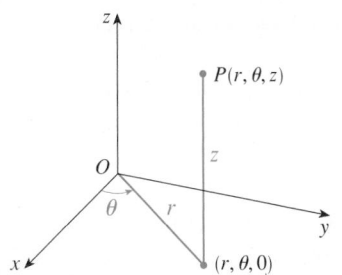

FIGURE 1
The cylindrical coordinates of a point

In the **cylindrical coordinate system**, a point P in three-dimensional space is represented by the ordered triple (r, θ, z), where r and θ are polar coordinates of the projection of P onto the xy-plane and z is the directed distance from the xy-plane to P (see Figure 1).

To convert from cylindrical to rectangular coordinates, we use the equations

1
$$x = r\cos\theta \qquad y = r\sin\theta \qquad z = z$$

whereas to convert from rectangular to cylindrical coordinates, we use

2
$$r^2 = x^2 + y^2 \qquad \tan\theta = \frac{y}{x} \qquad z = z$$

These equations follow from Equations 11.3.1 and 11.3.2.

EXAMPLE 1
(a) Plot the point with cylindrical coordinates $(2, 2\pi/3, 1)$ and find its rectangular coordinates.
(b) Find cylindrical coordinates of the point with rectangular coordinates $(3, -3, -7)$.

SOLUTION
(a) The point with cylindrical coordinates $(2, 2\pi/3, 1)$ is plotted in Figure 2. From Equations 1, its rectangular coordinates are

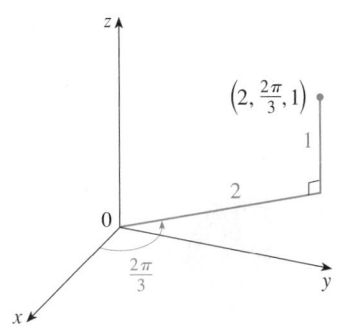

FIGURE 2

$$x = 2\cos\frac{2\pi}{3} = 2\left(-\frac{1}{2}\right) = -1$$

$$y = 2\sin\frac{2\pi}{3} = 2\left(\frac{\sqrt{3}}{2}\right) = \sqrt{3}$$

$$z = 1$$

Thus, the point is $\left(-1, \sqrt{3}, 1\right)$ in rectangular coordinates.

(b) From Equations 2 we have

$$r = \sqrt{3^2 + (-3)^2} = 3\sqrt{2}$$

$$\tan\theta = \frac{-3}{3} = -1 \qquad \text{so} \qquad \theta = \frac{7\pi}{4} + 2n\pi$$

$$z = -7$$

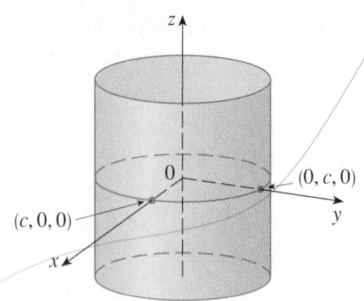

FIGURE 3

$r = c$, a cylinder

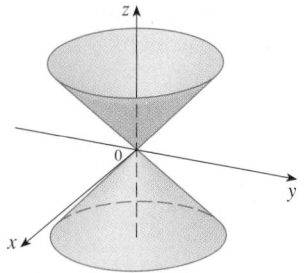

FIGURE 4

$z = r$, a cone

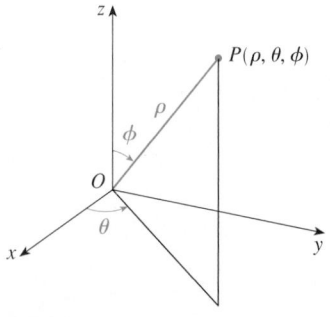

FIGURE 5

The spherical coordinates of a point

Therefore, one set of cylindrical coordinates is $\left(3\sqrt{2},\, 7\pi/4,\, -7\right)$. Another is $\left(3\sqrt{2},\, -\pi/4,\, -7\right)$. As with polar coordinates, there are infinitely many choices.

Cylindrical coordinates are useful in problems that involve symmetry about an axis, and the z-axis is chosen to coincide with this axis of symmetry. For instance, the axis of the circular cylinder with Cartesian equation $x^2 + y^2 = c^2$ is the z-axis. In cylindrical coordinates this cylinder has the very simple equation $r = c$. (See Figure 3.) This is the reason for the name "cylindrical" coordinates.

EXAMPLE 2 Describe the surface whose equation in cylindrical coordinates is $z = r$.

SOLUTION The equation says that the z-value, or height, of each point on the surface is the same as r, the distance from the point to the z-axis. Because θ doesn't appear, it can vary. So any horizontal trace in the plane $z = k$ $(k > 0)$ is a circle of radius k. These traces suggest that the surface is a cone. This prediction can be confirmed by converting the equation into rectangular coordinates. From the first equation in (2) we have

$$z^2 = r^2 = x^2 + y^2$$

We recognize the equation $z^2 = x^2 + y^2$ (by comparison with Table 1 in Section 13.6) as being a circular cone whose axis is the z-axis (see Figure 4).

EXAMPLE 3 Find an equation in cylindrical coordinates for the ellipsoid $4x^2 + 4y^2 + z^2 = 1$.

SOLUTION Since $r^2 = x^2 + y^2$ from Equations 2, we have

$$z^2 = 1 - 4(x^2 + y^2) = 1 - 4r^2$$

So an equation of the ellipsoid in cylindrical coordinates is $z^2 = 1 - 4r^2$.

|||| **Spherical Coordinates**

The **spherical coordinates** (ρ, θ, ϕ) of a point P in space are shown in Figure 5, where $\rho = |OP|$ is the distance from the origin to P, θ is the same angle as in cylindrical coordinates, and ϕ is the angle between the positive z-axis and the line segment OP. Note that

$$\rho \geqslant 0 \qquad 0 \leqslant \phi \leqslant \pi$$

The spherical coordinate system is especially useful in problems where there is symmetry about a point, and the origin is placed at this point. For example, the sphere with center the origin and radius c has the simple equation $\rho = c$ (see Figure 6); this is the reason for the name "spherical" coordinates. The graph of the equation $\theta = c$ is a vertical half-plane

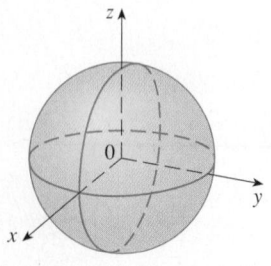

FIGURE 6 $\rho = c$, a sphere

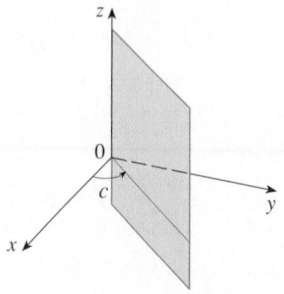

FIGURE 7 $\theta = c$, a half-plane

$0 < c < \pi/2$

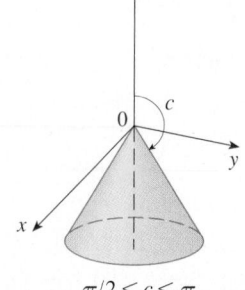

$\pi/2 < c < \pi$

FIGURE 8 $\phi = c$, a half-cone

(see Figure 7), and the equation $\phi = c$ represents a half-cone with the z-axis as its axis (see Figure 8).

The relationship between rectangular and spherical coordinates can be seen from Figure 9. From triangles OPQ and OPP' we have

$$z = \rho \cos \phi \qquad r = \rho \sin \phi$$

But $x = r \cos \theta$ and $y = r \sin \theta$, so to convert from spherical to rectangular coordinates, we use the equations

FIGURE 9

$$\boxed{3} \qquad x = \rho \sin \phi \cos \theta \qquad y = \rho \sin \phi \sin \theta \qquad z = \rho \cos \phi$$

Also, the distance formula shows that

$$\boxed{4} \qquad \rho^2 = x^2 + y^2 + z^2$$

We use this equation in converting from rectangular to spherical coordinates.

EXAMPLE 4 The point $(2, \pi/4, \pi/3)$ is given in spherical coordinates. Plot the point and find its rectangular coordinates.

SOLUTION We plot the point in Figure 10. From Equations 3 we have

$$x = \rho \sin \phi \cos \theta = 2 \sin \frac{\pi}{3} \cos \frac{\pi}{4} = 2\left(\frac{\sqrt{3}}{2}\right)\left(\frac{1}{\sqrt{2}}\right) = \sqrt{\frac{3}{2}}$$

$$y = \rho \sin \phi \sin \theta = 2 \sin \frac{\pi}{3} \sin \frac{\pi}{4} = 2\left(\frac{\sqrt{3}}{2}\right)\left(\frac{1}{\sqrt{2}}\right) = \sqrt{\frac{3}{2}}$$

$$z = \rho \cos \phi = 2 \cos \frac{\pi}{3} = 2\left(\tfrac{1}{2}\right) = 1$$

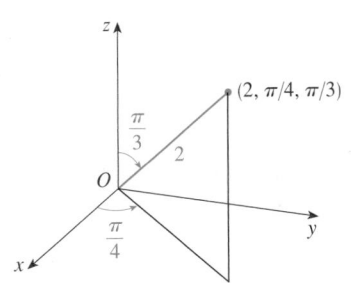

FIGURE 10

Thus, the point $(2, \pi/4, \pi/3)$ is $\left(\sqrt{3/2}, \sqrt{3/2}, 1\right)$ in rectangular coordinates.

EXAMPLE 5 The point $\left(0, 2\sqrt{3}, -2\right)$ is given in rectangular coordinates. Find spherical coordinates for this point.

SOLUTION From Equation 4 we have

$$\rho = \sqrt{x^2 + y^2 + z^2} = \sqrt{0 + 12 + 4} = 4$$

and so Equations 3 give

$$\cos \phi = \frac{z}{\rho} = \frac{-2}{4} = -\frac{1}{2} \qquad \phi = \frac{2\pi}{3}$$

$$\cos \theta = \frac{x}{\rho \sin \phi} = 0 \qquad \theta = \frac{\pi}{2}$$

(Note that $\theta \neq 3\pi/2$ because $y = 2\sqrt{3} > 0$.) Therefore, spherical coordinates of the given point are $(4, \pi/2, 2\pi/3)$.

EXAMPLE 6 Find an equation in spherical coordinates for the hyperboloid of two sheets with equation $x^2 - y^2 - z^2 = 1$.

SOLUTION Substituting the expressions in Equations 3 into the given equation, we have

$$\rho^2 \sin^2\phi \, \cos^2\theta - \rho^2 \sin^2\phi \, \sin^2\theta - \rho^2 \cos^2\phi = 1$$

$$\rho^2[\sin^2\phi \, (\cos^2\theta - \sin^2\theta) - \cos^2\phi] = 1$$

or

$$\rho^2(\sin^2\phi \, \cos 2\theta - \cos^2\phi) = 1$$

In Module 13.7 you can investigate families of surfaces in cylindrical and spherical coordinates.

EXAMPLE 7 Find a rectangular equation for the surface whose spherical equation is $\rho = \sin\theta \sin\phi$.

SOLUTION From Equations 4 and 3 we have

$$x^2 + y^2 + z^2 = \rho^2 = \rho \sin\theta \sin\phi = y$$

or

$$x^2 + \left(y - \tfrac{1}{2}\right)^2 + z^2 = \tfrac{1}{4}$$

which is the equation of a sphere with center $\left(0, \tfrac{1}{2}, 0\right)$ and radius $\tfrac{1}{2}$.

EXAMPLE 8 Use a computer to draw a picture of the solid that remains when a hole of radius 3 is drilled through the center of a sphere of radius 4.

SOLUTION To keep the equations simple, let's choose the coordinate system so that the center of the sphere is at the origin and the axis of the cylinder that forms the hole is the z-axis. We could use either cylindrical or spherical coordinates to describe the solid, but the description is somewhat simpler if we use cylindrical coordinates. Then the equation of the cylinder is $r = 3$ and the equation of the sphere is $x^2 + y^2 + z^2 = 16$, or $r^2 + z^2 = 16$. The points in the solid lie outside the cylinder and inside the sphere, so they satisfy the inequalities

$$3 \leqslant r \leqslant \sqrt{16 - z^2}$$

||||| Most three-dimensional graphing programs can graph surfaces whose equations are given in cylindrical or spherical coordinates. As Example 8 demonstrates, this is often the most convenient way of drawing a solid.

To ensure that the computer graphs only the appropriate parts of these surfaces, we find where they intersect by solving the equations $r = 3$ and $r = \sqrt{16 - z^2}$:

$$\sqrt{16 - z^2} = 3 \quad \Rightarrow \quad 16 - z^2 = 9 \quad \Rightarrow \quad z^2 = 7 \quad \Rightarrow \quad z = \pm\sqrt{7}$$

The solid lies between $z = -\sqrt{7}$ and $z = \sqrt{7}$, so we ask the computer to graph the surfaces with the following equations and domains:

$$r = 3 \qquad\qquad 0 \leqslant \theta \leqslant 2\pi \qquad\qquad -\sqrt{7} \leqslant z \leqslant \sqrt{7}$$

$$r = \sqrt{16 - z^2} \qquad 0 \leqslant \theta \leqslant 2\pi \qquad\qquad -\sqrt{7} \leqslant z \leqslant \sqrt{7}$$

FIGURE 11

The resulting picture, shown in Figure 11, is exactly what we want.

||||| **13.7** Exercises

1. What are cylindrical coordinates? For what types of surfaces do they provide convenient descriptions?

2. What are spherical coordinates? For what types of surfaces do they provide convenient descriptions?

3–8 ||||| Plot the point whose cylindrical coordinates are given. Then find the rectangular coordinates of the point.

3. $(2, \pi/4, 1)$

4. $(1, 3\pi/2, 2)$

5. $(3, 0, -6)$

6. $(1, \pi, e)$

7. $(4, -\pi/3, 5)$ **8.** $(5, \pi/6, 6)$

9–12 ▓ Change from rectangular to cylindrical coordinates.

9. $(1, -1, 4)$ **10.** $(3, 3, -2)$

11. $(-1, -\sqrt{3}, 2)$ **12.** $(3, 4, 5)$

13–18 ▓ Plot the point whose spherical coordinates are given. Then find the rectangular coordinates of the point.

13. $(1, 0, 0)$ **14.** $(3, 0, \pi)$

15. $(1, \pi/6, \pi/6)$ **16.** $(5, \pi, \pi/2)$

17. $(2, \pi/3, \pi/4)$ **18.** $(2, \pi/4, \pi/3)$

19–22 ▓ Change from rectangular to spherical coordinates.

19. $(1, \sqrt{3}, 2\sqrt{3})$ **20.** $(0, \sqrt{3}, 1)$

21. $(0, -1, -1)$ **22.** $(-1, 1, \sqrt{6})$

23–26 ▓ Change from cylindrical to spherical coordinates.

23. $(1, \pi/6, \sqrt{3})$ **24.** $(\sqrt{6}, \pi/4, \sqrt{2})$

25. $(\sqrt{3}, \pi/2, -1)$ **26.** $(4, \pi/8, 3)$

27–30 ▓ Change from spherical to cylindrical coordinates.

27. $(2, 0, 0)$ **28.** $(2\sqrt{2}, 3\pi/2, \pi/2)$

29. $(8, \pi/6, \pi/2)$ **30.** $(4, \pi/4, \pi/3)$

31–36 ▓ Describe in words the surface whose equation is given.

31. $r = 3$ **32.** $\rho = 3$

33. $\phi = 0$ **34.** $\phi = \pi/2$

35. $\phi = \pi/3$ **36.** $\theta = \pi/3$

37–48 ▓ Identify the surface whose equation is given.

37. $z = r^2$ **38.** $r = 4 \sin \theta$

39. $\rho \cos \phi = 2$ **40.** $\rho \sin \phi = 2$

41. $r = 2 \cos \theta$ **42.** $\rho = 2 \cos \phi$

43. $r^2 + z^2 = 25$ **44.** $r^2 - 2z^2 = 4$

45. $\rho^2(\sin^2\phi \, \cos^2\theta + \cos^2\phi) = 4$

46. $\rho^2(\sin^2\phi - 4\cos^2\phi) = 1$

47. $r^2 = r$ **48.** $\rho^2 - 6\rho + 8 = 0$

49–56 ▓ Write the equation (a) in cylindrical coordinates and (b) in spherical coordinates.

49. $z = x^2 + y^2$ **50.** $x^2 + y^2 + z^2 = 2$

51. $x = 3$ **52.** $x^2 + y^2 + z^2 + 2z = 0$

53. $x^2 - y^2 - 2z^2 = 4$ **54.** $y^2 + z^2 = 1$

55. $x^2 + y^2 = 2y$ **56.** $z = x^2 - y^2$

57–62 ▓ Sketch the solid described by the given inequalities.

57. $r^2 \leqslant z \leqslant 2 - r^2$

58. $0 \leqslant \theta \leqslant \pi/2, \quad r \leqslant z \leqslant 2$

59. $\rho \leqslant 2, \quad 0 \leqslant \phi \leqslant \pi/2, \quad 0 \leqslant \theta \leqslant \pi/2$

60. $2 \leqslant \rho \leqslant 3, \quad \pi/2 \leqslant \phi \leqslant \pi$

61. $-\pi/2 \leqslant \theta \leqslant \pi/2, \quad 0 \leqslant \phi \leqslant \pi/6, \quad 0 \leqslant \rho \leqslant \sec \phi$

62. $0 \leqslant \phi \leqslant \pi/3, \quad \rho \leqslant 2$

63. A cylindrical shell is 20 cm long, with inner radius 6 cm and outer radius 7 cm. Write inequalities that describe the shell in an appropriate coordinate system. Explain how you have positioned the coordinate system with respect to the shell.

64. (a) Find inequalities that describe a hollow ball with diameter 30 cm and thickness 0.5 cm. Explain how you have positioned the coordinate system that you have chosen.
(b) Suppose the ball is cut in half. Write inequalities that describe one of the halves.

65. A solid lies above the cone $z = \sqrt{x^2 + y^2}$ and below the sphere $x^2 + y^2 + z^2 = z$. Write a description of the solid in terms of inequalities involving spherical coordinates.

66. Use a graphing device to draw the solid enclosed by the paraboloids $z = x^2 + y^2$ and $z = 5 - x^2 - y^2$.

67. Use a graphing device to draw a silo consisting of a cylinder with radius 3 and height 10 surmounted by a hemisphere.

68. The latitude and longitude of a point P in the Northern Hemisphere are related to spherical coordinates ρ, θ, ϕ as follows. We take the origin to be the center of the Earth and the positive z-axis to pass through the North Pole. The positive x-axis passes through the point where the prime meridian (the meridian through Greenwich, England) intersects the equator. Then the latitude of P is $\alpha = 90° - \phi°$ and the longitude is $\beta = 360° - \theta°$. Find the great-circle distance from Los Angeles (lat. 34.06° N, long. 118.25° W) to Montréal (lat. 45.50° N, long. 73.60° W). Take the radius of the Earth to be 3960 mi. (A *great circle* is the circle of intersection of a sphere and a plane through the center of the sphere.)

|||| LABORATORY PROJECT

⌂ **Families of Surfaces**

In this project you will discover the interesting shapes that members of families of surfaces can take. You will also see how the shape of the surface evolves as you vary the constants.

1. Use a computer to investigate the family of surfaces

$$z = (ax^2 + by^2)e^{-x^2-y^2}$$

How does the shape of the graph depend on the numbers a and b?

2. Use a computer to investigate the family of surfaces $z = x^2 + y^2 + cxy$. In particular, you should determine the transitional values of c for which the surface changes from one type of quadric surface to another.

3. Members of the family of surfaces given in spherical coordinates by the equation

$$\rho = 1 + 0.2 \sin m\theta \sin n\phi$$

have been suggested as models for tumors and have been called *bumpy spheres* and *wrinkled spheres*. Use a computer to investigate this family of surfaces, assuming that m and n are positive integers. What roles do the values of m and n play in the shape of the surface?

|||| **13 Review** ━━━━━━━━━ ∘ CONCEPT CHECK ∘ ━━━━━━━━━

1. What is the difference between a vector and a scalar?

2. How do you add two vectors geometrically? How do you add them algebraically?

3. If **a** is a vector and c is a scalar, how is c**a** related to **a** geometrically? How do you find c**a** algebraically?

4. How do you find the vector from one point to another?

5. How do you find the dot product **a** · **b** of two vectors if you know their lengths and the angle between them? What if you know their components?

6. How are dot products useful?

7. Write expressions for the scalar and vector projections of **b** onto **a**. Illustrate with diagrams.

8. How do you find the cross product **a** × **b** of two vectors if you know their lengths and the angle between them? What if you know their components?

9. How are cross products useful?

10. (a) How do you find the area of the parallelogram determined by **a** and **b**?
    (b) How do you find the volume of the parallelepiped determined by **a**, **b**, and **c**?

11. How do you find a vector perpendicular to a plane?

12. How do you find the angle between two intersecting planes?

13. Write a vector equation, parametric equations, and symmetric equations for a line.

14. Write a vector equation and a scalar equation for a plane.

15. (a) How do you tell if two vectors are parallel?
    (b) How do you tell if two vectors are perpendicular?
    (c) How do you tell if two planes are parallel?

16. (a) Describe a method for determining whether three points P, Q, and R lie on the same line.
    (b) Describe a method for determining whether four points P, Q, R, and S lie in the same plane.

17. (a) How do you find the distance from a point to a line?
    (b) How do you find the distance from a point to a plane?
    (c) How do you find the distance between two lines?

18. What are the traces of a surface? How do you find them?

19. Write equations in standard form of the six types of quadric surfaces.

20. (a) Write the equations for converting from cylindrical to rectangular coordinates. In what situation would you use cylindrical coordinates?
    (b) Write the equations for converting from spherical to rectangular coordinates. In what situation would you use spherical coordinates?

— ▫ TRUE-FALSE QUIZ ▫ —

Determine whether the statement is true or false. If it is true, explain why.
If it is false, explain why or give an example that disproves the statement.

1. For any vectors $\mathbf{u}$ and $\mathbf{v}$ in V_3, $\mathbf{u} \cdot \mathbf{v} = \mathbf{v} \cdot \mathbf{u}$.

2. For any vectors $\mathbf{u}$ and $\mathbf{v}$ in V_3, $\mathbf{u} \times \mathbf{v} = \mathbf{v} \times \mathbf{u}$.

3. For any vectors $\mathbf{u}$ and $\mathbf{v}$ in V_3, $|\mathbf{u} \times \mathbf{v}| = |\mathbf{v} \times \mathbf{u}|$.

4. For any vectors $\mathbf{u}$ and $\mathbf{v}$ in V_3 and any scalar k,
$k(\mathbf{u} \cdot \mathbf{v}) = (k\mathbf{u}) \cdot \mathbf{v}$.

5. For any vectors $\mathbf{u}$ and $\mathbf{v}$ in V_3 and any scalar k,
$k(\mathbf{u} \times \mathbf{v}) = (k\mathbf{u}) \times \mathbf{v}$.

6. For any vectors $\mathbf{u}$, $\mathbf{v}$, and $\mathbf{w}$ in V_3,
$(\mathbf{u} + \mathbf{v}) \times \mathbf{w} = \mathbf{u} \times \mathbf{w} + \mathbf{v} \times \mathbf{w}$.

7. For any vectors $\mathbf{u}$, $\mathbf{v}$, and $\mathbf{w}$ in V_3,
$\mathbf{u} \cdot (\mathbf{v} \times \mathbf{w}) = (\mathbf{u} \times \mathbf{v}) \cdot \mathbf{w}$.

8. For any vectors $\mathbf{u}$, $\mathbf{v}$, and $\mathbf{w}$ in V_3,
$\mathbf{u} \times (\mathbf{v} \times \mathbf{w}) = (\mathbf{u} \times \mathbf{v}) \times \mathbf{w}$.

9. For any vectors $\mathbf{u}$ and $\mathbf{v}$ in V_3, $(\mathbf{u} \times \mathbf{v}) \cdot \mathbf{u} = 0$.

10. For any vectors $\mathbf{u}$ and $\mathbf{v}$ in V_3, $(\mathbf{u} + \mathbf{v}) \times \mathbf{v} = \mathbf{u} \times \mathbf{v}$.

11. The cross product of two unit vectors is a unit vector.

12. A linear equation $Ax + By + Cz + D = 0$ represents a line in space.

13. The set of points $\{(x, y, z) \mid x^2 + y^2 = 1\}$ is a circle.

14. If $\mathbf{u} = \langle u_1, u_2 \rangle$ and $\mathbf{v} = \langle v_1, v_2 \rangle$, then $\mathbf{u} \cdot \mathbf{v} = \langle u_1 v_1, u_2 v_2 \rangle$.

— ▫ EXERCISES ▫ —

1. (a) Find an equation of the sphere with center $(1, -1, 2)$ and radius 3.
(b) Find the center and radius of the sphere
$$x^2 + y^2 + z^2 + 4x + 6y - 10z + 2 = 0$$

2. Copy the vectors in the figure and use them to draw each of the following vectors.
(a) $\mathbf{a} + \mathbf{b}$ (b) $\mathbf{a} - \mathbf{b}$
(c) $-\frac{1}{2}\mathbf{a}$ (d) $2\mathbf{a} + \mathbf{b}$

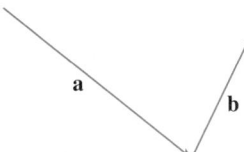

3. If $\mathbf{u}$ and $\mathbf{v}$ are the vectors shown in the figure, find $\mathbf{u} \cdot \mathbf{v}$ and $|\mathbf{u} \times \mathbf{v}|$. Is $\mathbf{u} \times \mathbf{v}$ directed into the page or out of it?

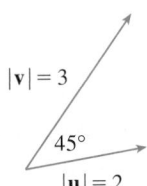

4. Calculate the given quantity if
$$\mathbf{a} = \mathbf{i} + \mathbf{j} - 2\mathbf{k} \qquad \mathbf{b} = 3\mathbf{i} - 2\mathbf{j} + \mathbf{k} \qquad \mathbf{c} = \mathbf{j} - 5\mathbf{k}$$
(a) $2\mathbf{a} + 3\mathbf{b}$ (b) $|\mathbf{b}|$
(c) $\mathbf{a} \cdot \mathbf{b}$ (d) $\mathbf{a} \times \mathbf{b}$
(e) $|\mathbf{b} \times \mathbf{c}|$ (f) $\mathbf{a} \cdot (\mathbf{b} \times \mathbf{c})$
(g) $\mathbf{c} \times \mathbf{c}$ (h) $\mathbf{a} \times (\mathbf{b} \times \mathbf{c})$
(i) $\mathrm{comp}_{\mathbf{a}} \mathbf{b}$ (j) $\mathrm{proj}_{\mathbf{a}} \mathbf{b}$
(k) The angle between $\mathbf{a}$ and $\mathbf{b}$ (correct to the nearest degree)

5. Find the values of x such that the vectors $\langle 3, 2, x \rangle$ and $\langle 2x, 4, x \rangle$ are orthogonal.

6. Find two unit vectors that are orthogonal to both $\mathbf{j} + 2\mathbf{k}$ and $\mathbf{i} - 2\mathbf{j} + 3\mathbf{k}$.

7. Suppose that $\mathbf{u} \cdot (\mathbf{v} \times \mathbf{w}) = 2$. Find
(a) $(\mathbf{u} \times \mathbf{v}) \cdot \mathbf{w}$ (b) $\mathbf{u} \cdot (\mathbf{w} \times \mathbf{v})$
(c) $\mathbf{v} \cdot (\mathbf{u} \times \mathbf{w})$ (d) $(\mathbf{u} \times \mathbf{v}) \cdot \mathbf{v}$

8. Show that if $\mathbf{a}$, $\mathbf{b}$, and $\mathbf{c}$ are in V_3, then
$$(\mathbf{a} \times \mathbf{b}) \cdot [(\mathbf{b} \times \mathbf{c}) \times (\mathbf{c} \times \mathbf{a})] = [\mathbf{a} \cdot (\mathbf{b} \times \mathbf{c})]^2$$

9. Find the acute angle between two diagonals of a cube.

10. Given the points $A(1, 0, 1)$, $B(2, 3, 0)$, $C(-1, 1, 4)$, and $D(0, 3, 2)$, find the volume of the parallelepiped with adjacent edges AB, AC, and AD.

11. (a) Find a vector perpendicular to the plane through the points $A(1, 0, 0)$, $B(2, 0, -1)$, and $C(1, 4, 3)$.
(b) Find the area of triangle ABC.

12. A constant force $\mathbf{F} = 3\mathbf{i} + 5\mathbf{j} + 10\mathbf{k}$ moves an object along the line segment from $(1, 0, 2)$ to $(5, 3, 8)$. Find the work done if the distance is measured in meters and the force in newtons.

13. A boat is pulled onto shore using two ropes, as shown in the diagram. If a force of 255 N is needed, find the magnitude of the force in each rope.

14. Find the magnitude of the torque about P if a 50-N force is applied as shown.

15–17 ▏▏▏▏ Find parametric equations for the line.

15. The line through $(4, -1, 2)$ and $(1, 1, 5)$

16. The line through $(1, 0, -1)$ and parallel to the line $\frac{1}{3}(x - 4) = \frac{1}{2}y = z + 2$

17. The line through $(-2, 2, 4)$ and perpendicular to the plane $2x - y + 5z = 12$

▫   ▫   ▫   ▫   ▫   ▫   ▫   ▫   ▫   ▫   ▫   ▫

18–20 ▏▏▏▏ Find an equation of the plane.

18. The plane through $(2, 1, 0)$ and parallel to $x + 4y - 3z = 1$

19. The plane through $(3, -1, 1)$, $(4, 0, 2)$, and $(6, 3, 1)$

20. The plane through $(1, 2, -2)$ that contains the line $x = 2t$, $y = 3 - t$, $z = 1 + 3t$

▫   ▫   ▫   ▫   ▫   ▫   ▫   ▫   ▫   ▫   ▫

21. Find the point in which the line with parametric equations $x = 2 - t$, $y = 1 + 3t$, $z = 4t$ intersects the plane $2x - y + z = 2$.

22. Find the distance from the origin to the line $x = 1 + t$, $y = 2 - t$, $z = -1 + 2t$.

23. Determine whether the lines given by the symmetric equations
$$\frac{x - 1}{2} = \frac{y - 2}{3} = \frac{z - 3}{4}$$
and
$$\frac{x + 1}{6} = \frac{y - 3}{-1} = \frac{z + 5}{2}$$
are parallel, skew, or intersecting.

24. (a) Show that the planes $x + y - z = 1$ and $2x - 3y + 4z = 5$ are neither parallel nor perpendicular.
(b) Find, correct to the nearest degree, the angle between these planes.

25. Find the distance between the planes $3x + y - 4z = 2$ and $3x + y - 4z = 24$.

26–34 ▏▏▏▏ Identify and sketch the graph of each surface.

26. $x = 3$ 　　　　　　　　　　 **27.** $x = z$

28. $y = z^2$ 　　　　　　　　　 **29.** $x^2 = y^2 + 4z^2$

30. $4x - y + 2z = 4$

31. $-4x^2 + y^2 - 4z^2 = 4$

32. $y^2 + z^2 = 1 + x^2$

33. $4x^2 + 4y^2 - 8y + z^2 = 0$

34. $x = y^2 + z^2 - 2y - 4z + 5$

▫   ▫   ▫   ▫   ▫   ▫   ▫   ▫   ▫   ▫   ▫

35. An ellipsoid is created by rotating the ellipse $4x^2 + y^2 = 16$ about the x-axis. Find an equation of the ellipsoid.

36. A surface consists of all points P such that the distance from P to the plane $y = 1$ is twice the distance from P to the point $(0, -1, 0)$. Find an equation for this surface and identify it.

37. The cylindrical coordinates of a point are $\left(2\sqrt{3}, \pi/3, 2\right)$. Find the rectangular and spherical coordinates of the point.

38. The rectangular coordinates of a point are $(2, 2, -1)$. Find the cylindrical and spherical coordinates of the point.

39. The spherical coordinates of a point are $(8, \pi/4, \pi/6)$. Find the rectangular and cylindrical coordinates of the point.

40–43 ▏▏▏▏ Identify the surface whose equation is given.

40. $\phi = \pi/4$ 　　　　　　　　 **41.** $\theta = \pi/4$

42. $r = \cos\theta$ 　　　　　　　 **43.** $\rho = 3\sec\phi$

▫   ▫   ▫   ▫   ▫   ▫   ▫   ▫   ▫   ▫   ▫

44–46 ▏▏▏▏ Write the equation in cylindrical coordinates and in spherical coordinates.

44. $x^2 + y^2 = 4$ 　　　　　　 **45.** $x^2 + y^2 + z^2 = 4$

46. $x^2 + y^2 + z^2 = 2x$

▫   ▫   ▫   ▫   ▫   ▫   ▫   ▫   ▫   ▫   ▫

47. The parabola $z = 4y^2$, $x = 0$ is rotated about the z-axis. Write an equation of the resulting surface in cylindrical coordinates.

48. Sketch the solid consisting of all points with spherical coordinates (ρ, θ, ϕ) such that $0 \leq \theta \leq \pi/2$, $0 \leq \phi \leq \pi/6$, and $0 \leq \rho \leq 2\cos\phi$.

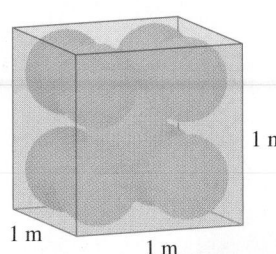

FIGURE FOR PROBLEM 1

1. Each edge of a cubical box has length 1 m. The box contains nine spherical balls with the same radius r. The center of one ball is at the center of the cube and it touches the other eight balls. Each of the other eight balls touches three sides of the box. Thus, the balls are tightly packed in the box. (See the figure.) Find r. (If you have trouble with this problem, read about the problem-solving strategy entitled *Use analogy* on page 58.)

2. Let B be a solid box with length L, width W, and height H. Let S be the set of all points that are a distance at most 1 from some point of B. Express the volume of S in terms of L, W, and H.

3. Let L be the line of intersection of the planes $cx + y + z = c$ and $x - cy + cz = -1$, where c is a real number.
   (a) Find symmetric equations for L.
   (b) As the number c varies, the line L sweeps out a surface S. Find an equation for the curve of intersection of S with the horizontal plane $z = t$ (the trace of S in the plane $z = t$).
   (c) Find the volume of the solid bounded by S and the planes $z = 0$ and $z = 1$.

4. A plane is capable of flying at a speed of 180 km/h in still air. The pilot takes off from an airfield and heads due north according to the plane's compass. After 30 minutes of flight time, the pilot notices that, due to the wind, the plane has actually traveled 80 km at an angle $5°$ east of north.
   (a) What is the wind velocity?
   (b) In what direction should the pilot have headed to reach the intended destination?

5. Suppose a block of mass m is placed on an inclined plane, as shown in the figure. The block's descent down the plane is slowed by friction; if θ is not too large, friction will prevent the block from moving at all. The forces acting on the block are the weight $\mathbf{W}$, where $|\mathbf{W}| = mg$ (g is the acceleration due to gravity); the normal force $\mathbf{N}$ (the normal component of the reactionary force of the plane on the block), where $|\mathbf{N}| = n$; and the force $\mathbf{F}$ due to friction, which acts parallel to the inclined plane, opposing the direction of motion. If the block is at rest and θ is increased, $|\mathbf{F}|$ must also increase until ultimately $|\mathbf{F}|$ reaches its maximum, beyond which the block begins to slide. At this angle θ_s, it has been observed that $|\mathbf{F}|$ is proportional to n. Thus, when $|\mathbf{F}|$ is maximal, we can say that $|\mathbf{F}| = \mu_s n$, where μ_s is called the *coefficient of static friction* and depends on the materials that are in contact.
   (a) Observe that $\mathbf{N} + \mathbf{F} + \mathbf{W} = \mathbf{0}$ and deduce that $\mu_s = \tan \theta_s$.
   (b) Suppose that, for $\theta > \theta_s$, an additional outside force $\mathbf{H}$ is applied to the block, horizontally from the left, and let $|\mathbf{H}| = h$. If h is small, the block may still slide down the plane; if h is large enough, the block will move up the plane. Let h_{min} be the smallest value of h that allows the block to remain motionless (so that $|\mathbf{F}|$ is maximal).

   By choosing the coordinate axes so that $\mathbf{F}$ lies along the x-axis, resolve each force into components parallel and perpendicular to the inclined plane and show that

$$h_{min} \sin \theta + mg \cos \theta = n \quad \text{and} \quad h_{min} \cos \theta + \mu_s n = mg \sin \theta$$

   (c) Show that
$$h_{min} = mg \tan(\theta - \theta_s)$$

   Does this equation seem reasonable? Does it make sense for $\theta = \theta_s$? As $\theta \to 90°$? Explain.
   (d) Let h_{max} be the largest value of h that allows the block to remain motionless. (In which direction is $\mathbf{F}$ heading?) Show that

$$h_{max} = mg \tan(\theta + \theta_s)$$

   Does this equation seem reasonable? Explain.

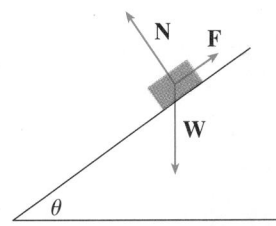

FIGURE FOR PROBLEM 5

CHAPTER 14

The calculus of vector-valued functions is used in Section 14.4 to prove Kepler's laws. These describe the motion of the planets about the Sun and also apply to the orbit of a satellite about the Earth, such as the Hubble Space Telescope.

NASA, STScI, and The Smithsonian Institution

Vector Functions

The functions that we have been using so far have been real-valued functions. We now study functions whose values are vectors because such functions are needed to describe curves and surfaces in space. We will also use vector-valued functions to describe the motion of objects through space. In particular, we will use them to derive Kepler's laws of planetary motion.

14.1 Vector Functions and Space Curves

In general, a function is a rule that assigns to each element in the domain an element in the range. A **vector-valued function**, or **vector function**, is simply a function whose domain is a set of real numbers and whose range is a set of vectors. We are most interested in vector functions $\mathbf{r}$ whose values are three-dimensional vectors. This means that for every number t in the domain of $\mathbf{r}$ there is a unique vector in V_3 denoted by $\mathbf{r}(t)$. If $f(t)$, $g(t)$, and $h(t)$ are the components of the vector $\mathbf{r}(t)$, then f, g, and h are real-valued functions called the **component functions** of $\mathbf{r}$ and we can write

$$\mathbf{r}(t) = \langle f(t), g(t), h(t) \rangle = f(t)\,\mathbf{i} + g(t)\,\mathbf{j} + h(t)\,\mathbf{k}$$

We use the letter t to denote the independent variable because it represents time in most applications of vector functions.

EXAMPLE 1 If

$$\mathbf{r}(t) = \left\langle t^3, \ln(3 - t), \sqrt{t} \right\rangle$$

then the component functions are

$$f(t) = t^3 \qquad g(t) = \ln(3 - t) \qquad h(t) = \sqrt{t}$$

By our usual convention, the domain of $\mathbf{r}$ consists of all values of t for which the expression for $\mathbf{r}(t)$ is defined. The expressions t^3, $\ln(3 - t)$, and $\sqrt{t}$ are all defined when $3 - t > 0$ and $t \geq 0$. Therefore, the domain of $\mathbf{r}$ is the interval $[0, 3)$.

The **limit** of a vector function $\mathbf{r}$ is defined by taking the limits of its component functions as follows.

||| If $\lim_{t \to a} \mathbf{r}(t) = \mathbf{L}$, this definition is equivalent to saying that the length and direction of the vector $\mathbf{r}(t)$ approach the length and direction of the vector $\mathbf{L}$.

> **1** If $\mathbf{r}(t) = \langle f(t), g(t), h(t) \rangle$, then
>
> $$\lim_{t \to a} \mathbf{r}(t) = \left\langle \lim_{t \to a} f(t), \lim_{t \to a} g(t), \lim_{t \to a} h(t) \right\rangle$$
>
> provided the limits of the component functions exist.

Equivalently, we could have used an ε-δ definition (see Exercise 43). Limits of vector functions obey the same rules as limits of real-valued functions (see Exercise 41).

EXAMPLE 2 Find $\lim\limits_{t \to 0} \mathbf{r}(t)$, where $\mathbf{r}(t) = (1 + t^3)\,\mathbf{i} + te^{-t}\,\mathbf{j} + \dfrac{\sin t}{t}\,\mathbf{k}$.

SOLUTION According to Definition 1, the limit of $\mathbf{r}$ is the vector whose components are the limits of the component functions of $\mathbf{r}$:

$$\lim_{t \to 0} \mathbf{r}(t) = \left[\lim_{t \to 0}(1 + t^3)\right]\mathbf{i} + \left[\lim_{t \to 0} te^{-t}\right]\mathbf{j} + \left[\lim_{t \to 0}\frac{\sin t}{t}\right]\mathbf{k}$$

$$= \mathbf{i} + \mathbf{k} \qquad \text{(by Equation 3.5.2)}$$

A vector function $\mathbf{r}$ is **continuous at a** if

$$\lim_{t \to a} \mathbf{r}(t) = \mathbf{r}(a)$$

In view of Definition 1, we see that $\mathbf{r}$ is continuous at a if and only if its component functions f, g, and h are continuous at a.

There is a close connection between continuous vector functions and space curves. Suppose that f, g, and h are continuous real-valued functions on an interval I. Then the set C of all points (x, y, z) in space, where

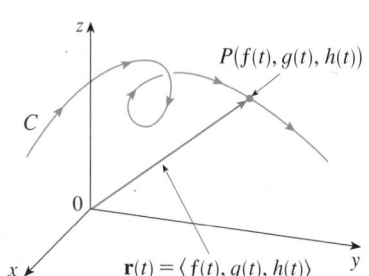

$$\boxed{2} \qquad x = f(t) \qquad y = g(t) \qquad z = h(t)$$

and t varies throughout the interval I, is called a **space curve**. The equations in (2) are called **parametric equations of C** and t is called a **parameter**. We can think of C as being traced out by a moving particle whose position at time t is $(f(t), g(t), h(t))$. If we now consider the vector function $\mathbf{r}(t) = \langle f(t), g(t), h(t)\rangle$, then $\mathbf{r}(t)$ is the position vector of the point $P(f(t), g(t), h(t))$ on C. Thus, any continuous vector function $\mathbf{r}$ defines a space curve C that is traced out by the tip of the moving vector $\mathbf{r}(t)$, as shown in Figure 1.

FIGURE 1

C is traced out by the tip of a moving position vector $\mathbf{r}(t)$.

EXAMPLE 3 Describe the curve defined by the vector function

$$\mathbf{r}(t) = \langle 1 + t, 2 + 5t, -1 + 6t\rangle$$

SOLUTION The corresponding parametric equations are

$$x = 1 + t \qquad y = 2 + 5t \qquad z = -1 + 6t$$

which we recognize from Equations 13.5.2 as parametric equations of a line passing through the point $(1, 2, -1)$ and parallel to the vector $\langle 1, 5, 6\rangle$. Alternatively, we could observe that the function can be written as $\mathbf{r} = \mathbf{r}_0 + t\mathbf{v}$, where $\mathbf{r}_0 = \langle 1, 2, -1\rangle$ and $\mathbf{v} = \langle 1, 5, 6\rangle$, and this is the vector equation of a line as given by Equation 13.5.1.

Plane curves can also be represented in vector notation. For instance, the curve given by the parametric equations $x = t^2 - 2t$ and $y = t + 1$ (see Example 1 in Section 11.1) could also be described by the vector equation

$$\mathbf{r}(t) = \langle t^2 - 2t, t + 1\rangle = (t^2 - 2t)\,\mathbf{i} + (t + 1)\,\mathbf{j}$$

where $\mathbf{i} = \langle 1, 0\rangle$ and $\mathbf{j} = \langle 0, 1\rangle$.

EXAMPLE 4 Sketch the curve whose vector equation is

$$\mathbf{r}(t) = \cos t\,\mathbf{i} + \sin t\,\mathbf{j} + t\,\mathbf{k}$$

Visual 14.1A shows several curves being traced out by position vectors, including those in Figures 1 and 2.

SOLUTION The parametric equations for this curve are

$$x = \cos t \qquad y = \sin t \qquad z = t$$

Since $x^2 + y^2 = \cos^2 t + \sin^2 t = 1$, the curve must lie on the circular cylinder $x^2 + y^2 = 1$. The point (x, y, z) lies directly above the point $(x, y, 0)$, which moves counterclockwise around the circle $x^2 + y^2 = 1$ in the xy-plane. (See Example 2 in Section 11.1.) Since $z = t$, the curve spirals upward around the cylinder as t increases. The curve, shown in Figure 2, is called a **helix**.

FIGURE 2

FIGURE 3

The corkscrew shape of the helix in Example 4 is familiar from its occurrence in coiled springs. It also occurs in the model of DNA (deoxyribonucleic acid, the genetic material of living cells). In 1953 James Watson and Francis Crick showed that the structure of the DNA molecule is that of two linked, parallel helices that are intertwined as in Figure 3.

In Examples 3 and 4 we were given vector equations of curves and asked for a geometric description or sketch. In the next two examples we are given a geometric description of a curve and are asked to find parametric equations for the curve.

EXAMPLE 5 Find a vector equation and parametric equations for the line segment that joins the point $P(1, 3, -2)$ to the point $Q(2, -1, 3)$.

SOLUTION In Section 13.5 we found a vector equation for the line segment that joins the tip of the vector $\mathbf{r}_0$ to the tip of the vector $\mathbf{r}_1$:

$$\mathbf{r}(t) = (1 - t)\mathbf{r}_0 + t\mathbf{r}_1 \qquad 0 \le t \le 1$$

(See Equation 13.5.4.) Here we take $\mathbf{r}_0 = \langle 1, 3, -2 \rangle$ and $\mathbf{r}_1 = \langle 2, -1, 3 \rangle$ to obtain a vector equation of the line segment from P to Q:

$$\mathbf{r}(t) = (1 - t)\langle 1, 3, -2 \rangle + t\langle 2, -1, 3 \rangle \qquad 0 \le t \le 1$$

or

$$\mathbf{r}(t) = \langle 1 + t, 3 - 4t, -2 + 5t \rangle \qquad 0 \le t \le 1$$

The corresponding parametric equations are

$$x = 1 + t \qquad y = 3 - 4t \qquad z = -2 + 5t \qquad 0 \le t \le 1$$

‖‖‖ Figure 4 shows the line segment PQ in Example 5.

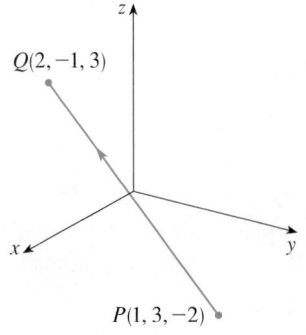

FIGURE 4

EXAMPLE 6 Find a vector function that represents the curve of intersection of the cylinder $x^2 + y^2 = 1$ and the plane $y + z = 2$.

SOLUTION Figure 5 shows how the plane and the cylinder intersect, and Figure 6 shows the curve of intersection C, which is an ellipse.

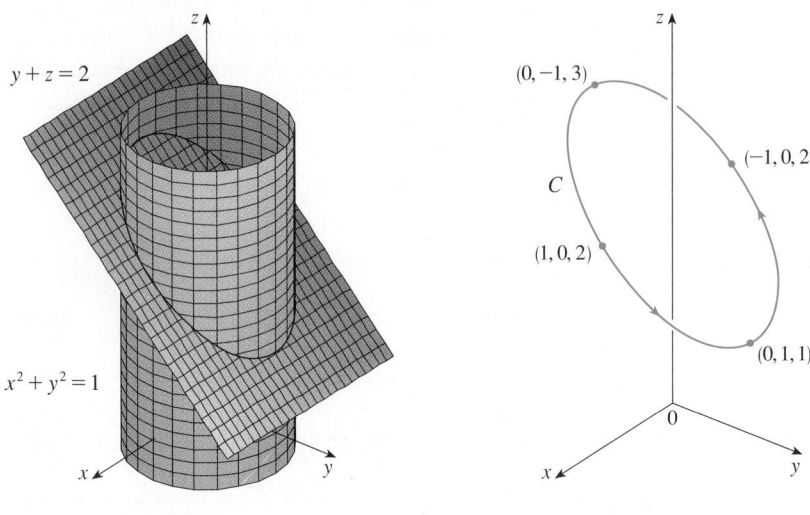

FIGURE 5   **FIGURE 6**

The projection of C onto the xy-plane is the circle $x^2 + y^2 = 1$, $z = 0$. So we know from Example 2 in Section 11.1 that we can write

$$x = \cos t \qquad y = \sin t \qquad 0 \leqslant t \leqslant 2\pi$$

From the equation of the plane, we have

$$z = 2 - y = 2 - \sin t$$

So we can write parametric equations for C as

$$x = \cos t \qquad y = \sin t \qquad z = 2 - \sin t \qquad 0 \leqslant t \leqslant 2\pi$$

The corresponding vector equation is

$$\mathbf{r}(t) = \cos t \, \mathbf{i} + \sin t \, \mathbf{j} + (2 - \sin t) \, \mathbf{k} \qquad 0 \leqslant t \leqslant 2\pi$$

This equation is called a *parametrization* of the curve C. The arrows in Figure 6 indicate the direction in which C is traced as the parameter t increases.

▦ ▎ **Using Computers to Draw Space Curves**

Space curves are inherently more difficult to draw by hand than plane curves; for an accurate representation we need to use technology. For instance, Figure 7 shows a computer-generated graph of the curve with parametric equations

$$x = (4 + \sin 20t) \cos t \qquad y = (4 + \sin 20t) \sin t \qquad z = \cos 20t$$

It's called a **toroidal spiral** because it lies on a torus. Another interesting curve, the **tre-**

foil knot, with equations

$$x = (2 + \cos 1.5t) \cos t \qquad y = (2 + \cos 1.5t) \sin t \qquad z = \sin 1.5t$$

is graphed in Figure 8. It wouldn't be easy to plot either of these curves by hand.

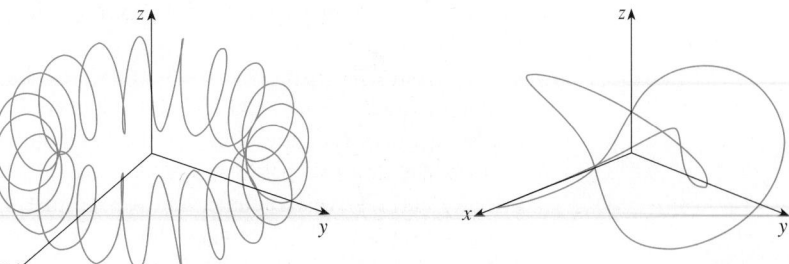

FIGURE 7 A toroidal spiral   **FIGURE 8** A trefoil knot

Even when a computer is used to draw a space curve, optical illusions make it difficult to get a good impression of what the curve really looks like. (This is especially true in Figure 8. See Exercise 42.) The next example shows how to cope with this problem.

EXAMPLE 7 Use a computer to sketch the curve with vector equation $\mathbf{r}(t) = \langle t, t^2, t^3 \rangle$. This curve is called a **twisted cubic**.

SOLUTION We start by using the computer to plot the curve with parametric equations $x = t$, $y = t^2$, $z = t^3$ for $-2 \leqslant t \leqslant 2$. The result is shown in Figure 9(a), but it's hard to see the true nature of the curve from that graph alone. Most three-dimensional computer graphing programs allow the user to enclose a curve or surface in a box instead of displaying the coordinate axes. When we look at the same curve in a box in Figure 9(b), we have a much clearer picture of the curve. We can see that it climbs from a lower corner of the box to the upper corner nearest us, and it twists as it climbs.

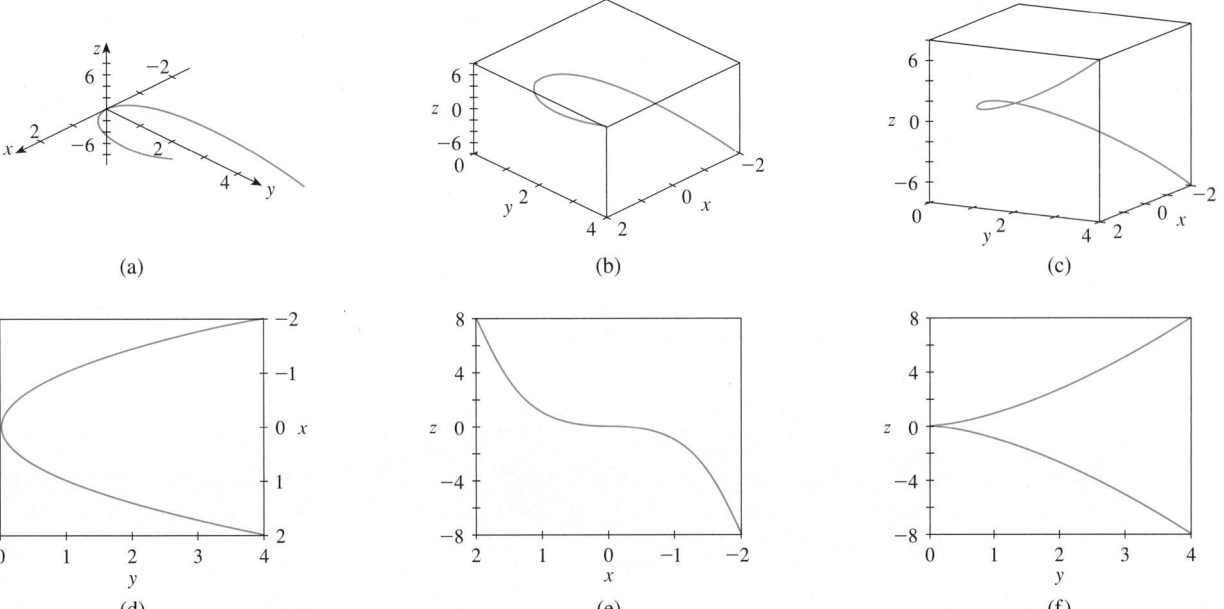

FIGURE 9 Views of the twisted cubic

In Visual 14.1B you can rotate the box in Figure 9 to see the curve from any viewpoint.

We get an even better idea of the curve when we view it from different vantage points. Part (c) shows the result of rotating the box to give another viewpoint. Parts (d), (e), and (f) show the views we get when we look directly at a face of the box. In particular, part (d) shows the view from directly above the box. It is the projection of the curve on the xy-plane, namely, the parabola $y = x^2$. Part (e) shows the projection on the xz-plane, the cubic curve $z = x^3$. It's now obvious why the given curve is called a twisted cubic.

Another method of visualizing a space curve is to draw it on a surface. For instance, the twisted cubic in Example 7 lies on the parabolic cylinder $y = x^2$. (Eliminate the parameter from the first two parametric equations, $x = t$ and $y = t^2$.) Figure 10 shows both the cylinder and the twisted cubic, and we see that the curve moves upward from the origin along the surface of the cylinder. We also used this method in Example 4 to visualize the helix lying on the circular cylinder (see Figure 2).

A third method for visualizing the twisted cubic is to realize that it also lies on the cylinder $z = x^3$. So it can be viewed as the curve of intersection of the cylinders $y = x^2$ and $z = x^3$. (See Figure 11.)

FIGURE 10

Visual 14.1C shows how curves arise as intersections of surfaces.

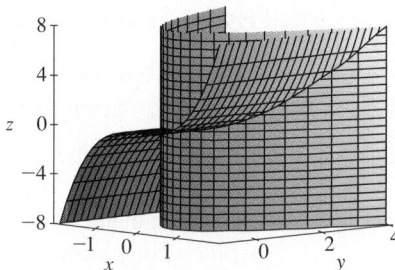

FIGURE 11

IIII Some computer algebra systems provide us with a clearer picture of a space curve by enclosing it in a tube. Such a plot enables us to see whether one part of a curve passes in front of or behind another part of the curve. For example, Figure 13 shows the curve of Figure 12(b) as rendered by the `tubeplot` command in Maple.

We have seen that an interesting space curve, the helix, occurs in the model of DNA. Another notable example of a space curve in science is the trajectory of a positively charged particle in orthogonally oriented electric and magnetic fields **E** and **B**. Depending on the initial velocity given the particle at the origin, the path of the particle is either a space curve whose projection on the horizontal plane is the cycloid we studied in Section 11.1 [Figure 12(a)] or a curve whose projection is the trochoid investigated in Exercise 38 in Section 11.1 [Figure 12(b)].

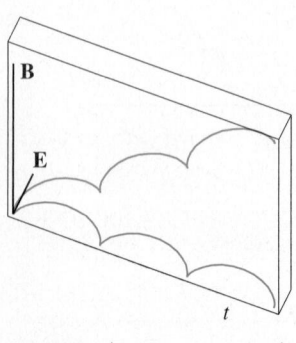

(a) $\mathbf{r}(t) = \langle t - \sin t, 1 - \cos t, t \rangle$

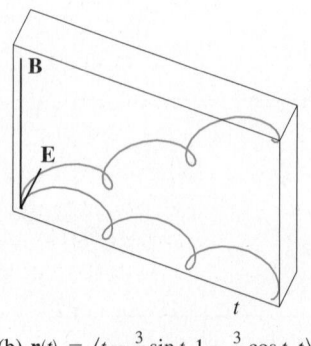

(b) $\mathbf{r}(t) = \langle t - \frac{3}{2} \sin t, 1 - \frac{3}{2} \cos t, t \rangle$

FIGURE 13

FIGURE 12
Motion of a charged particle in orthogonally oriented electric and magnetic fields

For further details concerning the physics involved and animations of the trajectories of the particles, see the following web sites:

▫ lompado.uah.edu/Links/CrossedFields.html

▫ www.phy.ntnu.edu.tw/java/emField/emField.html

▫ www.physics.ucla.edu/plasma-exp/Beam/

14.1 Exercises

1–2 ▥ Find the domain of the vector function.

1. $\mathbf{r}(t) = \langle t^2, \sqrt{t-1}, \sqrt{5-t} \rangle$

2. $\mathbf{r}(t) = \dfrac{t-2}{t+2}\,\mathbf{i} + \sin t\,\mathbf{j} + \ln(9-t^2)\,\mathbf{k}$

3–6 ▥ Find the limit.

3. $\displaystyle\lim_{t\to 0^+} \langle \cos t, \sin t, t \ln t \rangle$

4. $\displaystyle\lim_{t\to 0} \left\langle \dfrac{e^t-1}{t}, \dfrac{\sqrt{1+t}-1}{t}, \dfrac{3}{1+t} \right\rangle$

5. $\displaystyle\lim_{t\to 1} \left(\sqrt{t+3}\,\mathbf{i} + \dfrac{t-1}{t^2-1}\,\mathbf{j} + \dfrac{\tan t}{t}\,\mathbf{k} \right)$

6. $\displaystyle\lim_{t\to\infty} \left\langle \arctan t, e^{-2t}, \dfrac{\ln t}{t} \right\rangle$

7–14 ▥ Sketch the curve with the given vector equation. Indicate with an arrow the direction in which t increases.

7. $\mathbf{r}(t) = \langle t^4+1, t \rangle$ **8.** $\mathbf{r}(t) = \langle t^3, t^2 \rangle$

9. $\mathbf{r}(t) = \langle t, \cos 2t, \sin 2t \rangle$ **10.** $\mathbf{r}(t) = \langle 1+t, 3t, -t \rangle$

11. $\mathbf{r}(t) = \langle \sin t, 3, \cos t \rangle$

12. $\mathbf{r}(t) = t\,\mathbf{i} + t\,\mathbf{j} + \cos t\,\mathbf{k}$

13. $\mathbf{r}(t) = t^2\,\mathbf{i} + t^4\,\mathbf{j} + t^6\,\mathbf{k}$

14. $\mathbf{r}(t) = \sin t\,\mathbf{i} + \sin t\,\mathbf{j} + \sqrt{2}\,\cos t\,\mathbf{k}$

15–18 ▥ Find a vector equation and parametric equations for the line segment that joins P to Q.

15. $P(0, 0, 0), \quad Q(1, 2, 3)$ **16.** $P(1, 0, 1), \quad Q(2, 3, 1)$

17. $P(1, -1, 2), \quad Q(4, 1, 7)$ **18.** $P(-2, 4, 0), \quad Q(6, -1, 2)$

19–24 ▥ Match the parametric equations with the graphs (labeled I–VI). Give reasons for your choices.

19. $x = \cos 4t, \quad y = t, \quad z = \sin 4t$

20. $x = t, \quad y = t^2, \quad z = e^{-t}$

21. $x = t, \quad y = 1/(1+t^2), \quad z = t^2$

22. $x = e^{-t}\cos 10t, \quad y = e^{-t}\sin 10t, \quad z = e^{-t}$

23. $x = \cos t, \quad y = \sin t, \quad z = \sin 5t$

24. $x = \cos t, \quad y = \sin t, \quad z = \ln t$

I

II

III

IV

V

VI
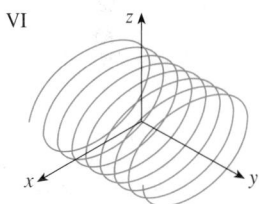

25. Show that the curve with parametric equations $x = t \cos t$, $y = t \sin t$, $z = t$ lies on the cone $z^2 = x^2 + y^2$, and use this fact to help sketch the curve.

26. Show that the curve with parametric equations $x = \sin t$, $y = \cos t$, $z = \sin^2 t$ is the curve of intersection of the surfaces $z = x^2$ and $x^2 + y^2 = 1$. Use this fact to help sketch the curve.

27–30 ▥ Use a computer to graph the curve with the given vector equation. Make sure you choose a parameter domain and viewpoints that reveal the true nature of the curve.

27. $\mathbf{r}(t) = \langle \sin t, \cos t, t^2 \rangle$ **28.** $\mathbf{r}(t) = \langle t^4 - t^2 + 1, t, t^2 \rangle$

29. $\mathbf{r}(t) = \langle t^2, \sqrt{t-1}, \sqrt{5-t} \rangle$

30. $\mathbf{r}(t) = \langle \sin t, \sin 2t, \sin 3t \rangle$

31. Graph the curve with parametric equations
$x = (1 + \cos 16t) \cos t$, $y = (1 + \cos 16t) \sin t$,
$z = 1 + \cos 16t$. Explain the appearance of the graph by
showing that it lies on a cone.

32. Graph the curve with parametric equations

$$x = \sqrt{1 - 0.25 \cos^2 10t} \cos t$$

$$y = \sqrt{1 - 0.25 \cos^2 10t} \sin t$$

$$z = 0.5 \cos 10t$$

Explain the appearance of the graph by showing that it lies on a
sphere.

33. Show that the curve with parametric equations $x = t^2$,
$y = 1 - 3t$, $z = 1 + t^3$ passes through the points $(1, 4, 0)$ and
$(9, -8, 28)$ but not through the point $(4, 7, -6)$.

34–36 ‖‖ Find a vector function that represents the curve of intersection of the two surfaces.

34. The cylinder $x^2 + y^2 = 4$ and the surface $z = xy$

35. The cone $z = \sqrt{x^2 + y^2}$ and the plane $z = 1 + y$

36. The paraboloid $z = 4x^2 + y^2$ and the parabolic cylinder $y = x^2$

37. Try to sketch by hand the curve of intersection of the circular
cylinder $x^2 + y^2 = 4$ and the parabolic cylinder $z = x^2$. Then
find parametric equations for this curve and use these equations
and a computer to graph the curve.

38. Try to sketch by hand the curve of intersection of the
parabolic cylinder $y = x^2$ and the top half of the ellipsoid
$x^2 + 4y^2 + 4z^2 = 16$. Then find parametric equations for
this curve and use these equations and a computer to graph
the curve.

39. If two objects travel through space along two different curves,
it's often important to know whether they will collide. (Will a
missile hit its moving target? Will two aircraft collide?) The
curves might intersect, but we need to know whether the
objects are in the same position *at the same time.* Suppose the

trajectories of two particles are given by the vector functions

$$\mathbf{r}_1(t) = \langle t^2, 7t - 12, t^2 \rangle \qquad \mathbf{r}_2(t) = \langle 4t - 3, t^2, 5t - 6 \rangle$$

for $t \geq 0$. Do the particles collide?

40. Two particles travel along the space curves

$$\mathbf{r}_1(t) = \langle t, t^2, t^3 \rangle \qquad \mathbf{r}_2(t) = \langle 1 + 2t, 1 + 6t, 1 + 14t \rangle$$

Do the particles collide? Do their paths intersect?

41. Suppose $\mathbf{u}$ and $\mathbf{v}$ are vector functions that possess limits as
$t \to a$ and let c be a constant. Prove the following properties of
limits.

(a) $\lim\limits_{t \to a} [\mathbf{u}(t) + \mathbf{v}(t)] = \lim\limits_{t \to a} \mathbf{u}(t) + \lim\limits_{t \to a} \mathbf{v}(t)$

(b) $\lim\limits_{t \to a} c\mathbf{u}(t) = c \lim\limits_{t \to a} \mathbf{u}(t)$

(c) $\lim\limits_{t \to a} [\mathbf{u}(t) \cdot \mathbf{v}(t)] = \lim\limits_{t \to a} \mathbf{u}(t) \cdot \lim\limits_{t \to a} \mathbf{v}(t)$

(d) $\lim\limits_{t \to a} [\mathbf{u}(t) \times \mathbf{v}(t)] = \lim\limits_{t \to a} \mathbf{u}(t) \times \lim\limits_{t \to a} \mathbf{v}(t)$

42. The view of the trefoil knot shown in Figure 8 is accurate, but
it doesn't reveal the whole story. Use the parametric equations

$$x = (2 + \cos 1.5t) \cos t \qquad y = (2 + \cos 1.5t) \sin t$$

$$z = \sin 1.5t$$

to sketch the curve by hand as viewed from above, with gaps
indicating where the curve passes over itself. Start by showing
that the projection of the curve onto the xy-plane has polar
coordinates $r = 2 + \cos 1.5t$ and $\theta = t$, so r varies between 1
and 3. Then show that z has maximum and minimum values
when the projection is halfway between $r = 1$ and $r = 3$.

When you have finished your sketch, use a computer to draw
the curve with viewpoint directly above and compare with your
sketch. Then use the computer to draw the curve from several
other viewpoints. You can get a better impression of the curve
if you plot a tube with radius 0.2 around the curve. (Use the
`tubeplot` command in Maple.)

43. Show that $\lim_{t \to a} \mathbf{r}(t) = \mathbf{b}$ if and only if for every $\varepsilon > 0$
there is a number $\delta > 0$ such that $|\mathbf{r}(t) - \mathbf{b}| < \varepsilon$ whenever
$0 < |t - a| < \delta$.

‖‖ 14.2 Derivatives and Integrals of Vector Functions

Later in this chapter we are going to use vector functions to describe the motion of planets and other objects through space. Here we prepare the way by developing the calculus
of vector functions.

‖‖ Derivatives

The **derivative** $\mathbf{r}'$ of a vector function $\mathbf{r}$ is defined in much the same way as for real-
valued functions:

$$\boxed{\textbf{1}} \qquad \frac{d\mathbf{r}}{dt} = \mathbf{r}'(t) = \lim_{h \to 0} \frac{\mathbf{r}(t + h) - \mathbf{r}(t)}{h}$$

if this limit exists. The geometric significance of this definition is shown in Figure 1. If the points P and Q have position vectors $\mathbf{r}(t)$ and $\mathbf{r}(t + h)$, then $\overrightarrow{PQ}$ represents the vector $\mathbf{r}(t + h) - \mathbf{r}(t)$, which can therefore be regarded as a secant vector. If $h > 0$, the scalar multiple $(1/h)(\mathbf{r}(t + h) - \mathbf{r}(t))$ has the same direction as $\mathbf{r}(t + h) - \mathbf{r}(t)$. As $h \to 0$, it appears that this vector approaches a vector that lies on the tangent line. For this reason, the vector $\mathbf{r}'(t)$ is called the **tangent vector** to the curve defined by $\mathbf{r}$ at the point P, provided that $\mathbf{r}'(t)$ exists and $\mathbf{r}'(t) \neq \mathbf{0}$. The **tangent line** to C at P is defined to be the line through P parallel to the tangent vector $\mathbf{r}'(t)$. We will also have occasion to consider the **unit tangent vector**, which is

$$\mathbf{T}(t) = \frac{\mathbf{r}'(t)}{|\mathbf{r}'(t)|}$$

Visual 14.2 shows an animation of Figure 1.

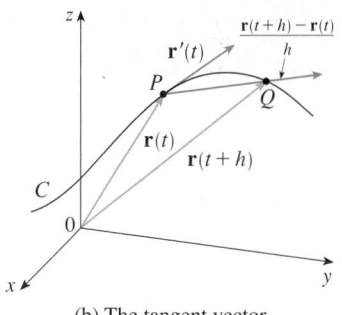

FIGURE 1

(a) The secant vector

(b) The tangent vector

The following theorem gives us a convenient method for computing the derivative of a vector function $\mathbf{r}$; just differentiate each component of $\mathbf{r}$.

$\boxed{\textbf{2}}$ **Theorem** If $\mathbf{r}(t) = \langle f(t), g(t), h(t) \rangle = f(t)\,\mathbf{i} + g(t)\,\mathbf{j} + h(t)\,\mathbf{k}$, where f, g, and h are differentiable functions, then

$$\mathbf{r}'(t) = \langle f'(t), g'(t), h'(t) \rangle = f'(t)\,\mathbf{i} + g'(t)\,\mathbf{j} + h'(t)\,\mathbf{k}$$

Proof

$$\mathbf{r}'(t) = \lim_{\Delta t \to 0} \frac{1}{\Delta t} [\mathbf{r}(t + \Delta t) - \mathbf{r}(t)]$$

$$= \lim_{\Delta t \to 0} \frac{1}{\Delta t} [\langle f(t + \Delta t), g(t + \Delta t), h(t + \Delta t) \rangle - \langle f(t), g(t), h(t) \rangle]$$

$$= \lim_{\Delta t \to 0} \left\langle \frac{f(t + \Delta t) - f(t)}{\Delta t}, \frac{g(t + \Delta t) - g(t)}{\Delta t}, \frac{h(t + \Delta t) - h(t)}{\Delta t} \right\rangle$$

$$= \left\langle \lim_{\Delta t \to 0} \frac{f(t + \Delta t) - f(t)}{\Delta t}, \lim_{\Delta t \to 0} \frac{g(t + \Delta t) - g(t)}{\Delta t}, \lim_{\Delta t \to 0} \frac{h(t + \Delta t) - h(t)}{\Delta t} \right\rangle$$

$$= \langle f'(t), g'(t), h'(t) \rangle$$

EXAMPLE 1
(a) Find the derivative of $\mathbf{r}(t) = (1 + t^3)\mathbf{i} + te^{-t}\mathbf{j} + \sin 2t\,\mathbf{k}$.
(b) Find the unit tangent vector at the point where $t = 0$.

SOLUTION
(a) According to Theorem 2, we differentiate each component of $\mathbf{r}$:

$$\mathbf{r}'(t) = 3t^2\mathbf{i} + (1 - t)e^{-t}\mathbf{j} + 2\cos 2t\,\mathbf{k}$$

(b) Since $\mathbf{r}(0) = \mathbf{i}$ and $\mathbf{r}'(0) = \mathbf{j} + 2\mathbf{k}$, the unit tangent vector at the point $(1, 0, 0)$ is

$$\mathbf{T}(0) = \frac{\mathbf{r}'(0)}{|\mathbf{r}'(0)|} = \frac{\mathbf{j} + 2\mathbf{k}}{\sqrt{1 + 4}} = \frac{1}{\sqrt{5}}\mathbf{j} + \frac{2}{\sqrt{5}}\mathbf{k}$$

EXAMPLE 2 For the curve $\mathbf{r}(t) = \sqrt{t}\,\mathbf{i} + (2 - t)\mathbf{j}$, find $\mathbf{r}'(t)$ and sketch the position vector $\mathbf{r}(1)$ and the tangent vector $\mathbf{r}'(1)$.

SOLUTION We have

$$\mathbf{r}'(t) = \frac{1}{2\sqrt{t}}\mathbf{i} - \mathbf{j} \qquad \text{and} \qquad \mathbf{r}'(1) = \frac{1}{2}\mathbf{i} - \mathbf{j}$$

The curve is a plane curve and elimination of the parameter from the equations $x = \sqrt{t}$, $y = 2 - t$ gives $y = 2 - x^2$, $x \geqslant 0$. In Figure 2 we draw the position vector $\mathbf{r}(1) = \mathbf{i} + \mathbf{j}$ starting at the origin and the tangent vector $\mathbf{r}'(1)$ starting at the corresponding point $(1, 1)$.

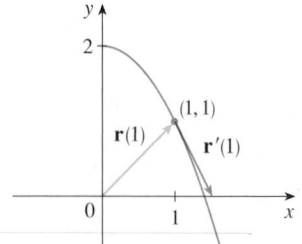

FIGURE 2

EXAMPLE 3 Find parametric equations for the tangent line to the helix with parametric equations

$$x = 2\cos t \qquad y = \sin t \qquad z = t$$

at the point $(0, 1, \pi/2)$.

SOLUTION The vector equation of the helix is $\mathbf{r}(t) = \langle 2\cos t, \sin t, t \rangle$, so

$$\mathbf{r}'(t) = \langle -2\sin t, \cos t, 1 \rangle$$

The parameter value corresponding to the point $(0, 1, \pi/2)$ is $t = \pi/2$, so the tangent vector there is $\mathbf{r}'(\pi/2) = \langle -2, 0, 1 \rangle$. The tangent line is the line through $(0, 1, \pi/2)$ parallel to the vector $\langle -2, 0, 1 \rangle$, so by Equations 13.5.2 its parametric equations are

$$x = -2t \qquad y = 1 \qquad z = \frac{\pi}{2} + t$$

|||| The helix and the tangent line in Example 3 are shown in Figure 3.

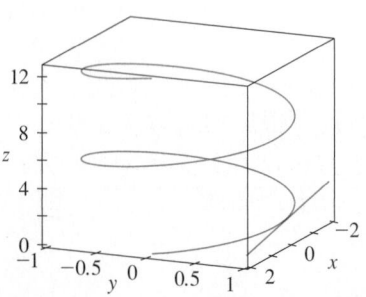

FIGURE 3

Just as for real-valued functions, the **second derivative** of a vector function $\mathbf{r}$ is the derivative of $\mathbf{r}'$, that is, $\mathbf{r}'' = (\mathbf{r}')'$. For instance, the second derivative of the function in Example 3 is

$$\mathbf{r}''(t) = \langle -2\cos t, -\sin t, 0 \rangle$$

A curve given by a vector function $\mathbf{r}(t)$ on an interval I is called **smooth** if $\mathbf{r}'$ is continuous and $\mathbf{r}'(t) \neq \mathbf{0}$ (except possibly at any endpoints of I). For instance, the helix in Example 3 is smooth because $\mathbf{r}'(t)$ is never $\mathbf{0}$.

EXAMPLE 4 Determine whether the semicubical parabola $\mathbf{r}(t) = \langle 1 + t^3, t^2 \rangle$ is smooth.

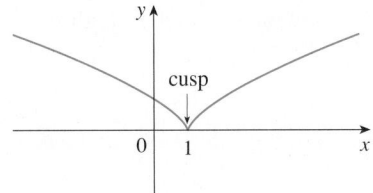

FIGURE 4

The curve $\mathbf{r}(t) = \langle 1 + t^3, t^2 \rangle$ is not smooth.

SOLUTION Since

$$\mathbf{r}'(t) = \langle 3t^2, 2t \rangle$$

we have $\mathbf{r}'(0) = \langle 0, 0 \rangle = \mathbf{0}$ and, therefore, the curve is not smooth. The point that corresponds to $t = 0$ is $(1, 0)$, and we see from the graph in Figure 4 that there is a sharp corner, called a **cusp**, at $(1, 0)$. Any curve with this type of behavior—an abrupt change in direction—is not smooth.

A curve, such as the semicubical parabola, that is made up of a finite number of smooth pieces is called **piecewise smooth**.

▕▏▏ Differentiation Rules

The next theorem shows that the differentiation formulas for real-valued functions have their counterparts for vector-valued functions.

> **3 Theorem** Suppose $\mathbf{u}$ and $\mathbf{v}$ are differentiable vector functions, c is a scalar, and f is a real-valued function. Then
>
> **1.** $\dfrac{d}{dt}[\mathbf{u}(t) + \mathbf{v}(t)] = \mathbf{u}'(t) + \mathbf{v}'(t)$
>
> **2.** $\dfrac{d}{dt}[c\mathbf{u}(t)] = c\mathbf{u}'(t)$
>
> **3.** $\dfrac{d}{dt}[f(t)\mathbf{u}(t)] = f'(t)\mathbf{u}(t) + f(t)\mathbf{u}'(t)$
>
> **4.** $\dfrac{d}{dt}[\mathbf{u}(t) \cdot \mathbf{v}(t)] = \mathbf{u}'(t) \cdot \mathbf{v}(t) + \mathbf{u}(t) \cdot \mathbf{v}'(t)$
>
> **5.** $\dfrac{d}{dt}[\mathbf{u}(t) \times \mathbf{v}(t)] = \mathbf{u}'(t) \times \mathbf{v}(t) + \mathbf{u}(t) \times \mathbf{v}'(t)$
>
> **6.** $\dfrac{d}{dt}[\mathbf{u}(f(t))] = f'(t)\mathbf{u}'(f(t))$ (Chain Rule)

This theorem can be proved either directly from Definition 1 or by using Theorem 2 and the corresponding differentiation formulas for real-valued functions. The proofs of Formulas 1, 2, 3, 5, and 6 are left as exercises.

Proof of Formula 4 Let

$$\mathbf{u}(t) = \langle f_1(t), f_2(t), f_3(t) \rangle \qquad \mathbf{v}(t) = \langle g_1(t), g_2(t), g_3(t) \rangle$$

Then

$$\mathbf{u}(t) \cdot \mathbf{v}(t) = f_1(t)g_1(t) + f_2(t)g_2(t) + f_3(t)g_3(t) = \sum_{i=1}^{3} f_i(t)g_i(t)$$

so the ordinary Product Rule gives

$$\frac{d}{dt}[\mathbf{u}(t) \cdot \mathbf{v}(t)] = \frac{d}{dt}\sum_{i=1}^{3} f_i(t)g_i(t) = \sum_{i=1}^{3} \frac{d}{dt}[f_i(t)g_i(t)]$$

$$= \sum_{i=1}^{3} [f_i'(t)g_i(t) + f_i(t)g_i'(t)]$$

$$= \sum_{i=1}^{3} f_i'(t)g_i(t) + \sum_{i=1}^{3} f_i(t)g_i'(t)$$

$$= \mathbf{u}'(t) \cdot \mathbf{v}(t) + \mathbf{u}(t) \cdot \mathbf{v}'(t)$$

EXAMPLE 5 Show that if $|\mathbf{r}(t)| = c$ (a constant), then $\mathbf{r}'(t)$ is orthogonal to $\mathbf{r}(t)$ for all t.

SOLUTION Since

$$\mathbf{r}(t) \cdot \mathbf{r}(t) = |\mathbf{r}(t)|^2 = c^2$$

and c^2 is a constant, Formula 4 of Theorem 3 gives

$$0 = \frac{d}{dt}[\mathbf{r}(t) \cdot \mathbf{r}(t)] = \mathbf{r}'(t) \cdot \mathbf{r}(t) + \mathbf{r}(t) \cdot \mathbf{r}'(t) = 2\mathbf{r}'(t) \cdot \mathbf{r}(t)$$

Thus, $\mathbf{r}'(t) \cdot \mathbf{r}(t) = 0$, which says that $\mathbf{r}'(t)$ is orthogonal to $\mathbf{r}(t)$.

Geometrically, this result says that if a curve lies on a sphere with center the origin, then the tangent vector $\mathbf{r}'(t)$ is always perpendicular to the position vector $\mathbf{r}(t)$.

▓ Integrals

The **definite integral** of a continuous vector function $\mathbf{r}(t)$ can be defined in much the same way as for real-valued functions except that the integral is a vector. But then we can express the integral of $\mathbf{r}$ in terms of the integrals of its component functions f, g, and h as follows. (We use the notation of Chapter 5.)

$$\int_a^b \mathbf{r}(t)\, dt = \lim_{n \to \infty} \sum_{i=1}^n \mathbf{r}(t_i^*)\, \Delta t$$

$$= \lim_{n \to \infty} \left[\left(\sum_{i=1}^n f(t_i^*)\, \Delta t \right) \mathbf{i} + \left(\sum_{i=1}^n g(t_i^*)\, \Delta t \right) \mathbf{j} + \left(\sum_{i=1}^n h(t_i^*)\, \Delta t \right) \mathbf{k} \right]$$

and so

$$\int_a^b \mathbf{r}(t)\, dt = \left(\int_a^b f(t)\, dt \right) \mathbf{i} + \left(\int_a^b g(t)\, dt \right) \mathbf{j} + \left(\int_a^b h(t)\, dt \right) \mathbf{k}$$

This means that we can evaluate an integral of a vector function by integrating each component function.

We can extend the Fundamental Theorem of Calculus to continuous vector functions as follows:

$$\int_a^b \mathbf{r}(t)\, dt = \mathbf{R}(t) \Big]_a^b = \mathbf{R}(b) - \mathbf{R}(a)$$

where $\mathbf{R}$ is an antiderivative of $\mathbf{r}$, that is, $\mathbf{R}'(t) = \mathbf{r}(t)$. We use the notation $\int \mathbf{r}(t)\, dt$ for indefinite integrals (antiderivatives).

EXAMPLE 6 If $\mathbf{r}(t) = 2 \cos t\, \mathbf{i} + \sin t\, \mathbf{j} + 2t\, \mathbf{k}$, then

$$\int \mathbf{r}(t)\, dt = \left(\int 2 \cos t\, dt \right) \mathbf{i} + \left(\int \sin t\, dt \right) \mathbf{j} + \left(\int 2t\, dt \right) \mathbf{k}$$

$$= 2 \sin t\, \mathbf{i} - \cos t\, \mathbf{j} + t^2\, \mathbf{k} + \mathbf{C}$$

where $\mathbf{C}$ is a vector constant of integration, and

$$\int_0^{\pi/2} \mathbf{r}(t)\, dt = \left[2 \sin t\, \mathbf{i} - \cos t\, \mathbf{j} + t^2\, \mathbf{k} \right]_0^{\pi/2} = 2\mathbf{i} + \mathbf{j} + \frac{\pi^2}{4} \mathbf{k}$$

14.2 Exercises

1. The figure shows a curve C given by a vector function $\mathbf{r}(t)$.
 (a) Draw the vectors $\mathbf{r}(4.5) - \mathbf{r}(4)$ and $\mathbf{r}(4.2) - \mathbf{r}(4)$.
 (b) Draw the vectors

$$\frac{\mathbf{r}(4.5) - \mathbf{r}(4)}{0.5} \quad \text{and} \quad \frac{\mathbf{r}(4.2) - \mathbf{r}(4)}{0.2}$$

 (c) Write expressions for $\mathbf{r}'(4)$ and the unit tangent vector $\mathbf{T}(4)$.
 (d) Draw the vector $\mathbf{T}(4)$.

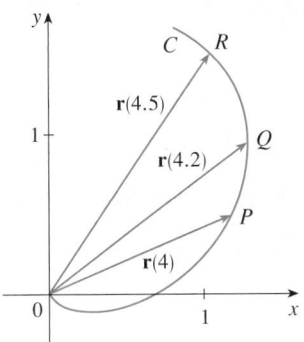

2. (a) Make a large sketch of the curve described by the vector
 function $\mathbf{r}(t) = \langle t^2, t \rangle$, $0 \le t \le 2$, and draw the vectors
 $\mathbf{r}(1)$, $\mathbf{r}(1.1)$, and $\mathbf{r}(1.1) - \mathbf{r}(1)$.
 (b) Draw the vector $\mathbf{r}'(1)$ starting at $(1, 1)$ and compare it with
 the vector

$$\frac{\mathbf{r}(1.1) - \mathbf{r}(1)}{0.1}$$

 Explain why these vectors are so close to each other in
 length and direction.

3–8 ▓
 (a) Sketch the plane curve with the given vector equation.
 (b) Find $\mathbf{r}'(t)$.
 (c) Sketch the position vector $\mathbf{r}(t)$ and the tangent vector $\mathbf{r}'(t)$ for
 the given value of t.

3. $\mathbf{r}(t) = \langle \cos t, \sin t \rangle$, $\quad t = \pi/4$

4. $\mathbf{r}(t) = \langle 1 + t, \sqrt{t} \rangle$, $\quad t = 1$

5. $\mathbf{r}(t) = (1 + t)\,\mathbf{i} + t^2\,\mathbf{j}$, $\quad t = 1$

6. $\mathbf{r}(t) = e^t\,\mathbf{i} + e^{-t}\,\mathbf{j}$, $\quad t = 0$

7. $\mathbf{r}(t) = e^t\,\mathbf{i} + e^{3t}\,\mathbf{j}$, $\quad t = 0$

8. $\mathbf{r}(t) = 2\sin t\,\mathbf{i} + 3\cos t\,\mathbf{j}$, $\quad t = \pi/3$

9–16 ▓ Find the derivative of the vector function.

9. $\mathbf{r}(t) = \langle t^2, 1 - t, \sqrt{t} \rangle$

10. $\mathbf{r}(t) = \langle \cos 3t, t, \sin 3t \rangle$

11. $\mathbf{r}(t) = \mathbf{i} - \mathbf{j} + e^{4t}\,\mathbf{k}$

12. $\mathbf{r}(t) = \sin^{-1}t\,\mathbf{i} + \sqrt{1 - t^2}\,\mathbf{j} + \mathbf{k}$

13. $\mathbf{r}(t) = e^{t^2}\mathbf{i} - \mathbf{j} + \ln(1 + 3t)\,\mathbf{k}$

14. $\mathbf{r}(t) = at\cos 3t\,\mathbf{i} + b\sin^3 t\,\mathbf{j} + c\cos^3 t\,\mathbf{k}$

15. $\mathbf{r}(t) = \mathbf{a} + t\,\mathbf{b} + t^2\,\mathbf{c}$

16. $\mathbf{r}(t) = t\,\mathbf{a} \times (\mathbf{b} + t\,\mathbf{c})$

17–20 ▓ Find the unit tangent vector $\mathbf{T}(t)$ at the point with the
given value of the parameter t.

17. $\mathbf{r}(t) = \langle 6t^5, 4t^3, 2t \rangle$, $\quad t = 1$

18. $\mathbf{r}(t) = 4\sqrt{t}\,\mathbf{i} + t^2\,\mathbf{j} + t\,\mathbf{k}$, $\quad t = 1$

19. $\mathbf{r}(t) = \cos t\,\mathbf{i} + 3t\,\mathbf{j} + 2\sin 2t\,\mathbf{k}$, $\quad t = 0$

20. $\mathbf{r}(t) = 2\sin t\,\mathbf{i} + 2\cos t\,\mathbf{j} + \tan t\,\mathbf{k}$, $\quad t = \pi/4$

21. If $\mathbf{r}(t) = \langle t, t^2, t^3 \rangle$, find $\mathbf{r}'(t)$, $\mathbf{T}(1)$, $\mathbf{r}''(t)$, and $\mathbf{r}'(t) \times \mathbf{r}''(t)$.

22. If $\mathbf{r}(t) = \langle e^{2t}, e^{-2t}, te^{2t} \rangle$, find $\mathbf{T}(0)$, $\mathbf{r}''(0)$, and $\mathbf{r}'(t) \cdot \mathbf{r}''(t)$.

23–26 ▓ Find parametric equations for the tangent line to the
curve with the given parametric equations at the specified point.

23. $x = t^5$, $y = t^4$, $z = t^3$; $\quad (1, 1, 1)$

24. $x = t^2 - 1$, $y = t^2 + 1$, $z = t + 1$; $\quad (-1, 1, 1)$

25. $x = e^{-t}\cos t$, $y = e^{-t}\sin t$, $z = e^{-t}$; $\quad (1, 0, 1)$

26. $x = \ln t$, $y = 2\sqrt{t}$, $z = t^2$; $\quad (0, 2, 1)$

27–28 ▓ Find parametric equations for the tangent line to the
curve with the given parametric equations at the specified point.
Illustrate by graphing both the curve and the tangent line on a common screen.

27. $x = t$, $y = \sqrt{2}\cos t$, $z = \sqrt{2}\sin t$; $\quad (\pi/4, 1, 1)$

28. $x = \cos t$, $y = 3e^{2t}$, $z = 3e^{-2t}$; $\quad (1, 3, 3)$

29. Determine whether the curve is smooth.
 (a) $\mathbf{r}(t) = \langle t^3, t^4, t^5 \rangle$ $\qquad$ (b) $\mathbf{r}(t) = \langle t^3 + t, t^4, t^5 \rangle$
 (c) $\mathbf{r}(t) = \langle \cos^3 t, \sin^3 t \rangle$

30. (a) Find the point of intersection of the tangent lines to the
 curve $\mathbf{r}(t) = \langle \sin \pi t, 2\sin \pi t, \cos \pi t \rangle$ at the points where
 $t = 0$ and $t = 0.5$.
 (b) Illustrate by graphing the curve and both tangent lines.

31. The curves $\mathbf{r}_1(t) = \langle t, t^2, t^3 \rangle$ and $\mathbf{r}_2(t) = \langle \sin t, \sin 2t, t \rangle$ intersect at the origin. Find their angle of intersection correct to the
 nearest degree.

32. At what point do the curves $\mathbf{r}_1(t) = \langle t, 1 - t, 3 + t^2 \rangle$ and
 $\mathbf{r}_2(s) = \langle 3 - s, s - 2, s^2 \rangle$ intersect? Find their angle of intersection correct to the nearest degree.

33–38 ▓▓ Evaluate the integral.

33. $\int_0^1 (16t^3\mathbf{i} - 9t^2\mathbf{j} + 25t^4\mathbf{k})\, dt$

34. $\int_0^1 \left(\dfrac{4}{1+t^2}\,\mathbf{j} + \dfrac{2t}{1+t^2}\,\mathbf{k} \right) dt$

35. $\int_0^{\pi/2} (3\sin^2 t \cos t\,\mathbf{i} + 3\sin t \cos^2 t\,\mathbf{j} + 2\sin t \cos t\,\mathbf{k})\, dt$

36. $\int_1^4 \left(\sqrt{t}\,\mathbf{i} + te^{-t}\,\mathbf{j} + \dfrac{1}{t^2}\,\mathbf{k} \right) dt$

37. $\int (e^t\mathbf{i} + 2t\,\mathbf{j} + \ln t\,\mathbf{k})\, dt$

38. $\int (\cos \pi t\,\mathbf{i} + \sin \pi t\,\mathbf{j} + t\,\mathbf{k})\, dt$

39. Find $\mathbf{r}(t)$ if $\mathbf{r}'(t) = t^2\mathbf{i} + 4t^3\mathbf{j} - t^2\mathbf{k}$ and $\mathbf{r}(0) = \mathbf{j}$.

40. Find $\mathbf{r}(t)$ if $\mathbf{r}'(t) = \sin t\,\mathbf{i} - \cos t\,\mathbf{j} + 2t\,\mathbf{k}$ and $\mathbf{r}(0) = \mathbf{i} + \mathbf{j} + 2\mathbf{k}$.

41. Prove Formula 1 of Theorem 3.

42. Prove Formula 3 of Theorem 3.

43. Prove Formula 5 of Theorem 3.

44. Prove Formula 6 of Theorem 3.

45. If $\mathbf{u}(t) = \mathbf{i} - 2t^2\mathbf{j} + 3t^3\mathbf{k}$ and $\mathbf{v}(t) = t\,\mathbf{i} + \cos t\,\mathbf{j} + \sin t\,\mathbf{k}$, find $(d/dt)\,[\mathbf{u}(t) \cdot \mathbf{v}(t)]$.

46. If $\mathbf{u}$ and $\mathbf{v}$ are the vector functions in Exercise 45, find $(d/dt)\,[\mathbf{u}(t) \times \mathbf{v}(t)]$.

47. Show that if $\mathbf{r}$ is a vector function such that $\mathbf{r}''$ exists, then

$$\frac{d}{dt}\,[\mathbf{r}(t) \times \mathbf{r}'(t)] = \mathbf{r}(t) \times \mathbf{r}''(t)$$

48. Find an expression for $\dfrac{d}{dt}\,[\mathbf{u}(t) \cdot (\mathbf{v}(t) \times \mathbf{w}(t))]$.

49. If $\mathbf{r}(t) \neq \mathbf{0}$, show that $\dfrac{d}{dt}\,|\,\mathbf{r}(t)\,| = \dfrac{1}{|\,\mathbf{r}(t)\,|}\,\mathbf{r}(t) \cdot \mathbf{r}'(t)$.

$\big[$*Hint:* $|\,\mathbf{r}(t)\,|^2 = \mathbf{r}(t) \cdot \mathbf{r}(t)\big]$

50. If a curve has the property that the position vector $\mathbf{r}(t)$ is always perpendicular to the tangent vector $\mathbf{r}'(t)$, show that the curve lies on a sphere with center the origin.

51. If $\mathbf{u}(t) = \mathbf{r}(t) \cdot [\mathbf{r}'(t) \times \mathbf{r}''(t)]$, show that

$$\mathbf{u}'(t) = \mathbf{r}(t) \cdot [\mathbf{r}'(t) \times \mathbf{r}'''(t)]$$

14.3 Arc Length and Curvature

In Section 11.2 we defined the length of a plane curve with parametric equations $x = f(t)$, $y = g(t)$, $a \leqslant t \leqslant b$, as the limit of lengths of inscribed polygons and, for the case where f' and g' are continuous, we arrived at the formula

$$\boxed{1} \qquad L = \int_a^b \sqrt{[f'(t)]^2 + [g'(t)]^2}\; dt = \int_a^b \sqrt{\left(\frac{dx}{dt}\right)^2 + \left(\frac{dy}{dt}\right)^2}\; dt$$

The length of a space curve is defined in exactly the same way (see Figure 1). Suppose that the curve has the vector equation $\mathbf{r}(t) = \langle f(t), g(t), h(t)\rangle$, $a \leqslant t \leqslant b$, or, equivalently, the parametric equations $x = f(t)$, $y = g(t)$, $z = h(t)$, where f', g', and h' are continuous. If the curve is traversed exactly once as t increases from a to b, then it can be shown that its length is

$$\boxed{2} \qquad L = \int_a^b \sqrt{[f'(t)]^2 + [g'(t)]^2 + [h'(t)]^2}\; dt$$

$$= \int_a^b \sqrt{\left(\frac{dx}{dt}\right)^2 + \left(\frac{dy}{dt}\right)^2 + \left(\frac{dz}{dt}\right)^2}\; dt$$

FIGURE 1
The length of a space curve is the limit of lengths of inscribed polygons.

Notice that both of the arc length formulas (1) and (2) can be put into the more compact form

$$\boxed{3} \qquad L = \int_a^b |\,\mathbf{r}'(t)\,|\; dt$$

because, for plane curves $\mathbf{r}(t) = f(t)\mathbf{i} + g(t)\mathbf{j}$,

$$|\mathbf{r}'(t)| = |f'(t)\mathbf{i} + g'(t)\mathbf{j}| = \sqrt{[f'(t)]^2 + [g'(t)]^2}$$

whereas, for space curves $\mathbf{r}(t) = f(t)\mathbf{i} + g(t)\mathbf{j} + h(t)\mathbf{k}$,

$$|\mathbf{r}'(t)| = |f'(t)\mathbf{i} + g'(t)\mathbf{j} + h'(t)\mathbf{k}| = \sqrt{[f'(t)]^2 + [g'(t)]^2 + [h'(t)]^2}$$

|||| Figure 2 shows the arc of the helix whose length is computed in Example 1.

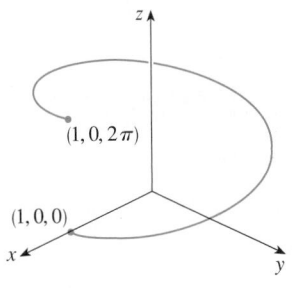

FIGURE 2

EXAMPLE 1 Find the length of the arc of the circular helix with vector equation $\mathbf{r}(t) = \cos t\,\mathbf{i} + \sin t\,\mathbf{j} + t\,\mathbf{k}$ from the point $(1, 0, 0)$ to the point $(1, 0, 2\pi)$.

SOLUTION Since $\mathbf{r}'(t) = -\sin t\,\mathbf{i} + \cos t\,\mathbf{j} + \mathbf{k}$, we have

$$|\mathbf{r}'(t)| = \sqrt{(-\sin t)^2 + \cos^2 t + 1} = \sqrt{2}$$

The arc from $(1, 0, 0)$ to $(1, 0, 2\pi)$ is described by the parameter interval $0 \le t \le 2\pi$ and so, from Formula 3, we have

$$L = \int_0^{2\pi} |\mathbf{r}'(t)|\,dt = \int_0^{2\pi} \sqrt{2}\,dt = 2\sqrt{2}\,\pi$$

A single curve C can be represented by more than one vector function. For instance, the twisted cubic

$$\boxed{4} \qquad\qquad \mathbf{r}_1(t) = \langle t, t^2, t^3 \rangle \qquad 1 \le t \le 2$$

could also be represented by the function

$$\boxed{5} \qquad\qquad \mathbf{r}_2(u) = \langle e^u, e^{2u}, e^{3u} \rangle \qquad 0 \le u \le \ln 2$$

where the connection between the parameters t and u is given by $t = e^u$. We say that Equations 4 and 5 are **parametrizations** of the curve C. If we were to use Equation 3 to compute the length of C using Equations 4 and 5, we would get the same answer. In general, it can be shown that when Equation 3 is used to compute the length of any piecewise-smooth curve, the arc length is independent of the parametrization that is used.

|||| Piecewise-smooth curves were introduced on page 895.

Now we suppose that C is a piecewise-smooth curve given by a vector function $\mathbf{r}(t) = f(t)\mathbf{i} + g(t)\mathbf{j} + h(t)\mathbf{k}$, $a \le t \le b$, and C is traversed exactly once as t increases from a to b. We define its **arc length function** s by

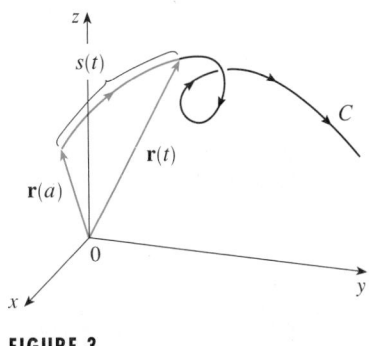

FIGURE 3

$$\boxed{6} \qquad s(t) = \int_a^t |\mathbf{r}'(u)|\,du = \int_a^t \sqrt{\left(\frac{dx}{du}\right)^2 + \left(\frac{dy}{du}\right)^2 + \left(\frac{dz}{du}\right)^2}\,du$$

Thus, $s(t)$ is the length of the part of C between $\mathbf{r}(a)$ and $\mathbf{r}(t)$. (See Figure 3.) If we differentiate both sides of Equation 6 using Part 1 of the Fundamental Theorem of Calculus, we obtain

$$\boxed{7} \qquad\qquad \frac{ds}{dt} = |\mathbf{r}'(t)|$$

It is often useful to **parametrize a curve with respect to arc length** because arc length arises naturally from the shape of the curve and does not depend on a particular coordinate system. If a curve $\mathbf{r}(t)$ is already given in terms of a parameter t and $s(t)$ is the arc length function given by Equation 6, then we may be able to solve for t as a function of s: $t = t(s)$. Then the curve can be reparametrized in terms of s by substituting for t: $\mathbf{r} = \mathbf{r}(t(s))$. Thus, if $s = 3$ for instance, $\mathbf{r}(t(3))$ is the position vector of the point 3 units of length along the curve from its starting point.

EXAMPLE 2 Reparametrize the helix $\mathbf{r}(t) = \cos t\,\mathbf{i} + \sin t\,\mathbf{j} + t\,\mathbf{k}$ with respect to arc length measured from $(1, 0, 0)$ in the direction of increasing t.

SOLUTION The initial point $(1, 0, 0)$ corresponds to the parameter value $t = 0$. From Example 1 we have

$$\frac{ds}{dt} = |\mathbf{r}'(t)| = \sqrt{2}$$

and so

$$s = s(t) = \int_0^t |\mathbf{r}'(u)|\,du = \int_0^t \sqrt{2}\,du = \sqrt{2}\,t$$

Therefore, $t = s/\sqrt{2}$ and the required reparametrization is obtained by substituting for t:

$$\mathbf{r}(t(s)) = \cos(s/\sqrt{2})\,\mathbf{i} + \sin(s/\sqrt{2})\,\mathbf{j} + (s/\sqrt{2})\,\mathbf{k}$$

||| Curvature

If C is a smooth curve defined by the vector function $\mathbf{r}$, then $\mathbf{r}'(t) \neq \mathbf{0}$. Recall that the unit tangent vector $\mathbf{T}(t)$ is given by

$$\mathbf{T}(t) = \frac{\mathbf{r}'(t)}{|\mathbf{r}'(t)|}$$

and indicates the direction of the curve. From Figure 4 you can see that $\mathbf{T}(t)$ changes direction very slowly when C is fairly straight, but it changes direction more quickly when C bends or twists more sharply.

The curvature of C at a given point is a measure of how quickly the curve changes direction at that point. Specifically, we define it to be the magnitude of the rate of change of the unit tangent vector with respect to arc length. (We use arc length so that the curvature will be independent of the parametrization.)

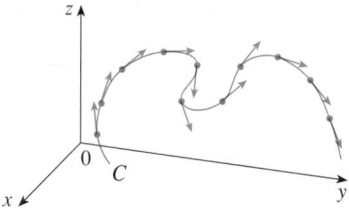

FIGURE 4

Unit tangent vectors at equally spaced points on C

Visual 14.3A shows animated unit tangent vectors, like those in Figure 4, for a variety of plane curves and space curves.

> **8** **Definition** The **curvature** of a curve is
>
> $$\kappa = \left|\frac{d\mathbf{T}}{ds}\right|$$
>
> where $\mathbf{T}$ is the unit tangent vector.

The curvature is easier to compute if it is expressed in terms of the parameter t instead of s, so we use the Chain Rule (Theorem 14.2.3, Formula 6) to write

$$\frac{d\mathbf{T}}{dt} = \frac{d\mathbf{T}}{ds}\frac{ds}{dt} \qquad \text{and} \qquad \kappa = \left|\frac{d\mathbf{T}}{ds}\right| = \left|\frac{d\mathbf{T}/dt}{ds/dt}\right|$$

But $ds/dt = |\mathbf{r}'(t)|$ from Equation 7, so

9
$$\kappa(t) = \frac{|\mathbf{T}'(t)|}{|\mathbf{r}'(t)|}$$

EXAMPLE 3 Show that the curvature of a circle of radius a is $1/a$.

SOLUTION We can take the circle to have center the origin, and then a parametrization is

$$\mathbf{r}(t) = a \cos t \, \mathbf{i} + a \sin t \, \mathbf{j}$$

Therefore $\qquad \mathbf{r}'(t) = -a \sin t \, \mathbf{i} + a \cos t \, \mathbf{j} \qquad$ and $\qquad |\mathbf{r}'(t)| = a$

so $$\mathbf{T}(t) = \frac{\mathbf{r}'(t)}{|\mathbf{r}'(t)|} = -\sin t \, \mathbf{i} + \cos t \, \mathbf{j}$$

and $$\mathbf{T}'(t) = -\cos t \, \mathbf{i} - \sin t \, \mathbf{j}$$

This gives $|\mathbf{T}'(t)| = 1$, so using Equation 9, we have

$$\kappa(t) = \frac{|\mathbf{T}'(t)|}{|\mathbf{r}'(t)|} = \frac{1}{a}$$

The result of Example 3 shows that small circles have large curvature and large circles have small curvature, in accordance with our intuition. We can see directly from the definition of curvature that the curvature of a straight line is always 0 because the tangent vector is constant.

Although Formula 9 can be used in all cases to compute the curvature, the formula given by the following theorem is often more convenient to apply.

---

10 Theorem The curvature of the curve given by the vector function $\mathbf{r}$ is

$$\kappa(t) = \frac{|\mathbf{r}'(t) \times \mathbf{r}''(t)|}{|\mathbf{r}'(t)|^3}$$

Proof Since $\mathbf{T} = \mathbf{r}'/|\mathbf{r}'|$ and $|\mathbf{r}'| = ds/dt$, we have

$$\mathbf{r}' = |\mathbf{r}'|\mathbf{T} = \frac{ds}{dt}\mathbf{T}$$

so the Product Rule (Theorem 14.2.3, Formula 3) gives

$$\mathbf{r}'' = \frac{d^2s}{dt^2}\mathbf{T} + \frac{ds}{dt}\mathbf{T}'$$

Using the fact that $\mathbf{T} \times \mathbf{T} = \mathbf{0}$ (see Example 2 in Section 13.4), we have

$$\mathbf{r}' \times \mathbf{r}'' = \left(\frac{ds}{dt}\right)^2 (\mathbf{T} \times \mathbf{T}')$$

Now $|\mathbf{T}(t)| = 1$ for all t, so $\mathbf{T}$ and $\mathbf{T}'$ are orthogonal by Example 5 in Section 14.2. Therefore, by Theorem 13.4.6,

$$|\mathbf{r}' \times \mathbf{r}''| = \left(\frac{ds}{dt}\right)^2 |\mathbf{T} \times \mathbf{T}'| = \left(\frac{ds}{dt}\right)^2 |\mathbf{T}||\mathbf{T}'| = \left(\frac{ds}{dt}\right)^2 |\mathbf{T}'|$$

Thus $$|\mathbf{T}'| = \frac{|\mathbf{r}' \times \mathbf{r}''|}{(ds/dt)^2} = \frac{|\mathbf{r}' \times \mathbf{r}''|}{|\mathbf{r}'|^2}$$

and $$\kappa = \frac{|\mathbf{T}'|}{|\mathbf{r}'|} = \frac{|\mathbf{r}' \times \mathbf{r}''|}{|\mathbf{r}'|^3}$$

EXAMPLE 4 Find the curvature of the twisted cubic $\mathbf{r}(t) = \langle t, t^2, t^3 \rangle$ at a general point and at $(0, 0, 0)$.

SOLUTION We first compute the required ingredients:

$$\mathbf{r}'(t) = \langle 1, 2t, 3t^2 \rangle \qquad \mathbf{r}''(t) = \langle 0, 2, 6t \rangle$$

$$|\mathbf{r}'(t)| = \sqrt{1 + 4t^2 + 9t^4}$$

$$\mathbf{r}'(t) \times \mathbf{r}''(t) = \begin{vmatrix} \mathbf{i} & \mathbf{j} & \mathbf{k} \\ 1 & 2t & 3t^2 \\ 0 & 2 & 6t \end{vmatrix} = 6t^2\,\mathbf{i} - 6t\,\mathbf{j} + 2\,\mathbf{k}$$

$$|\mathbf{r}'(t) \times \mathbf{r}''(t)| = \sqrt{36t^4 + 36t^2 + 4} = 2\sqrt{9t^4 + 9t^2 + 1}$$

Theorem 10 then gives

$$\kappa(t) = \frac{|\mathbf{r}'(t) \times \mathbf{r}''(t)|}{|\mathbf{r}'(t)|^3} = \frac{2\sqrt{1 + 9t^2 + 9t^4}}{(1 + 4t^2 + 9t^4)^{3/2}}$$

At the origin the curvature is $\kappa(0) = 2$.

For the special case of a plane curve with equation $y = f(x)$, we can choose x as the parameter and write $\mathbf{r}(x) = x\,\mathbf{i} + f(x)\,\mathbf{j}$. Then $\mathbf{r}'(x) = \mathbf{i} + f'(x)\,\mathbf{j}$ and $\mathbf{r}''(x) = f''(x)\,\mathbf{j}$. Since $\mathbf{i} \times \mathbf{j} = \mathbf{k}$ and $\mathbf{j} \times \mathbf{j} = \mathbf{0}$, we have $\mathbf{r}'(x) \times \mathbf{r}''(x) = f''(x)\,\mathbf{k}$. We also have $|\mathbf{r}'(x)| = \sqrt{1 + [f'(x)]^2}$ and so, by Theorem 10,

$$\boxed{11} \qquad \kappa(x) = \frac{|f''(x)|}{[1 + (f'(x))^2]^{3/2}}$$

EXAMPLE 5 Find the curvature of the parabola $y = x^2$ at the points $(0, 0)$, $(1, 1)$, and $(2, 4)$.

SOLUTION Since $y' = 2x$ and $y'' = 2$, Formula 11 gives

$$\kappa(x) = \frac{|y''|}{[1 + (y')^2]^{3/2}} = \frac{2}{(1 + 4x^2)^{3/2}}$$

The curvature at $(0, 0)$ is $\kappa(0) = 2$. At $(1, 1)$ it is $\kappa(1) = 2/5^{3/2} \approx 0.18$. At $(2, 4)$ it is $\kappa(2) = 2/17^{3/2} \approx 0.03$. Observe from the expression for $\kappa(x)$ or the graph of κ in Figure 5 that $\kappa(x) \to 0$ as $x \to \pm\infty$. This corresponds to the fact that the parabola appears to become flatter as $x \to \pm\infty$.

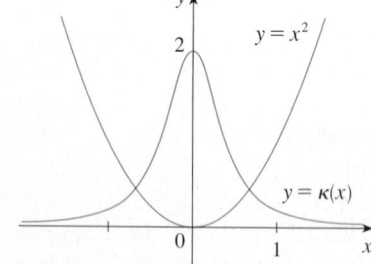

FIGURE 5

The parabola $y = x^2$ and its curvature function

The Normal and Binormal Vectors

At a given point on a smooth space curve $\mathbf{r}(t)$, there are many vectors that are orthogonal to the unit tangent vector $\mathbf{T}(t)$. We single out one by observing that, since $|\mathbf{T}(t)| = 1$ for all t, we have $\mathbf{T}(t) \cdot \mathbf{T}'(t) = 0$ by Example 5 in Section 14.2, so $\mathbf{T}'(t)$ is orthogonal to

‖ We can think of the normal vector as indicating the direction in which the curve is turning at each point.

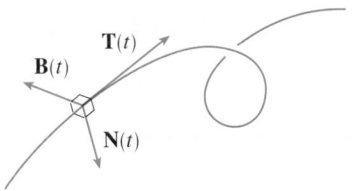

FIGURE 6

‖ Figure 7 illustrates Example 6 by showing the vectors **T**, **N**, and **B** at two locations on the helix. In general, the vectors **T**, **N**, and **B**, starting at the various points on a curve, form a set of orthogonal vectors, called the **TNB frame**, that moves along the curve as t varies. This **TNB** frame plays an important role in the branch of mathematics known as differential geometry and in its applications to the motion of spacecraft.

FIGURE 7

Visual 14.3B shows how the TNB frame moves along several curves.

$\mathbf{T}(t)$. Note that $\mathbf{T}'(t)$ is itself not a unit vector. But if $\mathbf{r}'$ is also smooth, we can define the **principal unit normal vector** $\mathbf{N}(t)$ (or simply **unit normal**) as

$$\mathbf{N}(t) = \frac{\mathbf{T}'(t)}{|\mathbf{T}'(t)|}$$

The vector $\mathbf{B}(t) = \mathbf{T}(t) \times \mathbf{N}(t)$ is called the **binormal vector**. It is perpendicular to both $\mathbf{T}$ and $\mathbf{N}$ and is also a unit vector. (See Figure 6.)

EXAMPLE 6 Find the unit normal and binormal vectors for the circular helix

$$\mathbf{r}(t) = \cos t\,\mathbf{i} + \sin t\,\mathbf{j} + t\,\mathbf{k}$$

SOLUTION We first compute the ingredients needed for the unit normal vector:

$$\mathbf{r}'(t) = -\sin t\,\mathbf{i} + \cos t\,\mathbf{j} + \mathbf{k} \qquad |\mathbf{r}'(t)| = \sqrt{2}$$

$$\mathbf{T}(t) = \frac{\mathbf{r}'(t)}{|\mathbf{r}'(t)|} = \frac{1}{\sqrt{2}}(-\sin t\,\mathbf{i} + \cos t\,\mathbf{j} + \mathbf{k})$$

$$\mathbf{T}'(t) = \frac{1}{\sqrt{2}}(-\cos t\,\mathbf{i} - \sin t\,\mathbf{j}) \qquad |\mathbf{T}'(t)| = \frac{1}{\sqrt{2}}$$

$$\mathbf{N}(t) = \frac{\mathbf{T}'(t)}{|\mathbf{T}'(t)|} = -\cos t\,\mathbf{i} - \sin t\,\mathbf{j} = \langle -\cos t, -\sin t, 0 \rangle$$

This shows that the normal vector at a point on the helix is horizontal and points toward the z-axis. The binormal vector is

$$\mathbf{B}(t) = \mathbf{T}(t) \times \mathbf{N}(t) = \frac{1}{\sqrt{2}}\begin{bmatrix} \mathbf{i} & \mathbf{j} & \mathbf{k} \\ -\sin t & \cos t & 1 \\ -\cos t & -\sin t & 0 \end{bmatrix} = \frac{1}{\sqrt{2}}\langle \sin t, -\cos t, 1 \rangle$$

The plane determined by the normal and binormal vectors $\mathbf{N}$ and $\mathbf{B}$ at a point P on a curve C is called the **normal plane** of C at P. It consists of all lines that are orthogonal to the tangent vector $\mathbf{T}$. The plane determined by the vectors $\mathbf{T}$ and $\mathbf{N}$ is called the **osculating plane** of C at P. The name comes from the Latin *osculum*, meaning "kiss." It is the plane that comes closest to containing the part of the curve near P. (For a plane curve, the osculating plane is simply the plane that contains the curve.)

The circle that lies in the osculating plane of C at P, has the same tangent as C at P, lies on the concave side of C (toward which $\mathbf{N}$ points), and has radius $\rho = 1/\kappa$ (the reciprocal of the curvature) is called the **osculating circle** (or the **circle of curvature**) of C at P. It is the circle that best describes how C behaves near P; it shares the same tangent, normal, and curvature at P.

EXAMPLE 7 Find the equations of the normal plane and osculating plane of the helix in Example 6 at the point $P(0, 1, \pi/2)$.

SOLUTION The normal plane at P has normal vector $\mathbf{r}'(\pi/2) = \langle -1, 0, 1 \rangle$, so an equation is

$$-1(x - 0) + 0(y - 1) + 1\left(z - \frac{\pi}{2}\right) = 0 \qquad \text{or} \qquad z = x + \frac{\pi}{2}$$

||| Figure 8 shows the helix and the osculating plane in Example 7.

FIGURE 8

FIGURE 9

 Visual 14.3C shows how the osculating circle changes as a point moves along a curve.

The osculating plane at P contains the vectors $\mathbf{T}$ and $\mathbf{N}$, so its normal vector is $\mathbf{T} \times \mathbf{N} = \mathbf{B}$. From Example 6 we have

$$\mathbf{B}(t) = \frac{1}{\sqrt{2}} \langle \sin t, -\cos t, 1 \rangle \qquad \mathbf{B}\left(\frac{\pi}{2}\right) = \left\langle \frac{1}{\sqrt{2}}, 0, \frac{1}{\sqrt{2}} \right\rangle$$

A simpler normal vector is $\langle 1, 0, 1 \rangle$, so an equation of the osculating plane is

$$1(x - 0) + 0(y - 1) + 1\left(z - \frac{\pi}{2}\right) = 0 \qquad \text{or} \qquad z = -x + \frac{\pi}{2}$$

EXAMPLE 8 Find and graph the osculating circle of the parabola $y = x^2$ at the origin.

SOLUTION From Example 5 the curvature of the parabola at the origin is $\kappa(0) = 2$. So the radius of the osculating circle at the origin is $1/\kappa = \frac{1}{2}$ and its center is $(0, \frac{1}{2})$. Its equation is therefore

$$x^2 + \left(y - \tfrac{1}{2}\right)^2 = \tfrac{1}{4}$$

For the graph in Figure 9 we use parametric equations of this circle:

$$x = \tfrac{1}{2} \cos t \qquad y = \tfrac{1}{2} + \tfrac{1}{2} \sin t$$

We summarize here the formulas for unit tangent, unit normal and binormal vectors, and curvature.

$$\mathbf{T}(t) = \frac{\mathbf{r}'(t)}{|\mathbf{r}'(t)|} \qquad \mathbf{N}(t) = \frac{\mathbf{T}'(t)}{|\mathbf{T}'(t)|} \qquad \mathbf{B}(t) = \mathbf{T}(t) \times \mathbf{N}(t)$$

$$\kappa = \left| \frac{d\mathbf{T}}{ds} \right| = \frac{|\mathbf{T}'(t)|}{|\mathbf{r}'(t)|} = \frac{|\mathbf{r}'(t) \times \mathbf{r}''(t)|}{|\mathbf{r}'(t)|^3}$$

||| 14.3 Exercises

1–6 ||| Find the length of the curve.

1. $\mathbf{r}(t) = \langle 2 \sin t, 5t, 2 \cos t \rangle, \quad -10 \le t \le 10$

2. $\mathbf{r}(t) = \langle t^2, \sin t - t \cos t, \cos t + t \sin t \rangle, \quad 0 \le t \le \pi$

3. $\mathbf{r}(t) = \sqrt{2}\,t\,\mathbf{i} + e^t\,\mathbf{j} + e^{-t}\,\mathbf{k}, \quad 0 \le t \le 1$

4. $\mathbf{r}(t) = t^2\,\mathbf{i} + 2t\,\mathbf{j} + \ln t\,\mathbf{k}, \quad 1 \le t \le e$

5. $\mathbf{r}(t) = \mathbf{i} + t^2\,\mathbf{j} + t^3\,\mathbf{k}, \quad 0 \le t \le 1$

6. $\mathbf{r}(t) = 12t\,\mathbf{i} + 8t^{3/2}\,\mathbf{j} + 3t^2\,\mathbf{k}, \quad 0 \le t \le 1$

7. Use Simpson's Rule with $n = 10$ to estimate the length of the arc of the twisted cubic $x = t$, $y = t^2$, $z = t^3$ from the origin to the point $(2, 4, 8)$.

8. Graph the curve with parametric equations $x = \cos t$, $y = \sin 3t$, $z = \sin t$. Find the total length of this curve correct to four decimal places.

9–11 ||| Reparametrize the curve with respect to arc length measured from the point where $t = 0$ in the direction of increasing t.

9. $\mathbf{r}(t) = 2t\,\mathbf{i} + (1 - 3t)\,\mathbf{j} + (5 + 4t)\,\mathbf{k}$

10. $\mathbf{r}(t) = e^{2t} \cos 2t\,\mathbf{i} + 2\,\mathbf{j} + e^{2t} \sin 2t\,\mathbf{k}$

11. $\mathbf{r}(t) = 3 \sin t\,\mathbf{i} + 4t\,\mathbf{j} + 3 \cos t\,\mathbf{k}$

12. Reparametrize the curve

$$\mathbf{r}(t) = \left(\frac{2}{t^2 + 1} - 1\right)\mathbf{i} + \frac{2t}{t^2 + 1}\,\mathbf{j}$$

with respect to arc length measured from the point $(1, 0)$ in the direction of increasing t. Express the reparametrization in its simplest form. What can you conclude about the curve?

13–16 ⅠⅠⅠⅠ
(a) Find the unit tangent and unit normal vectors $\mathbf{T}(t)$ and $\mathbf{N}(t)$.
(b) Use Formula 9 to find the curvature.

13. $\mathbf{r}(t) = \langle 2 \sin t, 5t, 2 \cos t \rangle$

14. $\mathbf{r}(t) = \langle t^2, \sin t - t \cos t, \cos t + t \sin t \rangle, \quad t > 0$

15. $\mathbf{r}(t) = \langle \sqrt{2}\,t, e^t, e^{-t} \rangle$ **16.** $\mathbf{r}(t) = \langle t^2, 2t, \ln t \rangle$

17–19 ⅠⅠⅠⅠ Use Theorem 10 to find the curvature.

17. $\mathbf{r}(t) = t^2\,\mathbf{i} + t\,\mathbf{k}$

18. $\mathbf{r}(t) = t\,\mathbf{i} + t\,\mathbf{j} + (1 + t^2)\,\mathbf{k}$

19. $\mathbf{r}(t) = 3t\,\mathbf{i} + 4 \sin t\,\mathbf{j} + 4 \cos t\,\mathbf{k}$

20. Find the curvature of $\mathbf{r}(t) = \langle e^t \cos t, e^t \sin t, t \rangle$ at the point $(1, 0, 0)$.

21. Find the curvature of $\mathbf{r}(t) = \langle t, t^2, t^3 \rangle$ at the point $(1, 1, 1)$.

22. Graph the curve with parametric equations

$$x = t \qquad y = 4t^{3/2} \qquad z = -t^2$$

and find the curvature at the point $(1, 4, -1)$.

23–25 ⅠⅠⅠⅠ Use Formula 11 to find the curvature.

23. $y = x^3$ **24.** $y = \cos x$ **25.** $y = 4x^{5/2}$

26–27 ⅠⅠⅠⅠ At what point does the curve have maximum curvature? What happens to the curvature as $x \to \infty$?

26. $y = \ln x$ **27.** $y = e^x$

28. Find an equation of a parabola that has curvature 4 at the origin.

29. (a) Is the curvature of the curve C shown in the figure greater at P or at Q? Explain.
(b) Estimate the curvature at P and at Q by sketching the osculating circles at those points.

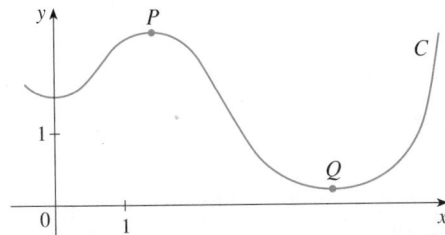

30–31 ⅠⅠⅠⅠ Use a graphing calculator or computer to graph both the curve and its curvature function $\kappa(x)$ on the same screen. Is the graph of κ what you would expect?

30. $y = xe^{-x}$ **31.** $y = x^4$

32–33 ⅠⅠⅠⅠ Two graphs, a and b, are shown. One is a curve $y = f(x)$ and the other is the graph of its curvature function $y = \kappa(x)$. Identify each curve and explain your choices.

32.

33.
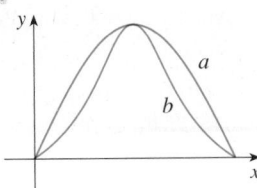

34. (a) Graph the curve $\mathbf{r}(t) = \langle \sin 3t, \sin 2t, \sin 3t \rangle$. At how many points on the curve does it appear that the curvature has a local or absolute maximum?
(b) Use a CAS to find and graph the curvature function. Does this graph confirm your conclusion from part (a)?

35. The graph of $\mathbf{r}(t) = \langle t - \frac{3}{2} \sin t, 1 - \frac{3}{2} \cos t, t \rangle$ is shown in Figure 12(b) in Section 14.1. Where do you think the curvature is largest? Use a CAS to find and graph the curvature function. For which values of t is the curvature largest?

36. Use Theorem 10 to show that the curvature of a plane parametric curve $x = f(t)$, $y = g(t)$ is

$$\kappa = \frac{|\dot{x}\ddot{y} - \dot{y}\ddot{x}|}{[\dot{x}^2 + \dot{y}^2]^{3/2}}$$

where the dots indicate derivatives with respect to t.

37–38 ⅠⅠⅠⅠ Use the formula in Exercise 36 to find the curvature.

37. $x = e^t \cos t, \quad y = e^t \sin t$

38. $x = 1 + t^3, \quad y = t + t^2$

39–40 ⅠⅠⅠⅠ Find the vectors $\mathbf{T}$, $\mathbf{N}$, and $\mathbf{B}$ at the given point.

39. $\mathbf{r}(t) = \langle t^2, \frac{2}{3}t^3, t \rangle, \quad (1, \frac{2}{3}, 1)$

40. $\mathbf{r}(t) = \langle e^t, e^t \sin t, e^t \cos t \rangle, \quad (1, 0, 1)$

41–42 ⅠⅠⅠⅠ Find equations of the normal plane and osculating plane of the curve at the given point.

41. $x = 2 \sin 3t, \ y = t, \ z = 2 \cos 3t; \quad (0, \pi, -2)$

42. $x = t, \ y = t^2, \ z = t^3; \quad (1, 1, 1)$

43. Find equations of the osculating circles of the ellipse $9x^2 + 4y^2 = 36$ at the points $(2, 0)$ and $(0, 3)$. Use a graphing calculator or computer to graph the ellipse and both osculating circles on the same screen.

44. Find equations of the osculating circles of the parabola $y = \frac{1}{2}x^2$ at the points $(0, 0)$ and $(1, \frac{1}{2})$. Graph both osculating circles and the parabola on the same screen.

45. At what point on the curve $x = t^3$, $y = 3t$, $z = t^4$ is the normal plane parallel to the plane $6x + 6y - 8z = 1$?

46. [CAS] Is there a point on the curve in Exercise 45 where the osculating plane is parallel to the plane $x + y + z = 1$? (*Note:* You will need a CAS for differentiating, for simplifying, and for computing a cross product.)

47. Show that the curvature κ is related to the tangent and normal vectors by the equation

$$\frac{d\mathbf{T}}{ds} = \kappa \mathbf{N}$$

48. Show that the curvature of a plane curve is $\kappa = |d\phi/ds|$, where ϕ is the angle between $\mathbf{T}$ and $\mathbf{i}$; that is, ϕ is the angle of inclination of the tangent line. (This shows that the definition of curvature is consistent with the definition for plane curves given in Exercise 69 in Section 11.2.)

49. (a) Show that $d\mathbf{B}/ds$ is perpendicular to $\mathbf{B}$.
(b) Show that $d\mathbf{B}/ds$ is perpendicular to $\mathbf{T}$.
(c) Deduce from parts (a) and (b) that $d\mathbf{B}/ds = -\tau(s)\mathbf{N}$ for some number $\tau(s)$ called the **torsion** of the curve. (The torsion measures the degree of twisting of a curve.)
(d) Show that for a plane curve the torsion is $\tau(s) = 0$.

50. The following formulas, called the **Frenet-Serret formulas**, are of fundamental importance in differential geometry:
1. $d\mathbf{T}/ds = \kappa \mathbf{N}$
2. $d\mathbf{N}/ds = -\kappa \mathbf{T} + \tau \mathbf{B}$
3. $d\mathbf{B}/ds = -\tau \mathbf{N}$
(Formula 1 comes from Exercise 47 and Formula 3 comes from Exercise 49.) Use the fact that $\mathbf{N} = \mathbf{B} \times \mathbf{T}$ to deduce Formula 2 from Formulas 1 and 3.

51. Use the Frenet-Serret formulas to prove each of the following. (Primes denote derivatives with respect to t. Start as in the proof of Theorem 10.)
(a) $\mathbf{r}'' = s''\mathbf{T} + \kappa(s')^2\mathbf{N}$

(b) $\mathbf{r}' \times \mathbf{r}'' = \kappa(s')^3\mathbf{B}$
(c) $\mathbf{r}''' = [s''' - \kappa^2(s')^3]\mathbf{T} + [3\kappa s's'' + \kappa'(s')^2]\mathbf{N} + \kappa\tau(s')^3\mathbf{B}$
(d) $\tau = \dfrac{(\mathbf{r}' \times \mathbf{r}'') \cdot \mathbf{r}'''}{|\mathbf{r}' \times \mathbf{r}''|^2}$

52. Show that the circular helix $\mathbf{r}(t) = \langle a \cos t, a \sin t, bt \rangle$, where a and b are positive constants, has constant curvature and constant torsion. [Use the result of Exercise 51(d).]

53. Use the formula in Exercise 51(d) to find the torsion of the curve $\mathbf{r}(t) = \langle t, \frac{1}{2}t^2, \frac{1}{3}t^3 \rangle$.

54. Find the curvature and torsion of the curve $x = \sinh t$, $y = \cosh t$, $z = t$ at the point $(0, 1, 0)$.

55. The DNA molecule has the shape of a double helix (see Figure 3 on page 887). The radius of each helix is about 10 angstroms ($1 \text{ Å} = 10^{-8}$ cm). Each helix rises about 34 Å during each complete turn, and there are about 2.9×10^8 complete turns. Estimate the length of each helix.

56. Let's consider the problem of designing a railroad track to make a smooth transition between sections of straight track. Existing track along the negative x-axis is to be joined smoothly to a track along the line $y = 1$ for $x \geq 1$.
(a) Find a polynomial $P = P(x)$ of degree 5 such that the function F defined by

$$F(x) = \begin{cases} 0 & \text{if } x \leq 0 \\ P(x) & \text{if } 0 < x < 1 \\ 1 & \text{if } x \geq 1 \end{cases}$$

is continuous and has continuous slope and continuous curvature.
(b) Use a graphing calculator or computer to draw the graph of F.

14.4 Motion in Space: Velocity and Acceleration

In this section we show how the ideas of tangent and normal vectors and curvature can be used in physics to study the motion of an object, including its velocity and acceleration, along a space curve. In particular, we follow in the footsteps of Newton by using these methods to derive Kepler's First Law of planetary motion.

Suppose a particle moves through space so that its position vector at time t is $\mathbf{r}(t)$. Notice from Figure 1 that, for small values of h, the vector

$$\boxed{1} \qquad \frac{\mathbf{r}(t + h) - \mathbf{r}(t)}{h}$$

FIGURE 1

approximates the direction of the particle moving along the curve $\mathbf{r}(t)$. Its magnitude measures the size of the displacement vector per unit time. The vector (1) gives the average velocity over a time interval of length h and its limit is the **velocity vector** $\mathbf{v}(t)$ at time t:

$$\boxed{2} \qquad \mathbf{v}(t) = \lim_{h \to 0} \frac{\mathbf{r}(t + h) - \mathbf{r}(t)}{h} = \mathbf{r}'(t)$$

Thus, the velocity vector is also the tangent vector and points in the direction of the tangent line.

The **speed** of the particle at time t is the magnitude of the velocity vector, that is, $|\mathbf{v}(t)|$. This is appropriate because, from (2) and from Equation 14.3.7, we have

$$|\mathbf{v}(t)| = |\mathbf{r}'(t)| = \frac{ds}{dt} = \text{rate of change of distance with respect to time}$$

As in the case of one-dimensional motion, the **acceleration** of the particle is defined as the derivative of the velocity:

$$\mathbf{a}(t) = \mathbf{v}'(t) = \mathbf{r}''(t)$$

EXAMPLE 1 The position vector of an object moving in a plane is given by $\mathbf{r}(t) = t^3\,\mathbf{i} + t^2\,\mathbf{j}$. Find its velocity, speed, and acceleration when $t = 1$ and illustrate geometrically.

SOLUTION The velocity and acceleration at time t are

$$\mathbf{v}(t) = \mathbf{r}'(t) = 3t^2\,\mathbf{i} + 2t\,\mathbf{j}$$

$$\mathbf{a}(t) = \mathbf{r}''(t) = 6t\,\mathbf{i} + 2\,\mathbf{j}$$

and the speed is

$$|\mathbf{v}(t)| = \sqrt{(3t^2)^2 + (2t)^2} = \sqrt{9t^4 + 4t^2}$$

When $t = 1$, we have

$$\mathbf{v}(1) = 3\,\mathbf{i} + 2\,\mathbf{j} \qquad \mathbf{a}(1) = 6\,\mathbf{i} + 2\,\mathbf{j} \qquad |\mathbf{v}(1)| = \sqrt{13}$$

These velocity and acceleration vectors are shown in Figure 2.

EXAMPLE 2 Find the velocity, acceleration, and speed of a particle with position vector $\mathbf{r}(t) = \langle t^2, e^t, te^t \rangle$.

SOLUTION

$$\mathbf{v}(t) = \mathbf{r}'(t) = \langle 2t, e^t, (1 + t)e^t \rangle$$

$$\mathbf{a}(t) = \mathbf{v}'(t) = \langle 2, e^t, (2 + t)e^t \rangle$$

$$|\mathbf{v}(t)| = \sqrt{4t^2 + e^{2t} + (1 + t)^2 e^{2t}}$$

The vector integrals that were introduced in Section 14.2 can be used to find position vectors when velocity or acceleration vectors are known, as in the following example.

FIGURE 2

Visual 14.4 shows animated velocity and acceleration vectors for objects moving along various curves.

⫿ Figure 3 shows the path of the particle in Example 2 with the velocity and acceleration vectors when $t = 1$.

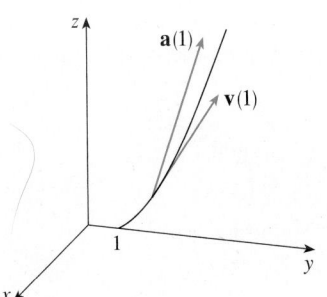

FIGURE 3

EXAMPLE 3 A moving particle starts at an initial position $\mathbf{r}(0) = \langle 1, 0, 0 \rangle$ with initial velocity $\mathbf{v}(0) = \mathbf{i} - \mathbf{j} + \mathbf{k}$. Its acceleration is $\mathbf{a}(t) = 4t\,\mathbf{i} + 6t\,\mathbf{j} + \mathbf{k}$. Find its velocity and position at time t.

SOLUTION Since $\mathbf{a}(t) = \mathbf{v}'(t)$, we have

$$\mathbf{v}(t) = \int \mathbf{a}(t)\,dt = \int (4t\,\mathbf{i} + 6t\,\mathbf{j} + \mathbf{k})\,dt$$

$$= 2t^2\,\mathbf{i} + 3t^2\,\mathbf{j} + t\,\mathbf{k} + \mathbf{C}$$

To determine the value of the constant vector $\mathbf{C}$, we use the fact that $\mathbf{v}(0) = \mathbf{i} - \mathbf{j} + \mathbf{k}$. The preceding equation gives $\mathbf{v}(0) = \mathbf{C}$, so $\mathbf{C} = \mathbf{i} - \mathbf{j} + \mathbf{k}$ and

$$\mathbf{v}(t) = 2t^2\,\mathbf{i} + 3t^2\,\mathbf{j} + t\,\mathbf{k} + \mathbf{i} - \mathbf{j} + \mathbf{k}$$

$$= (2t^2 + 1)\,\mathbf{i} + (3t^2 - 1)\,\mathbf{j} + (t + 1)\,\mathbf{k}$$

▐▐▐ The expression for $\mathbf{r}(t)$ that we obtained in Example 3 was used to plot the path of the particle in Figure 4 for $0 \leq t \leq 3$.

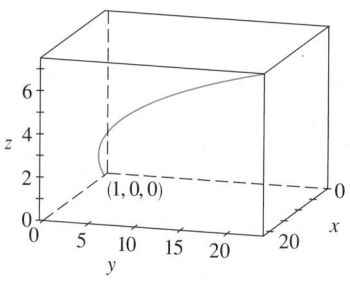

FIGURE 4

Since $\mathbf{v}(t) = \mathbf{r}'(t)$, we have

$$\mathbf{r}(t) = \int \mathbf{v}(t)\,dt$$

$$= \int \left[(2t^2 + 1)\,\mathbf{i} + (3t^2 - 1)\,\mathbf{j} + (t + 1)\,\mathbf{k} \right] dt$$

$$= \left(\tfrac{2}{3}t^3 + t \right)\mathbf{i} + (t^3 - t)\,\mathbf{j} + \left(\tfrac{1}{2}t^2 + t \right)\mathbf{k} + \mathbf{D}$$

Putting $t = 0$, we find that $\mathbf{D} = \mathbf{r}(0) = \mathbf{i}$, so

$$\mathbf{r}(t) = \left(\tfrac{2}{3}t^3 + t + 1 \right)\mathbf{i} + (t^3 - t)\,\mathbf{j} + \left(\tfrac{1}{2}t^2 + t \right)\mathbf{k}$$

In general, vector integrals allow us to recover velocity when acceleration is known and position when velocity is known:

$$\mathbf{v}(t) = \mathbf{v}(t_0) + \int_{t_0}^{t} \mathbf{a}(u)\,du \qquad \mathbf{r}(t) = \mathbf{r}(t_0) + \int_{t_0}^{t} \mathbf{v}(u)\,du$$

If the force that acts on a particle is known, then the acceleration can be found from **Newton's Second Law of Motion**. The vector version of this law states that if, at any time t, a force $\mathbf{F}(t)$ acts on an object of mass m producing an acceleration $\mathbf{a}(t)$, then

$$\mathbf{F}(t) = m\mathbf{a}(t)$$

▐▐▐ The angular speed of the object moving with position P is $\omega = d\theta/dt$, where θ is the angle shown in Figure 5.

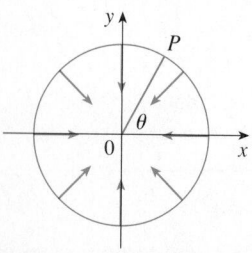

FIGURE 5

EXAMPLE 4 An object with mass m that moves in a circular path with constant angular speed ω has position vector $\mathbf{r}(t) = a \cos \omega t\,\mathbf{i} + a \sin \omega t\,\mathbf{j}$. Find the force acting on the object and show that it is directed toward the origin.

SOLUTION
$$\mathbf{v}(t) = \mathbf{r}'(t) = -a\omega \sin \omega t\,\mathbf{i} + a\omega \cos \omega t\,\mathbf{j}$$

$$\mathbf{a}(t) = \mathbf{v}'(t) = -a\omega^2 \cos \omega t\,\mathbf{i} - a\omega^2 \sin \omega t\,\mathbf{j}$$

Therefore, Newton's Second Law gives the force as

$$\mathbf{F}(t) = m\mathbf{a}(t) = -m\omega^2(a \cos \omega t\,\mathbf{i} + a \sin \omega t\,\mathbf{j})$$

Notice that $\mathbf{F}(t) = -m\omega^2\mathbf{r}(t)$. This shows that the force acts in the direction opposite to the radius vector $\mathbf{r}(t)$ and therefore points toward the origin (see Figure 5). Such a force is called a *centripetal* (center-seeking) force.

EXAMPLE 5 A projectile is fired with angle of elevation α and initial velocity $\mathbf{v}_0$. (See Figure 6.) Assuming that air resistance is negligible and the only external force is due to gravity, find the position function $\mathbf{r}(t)$ of the projectile. What value of α maximizes the range (the horizontal distance traveled)?

SOLUTION We set up the axes so that the projectile starts at the origin. Since the force due to gravity acts downward, we have

$$\mathbf{F} = m\mathbf{a} = -mg\,\mathbf{j}$$

where $g = |\mathbf{a}| \approx 9.8$ m/s^2. Thus

$$\mathbf{a} = -g\,\mathbf{j}$$

Since $\mathbf{v}'(t) = \mathbf{a}$, we have

$$\mathbf{v}(t) = -gt\,\mathbf{j} + \mathbf{C}$$

where $\mathbf{C} = \mathbf{v}(0) = \mathbf{v}_0$. Therefore

$$\mathbf{r}'(t) = \mathbf{v}(t) = -gt\,\mathbf{j} + \mathbf{v}_0$$

Integrating again, we obtain

$$\mathbf{r}(t) = -\tfrac{1}{2}gt^2\,\mathbf{j} + t\,\mathbf{v}_0 + \mathbf{D}$$

But $\mathbf{D} = \mathbf{r}(0) = \mathbf{0}$, so the position vector of the projectile is given by

$$\boxed{3} \qquad \mathbf{r}(t) = -\tfrac{1}{2}gt^2\,\mathbf{j} + t\,\mathbf{v}_0$$

If we write $|\mathbf{v}_0| = v_0$ (the initial speed of the projectile), then

$$\mathbf{v}_0 = v_0\cos\alpha\,\mathbf{i} + v_0\sin\alpha\,\mathbf{j}$$

and Equation 3 becomes

$$\mathbf{r}(t) = (v_0\cos\alpha)t\,\mathbf{i} + \left[(v_0\sin\alpha)t - \tfrac{1}{2}gt^2\right]\mathbf{j}$$

The parametric equations of the trajectory are therefore

||| If you eliminate t from Equations 4, you will see that y is a quadratic function of x. So the path of the projectile is part of a parabola.

$$\boxed{4} \qquad x = (v_0\cos\alpha)t \qquad y = (v_0\sin\alpha)t - \tfrac{1}{2}gt^2$$

The horizontal distance d is the value of x when $y = 0$. Setting $y = 0$, we obtain $t = 0$ or $t = (2v_0\sin\alpha)/g$. The latter value of t then gives

$$d = x = (v_0\cos\alpha)\frac{2v_0\sin\alpha}{g} = \frac{v_0^2(2\sin\alpha\cos\alpha)}{g} = \frac{v_0^2\sin 2\alpha}{g}$$

Clearly, d has its maximum value when $\sin 2\alpha = 1$, that is, $\alpha = \pi/4$.

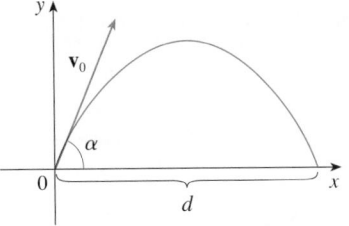

FIGURE 6

EXAMPLE 6 A projectile is fired with muzzle speed 150 m/s and angle of elevation 45° from a position 10 m above ground level. Where does the projectile hit the ground, and with what speed?

SOLUTION If we place the origin at ground level, then the initial position of the projectile is (0, 10) and so we need to adjust Equations 4 by adding 10 to the expression for y. With $v_0 = 150$ m/s, $\alpha = 45°$, and $g = 9.8$ m/s^2, we have

$$x = 150 \cos(\pi/4)t = 75\sqrt{2}\,t$$

$$y = 10 + 150 \sin(\pi/4)t - \tfrac{1}{2}(9.8)t^2 = 10 + 75\sqrt{2}\,t - 4.9t^2$$

Impact occurs when $y = 0$, that is, $4.9t^2 - 75\sqrt{2}\,t - 10 = 0$. Solving this quadratic equation (and using only the positive value of t), we get

$$t = \frac{75\sqrt{2} + \sqrt{11{,}250 + 196}}{9.8} \approx 21.74$$

Then $x \approx 75\sqrt{2}\,(21.74) \approx 2306$, so the projectile hits the ground about 2306 m away.

The velocity of the projectile is

$$\mathbf{v}(t) = \mathbf{r}'(t) = 75\sqrt{2}\,\mathbf{i} + \left(75\sqrt{2} - 9.8t\right)\mathbf{j}$$

So its speed at impact is

$$|\mathbf{v}(21.74)| = \sqrt{(75\sqrt{2})^2 + (75\sqrt{2} - 9.8 \cdot 21.74)^2} \approx 151 \text{ m/s}$$

‖ Tangential and Normal Components of Acceleration

When we study the motion of a particle, it is often useful to resolve the acceleration into two components, one in the direction of the tangent and the other in the direction of the normal. If we write $v = |\mathbf{v}|$ for the speed of the particle, then

$$\mathbf{T}(t) = \frac{\mathbf{r}'(t)}{|\mathbf{r}'(t)|} = \frac{\mathbf{v}(t)}{|\mathbf{v}(t)|} = \frac{\mathbf{v}}{v}$$

and so

$$\mathbf{v} = v\mathbf{T}$$

If we differentiate both sides of this equation with respect to t, we get

$$\boxed{5} \qquad \mathbf{a} = \mathbf{v}' = v'\mathbf{T} + v\mathbf{T}'$$

If we use the expression for the curvature given by Equation 14.3.9, then we have

$$\boxed{6} \qquad \kappa = \frac{|\mathbf{T}'|}{|\mathbf{r}'|} = \frac{|\mathbf{T}'|}{v} \qquad \text{so} \qquad |\mathbf{T}'| = \kappa v$$

The unit normal vector was defined in the preceding section as $\mathbf{N} = \mathbf{T}'/|\mathbf{T}'|$, so (6) gives

$$\mathbf{T}' = |\mathbf{T}'|\mathbf{N} = \kappa v\mathbf{N}$$

and Equation 5 becomes

$$\boxed{7} \qquad \mathbf{a} = v'\mathbf{T} + \kappa v^2 \mathbf{N}$$

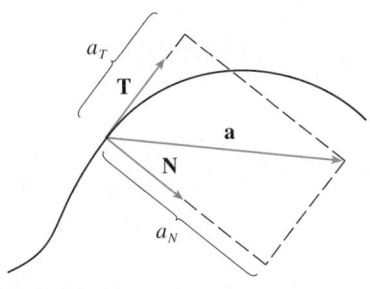

FIGURE 7

Writing a_T and a_N for the tangential and normal components of acceleration, we have

$$\mathbf{a} = a_T \mathbf{T} + a_N \mathbf{N}$$

where

$$\boxed{8} \qquad a_T = v' \qquad \text{and} \qquad a_N = \kappa v^2$$

This resolution is illustrated in Figure 7.

Let's look at what Formula 7 says. The first thing to notice is that the binormal vector **B** is absent. No matter how an object moves through space, its acceleration always lies in the plane of **T** and **N** (the osculating plane). (Recall that **T** gives the direction of motion and **N** points in the direction the curve is turning.) Next we notice that the tangential component of acceleration is v', the rate of change of speed, and the normal component of acceleration is κv^2, the curvature times the square of the speed. This makes sense if we think of a passenger in a car—a sharp turn in a road means a large value of the curvature κ, so the component of the acceleration perpendicular to the motion is large and the passenger is thrown against a car door. High speed around the turn has the same effect; in fact, if you double your speed, a_N is increased by a factor of 4.

Although we have expressions for the tangential and normal components of acceleration in Equations 8, it's desirable to have expressions that depend only on **r**, **r′**, and **r″**. To this end we take the dot product of $\mathbf{v} = v\mathbf{T}$ with **a** as given by Equation 7:

$$\mathbf{v} \cdot \mathbf{a} = v\mathbf{T} \cdot (v'\mathbf{T} + \kappa v^2 \mathbf{N})$$

$$= vv'\mathbf{T} \cdot \mathbf{T} + \kappa v^3 \mathbf{T} \cdot \mathbf{N}$$

$$= vv' \qquad\qquad \text{(since } \mathbf{T} \cdot \mathbf{T} = 1 \text{ and } \mathbf{T} \cdot \mathbf{N} = 0 \text{)}$$

Therefore

$$\boxed{9} \qquad a_T = v' = \frac{\mathbf{v} \cdot \mathbf{a}}{v} = \frac{\mathbf{r}'(t) \cdot \mathbf{r}''(t)}{|\mathbf{r}'(t)|}$$

Using the formula for curvature given by Theorem 14.3.10, we have

$$\boxed{10} \qquad a_N = \kappa v^2 = \frac{|\mathbf{r}'(t) \times \mathbf{r}''(t)|}{|\mathbf{r}'(t)|^3} |\mathbf{r}'(t)|^2 = \frac{|\mathbf{r}'(t) \times \mathbf{r}''(t)|}{|\mathbf{r}'(t)|}$$

EXAMPLE 7 A particle moves with position function $\mathbf{r}(t) = \langle t^2, t^2, t^3 \rangle$. Find the tangential and normal components of acceleration.

SOLUTION

$$\mathbf{r}(t) = t^2 \mathbf{i} + t^2 \mathbf{j} + t^3 \mathbf{k}$$

$$\mathbf{r}'(t) = 2t \mathbf{i} + 2t \mathbf{j} + 3t^2 \mathbf{k}$$

$$\mathbf{r}''(t) = 2 \mathbf{i} + 2 \mathbf{j} + 6t \mathbf{k}$$

$$|\mathbf{r}'(t)| = \sqrt{8t^2 + 9t^4}$$

Therefore, Equation 9 gives the tangential component as

$$a_T = \frac{\mathbf{r}'(t) \cdot \mathbf{r}''(t)}{|\mathbf{r}'(t)|} = \frac{8t + 18t^3}{\sqrt{8t^2 + 9t^4}}$$

Since
$$\mathbf{r}'(t) \times \mathbf{r}''(t) = \begin{vmatrix} \mathbf{i} & \mathbf{j} & \mathbf{k} \\ 2t & 2t & 3t^2 \\ 2 & 2 & 6t \end{vmatrix} = 6t^2\,\mathbf{i} - 6t^2\,\mathbf{j}$$

Equation 10 gives the normal component as

$$a_N = \frac{|\,\mathbf{r}'(t) \times \mathbf{r}''(t)\,|}{|\,\mathbf{r}'(t)\,|} = \frac{6\sqrt{2}\,t^2}{\sqrt{8t^2 + 9t^4}}$$

‖ Kepler's Laws of Planetary Motion

We now describe one of the great accomplishments of calculus by showing how the material of this chapter can be used to prove Kepler's laws of planetary motion. After 20 years of studying the astronomical observations of the Danish astronomer Tycho Brahe, the German mathematician and astronomer Johannes Kepler (1571–1630) formulated the following three laws.

> **Kepler's Laws**
>
> 1. A planet revolves around the Sun in an elliptical orbit with the Sun at one focus.
> 2. The line joining the Sun to a planet sweeps out equal areas in equal times.
> 3. The square of the period of revolution of a planet is proportional to the cube of the length of the major axis of its orbit.

In his book *Principia Mathematica* of 1687, Sir Isaac Newton was able to show that these three laws are consequences of two of his own laws, the Second Law of Motion and the Law of Universal Gravitation. In what follows we prove Kepler's First Law. The remaining laws are left as exercises (with hints).

Since the gravitational force of the Sun on a planet is so much larger than the forces exerted by other celestial bodies, we can safely ignore all bodies in the universe except the Sun and one planet revolving about it. We use a coordinate system with the Sun at the origin and we let $\mathbf{r} = \mathbf{r}(t)$ be the position vector of the planet. (Equally well, $\mathbf{r}$ could be the position vector of the Moon or a satellite moving around the Earth or a comet moving around a star.) The velocity vector is $\mathbf{v} = \mathbf{r}'$ and the acceleration vector is $\mathbf{a} = \mathbf{r}''$. We use the following laws of Newton:

$$\text{Second Law of Motion:} \quad \mathbf{F} = m\mathbf{a}$$

$$\text{Law of Gravitation:} \quad \mathbf{F} = -\frac{GMm}{r^3}\,\mathbf{r} = -\frac{GMm}{r^2}\,\mathbf{u}$$

where $\mathbf{F}$ is the gravitational force on the planet, m and M are the masses of the planet and the Sun, G is the gravitational constant, $r = |\mathbf{r}|$, and $\mathbf{u} = (1/r)\mathbf{r}$ is the unit vector in the direction of $\mathbf{r}$.

We first show that the planet moves in one plane. By equating the expressions for $\mathbf{F}$ in Newton's two laws, we find that

$$\mathbf{a} = -\frac{GM}{r^3}\,\mathbf{r}$$

and so **a** is parallel to **r**. It follows that $\mathbf{r} \times \mathbf{a} = \mathbf{0}$. We use Formula 5 in Theorem 14.2.3 to write

$$\frac{d}{dt}(\mathbf{r} \times \mathbf{v}) = \mathbf{r}' \times \mathbf{v} + \mathbf{r} \times \mathbf{v}'$$

$$= \mathbf{v} \times \mathbf{v} + \mathbf{r} \times \mathbf{a} = \mathbf{0} + \mathbf{0} = \mathbf{0}$$

Therefore
$$\mathbf{r} \times \mathbf{v} = \mathbf{h}$$

where **h** is a constant vector. (We may assume that $\mathbf{h} \neq \mathbf{0}$; that is, **r** and **v** are not parallel.) This means that the vector $\mathbf{r} = \mathbf{r}(t)$ is perpendicular to **h** for all values of t, so the planet always lies in the plane through the origin perpendicular to **h**. Thus, the orbit of the planet is a plane curve.

To prove Kepler's First Law we rewrite the vector **h** as follows:

$$\mathbf{h} = \mathbf{r} \times \mathbf{v} = \mathbf{r} \times \mathbf{r}' = r\mathbf{u} \times (r\mathbf{u})'$$

$$= r\mathbf{u} \times (r\mathbf{u}' + r'\mathbf{u}) = r^2(\mathbf{u} \times \mathbf{u}') + rr'(\mathbf{u} \times \mathbf{u})$$

$$= r^2(\mathbf{u} \times \mathbf{u}')$$

Then

$$\mathbf{a} \times \mathbf{h} = \frac{-GM}{r^2}\mathbf{u} \times (r^2\mathbf{u} \times \mathbf{u}') = -GM\,\mathbf{u} \times (\mathbf{u} \times \mathbf{u}')$$

$$= -GM[(\mathbf{u} \cdot \mathbf{u}')\mathbf{u} - (\mathbf{u} \cdot \mathbf{u})\mathbf{u}'] \qquad \text{(by Theorem 13.4.8, Property 6)}$$

But $\mathbf{u} \cdot \mathbf{u} = |\mathbf{u}|^2 = 1$ and, since $|\mathbf{u}(t)| = 1$, it follows from Example 5 in Section 14.2 that $\mathbf{u} \cdot \mathbf{u}' = 0$. Therefore

$$\mathbf{a} \times \mathbf{h} = GM\,\mathbf{u}'$$

and so
$$(\mathbf{v} \times \mathbf{h})' = \mathbf{v}' \times \mathbf{h} = \mathbf{a} \times \mathbf{h} = GM\,\mathbf{u}'$$

Integrating both sides of this equation, we get

$$\boxed{11} \qquad \mathbf{v} \times \mathbf{h} = GM\,\mathbf{u} + \mathbf{c}$$

where **c** is a constant vector.

At this point it is convenient to choose the coordinate axes so that the standard basis vector **k** points in the direction of the vector **h**. Then the planet moves in the xy-plane. Since both $\mathbf{v} \times \mathbf{h}$ and **u** are perpendicular to **h**, Equation 11 shows that **c** lies in the xy-plane. This means that we can choose the x- and y-axes so that the vector **i** lies in the direction of **c**, as shown in Figure 8.

If θ is the angle between **c** and **r**, then (r, θ) are polar coordinates of the planet. From Equation 11 we have

$$\mathbf{r} \cdot (\mathbf{v} \times \mathbf{h}) = \mathbf{r} \cdot (GM\,\mathbf{u} + \mathbf{c}) = GM\,\mathbf{r} \cdot \mathbf{u} + \mathbf{r} \cdot \mathbf{c}$$

$$= GMr\,\mathbf{u} \cdot \mathbf{u} + |\mathbf{r}||\mathbf{c}|\cos\theta = GMr + rc\cos\theta$$

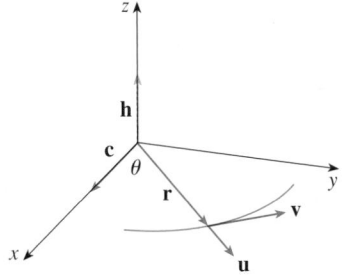

FIGURE 8

where $c = |\mathbf{c}|$. Then

$$r = \frac{\mathbf{r} \cdot (\mathbf{v} \times \mathbf{h})}{GM + c \cos \theta} = \frac{1}{GM} \frac{\mathbf{r} \cdot (\mathbf{v} \times \mathbf{h})}{1 + e \cos \theta}$$

where $e = c/(GM)$. But

$$\mathbf{r} \cdot (\mathbf{v} \times \mathbf{h}) = (\mathbf{r} \times \mathbf{v}) \cdot \mathbf{h} = \mathbf{h} \cdot \mathbf{h} = |\mathbf{h}|^2 = h^2$$

where $h = |\mathbf{h}|$. So

$$r = \frac{h^2/(GM)}{1 + e \cos \theta} = \frac{eh^2/c}{1 + e \cos \theta}$$

Writing $d = h^2/c$, we obtain the equation

[12]
$$r = \frac{ed}{1 + e \cos \theta}$$

Comparing with Theorem 11.6.6, we see that Equation 12 is the polar equation of a conic section with focus at the origin and eccentricity e. We know that the orbit of a planet is a closed curve and so the conic must be an ellipse.

This completes the derivation of Kepler's First Law. We will guide you through the derivation of the Second and Third Laws in the Applied Project on page 916. The proofs of these three laws show that the methods of this chapter provide a powerful tool for describing some of the laws of nature.

14.4 Exercises

1. The table gives coordinates of a particle moving through space along a smooth curve.
   (a) Find the average velocities over the time intervals [0, 1], [0.5, 1], [1, 2], and [1, 1.5].
   (b) Estimate the velocity and speed of the particle at $t = 1$.

t	x	y	z
0	2.7	9.8	3.7
0.5	3.5	7.2	3.3
1.0	4.5	6.0	3.0
1.5	5.9	6.4	2.8
2.0	7.3	7.8	2.7

2. The figure shows the path of a particle that moves with position vector $\mathbf{r}(t)$ at time t.
   (a) Draw a vector that represents the average velocity of the particle over the time interval $2 \le t \le 2.4$.
   (b) Draw a vector that represents the average velocity over the time interval $1.5 \le t \le 2$.
   (c) Write an expression for the velocity vector $\mathbf{v}(2)$.

   (d) Draw an approximation to the vector $\mathbf{v}(2)$ and estimate the speed of the particle at $t = 2$.

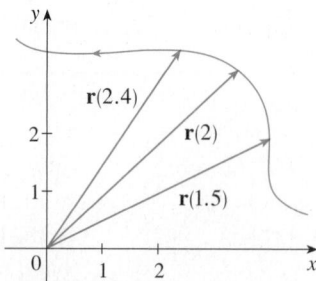

3–8 |||| Find the velocity, acceleration, and speed of a particle with the given position function. Sketch the path of the particle and draw the velocity and acceleration vectors for the specified value of t.

3. $\mathbf{r}(t) = \langle t^2 - 1, t \rangle$, $\quad t = 1$

4. $\mathbf{r}(t) = \langle 2 - t, 4\sqrt{t} \rangle$, $\quad t = 1$

5. $\mathbf{r}(t) = e^t \mathbf{i} + e^{-t} \mathbf{j}$, $\quad t = 0$

6. $\mathbf{r}(t) = \sin t\,\mathbf{i} + 2\cos t\,\mathbf{j}, \quad t = \pi/6$

7. $\mathbf{r}(t) = \sin t\,\mathbf{i} + t\,\mathbf{j} + \cos t\,\mathbf{k}, \quad t = 0$

8. $\mathbf{r}(t) = t\,\mathbf{i} + t^2\,\mathbf{j} + t^3\,\mathbf{k}, \quad t = 1$

9–14 ▨ Find the velocity, acceleration, and speed of a particle with the given position function.

9. $\mathbf{r}(t) = \langle t^2 + 1, t^3, t^2 - 1 \rangle$

10. $\mathbf{r}(t) = \langle 2\cos t, 3t, 2\sin t \rangle$

11. $\mathbf{r}(t) = \sqrt{2}\,t\,\mathbf{i} + e^t\,\mathbf{j} + e^{-t}\,\mathbf{k}$

12. $\mathbf{r}(t) = t^2\,\mathbf{i} + \ln t\,\mathbf{j} + t\,\mathbf{k}$

13. $\mathbf{r}(t) = e^t(\cos t\,\mathbf{i} + \sin t\,\mathbf{j} + t\,\mathbf{k})$

14. $\mathbf{r}(t) = t\sin t\,\mathbf{i} + t\cos t\,\mathbf{j} + t^2\,\mathbf{k}$

15–16 ▨ Find the velocity and position vectors of a particle that has the given acceleration and the given initial velocity and position.

15. $\mathbf{a}(t) = \mathbf{k}, \quad \mathbf{v}(0) = \mathbf{i} - \mathbf{j}, \quad \mathbf{r}(0) = \mathbf{0}$

16. $\mathbf{a}(t) = -10\,\mathbf{k}, \quad \mathbf{v}(0) = \mathbf{i} + \mathbf{j} - \mathbf{k}, \quad \mathbf{r}(0) = 2\,\mathbf{i} + 3\,\mathbf{j}$

17–18 ▨

(a) Find the position vector of a particle that has the given acceleration and the specified initial velocity and position.

(b) Use a computer to graph the path of the particle.

17. $\mathbf{a}(t) = \mathbf{i} + 2\,\mathbf{j} + 2t\,\mathbf{k}, \quad \mathbf{v}(0) = \mathbf{0}, \quad \mathbf{r}(0) = \mathbf{i} + \mathbf{k}$

18. $\mathbf{a}(t) = t\,\mathbf{i} + t^2\,\mathbf{j} + \cos 2t\,\mathbf{k}, \quad \mathbf{v}(0) = \mathbf{i} + \mathbf{k}, \quad \mathbf{r}(0) = \mathbf{j}$

19. The position function of a particle is given by $\mathbf{r}(t) = \langle t^2, 5t, t^2 - 16t \rangle$. When is the speed a minimum?

20. What force is required so that a particle of mass m has the position function $\mathbf{r}(t) = t^3\,\mathbf{i} + t^2\,\mathbf{j} + t^3\,\mathbf{k}$?

21. A force with magnitude 20 N acts directly upward from the xy-plane on an object with mass 4 kg. The object starts at the origin with initial velocity $\mathbf{v}(0) = \mathbf{i} - \mathbf{j}$. Find its position function and its speed at time t.

22. Show that if a particle moves with constant speed, then the velocity and acceleration vectors are orthogonal.

23. A projectile is fired with an initial speed of 500 m/s and angle of elevation 30°. Find (a) the range of the projectile, (b) the maximum height reached, and (c) the speed at impact.

24. Rework Exercise 23 if the projectile is fired from a position 200 m above the ground.

25. A ball is thrown at an angle of 45° to the ground. If the ball lands 90 m away, what was the initial speed of the ball?

26. A gun is fired with angle of elevation 30°. What is the muzzle speed if the maximum height of the shell is 500 m?

27. A gun has muzzle speed 150 m/s. Find two angles of elevation that can be used to hit a target 800 m away.

28. A batter hits a baseball 3 ft above the ground toward the center field fence, which is 10 ft high and 400 ft from home plate. The ball leaves the bat with speed 115 ft/s at an angle 50° above the horizontal. Is it a home run? (In other words, does the ball clear the fence?)

29. Water traveling along a straight portion of a river normally flows fastest in the middle, and the speed slows to almost zero at the banks. Consider a long stretch of river flowing north, with parallel banks 40 m apart. If the maximum water speed is 3 m/s, we can use a quadratic function as a basic model for the rate of water flow x units from the west bank: $f(x) = \frac{3}{400}x(40 - x)$.

(a) A boat proceeds at a constant speed of 5 m/s from a point A on the west bank while maintaining a heading perpendicular to the bank. How far down the river on the opposite bank will the boat touch shore? Graph the path of the boat.

(b) Suppose we would like to pilot the boat to land at the point B on the east bank directly opposite A. If we maintain a constant speed of 5 m/s and a constant heading, find the angle at which the boat should head. Then graph the actual path the boat follows. Does the path seem realistic?

30. Another reasonable model for the water speed of the river in Exercise 29 is a sine function: $f(x) = 3\sin(\pi x/40)$. If a boater would like to cross the river from A to B with constant heading and a constant speed of 5 m/s, determine the angle at which the boat should head.

31–36 ▨ Find the tangential and normal components of the acceleration vector.

31. $\mathbf{r}(t) = (3t - t^3)\,\mathbf{i} + 3t^2\,\mathbf{j}$

32. $\mathbf{r}(t) = (1 + t)\,\mathbf{i} + (t^2 - 2t)\,\mathbf{j}$

33. $\mathbf{r}(t) = \cos t\,\mathbf{i} + \sin t\,\mathbf{j} + t\,\mathbf{k}$

34. $\mathbf{r}(t) = t\,\mathbf{i} + t^2\,\mathbf{j} + 3t\,\mathbf{k}$

35. $\mathbf{r}(t) = e^t\,\mathbf{i} + \sqrt{2}\,t\,\mathbf{j} + e^{-t}\,\mathbf{k}$

36. $\mathbf{r}(t) = t\,\mathbf{i} + \cos^2 t\,\mathbf{j} + \sin^2 t\,\mathbf{k}$

37. The magnitude of the acceleration vector $\mathbf{a}$ is 10 cm/s². Use the figure to estimate the tangential and normal components of $\mathbf{a}$.

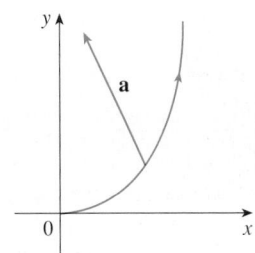

38. If a particle with mass m moves with position vector $\mathbf{r}(t)$, then its **angular momentum** is defined as $\mathbf{L}(t) = m\mathbf{r}(t) \times \mathbf{v}(t)$ and its **torque** as $\boldsymbol{\tau}(t) = m\mathbf{r}(t) \times \mathbf{a}(t)$. Show that $\mathbf{L}'(t) = \boldsymbol{\tau}(t)$. Deduce that if $\boldsymbol{\tau}(t) = \mathbf{0}$ for all t, then $\mathbf{L}(t)$ is constant. (This is the *law of conservation of angular momentum*.)

39. The position function of a spaceship is

$$\mathbf{r}(t) = (3 + t)\,\mathbf{i} + (2 + \ln t)\,\mathbf{j} + \left(7 - \frac{4}{t^2 + 1}\right)\mathbf{k}$$

and the coordinates of a space station are $(6, 4, 9)$. The captain wants the spaceship to coast into the space station. When should the engines be turned off?

40. A rocket burning its onboard fuel while moving through space has velocity $\mathbf{v}(t)$ and mass $m(t)$ at time t. If the exhaust gases escape with velocity $\mathbf{v}_e$ relative to the rocket, it can be deduced from Newton's Second Law of Motion that

$$m\frac{d\mathbf{v}}{dt} = \frac{dm}{dt}\,\mathbf{v}_e$$

(a) Show that $\mathbf{v}(t) = \mathbf{v}(0) - \ln\dfrac{m(0)}{m(t)}\,\mathbf{v}_e$.

(b) For the rocket to accelerate in a straight line from rest to twice the speed of its own exhaust gases, what fraction of its initial mass would the rocket have to burn as fuel?

▌▌▌▌ APPLIED PROJECT

Kepler's Laws

Johannes Kepler stated the following three laws of planetary motion on the basis of masses of data on the positions of the planets at various times.

> **Kepler's Laws**
>
> **1.** A planet revolves around the Sun in an elliptical orbit with the Sun at one focus.
>
> **2.** The line joining the Sun to a planet sweeps out equal areas in equal times.
>
> **3.** The square of the period of revolution of a planet is proportional to the cube of the length of the major axis of its orbit.

Kepler formulated these laws because they fitted the astronomical data. He wasn't able to see why they were true or how they related to each other. But Sir Isaac Newton, in his *Principia Mathematica* of 1687, showed how to deduce Kepler's three laws from two of Newton's own laws, the Second Law of Motion and the Law of Universal Gravitation. In Section 14.4 we proved Kepler's First Law using the calculus of vector functions. In this project we guide you through the proofs of Kepler's Second and Third Laws and explore some of their consequences.

1. Use the following steps to prove Kepler's Second Law. The notation is the same as in the proof of the First Law in Section 14.4. In particular, use polar coordinates so that $\mathbf{r} = (r\cos\theta)\,\mathbf{i} + (r\sin\theta)\,\mathbf{j}$.

(a) Show that $\mathbf{h} = r^2\dfrac{d\theta}{dt}\,\mathbf{k}$.

(b) Deduce that $r^2\dfrac{d\theta}{dt} = h$.

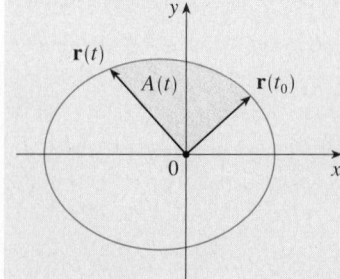

(c) If $A = A(t)$ is the area swept out by the radius vector $\mathbf{r} = \mathbf{r}(t)$ in the time interval $[t_0, t]$ as in the figure, show that

$$\frac{dA}{dt} = \tfrac{1}{2}r^2\frac{d\theta}{dt}$$

(d) Deduce that

$$\frac{dA}{dt} = \tfrac{1}{2}h = \text{constant}$$

This says that the rate at which A is swept out is constant and proves Kepler's Second Law.

2. Let T be the period of a planet about the Sun; that is, T is the time required for it to travel once around its elliptical orbit. Suppose that the lengths of the major and minor axes of the ellipse are $2a$ and $2b$.

   (a) Use part (d) of Problem 1 to show that $T = 2\pi ab/h$.

   (b) Show that $\dfrac{h^2}{GM} = ed = \dfrac{b^2}{a}$.

   (c) Use parts (a) and (b) to show that $T^2 = \dfrac{4\pi^2}{GM} a^3$.

   This proves Kepler's Third Law. [Notice that the proportionality constant $4\pi^2/(GM)$ is independent of the planet.]

3. The period of the Earth's orbit is approximately 365.25 days. Use this fact and Kepler's Third Law to find the length of the major axis of the Earth's orbit. You will need the mass of the Sun, $M = 1.99 \times 10^{30}$ kg, and the gravitational constant, $G = 6.67 \times 10^{-11}$ N·m²/kg².

4. It's possible to place a satellite into orbit about the Earth so that it remains fixed above a given location on the equator. Compute the altitude that is needed for such a satellite. The Earth's mass is 5.98×10^{24} kg; its radius is 6.37×10^6 m. (This orbit is called the Clarke Geosynchronous Orbit after Arthur C. Clarke, who first proposed the idea in 1948. The first such satellite, *Syncom II*, was launched in July 1963.)

14   Review

◦ CONCEPT CHECK ◦

1. What is a vector function? How do you find its derivative and its integral?

2. What is the connection between vector functions and space curves?

3. (a) What is a smooth curve?
   (b) How do you find the tangent vector to a smooth curve at a point? How do you find the tangent line? The unit tangent vector?

4. If $\mathbf{u}$ and $\mathbf{v}$ are differentiable vector functions, c is a scalar, and f is a real-valued function, write the rules for differentiating the following vector functions.
   (a) $\mathbf{u}(t) + \mathbf{v}(t)$ (b) $c\mathbf{u}(t)$ (c) $f(t)\mathbf{u}(t)$
   (d) $\mathbf{u}(t) \cdot \mathbf{v}(t)$ (e) $\mathbf{u}(t) \times \mathbf{v}(t)$ (f) $\mathbf{u}(f(t))$

5. How do you find the length of a space curve given by a vector function $\mathbf{r}(t)$?

6. (a) What is the definition of curvature?
   (b) Write a formula for curvature in terms of $\mathbf{r}'(t)$ and $\mathbf{T}'(t)$.
   (c) Write a formula for curvature in terms of $\mathbf{r}'(t)$ and $\mathbf{r}''(t)$.
   (d) Write a formula for the curvature of a plane curve with equation $y = f(x)$.

7. (a) Write formulas for the unit normal and binormal vectors of a smooth space curve $\mathbf{r}(t)$.
   (b) What is the normal plane of a curve at a point? What is the osculating plane? What is the osculating circle?

8. (a) How do you find the velocity, speed, and acceleration of a particle that moves along a space curve?
   (b) Write the acceleration in terms of its tangential and normal components.

9. State Kepler's Laws.

◦ TRUE-FALSE QUIZ ◦

Determine whether the statement is true or false. If it is true, explain why. If it is false, explain why or give an example that disproves the statement.

1. The curve with vector equation $\mathbf{r}(t) = t^3\,\mathbf{i} + 2t^3\,\mathbf{j} + 3t^3\,\mathbf{k}$ is a line.

2. The curve with vector equation $\mathbf{r}(t) = \langle t, t^3, t^5 \rangle$ is smooth.

3. The curve with vector equation $\mathbf{r}(t) = \langle \cos t, t^2, t^4 \rangle$ is smooth.

4. The derivative of a vector function is obtained by differentiating each component function.

5. If $\mathbf{u}(t)$ and $\mathbf{v}(t)$ are differentiable vector functions, then
$$\frac{d}{dt}[\mathbf{u}(t) \times \mathbf{v}(t)] = \mathbf{u}'(t) \times \mathbf{v}'(t)$$

6. If $\mathbf{r}(t)$ is a differentiable vector function, then
$$\frac{d}{dt}\,|\,\mathbf{r}(t)\,| = |\,\mathbf{r}'(t)\,|$$

7. If $\mathbf{T}(t)$ is the unit tangent vector of a smooth curve, then the curvature is $\kappa = |\,d\mathbf{T}/dt\,|$.

8. The binormal vector is $\mathbf{B}(t) = \mathbf{N}(t) \times \mathbf{T}(t)$.

9. The osculating circle of a curve C at a point has the same tangent vector, normal vector, and curvature as C at that point.

10. Different parametrizations of the same curve result in identical tangent vectors at a given point on the curve.

◦ EXERCISES ◦

1. (a) Sketch the curve with vector function
$$\mathbf{r}(t) = t\,\mathbf{i} + \cos \pi t\,\mathbf{j} + \sin \pi t\,\mathbf{k} \qquad t \geq 0$$
(b) Find $\mathbf{r}'(t)$ and $\mathbf{r}''(t)$.

2. Let $\mathbf{r}(t) = \langle \sqrt{2-t}, (e^t - 1)/t, \ln(t+1) \rangle$.
(a) Find the domain of $\mathbf{r}$.
(b) Find $\lim_{t \to 0} \mathbf{r}(t)$.
(c) Find $\mathbf{r}'(t)$.

3. Find a vector function that represents the curve of intersection of the cylinder $x^2 + y^2 = 16$ and the plane $x + z = 5$.

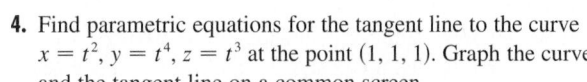 **4.** Find parametric equations for the tangent line to the curve $x = t^2$, $y = t^4$, $z = t^3$ at the point $(1, 1, 1)$. Graph the curve and the tangent line on a common screen.

5. If $\mathbf{r}(t) = t^2\,\mathbf{i} + t \cos \pi t\,\mathbf{j} + \sin \pi t\,\mathbf{k}$, evaluate $\int_0^1 \mathbf{r}(t)\,dt$.

6. Let C be the curve with equations $x = 2 - t^3$, $y = 2t - 1$, $z = \ln t$. Find (a) the point where C intersects the xz-plane, (b) parametric equations of the tangent line at $(1, 1, 0)$, and (c) an equation of the normal plane to C at $(1, 1, 0)$.

7. Use Simpson's Rule with $n = 4$ to estimate the length of the arc of the curve with equations $x = \sqrt{t}$, $y = 4/t$, $z = t^2 + 1$ from $(1, 4, 2)$ to $(2, 1, 17)$.

8. Find the length of the curve $\mathbf{r}(t) = \langle 2t^{3/2}, \cos 2t, \sin 2t \rangle$, $0 \leq t \leq 1$.

9. The helix $\mathbf{r}_1(t) = \cos t\,\mathbf{i} + \sin t\,\mathbf{j} + t\,\mathbf{k}$ intersects the curve $\mathbf{r}_2(t) = (1 + t)\,\mathbf{i} + t^2\,\mathbf{j} + t^3\,\mathbf{k}$ at the point $(1, 0, 0)$. Find the angle of intersection of these curves.

10. Reparametrize the curve $\mathbf{r}(t) = e^t\,\mathbf{i} + e^t \sin t\,\mathbf{j} + e^t \cos t\,\mathbf{k}$ with respect to arc length measured from the point $(1, 0, 1)$ in the direction of increasing t.

11. For the curve given by $\mathbf{r}(t) = \langle \frac{1}{3}t^3, \frac{1}{2}t^2, t \rangle$, find (a) the unit tangent vector, (b) the unit normal vector, and (c) the curvature.

12. Find the curvature of the ellipse $x = 3 \cos t$, $y = 4 \sin t$ at the points $(3, 0)$ and $(0, 4)$.

13. Find the curvature of the curve $y = x^4$ at the point $(1, 1)$.

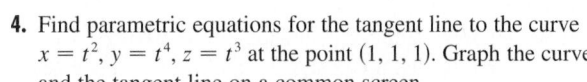 **14.** Find an equation of the osculating circle of the curve $y = x^4 - x^2$ at the origin. Graph both the curve and its osculating circle.

15. Find an equation of the osculating plane of the curve $x = \sin 2t$, $y = t$, $z = \cos 2t$ at the point $(0, \pi, 1)$.

16. The figure shows the curve C traced by a particle with position vector $\mathbf{r}(t)$ at time t.
(a) Draw a vector that represents the average velocity of the particle over the time interval $3 \leq t \leq 3.2$.
(b) Write an expression for the velocity $\mathbf{v}(3)$.
(c) Write an expression for the unit tangent vector $\mathbf{T}(3)$ and draw it.

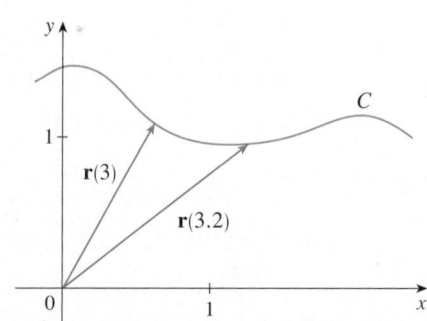

17. A particle moves with position function
$\mathbf{r}(t) = t \ln t\, \mathbf{i} + t\, \mathbf{j} + e^{-t}\, \mathbf{k}$. Find the velocity, speed, and acceleration of the particle.

18. A particle starts at the origin with initial velocity $\mathbf{i} - \mathbf{j} + 3\mathbf{k}$. Its acceleration is $\mathbf{a}(t) = 6t\, \mathbf{i} + 12t^2\, \mathbf{j} - 6t\, \mathbf{k}$. Find its position function.

19. An athlete throws a shot at an angle of $45°$ to the horizontal at an initial speed of 43 ft/s. It leaves his hand 7 ft above the ground.
(a) Where is the shot 2 seconds later?
(b) How high does the shot go?
(c) Where does the shot land?

20. Find the tangential and normal components of the acceleration vector of a particle with position function
$$\mathbf{r}(t) = t\, \mathbf{i} + 2t\, \mathbf{j} + t^2\, \mathbf{k}$$

21. A disk of radius 1 is rotating in the counterclockwise direction at a constant angular speed ω. A particle starts at the center of the disk and moves toward the edge along a fixed radius so that its position at time t, $t \geq 0$, is given by $\mathbf{r}(t) = t\mathbf{R}(t)$, where
$$\mathbf{R}(t) = \cos \omega t\, \mathbf{i} + \sin \omega t\, \mathbf{j}$$
(a) Show that the velocity $\mathbf{v}$ of the particle is
$$\mathbf{v} = \cos \omega t\, \mathbf{i} + \sin \omega t\, \mathbf{j} + t\mathbf{v}_d$$
where $\mathbf{v}_d = \mathbf{R}'(t)$ is the velocity of a point on the edge of the disk.
(b) Show that the acceleration $\mathbf{a}$ of the particle is
$$\mathbf{a} = 2\mathbf{v}_d + t\mathbf{a}_d$$
where $\mathbf{a}_d = \mathbf{R}''(t)$ is the acceleration of a point on the rim of the disk. The extra term $2\mathbf{v}_d$ is called the *Coriolis acceleration*; it is the result of the interaction of the rotation of the disk and the motion of the particle. One can obtain a physical demonstration of this acceleration by walking toward the edge of a moving merry-go-round.

(c) Determine the Coriolis acceleration of a particle that moves on a rotating disk according to the equation
$$\mathbf{r}(t) = e^{-t} \cos \omega t\, \mathbf{i} + e^{-t} \sin \omega t\, \mathbf{j}$$

22. In designing *transfer curves* to connect sections of straight railroad tracks, it's important to realize that the acceleration of the train should be continuous so that the reactive force exerted by the train on the track is also continuous. Because of the formulas for the components of acceleration in Section 14.4, this will be the case if the curvature varies continuously.
(a) A logical candidate for a transfer curve to join existing tracks given by $y = 1$ for $x \leq 0$ and $y = \sqrt{2} - x$ for $x \geq 1/\sqrt{2}$ might be the function $f(x) = \sqrt{1 - x^2}$, $0 < x < 1/\sqrt{2}$, whose graph is the arc of the circle shown in the figure. It looks reasonable at first glance. Show that the function
$$F(x) = \begin{cases} 1 & \text{if } x \leq 0 \\ \sqrt{1 - x^2} & \text{if } 0 < x < 1/\sqrt{2} \\ \sqrt{2} - x & \text{if } x \geq 1/\sqrt{2} \end{cases}$$
is continuous and has continuous slope, but does not have continuous curvature. Therefore, f is not an appropriate transfer curve.
(b) Find a fifth-degree polynomial to serve as a transfer curve between the following straight line segments: $y = 0$ for $x \leq 0$ and $y = x$ for $x \geq 1$. Could this be done with a fourth-degree polynomial? Use a graphing calculator or computer to sketch the graph of the "connected" function and check to see that it looks like the one in the figure.

FIGURE FOR PROBLEM 1

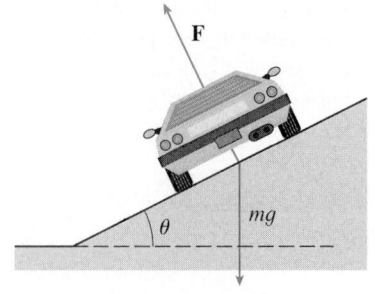

FIGURE FOR PROBLEM 2

1. A particle P moves with constant angular speed ω around a circle whose center is at the origin and whose radius is R. The particle is said to be in *uniform circular motion*. Assume that the motion is counterclockwise and that the particle is at the point $(R, 0)$ when $t = 0$. The position vector at time $t \geq 0$ is $\mathbf{r}(t) = R \cos \omega t\,\mathbf{i} + R \sin \omega t\,\mathbf{j}$.
   (a) Find the velocity vector $\mathbf{v}$ and show that $\mathbf{v} \cdot \mathbf{r} = 0$. Conclude that $\mathbf{v}$ is tangent to the circle and points in the direction of the motion.
   (b) Show that the speed $|\mathbf{v}|$ of the particle is the constant ωR. The *period* T of the particle is the time required for one complete revolution. Conclude that

$$T = \frac{2\pi R}{|\mathbf{v}|} = \frac{2\pi}{\omega}$$

   (c) Find the acceleration vector $\mathbf{a}$. Show that it is proportional to $\mathbf{r}$ and that it points toward the origin. An acceleration with this property is called a *centripetal acceleration*. Show that the magnitude of the acceleration vector is $|\mathbf{a}| = R\omega^2$.
   (d) Suppose that the particle has mass m. Show that the magnitude of the force $\mathbf{F}$ that is required to produce this motion, called a *centripetal force*, is

$$|\mathbf{F}| = \frac{m|\mathbf{v}|^2}{R}$$

2. A circular curve of radius R on a highway is banked at an angle θ so that a car can safely traverse the curve without skidding when there is no friction between the road and the tires. The loss of friction could occur, for example, if the road is covered with a film of water or ice. The rated speed v_R of the curve is the maximum speed that a car can attain without skidding. Suppose a car of mass m is traversing the curve at the rated speed v_R. Two forces are acting on the car: the vertical force, mg, due to the weight of the car, and a force $\mathbf{F}$ exerted by, and normal to, the road. (See the figure.)
   The vertical component of $\mathbf{F}$ balances the weight of the car, so that $|\mathbf{F}| \cos \theta = mg$. The horizontal component of $\mathbf{F}$ produces a centripetal force on the car so that, by Newton's Second Law and part (d) of Problem 1,

$$|\mathbf{F}| \sin \theta = \frac{mv_R^2}{R}$$

   (a) Show that $v_R^2 = Rg \tan \theta$.
   (b) Find the rated speed of a circular curve with radius 400 ft that is banked at an angle of $12°$.
   (c) Suppose the design engineers want to keep the banking at $12°$, but wish to increase the rated speed by 50%. What should the radius of the curve be?

3. A projectile is fired from the origin with angle of elevation α and initial speed v_0. Assuming that air resistance is negligible and that the only force acting on the projectile is gravity, g, we showed in Example 5 in Section 14.4 that the position vector of the projectile is $\mathbf{r}(t) = (v_0 \cos \alpha)t\,\mathbf{i} + \left[(v_0 \sin \alpha)t - \frac{1}{2}gt^2\right]\mathbf{j}$. We also showed that the maximum horizontal distance of the projectile is achieved when $\alpha = 45°$ and in this case the range is $R = v_0^2/g$.
   (a) At what angle should the projectile be fired to achieve maximum height and what is the maximum height?
   (b) Fix the initial speed v_0 and consider the parabola $x^2 + 2Ry - R^2 = 0$, whose graph is shown in the figure. Show that the projectile can hit any target inside or on the boundary

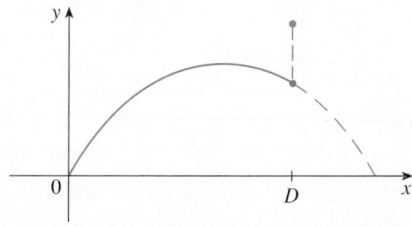

of the region bounded by the parabola and the x-axis, and that it can't hit any target outside this region.

(c) Suppose that the gun is elevated to an angle of inclination α in order to aim at a target that is suspended at a height h directly over a point D units downrange. The target is released at the instant the gun is fired. Show that the projectile always hits the target, regardless of the value v_0, provided the projectile does not hit the ground "before" D.

4. (a) A projectile is fired from the origin down an inclined plane that makes an angle θ with the horizontal. The angle of elevation of the gun and the initial speed of the projectile are α and v_0, respectively. Find the position vector of the projectile and the parametric equations of the path of the projectile as functions of the time t. (Ignore air resistance.)

(b) Show that the angle of elevation α that will maximize the downhill range is the angle halfway between the plane and the vertical.

(c) Suppose the projectile is fired up an inclined plane whose angle of inclination is θ. Show that, in order to maximize the (uphill) range, the projectile should be fired in the direction halfway between the plane and the vertical.

(d) In a paper presented in 1686, Edmond Halley summarized the laws of gravity and projectile motion and applied them to gunnery. One problem he posed involved firing a projectile to hit a target a distance R up an inclined plane. Show that the angle at which the projectile should be fired to hit the target but use the least amount of energy is the same as the angle in part (c). (Use the fact that the energy needed to fire the projectile is proportional to the square of the initial speed, so minimizing the energy is equivalent to minimizing the initial speed.)

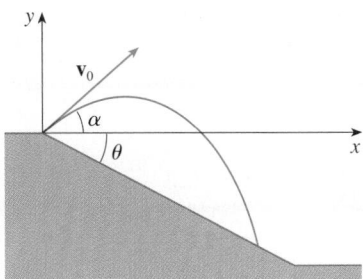

FIGURE FOR PROBLEM 4

5. A projectile of mass m is fired from the origin at an angle of elevation α. In addition to gravity, assume that air resistance provides a force that is proportional to the velocity and that opposes the motion. Then, by Newton's Second Law, the total force acting on the projectile satisfies the equation

$$\boxed{1} \qquad m\frac{d^2\mathbf{R}}{dt^2} = -mg\,\mathbf{j} - k\frac{d\mathbf{R}}{dt}$$

where $\mathbf{R}$ is the position vector and $k > 0$ is the constant of proportionality.

(a) Show that Equation 1 can be integrated to obtain the equation

$$\frac{d\mathbf{R}}{dt} + \frac{k}{m}\mathbf{R} = \mathbf{v}_0 - gt\,\mathbf{j}$$

where $\mathbf{v}_0 = \mathbf{v}(0) = \dfrac{d\mathbf{R}}{dt}(0)$.

(b) Multiply both sides of the equation in part (a) by $e^{(k/m)t}$ and show that the left-hand side of the resulting equation is the derivative of the product $e^{(k/m)t}\,\mathbf{R}(t)$. Then integrate to find an expression for the position vector $\mathbf{R}(t)$.

6. Find the curvature of the curve with parametric equations

$$x = \int_0^t \sin\left(\tfrac{1}{2}\pi\theta^2\right)d\theta \qquad y = \int_0^t \cos\left(\tfrac{1}{2}\pi\theta^2\right)d\theta$$

7. A ball rolls off a table with a speed of 2 ft/s. The table is 3.5 ft high.

(a) Determine the point at which the ball hits the floor and find its speed at the instant of impact.

(b) Find the angle θ between the path of the ball and the vertical line drawn through the point of impact. (See the figure.)

(c) Suppose the ball rebounds from the floor at the same angle with which it hits the floor, but loses 20% of its speed due to energy absorbed by the ball on impact. Where does the ball strike the floor on the second bounce?

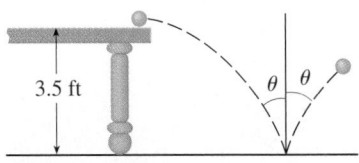

FIGURE FOR PROBLEM 7

8. A cable has radius r and length L and is wound around a spool with radius R without overlapping. What is the shortest length along the spool that is covered by the cable?

CHAPTER 15

We can visualize a function of two
variables by its graph (a surface) or
by its level curves (a contour map).

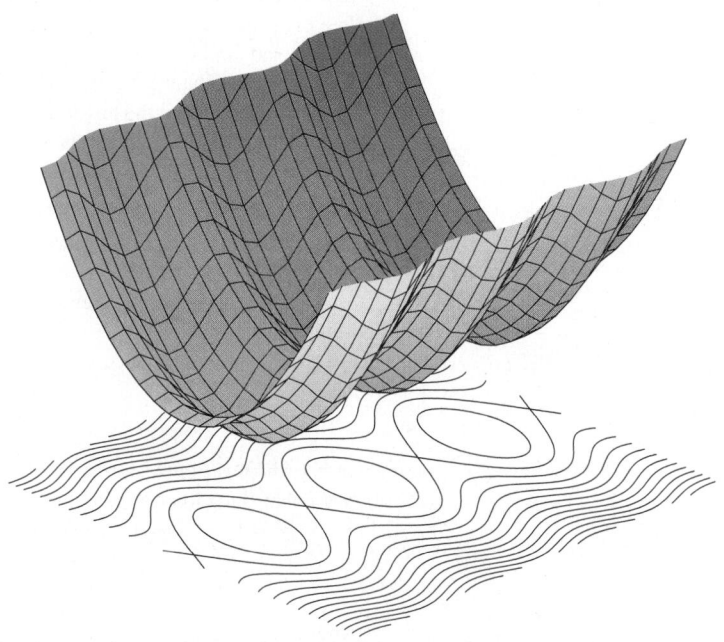

Partial Derivatives

So far we have dealt with the calculus of functions of a single variable. But, in the real world, physical quantities often depend on two or more variables, so in this chapter we turn our attention to functions of several variables and extend the basic ideas of differential calculus to such functions.

15.1 Functions of Several Variables

In this section we study functions of two or more variables from four points of view:

- verbally   (by a description in words)
- numerically   (by a table of values)
- algebraically   (by an explicit formula)
- visually   (by a graph or level curves)

Functions of Two Variables

The temperature T at a point on the surface of the Earth at any given time depends on the longitude x and latitude y of the point. We can think of T as being a function of the two variables x and y, or as a function of the pair (x, y). We indicate this functional dependence by writing $T = f(x, y)$.

The volume V of a circular cylinder depends on its radius r and height h. In fact, we know that $V = \pi r^2 h$. We say that V is a function of r and h, and we write $V(r, h) = \pi r^2 h$.

Definition   A **function f of two variables** is a rule that assigns to each ordered pair of real numbers (x, y) in a set D a unique real number denoted by $f(x, y)$. The set D is the **domain** of f and its **range** is the set of values that f takes on, that is, $\{f(x, y) \mid (x, y) \in D\}$.

We often write $z = f(x, y)$ to make explicit the value taken on by f at the general point (x, y). The variables x and y are **independent variables** and z is the **dependent variable**. [Compare this with the notation $y = f(x)$ for functions of a single variable.]

A function of two variables is just a function whose domain is a subset of $\mathbb{R}^2$ and whose range is a subset of $\mathbb{R}$. One way of visualizing such a function is by means of an arrow diagram (see Figure 1), where the domain D is represented as a subset of the xy-plane.

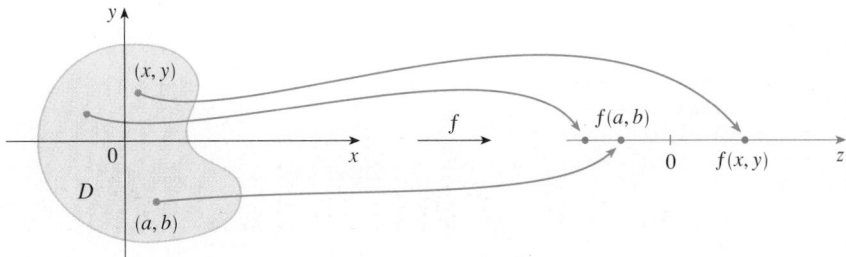

FIGURE 1

$x + y + 1 = 0$

FIGURE 2

Domain of $f(x, y) = \dfrac{\sqrt{x + y + 1}}{x - 1}$

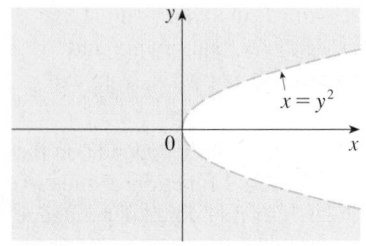

FIGURE 3

Domain of $f(x, y) = x \ln(y^2 - x)$

If a function f is given by a formula and no domain is specified, then the domain of f is understood to be the set of all pairs (x, y) for which the given expression is a well-defined real number.

EXAMPLE 1 Find the domains of the following functions and evaluate $f(3, 2)$.

(a) $f(x, y) = \dfrac{\sqrt{x + y + 1}}{x - 1}$ (b) $f(x, y) = x \ln(y^2 - x)$

SOLUTION

(a) $$f(3, 2) = \frac{\sqrt{3 + 2 + 1}}{3 - 1} = \frac{\sqrt{6}}{2}$$

The expression for f makes sense if the denominator is not 0 and the quantity under the square root sign is nonnegative. So the domain of f is

$$D = \{(x, y) \mid x + y + 1 \geqslant 0, \ x \neq 1\}$$

The inequality $x + y + 1 \geqslant 0$, or $y \geqslant -x - 1$, describes the points that lie on or above the line $y = -x - 1$, while $x \neq 1$ means that the points on the line $x = 1$ must be excluded from the domain. (See Figure 2.)

(b) $$f(3, 2) = 3 \ln(2^2 - 3) = 3 \ln 1 = 0$$

Since $\ln(y^2 - x)$ is defined only when $y^2 - x > 0$, that is, $x < y^2$, the domain of f is $D = \{(x, y) \mid x < y^2\}$. This is the set of points to the left of the parabola $x = y^2$. (See Figure 3.)

Not all functions are given by explicit formulas. The function in the next example is described verbally and by numerical estimates of its values.

EXAMPLE 2 In regions with severe winter weather, the *wind-chill index* is often used to describe the apparent severity of the cold. This index W is a subjective temperature that depends on the actual temperature T and the wind speed v. So W is a function of T and v, and we can write $W = f(T, v)$. Table 1 records values of W compiled by the National Weather Service of the U.S. and the Meteorological Service of Canada.

TABLE 1
Wind-chill index as a function of air temperature and wind speed

|||| THE NEW WIND-CHILL INDEX

A new wind-chill index was introduced in November of 2001 and is more accurate than the old index at measuring how cold it feels when it's windy. The new index is based on a model of how fast a human face loses heat. It was developed through clinical trials in which volunteers were exposed to a variety of temperatures and wind speeds in a refrigerated wind tunnel.

					Wind speed (km/h)						
T \ v	5	10	15	20	25	30	40	50	60	70	80
5	4	3	2	1	1	0	-1	-1	-2	-2	-3
0	-2	-3	-4	-5	-6	-6	-7	-8	-9	-9	-10
-5	-7	-9	-11	-12	-12	-13	-14	-15	-16	-16	-17
-10	-13	-15	-17	-18	-19	-20	-21	-22	-23	-23	-24
-15	-19	-21	-23	-24	-25	-26	-27	-29	-30	-30	-31
-20	-24	-27	-29	-30	-32	-33	-34	-35	-36	-37	-38
-25	-30	-33	-35	-37	-38	-39	-41	-42	-43	-44	-45
-30	-36	-39	-41	-43	-44	-46	-48	-49	-50	-51	-52
-35	-41	-45	-48	-49	-51	-52	-54	-56	-57	-58	-60
-40	-47	-51	-54	-56	-57	-59	-61	-63	-64	-65	-67

Actual temperature (°C)

For instance, the table shows that if the temperature is $-5°C$ and the wind speed is 50 km/h, then subjectively it would feel as cold as a temperature of about $-15°C$ with no wind. So

$$f(-5, 50) = -15$$

EXAMPLE 3 In 1928 Charles Cobb and Paul Douglas published a study in which they modeled the growth of the American economy during the period 1899–1922. They considered a simplified view of the economy in which production output is determined by the amount of labor involved and the amount of capital invested. While there are many other factors affecting economic performance, their model proved to be remarkably accurate. The function they used to model production was of the form

TABLE 2

Year	P	L	K
1899	100	100	100
1900	101	105	107
1901	112	110	114
1902	122	117	122
1903	124	122	131
1904	122	121	138
1905	143	125	149
1906	152	134	163
1907	151	140	176
1908	126	123	185
1909	155	143	198
1910	159	147	208
1911	153	148	216
1912	177	155	226
1913	184	156	236
1914	169	152	244
1915	189	156	266
1916	225	183	298
1917	227	198	335
1918	223	201	366
1919	218	196	387
1920	231	194	407
1921	179	146	417
1922	240	161	431

$$\boxed{1} \qquad P(L, K) = bL^{\alpha}K^{1-\alpha}$$

where P is the total production (the monetary value of all goods produced in a year), L is the amount of labor (the total number of person-hours worked in a year), and K is the amount of capital invested (the monetary worth of all machinery, equipment, and buildings). In Section 15.3 we will show how the form of Equation 1 follows from certain economic assumptions.

Cobb and Douglas used economic data published by the government to obtain Table 2. They took the year 1899 as a baseline and P, L, and K for 1899 were each assigned the value 100. The values for other years were expressed as percentages of the 1899 figures.

Cobb and Douglas used the method of least squares to fit the data of Table 2 to the function

$$\boxed{2} \qquad P(L, K) = 1.01L^{0.75}K^{0.25}$$

(See Exercise 71 for the details.)

If we use the model given by the function in Equation 2 to compute the production in the years 1910 and 1920, we get the values

$$P(147, 208) = 1.01(147)^{0.75}(208)^{0.25} \approx 161.9$$

$$P(194, 407) = 1.01(194)^{0.75}(407)^{0.25} \approx 235.8$$

which are quite close to the actual values, 159 and 231.

The production function (1) has subsequently been used in many settings, ranging from individual firms to global economic questions. It has become known as the **Cobb-Douglas production function**. Its domain is $\{(L, K) \mid L \geqslant 0, K \geqslant 0\}$ because L and K represent labor and capital and are therefore never negative.

EXAMPLE 4 Find the domain and range of

$$g(x, y) = \sqrt{9 - x^2 - y^2}$$

SOLUTION The domain of g is

$$D = \{(x, y) \mid 9 - x^2 - y^2 \geqslant 0\} = \{(x, y) \mid x^2 + y^2 \leqslant 9\}$$

which is the disk with center $(0, 0)$ and radius 3. (See Figure 4.) The range of g is

$$\{z \mid z = \sqrt{9 - x^2 - y^2}, (x, y) \in D\}$$

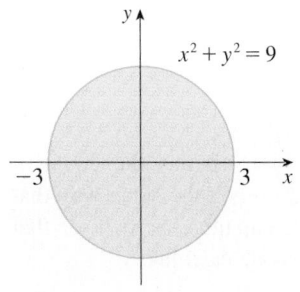

FIGURE 4
Domain of $g(x, y) = \sqrt{9 - x^2 - y^2}$

Since z is a positive square root, $z \geqslant 0$. Also

$$9 - x^2 - y^2 \leqslant 9 \quad \Rightarrow \quad \sqrt{9 - x^2 - y^2} \leqslant 3$$

So the range is

$$\{z \mid 0 \leqslant z \leqslant 3\} = [0, 3]$$

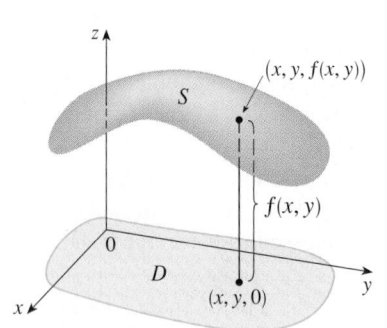

FIGURE 5

||| Graphs

Another way of visualizing the behavior of a function of two variables is to consider its graph.

> **Definition** If f is a function of two variables with domain D, then the **graph** of f is the set of all points (x, y, z) in $\mathbb{R}^3$ such that $z = f(x, y)$ and (x, y) is in D.

Just as the graph of a function f of one variable is a curve C with equation $y = f(x)$, so the graph of a function f of two variables is a surface S with equation $z = f(x, y)$. We can visualize the graph S of f as lying directly above or below its domain D in the xy-plane (see Figure 5).

EXAMPLE 5 Sketch the graph of the function $f(x, y) = 6 - 3x - 2y$.

SOLUTION The graph of f has the equation $z = 6 - 3x - 2y$, or $3x + 2y + z = 6$, which represents a plane. To graph the plane we first find the intercepts. Putting $y = z = 0$ in the equation, we get $x = 2$ as the x-intercept. Similarly, the y-intercept is 3 and the z-intercept is 6. This helps us sketch the portion of the graph that lies in the first octant (Figure 6).

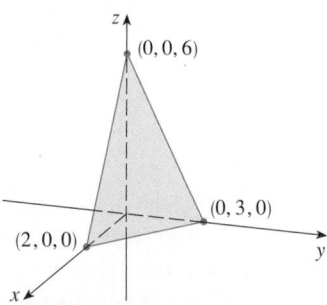

FIGURE 6

The function in Example 5 is a special case of the function

$$f(x, y) = ax + by + c$$

which is called a **linear function**. The graph of such a function has the equation $z = ax + by + c$, or $ax + by - z + c = 0$, so it is a plane. In much the same way that linear functions of one variable are important in single-variable calculus, we will see that linear functions of two variables play a central role in multivariable calculus.

EXAMPLE 6 Sketch the graph of $g(x, y) = \sqrt{9 - x^2 - y^2}$.

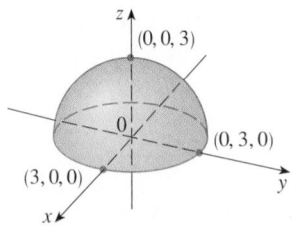

FIGURE 7
Graph of $g(x, y) = \sqrt{9 - x^2 - y^2}$

SOLUTION The graph has equation $z = \sqrt{9 - x^2 - y^2}$. We square both sides of this equation to obtain $z^2 = 9 - x^2 - y^2$, or $x^2 + y^2 + z^2 = 9$, which we recognize as an equation of the sphere with center the origin and radius 3. But, since $z \geqslant 0$, the graph of g is just the top half of this sphere (see Figure 7).

EXAMPLE 7 Use a computer to draw the graph of the Cobb-Douglas production function $P(L, K) = 1.01L^{0.75}K^{0.25}$.

SOLUTION Figure 8 shows the graph of P for values of the labor L and capital K that lie between 0 and 300. The computer has drawn the surface by plotting vertical traces. We see from these traces that the value of the production P increases as either L or K increases, as is to be expected.

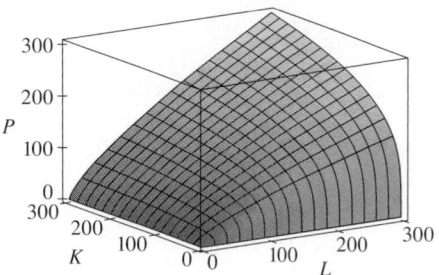

FIGURE 8

EXAMPLE 8 Find the domain and range and sketch the graph of $h(x, y) = 4x^2 + y^2$.

SOLUTION Notice that $h(x, y)$ is defined for all possible ordered pairs of real numbers (x, y), so the domain is $\mathbb{R}^2$, the entire xy-plane. The range of h is the set $[0, \infty)$ of all nonnegative real numbers. [Notice that $x^2 \geqslant 0$ and $y^2 \geqslant 0$, so $h(x, y) \geqslant 0$ for all x and y.]

The graph of h has the equation $z = 4x^2 + y^2$, which is the elliptic paraboloid that we sketched in Example 4 in Section 13.6. Horizontal traces are ellipses and vertical traces are parabolas (see Figure 9).

FIGURE 9
Graph of $h(x, y) = 4x^2 + y^2$

Computer programs are readily available for graphing functions of two variables. In most such programs, traces in the vertical planes $x = k$ and $y = k$ are drawn for equally spaced values of k and parts of the graph are eliminated using hidden line removal.

Figure 10 shows computer-generated graphs of several functions. Notice that we get an especially good picture of a function when rotation is used to give views from different vantage points. In parts (a) and (b) the graph of f is very flat and close to the xy-plane except near the origin; this is because $e^{-x^2-y^2}$ is very small when x or y is large.

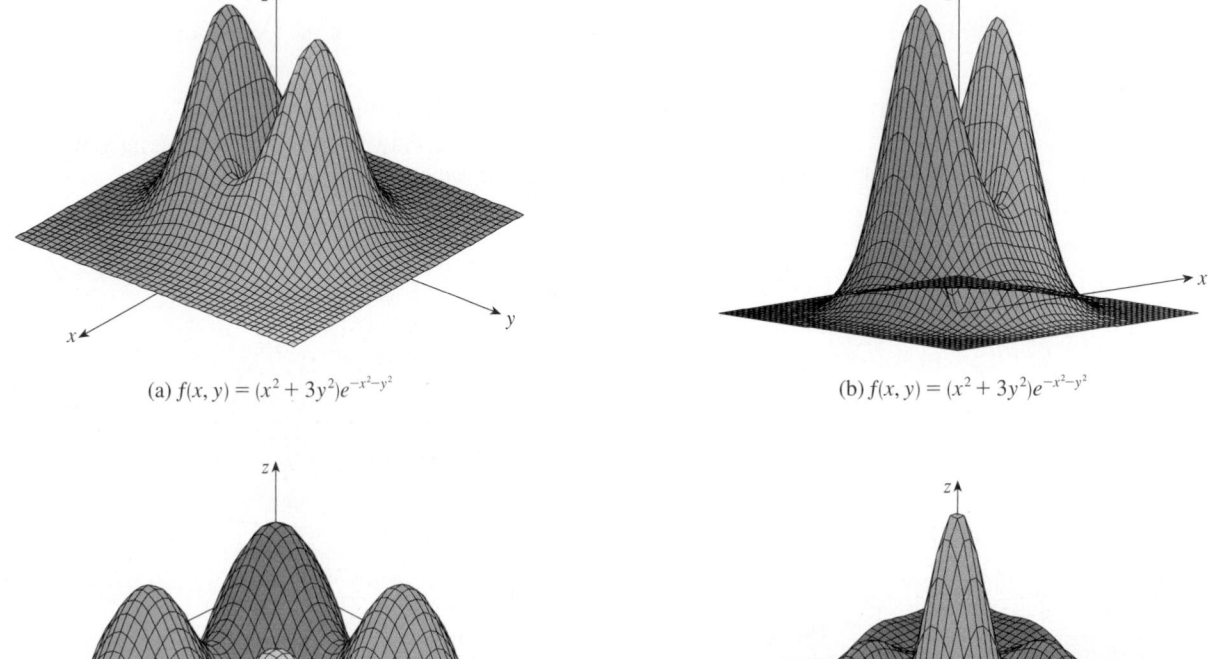

(a) $f(x, y) = (x^2 + 3y^2)e^{-x^2-y^2}$

(b) $f(x, y) = (x^2 + 3y^2)e^{-x^2-y^2}$

(c) $f(x, y) = \sin x + \sin y$

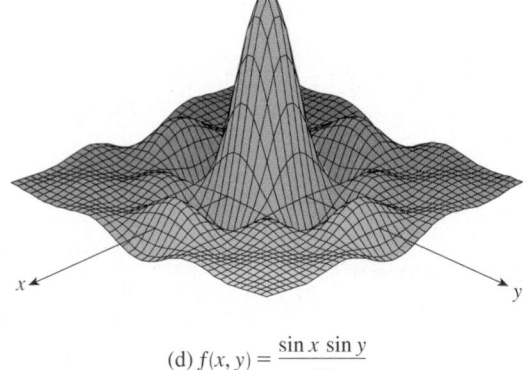

(d) $f(x, y) = \dfrac{\sin x \sin y}{xy}$

FIGURE 10

|||| Level Curves

So far we have two methods for visualizing functions: arrow diagrams and graphs. A third method, borrowed from mapmakers, is a contour map on which points of constant elevation are joined to form *contour curves,* or *level curves.*

Definition The **level curves** of a function f of two variables are the curves with equations $f(x, y) = k$, where k is a constant (in the range of f).

A level curve $f(x, y) = k$ is the set of all points in the domain of f at which f takes on a given value k. In other words, it shows where the graph of f has height k.

You can see from Figure 11 the relation between level curves and horizontal traces. The level curves $f(x, y) = k$ are just the traces of the graph of f in the horizontal plane $z = k$ projected down to the xy-plane. So if you draw the level curves of a function and visual-

FIGURE 11

FIGURE 12

 Visual 15.1A animates Figure 11 by showing level curves being lifted up to graphs of functions.

ize them being lifted up to the surface at the indicated height, then you can mentally piece together a picture of the graph. The surface is steep where the level curves are close together. It is somewhat flatter where they are farther apart.

One common example of level curves occurs in topographic maps of mountainous regions, such as the map in Figure 12. The level curves are curves of constant elevation above sea level. If you walk along one of these contour lines you neither ascend nor descend. Another common example is the temperature function introduced in the opening paragraph of this section. Here the level curves are called **isothermals** and join locations with the same temperature. Figure 13 shows a weather map of the world indicating the average January temperatures. The isothermals are the curves that separate the colored bands.

FIGURE 13

World mean sea-level temperatures in January in degrees Celsius

Tarbuck, *Atmosphere: Introduction to Meteorology*, 4th Edition, © 1989. Reprinted by permission of Pearson Education, Inc., Upper Saddle River, NJ.

FIGURE 14

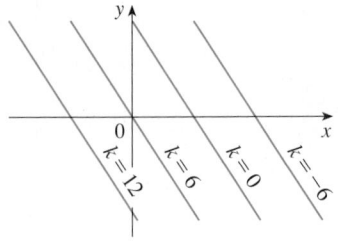

FIGURE 15
Contour map of $f(x, y) = 6 - 3x - 2y$

EXAMPLE 9 A contour map for a function f is shown in Figure 14. Use it to estimate the values of $f(1, 3)$ and $f(4, 5)$.

SOLUTION The point $(1, 3)$ lies partway between the level curves with z-values 70 and 80. We estimate that

$$f(1, 3) \approx 73$$

Similarly, we estimate that

$$f(4, 5) \approx 56$$

EXAMPLE 10 Sketch the level curves of the function $f(x, y) = 6 - 3x - 2y$ for the values $k = -6, 0, 6, 12$.

SOLUTION The level curves are

$$6 - 3x - 2y = k \qquad \text{or} \qquad 3x + 2y + (k - 6) = 0$$

This is a family of lines with slope $-\frac{3}{2}$. The four particular level curves with $k = -6, 0, 6,$ and 12 are $3x + 2y - 12 = 0$, $3x + 2y - 6 = 0$, $3x + 2y = 0$, and $3x + 2y + 6 = 0$. They are sketched in Figure 15. The level curves are equally spaced parallel lines because the graph of f is a plane (see Figure 6).

EXAMPLE 11 Sketch the level curves of the function

$$g(x, y) = \sqrt{9 - x^2 - y^2} \qquad \text{for} \quad k = 0, 1, 2, 3$$

SOLUTION The level curves are

$$\sqrt{9 - x^2 - y^2} = k \qquad \text{or} \qquad x^2 + y^2 = 9 - k^2$$

This is a family of concentric circles with center $(0, 0)$ and radius $\sqrt{9 - k^2}$. The cases $k = 0, 1, 2, 3$ are shown in Figure 16. Try to visualize these level curves lifted up to form a surface and compare with the graph of g (a hemisphere) in Figure 7. (See TEC Visual 15.1A.)

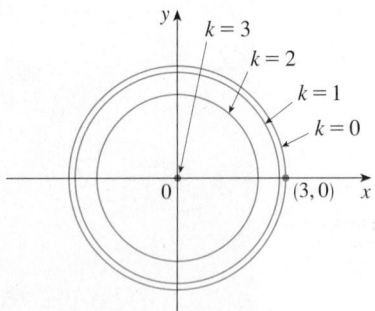

FIGURE 16
Contour map of $g(x, y) = \sqrt{9 - x^2 - y^2}$

EXAMPLE 12 Sketch some level curves of the function $h(x, y) = 4x^2 + y^2$.

SOLUTION The level curves are

$$4x^2 + y^2 = k \qquad \text{or} \qquad \frac{x^2}{k/4} + \frac{y^2}{k} = 1$$

which, for $k > 0$, describe a family of ellipses with semiaxes $\sqrt{k}/2$ and $\sqrt{k}$. Figure 17(a) shows a contour map of h drawn by a computer with level curves corresponding to $k = 0.25, 0.5, 0.75, \ldots, 4$. Figure 17(b) shows these level curves lifted up to the graph of h (an elliptic paraboloid) where they become horizontal traces. We see from Figure 17 how the graph of h is put together from the level curves.

Visual 15.1B demonstrates the connection between surfaces and their contour maps.

FIGURE 17

The graph of $h(x, y) = 4x^2 + y^2$
is formed by lifting the level curves.

(a) Contour map   (b) Horizontal traces are raised level curves

EXAMPLE 13 Plot level curves for the Cobb-Douglas production function of Example 3.

SOLUTION In Figure 18 we use a computer to draw a contour plot for the Cobb-Douglas production function

$$P(L, K) = 1.01 P^{0.75} K^{0.25}$$

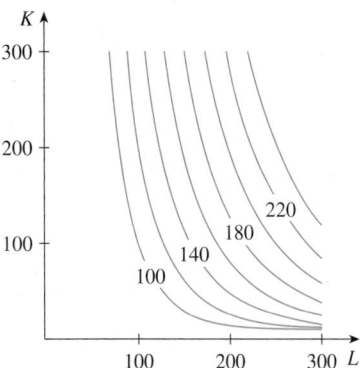

FIGURE 18

Level curves are labeled with the value of the production P. For instance, the level curve labeled 140 shows all values of the labor L and capital investment K that result in a production of $P = 140$. We see that, for a fixed value of P, as L increases K decreases, and vice versa.

For some purposes, a contour map is more useful than a graph. That is certainly true in Example 13. (Compare Figure 18 with Figure 8.) It is also true in estimating function values, as in Example 9.

Figure 19 shows some computer-generated level curves together with the corresponding computer-generated graphs. Notice that the level curves in part (c) crowd together near the origin. That corresponds to the fact that the graph in part (d) is very steep near the origin.

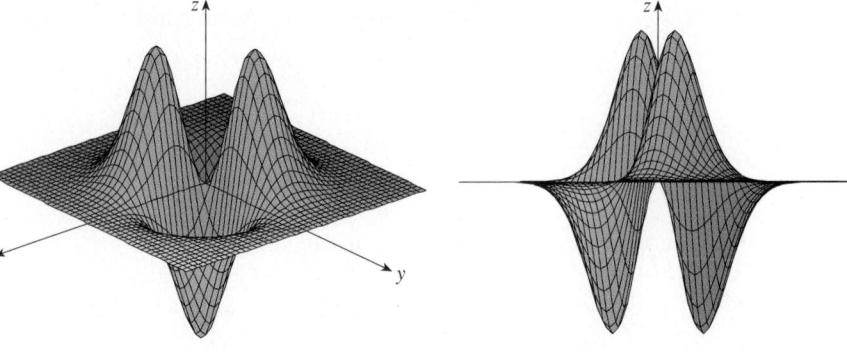

(a) Level curves of $f(x, y) = -xye^{-x^2-y^2}$

(b) Two views of $f(x, y) = -xye^{-x^2-y^2}$

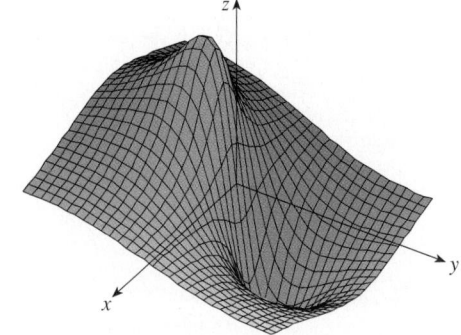

FIGURE 19

(c) Level curves of $f(x, y) = \dfrac{-3y}{x^2 + y^2 + 1}$

(d) $f(x, y) = \dfrac{-3y}{x^2 + y^2 + 1}$

▮▮▮ **Functions of Three or More Variables**

A **function of three variables**, f, is a rule that assigns to each ordered triple (x, y, z) in a domain $D \subset \mathbb{R}^3$ a unique real number denoted by $f(x, y, z)$. For instance, the temperature T at a point on the surface of the Earth depends on the longitude x and latitude y of the point and on the time t, so we could write $T = f(x, y, t)$.

EXAMPLE 14 Find the domain of f if

$$f(x, y, z) = \ln(z - y) + xy \sin z$$

SOLUTION The expression for $f(x, y, z)$ is defined as long as $z - y > 0$, so the domain of f is

$$D = \{(x, y, z) \in \mathbb{R}^3 \mid z > y\}$$

This is a **half-space** consisting of all points that lie above the plane $z = y$.

It's very difficult to visualize a function f of three variables by its graph, since that would lie in a four-dimensional space. However, we do gain some insight into f by examining its **level surfaces**, which are the surfaces with equations $f(x, y, z) = k$, where k is a constant. If the point (x, y, z) moves along a level surface, the value of $f(x, y, z)$ remains fixed.

EXAMPLE 15 Find the level surfaces of the function

$$f(x, y, z) = x^2 + y^2 + z^2$$

SOLUTION The level surfaces are $x^2 + y^2 + z^2 = k$, where $k \geqslant 0$. These form a family of concentric spheres with radius $\sqrt{k}$. (See Figure 20.) Thus, as (x, y, z) varies over any sphere with center O, the value of $f(x, y, z)$ remains fixed.

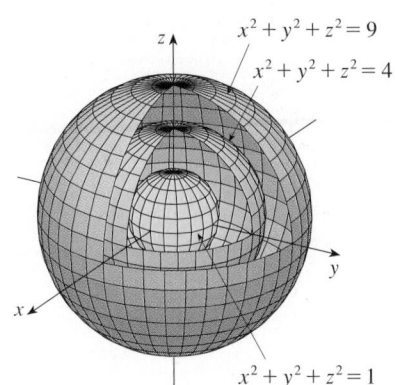

$x^2 + y^2 + z^2 = 9$
$x^2 + y^2 + z^2 = 4$
$x^2 + y^2 + z^2 = 1$

FIGURE 20

Functions of any number of variables can also be considered. A **function of n variables** is a rule that assigns a number $z = f(x_1, x_2, \ldots, x_n)$ to an n-tuple $(x_1, x_2, \ldots, x_n)$ of real numbers. We denote by $\mathbb{R}^n$ the set of all such n-tuples. For example, if a company uses n different ingredients in making a food product, c_i is the cost per unit of the ith ingredient, and x_i units of the ith ingredient are used, then the total cost C of the ingredients is a function of the n variables $x_1, x_2, \ldots, x_n$:

$$\boxed{3} \qquad C = f(x_1, x_2, \ldots, x_n) = c_1x_1 + c_2x_2 + \cdots + c_nx_n$$

The function f is a real-valued function whose domain is a subset of $\mathbb{R}^n$. Sometimes we will use vector notation to write such functions more compactly: If $\mathbf{x} = \langle x_1, x_2, \ldots, x_n \rangle$, we often write $f(\mathbf{x})$ in place of $f(x_1, x_2, \ldots, x_n)$. With this notation we can rewrite the function defined in Equation 3 as

$$f(\mathbf{x}) = \mathbf{c} \cdot \mathbf{x}$$

where $\mathbf{c} = \langle c_1, c_2, \ldots, c_n \rangle$ and $\mathbf{c} \cdot \mathbf{x}$ denotes the dot product of the vectors $\mathbf{c}$ and $\mathbf{x}$ in V_n.

In view of the one-to-one correspondence between points $(x_1, x_2, \ldots, x_n)$ in $\mathbb{R}^n$ and their position vectors $\mathbf{x} = \langle x_1, x_2, \ldots, x_n \rangle$ in V_n, we have three ways of looking at a function f defined on a subset of $\mathbb{R}^n$:

1. As a function of n real variables $x_1, x_2, \ldots, x_n$

2. As a function of a single point variable $(x_1, x_2, \ldots, x_n)$

3. As a function of a single vector variable $\mathbf{x} = \langle x_1, x_2, \ldots, x_n \rangle$

We will see that all three points of view are useful.

|||| 15.1 Exercises

1. In Example 2 we considered the function $W = f(T, v)$, where W is the wind-chill index, T is the actual temperature, and v is the wind speed. A numerical representation is given in Table 1.

(a) What is the value of $f(-15, 40)$? What is its meaning?

(b) Describe in words the meaning of the question "For what value of v is $f(-20, v) = -30$?" Then answer the question.

(c) Describe in words the meaning of the question "For what value of T is $f(T, 20) = -49$?" Then answer the question.

(d) What is the meaning of the function $W = f(-5, v)$? Describe the behavior of this function.

(e) What is the meaning of the function $W = f(T, 50)$? Describe the behavior of this function.

2. The *temperature-humidity index* I (or humidex, for short) is the perceived air temperature when the actual temperature is T and the relative humidity is h, so we can write $I = f(T, h)$. The following table of values of I is an excerpt from a table compiled by the National Oceanic and Atmospheric Administration.

TABLE 3   Apparent temperature as a function of temperature and humidity

Relative humidity (%)

T \ h	20	30	40	50	60	70
80	77	78	79	81	82	83
85	82	84	86	88	90	93
90	87	90	93	96	100	106
95	93	96	101	107	114	124
100	99	104	110	120	132	144

Actual temperature (°F)

(a) What is the value of $f(95, 70)$? What is its meaning?
(b) For what value of h is $f(90, h) = 100$?
(c) For what value of T is $f(T, 50) = 88$?
(d) What are the meanings of the functions $I = f(80, h)$ and $I = f(100, h)$? Compare the behavior of these two functions of h.

3. Verify for the Cobb-Douglas production function

$$P(L, K) = 1.01 L^{0.75} K^{0.25}$$

discussed in Example 3 that the production will be doubled if both the amount of labor and the amount of capital are doubled. Is this also true for the general production function $P(L, K) = bL^\alpha K^{1-\alpha}$?

4. The wind-chill index W discussed in Example 2 has been modeled by the following function:

$$W(T, v) = 13.12 + 0.6215T - 11.37v^{0.16} + 0.3965Tv^{0.16}$$

Check to see how closely this model agrees with the values in Table 1 for a few values of T and v.

5. The wave heights h in the open sea depend on the speed v of the wind and the length of time t that the wind has been blowing at that speed. Values of the function $h = f(v, t)$ are recorded in feet in the following table.
(a) What is the value of $f(40, 15)$? What is its meaning?
(b) What is the meaning of the function $h = f(30, t)$? Describe the behavior of this function.
(c) What is the meaning of the function $h = f(v, 30)$? Describe the behavior of this function.

Duration (hours)

v \ t	5	10	15	20	30	40	50
10	2	2	2	2	2	2	2
15	4	4	5	5	5	5	5
20	5	7	8	8	9	9	9
30	9	13	16	17	18	19	19
40	14	21	25	28	31	33	33
50	19	29	36	40	45	48	50
60	24	37	47	54	62	67	69

Wind speed (knots)

6. Let $f(x, y) = \ln(x + y - 1)$.
(a) Evaluate $f(1, 1)$.
(b) Evaluate $f(e, 1)$.
(c) Find and sketch the domain of f.
(d) Find the range of f.

7. Let $f(x, y) = x^2 e^{3xy}$.
(a) Evaluate $f(2, 0)$.
(b) Find the domain of f.
(c) Find the range of f.

8. Find and sketch the domain of the function $f(x, y) = \sqrt{1 + x - y^2}$. What is the range of f?

9. Let $f(x, y, z) = e^{\sqrt{z - x^2 - y^2}}$.
(a) Evaluate $f(2, -1, 6)$.
(b) Find the domain of f.
(c) Find the range of f.

10. Let $g(x, y, z) = \ln(25 - x^2 - y^2 - z^2)$.
(a) Evaluate $g(2, -2, 4)$.
(b) Find the domain of g.
(c) Find the range of g.

11–20 ||||| Find and sketch the domain of the function.

11. $f(x, y) = \sqrt{x + y}$

12. $f(x, y) = \sqrt{x} + \sqrt{y}$

13. $f(x, y) = \ln(9 - x^2 - 9y^2)$

14. $f(x, y) = \dfrac{x - 3y}{x + 3y}$

15. $f(x, y) = \dfrac{3x + 5y}{x^2 + y^2 - 4}$

16. $f(x, y) = \sqrt{y - x} \ln(y + x)$

17. $f(x, y) = \dfrac{\sqrt{y - x^2}}{1 - x^2}$

18. $f(x, y) = \sqrt{x^2 + y^2 - 1} + \ln(4 - x^2 - y^2)$

19. $f(x, y, z) = \sqrt{1 - x^2 - y^2 - z^2}$

20. $f(x, y, z) = \ln(16 - 4x^2 - 4y^2 - z^2)$

21–29 |||| Sketch the graph of the function.

21. $f(x, y) = 3$

22. $f(x, y) = y$

23. $f(x, y) = 1 - x - y$

24. $f(x, y) = \cos x$

25. $f(x, y) = 1 - x^2$

26. $f(x, y) = 3 - x^2 - y^2$

27. $f(x, y) = 4x^2 + y^2 + 1$

28. $f(x, y) = \sqrt{16 - x^2 - 16y^2}$

29. $f(x, y) = \sqrt{x^2 + y^2}$

30. Match the function with its graph (labeled I–VI). Give reasons for your choices.

(a) $f(x, y) = |x| + |y|$

(b) $f(x, y) = |xy|$

(c) $f(x, y) = \dfrac{1}{1 + x^2 + y^2}$

(d) $f(x, y) = (x^2 - y^2)^2$

(e) $f(x, y) = (x - y)^2$

(f) $f(x, y) = \sin(|x| + |y|)$

I

II

III

IV

V

VI
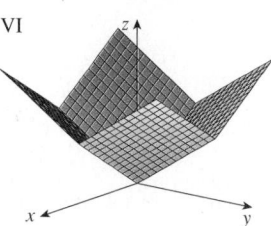

31. A contour map for a function f is shown. Use it to estimate the values of $f(-3, 3)$ and $f(3, -2)$. What can you say about the shape of the graph?

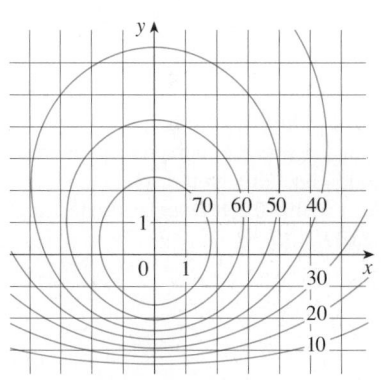

32. Two contour maps are shown. One is for a function f whose graph is a cone. The other is for a function g whose graph is a paraboloid. Which is which, and why?

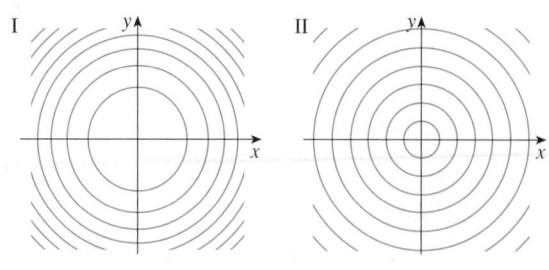

33. Locate the points A and B in the map of Lonesome Mountain (Figure 12). How would you describe the terrain near A? Near B?

34. Make a rough sketch of a contour map for the function whose graph is shown.

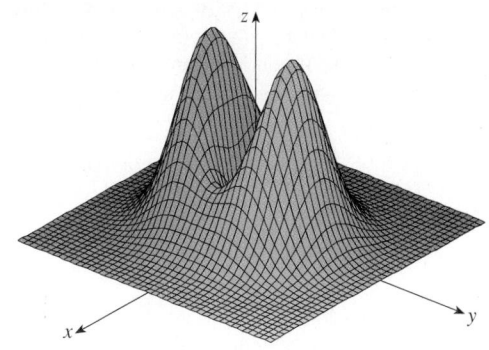

35–36 |||| A contour map of a function is shown. Use it to make a rough sketch of the graph of f.

35.

36.
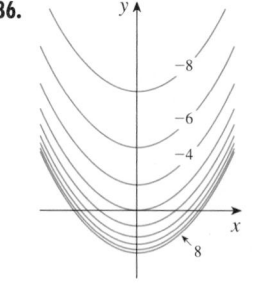

37–44 |||| Draw a contour map of the function showing several level curves.

37. $f(x, y) = xy$

38. $f(x, y) = x^2 - y^2$

39. $f(x, y) = y - \ln x$

40. $f(x, y) = e^{y/x}$

41. $f(x, y) = \sqrt{x + y}$

42. $f(x, y) = y \sec x$

43. $f(x, y) = x - y^2$

44. $f(x, y) = y/(x^2 + y^2)$

45–46 ‖‖‖ Sketch both a contour map and a graph of the function and compare them.

45. $f(x, y) = x^2 + 9y^2$

46. $f(x, y) = \sqrt{36 - 9x^2 - 4y^2}$

47. A thin metal plate, located in the xy-plane, has temperature $T(x, y)$ at the point (x, y). The level curves of T are called *isothermals* because at all points on an isothermal the temperature is the same. Sketch some isothermals if the temperature function is given by

$$T(x, y) = 100/(1 + x^2 + 2y^2)$$

48. If $V(x, y)$ is the electric potential at a point (x, y) in the xy-plane, then the level curves of V are called *equipotential curves* because at all points on such a curve the electric potential is the same. Sketch some equipotential curves if $V(x, y) = c/\sqrt{r^2 - x^2 - y^2}$, where c is a positive constant.

49–52 ‖‖‖ Use a computer to graph the function using various domains and viewpoints. Get a printout of one that, in your opinion, gives a good view. If your software also produces level curves, then plot some contour lines of the same function and compare with the graph.

49. $f(x, y) = x^3 + y^3$ **50.** $f(x, y) = \sin(ye^{-x})$

51. $f(x, y) = xy^2 - x^3$ (monkey saddle)

52. $f(x, y) = xy^3 - yx^3$ (dog saddle)

53–58 ‖‖‖ Match the function (a) with its graph (labeled A–F on page 937) and (b) with its contour map (labeled I–VI). Give reasons for your choices.

53. $z = \sin\sqrt{x^2 + y^2}$ **54.** $z = x^2y^2e^{-x^2-y^2}$

55. $z = \dfrac{1}{x^2 + 4y^2}$ **56.** $z = x^3 - 3xy^2$

57. $z = \sin x \sin y$ **58.** $z = \sin^2 x + \frac{1}{4}y^2$

59–62 ‖‖‖ Describe the level surfaces of the function.

59. $f(x, y, z) = x + 3y + 5z$

60. $f(x, y, z) = x^2 + 3y^2 + 5z^2$

61. $f(x, y, z) = x^2 - y^2 + z^2$

62. $f(x, y, z) = x^2 - y^2$

63–64 ‖‖‖ Describe how the graph of g is obtained from the graph of f.

63. (a) $g(x, y) = f(x, y) + 2$ (b) $g(x, y) = 2f(x, y)$
  (c) $g(x, y) = -f(x, y)$ (d) $g(x, y) = 2 - f(x, y)$

64. (a) $g(x, y) = f(x - 2, y)$ (b) $g(x, y) = f(x, y + 2)$
  (c) $g(x, y) = f(x + 3, y - 4)$

65–66 ‖‖‖ Use a computer to graph the function using various domains and viewpoints. Get a printout that gives a good view of the "peaks and valleys." Would you say the function has a maximum value? Can you identify any points on the graph that you might consider to be "local maximum points"? What about "local minimum points"?

65. $f(x, y) = 3x - x^4 - 4y^2 - 10xy$

66. $f(x, y) = xye^{-x^2-y^2}$

67–68 ‖‖‖ Use a computer to graph the function using various domains and viewpoints. Comment on the limiting behavior of the function. What happens as both x and y become large? What happens as (x, y) approaches the origin?

67. $f(x, y) = \dfrac{x + y}{x^2 + y^2}$ **68.** $f(x, y) = \dfrac{xy}{x^2 + y^2}$

69. Use a computer to investigate the family of functions $f(x, y) = e^{cx^2+y^2}$. How does the shape of the graph depend on c?

70. Graph the functions

$$f(x, y) = \sqrt{x^2 + y^2} \qquad\qquad f(x, y) = e^{\sqrt{x^2+y^2}}$$

$$f(x, y) = \ln\sqrt{x^2 + y^2} \qquad f(x, y) = \sin\left(\sqrt{x^2 + y^2}\right)$$

and $\qquad\qquad f(x, y) = \dfrac{1}{\sqrt{x^2 + y^2}}$

In general, if g is a function of one variable, how is the graph of $f(x, y) = g(\sqrt{x^2 + y^2})$ obtained from the graph of g?

71. (a) Show that, by taking logarithms, the general Cobb-Douglas function $P = bL^\alpha K^{1-\alpha}$ can be expressed as

$$\ln\frac{P}{K} = \ln b + \alpha \ln\frac{L}{K}$$

  (b) If we let $x = \ln(L/K)$ and $y = \ln(P/K)$, the equation in part (a) becomes the linear equation $y = \alpha x + \ln b$. Use Table 2 (in Example 3) to make a table of values of $\ln(L/K)$ and $\ln(P/K)$ for the years 1899–1922. Then use a graphing calculator or computer to find the least squares regression line through the points $(\ln(L/K), \ln(P/K))$.

  (c) Deduce that the Cobb-Douglas production function is $P = 1.01L^{0.75}K^{0.25}$.

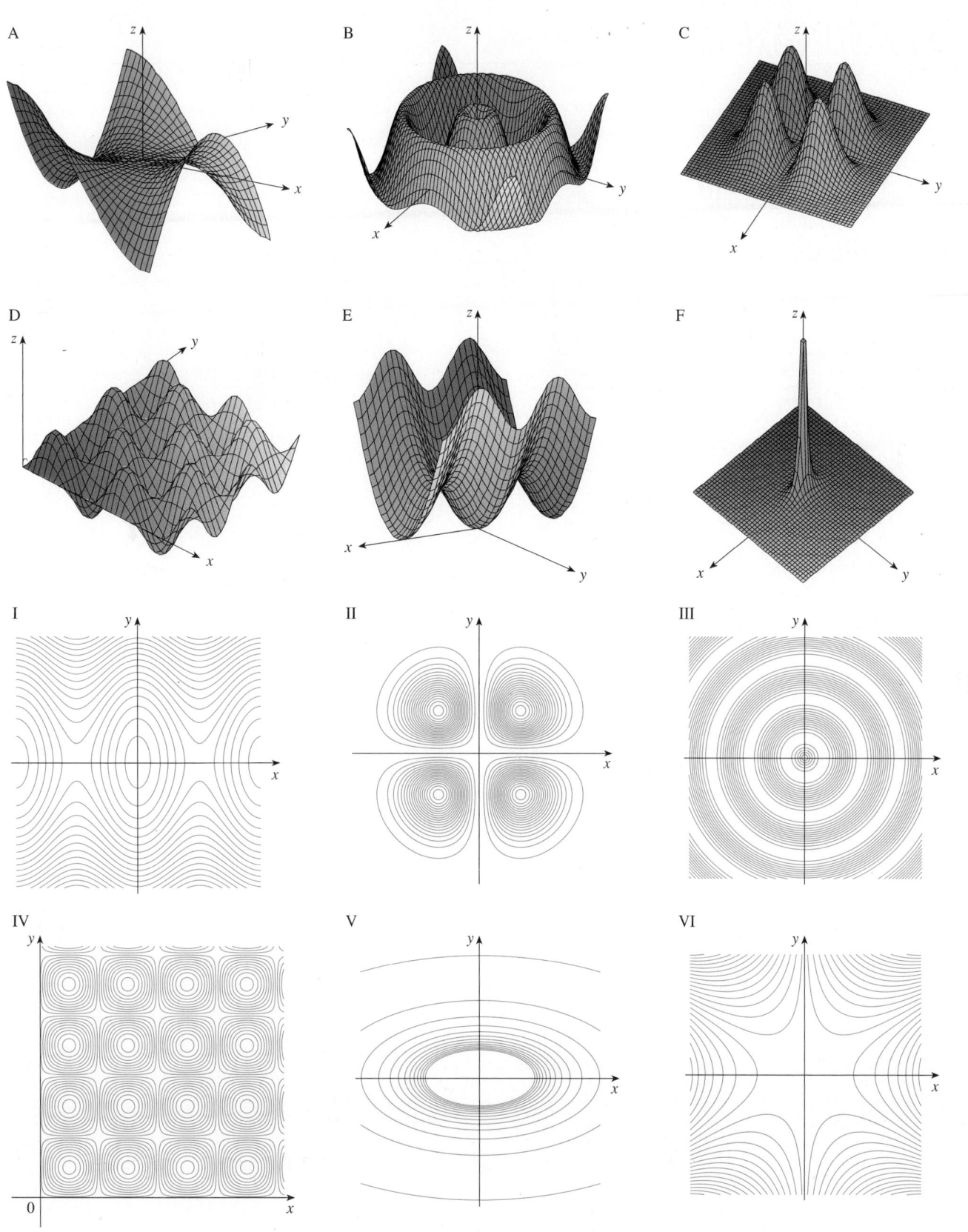

15.2 Limits and Continuity

Let's compare the behavior of the functions

$$f(x, y) = \frac{\sin(x^2 + y^2)}{x^2 + y^2} \qquad \text{and} \qquad g(x, y) = \frac{x^2 - y^2}{x^2 + y^2}$$

as x and y both approach 0 [and therefore the point (x, y) approaches the origin].

TABLE 1 Values of $f(x, y)$

x \ y	−1.0	−0.5	−0.2	0	0.2	0.5	1.0
−1.0	0.455	0.759	0.829	0.841	0.829	0.759	0.455
−0.5	0.759	0.959	0.986	0.990	0.986	0.959	0.759
−0.2	0.829	0.986	0.999	1.000	0.999	0.986	0.829
0	0.841	0.990	1.000		1.000	0.990	0.841
0.2	0.829	0.986	0.999	1.000	0.999	0.986	0.829
0.5	0.759	0.959	0.986	0.990	0.986	0.959	0.759
1.0	0.455	0.759	0.829	0.841	0.829	0.759	0.455

TABLE 2 Values of $g(x, y)$

x \ y	−1.0	−0.5	−0.2	0	0.2	0.5	1.0
−1.0	0.000	0.600	0.923	1.000	0.923	0.600	0.000
−0.5	−0.600	0.000	0.724	1.000	0.724	0.000	−0.600
−0.2	−0.923	−0.724	0.000	1.000	0.000	−0.724	−0.923
0	−1.000	−1.000	−1.000		−1.000	−1.000	−1.000
0.2	−0.923	−0.724	0.000	1.000	0.000	−0.724	−0.923
0.5	−0.600	0.000	0.724	1.000	0.724	0.000	−0.600
1.0	0.000	0.600	0.923	1.000	0.923	0.600	0.000

Tables 1 and 2 show values of $f(x, y)$ and $g(x, y)$, correct to three decimal places, for points (x, y) near the origin. (Notice that neither function is defined at the origin.) It appears that as (x, y) approaches $(0, 0)$, the values of $f(x, y)$ are approaching 1 whereas the values of $g(x, y)$ aren't approaching any number. It turns out that these guesses based on numerical evidence are correct, and we write

$$\lim_{(x, y) \to (0, 0)} \frac{\sin(x^2 + y^2)}{x^2 + y^2} = 1 \qquad \text{and} \qquad \lim_{(x, y) \to (0, 0)} \frac{x^2 - y^2}{x^2 + y^2} \quad \text{does not exist}$$

In general, we use the notation

$$\lim_{(x, y) \to (a, b)} f(x, y) = L$$

to indicate that the values of $f(x, y)$ approach the number L as the point (x, y) approaches the point (a, b) along any path that stays within the domain of f. In other words, we can make the values of $f(x, y)$ as close to L as we like by taking the point (x, y) sufficiently close to the point (a, b), but not equal to (a, b). A more precise definition follows.

---

1 **Definition** Let f be a function of two variables whose domain D includes points arbitrarily close to (a, b). Then we say that the **limit of $f(x, y)$ as (x, y) approaches (a, b)** is L and we write

$$\lim_{(x, y) \to (a, b)} f(x, y) = L$$

if for every number $\varepsilon > 0$ there is a corresponding number $\delta > 0$ such that

$$|f(x, y) - L| < \varepsilon \quad \text{whenever} \quad (x, y) \in D \quad \text{and} \quad 0 < \sqrt{(x - a)^2 + (y - b)^2} < \delta$$

Other notations for the limit in Definition 1 are

$$\lim_{\substack{x \to a \\ y \to b}} f(x, y) = L \qquad \text{and} \qquad f(x, y) \to L \ \text{as} \ (x, y) \to (a, b)$$

Notice that $|f(x, y) - L|$ is the distance between the numbers $f(x, y)$ and L, and $\sqrt{(x - a)^2 + (y - b)^2}$ is the distance between the point (x, y) and the point (a, b). Thus, Definition 1 says that the distance between $f(x, y)$ and L can be made arbitrarily small by making the distance from (x, y) to (a, b) sufficiently small (but not 0). Figure 1 illustrates Definition 1 by means of an arrow diagram. If any small interval $(L - \varepsilon, L + \varepsilon)$ is given around L, then we can find a disk D_δ with center (a, b) and radius $\delta > 0$ such that f maps all the points in D_δ [except possibly (a, b)] into the interval $(L - \varepsilon, L + \varepsilon)$.

FIGURE 1

FIGURE 2

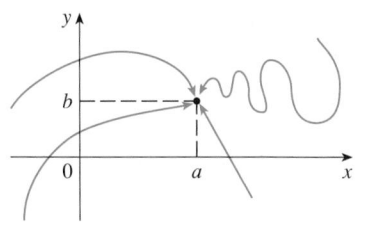

FIGURE 3

Another illustration of Definition 1 is given in Figure 2 where the surface S is the graph of f. If $\varepsilon > 0$ is given, we can find $\delta > 0$ such that if (x, y) is restricted to lie in the disk D_δ and $(x, y) \neq (a, b)$, then the corresponding part of S lies between the horizontal planes $z = L - \varepsilon$ and $z = L + \varepsilon$.

For functions of a single variable, when we let x approach a, there are only two possible directions of approach, from the left or from the right. We recall from Chapter 2 that if $\lim_{x \to a^-} f(x) \neq \lim_{x \to a^+} f(x)$, then $\lim_{x \to a} f(x)$ does not exist.

For functions of two variables the situation is not as simple because we can let (x, y) approach (a, b) from an infinite number of directions in any manner whatsoever (see Figure 3) as long as (x, y) stays within the domain of f.

Definition 1 says that the distance between $f(x, y)$ and L can be made arbitrarily small by making the distance from (x, y) to (a, b) sufficiently small (but not 0). The definition refers only to the *distance* between (x, y) and (a, b). It does not refer to the direction of approach. Therefore, if the limit exists, then $f(x, y)$ must approach the same limit no matter how (x, y) approaches (a, b). Thus, if we can find two different paths of approach along which the function $f(x, y)$ has different limits, then it follows that $\lim_{(x, y) \to (a, b)} f(x, y)$ does not exist.

> If $f(x, y) \to L_1$ as $(x, y) \to (a, b)$ along a path C_1 and $f(x, y) \to L_2$ as $(x, y) \to (a, b)$ along a path C_2, where $L_1 \neq L_2$, then $\lim_{(x, y) \to (a, b)} f(x, y)$ does not exist.

EXAMPLE 1 Show that $\displaystyle\lim_{(x, y) \to (0, 0)} \frac{x^2 - y^2}{x^2 + y^2}$ does not exist.

SOLUTION Let $f(x, y) = (x^2 - y^2)/(x^2 + y^2)$. First let's approach $(0, 0)$ along the x-axis. Then $y = 0$ gives $f(x, 0) = x^2/x^2 = 1$ for all $x \neq 0$, so

$$f(x, y) \to 1 \qquad \text{as} \qquad (x, y) \to (0, 0) \text{ along the } x\text{-axis}$$

FIGURE 4

FIGURE 5

In Visual 15.2 a rotating line on the surface in Figure 6 shows different limits at the origin from different directions.

We now approach along the y-axis by putting $x = 0$. Then $f(0, y) = \dfrac{-y^2}{y^2} = -1$ for all $y \neq 0$, so

$$f(x, y) \to -1 \qquad \text{as} \qquad (x, y) \to (0, 0) \text{ along the } y\text{-axis}$$

(See Figure 4.) Since f has two different limits along two different lines, the given limit does not exist. (This confirms the conjecture we made on the basis of numerical evidence at the beginning of this section.)

EXAMPLE 2 If $f(x, y) = xy/(x^2 + y^2)$, does $\displaystyle\lim_{(x, y) \to (0, 0)} f(x, y)$ exist?

SOLUTION If $y = 0$, then $f(x, 0) = 0/x^2 = 0$. Therefore

$$f(x, y) \to 0 \qquad \text{as} \qquad (x, y) \to (0, 0) \text{ along the } x\text{-axis}$$

If $x = 0$, then $f(0, y) = 0/y^2 = 0$, so

$$f(x, y) \to 0 \qquad \text{as} \qquad (x, y) \to (0, 0) \text{ along the } y\text{-axis}$$

Although we have obtained identical limits along the axes, that does not show that the given limit is 0. Let's now approach $(0, 0)$ along another line, say $y = x$. For all $x \neq 0$,

$$f(x, x) = \frac{x^2}{x^2 + x^2} = \frac{1}{2}$$

Therefore $\qquad f(x, y) \to \tfrac{1}{2} \qquad \text{as} \qquad (x, y) \to (0, 0) \text{ along } y = x$

(See Figure 5.) Since we have obtained different limits along different paths, the given limit does not exist.

Figure 6 sheds some light on Example 2. The ridge that occurs above the line $y = x$ corresponds to the fact that $f(x, y) = \tfrac{1}{2}$ for all points (x, y) on that line except the origin.

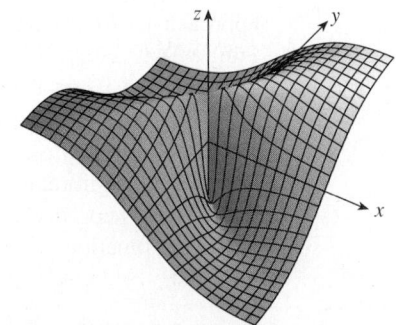

FIGURE 6
$$f(x, y) = \frac{xy}{x^2 + y^2}$$

EXAMPLE 3 If $f(x, y) = \dfrac{xy^2}{x^2 + y^4}$, does $\displaystyle\lim_{(x, y) \to (0, 0)} f(x, y)$ exist?

SOLUTION With the solution of Example 2 in mind, let's try to save time by letting $(x, y) \to (0, 0)$ along any nonvertical line through the origin. Then $y = mx$, where m is the slope, and

$$f(x, y) = f(x, mx) = \frac{x(mx)^2}{x^2 + (mx)^4} = \frac{m^2 x^3}{x^2 + m^4 x^4} = \frac{m^2 x}{1 + m^4 x^2}$$

So $\qquad\qquad f(x, y) \to 0 \qquad \text{as} \qquad (x, y) \to (0, 0) \text{ along } y = mx$

IIII Figure 7 shows the graph of the function in Example 3. Notice the ridge above the parabola $x = y^2$.

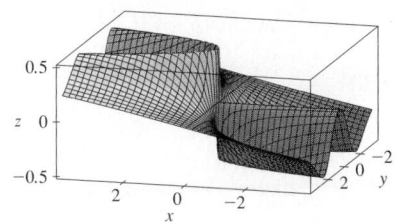

FIGURE 7

Thus, f has the same limiting value along every nonvertical line through the origin. But that does not show that the given limit is 0, for if we now let $(x, y) \to (0, 0)$ along the parabola $x = y^2$, we have

$$f(x, y) = f(y^2, y) = \frac{y^2 \cdot y^2}{(y^2)^2 + y^4} = \frac{y^4}{2y^4} = \frac{1}{2}$$

so $\qquad f(x, y) \to \frac{1}{2} \qquad$ as $\qquad (x, y) \to (0, 0)$ along $x = y^2$

Since different paths lead to different limiting values, the given limit does not exist.

Now let's look at limits that *do* exist. Just as for functions of one variable, the calculation of limits for functions of two variables can be greatly simplified by the use of properties of limits. The Limit Laws listed in Section 2.3 can be extended to functions of two variables. The limit of a sum is the sum of the limits, the limit of a product is the product of the limits, and so on. In particular, the following equations are true.

$$\boxed{2} \qquad \lim_{(x, y)\to(a, b)} x = a \qquad \lim_{(x, y)\to(a, b)} y = b \qquad \lim_{(x, y)\to(a, b)} c = c$$

The Squeeze Theorem also holds.

EXAMPLE 4 Find $\displaystyle\lim_{(x, y)\to(0, 0)} \frac{3x^2y}{x^2 + y^2}$ if it exists.

SOLUTION As in Example 3, we could show that the limit along any line through the origin is 0. This doesn't prove that the given limit is 0, but the limits along the parabolas $y = x^2$ and $x = y^2$ also turn out to be 0, so we begin to suspect that the limit does exist and is equal to 0.

Let $\varepsilon > 0$. We want to find $\delta > 0$ such that

$$\left| \frac{3x^2y}{x^2 + y^2} - 0 \right| < \varepsilon \qquad \text{whenever} \qquad 0 < \sqrt{x^2 + y^2} < \delta$$

that is, $\qquad \dfrac{3x^2|y|}{x^2 + y^2} < \varepsilon \qquad$ whenever $\qquad 0 < \sqrt{x^2 + y^2} < \delta$

But $x^2 \leq x^2 + y^2$ since $y^2 \geq 0$, so $x^2/(x^2 + y^2) \leq 1$ and therefore

$$\boxed{3} \qquad \frac{3x^2|y|}{x^2 + y^2} \leq 3|y| = 3\sqrt{y^2} \leq 3\sqrt{x^2 + y^2}$$

Thus, if we choose $\delta = \varepsilon/3$ and let $0 < \sqrt{x^2 + y^2} < \delta$, then

$$\left| \frac{3x^2y}{x^2 + y^2} - 0 \right| \leq 3\sqrt{x^2 + y^2} < 3\delta = 3\left(\frac{\varepsilon}{3}\right) = \varepsilon$$

IIII Another way to do Example 4 is to use the Squeeze Theorem instead of Definition 1. From (2) it follows that

$$\lim_{(x, y)\to(0, 0)} 3|y| = 0$$

and so the first inequality in (3) shows that the given limit is 0.

Hence, by Definition 1,

$$\lim_{(x, y)\to(0, 0)} \frac{3x^2y}{x^2 + y^2} = 0$$

||||| **Continuity**

Recall that evaluating limits of *continuous* functions of a single variable is easy. It can be accomplished by direct substitution because the defining property of a continuous function is $\lim_{x \to a} f(x) = f(a)$. Continuous functions of two variables are also defined by the direct substitution property.

---

4 **Definition** A function f of two variables is called **continuous at** (a, b) if

$$\lim_{(x, y) \to (a, b)} f(x, y) = f(a, b)$$

We say f is **continuous on** D if f is continuous at every point (a, b) in D.

The intuitive meaning of continuity is that if the point (x, y) changes by a small amount, then the value of $f(x, y)$ changes by a small amount. This means that a surface that is the graph of a continuous function has no hole or break.

Using the properties of limits, you can see that sums, differences, products, and quotients of continuous functions are continuous on their domains. Let's use this fact to give examples of continuous functions.

A **polynomial function of two variables** (or polynomial, for short) is a sum of terms of the form $cx^m y^n$, where c is a constant and m and n are nonnegative integers. A **rational function** is a ratio of polynomials. For instance,

$$f(x, y) = x^4 + 5x^3y^2 + 6xy^4 - 7y + 6$$

is a polynomial, whereas

$$g(x, y) = \frac{2xy + 1}{x^2 + y^2}$$

is a rational function.

The limits in (2) show that the functions $f(x, y) = x$, $g(x, y) = y$, and $h(x, y) = c$ are continuous. Since any polynomial can be built up out of the simple functions f, g, and h by multiplication and addition, it follows that *all polynomials are continuous on* $\mathbb{R}^2$. Likewise, any rational function is continuous on its domain because it is a quotient of continuous functions.

EXAMPLE 5 Evaluate $\lim_{(x, y) \to (1, 2)} (x^2y^3 - x^3y^2 + 3x + 2y)$.

SOLUTION Since $f(x, y) = x^2y^3 - x^3y^2 + 3x + 2y$ is a polynomial, it is continuous everywhere, so we can find the limit by direct substitution:

$$\lim_{(x, y) \to (1, 2)} (x^2y^3 - x^3y^2 + 3x + 2y) = 1^2 \cdot 2^3 - 1^3 \cdot 2^2 + 3 \cdot 1 + 2 \cdot 2 = 11 \quad \blacksquare$$

EXAMPLE 6 Where is the function $f(x, y) = \dfrac{x^2 - y^2}{x^2 + y^2}$ continuous?

SOLUTION The function f is discontinuous at $(0, 0)$ because it is not defined there. Since f is a rational function, it is continuous on its domain, which is the set $D = \{(x, y) \mid (x, y) \neq (0, 0)\}$. $\quad \blacksquare$

EXAMPLE 7 Let

$$g(x, y) = \begin{cases} \dfrac{x^2 - y^2}{x^2 + y^2} & \text{if } (x, y) \neq (0, 0) \\ 0 & \text{if } (x, y) = (0, 0) \end{cases}$$

Here g is defined at $(0, 0)$ but g is still discontinuous at 0 because $\lim_{(x,\,y)\to(0,\,0)} g(x, y)$ does not exist (see Example 1).

||| Figure 8 shows the graph of the continuous function in Example 8.

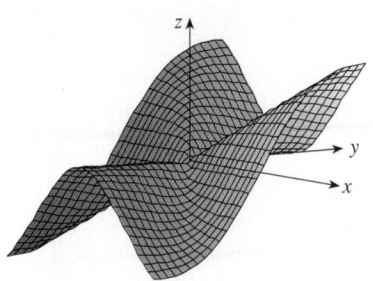

FIGURE 8

EXAMPLE 8 Let

$$f(x, y) = \begin{cases} \dfrac{3x^2y}{x^2 + y^2} & \text{if } (x, y) \neq (0, 0) \\ 0 & \text{if } (x, y) = (0, 0) \end{cases}$$

We know f is continuous for $(x, y) \neq (0, 0)$ since it is equal to a rational function there. Also, from Example 4, we have

$$\lim_{(x,\,y)\to(0,\,0)} f(x, y) = \lim_{(x,\,y)\to(0,\,0)} \frac{3x^2y}{x^2 + y^2} = 0 = f(0, 0)$$

Therefore, f is continuous at $(0, 0)$, and so it is continuous on $\mathbb{R}^2$.

Just as for functions of one variable, composition is another way of combining two continuous functions to get a third. In fact, it can be shown that if f is a continuous function of two variables and g is a continuous function of a single variable that is defined on the range of f, then the composite function $h = g \circ f$ defined by $h(x, y) = g(f(x, y))$ is also a continuous function.

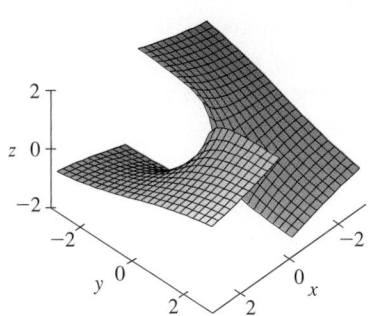

FIGURE 9
The function $h(x, y) = \arctan(y/x)$
is discontinuous where $x = 0$.

EXAMPLE 9 Where is the function $h(x, y) = \arctan(y/x)$ continuous?

SOLUTION The function $f(x, y) = y/x$ is a rational function and therefore continuous except on the line $x = 0$. The function $g(t) = \arctan t$ is continuous everywhere. So the composite function

$$g(f(x, y)) = \arctan(y/x) = h(x, y)$$

is continuous except where $x = 0$. The graph in Figure 9 shows the break in the graph of h above the y-axis.

||||| **Functions of Three or More Variables**

Everything that we have done in this section can be extended to functions of three or more variables. The notation

$$\lim_{(x,\,y,\,z)\to(a,\,b,\,c)} f(x, y, z) = L$$

means that the values of $f(x, y, z)$ approach the number L as the point (x, y, z) approaches the point (a, b, c) along any path in the domain of f. Because the distance between two points (x, y, z) and (a, b, c) in $\mathbb{R}^3$ is given by $\sqrt{(x - a)^2 + (y - b)^2 + (z - c)^2}$, we can write the precise definition as follows: For every number $\varepsilon > 0$ there is a corresponding number $\delta > 0$ such that

$$|f(x, y, z) - L| < \varepsilon \qquad \text{whenever} \qquad 0 < \sqrt{(x - a)^2 + (y - b)^2 + (z - c)^2} < \delta$$

and (x, y, z) is in the domain of f.

The function f is **continuous** at (a, b, c) if

$$\lim_{(x,\,y,\,z)\to(a,\,b,\,c)} f(x, y, z) = f(a, b, c)$$

For instance, the function

$$f(x, y, z) = \frac{1}{x^2 + y^2 + z^2 - 1}$$

is a rational function of three variables and so is continuous at every point in $\mathbb{R}^3$ except where $x^2 + y^2 + z^2 = 1$. In other words, it is discontinuous on the sphere with center the origin and radius 1.

If we use the vector notation introduced at the end of Section 15.1, then we can write the definitions of a limit for functions of two or three variables in a single compact form as follows.

> **5** If f is defined on a subset D of $\mathbb{R}^n$, then $\lim_{\mathbf{x} \to \mathbf{a}} f(\mathbf{x}) = L$ means that for every number $\varepsilon > 0$ there is a corresponding number $\delta > 0$ such that
>
> $$|f(\mathbf{x}) - L| < \varepsilon \quad \text{whenever } \mathbf{x} \in D \quad \text{and} \quad 0 < |\mathbf{x} - \mathbf{a}| < \delta$$

Notice that if $n = 1$, then $\mathbf{x} = x$ and $\mathbf{a} = a$, and (5) is just the definition of a limit for functions of a single variable. For the case $n = 2$, we have $\mathbf{x} = \langle x, y \rangle$, $\mathbf{a} = \langle a, b \rangle$, and $|\mathbf{x} - \mathbf{a}| = \sqrt{(x - a)^2 + (y - b)^2}$, so (5) becomes Definition 1. If $n = 3$, then $\mathbf{x} = \langle x, y, z \rangle$, $\mathbf{a} = \langle a, b, c \rangle$, and (5) becomes the definition of a limit of a function of three variables. In each case the definition of continuity can be written as

$$\lim_{\mathbf{x} \to \mathbf{a}} f(\mathbf{x}) = f(\mathbf{a})$$

15.2 Exercises

1. Suppose that $\lim_{(x, y) \to (3, 1)} f(x, y) = 6$. What can you say about the value of $f(3, 1)$? What if f is continuous?

2. Explain why each function is continuous or discontinuous.
   (a) The outdoor temperature as a function of longitude, latitude, and time
   (b) Elevation (height above sea level) as a function of longitude, latitude, and time
   (c) The cost of a taxi ride as a function of distance traveled and time

3–4 ▓▓▓▓ Use a table of numerical values of $f(x, y)$ for (x, y) near the origin to make a conjecture about the value of the limit of $f(x, y)$ as $(x, y) \to (0, 0)$. Then explain why your guess is correct.

3. $f(x, y) = \dfrac{x^2 y^3 + x^3 y^2 - 5}{2 - xy}$ **4.** $f(x, y) = \dfrac{2xy}{x^2 + 2y^2}$

5–20 ▓▓▓▓ Find the limit, if it exists, or show that the limit does not exist.

5. $\displaystyle\lim_{(x, y) \to (5, -2)} (x^5 + 4x^3 y - 5xy^2)$

6. $\displaystyle\lim_{(x, y) \to (6, 3)} xy \cos(x - 2y)$

7. $\displaystyle\lim_{(x, y) \to (0, 0)} \frac{x^2}{x^2 + y^2}$

8. $\displaystyle\lim_{(x, y) \to (0, 0)} \frac{x^2 + \sin^2 y}{2x^2 + y^2}$

9. $\displaystyle\lim_{(x, y) \to (0, 0)} \frac{xy \cos y}{3x^2 + y^2}$

10. $\displaystyle\lim_{(x, y) \to (0, 0)} \frac{6x^3 y}{2x^4 + y^4}$

11. $\displaystyle\lim_{(x, y) \to (0, 0)} \frac{xy}{\sqrt{x^2 + y^2}}$

12. $\displaystyle\lim_{(x, y) \to (0, 0)} \frac{x^4 - y^4}{x^2 + y^2}$

13. $\displaystyle\lim_{(x, y) \to (0, 0)} \frac{2x^2 y}{x^4 + y^2}$

14. $\displaystyle\lim_{(x, y) \to (0, 0)} \frac{x^2 \sin^2 y}{x^2 + 2y^2}$

15. $\displaystyle\lim_{(x, y) \to (0, 0)} \frac{x^2 + y^2}{\sqrt{x^2 + y^2 + 1} - 1}$

16. $\displaystyle\lim_{(x, y) \to (0, 0)} \frac{xy^4}{x^2 + y^8}$

17. $\displaystyle\lim_{(x, y, z) \to (3, 0, 1)} e^{-xy} \sin(\pi z / 2)$

18. $\displaystyle\lim_{(x, y, z) \to (0, 0, 0)} \frac{x^2 + 2y^2 + 3z^2}{x^2 + y^2 + z^2}$

19. $\displaystyle\lim_{(x, y, z) \to (0, 0, 0)} \frac{xy + yz^2 + xz^2}{x^2 + y^2 + z^4}$

20. $\displaystyle\lim_{(x, y, z) \to (0, 0, 0)} \frac{xy + yz + zx}{x^2 + y^2 + z^2}$

21–22 |||| Use a computer graph of the function to explain why the limit does not exist.

21. $\displaystyle\lim_{(x,y)\to(0,0)} \frac{2x^2 + 3xy + 4y^2}{3x^2 + 5y^2}$

22. $\displaystyle\lim_{(x,y)\to(0,0)} \frac{xy^3}{x^2 + y^6}$

23–24 |||| Find $h(x, y) = g(f(x, y))$ and the set on which h is continuous.

23. $g(t) = t^2 + \sqrt{t}, \quad f(x, y) = 2x + 3y - 6$

24. $g(t) = \dfrac{\sqrt{t} - 1}{\sqrt{t} + 1}, \quad f(x, y) = x^2 - y$

25–26 |||| Graph the function and observe where it is discontinuous. Then use the formula to explain what you have observed.

25. $f(x, y) = e^{1/(x-y)}$

26. $f(x, y) = \dfrac{1}{1 - x^2 - y^2}$

27–36 |||| Determine the set of points at which the function is continuous.

27. $F(x, y) = \dfrac{\sin(xy)}{e^x - y^2}$

28. $F(x, y) = \dfrac{x - y}{1 + x^2 + y^2}$

29. $F(x, y) = \arctan(x + \sqrt{y})$

30. $F(x, y) = e^{x^2 y} + \sqrt{x + y^2}$

31. $G(x, y) = \ln(x^2 + y^2 - 4)$

32. $G(x, y) = \sin^{-1}(x^2 + y^2)$

33. $f(x, y, z) = \dfrac{\sqrt{y}}{x^2 - y^2 + z^2}$

34. $f(x, y, z) = \sqrt{x + y + z}$

35. $f(x, y) = \begin{cases} \dfrac{x^2 y^3}{2x^2 + y^2} & \text{if } (x, y) \neq (0, 0) \\ 1 & \text{if } (x, y) = (0, 0) \end{cases}$

36. $f(x, y) = \begin{cases} \dfrac{xy}{x^2 + xy + y^2} & \text{if } (x, y) \neq (0, 0) \\ 0 & \text{if } (x, y) = (0, 0) \end{cases}$

37–38 |||| Use polar coordinates to find the limit. [If (r, θ) are polar coordinates of the point (x, y) with $r \geq 0$, note that $r \to 0^+$ as $(x, y) \to (0, 0)$.]

37. $\displaystyle\lim_{(x,y)\to(0,0)} \frac{x^3 + y^3}{x^2 + y^2}$

38. $\displaystyle\lim_{(x,y)\to(0,0)} (x^2 + y^2) \ln(x^2 + y^2)$

39. Use spherical coordinates to find

$$\lim_{(x,y,z)\to(0,0,0)} \frac{xyz}{x^2 + y^2 + z^2}$$

40. At the beginning of this section we considered the function

$$f(x, y) = \frac{\sin(x^2 + y^2)}{x^2 + y^2}$$

and guessed that $f(x, y) \to 1$ as $(x, y) \to (0, 0)$ on the basis of numerical evidence. Use polar coordinates to confirm the value of the limit. Then graph the function.

41. Show that the function f given by $f(\mathbf{x}) = |\mathbf{x}|$ is continuous on $\mathbb{R}^n$. [*Hint:* Consider $|\mathbf{x} - \mathbf{a}|^2 = (\mathbf{x} - \mathbf{a}) \cdot (\mathbf{x} - \mathbf{a})$.]

42. If $\mathbf{c} \in V_n$, show that the function f given by $f(\mathbf{x}) = \mathbf{c} \cdot \mathbf{x}$ is continuous on $\mathbb{R}^n$.

15.3 Partial Derivatives

On a hot day, extreme humidity makes us think the temperature is higher than it really is, whereas in very dry air we perceive the temperature to be lower than the thermometer indicates. The National Weather Service has devised the *heat index* (also called the temperature-humidity index, or humidex, in some countries) to describe the combined effects of temperature and humidity. The heat index I is the perceived air temperature when the actual temperature is T and the relative humidity is H. So I is a function of T and H and we can write $I = f(T, H)$. The following table of values of I is an excerpt from a table compiled by the National Weather Service.

TABLE 1

Heat index I as a function of
temperature and humidity

Relative humidity (%)

T \ H	50	55	60	65	70	75	80	85	90
90	96	98	100	103	106	109	112	115	119
92	100	103	105	108	112	115	119	123	128
94	104	107	111	114	118	122	127	132	137
96	109	113	116	121	125	130	135	141	146
98	114	118	123	127	133	138	144	150	157
100	119	124	129	135	141	147	154	161	168

Actual temperature (°F)

If we concentrate on the highlighted column of the table, which corresponds to a relative humidity of $H = 70\%$, we are considering the heat index as a function of the single variable T for a fixed value of H. Let's write $g(T) = f(T, 70)$. Then $g(T)$ describes how the heat index I increases as the actual temperature T increases when the relative humidity is 70%. The derivative of g when $T = 96°F$ is the rate of change of I with respect to T when $T = 96°F$:

$$g'(96) = \lim_{h \to 0} \frac{g(96 + h) - g(96)}{h} = \lim_{h \to 0} \frac{f(96 + h, 70) - f(96, 70)}{h}$$

We can approximate it using the values in Table 1 by taking $h = 2$ and -2:

$$g'(96) \approx \frac{g(98) - g(96)}{2} = \frac{f(98, 70) - f(96, 70)}{2} = \frac{133 - 125}{2} = 4$$

$$g'(96) \approx \frac{g(94) - g(96)}{-2} = \frac{f(94, 70) - f(96, 70)}{-2} = \frac{118 - 125}{-2} = 3.5$$

Averaging these values, we can say that the derivative $g'(96)$ is approximately 3.75. This means that, when the actual temperature is 96°F and the relative humidity is 70%, the apparent temperature (heat index) rises by about 3.75°F for every degree that the actual temperature rises!

Now let's look at the highlighted row in Table 1, which corresponds to a fixed temperature of $T = 96°F$. The numbers in this row are values of the function $G(H) = f(96, H)$, which describes how the heat index increases as the relative humidity H increases when the actual temperature is $T = 96°F$. The derivative of this function when $H = 70\%$ is the rate of change of I with respect to H when $H = 70\%$:

$$G'(70) = \lim_{h \to 0} \frac{G(70 + h) - G(70)}{h} = \lim_{h \to 0} \frac{f(96, 70 + h) - f(96, 70)}{h}$$

By taking $h = 5$ and -5, we approximate $G'(70)$ using the tabular values:

$$G'(70) \approx \frac{G(75) - G(70)}{5} = \frac{f(96, 75) - f(96, 70)}{5} = \frac{130 - 125}{5} = 1$$

$$G'(70) \approx \frac{G(65) - G(70)}{-5} = \frac{f(96, 65) - f(96, 70)}{-5} = \frac{121 - 125}{-5} = 0.8$$

By averaging these values we get the estimate $G'(70) \approx 0.9$. This says that, when the temperature is 96°F and the relative humidity is 70%, the heat index rises about 0.9°F for every percent that the relative humidity rises.

In general, if f is a function of two variables x and y, suppose we let only x vary while keeping y fixed, say $y = b$, where b is a constant. Then we are really considering a function of a single variable x, namely, $g(x) = f(x, b)$. If g has a derivative at a, then we call it the **partial derivative of f with respect to x at (a, b)** and denote it by $f_x(a, b)$. Thus

1
$$f_x(a, b) = g'(a) \qquad \text{where} \qquad g(x) = f(x, b)$$

By the definition of a derivative, we have

$$g'(a) = \lim_{h \to 0} \frac{g(a + h) - g(a)}{h}$$

and so Equation 1 becomes

2
$$f_x(a, b) = \lim_{h \to 0} \frac{f(a + h, b) - f(a, b)}{h}$$

Similarly, the **partial derivative of f with respect to y at (a, b)**, denoted by $f_y(a, b)$, is obtained by keeping x fixed $(x = a)$ and finding the ordinary derivative at b of the function $G(y) = f(a, y)$:

3
$$f_y(a, b) = \lim_{h \to 0} \frac{f(a, b + h) - f(a, b)}{h}$$

With this notation for partial derivatives, we can write the rates of change of the heat index I with respect to the actual temperature T and relative humidity H when $T = 96$°F and $H = 70\%$ as follows:

$$f_T(96, 70) \approx 3.75 \qquad f_H(96, 70) \approx 0.9$$

If we now let the point (a, b) vary in Equations 2 and 3, f_x and f_y become functions of two variables.

4 If f is a function of two variables, its **partial derivatives** are the functions f_x and f_y defined by

$$f_x(x, y) = \lim_{h \to 0} \frac{f(x + h, y) - f(x, y)}{h}$$

$$f_y(x, y) = \lim_{h \to 0} \frac{f(x, y + h) - f(x, y)}{h}$$

There are many alternative notations for partial derivatives. For instance, instead of f_x we can write f_1 or $D_1 f$ (to indicate differentiation with respect to the *first* variable) or $\partial f/\partial x$. But here $\partial f/\partial x$ can't be interpreted as a ratio of differentials.

Notations for Partial Derivatives If $z = f(x, y)$, we write

$$f_x(x, y) = f_x = \frac{\partial f}{\partial x} = \frac{\partial}{\partial x} f(x, y) = \frac{\partial z}{\partial x} = f_1 = D_1 f = D_x f$$

$$f_y(x, y) = f_y = \frac{\partial f}{\partial y} = \frac{\partial}{\partial y} f(x, y) = \frac{\partial z}{\partial y} = f_2 = D_2 f = D_y f$$

To compute partial derivatives, all we have to do is remember from Equation 1 that the partial derivative with respect to x is just the *ordinary* derivative of the function g of a single variable that we get by keeping y fixed. Thus, we have the following rule.

Rule for Finding Partial Derivatives of $z = f(x, y)$

1. To find f_x, regard y as a constant and differentiate $f(x, y)$ with respect to x.

2. To find f_y, regard x as a constant and differentiate $f(x, y)$ with respect to y.

EXAMPLE 1 If $f(x, y) = x^3 + x^2 y^3 - 2y^2$, find $f_x(2, 1)$ and $f_y(2, 1)$.

SOLUTION Holding y constant and differentiating with respect to x, we get

$$f_x(x, y) = 3x^2 + 2xy^3$$

and so

$$f_x(2, 1) = 3 \cdot 2^2 + 2 \cdot 2 \cdot 1^3 = 16$$

Holding x constant and differentiating with respect to y, we get

$$f_y(x, y) = 3x^2 y^2 - 4y$$

$$f_y(2, 1) = 3 \cdot 2^2 \cdot 1^2 - 4 \cdot 1 = 8$$

|||| Interpretations of Partial Derivatives

To give a geometric interpretation of partial derivatives, we recall that the equation $z = f(x, y)$ represents a surface S (the graph of f). If $f(a, b) = c$, then the point $P(a, b, c)$ lies on S. By fixing $y = b$, we are restricting our attention to the curve C_1 in which the vertical plane $y = b$ intersects S. (In other words, C_1 is the trace of S in the plane $y = b$.) Likewise, the vertical plane $x = a$ intersects S in a curve C_2. Both of the curves C_1 and C_2 pass through the point P. (See Figure 1.)

Notice that the curve C_1 is the graph of the function $g(x) = f(x, b)$, so the slope of its tangent T_1 at P is $g'(a) = f_x(a, b)$. The curve C_2 is the graph of the function $G(y) = f(a, y)$, so the slope of its tangent T_2 at P is $G'(b) = f_y(a, b)$.

Thus, the partial derivatives $f_x(a, b)$ and $f_y(a, b)$ can be interpreted geometrically as the slopes of the tangent lines at $P(a, b, c)$ to the traces C_1 and C_2 of S in the planes $y = b$ and $x = a$.

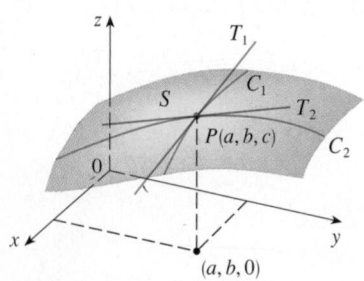

FIGURE 1

The partial derivatives of f at (a, b) are the slopes of the tangents to C_1 and C_2.

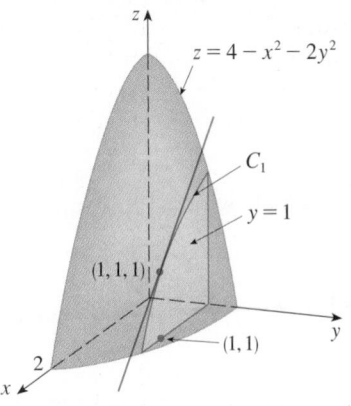

$z = 4 - x^2 - 2y^2$

C_1

$y = 1$

$(1, 1, 1)$

$(1, 1)$

2

FIGURE 2

As we have seen in the case of the heat index function, partial derivatives can also be interpreted as *rates of change*. If $z = f(x, y)$, then $\partial z / \partial x$ represents the rate of change of z with respect to x when y is fixed. Similarly, $\partial z / \partial y$ represents the rate of change of z with respect to y when x is fixed.

EXAMPLE 2 If $f(x, y) = 4 - x^2 - 2y^2$, find $f_x(1, 1)$ and $f_y(1, 1)$ and interpret these numbers as slopes.

SOLUTION We have

$$f_x(x, y) = -2x \qquad f_y(x, y) = -4y$$

$$f_x(1, 1) = -2 \qquad f_y(1, 1) = -4$$

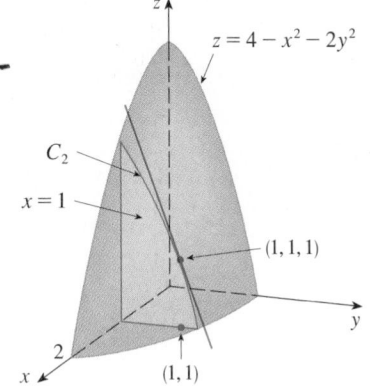

$z = 4 - x^2 - 2y^2$

C_2

$x = 1$

$(1, 1, 1)$

2

$(1, 1)$

FIGURE 3

The graph of f is the paraboloid $z = 4 - x^2 - 2y^2$ and the vertical plane $y = 1$ intersects it in the parabola $z = 2 - x^2$, $y = 1$. (As in the preceding discussion, we label it C_1 in Figure 2.) The slope of the tangent line to this parabola at the point $(1, 1, 1)$ is $f_x(1, 1) = -2$. Similarly, the curve C_2 in which the plane $x = 1$ intersects the paraboloid is the parabola $z = 3 - 2y^2$, $x = 1$, and the slope of the tangent line at $(1, 1, 1)$ is $f_y(1, 1) = -4$. (See Figure 3.)

Figure 4 is a computer-drawn counterpart to Figure 2. Part (a) shows the plane $y = 1$ intersecting the surface to form the curve C_1 and part (b) shows C_1 and T_1. [We have used the vector equations $\mathbf{r}(t) = \langle t, 1, 2 - t^2 \rangle$ for C_1 and $\mathbf{r}(t) = \langle 1 + t, 1, 1 - 2t \rangle$ for T_1.] Similarly, Figure 5 corresponds to Figure 3.

FIGURE 4   (a)   (b)

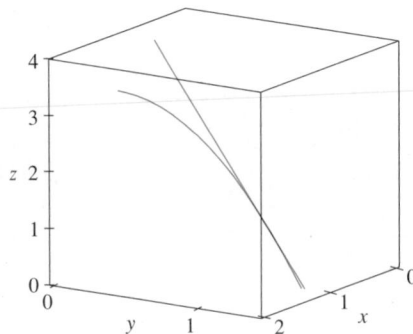

FIGURE 5

EXAMPLE 3 If $f(x, y) = \sin\left(\dfrac{x}{1 + y}\right)$, calculate $\dfrac{\partial f}{\partial x}$ and $\dfrac{\partial f}{\partial y}$.

SOLUTION Using the Chain Rule for functions of one variable, we have

$$\frac{\partial f}{\partial x} = \cos\left(\frac{x}{1 + y}\right) \cdot \frac{\partial}{\partial x}\left(\frac{x}{1 + y}\right) = \cos\left(\frac{x}{1 + y}\right) \cdot \frac{1}{1 + y}$$

$$\frac{\partial f}{\partial y} = \cos\left(\frac{x}{1 + y}\right) \cdot \frac{\partial}{\partial y}\left(\frac{x}{1 + y}\right) = -\cos\left(\frac{x}{1 + y}\right) \cdot \frac{x}{(1 + y)^2}$$

||| Some computer algebra systems can plot surfaces defined by implicit equations in three variables. Figure 6 shows such a plot of the surface defined by the equation in Example 4.

EXAMPLE 4 Find $\partial z/\partial x$ and $\partial z/\partial y$ if z is defined implicitly as a function of x and y by the equation

$$x^3 + y^3 + z^3 + 6xyz = 1$$

SOLUTION To find $\partial z/\partial x$, we differentiate implicitly with respect to x, being careful to treat y as a constant:

$$3x^2 + 3z^2\frac{\partial z}{\partial x} + 6yz + 6xy\frac{\partial z}{\partial x} = 0$$

Solving this equation for $\partial z/\partial x$, we obtain

$$\frac{\partial z}{\partial x} = -\frac{x^2 + 2yz}{z^2 + 2xy}$$

FIGURE 6

In Visual 15.3 you can zoom and rotate the surfaces in Figure 6 and Exercises 41–44.

Similarly, implicit differentiation with respect to y gives

$$\frac{\partial z}{\partial y} = -\frac{y^2 + 2xz}{z^2 + 2xy}$$

||| **Functions of More than Two Variables**

Partial derivatives can also be defined for functions of three or more variables. For example, if f is a function of three variables x, y, and z, then its partial derivative with respect to x is defined as

$$f_x(x, y, z) = \lim_{h \to 0} \frac{f(x + h, y, z) - f(x, y, z)}{h}$$

and it is found by regarding y and z as constants and differentiating $f(x, y, z)$ with respect to x. If $w = f(x, y, z)$, then $f_x = \partial w/\partial x$ can be interpreted as the rate of change of w with respect to x when y and z are held fixed. But we can't interpret it geometrically because the graph of f lies in four-dimensional space.

In general, if u is a function of n variables, $u = f(x_1, x_2, \ldots, x_n)$, its partial derivative with respect to the ith variable x_i is

$$\frac{\partial u}{\partial x_i} = \lim_{h \to 0} \frac{f(x_1, \ldots, x_{i-1}, x_i + h, x_{i+1}, \ldots, x_n) - f(x_1, \ldots, x_i, \ldots, x_n)}{h}$$

and we also write

$$\frac{\partial u}{\partial x_i} = \frac{\partial f}{\partial x_i} = f_{x_i} = f_i = D_i f$$

EXAMPLE 5 Find f_x, f_y, and f_z if $f(x, y, z) = e^{xy} \ln z$.

SOLUTION Holding y and z constant and differentiating with respect to x, we have

$$f_x = ye^{xy} \ln z$$

Similarly, $\qquad\qquad f_y = xe^{xy} \ln z \qquad$ and $\qquad f_z = \dfrac{e^{xy}}{z}$

Higher Derivatives

If f is a function of two variables, then its partial derivatives f_x and f_y are also functions of two variables, so we can consider their partial derivatives $(f_x)_x$, $(f_x)_y$, $(f_y)_x$, and $(f_y)_y$, which are called the **second partial derivatives** of f. If $z = f(x, y)$, we use the following notation:

$$(f_x)_x = f_{xx} = f_{11} = \frac{\partial}{\partial x}\left(\frac{\partial f}{\partial x}\right) = \frac{\partial^2 f}{\partial x^2} = \frac{\partial^2 z}{\partial x^2}$$

$$(f_x)_y = f_{xy} = f_{12} = \frac{\partial}{\partial y}\left(\frac{\partial f}{\partial x}\right) = \frac{\partial^2 f}{\partial y\, \partial x} = \frac{\partial^2 z}{\partial y\, \partial x}$$

$$(f_y)_x = f_{yx} = f_{21} = \frac{\partial}{\partial x}\left(\frac{\partial f}{\partial y}\right) = \frac{\partial^2 f}{\partial x\, \partial y} = \frac{\partial^2 z}{\partial x\, \partial y}$$

$$(f_y)_y = f_{yy} = f_{22} = \frac{\partial}{\partial y}\left(\frac{\partial f}{\partial y}\right) = \frac{\partial^2 f}{\partial y^2} = \frac{\partial^2 z}{\partial y^2}$$

Thus, the notation f_{xy} (or $\partial^2 f / \partial y\, \partial x$) means that we first differentiate with respect to x and then with respect to y, whereas in computing f_{yx} the order is reversed.

EXAMPLE 6 Find the second partial derivatives of

$$f(x, y) = x^3 + x^2 y^3 - 2y^2$$

SOLUTION In Example 1 we found that

$$f_x(x, y) = 3x^2 + 2xy^3 \qquad\qquad f_y(x, y) = 3x^2 y^2 - 4y$$

Therefore

$$f_{xx} = \frac{\partial}{\partial x}\,(3x^2 + 2xy^3) = 6x + 2y^3 \qquad f_{xy} = \frac{\partial}{\partial y}\,(3x^2 + 2xy^3) = 6xy^2$$

$$f_{yx} = \frac{\partial}{\partial x}\,(3x^2 y^2 - 4y) = 6xy^2 \qquad f_{yy} = \frac{\partial}{\partial y}\,(3x^2 y^2 - 4y) = 6x^2 y - 4$$

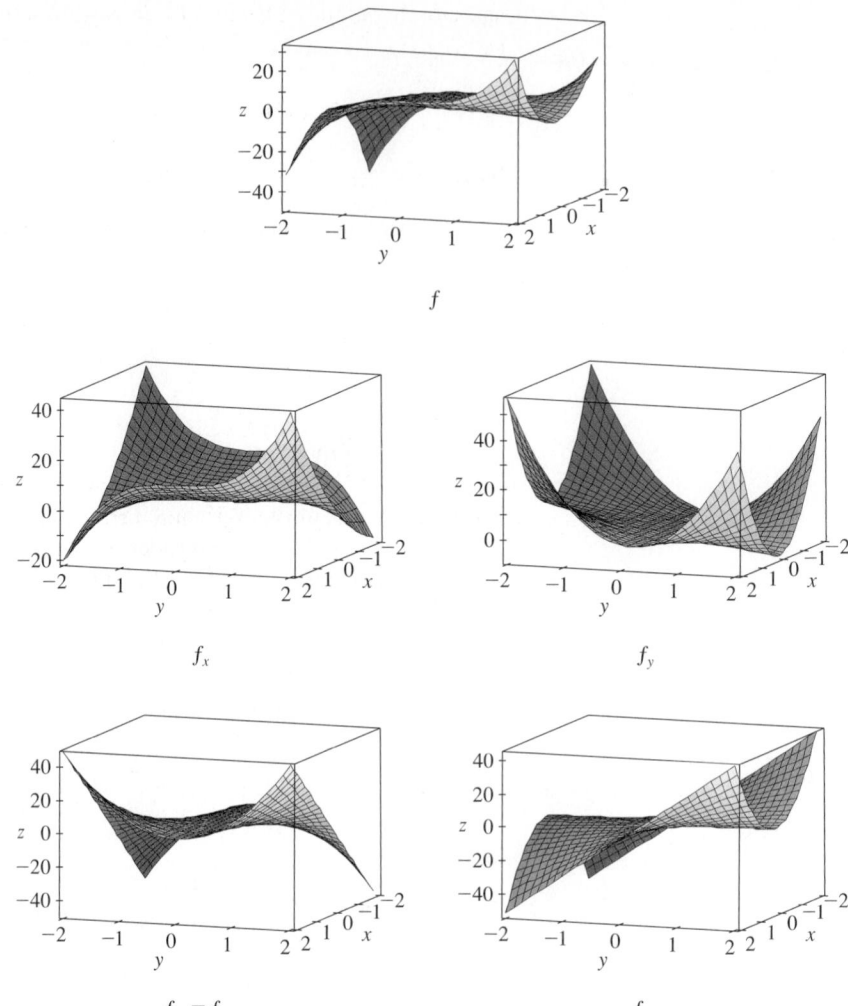

|||| Figure 7 shows the graph of the function f in Example 6 and the graphs of its first- and second-order partial derivatives for $-2 \leqslant x \leqslant 2$, $-2 \leqslant y \leqslant 2$. Notice that these graphs are consistent with our interpretations of f_x and f_y as slopes of tangent lines to traces of the graph of f. For instance, the graph of f decreases if we start at $(0, -2)$ and move in the positive x-direction. This is reflected in the negative values of f_x. You should compare the graphs of f_{yx} and f_{yy} with the graph of f_y to see the relationships.

f

f_x

f_y

f_{xx}

$f_{xy} = f_{yx}$

f_{yy}

FIGURE 7

Notice that $f_{xy} = f_{yx}$ in Example 6. This is not just a coincidence. It turns out that the mixed partial derivatives f_{xy} and f_{yx} are equal for most functions that one meets in practice. The following theorem, which was discovered by the French mathematician Alexis Clairaut (1713–1765), gives conditions under which we can assert that $f_{xy} = f_{yx}$. The proof is given in Appendix F.

|||| Alexis Clairaut was a child prodigy in mathematics, having read l'Hospital's textbook on calculus when he was ten and presented a paper on geometry to the French Academy of Sciences when he was 13. At the age of 18, Clairaut published *Recherches sur les courbes à double courbure*, which was the first systematic treatise on three-dimensional analytic geometry and included the calculus of space curves.

Clairaut's Theorem Suppose f is defined on a disk D that contains the point (a, b). If the functions f_{xy} and f_{yx} are both continuous on D, then

$$f_{xy}(a, b) = f_{yx}(a, b)$$

Partial derivatives of order 3 or higher can also be defined. For instance,

$$f_{xyy} = (f_{xy})_y = \frac{\partial}{\partial y}\left(\frac{\partial^2 f}{\partial y\, \partial x}\right) = \frac{\partial^3 f}{\partial y^2\, \partial x}$$

and using Clairaut's Theorem it can be shown that $f_{xyy} = f_{yxy} = f_{yyx}$ if these functions are continuous.

EXAMPLE 7 Calculate f_{xxyz} if $f(x, y, z) = \sin(3x + yz)$.

SOLUTION
$$f_x = 3 \cos(3x + yz)$$

$$f_{xx} = -9 \sin(3x + yz)$$

$$f_{xxy} = -9z \cos(3x + yz)$$

$$f_{xxyz} = -9 \cos(3x + yz) + 9yz \sin(3x + yz)$$

⏐⏐⏐⏐ **Partial Differential Equations**

Partial derivatives occur in *partial differential equations* that express certain physical laws. For instance, the partial differential equation

$$\frac{\partial^2 u}{\partial x^2} + \frac{\partial^2 u}{\partial y^2} = 0$$

is called **Laplace's equation** after Pierre Laplace (1749–1827). Solutions of this equation are called **harmonic functions** and play a role in problems of heat conduction, fluid flow, and electric potential.

EXAMPLE 8 Show that the function $u(x, y) = e^x \sin y$ is a solution of Laplace's equation.

SOLUTION
$$u_x = e^x \sin y \qquad\qquad u_y = e^x \cos y$$

$$u_{xx} = e^x \sin y \qquad\qquad u_{yy} = -e^x \sin y$$

$$u_{xx} + u_{yy} = e^x \sin y - e^x \sin y = 0$$

Therefore, u satisfies Laplace's equation.

The **wave equation**
$$\frac{\partial^2 u}{\partial t^2} = a^2 \frac{\partial^2 u}{\partial x^2}$$

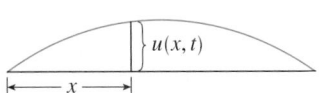

FIGURE 8

describes the motion of a waveform, which could be an ocean wave, a sound wave, a light wave, or a wave traveling along a vibrating string. For instance, if $u(x, t)$ represents the displacement of a vibrating violin string at time t and at a distance x from one end of the string (as in Figure 8), then $u(x, t)$ satisfies the wave equation. Here the constant a depends on the density of the string and on the tension in the string.

EXAMPLE 9 Verify that the function $u(x, t) = \sin(x - at)$ satisfies the wave equation.

SOLUTION
$$u_x = \cos(x - at) \qquad\qquad u_{xx} = -\sin(x - at)$$

$$u_t = -a \cos(x - at) \qquad\qquad u_{tt} = -a^2 \sin(x - at) = a^2 u_{xx}$$

So u satisfies the wave equation.

▥ The Cobb-Douglas Production Function

In Example 3 in Section 15.1 we described the work of Cobb and Douglas in modeling the total production P of an economic system as a function of the amount of labor L and the capital investment K. Here we use partial derivatives to show how the particular form of their model follows from certain assumptions they made about the economy.

If the production function is denoted by $P = P(L, K)$, then the partial derivative $\partial P/\partial L$ is the rate at which production changes with respect to the amount of labor. Economists call it the marginal production with respect to labor or the *marginal productivity of labor.* Likewise, the partial derivative $\partial P/\partial K$ is the rate of change of production with respect to capital and is called the *marginal productivity of capital.* In these terms, the assumptions made by Cobb and Douglas can be stated as follows.

(i) If either labor or capital vanishes, then so will production.

(ii) The marginal productivity of labor is proportional to the amount of production per unit of labor.

(iii) The marginal productivity of capital is proportional to the amount of production per unit of capital.

Because the production per unit of labor is P/L, assumption (ii) says that

$$\frac{\partial P}{\partial L} = \alpha \frac{P}{L}$$

for some constant α. If we keep K constant ($K = K_0$), then this partial differential equation becomes an ordinary differential equation:

$$\boxed{5} \qquad\qquad \frac{dP}{dL} = \alpha \frac{P}{L}$$

If we solve this separable differential equation by the methods of Section 10.3 (see also Exercise 75), we get

$$\boxed{6} \qquad\qquad P(L, K_0) = C_1(K_0)L^\alpha$$

Notice that we have written the constant C_1 as a function of K_0 because it could depend on the value of K_0.

Similarly, assumption (iii) says that

$$\frac{\partial P}{\partial K} = \beta \frac{P}{K}$$

and we can solve this differential equation to get

$$\boxed{7} \qquad\qquad P(L_0, K) = C_2(L_0)K^\beta$$

Comparing Equations 6 and 7, we have

$$\boxed{8} \qquad\qquad P(L, K) = bL^\alpha K^\beta$$

where b is a constant that is independent of both L and K. Assumption (i) shows that $\alpha > 0$ and $\beta > 0$.

Notice from Equation 8 that if labor and capital are both increased by a factor m, then

$$P(mL, mK) = b(mL)^{\alpha}(mK)^{\beta} = m^{\alpha+\beta}bL^{\alpha}K^{\beta} = m^{\alpha+\beta}P(L, K)$$

If $\alpha + \beta = 1$, then $P(mL, mK) = mP(L, K)$, which means that production is also increased by a factor of m. That is why Cobb and Douglas assumed that $\alpha + \beta = 1$ and therefore

$$P(L, K) = bL^{\alpha}K^{1-\alpha}$$

This is the Cobb-Douglas production function that we discussed in Section 15.1.

15.3 Exercises

1. The temperature T at a location in the Northern Hemisphere depends on the longitude x, latitude y, and time t, so we can write $T = f(x, y, t)$. Let's measure time in hours from the beginning of January.
   (a) What are the meanings of the partial derivatives $\partial T/\partial x$, $\partial T/\partial y$, and $\partial T/\partial t$?
   (b) Honolulu has longitude 158°W and latitude 21°N. Suppose that at 9:00 A.M. on January 1 the wind is blowing hot air to the northeast, so the air to the west and south is warm and the air to the north and east is cooler. Would you expect $f_x(158, 21, 9)$, $f_y(158, 21, 9)$, and $f_t(158, 21, 9)$ to be positive or negative? Explain.

2. At the beginning of this section we discussed the function $I = f(T, H)$, where I is the heat index, T is the temperature, and H is the relative humidity. Use Table 1 to estimate $f_T(92, 60)$ and $f_H(92, 60)$. What are the practical interpretations of these values?

3. The wind-chill index W is the perceived temperature when the actual temperature is T and the wind speed is v, so we can write $W = f(T, v)$. The following table of values is an excerpt from Table 1 in Section 15.1.

Wind speed (km/h)

T \ v	20	30	40	50	60	70
−10	−18	−20	−21	−22	−23	−23
−15	−24	−26	−27	−29	−30	−30
−20	−30	−33	−34	−35	−36	−37
−25	−37	−39	−41	−42	−43	−44

Actual temperature (°C)

(a) Estimate the values of $f_T(-15, 30)$ and $f_v(-15, 30)$. What are the practical interpretations of these values?

(b) In general, what can you say about the signs of $\partial W/\partial T$ and $\partial W/\partial v$?
(c) What appears to be the value of the following limit?

$$\lim_{v \to \infty} \frac{\partial W}{\partial v}$$

4. The wave heights h in the open sea depend on the speed v of the wind and the length of time t that the wind has been blowing at that speed. Values of the function $h = f(v, t)$ are recorded in feet in the following table.

Duration (hours)

v \ t	5	10	15	20	30	40	50
10	2	2	2	2	2	2	2
15	4	4	5	5	5	5	5
20	5	7	8	8	9	9	9
30	9	13	16	17	18	19	19
40	14	21	25	28	31	33	33
50	19	29	36	40	45	48	50
60	24	37	47	54	62	67	69

Wind speed (knots)

(a) What are the meanings of the partial derivatives $\partial h/\partial v$ and $\partial h/\partial t$?
(b) Estimate the values of $f_v(40, 15)$ and $f_t(40, 15)$. What are the practical interpretations of these values?
(c) What appears to be the value of the following limit?

$$\lim_{t \to \infty} \frac{\partial h}{\partial t}$$

5–6 ▐▐▐ Determine the signs of the partial derivatives for the function f whose graph is shown.

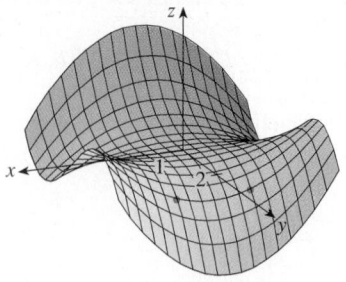

5. (a) $f_x(1, 2)$ (b) $f_y(1, 2)$

6. (a) $f_x(-1, 2)$ (b) $f_y(-1, 2)$
   (c) $f_{xx}(-1, 2)$ (d) $f_{yy}(-1, 2)$

7. The following surfaces, labeled a, b, and c, are graphs of a function f and its partial derivatives f_x and f_y. Identify each surface and give reasons for your choices.

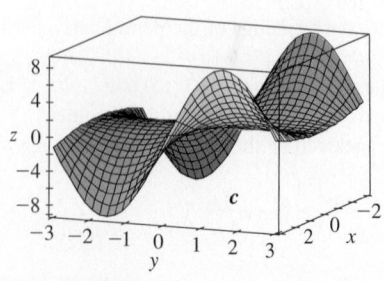

8. A contour map is given for a function f. Use it to estimate $f_x(2, 1)$ and $f_y(2, 1)$.

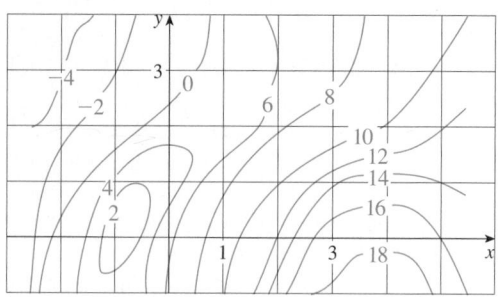

9. If $f(x, y) = 16 - 4x^2 - y^2$, find $f_x(1, 2)$ and $f_y(1, 2)$ and interpret these numbers as slopes. Illustrate with either hand-drawn sketches or computer plots.

10. If $f(x, y) = \sqrt{4 - x^2 - 4y^2}$, find $f_x(1, 0)$ and $f_y(1, 0)$ and interpret these numbers as slopes. Illustrate with either hand-drawn sketches or computer plots.

11–12 ▐▐▐ Find f_x and f_y and graph f, f_x, and f_y with domains and viewpoints that enable you to see the relationships between them.

11. $f(x, y) = x^2 + y^2 + x^2 y$ **12.** $f(x, y) = xe^{-x^2-y^2}$

13–34 ▐▐▐ Find the first partial derivatives of the function.

13. $f(x, y) = 3x - 2y^4$

14. $f(x, y) = x^5 + 3x^3 y^2 + 3xy^4$

15. $z = xe^{3y}$ **16.** $z = y \ln x$

17. $f(x, y) = \dfrac{x - y}{x + y}$ **18.** $f(x, y) = x^y$

19. $w = \sin \alpha \cos \beta$ **20.** $f(s, t) = st^2/(s^2 + t^2)$

21. $f(r, s) = r \ln(r^2 + s^2)$ **22.** $f(x, t) = \arctan(x\sqrt{t})$

23. $u = te^{w/t}$ **24.** $f(x, y) = \displaystyle\int_y^x \cos(t^2)\, dt$

25. $f(x, y, z) = xy^2 z^3 + 3yz$ **26.** $f(x, y, z) = x^2 e^{yz}$

27. $w = \ln(x + 2y + 3z)$ **28.** $w = \sqrt{r^2 + s^2 + t^2}$

29. $u = xe^{-t} \sin \theta$ **30.** $u = x^{y/z}$

31. $f(x, y, z, t) = xyz^2 \tan(yt)$ **32.** $f(x, y, z, t) = \dfrac{xy^2}{t + 2z}$

33. $u = \sqrt{x_1^2 + x_2^2 + \cdots + x_n^2}$

34. $u = \sin(x_1 + 2x_2 + \cdots + nx_n)$

35–38 ▐▐▐ Find the indicated partial derivatives.

35. $f(x, y) = \sqrt{x^2 + y^2}$; $f_x(3, 4)$

36. $f(x, y) = \sin(2x + 3y)$; $f_y(-6, 4)$

37. $f(x, y, z) = x/(y + z)$; $f_z(3, 2, 1)$

38. $f(u, v, w) = w \tan(uv)$; $f_v(2, 0, 3)$

□ □ □ □ □ □ □ □ □ □ □ □

39–40 ▓ Use the definition of partial derivatives as limits (4) to find $f_x(x, y)$ and $f_y(x, y)$.

39. $f(x, y) = x^2 - xy + 2y^2$ **40.** $f(x, y) = \sqrt{3x - y}$

□ □ □ □ □ □ □ □

41–44 ▓ Use implicit differentiation to find $\partial z/\partial x$ and $\partial z/\partial y$. (You can see what these surfaces look like in TEC Visual 15.3.)

41. $x^2 + y^2 + z^2 = 3xyz$ **42.** $yz = \ln(x + z)$

43. $x - z = \arctan(yz)$ **44.** $\sin(xyz) = x + 2y + 3z$

□ □ □ □ □ □ □ □ □

45–46 ▓ Find $\partial z/\partial x$ and $\partial z/\partial y$.

45. (a) $z = f(x) + g(y)$ (b) $z = f(x + y)$

46. (a) $z = f(x)g(y)$ (b) $z = f(xy)$
  (c) $z = f(x/y)$

□ □ □ □ □ □ □ □

47–52 ▓ Find all the second partial derivatives.

47. $f(x, y) = x^4 - 3x^2y^3$ **48.** $f(x, y) = \ln(3x + 5y)$

49. $z = x/(x + y)$ **50.** $z = y \tan 2x$

51. $u = e^{-s} \sin t$ **52.** $v = \sqrt{x + y^2}$

□ □ □ □ □ □ □ □ □

53–56 ▓ Verify that the conclusion of Clairaut's Theorem holds, that is, $u_{xy} = u_{yx}$.

53. $u = x \sin(x + 2y)$ **54.** $u = x^4y^2 - 2xy^5$

55. $u = \ln\sqrt{x^2 + y^2}$ **56.** $u = xye^y$

□ □ □ □ □ □ □ □ □

57–64 ▓ Find the indicated partial derivative.

57. $f(x, y) = 3xy^4 + x^3y^2$; f_{xxy}, f_{yyy}

58. $f(x, t) = x^2e^{-ct}$; f_{ttt}, f_{txx}

59. $f(x, y, z) = \cos(4x + 3y + 2z)$; f_{xyz}, f_{yzz}

60. $f(r, s, t) = r \ln(rs^2t^3)$; f_{rss}, f_{rst}

61. $u = e^{r\theta} \sin\theta$; $\dfrac{\partial^3 u}{\partial r^2 \partial\theta}$

62. $z = u\sqrt{v - w}$; $\dfrac{\partial^3 z}{\partial u\,\partial v\,\partial w}$

63. $w = \dfrac{x}{y + 2z}$; $\dfrac{\partial^3 w}{\partial z\,\partial y\,\partial x}$, $\dfrac{\partial^3 w}{\partial x^2\,\partial y}$

64. $u = x^a y^b z^c$; $\dfrac{\partial^6 u}{\partial x\,\partial y^2\,\partial z^3}$

□ □ □ □ □ □ □ □ □

65. Use the table of values of $f(x, y)$ to estimate the values of $f_x(3, 2)$, $f_x(3, 2.2)$, and $f_{xy}(3, 2)$.

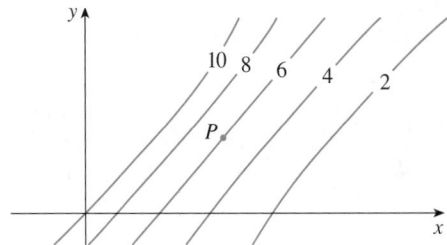

x \ y	1.8	2.0	2.2
2.5	12.5	10.2	9.3
3.0	18.1	17.5	15.9
3.5	20.0	22.4	26.1

66. Level curves are shown for a function f. Determine whether the following partial derivatives are positive or negative at the point P.

(a) f_x (b) f_y (c) f_{xx}
(d) f_{xy} (e) f_{yy}

67. Verify that the function $u = e^{-\alpha^2 k^2 t} \sin kx$ is a solution of the *heat conduction equation* $u_t = \alpha^2 u_{xx}$.

68. Determine whether each of the following functions is a solution of Laplace's equation $u_{xx} + u_{yy} = 0$.
(a) $u = x^2 + y^2$
(b) $u = x^2 - y^2$
(c) $u = x^3 + 3xy^2$
(d) $u = \ln\sqrt{x^2 + y^2}$
(e) $u = \sin x \cosh y + \cos x \sinh y$
(f) $u = e^{-x} \cos y - e^{-y} \cos x$

69. Verify that the function $u = 1/\sqrt{x^2 + y^2 + z^2}$ is a solution of the three-dimensional Laplace equation $u_{xx} + u_{yy} + u_{zz} = 0$.

70. Show that each of the following functions is a solution of the wave equation $u_{tt} = a^2 u_{xx}$.
(a) $u = \sin(kx) \sin(akt)$
(b) $u = t/(a^2t^2 - x^2)$
(c) $u = (x - at)^6 + (x + at)^6$
(d) $u = \sin(x - at) + \ln(x + at)$

71. If f and g are twice differentiable functions of a single variable, show that the function

$$u(x, t) = f(x + at) + g(x - at)$$

is a solution of the wave equation given in Exercise 70.

72. If $u = e^{a_1 x_1 + a_2 x_2 + \cdots + a_n x_n}$, where $a_1^2 + a_2^2 + \cdots + a_n^2 = 1$, show that

$$\frac{\partial^2 u}{\partial x_1^2} + \frac{\partial^2 u}{\partial x_2^2} + \cdots + \frac{\partial^2 u}{\partial x_n^2} = u$$

73. Show that the function $z = xe^y + ye^x$ is a solution of the equation

$$\frac{\partial^3 z}{\partial x^3} + \frac{\partial^3 z}{\partial y^3} = x \frac{\partial^3 z}{\partial x \, \partial y^2} + y \frac{\partial^3 z}{\partial x^2 \, \partial y}$$

74. Show that the Cobb-Douglas production function $P = bL^\alpha K^\beta$ satisfies the equation

$$L \frac{\partial P}{\partial L} + K \frac{\partial P}{\partial K} = (\alpha + \beta)P$$

75. Show that the Cobb-Douglas production function satisfies $P(L, K_0) = C_1(K_0)L^\alpha$ by solving the differential equation

$$\frac{dP}{dL} = \alpha \frac{P}{L}$$

(See Equation 5.)

76. The temperature at a point (x, y) on a flat metal plate is given by $T(x, y) = 60/(1 + x^2 + y^2)$, where T is measured in °C and x, y in meters. Find the rate of change of temperature with respect to distance at the point $(2, 1)$ in (a) the x-direction and (b) the y-direction.

77. The total resistance R produced by three conductors with resistances R_1, R_2, R_3 connected in a parallel electrical circuit is given by the formula

$$\frac{1}{R} = \frac{1}{R_1} + \frac{1}{R_2} + \frac{1}{R_3}$$

Find $\partial R/\partial R_1$.

78. The gas law for a fixed mass m of an ideal gas at absolute temperature T, pressure P, and volume V is $PV = mRT$, where R is the gas constant. Show that

$$\frac{\partial P}{\partial V} \frac{\partial V}{\partial T} \frac{\partial T}{\partial P} = -1$$

79. For the ideal gas of Exercise 78, show that

$$T \frac{\partial P}{\partial T} \frac{\partial V}{\partial T} = mR$$

80. The wind-chill index is modeled by the function

$$W = 13.12 + 0.6215T - 11.37v^{0.16} + 0.3965Tv^{0.16}$$

where T is the temperature (°C) and v is the wind speed (km/h). When $T = -15$°C and $v = 30$ km/h, by how much would you expect the apparent temperature to drop if the actual temperature decreases by 1°C? What if the wind speed increases by 1 km/h?

81. The kinetic energy of a body with mass m and velocity v is $K = \frac{1}{2}mv^2$. Show that

$$\frac{\partial K}{\partial m} \frac{\partial^2 K}{\partial v^2} = K$$

82. If a, b, c are the sides of a triangle and A, B, C are the opposite angles, find $\partial A/\partial a$, $\partial A/\partial b$, $\partial A/\partial c$ by implicit differentiation of the Law of Cosines.

83. You are told that there is a function f whose partial derivatives are $f_x(x, y) = x + 4y$ and $f_y(x, y) = 3x - y$. Should you believe it?

84. The paraboloid $z = 6 - x - x^2 - 2y^2$ intersects the plane $x = 1$ in a parabola. Find parametric equations for the tangent line to this parabola at the point $(1, 2, -4)$. Use a computer to graph the paraboloid, the parabola, and the tangent line on the same screen.

85. The ellipsoid $4x^2 + 2y^2 + z^2 = 16$ intersects the plane $y = 2$ in an ellipse. Find parametric equations for the tangent line to this ellipse at the point $(1, 2, 2)$.

86. In a study of frost penetration it was found that the temperature T at time t (measured in days) at a depth x (measured in feet) can be modeled by the function

$$T(x, t) = T_0 + T_1 e^{-\lambda x} \sin(\omega t - \lambda x)$$

where $\omega = 2\pi/365$ and λ is a positive constant.
(a) Find $\partial T/\partial x$. What is its physical significance?
(b) Find $\partial T/\partial t$. What is its physical significance?
(c) Show that T satisfies the heat equation $T_t = kT_{xx}$ for a certain constant k.
(d) If $\lambda = 0.2$, $T_0 = 0$, and $T_1 = 10$, use a computer to graph $T(x, t)$.
(e) What is the physical significance of the term $-\lambda x$ in the expression $\sin(\omega t - \lambda x)$?

87. Use Clairaut's Theorem to show that if the third-order partial derivatives of f are continuous, then

$$f_{xyy} = f_{yxy} = f_{yyx}$$

88. (a) How many nth-order partial derivatives does a function of two variables have?
(b) If these partial derivatives are all continuous, how many of them can be distinct?
(c) Answer the question in part (a) for a function of three variables.

89. If $f(x, y) = x(x^2 + y^2)^{-3/2}e^{\sin(x^2 y)}$, find $f_x(1, 0)$.
[*Hint:* Instead of finding $f_x(x, y)$ first, note that it's easier to use Equation 1 or Equation 2.]

90. If $f(x, y) = \sqrt[3]{x^3 + y^3}$, find $f_x(0, 0)$.

91. Let

$$f(x, y) = \begin{cases} \dfrac{x^3 y - xy^3}{x^2 + y^2} & \text{if } (x, y) \neq (0, 0) \\ 0 & \text{if } (x, y) = (0, 0) \end{cases}$$

(a) Use a computer to graph f.
(b) Find $f_x(x, y)$ and $f_y(x, y)$ when $(x, y) \neq (0, 0)$.
(c) Find $f_x(0, 0)$ and $f_y(0, 0)$ using Equations 2 and 3.
(d) Show that $f_{xy}(0, 0) = -1$ and $f_{yx}(0, 0) = 1$.
(e) Does the result of part (d) contradict Clairaut's Theorem? Use graphs of f_{xy} and f_{yx} to illustrate your answer.

15.4 Tangent Planes and Linear Approximations

One of the most important ideas in single-variable calculus is that as we zoom in toward a point on the graph of a differentiable function, the graph becomes indistinguishable from its tangent line and we can approximate the function by a linear function. (See Section 3.10.) Here we develop similar ideas in three dimensions. As we zoom in toward a point on a surface that is the graph of a differentiable function of two variables, the surface looks more and more like a plane (its tangent plane) and we can approximate the function by a linear function of two variables. We also extend the idea of a differential to functions of two or more variables.

Tangent Planes

Suppose a surface S has equation $z = f(x, y)$, where f has continuous first partial derivatives, and let $P(x_0, y_0, z_0)$ be a point on S. As in the preceding section, let C_1 and C_2 be the curves obtained by intersecting the vertical planes $y = y_0$ and $x = x_0$ with the surface S. Then the point P lies on both C_1 and C_2. Let T_1 and T_2 be the tangent lines to the curves C_1 and C_2 at the point P. Then the **tangent plane** to the surface S at the point P is defined to be the plane that contains both tangent lines T_1 and T_2. (See Figure 1.)

We will see in Section 15.6 that if C is any other curve that lies on the surface S and passes through P, then its tangent line at P also lies in the tangent plane. Therefore, you can think of the tangent plane to S at P as consisting of all possible tangent lines at P to curves that lie on S and pass through P. The tangent plane at P is the plane that most closely approximates the surface S near the point P.

We know from Equation 13.5.7 that any plane passing through the point $P(x_0, y_0, z_0)$ has an equation of the form

$$A(x - x_0) + B(y - y_0) + C(z - z_0) = 0$$

By dividing this equation by C and letting $a = -A/C$ and $b = -B/C$, we can write it in the form

1 $$z - z_0 = a(x - x_0) + b(y - y_0)$$

If Equation 1 represents the tangent plane at P, then its intersection with the plane $y = y_0$ must be the tangent line T_1. Setting $y = y_0$ in Equation 1 gives

$$z - z_0 = a(x - x_0) \qquad y = y_0$$

and we recognize these as the equations (in point-slope form) of a line with slope a. But from Section 15.3 we know that the slope of the tangent T_1 is $f_x(x_0, y_0)$. Therefore, $a = f_x(x_0, y_0)$.

Similarly, putting $x = x_0$ in Equation 1, we get $z - z_0 = b(y - y_0)$, which must represent the tangent line T_2, so $b = f_y(x_0, y_0)$.

FIGURE 1
The tangent plane contains the tangent lines T_1 and T_2.

Note the similarity between the equation of a tangent plane and the equation of a tangent line:
$$y - y_0 = f'(x_0)(x - x_0)$$

2   Suppose f has continuous partial derivatives. An equation of the tangent plane to the surface $z = f(x, y)$ at the point $P(x_0, y_0, z_0)$ is

$$z - z_0 = f_x(x_0, y_0)(x - x_0) + f_y(x_0, y_0)(y - y_0)$$

EXAMPLE 1 Find the tangent plane to the elliptic paraboloid $z = 2x^2 + y^2$ at the point (1, 1, 3).

SOLUTION Let $f(x, y) = 2x^2 + y^2$. Then

$$f_x(x, y) = 4x \qquad f_y(x, y) = 2y$$

$$f_x(1, 1) = 4 \qquad f_y(1, 1) = 2$$

Then (2) gives the equation of the tangent plane at (1, 1, 3) as

$$z - 3 = 4(x - 1) + 2(y - 1)$$

or
$$z = 4x + 2y - 3$$

Visual 15.4 shows an animation of Figures 2 and 3.

Figure 2(a) shows the elliptic paraboloid and its tangent plane at (1, 1, 3) that we found in Example 1. In parts (b) and (c) we zoom in toward the point (1, 1, 3) by restricting the domain of the function $f(x, y) = 2x^2 + y^2$. Notice that the more we zoom in, the flatter the graph appears and the more it resembles its tangent plane.

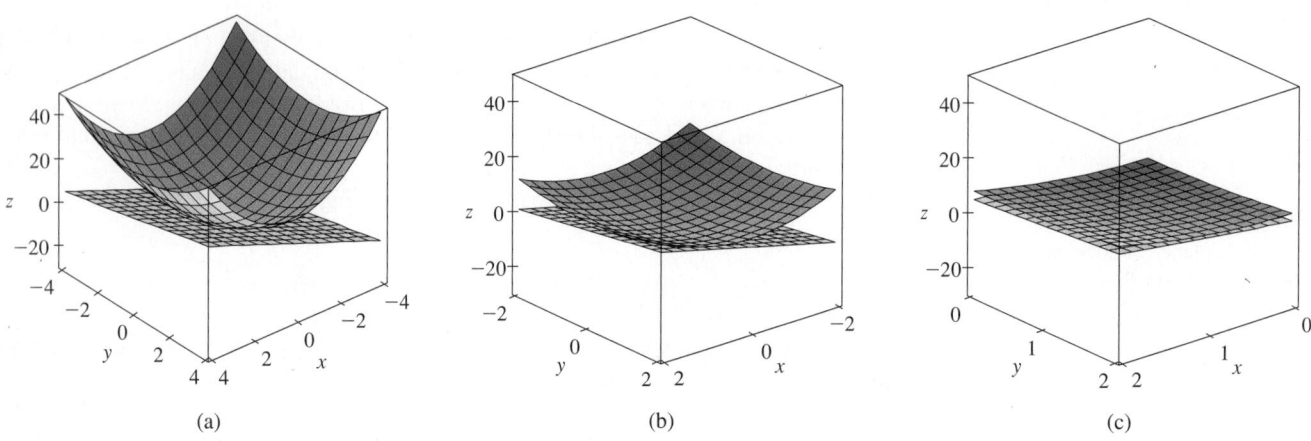

(a)   (b)   (c)

FIGURE 2 The elliptic paraboloid $z = 2x^2 + y^2$ appears to coincide with its tangent plane as we zoom in toward (1, 1, 3).

In Figure 3 we corroborate this impression by zooming in toward the point (1, 1) on a contour map of the function $f(x, y) = 2x^2 + y^2$. Notice that the more we zoom in, the more the level curves look like equally spaced parallel lines, which is characteristic of a plane.

FIGURE 3
Zooming in toward (1, 1)
on a contour map of
$f(x, y) = 2x^2 + y^2$

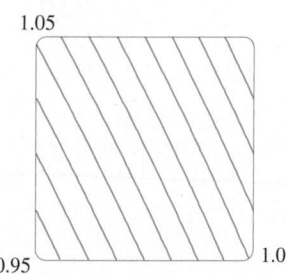

||| Linear Approximations

In Example 1 we found that an equation of the tangent plane to the graph of the function $f(x, y) = 2x^2 + y^2$ at the point $(1, 1, 3)$ is $z = 4x + 2y - 3$. Therefore, in view of the visual evidence in Figures 2 and 3, the linear function of two variables

$$L(x, y) = 4x + 2y - 3$$

is a good approximation to $f(x, y)$ when (x, y) is near $(1, 1)$. The function L is called the *linearization* of f at $(1, 1)$ and the approximation

$$f(x, y) \approx 4x + 2y - 3$$

is called the *linear approximation* or *tangent plane approximation* of f at $(1, 1)$.

For instance, at the point $(1.1, 0.95)$ the linear approximation gives

$$f(1.1, 0.95) \approx 4(1.1) + 2(0.95) - 3 = 3.3$$

which is quite close to the true value of $f(1.1, 0.95) = 2(1.1)^2 + (0.95)^2 = 3.3225$. But if we take a point farther away from $(1, 1)$, such as $(2, 3)$, we no longer get a good approximation. In fact, $L(2, 3) = 11$ whereas $f(2, 3) = 17$.

In general, we know from (2) that an equation of the tangent plane to the graph of a function f of two variables at the point $(a, b, f(a, b))$ is

$$z = f(a, b) + f_x(a, b)(x - a) + f_y(a, b)(y - b)$$

The linear function whose graph is this tangent plane, namely

3 $$L(x, y) = f(a, b) + f_x(a, b)(x - a) + f_y(a, b)(y - b)$$

is called the **linearization** of f at (a, b) and the approximation

4 $$f(x, y) \approx f(a, b) + f_x(a, b)(x - a) + f_y(a, b)(y - b)$$

is called the **linear approximation** or the **tangent plane approximation** of f at (a, b).

We have defined tangent planes for surfaces $z = f(x, y)$, where f has continuous first partial derivatives. What happens if f_x and f_y are not continuous? Figure 4 pictures such a function; its equation is

$$f(x, y) = \begin{cases} \dfrac{xy}{x^2 + y^2} & \text{if } (x, y) \neq (0, 0) \\ 0 & \text{if } (x, y) = (0, 0) \end{cases}$$

You can verify (see Exercise 42) that its partial derivatives exist at the origin and, in fact, $f_x(0, 0) = 0$ and $f_y(0, 0) = 0$, but f_x and f_y are not continuous. The linear approximation would be $f(x, y) \approx 0$, but $f(x, y) = \frac{1}{2}$ at all points on the line $y = x$. So a function of two variables can behave badly even though both of its partial derivatives exist. To rule out such behavior, we formulate the idea of a differentiable function of two variables.

Recall that for a function of one variable, $y = f(x)$, if x changes from a to $a + \Delta x$, we defined the increment of y as

$$\Delta y = f(a + \Delta x) - f(a)$$

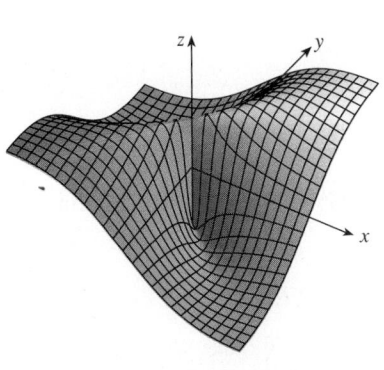

FIGURE 4

$f(x, y) = \dfrac{xy}{x^2 + y^2}$ if $(x, y) \neq (0, 0)$,

$f(0, 0) = 0$

In Chapter 3 we showed that if f is differentiable at a, then

||| This is Equation 3.6.5.

> **5**
$$\Delta y = f'(a)\,\Delta x + \varepsilon\,\Delta x \qquad \text{where } \varepsilon \to 0 \text{ as } \Delta x \to 0$$

Now consider a function of two variables, $z = f(x, y)$, and suppose x changes from a to $a + \Delta x$ and y changes from b to $b + \Delta y$. Then the corresponding **increment** of z is

> **6**
$$\Delta z = f(a + \Delta x, b + \Delta y) - f(a, b)$$

Thus, the increment Δz represents the change in the value of f when (x, y) changes from (a, b) to $(a + \Delta x, b + \Delta y)$. By analogy with (5) we define the differentiability of a function of two variables as follows.

> **7 Definition**   If $z = f(x, y)$, then f is **differentiable** at (a, b) if Δz can be expressed in the form
>
> $$\Delta z = f_x(a, b)\,\Delta x + f_y(a, b)\,\Delta y + \varepsilon_1\,\Delta x + \varepsilon_2\,\Delta y$$
>
> where ε_1 and $\varepsilon_2 \to 0$ as $(\Delta x, \Delta y) \to (0, 0)$.

Definition 7 says that a differentiable function is one for which the linear approximation (4) is a good approximation when (x, y) is near (a, b). In other words, the tangent plane approximates the graph of f well near the point of tangency.

It's sometimes hard to use Definition 7 directly to check the differentiability of a function, but the following theorem provides a convenient sufficient condition for differentiability.

||| Theorem 8 is proved in Appendix F.

> **8 Theorem**   If the partial derivatives f_x and f_y exist near (a, b) and are continuous at (a, b), then f is differentiable at (a, b).

EXAMPLE 2 Show that $f(x, y) = xe^{xy}$ is differentiable at $(1, 0)$ and find its linearization there. Then use it to approximate $f(1.1, -0.1)$.

SOLUTION The partial derivatives are

$$f_x(x, y) = e^{xy} + xye^{xy} \qquad f_y(x, y) = x^2 e^{xy}$$

$$f_x(1, 0) = 1 \qquad\qquad\qquad f_y(1, 0) = 1$$

Both f_x and f_y are continuous functions, so f is differentiable by Theorem 8. The linearization is

$$L(x, y) = f(1, 0) + f_x(1, 0)(x - 1) + f_y(1, 0)(y - 0)$$

$$= 1 + 1(x - 1) + 1 \cdot y = x + y$$

The corresponding linear approximation is

$$xe^{xy} \approx x + y$$

||| Figure 5 shows the graphs of the function f and its linearization L in Example 2.

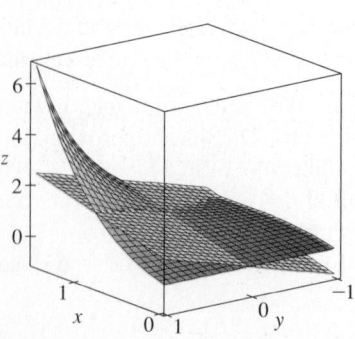

so
$$f(1.1, -0.1) \approx 1.1 - 0.1 = 1$$

Compare this with the actual value of $f(1.1, -0.1) = 1.1e^{-0.11} \approx 0.98542$.

FIGURE 5

EXAMPLE 3 At the beginning of Section 15.3 we discussed the heat index (perceived temperature) I as a function of the actual temperature T and the relative humidity H and gave the following table of values from the National Weather Service.

Relative humidity (%)

T \ H	50	55	60	65	70	75	80	85	90
90	96	98	100	103	106	109	112	115	119
92	100	103	105	108	112	115	119	123	128
94	104	107	111	114	118´	122	127	132	137
96	109	113	116	121	125	130	135	141	146
98	114	118	123	127	133	138	144	150	157
100	119	124	129	135	141	147	154	161	168

Actual temperature (°F)

Find a linear approximation for the heat index $I = f(T, H)$ when T is near 96°F and H is near 70%. Use it to estimate the heat index when the temperature is 97°F and the relative humidity is 72%.

SOLUTION We read from the table that $f(96, 70) = 125$. In Section 15.3 we used the tabular values to estimate that $f_T(96, 70) \approx 3.75$ and $f_H(96, 70) \approx 0.9$. (See pages 946–947.) So the linear approximation is

$$f(T, H) \approx f(96, 70) + f_T(96, 70)(T - 96) + f_H(96, 70)(H - 70)$$

$$\approx 125 + 3.75(T - 96) + 0.9(H - 70)$$

In particular,

$$f(97, 72) \approx 125 + 3.75(1) + 0.9(2) = 130.55$$

Therefore, when $T = 97°F$ and $H = 72\%$, the heat index is

$$I \approx 131°F$$

||||| **Differentials**

For a differentiable function of one variable, $y = f(x)$, we define the differential dx to be an independent variable; that is, dx can be given the value of any real number. The differential of y is then defined as

$$\boxed{9} \qquad dy = f'(x)\, dx$$

(See Section 3.10.) Figure 6 shows the relationship between the increment Δy and the differential dy: Δy represents the change in height of the curve $y = f(x)$ and dy represents the change in height of the tangent line when x changes by an amount $dx = \Delta x$.

For a differentiable function of two variables, $z = f(x, y)$, we define the **differentials** dx and dy to be independent variables; that is, they can be given any values. Then the **differential** dz, also called the **total differential**, is defined by

$$\boxed{10} \qquad dz = f_x(x, y)\, dx + f_y(x, y)\, dy = \frac{\partial z}{\partial x} dx + \frac{\partial z}{\partial y} dy$$

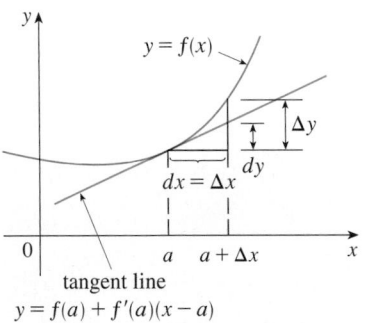

FIGURE 6

(Compare with Equation 9.) Sometimes the notation df is used in place of dz.

If we take $dx = \Delta x = x - a$ and $dy = \Delta y = y - b$ in Equation 10, then the differential of z is

$$dz = f_x(a, b)(x - a) + f_y(a, b)(y - b)$$

So, in the notation of differentials, the linear approximation (4) can be written as

$$f(x, y) \approx f(a, b) + dz$$

Figure 7 is the three-dimensional counterpart of Figure 6 and shows the geometric interpretation of the differential dz and the increment Δz: dz represents the change in height of the tangent plane, whereas Δz represents the change in height of the surface $z = f(x, y)$ when (x, y) changes from (a, b) to $(a + \Delta x, b + \Delta y)$.

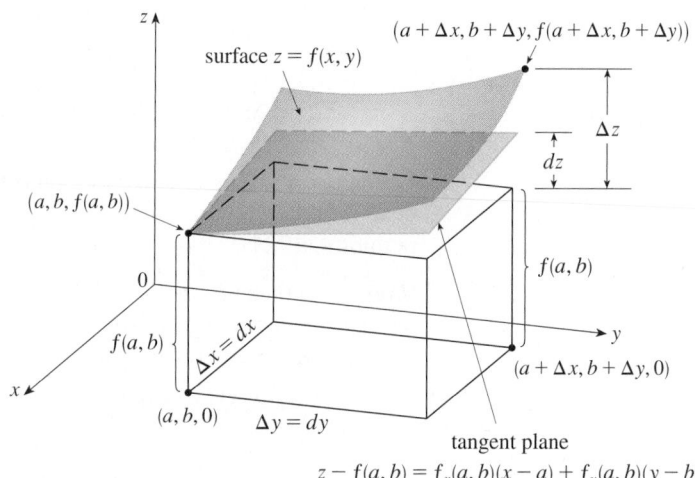

FIGURE 7

EXAMPLE 4
(a) If $z = f(x, y) = x^2 + 3xy - y^2$, find the differential dz.
(b) If x changes from 2 to 2.05 and y changes from 3 to 2.96, compare the values of Δz and dz.

SOLUTION
(a) Definition 10 gives

$$dz = \frac{\partial z}{\partial x}\, dx + \frac{\partial z}{\partial y}\, dy = (2x + 3y)\, dx + (3x - 2y)\, dy$$

(b) Putting $x = 2$, $dx = \Delta x = 0.05$, $y = 3$, and $dy = \Delta y = -0.04$, we get

$$dz = [2(2) + 3(3)]0.05 + [3(2) - 2(3)](-0.04)$$

$$= 0.65$$

The increment of z is

$$\Delta z = f(2.05, 2.96) - f(2, 3)$$

$$= [(2.05)^2 + 3(2.05)(2.96) - (2.96)^2] - [2^2 + 3(2)(3) - 3^2]$$

$$= 0.6449$$

Notice that $\Delta z \approx dz$ but dz is easier to compute.

|||| In Example 4, dz is close to Δz because the tangent plane is a good approximation to the surface $z = x^2 + 3xy - y^2$ near (2, 3, 13). (See Figure 8.)

FIGURE 8

EXAMPLE 5 The base radius and height of a right circular cone are measured as 10 cm and 25 cm, respectively, with a possible error in measurement of as much as 0.1 cm in each. Use differentials to estimate the maximum error in the calculated volume of the cone.

SOLUTION The volume V of a cone with base radius r and height h is $V = \pi r^2 h/3$. So the differential of V is

$$dV = \frac{\partial V}{\partial r}\, dr + \frac{\partial V}{\partial h}\, dh = \frac{2\pi rh}{3}\, dr + \frac{\pi r^2}{3}\, dh$$

Since each error is at most 0.1 cm, we have $|\Delta r| \leqslant 0.1$, $|\Delta h| \leqslant 0.1$. To find the largest error in the volume we take the largest error in the measurement of r and of h. Therefore, we take $dr = 0.1$ and $dh = 0.1$ along with $r = 10$, $h = 25$. This gives

$$dV = \frac{500\pi}{3}(0.1) + \frac{100\pi}{3}(0.1) = 20\pi$$

Thus, the maximum error in the calculated volume is about 20π cm$^3 \approx 63$ cm^3. ▬

⦀ Functions of Three or More Variables

Linear approximations, differentiability, and differentials can be defined in a similar manner for functions of more than two variables. A differentiable function is defined by an expression similar to the one in Definition 7. For such functions the **linear approximation** is

$$f(x, y, z) \approx f(a, b, c) + f_x(a, b, c)(x - a) + f_y(a, b, c)(y - b) + f_z(a, b, c)(z - c)$$

and the linearization $L(x, y, z)$ is the right side of this expression.

If $w = f(x, y, z)$, then the **increment** of w is

$$\Delta w = f(x + \Delta x, y + \Delta y, z + \Delta z) - f(x, y, z)$$

The **differential** dw is defined in terms of the differentials dx, dy, and dz of the independent variables by

$$dw = \frac{\partial w}{\partial x}\, dx + \frac{\partial w}{\partial y}\, dy + \frac{\partial w}{\partial z}\, dz$$

EXAMPLE 6 The dimensions of a rectangular box are measured to be 75 cm, 60 cm, and 40 cm, and each measurement is correct to within 0.2 cm. Use differentials to estimate the largest possible error when the volume of the box is calculated from these measurements.

SOLUTION If the dimensions of the box are x, y, and z, its volume is $V = xyz$ and so

$$dV = \frac{\partial V}{\partial x}\, dx + \frac{\partial V}{\partial y}\, dy + \frac{\partial V}{\partial z}\, dz = yz\, dx + xz\, dy + xy\, dz$$

We are given that $|\Delta x| \leqslant 0.2$, $|\Delta y| \leqslant 0.2$, and $|\Delta z| \leqslant 0.2$. To find the largest error in the volume, we therefore use $dx = 0.2$, $dy = 0.2$, and $dz = 0.2$ together with $x = 75$, $y = 60$, and $z = 40$:

$$\Delta V \approx dV = (60)(40)(0.2) + (75)(40)(0.2) + (75)(60)(0.2)$$

$$= 1980$$

Thus, an error of only 0.2 cm in measuring each dimension could lead to an error of as much as 1980 cm^3 in the calculated volume! This may seem like a large error, but it's only about 1% of the volume of the box. ▬

▮▮ 15.4 Exercises

1–6 ▮▮▮ Find an equation of the tangent plane to the given surface at the specified point.

1. $z = 4x^2 - y^2 + 2y$, $(-1, 2, 4)$

2. $z = 9x^2 + y^2 + 6x - 3y + 5$, $(1, 2, 18)$

3. $z = \sqrt{4 - x^2 - 2y^2}$, $(1, -1, 1)$

4. $z = y \ln x$, $(1, 4, 0)$

5. $z = y \cos(x - y)$, $(2, 2, 2)$

6. $z = e^{x^2 - y^2}$, $(1, -1, 1)$

7–8 ▮▮▮ Graph the surface and the tangent plane at the given point. (Choose the domain and viewpoint so that you get a good view of both the surface and the tangent plane.) Then zoom in until the surface and the tangent plane become indistinguishable.

7. $z = x^2 + xy + 3y^2$, $(1, 1, 5)$

8. $z = \arctan(xy^2)$, $(1, 1, \pi/4)$

CAS **9–10** ▮▮▮ Draw the graph of f and its tangent plane at the given point. (Use your computer algebra system both to compute the partial derivatives and to graph the surface and its tangent plane.) Then zoom in until the surface and the tangent plane become indistinguishable.

9. $f(x, y) = e^{-(x^2+y^2)/15}(\sin^2 x + \cos^2 y)$, $(2, 3, f(2, 3))$

10. $f(x, y) = \dfrac{\sqrt{1 + 4x^2 + 4y^2}}{1 + x^4 + y^4}$, $(1, 1, 1)$

11–16 ▮▮▮ Explain why the function is differentiable at the given point. Then find the linearization $L(x, y)$ of the function at that point.

11. $f(x, y) = x\sqrt{y}$, $(1, 4)$ **12.** $f(x, y) = x/y$, $(6, 3)$

13. $f(x, y) = e^x \cos xy$, $(0, 0)$ **14.** $f(x, y) = \sqrt{x + e^{4y}}$, $(3, 0)$

15. $f(x, y) = \tan^{-1}(x + 2y)$, $(1, 0)$

16. $f(x, y) = \sin(2x + 3y)$, $(-3, 2)$

17. Find the linear approximation of the function $f(x, y) = \sqrt{20 - x^2 - 7y^2}$ at $(2, 1)$ and use it to approximate $f(1.95, 1.08)$.

18. Find the linear approximation of the function $f(x, y) = \ln(x - 3y)$ at $(7, 2)$ and use it to approximate $f(6.9, 2.06)$. Illustrate by graphing f and the tangent plane.

19. Find the linear approximation of the function $f(x, y, z) = \sqrt{x^2 + y^2 + z^2}$ at $(3, 2, 6)$ and use it to approximate the number $\sqrt{(3.02)^2 + (1.97)^2 + (5.99)^2}$.

20. The wave heights h in the open sea depend on the speed v of the wind and the length of time t that the wind has been blowing at that speed. Values of the function $h = f(v, t)$ are recorded in the following table.

	Duration (hours)						
t ╲ v	5	10	15	20	30	40	50
20	5	7	8	8	9	9	9
30	9	13	16	17	18	19	19
40	14	21	25	28	31	33	33
50	19	29	36	40	45	48	50
60	24	37	47	54	62	67	69

Wind speed (knots)

Use the table to find a linear approximation to the wave height function when v is near 40 knots and t is near 20 hours. Then estimate the wave heights when the wind has been blowing for 24 hours at 43 knots.

21. Use the table in Example 3 to find a linear approximation to the heat index function when the temperature is near 94°F and the relative humidity is near 80%. Then estimate the heat index when the temperature is 95°F and the relative humidity is 78%.

22. The wind-chill index W is the perceived temperature when the actual temperature is T and the wind speed is v, so we can write $W = f(T, v)$. The following table of values is an excerpt from Table 1 in Section 15.1.

	Wind speed (km/h)					
T ╲ v	20	30	40	50	60	70
-10	-18	-20	-21	-22	-23	-23
-15	-24	-26	-27	-29	-30	-30
-20	-30	-33	-34	-35	-36	-37
-25	-37	-39	$-41·$	-42	-43	-44

Actual temperature (°C)

Use the table to find a linear approximation to the wind-chill index function when T is near -15°C and v is near 50 km/h. Then estimate the wind-chill index when the temperature is -17°C and the wind speed is 55 km/h.

23–28 ▮▮▮ Find the differential of the function.

23. $z = x^3 \ln(y^2)$ **24.** $v = y \cos xy$

25. $u = e^t \sin \theta$ **26.** $u = r/(s + 2t)$

27. $w = \ln\sqrt{x^2 + y^2 + z^2}$ **28.** $w = xye^{xz}$

29. If $z = 5x^2 + y^2$ and (x, y) changes from $(1, 2)$ to $(1.05, 2.1)$, compare the values of Δz and dz.

30. If $z = x^2 - xy + 3y^2$ and (x, y) changes from $(3, -1)$ to $(2.96, -0.95)$, compare the values of Δz and dz.

31. The length and width of a rectangle are measured as 30 cm and 24 cm, respectively, with an error in measurement of at most 0.1 cm in each. Use differentials to estimate the maximum error in the calculated area of the rectangle.

32. The dimensions of a closed rectangular box are measured as 80 cm, 60 cm, and 50 cm, respectively, with a possible error of 0.2 cm in each dimension. Use differentials to estimate the maximum error in calculating the surface area of the box.

33. Use differentials to estimate the amount of tin in a closed tin can with diameter 8 cm and height 12 cm if the tin is 0.04 cm thick.

34. Use differentials to estimate the amount of metal in a closed cylindrical can that is 10 cm high and 4 cm in diameter if the metal in the top and bottom is 0.1 cm thick and the metal in the sides is 0.05 cm thick.

35. A boundary stripe 3 in. wide is painted around a rectangle whose dimensions are 100 ft by 200 ft. Use differentials to approximate the number of square feet of paint in the stripe.

36. The pressure, volume, and temperature of a mole of an ideal gas are related by the equation $PV = 8.31T$, where P is measured in kilopascals, V in liters, and T in kelvins. Use differentials to find the approximate change in the pressure if the volume increases from 12 L to 12.3 L and the temperature decreases from 310 K to 305 K.

37. If R is the total resistance of three resistors, connected in parallel, with resistances R_1, R_2, R_3, then

$$\frac{1}{R} = \frac{1}{R_1} + \frac{1}{R_2} + \frac{1}{R_3}$$

If the resistances are measured in ohms as $R_1 = 25\ \Omega$, $R_2 = 40\ \Omega$, and $R_3 = 50\ \Omega$, with a possible error of 0.5% in each case, estimate the maximum error in the calculated value of R.

38. Four positive numbers, each less than 50, are rounded to the first decimal place and then multiplied together. Use differentials to estimate the maximum possible error in the computed product that might result from the rounding.

39–40 ▒ Show that the function is differentiable by finding values of ε_1 and ε_2 that satisfy Definition 7.

39. $f(x, y) = x^2 + y^2$ **40.** $f(x, y) = xy - 5y^2$

41. Prove that if f is a function of two variables that is differentiable at (a, b), then f is continuous at (a, b).

   Hint: Show that

$$\lim_{(\Delta x, \Delta y) \to (0, 0)} f(a + \Delta x, b + \Delta y) = f(a, b)$$

42. (a) The function

$$f(x, y) = \begin{cases} \dfrac{xy}{x^2 + y^2} & \text{if } (x, y) \neq (0, 0) \\ 0 & \text{if } (x, y) = (0, 0) \end{cases}$$

   was graphed in Figure 4. Show that $f_x(0, 0)$ and $f_y(0, 0)$ both exist but f is not differentiable at $(0, 0)$. [*Hint:* Use the result of Exercise 41.]

   (b) Explain why f_x and f_y are not continuous at $(0, 0)$.

15.5 The Chain Rule

Recall that the Chain Rule for functions of a single variable gives the rule for differentiating a composite function: If $y = f(x)$ and $x = g(t)$, where f and g are differentiable functions, then y is indirectly a differentiable function of t and

$$\frac{dy}{dt} = \frac{dy}{dx}\frac{dx}{dt}$$

   For functions of more than one variable, the Chain Rule has several versions, each of them giving a rule for differentiating a composite function. The first version (Theorem 2) deals with the case where $z = f(x, y)$ and each of the variables x and y is, in turn, a function of a variable t. This means that z is indirectly a function of t, $z = f(g(t), h(t))$, and the Chain Rule gives a formula for differentiating z as a function of t. We assume that f is differentiable (Definition 15.4.7). Recall that this is the case when f_x and f_y are continuous (Theorem 15.4.8).

2 The Chain Rule (Case 1) Suppose that $z = f(x, y)$ is a differentiable function of x and y, where $x = g(t)$ and $y = h(t)$ are both differentiable functions of t. Then z is a differentiable function of t and

$$\frac{dz}{dt} = \frac{\partial f}{\partial x}\frac{dx}{dt} + \frac{\partial f}{\partial y}\frac{dy}{dt}$$

Proof A change of Δt in t produces changes of Δx in x and Δy in y. These, in turn, produce a change of Δz in z, and from Definition 15.4.7 we have

$$\Delta z = \frac{\partial f}{\partial x}\Delta x + \frac{\partial f}{\partial y}\Delta y + \varepsilon_1\,\Delta x + \varepsilon_2\,\Delta y$$

where $\varepsilon_1 \to 0$ and $\varepsilon_2 \to 0$ as $(\Delta x, \Delta y) \to (0, 0)$. [If the functions ε_1 and ε_2 are not defined at $(0, 0)$, we can define them to be 0 there.] Dividing both sides of this equation by Δt, we have

$$\frac{\Delta z}{\Delta t} = \frac{\partial f}{\partial x}\frac{\Delta x}{\Delta t} + \frac{\partial f}{\partial y}\frac{\Delta y}{\Delta t} + \varepsilon_1\frac{\Delta x}{\Delta t} + \varepsilon_2\frac{\Delta y}{\Delta t}$$

If we now let $\Delta t \to 0$, then $\Delta x = g(t + \Delta t) - g(t) \to 0$ because g is differentiable and therefore continuous. Similarly, $\Delta y \to 0$. This, in turn, means that $\varepsilon_1 \to 0$ and $\varepsilon_2 \to 0$, so

$$\frac{dz}{dt} = \lim_{\Delta t \to 0}\frac{\Delta z}{\Delta t}$$

$$= \frac{\partial f}{\partial x}\lim_{\Delta t \to 0}\frac{\Delta x}{\Delta t} + \frac{\partial f}{\partial y}\lim_{\Delta t \to 0}\frac{\Delta y}{\Delta t} + \lim_{\Delta t \to 0}\varepsilon_1\lim_{\Delta t \to 0}\frac{\Delta x}{\Delta t} + \lim_{\Delta t \to 0}\varepsilon_2\lim_{\Delta t \to 0}\frac{\Delta y}{\Delta t}$$

$$= \frac{\partial f}{\partial x}\frac{dx}{dt} + \frac{\partial f}{\partial y}\frac{dy}{dt} + 0\cdot\frac{dx}{dt} + 0\cdot\frac{dy}{dt}$$

$$= \frac{\partial f}{\partial x}\frac{dx}{dt} + \frac{\partial f}{\partial y}\frac{dy}{dt}$$

Since we often write $\partial z/\partial x$ in place of $\partial f/\partial x$, we can rewrite the Chain Rule in the form

$$\frac{dz}{dt} = \frac{\partial z}{\partial x}\frac{dx}{dt} + \frac{\partial z}{\partial y}\frac{dy}{dt}$$

||| Notice the similarity to the definition of the differential:

$$dz = \frac{\partial z}{\partial x}dx + \frac{\partial z}{\partial y}dy$$

EXAMPLE 1 If $z = x^2 y + 3xy^4$, where $x = \sin 2t$ and $y = \cos t$, find dz/dt when $t = 0$.

SOLUTION The Chain Rule gives

$$\frac{dz}{dt} = \frac{\partial z}{\partial x}\frac{dx}{dt} + \frac{\partial z}{\partial y}\frac{dy}{dt}$$

$$= (2xy + 3y^4)(2\cos 2t) + (x^2 + 12xy^3)(-\sin t)$$

It's not necessary to substitute the expressions for x and y in terms of t. We simply observe that when $t = 0$ we have $x = \sin 0 = 0$ and $y = \cos 0 = 1$. Therefore,

$$\left.\frac{dz}{dt}\right|_{t=0} = (0 + 3)(2 \cos 0) + (0 + 0)(-\sin 0) = 6$$

The derivative in Example 1 can be interpreted as the rate of change of z with respect to t as the point (x, y) moves along the curve C with parametric equations $x = \sin 2t$, $y = \cos t$. (See Figure 1.) In particular, when $t = 0$, the point (x, y) is $(0, 1)$ and $dz/dt = 6$ is the rate of increase as we move along the curve C through $(0, 1)$. If, for instance, $z = T(x, y) = x^2y + 3xy^4$ represents the temperature at the point (x, y), then the composite function $z = T(\sin 2t, \cos t)$ represents the temperature at points on C and the derivative dz/dt represents the rate at which the temperature changes along C.

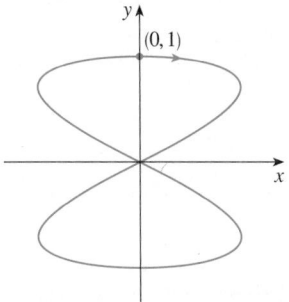

FIGURE 1

The curve $x = \sin 2t$, $y = \cos t$

EXAMPLE 2 The pressure P (in kilopascals), volume V (in liters), and temperature T (in kelvins) of a mole of an ideal gas are related by the equation $PV = 8.31T$. Find the rate at which the pressure is changing when the temperature is 300 K and increasing at a rate of 0.1 K/s and the volume is 100 L and increasing at a rate of 0.2 L/s.

SOLUTION If t represents the time elapsed in seconds, then at the given instant we have $T = 300$, $dT/dt = 0.1$, $V = 100$, $dV/dt = 0.2$. Since

$$P = 8.31\frac{T}{V}$$

the Chain Rule gives

$$\frac{dP}{dt} = \frac{\partial P}{\partial T}\frac{dT}{dt} + \frac{\partial P}{\partial V}\frac{dV}{dt} = \frac{8.31}{V}\frac{dT}{dt} - \frac{8.31T}{V^2}\frac{dV}{dt}$$

$$= \frac{8.31}{100}(0.1) - \frac{8.31(300)}{100^2}(0.2) = -0.04155$$

The pressure is decreasing at a rate of about 0.042 kPa/s.

We now consider the situation where $z = f(x, y)$ but each of x and y is a function of two variables s and t: $x = g(s, t)$, $y = h(s, t)$. Then z is indirectly a function of s and t and we wish to find $\partial z/\partial s$ and $\partial z/\partial t$. Recall that in computing $\partial z/\partial t$ we hold s fixed and compute the ordinary derivative of z with respect to t. Therefore, we can apply Theorem 2 to obtain

$$\frac{\partial z}{\partial t} = \frac{\partial z}{\partial x}\frac{\partial x}{\partial t} + \frac{\partial z}{\partial y}\frac{\partial y}{\partial t}$$

A similar argument holds for $\partial z/\partial s$ and so we have proved the following version of the Chain Rule.

---

3 **The Chain Rule (Case 2)** Suppose that $z = f(x, y)$ is a differentiable function of x and y, where $x = g(s, t)$ and $y = h(s, t)$ are differentiable functions of s and t. Then

$$\frac{\partial z}{\partial s} = \frac{\partial z}{\partial x}\frac{\partial x}{\partial s} + \frac{\partial z}{\partial y}\frac{\partial y}{\partial s} \qquad \frac{\partial z}{\partial t} = \frac{\partial z}{\partial x}\frac{\partial x}{\partial t} + \frac{\partial z}{\partial y}\frac{\partial y}{\partial t}$$

EXAMPLE 3 If $z = e^x \sin y$, where $x = st^2$ and $y = s^2t$, find $\partial z/\partial s$ and $\partial z/\partial t$.

SOLUTION Applying Case 2 of the Chain Rule, we get

$$\frac{\partial z}{\partial s} = \frac{\partial z}{\partial x}\frac{\partial x}{\partial s} + \frac{\partial z}{\partial y}\frac{\partial y}{\partial s} = (e^x \sin y)(t^2) + (e^x \cos y)(2st)$$

$$= t^2 e^{st^2} \sin(s^2t) + 2ste^{st^2} \cos(s^2t)$$

$$\frac{\partial z}{\partial t} = \frac{\partial z}{\partial x}\frac{\partial x}{\partial t} + \frac{\partial z}{\partial y}\frac{\partial y}{\partial t} = (e^x \sin y)(2st) + (e^x \cos y)(s^2)$$

$$= 2ste^{st^2} \sin(s^2t) + s^2 e^{st^2} \cos(s^2t)$$

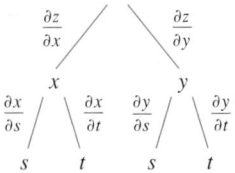

FIGURE 2

Case 2 of the Chain Rule contains three types of variables: s and t are **independent** variables, x and y are called **intermediate** variables, and z is the **dependent** variable. Notice that Theorem 3 has one term for each intermediate variable and each of these terms resembles the one-dimensional Chain Rule in Equation 1.

To remember the Chain Rule it's helpful to draw the **tree diagram** in Figure 2. We draw branches from the dependent variable z to the intermediate variables x and y to indicate that z is a function of x and y. Then we draw branches from x and y to the independent variables s and t. On each branch we write the corresponding partial derivative. To find $\partial z/\partial s$ we find the product of the partial derivatives along each path from z to s and then add these products:

$$\frac{\partial z}{\partial s} = \frac{\partial z}{\partial x}\frac{\partial x}{\partial s} + \frac{\partial z}{\partial y}\frac{\partial y}{\partial s}$$

Similarly, we find $\partial z/\partial t$ by using the paths from z to t.

Now we consider the general situation in which a dependent variable u is a function of n intermediate variables $x_1, \ldots, x_n$, each of which is, in turn, a function of m independent variables $t_1, \ldots, t_m$. Notice that there are n terms, one for each intermediate variable. The proof is similar to that of Case 1.

---

4 The Chain Rule (General Version) Suppose that u is a differentiable function of the n variables $x_1, x_2, \ldots, x_n$ and each x_j is a differentiable function of the m variables $t_1, t_2, \ldots, t_m$. Then u is a function of $t_1, t_2, \ldots, t_m$ and

$$\frac{\partial u}{\partial t_i} = \frac{\partial u}{\partial x_1}\frac{\partial x_1}{\partial t_i} + \frac{\partial u}{\partial x_2}\frac{\partial x_2}{\partial t_i} + \cdots + \frac{\partial u}{\partial x_n}\frac{\partial x_n}{\partial t_i}$$

for each $i = 1, 2, \ldots, m$.

EXAMPLE 4 Write out the Chain Rule for the case where $w = f(x, y, z, t)$ and $x = x(u, v)$, $y = y(u, v)$, $z = z(u, v)$, and $t = t(u, v)$.

SOLUTION We apply Theorem 4 with $n = 4$ and $m = 2$. Figure 3 shows the tree diagram. Although we haven't written the derivatives on the branches, it's understood that if a branch leads from y to u, then the partial derivative for that branch is $\partial y/\partial u$. With the aid

FIGURE 3

of the tree diagram we can now write the required expressions:

$$\frac{\partial w}{\partial u} = \frac{\partial w}{\partial x}\frac{\partial x}{\partial u} + \frac{\partial w}{\partial y}\frac{\partial y}{\partial u} + \frac{\partial w}{\partial z}\frac{\partial z}{\partial u} + \frac{\partial w}{\partial t}\frac{\partial t}{\partial u}$$

$$\frac{\partial w}{\partial v} = \frac{\partial w}{\partial x}\frac{\partial x}{\partial v} + \frac{\partial w}{\partial y}\frac{\partial y}{\partial v} + \frac{\partial w}{\partial z}\frac{\partial z}{\partial v} + \frac{\partial w}{\partial t}\frac{\partial t}{\partial v}$$

EXAMPLE 5 If $u = x^4y + y^2z^3$, where $x = rse^t$, $y = rs^2e^{-t}$, and $z = r^2s \sin t$, find the value of $\partial u/\partial s$ when $r = 2$, $s = 1$, $t = 0$.

SOLUTION With the help of the tree diagram in Figure 4, we have

$$\frac{\partial u}{\partial s} = \frac{\partial u}{\partial x}\frac{\partial x}{\partial s} + \frac{\partial u}{\partial y}\frac{\partial y}{\partial s} + \frac{\partial u}{\partial z}\frac{\partial z}{\partial s}$$

$$= (4x^3y)(re^t) + (x^4 + 2yz^3)(2rse^{-t}) + (3y^2z^2)(r^2 \sin t)$$

When $r = 2$, $s = 1$, and $t = 0$, we have $x = 2$, $y = 2$, and $z = 0$, so

$$\frac{\partial u}{\partial s} = (64)(2) + (16)(4) + (0)(0) = 192$$

EXAMPLE 6 If $g(s, t) = f(s^2 - t^2, t^2 - s^2)$ and f is differentiable, show that g satisfies the equation

$$t\frac{\partial g}{\partial s} + s\frac{\partial g}{\partial t} = 0$$

SOLUTION Let $x = s^2 - t^2$ and $y = t^2 - s^2$. Then $g(s, t) = f(x, y)$ and the Chain Rule gives

$$\frac{\partial g}{\partial s} = \frac{\partial f}{\partial x}\frac{\partial x}{\partial s} + \frac{\partial f}{\partial y}\frac{\partial y}{\partial s} = \frac{\partial f}{\partial x}(2s) + \frac{\partial f}{\partial y}(-2s)$$

$$\frac{\partial g}{\partial t} = \frac{\partial f}{\partial x}\frac{\partial x}{\partial t} + \frac{\partial f}{\partial y}\frac{\partial y}{\partial t} = \frac{\partial f}{\partial x}(-2t) + \frac{\partial f}{\partial y}(2t)$$

Therefore

$$t\frac{\partial g}{\partial s} + s\frac{\partial g}{\partial t} = \left(2st\frac{\partial f}{\partial x} - 2st\frac{\partial f}{\partial y}\right) + \left(-2st\frac{\partial f}{\partial x} + 2st\frac{\partial f}{\partial y}\right) = 0$$

EXAMPLE 7 If $z = f(x, y)$ has continuous second-order partial derivatives and $x = r^2 + s^2$ and $y = 2rs$, find (a) $\partial z/\partial r$ and (b) $\partial^2z/\partial r^2$.

SOLUTION
(a) The Chain Rule gives

$$\frac{\partial z}{\partial r} = \frac{\partial z}{\partial x}\frac{\partial x}{\partial r} + \frac{\partial z}{\partial y}\frac{\partial y}{\partial r} = \frac{\partial z}{\partial x}(2r) + \frac{\partial z}{\partial y}(2s)$$

(b) Applying the Product Rule to the expression in part (a), we get

5

$$\frac{\partial^2z}{\partial r^2} = \frac{\partial}{\partial r}\left(2r\frac{\partial z}{\partial x} + 2s\frac{\partial z}{\partial y}\right)$$

$$= 2\frac{\partial z}{\partial x} + 2r\frac{\partial}{\partial r}\left(\frac{\partial z}{\partial x}\right) + 2s\frac{\partial}{\partial r}\left(\frac{\partial z}{\partial y}\right)$$

FIGURE 4

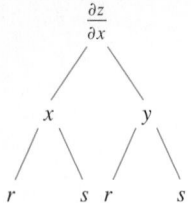

FIGURE 5

But, using the Chain Rule again (see Figure 5), we have

$$\frac{\partial}{\partial r}\left(\frac{\partial z}{\partial x}\right) = \frac{\partial}{\partial x}\left(\frac{\partial z}{\partial x}\right)\frac{\partial x}{\partial r} + \frac{\partial}{\partial y}\left(\frac{\partial z}{\partial x}\right)\frac{\partial y}{\partial r}$$

$$= \frac{\partial^2 z}{\partial x^2}(2r) + \frac{\partial^2 z}{\partial y\,\partial x}(2s)$$

$$\frac{\partial}{\partial r}\left(\frac{\partial z}{\partial y}\right) = \frac{\partial}{\partial x}\left(\frac{\partial z}{\partial y}\right)\frac{\partial x}{\partial r} + \frac{\partial}{\partial y}\left(\frac{\partial z}{\partial y}\right)\frac{\partial y}{\partial r}$$

$$= \frac{\partial^2 z}{\partial x\,\partial y}(2r) + \frac{\partial^2 z}{\partial y^2}(2s)$$

Putting these expressions into Equation 5 and using the equality of the mixed second-order derivatives, we obtain

$$\frac{\partial^2 z}{\partial r^2} = 2\frac{\partial z}{\partial x} + 2r\left(2r\frac{\partial^2 z}{\partial x^2} + 2s\frac{\partial^2 z}{\partial y\,\partial x}\right) + 2s\left(2r\frac{\partial^2 z}{\partial x\,\partial y} + 2s\frac{\partial^2 z}{\partial y^2}\right)$$

$$= 2\frac{\partial z}{\partial x} + 4r^2\frac{\partial^2 z}{\partial x^2} + 8rs\frac{\partial^2 z}{\partial x\,\partial y} + 4s^2\frac{\partial^2 z}{\partial y^2}$$

▥ Implicit Differentiation

The Chain Rule can be used to give a more complete description of the process of implicit differentiation that was introduced in Sections 3.7 and 15.3. We suppose that an equation of the form $F(x, y) = 0$ defines y implicitly as a differentiable function of x, that is, $y = f(x)$, where $F(x, f(x)) = 0$ for all x in the domain of f. If F is differentiable, we can apply Case 1 of the Chain Rule to differentiate both sides of the equation $F(x, y) = 0$ with respect to x. Since both x and y are functions of x, we obtain

$$\frac{\partial F}{\partial x}\frac{dx}{dx} + \frac{\partial F}{\partial y}\frac{dy}{dx} = 0$$

But $dx/dx = 1$, so if $\partial F/\partial y \neq 0$ we solve for dy/dx and obtain

$$\boxed{6} \qquad \frac{dy}{dx} = -\frac{\dfrac{\partial F}{\partial x}}{\dfrac{\partial F}{\partial y}} = -\frac{F_x}{F_y}$$

To derive this equation we assumed that $F(x, y) = 0$ defines y implicitly as a function of x. The **Implicit Function Theorem**, proved in advanced calculus, gives conditions under which this assumption is valid. It states that if F is defined on a disk containing (a, b), where $F(a, b) = 0$, $F_y(a, b) \neq 0$, and F_x and F_y are continuous on the disk, then the equation $F(x, y) = 0$ defines y as a function of x near the point (a, b) and the derivative of this function is given by Equation 6.

EXAMPLE 8 Find y' if $x^3 + y^3 = 6xy$.

SOLUTION The given equation can be written as

$$F(x, y) = x^3 + y^3 - 6xy = 0$$

so Equation 6 gives

▒▒ The solution to Example 8 should be
compared to the one in Example 2 in
Section 3.7.

$$\frac{dy}{dx} = -\frac{F_x}{F_y} = -\frac{3x^2 - 6y}{3y^2 - 6x} = -\frac{x^2 - 2y}{y^2 - 2x}$$

Now we suppose that z is given implicitly as a function $z = f(x, y)$ by an equation of the form $F(x, y, z) = 0$. This means that $F(x, y, f(x, y)) = 0$ for all (x, y) in the domain of f. If F and f are differentiable, then we can use the Chain Rule to differentiate the equation $F(x, y, z) = 0$ as follows:

$$\frac{\partial F}{\partial x}\frac{\partial x}{\partial x} + \frac{\partial F}{\partial y}\frac{\partial y}{\partial x} + \frac{\partial F}{\partial z}\frac{\partial z}{\partial x} = 0$$

But

$$\frac{\partial}{\partial x}(x) = 1 \qquad \text{and} \qquad \frac{\partial}{\partial x}(y) = 0$$

so this equation becomes

$$\frac{\partial F}{\partial x} + \frac{\partial F}{\partial z}\frac{\partial z}{\partial x} = 0$$

If $\partial F/\partial z \neq 0$, we solve for $\partial z/\partial x$ and obtain the first formula in Equations 7. The formula for $\partial z/\partial y$ is obtained in a similar manner.

7

$$\frac{\partial z}{\partial x} = -\frac{\dfrac{\partial F}{\partial x}}{\dfrac{\partial F}{\partial z}} \qquad\qquad \frac{\partial z}{\partial y} = -\frac{\dfrac{\partial F}{\partial y}}{\dfrac{\partial F}{\partial z}}$$

Again, a version of the **Implicit Function Theorem** gives conditions under which our assumption is valid. If F is defined within a sphere containing (a, b, c), where $F(a, b, c) = 0$, $F_z(a, b, c) \neq 0$, and F_x, F_y, and F_z are continuous inside the sphere, then the equation $F(x, y, z) = 0$ defines z as a function of x and y near the point (a, b, c) and this function is differentiable, with partial derivatives given by (7).

EXAMPLE 9 Find $\dfrac{\partial z}{\partial x}$ and $\dfrac{\partial z}{\partial y}$ if $x^3 + y^3 + z^3 + 6xyz = 1$.

SOLUTION Let $F(x, y, z) = x^3 + y^3 + z^3 + 6xyz - 1$. Then, from Equations 7, we have

▒▒ The solution to Example 9 should be
compared to the one in Example 4 in
Section 15.3.

$$\frac{\partial z}{\partial x} = -\frac{F_x}{F_z} = -\frac{3x^2 + 6yz}{3z^2 + 6xy} = -\frac{x^2 + 2yz}{z^2 + 2xy}$$

$$\frac{\partial z}{\partial y} = -\frac{F_y}{F_z} = -\frac{3y^2 + 6xz}{3z^2 + 6xy} = -\frac{y^2 + 2xz}{z^2 + 2xy}$$

15.5 Exercises

1–6 ▓ Use the Chain Rule to find dz/dt or dw/dt.

1. $z = x^2 y + xy^2$, $\quad x = 2 + t^4$, $\quad y = 1 - t^3$

2. $z = \sqrt{x^2 + y^2}$, $\quad x = e^{2t}$, $\quad y = e^{-2t}$

3. $z = \sin x \cos y$, $\quad x = \pi t$, $\quad y = \sqrt{t}$

4. $z = x \ln(x + 2y)$, $\quad x = \sin t$, $\quad y = \cos t$

5. $w = xe^{y/z}$, $\quad x = t^2$, $\quad y = 1 - t$, $\quad z = 1 + 2t$

6. $w = xy + yz^2$, $\quad x = e^t$, $\quad y = e^t \sin t$, $\quad z = e^t \cos t$

7–12 ▓ Use the Chain Rule to find $\partial z/\partial s$ and $\partial z/\partial t$.

7. $z = x^2 + xy + y^2$, $\quad x = s + t$, $\quad y = st$

8. $z = x/y$, $\quad x = se^t$, $\quad y = 1 + se^{-t}$

9. $z = \arctan(2x + y)$, $\quad x = s^2 t$, $\quad y = s \ln t$

10. $z = e^{xy} \tan y$, $\quad x = s + 2t$, $\quad y = s/t$

11. $z = e^r \cos \theta$, $\quad r = st$, $\quad \theta = \sqrt{s^2 + t^2}$

12. $z = \sin \alpha \tan \beta$, $\quad \alpha = 3s + t$, $\quad \beta = s - t$

13. If $z = f(x, y)$, where f is differentiable, $x = g(t)$, $y = h(t)$, $g(3) = 2$, $g'(3) = 5$, $h(3) = 7$, $h'(3) = -4$, $f_x(2, 7) = 6$, and $f_y(2, 7) = -8$, find dz/dt when $t = 3$.

14. Let $W(s, t) = F(u(s, t), v(s, t))$, where F, u, and v are differentiable, $u(1, 0) = 2$, $u_s(1, 0) = -2$, $u_t(1, 0) = 6$, $v(1, 0) = 3$, $v_s(1, 0) = 5$, $v_t(1, 0) = 4$, $F_u(2, 3) = -1$, and $F_v(2, 3) = 10$. Find $W_s(1, 0)$ and $W_t(1, 0)$.

15. Suppose f is a differentiable function of x and y, and $g(u, v) = f(e^u + \sin v, e^u + \cos v)$. Use the table of values to calculate $g_u(0, 0)$ and $g_v(0, 0)$.

	f	g	f_x	f_y
(0, 0)	3	6	4	8
(1, 2)	6	3	2	5

16. Suppose f is a differentiable function of x and y, and $g(r, s) = f(2r - s, s^2 - 4r)$. Use the table of values in Exercise 15 to calculate $g_r(1, 2)$ and $g_s(1, 2)$.

17–20 ▓ Use a tree diagram to write out the Chain Rule for the given case. Assume all functions are differentiable.

17. $u = f(x, y)$, $\quad$ where $x = x(r, s, t)$, $y = y(r, s, t)$

18. $w = f(x, y, z)$, $\quad$ where $x = x(t, u)$, $y = y(t, u)$, $z = z(t, u)$

19. $v = f(p, q, r)$, $\quad$ where $p = p(x, y, z)$, $q = q(x, y, z)$, $r = r(x, y, z)$

20. $u = f(s, t)$, $\quad$ where $s = s(w, x, y, z)$, $t = t(w, x, y, z)$

21–26 ▓ Use the Chain Rule to find the indicated partial derivatives.

21. $z = x^2 + xy^3$, $\quad x = uv^2 + w^3$, $\quad y = u + ve^w$;
$\dfrac{\partial z}{\partial u}$, $\dfrac{\partial z}{\partial v}$, $\dfrac{\partial z}{\partial w}$ $\quad$ when $u = 2, v = 1, w = 0$

22. $u = \sqrt{r^2 + s^2}$, $\quad r = y + x \cos t$, $\quad s = x + y \sin t$;
$\dfrac{\partial u}{\partial x}$, $\dfrac{\partial u}{\partial y}$, $\dfrac{\partial u}{\partial t}$ $\quad$ when $x = 1, y = 2, t = 0$

23. $R = \ln(u^2 + v^2 + w^2)$, $\quad u = x + 2y$, $\quad v = 2x - y$, $w = 2xy$;
$\dfrac{\partial R}{\partial x}$, $\dfrac{\partial R}{\partial y}$ $\quad$ when $x = y = 1$

24. $M = xe^{y - z^2}$, $\quad x = 2uv$, $\quad y = u - v$, $\quad z = u + v$;
$\dfrac{\partial M}{\partial u}$, $\dfrac{\partial M}{\partial v}$ $\quad$ when $u = 3, v = -1$

25. $u = x^2 + yz$, $\quad x = pr \cos \theta$, $\quad y = pr \sin \theta$, $\quad z = p + r$;
$\dfrac{\partial u}{\partial p}$, $\dfrac{\partial u}{\partial r}$, $\dfrac{\partial u}{\partial \theta}$ $\quad$ when $p = 2, r = 3, \theta = 0$

26. $Y = w \tan^{-1}(uv)$, $\quad u = r + s$, $\quad v = s + t$, $\quad w = t + r$;
$\dfrac{\partial Y}{\partial r}$, $\dfrac{\partial Y}{\partial s}$, $\dfrac{\partial Y}{\partial t}$ $\quad$ when $r = 1, s = 0, t = 1$

27–30 ▓ Use Equation 6 to find dy/dx.

27. $\sqrt{xy} = 1 + x^2 y$ $\qquad$ **28.** $y^5 + x^2 y^3 = 1 + ye^{x^2}$

29. $\cos(x - y) = xe^y$ $\qquad$ **30.** $\sin x + \cos y = \sin x \cos y$

31–34 ▓ Use Equations 7 to find $\partial z/\partial x$ and $\partial z/\partial y$.

31. $x^2 + y^2 + z^2 = 3xyz$ $\qquad$ **32.** $xyz = \cos(x + y + z)$

33. $x - z = \arctan(yz)$ $\qquad$ **34.** $yz = \ln(x + z)$

35. The temperature at a point (x, y) is $T(x, y)$, measured in degrees Celsius. A bug crawls so that its position after t seconds is given by $x = \sqrt{1 + t}$, $y = 2 + \frac{1}{3}t$, where x and y are measured in centimeters. The temperature function satisfies $T_x(2, 3) = 4$ and $T_y(2, 3) = 3$. How fast is the temperature rising on the bug's path after 3 seconds?

36. Wheat production in a given year, W, depends on the average temperature T and the annual rainfall R. Scientists estimate that the average temperature is rising at a rate of $0.15°C/\text{year}$ and rainfall is decreasing at a rate of 0.1 cm/year. They also estimate that, at current production levels, $\partial W/\partial T = -2$ and $\partial W/\partial R = 8$.
(a) What is the significance of the signs of these partial derivatives?
(b) Estimate the current rate of change of wheat production, dW/dt.

37. The speed of sound traveling through ocean water with salinity 35 parts per thousand has been modeled by the equation

$$C = 1449.2 + 4.6T - 0.055T^2 + 0.00029T^3 + 0.016D$$

where C is the speed of sound (in meters per second), T is the temperature (in degrees Celsius), and D is the depth below the ocean surface (in meters). A scuba diver began a leisurely dive into the ocean water; the diver's depth and surrounding water temperature over time are recorded in the following graphs. Estimate the rate of change (with respect to time) of the speed of sound through the ocean water experienced by the diver 20 minutes into the dive. What are the units?

 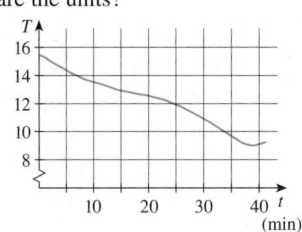

38. The radius of a right circular cone is increasing at a rate of 1.8 in/s while its height is decreasing at a rate of 2.5 in/s. At what rate is the volume of the cone changing when the radius is 120 in. and the height is 140 in.?

39. The length ℓ, width w, and height h of a box change with time. At a certain instant the dimensions are $\ell = 1$ m and $w = h = 2$ m, and ℓ and w are increasing at a rate of 2 m/s while h is decreasing at a rate of 3 m/s. At that instant find the rates at which the following quantities are changing.
(a) The volume   (b) The surface area
(c) The length of a diagonal

40. The voltage V in a simple electrical circuit is slowly decreasing as the battery wears out. The resistance R is slowly increasing as the resistor heats up. Use Ohm's Law, $V = IR$, to find how the current I is changing at the moment when $R = 400\ \Omega$, $I = 0.08$ A, $dV/dt = -0.01$ V/s, and $dR/dt = 0.03\ \Omega$/s.

41. The pressure of 1 mole of an ideal gas is increasing at a rate of 0.05 kPa/s and the temperature is increasing at a rate of 0.15 K/s. Use the equation in Example 2 to find the rate of change of the volume when the pressure is 20 kPa and the temperature is 320 K.

42. Car A is traveling north on Highway 16 and car B is traveling west on Highway 83. Each car is approaching the intersection of these highways. At a certain moment, car A is 0.3 km from the intersection and traveling at 90 km/h while car B is 0.4 km from the intersection and traveling at 80 km/h. How fast is the distance between the cars changing at that moment?

43–46 ▮▮▮ Assume that all the given functions are differentiable.

43. If $z = f(x, y)$, where $x = r\cos\theta$ and $y = r\sin\theta$, (a) find $\partial z/\partial r$ and $\partial z/\partial\theta$ and (b) show that

$$\left(\frac{\partial z}{\partial x}\right)^2 + \left(\frac{\partial z}{\partial y}\right)^2 = \left(\frac{\partial z}{\partial r}\right)^2 + \frac{1}{r^2}\left(\frac{\partial z}{\partial\theta}\right)^2$$

44. If $u = f(x, y)$, where $x = e^s\cos t$ and $y = e^s\sin t$, show that

$$\left(\frac{\partial u}{\partial x}\right)^2 + \left(\frac{\partial u}{\partial y}\right)^2 = e^{-2s}\left[\left(\frac{\partial u}{\partial s}\right)^2 + \left(\frac{\partial u}{\partial t}\right)^2\right]$$

45. If $z = f(x - y)$, show that $\dfrac{\partial z}{\partial x} + \dfrac{\partial z}{\partial y} = 0$.

46. If $z = f(x, y)$, where $x = s + t$ and $y = s - t$, show that

$$\left(\frac{\partial z}{\partial x}\right)^2 - \left(\frac{\partial z}{\partial y}\right)^2 = \frac{\partial z}{\partial s}\frac{\partial z}{\partial t}$$

47–52 ▮▮▮ Assume that all the given functions have continuous second-order partial derivatives.

47. Show that any function of the form

$$z = f(x + at) + g(x - at)$$

is a solution of the wave equation

$$\frac{\partial^2 z}{\partial t^2} = a^2\frac{\partial^2 z}{\partial x^2}$$

[*Hint:* Let $u = x + at$, $v = x - at$.]

48. If $u = f(x, y)$, where $x = e^s\cos t$ and $y = e^s\sin t$, show that

$$\frac{\partial^2 u}{\partial x^2} + \frac{\partial^2 u}{\partial y^2} = e^{-2s}\left[\frac{\partial^2 u}{\partial s^2} + \frac{\partial^2 u}{\partial t^2}\right]$$

49. If $z = f(x, y)$, where $x = r^2 + s^2$, $y = 2rs$, find $\partial^2 z/\partial r\,\partial s$. (Compare with Example 7.)

50. If $z = f(x, y)$, where $x = r\cos\theta$, $y = r\sin\theta$, find (a) $\partial z/\partial r$, (b) $\partial z/\partial\theta$, and (c) $\partial^2 z/\partial r\,\partial\theta$.

51. If $z = f(x, y)$, where $x = r\cos\theta$, $y = r\sin\theta$, show that

$$\frac{\partial^2 z}{\partial x^2} + \frac{\partial^2 z}{\partial y^2} = \frac{\partial^2 z}{\partial r^2} + \frac{1}{r^2}\frac{\partial^2 z}{\partial\theta^2} + \frac{1}{r}\frac{\partial z}{\partial r}$$

52. Suppose $z = f(x, y)$, where $x = g(s, t)$ and $y = h(s, t)$.
(a) Show that

$$\frac{\partial^2 z}{\partial t^2} = \frac{\partial^2 z}{\partial x^2}\left(\frac{\partial x}{\partial t}\right)^2 + 2\frac{\partial^2 z}{\partial x\,\partial y}\frac{\partial x}{\partial t}\frac{\partial y}{\partial t} + \frac{\partial^2 z}{\partial y^2}\left(\frac{\partial y}{\partial t}\right)^2$$

$$+ \frac{\partial z}{\partial x}\frac{\partial^2 x}{\partial t^2} + \frac{\partial z}{\partial y}\frac{\partial^2 y}{\partial t^2}$$

(b) Find a similar formula for $\partial^2 z/\partial s\,\partial t$.

53. A function f is called **homogeneous of degree n** if it satisfies the equation $f(tx, ty) = t^n f(x, y)$ for all t, where n is a positive integer and f has continuous second-order partial derivatives.
(a) Verify that $f(x, y) = x^2 y + 2xy^2 + 5y^3$ is homogeneous of degree 3.

(b) Show that if f is homogeneous of degree n, then

$$x \frac{\partial f}{\partial x} + y \frac{\partial f}{\partial y} = nf(x, y)$$

[*Hint:* Use the Chain Rule to differentiate $f(tx, ty)$ with respect to t.]

54. If f is homogeneous of degree n, show that

$$x^2 \frac{\partial^2 f}{\partial x^2} + 2xy \frac{\partial^2 f}{\partial x \, \partial y} + y^2 \frac{\partial^2 f}{\partial y^2} = n(n-1)f(x, y)$$

55. If f is homogeneous of degree n, show that

$$f_x(tx, ty) = t^{n-1}f_x(x, y)$$

56. Suppose that the equation $F(x, y, z) = 0$ implicitly defines each of the three variables x, y, and z as functions of the other two: $z = f(x, y)$, $y = g(x, z)$, $x = h(y, z)$. If F is differentiable and F_x, F_y, and F_z are all nonzero, show that

$$\frac{\partial z}{\partial x} \frac{\partial x}{\partial y} \frac{\partial y}{\partial z} = -1$$

▐▐▐ **15.6** Directional Derivatives and the Gradient Vector

The weather map in Figure 1 shows a contour map of the temperature function $T(x, y)$ for the states of California and Nevada at 3:00 P.M. on a day in October. The level curves, or isothermals, join locations with the same temperature. The partial derivative T_x at a location such as Reno is the rate of change of temperature with respect to distance if we travel east from Reno; T_y is the rate of change of temperature if we travel north. But what if we want to know the rate of change of temperature when we travel southeast (toward Las Vegas), or in some other direction? In this section we introduce a type of derivative, called a *directional derivative,* that enables us to find the rate of change of a function of two or more variables in any direction.

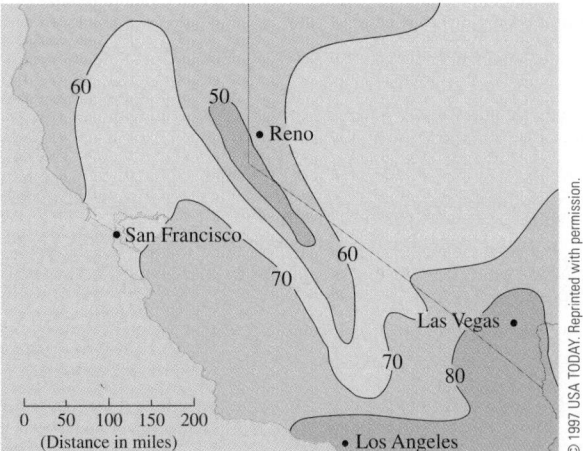

FIGURE 1

© 1997 USA TODAY. Reprinted with permission.

▐▐▐ Directional Derivatives

Recall that if $z = f(x, y)$, then the partial derivatives f_x and f_y are defined as

$$\boxed{1}$$

$$f_x(x_0, y_0) = \lim_{h \to 0} \frac{f(x_0 + h, y_0) - f(x_0, y_0)}{h}$$

$$f_y(x_0, y_0) = \lim_{h \to 0} \frac{f(x_0, y_0 + h) - f(x_0, y_0)}{h}$$

and represent the rates of change of z in the x- and y-directions, that is, in the directions of the unit vectors **i** and **j**.

Suppose that we now wish to find the rate of change of z at (x_0, y_0) in the direction of an arbitrary unit vector $\mathbf{u} = \langle a, b \rangle$. (See Figure 2.) To do this we consider the surface S with equation $z = f(x, y)$ (the graph of f) and we let $z_0 = f(x_0, y_0)$. Then the point

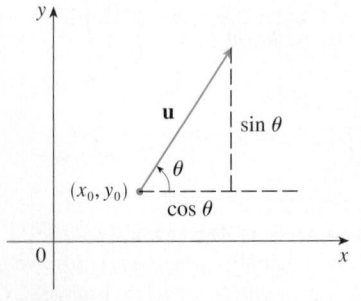

FIGURE 2

A unit vector $\mathbf{u} = \langle a, b \rangle = \langle \cos \theta, \sin \theta \rangle$

$P(x_0, y_0, z_0)$ lies on S. The vertical plane that passes through P in the direction of $\mathbf{u}$ intersects S in a curve C. (See Figure 3.) The slope of the tangent line T to C at the point P is the rate of change of z in the direction of $\mathbf{u}$.

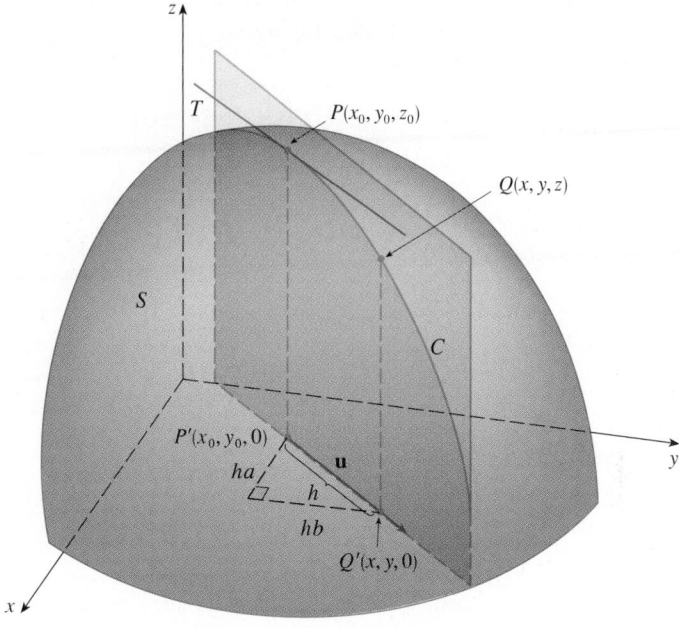

Visual 15.6A animates Figure 3 by rotating $\mathbf{u}$ and therefore T.

FIGURE 3

If $Q(x, y, z)$ is another point on C and P', Q' are the projections of P, Q on the xy-plane, then the vector $\overrightarrow{P'Q'}$ is parallel to $\mathbf{u}$ and so

$$\overrightarrow{P'Q'} = h\mathbf{u} = \langle ha, hb \rangle$$

for some scalar h. Therefore, $x - x_0 = ha$, $y - y_0 = hb$, so $x = x_0 + ha$, $y = y_0 + hb$, and

$$\frac{\Delta z}{h} = \frac{z - z_0}{h} = \frac{f(x_0 + ha, y_0 + hb) - f(x_0, y_0)}{h}$$

If we take the limit as $h \to 0$, we obtain the rate of change of z (with respect to distance) in the direction of $\mathbf{u}$, which is called the directional derivative of f in the direction of $\mathbf{u}$.

> **2 Definition** The **directional derivative** of f at (x_0, y_0) in the direction of a unit vector $\mathbf{u} = \langle a, b \rangle$ is
>
> $$D_{\mathbf{u}} f(x_0, y_0) = \lim_{h \to 0} \frac{f(x_0 + ha, y_0 + hb) - f(x_0, y_0)}{h}$$
>
> if this limit exists.

By comparing Definition 2 with (1), we see that if $\mathbf{u} = \mathbf{i} = \langle 1, 0 \rangle$, then $D_{\mathbf{i}} f = f_x$ and if $\mathbf{u} = \mathbf{j} = \langle 0, 1 \rangle$, then $D_{\mathbf{j}} f = f_y$. In other words, the partial derivatives of f with respect to x and y are just special cases of the directional derivative.

EXAMPLE 1 Use the weather map in Figure 1 to estimate the value of the directional derivative of the temperature function at Reno in the southeasterly direction.

SOLUTION The unit vector directed toward the southeast is $\mathbf{u} = (\mathbf{i} - \mathbf{j})/\sqrt{2}$, but we won't need to use this expression. We start by drawing a line through Reno toward the southeast. (See Figure 4.)

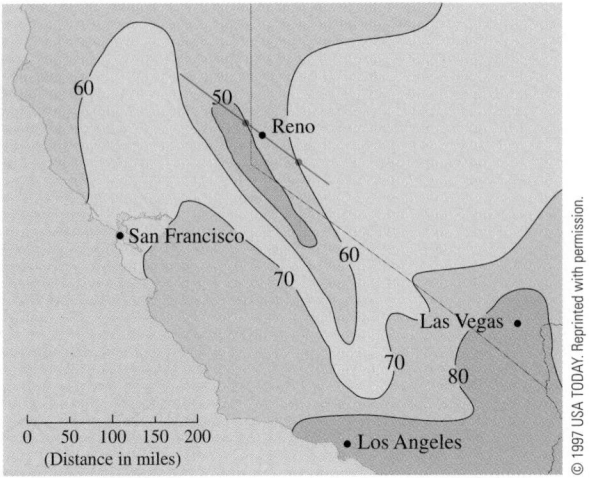

FIGURE 4

We approximate the directional derivative $D_{\mathbf{u}}T$ by the average rate of change of the temperature between the points where this line intersects the isothermals $T = 50$ and $T = 60$. The temperature at the point southeast of Reno is $T = 60°F$ and the temperature at the point northwest of Reno is $T = 50°F$. The distance between these points looks to be about 75 miles. So the rate of change of the temperature in the southeasterly direction is

$$D_{\mathbf{u}}T \approx \frac{60 - 50}{75} = \frac{10}{75} \approx 0.13°F/mi$$

When we compute the directional derivative of a function defined by a formula, we generally use the following theorem.

> **3** **Theorem** If f is a differentiable function of x and y, then f has a directional derivative in the direction of any unit vector $\mathbf{u} = \langle a, b \rangle$ and
>
> $$D_{\mathbf{u}}f(x, y) = f_x(x, y)a + f_y(x, y)b$$

Proof If we define a function g of the single variable h by

$$g(h) = f(x_0 + ha, y_0 + hb)$$

then by the definition of a derivative we have

$$\boxed{4} \qquad g'(0) = \lim_{h \to 0} \frac{g(h) - g(0)}{h} = \lim_{h \to 0} \frac{f(x_0 + ha, y_0 + hb) - f(x_0, y_0)}{h}$$

$$= D_{\mathbf{u}}f(x_0, y_0)$$

On the other hand, we can write $g(h) = f(x, y)$, where $x = x_0 + ha$, $y = y_0 + hb$, so the Chain Rule (Theorem 15.5.2) gives

$$g'(h) = \frac{\partial f}{\partial x}\frac{dx}{dh} + \frac{\partial f}{\partial y}\frac{dy}{dh} = f_x(x, y)a + f_y(x, y)b$$

If we now put $h = 0$, then $x = x_0$, $y = y_0$, and

$$\boxed{5} \qquad g'(0) = f_x(x_0, y_0)a + f_y(x_0, y_0)b$$

Comparing Equations 4 and 5, we see that

$$D_\mathbf{u} f(x_0, y_0) = f_x(x_0, y_0)a + f_y(x_0, y_0)b$$

If the unit vector $\mathbf{u}$ makes an angle θ with the positive x-axis (as in Figure 2), then we can write $\mathbf{u} = \langle \cos\theta, \sin\theta \rangle$ and the formula in Theorem 3 becomes

$$\boxed{6} \qquad D_\mathbf{u} f(x, y) = f_x(x, y)\cos\theta + f_y(x, y)\sin\theta$$

▏▏▏ The directional derivative $D_\mathbf{u} f(1, 2)$ in Example 2 represents the rate of change of z in the direction of $\mathbf{u}$. This is the slope of the tangent line to the curve of intersection of the surface $z = x^3 - 3xy + 4y^2$ and the vertical plane through $(1, 2, 0)$ in the direction of $\mathbf{u}$ shown in Figure 5.

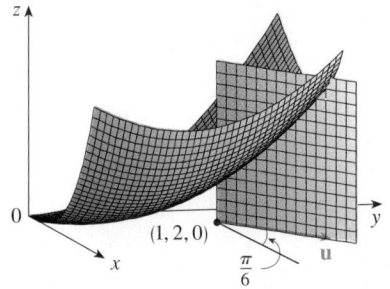

FIGURE 5

EXAMPLE 2 Find the directional derivative $D_\mathbf{u} f(x, y)$ if

$$f(x, y) = x^3 - 3xy + 4y^2$$

and $\mathbf{u}$ is the unit vector given by angle $\theta = \pi/6$. What is $D_\mathbf{u} f(1, 2)$?

SOLUTION Formula 6 gives

$$D_\mathbf{u} f(x, y) = f_x(x, y)\cos\frac{\pi}{6} + f_y(x, y)\sin\frac{\pi}{6}$$

$$= (3x^2 - 3y)\frac{\sqrt{3}}{2} + (-3x + 8y)\tfrac{1}{2}$$

$$= \tfrac{1}{2}\left[3\sqrt{3}x^2 - 3x + \left(8 - 3\sqrt{3}\right)y\right]$$

Therefore

$$D_\mathbf{u} f(1, 2) = \tfrac{1}{2}\left[3\sqrt{3}(1)^2 - 3(1) + \left(8 - 3\sqrt{3}\right)(2)\right] = \frac{13 - 3\sqrt{3}}{2}$$

▏▏▏▏▏ **The Gradient Vector**

Notice from Theorem 3 that the directional derivative can be written as the dot product of two vectors:

$$\boxed{7} \qquad D_\mathbf{u} f(x, y) = f_x(x, y)a + f_y(x, y)b$$

$$= \langle f_x(x, y), f_y(x, y) \rangle \cdot \langle a, b \rangle$$

$$= \langle f_x(x, y), f_y(x, y) \rangle \cdot \mathbf{u}$$

The first vector in this dot product occurs not only in computing directional derivatives but in many other contexts as well. So we give it a special name (the *gradient* of f) and a special notation (**grad** f or ∇f, which is read "del f").

8 **Definition** If f is a function of two variables x and y, then the **gradient** of f is the vector function ∇f defined by

$$\nabla f(x, y) = \langle f_x(x, y), f_y(x, y) \rangle = \frac{\partial f}{\partial x}\mathbf{i} + \frac{\partial f}{\partial y}\mathbf{j}$$

EXAMPLE 3 If $f(x, y) = \sin x + e^{xy}$, then

$$\nabla f(x, y) = \langle f_x, f_y \rangle = \langle \cos x + ye^{xy}, xe^{xy} \rangle$$

and $\qquad\qquad \nabla f(0, 1) = \langle 2, 0 \rangle$

With this notation for the gradient vector, we can rewrite the expression (7) for the directional derivative as

9

$$D_{\mathbf{u}} f(x, y) = \nabla f(x, y) \cdot \mathbf{u}$$

This expresses the directional derivative in the direction of $\mathbf{u}$ as the scalar projection of the gradient vector onto $\mathbf{u}$.

▏▏ The gradient vector $\nabla f(2, -1)$ in Example 4 is shown in Figure 6 with initial point $(2, -1)$. Also shown is the vector $\mathbf{v}$ that gives the direction of the directional derivative. Both of these vectors are superimposed on a contour plot of the graph of f.

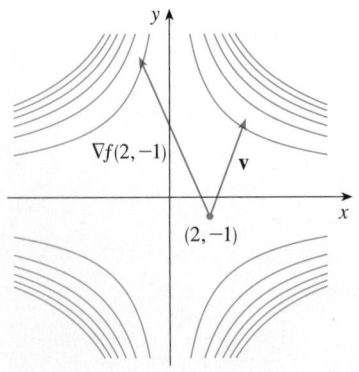

FIGURE 6

EXAMPLE 4 Find the directional derivative of the function $f(x, y) = x^2 y^3 - 4y$ at the point $(2, -1)$ in the direction of the vector $\mathbf{v} = 2\mathbf{i} + 5\mathbf{j}$.

SOLUTION We first compute the gradient vector at $(2, -1)$:

$$\nabla f(x, y) = 2xy^3\mathbf{i} + (3x^2y^2 - 4)\mathbf{j}$$

$$\nabla f(2, -1) = -4\mathbf{i} + 8\mathbf{j}$$

Note that $\mathbf{v}$ is not a unit vector, but since $|\mathbf{v}| = \sqrt{29}$, the unit vector in the direction of $\mathbf{v}$ is

$$\mathbf{u} = \frac{\mathbf{v}}{|\mathbf{v}|} = \frac{2}{\sqrt{29}}\mathbf{i} + \frac{5}{\sqrt{29}}\mathbf{j}$$

Therefore, by Equation 9, we have

$$D_{\mathbf{u}} f(2, -1) = \nabla f(2, -1) \cdot \mathbf{u} = (-4\mathbf{i} + 8\mathbf{j}) \cdot \left(\frac{2}{\sqrt{29}}\mathbf{i} + \frac{5}{\sqrt{29}}\mathbf{j} \right)$$

$$= \frac{-4 \cdot 2 + 8 \cdot 5}{\sqrt{29}} = \frac{32}{\sqrt{29}}$$

▏▏▏▏▏ **Functions of Three Variables**

For functions of three variables we can define directional derivatives in a similar manner. Again $D_{\mathbf{u}} f(x, y, z)$ can be interpreted as the rate of change of the function in the direction of a unit vector $\mathbf{u}$.

> **10** **Definition** The **directional derivative** of f at (x_0, y_0, z_0) in the direction of a unit vector $\mathbf{u} = \langle a, b, c \rangle$ is
>
> $$D_\mathbf{u} f(x_0, y_0, z_0) = \lim_{h \to 0} \frac{f(x_0 + ha, y_0 + hb, z_0 + hc) - f(x_0, y_0, z_0)}{h}$$
>
> if this limit exists.

If we use vector notation, then we can write both definitions (2 and 10) of the directional derivative in the compact form

$$D_\mathbf{u} f(\mathbf{x}_0) = \lim_{h \to 0} \frac{f(\mathbf{x}_0 + h\mathbf{u}) - f(\mathbf{x}_0)}{h} \qquad \boxed{11}$$

where $\mathbf{x}_0 = \langle x_0, y_0 \rangle$ if $n = 2$ and $\mathbf{x}_0 = \langle x_0, y_0, z_0 \rangle$ if $n = 3$. This is reasonable since the vector equation of the line through $\mathbf{x}_0$ in the direction of the vector $\mathbf{u}$ is given by $\mathbf{x} = \mathbf{x}_0 + t\mathbf{u}$ (Equation 13.5.1) and so $f(\mathbf{x}_0 + h\mathbf{u})$ represents the value of f at a point on this line.

If $f(x, y, z)$ is differentiable and $\mathbf{u} = \langle a, b, c \rangle$, then the same method that was used to prove Theorem 3 can be used to show that

$$\boxed{12} \qquad D_\mathbf{u} f(x, y, z) = f_x(x, y, z)a + f_y(x, y, z)b + f_z(x, y, z)c$$

For a function f of three variables, the **gradient vector**, denoted by ∇f or **grad** f, is

$$\nabla f(x, y, z) = \langle f_x(x, y, z), f_y(x, y, z), f_z(x, y, z) \rangle$$

or, for short,

$$\boxed{13} \qquad \nabla f = \langle f_x, f_y, f_z \rangle = \frac{\partial f}{\partial x}\mathbf{i} + \frac{\partial f}{\partial y}\mathbf{j} + \frac{\partial f}{\partial z}\mathbf{k}$$

Then, just as with functions of two variables, Formula 12 for the directional derivative can be rewritten as

$$\boxed{14} \qquad D_\mathbf{u} f(x, y, z) = \nabla f(x, y, z) \cdot \mathbf{u}$$

EXAMPLE 5 If $f(x, y, z) = x \sin yz$, (a) find the gradient of f and (b) find the directional derivative of f at $(1, 3, 0)$ in the direction of $\mathbf{v} = \mathbf{i} + 2\mathbf{j} - \mathbf{k}$.

SOLUTION
(a) The gradient of f is

$$\nabla f(x, y, z) = \langle f_x(x, y, z), f_y(x, y, z), f_z(x, y, z) \rangle$$

$$= \langle \sin yz, xz \cos yz, xy \cos yz \rangle$$

(b) At $(1, 3, 0)$ we have $\nabla f(1, 3, 0) = \langle 0, 0, 3 \rangle$. The unit vector in the direction of $\mathbf{v} = \mathbf{i} + 2\mathbf{j} - \mathbf{k}$ is

$$\mathbf{u} = \frac{1}{\sqrt{6}} \mathbf{i} + \frac{2}{\sqrt{6}} \mathbf{j} - \frac{1}{\sqrt{6}} \mathbf{k}$$

Therefore, Equation 14 gives

$$D_{\mathbf{u}} f(1, 3, 0) = \nabla f(1, 3, 0) \cdot \mathbf{u}$$
$$= 3\mathbf{k} \cdot \left(\frac{1}{\sqrt{6}} \mathbf{i} + \frac{2}{\sqrt{6}} \mathbf{j} - \frac{1}{\sqrt{6}} \mathbf{k} \right)$$
$$= 3\left(-\frac{1}{\sqrt{6}} \right) = -\sqrt{\frac{3}{2}}$$

▓▓▓ Maximizing the Directional Derivative

Suppose we have a function f of two or three variables and we consider all possible directional derivatives of f at a given point. These give the rates of change of f in all possible directions. We can then ask the questions: In which of these directions does f change fastest and what is the maximum rate of change? The answers are provided by the following theorem.

Visual 15.6B provides visual confirmation of Theorem 15.

> **15 Theorem** Suppose f is a differentiable function of two or three variables. The maximum value of the directional derivative $D_{\mathbf{u}} f(\mathbf{x})$ is $|\nabla f(\mathbf{x})|$ and it occurs when $\mathbf{u}$ has the same direction as the gradient vector $\nabla f(\mathbf{x})$.

Proof From Equation 9 or 14 we have

$$D_{\mathbf{u}} f = \nabla f \cdot \mathbf{u} = |\nabla f| |\mathbf{u}| \cos \theta = |\nabla f| \cos \theta$$

where θ is the angle between ∇f and $\mathbf{u}$. The maximum value of $\cos \theta$ is 1 and this occurs when $\theta = 0$. Therefore, the maximum value of $D_{\mathbf{u}} f$ is $|\nabla f|$ and it occurs when $\theta = 0$, that is, when $\mathbf{u}$ has the same direction as ∇f.

EXAMPLE 6
(a) If $f(x, y) = xe^y$, find the rate of change of f at the point $P(2, 0)$ in the direction from P to $Q(\frac{1}{2}, 2)$.
(b) In what direction does f have the maximum rate of change? What is this maximum rate of change?

SOLUTION
(a) We first compute the gradient vector:

$$\nabla f(x, y) = \langle f_x, f_y \rangle = \langle e^y, xe^y \rangle$$
$$\nabla f(2, 0) = \langle 1, 2 \rangle$$

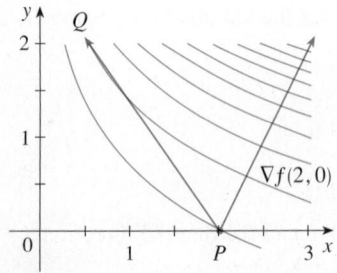

FIGURE 7

▓▓▓ At $(2, 0)$ the function in Example 6 increases fastest in the direction of the gradient vector $\nabla f(2, 0) = \langle 1, 2 \rangle$. Notice from Figure 7 that this vector appears to be perpendicular to the level curve through $(2, 0)$. Figure 8 shows the graph of f and the gradient vector.

The unit vector in the direction of $\overrightarrow{PQ} = \langle -1.5, 2 \rangle$ is $\mathbf{u} = \left\langle -\frac{3}{5}, \frac{4}{5} \right\rangle$, so the rate of change of f in the direction from P to Q is

$$D_{\mathbf{u}} f(2, 0) = \nabla f(2, 0) \cdot \mathbf{u} = \langle 1, 2 \rangle \cdot \left\langle -\frac{3}{5}, \frac{4}{5} \right\rangle$$
$$= 1\left(-\frac{3}{5} \right) + 2\left(\frac{4}{5} \right) = 1$$

FIGURE 8

(b) According to Theorem 15, f increases fastest in the direction of the gradient vector $\nabla f(2, 0) = \langle 1, 2 \rangle$. The maximum rate of change is

$$|\nabla f(2, 0)| = |\langle 1, 2 \rangle| = \sqrt{5}$$

EXAMPLE 7 Suppose that the temperature at a point (x, y, z) in space is given by $T(x, y, z) = 80/(1 + x^2 + 2y^2 + 3z^2)$, where T is measured in degrees Celsius and x, y, z in meters. In which direction does the temperature increase fastest at the point $(1, 1, -2)$? What is the maximum rate of increase?

SOLUTION The gradient of T is

$$\nabla T = \frac{\partial T}{\partial x}\mathbf{i} + \frac{\partial T}{\partial y}\mathbf{j} + \frac{\partial T}{\partial z}\mathbf{k}$$

$$= -\frac{160x}{(1 + x^2 + 2y^2 + 3z^2)^2}\mathbf{i} - \frac{320y}{(1 + x^2 + 2y^2 + 3z^2)^2}\mathbf{j} - \frac{480z}{(1 + x^2 + 2y^2 + 3z^2)^2}\mathbf{k}$$

$$= \frac{160}{(1 + x^2 + 2y^2 + 3z^2)^2}(-x\mathbf{i} - 2y\mathbf{j} - 3z\mathbf{k})$$

At the point $(1, 1, -2)$ the gradient vector is

$$\nabla T(1, 1, -2) = \tfrac{160}{256}(-\mathbf{i} - 2\mathbf{j} + 6\mathbf{k}) = \tfrac{5}{8}(-\mathbf{i} - 2\mathbf{j} + 6\mathbf{k})$$

By Theorem 15 the temperature increases fastest in the direction of the gradient vector $\nabla T(1, 1, -2) = \tfrac{5}{8}(-\mathbf{i} - 2\mathbf{j} + 6\mathbf{k})$ or, equivalently, in the direction of $-\mathbf{i} - 2\mathbf{j} + 6\mathbf{k}$ or the unit vector $(-\mathbf{i} - 2\mathbf{j} + 6\mathbf{k})/\sqrt{41}$. The maximum rate of increase is the length of the gradient vector:

$$|\nabla T(1, 1, -2)| = \tfrac{5}{8}|-\mathbf{i} - 2\mathbf{j} + 6\mathbf{k}| = \frac{5\sqrt{41}}{8}$$

Therefore, the maximum rate of increase of temperature is $5\sqrt{41}/8 \approx 4°C/m$. ▬

Tangent Planes to Level Surfaces

Suppose S is a surface with equation $F(x, y, z) = k$, that is, it is a level surface of a function F of three variables, and let $P(x_0, y_0, z_0)$ be a point on S. Let C be any curve that lies on the surface S and passes through the point P. Recall from Section 14.1 that the curve C is described by a continuous vector function $\mathbf{r}(t) = \langle x(t), y(t), z(t) \rangle$. Let t_0 be the parameter value corresponding to P; that is, $\mathbf{r}(t_0) = \langle x_0, y_0, z_0 \rangle$. Since C lies on S, any point $(x(t), y(t), z(t))$ must satisfy the equation of S, that is,

16    $$F(x(t), y(t), z(t)) = k$$

If x, y, and z are differentiable functions of t and F is also differentiable, then we can use the Chain Rule to differentiate both sides of Equation 16 as follows:

17    $$\frac{\partial F}{\partial x}\frac{dx}{dt} + \frac{\partial F}{\partial y}\frac{dy}{dt} + \frac{\partial F}{\partial z}\frac{dz}{dt} = 0$$

But, since $\nabla F = \langle F_x, F_y, F_z \rangle$ and $\mathbf{r}'(t) = \langle x'(t), y'(t), z'(t) \rangle$, Equation 17 can be written in terms of a dot product as

$$\nabla F \cdot \mathbf{r}'(t) = 0$$

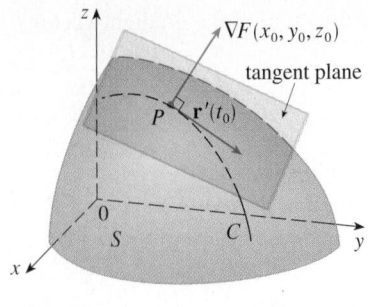

FIGURE 9

In particular, when $t = t_0$ we have $\mathbf{r}(t_0) = \langle x_0, y_0, z_0 \rangle$, so

$$\boxed{18} \qquad \nabla F(x_0, y_0, z_0) \cdot \mathbf{r}'(t_0) = 0$$

Equation 18 says that *the gradient vector at P, $\nabla F(x_0, y_0, z_0)$, is perpendicular to the tangent vector $\mathbf{r}'(t_0)$ to any curve C on S that passes through P.* (See Figure 9.) If $\nabla F(x_0, y_0, z_0) \neq \mathbf{0}$, it is therefore natural to define the **tangent plane to the level surface** $F(x, y, z) = k$ **at** $P(x_0, y_0, z_0)$ as the plane that passes through P and has normal vector $\nabla F(x_0, y_0, z_0)$. Using the standard equation of a plane (Equation 13.5.7), we can write the equation of this tangent plane as

$$\boxed{19} \qquad F_x(x_0, y_0, z_0)(x - x_0) + F_y(x_0, y_0, z_0)(y - y_0) + F_z(x_0, y_0, z_0)(z - z_0) = 0$$

The **normal line** to S at P is the line passing through P and perpendicular to the tangent plane. The direction of the normal line is therefore given by the gradient vector $\nabla F(x_0, y_0, z_0)$ and so, by Equation 13.5.3, its symmetric equations are

$$\boxed{20} \qquad \frac{x - x_0}{F_x(x_0, y_0, z_0)} = \frac{y - y_0}{F_y(x_0, y_0, z_0)} = \frac{z - z_0}{F_z(x_0, y_0, z_0)}$$

In the special case in which the equation of a surface S is of the form $z = f(x, y)$ (that is, S is the graph of a function f of two variables), we can rewrite the equation as

$$F(x, y, z) = f(x, y) - z = 0$$

and regard S as a level surface (with $k = 0$) of F. Then

$$F_x(x_0, y_0, z_0) = f_x(x_0, y_0)$$

$$F_y(x_0, y_0, z_0) = f_y(x_0, y_0)$$

$$F_z(x_0, y_0, z_0) = -1$$

so Equation 19 becomes

$$f_x(x_0, y_0)(x - x_0) + f_y(x_0, y_0)(y - y_0) - (z - z_0) = 0$$

which is equivalent to Equation 15.4.2. Thus, our new, more general, definition of a tangent plane is consistent with the definition that was given for the special case of Section 15.4.

EXAMPLE 8 Find the equations of the tangent plane and normal line at the point $(-2, 1, -3)$ to the ellipsoid

$$\frac{x^2}{4} + y^2 + \frac{z^2}{9} = 3$$

SOLUTION The ellipsoid is the level surface (with $k = 3$) of the function

$$F(x, y, z) = \frac{x^2}{4} + y^2 + \frac{z^2}{9}$$

▥ Figure 10 shows the ellipsoid, tangent plane, and normal line in Example 8.

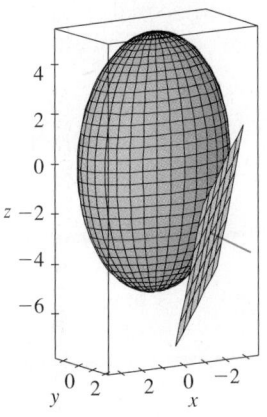

FIGURE 10

Therefore, we have

$$F_x(x, y, z) = \frac{x}{2} \qquad F_y(x, y, z) = 2y \qquad F_z(x, y, z) = \frac{2z}{9}$$

$$F_x(-2, 1, -3) = -1 \qquad F_y(-2, 1, -3) = 2 \qquad F_z(-2, 1, -3) = -\tfrac{2}{3}$$

Then Equation 19 gives the equation of the tangent plane at $(-2, 1, -3)$ as

$$-1(x + 2) + 2(y - 1) - \tfrac{2}{3}(z + 3) = 0$$

which simplifies to $3x - 6y + 2z + 18 = 0$.

By Equation 20, symmetric equations of the normal line are

$$\frac{x + 2}{-1} = \frac{y - 1}{2} = \frac{z + 3}{-\tfrac{2}{3}}$$

▥ **Significance of the Gradient Vector**

We now summarize the ways in which the gradient vector is significant. We first consider a function f of three variables and a point $P(x_0, y_0, z_0)$ in its domain. On the one hand, we know from Theorem 15 that the gradient vector $\nabla f(x_0, y_0, z_0)$ gives the direction of fastest increase of f. On the other hand, we know that $\nabla f(x_0, y_0, z_0)$ is orthogonal to the level surface S of f through P. (Refer to Figure 9.) These two properties are quite compatible intuitively because as we move away from P on the level surface S, the value of f does not change at all. So it seems reasonable that if we move in the perpendicular direction, we get the maximum increase.

In like manner we consider a function f of two variables and a point $P(x_0, y_0)$ in its domain. Again the gradient vector $\nabla f(x_0, y_0)$ gives the direction of fastest increase of f. Also, by considerations similar to our discussion of tangent planes, it can be shown that $\nabla f(x_0, y_0)$ is perpendicular to the level curve $f(x, y) = k$ that passes through P. Again this is intuitively plausible because the values of f remain constant as we move along the curve. (See Figure 11.)

FIGURE 11

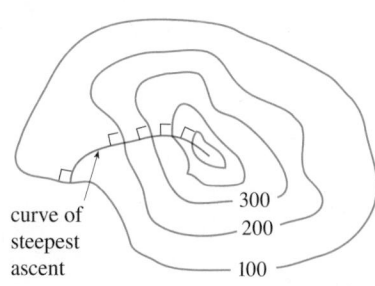

FIGURE 12

If we consider a topographical map of a hill and let $f(x, y)$ represent the height above sea level at a point with coordinates (x, y), then a curve of steepest ascent can be drawn as in Figure 12 by making it perpendicular to all of the contour lines. This phenomenon can also be noticed in Figure 12 in Section 15.1, where Lonesome Creek follows a curve of steepest descent.

Computer algebra systems have commands that plot sample gradient vectors. Each gradient vector $\nabla f(a, b)$ is plotted starting at the point (a, b). Figure 13 shows such a plot (called a *gradient vector field*) for the function $f(x, y) = x^2 - y^2$ superimposed on a contour map of f. As expected, the gradient vectors point "uphill" and are perpendicular to the level curves.

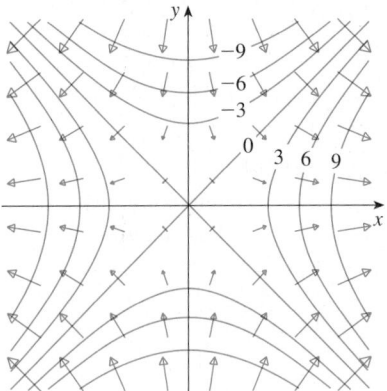

FIGURE 13

15.6 Exercises

1. A contour map of barometric pressure (in millibars) is shown for 7:00 A.M. on September 12, 1960, when Hurricane Donna was raging. Estimate the value of the directional derivative of the pressure function at Raleigh, North Carolina, in the direction of the eye of the hurricane. What are the units of the directional derivative?

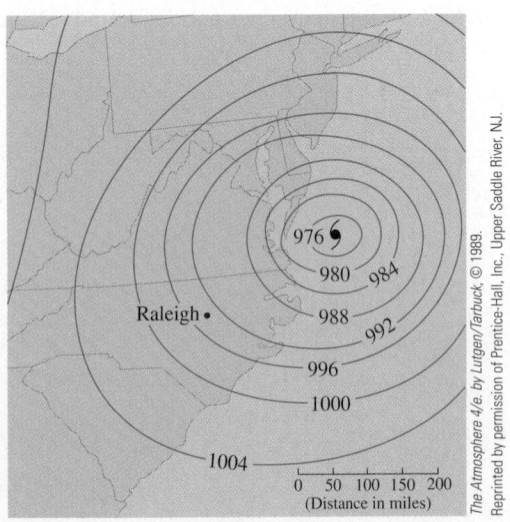

The Atmosphere 4/e. by Lutgen/Tarbuck, © 1989. Reprinted by permission of Prentice-Hall, Inc., Upper Saddle River, NJ.

2. The contour map shows the average annual snowfall (in inches) near Lake Michigan. Estimate the value of the

directional derivative of this snowfall function at Muskegon, Michigan, in the direction of Ludington. What are the units?

3. A table of values for the wind-chill index $W = f(T, v)$ is given in Exercise 3 on page 955. Use the table to estimate the value of $D_{\mathbf{u}} f(-20, 30)$, where $\mathbf{u} = (\mathbf{i} + \mathbf{j})/\sqrt{2}$.

4–6 |||| Find the directional derivative of f at the given point in the direction indicated by the angle θ.

4. $f(x, y) = x^2 y^3 - y^4$, $(2, 1)$, $\theta = \pi/4$

5. $f(x, y) = \sqrt{5x - 4y}$, $(4, 1)$, $\theta = -\pi/6$

6. $f(x, y) = x \sin(xy)$, $(2, 0)$, $\theta = \pi/3$

7–10 ▥

(a) Find the gradient of f.

(b) Evaluate the gradient at the point P.

(c) Find the rate of change of f at P in the direction of the vector $\mathbf{u}$.

7. $f(x, y) = 5xy^2 - 4x^3y$, $P(1, 2)$, $\mathbf{u} = \left\langle \frac{5}{13}, \frac{12}{13} \right\rangle$

8. $f(x, y) = y \ln x$, $P(1, -3)$, $\mathbf{u} = \left\langle -\frac{4}{5}, \frac{3}{5} \right\rangle$

9. $f(x, y, z) = xe^{2yz}$, $P(3, 0, 2)$, $\mathbf{u} = \left\langle \frac{2}{3}, -\frac{2}{3}, \frac{1}{3} \right\rangle$

10. $f(x, y, z) = \sqrt{x + yz}$, $P(1, 3, 1)$, $\mathbf{u} = \left\langle \frac{2}{7}, \frac{3}{7}, \frac{6}{7} \right\rangle$

11–17 ▥ Find the directional derivative of the function at the given point in the direction of the vector $\mathbf{v}$.

11. $f(x, y) = 1 + 2x\sqrt{y}$, $(3, 4)$, $\mathbf{v} = \langle 4, -3 \rangle$

12. $f(x, y) = \ln(x^2 + y^2)$, $(2, 1)$, $\mathbf{v} = \langle -1, 2 \rangle$

13. $g(s, t) = s^2 e^t$, $(2, 0)$, $\mathbf{v} = \mathbf{i} + \mathbf{j}$

14. $g(r, \theta) = e^{-r} \sin \theta$, $(0, \pi/3)$, $\mathbf{v} = 3\mathbf{i} - 2\mathbf{j}$

15. $f(x, y, z) = \sqrt{x^2 + y^2 + z^2}$, $(1, 2, -2)$, $\mathbf{v} = \langle -6, 6, -3 \rangle$

16. $f(x, y, z) = x/(y + z)$, $(4, 1, 1)$, $\mathbf{v} = \langle 1, 2, 3 \rangle$

17. $g(x, y, z) = (x + 2y + 3z)^{3/2}$, $(1, 1, 2)$, $\mathbf{v} = 2\mathbf{j} - \mathbf{k}$

---

18. Use the figure to estimate $D_{\mathbf{u}} f(2, 2)$.

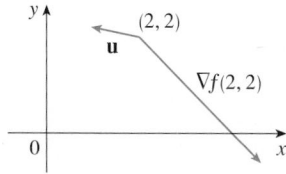

19. Find the directional derivative of $f(x, y) = \sqrt{xy}$ at $P(2, 8)$ in the direction of $Q(5, 4)$.

20. Find the directional derivative of $f(x, y, z) = x^2 + y^2 + z^2$ at $P(2, 1, 3)$ in the direction of the origin.

21–26 ▥ Find the maximum rate of change of f at the given point and the direction in which it occurs.

21. $f(x, y) = y^2/x$, $(2, 4)$

22. $f(p, q) = qe^{-p} + pe^{-q}$, $(0, 0)$

23. $f(x, y) = \sin(xy)$, $(1, 0)$

24. $f(x, y, z) = x^2y^3z^4$, $(1, 1, 1)$

25. $f(x, y, z) = \ln(xy^2z^3)$, $(1, -2, -3)$

26. $f(x, y, z) = \tan(x + 2y + 3z)$, $(-5, 1, 1)$

---

27. (a) Show that a differentiable function f decreases most rapidly at $\mathbf{x}$ in the direction opposite to the gradient vector, that is, in the direction of $-\nabla f(\mathbf{x})$.

(b) Use the result of part (a) to find the direction in which the function $f(x, y) = x^4y - x^2y^3$ decreases fastest at the point $(2, -3)$.

28. Find the directions in which the directional derivative of $f(x, y) = x^2 + \sin xy$ at the point $(1, 0)$ has the value 1.

29. Find all points at which the direction of fastest change of the function $f(x, y) = x^2 + y^2 - 2x - 4y$ is $\mathbf{i} + \mathbf{j}$.

30. Near a buoy, the depth of a lake at the point with coordinates (x, y) is $z = 200 + 0.02x^2 - 0.001y^3$, where x, y, and z are measured in meters. A fisherman in a small boat starts at the point $(80, 60)$ and moves toward the buoy, which is located at $(0, 0)$. Is the water under the boat getting deeper or shallower when he departs? Explain.

31. The temperature T in a metal ball is inversely proportional to the distance from the center of the ball, which we take to be the origin. The temperature at the point $(1, 2, 2)$ is $120°$.

(a) Find the rate of change of T at $(1, 2, 2)$ in the direction toward the point $(2, 1, 3)$.

(b) Show that at any point in the ball the direction of greatest increase in temperature is given by a vector that points toward the origin.

32. The temperature at a point (x, y, z) is given by

$$T(x, y, z) = 200e^{-x^2 - 3y^2 - 9z^2}$$

where T is measured in °C and x, y, z in meters.

(a) Find the rate of change of temperature at the point $P(2, -1, 2)$ in the direction toward the point $(3, -3, 3)$.

(b) In which direction does the temperature increase fastest at P?

(c) Find the maximum rate of increase at P.

33. Suppose that over a certain region of space the electrical potential V is given by $V(x, y, z) = 5x^2 - 3xy + xyz$.

(a) Find the rate of change of the potential at $P(3, 4, 5)$ in the direction of the vector $\mathbf{v} = \mathbf{i} + \mathbf{j} - \mathbf{k}$.

(b) In which direction does V change most rapidly at P?

(c) What is the maximum rate of change at P?

34. Suppose you are climbing a hill whose shape is given by the equation $z = 1000 - 0.01x^2 - 0.02y^2$, where x, y, and z are measured in meters, and you are standing at a point with coordinates $(50, 80, 847)$. The positive x-axis points east and the positive y-axis points north.

(a) If you walk due south, will you start to ascend or descend? At what rate?

(b) If you walk northwest, will you start to ascend or descend? At what rate?

(c) In which direction is the slope largest? What is the rate of ascent in that direction? At what angle above the horizontal does the path in that direction begin?

35. Let f be a function of two variables that has continuous partial derivatives and consider the points $A(1, 3)$, $B(3, 3)$, $C(1, 7)$, and $D(6, 15)$. The directional derivative of f at A in the direction of the vector $\overrightarrow{AB}$ is 3 and the directional derivative at A in the direction of $\overrightarrow{AC}$ is 26. Find the directional derivative of f at A in the direction of the vector $\overrightarrow{AD}$.

36. For the given contour map draw the curves of steepest ascent starting at P and at Q.

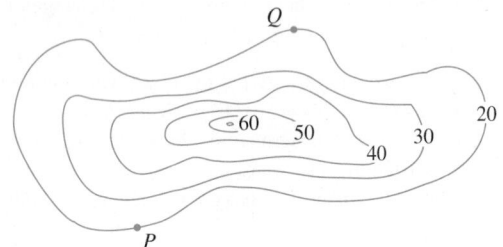

37. Show that the operation of taking the gradient of a function has the given property. Assume that u and v are differentiable functions of x and y and a, b are constants.
(a) $\nabla(au + bv) = a\,\nabla u + b\,\nabla v$
(b) $\nabla(uv) = u\,\nabla v + v\,\nabla u$
(c) $\nabla\left(\dfrac{u}{v}\right) = \dfrac{v\,\nabla u - u\,\nabla v}{v^2}$
(d) $\nabla u^n = nu^{n-1}\,\nabla u$

38. Sketch the gradient vector $\nabla f(4, 6)$ for the function f whose level curves are shown. Explain how you chose the direction and length of this vector.

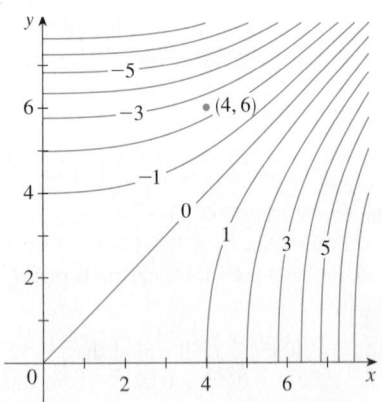

39–44 |||| Find equations of (a) the tangent plane and (b) the normal line to the given surface at the specified point.

39. $x^2 + 2y^2 + 3z^2 = 21$, $(4, -1, 1)$

40. $x = y^2 + z^2 - 2$, $(-1, 1, 0)$

41. $x^2 - 2y^2 + z^2 + yz = 2$, $(2, 1, -1)$

42. $x - z = 4\arctan(yz)$, $(1 + \pi, 1, 1)$

43. $z + 1 = xe^y \cos z$, $(1, 0, 0)$

44. $yz = \ln(x + z)$, $(0, 0, 1)$

45–46 |||| Use a computer to graph the surface, the tangent plane, and the normal line on the same screen. Choose the domain carefully so that you avoid extraneous vertical planes. Choose the viewpoint so that you get a good view of all three objects.

45. $xy + yz + zx = 3$, $(1, 1, 1)$

46. $xyz = 6$, $(1, 2, 3)$

47. If $f(x, y) = x^2 + 4y^2$, find the gradient vector $\nabla f(2, 1)$ and use it to find the tangent line to the level curve $f(x, y) = 8$ at the point $(2, 1)$. Sketch the level curve, the tangent line, and the gradient vector.

48. If $g(x, y) = x - y^2$, find the gradient vector $\nabla g(3, -1)$ and use it to find the tangent line to the level curve $g(x, y) = 2$ at the point $(3, -1)$. Sketch the level curve, the tangent line, and the gradient vector.

49. Show that the equation of the tangent plane to the ellipsoid $x^2/a^2 + y^2/b^2 + z^2/c^2 = 1$ at the point (x_0, y_0, z_0) can be written as
$$\frac{xx_0}{a^2} + \frac{yy_0}{b^2} + \frac{zz_0}{c^2} = 1$$

50. Find the equation of the tangent plane to the hyperboloid $x^2/a^2 + y^2/b^2 - z^2/c^2 = 1$ at (x_0, y_0, z_0) and express it in a form similar to the one in Exercise 49.

51. Show that the equation of the tangent plane to the elliptic paraboloid $z/c = x^2/a^2 + y^2/b^2$ at the point (x_0, y_0, z_0) can be written as
$$\frac{2xx_0}{a^2} + \frac{2yy_0}{b^2} = \frac{z + z_0}{c}$$

52. Find the points on the ellipsoid $x^2 + 2y^2 + 3z^2 = 1$ where the tangent plane is parallel to the plane $3x - y + 3z = 1$.

53. Find the points on the hyperboloid $x^2 - y^2 + 2z^2 = 1$ where the normal line is parallel to the line that joins the points $(3, -1, 0)$ and $(5, 3, 6)$.

54. Show that the ellipsoid $3x^2 + 2y^2 + z^2 = 9$ and the sphere $x^2 + y^2 + z^2 - 8x - 6y - 8z + 24 = 0$ are tangent to each other at the point $(1, 1, 2)$. (This means that they have a common tangent plane at the point.)

55. Show that every plane that is tangent to the cone $x^2 + y^2 = z^2$ passes through the origin.

56. Show that every normal line to the sphere $x^2 + y^2 + z^2 = r^2$ passes through the center of the sphere.

57. Show that the sum of the x-, y-, and z-intercepts of any tangent plane to the surface $\sqrt{x} + \sqrt{y} + \sqrt{z} = \sqrt{c}$ is a constant.

58. Show that the product of the x-, y-, and z-intercepts of any tangent plane to the surface $xyz = c^3$ is a constant.

59. Find parametric equations for the tangent line to the curve of intersection of the paraboloid $z = x^2 + y^2$ and the ellipsoid $4x^2 + y^2 + z^2 = 9$ at the point $(-1, 1, 2)$.

60. (a) The plane $y + z = 3$ intersects the cylinder $x^2 + y^2 = 5$ in an ellipse. Find parametric equations for the tangent line to this ellipse at the point $(1, 2, 1)$.

(b) Graph the cylinder, the plane, and the tangent line on the same screen.

61. (a) Two surfaces are called **orthogonal** at a point of intersection if their normal lines are perpendicular at that point. Show that surfaces with equations $F(x, y, z) = 0$ and $G(x, y, z) = 0$ are orthogonal at a point P where $\nabla F \neq \mathbf{0}$ and $\nabla G \neq \mathbf{0}$ if and only if $F_x G_x + F_y G_y + F_z G_z = 0$ at P.

(b) Use part (a) to show that the surfaces $z^2 = x^2 + y^2$ and $x^2 + y^2 + z^2 = r^2$ are orthogonal at every point of intersection. Can you see why this is true without using calculus?

62. (a) Show that the function $f(x, y) = \sqrt[3]{xy}$ is continuous and the partial derivatives f_x and f_y exist at the origin but the directional derivatives in all other directions do not exist.

(b) Graph f near the origin and comment on how the graph confirms part (a).

63. Suppose that the directional derivatives of $f(x, y)$ are known at a given point in two nonparallel directions given by unit vectors $\mathbf{u}$ and $\mathbf{v}$. Is it possible to find ∇f at this point? If so, how would you do it?

64. Show that if $z = f(x, y)$ is differentiable at $\mathbf{x}_0 = \langle x_0, y_0 \rangle$, then

$$\lim_{\mathbf{x} \to \mathbf{x}_0} \frac{f(\mathbf{x}) - f(\mathbf{x}_0) - \nabla f(\mathbf{x}_0) \cdot (\mathbf{x} - \mathbf{x}_0)}{|\mathbf{x} - \mathbf{x}_0|} = 0$$

[*Hint:* Use Definition 15.4.7 directly.]

▥ 15.7 Maximum and Minimum Values

As we saw in Chapter 4, one of the main uses of ordinary derivatives is in finding maximum and minimum values. In this section we see how to use partial derivatives to locate maxima and minima of functions of two variables. In particular, in Example 6 we will see how to maximize the volume of a box without a lid if we have a fixed amount of cardboard to work with.

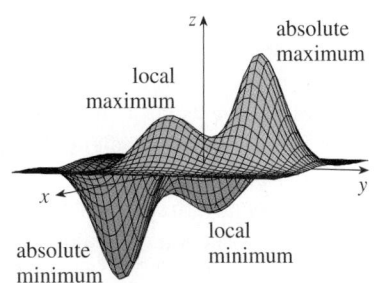

FIGURE 1

> **1 Definition** A function of two variables has a **local maximum** at (a, b) if $f(x, y) \leq f(a, b)$ when (x, y) is near (a, b). [This means that $f(x, y) \leq f(a, b)$ for all points (x, y) in some disk with center (a, b).] The number $f(a, b)$ is called a **local maximum value**. If $f(x, y) \geq f(a, b)$ when (x, y) is near (a, b), then $f(a, b)$ is a **local minimum value**.

If the inequalities in Definition 1 hold for *all* points (x, y) in the domain of f, then f has an **absolute maximum** (or **absolute minimum**) at (a, b).

The graph of a function with several maxima and minima is shown in Figure 1. You can think of the local maxima as mountain peaks and the local minima as valley bottoms.

▥ Notice that the conclusion of Theorem 2 can be stated in the notation of gradient vectors as $\nabla f(a, b) = \mathbf{0}$.

> **2 Theorem** If f has a local maximum or minimum at (a, b) and the first-order partial derivatives of f exist there, then $f_x(a, b) = 0$ and $f_y(a, b) = 0$.

Proof Let $g(x) = f(x, b)$. If f has a local maximum (or minimum) at (a, b), then g has a local maximum (or minimum) at a, so $g'(a) = 0$ by Fermat's Theorem (see Theorem 4.1.4). But $g'(a) = f_x(a, b)$ (see Equation 15.3.1) and so $f_x(a, b) = 0$. Similarly, by applying Fermat's Theorem to the function $G(y) = f(a, y)$, we obtain $f_y(a, b) = 0$.

If we put $f_x(a, b) = 0$ and $f_y(a, b) = 0$ in the equation of a tangent plane (Equation 15.4.2), we get $z = z_0$. Thus, the geometric interpretation of Theorem 2 is that if the graph of f has a tangent plane at a local maximum or minimum, then the tangent plane must be horizontal.

A point (a, b) is called a **critical point** (or *stationary point*) of f if $f_x(a, b) = 0$ and $f_y(a, b) = 0$, or if one of these partial derivatives does not exist. Theorem 2 says that if f has a local maximum or minimum at (a, b), then (a, b) is a critical point of f. However, as in single-variable calculus, not all critical points give rise to maxima or minima. At a critical point, a function could have a local maximum or a local minimum or neither.

EXAMPLE 1 Let $f(x, y) = x^2 + y^2 - 2x - 6y + 14$. Then

$$f_x(x, y) = 2x - 2 \qquad f_y(x, y) = 2y - 6$$

These partial derivatives are equal to 0 when $x = 1$ and $y = 3$, so the only critical point is $(1, 3)$. By completing the square, we find that

$$f(x, y) = 4 + (x - 1)^2 + (y - 3)^2$$

Since $(x - 1)^2 \geq 0$ and $(y - 3)^2 \geq 0$, we have $f(x, y) \geq 4$ for all values of x and y. Therefore, $f(1, 3) = 4$ is a local minimum, and in fact it is the absolute minimum of f. This can be confirmed geometrically from the graph of f, which is the elliptic paraboloid with vertex $(1, 3, 4)$ shown in Figure 2.

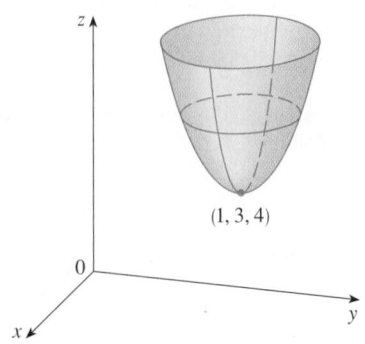

FIGURE 2
$z = x^2 + y^2 - 2x - 6y + 14$

EXAMPLE 2 Find the extreme values of $f(x, y) = y^2 - x^2$.

SOLUTION Since $f_x = -2x$ and $f_y = 2y$, the only critical point is $(0, 0)$. Notice that for points on the x-axis we have $y = 0$, so $f(x, y) = -x^2 < 0$ (if $x \neq 0$). However, for points on the y-axis we have $x = 0$, so $f(x, y) = y^2 > 0$ (if $y \neq 0$). Thus, every disk with center $(0, 0)$ contains points where f takes positive values as well as points where f takes negative values. Therefore, $f(0, 0) = 0$ can't be an extreme value for f, so f has no extreme value.

Example 2 illustrates the fact that a function need not have a maximum or minimum value at a critical point. Figure 3 shows how this is possible. The graph of f is the hyperbolic paraboloid $z = y^2 - x^2$, which has a horizontal tangent plane ($z = 0$) at the origin. You can see that $f(0, 0) = 0$ is a maximum in the direction of the x-axis but a minimum in the direction of the y-axis. Near the origin the graph has the shape of a saddle and so $(0, 0)$ is called a *saddle point* of f.

We need to be able to determine whether or not a function has an extreme value at a critical point. The following test, which is proved at the end of this section, is analogous to the Second Derivative Test for functions of one variable.

FIGURE 3
$z = y^2 - x^2$

> **3** **Second Derivatives Test** Suppose the second partial derivatives of f are continuous on a disk with center (a, b), and suppose that $f_x(a, b) = 0$ and $f_y(a, b) = 0$ [that is, (a, b) is a critical point of f]. Let
>
> $$D = D(a, b) = f_{xx}(a, b) f_{yy}(a, b) - [f_{xy}(a, b)]^2$$
>
> (a) If $D > 0$ and $f_{xx}(a, b) > 0$, then $f(a, b)$ is a local minimum.
> (b) If $D > 0$ and $f_{xx}(a, b) < 0$, then $f(a, b)$ is a local maximum.
> (c) If $D < 0$, then $f(a, b)$ is not a local maximum or minimum.

NOTE 1 □ In case (c) the point (a, b) is called a **saddle point** of f and the graph of f crosses its tangent plane at (a, b).

NOTE 2 □ If $D = 0$, the test gives no information: f could have a local maximum or local minimum at (a, b), or (a, b) could be a saddle point of f.

NOTE 3 □ To remember the formula for D it's helpful to write it as a determinant:

$$D = \begin{vmatrix} f_{xx} & f_{xy} \\ f_{yx} & f_{yy} \end{vmatrix} = f_{xx}f_{yy} - (f_{xy})^2$$

EXAMPLE 3 Find the local maximum and minimum values and saddle points of $f(x, y) = x^4 + y^4 - 4xy + 1$.

SOLUTION We first locate the critical points:

$$f_x = 4x^3 - 4y \qquad f_y = 4y^3 - 4x$$

Setting these partial derivatives equal to 0, we obtain the equations

$$x^3 - y = 0 \qquad \text{and} \qquad y^3 - x = 0$$

To solve these equations we substitute $y = x^3$ from the first equation into the second one. This gives

$$0 = x^9 - x = x(x^8 - 1) = x(x^4 - 1)(x^4 + 1) = x(x^2 - 1)(x^2 + 1)(x^4 + 1)$$

so there are three real roots: $x = 0, 1, -1$. The three critical points are $(0, 0)$, $(1, 1)$, and $(-1, -1)$.

Next we calculate the second partial derivatives and $D(x, y)$:

$$f_{xx} = 12x^2 \qquad f_{xy} = -4 \qquad f_{yy} = 12y^2$$

$$D(x, y) = f_{xx}f_{yy} - (f_{xy})^2 = 144x^2y^2 - 16$$

Since $D(0, 0) = -16 < 0$, it follows from case (c) of the Second Derivatives Test that the origin is a saddle point; that is, f has no local maximum or minimum at $(0, 0)$. Since $D(1, 1) = 128 > 0$ and $f_{xx}(1, 1) = 12 > 0$, we see from case (a) of the test that $f(1, 1) = -1$ is a local minimum. Similarly, we have $D(-1, -1) = 128 > 0$ and $f_{xx}(-1, -1) = 12 > 0$, so $f(-1, -1) = -1$ is also a local minimum.

The graph of f is shown in Figure 4.

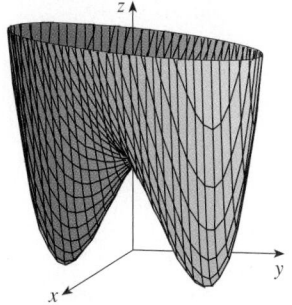

FIGURE 4
$z = x^4 + y^4 - 4xy + 1$

‖‖ A contour map of the function f in Example 3 is shown in Figure 5. The level curves near $(1, 1)$ and $(-1, -1)$ are oval in shape and indicate that as we move away from $(1, 1)$ or $(-1, -1)$ in any direction the values of f are increasing. The level curves near $(0, 0)$, on the other hand, resemble hyperbolas. They reveal that as we move away from the origin (where the value of f is 1), the values of f decrease in some directions but increase in other directions. Thus, the contour map suggests the presence of the minima and saddle point that we found in Example 3.

FIGURE 5

In Module 15.7 you can use contour maps to estimate the locations of critical points.

EXAMPLE 4 Find and classify the critical points of the function

$$f(x, y) = 10x^2y - 5x^2 - 4y^2 - x^4 - 2y^4$$

Also find the highest point on the graph of f.

SOLUTION The first-order partial derivatives are

$$f_x = 20xy - 10x - 4x^3 \qquad f_y = 10x^2 - 8y - 8y^3$$

So to find the critical points we need to solve the equations

$$\boxed{4} \qquad\qquad\qquad 2x(10y - 5 - 2x^2) = 0$$

$$\boxed{5} \qquad\qquad\qquad 5x^2 - 4y - 4y^3 = 0$$

From Equation 4 we see that either

$$x = 0 \qquad \text{or} \qquad 10y - 5 - 2x^2 = 0$$

In the first case ($x = 0$), Equation 5 becomes $-4y(1 + y^2) = 0$, so $y = 0$ and we have the critical point $(0, 0)$.

In the second case ($10y - 5 - 2x^2 = 0$), we get

$$\boxed{6} \qquad\qquad\qquad x^2 = 5y - 2.5$$

and, putting this in Equation 5, we have $25y - 12.5 - 4y - 4y^3 = 0$. So we have to solve the cubic equation

$$\boxed{7} \qquad\qquad\qquad 4y^3 - 21y + 12.5 = 0$$

Using a graphing calculator or computer to graph the function

$$g(y) = 4y^3 - 21y + 12.5$$

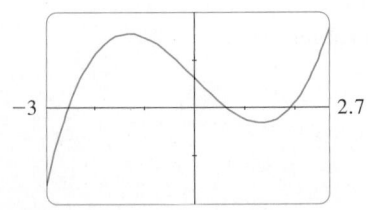

FIGURE 6

as in Figure 6, we see that Equation 7 has three real roots. By zooming in, we can find the roots to four decimal places:

$$y \approx -2.5452 \qquad y \approx 0.6468 \qquad y \approx 1.8984$$

(Alternatively, we could have used Newton's method or a rootfinder to locate these roots.) From Equation 6, the corresponding x-values are given by

$$x = \pm\sqrt{5y - 2.5}$$

If $y \approx -2.5452$, then x has no corresponding real values. If $y \approx 0.6468$, then $x \approx \pm0.8567$. If $y \approx 1.8984$, then $x \approx \pm2.6442$. So we have a total of five critical points, which are analyzed in the following chart. All quantities are rounded to two decimal places.

Critical point	Value of f	f_{xx}	D	Conclusion
$(0, 0)$	0.00	-10.00	80.00	local maximum
$(\pm 2.64, 1.90)$	8.50	-55.93	2488.72	local maximum
$(\pm 0.86, 0.65)$	-1.48	-5.87	-187.64	saddle point

Figures 7 and 8 give two views of the graph of f and we see that the surface opens downward. [This can also be seen from the expression for $f(x, y)$: The dominant terms are $-x^4 - 2y^4$ when $|x|$ and $|y|$ are large.] Comparing the values of f at its local maximum points, we see that the absolute maximum value of f is $f(\pm 2.64, 1.90) \approx 8.50$. In other words, the highest points on the graph of f are $(\pm 2.64, 1.90, 8.50)$.

Visual 15.7 shows several families of surfaces. The surface in Figures 7 and 8 is a member of one of these families.

FIGURE 7

FIGURE 8

|||| The five critical points of the function f in Example 4 are shown in red in the contour map of f in Figure 9.

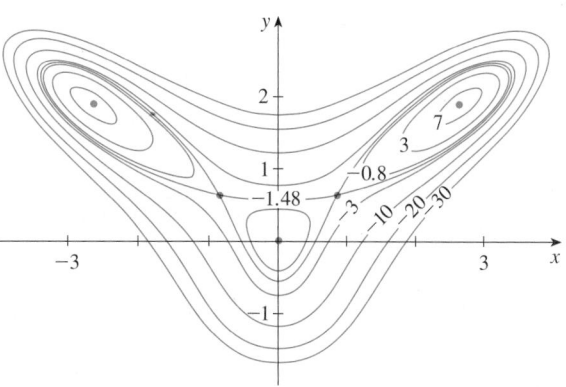

FIGURE 9

EXAMPLE 5 Find the shortest distance from the point $(1, 0, -2)$ to the plane $x + 2y + z = 4$.

SOLUTION The distance from any point (x, y, z) to the point $(1, 0, -2)$ is

$$d = \sqrt{(x - 1)^2 + y^2 + (z + 2)^2}$$

but if (x, y, z) lies on the plane $x + 2y + z = 4$, then $z = 4 - x - 2y$ and so we have $d = \sqrt{(x - 1)^2 + y^2 + (6 - x - 2y)^2}$. We can minimize d by minimizing the simpler expression

$$d^2 = f(x, y) = (x - 1)^2 + y^2 + (6 - x - 2y)^2$$

By solving the equations

$$f_x = 2(x - 1) - 2(6 - x - 2y) = 4x + 4y - 14 = 0$$

$$f_y = 2y - 4(6 - x - 2y) = 4x + 10y - 24 = 0$$

we find that the only critical point is $\left(\frac{11}{6}, \frac{5}{3}\right)$. Since $f_{xx} = 4$, $f_{xy} = 4$, and $f_{yy} = 10$, we have $D(x, y) = f_{xx}f_{yy} - (f_{xy})^2 = 24 > 0$ and $f_{xx} > 0$, so by the Second Derivatives Test f has a local minimum at $\left(\frac{11}{6}, \frac{5}{3}\right)$. Intuitively, we can see that this local minimum is actually an absolute minimum because there must be a point on the given plane that is closest to $(1, 0, -2)$. If $x = \frac{11}{6}$ and $y = \frac{5}{3}$, then

$$d = \sqrt{(x - 1)^2 + y^2 + (6 - x - 2y)^2} = \sqrt{\left(\frac{5}{6}\right)^2 + \left(\frac{5}{3}\right)^2 + \left(\frac{5}{6}\right)^2} = \frac{5\sqrt{6}}{6}$$

The shortest distance from $(1, 0, -2)$ to the plane $x + 2y + z = 4$ is $5\sqrt{6}/6$. ▬

|||| Example 5 could also be solved using vectors. Compare with the methods of Section 13.5.

EXAMPLE 6 A rectangular box without a lid is to be made from 12 m² of cardboard. Find the maximum volume of such a box.

SOLUTION Let the length, width, and height of the box (in meters) be x, y, and z, as shown in Figure 10. Then the volume of the box is

$$V = xyz$$

We can express V as a function of just two variables x and y by using the fact that the area of the four sides and the bottom of the box is

$$2xz + 2yz + xy = 12$$

Solving this equation for z, we get $z = (12 - xy)/[2(x + y)]$, so the expression for V becomes

$$V = xy\,\frac{12 - xy}{2(x + y)} = \frac{12xy - x^2y^2}{2(x + y)}$$

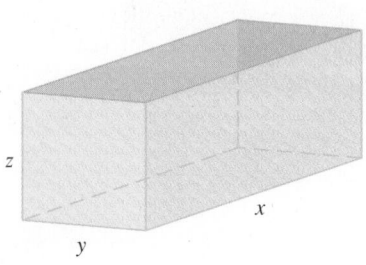

FIGURE 10

We compute the partial derivatives:

$$\frac{\partial V}{\partial x} = \frac{y^2(12 - 2xy - x^2)}{2(x + y)^2} \qquad \frac{\partial V}{\partial y} = \frac{x^2(12 - 2xy - y^2)}{2(x + y)^2}$$

If V is a maximum, then $\partial V/\partial x = \partial V/\partial y = 0$, but $x = 0$ or $y = 0$ gives $V = 0$, so we must solve the equations

$$12 - 2xy - x^2 = 0 \qquad 12 - 2xy - y^2 = 0$$

These imply that $x^2 = y^2$ and so $x = y$. (Note that x and y must both be positive in this problem.) If we put $x = y$ in either equation we get $12 - 3x^2 = 0$, which gives $x = 2$, $y = 2$, and $z = (12 - 2 \cdot 2)/[2(2 + 2)] = 1$.

We could use the Second Derivatives Test to show that this gives a local maximum of V, or we could simply argue from the physical nature of this problem that there must be an absolute maximum volume, which has to occur at a critical point of V, so it must occur when $x = 2$, $y = 2$, $z = 1$. Then $V = 2 \cdot 2 \cdot 1 = 4$, so the maximum volume of the box is 4 m³. ▬

||| Absolute Maximum and Minimum Values

For a function f of one variable the Extreme Value Theorem says that if f is continuous on a closed interval $[a, b]$, then f has an absolute minimum value and an absolute maximum value. According to the Closed Interval Method in Section 4.1, we found these by evaluating f not only at the critical numbers but also at the endpoints a and b.

There is a similar situation for functions of two variables. Just as a closed interval contains its endpoints, a **closed set** in $\mathbb{R}^2$ is one that contains all its boundary points. [A boundary point of D is a point (a, b) such that every disk with center (a, b) contains points in D and also points not in D.] For instance, the disk

$$D = \{(x, y) \mid x^2 + y^2 \leq 1\}$$

which consists of all points on and inside the circle $x^2 + y^2 = 1$, is a closed set because it contains all of its boundary points (which are the points on the circle $x^2 + y^2 = 1$). But if even one point on the boundary curve were omitted, the set would not be closed. (See Figure 11.)

A **bounded set** in $\mathbb{R}^2$ is one that is contained within some disk. In other words, it is finite in extent. Then, in terms of closed and bounded sets, we can state the following counterpart of the Extreme Value Theorem in two dimensions.

(a) Closed sets

(b) Sets that are not closed

FIGURE 11

> **8 Extreme Value Theorem for Functions of Two Variables** If f is continuous on a closed, bounded set D in $\mathbb{R}^2$, then f attains an absolute maximum value $f(x_1, y_1)$ and an absolute minimum value $f(x_2, y_2)$ at some points (x_1, y_1) and (x_2, y_2) in D.

To find the extreme values guaranteed by Theorem 8, we note that, by Theorem 2, if f has an extreme value at (x_1, y_1), then (x_1, y_1) is either a critical point of f or a boundary point of D. Thus, we have the following extension of the Closed Interval Method.

> **9** To find the absolute maximum and minimum values of a continuous function f on a closed, bounded set D:
>
> **1.** Find the values of f at the critical points of f in D.
>
> **2.** Find the extreme values of f on the boundary of D.
>
> **3.** The largest of the values from steps 1 and 2 is the absolute maximum value; the smallest of these values is the absolute minimum value.

EXAMPLE 7 Find the absolute maximum and minimum values of the function $f(x, y) = x^2 - 2xy + 2y$ on the rectangle $D = \{(x, y) \mid 0 \leq x \leq 3, 0 \leq y \leq 2\}$.

SOLUTION Since f is a polynomial, it is continuous on the closed, bounded rectangle D, so Theorem 8 tells us there is both an absolute maximum and an absolute minimum. According to step 1 in (9), we first find the critical points. These occur when

$$f_x = 2x - 2y = 0 \qquad f_y = -2x + 2 = 0$$

so the only critical point is $(1, 1)$, and the value of f there is $f(1, 1) = 1$.

FIGURE 12

In step 2 we look at the values of f on the boundary of D, which consists of the four line segments L_1, L_2, L_3, L_4 shown in Figure 12. On L_1 we have $y = 0$ and

$$f(x, 0) = x^2 \qquad 0 \leqslant x \leqslant 3$$

This is an increasing function of x, so its minimum value is $f(0, 0) = 0$ and its maximum value is $f(3, 0) = 9$. On L_2 we have $x = 3$ and

$$f(3, y) = 9 - 4y \qquad 0 \leqslant y \leqslant 2$$

This is a decreasing function of y, so its maximum value is $f(3, 0) = 9$ and its minimum value is $f(3, 2) = 1$. On L_3 we have $y = 2$ and

$$f(x, 2) = x^2 - 4x + 4 \qquad 0 \leqslant x \leqslant 3$$

By the methods of Chapter 4, or simply by observing that $f(x, 2) = (x - 2)^2$, we see that the minimum value of this function is $f(2, 2) = 0$ and the maximum value is $f(0, 2) = 4$. Finally, on L_4 we have $x = 0$ and

$$f(0, y) = 2y \qquad 0 \leqslant y \leqslant 2$$

with maximum value $f(0, 2) = 4$ and minimum value $f(0, 0) = 0$. Thus, on the boundary, the minimum value of f is 0 and the maximum is 9.

In step 3 we compare these values with the value $f(1, 1) = 1$ at the critical point and conclude that the absolute maximum value of f on D is $f(3, 0) = 9$ and the absolute minimum value is $f(0, 0) = f(2, 2) = 0$. Figure 13 shows the graph of f.

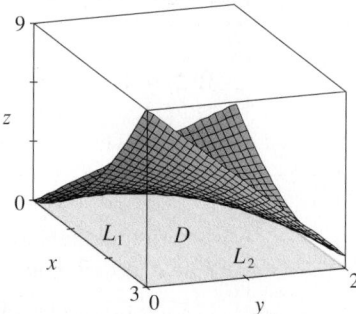

FIGURE 13
$f(x, y) = x^2 - 2xy + 2y$

We close this section by giving a proof of the first part of the Second Derivatives Test. Part (b) has a similar proof.

Proof of Theorem 3, Part (a) We compute the second-order directional derivative of f in the direction of $\mathbf{u} = \langle h, k \rangle$. The first-order derivative is given by Theorem 15.6.3:

$$D_{\mathbf{u}} f = f_x h + f_y k$$

Applying this theorem a second time, we have

$$D_{\mathbf{u}}^2 f = D_{\mathbf{u}}(D_{\mathbf{u}} f) = \frac{\partial}{\partial x}(D_{\mathbf{u}} f)h + \frac{\partial}{\partial y}(D_{\mathbf{u}} f)k$$

$$= (f_{xx} h + f_{yx} k)h + (f_{xy} h + f_{yy} k)k$$

$$= f_{xx} h^2 + 2f_{xy} hk + f_{yy} k^2 \qquad \text{(by Clairaut's Theorem)}$$

If we complete the square in this expression, we obtain

$$\boxed{10} \qquad D_{\mathbf{u}}^2 f = f_{xx}\left(h + \frac{f_{xy}}{f_{xx}}k\right)^2 + \frac{k^2}{f_{xx}}(f_{xx}f_{yy} - f_{xy}^2)$$

We are given that $f_{xx}(a, b) > 0$ and $D(a, b) > 0$. But f_{xx} and $D = f_{xx}f_{yy} - f_{xy}^2$ are continuous functions, so there is a disk B with center (a, b) and radius $\delta > 0$ such that $f_{xx}(x, y) > 0$ and $D(x, y) > 0$ whenever (x, y) is in B. Therefore, by looking at Equation 10, we see that $D_{\mathbf{u}}^2 f(x, y) > 0$ whenever (x, y) is in B. This means that if C is the curve obtained by intersecting the graph of f with the vertical plane through $P(a, b, f(a, b))$ in the direction of $\mathbf{u}$, then C is concave upward on an interval of length 2δ. This is true in the direction of every vector $\mathbf{u}$, so if we restrict (x, y) to lie in B, the graph of f lies above its horizontal tangent plane at P. Thus, $f(x, y) \geqslant f(a, b)$ whenever (x, y) is in B. This shows that $f(a, b)$ is a local minimum.

15.7 Exercises

1. Suppose $(1, 1)$ is a critical point of a function f with continuous second derivatives. In each case, what can you say about f?
(a) $f_{xx}(1, 1) = 4$, $\quad f_{xy}(1, 1) = 1$, $\quad f_{yy}(1, 1) = 2$
(b) $f_{xx}(1, 1) = 4$, $\quad f_{xy}(1, 1) = 3$, $\quad f_{yy}(1, 1) = 2$

2. Suppose $(0, 2)$ is a critical point of a function g with continuous second derivatives. In each case, what can you say about g?
(a) $g_{xx}(0, 2) = -1$, $\quad g_{xy}(0, 2) = 6$, $\quad g_{yy}(0, 2) = 1$
(b) $g_{xx}(0, 2) = -1$, $\quad g_{xy}(0, 2) = 2$, $\quad g_{yy}(0, 2) = -8$
(c) $g_{xx}(0, 2) = 4$, $\quad g_{xy}(0, 2) = 6$, $\quad g_{yy}(0, 2) = 9$

3–4 ▓ Use the level curves in the figure to predict the location of the critical points of f and whether f has a saddle point or a local maximum or minimum at each of those points. Explain your reasoning. Then use the Second Derivatives Test to confirm your predictions.

3. $f(x, y) = 4 + x^3 + y^3 - 3xy$

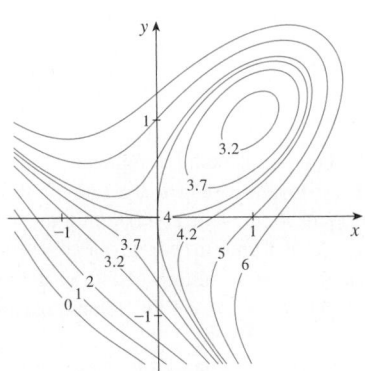

4. $f(x, y) = 3x - x^3 - 2y^2 + y^4$

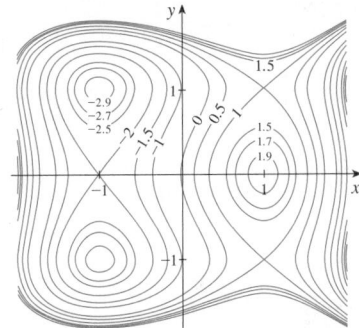

5–18 ▓ Find the local maximum and minimum values and saddle point(s) of the function. If you have three-dimensional graphing software, graph the function with a domain and viewpoint that reveal all the important aspects of the function.

5. $f(x, y) = 9 - 2x + 4y - x^2 - 4y^2$

6. $f(x, y) = x^3y + 12x^2 - 8y$

7. $f(x, y) = x^4 + y^4 - 4xy + 2$

8. $f(x, y) = e^{4y - x^2 - y^2}$

9. $f(x, y) = (1 + xy)(x + y)$

10. $f(x, y) = 2x^3 + xy^2 + 5x^2 + y^2$

11. $f(x, y) = 1 + 2xy - x^2 - y^2$

12. $f(x, y) = xy(1 - x - y)$

13. $f(x, y) = e^x \cos y$

14. $f(x, y) = x^2 + y^2 + \dfrac{1}{x^2 y^2}$

15. $f(x, y) = x \sin y$

16. $f(x, y) = (2x - x^2)(2y - y^2)$

17. $f(x, y) = (x^2 + y^2)e^{y^2 - x^2}$

18. $f(x, y) = x^2 y e^{-x^2 - y^2}$

19–22 ||||| Use a graph and/or level curves to estimate the local maximum and minimum values and saddle point(s) of the function. Then use calculus to find these values precisely.

19. $f(x, y) = 3x^2y + y^3 - 3x^2 - 3y^2 + 2$

20. $f(x, y) = xye^{-x^2-y^2}$

21. $f(x, y) = \sin x + \sin y + \sin(x + y)$,
$0 \leqslant x \leqslant 2\pi, \ 0 \leqslant y \leqslant 2\pi$

22. $f(x, y) = \sin x + \sin y + \cos(x + y)$,
$0 \leqslant x \leqslant \pi/4, \ 0 \leqslant y \leqslant \pi/4$

23–26 ||||| Use a graphing device as in Example 4 (or Newton's method or a rootfinder) to find the critical points of f correct to three decimal places. Then classify the critical points and find the highest or lowest points on the graph.

23. $f(x, y) = x^4 - 5x^2 + y^2 + 3x + 2$

24. $f(x, y) = 5 - 10xy - 4x^2 + 3y - y^4$

25. $f(x, y) = 2x + 4x^2 - y^2 + 2xy^2 - x^4 - y^4$

26. $f(x, y) = e^x + y^4 - x^3 + 4\cos y$

27–34 ||||| Find the absolute maximum and minimum values of f on the set D.

27. $f(x, y) = 1 + 4x - 5y$, D is the closed triangular region with vertices $(0, 0)$, $(2, 0)$, and $(0, 3)$

28. $f(x, y) = 3 + xy - x - 2y$, D is the closed triangular region with vertices $(1, 0)$, $(5, 0)$, and $(1, 4)$

29. $f(x, y) = x^2 + y^2 + x^2y + 4$,
$D = \{(x, y) \,|\, |x| \leqslant 1, |y| \leqslant 1\}$

30. $f(x, y) = 4x + 6y - x^2 - y^2$,
$D = \{(x, y) \,|\, 0 \leqslant x \leqslant 4, 0 \leqslant y \leqslant 5\}$

31. $f(x, y) = x^4 + y^4 - 4xy + 2$,
$D = \{(x, y) \,|\, 0 \leqslant x \leqslant 3, 0 \leqslant y \leqslant 2\}$

32. $f(x, y) = xy^2$, $D = \{(x, y) \,|\, x \geqslant 0, y \geqslant 0, x^2 + y^2 \leqslant 3\}$

33. $f(x, y) = 2x^3 + y^4$, $D = \{(x, y) \,|\, x^2 + y^2 \leqslant 1\}$

34. $f(x, y) = x^3 - 3x - y^3 + 12y$, D is the quadrilateral whose vertices are $(-2, 3)$, $(2, 3)$, $(2, 2)$, and $(-2, -2)$.

35. For functions of one variable it is impossible for a continuous function to have two local maxima and no local minimum. But for functions of two variables such functions exist. Show that the function
$$f(x, y) = -(x^2 - 1)^2 - (x^2y - x - 1)^2$$
has only two critical points, but has local maxima at both of them. Then use a computer to produce a graph with a carefully chosen domain and viewpoint to see how this is possible.

36. If a function of one variable is continuous on an interval and has only one critical number, then a local maximum has to be

an absolute maximum. But this is not true for functions of two variables. Show that the function
$$f(x, y) = 3xe^y - x^3 - e^{3y}$$
has exactly one critical point, and that f has a local maximum there that is not an absolute maximum. Then use a computer to produce a graph with a carefully chosen domain and viewpoint to see how this is possible.

37. Find the shortest distance from the point $(2, 1, -1)$ to the plane $x + y - z = 1$.

38. Find the point on the plane $x - y + z = 4$ that is closest to the point $(1, 2, 3)$.

39. Find the points on the surface $z^2 = xy + 1$ that are closest to the origin.

40. Find the points on the surface $x^2y^2z = 1$ that are closest to the origin.

41. Find three positive numbers whose sum is 100 and whose product is a maximum.

42. Find three positive numbers x, y, and z whose sum is 100 such that $x^ay^bz^c$ is a maximum.

43. Find the volume of the largest rectangular box with edges parallel to the axes that can be inscribed in the ellipsoid
$$9x^2 + 36y^2 + 4z^2 = 36$$

44. Solve the problem in Exercise 43 for a general ellipsoid
$$\frac{x^2}{a^2} + \frac{y^2}{b^2} + \frac{z^2}{c^2} = 1$$

45. Find the volume of the largest rectangular box in the first octant with three faces in the coordinate planes and one vertex in the plane $x + 2y + 3z = 6$.

46. Find the dimensions of the rectangular box with largest volume if the total surface area is given as 64 cm^2.

47. Find the dimensions of a rectangular box of maximum volume such that the sum of the lengths of its 12 edges is a constant c.

48. The base of an aquarium with given volume V is made of slate and the sides are made of glass. If slate costs five times as much (per unit area) as glass, find the dimensions of the aquarium that minimize the cost of the materials.

49. A cardboard box without a lid is to have a volume of $32,000 \text{ cm}^3$. Find the dimensions that minimize the amount of cardboard used.

50. A rectangular building is being designed to minimize heat loss. The east and west walls lose heat at a rate of 10 units/m² per day, the north and south walls at a rate of 8 units/m² per day, the floor at a rate of 1 unit/m² per day, and the roof at a rate of 5 units/m² per day. Each wall must be at least 30 m long, the height must be at least 4 m, and the volume must be exactly 4000 m^3.
(a) Find and sketch the domain of the heat loss as a function of the lengths of the sides.

(b) Find the dimensions that minimize heat loss. (Check both the critical points and the points on the boundary of the domain.)

(c) Could you design a building with even less heat loss if the restrictions on the lengths of the walls were removed?

51. If the length of the diagonal of a rectangular box must be L, what is the largest possible volume?

52. Three alleles (alternative versions of a gene) A, B, and O determine the four blood types A (AA or AO), B (BB or BO), O (OO), and AB. The Hardy-Weinberg Law states that the proportion of individuals in a population who carry two different alleles is

$$P = 2pq + 2pr + 2rq$$

where p, q, and r are the proportions of A, B, and O in the population. Use the fact that $p + q + r = 1$ to show that P is at most $\frac{2}{3}$.

53. Suppose that a scientist has reason to believe that two quantities x and y are related linearly, that is, $y = mx + b$, at least approximately, for some values of m and b. The scientist performs an experiment and collects data in the form of points (x_1, y_1), (x_2, y_2), ..., (x_n, y_n), and then plots these points. The points don't lie exactly on a straight line, so the scientist wants to find constants m and b so that the line $y = mx + b$ "fits" the points as well as possible. (See the figure.)

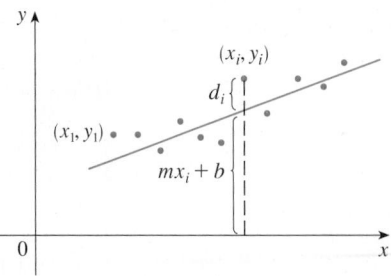

Let $d_i = y_i - (mx_i + b)$ be the vertical deviation of the point (x_i, y_i) from the line. The **method of least squares** determines m and b so as to minimize $\sum_{i=1}^{n} d_i^2$, the sum of the squares of these deviations. Show that, according to this method, the line of best fit is obtained when

$$m \sum_{i=1}^{n} x_i + bn = \sum_{i=1}^{n} y_i$$

$$m \sum_{i=1}^{n} x_i^2 + b \sum_{i=1}^{n} x_i = \sum_{i=1}^{n} x_i y_i$$

Thus, the line is found by solving these two equations in the two unknowns m and b. (See Section 1.2 for a further discussion and applications of the method of least squares.)

54. Find an equation of the plane that passes through the point $(1, 2, 3)$ and cuts off the smallest volume in the first octant.

APPLIED PROJECT

Designing a Dumpster

For this project we locate a trash dumpster in order to study its shape and construction. We then attempt to determine the dimensions of a container of similar design that minimize construction cost.

1. First locate a trash dumpster in your area. Carefully study and describe all details of its construction, and determine its volume. Include a sketch of the container.

2. While maintaining the general shape and method of construction, determine the dimensions such a container of the same volume should have in order to minimize the cost of construction. Use the following assumptions in your analysis:

- The sides, back, and front are to be made from 12-gauge (0.1046 inch thick) steel sheets, which cost $0.70 per square foot (including any required cuts or bends).
- The base is to be made from a 10-gauge (0.1345 inch thick) steel sheet, which costs $0.90 per square foot.
- Lids cost approximately $50.00 each, regardless of dimensions.
- Welding costs approximately $0.18 per foot for material and labor combined.

Give justification of any further assumptions or simplifications made of the details of construction.

3. Describe how any of your assumptions or simplifications may affect the final result.

4. If you were hired as a consultant on this investigation, what would your conclusions be? Would you recommend altering the design of the dumpster? If so, describe the savings that would result.

▟▟▟▏ DISCOVERY PROJECT

Quadratic Approximations and Critical Points

The Taylor polynomial approximation to functions of one variable that we discussed in Chapter 12 can be extended to functions of two or more variables. Here we investigate quadratic approximations to functions of two variables and use them to give insight into the Second Derivatives Test for classifying critical points.

In Section 15.4 we discussed the linearization of a function f of two variables at a point (a, b):

$$L(x, y) = f(a, b) + f_x(a, b)(x - a) + f_y(a, b)(y - b)$$

Recall that the graph of L is the tangent plane to the surface $z = f(x, y)$ at $(a, b, f(a, b))$ and the corresponding linear approximation is $f(x, y) \approx L(x, y)$. The linearization L is also called the **first-degree Taylor polynomial** of f at (a, b).

1. If f has continuous second-order partial derivatives at (a, b), then the **second-degree Taylor polynomial** of f at (a, b) is

$$Q(x, y) = f(a, b) + f_x(a, b)(x - a) + f_y(a, b)(y - b)$$
$$+ \tfrac{1}{2}f_{xx}(a, b)(x - a)^2 + f_{xy}(a, b)(x - a)(y - b) + \tfrac{1}{2}f_{yy}(a, b)(y - b)^2$$

and the approximation $f(x, y) \approx Q(x, y)$ is called the **quadratic approximation** to f at (a, b). Verify that Q has the same first- and second-order partial derivatives as f at (a, b).

2. (a) Find the first- and second-degree Taylor polynomials L and Q of $f(x, y) = e^{-x^2 - y^2}$ at $(0, 0)$.

(b) Graph f, L, and Q. Comment on how well L and Q approximate f.

3. (a) Find the first- and second-degree Taylor polynomials L and Q for $f(x, y) = xe^y$ at $(1, 0)$.

(b) Compare the values of L, Q, and f at $(0.9, 0.1)$.

(c) Graph f, L, and Q. Comment on how well L and Q approximate f.

4. In this problem we analyze the behavior of the polynomial $f(x, y) = ax^2 + bxy + cy^2$ (without using the Second Derivatives Test) by identifying the graph as a paraboloid.

(a) By completing the square, show that if $a \neq 0$, then

$$f(x, y) = ax^2 + bxy + cy^2 = a\left[\left(x + \frac{b}{2a}y \right)^2 + \left(\frac{4ac - b^2}{4a^2} \right)y^2 \right]$$

(b) Let $D = 4ac - b^2$. Show that if $D > 0$ and $a > 0$, then f has a local minimum at $(0, 0)$.

(c) Show that if $D > 0$ and $a < 0$, then f has a local maximum at $(0, 0)$.

(d) Show that if $D < 0$, then $(0, 0)$ is a saddle point.

5. (a) Suppose f is any function with continuous second-order partial derivatives such that $f(0, 0) = 0$ and $(0, 0)$ is a critical point of f. Write an expression for the second-degree Taylor polynomial, Q, of f at $(0, 0)$.

(b) What can you conclude about Q from Problem 4?

(c) In view of the quadratic approximation $f(x, y) \approx Q(x, y)$, what does part (b) suggest about f?

15.8 Lagrange Multipliers

In Example 6 in Section 15.7 we maximized a volume function $V = xyz$ subject to the constraint $2xz + 2yz + xy = 12$, which expressed the side condition that the surface area was 12 m². In this section we present Lagrange's method for maximizing or minimizing a general function $f(x, y, z)$ subject to a constraint (or side condition) of the form $g(x, y, z) = k$.

It's easier to explain the geometric basis of Lagrange's method for functions of two variables. So we start by trying to find the extreme values of $f(x, y)$ subject to a constraint of the form $g(x, y) = k$. In other words, we seek the extreme values of $f(x, y)$ when the point (x, y) is restricted to lie on the level curve $g(x, y) = k$. Figure 1 shows this curve together with several level curves of f. These have the equations $f(x, y) = c$, where $c = 7$, 8, 9, 10, 11. To maximize $f(x, y)$ subject to $g(x, y) = k$ is to find the largest value of c such that the level curve $f(x, y) = c$ intersects $g(x, y) = k$. It appears from Figure 1 that this happens when these curves just touch each other, that is, when they have a common tangent line. (Otherwise, the value of c could be increased further.) This means that the normal lines at the point (x_0, y_0) where they touch are identical. So the gradient vectors are parallel; that is, $\nabla f(x_0, y_0) = \lambda \nabla g(x_0, y_0)$ for some scalar λ.

Visual 15.8 animates Figure 1 for both level curves and level surfaces.

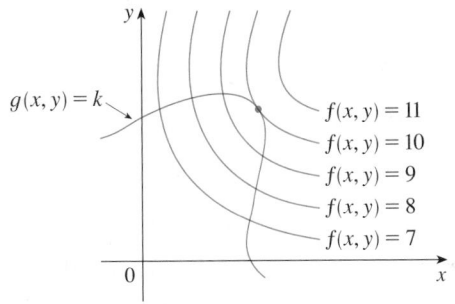

$g(x, y) = k$

$f(x, y) = 11$
$f(x, y) = 10$
$f(x, y) = 9$
$f(x, y) = 8$
$f(x, y) = 7$

FIGURE 1

This kind of argument also applies to the problem of finding the extreme values of $f(x, y, z)$ subject to the constraint $g(x, y, z) = k$. Thus, the point (x, y, z) is restricted to lie on the level surface S with equation $g(x, y, z) = k$. Instead of the level curves in Figure 1, we consider the level surfaces $f(x, y, z) = c$ and argue that if the maximum value of f is $f(x_0, y_0, z_0) = c$, then the level surface $f(x, y, z) = c$ is tangent to the level surface $g(x, y, z) = k$ and so the corresponding gradient vectors are parallel.

This intuitive argument can be made precise as follows. Suppose that a function f has an extreme value at a point $P(x_0, y_0, z_0)$ on the surface S and let C be a curve with vector equation $\mathbf{r}(t) = \langle x(t), y(t), z(t) \rangle$ that lies on S and passes through P. If t_0 is the parameter value corresponding to the point P, then $\mathbf{r}(t_0) = \langle x_0, y_0, z_0 \rangle$. The composite function $h(t) = f(x(t), y(t), z(t))$ represents the values that f takes on the curve C. Since f has an extreme value at (x_0, y_0, z_0), it follows that h has an extreme value at t_0, so $h'(t_0) = 0$. But if f is differentiable, we can use the Chain Rule to write

$$0 = h'(t_0) = f_x(x_0, y_0, z_0)x'(t_0) + f_y(x_0, y_0, z_0)y'(t_0) + f_z(x_0, y_0, z_0)z'(t_0)$$

$$= \nabla f(x_0, y_0, z_0) \cdot \mathbf{r}'(t_0)$$

This shows that the gradient vector $\nabla f(x_0, y_0, z_0)$ is orthogonal to the tangent vector $\mathbf{r}'(t_0)$ to every such curve C. But we already know from Section 15.6 that the gradient vector of g, $\nabla g(x_0, y_0, z_0)$, is also orthogonal to $\mathbf{r}'(t_0)$. (See Equation 15.6.18.) This means that the gradient vectors $\nabla f(x_0, y_0, z_0)$ and $\nabla g(x_0, y_0, z_0)$ must be parallel. Therefore, if $\nabla g(x_0, y_0, z_0) \neq \mathbf{0}$, there is a number λ such that

|||| Lagrange multipliers are named after the French-Italian mathematician Joseph-Louis Lagrange (1736–1813). See page 236 for a biographical sketch of Lagrange.

$\boxed{1}$

$$\nabla f(x_0, y_0, z_0) = \lambda\, \nabla g(x_0, y_0, z_0)$$

The number λ in Equation 1 is called a **Lagrange multiplier**. The procedure based on Equation 1 is as follows.

|||| In deriving Lagrange's method we assumed that $\nabla g \neq \mathbf{0}$. In each of our examples you can check that $\nabla g \neq \mathbf{0}$ at all points where $g(x, y, z) = k$.

> **Method of Lagrange Multipliers**   To find the maximum and minimum values of $f(x, y, z)$ subject to the constraint $g(x, y, z) = k$ [assuming that these extreme values exist and $\nabla g \neq \mathbf{0}$ on the surface $g(x, y, z) = k$]:
>
> (a) Find all values of x, y, z, and λ such that
>
> $$\nabla f(x, y, z) = \lambda\, \nabla g(x, y, z)$$
>
> and $\qquad\qquad g(x, y, z) = k$
>
> (b) Evaluate f at all the points (x, y, z) that result from step (a). The largest of these values is the maximum value of f; the smallest is the minimum value of f.

If we write the vector equation $\nabla f = \lambda\, \nabla g$ in terms of its components, then the equations in step (a) become

$$f_x = \lambda g_x \qquad f_y = \lambda g_y \qquad f_z = \lambda g_z \qquad g(x, y, z) = k$$

This is a system of four equations in the four unknowns x, y, z, and λ, but it is not necessary to find explicit values for λ.

For functions of two variables the method of Lagrange multipliers is similar to the method just described. To find the extreme values of $f(x, y)$ subject to the constraint $g(x, y) = k$, we look for values of x, y, and λ such that

$$\nabla f(x, y) = \lambda\, \nabla g(x, y) \qquad \text{and} \qquad g(x, y) = k$$

This amounts to solving three equations in three unknowns:

$$f_x = \lambda g_x \qquad f_y = \lambda g_y \qquad g(x, y) = k$$

Our first illustration of Lagrange's method is to reconsider the problem given in Example 6 in Section 15.7.

EXAMPLE 1   A rectangular box without a lid is to be made from 12 m² of cardboard. Find the maximum volume of such a box.

SOLUTION   As in Example 6 in Section 15.7 we let x, y, and z be the length, width, and height, respectively, of the box in meters. Then we wish to maximize

$$V = xyz$$

subject to the constraint

$$g(x, y, z) = 2xz + 2yz + xy = 12$$

Using the method of Lagrange multipliers, we look for values of x, y, z, and λ such that $\nabla V = \lambda \nabla g$ and $g(x, y, z) = 12$. This gives the equations

$$V_x = \lambda g_x \qquad V_y = \lambda g_y \qquad V_z = \lambda g_z \qquad 2xz + 2yz + xy = 12$$

which become

$$\boxed{2} \qquad\qquad\qquad yz = \lambda(2z + y)$$

$$\boxed{3} \qquad\qquad\qquad xz = \lambda(2z + x)$$

$$\boxed{4} \qquad\qquad\qquad xy = \lambda(2x + 2y)$$

$$\boxed{5} \qquad\qquad\qquad 2xz + 2yz + xy = 12$$

There are no general rules for solving systems of equations. Sometimes some ingenuity is required. In the present example you might notice that if we multiply (2) by x, (3) by y, and (4) by z, then the left sides of these equations will be identical. Doing this, we have

||| Another method for solving the system of equations (2–5) is to solve each of Equations 2, 3, and 4 for λ and then to equate the resulting expressions.

$$\boxed{6} \qquad\qquad\qquad xyz = \lambda(2xz + xy)$$

$$\boxed{7} \qquad\qquad\qquad xyz = \lambda(2yz + xy)$$

$$\boxed{8} \qquad\qquad\qquad xyz = \lambda(2xz + 2yz)$$

We observe that $\lambda \neq 0$ because $\lambda = 0$ would imply $yz = xz = xy = 0$ from (2), (3), and (4) and this would contradict (5). Therefore, from (6) and (7) we have

$$2xz + xy = 2yz + xy$$

which gives $xz = yz$. But $z \neq 0$ (since $z = 0$ would give $V = 0$), so $x = y$. From (7) and (8) we have

$$2yz + xy = 2xz + 2yz$$

which gives $2xz = xy$ and so (since $x \neq 0$) $y = 2z$. If we now put $x = y = 2z$ in (5), we get

$$4z^2 + 4z^2 + 4z^2 = 12$$

Since x, y, and z are all positive, we therefore have $z = 1$, $x = 2$, and $y = 2$ as before.

EXAMPLE 2 Find the extreme values of the function $f(x, y) = x^2 + 2y^2$ on the circle $x^2 + y^2 = 1$.

SOLUTION We are asked for the extreme values of f subject to the constraint $g(x, y) = x^2 + y^2 = 1$. Using Lagrange multipliers, we solve the equations $\nabla f = \lambda \nabla g$, $g(x, y) = 1$, which can be written as

$$f_x = \lambda g_x \qquad f_y = \lambda g_y \qquad g(x, y) = 1$$

or as

$$\boxed{9} \qquad\qquad\qquad 2x = 2x\lambda$$

$$\boxed{10} \qquad\qquad\qquad 4y = 2y\lambda$$

$$\boxed{11} \qquad\qquad\qquad x^2 + y^2 = 1$$

||| In geometric terms, Example 2 asks for the highest and lowest points on the curve C in Figure 2 that lies on the paraboloid $z = x^2 + 2y^2$ and directly above the constraint circle $x^2 + y^2 = 1$.

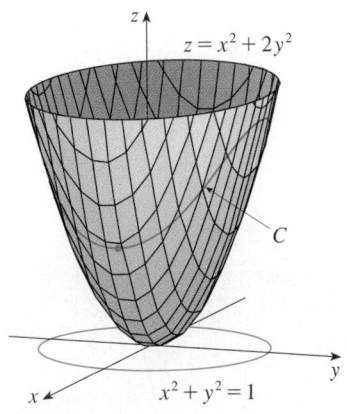

$z = x^2 + 2y^2$

C

$x^2 + y^2 = 1$

FIGURE 2

▏▏▏▏ The geometry behind the use of Lagrange multipliers in Example 2 is shown in Figure 3. The extreme values of $f(x, y) = x^2 + 2y^2$ correspond to the level curves that touch the circle $x^2 + y^2 = 1$.

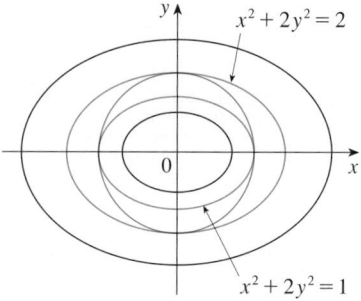

FIGURE 3

From (9) we have $x = 0$ or $\lambda = 1$. If $x = 0$, then (11) gives $y = \pm 1$. If $\lambda = 1$, then $y = 0$ from (10), so then (11) gives $x = \pm 1$. Therefore, f has possible extreme values at the points $(0, 1)$, $(0, -1)$, $(1, 0)$, and $(-1, 0)$. Evaluating f at these four points, we find that

$$f(0, 1) = 2 \qquad f(0, -1) = 2 \qquad f(1, 0) = 1 \qquad f(-1, 0) = 1$$

Therefore, the maximum value of f on the circle $x^2 + y^2 = 1$ is $f(0, \pm 1) = 2$ and the minimum value is $f(\pm 1, 0) = 1$. Checking with Figure 2, we see that these values look reasonable.

EXAMPLE 3 Find the extreme values of $f(x, y) = x^2 + 2y^2$ on the disk $x^2 + y^2 \leqslant 1$.

SOLUTION According to the procedure in (15.7.9), we compare the values of f at the critical points with values at the points on the boundary. Since $f_x = 2x$ and $f_y = 4y$, the only critical point is $(0, 0)$. We compare the value of f at that point with the extreme values on the boundary from Example 2:

$$f(0, 0) = 0 \qquad f(\pm 1, 0) = 1 \qquad f(0, \pm 1) = 2$$

Therefore, the maximum value of f on the disk $x^2 + y^2 \leqslant 1$ is $f(0, \pm 1) = 2$ and the minimum value is $f(0, 0) = 0$.

EXAMPLE 4 Find the points on the sphere $x^2 + y^2 + z^2 = 4$ that are closest to and farthest from the point $(3, 1, -1)$.

SOLUTION The distance from a point (x, y, z) to the point $(3, 1, -1)$ is

$$d = \sqrt{(x - 3)^2 + (y - 1)^2 + (z + 1)^2}$$

but the algebra is simpler if we instead maximize and minimize the square of the distance:

$$d^2 = f(x, y, z) = (x - 3)^2 + (y - 1)^2 + (z + 1)^2$$

The constraint is that the point (x, y, z) lies on the sphere, that is,

$$g(x, y, z) = x^2 + y^2 + z^2 = 4$$

According to the method of Lagrange multipliers, we solve $\nabla f = \lambda \nabla g$, $g = 4$. This gives

$$\boxed{12} \qquad\qquad\qquad 2(x - 3) = 2x\lambda$$

$$\boxed{13} \qquad\qquad\qquad 2(y - 1) = 2y\lambda$$

$$\boxed{14} \qquad\qquad\qquad 2(z + 1) = 2z\lambda$$

$$\boxed{15} \qquad\qquad\qquad x^2 + y^2 + z^2 = 4$$

The simplest way to solve these equations is to solve for x, y, and z in terms of λ from (12), (13), and (14), and then substitute these values into (15). From (12) we have

$$x - 3 = x\lambda \qquad \text{or} \qquad x(1 - \lambda) = 3 \qquad \text{or} \qquad x = \frac{3}{1 - \lambda}$$

IIII Figure 4 shows the sphere and the nearest point P in Example 4. Can you see how to find the coordinates of P without using calculus?

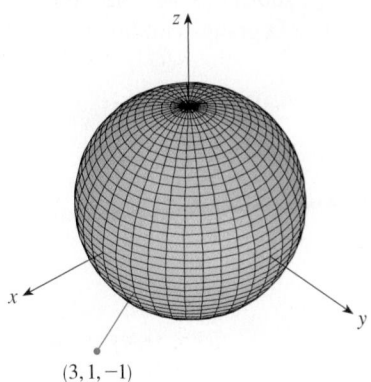

(3, 1, −1)

FIGURE 4

[Note that $1 - \lambda \neq 0$ because $\lambda = 1$ is impossible from (12).] Similarly, (13) and (14) give

$$y = \frac{1}{1 - \lambda} \qquad z = -\frac{1}{1 - \lambda}$$

Therefore, from (15) we have

$$\frac{3^2}{(1 - \lambda)^2} + \frac{1^2}{(1 - \lambda)^2} + \frac{(-1)^2}{(1 - \lambda)^2} = 4$$

which gives $(1 - \lambda)^2 = \frac{11}{4}$, $1 - \lambda = \pm\sqrt{11}/2$, so

$$\lambda = 1 \pm \frac{\sqrt{11}}{2}$$

These values of λ then give the corresponding points (x, y, z):

$$\left(\frac{6}{\sqrt{11}}, \frac{2}{\sqrt{11}}, -\frac{2}{\sqrt{11}}\right) \qquad \text{and} \qquad \left(-\frac{6}{\sqrt{11}}, -\frac{2}{\sqrt{11}}, \frac{2}{\sqrt{11}}\right)$$

It's easy to see that f has a smaller value at the first of these points, so the closest point is $\left(6/\sqrt{11}, 2/\sqrt{11}, -2/\sqrt{11}\right)$ and the farthest is $\left(-6/\sqrt{11}, -2/\sqrt{11}, 2/\sqrt{11}\right)$. ▬

Two Constraints

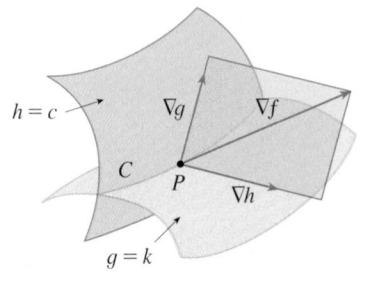

FIGURE 5

Suppose now that we want to find the maximum and minimum values of a function $f(x, y, z)$ subject to two constraints (side conditions) of the form $g(x, y, z) = k$ and $h(x, y, z) = c$. Geometrically, this means that we are looking for the extreme values of f when (x, y, z) is restricted to lie on the curve of intersection C of the level surfaces $g(x, y, z) = k$ and $h(x, y, z) = c$. (See Figure 5.) Suppose f has such an extreme value at a point $P(x_0, y_0, z_0)$. We know from the beginning of this section that ∇f is orthogonal to C there. But we also know that ∇g is orthogonal to $g(x, y, z) = k$ and ∇h is orthogonal to $h(x, y, z) = c$, so ∇g and ∇h are both orthogonal to C. This means that the gradient vector $\nabla f(x_0, y_0, z_0)$ is in the plane determined by $\nabla g(x_0, y_0, z_0)$ and $\nabla h(x_0, y_0, z_0)$. (We assume that these gradient vectors are not zero and not parallel.) So there are numbers λ and μ (called Lagrange multipliers) such that

| 16 | $$\nabla f(x_0, y_0, z_0) = \lambda \nabla g(x_0, y_0, z_0) + \mu \nabla h(x_0, y_0, z_0)$$ |

In this case Lagrange's method is to look for extreme values by solving five equations in the five unknowns x, y, z, λ, and μ. These equations are obtained by writing Equation 16 in terms of its components and using the constraint equations:

$$f_x = \lambda g_x + \mu h_x$$

$$f_y = \lambda g_y + \mu h_y$$

$$f_z = \lambda g_z + \mu h_z$$

$$g(x, y, z) = k$$

$$h(x, y, z) = c$$

‖‖ The cylinder $x^2 + y^2 = 1$ intersects the plane $x - y + z = 1$ in an ellipse (Figure 6). Example 5 asks for the maximum value of f when (x, y, z) is restricted to lie on the ellipse.

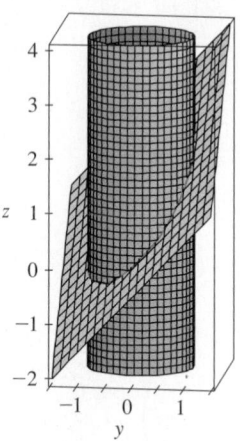

FIGURE 6

EXAMPLE 5 Find the maximum value of the function $f(x, y, z) = x + 2y + 3z$ on the curve of intersection of the plane $x - y + z = 1$ and the cylinder $x^2 + y^2 = 1$.

SOLUTION We maximize the function $f(x, y, z) = x + 2y + 3z$ subject to the constraints $g(x, y, z) = x - y + z = 1$ and $h(x, y, z) = x^2 + y^2 = 1$. The Lagrange condition is $\nabla f = \lambda \nabla g + \mu \nabla h$, so we solve the equations

| 17 | $1 = \lambda + 2x\mu$ |

| 18 | $2 = -\lambda + 2y\mu$ |

| 19 | $3 = \lambda$ |

| 20 | $x - y + z = 1$ |

| 21 | $x^2 + y^2 = 1$ |

Putting $\lambda = 3$ [from (19)] in (17), we get $2x\mu = -2$, so $x = -1/\mu$. Similarly, (18) gives $y = 5/(2\mu)$. Substitution in (21) then gives

$$\frac{1}{\mu^2} + \frac{25}{4\mu^2} = 1$$

and so $\mu^2 = \frac{29}{4}$, $\mu = \pm\sqrt{29}/2$. Then $x = \mp 2/\sqrt{29}$, $y = \pm 5/\sqrt{29}$, and, from (20), $z = 1 - x + y = 1 \pm 7/\sqrt{29}$. The corresponding values of f are

$$\mp\frac{2}{\sqrt{29}} + 2\left(\pm\frac{5}{\sqrt{29}}\right) + 3\left(1 \pm \frac{7}{\sqrt{29}}\right) = 3 \pm \sqrt{29}$$

Therefore, the maximum value of f on the given curve is $3 + \sqrt{29}$.

15.8 Exercises

1. Pictured are a contour map of f and a curve with equation $g(x, y) = 8$. Estimate the maximum and minimum values of f subject to the constraint that $g(x, y) = 8$. Explain your reasoning.

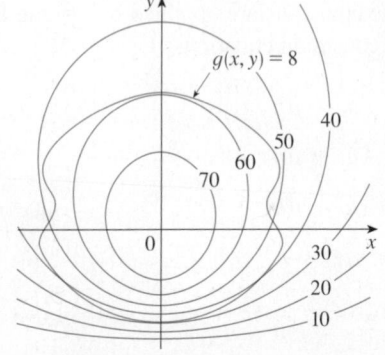

2. (a) Use a graphing calculator or computer to graph the circle $x^2 + y^2 = 1$. On the same screen, graph several curves of the form $x^2 + y = c$ until you find two that just touch the circle. What is the significance of the values of c for these two curves?
   (b) Use Lagrange multipliers to find the extreme values of $f(x, y) = x^2 + y$ subject to the constraint $x^2 + y^2 = 1$. Compare your answers with those in part (a).

3–17 ▓ Use Lagrange multipliers to find the maximum and minimum values of the function subject to the given constraint(s).

3. $f(x, y) = x^2 - y^2$; $\quad x^2 + y^2 = 1$

4. $f(x, y) = 4x + 6y$; $\quad x^2 + y^2 = 13$

5. $f(x, y) = x^2 y$; $\quad x^2 + 2y^2 = 6$

6. $f(x, y) = x^2 + y^2$; $\quad x^4 + y^4 = 1$

7. $f(x, y, z) = 2x + 6y + 10z;$ $x^2 + y^2 + z^2 = 35$

8. $f(x, y, z) = 8x - 4z;$ $x^2 + 10y^2 + z^2 = 5$

9. $f(x, y, z) = xyz;$ $x^2 + 2y^2 + 3z^2 = 6$

10. $f(x, y, z) = x^2 y^2 z^2;$ $x^2 + y^2 + z^2 = 1$

11. $f(x, y, z) = x^2 + y^2 + z^2;$ $x^4 + y^4 + z^4 = 1$

12. $f(x, y, z) = x^4 + y^4 + z^4;$ $x^2 + y^2 + z^2 = 1$

13. $f(x, y, z, t) = x + y + z + t;$ $x^2 + y^2 + z^2 + t^2 = 1$

14. $f(x_1, x_2, \ldots, x_n) = x_1 + x_2 + \cdots + x_n;$
$x_1^2 + x_2^2 + \cdots + x_n^2 = 1$

15. $f(x, y, z) = x + 2y;$ $x + y + z = 1,$ $y^2 + z^2 = 4$

16. $f(x, y, z) = 3x - y - 3z;$
$x + y - z = 0,$ $x^2 + 2z^2 = 1$

17. $f(x, y, z) = yz + xy;$ $xy = 1,$ $y^2 + z^2 = 1$

18–19 ▐▐ Find the extreme values of f on the region described by the inequality.

18. $f(x, y) = 2x^2 + 3y^2 - 4x - 5,$ $x^2 + y^2 \leqslant 16$

19. $f(x, y) = e^{-xy},$ $x^2 + 4y^2 \leqslant 1$

[CAS] **20.** (a) If your computer algebra system plots implicitly defined curves, use it to estimate the minimum and maximum values of $f(x, y) = x^3 + y^3 + 3xy$ subject to the constraint $(x - 3)^2 + (y - 3)^2 = 9$ by graphical methods.
(b) Solve the problem in part (a) with the aid of Lagrange multipliers. Use your CAS to solve the equations numerically. Compare your answers with those in part (a).

21. The total production P of a certain product depends on the amount L of labor used and the amount K of capital investment. In Sections 15.1 and 15.3 we discussed how the Cobb-Douglas model $P = bL^\alpha K^{1-\alpha}$ follows from certain economic assumptions, where b and α are positive constants and $\alpha < 1$. If the cost of a unit of labor is m and the cost of a unit of capital is n, and the company can spend only p dollars as its total budget, then maximizing the production P is subject to the constraint $mL + nK = p$. Show that the maximum production occurs when

$$L = \frac{\alpha p}{m} \quad \text{and} \quad K = \frac{(1 - \alpha)p}{n}$$

22. Referring to Exercise 21, we now suppose that the production is fixed at $bL^\alpha K^{1-\alpha} = Q$, where Q is a constant. What values of L and K minimize the cost function $C(L, K) = mL + nK$?

23. Use Lagrange multipliers to prove that the rectangle with maximum area that has a given perimeter p is a square.

24. Use Lagrange multipliers to prove that the triangle with maximum area that has a given perimeter p is equilateral.

[*Hint:* Use Heron's formula for the area:
$A = \sqrt{s(s - x)(s - y)(s - z)}$, where $s = p/2$ and x, y, z are the lengths of the sides.]

25–37 ▐▐ Use Lagrange multipliers to give an alternate solution to the indicated exercise in Section 15.7.

25. Exercise 37	**26.** Exercise 38
27. Exercise 39	**28.** Exercise 40
29. Exercise 41	**30.** Exercise 42
31. Exercise 43	**32.** Exercise 44
33. Exercise 45	**34.** Exercise 46
35. Exercise 47	**36.** Exercise 48
37. Exercise 51	

38. Find the maximum and minimum volumes of a rectangular box whose surface area is 1500 cm^2 and whose total edge length is 200 cm.

39. The plane $x + y + 2z = 2$ intersects the paraboloid $z = x^2 + y^2$ in an ellipse. Find the points on this ellipse that are nearest to and farthest from the origin.

40. The plane $4x - 3y + 8z = 5$ intersects the cone $z^2 = x^2 + y^2$ in an ellipse.
(a) Graph the cone, the plane, and the ellipse.
(b) Use Lagrange multipliers to find the highest and lowest points on the ellipse.

[CAS] **41–42** ▐▐ Find the maximum and minimum values of f subject to the given constraints. Use a computer algebra system to solve the system of equations that arises in using Lagrange multipliers. (If your CAS finds only one solution, you may need to use additional commands.)

41. $f(x, y, z) = ye^{x-z};$ $9x^2 + 4y^2 + 36z^2 = 36,$ $xy + yz = 1$

42. $f(x, y, z) = x + y + z;$ $x^2 - y^2 = z,$ $x^2 + z^2 = 4$

43. (a) Find the maximum value of

$$f(x_1, x_2, \ldots, x_n) = \sqrt[n]{x_1 x_2 \cdots x_n}$$

given that $x_1, x_2, \ldots, x_n$ are positive numbers and $x_1 + x_2 + \cdots + x_n = c$, where c is a constant.
(b) Deduce from part (a) that if $x_1, x_2, \ldots, x_n$ are positive numbers, then

$$\sqrt[n]{x_1 x_2 \cdots x_n} \leqslant \frac{x_1 + x_2 + \cdots + x_n}{n}$$

This inequality says that the geometric mean of n numbers is no larger than the arithmetic mean of the numbers. Under what circumstances are these two means equal?

44. (a) Maximize $\sum_{i=1}^{n} x_i y_i$ subject to the constraints $\sum_{i=1}^{n} x_i^2 = 1$ and $\sum_{i=1}^{n} y_i^2 = 1$.

(b) Put

$$x_i = \frac{a_i}{\sqrt{\sum a_j^2}} \qquad \text{and} \qquad y_i = \frac{b_i}{\sqrt{\sum b_j^2}}$$

to show that

$$\sum a_i b_i \leq \sqrt{\sum a_j^2} \ \sqrt{\sum b_j^2}$$

for any numbers $a_1, \ldots, a_n, b_1, \ldots, b_n$. This inequality is known as the Cauchy-Schwarz Inequality.

APPLIED PROJECT

Courtesy of Orbital Sciences Corporation

Rocket Science

Many rockets, such as the *Pegasus XL* currently used to launch satellites and the *Saturn V* that first put men on the Moon, are designed to use three stages in their ascent into space. A large first stage initially propels the rocket until its fuel is consumed, at which point the stage is jettisoned to reduce the mass of the rocket. The smaller second and third stages function similarly in order to place the rocket's payload into orbit about the Earth. (With this design, at least two stages are required in order to reach the necessary velocities, and using three stages has proven to be a good compromise between cost and performance.) Our goal here is to determine the individual masses of the three stages to be designed in such a way as to minimize the total mass of the rocket while enabling it to reach a desired velocity.

For a single-stage rocket consuming fuel at a constant rate, the change in velocity resulting from the acceleration of the rocket vehicle has been modeled by

$$\Delta V = -c \ln\left(1 - \frac{(1 - S)M_r}{P + M_r} \right)$$

where M_r is the mass of the rocket engine including initial fuel, P is the mass of the payload, S is a *structural factor* determined by the design of the rocket (specifically, it is the ratio of the mass of the rocket vehicle without fuel to the total mass of the rocket with payload), and c is the (constant) speed of exhaust relative to the rocket.

Now consider a rocket with three stages and a payload of mass A. Assume that outside forces are negligible and that c and S remain constant for each stage. If M_i is the mass of the ith stage, we can initially consider the rocket engine to have mass M_1 and its payload to have mass $M_2 + M_3 + A$; the second and third stages can be handled similarly.

1. Show that the velocity attained after all three stages have been jettisoned is given by

$$v_f = c\left[\ln\left(\frac{M_1 + M_2 + M_3 + A}{SM_1 + M_2 + M_3 + A} \right) + \ln\left(\frac{M_2 + M_3 + A}{SM_2 + M_3 + A} \right) + \ln\left(\frac{M_3 + A}{SM_3 + A} \right) \right]$$

2. We wish to minimize the total mass $M = M_1 + M_2 + M_3$ of the rocket engine subject to the constraint that the desired velocity v_f from Problem 1 is attained. The method of Lagrange multipliers is appropriate here, but difficult to implement using the current expressions. To simplify, we define variables N_i so that the constraint equation may be expressed as $v_f = c(\ln N_1 + \ln N_2 + \ln N_3)$. Since M is now difficult to express in terms of the N_i's, we wish to use a simpler function that will be minimized at the same place as M. Show that

$$\frac{M_1 + M_2 + M_3 + A}{M_2 + M_3 + A} = \frac{(1 - S)N_1}{1 - SN_1}$$

$$\frac{M_2 + M_3 + A}{M_3 + A} = \frac{(1 - S)N_2}{1 - SN_2}$$

$$\frac{M_3 + A}{A} = \frac{(1 - S)N_3}{1 - SN_3}$$

and conclude that

$$\frac{M + A}{A} = \frac{(1 - S)^3 N_1 N_2 N_3}{(1 - SN_1)(1 - SN_2)(1 - SN_3)}$$

3. Verify that $\ln((M + A)/A)$ is minimized at the same location as M; use Lagrange multipliers and the results of Problem 2 to find expressions for the values of N_i where the minimum occurs subject to the constraint $v_f = c(\ln N_1 + \ln N_2 + \ln N_3)$. [*Hint:* Use properties of logarithms to help simplify the expressions.]

4. Find an expression for the minimum value of M as a function of v_f.

5. If we want to put a three-stage rocket into orbit 100 miles above the Earth's surface, a final velocity of approximately 17,500 mi/h is required. Suppose that each stage is built with a structural factor $S = 0.2$ and an exhaust speed of $c = 6000$ mi/h.
(a) Find the minimum total mass M of the rocket engines as a function of A.
(b) Find the mass of each individual stage as a function of A. (They are not equally sized!)

6. The same rocket would require a final velocity of approximately 24,700 mi/h in order to escape Earth's gravity. Find the mass of each individual stage that would minimize the total mass of the rocket engines and allow the rocket to propel a 500-pound probe into deep space.

▦ APPLIED PROJECT

Hydro-Turbine Optimization

The Great Northern Paper Company in Millinocket, Maine, operates a hydroelectric generating station on the Penobscot River. Water is piped from a dam to the power station. The rate at which the water flows through the pipe varies, depending on external conditions.

The power station has three different hydroelectric turbines, each with a known (and unique) power function that gives the amount of electric power generated as a function of the water flow arriving at the turbine. The incoming water can be apportioned in different volumes to each turbine, so the goal is to determine how to distribute water among the turbines to give the maximum total energy production for any rate of flow.

Using experimental evidence and *Bernoulli's equation*, the following quadratic models were determined for the power output of each turbine, along with the allowable flows of operation:

$$KW_1 = (-18.89 + 0.1277Q_1 - 4.08 \cdot 10^{-5}Q_1^2)(170 - 1.6 \cdot 10^{-6}Q_T^2)$$
$$KW_2 = (-24.51 + 0.1358Q_2 - 4.69 \cdot 10^{-5}Q_2^2)(170 - 1.6 \cdot 10^{-6}Q_T^2)$$
$$KW_3 = (-27.02 + 0.1380Q_3 - 3.84 \cdot 10^{-5}Q_3^2)(170 - 1.6 \cdot 10^{-6}Q_T^2)$$

$$250 \leq Q_1 \leq 1110, \quad 250 \leq Q_2 \leq 1110, \quad 250 \leq Q_3 \leq 1225$$

where

$$Q_i = \text{flow through turbine } i \text{ in cubic feet per second}$$
$$KW_i = \text{power generated by turbine } i \text{ in kilowatts}$$
$$Q_T = \text{total flow through the station in cubic feet per second}$$

1. If all three turbines are being used, we wish to determine the flow Q_i to each turbine that will give the maximum total energy production. Our limitations are that the flows must sum to the total incoming flow and the given domain restrictions must be observed. Consequently, use Lagrange multipliers to find the values for the individual flows (as functions of Q_T) that maximize the total energy production $KW_1 + KW_2 + KW_3$ subject to the constraints $Q_1 + Q_2 + Q_3 = Q_T$ and the domain restrictions on each Q_i.

2. For which values of Q_T is your result valid?

3. For an incoming flow of 2500 ft³/s, determine the distribution to the turbines and verify (by trying some nearby distributions) that your result is indeed a maximum.

4. Until now we assumed that all three turbines are operating; is it possible in some situations that more power could be produced by using only one turbine? Make a graph of the three power functions and use it to help decide if an incoming flow of 1000 ft³/s should be distributed to all three turbines or routed to just one. (If you determine that only one turbine should be used, which one?) What if the flow is only 600 ft³/s?

5. Perhaps for some flow levels it would be advantageous to use two turbines. If the incoming flow is 1500 ft³/s, which two turbines would you recommend using? Use Lagrange multipliers to determine how the flow should be distributed between the two turbines to maximize the energy produced. For this flow, is using two turbines more efficient than using all three?

6. If the incoming flow is 3400 ft³/s, what would you recommend to the company?

|||| **15 Review** ———————— ∘ CONCEPT CHECK ∘ ————————

1. (a) What is a function of two variables?
(b) Describe three methods for visualizing a function of two variables.

2. What is a function of three variables? How can you visualize such a function?

3. What does
$$\lim_{(x,\,y)\to(a,\,b)} f(x,y) = L$$
mean? How can you show that such a limit does not exist?

4. (a) What does it mean to say that f is continuous at (a, b)?
(b) If f is continuous on $\mathbb{R}^2$, what can you say about its graph?

5. (a) Write expressions for the partial derivatives $f_x(a, b)$ and $f_y(a, b)$ as limits.
(b) How do you interpret $f_x(a, b)$ and $f_y(a, b)$ geometrically? How do you interpret them as rates of change?
(c) If $f(x, y)$ is given by a formula, how do you calculate f_x and f_y?

6. What does Clairaut's Theorem say?

7. How do you find a tangent plane to each of the following types of surfaces?
(a) A graph of a function of two variables, $z = f(x, y)$
(b) A level surface of a function of three variables, $F(x, y, z) = k$

8. Define the linearization of f at (a, b). What is the corresponding linear approximation? What is the geometric interpretation of the linear approximation?

9. (a) What does it mean to say that f is differentiable at (a, b)?
(b) How do you usually verify that f is differentiable?

10. If $z = f(x, y)$, what are the differentials dx, dy, and dz?

11. State the Chain Rule for the case where $z = f(x, y)$ and x and y are functions of one variable. What if x and y are functions of two variables?

12. If z is defined implicitly as a function of x and y by an equation of the form $F(x, y, z) = 0$, how do you find $\partial z/\partial x$ and $\partial z/\partial y$?

13. (a) Write an expression as a limit for the directional derivative of f at (x_0, y_0) in the direction of a unit vector $\mathbf{u} = \langle a, b \rangle$. How do you interpret it as a rate? How do you interpret it geometrically?
(b) If f is differentiable, write an expression for $D_\mathbf{u} f(x_0, y_0)$ in terms of f_x and f_y.

14. (a) Define the gradient vector ∇f for a function f of two or three variables.
(b) Express $D_\mathbf{u} f$ in terms of ∇f.
(c) Explain the geometric significance of the gradient.

15. What do the following statements mean?
(a) f has a local maximum at (a, b).
(b) f has an absolute maximum at (a, b).
(c) f has a local minimum at (a, b).
(d) f has an absolute minimum at (a, b).
(e) f has a saddle point at (a, b).

16. (a) If f has a local maximum at (a, b), what can you say about its partial derivatives at (a, b)?
(b) What is a critical point of f?

17. State the Second Derivatives Test.

18. (a) What is a closed set in $\mathbb{R}^2$? What is a bounded set?
(b) State the Extreme Value Theorem for functions of two variables.
(c) How do you find the values that the Extreme Value Theorem guarantees?

19. Explain how the method of Lagrange multipliers works in finding the extreme values of $f(x, y, z)$ subject to the constraint $g(x, y, z) = k$. What if there is a second constraint $h(x, y, z) = c$?

─── ▫ TRUE-FALSE QUIZ ▫ ───

Determine whether the statement is true or false. If it is true, explain why. If it is false, explain why or give an example that disproves the statement.

1. $f_y(a, b) = \lim_{y \to b} \dfrac{f(a, y) - f(a, b)}{y - b}$

2. There exists a function f with continuous second-order partial derivatives such that $f_x(x, y) = x + y^2$ and $f_y(x, y) = x - y^2$.

3. $f_{xy} = \dfrac{\partial^2 f}{\partial x\, \partial y}$

4. $D_{\mathbf{k}} f(x, y, z) = f_z(x, y, z)$

5. If $f(x, y) \to L$ as $(x, y) \to (a, b)$ along every straight line through (a, b), then $\lim_{(x, y) \to (a, b)} f(x, y) = L$.

6. If $f_x(a, b)$ and $f_y(a, b)$ both exist, then f is differentiable at (a, b).

7. If f has a local minimum at (a, b) and f is differentiable at (a, b), then $\nabla f(a, b) = \mathbf{0}$.

8. If f is a function, then $\lim_{(x, y) \to (2, 5)} f(x, y) = f(2, 5)$.

9. If $f(x, y) = \ln y$, then $\nabla f(x, y) = 1/y$.

10. If $(2, 1)$ is a critical point of f and

$$f_{xx}(2, 1) f_{yy}(2, 1) < [f_{xy}(2, 1)]^2$$

then f has a saddle point at $(2, 1)$.

11. If $f(x, y) = \sin x + \sin y$, then $-\sqrt{2} \le D_{\mathbf{u}} f(x, y) \le \sqrt{2}$.

12. If $f(x, y)$ has two local maxima, then f must have a local minimum.

─── ▫ EXERCISES ▫ ───

1–2 �…▌ Find and sketch the domain of the function.

1. $f(x, y) = \sin^{-1} x + \tan^{-1} y$ **2.** $f(x, y, z) = \sqrt{z - x^2 - y^2}$

3–4 ▌▌ Sketch the graph of the function.

3. $f(x, y) = 1 - x^2 - y^2$ **4.** $f(x, y) = \sqrt{x^2 + y^2 - 1}$

5–6 ▌▌ Sketch several level curves of the function.

5. $f(x, y) = e^{-(x^2+y^2)}$ **6.** $f(x, y) = x^2 + 4y$

7. Make a rough sketch of a contour map for the function whose graph is shown.

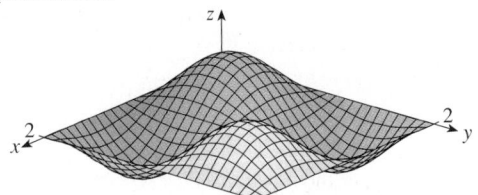

8. A contour map of a function f is shown. Use it to make a rough sketch of the graph of f.

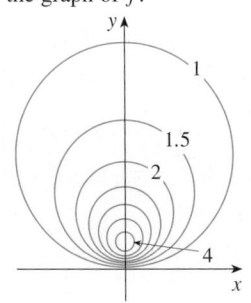

9–10 ▌▌ Evaluate the limit or show that it does not exist.

9. $\lim_{(x, y) \to (1, 1)} \dfrac{2xy}{x^2 + 2y^2}$ **10.** $\lim_{(x, y) \to (0, 0)} \dfrac{2xy}{x^2 + 2y^2}$

11. A metal plate is situated in the xy-plane and occupies the rectangle $0 \le x \le 10$, $0 \le y \le 8$, where x and y are measured in meters. The temperature at the point (x, y) in the plate is $T(x, y)$, where T is measured in degrees Celsius. Temperatures at equally spaced points were measured and recorded in the table.
(a) Estimate the values of the partial derivatives $T_x(6, 4)$ and $T_y(6, 4)$. What are the units?
(b) Estimate the value of $D_{\mathbf{u}} T(6, 4)$, where $\mathbf{u} = (\mathbf{i} + \mathbf{j})/\sqrt{2}$. Interpret your result.
(c) Estimate the value of $T_{xy}(6, 4)$.

y⁄x	0	2	4	6	8
0	30	38	45	51	55
2	52	56	60	62	61
4	78	74	72	68	66
6	98	87	80	75	71
8	96	90	86	80	75
10	92	92	91	87	78

12. Find a linear approximation to the temperature function $T(x, y)$ in Exercise 11 near the point $(6, 4)$. Then use it to estimate the temperature at the point $(5, 3.8)$.

13–17 ▏▏ Find the first partial derivatives.

13. $f(x, y) = \sqrt{2x + y^2}$

14. $u = e^{-r} \sin 2\theta$

15. $g(u, v) = u \tan^{-1} v$

16. $w = \dfrac{x}{y - z}$

17. $T(p, q, r) = p \ln(q + e^r)$

18. The speed of sound traveling through ocean water is a function of temperature, salinity, and pressure. It has been modeled by the function

$$C = 1449.2 + 4.6T - 0.055T^2 + 0.00029T^3$$
$$+ (1.34 - 0.01T)(S - 35) + 0.016D$$

where C is the speed of sound (in meters per second), T is the temperature (in degrees Celsius), S is the salinity (the concentration of salts in parts per thousand, which means the number of grams of dissolved solids per 1000 g of water), and D is the depth below the ocean surface (in meters). Compute $\partial C/\partial T$, $\partial C/\partial S$, and $\partial C/\partial D$ when $T = 10°C$, $S = 35$ parts per thousand, and $D = 100$ m. Explain the physical significance of these partial derivatives.

19–22 ▏▏ Find all second partial derivatives of f.

19. $f(x, y) = 4x^3 - xy^2$

20. $z = xe^{-2y}$

21. $f(x, y, z) = x^k y^l z^m$

22. $v = r \cos(s + 2t)$

23. If $u = x^y$, show that $\dfrac{x}{y}\dfrac{\partial u}{\partial x} + \dfrac{1}{\ln x}\dfrac{\partial u}{\partial y} = 2u$.

24. If $\rho = \sqrt{x^2 + y^2 + z^2}$, show that

$$\frac{\partial^2 \rho}{\partial x^2} + \frac{\partial^2 \rho}{\partial y^2} + \frac{\partial^2 \rho}{\partial z^2} = \frac{2}{\rho}$$

25–29 ▏▏ Find equations of (a) the tangent plane and (b) the normal line to the given surface at the specified point.

25. $z = 3x^2 - y^2 + 2x$, $(1, -2, 1)$

26. $z = e^x \cos y$, $(0, 0, 1)$

27. $x^2 + 2y^2 - 3z^2 = 3$, $(2, -1, 1)$

28. $xy + yz + zx = 3$, $(1, 1, 1)$

29. $\sin(xyz) = x + 2y + 3z$, $(2, -1, 0)$

30. Use a computer to graph the surface $z = x^3 + 2xy$ and its tangent plane and normal line at $(1, 2, 5)$ on the same screen. Choose the domain and viewpoint so that you get a good view of all three objects.

31. Find the points on the sphere $x^2 + y^2 + z^2 = 1$ where the tangent plane is parallel to the plane $2x + y - 3z = 2$.

32. Find dz if $z = x^2 \tan^{-1} y$.

33. Find the linear approximation of the function $f(x, y, z) = x^3 \sqrt{y^2 + z^2}$ at the point $(2, 3, 4)$ and use it to estimate the number $(1.98)^3 \sqrt{(3.01)^2 + (3.97)^2}$.

34. The two legs of a right triangle are measured as 5 m and 12 m with a possible error in measurement of at most 0.2 cm in each. Use differentials to estimate the maximum error in the calculated value of (a) the area of the triangle and (b) the length of the hypotenuse.

35. If $w = \sqrt{x} + y^2/z$, where $x = e^{2t}$, $y = t^3 + 4t$, and $z = t^2 - 4$, use the Chain Rule to find dw/dt.

36. If $z = \cos xy + y \cos x$, where $x = u^2 + v$ and $y = u - v^2$, use the Chain Rule to find $\partial z/\partial u$ and $\partial z/\partial v$.

37. Suppose $z = f(x, y)$, where $x = g(s, t)$, $y = h(s, t)$, $g(1, 2) = 3$, $g_s(1, 2) = -1$, $g_t(1, 2) = 4$, $h(1, 2) = 6$, $h_s(1, 2) = -5$, $h_t(1, 2) = 10$, $f_x(3, 6) = 7$, and $f_y(3, 6) = 8$. Find $\partial z/\partial s$ and $\partial z/\partial t$ when $s = 1$ and $t = 2$.

38. Use a tree diagram to write out the Chain Rule for the case where $w = f(t, u, v)$, $t = t(p, q, r, s)$, $u = u(p, q, r, s)$, and $v = v(p, q, r, s)$ are all differentiable functions.

39. If $z = y + f(x^2 - y^2)$, where f is differentiable, show that

$$y \frac{\partial z}{\partial x} + x \frac{\partial z}{\partial y} = x$$

40. The length x of a side of a triangle is increasing at a rate of 3 in/s, the length y of another side is decreasing at a rate of 2 in/s, and the contained angle θ is increasing at a rate of 0.05 radian/s. How fast is the area of the triangle changing when $x = 40$ in, $y = 50$ in, and $\theta = \pi/6$?

41. If $z = f(u, v)$, where $u = xy$, $v = y/x$, and f has continuous second partial derivatives, show that

$$x^2 \frac{\partial^2 z}{\partial x^2} - y^2 \frac{\partial^2 z}{\partial y^2} = -4uv \frac{\partial^2 z}{\partial u \partial v} + 2v \frac{\partial z}{\partial v}$$

42. If $yz^4 + x^2z^3 = e^{xyz}$, find $\dfrac{\partial z}{\partial x}$ and $\dfrac{\partial z}{\partial y}$.

43. Find the gradient of the function $f(x, y, z) = z^2 e^{x\sqrt{y}}$.

44. (a) When is the directional derivative of f a maximum?
(b) When is it a minimum?
(c) When is it 0?
(d) When is it half of its maximum value?

45–46 ▏▏ Find the directional derivative of f at the given point in the indicated direction.

45. $f(x, y) = 2\sqrt{x} - y^2$, $(1, 5)$,
in the direction toward the point $(4, 1)$

46. $f(x, y, z) = x^2y + x\sqrt{1 + z}$, $(1, 2, 3)$,
in the direction of $\mathbf{v} = 2\mathbf{i} + \mathbf{j} - 2\mathbf{k}$

47. Find the maximum rate of change of $f(x, y) = x^2 y + \sqrt{y}$ at the point $(2, 1)$. In which direction does it occur?

48. Find the direction in which $f(x, y, z) = ze^{xy}$ increases most rapidly at the point $(0, 1, 2)$. What is the maximum rate of increase?

49. The contour map shows wind speed in knots during Hurricane Andrew on August 24, 1992. Use it to estimate the value of the directional derivative of the wind speed at Homestead, Florida, in the direction of the eye of the hurricane.

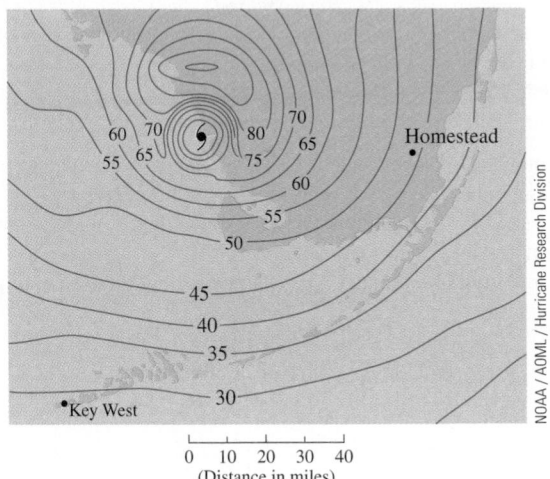

0 10 20 30 40
(Distance in miles)

50. Find parametric equations of the tangent line at the point $(-2, 2, 4)$ to the curve of intersection of the surface $z = 2x^2 - y^2$ and the plane $z = 4$.

51–54 ||| Find the local maximum and minimum values and saddle points of the function. If you have three-dimensional graphing software, graph the function with a domain and viewpoint that reveal all the important aspects of the function.

51. $f(x, y) = x^2 - xy + y^2 + 9x - 6y + 10$

52. $f(x, y) = x^3 - 6xy + 8y^3$

53. $f(x, y) = 3xy - x^2 y - xy^2$

54. $f(x, y) = (x^2 + y)e^{y/2}$

55–56 ||| Find the absolute maximum and minimum values of f on the set D.

55. $f(x, y) = 4xy^2 - x^2 y^2 - xy^3$; D is the closed triangular region in the xy-plane with vertices $(0, 0)$, $(0, 6)$, and $(6, 0)$

56. $f(x, y) = e^{-x^2-y^2}(x^2 + 2y^2)$; D is the disk $x^2 + y^2 \le 4$

57. Use a graph and/or level curves to estimate the local maximum and minimum values and saddle points of $f(x, y) = x^3 - 3x + y^4 - 2y^2$. Then use calculus to find these values precisely.

58. Use a graphing calculator or computer (or Newton's method or a computer algebra system) to find the critical points of $f(x, y) = 12 + 10y - 2x^2 - 8xy - y^4$ correct to three decimal places. Then classify the critical points and find the highest point on the graph.

59–62 ||| Use Lagrange multipliers to find the maximum and minimum values of f subject to the given constraint(s).

59. $f(x, y) = x^2 y$; $x^2 + y^2 = 1$

60. $f(x, y) = \dfrac{1}{x} + \dfrac{1}{y}$; $\dfrac{1}{x^2} + \dfrac{1}{y^2} = 1$

61. $f(x, y, z) = xyz$; $x^2 + y^2 + z^2 = 3$

62. $f(x, y, z) = x^2 + 2y^2 + 3z^2$;
$x + y + z = 1$, $x - y + 2z = 2$

63. Find the points on the surface $xy^2 z^3 = 2$ that are closest to the origin.

64. A package in the shape of a rectangular box can be mailed by U.S. Parcel Post if the sum of its length and girth (the perimeter of a cross-section perpendicular to the length) is at most 108 in. Find the dimensions of the package with largest volume that can be mailed by Parcel Post.

65. A pentagon is formed by placing an isosceles triangle on a rectangle, as shown in the figure. If the pentagon has fixed perimeter P, find the lengths of the sides of the pentagon that maximize the area of the pentagon.

66. A particle of mass m moves on the surface $z = f(x, y)$. Let $x = x(t)$, $y = y(t)$ be the x- and y-coordinates of the particle at time t.
(a) Find the velocity vector $\mathbf{v}$ and the kinetic energy $K = \frac{1}{2}m|\mathbf{v}|^2$ of the particle.
(b) Determine the acceleration vector $\mathbf{a}$.
(c) Let $z = x^2 + y^2$ and $x(t) = t \cos t$, $y(t) = t \sin t$. Find the velocity vector, the kinetic energy, and the acceleration vector.

1. A rectangle with length L and width W is cut into four smaller rectangles by two lines parallel to the sides. Find the maximum and minimum values of the sum of the squares of the areas of the smaller rectangles.

2. Marine biologists have determined that when a shark detects the presence of blood in the water, it will swim in the direction in which the concentration of the blood increases most rapidly. Based on certain tests, the concentration of blood (in parts per million) at a point $P(x, y)$ on the surface of seawater is approximated by

$$C(x, y) = e^{-(x^2 + 2y^2)/10^4}$$

where x and y are measured in meters in a rectangular coordinate system with the blood source at the origin.
   (a) Identify the level curves of the concentration function and sketch several members of this family together with a path that a shark will follow to the source.
   (b) Suppose a shark is at the point (x_0, y_0) when it first detects the presence of blood in the water. Find an equation of the shark's path by setting up and solving a differential equation.

3. A long piece of galvanized sheet metal w inches wide is to be bent into a symmetric form with three straight sides to make a rain gutter. A cross-section is shown in the figure.
   (a) Determine the dimensions that allow the maximum possible flow; that is, find the dimensions that give the maximum possible cross-sectional area.
   (b) Would it be better to bend the metal into a gutter with a semicircular cross-section than a three-sided cross-section?

$$w - 2x$$

4. For what values of the number r is the function

$$f(x, y, z) = \begin{cases} \dfrac{(x + y + z)^r}{x^2 + y^2 + z^2} & \text{if } (x, y, z) \neq 0 \\ 0 & \text{if } (x, y, z) = 0 \end{cases}$$

continuous on $\mathbb{R}^3$?

5. Suppose f is a differentiable function of one variable. Show that all tangent planes to the surface $z = xf(y/x)$ intersect in a common point.

6. (a) Newton's method for approximating a root of an equation $f(x) = 0$ (see Section 4.9) can be adapted to approximating a solution of a system of equations $f(x, y) = 0$ and $g(x, y) = 0$. The surfaces $z = f(x, y)$ and $z = g(x, y)$ intersect in a curve that intersects the xy-plane at the point (r, s), which is the solution of the system. If an initial approximation (x_1, y_1) is close to this point, then the tangent planes to the surfaces at (x_1, y_1) intersect in a straight line that intersects the xy-plane in a point (x_2, y_2), which should be closer to (r, s). (Compare with Figure 2 in Section 4.9.) Show that

$$x_2 = x_1 - \frac{fg_y - f_y g}{f_x g_y - f_y g_x} \quad \text{and} \quad y_2 = y_1 - \frac{f_x g - fg_x}{f_x g_y - f_y g_x}$$

where f, g, and their partial derivatives are evaluated at (x_1, y_1). If we continue this procedure, we obtain successive approximations (x_n, y_n).

(b) It was Thomas Simpson (1710–1761) who formulated Newton's method as we know it today and who extended it to functions of two variables as in part (a). (See the biography of Simpson on page 560.) The example that he gave to illustrate the method was to solve the system of equations

$$x^x + y^y = 1000 \qquad x^y + y^x = 100$$

In other words, he found the points of intersection of the curves in the figure. Use the method of part (a) to find the coordinates of the points of intersection correct to six decimal places.

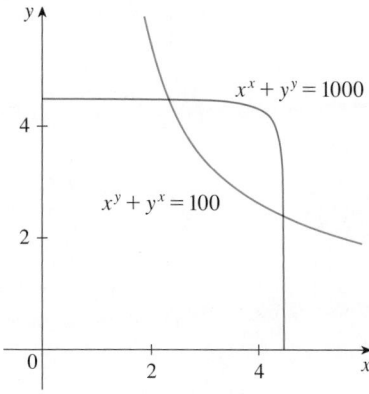

7. (a) Show that when Laplace's equation

$$\frac{\partial^2 u}{\partial x^2} + \frac{\partial^2 u}{\partial y^2} + \frac{\partial^2 u}{\partial z^2} = 0$$

is written in cylindrical coordinates, it becomes

$$\frac{\partial^2 u}{\partial r^2} + \frac{1}{r}\frac{\partial u}{\partial r} + \frac{1}{r^2}\frac{\partial^2 u}{\partial \theta^2} + \frac{\partial^2 u}{\partial z^2} = 0$$

(b) Show that when Laplace's equation is written in spherical coordinates, it becomes

$$\frac{\partial^2 u}{\partial \rho^2} + \frac{2}{\rho}\frac{\partial u}{\partial \rho} + \frac{\cot\phi}{\rho^2}\frac{\partial u}{\partial \phi} + \frac{1}{\rho^2}\frac{\partial^2 u}{\partial \phi^2} + \frac{1}{\rho^2 \sin^2\phi}\frac{\partial^2 u}{\partial \theta^2} = 0$$

8. Among all planes that are tangent to the surface $xy^2z^2 = 1$, find the ones that are farthest from the origin.

9. If the ellipse $x^2/a^2 + y^2/b^2 = 1$ is to enclose the circle $x^2 + y^2 = 2y$, what values of a and b minimize the area of the ellipse?

CHAPTER 16

If we approximate a solid by rectangular columns and let the number of columns increase, the limit of sums of volumes of columns is the volume of the solid.

Multiple Integrals

In this chapter we extend the idea of a definite integral to double and triple integrals of functions of two or three variables. These ideas are then used to compute volumes, surface areas, masses, and centroids of more general regions than we were able to consider in Chapters 6 and 9. We also use double integrals to calculate probabilities when two random variables are involved.

16.1 Double Integrals over Rectangles

In much the same way that our attempt to solve the area problem led to the definition of a definite integral, we now seek to find the volume of a solid and in the process we arrive at the definition of a double integral.

Review of the Definite Integral

First let's recall the basic facts concerning definite integrals of functions of a single variable. If $f(x)$ is defined for $a \leq x \leq b$, we start by dividing the interval $[a, b]$ into n subintervals $[x_{i-1}, x_i]$ of equal width $\Delta x = (b - a)/n$ and we choose sample points x_i^* in these subintervals. Then we form the Riemann sum

$$\boxed{1} \qquad \sum_{i=1}^{n} f(x_i^*)\, \Delta x$$

and take the limit of such sums as $n \to \infty$ to obtain the definite integral of f from a to b:

$$\boxed{2} \qquad \int_a^b f(x)\, dx = \lim_{n \to \infty} \sum_{i=1}^{n} f(x_i^*)\, \Delta x$$

In the special case where $f(x) \geq 0$, the Riemann sum can be interpreted as the sum of the areas of the approximating rectangles in Figure 1, and $\int_a^b f(x)\, dx$ represents the area under the curve $y = f(x)$ from a to b.

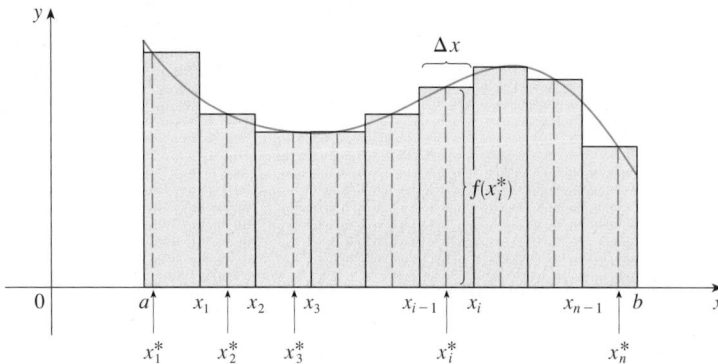

FIGURE 1

Volumes and Double Integrals

In a similar manner we consider a function f of two variables defined on a closed rectangle

$$R = [a, b] \times [c, d] = \{(x, y) \in \mathbb{R}^2 \mid a \leq x \leq b,\ c \leq y \leq d\}$$

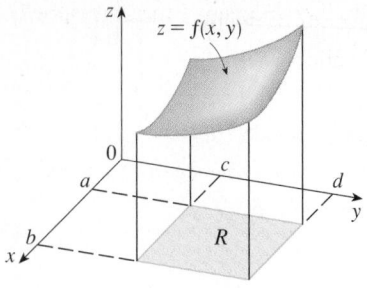

FIGURE 2

and we first suppose that $f(x, y) \geq 0$. The graph of f is a surface with equation $z = f(x, y)$. Let S be the solid that lies above R and under the graph of f, that is,

$$S = \{(x, y, z) \in \mathbb{R}^3 \,|\, 0 \leq z \leq f(x, y), \ (x, y) \in R\}$$

(See Figure 2.) Our goal is to find the volume of S.

The first step is to divide the rectangle R into subrectangles. We do this by dividing the interval $[a, b]$ into m subintervals $[x_{i-1}, x_i]$ of equal width $\Delta x = (b - a)/m$ and dividing $[c, d]$ into n subintervals $[y_{j-1}, y_j]$ of equal width $\Delta y = (d - c)/n$. By drawing lines parallel to the coordinate axes through the endpoints of these subintervals as in Figure 3, we form the subrectangles

$$R_{ij} = [x_{i-1}, x_i] \times [y_{j-1}, y_j] = \{(x, y) \,|\, x_{i-1} \leq x \leq x_i, \ y_{j-1} \leq y \leq y_j\}$$

each with area $\Delta A = \Delta x \, \Delta y$.

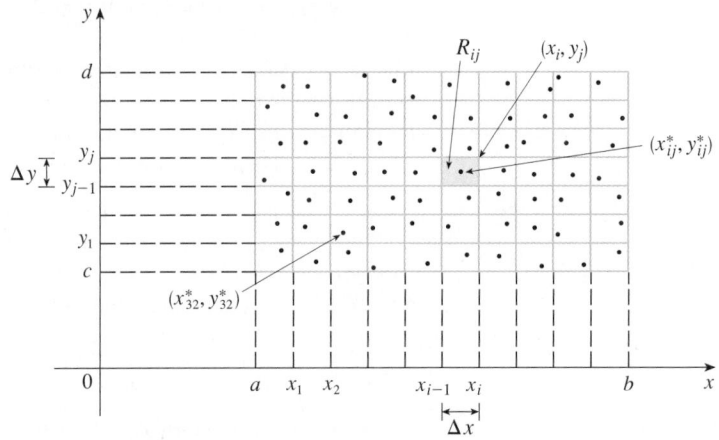

FIGURE 3

Dividing R into subrectangles

If we choose a **sample point** (x_{ij}^*, y_{ij}^*) in each R_{ij}, then we can approximate the part of S that lies above each R_{ij} by a thin rectangular box (or "column") with base R_{ij} and height $f(x_{ij}^*, y_{ij}^*)$ as shown in Figure 4. (Compare with Figure 1.) The volume of this box is the height of the box times the area of the base rectangle:

$$f(x_{ij}^*, y_{ij}^*) \, \Delta A$$

FIGURE 4

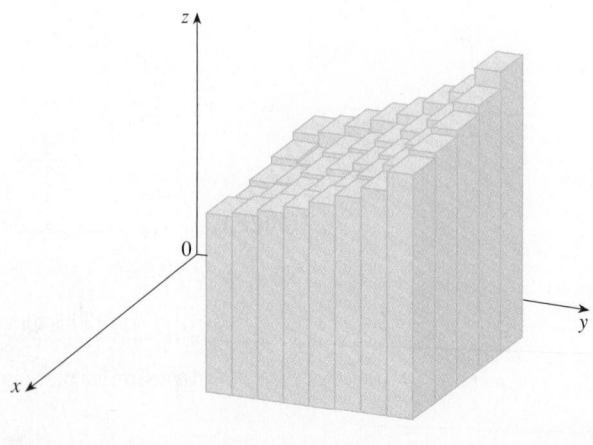

FIGURE 5

If we follow this procedure for all the rectangles and add the volumes of the corresponding boxes, we get an approximation to the total volume of S:

$$\boxed{3}\qquad V \approx \sum_{i=1}^{m}\sum_{j=1}^{n} f(x_{ij}^*, y_{ij}^*)\,\Delta A$$

(See Figure 5.) This double sum means that for each subrectangle we evaluate f at the chosen point and multiply by the area of the subrectangle, and then we add the results.

Our intuition tells us that the approximation given in (3) becomes better as m and n become larger and so we would expect that

$$\boxed{4}\qquad V = \lim_{m,\,n\to\infty}\sum_{i=1}^{m}\sum_{j=1}^{n} f(x_{ij}^*, y_{ij}^*)\,\Delta A$$

We use the expression in Equation 4 to define the **volume** of the solid S that lies under the graph of f and above the rectangle R. (It can be shown that this definition is consistent with our formula for volume in Section 6.2.)

Limits of the type that appear in Equation 4 occur frequently, not just in finding volumes but in a variety of other situations as well—as we will see in Section 16.5—even when f is not a positive function. So we make the following definition.

> $\boxed{5}$ **Definition** The **double integral** of f over the rectangle R is
> $$\iint_R f(x,y)\,dA = \lim_{m,\,n\to\infty}\sum_{i=1}^{m}\sum_{j=1}^{n} f(x_{ij}^*, y_{ij}^*)\,\Delta A$$
> if this limit exists.

The precise meaning of the limit in Definition 5 is that for every number $\varepsilon > 0$ there is an integer N such that

$$\left| \iint_R f(x,y)\,dA - \sum_{i=1}^{m}\sum_{j=1}^{n} f(x_{ij}^*, y_{ij}^*)\,\Delta A \right| < \varepsilon$$

for all integers m and n greater than N and for any choice of sample points (x_{ij}^*, y_{ij}^*) in R_{ij}.

It can be proved that the limit in Definition 5 exists if f is a continuous function. (It also exists for some discontinuous functions as long as they are reasonably "well behaved.")

The sample point (x_{ij}^*, y_{ij}^*) can be chosen to be any point in the subrectangle R_{ij}, but if we choose it to be the upper right-hand corner of R_{ij} [namely (x_i, y_j), see Figure 3], then the expression for the double integral looks simpler:

$$\boxed{6}\qquad \iint_R f(x,y)\,dA = \lim_{m,\,n\to\infty}\sum_{i=1}^{m}\sum_{j=1}^{n} f(x_i, y_j)\,\Delta A$$

By comparing Definitions 4 and 5, we see that a volume can be written as a double integral:

> If $f(x,y) \geqslant 0$, then the volume V of the solid that lies above the rectangle R and below the surface $z = f(x,y)$ is
> $$V = \iint_R f(x,y)\,dA$$

The sum in Definition 5,

$$\sum_{i=1}^{m} \sum_{j=1}^{n} f(x_{ij}^*, y_{ij}^*) \, \Delta A$$

is called a **double Riemann sum** and is used as an approximation to the value of the double integral. [Notice how similar it is to the Riemann sum in (1) for a function of a single variable.] If f happens to be a *positive* function, then the double Riemann sum represents the sum of volumes of columns, as in Figure 5, and is an approximation to the volume under the graph of f.

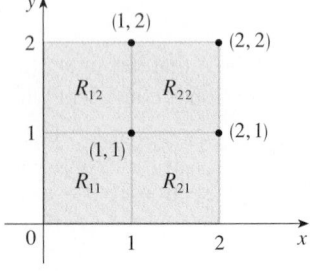

FIGURE 6

EXAMPLE 1 Estimate the volume of the solid that lies above the square $R = [0, 2] \times [0, 2]$ and below the elliptic paraboloid $z = 16 - x^2 - 2y^2$. Divide R into four equal squares and choose the sample point to be the upper right corner of each square R_{ij}. Sketch the solid and the approximating rectangular boxes.

SOLUTION The squares are shown in Figure 6. The paraboloid is the graph of $f(x, y) = 16 - x^2 - 2y^2$ and the area of each square is 1. Approximating the volume by the Riemann sum with $m = n = 2$, we have

$$V \approx \sum_{i=1}^{2} \sum_{j=1}^{2} f(x_i, y_j) \, \Delta A$$

$$= f(1, 1) \, \Delta A + f(1, 2) \, \Delta A + f(2, 1) \, \Delta A + f(2, 2) \, \Delta A$$

$$= 13(1) + 7(1) + 10(1) + 4(1) = 34$$

This is the volume of the approximating rectangular boxes shown in Figure 7.

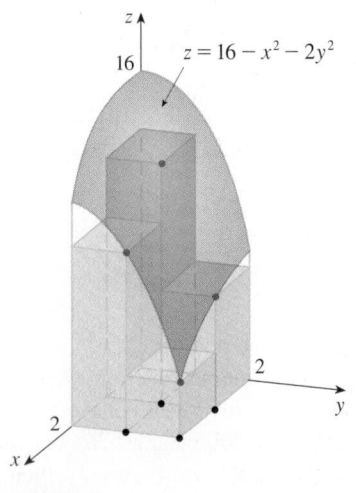

FIGURE 7

We get better approximations to the volume in Example 1 if we increase the number of squares. Figure 8 shows how the columns start to look more like the actual solid and the corresponding approximations become more accurate when we use 16, 64, and 256 squares. In the next section we will be able to show that the exact volume is 48.

FIGURE 8

The Riemann sum approximations to
the volume under $z = 16 - x^2 - 2y^2$
become more accurate as m and
n increase.

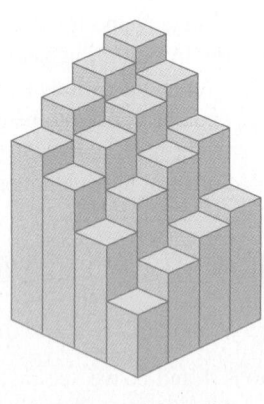

(a) $m = n = 4$, $V \approx 41.5$

(b) $m = n = 8$, $V \approx 44.875$

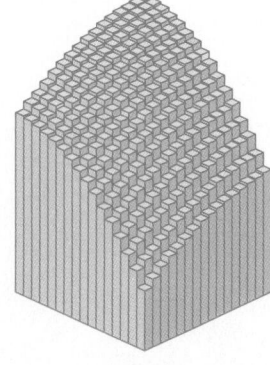

(c) $m = n = 16$, $V \approx 46.46875$

EXAMPLE 2 If $R = \{(x, y) \mid -1 \leqslant x \leqslant 1, -2 \leqslant y \leqslant 2\}$, evaluate the integral

$$\iint_R \sqrt{1 - x^2} \, dA$$

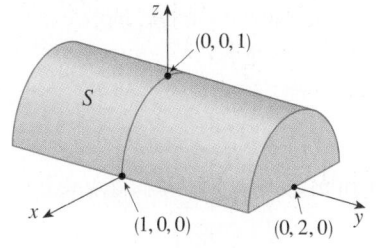

FIGURE 9

SOLUTION It would be very difficult to evaluate this integral directly from Definition 5 but, because $\sqrt{1 - x^2} \geqslant 0$, we can compute the integral by interpreting it as a volume. If $z = \sqrt{1 - x^2}$, then $x^2 + z^2 = 1$ and $z \geqslant 0$, so the given double integral represents the volume of the solid S that lies below the circular cylinder $x^2 + z^2 = 1$ and above the rectangle R. (See Figure 9.) The volume of S is the area of a semicircle with radius 1 times the length of the cylinder. Thus

$$\iint_R \sqrt{1 - x^2}\, dA = \tfrac{1}{2}\pi(1)^2 \times 4 = 2\pi$$

The Midpoint Rule

The methods that we used for approximating single integrals (the Midpoint Rule, the Trapezoidal Rule, Simpson's Rule) all have counterparts for double integrals. Here we consider only the Midpoint Rule for double integrals. This means that we use a double Riemann sum to approximate the double integral, where the sample point (x_{ij}^*, y_{ij}^*) in R_{ij} is chosen to be the center $(\bar{x}_i, \bar{y}_j)$ of R_{ij}. In other words, $\bar{x}_i$ is the midpoint of $[x_{i-1}, x_i]$ and $\bar{y}_j$ is the midpoint of $[y_{j-1}, y_j]$.

> **Midpoint Rule for Double Integrals**
>
> $$\iint_R f(x, y)\, dA \approx \sum_{i=1}^{m} \sum_{j=1}^{n} f(\bar{x}_i, \bar{y}_j)\, \Delta A$$
>
> where $\bar{x}_i$ is the midpoint of $[x_{i-1}, x_i]$ and $\bar{y}_j$ is the midpoint of $[y_{j-1}, y_j]$.

EXAMPLE 3 Use the Midpoint Rule with $m = n = 2$ to estimate the value of the integral $\iint_R (x - 3y^2)\, dA$, where $R = \{(x, y) \mid 0 \leqslant x \leqslant 2, 1 \leqslant y \leqslant 2\}$.

SOLUTION In using the Midpoint Rule with $m = n = 2$, we evaluate $f(x, y) = x - 3y^2$ at the centers of the four subrectangles shown in Figure 10. So $\bar{x}_1 = \tfrac{1}{2}$, $\bar{x}_2 = \tfrac{3}{2}$, $\bar{y}_1 = \tfrac{5}{4}$, and $\bar{y}_2 = \tfrac{7}{4}$. The area of each subrectangle is $\Delta A = \tfrac{1}{2}$. Thus

$$\iint_R (x - 3y^2)\, dA \approx \sum_{i=1}^{2} \sum_{j=1}^{2} f(\bar{x}_i, \bar{y}_j)\, \Delta A$$

$$= f(\bar{x}_1, \bar{y}_1)\, \Delta A + f(\bar{x}_1, \bar{y}_2)\, \Delta A + f(\bar{x}_2, \bar{y}_1)\, \Delta A + f(\bar{x}_2, \bar{y}_2)\, \Delta A$$

$$= f\!\left(\tfrac{1}{2}, \tfrac{5}{4}\right) \Delta A + f\!\left(\tfrac{1}{2}, \tfrac{7}{4}\right) \Delta A + f\!\left(\tfrac{3}{2}, \tfrac{5}{4}\right) \Delta A + f\!\left(\tfrac{3}{2}, \tfrac{7}{4}\right) \Delta A$$

$$= \left(-\tfrac{67}{16}\right)\tfrac{1}{2} + \left(-\tfrac{139}{16}\right)\tfrac{1}{2} + \left(-\tfrac{51}{16}\right)\tfrac{1}{2} + \left(-\tfrac{123}{16}\right)\tfrac{1}{2}$$

$$= -\tfrac{95}{8} = -11.875$$

Thus, we have

$$\iint_R (x - 3y^2)\, dA \approx -11.875$$

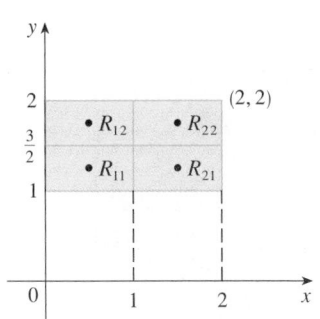

FIGURE 10

NOTE □ In the next section we will develop an efficient method for computing double integrals and then we will see that the exact value of the double integral in Example 3 is -12. (Remember that the interpretation of a double integral as a volume is valid only when the integrand f is a *positive* function. The integrand in Example 3 is not a positive function, so its integral is not a volume. In Examples 2 and 3 in Section 16.2 we will discuss how to interpret integrals of functions that are not always positive in terms of volumes.) If we keep dividing each subrectangle in Figure 10 into four smaller ones with similar shape,

Number of subrectangles	Midpoint Rule approximations
1	−11.5000
4	−11.8750
16	−11.9687
64	−11.9922
256	−11.9980
1024	−11.9995

we get the Midpoint Rule approximations displayed in the chart in the margin. Notice how these approximations approach the exact value of the double integral, −12.

▏▏▏ Average Value

Recall from Section 6.5 that the average value of a function f of one variable defined on an interval $[a, b]$ is

$$f_{ave} = \frac{1}{b - a} \int_a^b f(x) \, dx$$

In a similar fashion we define the **average value** of a function f of two variables defined on a rectangle R to be

$$f_{ave} = \frac{1}{A(R)} \iint_R f(x, y) \, dA$$

where $A(R)$ is the area of R.

If $f(x, y) \geq 0$, the equation

$$A(R) \times f_{ave} = \iint_R f(x, y) \, dA$$

says that the box with base R and height f_{ave} has the same volume as the solid that lies under the graph of f. [If $z = f(x, y)$ describes a mountainous region and you chop off the tops of the mountains at height f_{ave}, then you can use them to fill in the valleys so that the region becomes completely flat. See Figure 11.]

FIGURE 11

EXAMPLE 4 The contour map in Figure 12 shows the snowfall, in inches, that fell on the state of Colorado on December 24, 1982. (The state is in the shape of a rectangle that measures 388 mi west to east and 276 mi south to north.) Use the contour map to estimate the average snowfall for Colorado as a whole on December 24.

FIGURE 12

SOLUTION Let's place the origin at the southwest corner of the state. Then $0 \leqslant x \leqslant 388$, $0 \leqslant y \leqslant 276$, and $f(x, y)$ is the snowfall, in inches, at a location x miles to the east and y miles to the north of the origin. If R is the rectangle that represents Colorado, then the average snowfall for the state on December 24 was

$$f_{\text{ave}} = \frac{1}{A(R)} \iint\limits_{R} f(x, y) \, dA$$

where $A(R) = 388 \cdot 276$. To estimate the value of this double integral let's use the Midpoint Rule with $m = n = 4$. In other words, we divide R into 16 subrectangles of equal size, as in Figure 13. The area of each subrectangle is

$$\Delta A = \tfrac{1}{16}(388)(276) = 6693 \text{ mi}^2$$

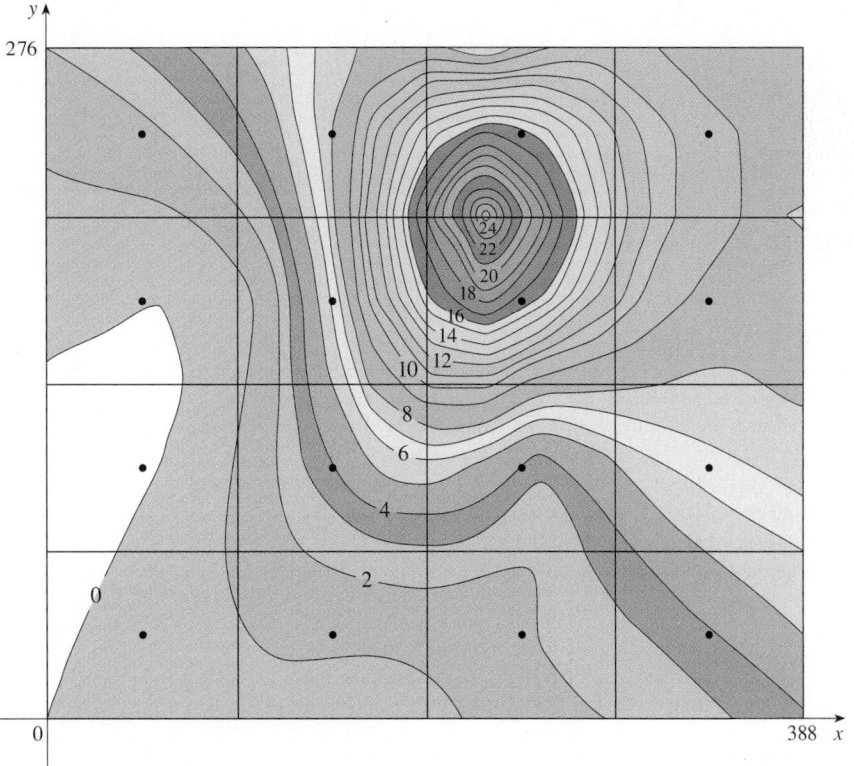

FIGURE 13

Using the contour map to estimate the value of f at the center of each subrectangle, we get

$$\iint\limits_{R} f(x, y) \, dA \approx \sum_{i=1}^{4} \sum_{j=1}^{4} f(\bar{x}_i, \bar{y}_j) \, \Delta A$$

$$\approx \Delta A[0.4 + 1.2 + 1.8 + 3.9 + 0 + 3.9 + 4.0 + 6.5$$

$$+ 0.1 + 6.1 + 16.5 + 8.8 + 1.8 + 8.0 + 16.2 + 9.4]$$

$$= (6693)(88.6)$$

Therefore

$$f_{\text{ave}} \approx \frac{(6693)(88.6)}{(388)(276)} \approx 5.5$$

On December 24, 1982, Colorado received an average of approximately $5\tfrac{1}{2}$ inches of snow.

Properties of Double Integrals

We list here three properties of double integrals that can be proved in the same manner as in Section 5.2. We assume that all of the integrals exist. Properties 7 and 8 are referred to as the *linearity* of the integral.

▓ Double integrals behave this way because the double sums that define them behave this way.

$$\boxed{7} \qquad \iint_R [f(x, y) + g(x, y)]\, dA = \iint_R f(x, y)\, dA + \iint_R g(x, y)\, dA$$

$$\boxed{8} \qquad \iint_R cf(x, y)\, dA = c \iint_R f(x, y)\, dA \qquad \text{where } c \text{ is a constant}$$

If $f(x, y) \geq g(x, y)$ for all (x, y) in R, then

$$\boxed{9} \qquad \iint_R f(x, y)\, dA \geq \iint_R g(x, y)\, dA$$

16.1 Exercises

1. (a) Estimate the volume of the solid that lies below the surface $z = xy$ and above the rectangle $R = \{(x, y) \mid 0 \leq x \leq 6, 0 \leq y \leq 4\}$. Use a Riemann sum with $m = 3$, $n = 2$, and take the sample point to be the upper right corner of each subrectangle.
   (b) Use the Midpoint Rule to estimate the volume of the solid in part (a).

2. If $R = [-1, 3] \times [0, 2]$, use a Riemann sum with $m = 4$, $n = 2$ to estimate the value of $\iint_R (y^2 - 2x^2)\, dA$. Take the sample points to be the upper left corners of the subrectangles.

3. (a) Use a Riemann sum with $m = n = 2$ to estimate the value of $\iint_R \sin(x + y)\, dA$, where $R = [0, \pi] \times [0, \pi]$. Take the sample points to be lower left corners.
   (b) Use the Midpoint Rule to estimate the integral in part (a).

4. (a) Estimate the volume of the solid that lies below the surface $z = x + 2y^2$ and above the rectangle $R = [0, 2] \times [0, 4]$. Use a Riemann sum with $m = n = 2$ and choose the sample points to be lower right corners.
   (b) Use the Midpoint Rule to estimate the volume in part (a).

5. A table of values is given for a function $f(x, y)$ defined on $R = [1, 3] \times [0, 4]$.
   (a) Estimate $\iint_R f(x, y)\, dA$ using the Midpoint Rule with $m = n = 2$.
   (b) Estimate the double integral with $m = n = 4$ by choosing the sample points to be the points farthest from the origin.

y \ x	0	1	2	3	4
1.0	2	0	−3	−6	−5
1.5	3	1	−4	−8	−6
2.0	4	3	0	−5	−8
2.5	5	5	3	−1	−4
3.0	7	8	6	3	0

6. A 20-ft-by-30-ft swimming pool is filled with water. The depth is measured at 5-ft intervals, starting at one corner of the pool, and the values are recorded in the table. Estimate the volume of water in the pool.

	0	5	10	15	20	25	30
0	2	3	4	6	7	8	8
5	2	3	4	7	8	10	8
10	2	4	6	8	10	12	10
15	2	3	4	5	6	8	7
20	2	2	2	2	3	4	4

7. Let V be the volume of the solid that lies under the graph of $f(x, y) = \sqrt{52 - x^2 - y^2}$ and above the rectangle given by $2 \leq x \leq 4$, $2 \leq y \leq 6$. We use the lines $x = 3$ and $y = 4$ to divide R into subrectangles. Let L and U be the Riemann sums computed using lower left corners and upper right corners, respectively. Without calculating the numbers V, L, and U, arrange them in increasing order and explain your reasoning.

8. The figure shows level curves of a function f in the square $R = [0, 1] \times [0, 1]$. Use them to estimate $\iint_R f(x, y)\, dA$ to the nearest integer.

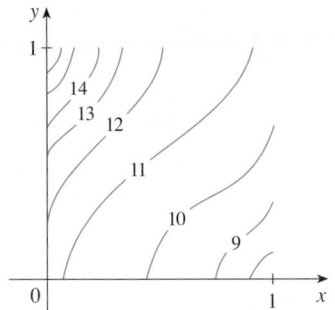

9. A contour map is shown for a function f on the square $R = [0, 4] \times [0, 4]$.
   (a) Use the Midpoint Rule with $m = n = 2$ to estimate the value of $\iint_R f(x, y)\, dA$.
   (b) Estimate the average value of f.

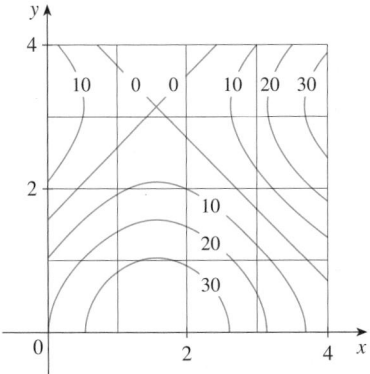

10. The contour map shows the temperature, in degrees Fahrenheit, at 3:00 P.M. on May 1, 1996, in Colorado. (The state measures 388 mi east to west and 276 mi north to south.) Use the Midpoint Rule with $m = n = 4$ to estimate the average temperature in Colorado at that time.

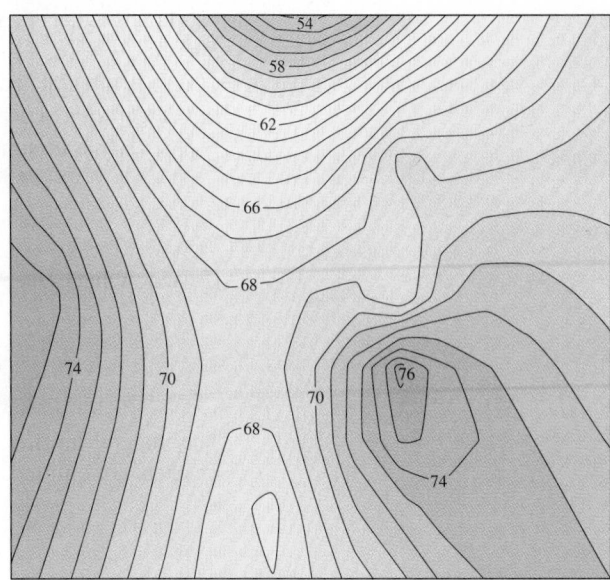

11–13 |||| Evaluate the double integral by first identifying it as the volume of a solid.

11. $\iint_R 3\, dA$, $R = \{(x, y) \mid -2 \leqslant x \leqslant 2,\, 1 \leqslant y \leqslant 6\}$

12. $\iint_R (5 - x)\, dA$, $R = \{(x, y) \mid 0 \leqslant x \leqslant 5,\, 0 \leqslant y \leqslant 3\}$

13. $\iint_R (4 - 2y)\, dA$, $R = [0, 1] \times [0, 1]$

14. The integral $\iint_R \sqrt{9 - y^2}\, dA$, where $R = [0, 4] \times [0, 2]$, represents the volume of a solid. Sketch the solid.

15. Use a programmable calculator or computer (or the sum command on a CAS) to estimate

$$\iint\limits_R e^{-x^2 - y^2}\, dA$$

where $R = [0, 1] \times [0, 1]$. Use the Midpoint Rule with the following numbers of squares of equal size: 1, 4, 16, 64, 256, and 1024.

16. Repeat Exercise 15 for the integral $\iint_R \cos(x^4 + y^4)\, dA$.

17. If f is a constant function, $f(x, y) = k$, and $R = [a, b] \times [c, d]$, show that $\iint_R k\, dA = k(b - a)(d - c)$.

18. If $R = [0, 1] \times [0, 1]$, show that $0 \leqslant \iint_R \sin(x + y)\, dA \leqslant 1$.

16.2 Iterated Integrals

Recall that it is usually difficult to evaluate single integrals directly from the definition of an integral, but the Fundamental Theorem of Calculus provides a much easier method. The evaluation of double integrals from first principles is even more difficult, but in this section we see how to express a double integral as an iterated integral, which can then be evaluated by calculating two single integrals.

Suppose that f is a function of two variables that is continuous on the rectangle $R = [a, b] \times [c, d]$. We use the notation $\int_c^d f(x, y)\, dy$ to mean that x is held fixed and $f(x, y)$ is integrated with respect to y from $y = c$ to $y = d$. This procedure is called *partial integration with respect to y*. (Notice its similarity to partial differentiation.) Now $\int_c^d f(x, y)\, dy$ is a number that depends on the value of x, so it defines a function of x:

$$A(x) = \int_c^d f(x, y)\, dy$$

If we now integrate the function A with respect to x from $x = a$ to $x = b$, we get

| 1 |

$$\int_a^b A(x)\, dx = \int_a^b \left[\int_c^d f(x, y)\, dy \right] dx$$

The integral on the right side of Equation 1 is called an **iterated integral**. Usually the brackets are omitted. Thus

| 2 |

$$\int_a^b \int_c^d f(x, y)\, dy\, dx = \int_a^b \left[\int_c^d f(x, y)\, dy \right] dx$$

means that we first integrate with respect to y from c to d and then with respect to x from a to b.

Similarly, the iterated integral

| 3 |

$$\int_c^d \int_a^b f(x, y)\, dx\, dy = \int_c^d \left[\int_a^b f(x, y)\, dx \right] dy$$

means that we first integrate with respect to x (holding y fixed) from $x = a$ to $x = b$ and then we integrate the resulting function of y with respect to y from $y = c$ to $y = d$. Notice that in both Equations 2 and 3 we work *from the inside out*.

EXAMPLE 1 Evaluate the iterated integrals.

(a) $\displaystyle\int_0^3 \int_1^2 x^2 y\, dy\, dx$ (b) $\displaystyle\int_1^2 \int_0^3 x^2 y\, dx\, dy$

SOLUTION
(a) Regarding x as a constant, we obtain

$$\int_1^2 x^2 y\, dy = \left[x^2 \frac{y^2}{2} \right]_{y=1}^{y=2}$$

$$= x^2 \left(\frac{2^2}{2} \right) - x^2 \left(\frac{1^2}{2} \right) = \tfrac{3}{2} x^2$$

Thus, the function A in the preceding discussion is given by $A(x) = \tfrac{3}{2} x^2$ in this example. We now integrate this function of x from 0 to 3:

$$\int_0^3 \int_1^2 x^2 y\, dy\, dx = \int_0^3 \left[\int_1^2 x^2 y\, dy \right] dx$$

$$= \int_0^3 \tfrac{3}{2} x^2\, dx = \frac{x^3}{2} \Bigg]_0^3 = \frac{27}{2}$$

(b) Here we first integrate with respect to x:

$$\int_1^2 \int_0^3 x^2 y \, dx \, dy = \int_1^2 \left[\int_0^3 x^2 y \, dx \right] dy = \int_1^2 \left[\frac{x^3}{3} y \right]_{x=0}^{x=3} dy$$

$$= \int_1^2 9y \, dy = 9 \frac{y^2}{2} \Big]_1^2 = \frac{27}{2}$$

Notice that in Example 1 we obtained the same answer whether we integrated with respect to y or x first. In general, it turns out (see Theorem 4) that the two iterated integrals in Equations 2 and 3 are always equal; that is, the order of integration does not matter. (This is similar to Clairaut's Theorem on the equality of the mixed partial derivatives.)

The following theorem gives a practical method for evaluating a double integral by expressing it as an iterated integral (in either order).

|||| Theorem 4 is named after the Italian mathematician Guido Fubini (1879–1943), who proved a very general version of this theorem in 1907. But the version for continuous functions was known to the French mathematician Augustin-Louis Cauchy almost a century earlier.

---

4 Fubini's Theorem If f is continuous on the rectangle $R = \{(x, y) \mid a \leqslant x \leqslant b, c \leqslant y \leqslant d\}$, then

$$\iint_R f(x, y) \, dA = \int_a^b \int_c^d f(x, y) \, dy \, dx = \int_c^d \int_a^b f(x, y) \, dx \, dy$$

More generally, this is true if we assume that f is bounded on R, f is discontinuous only on a finite number of smooth curves, and the iterated integrals exist.

The proof of Fubini's Theorem is too difficult to include in this book, but we can at least give an intuitive indication of why it is true for the case where $f(x, y) \geqslant 0$. Recall that if f is positive, then we can interpret the double integral $\iint_R f(x, y) \, dA$ as the volume V of the solid S that lies above R and under the surface $z = f(x, y)$. But we have another formula that we used for volume in Chapter 6, namely,

$$V = \int_a^b A(x) \, dx$$

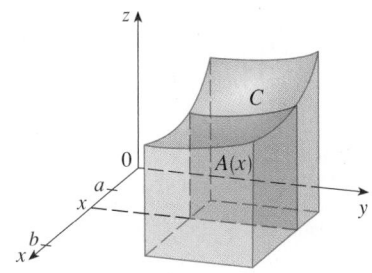

FIGURE 1

where $A(x)$ is the area of a cross-section of S in the plane through x perpendicular to the x-axis. From Figure 1 you can see that $A(x)$ is the area under the curve C whose equation is $z = f(x, y)$, where x is held constant and $c \leqslant y \leqslant d$. Therefore

$$A(x) = \int_c^d f(x, y) \, dy$$

and we have

$$\iint_R f(x, y) \, dA = V = \int_a^b A(x) \, dx = \int_a^b \int_c^d f(x, y) \, dy \, dx$$

Visual 16.2 illustrates Fubini's Theorem by showing an animation of Figures 1 and 2.

A similar argument, using cross-sections perpendicular to the y-axis as in Figure 2, shows that

$$\iint_R f(x, y) \, dA = \int_c^d \int_a^b f(x, y) \, dx \, dy$$

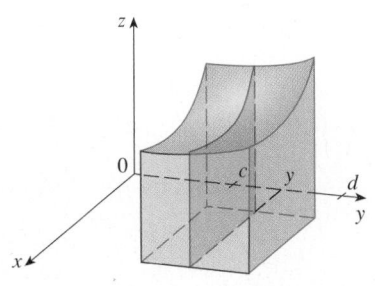

FIGURE 2

EXAMPLE 2 Evaluate the double integral $\iint_R (x - 3y^2) \, dA$, where $R = \{(x, y) \mid 0 \leqslant x \leqslant 2, 1 \leqslant y \leqslant 2\}$. (Compare with Example 3 in Section 16.1.)

‖‖ Notice the negative answer in Example 2; nothing is wrong with that. The function f in that example is not a positive function, so its integral doesn't represent a volume. From Figure 3 we see that f is always negative on R, so the value of the integral is the *negative* of the volume that lies *above* the graph of f and *below* R.

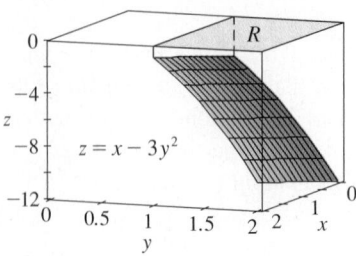

FIGURE 3

SOLUTION 1 Fubini's Theorem gives

$$\iint\limits_R (x - 3y^2)\, dA = \int_0^2 \int_1^2 (x - 3y^2)\, dy\, dx$$

$$= \int_0^2 \left[xy - y^3\right]_{y=1}^{y=2} dx$$

$$= \int_0^2 (x - 7)\, dx = \frac{x^2}{2} - 7x\Bigg]_0^2 = -12$$

SOLUTION 2 Again applying Fubini's Theorem, but this time integrating with respect to x first, we have

$$\iint\limits_R (x - 3y^2)\, dA = \int_1^2 \int_0^2 (x - 3y^2)\, dx\, dy$$

$$= \int_1^2 \left[\frac{x^2}{2} - 3xy^2\right]_{x=0}^{x=2} dy$$

$$= \int_1^2 (2 - 6y^2)\, dy = 2y - 2y^3\Big]_1^2 = -12$$

EXAMPLE 3 Evaluate $\iint_R y\sin(xy)\, dA$, where $R = [1, 2] \times [0, \pi]$.

SOLUTION 1 If we first integrate with respect to x, we get

$$\iint\limits_R y\sin(xy)\, dA = \int_0^\pi \int_1^2 y\sin(xy)\, dx\, dy$$

$$= \int_0^\pi \left[-\cos(xy)\right]_{x=1}^{x=2} dy$$

$$= \int_0^\pi (-\cos 2y + \cos y)\, dy$$

$$= -\tfrac{1}{2}\sin 2y + \sin y\Big]_0^\pi = 0$$

SOLUTION 2 If we reverse the order of integration, we get

$$\iint\limits_R y\sin(xy)\, dA = \int_1^2 \int_0^\pi y\sin(xy)\, dy\, dx$$

To evaluate the inner integral we use integration by parts with

$$u = y \qquad\qquad dv = \sin(xy)\, dy$$

$$du = dy \qquad\qquad v = -\frac{\cos(xy)}{x}$$

‖‖ For a function f that takes on both positive and negative values, $\iint_R f(x, y)\, dA$ is a difference of volumes: $V_1 - V_2$, where V_1 is the volume above R and below the graph of f and V_2 is the volume below R and above the graph. The fact that the integral in Example 3 is 0 means that these two volumes V_1 and V_2 are equal. (See Figure 4.)

and so

$$\int_0^\pi y\sin(xy)\, dy = -\frac{y\cos(xy)}{x}\Bigg]_{y=0}^{y=\pi} + \frac{1}{x}\int_0^\pi \cos(xy)\, dy$$

$$= -\frac{\pi\cos \pi x}{x} + \frac{1}{x^2}\left[\sin(xy)\right]_{y=0}^{y=\pi}$$

$$= -\frac{\pi\cos \pi x}{x} + \frac{\sin \pi x}{x^2}$$

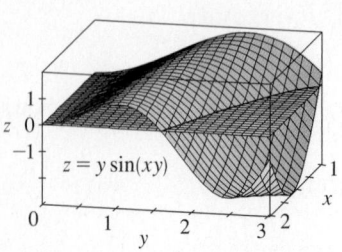

FIGURE 4

If we now integrate the first term by parts with $u = -1/x$ and $dv = \pi \cos \pi x \, dx$, we get $du = dx/x^2$, $v = \sin \pi x$, and

$$\int \left(-\frac{\pi \cos \pi x}{x} \right) dx = -\frac{\sin \pi x}{x} - \int \frac{\sin \pi x}{x^2} \, dx$$

Therefore

$$\int \left(-\frac{\pi \cos \pi x}{x} + \frac{\sin \pi x}{x^2} \right) dx = -\frac{\sin \pi x}{x}$$

and so

$$\int_1^2 \int_0^\pi y \sin(xy) \, dy \, dx = \left[-\frac{\sin \pi x}{x} \right]_1^2$$

$$= -\frac{\sin 2\pi}{2} + \sin \pi = 0$$

‖‖‖ In Example 2, Solutions 1 and 2 are equally straightforward, but in Example 3 the first solution is much easier than the second one. Therefore, when we evaluate double integrals it is wise to choose the order of integration that gives simpler integrals.

EXAMPLE 4 Find the volume of the solid S that is bounded by the elliptic paraboloid $x^2 + 2y^2 + z = 16$, the planes $x = 2$ and $y = 2$, and the three coordinate planes.

SOLUTION We first observe that S is the solid that lies under the surface $z = 16 - x^2 - 2y^2$ and above the square $R = [0, 2] \times [0, 2]$. (See Figure 5.) This solid was considered in Example 1 in Section 16.1, but we are now in a position to evaluate the double integral using Fubini's Theorem. Therefore

$$V = \iint_R (16 - x^2 - 2y^2) \, dA = \int_0^2 \int_0^2 (16 - x^2 - 2y^2) \, dx \, dy$$

$$= \int_0^2 \left[16x - \tfrac{1}{3}x^3 - 2y^2 x \right]_{x=0}^{x=2} dy$$

$$= \int_0^2 \left(\tfrac{88}{3} - 4y^2 \right) dy = \left[\tfrac{88}{3}y - \tfrac{4}{3}y^3 \right]_0^2 = 48$$

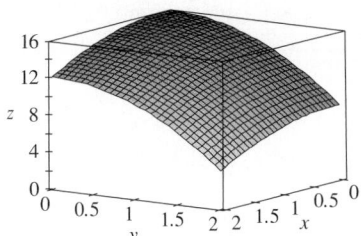

FIGURE 5

In the special case where $f(x, y)$ can be factored as the product of a function of x only and a function of y only, the double integral of f can be written in a particularly simple form. To be specific, suppose that $f(x, y) = g(x)h(y)$ and $R = [a, b] \times [c, d]$. Then Fubini's Theorem gives

$$\iint_R f(x, y) \, dA = \int_c^d \int_a^b g(x)h(y) \, dx \, dy = \int_c^d \left[\int_a^b g(x)h(y) \, dx \right] dy$$

In the inner integral y is a constant, so $h(y)$ is a constant and we can write

$$\int_c^d \left[\int_a^b g(x)h(y) \, dx \right] dy = \int_c^d \left[h(y) \left(\int_a^b g(x) \, dx \right) \right] dy$$

$$= \int_a^b g(x) \, dx \int_c^d h(y) \, dy$$

since $\int_a^b g(x) \, dx$ is a constant. Therefore, in this case, the double integral of f can be written as the product of two single integrals:

$$\iint_R g(x)h(y) \, dA = \int_a^b g(x) \, dx \int_c^d h(y) \, dy \qquad \text{where } R = [a, b] \times [c, d]$$

EXAMPLE 5 If $R = [0, \pi/2] \times [0, \pi/2]$, then

$$\iint_R \sin x \cos y \, dA = \int_0^{\pi/2} \sin x \, dx \int_0^{\pi/2} \cos y \, dy$$

$$= \left[-\cos x\right]_0^{\pi/2} \left[\sin y\right]_0^{\pi/2} = 1 \cdot 1 = 1$$

‖‖‖ The function $f(x, y) = \sin x \cos y$ in Example 5 is positive on R, so the integral represents the volume of the solid that lies above R and below the graph of f shown in Figure 6.

FIGURE 6

16.2 Exercises

1–2 ‖‖‖ Find $\int_0^3 f(x, y) \, dx$ and $\int_0^4 f(x, y) \, dy$.

1. $f(x, y) = 2x + 3x^2 y$　　**2.** $f(x, y) = \dfrac{y}{x + 2}$

3–12 ‖‖‖ Calculate the iterated integral.

3. $\int_1^3 \int_0^1 (1 + 4xy) \, dx \, dy$　　**4.** $\int_2^4 \int_{-1}^1 (x^2 + y^2) \, dy \, dx$

5. $\int_0^2 \int_0^{\pi/2} x \sin y \, dy \, dx$　　**6.** $\int_1^4 \int_0^2 (x + \sqrt{y}) \, dx \, dy$

7. $\int_0^2 \int_0^1 (2x + y)^8 \, dx \, dy$　　**8.** $\int_0^1 \int_1^2 \dfrac{xe^x}{y} \, dy \, dx$

9. $\int_1^4 \int_1^2 \left(\dfrac{x}{y} + \dfrac{y}{x}\right) dy \, dx$　　**10.** $\int_1^2 \int_0^1 (x + y)^{-2} \, dx \, dy$

11. $\int_0^{\ln 2} \int_0^{\ln 5} e^{2x-y} \, dx \, dy$

12. $\int_0^1 \int_0^1 \dfrac{xy}{\sqrt{x^2 + y^2 + 1}} \, dy \, dx$

13–20 ‖‖‖ Calculate the double integral.

13. $\iint_R (6x^2 y^3 - 5y^4) \, dA, \quad R = \{(x, y) \,|\, 0 \leqslant x \leqslant 3, \ 0 \leqslant y \leqslant 1\}$

14. $\iint_R \cos(x + 2y) \, dA, \quad R = \{(x, y) \,|\, 0 \leqslant x \leqslant \pi, \ 0 \leqslant y \leqslant \pi/2\}$

15. $\iint_R \dfrac{xy^2}{x^2 + 1} \, dA, \quad R = \{(x, y) \,|\, 0 \leqslant x \leqslant 1, \ -3 \leqslant y \leqslant 3\}$

16. $\iint_R \dfrac{1 + x^2}{1 + y^2} \, dA, \quad R = \{(x, y) \,|\, 0 \leqslant x \leqslant 1, \ 0 \leqslant y \leqslant 1\}$

17. $\iint_R x \sin(x + y) \, dA, \quad R = [0, \pi/6] \times [0, \pi/3]$

18. $\iint_R \dfrac{x}{1 + xy} \, dA, \quad R = [0, 1] \times [0, 1]$

19. $\iint_R xye^{x^2 y} \, dA, \quad R = [0, 1] \times [0, 2]$

20. $\iint_R \dfrac{x}{x^2 + y^2} \, dA, \quad R = [1, 2] \times [0, 1]$

21–22 ‖‖‖ Sketch the solid whose volume is given by the iterated integral.

21. $\int_0^1 \int_0^1 (4 - x - 2y) \, dx \, dy$

22. $\int_0^1 \int_0^1 (2 - x^2 - y^2) \, dy \, dx$

---

23. Find the volume of the solid that lies under the plane $3x + 2y + z = 12$ and above the rectangle $R = \{(x, y) \,|\, 0 \leqslant x \leqslant 1, \ -2 \leqslant y \leqslant 3\}$.

24. Find the volume of the solid that lies under the hyperbolic paraboloid $z = 4 + x^2 - y^2$ and above the square $R = [-1, 1] \times [0, 2]$.

25. Find the volume of the solid lying under the elliptic paraboloid $x^2/4 + y^2/9 + z = 1$ and above the rectangle $R = [-1, 1] \times [-2, 2]$.

26. Find the volume of the solid enclosed by the surface $z = 1 + e^x \sin y$ and the planes $x = \pm 1$, $y = 0$, $y = \pi$, and $z = 0$.

27. Find the volume of the solid bounded by the surface $z = x\sqrt{x^2 + y}$ and the planes $x = 0$, $x = 1$, $y = 0$, $y = 1$, and $z = 0$.

28. Find the volume of the solid bounded by the elliptic paraboloid $z = 1 + (x - 1)^2 + 4y^2$, the planes $x = 3$ and $y = 2$, and the coordinate planes.

29. Find the volume of the solid in the first octant bounded by the cylinder $z = 9 - y^2$ and the plane $x = 2$.

30. (a) Find the volume of the solid bounded by the surface $z = 6 - xy$ and the planes $x = 2$, $x = -2$, $y = 0$, $y = 3$, and $z = 0$.
(b) Use a computer to draw the solid.

CAS **31.** Use a computer algebra system to find the exact value of the integral $\iint_R x^5 y^3 e^{xy} \, dA$, where $R = [0, 1] \times [0, 1]$. Then use the CAS to draw the solid whose volume is given by the integral.

CAS **32.** Graph the solid that lies between the surfaces $z = e^{-x^2} \cos(x^2 + y^2)$ and $z = 2 - x^2 - y^2$ for $|x| \leq 1$, $|y| \leq 1$. Use a computer algebra system to approximate the volume of this solid correct to four decimal places.

33–34 ▥ Find the average value of f over the given rectangle.

33. $f(x, y) = x^2 y$, R has vertices $(-1, 0)$, $(-1, 5)$, $(1, 5)$, $(1, 0)$

34. $f(x, y) = e^y \sqrt{x + e^y}$, $R = [0, 4] \times [0, 1]$

▱ ▱ ▱ ▱ ▱ ▱ ▱ ▱ ▱ ▱ ▱ ▱

CAS **35.** Use your CAS to compute the iterated integrals

$$\int_0^1 \int_0^1 \frac{x - y}{(x + y)^3} \, dy \, dx \qquad \text{and} \qquad \int_0^1 \int_0^1 \frac{x - y}{(x + y)^3} \, dx \, dy$$

Do the answers contradict Fubini's Theorem? Explain what is happening.

36. (a) In what way are the theorems of Fubini and Clairaut similar?
(b) If $f(x, y)$ is continuous on $[a, b] \times [c, d]$ and

$$g(x, y) = \int_a^x \int_c^y f(s, t) \, dt \, ds$$

for $a < x < b$, $c < y < d$, show that $g_{xy} = g_{yx} = f(x, y)$.

16.3 Double Integrals over General Regions

For single integrals, the region over which we integrate is always an interval. But for double integrals, we want to be able to integrate a function f not just over rectangles but also over regions D of more general shape, such as the one illustrated in Figure 1. We suppose that D is a bounded region, which means that D can be enclosed in a rectangular region R as in Figure 2. Then we define a new function F with domain R by

$$\boxed{1} \qquad F(x, y) = \begin{cases} f(x, y) & \text{if } (x, y) \text{ is in } D \\ 0 & \text{if } (x, y) \text{ is in } R \text{ but not in } D \end{cases}$$

FIGURE 1

FIGURE 2

FIGURE 3

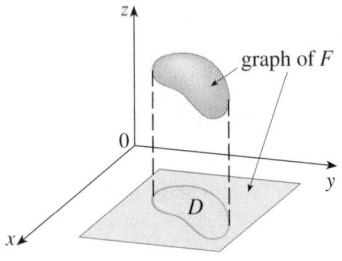

FIGURE 4

If the double integral of F exists over R, then we define the **double integral of f over D** by

> **2** $$\iint_D f(x, y)\, dA = \iint_R F(x, y)\, dA \qquad \text{where } F \text{ is given by Equation 1}$$

Definition 2 makes sense because R is a rectangle and so $\iint_R F(x, y)\, dA$ has been previously defined in Section 16.1. The procedure that we have used is reasonable because the values of $F(x, y)$ are 0 when (x, y) lies outside D and so they contribute nothing to the integral. This means that it doesn't matter what rectangle R we use as long as it contains D.

In the case where $f(x, y) \geqslant 0$ we can still interpret $\iint_D f(x, y)\, dA$ as the volume of the solid that lies above D and under the surface $z = f(x, y)$ (the graph of f). You can see that this is reasonable by comparing the graphs of f and F in Figures 3 and 4 and remembering that $\iint_R F(x, y)\, dA$ is the volume under the graph of F.

Figure 4 also shows that F is likely to have discontinuities at the boundary points of D. Nonetheless, if f is continuous on D and the boundary curve of D is "well behaved" (in a sense outside the scope of this book), then it can be shown that $\iint_R F(x, y)\, dA$ exists and therefore $\iint_D f(x, y)\, dA$ exists. In particular, this is the case for the following types of regions.

A plane region D is said to be of **type I** if it lies between the graphs of two continuous functions of x, that is,

$$D = \{(x, y) \mid a \leqslant x \leqslant b,\ g_1(x) \leqslant y \leqslant g_2(x)\}$$

where g_1 and g_2 are continuous on $[a, b]$. Some examples of type I regions are shown in Figure 5.

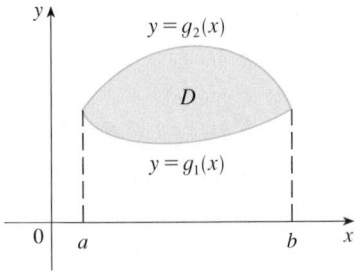

FIGURE 5 Some type I regions

In order to evaluate $\iint_D f(x, y)\, dA$ when D is a region of type I, we choose a rectangle $R = [a, b] \times [c, d]$ that contains D, as in Figure 6, and we let F be the function given by Equation 1; that is, F agrees with f on D and F is 0 outside D. Then, by Fubini's Theorem,

$$\iint_D f(x, y)\, dA = \iint_R F(x, y)\, dA = \int_a^b \int_c^d F(x, y)\, dy\, dx$$

Observe that $F(x, y) = 0$ if $y < g_1(x)$ or $y > g_2(x)$ because (x, y) then lies outside D. Therefore

$$\int_c^d F(x, y)\, dy = \int_{g_1(x)}^{g_2(x)} F(x, y)\, dy = \int_{g_1(x)}^{g_2(x)} f(x, y)\, dy$$

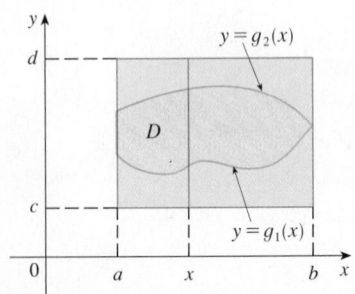

FIGURE 6

because $F(x, y) = f(x, y)$ when $g_1(x) \leq y \leq g_2(x)$. Thus, we have the following formula that enables us to evaluate the double integral as an iterated integral.

---

3 If f is continuous on a type I region D such that

$$D = \{(x, y) \mid a \leq x \leq b, \ g_1(x) \leq y \leq g_2(x)\}$$

then

$$\iint_D f(x, y) \, dA = \int_a^b \int_{g_1(x)}^{g_2(x)} f(x, y) \, dy \, dx$$

The integral on the right side of (3) is an iterated integral that is similar to the ones we considered in the preceding section, except that in the inner integral we regard x as being constant not only in $f(x, y)$ but also in the limits of integration, $g_1(x)$ and $g_2(x)$.

We also consider plane regions of **type II**, which can be expressed as

4
$$D = \{(x, y) \mid c \leq y \leq d, \ h_1(y) \leq x \leq h_2(y)\}$$

where h_1 and h_2 are continuous. Two such regions are illustrated in Figure 7.

Using the same methods that were used in establishing (3), we can show that

---

5
$$\iint_D f(x, y) \, dA = \int_c^d \int_{h_1(y)}^{h_2(y)} f(x, y) \, dx \, dy$$

---

where D is a type II region given by Equation 4.

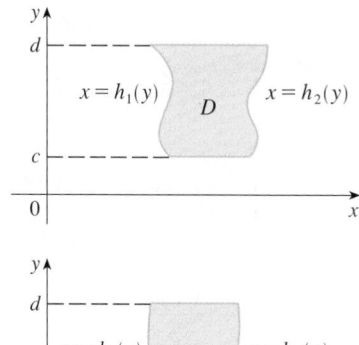

FIGURE 7
Some type II regions

EXAMPLE 1 Evaluate $\iint_D (x + 2y) \, dA$, where D is the region bounded by the parabolas $y = 2x^2$ and $y = 1 + x^2$.

SOLUTION The parabolas intersect when $2x^2 = 1 + x^2$, that is, $x^2 = 1$, so $x = \pm 1$. We note that the region D, sketched in Figure 8, is a type I region but not a type II region and we can write

$$D = \{(x, y) \mid -1 \leq x \leq 1, \ 2x^2 \leq y \leq 1 + x^2\}$$

Since the lower boundary is $y = 2x^2$ and the upper boundary is $y = 1 + x^2$, Equation 3 gives

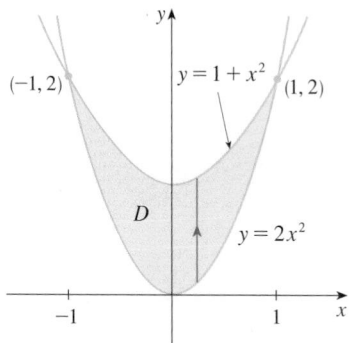

FIGURE 8

$$\iint_D (x + 2y) \, dA = \int_{-1}^{1} \int_{2x^2}^{1+x^2} (x + 2y) \, dy \, dx$$

$$= \int_{-1}^{1} \left[xy + y^2 \right]_{y=2x^2}^{y=1+x^2} dx$$

$$= \int_{-1}^{1} \left[x(1 + x^2) + (1 + x^2)^2 - x(2x^2) - (2x^2)^2 \right] dx$$

$$= \int_{-1}^{1} (-3x^4 - x^3 + 2x^2 + x + 1) \, dx$$

$$= -3 \frac{x^5}{5} - \frac{x^4}{4} + 2 \frac{x^3}{3} + \frac{x^2}{2} + x \bigg]_{-1}^{1} = \frac{32}{15}$$

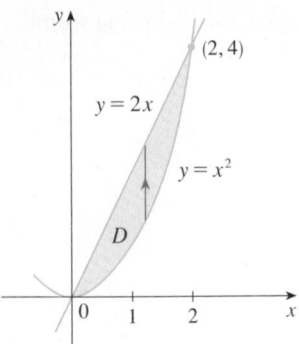

FIGURE 9

D as a type I region

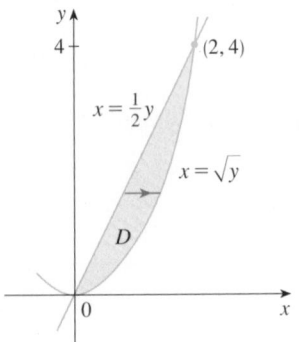

FIGURE 10

D as a type II region

▥ Figure 11 shows the solid whose volume is calculated in Example 2. It lies above the xy-plane, below the paraboloid $z = x^2 + y^2$, and between the plane $y = 2x$ and the parabolic cylinder $y = x^2$.

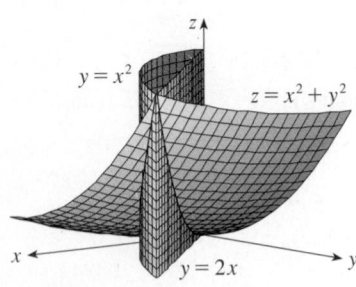

FIGURE 11

NOTE ▫ When we set up a double integral as in Example 1, it is essential to draw a diagram. Often it is helpful to draw a vertical arrow as in Figure 8. Then the limits of integration for the *inner* integral can be read from the diagram as follows: The arrow starts at the lower boundary $y = g_1(x)$, which gives the lower limit in the integral, and the arrow ends at the upper boundary $y = g_2(x)$, which gives the upper limit of integration. For a type II region the arrow is drawn horizontally from the left boundary to the right boundary.

EXAMPLE 2 Find the volume of the solid that lies under the paraboloid $z = x^2 + y^2$ and above the region D in the xy-plane bounded by the line $y = 2x$ and the parabola $y = x^2$.

SOLUTION 1 From Figure 9 we see that D is a type I region and

$$D = \{(x, y) \mid 0 \le x \le 2, \ x^2 \le y \le 2x\}$$

Therefore, the volume under $z = x^2 + y^2$ and above D is

$$V = \iint_D (x^2 + y^2)\, dA = \int_0^2 \int_{x^2}^{2x} (x^2 + y^2)\, dy\, dx$$

$$= \int_0^2 \left[x^2 y + \frac{y^3}{3} \right]_{y=x^2}^{y=2x} dx = \int_0^2 \left[x^2(2x) + \frac{(2x)^3}{3} - x^2 x^2 - \frac{(x^2)^3}{3} \right] dx$$

$$= \int_0^2 \left(-\frac{x^6}{3} - x^4 + \frac{14x^3}{3} \right) dx = -\frac{x^7}{21} - \frac{x^5}{5} + \frac{7x^4}{6} \Big]_0^2 = \frac{216}{35}$$

SOLUTION 2 From Figure 10 we see that D can also be written as a type II region:

$$D = \left\{ (x, y) \mid 0 \le y \le 4, \ \tfrac{1}{2}y \le x \le \sqrt{y} \right\}$$

Therefore, another expression for V is

$$V = \iint_D (x^2 + y^2)\, dA = \int_0^4 \int_{\frac{1}{2}y}^{\sqrt{y}} (x^2 + y^2)\, dx\, dy$$

$$= \int_0^4 \left[\frac{x^3}{3} + y^2 x \right]_{x=\frac{1}{2}y}^{x=\sqrt{y}} dy = \int_0^4 \left(\frac{y^{3/2}}{3} + y^{5/2} - \frac{y^3}{24} - \frac{y^3}{2} \right) dy$$

$$= \tfrac{2}{15} y^{5/2} + \tfrac{2}{7} y^{7/2} - \tfrac{13}{96} y^4 \Big]_0^4 = \tfrac{216}{35}$$

EXAMPLE 3 Evaluate $\iint_D xy\, dA$, where D is the region bounded by the line $y = x - 1$ and the parabola $y^2 = 2x + 6$.

SOLUTION The region D is shown in Figure 12. Again D is both type I and type II, but the description of D as a type I region is more complicated because the lower boundary consists of two parts. Therefore, we prefer to express D as a type II region:

$$D = \left\{ (x, y) \mid -2 \le y \le 4, \ \tfrac{1}{2}y^2 - 3 \le x \le y + 1 \right\}$$

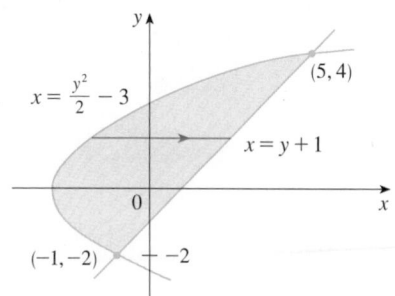

FIGURE 12   (a) D as a type I region   (b) D as a type II region

Then (5) gives

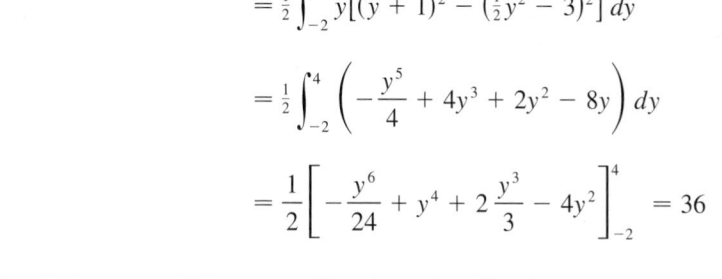

$$\iint\limits_{D} xy \, dA = \int_{-2}^{4} \int_{\frac{1}{2}y^2-3}^{y+1} xy \, dx \, dy = \int_{-2}^{4} \left[\frac{x^2}{2} \, y \right]_{x=\frac{1}{2}y^2-3}^{x=y+1} dy$$

$$= \frac{1}{2} \int_{-2}^{4} y\left[(y+1)^2 - \left(\frac{1}{2}y^2 - 3 \right)^2 \right] dy$$

$$= \frac{1}{2} \int_{-2}^{4} \left(-\frac{y^5}{4} + 4y^3 + 2y^2 - 8y \right) dy$$

$$= \frac{1}{2} \left[-\frac{y^6}{24} + y^4 + 2\frac{y^3}{3} - 4y^2 \right]_{-2}^{4} = 36$$

If we had expressed D as a type I region using Figure 12(a), then we would have obtained

$$\iint\limits_{D} xy \, dA = \int_{-3}^{-1} \int_{-\sqrt{2x+6}}^{\sqrt{2x+6}} xy \, dy \, dx + \int_{-1}^{5} \int_{x-1}^{\sqrt{2x+6}} xy \, dy \, dx$$

but this would have involved more work than the other method.

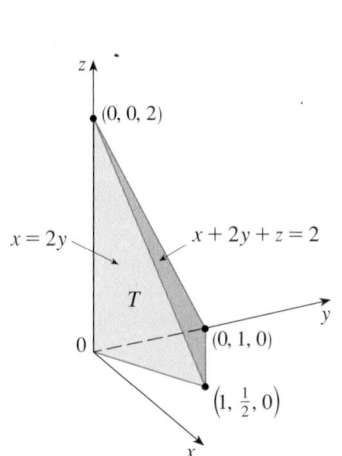

FIGURE 13

EXAMPLE 4 Find the volume of the tetrahedron bounded by the planes $x + 2y + z = 2$, $x = 2y$, $x = 0$, and $z = 0$.

SOLUTION In a question such as this, it's wise to draw two diagrams: one of the three-dimensional solid and another of the plane region D over which it lies. Figure 13 shows the tetrahedron T bounded by the coordinate planes $x = 0$, $z = 0$, the vertical plane $x = 2y$, and the plane $x + 2y + z = 2$. Since the plane $x + 2y + z = 2$ intersects the xy-plane (whose equation is $z = 0$) in the line $x + 2y = 2$, we see that T lies above the triangular region D in the xy-plane bounded by the lines $x = 2y$, $x + 2y = 2$, and $x = 0$. (See Figure 14.)

The plane $x + 2y + z = 2$ can be written as $z = 2 - x - 2y$, so the required volume lies under the graph of the function $z = 2 - x - 2y$ and above

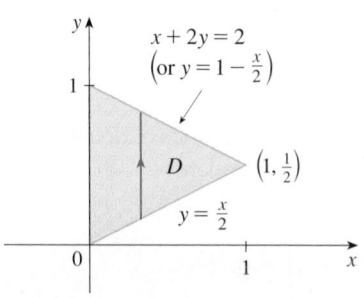

FIGURE 14

$$D = \left\{ (x, y) \mid 0 \leqslant x \leqslant 1, \ x/2 \leqslant y \leqslant 1 - x/2 \right\}$$

Therefore

$$V = \iint\limits_{D} (2 - x - 2y)\, dA = \int_0^1 \int_{x/2}^{1-x/2} (2 - x - 2y)\, dy\, dx$$

$$= \int_0^1 \left[2y - xy - y^2 \right]_{y=x/2}^{y=1-x/2}\, dx$$

$$= \int_0^1 \left[2 - x - x\left(1 - \frac{x}{2}\right) - \left(1 - \frac{x}{2}\right)^2 - x + \frac{x^2}{2} + \frac{x^2}{4} \right] dx$$

$$= \int_0^1 (x^2 - 2x + 1)\, dx = \frac{x^3}{3} - x^2 + x \Big]_0^1 = \frac{1}{3}$$

EXAMPLE 5 Evaluate the iterated integral $\int_0^1 \int_x^1 \sin(y^2)\, dy\, dx$.

SOLUTION If we try to evaluate the integral as it stands, we are faced with the task of first evaluating $\int \sin(y^2)\, dy$. But it's impossible to do so in finite terms since $\int \sin(y^2)\, dy$ is not an elementary function. (See the end of Section 8.5.) So we must change the order of integration. This is accomplished by first expressing the given iterated integral as a double integral. Using (3) backward, we have

$$\int_0^1 \int_x^1 \sin(y^2)\, dy\, dx = \iint\limits_{D} \sin(y^2)\, dA$$

where

$$D = \{(x, y) \mid 0 \le x \le 1,\ x \le y \le 1\}$$

We sketch this region D in Figure 15. Then from Figure 16 we see that an alternative description of D is

$$D = \{(x, y) \mid 0 \le y \le 1,\ 0 \le x \le y\}$$

This enables us to use (5) to express the double integral as an iterated integral in the reverse order:

$$\int_0^1 \int_x^1 \sin(y^2)\, dy\, dx = \iint\limits_{D} \sin(y^2)\, dA$$

$$= \int_0^1 \int_0^y \sin(y^2)\, dx\, dy = \int_0^1 \left[x\sin(y^2) \right]_{x=0}^{x=y}\, dy$$

$$= \int_0^1 y\sin(y^2)\, dy = -\tfrac{1}{2}\cos(y^2) \Big]_0^1$$

$$= \tfrac{1}{2}(1 - \cos 1)$$

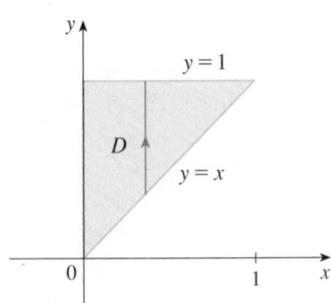

FIGURE 15

D as a type I region

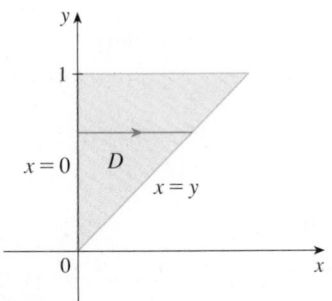

FIGURE 16

D as a type II region

▮▮▮▮ **Properties of Double Integrals**

We assume that all of the following integrals exist. The first three properties of double integrals over a region D follow immediately from Definition 2 and Properties 7, 8, and 9 in Section 16.1.

6
$$\iint\limits_{D} [f(x, y) + g(x, y)]\, dA = \iint\limits_{D} f(x, y)\, dA + \iint\limits_{D} g(x, y)\, dA$$

7
$$\iint\limits_{D} cf(x, y)\, dA = c \iint\limits_{D} f(x, y)\, dA$$

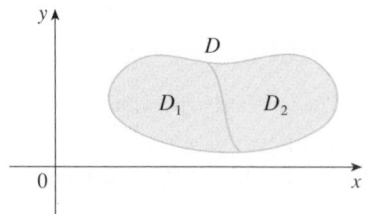

FIGURE 17

If $f(x, y) \geq g(x, y)$ for all (x, y) in D, then

$$\boxed{8} \qquad \iint_D f(x, y) \, dA \geq \iint_D g(x, y) \, dA$$

The next property of double integrals is similar to the property of single integrals given by the equation $\int_a^b f(x) \, dx = \int_a^c f(x) \, dx + \int_c^b f(x) \, dx$.

If $D = D_1 \cup D_2$, where D_1 and D_2 don't overlap except perhaps on their boundaries (see Figure 17), then

$$\boxed{9} \qquad \iint_D f(x, y) \, dA = \iint_{D_1} f(x, y) \, dA + \iint_{D_2} f(x, y) \, dA$$

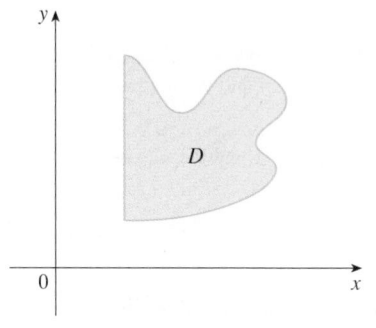

(a) D is neither type I nor type II.

Property 9 can be used to evaluate double integrals over regions D that are neither type I nor type II but can be expressed as a union of regions of type I or type II. Figure 18 illustrates this procedure. (See Exercises 49 and 50.)

The next property of integrals says that if we integrate the constant function $f(x, y) = 1$ over a region D, we get the area of D:

$$\boxed{10} \qquad \iint_D 1 \, dA = A(D)$$

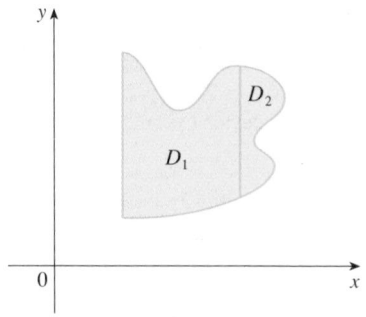

(b) $D = D_1 \cup D_2$,
    D_1 is type I, D_2 is type II.

FIGURE 18

Figure 19 illustrates why Equation 10 is true: A solid cylinder whose base is D and whose height is 1 has volume $A(D) \cdot 1 = A(D)$, but we know that we can also write its volume as $\iint_D 1 \, dA$.

Finally, we can combine Properties 7, 8, and 10 to prove the following property. (See Exercise 53.)

$$\boxed{11} \quad \text{If } m \leq f(x, y) \leq M \text{ for all } (x, y) \text{ in } D, \text{ then}$$

$$mA(D) \leq \iint_D f(x, y) \, dA \leq MA(D)$$

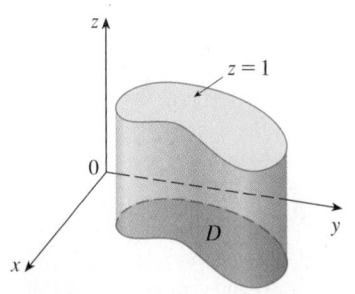

FIGURE 19
Cylinder with base D and height 1

EXAMPLE 6 Use Property 11 to estimate the integral $\iint_D e^{\sin x \cos y} \, dA$, where D is the disk with center the origin and radius 2.

SOLUTION Since $-1 \leq \sin x \leq 1$ and $-1 \leq \cos y \leq 1$, we have $-1 \leq \sin x \cos y \leq 1$ and therefore

$$e^{-1} \leq e^{\sin x \cos y} \leq e^1 = e$$

Thus, using $m = e^{-1} = 1/e$, $M = e$, and $A(D) = \pi(2)^2$ in Property 11, we obtain

$$\frac{4\pi}{e} \leq \iint_D e^{\sin x \cos y} \, dA \leq 4\pi e$$

16.3 Exercises

1–6 ▨ Evaluate the iterated integral.

1. $\int_0^1 \int_0^{x^2} (x + 2y)\, dy\, dx$

2. $\int_1^2 \int_y^2 xy\, dx\, dy$

3. $\int_0^1 \int_y^{e^y} \sqrt{x}\, dx\, dy$

4. $\int_0^1 \int_x^{2-x} (x^2 - y)\, dy\, dx$

5. $\int_0^{\pi/2} \int_0^{\cos\theta} e^{\sin\theta}\, dr\, d\theta$

6. $\int_0^1 \int_0^v \sqrt{1 - v^2}\, du\, dv$

7–18 ▨ Evaluate the double integral.

7. $\iint_D x^3 y^2\, dA$, $D = \{(x, y) \mid 0 \le x \le 2, -x \le y \le x\}$

8. $\iint_D \frac{4y}{x^3 + 2}\, dA$, $D = \{(x, y) \mid 1 \le x \le 2, 0 \le y \le 2x\}$

9. $\iint_D \frac{2y}{x^2 + 1}\, dA$, $D = \{(x, y) \mid 0 \le x \le 1, 0 \le y \le \sqrt{x}\}$

10. $\iint_D e^{y^2}\, dA$, $D = \{(x, y) \mid 0 \le y \le 1, 0 \le x \le y\}$

11. $\iint_D e^{x/y}\, dA$, $D = \{(x, y) \mid 1 \le y \le 2, y \le x \le y^3\}$

12. $\iint_D x\sqrt{y^2 - x^2}\, dA$, $D = \{(x, y) \mid 0 \le y \le 1, 0 \le x \le y\}$

13. $\iint_D x \cos y\, dA$, D is bounded by $y = 0$, $y = x^2$, $x = 1$

14. $\iint_D (x + y)\, dA$, D is bounded by $y = \sqrt{x}$ and $y = x^2$

15. $\iint_D y^3\, dA$, D is the triangular region with vertices $(0, 2)$, $(1, 1)$, and $(3, 2)$

16. $\iint_D xy^2\, dA$, D is enclosed by $x = 0$ and $x = \sqrt{1 - y^2}$

17. $\iint_D (2x - y)\, dA$, D is bounded by the circle with center the origin and radius 2

18. $\iint_D 2xy\, dA$, D is the triangular region with vertices $(0, 0)$, $(1, 2)$, and $(0, 3)$

19–28 ▨ Find the volume of the given solid.

19. Under the plane $x + 2y - z = 0$ and above the region bounded by $y = x$ and $y = x^4$

20. Under the surface $z = 2x + y^2$ and above the region bounded by $x = y^2$ and $x = y^3$

21. Under the surface $z = xy$ and above the triangle with vertices $(1, 1)$, $(4, 1)$, and $(1, 2)$

22. Enclosed by the paraboloid $z = x^2 + 3y^2$ and the planes $x = 0$, $y = 1$, $y = x$, $z = 0$

23. Bounded by the planes $x = 0$, $y = 0$, $z = 0$, and $x + y + z = 1$

24. Bounded by the planes $z = x$, $y = x$, $x + y = 2$, and $z = 0$

25. Enclosed by the cylinders $z = x^2$, $y = x^2$ and the planes $z = 0$, $y = 4$

26. Bounded by the cylinder $y^2 + z^2 = 4$ and the planes $x = 2y$, $x = 0$, $z = 0$ in the first octant

27. Bounded by the cylinder $x^2 + y^2 = 1$ and the planes $y = z$, $x = 0$, $z = 0$ in the first octant

28. Bounded by the cylinders $x^2 + y^2 = r^2$ and $y^2 + z^2 = r^2$

29. Use a graphing calculator or computer to estimate the x-coordinates of the points of intersection of the curves $y = x^4$ and $y = 3x - x^2$. If D is the region bounded by these curves, estimate $\iint_D x\, dA$.

30. Find the approximate volume of the solid in the first octant that is bounded by the planes $y = x$, $z = 0$, and $z = x$ and the cylinder $y = \cos x$. (Use a graphing device to estimate the points of intersection.)

31–32 ▨ Find the volume of the solid by subtracting two volumes.

31. The solid enclosed by the parabolic cylinders $y = 1 - x^2$, $y = x^2 - 1$ and the planes $x + y + z = 2$, $2x + 2y - z + 10 = 0$

32. The solid enclosed by the parabolic cylinder $y = x^2$ and the planes $z = 3y$, $z = 2 + y$

33–36 ▨ Use a computer algebra system to find the exact volume of the solid.

33. Under the surface $z = x^3 y^4 + xy^2$ and above the region bounded by the curves $y = x^3 - x$ and $y = x^2 + x$ for $x \ge 0$

34. Between the paraboloids $z = 2x^2 + y^2$ and $z = 8 - x^2 - 2y^2$ and inside the cylinder $x^2 + y^2 = 1$

35. Enclosed by $z = 1 - x^2 - y^2$ and $z = 0$

36. Enclosed by $z = x^2 + y^2$ and $z = 2y$

37–42 ▨ Sketch the region of integration and change the order of integration.

37. $\int_0^4 \int_0^{\sqrt{x}} f(x, y)\, dy\, dx$

38. $\int_0^1 \int_{4x}^4 f(x, y)\, dy\, dx$

39. $\int_0^3 \int_{-\sqrt{9-y^2}}^{\sqrt{9-y^2}} f(x, y) \, dx \, dy$

40. $\int_0^3 \int_0^{\sqrt{9-y}} f(x, y) \, dx \, dy$

41. $\int_1^2 \int_0^{\ln x} f(x, y) \, dy \, dx$

42. $\int_0^1 \int_{\arctan x}^{\pi/4} f(x, y) \, dy \, dx$

43–48 ▓ Evaluate the integral by reversing the order of integration.

43. $\int_0^1 \int_{3y}^3 e^{x^2} \, dx \, dy$

44. $\int_0^1 \int_{\sqrt{y}}^1 \sqrt{x^3 + 1} \, dx \, dy$

45. $\int_0^3 \int_{y^2}^9 y \cos(x^2) \, dx \, dy$

46. $\int_0^1 \int_{x^2}^1 x^3 \sin(y^3) \, dy \, dx$

47. $\int_0^1 \int_{\arcsin y}^{\pi/2} \cos x \sqrt{1 + \cos^2 x} \, dx \, dy$

48. $\int_0^8 \int_{\sqrt[3]{y}}^2 e^{x^4} \, dx \, dy$

49–50 ▓ Express D as a union of regions of type I or type II and evaluate the integral.

49. $\iint_D x^2 \, dA$

50. $\iint_D xy \, dA$

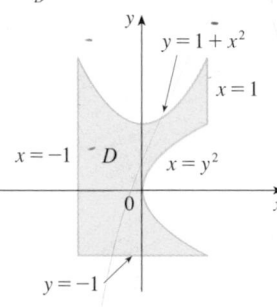

51–52 ▓ Use Property 11 to estimate the value of the integral.

51. $\iint_D \sqrt{x^3 + y^3} \, dA, \quad D = [0, 1] \times [0, 1]$

52. $\iint_D e^{x^2+y^2} \, dA, \quad D$ is the disk with center the origin and radius $\frac{1}{2}$

---

53. Prove Property 11.

54. In evaluating a double integral over a region D, a sum of iterated integrals was obtained as follows:

$$\iint_D f(x, y) \, dA = \int_0^1 \int_0^{2y} f(x, y) \, dx \, dy + \int_1^3 \int_0^{3-y} f(x, y) \, dx \, dy$$

Sketch the region D and express the double integral as an iterated integral with reversed order of integration.

55. Evaluate $\iint_D (x^2 \tan x + y^3 + 4) \, dA$, where $D = \{(x, y) \mid x^2 + y^2 \leq 2\}$.
[*Hint:* Exploit the fact that D is symmetric with respect to both axes.]

56. Use symmetry to evaluate $\iint_D (2 - 3x + 4y) \, dA$, where D is the region bounded by the square with vertices $(\pm 5, 0)$ and $(0, \pm 5)$.

57. Compute $\iint_D \sqrt{1 - x^2 - y^2} \, dA$, where D is the disk $x^2 + y^2 \leq 1$, by first identifying the integral as the volume of a solid.

CAS 58. Graph the solid bounded by the plane $x + y + z = 1$ and the paraboloid $z = 4 - x^2 - y^2$ and find its exact volume. (Use your CAS to do the graphing, to find the equations of the boundary curves of the region of integration, and to evaluate the double integral.)

16.4 Double Integrals in Polar Coordinates

Suppose that we want to evaluate a double integral $\iint_R f(x, y) \, dA$, where R is one of the regions shown in Figure 1. In either case the description of R in terms of rectangular coordinates is rather complicated but R is easily described using polar coordinates.

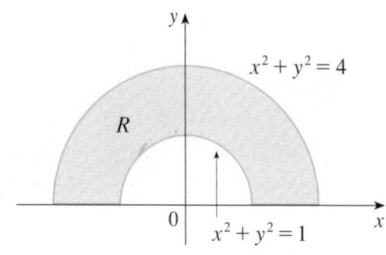

FIGURE 1   (a) $R = \{(r, \theta) \mid 0 \leq r \leq 1, 0 \leq \theta \leq 2\pi\}$ (b) $R = \{(r, \theta) \mid 1 \leq r \leq 2, 0 \leq \theta \leq \pi\}$

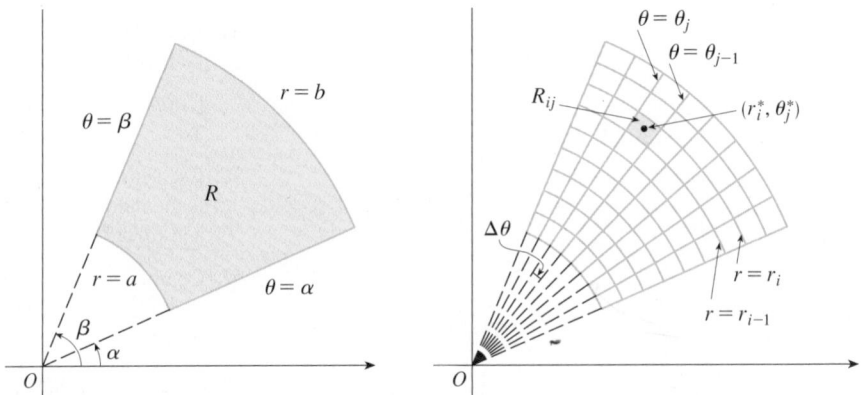

Recall from Figure 2 that the polar coordinates (r, θ) of a point are related to the rectangular coordinates (x, y) by the equations

$$r^2 = x^2 + y^2 \qquad x = r\cos\theta \qquad y = r\sin\theta$$

(See Section 11.3.)

The regions in Figure 1 are special cases of a **polar rectangle**

$$R = \{(r, \theta) \mid a \le r \le b, \alpha \le \theta \le \beta\}$$

which is shown in Figure 3. In order to compute the double integral $\iint_R f(x, y)\, dA$, where R is a polar rectangle, we divide the interval $[a, b]$ into m subintervals $[r_{i-1}, r_i]$ of equal width $\Delta r = (b - a)/m$ and we divide the interval $[\alpha, \beta]$ into n subintervals $[\theta_{j-1}, \theta_j]$ of equal width $\Delta\theta = (\beta - \alpha)/n$. Then the circles $r = r_i$ and the rays $\theta = \theta_j$ divide the polar rectangle R into the small polar rectangles shown in Figure 4.

FIGURE 2

FIGURE 3 Polar rectangle

FIGURE 4 Dividing R into polar subrectangles

The "center" of the polar subrectangle

$$R_{ij} = \{(r, \theta) \mid r_{i-1} \le r \le r_i, \theta_{j-1} \le \theta \le \theta_j\}$$

has polar coordinates

$$r_i^* = \tfrac{1}{2}(r_{i-1} + r_i) \qquad \theta_j^* = \tfrac{1}{2}(\theta_{j-1} + \theta_j)$$

We compute the area of R_{ij} using the fact that the area of a sector of a circle with radius r and central angle θ is $\frac{1}{2}r^2\theta$. Subtracting the areas of two such sectors, each of which has central angle $\Delta\theta = \theta_j - \theta_{j-1}$, we find that the area of R_{ij} is

$$\Delta A_i = \tfrac{1}{2}r_i^2\,\Delta\theta - \tfrac{1}{2}r_{i-1}^2\,\Delta\theta = \tfrac{1}{2}(r_i^2 - r_{i-1}^2)\,\Delta\theta$$

$$= \tfrac{1}{2}(r_i + r_{i-1})(r_i - r_{i-1})\,\Delta\theta = r_i^*\,\Delta r\,\Delta\theta$$

Although we have defined the double integral $\iint_R f(x, y)\, dA$ in terms of ordinary rectangles, it can be shown that, for continuous functions f, we always obtain the same answer using polar rectangles. The rectangular coordinates of the center of R_{ij} are $(r_i^* \cos\theta_j^*, r_i^* \sin\theta_j^*)$, so a typical Riemann sum is

$$\boxed{1} \quad \sum_{i=1}^{m}\sum_{j=1}^{n} f(r_i^* \cos\theta_j^*, r_i^* \sin\theta_j^*)\,\Delta A_i = \sum_{i=1}^{m}\sum_{j=1}^{n} f(r_i^* \cos\theta_j^*, r_i^* \sin\theta_j^*)\, r_i^*\,\Delta r\,\Delta\theta$$

If we write $g(r, \theta) = rf(r\cos\theta, r\sin\theta)$, then the Riemann sum in Equation 1 can be written as

$$\sum_{i=1}^{m}\sum_{j=1}^{n} g(r_i^*, \theta_j^*)\,\Delta r\,\Delta\theta$$

which is a Riemann sum for the double integral

$$\int_{\alpha}^{\beta}\int_{a}^{b} g(r, \theta)\,dr\,d\theta$$

Therefore, we have

$$\iint_{R} f(x, y)\,dA = \lim_{m,n\to\infty}\sum_{i=1}^{m}\sum_{j=1}^{n} f(r_i^*\cos\theta_j^*, r_i^*\sin\theta_j^*)\,\Delta A_i$$

$$= \lim_{m,n\to\infty}\sum_{i=1}^{m}\sum_{j=1}^{n} g(r_i^*, \theta_j^*)\,\Delta r\,\Delta\theta = \int_{\alpha}^{\beta}\int_{a}^{b} g(r, \theta)\,dr\,d\theta$$

$$= \int_{\alpha}^{\beta}\int_{a}^{b} f(r\cos\theta, r\sin\theta)\,r\,dr\,d\theta$$

> **2** **Change to Polar Coordinates in a Double Integral** If f is continuous on a polar rectangle R given by $0 \leqslant a \leqslant r \leqslant b$, $\alpha \leqslant \theta \leqslant \beta$, where $0 \leqslant \beta - \alpha \leqslant 2\pi$, then
>
> $$\iint_{R} f(x, y)\,dA = \int_{\alpha}^{\beta}\int_{a}^{b} f(r\cos\theta, r\sin\theta)\,r\,dr\,d\theta$$

The formula in (2) says that we convert from rectangular to polar coordinates in a double integral by writing $x = r\cos\theta$ and $y = r\sin\theta$, using the appropriate limits of integration for r and θ, and replacing dA by $r\,dr\,d\theta$. Be careful not to forget the additional factor r on the right side of Formula 2. A classical method for remembering this is shown in Figure 5, where the "infinitesimal" polar rectangle can be thought of as an ordinary rectangle with dimensions $r\,d\theta$ and dr and therefore has "area" $dA = r\,dr\,d\theta$.

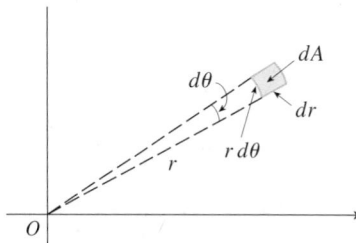

FIGURE 5

EXAMPLE 1 Evaluate $\iint_{R} (3x + 4y^2)\,dA$, where R is the region in the upper half-plane bounded by the circles $x^2 + y^2 = 1$ and $x^2 + y^2 = 4$.

SOLUTION The region R can be described as

$$R = \{(x, y)\,|\,y \geqslant 0,\ 1 \leqslant x^2 + y^2 \leqslant 4\}$$

It is the half-ring shown in Figure 1(b), and in polar coordinates it is given by $1 \leqslant r \leqslant 2$,

$0 \leqslant \theta \leqslant \pi$. Therefore, by Formula 2,

$$\iint\limits_{R} (3x + 4y^2)\, dA = \int_0^{\pi} \int_1^2 (3r\cos\theta + 4r^2\sin^2\theta)\, r\, dr\, d\theta$$

$$= \int_0^{\pi} \int_1^2 (3r^2\cos\theta + 4r^3\sin^2\theta)\, dr\, d\theta$$

$$= \int_0^{\pi} \big[r^3\cos\theta + r^4\sin^2\theta\big]_{r=1}^{r=2}\, d\theta = \int_0^{\pi} (7\cos\theta + 15\sin^2\theta)\, d\theta$$

$$= \int_0^{\pi} \big[7\cos\theta + \tfrac{15}{2}(1 - \cos 2\theta)\big]\, d\theta$$

$$= 7\sin\theta + \frac{15\theta}{2} - \frac{15}{4}\sin 2\theta \bigg]_0^{\pi} = \frac{15\pi}{2}$$

▮▮▮ Here we use the trigonometric identity

$$\sin^2\theta = \tfrac{1}{2}(1 - \cos 2\theta)$$

See Section 8.2 for advice on integrating trigonometric functions.

EXAMPLE 2 Find the volume of the solid bounded by the plane $z = 0$ and the paraboloid $z = 1 - x^2 - y^2$.

SOLUTION If we put $z = 0$ in the equation of the paraboloid, we get $x^2 + y^2 = 1$. This means that the plane intersects the paraboloid in the circle $x^2 + y^2 = 1$, so the solid lies under the paraboloid and above the circular disk D given by $x^2 + y^2 \leqslant 1$ [see Figures 6 and 1(a)]. In polar coordinates D is given by $0 \leqslant r \leqslant 1$, $0 \leqslant \theta \leqslant 2\pi$. Since $1 - x^2 - y^2 = 1 - r^2$, the volume is

$$V = \iint\limits_{D} (1 - x^2 - y^2)\, dA = \int_0^{2\pi} \int_0^1 (1 - r^2)\, r\, dr\, d\theta$$

$$= \int_0^{2\pi} d\theta \int_0^1 (r - r^3)\, dr = 2\pi \left[\frac{r^2}{2} - \frac{r^4}{4} \right]_0^1 = \frac{\pi}{2}$$

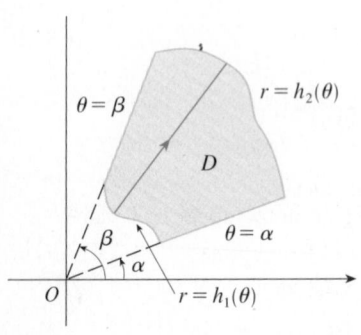

FIGURE 6

If we had used rectangular coordinates instead of polar coordinates, then we would have obtained

$$V = \iint\limits_{D} (1 - x^2 - y^2)\, dA = \int_{-1}^1 \int_{-\sqrt{1-x^2}}^{\sqrt{1-x^2}} (1 - x^2 - y^2)\, dy\, dx$$

which is not easy to evaluate because it involves finding $\int (1 - x^2)^{3/2}\, dx$.

What we have done so far can be extended to the more complicated type of region shown in Figure 7. It's similar to the type II rectangular regions considered in Section 16.3. In fact, by combining Formula 2 in this section with Formula 16.3.5, we obtain the following formula.

3 If f is continuous on a polar region of the form

$$D = \{(r, \theta) \mid \alpha \leqslant \theta \leqslant \beta,\ h_1(\theta) \leqslant r \leqslant h_2(\theta)\}$$

then

$$\iint\limits_{D} f(x, y)\, dA = \int_{\alpha}^{\beta} \int_{h_1(\theta)}^{h_2(\theta)} f(r\cos\theta, r\sin\theta)\, r\, dr\, d\theta$$

FIGURE 7

$D = \{(r, \theta) \mid \alpha \leqslant \theta \leqslant \beta,\ h_1(\theta) \leqslant r \leqslant h_2(\theta)\}$

In particular, taking $f(x, y) = 1$, $h_1(\theta) = 0$, and $h_2(\theta) = h(\theta)$ in this formula, we see that the area of the region D bounded by $\theta = \alpha$, $\theta = \beta$, and $r = h(\theta)$ is

$$A(D) = \iint_D 1\, dA = \int_\alpha^\beta \int_0^{h(\theta)} r\, dr\, d\theta$$

$$= \int_\alpha^\beta \left[\frac{r^2}{2}\right]_0^{h(\theta)} d\theta = \int_\alpha^\beta \tfrac{1}{2}[h(\theta)]^2\, d\theta$$

and this agrees with Formula 11.4.3.

EXAMPLE 3 Use a double integral to find the area enclosed by one loop of the four-leaved rose $r = \cos 2\theta$.

SOLUTION From the sketch of the curve in Figure 8 we see that a loop is given by the region

$$D = \left\{(r, \theta) \mid -\pi/4 \leqslant \theta \leqslant \pi/4,\ 0 \leqslant r \leqslant \cos 2\theta\right\}$$

So the area is

$$A(D) = \iint_D dA = \int_{-\pi/4}^{\pi/4} \int_0^{\cos 2\theta} r\, dr\, d\theta$$

$$= \int_{-\pi/4}^{\pi/4} \left[\tfrac{1}{2}r^2\right]_0^{\cos 2\theta} d\theta = \tfrac{1}{2}\int_{-\pi/4}^{\pi/4} \cos^2 2\theta\, d\theta$$

$$= \tfrac{1}{4}\int_{-\pi/4}^{\pi/4}(1 + \cos 4\theta)\, d\theta = \tfrac{1}{4}\left[\theta + \tfrac{1}{4}\sin 4\theta\right]_{-\pi/4}^{\pi/4} = \frac{\pi}{8}$$

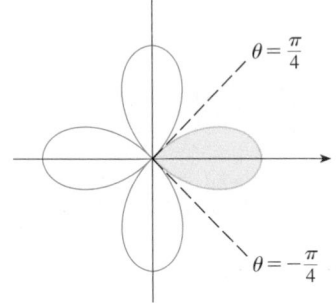

$\theta = \dfrac{\pi}{4}$

$\theta = -\dfrac{\pi}{4}$

FIGURE 8

EXAMPLE 4 Find the volume of the solid that lies under the paraboloid $z = x^2 + y^2$, above the xy-plane, and inside the cylinder $x^2 + y^2 = 2x$.

SOLUTION The solid lies above the disk D whose boundary circle has equation $x^2 + y^2 = 2x$ or, after completing the square,

$$(x - 1)^2 + y^2 = 1$$

(see Figures 9 and 10). In polar coordinates we have $x^2 + y^2 = r^2$ and $x = r\cos\theta$, so the boundary circle becomes $r^2 = 2r\cos\theta$, or $r = 2\cos\theta$. Thus, the disk D is given by

$$D = \left\{(r, \theta) \mid -\pi/2 \leqslant \theta \leqslant \pi/2,\ 0 \leqslant r \leqslant 2\cos\theta\right\}$$

and, by Formula 3, we have

$$V = \iint_D (x^2 + y^2)\, dA = \int_{-\pi/2}^{\pi/2} \int_0^{2\cos\theta} r^2\, r\, dr\, d\theta$$

$$= \int_{-\pi/2}^{\pi/2} \left[\frac{r^4}{4}\right]_0^{2\cos\theta} d\theta = 4\int_{-\pi/2}^{\pi/2} \cos^4\theta\, d\theta$$

$$= 8\int_0^{\pi/2} \cos^4\theta\, d\theta = 8\int_0^{\pi/2} \left(\frac{1 + \cos 2\theta}{2}\right)^2 d\theta$$

$$= 2\int_0^{\pi/2} \left[1 + 2\cos 2\theta + \tfrac{1}{2}(1 + \cos 4\theta)\right] d\theta$$

$$= 2\left[\tfrac{3}{2}\theta + \sin 2\theta + \tfrac{1}{8}\sin 4\theta\right]_0^{\pi/2} = 2\left(\frac{3}{2}\right)\left(\frac{\pi}{2}\right) = \frac{3\pi}{2}$$

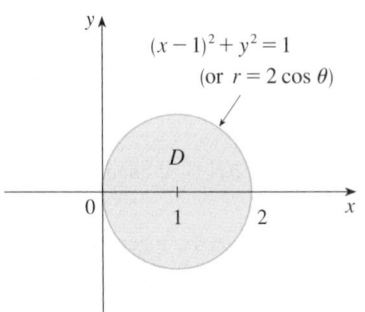

$(x - 1)^2 + y^2 = 1$
(or $r = 2\cos\theta$)

D

FIGURE 9

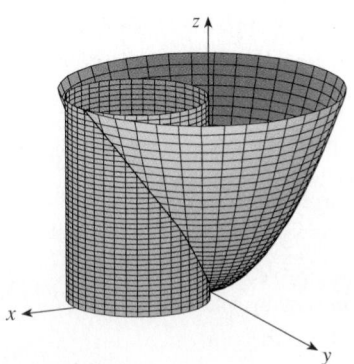

FIGURE 10

||| 16.4 Exercises

1–6 ||| A region R is shown. Decide whether to use polar coordinates or rectangular coordinates and write $\iint_R f(x, y)\, dA$ as an iterated integral, where f is an arbitrary continuous function on R.

1.

2.

3.

4.

5.

6.

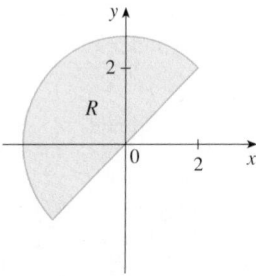

7–8 ||| Sketch the region whose area is given by the integral and evaluate the integral.

7. $\displaystyle\int_{\pi}^{2\pi}\int_{4}^{7} r\, dr\, d\theta$

8. $\displaystyle\int_{0}^{\pi/2}\int_{0}^{4\cos\theta} r\, dr\, d\theta$

9–16 ||| Evaluate the given integral by changing to polar coordinates.

9. $\iint_D xy\, dA$,
where D is the disk with center the origin and radius 3

10. $\iint_R (x + y)\, dA$, where R is the region that lies to the left of the y-axis between the circles $x^2 + y^2 = 1$ and $x^2 + y^2 = 4$

11. $\iint_R \cos(x^2 + y^2)\, dA$, where R is the region that lies above the x-axis within the circle $x^2 + y^2 = 9$

12. $\iint_R \sqrt{4 - x^2 - y^2}\, dA$,
where $R = \{(x, y)\,|\,x^2 + y^2 \leqslant 4,\ x \geqslant 0\}$

13. $\iint_D e^{-x^2-y^2}\, dA$, where D is the region bounded by the semicircle $x = \sqrt{4 - y^2}$ and the y-axis

14. $\iint_R ye^x\, dA$, where R is the region in the first quadrant enclosed by the circle $x^2 + y^2 = 25$

15. $\iint_R \arctan(y/x)\, dA$,
where $R = \{(x, y)\,|\,1 \leqslant x^2 + y^2 \leqslant 4,\ 0 \leqslant y \leqslant x\}$

16. $\iint_D x\, dA$, where D is the region in the first quadrant that lies between the circles $x^2 + y^2 = 4$ and $x^2 + y^2 = 2x$

17–20 ||| Use a double integral to find the area of the region.

17. One loop of the rose $r = \cos 3\theta$

18. The region enclosed by the curve $r = 4 + 3\cos\theta$

19. The region within both of the circles $r = \cos\theta$ and $r = \sin\theta$

20. The region inside the circle $r = 4\sin\theta$ and outside the circle $r = 2$

21–27 ||| Use polar coordinates to find the volume of the given solid.

21. Under the paraboloid $z = x^2 + y^2$ and above the disk $x^2 + y^2 \leqslant 9$

22. Inside the sphere $x^2 + y^2 + z^2 = 16$ and outside the cylinder $x^2 + y^2 = 4$

23. A sphere of radius a

24. Bounded by the paraboloid $z = 10 - 3x^2 - 3y^2$ and the plane $z = 4$

25. Above the cone $z = \sqrt{x^2 + y^2}$ and below the sphere $x^2 + y^2 + z^2 = 1$

26. Bounded by the paraboloids $z = 3x^2 + 3y^2$ and $z = 4 - x^2 - y^2$

27. Inside both the cylinder $x^2 + y^2 = 4$ and the ellipsoid $4x^2 + 4y^2 + z^2 = 64$

28. (a) A cylindrical drill with radius r_1 is used to bore a hole through the center of a sphere of radius r_2. Find the volume of the ring-shaped solid that remains.
(b) Express the volume in part (a) in terms of the height h of the ring. Notice that the volume depends only on h, not on r_1 or r_2.

29–32 ||| Evaluate the iterated integral by converting to polar coordinates.

29. $\displaystyle\int_{0}^{1}\int_{0}^{\sqrt{1-x^2}} e^{x^2+y^2}\, dy\, dx$

30. $\displaystyle\int_{-a}^{a}\int_{0}^{\sqrt{a^2-y^2}} (x^2 + y^2)^{3/2}\, dx\, dy$

31. $\int_0^2 \int_{-\sqrt{4-y^2}}^{\sqrt{4-y^2}} x^2 y^2 \, dx \, dy$ **32.** $\int_0^2 \int_0^{\sqrt{2x-x^2}} \sqrt{x^2+y^2} \, dy \, dx$

33. A swimming pool is circular with a 40-ft diameter. The depth is constant along east-west lines and increases linearly from 2 ft at the south end to 7 ft at the north end. Find the volume of water in the pool.

34. An agricultural sprinkler distributes water in a circular pattern of radius 100 ft. It supplies water to a depth of e^{-r} feet per hour at a distance of r feet from the sprinkler.
   (a) What is the total amount of water supplied per hour to the region inside the circle of radius R centered at the sprinkler?
   (b) Determine an expression for the average amount of water per hour per square foot supplied to the region inside the circle of radius R.

35. Use polar coordinates to combine the sum

$$\int_{1/\sqrt{2}}^1 \int_{\sqrt{1-x^2}}^x xy \, dy \, dx + \int_1^{\sqrt{2}} \int_0^x xy \, dy \, dx + \int_{\sqrt{2}}^2 \int_0^{\sqrt{4-x^2}} xy \, dy \, dx$$

into one double integral. Then evaluate the double integral.

36. (a) We define the improper integral (over the entire plane $\mathbb{R}^2$)

$$I = \iint_{\mathbb{R}^2} e^{-(x^2+y^2)} \, dA = \int_{-\infty}^{\infty} \int_{-\infty}^{\infty} e^{-(x^2+y^2)} \, dy \, dx$$

$$= \lim_{a \to \infty} \iint_{D_a} e^{-(x^2+y^2)} \, dA$$

where D_a is the disk with radius a and center the origin. Show that

$$\int_{-\infty}^{\infty} \int_{-\infty}^{\infty} e^{-(x^2+y^2)} \, dA = \pi$$

(b) An equivalent definition of the improper integral in part (a) is

$$\iint_{\mathbb{R}^2} e^{-(x^2+y^2)} \, dA = \lim_{a \to \infty} \iint_{S_a} e^{-(x^2+y^2)} \, dA$$

where S_a is the square with vertices $(\pm a, \pm a)$. Use this to show that

$$\int_{-\infty}^{\infty} e^{-x^2} \, dx \int_{-\infty}^{\infty} e^{-y^2} \, dy = \pi$$

(c) Deduce that

$$\int_{-\infty}^{\infty} e^{-x^2} \, dx = \sqrt{\pi}$$

(d) By making the change of variable $t = \sqrt{2}\, x$, show that

$$\int_{-\infty}^{\infty} e^{-x^2/2} \, dx = \sqrt{2\pi}$$

(This is a fundamental result for probability and statistics.)

37. Use the result of Exercise 36 part (c) to evaluate the following integrals.
   (a) $\int_0^{\infty} x^2 e^{-x^2} \, dx$ (b) $\int_0^{\infty} \sqrt{x}\, e^{-x} \, dx$

16.5 Applications of Double Integrals

We have already seen one application of double integrals: computing volumes. Another geometric application is finding areas of surfaces and this will be done in the next section. In this section we explore physical applications such as computing mass, electric charge, center of mass, and moment of inertia. We will see that these physical ideas are also important when applied to probability density functions of two random variables.

Density and Mass

In Section 9.3 we were able to use single integrals to compute moments and the center of mass of a thin plate or lamina with constant density. But now, equipped with the double integral, we can consider a lamina with variable density. Suppose the lamina occupies a region D of the xy-plane and its **density** (in units of mass per unit area) at a point (x, y) in D is given by $\rho(x, y)$, where ρ is a continuous function on D. This means that

$$\rho(x, y) = \lim \frac{\Delta m}{\Delta A}$$

where Δm and ΔA are the mass and area of a small rectangle that contains (x, y) and the limit is taken as the dimensions of the rectangle approach 0. (See Figure 1.)

FIGURE 1

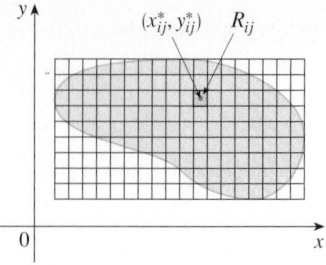

FIGURE 2

To find the total mass m of the lamina we divide a rectangle R containing D into sub-rectangles R_{ij} of the same size (as in Figure 2) and consider $\rho(x, y)$ to be 0 outside D. If we choose a point (x_{ij}^*, y_{ij}^*) in R_{ij}, then the mass of the part of the lamina that occupies R_{ij} is approximately $\rho(x_{ij}^*, y_{ij}^*) \, \Delta A$, where ΔA is the area of R_{ij}. If we add all such masses, we get an approximation to the total mass:

$$m \approx \sum_{i=1}^{k} \sum_{j=1}^{l} \rho(x_{ij}^*, y_{ij}^*) \, \Delta A$$

If we now increase the number of subrectangles, we obtain the total mass m of the lamina as the limiting value of the approximations:

$$\boxed{1} \qquad m = \lim_{k, l \to \infty} \sum_{i=1}^{k} \sum_{j=1}^{l} \rho(x_{ij}^*, y_{ij}^*) \, \Delta A = \iint_D \rho(x, y) \, dA$$

Physicists also consider other types of density that can be treated in the same manner. For example, if an electric charge is distributed over a region D and the charge density (in units of charge per unit area) is given by $\sigma(x, y)$ at a point (x, y) in D, then the total charge Q is given by

$$\boxed{2} \qquad Q = \iint_D \sigma(x, y) \, dA$$

EXAMPLE 1 Charge is distributed over the triangular region D in Figure 3 so that the charge density at (x, y) is $\sigma(x, y) = xy$, measured in coulombs per square meter (C/m^2). Find the total charge.

SOLUTION From Equation 2 and Figure 3 we have

$$Q = \iint_D \sigma(x, y) \, dA = \int_0^1 \int_{1-x}^1 xy \, dy \, dx$$

$$= \int_0^1 \left[x \frac{y^2}{2} \right]_{y=1-x}^{y=1} dx = \int_0^1 \frac{x}{2} [1^2 - (1 - x)^2] \, dx$$

$$= \frac{1}{2} \int_0^1 (2x^2 - x^3) \, dx = \frac{1}{2} \left[\frac{2x^3}{3} - \frac{x^4}{4} \right]_0^1 = \frac{5}{24}$$

Thus, the total charge is $\frac{5}{24}$ C.

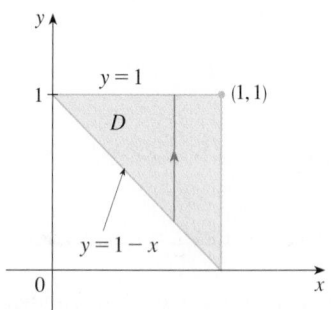

FIGURE 3

Moments and Centers of Mass

In Section 9.3 we found the center of mass of a lamina with constant density; here we consider a lamina with variable density. Suppose the lamina occupies a region D and has density function $\rho(x, y)$. Recall from Chapter 9 that we defined the moment of a particle about an axis as the product of its mass and its directed distance from the axis. We divide D into small rectangles as in Figure 2. Then the mass of R_{ij} is approximately $\rho(x_{ij}^*, y_{ij}^*) \, \Delta A$, so we can approximate the moment of R_{ij} with respect to the x-axis by

$$[\rho(x_{ij}^*, y_{ij}^*) \, \Delta A] y_{ij}^*$$

If we now add these quantities and take the limit as the number of subrectangles becomes large, we obtain the **moment** of the entire lamina **about the x-axis**:

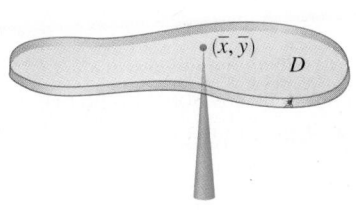

FIGURE 4

$$\boxed{\;\mathbf{3}\quad M_x = \lim_{m, n \to \infty} \sum_{i=1}^{m} \sum_{j=1}^{n} y_{ij}^* \, \rho(x_{ij}^*, y_{ij}^*) \, \Delta A = \iint_D y \rho(x, y) \, dA\;}$$

Similarly, the **moment about the y-axis** is

$$\boxed{\;\mathbf{4}\quad M_y = \lim_{m, n \to \infty} \sum_{i=1}^{m} \sum_{j=1}^{n} x_{ij}^* \, \rho(x_{ij}^*, y_{ij}^*) \, \Delta A = \iint_D x \rho(x, y) \, dA\;}$$

As before, we define the center of mass $(\bar{x}, \bar{y})$ so that $m\bar{x} = M_y$ and $m\bar{y} = M_x$. The physical significance is that the lamina behaves as if its entire mass is concentrated at its center of mass. Thus, the lamina balances horizontally when supported at its center of mass (see Figure 4).

5 The coordinates $(\bar{x}, \bar{y})$ of the center of mass of a lamina occupying the region D and having density function $\rho(x, y)$ are

$$\bar{x} = \frac{M_y}{m} = \frac{1}{m} \iint_D x \rho(x, y) \, dA \qquad \bar{y} = \frac{M_x}{m} = \frac{1}{m} \iint_D y \rho(x, y) \, dA$$

where the mass m is given by

$$m = \iint_D \rho(x, y) \, dA$$

EXAMPLE 2 Find the mass and center of mass of a triangular lamina with vertices $(0, 0)$, $(1, 0)$, and $(0, 2)$ if the density function is $\rho(x, y) = 1 + 3x + y$.

SOLUTION The triangle is shown in Figure 5. (Note that the equation of the upper boundary is $y = 2 - 2x$.) The mass of the lamina is

$$m = \iint_D \rho(x, y) \, dA = \int_0^1 \int_0^{2-2x} (1 + 3x + y) \, dy \, dx$$

$$= \int_0^1 \left[y + 3xy + \frac{y^2}{2} \right]_{y=0}^{y=2-2x} dx$$

$$= 4 \int_0^1 (1 - x^2) \, dx = 4 \left[x - \frac{x^3}{3} \right]_0^1 = \frac{8}{3}$$

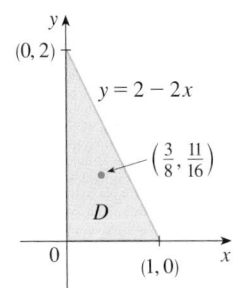

FIGURE 5

Then the formulas in (5) give

$$\bar{x} = \frac{1}{m} \iint_D x \rho(x, y) \, dA = \tfrac{3}{8} \int_0^1 \int_0^{2-2x} (x + 3x^2 + xy) \, dy \, dx$$

$$= \frac{3}{8} \int_0^1 \left[xy + 3x^2y + x\frac{y^2}{2} \right]_{y=0}^{y=2-2x} dx$$

$$= \frac{3}{2} \int_0^1 (x - x^3) \, dx = \frac{3}{2} \left[\frac{x^2}{2} - \frac{x^4}{4} \right]_0^1 = \frac{3}{8}$$

$$\bar{y} = \frac{1}{m} \iint_D y\rho(x, y)\, dA = \frac{3}{8} \int_0^1 \int_0^{2-2x} (y + 3xy + y^2)\, dy\, dx$$

$$= \frac{3}{8} \int_0^1 \left[\frac{y^2}{2} + 3x\frac{y^2}{2} + \frac{y^3}{3} \right]_{y=0}^{y=2-2x} dx = \frac{1}{4} \int_0^1 (7 - 9x - 3x^2 + 5x^3)\, dx$$

$$= \frac{1}{4} \left[7x - 9\frac{x^2}{2} - x^3 + 5\frac{x^4}{4} \right]_0^1 = \frac{11}{16}$$

The center of mass is at the point $\left(\frac{3}{8}, \frac{11}{16}\right)$.

EXAMPLE 3 The density at any point on a semicircular lamina is proportional to the distance from the center of the circle. Find the center of mass of the lamina.

SOLUTION Let's place the lamina as the upper half of the circle $x^2 + y^2 = a^2$ (see Figure 6). Then the distance from a point (x, y) to the center of the circle (the origin) is $\sqrt{x^2 + y^2}$. Therefore, the density function is

$$\rho(x, y) = K\sqrt{x^2 + y^2}$$

where K is some constant. Both the density function and the shape of the lamina suggest that we convert to polar coordinates. Then $\sqrt{x^2 + y^2} = r$ and the region D is given by $0 \leq r \leq a$, $0 \leq \theta \leq \pi$. Thus, the mass of the lamina is

$$m = \iint_D \rho(x, y)\, dA = \iint_D K\sqrt{x^2 + y^2}\, dA$$

$$= \int_0^\pi \int_0^a (Kr)\, r\, dr\, d\theta = K \int_0^\pi d\theta \int_0^a r^2\, dr$$

$$= K\pi \frac{r^3}{3} \Big]_0^a = \frac{K\pi a^3}{3}$$

Both the lamina and the density function are symmetric with respect to the y-axis, so the center of mass must lie on the y-axis, that is, $\bar{x} = 0$. The y-coordinate is given by

$$\bar{y} = \frac{1}{m} \iint_D y\rho(x, y)\, dA = \frac{3}{K\pi a^3} \int_0^\pi \int_0^a r\sin\theta\,(Kr)\, r\, dr\, d\theta$$

$$= \frac{3}{\pi a^3} \int_0^\pi \sin\theta\, d\theta \int_0^a r^3\, dr = \frac{3}{\pi a^3} \left[-\cos\theta\right]_0^\pi \left[\frac{r^4}{4}\right]_0^a$$

$$= \frac{3}{\pi a^3} \frac{2a^4}{4} = \frac{3a}{2\pi}$$

Therefore, the center of mass is located at the point $(0, 3a/(2\pi))$.

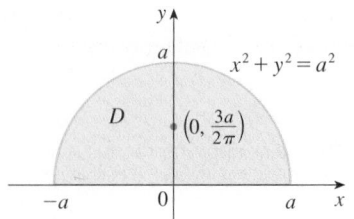

FIGURE 6

||| Compare the location of the center of mass in Example 3 with Example 4 in Section 9.3 where we found that the center of mass of a lamina with the same shape but uniform density is located at the point $(0, 4a/(3\pi))$.

||| **Moment of Inertia**

The **moment of inertia** (also called the **second moment**) of a particle of mass m about an axis is defined to be mr^2, where r is the distance from the particle to the axis. We extend this concept to a lamina with density function $\rho(x, y)$ and occupying a region D by proceeding as we did for ordinary moments. We divide D into small rectangles, approximate the moment of inertia of each subrectangle about the x-axis, and take the limit of the sum as the number of subrectangles becomes large. The result is the **moment of inertia** of the lamina **about the x-axis**:

| 6 | $$I_x = \lim_{m,\,n \to \infty} \sum_{i=1}^{m} \sum_{j=1}^{n} (y_{ij}^*)^2 \rho(x_{ij}^*, y_{ij}^*)\, \Delta A = \iint_D y^2 \rho(x, y)\, dA$$ |

Similarly, the **moment of inertia about the y-axis** is

| 7 | $$I_y = \lim_{m,\,n \to \infty} \sum_{i=1}^{m} \sum_{j=1}^{n} (x_{ij}^*)^2 \rho(x_{ij}^*, y_{ij}^*)\, \Delta A = \iint_D x^2 \rho(x, y)\, dA$$ |

It is also of interest to consider the **moment of inertia about the origin**, also called the **polar moment of inertia**:

| 8 | $$I_0 = \lim_{m,\,n \to \infty} \sum_{i=1}^{m} \sum_{j=1}^{n} [(x_{ij}^*)^2 + (y_{ij}^*)^2]\, \rho(x_{ij}^*, y_{ij}^*)\, \Delta A = \iint_D (x^2 + y^2)\rho(x, y)\, dA$$ |

Note that $I_0 = I_x + I_y$.

EXAMPLE 4 Find the moments of inertia I_x, I_y, and I_0 of a homogeneous disk D with density $\rho(x, y) = \rho$, center the origin, and radius a.

SOLUTION The boundary of D is the circle $x^2 + y^2 = a^2$ and in polar coordinates D is described by $0 \leqslant \theta \leqslant 2\pi$, $0 \leqslant r \leqslant a$. Let's compute I_0 first:

$$I_0 = \iint_D (x^2 + y^2)\rho\, dA = \rho \int_0^{2\pi} \int_0^a r^2\, r\, dr\, d\theta$$

$$= \rho \int_0^{2\pi} d\theta \int_0^a r^3\, dr = 2\pi\rho \left[\frac{r^4}{4}\right]_0^a = \frac{\pi\rho a^4}{2}.$$

Instead of computing I_x and I_y directly, we use the facts that $I_x + I_y = I_0$ and $I_x = I_y$ (from the symmetry of the problem). Thus

$$I_x = I_y = \frac{I_0}{2} = \frac{\pi\rho a^4}{4}$$

In Example 4 notice that the mass of the disk is

$$m = \text{density} \times \text{area} = \rho(\pi a^2)$$

so the moment of inertia of the disk about the origin (like a wheel about its axle) can be written as

$$I_0 = \tfrac{1}{2}ma^2$$

Thus, if we increase the mass or the radius of the disk, we thereby increase the moment of inertia. In general, the moment of inertia plays much the same role in rotational motion that mass plays in linear motion. The moment of inertia of a wheel is what makes it difficult to start or stop the rotation of the wheel, just as the mass of a car is what makes it difficult to start or stop the motion of the car.

The **radius of gyration of a lamina about an axis** is the number R such that

$$\boxed{9} \qquad mR^2 = I$$

where m is the mass of the lamina and I is the moment of inertia about the given axis. Equation 9 says that if the mass of the lamina were concentrated at a distance R from the axis, then the moment of inertia of this "point mass" would be the same as the moment of inertia of the lamina.

In particular, the radius of gyration $\bar{\bar{y}}$ with respect to the x-axis and the radius of gyration $\bar{\bar{x}}$ with respect to the y-axis are given by the equations

$$\boxed{10} \qquad m\bar{\bar{y}}^2 = I_x \qquad m\bar{\bar{x}}^2 = I_y$$

Thus $(\bar{\bar{x}}, \bar{\bar{y}})$ is the point at which the mass of the lamina can be concentrated without changing the moments of inertia with respect to the coordinate axes. (Note the analogy with the center of mass.)

EXAMPLE 5 Find the radius of gyration about the x-axis of the disk in Example 4.

SOLUTION As noted, the mass of the disk is $m = \rho \pi a^2$, so from Equations 10 we have

$$\bar{\bar{y}}^2 = \frac{I_x}{m} = \frac{\frac{1}{4}\pi\rho a^4}{\rho\pi a^2} = \frac{a^2}{4}$$

Therefore, the radius of gyration about the x-axis is

$$\bar{\bar{y}} = \frac{a}{2}$$

which is half the radius of the disk.

||||| Probability

In Section 9.5 we considered the *probability density function* f of a continuous random variable X. This means that $f(x) \geq 0$ for all x, $\int_{-\infty}^{\infty} f(x)\,dx = 1$, and the probability that X lies between a and b is found by integrating f from a to b:

$$P(a \leq X \leq b) = \int_a^b f(x)\,dx$$

Now we consider a pair of continuous random variables X and Y, such as the lifetimes of two components of a machine or the height and weight of an adult female chosen at random. The **joint density function** of X and Y is a function f of two variables such that the probability that (X, Y) lies in a region D is

$$P((X, Y) \in D) = \iint_D f(x, y)\,dA$$

In particular, if the region is a rectangle, the probability that X lies between a and b and Y lies between c and d is

$$P(a \leqslant X \leqslant b, \ c \leqslant Y \leqslant d) = \int_a^b \int_c^d f(x, y) \, dy \, dx$$

(See Figure 7.)

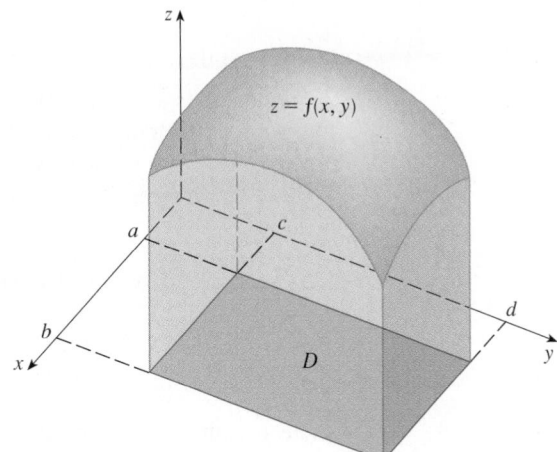

FIGURE 7

The probability that X lies between a and b and Y lies between c and d is the volume that lies above the rectangle $D = [a, b] \times [c, d]$ and below the graph of the joint density function.

Because probabilities aren't negative and are measured on a scale from 0 to 1, the joint density function has the following properties:

$$f(x, y) \geqslant 0 \qquad \iint_{\mathbb{R}^2} f(x, y) \, dA = 1$$

As in Exercise 36 in Section 16.4, the double integral over $\mathbb{R}^2$ is an improper integral defined as the limit of double integrals over expanding circles or squares and we can write

$$\iint_{\mathbb{R}^2} f(x, y) \, dA = \int_{-\infty}^{\infty} \int_{-\infty}^{\infty} f(x, y) \, dx \, dy = 1$$

EXAMPLE 6 If the joint density function for X and Y is given by

$$f(x, y) = \begin{cases} C(x + 2y) & \text{if } 0 \leqslant x \leqslant 10, \ 0 \leqslant y \leqslant 10 \\ 0 & \text{otherwise} \end{cases}$$

find the value of the constant C. Then find $P(X \leqslant 7, Y \geqslant 2)$.

SOLUTION We find the value of C by ensuring that the double integral of f is equal to 1. Because $f(x, y) = 0$ outside the rectangle $[0, 10] \times [0, 10]$, we have

$$\int_{-\infty}^{\infty} \int_{-\infty}^{\infty} f(x, y) \, dy \, dx = \int_0^{10} \int_0^{10} C(x + 2y) \, dy \, dx = C \int_0^{10} \left[xy + y^2 \right]_{y=0}^{y=10} dx$$

$$= C \int_0^{10} (10x + 100) \, dx = 1500C$$

Therefore, $1500C = 1$ and so $C = \frac{1}{1500}$.

Now we can compute the probability that X is at most 7 and Y is at least 2:

$$P(X \leqslant 7, Y \geqslant 2) = \int_{-\infty}^{7} \int_{2}^{\infty} f(x, y) \, dy \, dx = \int_{0}^{7} \int_{2}^{10} \tfrac{1}{1500}(x + 2y) \, dy \, dx$$

$$= \tfrac{1}{1500} \int_{0}^{7} \left[xy + y^2 \right]_{y=2}^{y=10} dx = \tfrac{1}{1500} \int_{0}^{7} (8x + 96) \, dx$$

$$= \tfrac{868}{1500} \approx 0.5787$$

Suppose X is a random variable with probability density function $f_1(x)$ and Y is a random variable with density function $f_2(y)$. Then X and Y are called **independent random variables** if their joint density function is the product of their individual density functions:

$$f(x, y) = f_1(x)f_2(y)$$

In Section 9.5 we modeled waiting times by using exponential density functions

$$f(t) = \begin{cases} 0 & \text{if } t < 0 \\ \mu^{-1}e^{-t/\mu} & \text{if } t \geqslant 0 \end{cases}$$

where μ is the mean waiting time. In the next example we consider a situation with two independent waiting times.

EXAMPLE 7 The manager of a movie theater determines that the average time moviegoers wait in line to buy a ticket for this week's film is 10 minutes and the average time they wait to buy popcorn is 5 minutes. Assuming that the waiting times are independent, find the probability that a moviegoer waits a total of less than 20 minutes before taking his or her seat.

SOLUTION Assuming that both the waiting time X for the ticket purchase and the waiting time Y in the refreshment line are modeled by exponential probability density functions, we can write the individual density functions as

$$f_1(x) = \begin{cases} 0 & \text{if } x < 0 \\ \tfrac{1}{10}e^{-x/10} & \text{if } x \geqslant 0 \end{cases} \qquad f_2(y) = \begin{cases} 0 & \text{if } y < 0 \\ \tfrac{1}{5}e^{-y/5} & \text{if } y \geqslant 0 \end{cases}$$

Since X and Y are independent, the joint density function is the product:

$$f(x, y) = f_1(x)f_2(y) = \begin{cases} \tfrac{1}{50}e^{-x/10}e^{-y/5} & \text{if } x \geqslant 0, \ y \geqslant 0 \\ 0 & \text{otherwise} \end{cases}$$

We are asked for the probability that $X + Y < 20$:

$$P(X + Y < 20) = P((X, Y) \in D)$$

where D is the triangular region shown in Figure 8. Thus

$$P(X + Y < 20) = \iint_{D} f(x, y) \, dA = \int_{0}^{20} \int_{0}^{20-x} \tfrac{1}{50}e^{-x/10}e^{-y/5} \, dy \, dx$$

$$= \tfrac{1}{50} \int_{0}^{20} \left[e^{-x/10}(-5)e^{-y/5} \right]_{y=0}^{y=20-x} dx$$

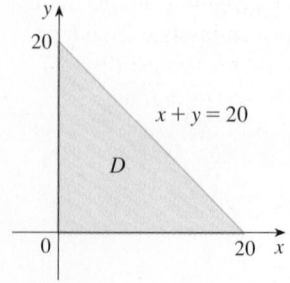

FIGURE 8

$$= \frac{1}{10} \int_0^{20} e^{-x/10} (1 - e^{(x-20)/5}) \, dx$$

$$= \frac{1}{10} \int_0^{20} (e^{-x/10} - e^{-4} e^{x/10}) \, dx$$

$$= 1 + e^{-4} - 2e^{-2} \approx 0.7476$$

This means that about 75% of the moviegoers wait less than 20 minutes before taking their seats.

Expected Values

Recall from Section 9.5 that if X is a random variable with probability density function f, then its *mean* is

$$\mu = \int_{-\infty}^{\infty} x f(x) \, dx$$

Now if X and Y are random variables with joint density function f, we define the **X-mean** and **Y-mean**, also called the **expected values** of X and Y, to be

$$\boxed{11} \qquad \mu_1 = \iint_{\mathbb{R}^2} x f(x, y) \, dA \qquad \mu_2 = \iint_{\mathbb{R}^2} y f(x, y) \, dA$$

Notice how closely the expressions for μ_1 and μ_2 in (11) resemble the moments M_x and M_y of a lamina with density function ρ in Equations 3 and 4. In fact, we can think of probability as being like continuously distributed mass. We calculate probability the way we calculate mass—by integrating a density function. And because the total "probability mass" is 1, the expressions for $\bar{x}$ and $\bar{y}$ in (5) show that we can think of the expected values of X and Y, μ_1 and μ_2, as the coordinates of the "center of mass" of the probability distribution.

In the next example we deal with normal distributions. As in Section 9.5, a single random variable is *normally distributed* if its probability density function is of the form

$$f(x) = \frac{1}{\sigma \sqrt{2\pi}} e^{-(x-\mu)^2/(2\sigma^2)}$$

where μ is the mean and σ is the standard deviation.

EXAMPLE 8 A factory produces (cylindrically shaped) roller bearings that are sold as having diameter 4.0 cm and length 6.0 cm. In fact, the diameters X are normally distributed with mean 4.0 cm and standard deviation 0.01 cm while the lengths Y are normally distributed with mean 6.0 cm and standard deviation 0.01 cm. Assuming that X and Y are independent, write the joint density function and graph it. Find the probability that a bearing randomly chosen from the production line has either length or diameter that differs from the mean by more than 0.02 cm.

SOLUTION We are given that X and Y are normally distributed with $\mu_1 = 4.0$, $\mu_2 = 6.0$, and $\sigma_1 = \sigma_2 = 0.01$. So the individual density functions for X and Y are

$$f_1(x) = \frac{1}{0.01 \sqrt{2\pi}} e^{-(x-4)^2/0.0002} \qquad f_2(y) = \frac{1}{0.01 \sqrt{2\pi}} e^{-(y-6)^2/0.0002}$$

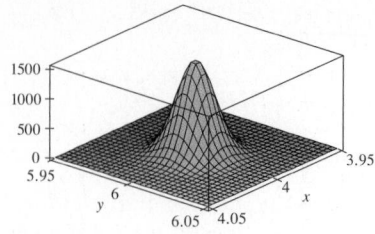

FIGURE 9

Graph of the bivariate normal joint
density function in Example 8

Since X and Y are independent, the joint density function is the product:

$$f(x, y) = f_1(x)f_2(y) = \frac{1}{0.0002\pi} e^{-(x-4)^2/0.0002} e^{-(y-6)^2/0.0002}$$

$$= \frac{5000}{\pi} e^{-5000[(x-4)^2+(y-6)^2]}$$

A graph of this function is shown in Figure 9.

Let's first calculate the probability that both X and Y differ from their means by less than 0.02 cm. Using a calculator or computer to estimate the integral, we have

$$P(3.98 < X < 4.02, 5.98 < Y < 6.02) = \int_{3.98}^{4.02} \int_{5.98}^{6.02} f(x, y)\, dy\, dx$$

$$= \frac{5000}{\pi} \int_{3.98}^{4.02} \int_{5.98}^{6.02} e^{-5000[(x-4)^2+(y-6)^2]}\, dy\, dx$$

$$\approx 0.91$$

Then the probability that either X or Y differs from its mean by more than 0.02 cm is approximately

$$1 - 0.91 = 0.09$$

16.5 Exercises

1. Electric charge is distributed over the rectangle $1 \leqslant x \leqslant 3$, $0 \leqslant y \leqslant 2$ so that the charge density at (x, y) is $\sigma(x, y) = 2xy + y^2$ (measured in coulombs per square meter). Find the total charge on the rectangle.

2. Electric charge is distributed over the disk $x^2 + y^2 \leqslant 4$ so that the charge density at (x, y) is $\sigma(x, y) = x + y + x^2 + y^2$ (measured in coulombs per square meter). Find the total charge on the disk.

3–10 ▮▮▮ Find the mass and center of mass of the lamina that occupies the region D and has the given density function ρ.

3. $D = \{(x, y) \mid 0 \leqslant x \leqslant 2, -1 \leqslant y \leqslant 1\}$; $\rho(x, y) = xy^2$

4. $D = \{(x, y) \mid 0 \leqslant x \leqslant a, 0 \leqslant y \leqslant b\}$; $\rho(x, y) = cxy$

5. D is the triangular region with vertices $(0, 0)$, $(2, 1)$, $(0, 3)$; $\rho(x, y) = x + y$

6. D is the triangular region with vertices $(0, 0)$, $(1, 1)$, $(4, 0)$; $\rho(x, y) = x$

7. D is bounded by $y = e^x$, $y = 0$, $x = 0$, and $x = 1$; $\rho(x, y) = y$

8. D is bounded by $y = \sqrt{x}$, $y = 0$, and $x = 1$; $\rho(x, y) = x$

9. D is bounded by the parabola $x = y^2$ and the line $y = x - 2$; $\rho(x, y) = 3$

10. $D = \{(x, y) \mid 0 \leqslant y \leqslant \cos x, 0 \leqslant x \leqslant \pi/2\}$; $\rho(x, y) = x$

11. A lamina occupies the part of the disk $x^2 + y^2 \leqslant 1$ in the first quadrant. Find its center of mass if the density at any point is proportional to its distance from the x-axis.

12. Find the center of mass of the lamina in Exercise 11 if the density at any point is proportional to the square of its distance from the origin.

13. Find the center of mass of a lamina in the shape of an isosceles right triangle with equal sides of length a if the density at any point is proportional to the square of the distance from the vertex opposite the hypotenuse.

14. A lamina occupies the region inside the circle $x^2 + y^2 = 2y$ but outside the circle $x^2 + y^2 = 1$. Find the center of mass if the density at any point is inversely proportional to its distance from the origin.

15. Find the moments of inertia I_x, I_y, I_0 for the lamina of Exercise 7.

16. Find the moments of inertia I_x, I_y, I_0 for the lamina of Exercise 12.

17. Find the moments of inertia I_x, I_y, I_0 for the lamina of Exercise 9.

18. Consider a square fan blade with sides of length 2 and the lower left corner placed at the origin. If the density of the blade is $\rho(x, y) = 1 + 0.1x$, is it more difficult to rotate the blade about the x-axis or the y-axis?

CAS **19–20** ▐▐ Use a computer algebra system to find the mass, center of mass, and moments of inertia of the lamina that occupies the region D and has the given density function.

19. $D = \{(x, y) \mid 0 \leqslant y \leqslant \sin x, \ 0 \leqslant x \leqslant \pi\}$; $\rho(x, y) = xy$

20. D is enclosed by the cardioid $r = 1 + \cos \theta$;
$\rho(x, y) = \sqrt{x^2 + y^2}$

21. A lamina with constant density $\rho(x, y) = \rho$ occupies a square with vertices $(0, 0)$, $(a, 0)$, (a, a), and $(0, a)$. Find the moments of inertia I_x and I_y and the radii of gyration $\bar{\bar{x}}$ and $\bar{\bar{y}}$.

22. A lamina with constant density $\rho(x, y) = \rho$ occupies the region under the curve $y = \sin x$ from $x = 0$ to $x = \pi$. Find the moments of inertia I_x and I_y and the radii of gyration $\bar{\bar{x}}$ and $\bar{\bar{y}}$.

23. The joint density function for a pair of random variables X and Y is

$$f(x, y) = \begin{cases} Cx(1 + y) & \text{if } 0 \leqslant x \leqslant 1, \ 0 \leqslant y \leqslant 2 \\ 0 & \text{otherwise} \end{cases}$$

(a) Find the value of the constant C.
(b) Find $P(X \leqslant 1, Y \leqslant 1)$.
(c) Find $P(X + Y \leqslant 1)$.

24. (a) Verify that

$$f(x, y) = \begin{cases} 4xy & \text{if } 0 \leqslant x \leqslant 1, \ 0 \leqslant y \leqslant 1 \\ 0 & \text{otherwise} \end{cases}$$

is a joint density function.
(b) If X and Y are random variables whose joint density function is the function f in part (a), find
  (i) $P(X \geqslant \frac{1}{2})$ (ii) $P(X \geqslant \frac{1}{2}, Y \leqslant \frac{1}{2})$
(c) Find the expected values of X and Y.

25. Suppose X and Y are random variables with joint density function

$$f(x, y) = \begin{cases} 0.1e^{-(0.5x + 0.2y)} & \text{if } x \geqslant 0, \ y \geqslant 0 \\ 0 & \text{otherwise} \end{cases}$$

(a) Verify that f is indeed a joint density function.
(b) Find the following probabilities.
  (i) $P(Y \geqslant 1)$ (ii) $P(X \leqslant 2, Y \leqslant 4)$
(c) Find the expected values of X and Y.

26. (a) A lamp has two bulbs of a type with an average lifetime of 1000 hours. Assuming that we can model the probability of failure of these bulbs by an exponential density function

with mean $\mu = 1000$, find the probability that both of the lamp's bulbs fail within 1000 hours.
(b) Another lamp has just one bulb of the same type as in part (a). If one bulb burns out and is replaced by a bulb of the same type, find the probability that the two bulbs fail within a total of 1000 hours.

CAS **27.** Suppose that X and Y are independent random variables, where X is normally distributed with mean 45 and standard deviation 0.5 and Y is normally distributed with mean 20 and standard deviation 0.1.
(a) Find $P(40 \leqslant X \leqslant 50, 20 \leqslant Y \leqslant 25)$.
(b) Find $P(4(X - 45)^2 + 100(Y - 20)^2 \leqslant 2)$.

28. Xavier and Yolanda both have classes that end at noon and they agree to meet every day after class. They arrive at the coffee shop independently. Xavier's arrival time is X and Yolanda's arrival time is Y, where X and Y are measured in minutes after noon. The individual density functions are

$$f_1(x) = \begin{cases} e^{-x} & \text{if } x \geqslant 0 \\ 0 & \text{if } x < 0 \end{cases} \qquad f_2(y) = \begin{cases} \frac{1}{50}y & \text{if } 0 \leqslant y \leqslant 10 \\ 0 & \text{otherwise} \end{cases}$$

(Xavier arrives sometime after noon and is more likely to arrive promptly than late. Yolanda always arrives by 12:10 P.M. and is more likely to arrive late than promptly.) After Yolanda arrives, she'll wait for up to half an hour for Xavier, but he won't wait for her. Find the probability that they meet.

29. When studying the spread of an epidemic, we assume that the probability that an infected individual will spread the disease to an uninfected individual is a function of the distance between them. Consider a circular city of radius 10 mi in which the population is uniformly distributed. For an uninfected individual at a fixed point $A(x_0, y_0)$, assume that the probability function is given by

$$f(P) = \tfrac{1}{20}[20 - d(P, A)]$$

where $d(P, A)$ denotes the distance between P and A.
(a) Suppose the exposure of a person to the disease is the sum of the probabilities of catching the disease from all members of the population. Assume that the infected people are uniformly distributed throughout the city, with k infected individuals per square mile. Find a double integral that represents the exposure of a person residing at A.
(b) Evaluate the integral for the case in which A is the center of the city and for the case in which A is located on the edge of the city. Where would you prefer to live?

▐▐▐ 16.6 Surface Area

▐▐▐▐ In Section 17.6 we will deal with areas of more general surfaces, called parametric surfaces, and so it is possible to omit this section if that later section will be covered.

In this section we apply double integrals to the problem of computing the area of a surface. In Section 9.2 we found the area of a very special type of surface—a surface of revolution—by the methods of single-variable calculus. Here we compute the area of a surface with equation $z = f(x, y)$, the graph of a function of two variables.

FIGURE 1

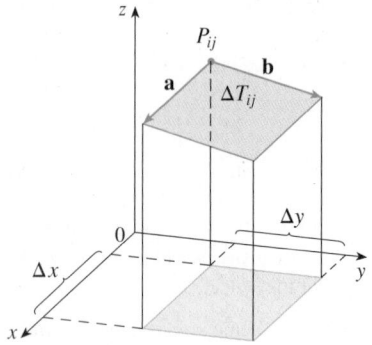

FIGURE 2

Let S be a surface with equation $z = f(x, y)$, where f has continuous partial derivatives. For simplicity in deriving the surface area formula, we assume that $f(x, y) \geqslant 0$ and the domain D of f is a rectangle. We divide D into small rectangles R_{ij} with area $\Delta A = \Delta x \, \Delta y$. If (x_i, y_j) is the corner of R_{ij} closest to the origin, let $P_{ij}(x_i, y_j, f(x_i, y_j))$ be the point on S directly above it (see Figure 1). The tangent plane to S at P_{ij} is an approximation to S near P_{ij}. So the area ΔT_{ij} of the part of this tangent plane (a parallelogram) that lies directly above R_{ij} is an approximation to the area ΔS_{ij} of the part of S that lies directly above R_{ij}. Thus, the sum $\Sigma\Sigma \, \Delta T_{ij}$ is an approximation to the total area of S, and this approximation appears to improve as the number of rectangles increases. Therefore, we define the **surface area** of S to be

$$\boxed{1} \qquad A(S) = \lim_{m,\,n \to \infty} \sum_{i=1}^{m} \sum_{j=1}^{n} \Delta T_{ij}$$

To find a formula that is more convenient than Equation 1 for computational purposes, we let $\mathbf{a}$ and $\mathbf{b}$ be the vectors that start at P_{ij} and lie along the sides of the parallelogram with area ΔT_{ij}. (See Figure 2.) Then $\Delta T_{ij} = |\mathbf{a} \times \mathbf{b}|$. Recall from Section 15.3 that $f_x(x_i, y_j)$ and $f_y(x_i, y_j)$ are the slopes of the tangent lines through P_{ij} in the directions of $\mathbf{a}$ and $\mathbf{b}$. Therefore

$$\mathbf{a} = \Delta x \, \mathbf{i} + f_x(x_i, y_j) \, \Delta x \, \mathbf{k}$$

$$\mathbf{b} = \Delta y \, \mathbf{j} + f_y(x_i, y_j) \, \Delta y \, \mathbf{k}$$

and

$$\mathbf{a} \times \mathbf{b} = \begin{vmatrix} \mathbf{i} & \mathbf{j} & \mathbf{k} \\ \Delta x & 0 & f_x(x_i, y_j) \, \Delta x \\ 0 & \Delta y & f_y(x_i, y_j) \, \Delta y \end{vmatrix}$$

$$= -f_x(x_i, y_j) \, \Delta x \, \Delta y \, \mathbf{i} - f_y(x_i, y_j) \, \Delta x \, \Delta y \, \mathbf{j} + \Delta x \, \Delta y \, \mathbf{k}$$

$$= [-f_x(x_i, y_j)\mathbf{i} - f_y(x_i, y_j)\mathbf{j} + \mathbf{k}] \, \Delta A$$

Thus $\qquad \Delta T_{ij} = |\mathbf{a} \times \mathbf{b}| = \sqrt{[f_x(x_i, y_j)]^2 + [f_y(x_i, y_j)]^2 + 1} \; \Delta A$

From Definition 1 we then have

$$A(S) = \lim_{m,\,n \to \infty} \sum_{i=1}^{m} \sum_{j=1}^{n} \Delta T_{ij}$$

$$= \lim_{m,\,n \to \infty} \sum_{i=1}^{m} \sum_{j=1}^{n} \sqrt{[f_x(x_i, y_j)]^2 + [f_y(x_i, y_j)]^2 + 1} \; \Delta A$$

and by the definition of a double integral we get the following formula.

$\boxed{2}$ The area of the surface with equation $z = f(x, y)$, $(x, y) \in D$, where f_x and f_y are continuous, is

$$A(S) = \iint\limits_{D} \sqrt{[f_x(x, y)]^2 + [f_y(x, y)]^2 + 1} \; dA$$

We will verify in Section 17.6 that this formula is consistent with our previous formula for the area of a surface of revolution. If we use the alternative notation for partial derivatives, we can rewrite Formula 2 as follows:

$$\boxed{3} \qquad A(S) = \iint_D \sqrt{1 + \left(\frac{\partial z}{\partial x}\right)^2 + \left(\frac{\partial z}{\partial y}\right)^2}\ dA$$

Notice the similarity between the surface area formula in Equation 3 and the arc length formula from Section 9.1:

$$L = \int_a^b \sqrt{1 + \left(\frac{dy}{dx}\right)^2}\ dx$$

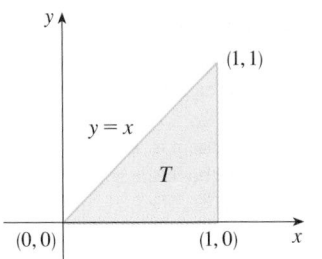

FIGURE 3

EXAMPLE 1 Find the surface area of the part of the surface $z = x^2 + 2y$ that lies above the triangular region T in the xy-plane with vertices $(0, 0)$, $(1, 0)$, and $(1, 1)$.

SOLUTION The region T is shown in Figure 3 and is described by

$$T = \{(x, y) \mid 0 \le x \le 1,\ 0 \le y \le x\}$$

Using Formula 2 with $f(x, y) = x^2 + 2y$, we get

$$A = \iint_T \sqrt{(2x)^2 + (2)^2 + 1}\ dA = \int_0^1 \int_0^x \sqrt{4x^2 + 5}\ dy\ dx$$

$$= \int_0^1 x\sqrt{4x^2 + 5}\ dx = \tfrac{1}{8} \cdot \tfrac{2}{3}(4x^2 + 5)^{3/2}\big]_0^1 = \tfrac{1}{12}\left(27 - 5\sqrt{5}\right)$$

FIGURE 4

Figure 4 shows the portion of the surface whose area we have just computed.

EXAMPLE 2 Find the area of the part of the paraboloid $z = x^2 + y^2$ that lies under the plane $z = 9$.

SOLUTION The plane intersects the paraboloid in the circle $x^2 + y^2 = 9$, $z = 9$. Therefore, the given surface lies above the disk D with center the origin and radius 3 (see Figure 5). Using Formula 3, we have

$$A = \iint_D \sqrt{1 + \left(\frac{\partial z}{\partial x}\right)^2 + \left(\frac{\partial z}{\partial y}\right)^2}\ dA = \iint_D \sqrt{1 + (2x)^2 + (2y)^2}\ dA$$

$$= \iint_D \sqrt{1 + 4(x^2 + y^2)}\ dA$$

Converting to polar coordinates, we obtain

$$A = \int_0^{2\pi} \int_0^3 \sqrt{1 + 4r^2}\ r\ dr\ d\theta = \int_0^{2\pi} d\theta \int_0^3 \tfrac{1}{8}\sqrt{1 + 4r^2}\ (8r)\ dr$$

$$= 2\pi\left(\tfrac{1}{8}\right)\tfrac{2}{3}(1 + 4r^2)^{3/2}\big]_0^3 = \frac{\pi}{6}\left(37\sqrt{37} - 1\right)$$

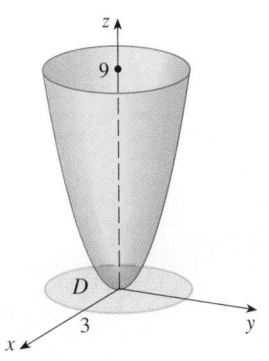

FIGURE 5

16.6 Exercises

1–12 ▐▐▐ Find the area of the surface.

1. The part of the plane $z = 2 + 3x + 4y$ that lies above the rectangle $[0, 5] \times [1, 4]$

2. The part of the plane $2x + 5y + z = 10$ that lies inside the cylinder $x^2 + y^2 = 9$

3. The part of the plane $3x + 2y + z = 6$ that lies in the first octant

4. The part of the surface $z = 1 + 3x + 2y^2$ that lies above the triangle with vertices $(0, 0)$, $(0, 1)$, and $(2, 1)$

5. The part of the cylinder $y^2 + z^2 = 9$ that lies above the rectangle with vertices $(0, 0)$, $(4, 0)$, $(0, 2)$, and $(4, 2)$

6. The part of the paraboloid $z = 4 - x^2 - y^2$ that lies above the xy-plane

7. The part of the hyperbolic paraboloid $z = y^2 - x^2$ that lies between the cylinders $x^2 + y^2 = 1$ and $x^2 + y^2 = 4$

8. The surface $z = \frac{2}{3}(x^{3/2} + y^{3/2})$, $0 \le x \le 1$, $0 \le y \le 1$

9. The part of the surface $z = xy$ that lies within the cylinder $x^2 + y^2 = 1$

10. The part of the sphere $x^2 + y^2 + z^2 = 4$ that lies above the plane $z = 1$

11. The part of the sphere $x^2 + y^2 + z^2 = a^2$ that lies within the cylinder $x^2 + y^2 = ax$ and above the xy-plane

12. The part of the sphere $x^2 + y^2 + z^2 = 4z$ that lies inside the paraboloid $z = x^2 + y^2$

13–14 ▐▐▐ Find the area of the surface correct to four decimal places by expressing the area in terms of a single integral and using your calculator to estimate the integral.

13. The part of the surface $z = e^{-x^2 - y^2}$ that lies above the disk $x^2 + y^2 \le 4$

14. The part of the surface $z = \cos(x^2 + y^2)$ that lies inside the cylinder $x^2 + y^2 = 1$

15. (a) Use the Midpoint Rule for double integrals (see Section 16.1) with four squares to estimate the surface area of the portion of the paraboloid $z = x^2 + y^2$ that lies above the square $[0, 1] \times [0, 1]$.

(b) Use a computer algebra system to approximate the surface area in part (a) to four decimal places. Compare with the answer to part (a).

16. (a) Use the Midpoint Rule for double integrals with $m = n = 2$ to estimate the area of the surface $z = xy + x^2 + y^2$, $0 \le x \le 2$, $0 \le y \le 2$.

(b) Use a computer algebra system to approximate the surface area in part (a) to four decimal places. Compare with the answer to part (a).

17. Find the exact area of the surface $z = 1 + 2x + 3y + 4y^2$, $1 \le x \le 4$, $0 \le y \le 1$.

18. Find the exact area of the surface

$$z = 1 + x + y + x^2 \qquad -2 \le x \le 1 \quad -1 \le y \le 1$$

Illustrate by graphing the surface.

19. Find, to four decimal places, the area of the part of the surface $z = 1 + x^2 y^2$ that lies above the disk $x^2 + y^2 \le 1$.

20. Find, to four decimal places, the area of the part of the surface $z = (1 + x^2)/(1 + y^2)$ that lies above the square $|x| + |y| \le 1$. Illustrate by graphing this part of the surface.

21. Show that the area of the part of the plane $z = ax + by + c$ that projects onto a region D in the xy-plane with area $A(D)$ is $\sqrt{a^2 + b^2 + 1}\, A(D)$.

22. If you attempt to use Formula 2 to find the area of the top half of the sphere $x^2 + y^2 + z^2 = a^2$, you have a slight problem because the double integral is improper. In fact, the integrand has an infinite discontinuity at every point of the boundary circle $x^2 + y^2 = a^2$. However, the integral can be computed as the limit of the integral over the disk $x^2 + y^2 \le t^2$ as $t \to a^-$. Use this method to show that the area of a sphere of radius a is $4\pi a^2$.

23. Find the area of the finite part of the paraboloid $y = x^2 + z^2$ cut off by the plane $y = 25$. [*Hint:* Project the surface onto the xz-plane.]

24. The figure shows the surface created when the cylinder $y^2 + z^2 = 1$ intersects the cylinder $x^2 + z^2 = 1$. Find the area of this surface.

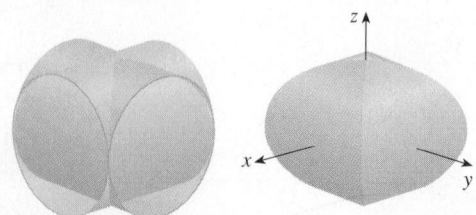

16.7 Triple Integrals

Just as we defined single integrals for functions of one variable and double integrals for functions of two variables, so we can define triple integrals for functions of three variables. Let's first deal with the simplest case where f is defined on a rectangular box:

$$\boxed{1} \qquad B = \{(x, y, z) \mid a \leqslant x \leqslant b,\ c \leqslant y \leqslant d,\ r \leqslant z \leqslant s\}$$

The first step is to divide B into sub-boxes. We do this by dividing the interval $[a, b]$ into l subintervals $[x_{i-1}, x_i]$ of equal width Δx, dividing $[c, d]$ into m subintervals of width Δy, and dividing $[r, s]$ into n subintervals of width Δz. The planes through the endpoints of these subintervals parallel to the coordinate planes divide the box B into lmn sub-boxes

$$B_{ijk} = [x_{i-1}, x_i] \times [y_{j-1}, y_j] \times [z_{k-1}, z_k]$$

which are shown in Figure 1. Each sub-box has volume $\Delta V = \Delta x\, \Delta y\, \Delta z$.

Then we form the **triple Riemann sum**

$$\boxed{2} \qquad \sum_{i=1}^{l} \sum_{j=1}^{m} \sum_{k=1}^{n} f(x_{ijk}^*, y_{ijk}^*, z_{ijk}^*)\, \Delta V$$

where the sample point $(x_{ijk}^*, y_{ijk}^*, z_{ijk}^*)$ is in B_{ijk}. By analogy with the definition of a double integral (16.1.5), we define the triple integral as the limit of the triple Riemann sums in (2).

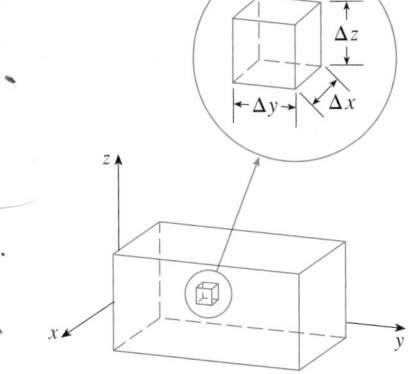

FIGURE 1

> **3 Definition** The **triple integral** of f over the box B is
>
> $$\iiint_B f(x, y, z)\, dV = \lim_{l, m, n \to \infty} \sum_{i=1}^{l} \sum_{j=1}^{m} \sum_{k=1}^{n} f(x_{ijk}^*, y_{ijk}^*, z_{ijk}^*)\, \Delta V$$
>
> if this limit exists.

Again, the triple integral always exists if f is continuous. We can choose the sample point to be any point in the sub-box, but if we choose it to be the point (x_i, y_j, z_k) we get a simpler-looking expression for the triple integral:

$$\iiint_B f(x, y, z)\, dV = \lim_{l, m, n \to \infty} \sum_{i=1}^{l} \sum_{j=1}^{m} \sum_{k=1}^{n} f(x_i, y_j, z_k)\, \Delta V$$

Just as for double integrals, the practical method for evaluating triple integrals is to express them as iterated integrals as follows.

> **4 Fubini's Theorem for Triple Integrals** If f is continuous on the rectangular box $B = [a, b] \times [c, d] \times [r, s]$, then
>
> $$\iiint_B f(x, y, z)\, dV = \int_r^s \int_c^d \int_a^b f(x, y, z)\, dx\, dy\, dz$$

The iterated integral on the right side of Fubini's Theorem means that we integrate first with respect to x (keeping y and z fixed), then we integrate with respect to y (keeping z fixed), and finally we integrate with respect to z. There are five other possible orders in which we can integrate, all of which give the same value. For instance, if we integrate with respect to y, then z, and then x, we have

$$\iiint_B f(x, y, z)\, dV = \int_a^b \int_r^s \int_c^d f(x, y, z)\, dy\, dz\, dx$$

EXAMPLE 1 Evaluate the triple integral $\iiint_B xyz^2\, dV$, where B is the rectangular box given by

$$B = \{(x, y, z) \mid 0 \leqslant x \leqslant 1,\ -1 \leqslant y \leqslant 2,\ 0 \leqslant z \leqslant 3\}$$

SOLUTION We could use any of the six possible orders of integration. If we choose to integrate with respect to x, then y, and then z, we obtain

$$\iiint_B xyz^2\, dV = \int_0^3 \int_{-1}^2 \int_0^1 xyz^2\, dx\, dy\, dz = \int_0^3 \int_{-1}^2 \left[\frac{x^2 yz^2}{2} \right]_{x=0}^{x=1} dy\, dz$$

$$= \int_0^3 \int_{-1}^2 \frac{yz^2}{2}\, dy\, dz = \int_0^3 \left[\frac{y^2 z^2}{4} \right]_{y=-1}^{y=2} dz$$

$$= \int_0^3 \frac{3z^2}{4}\, dz = \frac{z^3}{4} \bigg]_0^3 = \frac{27}{4}$$

Now we define the **triple integral over a general bounded region E** in three-dimensional space (a solid) by much the same procedure that we used for double integrals (16.3.2). We enclose E in a box B of the type given by Equation 1. Then we define a function F so that it agrees with f on E but is 0 for points in B that are outside E. By definition,

$$\iiint_E f(x, y, z)\, dV = \iiint_B F(x, y, z)\, dV$$

This integral exists if f is continuous and the boundary of E is "reasonably smooth." The triple integral has essentially the same properties as the double integral (Properties 6–9 in Section 16.3).

We restrict our attention to continuous functions f and to certain simple types of regions. A solid region E is said to be of **type 1** if it lies between the graphs of two continuous functions of x and y, that is,

$$\boxed{5} \qquad E = \{(x, y, z) \mid (x, y) \in D,\ u_1(x, y) \leqslant z \leqslant u_2(x, y)\}$$

where D is the projection of E onto the xy-plane as shown in Figure 2. Notice that the upper boundary of the solid E is the surface with equation $z = u_2(x, y)$, while the lower boundary is the surface $z = u_1(x, y)$.

By the same sort of argument that led to (16.3.3), it can be shown that if E is a type 1 region given by Equation 5, then

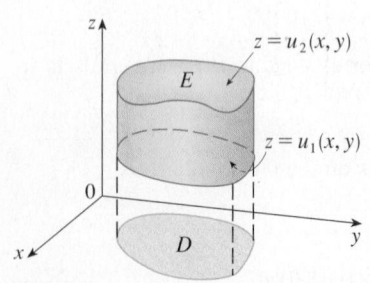

FIGURE 2
A type 1 solid region

$$\boxed{6} \qquad \iiint_E f(x, y, z)\, dV = \iint_D \left[\int_{u_1(x, y)}^{u_2(x, y)} f(x, y, z)\, dz \right] dA$$

The meaning of the inner integral on the right side of Equation 6 is that x and y are held fixed, and therefore $u_1(x, y)$ and $u_2(x, y)$ are regarded as constants, while $f(x, y, z)$ is integrated with respect to z.

In particular, if the projection D of E onto the xy-plane is a type I plane region (as in Figure 3), then

$$E = \{(x, y, z) \mid a \leqslant x \leqslant b, \ g_1(x) \leqslant y \leqslant g_2(x), \ u_1(x, y) \leqslant z \leqslant u_2(x, y)\}$$

and Equation 6 becomes

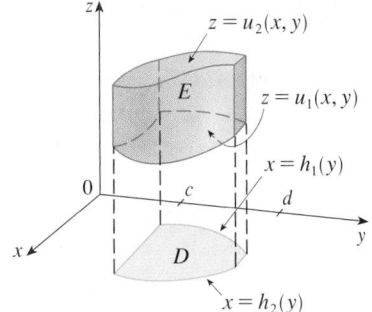

FIGURE 3

A type 1 solid region

[7]
$$\iiint_E f(x, y, z) \, dV = \int_a^b \int_{g_1(x)}^{g_2(x)} \int_{u_1(x, y)}^{u_2(x, y)} f(x, y, z) \, dz \, dy \, dx$$

If, on the other hand, D is a type II plane region (as in Figure 4), then

$$E = \{(x, y, z) \mid c \leqslant y \leqslant d, \ h_1(y) \leqslant x \leqslant h_2(y), \ u_1(x, y) \leqslant z \leqslant u_2(x, y)\}$$

and Equation 6 becomes

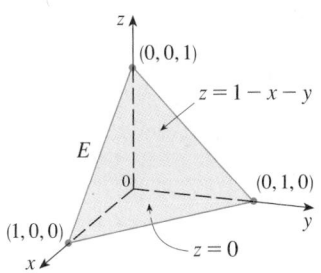

FIGURE 4

Another type 1 solid region

[8]
$$\iiint_E f(x, y, z) \, dV = \int_c^d \int_{h_1(y)}^{h_2(y)} \int_{u_1(x, y)}^{u_2(x, y)} f(x, y, z) \, dz \, dx \, dy$$

EXAMPLE 2 Evaluate $\iiint_E z \, dV$, where E is the solid tetrahedron bounded by the four planes $x = 0$, $y = 0$, $z = 0$, and $x + y + z = 1$.

SOLUTION When we set up a triple integral it's wise to draw *two* diagrams: one of the solid region E (see Figure 5) and one of its projection D on the xy-plane (see Figure 6). The lower boundary of the tetrahedron is the plane $z = 0$ and the upper boundary is the plane $x + y + z = 1$ (or $z = 1 - x - y$), so we use $u_1(x, y) = 0$ and $u_2(x, y) = 1 - x - y$ in Formula 7. Notice that the planes $x + y + z = 1$ and $z = 0$ intersect in the line $x + y = 1$ (or $y = 1 - x$) in the xy-plane. So the projection of E is the triangular region shown in Figure 6, and we have

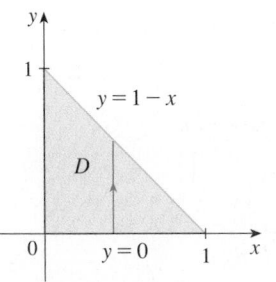

FIGURE 5

[9]
$$E = \{(x, y, z) \mid 0 \leqslant x \leqslant 1, \ 0 \leqslant y \leqslant 1 - x, \ 0 \leqslant z \leqslant 1 - x - y\}$$

This description of E as a type 1 region enables us to evaluate the integral as follows:

$$\iiint_E z \, dV = \int_0^1 \int_0^{1-x} \int_0^{1-x-y} z \, dz \, dy \, dx = \int_0^1 \int_0^{1-x} \left[\frac{z^2}{2}\right]_{z=0}^{z=1-x-y} dy \, dx$$

$$= \frac{1}{2} \int_0^1 \int_0^{1-x} (1 - x - y)^2 \, dy \, dx$$

$$= \frac{1}{2} \int_0^1 \left[-\frac{(1 - x - y)^3}{3}\right]_{y=0}^{y=1-x} dx$$

$$= \frac{1}{6} \int_0^1 (1 - x)^3 \, dx = \frac{1}{6} \left[-\frac{(1 - x)^4}{4}\right]_0^1 = \frac{1}{24}$$

FIGURE 6

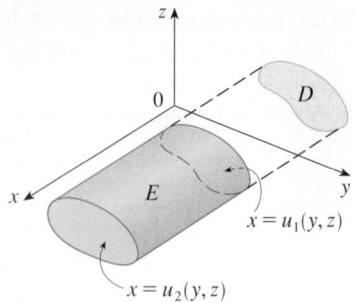

FIGURE 7

A type 2 region

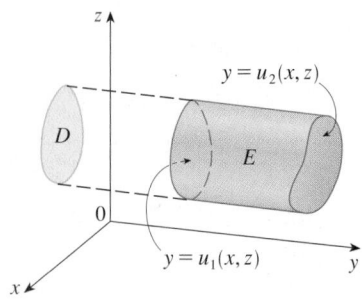

FIGURE 8

A type 3 region

Visual 16.7 illustrates how solid regions (including the one in Figure 9) project onto coordinate planes.

A solid region E is of **type 2** if it is of the form

$$E = \{(x, y, z) \,|\, (y, z) \in D, \; u_1(y, z) \leqslant x \leqslant u_2(y, z)\}$$

where, this time, D is the projection of E onto the yz-plane (see Figure 7). The back surface is $x = u_1(y, z)$, the front surface is $x = u_2(y, z)$, and we have

$$\boxed{10} \qquad \iiint_E f(x, y, z)\, dV = \iint_D \left[\int_{u_1(y,z)}^{u_2(y,z)} f(x, y, z)\, dx \right] dA$$

Finally, a **type 3** region is of the form

$$E = \{(x, y, z) \,|\, (x, z) \in D, \; u_1(x, z) \leqslant y \leqslant u_2(x, z)\}$$

where D is the projection of E onto the xz-plane, $y = u_1(x, z)$ is the left surface, and $y = u_2(x, z)$ is the right surface (see Figure 8). For this type of region we have

$$\boxed{11} \qquad \iiint_E f(x, y, z)\, dV = \iint_D \left[\int_{u_1(x,z)}^{u_2(x,z)} f(x, y, z)\, dy \right] dA$$

In each of Equations 10 and 11 there may be two possible expressions for the integral depending on whether D is a type I or type II plane region (and corresponding to Equations 7 and 8).

EXAMPLE 3 Evaluate $\iiint_E \sqrt{x^2 + z^2}\, dV$, where E is the region bounded by the paraboloid $y = x^2 + z^2$ and the plane $y = 4$.

SOLUTION The solid E is shown in Figure 9. If we regard it as a type 1 region, then we need to consider its projection D_1 onto the xy-plane, which is the parabolic region in Figure 10. (The trace of $y = x^2 + z^2$ in the plane $z = 0$ is the parabola $y = x^2$.)

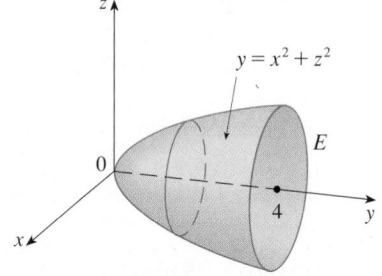

FIGURE 9

Region of integration

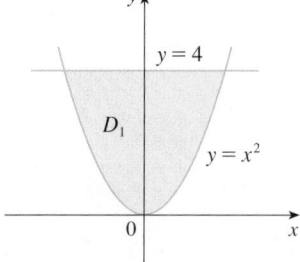

FIGURE 10

Projection on xy-plane

From $y = x^2 + z^2$ we obtain $z = \pm\sqrt{y - x^2}$, so the lower boundary surface of E is $z = -\sqrt{y - x^2}$ and the upper surface is $z = \sqrt{y - x^2}$. Therefore, the description of E as a type 1 region is

$$E = \left\{ (x, y, z) \,\middle|\, -2 \leqslant x \leqslant 2, \; x^2 \leqslant y \leqslant 4, \; -\sqrt{y - x^2} \leqslant z \leqslant \sqrt{y - x^2} \right\}$$

and so we obtain

$$\iiint_E \sqrt{x^2 + z^2}\, dV = \int_{-2}^{2} \int_{x^2}^{4} \int_{-\sqrt{y-x^2}}^{\sqrt{y-x^2}} \sqrt{x^2 + z^2}\, dz\, dy\, dx$$

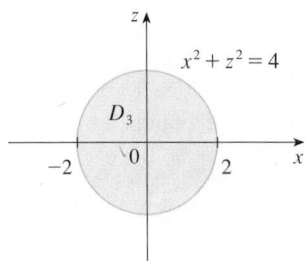

FIGURE 11
Projection on xz-plane

Although this expression is correct, it is extremely difficult to evaluate. So let's instead consider E as a type 3 region. As such, its projection D_3 onto the xz-plane is the disk $x^2 + z^2 \leqslant 4$ shown in Figure 11.

Then the left boundary of E is the paraboloid $y = x^2 + z^2$ and the right boundary is the plane $y = 4$, so taking $u_1(x, z) = x^2 + z^2$ and $u_2(x, z) = 4$ in Equation 11, we have

$$\iiint_E \sqrt{x^2 + z^2}\, dV = \iint_{D_3} \left[\int_{x^2+z^2}^{4} \sqrt{x^2 + z^2}\, dy \right] dA$$

$$= \iint_{D_3} (4 - x^2 - z^2)\sqrt{x^2 + z^2}\, dA$$

Although this integral could be written as

$$\int_{-2}^{2} \int_{-\sqrt{4-x^2}}^{\sqrt{4-x^2}} (4 - x^2 - z^2)\sqrt{x^2 + z^2}\, dz\, dx$$

⊘ The most difficult step in evaluating a triple integral is setting up an expression for the region of integration (such as Equation 9 in Example 2). Remember that the limits of integration in the inner integral contain at most two variables, the limits of integration in the middle integral contain at most one variable, and the limits of integration in the outer integral must be constants.

it's easier to convert to polar coordinates in the xz-plane: $x = r \cos \theta$, $z = r \sin \theta$. This gives

$$\iiint_E \sqrt{x^2 + z^2}\, dV = \iint_{D_3} (4 - x^2 - z^2)\sqrt{x^2 + z^2}\, dA$$

$$= \int_{0}^{2\pi} \int_{0}^{2} (4 - r^2) r\, r\, dr\, d\theta = \int_{0}^{2\pi} d\theta \int_{0}^{2} (4r^2 - r^4)\, dr$$

$$= 2\pi \left[\frac{4r^3}{3} - \frac{r^5}{5} \right]_{0}^{2} = \frac{128\pi}{15}$$

‖‖‖‖ Applications of Triple Integrals

Recall that if $f(x) \geqslant 0$, then the single integral $\int_a^b f(x)\, dx$ represents the area under the curve $y = f(x)$ from a to b, and if $f(x, y) \geqslant 0$, then the double integral $\iint_D f(x, y)\, dA$ represents the volume under the surface $z = f(x, y)$ and above D. The corresponding interpretation of a triple integral $\iiint_E f(x, y, z)\, dV$, where $f(x, y, z) \geqslant 0$, is not very useful because it would be the "hypervolume" of a four-dimensional object and, of course, that is very difficult to visualize. (Remember that E is just the *domain* of the function f; the graph of f lies in four-dimensional space.) Nonetheless, the triple integral $\iiint_E f(x, y, z)\, dV$ can be interpreted in different ways in different physical situations, depending on the physical interpretations of x, y, z and $f(x, y, z)$.

Let's begin with the special case where $f(x, y, z) = 1$ for all points in E. Then the triple integral does represent the volume of E:

12
$$V(E) = \iiint_E dV$$

For example, you can see this in the case of a type 1 region by putting $f(x, y, z) = 1$ in Formula 6:

$$\iiint_E 1\, dV = \iint_D \left[\int_{u_1(x, y)}^{u_2(x, y)} dz \right] dA = \iint_D [u_2(x, y) - u_1(x, y)]\, dA$$

and from Section 16.3 we know this represents the volume that lies between the surfaces $z = u_1(x, y)$ and $z = u_2(x, y)$.

EXAMPLE 4 Use a triple integral to find the volume of the tetrahedron T bounded by the planes $x + 2y + z = 2$, $x = 2y$, $x = 0$, and $z = 0$.

SOLUTION The tetrahedron T and its projection D on the xy-plane are shown in Figures 12 and 13. The lower boundary of T is the plane $z = 0$ and the upper boundary is the plane $x + 2y + z = 2$, that is, $z = 2 - x - 2y$. Therefore, we have

$$V(T) = \iiint_T dV = \int_0^1 \int_{x/2}^{1-x/2} \int_0^{2-x-2y} dz\, dy\, dx$$

$$= \int_0^1 \int_{x/2}^{1-x/2} (2 - x - 2y)\, dy\, dx = \tfrac{1}{3}$$

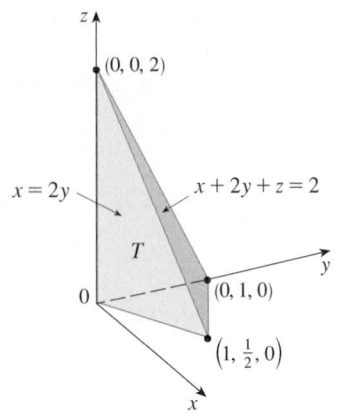

$x = 2y$ $x + 2y + z = 2$ $(0, 0, 2)$ $(0, 1, 0)$ $\left(1, \tfrac{1}{2}, 0\right)$ T

FIGURE 12

by the same calculation as in Example 4 in Section 16.3.

(Notice that it is not necessary to use triple integrals to compute volumes. They simply give an alternative method for setting up the calculation.)

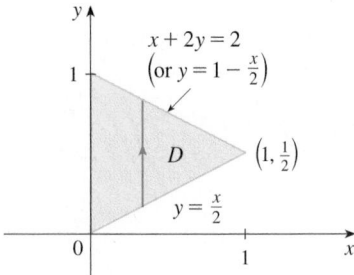

$x + 2y = 2$ $\left(\text{or } y = 1 - \tfrac{x}{2}\right)$ D $\left(1, \tfrac{1}{2}\right)$ $y = \tfrac{x}{2}$

FIGURE 13

All the applications of double integrals in Section 16.5 can be immediately extended to triple integrals. For example, if the density function of a solid object that occupies the region E is $\rho(x, y, z)$, in units of mass per unit volume, at any given point (x, y, z), then its **mass** is

$$\boxed{13} \qquad m = \iiint_E \rho(x, y, z)\, dV$$

and its **moments** about the three coordinate planes are

$$\boxed{14} \qquad M_{yz} = \iiint_E x\rho(x, y, z)\, dV \qquad M_{xz} = \iiint_E y\rho(x, y, z)\, dV$$

$$M_{xy} = \iiint_E z\rho(x, y, z)\, dV$$

The **center of mass** is located at the point $(\bar{x}, \bar{y}, \bar{z})$, where

$$\boxed{15} \qquad \bar{x} = \frac{M_{yz}}{m} \qquad \bar{y} = \frac{M_{xz}}{m} \qquad \bar{z} = \frac{M_{xy}}{m}$$

If the density is constant, the center of mass of the solid is called the **centroid** of E. The **moments of inertia** about the three coordinate axes are

$$\boxed{16} \qquad I_x = \iiint_E (y^2 + z^2)\rho(x, y, z)\, dV \qquad I_y = \iiint_E (x^2 + z^2)\rho(x, y, z)\, dV$$

$$I_z = \iiint_E (x^2 + y^2)\rho(x, y, z)\, dV$$

As in Section 16.5, the total **electric charge** on a solid object occupying a region E and having charge density $\sigma(x, y, z)$ is

$$Q = \iiint\limits_{E} \sigma(x, y, z)\, dV$$

If we have three continuous random variables X, Y, and Z, their **joint density function** is a function of three variables such that the probability that (X, Y, Z) lies in E is

$$P((X, Y, Z) \in E) = \iiint\limits_{E} f(x, y, z)\, dV$$

In particular,

$$P(a \le X \le b,\ c \le Y \le d,\ r \le Z \le s) = \int_{a}^{b} \int_{c}^{d} \int_{r}^{s} f(x, y, z)\, dz\, dy\, dx$$

The joint density function satisfies

$$f(x, y, z) \ge 0 \qquad \int_{-\infty}^{\infty} \int_{-\infty}^{\infty} \int_{-\infty}^{\infty} f(x, y, z)\, dz\, dy\, dx = 1$$

EXAMPLE 5 Find the center of mass of a solid of constant density that is bounded by the parabolic cylinder $x = y^2$ and the planes $x = z$, $z = 0$, and $x = 1$.

SOLUTION The solid E and its projection onto the xy-plane are shown in Figure 14. The lower and upper surfaces of E are the planes $z = 0$ and $z = x$, so we describe E as a type 1 region:

$$E = \{(x, y, z) \mid -1 \le y \le 1,\ y^2 \le x \le 1,\ 0 \le z \le x\}$$

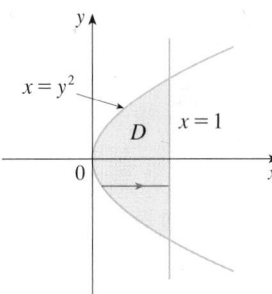

FIGURE 14

Then, if the density is $\rho(x, y, z) = \rho$, the mass is

$$m = \iiint\limits_{E} \rho\, dV = \int_{-1}^{1} \int_{y^2}^{1} \int_{0}^{x} \rho\, dz\, dx\, dy$$

$$= \rho \int_{-1}^{1} \int_{y^2}^{1} x\, dx\, dy = \rho \int_{-1}^{1} \left[\frac{x^2}{2} \right]_{x=y^2}^{x=1} dy$$

$$= \frac{\rho}{2} \int_{-1}^{1} (1 - y^4)\, dy = \rho \int_{0}^{1} (1 - y^4)\, dy$$

$$= \rho \left[y - \frac{y^5}{5} \right]_{0}^{1} = \frac{4\rho}{5}$$

Because of the symmetry of E and ρ about the xz-plane, we can immediately say that $M_{xz} = 0$ and, therefore, $\bar{y} = 0$. The other moments are

$$M_{yz} = \iiint_E x\rho \, dV = \int_{-1}^1 \int_{y^2}^1 \int_0^x x\rho \, dz \, dx \, dy$$

$$= \rho \int_{-1}^1 \int_{y^2}^1 x^2 \, dx \, dy = \rho \int_{-1}^1 \left[\frac{x^3}{3} \right]_{x=y^2}^{x=1} dy$$

$$= \frac{2\rho}{3} \int_0^1 (1 - y^6) \, dy = \frac{2\rho}{3} \left[y - \frac{y^7}{7} \right]_0^1 = \frac{4\rho}{7}$$

$$M_{xy} = \iiint_E z\rho \, dV = \int_{-1}^1 \int_{y^2}^1 \int_0^x z\rho \, dz \, dx \, dy$$

$$= \rho \int_{-1}^1 \int_{y^2}^1 \left[\frac{z^2}{2} \right]_{z=0}^{z=x} dx \, dy = \frac{\rho}{2} \int_{-1}^1 \int_{y^2}^1 x^2 \, dx \, dy$$

$$= \frac{\rho}{3} \int_0^1 (1 - y^6) \, dy = \frac{2\rho}{7}$$

Therefore, the center of mass is

$$(\bar{x}, \bar{y}, \bar{z}) = \left(\frac{M_{yz}}{m}, \frac{M_{xz}}{m}, \frac{M_{xy}}{m} \right) = \left(\tfrac{5}{7}, 0, \tfrac{5}{14} \right)$$

16.7 Exercises

1. Evaluate the integral in Example 1, integrating first with respect to z, then x, and then y.

2. Evaluate the integral $\iiint_E (xz - y^3) \, dV$, where

$$E = \{(x, y, z) \mid -1 \le x \le 1, 0 \le y \le 2, 0 \le z \le 1\}$$

using three different orders of integration.

3–6 |||| Evaluate the iterated integral.

3. $\int_0^1 \int_0^z \int_0^{x+z} 6xz \, dy \, dx \, dz$

4. $\int_0^1 \int_x^{2x} \int_0^y 2xyz \, dz \, dy \, dx$

5. $\int_0^3 \int_0^1 \int_0^{\sqrt{1-z^2}} ze^y \, dx \, dz \, dy$

6. $\int_0^1 \int_0^z \int_0^y ze^{-y^2} \, dx \, dy \, dz$

7–16 |||| Evaluate the triple integral.

7. $\iiint_E 2x \, dV$, where
$E = \{(x, y, z) \mid 0 \le y \le 2, 0 \le x \le \sqrt{4 - y^2}, 0 \le z \le y\}$

8. $\iiint_E yz \cos(x^5) \, dV$, where
$E = \{(x, y, z) \mid 0 \le x \le 1, 0 \le y \le x, x \le z \le 2x\}$

9. $\iiint_E 6xy \, dV$, where E lies under the plane $z = 1 + x + y$ and above the region in the xy-plane bounded by the curves $y = \sqrt{x}, y = 0$, and $x = 1$

10. $\iiint_E y \, dV$, where E is bounded by the planes $x = 0, y = 0, z = 0$, and $2x + 2y + z = 4$

11. $\iiint_E xy \, dV$, where E is the solid tetrahedron with vertices $(0, 0, 0), (1, 0, 0), (0, 2, 0)$, and $(0, 0, 3)$

12. $\iiint_E xz \, dV$, where E is the solid tetrahedron with vertices $(0, 0, 0), (0, 1, 0), (1, 1, 0)$, and $(0, 1, 1)$

13. $\iiint_E x^2 e^y \, dV$, where E is bounded by the parabolic cylinder $z = 1 - y^2$ and the planes $z = 0, x = 1$, and $x = -1$

14. $\iiint_E (x + 2y) \, dV$, where E is bounded by the parabolic cylinder $y = x^2$ and the planes $x = z, x = y$, and $z = 0$

15. $\iiint_E x \, dV$, where E is bounded by the paraboloid $x = 4y^2 + 4z^2$ and the plane $x = 4$

16. $\iiint_E z \, dV$, where E is bounded by the cylinder $y^2 + z^2 = 9$ and the planes $x = 0, y = 3x$, and $z = 0$ in the first octant

17–20 |||| Use a triple integral to find the volume of the given solid.

17. The tetrahedron enclosed by the coordinate planes and the plane $2x + y + z = 4$

18. The solid bounded by the cylinder $y = x^2$ and the planes $z = 0, z = 4$, and $y = 9$

19. The solid enclosed by the cylinder $x^2 + y^2 = 9$ and the planes $y + z = 5$ and $z = 1$

20. The solid enclosed by the paraboloid $x = y^2 + z^2$ and the plane $x = 16$

---

21. (a) Express the volume of the wedge in the first octant that is cut from the cylinder $y^2 + z^2 = 1$ by the planes $y = x$ and $x = 1$ as a triple integral.

AS (b) Use either the Table of Integrals (on the back Reference Pages) or a computer algebra system to find the exact value of the triple integral in part (a).

22. (a) In the **Midpoint Rule for triple integrals** we use a triple Riemann sum to approximate a triple integral over a box B, where $f(x, y, z)$ is evaluated at the center $(\bar{x}_i, \bar{y}_j, \bar{z}_k)$ of the box B_{ijk}. Use the Midpoint Rule to estimate $\iiint_B e^{-x^2-y^2-z^2} \, dV$, where B is the cube defined by $0 \le x \le 1$, $0 \le y \le 1$, $0 \le z \le 1$. Divide B into eight cubes of equal size.

Ⅰ⑤ (b) Use a computer algebra system to approximate the integral in part (a) correct to two decimal places. Compare with the answer to part (a).

23–24 ▓ Use the Midpoint Rule for triple integrals (Exercise 22) to estimate the value of the integral. Divide B into eight sub-boxes of equal size.

23. $\iiint_B \dfrac{1}{\ln(1 + x + y + z)} \, dV$, where
$B = \{(x, y, z) \mid 0 \le x \le 4,\ 0 \le y \le 8,\ 0 \le z \le 4\}$

24. $\iiint_B \sin(xy^2z^3) \, dV$, where
$B = \{(x, y, z) \mid 0 \le x \le 4,\ 0 \le y \le 2,\ 0 \le z \le 1\}$

25–26 ▓ Sketch the solid whose volume is given by the iterated integral.

25. $\displaystyle\int_0^1 \int_0^{1-x} \int_0^{2-2z} dy \, dz \, dx$

26. $\displaystyle\int_0^2 \int_0^{2-y} \int_0^{4-y^2} dx \, dz \, dy$

27–30 ▓ Express the integral $\iiint_E f(x, y, z) \, dV$ as an iterated integral in six different ways, where E is the solid bounded by the given surfaces.

27. $x^2 + z^2 = 4,\quad y = 0,\quad y = 6$

28. $z = 0,\quad x = 0,\quad y = 2,\quad z = y - 2x$

29. $z = 0,\quad z = y,\quad x^2 = 1 - y$

30. $9x^2 + 4y^2 + z^2 = 1$

31. The figure shows the region of integration for the integral

$$\int_0^1 \int_{\sqrt{x}}^1 \int_0^{1-y} f(x, y, z) \, dz \, dy \, dx$$

Rewrite this integral as an equivalent iterated integral in the five other orders.

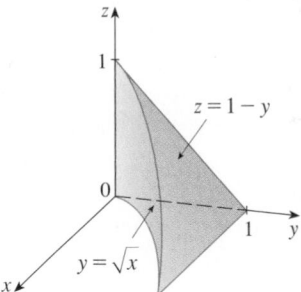

32. The figure shows the region of integration for the integral

$$\int_0^1 \int_0^{1-x^2} \int_0^{1-x} f(x, y, z) \, dy \, dz \, dx$$

Rewrite this integral as an equivalent iterated integral in the five other orders.

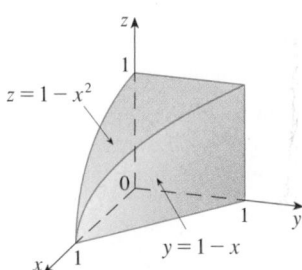

33–34 ▓ Write five other iterated integrals that are equal to the given iterated integral.

33. $\displaystyle\int_0^1 \int_y^1 \int_0^y f(x, y, z) \, dz \, dx \, dy$

34. $\displaystyle\int_0^1 \int_0^{x^2} \int_0^y f(x, y, z) \, dz \, dy \, dx$

35–38 ▓ Find the mass and center of mass of the solid E with the given density function ρ.

35. E is the solid of Exercise 9; $\rho(x, y, z) = 2$

36. E is bounded by the parabolic cylinder $z = 1 - y^2$ and the planes $x + z = 1$, $x = 0$, and $z = 0$; $\rho(x, y, z) = 4$

37. E is the cube given by $0 \le x \le a$, $0 \le y \le a$, $0 \le z \le a$; $\rho(x, y, z) = x^2 + y^2 + z^2$

38. E is the tetrahedron bounded by the planes $x = 0$, $y = 0$, $z = 0$, $x + y + z = 1$; $\rho(x, y, z) = y$

39–40 ||||| Set up, but do not evaluate, integral expressions for (a) the mass, (b) the center of mass, and (c) the moment of inertia about the z-axis.

39. The solid of Exercise 19; $\rho(x, y, z) = \sqrt{x^2 + y^2}$

40. The hemisphere $x^2 + y^2 + z^2 \leqslant 1$, $z \geqslant 0$; $\rho(x, y, z) = \sqrt{x^2 + y^2 + z^2}$

CAS **41.** Let E be the solid in the first octant bounded by the cylinder $x^2 + y^2 = 1$ and the planes $y = z$, $x = 0$, and $z = 0$ with the density function $\rho(x, y, z) = 1 + x + y + z$. Use a computer algebra system to find the exact values of the following quantities for E.
(a) The mass
(b) The center of mass
(c) The moment of inertia about the z-axis

CAS **42.** If E is the solid of Exercise 16 with density function $\rho(x, y, z) = x^2 + y^2$, find the following quantities, correct to three decimal places.
(a) The mass
(b) The center of mass
(c) The moment of inertia about the z-axis

43. Find the moments of inertia for a cube of constant density k and side length L if one vertex is located at the origin and three edges lie along the coordinate axes.

44. Find the moments of inertia for a rectangular brick with dimensions a, b, and c, mass M, and constant density if the center of the brick is situated at the origin and the edges are parallel to the coordinate axes.

45. The joint density function for random variables X, Y, and Z is $f(x, y, z) = Cxyz$ if $0 \leqslant x \leqslant 2$, $0 \leqslant y \leqslant 2$, $0 \leqslant z \leqslant 2$, and $f(x, y, z) = 0$ otherwise.
(a) Find the value of the constant C.
(b) Find $P(X \leqslant 1, Y \leqslant 1, Z \leqslant 1)$.
(c) Find $P(X + Y + Z \leqslant 1)$.

46. Suppose X, Y, and Z are random variables with joint density function $f(x, y, z) = Ce^{-(0.5x + 0.2y + 0.1z)}$ if $x \geqslant 0$, $y \geqslant 0$, $z \geqslant 0$, and $f(x, y, z) = 0$ otherwise.
(a) Find the value of the constant C.
(b) Find $P(X \leqslant 1, Y \leqslant 1)$.
(c) Find $P(X \leqslant 1, Y \leqslant 1, Z \leqslant 1)$.

47–48 ||||| The **average value** of a function $f(x, y, z)$ over a solid region E is defined to be

$$f_{ave} = \frac{1}{V(E)} \iiint_E f(x, y, z)\, dV$$

where $V(E)$ is the volume of E. For instance, if ρ is a density function, then ρ_{ave} is the average density of E.

47. Find the average value of the function $f(x, y, z) = xyz$ over the cube with side length L that lies in the first octant with one vertex at the origin and edges parallel to the coordinate axes.

48. Find the average value of the function $f(x, y, z) = x^2z + y^2z$ over the region enclosed by the paraboloid $z = 1 - x^2 - y^2$ and the plane $z = 0$.

49. Find the region E for which the triple integral

$$\iiint_E (1 - x^2 - 2y^2 - 3z^2)\, dV$$

is a maximum.

||||| DISCOVERY PROJECT

Volumes of Hyperspheres

In this project we find formulas for the volume enclosed by a hypersphere in n-dimensional space.

1. Use a double integral and trigonometric substitution, together with Formula 64 in the Table of Integrals, to find the area of a circle with radius r.

2. Use a triple integral and trigonometric substitution to find the volume of a sphere with radius r.

3. Use a quadruple integral to find the hypervolume enclosed by the hypersphere $x^2 + y^2 + z^2 + w^2 = r^2$ in $\mathbb{R}^4$. (Use only trigonometric substitution and the reduction formulas for $\int \sin^n x\, dx$ or $\int \cos^n x\, dx$.)

4. Use an n-tuple integral to find the volume enclosed by a hypersphere of radius r in n-dimensional space $\mathbb{R}^n$. [*Hint:* The formulas are different for n even and n odd.]

16.8 Triple Integrals in Cylindrical and Spherical Coordinates

We saw in Section 16.4 that some double integrals are easier to evaluate using polar coordinates. In this section we see that some triple integrals are easier to evaluate using cylindrical or spherical coordinates.

||||| Cylindrical Coordinates

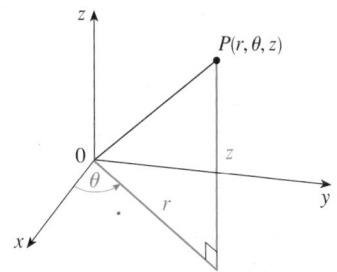

FIGURE 1

Recall from Section 13.7 that the cylindrical coordinates of a point P are (r, θ, z), where r, θ, and z are shown in Figure 1. Suppose that E is a type 1 region whose projection D on the xy-plane is conveniently described in polar coordinates (see Figure 2). In particular, suppose that f is continuous and

$$E = \{(x, y, z) \mid (x, y) \in D, \ u_1(x, y) \leq z \leq u_2(x, y)\}$$

where D is given in polar coordinates by

$$D = \{(r, \theta) \mid \alpha \leq \theta \leq \beta, \ h_1(\theta) \leq r \leq h_2(\theta)\}$$

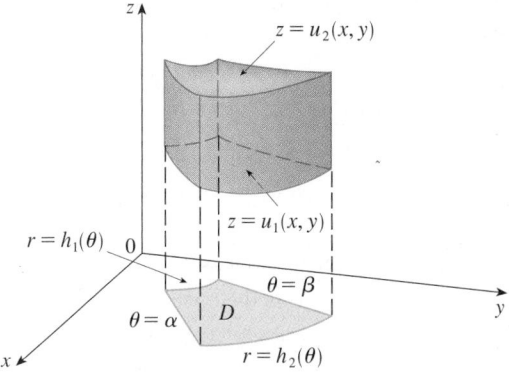

FIGURE 2

We know from Equation 16.7.6 that

$$\boxed{1} \qquad \iiint_E f(x, y, z) \, dV = \iint_D \left[\int_{u_1(x, y)}^{u_2(x, y)} f(x, y, z) \, dz \right] dA$$

But we also know how to evaluate double integrals in polar coordinates. In fact, combining Equation 1 with Equation 16.4.3, we obtain

$$\boxed{2} \qquad \iiint_E f(x, y, z) \, dV = \int_\alpha^\beta \int_{h_1(\theta)}^{h_2(\theta)} \int_{u_1(r \cos \theta, r \sin \theta)}^{u_2(r \cos \theta, r \sin \theta)} f(r \cos \theta, r \sin \theta, z) \, r \, dz \, dr \, d\theta$$

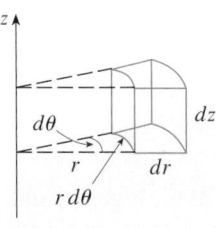

FIGURE 3

Volume element in cylindrical coordinates: $dV = r \, dz \, dr \, d\theta$

Formula 2 is the **formula for triple integration in cylindrical coordinates**. It says that we convert a triple integral from rectangular to cylindrical coordinates by writing $x = r \cos \theta$, $y = r \sin \theta$, leaving z as it is, using the appropriate limits of integration for z, r, and θ, and replacing dV by $r \, dz \, dr \, d\theta$. (Figure 3 shows how to remember this.) It is worthwhile to use this formula when E is a solid region easily described in cylindrical coordinates, and especially when the function $f(x, y, z)$ involves the expression $x^2 + y^2$.

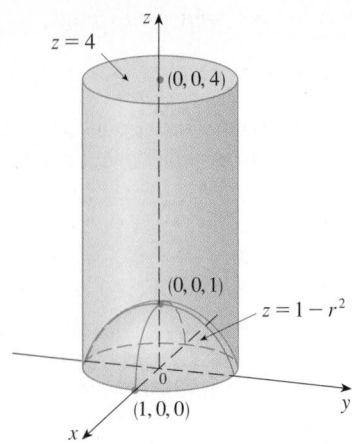

FIGURE 4

EXAMPLE 1 A solid E lies within the cylinder $x^2 + y^2 = 1$, below the plane $z = 4$, and above the paraboloid $z = 1 - x^2 - y^2$. (See Figure 4.) The density at any point is proportional to its distance from the axis of the cylinder. Find the mass of E.

SOLUTION In cylindrical coordinates the cylinder is $r = 1$ and the paraboloid is $z = 1 - r^2$, so we can write

$$E = \{(r, \theta, z) \mid 0 \leqslant \theta \leqslant 2\pi, \ 0 \leqslant r \leqslant 1, \ 1 - r^2 \leqslant z \leqslant 4\}$$

Since the density at (x, y, z) is proportional to the distance from the z-axis, the density function is

$$f(x, y, z) = K\sqrt{x^2 + y^2} = Kr$$

where K is the proportionality constant. Therefore, from Formula 16.7.13, the mass of E is

$$m = \iiint_E K\sqrt{x^2 + y^2}\, dV = \int_0^{2\pi} \int_0^1 \int_{1-r^2}^4 (Kr)\, r\, dz\, dr\, d\theta$$

$$= \int_0^{2\pi} \int_0^1 Kr^2 [4 - (1 - r^2)]\, dr\, d\theta = K \int_0^{2\pi} d\theta \int_0^1 (3r^2 + r^4)\, dr$$

$$= 2\pi K \left[r^3 + \frac{r^5}{5} \right]_0^1 = \frac{12\pi K}{5}$$

EXAMPLE 2 Evaluate $\displaystyle\int_{-2}^2 \int_{-\sqrt{4-x^2}}^{\sqrt{4-x^2}} \int_{\sqrt{x^2+y^2}}^2 (x^2 + y^2)\, dz\, dy\, dx$.

SOLUTION This iterated integral is a triple integral over the solid region

$$E = \left\{(x, y, z) \mid -2 \leqslant x \leqslant 2, \ -\sqrt{4 - x^2} \leqslant y \leqslant \sqrt{4 - x^2}, \ \sqrt{x^2 + y^2} \leqslant z \leqslant 2\right\}$$

and the projection of E onto the xy-plane is the disk $x^2 + y^2 \leqslant 4$. The lower surface of E is the cone $z = \sqrt{x^2 + y^2}$ and its upper surface is the plane $z = 2$. (See Figure 5.) This region has a much simpler description in cylindrical coordinates:

$$E = \{(r, \theta, z) \mid 0 \leqslant \theta \leqslant 2\pi, \ 0 \leqslant r \leqslant 2, \ r \leqslant z \leqslant 2\}$$

Therefore, we have

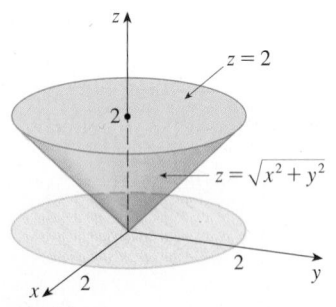

FIGURE 5

$$\int_{-2}^2 \int_{-\sqrt{4-x^2}}^{\sqrt{4-x^2}} \int_{\sqrt{x^2+y^2}}^2 (x^2 + y^2)\, dz\, dy\, dx = \iiint_E (x^2 + y^2)\, dV$$

$$= \int_0^{2\pi} \int_0^2 \int_r^2 r^2\, r\, dz\, dr\, d\theta$$

$$= \int_0^{2\pi} d\theta \int_0^2 r^3(2 - r)\, dr$$

$$= 2\pi \left[\tfrac{1}{2}r^4 - \tfrac{1}{5}r^5 \right]_0^2 = \tfrac{16}{5}\pi$$

||| **Spherical Coordinates**

In Section 13.7 we defined the spherical coordinates (ρ, θ, ϕ) of a point (see Figure 6) and we demonstrated the following relationships between rectangular coordinates and spherical coordinates:

3

$$x = \rho \sin\phi \cos\theta \qquad y = \rho \sin\phi \sin\theta \qquad z = \rho \cos\phi$$

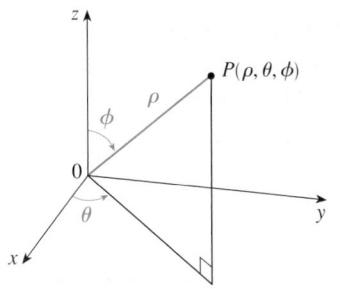

FIGURE 6

Spherical coordinates of P

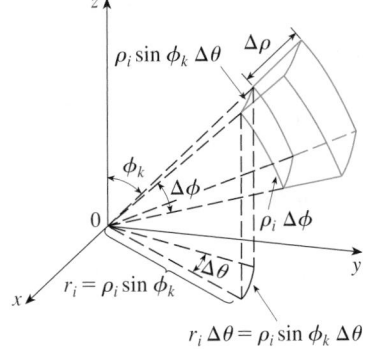

FIGURE 7

In this coordinate system the counterpart of a rectangular box is a **spherical wedge**

$$E = \{(\rho, \theta, \phi) \mid a \leq \rho \leq b, \ \alpha \leq \theta \leq \beta, \ c \leq \phi \leq d\}$$

where $a \geq 0$, $\beta - \alpha \leq 2\pi$, and $d - c \leq \pi$. Although we defined triple integrals by dividing solids into small boxes, it can be shown that dividing a solid into small spherical wedges always gives the same result. So we divide E into smaller spherical wedges E_{ijk} by means of equally spaced spheres $\rho = \rho_i$, half-planes $\theta = \theta_j$, and half-cones $\phi = \phi_k$. Figure 7 shows that E_{ijk} is approximately a rectangular box with dimensions $\Delta\rho$, $\rho_i\,\Delta\phi$ (arc of a circle with radius ρ_i, angle $\Delta\phi$), and $\rho_i \sin\phi_k\,\Delta\theta$ (arc of a circle with radius $\rho_i \sin\phi_k$, angle $\Delta\theta$). So an approximation to the volume of E_{ijk} is given by

$$\Delta V_{ijk} \approx (\Delta\rho)(\rho_i\,\Delta\phi)(\rho_i \sin\phi_k\,\Delta\theta) = \rho_i^2 \sin\phi_k\,\Delta\rho\,\Delta\theta\,\Delta\phi$$

In fact, it can be shown, with the aid of the Mean Value Theorem (Exercise 39), that the volume of E_{ijk} is given exactly by

$$\Delta V_{ijk} = \tilde{\rho}_i^2 \sin\tilde{\phi}_k\,\Delta\rho\,\Delta\theta\,\Delta\phi$$

where $(\tilde{\rho}_i, \tilde{\theta}_j, \tilde{\phi}_k)$ is some point in E_{ijk}. Let $(x_{ijk}^*, y_{ijk}^*, z_{ijk}^*)$ be the rectangular coordinates of this point. Then

$$\iiint_E f(x, y, z)\,dV = \lim_{l, m, n \to \infty} \sum_{i=1}^{l} \sum_{j=1}^{m} \sum_{k=1}^{n} f(x_{ijk}^*, y_{ijk}^*, z_{ijk}^*)\,\Delta V_{ijk}$$

$$= \lim_{l, m, n \to \infty} \sum_{i=1}^{l} \sum_{j=1}^{m} \sum_{k=1}^{n} f(\tilde{\rho}_i \sin\tilde{\phi}_k \cos\tilde{\theta}_j, \tilde{\rho}_i \sin\tilde{\phi}_k \sin\tilde{\theta}_j, \tilde{\rho}_i \cos\tilde{\phi}_k)\,\tilde{\rho}_i^2 \sin\tilde{\phi}_k\,\Delta\rho\,\Delta\theta\,\Delta\phi$$

But this sum is a Riemann sum for the function

$$F(\rho, \theta, \phi) = \rho^2 \sin\phi\, f(\rho \sin\phi \cos\theta, \rho \sin\phi \sin\theta, \rho \cos\phi)$$

Consequently, we have arrived at the following **formula for triple integration in spherical coordinates**.

4
$$\iiint_E f(x, y, z)\,dV$$

$$= \int_c^d \int_\alpha^\beta \int_a^b f(\rho \sin\phi \cos\theta, \rho \sin\phi \sin\theta, \rho \cos\phi)\,\rho^2 \sin\phi\,d\rho\,d\theta\,d\phi$$

where E is a spherical wedge given by

$$E = \{(\rho, \theta, \phi) \mid a \leq \rho \leq b, \ \alpha \leq \theta \leq \beta, \ c \leq \phi \leq d\}$$

Formula 4 says that we convert a triple integral from rectangular coordinates to spherical coordinates by writing

$$x = \rho \sin\phi \cos\theta \qquad y = \rho \sin\phi \sin\theta \qquad z = \rho \cos\phi$$

using the appropriate limits of integration, and replacing dV by $\rho^2 \sin\phi\,d\rho\,d\theta\,d\phi$. This is illustrated in Figure 8.

This formula can be extended to include more general spherical regions such as

$$E = \{(\rho, \theta, \phi) \mid \alpha \leq \theta \leq \beta, \ c \leq \phi \leq d, \ g_1(\theta, \phi) \leq \rho \leq g_2(\theta, \phi)\}$$

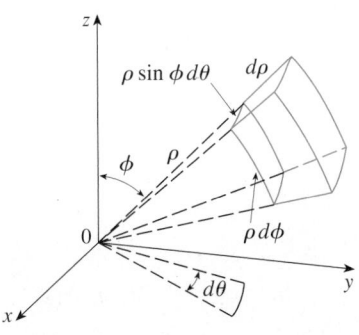

FIGURE 8

Volume element in spherical coordinates: $dV = \rho^2 \sin\phi\,d\rho\,d\theta\,d\phi$

In this case the formula is the same as in (4) except that the limits of integration for ρ are $g_1(\theta, \phi)$ and $g_2(\theta, \phi)$.

Usually, spherical coordinates are used in triple integrals when surfaces such as cones and spheres form the boundary of the region of integration.

EXAMPLE 3 Evaluate $\iiint_B e^{(x^2+y^2+z^2)^{3/2}} \, dV$, where B is the unit ball:

$$B = \{(x, y, z) \,|\, x^2 + y^2 + z^2 \leqslant 1\}$$

SOLUTION Since the boundary of B is a sphere, we use spherical coordinates:

$$B = \{(\rho, \theta, \phi) \,|\, 0 \leqslant \rho \leqslant 1, \ 0 \leqslant \theta \leqslant 2\pi, \ 0 \leqslant \phi \leqslant \pi\}$$

In addition, spherical coordinates are appropriate because

$$x^2 + y^2 + z^2 = \rho^2$$

Thus, (4) gives

$$\iiint_B e^{(x^2+y^2+z^2)^{3/2}} \, dV = \int_0^\pi \int_0^{2\pi} \int_0^1 e^{(\rho^2)^{3/2}} \rho^2 \sin\phi \, d\rho \, d\theta \, d\phi$$

$$= \int_0^\pi \sin\phi \, d\phi \int_0^{2\pi} d\theta \int_0^1 \rho^2 e^{\rho^3} \, d\rho$$

$$= \left[-\cos\phi\right]_0^\pi (2\pi) \left[\tfrac{1}{3}e^{\rho^3}\right]_0^1 = \tfrac{4}{3}\pi(e - 1)$$

NOTE □ It would have been extremely awkward to evaluate the integral in Example 3 without spherical coordinates. In rectangular coordinates the iterated integral would have been

$$\int_{-1}^1 \int_{-\sqrt{1-x^2}}^{\sqrt{1-x^2}} \int_{-\sqrt{1-x^2-y^2}}^{\sqrt{1-x^2-y^2}} e^{(x^2+y^2+z^2)^{3/2}} \, dz \, dy \, dx$$

EXAMPLE 4 Use spherical coordinates to find the volume of the solid that lies above the cone $z = \sqrt{x^2 + y^2}$ and below the sphere $x^2 + y^2 + z^2 = z$. (See Figure 9.)

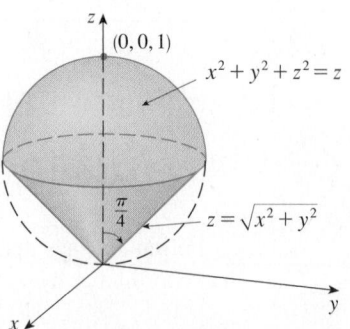

FIGURE 9

SOLUTION Notice that the sphere passes through the origin and has center $\left(0, 0, \tfrac{1}{2}\right)$. We write the equation of the sphere in spherical coordinates as

$$\rho^2 = \rho \cos\phi \qquad \text{or} \qquad \rho = \cos\phi$$

||||| Figure 10 gives another look (this time drawn by Maple) at the solid of Example 4.

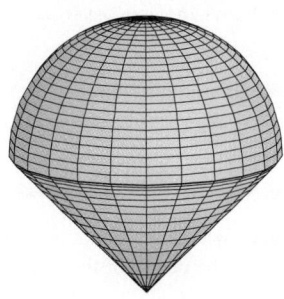

FIGURE 10

The equation of the cone can be written as

$$\rho \cos \phi = \sqrt{\rho^2 \sin^2\phi \, \cos^2\theta + \rho^2 \sin^2\phi \, \sin^2\theta} = \rho \sin \phi$$

This gives $\sin \phi = \cos \phi$, or $\phi = \pi/4$. Therefore, the description of the solid E in spherical coordinates is

$$E = \{(\rho, \theta, \phi) \mid 0 \le \theta \le 2\pi, \ 0 \le \phi \le \pi/4, \ 0 \le \rho \le \cos \phi\}$$

Figure 11 shows how E is swept out if we integrate first with respect to ρ, then ϕ, and then θ. The volume of E is

$$V(E) = \iiint_E dV = \int_0^{2\pi} \int_0^{\pi/4} \int_0^{\cos \phi} \rho^2 \sin \phi \, d\rho \, d\phi \, d\theta$$

$$= \int_0^{2\pi} d\theta \int_0^{\pi/4} \sin \phi \left[\frac{\rho^3}{3} \right]_{\rho=0}^{\rho=\cos \phi} d\phi$$

$$= \frac{2\pi}{3} \int_0^{\pi/4} \sin \phi \cos^3\phi \, d\phi = \frac{2\pi}{3} \left[-\frac{\cos^4\phi}{4} \right]_0^{\pi/4} = \frac{\pi}{8}$$

[TEC] Visual 16.8 shows an animation of Figure 11.

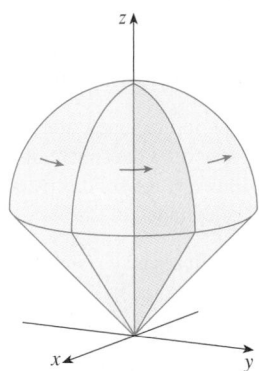

FIGURE 11

ρ varies from 0 to $\cos \phi$ while ϕ and θ are constant.

ϕ varies from 0 to $\pi/4$ while θ is constant.

θ varies from 0 to 2π.

||||| **16.8 Exercises**

1–4 ||||| Sketch the solid whose volume is given by the integral and evaluate the integral.

1. $\int_0^4 \int_0^{2\pi} \int_r^4 r \, dz \, d\theta \, dr$

2. $\int_0^{\pi/2} \int_0^2 \int_0^{9-r^2} r \, dz \, dr \, d\theta$

3. $\int_0^{\pi/6} \int_0^{\pi/2} \int_0^3 \rho^2 \sin \phi \, d\rho \, d\theta \, d\phi$

4. $\int_0^{2\pi} \int_{\pi/2}^{\pi} \int_1^2 \rho^2 \sin \phi \, d\rho \, d\phi \, d\theta$

5–6 ||||| Set up the triple integral of an arbitrary continuous function $f(x, y, z)$ in cylindrical or spherical coordinates over the solid shown.

5.

6.

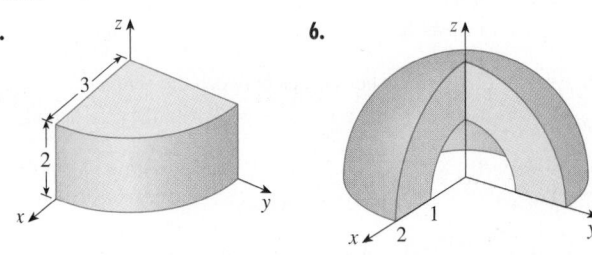

7–16 |||| Use cylindrical coordinates.

7. Evaluate $\iiint_E \sqrt{x^2 + y^2} \, dV$, where E is the region that lies inside the cylinder $x^2 + y^2 = 16$ and between the planes $z = -5$ and $z = 4$.

8. Evaluate $\iiint_E (x^3 + xy^2) \, dV$, where E is the solid in the first octant that lies beneath the paraboloid $z = 1 - x^2 - y^2$.

9. Evaluate $\iiint_E e^z \, dV$, where E is enclosed by the paraboloid $z = 1 + x^2 + y^2$, the cylinder $x^2 + y^2 = 5$, and the xy-plane.

10. Evaluate $\iiint_E x \, dV$, where E is enclosed by the planes $z = 0$ and $z = x + y + 5$ and by the cylinders $x^2 + y^2 = 4$ and $x^2 + y^2 = 9$.

11. Evaluate $\iiint_E x^2 \, dV$, where E is the solid that lies within the cylinder $x^2 + y^2 = 1$, above the plane $z = 0$, and below the cone $z^2 = 4x^2 + 4y^2$.

12. Find the volume of the solid that lies within both the cylinder $x^2 + y^2 = 1$ and the sphere $x^2 + y^2 + z^2 = 4$.

13. (a) Find the volume of the region E bounded by the paraboloids $z = x^2 + y^2$ and $z = 36 - 3x^2 - 3y^2$.
(b) Find the centroid of E (the center of mass in the case where the density is constant).

14. (a) Find the volume of the solid that the cylinder $r = a \cos \theta$ cuts out of the sphere of radius a centered at the origin.
(b) Illustrate the solid of part (a) by graphing the sphere and the cylinder on the same screen.

15. Find the mass and center of mass of the solid S bounded by the paraboloid $z = 4x^2 + 4y^2$ and the plane $z = a$ $(a > 0)$ if S has constant density K.

16. Find the mass of a ball B given by $x^2 + y^2 + z^2 \leq a^2$ if the density at any point is proportional to its distance from the z-axis.

17–28 |||| Use spherical coordinates.

17. Evaluate $\iiint_B (x^2 + y^2 + z^2) \, dV$, where B is the unit ball $x^2 + y^2 + z^2 \leq 1$.

18. Evaluate $\iiint_H (x^2 + y^2) \, dV$, where H is the hemispherical region that lies above the xy-plane and below the sphere $x^2 + y^2 + z^2 = 1$.

19. Evaluate $\iiint_E z \, dV$, where E lies between the spheres $x^2 + y^2 + z^2 = 1$ and $x^2 + y^2 + z^2 = 4$ in the first octant.

20. Evaluate $\iiint_E e^{\sqrt{x^2+y^2+z^2}} \, dV$, where E is enclosed by the sphere $x^2 + y^2 + z^2 = 9$ in the first octant.

21. Evaluate $\iiint_E x^2 \, dV$, where E is bounded by the xz-plane and the hemispheres $y = \sqrt{9 - x^2 - z^2}$ and $y = \sqrt{16 - x^2 - z^2}$.

22. Evaluate $\iiint_E xyz \, dV$, where E lies between the spheres $\rho = 2$ and $\rho = 4$ and above the cone $\phi = \pi/3$.

23. Find the volume of the solid that lies above the cone $\phi = \pi/3$ and below the sphere $\rho = 4 \cos \phi$.

24. Find the volume of the solid that lies within the sphere $x^2 + y^2 + z^2 = 4$, above the xy-plane, and below the cone $z = \sqrt{x^2 + y^2}$.

25. Find the centroid of the solid in Exercise 21.

26. Let H be a solid hemisphere of radius a whose density at any point is proportional to its distance from the center of the base.
(a) Find the mass of H.
(b) Find the center of mass of H.
(c) Find the moment of inertia of H about its axis.

27. (a) Find the centroid of a solid homogeneous hemisphere of radius a.
(b) Find the moment of inertia of the solid in part (a) about a diameter of its base.

28. Find the mass and center of mass of a solid hemisphere of radius a if the density at any point is proportional to its distance from the base.

29–32 |||| Use cylindrical or spherical coordinates, whichever seems more appropriate.

29. Find the volume and centroid of the solid E that lies above the cone $z = \sqrt{x^2 + y^2}$ and below the sphere $x^2 + y^2 + z^2 = 1$.

30. Find the volume of the smaller wedge cut from a sphere of radius a by two planes that intersect along a diameter at an angle of $\pi/6$.

31. Evaluate $\iiint_E z \, dV$, where E lies above the paraboloid $z = x^2 + y^2$ and below the plane $z = 2y$. Use either the Table of Integrals (on the back Reference Pages) or a computer algebra system to evaluate the integral.

32. (a) Find the volume enclosed by the torus $\rho = \sin \phi$.
(b) Use a computer to draw the torus.

33–34 |||| Evaluate the integral by changing to cylindrical coordinates.

33. $\int_{-1}^{1} \int_{-\sqrt{1-x^2}}^{\sqrt{1-x^2}} \int_{\sqrt{x^2+y^2}}^{2-x^2-y^2} (x^2 + y^2)^{3/2} \, dz \, dy \, dx$

34. $\int_{0}^{1} \int_{0}^{\sqrt{1-y^2}} \int_{\sqrt{x^2+y^2}}^{\sqrt{x^2+y^2}} xyz \, dz \, dx \, dy$

35–36 |||| Evaluate the integral by changing to spherical coordinates.

35. $\int_{-3}^{3} \int_{-\sqrt{9-x^2}}^{\sqrt{9-x^2}} \int_{0}^{\sqrt{9-x^2-y^2}} z \sqrt{x^2 + y^2 + z^2} \, dz \, dy \, dx$

36. $\int_{0}^{3} \int_{0}^{\sqrt{9-y^2}} \int_{\sqrt{x^2+y^2}}^{\sqrt{18-x^2-y^2}} (x^2 + y^2 + z^2) \, dz \, dx \, dy$

37. In the Laboratory Project on page 880 we investigated the family of surfaces $\rho = 1 + \frac{1}{5} \sin m\theta \sin n\phi$ that have been used as models for tumors. The "bumpy sphere" with $m = 6$ and $n = 5$ is shown. Use a computer algebra system to find the volume it encloses.

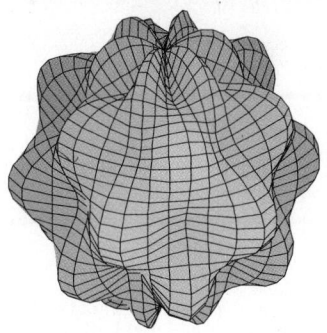

38. Show that

$$\int_{-\infty}^{\infty} \int_{-\infty}^{\infty} \int_{-\infty}^{\infty} \sqrt{x^2 + y^2 + z^2}\, e^{-(x^2+y^2+z^2)}\, dx\, dy\, dz = 2\pi$$

(The improper triple integral is defined as the limit of a triple integral over a solid sphere as the radius of the sphere increases indefinitely.)

39. (a) Use cylindrical coordinates to show that the volume of the solid bounded above by the sphere $r^2 + z^2 = a^2$ and below by the cone $z = r \cot \phi_0$ (or $\phi = \phi_0$), where $0 < \phi_0 < \pi/2$, is

$$V = \frac{2\pi a^3}{3} (1 - \cos \phi_0)$$

(b) Deduce that the volume of the spherical wedge given by $\rho_1 \le \rho \le \rho_2$, $\theta_1 \le \theta \le \theta_2$, $\phi_1 \le \phi \le \phi_2$ is

$$\Delta V = \frac{\rho_2^3 - \rho_1^3}{3} (\cos \phi_1 - \cos \phi_2)(\theta_2 - \theta_1)$$

(c) Use the Mean Value Theorem to show that the volume in part (b) can be written as

$$\Delta V = \bar{\rho}^2 \sin \bar{\phi}\, \Delta\rho\, \Delta\theta\, \Delta\phi$$

where $\bar{\rho}$ lies between ρ_1 and ρ_2, $\bar{\phi}$ lies between ϕ_1 and ϕ_2, $\Delta\rho = \rho_2 - \rho_1$, $\Delta\theta = \theta_2 - \theta_1$, and $\Delta\phi = \phi_2 - \phi_1$.

40. When studying the formation of mountain ranges, geologists estimate the amount of work required to lift a mountain from sea level. Consider a mountain that is essentially in the shape of a right circular cone. Suppose that the weight density of the material in the vicinity of a point P is $g(P)$ and the height is $h(P)$.

(a) Find a definite integral that represents the total work done in forming the mountain.

(b) Assume that Mount Fuji in Japan is in the shape of a right circular cone with radius 62,000 ft, height 12,400 ft, and density a constant 200 lb/ft³. How much work was done in forming Mount Fuji if the land was initially at sea level?

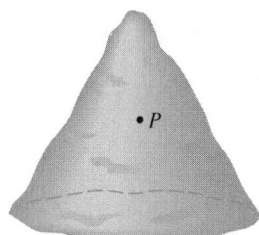

||| APPLIED PROJECT

Roller Derby

Suppose that a solid ball (a marble), a hollow ball (a squash ball), a solid cylinder (a steel bar), and a hollow cylinder (a lead pipe) roll down a slope. Which of these objects reaches the bottom first? (Make a guess before proceeding.)

To answer this question we consider a ball or cylinder with mass m, radius r, and moment of inertia I (about the axis of rotation). If the vertical drop is h, then the potential energy at the top is mgh. Suppose the object reaches the bottom with velocity v and angular velocity ω, so $v = \omega r$. The kinetic energy at the bottom consists of two parts: $\frac{1}{2}mv^2$ from translation (moving down the slope) and $\frac{1}{2}I\omega^2$ from rotation. If we assume that energy loss from rolling friction is negligible, then conservation of energy gives

$$mgh = \tfrac{1}{2}mv^2 + \tfrac{1}{2}I\omega^2$$

1. Show that

$$v^2 = \frac{2gh}{1 + I^*} \qquad \text{where } I^* = \frac{I}{mr^2}$$

2. If $y(t)$ is the vertical distance traveled at time t, then the same reasoning as used in Problem 1 shows that $v^2 = 2gy/(1 + I^*)$ at any time t. Use this result to show that y satisfies the differential equation

$$\frac{dy}{dt} = \sqrt{\frac{2g}{1 + I^*}} \,(\sin \alpha)\sqrt{y}$$

where α is the angle of inclination of the plane.

3. By solving the differential equation in Problem 2, show that the total travel time is

$$T = \sqrt{\frac{2h(1 + I^*)}{g \sin^2\alpha}}$$

This shows that the object with the smallest value of I^* wins the race.

4. Show that $I^* = \frac{1}{2}$ for a solid cylinder and $I^* = 1$ for a hollow cylinder.

5. Calculate I^* for a partly hollow ball with inner radius a and outer radius r. Express your answer in terms of $b = a/r$. What happens as $a \to 0$ and as $a \to r$?

6. Show that $I^* = \frac{2}{5}$ for a solid ball and $I^* = \frac{2}{3}$ for a hollow ball. Thus, the objects finish in the following order: solid ball, solid cylinder, hollow ball, hollow cylinder.

||| DISCOVERY PROJECT

The Intersection of Three Cylinders

The figure shows the solid enclosed by three circular cylinders with the same diameter that intersect at right angles. In this project we compute its volume and determine how its shape changes if the cylinders have different diameters.

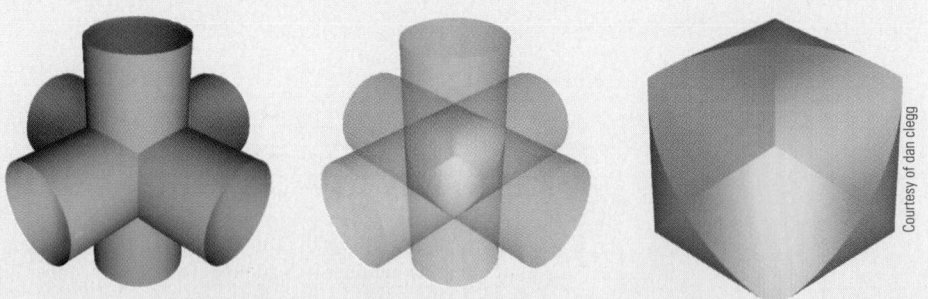

Courtesy of dan clegg

1. Sketch carefully the solid enclosed by the three cylinders $x^2 + y^2 = 1$, $x^2 + z^2 = 1$, and $y^2 + z^2 = 1$. Indicate the positions of the coordinate axes and label the faces with the equations of the corresponding cylinders.

2. Find the volume of the solid in Problem 1.

CAS 3. Use a computer algebra system to draw the edges of the solid.

4. What happens to the solid in Problem 1 if the radius of the first cylinder is different from 1? Illustrate with a hand-drawn sketch or a computer graph.

5. If the first cylinder is $x^2 + y^2 = a^2$, where $a < 1$, set up, but do not evaluate, a double integral for the volume of the solid. What if $a > 1$?

16.9 Change of Variables in Multiple Integrals

In one-dimensional calculus we often use a change of variable (a substitution) to simplify an integral. By reversing the roles of x and u, we can write the Substitution Rule (5.5.5) as

$$\boxed{1} \qquad \int_a^b f(x)\, dx = \int_c^d f(g(u))\, g'(u)\, du$$

where $x = g(u)$ and $a = g(c)$, $b = g(d)$. Another way of writing Formula 1 is as follows:

$$\boxed{2} \qquad \int_a^b f(x)\, dx = \int_c^d f(x(u)) \frac{dx}{du}\, du$$

A change of variables can also be useful in double integrals. We have already seen one example of this: conversion to polar coordinates. The new variables r and θ are related to the old variables x and y by the equations

$$x = r \cos \theta \qquad y = r \sin \theta$$

and the change of variables formula (16.4.2) can be written as

$$\iint\limits_R f(x, y)\, dA = \iint\limits_S f(r \cos \theta, r \sin \theta)\, r\, dr\, d\theta$$

where S is the region in the $r\theta$-plane that corresponds to the region R in the xy-plane.

More generally, we consider a change of variables that is given by a **transformation** T from the uv-plane to the xy-plane:

$$T(u, v) = (x, y)$$

where x and y are related to u and v by the equations

$$\boxed{3} \qquad x = g(u, v) \qquad y = h(u, v)$$

or, as we sometimes write,

$$x = x(u, v) \qquad y = y(u, v)$$

We usually assume that T is a C^1 **transformation**, which means that g and h have continuous first-order partial derivatives.

A transformation T is really just a function whose domain and range are both subsets of $\mathbb{R}^2$. If $T(u_1, v_1) = (x_1, y_1)$, then the point (x_1, y_1) is called the **image** of the point (u_1, v_1). If no two points have the same image, T is called **one-to-one**. Figure 1 shows the effect of a transformation T on a region S in the uv-plane. T transforms S into a region R in the xy-plane called the **image of S**, consisting of the images of all points in S.

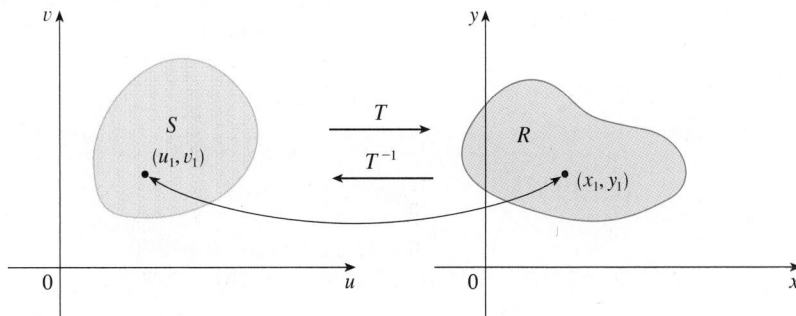

FIGURE 1

If T is a one-to-one transformation, then it has an **inverse transformation** T^{-1} from the xy-plane to the uv-plane and it may be possible to solve Equations 3 for u and v in terms of x and y:

$$u = G(x, y) \qquad v = H(x, y)$$

EXAMPLE 1 A transformation is defined by the equations

$$x = u^2 - v^2 \qquad y = 2uv$$

Find the image of the square $S = \{(u, v) \mid 0 \leqslant u \leqslant 1,\ 0 \leqslant v \leqslant 1\}$.

SOLUTION The transformation maps the boundary of S into the boundary of the image. So we begin by finding the images of the sides of S. The first side, S_1, is given by $v = 0$ $(0 \leqslant u \leqslant 1)$. (See Figure 2.) From the given equations we have $x = u^2$, $y = 0$, and so $0 \leqslant x \leqslant 1$. Thus, S_1 is mapped into the line segment from $(0, 0)$ to $(1, 0)$ in the xy-plane. The second side, S_2, is $u = 1$ $(0 \leqslant v \leqslant 1)$ and, putting $u = 1$ in the given equations, we get

$$x = 1 - v^2 \qquad y = 2v$$

Eliminating v, we obtain

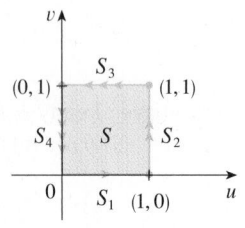

$$\boxed{4} \qquad\qquad x = 1 - \frac{y^2}{4} \qquad 0 \leqslant x \leqslant 1$$

which is part of a parabola. Similarly, S_3 is given by $v = 1$ $(0 \leqslant u \leqslant 1)$, whose image is the parabolic arc

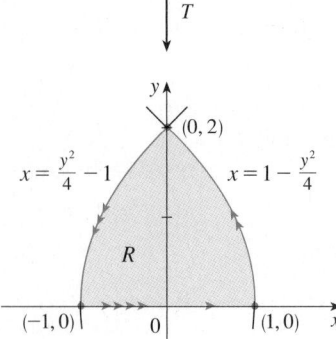

$$\boxed{5} \qquad\qquad x = \frac{y^2}{4} - 1 \qquad -1 \leqslant x \leqslant 0$$

Finally, S_4 is given by $u = 0$ $(0 \leqslant v \leqslant 1)$ whose image is $x = -v^2$, $y = 0$, that is, $-1 \leqslant x \leqslant 0$. (Notice that as we move around the square in the counterclockwise direction, we also move around the parabolic region in the counterclockwise direction.) The image of S is the region R (shown in Figure 2) bounded by the x-axis and the parabolas given by Equations 4 and 5.

FIGURE 2

Now let's see how a change of variables affects a double integral. We start with a small rectangle S in the uv-plane whose lower left corner is the point (u_0, v_0) and whose dimensions are Δu and Δv. (See Figure 3.)

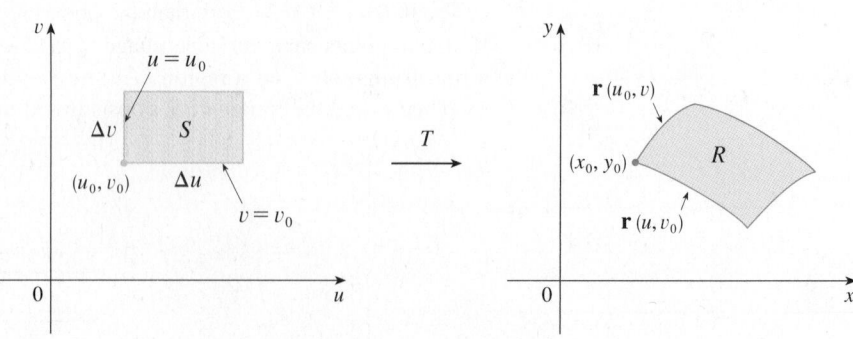

FIGURE 3

The image of S is a region R in the xy-plane, one of whose boundary points is $(x_0, y_0) = T(u_0, v_0)$. The vector

$$\mathbf{r}(u, v) = g(u, v)\,\mathbf{i} + h(u, v)\,\mathbf{j}$$

is the position vector of the image of the point (u, v). The equation of the lower side of S is $v = v_0$, whose image curve is given by the vector function $\mathbf{r}(u, v_0)$. The tangent vector at (x_0, y_0) to this image curve is

$$\mathbf{r}_u = g_u(u_0, v_0)\,\mathbf{i} + h_u(u_0, v_0)\,\mathbf{j} = \frac{\partial x}{\partial u}\,\mathbf{i} + \frac{\partial y}{\partial u}\,\mathbf{j}$$

Similarly, the tangent vector at (x_0, y_0) to the image curve of the left side of S (namely, $u = u_0$) is

$$\mathbf{r}_v = g_v(u_0, v_0)\,\mathbf{i} + h_v(u_0, v_0)\,\mathbf{j} = \frac{\partial x}{\partial v}\,\mathbf{i} + \frac{\partial y}{\partial v}\,\mathbf{j}$$

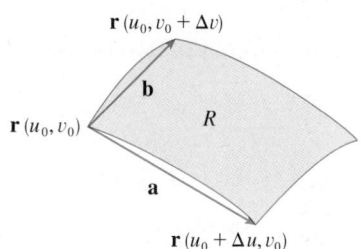

FIGURE 4

We can approximate the image region $R = T(S)$ by a parallelogram determined by the secant vectors

$$\mathbf{a} = \mathbf{r}(u_0 + \Delta u, v_0) - \mathbf{r}(u_0, v_0) \qquad \mathbf{b} = \mathbf{r}(u_0, v_0 + \Delta v) - \mathbf{r}(u_0, v_0)$$

shown in Figure 4. But

$$\mathbf{r}_u = \lim_{\Delta u \to 0} \frac{\mathbf{r}(u_0 + \Delta u, v_0) - \mathbf{r}(u_0, v_0)}{\Delta u}$$

and so

$$\mathbf{r}(u_0 + \Delta u, v_0) - \mathbf{r}(u_0, v_0) \approx \Delta u\,\mathbf{r}_u$$

Similarly

$$\mathbf{r}(u_0, v_0 + \Delta v) - \mathbf{r}(u_0, v_0) \approx \Delta v\,\mathbf{r}_v$$

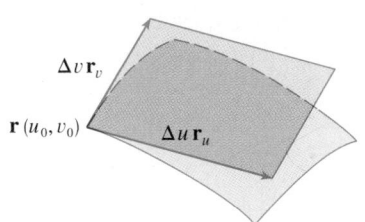

FIGURE 5

This means that we can approximate R by a parallelogram determined by the vectors $\Delta u\,\mathbf{r}_u$ and $\Delta v\,\mathbf{r}_v$. (See Figure 5.) Therefore, we can approximate the area of R by the area of this parallelogram, which, from Section 13.4, is

$$\boxed{6} \qquad |(\Delta u\,\mathbf{r}_u) \times (\Delta v\,\mathbf{r}_v)| = |\mathbf{r}_u \times \mathbf{r}_v|\,\Delta u\,\Delta v$$

Computing the cross product, we obtain

$$\mathbf{r}_u \times \mathbf{r}_v = \begin{vmatrix} \mathbf{i} & \mathbf{j} & \mathbf{k} \\ \dfrac{\partial x}{\partial u} & \dfrac{\partial y}{\partial u} & 0 \\ \dfrac{\partial x}{\partial v} & \dfrac{\partial y}{\partial v} & 0 \end{vmatrix} = \begin{vmatrix} \dfrac{\partial x}{\partial u} & \dfrac{\partial y}{\partial u} \\ \dfrac{\partial x}{\partial v} & \dfrac{\partial y}{\partial v} \end{vmatrix}\mathbf{k} = \begin{vmatrix} \dfrac{\partial x}{\partial u} & \dfrac{\partial x}{\partial v} \\ \dfrac{\partial y}{\partial u} & \dfrac{\partial y}{\partial v} \end{vmatrix}\mathbf{k}$$

The determinant that arises in this calculation is called the *Jacobian* of the transformation and is given a special notation.

▓ The Jacobian is named after the German mathematician Carl Gustav Jacob Jacobi (1804–1851). Although the French mathematician Cauchy first used these special determinants involving partial derivatives, Jacobi developed them into a method for evaluating multiple integrals.

> **7 Definition** The **Jacobian** of the transformation T given by $x = g(u, v)$ and $y = h(u, v)$ is
>
> $$\frac{\partial(x, y)}{\partial(u, v)} = \begin{vmatrix} \dfrac{\partial x}{\partial u} & \dfrac{\partial x}{\partial v} \\ \dfrac{\partial y}{\partial u} & \dfrac{\partial y}{\partial v} \end{vmatrix} = \frac{\partial x}{\partial u}\frac{\partial y}{\partial v} - \frac{\partial x}{\partial v}\frac{\partial y}{\partial u}$$

With this notation we can use Equation 6 to give an approximation to the area ΔA of R:

$$\boxed{8} \qquad \Delta A \approx \left| \frac{\partial(x, y)}{\partial(u, v)} \right| \Delta u \, \Delta v$$

where the Jacobian is evaluated at (u_0, v_0).

Next we divide a region S in the uv-plane into rectangles S_{ij} and call their images in the xy-plane R_{ij}. (See Figure 6.)

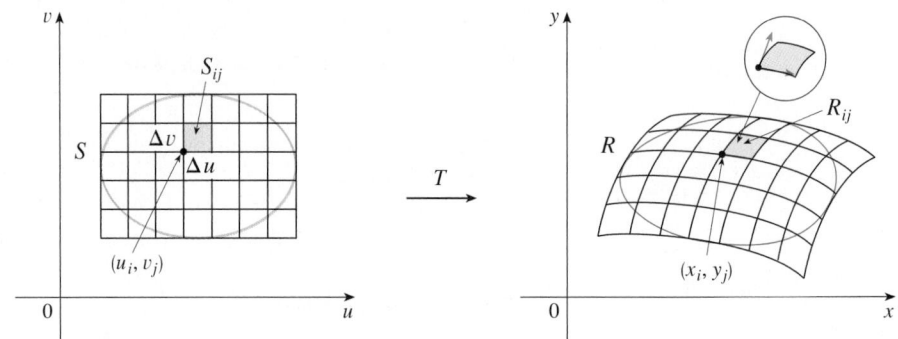

FIGURE 6

Applying the approximation (8) to each R_{ij}, we approximate the double integral of f over R as follows:

$$\iint_R f(x, y) \, dA \approx \sum_{i=1}^{m} \sum_{j=1}^{n} f(x_i, y_j) \, \Delta A$$

$$\approx \sum_{i=1}^{m} \sum_{j=1}^{n} f(g(u_i, v_j), h(u_i, v_j)) \left| \frac{\partial(x, y)}{\partial(u, v)} \right| \Delta u \, \Delta v$$

where the Jacobian is evaluated at (u_i, v_j). Notice that this double sum is a Riemann sum for the integral

$$\iint_S f(g(u, v), h(u, v)) \left| \frac{\partial(x, y)}{\partial(u, v)} \right| du \, dv$$

The foregoing argument suggests that the following theorem is true. (A full proof is given in books on advanced calculus.)

$\boxed{9}$ **Change of Variables in a Double Integral** Suppose that T is a C^1 transformation whose Jacobian is nonzero and that maps a region S in the uv-plane onto a region R in the xy-plane. Suppose that f is continuous on R and that R and S are type I or type II plane regions. Suppose also that T is one-to-one, except perhaps on the boundary of S. Then

$$\iint_R f(x, y) \, dA = \iint_S f(x(u, v), y(u, v)) \left| \frac{\partial(x, y)}{\partial(u, v)} \right| du \, dv$$

Theorem 9 says that we change from an integral in x and y to an integral in u and v by expressing x and y in terms of u and v and writing

$$dA = \left| \frac{\partial(x, y)}{\partial(u, v)} \right| du \, dv$$

Notice the similarity between Theorem 9 and the one-dimensional formula in Equation 2. Instead of the derivative dx/du, we have the absolute value of the Jacobian, that is, $|\partial(x, y)/\partial(u, v)|$.

As a first illustration of Theorem 9, we show that the formula for integration in polar coordinates is just a special case. Here the transformation T from the $r\theta$-plane to the xy-plane is given by

$$x = g(r, \theta) = r\cos\theta \qquad y = h(r, \theta) = r\sin\theta$$

and the geometry of the transformation is shown in Figure 7. T maps an ordinary rectangle in the $r\theta$-plane to a polar rectangle in the xy-plane. The Jacobian of T is

$$\frac{\partial(x, y)}{\partial(r, \theta)} = \begin{vmatrix} \dfrac{\partial x}{\partial r} & \dfrac{\partial x}{\partial \theta} \\ \dfrac{\partial y}{\partial r} & \dfrac{\partial y}{\partial \theta} \end{vmatrix} = \begin{vmatrix} \cos\theta & -r\sin\theta \\ \sin\theta & r\cos\theta \end{vmatrix} = r\cos^2\theta + r\sin^2\theta = r > 0$$

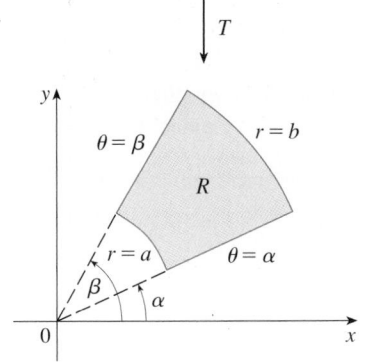

FIGURE 7

The polar coordinate transformation

Thus, Theorem 9 gives

$$\iint_R f(x, y)\, dx\, dy = \iint_S f(r\cos\theta, r\sin\theta) \left| \frac{\partial(x, y)}{\partial(r, \theta)} \right| dr\, d\theta$$

$$= \int_\alpha^\beta \int_a^b f(r\cos\theta, r\sin\theta)\, r\, dr\, d\theta$$

which is the same as Formula 16.4.2.

EXAMPLE 2 Use the change of variables $x = u^2 - v^2$, $y = 2uv$ to evaluate the integral $\iint_R y\, dA$, where R is the region bounded by the x-axis and the parabolas $y^2 = 4 - 4x$ and $y^2 = 4 + 4x$.

SOLUTION The region R is pictured in Figure 2. In Example 1 we discovered that $T(S) = R$, where S is the square $[0, 1] \times [0, 1]$. Indeed, the reason for making the change of variables to evaluate the integral is that S is a much simpler region than R. First we need to compute the Jacobian:

$$\frac{\partial(x, y)}{\partial(u, v)} = \begin{vmatrix} \dfrac{\partial x}{\partial u} & \dfrac{\partial x}{\partial v} \\ \dfrac{\partial y}{\partial u} & \dfrac{\partial y}{\partial v} \end{vmatrix} = \begin{vmatrix} 2u & -2v \\ 2v & 2u \end{vmatrix} = 4u^2 + 4v^2 > 0$$

Therefore, by Theorem 9,

$$\iint_R y\, dA = \iint_S 2uv \left| \frac{\partial(x, y)}{\partial(u, v)} \right| dA = \int_0^1 \int_0^1 (2uv)4(u^2 + v^2)\, du\, dv$$

$$= 8 \int_0^1 \int_0^1 (u^3 v + uv^3)\, du\, dv = 8 \int_0^1 \left[\tfrac{1}{4}u^4 v + \tfrac{1}{2}u^2 v^3 \right]_{u=0}^{u=1} dv$$

$$= \int_0^1 (2v + 4v^3)\, dv = \left[v^2 + v^4 \right]_0^1 = 2$$

NOTE ▫ Example 2 was not a very difficult problem to solve because we were given a suitable change of variables. If we are not supplied with a transformation, then the first step is to think of an appropriate change of variables. If $f(x, y)$ is difficult to integrate, then the form of $f(x, y)$ may suggest a transformation. If the region of integration R is awkward, then the transformation should be chosen so that the corresponding region S in the uv-plane has a convenient description.

EXAMPLE 3 Evaluate the integral $\iint_R e^{(x+y)/(x-y)} \, dA$, where R is the trapezoidal region with vertices $(1, 0)$, $(2, 0)$, $(0, -2)$, and $(0, -1)$.

SOLUTION Since it isn't easy to integrate $e^{(x+y)/(x-y)}$, we make a change of variables suggested by the form of this function:

[10]
$$u = x + y \qquad v = x - y$$

These equations define a transformation T^{-1} from the xy-plane to the uv-plane. Theorem 9 talks about a transformation T from the uv-plane to the xy-plane. It is obtained by solving Equations 10 for x and y:

[11]
$$x = \tfrac{1}{2}(u + v) \qquad y = \tfrac{1}{2}(u - v)$$

The Jacobian of T is

$$\frac{\partial(x, y)}{\partial(u, v)} = \begin{vmatrix} \dfrac{\partial x}{\partial u} & \dfrac{\partial x}{\partial v} \\[2mm] \dfrac{\partial y}{\partial u} & \dfrac{\partial y}{\partial v} \end{vmatrix} = \begin{vmatrix} \tfrac{1}{2} & \tfrac{1}{2} \\[2mm] \tfrac{1}{2} & -\tfrac{1}{2} \end{vmatrix} = -\tfrac{1}{2}$$

To find the region S in the uv-plane corresponding to R, we note that the sides of R lie on the lines

$$y = 0 \qquad x - y = 2 \qquad x = 0 \qquad x - y = 1$$

and, from either Equations 10 or Equations 11, the image lines in the uv-plane are

$$u = v \qquad v = 2 \qquad u = -v \qquad v = 1$$

Thus, the region S is the trapezoidal region with vertices $(1, 1)$, $(2, 2)$, $(-2, 2)$, and $(-1, 1)$ shown in Figure 8. Since

$$S = \{(u, v) \mid 1 \leqslant v \leqslant 2, \ -v \leqslant u \leqslant v\}$$

Theorem 9 gives

$$\iint_R e^{(x+y)/(x-y)} \, dA = \iint_S e^{u/v} \left| \frac{\partial(x, y)}{\partial(u, v)} \right| \, du \, dv$$

$$= \int_1^2 \int_{-v}^{v} e^{u/v} \left(\tfrac{1}{2}\right) du \, dv = \tfrac{1}{2} \int_1^2 \left[v e^{u/v} \right]_{u=-v}^{u=v} \, dv$$

$$= \tfrac{1}{2} \int_1^2 (e - e^{-1}) v \, dv = \tfrac{3}{4}(e - e^{-1})$$

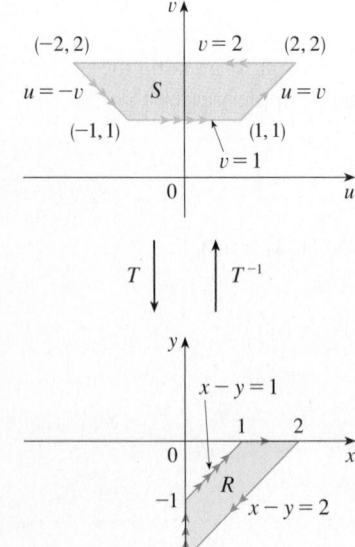

FIGURE 8

‖ **Triple Integrals**

There is a similar change of variables formula for triple integrals. Let T be a transformation that maps a region S in uvw-space onto a region R in xyz-space by means of the equations

$$x = g(u, v, w) \qquad y = h(u, v, w) \qquad z = k(u, v, w)$$

The **Jacobian** of T is the following 3×3 determinant:

$$\boxed{12} \qquad \frac{\partial(x, y, z)}{\partial(u, v, w)} = \begin{vmatrix} \dfrac{\partial x}{\partial u} & \dfrac{\partial x}{\partial v} & \dfrac{\partial x}{\partial w} \\[2mm] \dfrac{\partial y}{\partial u} & \dfrac{\partial y}{\partial v} & \dfrac{\partial y}{\partial w} \\[2mm] \dfrac{\partial z}{\partial u} & \dfrac{\partial z}{\partial v} & \dfrac{\partial z}{\partial w} \end{vmatrix}$$

Under hypotheses similar to those in Theorem 9, we have the following formula for triple integrals:

$$\boxed{13} \qquad \iiint\limits_{R} f(x, y, z)\, dV = \iiint\limits_{S} f(x(u, v, w), y(u, v, w), z(u, v, w)) \left| \frac{\partial(x, y, z)}{\partial(u, v, w)} \right| du\, dv\, dw$$

EXAMPLE 4 Use Formula 13 to derive the formula for triple integration in spherical coordinates.

SOLUTION Here the change of variables is given by

$$x = \rho \sin \phi \cos \theta \qquad y = \rho \sin \phi \sin \theta \qquad z = \rho \cos \phi$$

We compute the Jacobian as follows:

$$\frac{\partial(x, y, z)}{\partial(\rho, \theta, \phi)} = \begin{vmatrix} \sin \phi \cos \theta & -\rho \sin \phi \sin \theta & \rho \cos \phi \cos \theta \\ \sin \phi \sin \theta & \rho \sin \phi \cos \theta & \rho \cos \phi \sin \theta \\ \cos \phi & 0 & -\rho \sin \phi \end{vmatrix}$$

$$= \cos \phi \begin{vmatrix} -\rho \sin \phi \sin \theta & \rho \cos \phi \cos \theta \\ \rho \sin \phi \cos \theta & \rho \cos \phi \sin \theta \end{vmatrix} - \rho \sin \phi \begin{vmatrix} \sin \phi \cos \theta & -\rho \sin \phi \sin \theta \\ \sin \phi \sin \theta & \rho \sin \phi \cos \theta \end{vmatrix}$$

$$= \cos \phi \left(-\rho^2 \sin \phi \cos \phi \sin^2\theta - \rho^2 \sin \phi \cos \phi \cos^2\theta \right)$$

$$\qquad - \rho \sin \phi \left(\rho \sin^2\phi \cos^2\theta + \rho \sin^2\phi \sin^2\theta \right)$$

$$= -\rho^2 \sin \phi \cos^2\phi - \rho^2 \sin \phi \sin^2\phi = -\rho^2 \sin \phi$$

Since $0 \leqslant \phi \leqslant \pi$, we have $\sin \phi \geqslant 0$. Therefore

$$\left| \frac{\partial(x, y, z)}{\partial(\rho, \theta, \phi)} \right| = \left| -\rho^2 \sin \phi \right| = \rho^2 \sin \phi$$

and Formula 13 gives

$$\iiint\limits_{R} f(x, y, z)\, dV = \iiint\limits_{S} f(\rho \sin \phi \cos \theta, \rho \sin \phi \sin \theta, \rho \cos \phi)\, \rho^2 \sin \phi\, d\rho\, d\theta\, d\phi$$

which is equivalent to Formula 16.8.4.

16.9 Exercises

1–6 |||| Find the Jacobian of the transformation.

1. $x = u + 4v, \quad y = 3u - 2v$

2. $x = u^2 - v^2, \quad y = u^2 + v^2$

3. $x = \dfrac{u}{u+v}, \quad y = \dfrac{v}{u-v}$

4. $x = \alpha \sin \beta, \quad y = \alpha \cos \beta$

5. $x = uv, \quad y = vw, \quad z = uw$

6. $x = e^{u-v}, \quad y = e^{u+v}, \quad z = e^{u+v+w}$

7–10 |||| Find the image of the set S under the given transformation.

7. $S = \{(u, v) \mid 0 \le u \le 3, \ 0 \le v \le 2\};$
$x = 2u + 3v, \ y = u - v$

8. S is the square bounded by the lines $u = 0, u = 1, v = 0,$
$v = 1; \quad x = v, \ y = u(1 + v^2)$

9. S is the triangular region with vertices $(0, 0), (1, 1), (0, 1);$
$x = u^2, \ y = v$

10. S is the disk given by $u^2 + v^2 \le 1; \quad x = au, \ y = bv$

11–16 |||| Use the given transformation to evaluate the integral.

11. $\iint_R (x - 3y)\, dA$, where R is the triangular region with
vertices $(0, 0), (2, 1),$ and $(1, 2); \quad x = 2u + v, \ y = u + 2v$

12. $\iint_R (4x + 8y)\, dA$, where R is the parallelogram with
vertices $(-1, 3), (1, -3), (3, -1),$ and $(1, 5);$
$x = \frac{1}{4}(u + v), \ y = \frac{1}{4}(v - 3u)$

13. $\iint_R x^2\, dA$, where R is the region bounded by the ellipse
$9x^2 + 4y^2 = 36; \quad x = 2u, \ y = 3v$

14. $\iint_R (x^2 - xy + y^2)\, dA$, where R is the region bounded
by the ellipse $x^2 - xy + y^2 = 2;$
$x = \sqrt{2}u - \sqrt{2/3}v, \ y = \sqrt{2}u + \sqrt{2/3}v$

15. $\iint_R xy\, dA$, where R is the region in the first quadrant bounded
by the lines $y = x$ and $y = 3x$ and the hyperbolas $xy = 1,$
$xy = 3; \quad x = u/v, \ y = v$

16. $\iint_R y^2\, dA$, where R is the region bounded by the curves $xy = 1,$
$xy = 2, xy^2 = 1, xy^2 = 2; \quad u = xy, \ v = xy^2$. Illustrate by
using a graphing calculator or computer to draw R.

17. (a) Evaluate $\iiint_E dV$, where E is the solid enclosed by the
ellipsoid $x^2/a^2 + y^2/b^2 + z^2/c^2 = 1$. Use the transformation $x = au, \ y = bv, \ z = cw$.

(b) The Earth is not a perfect sphere; rotation has resulted in
flattening at the poles. So the shape can be approximated by
an ellipsoid with $a = b = 6378$ km and $c = 6356$ km. Use
part (a) to estimate the volume of the Earth.

18. Evaluate $\iiint_E x^2 y\, dV$, where E is the solid of Exercise 17(a).

19–23 |||| Evaluate the integral by making an appropriate change of
variables.

19. $\displaystyle\iint_R \frac{x - 2y}{3x - y}\, dA$, where R is the parallelogram enclosed by the
lines $x - 2y = 0, x - 2y = 4, 3x - y = 1,$ and $3x - y = 8$

20. $\iint_R (x + y)e^{x^2 - y^2}\, dA$, where R is the rectangle enclosed by the
lines $x - y = 0, x - y = 2, x + y = 0,$ and $x + y = 3$

21. $\displaystyle\iint_R \cos\left(\frac{y - x}{y + x}\right) dA$, where R is the trapezoidal region
with vertices $(1, 0), (2, 0), (0, 2),$ and $(0, 1)$

22. $\iint_R \sin(9x^2 + 4y^2)\, dA$, where R is the region in the first quadrant bounded by the ellipse $9x^2 + 4y^2 = 1$

23. $\iint_R e^{x+y}\, dA$, where R is given by the inequality $|x| + |y| \le 1$

24. Let f be continuous on $[0, 1]$ and let R be the triangular region
with vertices $(0, 0), (1, 0),$ and $(0, 1)$. Show that

$$\iint_R f(x + y)\, dA = \int_0^1 u f(u)\, du$$

16 Review

1. Suppose f is a continuous function defined on a rectangle $R = [a, b] \times [c, d]$.
(a) Write an expression for a double Riemann sum of f. If $f(x, y) \geqslant 0$, what does the sum represent?
(b) Write the definition of $\iint_R f(x, y) \, dA$ as a limit.
(c) What is the geometric interpretation of $\iint_R f(x, y) \, dA$ if $f(x, y) \geqslant 0$? What if f takes on both positive and negative values?
(d) How do you evaluate $\iint_R f(x, y) \, dA$?
(e) What does the Midpoint Rule for double integrals say?
(f) Write an expression for the average value of f.

2. (a) How do you define $\iint_D f(x, y) \, dA$ if D is a bounded region that is not a rectangle?
(b) What is a type I region? How do you evaluate $\iint_D f(x, y) \, dA$ if D is a type I region?
(c) What is a type II region? How do you evaluate $\iint_D f(x, y) \, dA$ if D is a type II region?
(d) What properties do double integrals have?

3. How do you change from rectangular coordinates to polar coordinates in a double integral? Why would you want to do it?

4. If a lamina occupies a plane region D and has density function $\rho(x, y)$, write expressions for each of the following in terms of double integrals.
(a) The mass
(b) The moments about the axes
(c) The center of mass
(d) The moments of inertia about the axes and the origin

5. Let f be a joint density function of a pair of continuous random variables X and Y.
(a) Write a double integral for the probability that X lies between a and b and Y lies between c and d.

(b) What properties does f possess?
(c) What are the expected values of X and Y?

6. Write an expression for the area of a surface with equation $z = f(x, y)$, $(x, y) \in D$.

7. (a) Write the definition of the triple integral of f over a rectangular box B.
(b) How do you evaluate $\iiint_B f(x, y, z) \, dV$?
(c) How do you define $\iiint_E f(x, y, z) \, dV$ if E is a bounded solid region that is not a box?
(d) What is a type 1 solid region? How do you evaluate $\iiint_E f(x, y, z) \, dV$ if E is such a region?
(e) What is a type 2 solid region? How do you evaluate $\iiint_E f(x, y, z) \, dV$ if E is such a region?
(f) What is a type 3 solid region? How do you evaluate $\iiint_E f(x, y, z) \, dV$ if E is such a region?

8. Suppose a solid object occupies the region E and has density function $\rho(x, y, z)$. Write expressions for each of the following.
(a) The mass
(b) The moments about the coordinate planes
(c) The coordinates of the center of mass
(d) The moments of inertia about the axes

9. (a) How do you change from rectangular coordinates to cylindrical coordinates in a triple integral?
(b) How do you change from rectangular coordinates to spherical coordinates in a triple integral?
(c) In what situations would you change to cylindrical or spherical coordinates?

10. (a) If a transformation T is given by $x = g(u, v)$, $y = h(u, v)$, what is the Jacobian of T?
(b) How do you change variables in a double integral?
(c) How do you change variables in a triple integral?

Determine whether the statement is true or false. If it is true, explain why. If it is false, explain why or give an example that disproves the statement.

1. $\int_{-1}^{2} \int_{0}^{6} x^2 \sin(x - y) \, dx \, dy = \int_{0}^{6} \int_{-1}^{2} x^2 \sin(x - y) \, dy \, dx$

2. $\int_{0}^{1} \int_{0}^{x} \sqrt{x + y^2} \, dy \, dx = \int_{0}^{x} \int_{0}^{1} \sqrt{x + y^2} \, dx \, dy$

3. $\int_{1}^{2} \int_{3}^{4} x^2 e^y \, dy \, dx = \int_{1}^{2} x^2 \, dx \int_{3}^{4} e^y \, dy$

4. $\int_{-1}^{1} \int_{0}^{1} e^{x^2 + y^2} \sin y \, dx \, dy = 0$

5. If D is the disk given by $x^2 + y^2 \leqslant 4$, then
$$\iint_D \sqrt{4 - x^2 - y^2} \, dA = \tfrac{16}{3}\pi$$

6. $\int_{1}^{4} \int_{0}^{1} \left(x^2 + \sqrt{y} \right) \sin(x^2 y^2) \, dx \, dy \leqslant 9$

7. The integral
$$\int_{0}^{2\pi} \int_{0}^{2} \int_{r}^{2} dz \, dr \, d\theta$$
represents the volume enclosed by the cone $z = \sqrt{x^2 + y^2}$ and the plane $z = 2$.

8. The integral $\iiint_E k r^3 \, dz \, dr \, d\theta$ represents the moment of inertia about the z-axis of a solid E with constant density k.

· EXERCISES ·

---

1. A contour map is shown for a function f on the square $R = [0, 3] \times [0, 3]$. Use a Riemann sum with nine terms to estimate the value of $\iint_R f(x, y)\, dA$. Take the sample points to be the upper right corners of the squares.

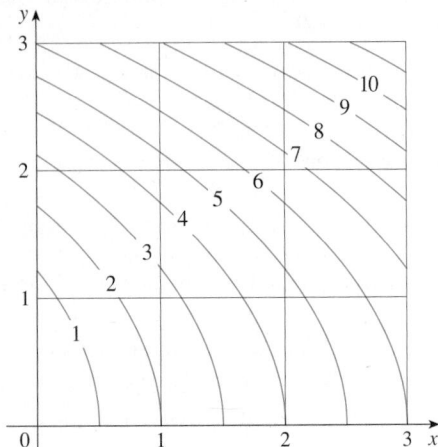

2. Use the Midpoint Rule to estimate the integral in Exercise 1.

3–8 IIII Calculate the iterated integral.

3. $\displaystyle\int_1^2 \int_0^2 (y + 2xe^y)\, dx\, dy$

4. $\displaystyle\int_0^1 \int_0^1 ye^{xy}\, dx\, dy$

5. $\displaystyle\int_0^1 \int_0^x \cos(x^2)\, dy\, dx$

6. $\displaystyle\int_0^1 \int_x^{e^x} 3xy^2\, dy\, dx$

7. $\displaystyle\int_0^\pi \int_0^1 \int_0^{\sqrt{1-y^2}} y \sin x\, dz\, dy\, dx$

8. $\displaystyle\int_0^1 \int_0^y \int_x^1 6xyz\, dz\, dx\, dy$

9–10 IIII Write $\iint_R f(x, y)\, dA$ as an iterated integral, where R is the region shown and f is an arbitrary continuous function on R.

9.

10.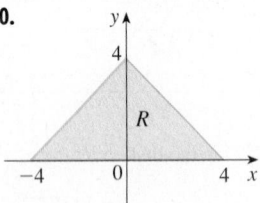

---

11. Describe the region whose area is given by the integral

$$\int_0^{\pi/2} \int_0^{\sin 2\theta} r\, dr\, d\theta$$

12. Describe the solid whose volume is given by the integral

$$\int_0^{\pi/2} \int_0^{\pi/2} \int_1^2 \rho^2 \sin\phi\, d\rho\, d\phi\, d\theta$$

and evaluate the integral.

13–14 IIII Calculate the iterated integral by first reversing the order of integration.

13. $\displaystyle\int_0^1 \int_x^1 \cos(y^2)\, dy\, dx$

14. $\displaystyle\int_0^1 \int_{\sqrt{y}}^1 \frac{ye^{x^2}}{x^3}\, dx\, dy$

15–28 IIII Calculate the value of the multiple integral.

15. $\iint_R ye^{xy}\, dA$, where $R = \{(x, y) \mid 0 \le x \le 2,\ 0 \le y \le 3\}$

16. $\iint_D xy\, dA$, where $D = \{(x, y) \mid 0 \le y \le 1,\ y^2 \le x \le y + 2\}$

17. $\displaystyle\iint_D \frac{y}{1 + x^2}\, dA$, where D is bounded by $y = \sqrt{x},\ y = 0,\ x = 1$

18. $\displaystyle\iint_D \frac{1}{1 + x^2}\, dA$, where D is the triangular region with vertices $(0, 0),\ (1, 1),$ and $(0, 1)$

19. $\iint_D y\, dA$, where D is the region in the first quadrant bounded by the parabolas $x = y^2$ and $x = 8 - y^2$

20. $\iint_D y\, dA$, where D is the region in the first quadrant that lies above the hyperbola $xy = 1$ and the line $y = x$ and below the line $y = 2$

21. $\iint_D (x^2 + y^2)^{3/2}\, dA$, where D is the region in the first quadrant bounded by the lines $y = 0$ and $y = \sqrt{3}x$ and the circle $x^2 + y^2 = 9$

22. $\iint_D x\, dA$, where D is the region in the first quadrant that lies between the circles $x^2 + y^2 = 1$ and $x^2 + y^2 = 2$

23. $\iiint_E xy\, dV$, where $E = \{(x, y, z) \mid 0 \le x \le 3,\ 0 \le y \le x,\ 0 \le z \le x + y\}$

24. $\iiint_T xy\, dV$, where T is the solid tetrahedron with vertices $(0, 0, 0),\ (\frac{1}{3}, 0, 0),\ (0, 1, 0),$ and $(0, 0, 1)$

25. $\iiint_E y^2z^2\, dV$, where E is bounded by the paraboloid $x = 1 - y^2 - z^2$ and the plane $x = 0$

26. $\iiint_E z\, dV$, where E is bounded by the planes $y = 0,\ z = 0,$ $x + y = 2$ and the cylinder $y^2 + z^2 = 1$ in the first octant

27. $\iiint_E yz\, dV$, where E lies above the plane $z = 0$, below the plane $z = y$, and inside the cylinder $x^2 + y^2 = 4$

28. $\iiint_H z^3\sqrt{x^2 + y^2 + z^2}\, dV$, where H is the solid hemisphere that lies above the xy-plane and has center the origin and radius 1

29–34 IIII Find the volume of the given solid.

29. Under the paraboloid $z = x^2 + 4y^2$ and above the rectangle $R = [0, 2] \times [1, 4]$

30. Under the surface $z = x^2y$ and above the triangle in the xy-plane with vertices $(1, 0),\ (2, 1),$ and $(4, 0)$

31. The solid tetrahedron with vertices $(0, 0, 0),\ (0, 0, 1),\ (0, 2, 0),$ and $(2, 2, 0)$

32. Bounded by the cylinder $x^2 + y^2 = 4$ and the planes $z = 0$ and $y + z = 3$

33. One of the wedges cut from the cylinder $x^2 + 9y^2 = a^2$ by the planes $z = 0$ and $z = mx$

34. Above the paraboloid $z = x^2 + y^2$ and below the half-cone $z = \sqrt{x^2 + y^2}$

35. Consider a lamina that occupies the region D bounded by the parabola $x = 1 - y^2$ and the coordinate axes in the first quadrant with density function $\rho(x, y) = y$.
(a) Find the mass of the lamina.
(b) Find the center of mass.
(c) Find the moments of inertia and radii of gyration about the x- and y-axes.

36. A lamina occupies the part of the disk $x^2 + y^2 \leqslant a^2$ that lies in the first quadrant.
(a) Find the centroid of the lamina.
(b) Find the center of mass of the lamina if the density function is $\rho(x, y) = xy^2$.

37. (a) Find the centroid of a right circular cone with height h and base radius a. (Place the cone so that its base is in the xy-plane with center the origin and its axis along the positive z-axis.)
(b) Find the moment of inertia of the cone about its axis (the z-axis).

38. Find the area of the part of the cone $z^2 = a^2(x^2 + y^2)$ between the planes $z = 1$ and $z = 2$.

39. Find the area of the part of the surface $z = x^2 + y$ that lies above the triangle with vertices $(0, 0)$, $(1, 0)$, and $(0, 2)$.

CAS **40.** Graph the surface $z = x \sin y$, $-3 \leqslant x \leqslant 3$, $-\pi \leqslant y \leqslant \pi$, and find its surface area correct to four decimal places.

41. Use polar coordinates to evaluate $\int_0^3 \int_{-\sqrt{9-x^2}}^{\sqrt{9-x^2}} (x^3 + xy^2)\, dy\, dx$.

42. Use spherical coordinates to evaluate
$$\int_{-2}^{2} \int_{0}^{\sqrt{4-y^2}} \int_{-\sqrt{4-x^2-y^2}}^{\sqrt{4-x^2-y^2}} y^2 \sqrt{x^2 + y^2 + z^2}\, dz\, dx\, dy$$

43. If D is the region bounded by the curves $y = 1 - x^2$ and $y = e^x$, find the approximate value of the integral $\iint_D y^2\, dA$. (Use a graphing device to estimate the points of intersection of the curves.)

CAS **44.** Find the center of mass of the solid tetrahedron with vertices $(0, 0, 0)$, $(1, 0, 0)$, $(0, 2, 0)$, $(0, 0, 3)$ and density function $\rho(x, y, z) = x^2 + y^2 + z^2$.

45. The joint density function for random variables X and Y is
$$f(x, y) = \begin{cases} C(x + y) & \text{if } 0 \leqslant x \leqslant 3,\ 0 \leqslant y \leqslant 2 \\ 0 & \text{otherwise} \end{cases}$$
(a) Find the value of the constant C.
(b) Find $P(X \leqslant 2, Y \geqslant 1)$.
(c) Find $P(X + Y \leqslant 1)$.

46. A lamp has three bulbs, each of a type with average lifetime 800 hours. If we model the probability of failure of the bulbs by an exponential density function with mean 800, find the probability that all three bulbs fail within a total of 1000 hours.

47. Rewrite the integral
$$\int_{-1}^{1} \int_{x^2}^{1} \int_{0}^{1-y} f(x, y, z)\, dz\, dy\, dx$$
as an iterated integral in the order $dx\, dy\, dz$.

48. Give five other iterated integrals that are equal to
$$\int_{0}^{2} \int_{0}^{y^3} \int_{0}^{y^2} f(x, y, z)\, dz\, dx\, dy$$

49. Use the transformation $u = x - y$, $v = x + y$ to evaluate $\iint_R (x - y)/(x + y)\, dA$, where R is the square with vertices $(0, 2)$, $(1, 1)$, $(2, 2)$, and $(1, 3)$.

50. Use the transformation $x = u^2$, $y = v^2$, $z = w^2$ to find the volume of the region bounded by the surface $\sqrt{x} + \sqrt{y} + \sqrt{z} = 1$ and the coordinate planes.

51. Use the change of variables formula and an appropriate transformation to evaluate $\iint_R xy\, dA$, where R is the square with vertices $(0, 0)$, $(1, 1)$, $(2, 0)$, and $(1, -1)$.

52. The **Mean Value Theorem for double integrals** says that if f is a continuous function on a plane region D that is of type I or II, then there exists a point (x_0, y_0) in D such that
$$\iint_D f(x, y)\, dA = f(x_0, y_0)\, A(D)$$
Use the Extreme Value Theorem (15.7.8) and Property 16.3.11 of integrals to prove this theorem. (Use the proof of the single-variable version in Section 6.5 as a guide.)

53. Suppose that f is continuous on a disk that contains the point (a, b). Let D_r be the closed disk with center (a, b) and radius r. Use the Mean Value Theorem for double integrals (see Exercise 52) to show that
$$\lim_{r \to 0} \frac{1}{\pi r^2} \iint_{D_r} f(x, y)\, dA = f(a, b)$$

54. (a) Evaluate $\displaystyle\iint_D \frac{1}{(x^2 + y^2)^{n/2}}\, dA$, where n is an integer and D is the region bounded by the circles with center the origin and radii r and R, $0 < r < R$.
(b) For what values of n does the integral in part (a) have a limit as $r \to 0^+$?
(c) Find $\displaystyle\iiint_E \frac{1}{(x^2 + y^2 + z^2)^{n/2}}\, dV$, where E is the region bounded by the spheres with center the origin and radii r and R, $0 < r < R$.
(d) For what values of n does the integral in part (c) have a limit as $r \to 0^+$?

1. If $[\![x]\!]$ denotes the greatest integer in x, evaluate the integral

$$\iint_R [\![x + y]\!]\, dA$$

where $R = \{(x, y) \mid 1 \leqslant x \leqslant 3,\ 2 \leqslant y \leqslant 5\}$.

2. Evaluate the integral

$$\int_0^1 \int_0^1 e^{\max\{x^2,\, y^2\}}\, dy\, dx$$

where $\max\{x^2, y^2\}$ means the larger of the numbers x^2 and y^2.

3. Find the average value of the function $f(x) = \int_x^1 \cos(t^2)\, dt$ on the interval $[0, 1]$.

4. If $\mathbf{a}$, $\mathbf{b}$, and $\mathbf{c}$ are constant vectors, $\mathbf{r}$ is the position vector $x\mathbf{i} + y\mathbf{j} + z\mathbf{k}$, and E is given by the inequalities $0 \leqslant \mathbf{a} \cdot \mathbf{r} \leqslant \alpha$, $0 \leqslant \mathbf{b} \cdot \mathbf{r} \leqslant \beta$, $0 \leqslant \mathbf{c} \cdot \mathbf{r} \leqslant \gamma$, show that

$$\iiint_E (\mathbf{a} \cdot \mathbf{r})(\mathbf{b} \cdot \mathbf{r})(\mathbf{c} \cdot \mathbf{r})\, dV = \frac{(\alpha\beta\gamma)^2}{8|\mathbf{a} \cdot (\mathbf{b} \times \mathbf{c})|}$$

5. The double integral $\int_0^1 \int_0^1 \dfrac{1}{1 - xy}\, dx\, dy$ is an improper integral and could be defined as the limit of double integrals over the rectangle $[0, t] \times [0, t]$ as $t \to 1^-$. But if we expand the integrand as a geometric series, we can express the integral as the sum of an infinite series. Show that

$$\int_0^1 \int_0^1 \frac{1}{1 - xy}\, dx\, dy = \sum_{n=1}^{\infty} \frac{1}{n^2}$$

6. Leonhard Euler was able to find the exact sum of the series in Problem 5. In 1736 he proved that

$$\sum_{n=1}^{\infty} \frac{1}{n^2} = \frac{\pi^2}{6}$$

In this problem we ask you to prove this fact by evaluating the double integral in Problem 5. Start by making the change of variables

$$x = \frac{u - v}{\sqrt{2}} \qquad y = \frac{u + v}{\sqrt{2}}$$

This gives a rotation about the origin through the angle $\pi/4$. You will need to sketch the corresponding region in the uv-plane.

    [*Hint:* If, in evaluating the integral, you encounter either of the expressions $(1 - \sin\theta)/\cos\theta$ or $(\cos\theta)/(1 + \sin\theta)$, you might like to use the identity $\cos\theta = \sin((\pi/2) - \theta)$ and the corresponding identity for $\sin\theta$.]

7. (a) Show that

$$\int_0^1 \int_0^1 \int_0^1 \frac{1}{1 - xyz}\, dx\, dy\, dz = \sum_{n=1}^{\infty} \frac{1}{n^3}$$

(Nobody has ever been able to find the exact value of the sum of this series.)

(b) Show that

$$\int_0^1 \int_0^1 \int_0^1 \frac{1}{1 + xyz}\, dx\, dy\, dz = \sum_{n=1}^{\infty} \frac{(-1)^{n-1}}{n^3}$$

Use this equation to evaluate the triple integral correct to two decimal places.

8. Show that

$$\int_0^{\infty} \frac{\arctan \pi x - \arctan x}{x}\, dx = \frac{\pi}{2} \ln \pi$$

by first expressing the integral as an iterated integral.

9. If f is continuous, show that

$$\int_0^x \int_0^y \int_0^z f(t)\, dt\, dz\, dy = \frac{1}{2} \int_0^x (x - t)^2 f(t)\, dt$$

10. (a) A lamina has constant density ρ and takes the shape of a disk with center the origin and radius R. Use Newton's Law of Gravitation (see Section 14.4) to show that the magnitude of the force of attraction that the lamina exerts on a body with mass m located at the point $(0, 0, d)$ on the positive z-axis is

$$F = 2\pi Gm\rho d\left(\frac{1}{d} - \frac{1}{\sqrt{R^2 + d^2}}\right)$$

[*Hint:* Divide the disk as in Figure 4 in Section 16.4 and first compute the vertical component of the force exerted by the polar subrectangle R_{ij}.]

(b) Show that the magnitude of the force of attraction of a lamina with density ρ that occupies an entire plane on an object with mass m located at a distance d from the plane is

$$F = 2\pi Gm\rho$$

Notice that this expression does not depend on d.

CHAPTER 17

The collection of wind velocity vectors
at any given time during a tornado is an
example of a vector field.

Vector Calculus

In this chapter we study the calculus of vector fields. (These are functions that assign vectors to points in space.) In particular we define line integrals (which can be used to find the work done by a force field in moving an object along a curve). Then we define surface integrals (which can be used to find the rate of fluid flow across a surface). The connections between these new types of integrals and the single, double, and triple integrals that we have already met are given by the higher-dimensional versions of the Fundamental Theorem of Calculus: Green's Theorem, Stokes' Theorem, and the Divergence Theorem.

17.1 Vector Fields

The vectors in Figure 1 are air velocity vectors that indicate the wind speed and direction at points 10 m above the surface elevation in the San Francisco Bay area. We see at a glance from the largest arrows in part (a) that the greatest wind speeds at that time occurred as the winds entered the bay across the Golden Gate Bridge. Part (b) shows the very different wind pattern at a later date. Associated with every point in the air we can imagine a wind velocity vector. This is an example of a *velocity vector field*.

(a) 12:00 P.M., June 11, 2002 (b) 4:00 P.M., June 30, 2002

FIGURE 1 Velocity vector fields showing San Francisco Bay wind patterns

Other examples of velocity vector fields are illustrated in Figure 2: ocean currents and flow past an airfoil.

(a) Ocean currents off the coast of Nova Scotia

(b) Airflow past an inclined airfoil

FIGURE 2 Velocity vector fields

Another type of vector field, called a *force field,* associates a force vector with each point in a region. An example is the gravitational force field that we will look at in Example 4.

In general, a vector field is a function whose domain is a set of points in $\mathbb{R}^2$ (or $\mathbb{R}^3$) and whose range is a set of vectors in V_2 (or V_3).

> **1 Definition** Let D be a set in $\mathbb{R}^2$ (a plane region). A **vector field on** $\mathbb{R}^2$ is a function $\mathbf{F}$ that assigns to each point (x, y) in D a two-dimensional vector $\mathbf{F}(x, y)$.

The best way to picture a vector field is to draw the arrow representing the vector $\mathbf{F}(x, y)$ starting at the point (x, y). Of course, it's impossible to do this for all points (x, y), but we can gain a reasonable impression of $\mathbf{F}$ by doing it for a few representative points in D as in Figure 3. Since $\mathbf{F}(x, y)$ is a two-dimensional vector, we can write it in terms of its **component functions** P and Q as follows:

$$\mathbf{F}(x, y) = P(x, y)\,\mathbf{i} + Q(x, y)\,\mathbf{j} = \langle P(x, y), Q(x, y) \rangle$$

or, for short,
$$\mathbf{F} = P\,\mathbf{i} + Q\,\mathbf{j}$$

Notice that P and Q are scalar functions of two variables and are sometimes called **scalar fields** to distinguish them from vector fields.

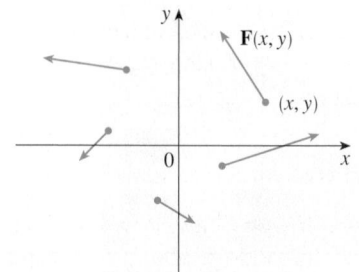

FIGURE 3
Vector field on $\mathbb{R}^2$

> **2 Definition** Let E be a subset of $\mathbb{R}^3$. A **vector field on** $\mathbb{R}^3$ is a function $\mathbf{F}$ that assigns to each point (x, y, z) in E a three-dimensional vector $\mathbf{F}(x, y, z)$.

A vector field $\mathbf{F}$ on $\mathbb{R}^3$ is pictured in Figure 4. We can express it in terms of its component functions P, Q, and R as

$$\mathbf{F}(x, y, z) = P(x, y, z)\,\mathbf{i} + Q(x, y, z)\,\mathbf{j} + R(x, y, z)\,\mathbf{k}$$

As with the vector functions in Section 14.1, we can define continuity of vector fields and show that $\mathbf{F}$ is continuous if and only if its component functions P, Q, and R are continuous.

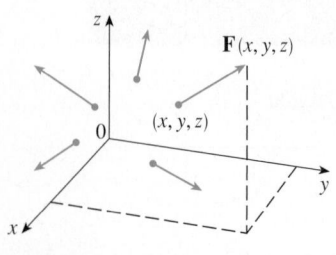

FIGURE 4
Vector field on $\mathbb{R}^3$

We sometimes identify a point (x, y, z) with its position vector $\mathbf{x} = \langle x, y, z \rangle$ and write $\mathbf{F}(\mathbf{x})$ instead of $\mathbf{F}(x, y, z)$. Then $\mathbf{F}$ becomes a function that assigns a vector $\mathbf{F}(\mathbf{x})$ to a vector $\mathbf{x}$.

EXAMPLE 1 A vector field on $\mathbb{R}^2$ is defined by

$$\mathbf{F}(x, y) = -y\,\mathbf{i} + x\,\mathbf{j}$$

Describe $\mathbf{F}$ by sketching some of the vectors $\mathbf{F}(x, y)$ as in Figure 3.

SOLUTION Since $\mathbf{F}(1, 0) = \mathbf{j}$, we draw the vector $\mathbf{j} = \langle 0, 1 \rangle$ starting at the point $(1, 0)$ in Figure 5. Since $\mathbf{F}(0, 1) = -\mathbf{i}$, we draw the vector $\langle -1, 0 \rangle$ with starting point $(0, 1)$. Continuing in this way, we calculate several other representative values of $\mathbf{F}(x, y)$ in the table and draw the corresponding vectors to represent the vector field in Figure 5.

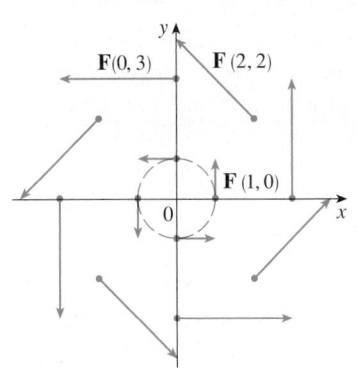

FIGURE 5

$\mathbf{F}(x, y) = -y\,\mathbf{i} + x\,\mathbf{j}$

(x, y)	$\mathbf{F}(x, y)$	(x, y)	$\mathbf{F}(x, y)$
$(1, 0)$	$\langle 0, 1 \rangle$	$(-1, 0)$	$\langle 0, -1 \rangle$
$(2, 2)$	$\langle -2, 2 \rangle$	$(-2, -2)$	$\langle 2, -2 \rangle$
$(3, 0)$	$\langle 0, 3 \rangle$	$(-3, 0)$	$\langle 0, -3 \rangle$
$(0, 1)$	$\langle -1, 0 \rangle$	$(0, -1)$	$\langle 1, 0 \rangle$
$(-2, 2)$	$\langle -2, -2 \rangle$	$(2, -2)$	$\langle 2, 2 \rangle$
$(0, 3)$	$\langle -3, 0 \rangle$	$(0, -3)$	$\langle 3, 0 \rangle$

It appears from Figure 5 that each arrow is tangent to a circle with center the origin. To confirm this, we take the dot product of the position vector $\mathbf{x} = x\,\mathbf{i} + y\,\mathbf{j}$ with the vector $\mathbf{F}(\mathbf{x}) = \mathbf{F}(x, y)$:

$$\mathbf{x} \cdot \mathbf{F}(\mathbf{x}) = (x\,\mathbf{i} + y\,\mathbf{j}) \cdot (-y\,\mathbf{i} + x\,\mathbf{j})$$

$$= -xy + yx = 0$$

This shows that $\mathbf{F}(x, y)$ is perpendicular to the position vector $\langle x, y \rangle$ and is therefore tangent to a circle with center the origin and radius $|\mathbf{x}| = \sqrt{x^2 + y^2}$. Notice also that

$$|\mathbf{F}(x, y)| = \sqrt{(-y)^2 + x^2} = \sqrt{x^2 + y^2} = |\mathbf{x}|$$

so the magnitude of the vector $\mathbf{F}(x, y)$ is equal to the radius of the circle.

Some computer algebra systems are capable of plotting vector fields in two or three dimensions. They give a better impression of the vector field than is possible by hand because the computer can plot a large number of representative vectors. Figure 6 shows a computer plot of the vector field in Example 1; Figures 7 and 8 show two other vector fields. Notice that the computer scales the lengths of the vectors so they are not too long and yet are proportional to their true lengths.

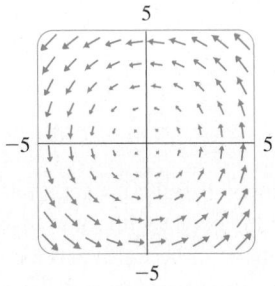

FIGURE 6

$\mathbf{F}(x, y) = \langle -y, x \rangle$

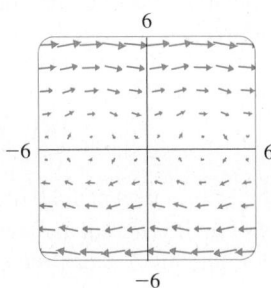

FIGURE 7

$\mathbf{F}(x, y) = \langle y, \sin x \rangle$

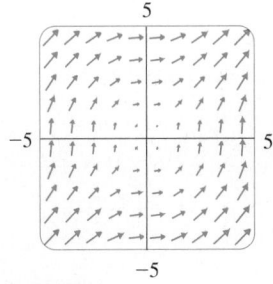

FIGURE 8

$\mathbf{F}(x, y) = \langle \ln(1 + y^2), \ln(1 + x^2) \rangle$

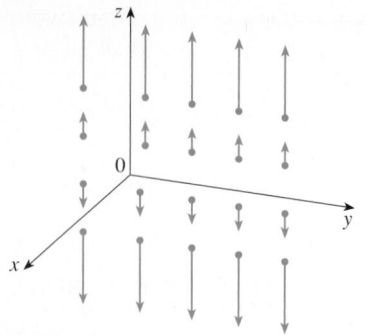

FIGURE 9

$\mathbf{F}(x, y, z) = z\,\mathbf{k}$

EXAMPLE 2 Sketch the vector field on $\mathbb{R}^3$ given by $\mathbf{F}(x, y, z) = z\,\mathbf{k}$.

SOLUTION The sketch is shown in Figure 9. Notice that all vectors are vertical and point upward above the xy-plane or downward below it. The magnitude increases with the distance from the xy-plane.

We were able to draw the vector field in Example 2 by hand because of its particularly simple formula. Most three-dimensional vector fields, however, are virtually impossible to sketch by hand and so we need to resort to a computer algebra system. Examples are shown in Figures 10, 11, and 12. Notice that the vector fields in Figures 10 and 11 have similar formulas, but all the vectors in Figure 11 point in the general direction of the negative y-axis because their y-components are all -2. If the vector field in Figure 12 represents a velocity field, then a particle would be swept upward and would spiral around the z-axis in the clockwise direction as viewed from above.

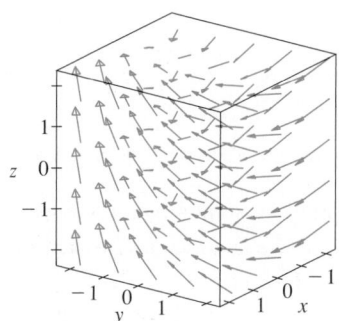

FIGURE 10

$\mathbf{F}(x, y, z) = y\,\mathbf{i} + z\,\mathbf{j} + x\,\mathbf{k}$

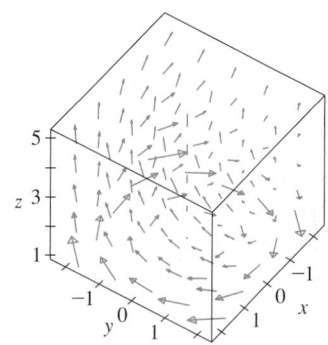

FIGURE 11

$\mathbf{F}(x, y, z) = y\,\mathbf{i} - 2\,\mathbf{j} + x\,\mathbf{k}$

FIGURE 12

$\mathbf{F}(x, y, z) = \dfrac{y}{z}\,\mathbf{i} - \dfrac{x}{z}\,\mathbf{j} + \dfrac{z}{4}\,\mathbf{k}$

 In Visual 17.1 you can rotate the vector fields in Figures 10–12 as well as additional fields.

EXAMPLE 3 Imagine a fluid flowing steadily along a pipe and let $\mathbf{V}(x, y, z)$ be the velocity vector at a point (x, y, z). Then $\mathbf{V}$ assigns a vector to each point (x, y, z) in a certain domain E (the interior of the pipe) and so $\mathbf{V}$ is a vector field on $\mathbb{R}^3$ called a **velocity field**. A possible velocity field is illustrated in Figure 13. The speed at any given point is indicated by the length of the arrow.

Velocity fields also occur in other areas of physics. For instance, the vector field in Example 1 could be used as the velocity field describing the counterclockwise rotation of a wheel. We have seen other examples of velocity fields in Figures 1 and 2.

FIGURE 13

Velocity field in fluid flow

EXAMPLE 4 Newton's Law of Gravitation states that the magnitude of the gravitational force between two objects with masses m and M is

$$|\mathbf{F}| = \frac{mMG}{r^2}$$

where r is the distance between the objects and G is the gravitational constant. (This is an example of an inverse square law.) Let's assume that the object with mass M is located at the origin in $\mathbb{R}^3$. (For instance, M could be the mass of the Earth and the origin would be at its center.) Let the position vector of the object with mass m be $\mathbf{x} = \langle x, y, z \rangle$. Then $r = |\mathbf{x}|$, so $r^2 = |\mathbf{x}|^2$. The gravitational force exerted on this second object acts toward the origin, and the unit vector in this direction is

$$-\frac{\mathbf{x}}{|\mathbf{x}|}$$

Therefore, the gravitational force acting on the object at $\mathbf{x} = \langle x, y, z \rangle$ is

> [3]

$$\mathbf{F}(\mathbf{x}) = -\frac{mMG}{|\mathbf{x}|^3}\mathbf{x}$$

[Physicists often use the notation $\mathbf{r}$ instead of $\mathbf{x}$ for the position vector, so you may see Formula 3 written in the form $\mathbf{F} = -(mMG/r^3)\mathbf{r}$.] The function given by Equation 3 is an example of a vector field, called the **gravitational field**, because it associates a vector [the force $\mathbf{F}(\mathbf{x})$] with every point $\mathbf{x}$ in space.

Formula 3 is a compact way of writing the gravitational field, but we can also write it in terms of its component functions by using the facts that $\mathbf{x} = x\,\mathbf{i} + y\,\mathbf{j} + z\,\mathbf{k}$ and $|\mathbf{x}| = \sqrt{x^2 + y^2 + z^2}$:

$$\mathbf{F}(x, y, z) = \frac{-mMGx}{(x^2 + y^2 + z^2)^{3/2}}\mathbf{i} + \frac{-mMGy}{(x^2 + y^2 + z^2)^{3/2}}\mathbf{j} + \frac{-mMGz}{(x^2 + y^2 + z^2)^{3/2}}\mathbf{k}$$

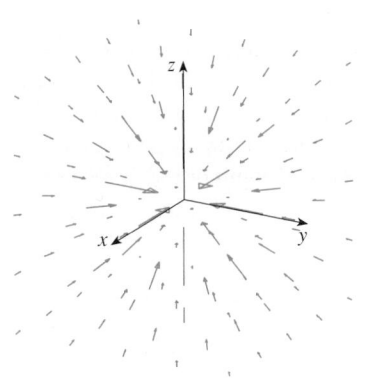

FIGURE 14
Gravitational force field

The gravitational field $\mathbf{F}$ is pictured in Figure 14.

EXAMPLE 5 Suppose an electric charge Q is located at the origin. According to Coulomb's Law, the electric force $\mathbf{F}(\mathbf{x})$ exerted by this charge on a charge q located at a point (x, y, z) with position vector $\mathbf{x} = \langle x, y, z \rangle$ is

> [4]

$$\mathbf{F}(\mathbf{x}) = \frac{\varepsilon q Q}{|\mathbf{x}|^3}\mathbf{x}$$

where ε is a constant (that depends on the units used). For like charges, we have $qQ > 0$ and the force is repulsive; for unlike charges, we have $qQ < 0$ and the force is attractive. Notice the similarity between Formulas 3 and 4. Both vector fields are examples of **force fields**.

Instead of considering the electric force $\mathbf{F}$, physicists often consider the force per unit charge:

$$\mathbf{E}(\mathbf{x}) = \frac{1}{q}\mathbf{F}(\mathbf{x}) = \frac{\varepsilon Q}{|\mathbf{x}|^3}\mathbf{x}$$

Then $\mathbf{E}$ is a vector field on $\mathbb{R}^3$ called the **electric field** of Q.

||| Gradient Fields

If f is a scalar function of two variables, recall from Section 15.6 that its gradient ∇f (or grad f) is defined by

$$\nabla f(x, y) = f_x(x, y)\,\mathbf{i} + f_y(x, y)\,\mathbf{j}$$

Therefore, ∇f is really a vector field on $\mathbb{R}^2$ and is called a **gradient vector field**. Likewise, if f is a scalar function of three variables, its gradient is a vector field on $\mathbb{R}^3$ given by

$$\nabla f(x, y, z) = f_x(x, y, z)\,\mathbf{i} + f_y(x, y, z)\,\mathbf{j} + f_z(x, y, z)\,\mathbf{k}$$

EXAMPLE 6 Find the gradient vector field of $f(x, y) = x^2 y - y^3$. Plot the gradient vector field together with a contour map of f. How are they related?

SOLUTION The gradient vector field is given by

$$\nabla f(x, y) = \frac{\partial f}{\partial x} \mathbf{i} + \frac{\partial f}{\partial y} \mathbf{j} = 2xy \, \mathbf{i} + (x^2 - 3y^2) \mathbf{j}$$

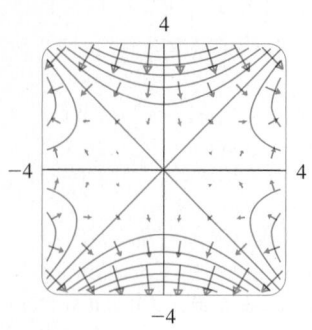

FIGURE 15

Figure 15 shows a contour map of f with the gradient vector field. Notice that the gradient vectors are perpendicular to the level curves, as we would expect from Section 15.6. Notice also that the gradient vectors are long where the level curves are close to each other and short where they are farther apart. That's because the length of the gradient vector is the value of the directional derivative of f and close level curves indicate a steep graph.

A vector field **F** is called a **conservative vector field** if it is the gradient of some scalar function, that is, if there exists a function f such that $\mathbf{F} = \nabla f$. In this situation f is called a **potential function** for **F**.

Not all vector fields are conservative, but such fields do arise frequently in physics. For example, the gravitational field **F** in Example 4 is conservative because if we define

$$f(x, y, z) = \frac{mMG}{\sqrt{x^2 + y^2 + z^2}}$$

then

$$\nabla f(x, y, z) = \frac{\partial f}{\partial x} \mathbf{i} + \frac{\partial f}{\partial y} \mathbf{j} + \frac{\partial f}{\partial z} \mathbf{k}$$

$$= \frac{-mMGx}{(x^2 + y^2 + z^2)^{3/2}} \mathbf{i} + \frac{-mMGy}{(x^2 + y^2 + z^2)^{3/2}} \mathbf{j} + \frac{-mMGz}{(x^2 + y^2 + z^2)^{3/2}} \mathbf{k}$$

$$= \mathbf{F}(x, y, z)$$

In Sections 17.3 and 17.5 we will learn how to tell whether or not a given vector field is conservative.

17.1 Exercises

1–10 ▏▏▎ Sketch the vector field **F** by drawing a diagram like Figure 5 or Figure 9.

1. $\mathbf{F}(x, y) = \frac{1}{2}(\mathbf{i} + \mathbf{j})$

2. $\mathbf{F}(x, y) = \mathbf{i} + x \mathbf{j}$

3. $\mathbf{F}(x, y) = y \mathbf{i} + \frac{1}{2} \mathbf{j}$

4. $\mathbf{F}(x, y) = (x - y) \mathbf{i} + x \mathbf{j}$

5. $\mathbf{F}(x, y) = \dfrac{y \mathbf{i} + x \mathbf{j}}{\sqrt{x^2 + y^2}}$

6. $\mathbf{F}(x, y) = \dfrac{y \mathbf{i} - x \mathbf{j}}{\sqrt{x^2 + y^2}}$

7. $\mathbf{F}(x, y, z) = \mathbf{j}$

8. $\mathbf{F}(x, y, z) = z \mathbf{j}$

9. $\mathbf{F}(x, y, z) = y \mathbf{j}$

10. $\mathbf{F}(x, y, z) = \mathbf{j} - \mathbf{i}$

11–14 ▏▏▎ Match the vector fields **F** with the plots labeled I–IV. Give reasons for your choices.

11. $\mathbf{F}(x, y) = \langle y, x \rangle$

12. $\mathbf{F}(x, y) = \langle 1, \sin y \rangle$

13. $\mathbf{F}(x, y) = \langle x - 2, x + 1 \rangle$

14. $\mathbf{F}(x, y) = \langle y, 1/x \rangle$

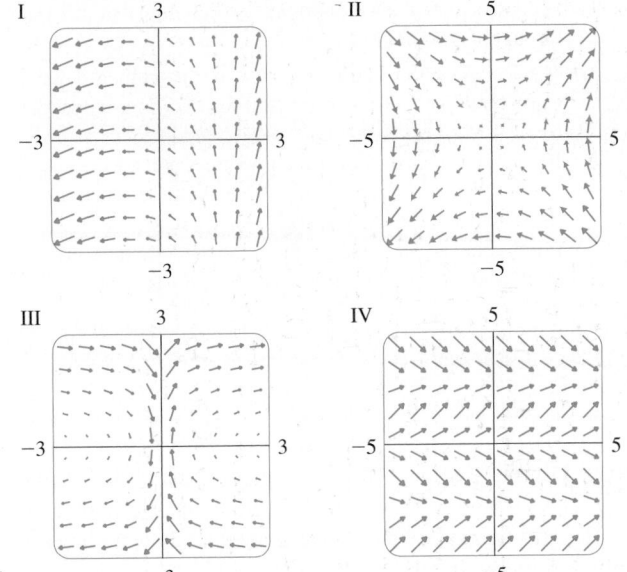

15–18 ▥ Match the vector fields **F** on $\mathbb{R}^3$ with the plots labeled I–IV. Give reasons for your choices.

15. $\mathbf{F}(x, y, z) = \mathbf{i} + 2\mathbf{j} + 3\mathbf{k}$

16. $\mathbf{F}(x, y, z) = \mathbf{i} + 2\mathbf{j} + z\mathbf{k}$

17. $\mathbf{F}(x, y, z) = x\mathbf{i} + y\mathbf{j} + 3\mathbf{k}$

18. $\mathbf{F}(x, y, z) = x\mathbf{i} + y\mathbf{j} + z\mathbf{k}$

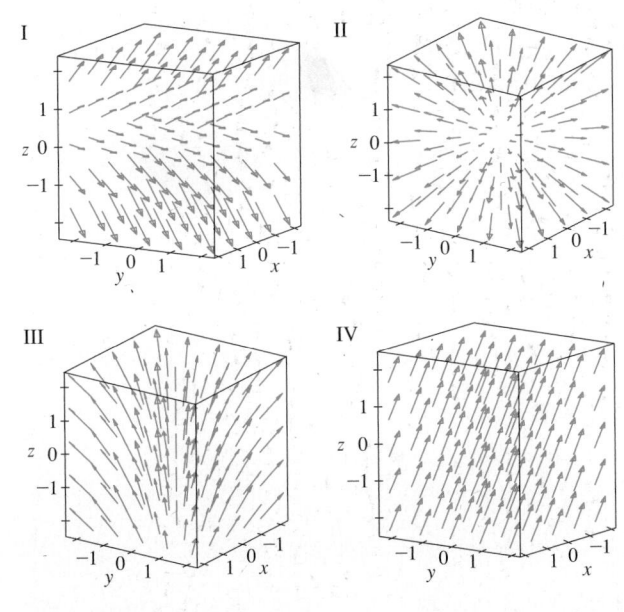

CAS **19.** If you have a CAS that plots vector fields (the command is fieldplot in Maple and PlotVectorField in

Mathematica), use it to plot

$$\mathbf{F}(x, y) = (y^2 - 2xy)\,\mathbf{i} + (3xy - 6x^2)\,\mathbf{j}$$

Explain the appearance by finding the set of points (x, y) such that $\mathbf{F}(x, y) = \mathbf{0}$.

CAS **20.** Let $\mathbf{F}(\mathbf{x}) = (r^2 - 2r)\mathbf{x}$, where $\mathbf{x} = \langle x, y \rangle$ and $r = |\mathbf{x}|$. Use a CAS to plot this vector field in various domains until you can see what is happening. Describe the appearance of the plot and explain it by finding the points where $\mathbf{F}(\mathbf{x}) = \mathbf{0}$.

21–24 ▥ Find the gradient vector field of f.

21. $f(x, y) = \ln(x + 2y)$ **22.** $f(x, y) = x^\alpha e^{-\beta x}$

23. $f(x, y, z) = \sqrt{x^2 + y^2 + z^2}$ **24.** $f(x, y, z) = x\cos(y/z)$

25–26 ▥ Find the gradient vector field ∇f of f and sketch it.

25. $f(x, y) = xy - 2x$ **26.** $f(x, y) = \frac{1}{4}(x + y)^2$

CAS **27–28** ▥ Plot the gradient vector field of f together with a contour map of f. Explain how they are related to each other.

27. $f(x, y) = \sin x + \sin y$ **28.** $f(x, y) = \sin(x + y)$

29–32 ▥ Match the functions f with the plots of their gradient vector fields (labeled I–IV). Give reasons for your choices.

29. $f(x, y) = xy$ **30.** $f(x, y) = x^2 - y^2$

31. $f(x, y) = x^2 + y^2$ **32.** $f(x, y) = \sqrt{x^2 + y^2}$

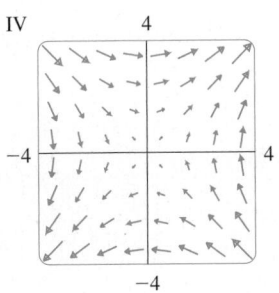

33. The **flow lines** (or **streamlines**) of a vector field are the paths followed by a particle whose velocity field is the given vector field. Thus, the vectors in a vector field are tangent to the flow lines.

(a) Use a sketch of the vector field $\mathbf{F}(x, y) = x\,\mathbf{i} - y\,\mathbf{j}$ to draw some flow lines. From your sketches, can you guess the equations of the flow lines?

(b) If parametric equations of a flow line are $x = x(t)$, $y = y(t)$, explain why these functions satisfy the differential equations $dx/dt = x$ and $dy/dt = -y$. Then solve the differential

equations to find an equation of the flow line that passes through the point $(1, 1)$.

34. (a) Sketch the vector field $\mathbf{F}(x, y) = \mathbf{i} + x\,\mathbf{j}$ and then sketch some flow lines. What shape do these flow lines appear to have?

(b) If parametric equations of the flow lines are $x = x(t)$, $y = y(t)$, what differential equations do these functions satisfy? Deduce that $dy/dx = x$.

(c) If a particle starts at the origin in the velocity field given by $\mathbf{F}$, find an equation of the path it follows.

17.2 Line Integrals

In this section we define an integral that is similar to a single integral except that instead of integrating over an interval $[a, b]$, we integrate over a curve C. Such integrals are called *line integrals,* although "curve integrals" would be better terminology. They were invented in the early 19th century to solve problems involving fluid flow, forces, electricity, and magnetism.

We start with a plane curve C given by the parametric equations

$$\boxed{1} \qquad x = x(t) \qquad y = y(t) \qquad a \leqslant t \leqslant b$$

or, equivalently, by the vector equation $\mathbf{r}(t) = x(t)\,\mathbf{i} + y(t)\,\mathbf{j}$, and we assume that C is a smooth curve. [This means that $\mathbf{r}'$ is continuous and $\mathbf{r}'(t) \neq \mathbf{0}$. See Section 14.2.] If we divide the parameter interval $[a, b]$ into n subintervals $[t_{i-1}, t_i]$ of equal width and we let $x_i = x(t_i)$ and $y_i = y(t_i)$, then the corresponding points $P_i(x_i, y_i)$ divide C into n subarcs with lengths $\Delta s_1, \Delta s_2, \ldots, \Delta s_n$. (See Figure 1.) We choose any point $P_i^*(x_i^*, y_i^*)$ in the ith subarc. (This corresponds to a point t_i^* in $[t_{i-1}, t_i]$.) Now if f is any function of two variables whose domain includes the curve C, we evaluate f at the point (x_i^*, y_i^*), multiply by the length Δs_i of the subarc, and form the sum

$$\sum_{i=1}^{n} f(x_i^*, y_i^*)\,\Delta s_i$$

which is similar to a Riemann sum. Then we take the limit of these sums and make the following definition by analogy with a single integral.

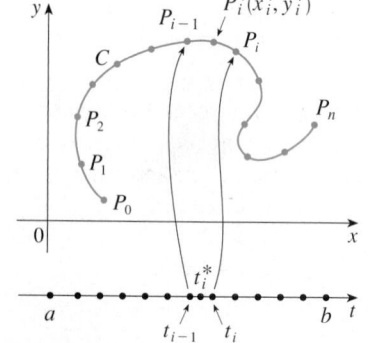

FIGURE 1

> $\boxed{2}$ **Definition** If f is defined on a smooth curve C given by Equations 1, then the **line integral of f along C** is
>
> $$\int_C f(x, y)\,ds = \lim_{n \to \infty} \sum_{i=1}^{n} f(x_i^*, y_i^*)\,\Delta s_i$$
>
> if this limit exists.

In Section 11.2 we found that the length of C is

$$L = \int_a^b \sqrt{\left(\frac{dx}{dt}\right)^2 + \left(\frac{dy}{dt}\right)^2}\,dt$$

A similar type of argument can be used to show that if f is a continuous function, then the limit in Definition 2 always exists and the following formula can be used to evaluate the line integral:

$$\boxed{3} \qquad \int_C f(x, y) \, ds = \int_a^b f(x(t), y(t)) \sqrt{\left(\frac{dx}{dt}\right)^2 + \left(\frac{dy}{dt}\right)^2} \, dt$$

The value of the line integral does not depend on the parametrization of the curve, provided that the curve is traversed exactly once as t increases from a to b.

If $s(t)$ is the length of C between $\mathbf{r}(a)$ and $\mathbf{r}(t)$, then

$$\frac{ds}{dt} = \sqrt{\left(\frac{dx}{dt}\right)^2 + \left(\frac{dy}{dt}\right)^2}$$

▥ The arc length function s is discussed in Section 14.3.

So the way to remember Formula 3 is to express everything in terms of the parameter t: Use the parametric equations to express x and y in terms of t and write ds as

$$ds = \sqrt{\left(\frac{dx}{dt}\right)^2 + \left(\frac{dy}{dt}\right)^2} \, dt$$

In the special case where C is the line segment that joins $(a, 0)$ to $(b, 0)$, using x as the parameter, we can write the parametric equations of C as follows: $x = x$, $y = 0$, $a \le x \le b$. Formula 3 then becomes

$$\int_C f(x, y) \, ds = \int_a^b f(x, 0) \, dx$$

and so the line integral reduces to an ordinary single integral in this case.

Just as for an ordinary single integral, we can interpret the line integral of a *positive* function as an area. In fact, if $f(x, y) \ge 0$, $\int_C f(x, y) \, ds$ represents the area of one side of the "fence" or "curtain" in Figure 2, whose base is C and whose height above the point (x, y) is $f(x, y)$.

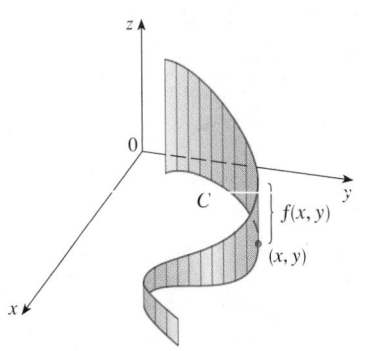

FIGURE 2

EXAMPLE 1 Evaluate $\int_C (2 + x^2 y) \, ds$, where C is the upper half of the unit circle $x^2 + y^2 = 1$.

SOLUTION In order to use Formula 3 we first need parametric equations to represent C. Recall that the unit circle can be parametrized by means of the equations

$$x = \cos t \qquad y = \sin t$$

and the upper half of the circle is described by the parameter interval $0 \le t \le \pi$. (See Figure 3.) Therefore, Formula 3 gives

$$\int_C (2 + x^2 y) \, ds = \int_0^\pi (2 + \cos^2 t \sin t) \sqrt{\left(\frac{dx}{dt}\right)^2 + \left(\frac{dy}{dt}\right)^2} \, dt$$

$$= \int_0^\pi (2 + \cos^2 t \sin t) \sqrt{\sin^2 t + \cos^2 t} \, dt$$

$$= \int_0^\pi (2 + \cos^2 t \sin t) \, dt = \left[2t - \frac{\cos^3 t}{3} \right]_0^\pi$$

$$= 2\pi + \tfrac{2}{3}$$

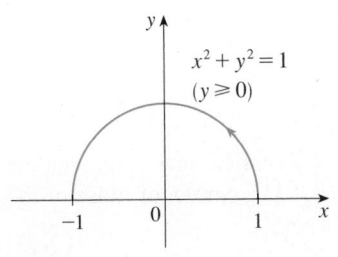

$x^2 + y^2 = 1$
$(y \ge 0)$

FIGURE 3

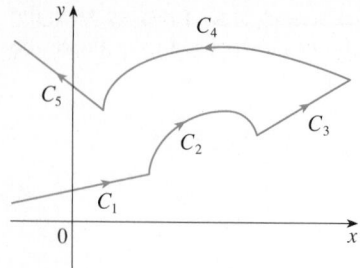

FIGURE 4

A piecewise-smooth curve

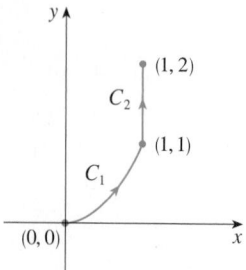

FIGURE 5

$C = C_1 \cup C_2$

Suppose now that C is a **piecewise-smooth curve**; that is, C is a union of a finite number of smooth curves $C_1, C_2, \ldots, C_n$, where, as illustrated in Figure 4, the initial point of C_{i+1} is the terminal point of C_i. Then we define the integral of f along C as the sum of the integrals of f along each of the smooth pieces of C:

$$\int_C f(x, y)\, ds = \int_{C_1} f(x, y)\, ds + \int_{C_2} f(x, y)\, ds + \cdots + \int_{C_n} f(x, y)\, ds$$

EXAMPLE 2 Evaluate $\int_C 2x\, ds$, where C consists of the arc C_1 of the parabola $y = x^2$ from $(0, 0)$ to $(1, 1)$ followed by the vertical line segment C_2 from $(1, 1)$ to $(1, 2)$.

SOLUTION The curve C is shown in Figure 5. C_1 is the graph of a function of x, so we can choose x as the parameter and the equations for C_1 become

$$x = x \qquad y = x^2 \qquad 0 \le x \le 1$$

Therefore

$$\int_{C_1} 2x\, ds = \int_0^1 2x \sqrt{\left(\frac{dx}{dx}\right)^2 + \left(\frac{dy}{dx}\right)^2}\, dx$$

$$= \int_0^1 2x \sqrt{1 + 4x^2}\, dx = \tfrac14 \cdot \tfrac23 (1 + 4x^2)^{3/2}\big]_0^1 = \frac{5\sqrt5 - 1}{6}$$

On C_2 we choose y as the parameter, so the equations of C_2 are

$$x = 1 \qquad y = y \qquad 1 \le y \le 2$$

and

$$\int_{C_2} 2x\, ds = \int_1^2 2(1) \sqrt{\left(\frac{dx}{dy}\right)^2 + \left(\frac{dy}{dy}\right)^2}\, dy = \int_1^2 2\, dy = 2$$

Thus

$$\int_C 2x\, ds = \int_{C_1} 2x\, ds + \int_{C_2} 2x\, ds = \frac{5\sqrt5 - 1}{6} + 2$$

Any physical interpretation of a line integral $\int_C f(x, y)\, ds$ depends on the physical interpretation of the function f. Suppose that $\rho(x, y)$ represents the linear density at a point (x, y) of a thin wire shaped like a curve C. Then the mass of the part of the wire from P_{i-1} to P_i in Figure 1 is approximately $\rho(x_i^*, y_i^*)\, \Delta s_i$ and so the total mass of the wire is approximately $\Sigma\, \rho(x_i^*, y_i^*)\, \Delta s_i$. By taking more and more points on the curve, we obtain the **mass** m of the wire as the limiting value of these approximations:

$$m = \lim_{n \to \infty} \sum_{i=1}^n \rho(x_i^*, y_i^*)\, \Delta s_i = \int_C \rho(x, y)\, ds$$

[For example, if $f(x, y) = 2 + x^2 y$ represents the density of a semicircular wire, then the integral in Example 1 would represent the mass of the wire.] The **center of mass** of the wire with density function ρ is located at the point $(\bar x, \bar y)$, where

4
$$\bar x = \frac1m \int_C x\rho(x, y)\, ds \qquad \bar y = \frac1m \int_C y\rho(x, y)\, ds$$

Other physical interpretations of line integrals will be discussed later in this chapter.

EXAMPLE 3 A wire takes the shape of the semicircle $x^2 + y^2 = 1$, $y \geq 0$, and is thicker near its base than near the top. Find the center of mass of the wire if the linear density at any point is proportional to its distance from the line $y = 1$.

SOLUTION As in Example 1 we use the parametrization $x = \cos t$, $y = \sin t$, $0 \leq t \leq \pi$, and find that $ds = dt$. The linear density is

$$\rho(x, y) = k(1 - y)$$

where k is a constant, and so the mass of the wire is

$$m = \int_C k(1 - y)\, ds = \int_0^\pi k(1 - \sin t)\, dt$$

$$= k\left[t + \cos t\right]_0^\pi = k(\pi - 2)$$

From Equations 4 we have

$$\bar{y} = \frac{1}{m} \int_C y\rho(x, y)\, ds = \frac{1}{k(\pi - 2)} \int_C yk(1 - y)\, ds$$

$$= \frac{1}{\pi - 2} \int_0^\pi (\sin t - \sin^2 t)\, dt = \frac{1}{\pi - 2}\left[-\cos t - \tfrac{1}{2}t + \tfrac{1}{4}\sin 2t\right]_0^\pi$$

$$= \frac{4 - \pi}{2(\pi - 2)}$$

By symmetry we see that $\bar{x} = 0$, so the center of mass is

$$\left(0, \frac{4 - \pi}{2(\pi - 2)}\right) \approx (0, 0.38)$$

center of mass

FIGURE 6

See Figure 6.

Two other line integrals are obtained by replacing Δs_i by either $\Delta x_i = x_i - x_{i-1}$ or $\Delta y_i = y_i - y_{i-1}$ in Definition 2. They are called the **line integrals of f along C with respect to x and y:**

5
$$\int_C f(x, y)\, dx = \lim_{n \to \infty} \sum_{i=1}^n f(x_i^*, y_i^*)\, \Delta x_i$$

6
$$\int_C f(x, y)\, dy = \lim_{n \to \infty} \sum_{i=1}^n f(x_i^*, y_i^*)\, \Delta y_i$$

When we want to distinguish the original line integral $\int_C f(x, y)\, ds$ from those in Equations 5 and 6, we call it the **line integral with respect to arc length**.

The following formulas say that line integrals with respect to x and y can also be evaluated by expressing everything in terms of t: $x = x(t)$, $y = y(t)$, $dx = x'(t)\, dt$, $dy = y'(t)\, dt$.

7

$$\int_C f(x, y)\, dx = \int_a^b f(x(t), y(t))\, x'(t)\, dt$$

$$\int_C f(x, y)\, dy = \int_a^b f(x(t), y(t))\, y'(t)\, dt$$

It frequently happens that line integrals with respect to x and y occur together. When this happens, it's customary to abbreviate by writing

$$\int_C P(x, y)\, dx + \int_C Q(x, y)\, dy = \int_C P(x, y)\, dx + Q(x, y)\, dy$$

When we are setting up a line integral, sometimes the most difficult thing is to think of a parametric representation for a curve whose geometric description is given. In particular, we often need to parametrize a line segment, so it's useful to remember that a vector representation of the line segment that starts at $\mathbf{r}_0$ and ends at $\mathbf{r}_1$ is given by

$$\boxed{\mathbf{r}(t) = (1 - t)\mathbf{r}_0 + t\mathbf{r}_1 \qquad 0 \le t \le 1}$$

[8]

(See Equation 13.5.4.)

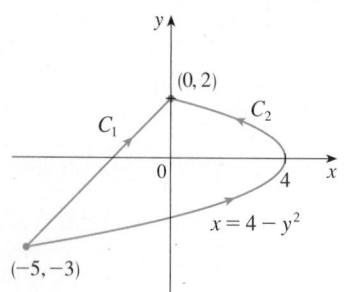

C_1 $(0, 2)$ C_2

$x = 4 - y^2$

$(-5, -3)$

FIGURE 7

EXAMPLE 4 Evaluate $\int_C y^2\, dx + x\, dy$, where (a) $C = C_1$ is the line segment from $(-5, -3)$ to $(0, 2)$ and (b) $C = C_2$ is the arc of the parabola $x = 4 - y^2$ from $(-5, -3)$ to $(0, 2)$. (See Figure 7.)

SOLUTION

(a) A parametric representation for the line segment is

$$x = 5t - 5 \qquad y = 5t - 3 \qquad 0 \le t \le 1$$

(Use Equation 8 with $\mathbf{r}_0 = \langle -5, -3 \rangle$ and $\mathbf{r}_1 = \langle 0, 2 \rangle$.) Then $dx = 5\, dt$, $dy = 5\, dt$, and Formula 7 gives

$$\int_{C_1} y^2\, dx + x\, dy = \int_0^1 (5t - 3)^2 (5\, dt) + (5t - 5)(5\, dt)$$

$$= 5 \int_0^1 (25t^2 - 25t + 4)\, dt$$

$$= 5 \left[\frac{25t^3}{3} - \frac{25t^2}{2} + 4t \right]_0^1 = -\frac{5}{6}$$

(b) Since the parabola is given as a function of y, let's take y as the parameter and write C_2 as

$$x = 4 - y^2 \qquad y = y \qquad -3 \le y \le 2$$

Then $dx = -2y\, dy$ and by Formula 7 we have

$$\int_{C_2} y^2\, dx + x\, dy = \int_{-3}^2 y^2(-2y)\, dy + (4 - y^2)\, dy$$

$$= \int_{-3}^2 (-2y^3 - y^2 + 4)\, dy$$

$$= \left[-\frac{y^4}{2} - \frac{y^3}{3} + 4y \right]_{-3}^2 = 40\tfrac{5}{6}$$

Notice that we got different answers in parts (a) and (b) of Example 4 even though the two curves had the same endpoints. Thus, in general, the value of a line integral depends not just on the endpoints of the curve but also on the path. (But see Section 17.3 for conditions under which the integral is independent of the path.)

Notice also that the answers in Example 4 depend on the direction, or orientation, of the curve. If $-C_1$ denotes the line segment from $(0, 2)$ to $(-5, -3)$, you can verify, using the parametrization

$$x = -5t \qquad y = 2 - 5t \qquad 0 \leqslant t \leqslant 1$$

that

$$\int_{-C_1} y^2 \, dx + x \, dy = \tfrac{5}{6}$$

In general, a given parametrization $x = x(t)$, $y = y(t)$, $a \leqslant t \leqslant b$, determines an **orientation** of a curve C, with the positive direction corresponding to increasing values of the parameter t. (See Figure 8, where the initial point A corresponds to the parameter value a and the terminal point B corresponds to $t = b$.)

If $-C$ denotes the curve consisting of the same points as C but with the opposite orientation (from initial point B to terminal point A in Figure 8), then we have

$$\int_{-C} f(x, y) \, dx = -\int_{C} f(x, y) \, dx \qquad \int_{-C} f(x, y) \, dy = -\int_{C} f(x, y) \, dy$$

But if we integrate with respect to arc length, the value of the line integral does *not* change when we reverse the orientation of the curve:

$$\int_{-C} f(x, y) \, ds = \int_{C} f(x, y) \, ds$$

This is because Δs_i is always positive, whereas Δx_i and Δy_i change sign when we reverse the orientation of C.

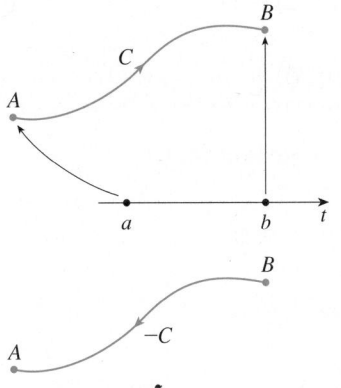

FIGURE 8

Line Integrals in Space

We now suppose that C is a smooth space curve given by the parametric equations

$$x = x(t) \qquad y = y(t) \qquad z = z(t) \qquad a \leqslant t \leqslant b$$

or by a vector equation $\mathbf{r}(t) = x(t)\,\mathbf{i} + y(t)\,\mathbf{j} + z(t)\,\mathbf{k}$. If f is a function of three variables that is continuous on some region containing C, then we define the **line integral of f along C** (with respect to arc length) in a manner similar to that for plane curves:

$$\int_{C} f(x, y, z) \, ds = \lim_{n \to \infty} \sum_{i=1}^{n} f(x_i^*, y_i^*, z_i^*) \, \Delta s_i$$

We evaluate it using a formula similar to Formula 3:

$$\boxed{9} \quad \int_{C} f(x, y, z) \, ds = \int_{a}^{b} f(x(t), y(t), z(t)) \sqrt{\left(\frac{dx}{dt}\right)^2 + \left(\frac{dy}{dt}\right)^2 + \left(\frac{dz}{dt}\right)^2} \, dt$$

Observe that the integrals in both Formulas 3 and 9 can be written in the more compact vector notation

$$\int_{a}^{b} f(\mathbf{r}(t)) \, |\, \mathbf{r}'(t)\, | \, dt$$

For the special case $f(x, y, z) = 1$, we get

$$\int_C ds = \int_a^b |\mathbf{r}'(t)|\, dt = L$$

where L is the length of the curve C (see Formula 14.3.3).

Line integrals along C with respect to x, y, and z can also be defined. For example,

$$\int_C f(x, y, z)\, dz = \lim_{n \to \infty} \sum_{i=1}^n f(x_i^*, y_i^*, z_i^*)\, \Delta z_i$$

$$= \int_a^b f(x(t), y(t), z(t)) z'(t)\, dt$$

Therefore, as with line integrals in the plane, we evaluate integrals of the form

10          $$\int_C P(x, y, z)\, dx + Q(x, y, z)\, dy + R(x, y, z)\, dz$$

by expressing everything (x, y, z, dx, dy, dz) in terms of the parameter t.

EXAMPLE 5 Evaluate $\int_C y \sin z\, ds$, where C is the circular helix given by the equations $x = \cos t$, $y = \sin t$, $z = t$, $0 \leqslant t \leqslant 2\pi$. (See Figure 9.)

SOLUTION Formula 9 gives

$$\int_C y \sin z\, ds = \int_0^{2\pi} (\sin t) \sin t \sqrt{\left(\frac{dx}{dt}\right)^2 + \left(\frac{dy}{dt}\right)^2 + \left(\frac{dz}{dt}\right)^2}\, dt$$

$$= \int_0^{2\pi} \sin^2 t \sqrt{\sin^2 t + \cos^2 t + 1}\, dt$$

$$= \sqrt{2} \int_0^{2\pi} \tfrac{1}{2}(1 - \cos 2t)\, dt = \frac{\sqrt{2}}{2} \left[t - \tfrac{1}{2} \sin 2t \right]_0^{2\pi} = \sqrt{2}\,\pi$$

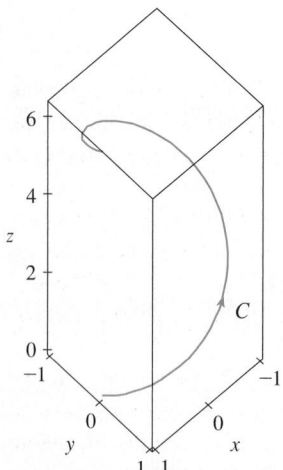

FIGURE 9

EXAMPLE 6 Evaluate $\int_C y\, dx + z\, dy + x\, dz$, where C consists of the line segment C_1 from $(2, 0, 0)$ to $(3, 4, 5)$ followed by the vertical line segment C_2 from $(3, 4, 5)$ to $(3, 4, 0)$.

SOLUTION The curve C is shown in Figure 10. Using Equation 8, we write C_1 as

$$\mathbf{r}(t) = (1 - t)\langle 2, 0, 0 \rangle + t \langle 3, 4, 5 \rangle = \langle 2 + t, 4t, 5t \rangle$$

or, in parametric form, as

$$x = 2 + t \qquad y = 4t \qquad z = 5t \qquad 0 \leqslant t \leqslant 1$$

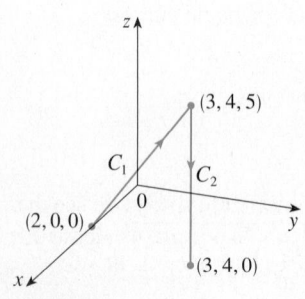

FIGURE 10

Thus

$$\int_{C_1} y\, dx + z\, dy + x\, dz = \int_0^1 (4t)\, dt + (5t)4\, dt + (2 + t)5\, dt$$

$$= \int_0^1 (10 + 29t)\, dt = 10t + 29\frac{t^2}{2}\bigg]_0^1 = 24.5$$

Likewise, C_2 can be written in the form

$$\mathbf{r}(t) = (1-t)\langle 3,4,5\rangle + t\langle 3,4,0\rangle = \langle 3,4,5-5t\rangle$$

or
$$x=3 \qquad y=4 \qquad z=5-5t \qquad 0\leqslant t\leqslant 1$$

Then $dx=0=dy$, so

$$\int_{C_2} y\,dx + z\,dy + x\,dz = \int_0^1 3(-5)\,dt = -15$$

Adding the values of these integrals, we obtain

$$\int_C y\,dx + z\,dy + x\,dz = 24.5 - 15 = 9.5$$

▏▏▏ Line Integrals of Vector Fields

Recall from Section 6.4 that the work done by a variable force $f(x)$ in moving a particle from a to b along the x-axis is $W = \int_a^b f(x)\,dx$. Then in Section 13.3 we found that the work done by a constant force $\mathbf{F}$ in moving an object from a point P to another point Q in space is $W = \mathbf{F}\cdot\mathbf{D}$, where $\mathbf{D} = \overrightarrow{PQ}$ is the displacement vector.

Now suppose that $\mathbf{F} = P\,\mathbf{i} + Q\,\mathbf{j} + R\,\mathbf{k}$ is a continuous force field on $\mathbb{R}^3$, such as the gravitational field of Example 4 in Section 17.1 or the electric force field of Example 5 in Section 17.1. (A force field on $\mathbb{R}^2$ could be regarded as a special case where $R=0$ and P and Q depend only on x and y.) We wish to compute the work done by this force in moving a particle along a smooth curve C.

We divide C into subarcs $P_{i-1}P_i$ with lengths Δs_i by dividing the parameter interval $[a,b]$ into subintervals of equal width. (See Figure 1 for the two-dimensional case or Figure 11 for the three-dimensional case.) Choose a point $P_i^*(x_i^*, y_i^*, z_i^*)$ on the ith subarc corresponding to the parameter value t_i^*. If Δs_i is small, then as the particle moves from P_{i-1} to P_i along the curve, it proceeds approximately in the direction of $\mathbf{T}(t_i^*)$, the unit tangent vector at P_i^*. Thus, the work done by the force $\mathbf{F}$ in moving the particle from P_{i-1} to P_i is approximately

$$\mathbf{F}(x_i^*, y_i^*, z_i^*) \cdot [\Delta s_i\,\mathbf{T}(t_i^*)] = [\mathbf{F}(x_i^*, y_i^*, z_i^*) \cdot \mathbf{T}(t_i^*)]\,\Delta s_i$$

and the total work done in moving the particle along C is approximately

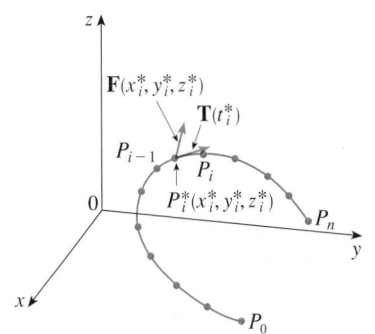

FIGURE 11

$$\boxed{11} \qquad \sum_{i=1}^n [\mathbf{F}(x_i^*, y_i^*, z_i^*) \cdot \mathbf{T}(x_i^*, y_i^*, z_i^*)]\,\Delta s_i$$

where $\mathbf{T}(x,y,z)$ is the unit tangent vector at the point (x,y,z) on C. Intuitively, we see that these approximations ought to become better as n becomes larger. Therefore, we define the **work** W done by the force field $\mathbf{F}$ as the limit of the Riemann sums in (11), namely,

$$\boxed{12} \qquad W = \int_C \mathbf{F}(x,y,z) \cdot \mathbf{T}(x,y,z)\,ds = \int_C \mathbf{F}\cdot\mathbf{T}\,ds$$

Equation 12 says that *work is the line integral with respect to arc length of the tangential component of the force.*

If the curve C is given by the vector equation $\mathbf{r}(t) = x(t)\,\mathbf{i} + y(t)\,\mathbf{j} + z(t)\,\mathbf{k}$, then $\mathbf{T}(t) = \mathbf{r}'(t)/|\mathbf{r}'(t)|$, so using Equation 9 we can rewrite Equation 12 in the form

$$W = \int_a^b \left[\mathbf{F}(\mathbf{r}(t)) \cdot \frac{\mathbf{r}'(t)}{|\mathbf{r}'(t)|} \right] |\mathbf{r}'(t)|\, dt = \int_a^b \mathbf{F}(\mathbf{r}(t)) \cdot \mathbf{r}'(t)\, dt$$

This integral is often abbreviated as $\int_C \mathbf{F} \cdot d\mathbf{r}$ and occurs in other areas of physics as well. Therefore, we make the following definition for the line integral of *any* continuous vector field.

> **13 Definition** Let $\mathbf{F}$ be a continuous vector field defined on a smooth curve C given by a vector function $\mathbf{r}(t)$, $a \le t \le b$. Then the **line integral of F along** C is
>
> $$\int_C \mathbf{F} \cdot d\mathbf{r} = \int_a^b \mathbf{F}(\mathbf{r}(t)) \cdot \mathbf{r}'(t)\, dt = \int_C \mathbf{F} \cdot \mathbf{T}\, ds$$

When using Definition 13, remember that $\mathbf{F}(\mathbf{r}(t))$ is just an abbreviation for $\mathbf{F}(x(t), y(t), z(t))$, so we evaluate $\mathbf{F}(\mathbf{r}(t))$ simply by putting $x = x(t)$, $y = y(t)$, and $z = z(t)$ in the expression for $\mathbf{F}(x, y, z)$. Notice also that we can formally write $d\mathbf{r} = \mathbf{r}'(t)\,dt$.

|||| Figure 12 shows the force field and the curve in Example 7. The work done is negative because the field impedes movement along the curve.

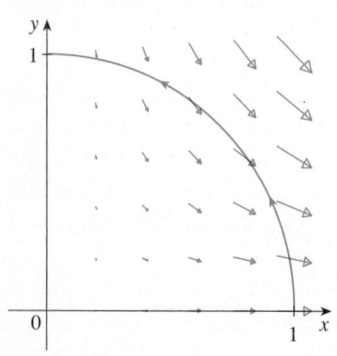

FIGURE 12

EXAMPLE 7 Find the work done by the force field $\mathbf{F}(x, y) = x^2\,\mathbf{i} - xy\,\mathbf{j}$ in moving a particle along the quarter-circle $\mathbf{r}(t) = \cos t\,\mathbf{i} + \sin t\,\mathbf{j}$, $0 \le t \le \pi/2$.

SOLUTION Since $x = \cos t$ and $y = \sin t$, we have

$$\mathbf{F}(\mathbf{r}(t)) = \cos^2 t\,\mathbf{i} - \cos t \sin t\,\mathbf{j}$$

and

$$\mathbf{r}'(t) = -\sin t\,\mathbf{i} + \cos t\,\mathbf{j}$$

Therefore, the work done is

$$\int_C \mathbf{F} \cdot d\mathbf{r} = \int_0^{\pi/2} \mathbf{F}(\mathbf{r}(t)) \cdot \mathbf{r}'(t)\, dt = \int_0^{\pi/2} (-2\cos^2 t \sin t)\, dt$$

$$= 2\,\frac{\cos^3 t}{3}\Bigg]_0^{\pi/2} = -\frac{2}{3}$$

NOTE • Even though $\int_C \mathbf{F} \cdot d\mathbf{r} = \int_C \mathbf{F} \cdot \mathbf{T}\, ds$ and integrals with respect to arc length are unchanged when orientation is reversed, it is still true that

$$\int_{-C} \mathbf{F} \cdot d\mathbf{r} = -\int_C \mathbf{F} \cdot d\mathbf{r}$$

because the unit tangent vector $\mathbf{T}$ is replaced by its negative when C is replaced by $-C$.

EXAMPLE 8 Evaluate $\int_C \mathbf{F} \cdot d\mathbf{r}$, where $\mathbf{F}(x, y, z) = xy\,\mathbf{i} + yz\,\mathbf{j} + zx\,\mathbf{k}$ and C is the twisted cubic given by

$$x = t \qquad y = t^2 \qquad z = t^3 \qquad 0 \le t \le 1$$

|||| Figure 13 shows the twisted cubic C in Example 8 and some typical vectors acting at three points on C.

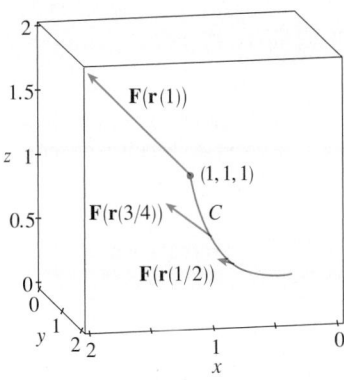

FIGURE 13

SOLUTION We have

$$\mathbf{r}(t) = t\,\mathbf{i} + t^2\,\mathbf{j} + t^3\,\mathbf{k}$$

$$\mathbf{r}'(t) = \mathbf{i} + 2t\,\mathbf{j} + 3t^2\,\mathbf{k}$$

$$\mathbf{F}(\mathbf{r}(t)) = t^3\,\mathbf{i} + t^5\,\mathbf{j} + t^4\,\mathbf{k}$$

Thus

$$\int_C \mathbf{F} \cdot d\mathbf{r} = \int_0^1 \mathbf{F}(\mathbf{r}(t)) \cdot \mathbf{r}'(t)\,dt$$

$$= \int_0^1 (t^3 + 5t^6)\,dt = \frac{t^4}{4} + \frac{5t^7}{7}\Big]_0^1 = \frac{27}{28}$$

Finally, we note the connection between line integrals of vector fields and line integrals of scalar fields. Suppose the vector field $\mathbf{F}$ on $\mathbb{R}^3$ is given in component form by the equation $\mathbf{F} = P\,\mathbf{i} + Q\,\mathbf{j} + R\,\mathbf{k}$. We use Definition 13 to compute its line integral along C:

$$\int_C \mathbf{F} \cdot d\mathbf{r} = \int_a^b \mathbf{F}(\mathbf{r}(t)) \cdot \mathbf{r}'(t)\,dt$$

$$= \int_a^b (P\,\mathbf{i} + Q\,\mathbf{j} + R\,\mathbf{k}) \cdot (x'(t)\,\mathbf{i} + y'(t)\,\mathbf{j} + z'(t)\,\mathbf{k})\,dt$$

$$= \int_a^b [P(x(t), y(t), z(t))x'(t) + Q(x(t), y(t), z(t))y'(t) + R(x(t), y(t), z(t))z'(t)]\,dt$$

But this last integral is precisely the line integral in (10). Therefore, we have

$$\int_C \mathbf{F} \cdot d\mathbf{r} = \int_C P\,dx + Q\,dy + R\,dz \qquad \text{where } \mathbf{F} = P\,\mathbf{i} + Q\,\mathbf{j} + R\,\mathbf{k}$$

For example, the integral $\int_C y\,dx + z\,dy + x\,dz$ in Example 6 could be expressed as $\int_C \mathbf{F} \cdot d\mathbf{r}$ where

$$\mathbf{F}(x, y, z) = y\,\mathbf{i} + z\,\mathbf{j} + x\,\mathbf{k}$$

|||| 17.2 Exercises

1–16 |||| Evaluate the line integral, where C is the given curve.

1. $\int_C y\,ds$, $C: x = t^2$, $y = t$, $0 \le t \le 2$

2. $\int_C (y/x)\,ds$, $C: x = t^4$, $y = t^3$, $\frac{1}{2} \le t \le 1$

3. $\int_C xy^4\,ds$, C is the right half of the circle $x^2 + y^2 = 16$

4. $\int_C ye^x\,ds$, C is the line segment joining $(1, 2)$ to $(4, 7)$

5. $\int_C (xy + \ln x)\,dy$, C is the arc of the parabola $y = x^2$ from $(1, 1)$ to $(3, 9)$

6. $\int_C xe^y\,dx$, C is the arc of the curve $x = e^y$ from $(1, 0)$ to $(e, 1)$

7. $\int_C xy\,dx + (x - y)\,dy$, C consists of line segments from $(0, 0)$ to $(2, 0)$ and from $(2, 0)$ to $(3, 2)$

8. $\int_C \sin x\,dx + \cos y\,dy$, C consists of the top half of the circle $x^2 + y^2 = 1$ from $(1, 0)$ to $(-1, 0)$ and the line segment from $(-1, 0)$ to $(-2, 3)$

9. $\int_C xy^3\,ds$, $C: x = 4\sin t$, $y = 4\cos t$, $z = 3t$, $0 \le t \le \pi/2$

10. $\int_C x^2z\,ds$, C is the line segment from $(0, 6, -1)$ to $(4, 1, 5)$

11. $\int_C xe^{yz}\,ds$, C is the line segment from $(0, 0, 0)$ to $(1, 2, 3)$

12. $\int_C (2x + 9z)\,ds$, $C: x = t$, $y = t^2$, $z = t^3$, $0 \le t \le 1$

13. $\int_C x^2 y \sqrt{z}\, dz,$ $C: x = t^3,\ y = t,\ z = t^2,\ 0 \le t \le 1$

14. $\int_C z\, dx + x\, dy + y\, dz,$ $C: x = t^2,\ y = t^3,\ z = t^2,\ 0 \le t \le 1$

15. $\int_C (x + yz)\, dx + 2x\, dy + xyz\, dz,$ C consists of line segments from $(1, 0, 1)$ to $(2, 3, 1)$ and from $(2, 3, 1)$ to $(2, 5, 2)$

16. $\int_C x^2\, dx + y^2\, dy + z^2\, dz,$ C consists of line segments from $(0, 0, 0)$ to $(1, 2, -1)$ and from $(1, 2, -1)$ to $(3, 2, 0)$

17. Let $\mathbf{F}$ be the vector field shown in the figure.
(a) If C_1 is the vertical line segment from $(-3, -3)$ to $(-3, 3)$, determine whether $\int_{C_1} \mathbf{F} \cdot d\mathbf{r}$ is positive, negative, or zero.
(b) If C_2 is the counterclockwise-oriented circle with radius 3 and center the origin, determine whether $\int_{C_2} \mathbf{F} \cdot d\mathbf{r}$ is positive, negative, or zero.

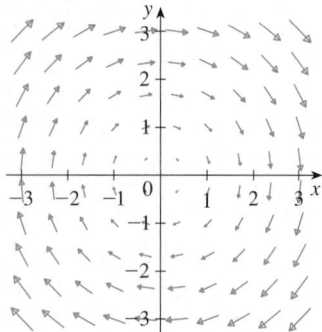

18. The figure shows a vector field $\mathbf{F}$ and two curves C_1 and C_2. Are the line integrals of $\mathbf{F}$ over C_1 and C_2 positive, negative, or zero? Explain.

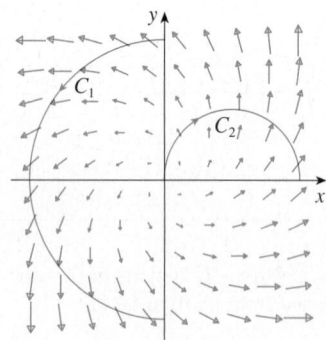

19–22 |||| Evaluate the line integral $\int_C \mathbf{F} \cdot d\mathbf{r}$, where C is given by the vector function $\mathbf{r}(t)$.

19. $\mathbf{F}(x, y) = x^2 y^3\, \mathbf{i} - y\sqrt{x}\, \mathbf{j},$
$\mathbf{r}(t) = t^2\, \mathbf{i} - t^3\, \mathbf{j},\ 0 \le t \le 1$

20. $\mathbf{F}(x, y, z) = yz\, \mathbf{i} + xz\, \mathbf{j} + xy\, \mathbf{k},$
$\mathbf{r}(t) = t\, \mathbf{i} + t^2\, \mathbf{j} + t^3\, \mathbf{k},\ 0 \le t \le 2$

21. $\mathbf{F}(x, y, z) = \sin x\, \mathbf{i} + \cos y\, \mathbf{j} + xz\, \mathbf{k},$
$\mathbf{r}(t) = t^3\, \mathbf{i} - t^2\, \mathbf{j} + t\, \mathbf{k},\ 0 \le t \le 1$

22. $\mathbf{F}(x, y, z) = z\, \mathbf{i} + y\, \mathbf{j} - x\, \mathbf{k},$
$\mathbf{r}(t) = t\, \mathbf{i} + \sin t\, \mathbf{j} + \cos t\, \mathbf{k},\ 0 \le t \le \pi$

CAS 23–24 |||| Use a graph of the vector field $\mathbf{F}$ and the curve C to guess whether the line integral of $\mathbf{F}$ over C is positive, negative, or zero. Then evaluate the line integral.

23. $\mathbf{F}(x, y) = (x - y)\, \mathbf{i} + xy\, \mathbf{j},$
C is the arc of the circle $x^2 + y^2 = 4$ traversed counterclockwise from $(2, 0)$ to $(0, -2)$

24. $\mathbf{F}(x, y) = \dfrac{x}{\sqrt{x^2 + y^2}}\, \mathbf{i} + \dfrac{y}{\sqrt{x^2 + y^2}}\, \mathbf{j},$
C is the parabola $y = 1 + x^2$ from $(-1, 2)$ to $(1, 2)$

25. (a) Evaluate the line integral $\int_C \mathbf{F} \cdot d\mathbf{r}$, where $\mathbf{F}(x, y) = e^{x-1}\, \mathbf{i} + xy\, \mathbf{j}$ and C is given by $\mathbf{r}(t) = t^2\, \mathbf{i} + t^3\, \mathbf{j},\ 0 \le t \le 1.$
(b) Illustrate part (a) by using a graphing calculator or computer to graph C and the vectors from the vector field corresponding to $t = 0,\ 1/\sqrt{2}$, and 1 (as in Figure 13).

26. (a) Evaluate the line integral $\int_C \mathbf{F} \cdot d\mathbf{r}$, where $\mathbf{F}(x, y, z) = x\, \mathbf{i} - z\, \mathbf{j} + y\, \mathbf{k}$ and C is given by $\mathbf{r}(t) = 2t\, \mathbf{i} + 3t\, \mathbf{j} - t^2\, \mathbf{k},\ -1 \le t \le 1.$
(b) Illustrate part (a) by using a computer to graph C and the vectors from the vector field corresponding to $t = \pm 1$ and $\pm \frac{1}{2}$ (as in Figure 13).

CAS 27. Find the exact value of $\int_C x^3 y^5\, ds$, where C is the part of the astroid $x = \cos^3 t,\ y = \sin^3 t$ in the first quadrant.

CAS 28. Find the exact value of $\int_C \mathbf{F} \cdot d\mathbf{r}$, where $\mathbf{F}(x, y, z) = x^4 e^y\, \mathbf{i} + \ln z\, \mathbf{j} + \sqrt{y^2 + z^2}\, \mathbf{k}$ and C is the line segment from $(1, 2, 1)$ to $(6, 4, 5)$.

29. If C is the curve with parametric equations $x = \ln t,\ y = e^{-t},\ 1 \le t \le 2$, use a calculator or CAS to evaluate the line integral $\int_C x \sin y\, ds$ correct to three decimal places.

30. (a) Find the work done by the force field $\mathbf{F}(x, y) = x^2\, \mathbf{i} + xy\, \mathbf{j}$ on a particle that moves once around the circle $x^2 + y^2 = 4$ oriented in the counterclockwise direction.
CAS (b) Use a computer algebra system to graph the force field and circle on the same screen. Use the graph to explain your answer to part (a).

31. A thin wire is bent into the shape of a semicircle $x^2 + y^2 = 4$, $x \ge 0$. If the linear density is a constant k, find the mass and center of mass of the wire.

32. Find the mass and center of mass of a thin wire in the shape of a quarter-circle $x^2 + y^2 = r^2,\ x \ge 0,\ y \ge 0$, if the density function is $\rho(x, y) = x + y$.

33. (a) Write the formulas similar to Equations 4 for the center of mass $(\bar{x}, \bar{y}, \bar{z})$ of a thin wire with density function $\rho(x, y, z)$ in the shape of a space curve C.

(b) Find the center of mass of a wire in the shape of the helix $x = 2 \sin t$, $y = 2 \cos t$, $z = 3t$, $0 \le t \le 2\pi$, if the density is a constant k.

34. Find the mass and center of mass of a wire in the shape of the helix $x = t$, $y = \cos t$, $z = \sin t$, $0 \le t \le 2\pi$, if the density at any point is equal to the square of the distance from the origin.

35. If a wire with linear density $\rho(x, y)$ lies along a plane curve C, its **moments of inertia** about the x- and y-axes are defined as

$$I_x = \int_C y^2 \rho(x, y)\, ds \qquad I_y = \int_C x^2 \rho(x, y)\, ds$$

Find the moments of inertia for the wire in Example 3.

36. If a wire with linear density $\rho(x, y, z)$ lies along a space curve C, its **moments of inertia** about the x-, y-, and z-axes are defined as

$$I_x = \int_C (y^2 + z^2)\rho(x, y, z)\, ds$$

$$I_y = \int_C (x^2 + z^2)\rho(x, y, z)\, ds$$

$$I_z = \int_C (x^2 + y^2)\rho(x, y, z)\, ds$$

Find the moments of inertia for the wire in Exercise 33.

37. Find the work done by the force field $\mathbf{F}(x, y) = x\,\mathbf{i} + (y + 2)\,\mathbf{j}$ in moving an object along an arch of the cycloid $\mathbf{r}(t) = (t - \sin t)\,\mathbf{i} + (1 - \cos t)\,\mathbf{j}$, $0 \le t \le 2\pi$.

38. Find the work done by the force field $\mathbf{F}(x, y) = x \sin y\,\mathbf{i} + y\,\mathbf{j}$ on a particle that moves along the parabola $y = x^2$ from $(-1, 1)$ to $(2, 4)$.

39. Find the work done by the force field $\mathbf{F}(x, y, z) = \langle y + z, x + z, x + y \rangle$ on a particle that moves along the line segment from $(1, 0, 0)$ to $(3, 4, 2)$.

40. The force exerted by an electric charge at the origin on a charged particle at a point (x, y, z) with position vector $\mathbf{r} = \langle x, y, z \rangle$ is $\mathbf{F}(\mathbf{r}) = K\mathbf{r}/|\mathbf{r}|^3$ where K is a constant. (See Example 5 in Section 17.1.) Find the work done as the particle moves along a straight line from $(2, 0, 0)$ to $(2, 1, 5)$.

41. A 160-lb man carries a 25-lb can of paint up a helical staircase that encircles a silo with a radius of 20 ft. If the silo is 90 ft high and the man makes exactly three complete revolutions, how much work is done by the man against gravity in climbing to the top?

42. Suppose there is a hole in the can of paint in Exercise 41 and 9 lb of paint leaks steadily out of the can during the man's ascent. How much work is done?

43. (a) Show that a constant force field does zero work on a particle that moves once uniformly around the circle $x^2 + y^2 = 1$.

(b) Is this also true for a force field $\mathbf{F}(\mathbf{x}) = k\mathbf{x}$, where k is a constant and $\mathbf{x} = \langle x, y \rangle$?

44. The base of a circular fence with radius 10 m is given by $x = 10 \cos t$, $y = 10 \sin t$. The height of the fence at position (x, y) is given by the function $h(x, y) = 4 + 0.01(x^2 - y^2)$, so the height varies from 3 m to 5 m. Suppose that 1 L of paint covers 100 m². Sketch the fence and determine how much paint you will need if you paint both sides of the fence.

45. An object moves along the curve C shown in the figure from $(1, 2)$ to $(9, 8)$. The lengths of the vectors in the force field $\mathbf{F}$ are measured in newtons by the scales on the axes. Estimate the work done by $\mathbf{F}$ on the object.

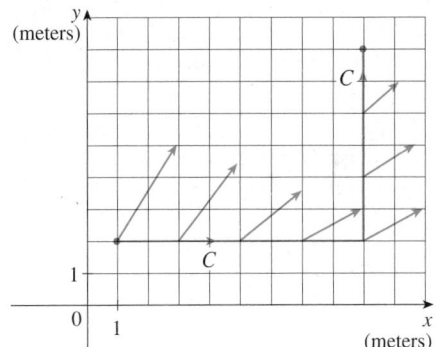

46. Experiments show that a steady current I in a long wire produces a magnetic field $\mathbf{B}$ that is tangent to any circle that lies in the plane perpendicular to the wire and whose center is the axis of the wire (as in the figure). *Ampère's Law* relates the electric current to its magnetic effects and states that

$$\int_C \mathbf{B} \cdot d\mathbf{r} = \mu_0 I$$

where I is the net current that passes through any surface bounded by a closed curve C and μ_0 is a constant called the permeability of free space. By taking C to be a circle with radius r, show that the magnitude $B = |\mathbf{B}|$ of the magnetic field at a distance r from the center of the wire is

$$B = \frac{\mu_0 I}{2\pi r}$$

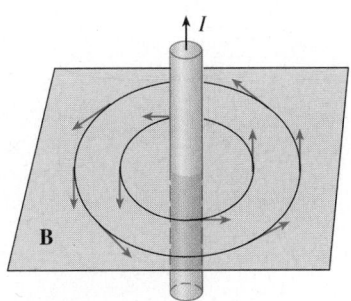

17.3 The Fundamental Theorem for Line Integrals

Recall from Section 5.3 that Part 2 of the Fundamental Theorem of Calculus can be written as

$$\boxed{1} \qquad \int_a^b F'(x)\,dx = F(b) - F(a)$$

where F' is continuous on $[a, b]$. We also called Equation 1 the Net Change Theorem: The integral of a rate of change is the net change.

If we think of the gradient vector ∇f of a function f of two or three variables as a sort of derivative of f, then the following theorem can be regarded as a version of the Fundamental Theorem for line integrals.

> $\boxed{2}$ **Theorem** Let C be a smooth curve given by the vector function $\mathbf{r}(t)$, $a \leqslant t \leqslant b$. Let f be a differentiable function of two or three variables whose gradient vector ∇f is continuous on C. Then
>
> $$\int_C \nabla f \cdot d\mathbf{r} = f(\mathbf{r}(b)) - f(\mathbf{r}(a))$$

NOTE □ Theorem 2 says that we can evaluate the line integral of a conservative vector field (the gradient vector field of the potential function f) simply by knowing the value of f at the endpoints of C. In fact, Theorem 2 says that the line integral of ∇f is the net change in f. If f is a function of two variables and C is a plane curve with initial point $A(x_1, y_1)$ and terminal point $B(x_2, y_2)$, as in Figure 1, then Theorem 2 becomes

$$\int_C \nabla f \cdot d\mathbf{r} = f(x_2, y_2) - f(x_1, y_1)$$

If f is a function of three variables and C is a space curve joining the point $A(x_1, y_1, z_1)$ to the point $B(x_2, y_2, z_2)$, then we have

$$\int_C \nabla f \cdot d\mathbf{r} = f(x_2, y_2, z_2) - f(x_1, y_1, z_1)$$

Let's prove Theorem 2 for this case.

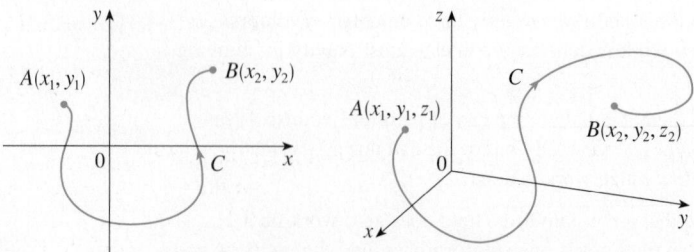

FIGURE 1

Proof of Theorem 2   Using Definition 17.2.13, we have

$$\int_C \nabla f \cdot d\mathbf{r} = \int_a^b \nabla f(\mathbf{r}(t)) \cdot \mathbf{r}'(t)\, dt$$

$$= \int_a^b \left(\frac{\partial f}{\partial x} \frac{dx}{dt} + \frac{\partial f}{\partial y} \frac{dy}{dt} + \frac{\partial f}{\partial z} \frac{dz}{dt} \right) dt$$

$$= \int_a^b \frac{d}{dt} f(\mathbf{r}(t))\, dt \qquad\qquad \text{(by the Chain Rule)}$$

$$= f(\mathbf{r}(b)) - f(\mathbf{r}(a))$$

The last step follows from the Fundamental Theorem of Calculus (Equation 1).

Although we have proved Theorem 2 for smooth curves, it is also true for piecewise-smooth curves. This can be seen by subdividing C into a finite number of smooth curves and adding the resulting integrals.

EXAMPLE 1   Find the work done by the gravitational field

$$\mathbf{F}(\mathbf{x}) = -\frac{mMG}{|\mathbf{x}|^3} \mathbf{x}$$

in moving a particle with mass m from the point $(3, 4, 12)$ to the point $(2, 2, 0)$ along a piecewise-smooth curve C. (See Example 4 in Section 17.1.)

SOLUTION   From Section 17.1 we know that $\mathbf{F}$ is a conservative vector field and, in fact, $\mathbf{F} = \nabla f$, where

$$f(x, y, z) = \frac{mMG}{\sqrt{x^2 + y^2 + z^2}}$$

Therefore, by Theorem 2, the work done is

$$W = \int_C \mathbf{F} \cdot d\mathbf{r} = \int_C \nabla f \cdot d\mathbf{r}$$

$$= f(2, 2, 0) - f(3, 4, 12)$$

$$= \frac{mMG}{\sqrt{2^2 + 2^2}} - \frac{mMG}{\sqrt{3^2 + 4^2 + 12^2}} = mMG \left(\frac{1}{2\sqrt{2}} - \frac{1}{13} \right)$$

||| Independence of Path

Suppose C_1 and C_2 are two piecewise-smooth curves (which are called **paths**) that have the same initial point A and terminal point B. We know from Example 4 in Section 17.2 that, in general, $\int_{C_1} \mathbf{F} \cdot d\mathbf{r} \neq \int_{C_2} \mathbf{F} \cdot d\mathbf{r}$. But one implication of Theorem 2 is that

$$\int_{C_1} \nabla f \cdot d\mathbf{r} = \int_{C_2} \nabla f \cdot d\mathbf{r}$$

whenever ∇f is continuous. In other words, the line integral of a *conservative* vector field depends only on the initial point and terminal point of a curve.

In general, if $\mathbf{F}$ is a continuous vector field with domain D, we say that the line integral $\int_C \mathbf{F} \cdot d\mathbf{r}$ is **independent of path** if $\int_{C_1} \mathbf{F} \cdot d\mathbf{r} = \int_{C_2} \mathbf{F} \cdot d\mathbf{r}$ for any two paths C_1 and C_2 in

FIGURE 2

A closed curve

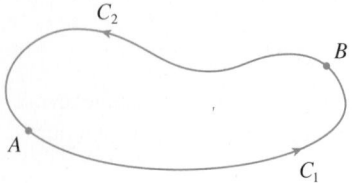

FIGURE 3

D that have the same initial and terminal points. With this terminology we can say that *line integrals of conservative vector fields are independent of path.*

A curve is called **closed** if its terminal point coincides with its initial point, that is, $\mathbf{r}(b) = \mathbf{r}(a)$. (See Figure 2.) If $\int_C \mathbf{F} \cdot d\mathbf{r}$ is independent of path in D and C is any closed path in D, we can choose any two points A and B on C and regard C as being composed of the path C_1 from A to B followed by the path C_2 from B to A. (See Figure 3.) Then

$$\int_C \mathbf{F} \cdot d\mathbf{r} = \int_{C_1} \mathbf{F} \cdot d\mathbf{r} + \int_{C_2} \mathbf{F} \cdot d\mathbf{r} = \int_{C_1} \mathbf{F} \cdot d\mathbf{r} - \int_{-C_2} \mathbf{F} \cdot d\mathbf{r} = 0$$

since C_1 and $-C_2$ have the same initial and terminal points.

Conversely, if it is true that $\int_C \mathbf{F} \cdot d\mathbf{r} = 0$ whenever C is a closed path in D, then we demonstrate independence of path as follows. Take any two paths C_1 and C_2 from A to B in D and define C to be the curve consisting of C_1 followed by $-C_2$. Then

$$0 = \int_C \mathbf{F} \cdot d\mathbf{r} = \int_{C_1} \mathbf{F} \cdot d\mathbf{r} + \int_{-C_2} \mathbf{F} \cdot d\mathbf{r} = \int_{C_1} \mathbf{F} \cdot d\mathbf{r} - \int_{C_2} \mathbf{F} \cdot d\mathbf{r}$$

and so $\int_{C_1} \mathbf{F} \cdot d\mathbf{r} = \int_{C_2} \mathbf{F} \cdot d\mathbf{r}$. Thus, we have proved the following theorem.

> **3 Theorem** $\int_C \mathbf{F} \cdot d\mathbf{r}$ is independent of path in D if and only if $\int_C \mathbf{F} \cdot d\mathbf{r} = 0$ for every closed path C in D.

Since we know that the line integral of any conservative vector field $\mathbf{F}$ is independent of path, it follows that $\int_C \mathbf{F} \cdot d\mathbf{r} = 0$ for any closed path. The physical interpretation is that the work done by a conservative force field (such as the gravitational or electric field in Section 17.1) as it moves an object around a closed path is 0.

The following theorem says that the *only* vector fields that are independent of path are conservative. It is stated and proved for plane curves, but there is a similar version for space curves. We assume that D is **open**, which means that for every point P in D there is a disk with center P that lies entirely in D. (So D doesn't contain any of its boundary points.) In addition, we assume that D is **connected**. This means that any two points in D can be joined by a path that lies in D.

> **4 Theorem** Suppose $\mathbf{F}$ is a vector field that is continuous on an open connected region D. If $\int_C \mathbf{F} \cdot d\mathbf{r}$ is independent of path in D, then $\mathbf{F}$ is a conservative vector field on D; that is, there exists a function f such that $\nabla f = \mathbf{F}$.

Proof Let $A(a, b)$ be a fixed point in D. We construct the desired potential function f by defining

$$f(x, y) = \int_{(a, b)}^{(x, y)} \mathbf{F} \cdot d\mathbf{r}$$

for any point (x, y) in D. Since $\int_C \mathbf{F} \cdot d\mathbf{r}$ is independent of path, it does not matter which path C from (a, b) to (x, y) is used to evaluate $f(x, y)$. Since D is open, there exists a disk contained in D with center (x, y). Choose any point (x_1, y) in the disk with $x_1 < x$ and let C consist of any path C_1 from (a, b) to (x_1, y) followed by the horizontal line segment C_2 from (x_1, y) to (x, y). (See Figure 4.) Then

$$f(x, y) = \int_{C_1} \mathbf{F} \cdot d\mathbf{r} + \int_{C_2} \mathbf{F} \cdot d\mathbf{r} = \int_{(a, b)}^{(x_1, y)} \mathbf{F} \cdot d\mathbf{r} + \int_{C_2} \mathbf{F} \cdot d\mathbf{r}$$

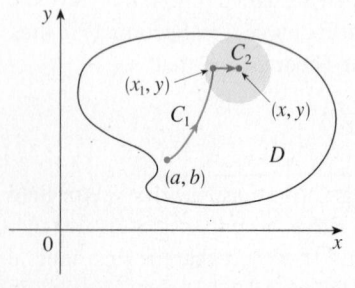

FIGURE 4

Notice that the first of these integrals does not depend on x, so

$$\frac{\partial}{\partial x} f(x, y) = 0 + \frac{\partial}{\partial x} \int_{C_2} \mathbf{F} \cdot d\mathbf{r}$$

If we write $\mathbf{F} = P\,\mathbf{i} + Q\,\mathbf{j}$, then

$$\int_{C_2} \mathbf{F} \cdot d\mathbf{r} = \int_{C_2} P\,dx + Q\,dy$$

On C_2, y is constant, so $dy = 0$. Using t as the parameter, where $x_1 \leqslant t \leqslant x$, we have

$$\frac{\partial}{\partial x} f(x, y) = \frac{\partial}{\partial x} \int_{C_2} P\,dx + Q\,dy = \frac{\partial}{\partial x} \int_{x_1}^{x} P(t, y)\,dt = P(x, y)$$

by Part 1 of the Fundamental Theorem of Calculus (see Section 5.3). A similar argument, using a vertical line segment (see Figure 5), shows that

$$\frac{\partial}{\partial y} f(x, y) = \frac{\partial}{\partial y} \int_{C_2} P\,dx + Q\,dy = \frac{\partial}{\partial y} \int_{y_1}^{y} Q(x, t)\,dt = Q(x, y)$$

y↑

(x, y) C_2
(x, y_1)
C_1
D
(a, b)

0 x

FIGURE 5

Thus

$$\mathbf{F} = P\,\mathbf{i} + Q\,\mathbf{j} = \frac{\partial f}{\partial x}\,\mathbf{i} + \frac{\partial f}{\partial y}\,\mathbf{j} = \nabla f$$

which says that $\mathbf{F}$ is conservative.

The question remains: How is it possible to determine whether or not a vector field $\mathbf{F}$ is conservative? Suppose it is known that $\mathbf{F} = P\,\mathbf{i} + Q\,\mathbf{j}$ is conservative, where P and Q have continuous first-order partial derivatives. Then there is a function f such that $\mathbf{F} = \nabla f$, that is,

$$P = \frac{\partial f}{\partial x} \qquad \text{and} \qquad Q = \frac{\partial f}{\partial y}$$

Therefore, by Clairaut's Theorem,

$$\frac{\partial P}{\partial y} = \frac{\partial^2 f}{\partial y\,\partial x} = \frac{\partial^2 f}{\partial x\,\partial y} = \frac{\partial Q}{\partial x}$$

> **5 Theorem** If $\mathbf{F}(x, y) = P(x, y)\,\mathbf{i} + Q(x, y)\,\mathbf{j}$ is a conservative vector field, where P and Q have continuous first-order partial derivatives on a domain D, then throughout D we have
>
> $$\frac{\partial P}{\partial y} = \frac{\partial Q}{\partial x}$$

The converse of Theorem 5 is true only for a special type of region. To explain this, we first need the concept of a **simple curve**, which is a curve that doesn't intersect itself anywhere between its endpoints. [See Figure 6; $\mathbf{r}(a) = \mathbf{r}(b)$ for a simple closed curve, but $\mathbf{r}(t_1) \neq \mathbf{r}(t_2)$ when $a < t_1 < t_2 < b$.]

In Theorem 4 we needed an open connected region. For the next theorem we need a stronger condition. A **simply-connected region** in the plane is a connected region D such

simple,
not closed

not simple,
not closed

simple,
closed

not simple,
closed

FIGURE 6
Types of curves

simply-connected region

regions that are not simply-connected

FIGURE 7

that every simple closed curve in D encloses only points that are in D. Notice from Figure 7 that, intuitively speaking, a simply-connected region contains no hole and can't consist of two separate pieces.

In terms of simply-connected regions we can now state a partial converse to Theorem 5 that gives a convenient method for verifying that a vector field on $\mathbb{R}^2$ is conservative. The proof will be sketched in the next section as a consequence of Green's Theorem.

> **6 Theorem** Let $\mathbf{F} = P\,\mathbf{i} + Q\,\mathbf{j}$ be a vector field on an open simply-connected region D. Suppose that P and Q have continuous first-order derivatives and
>
> $$\frac{\partial P}{\partial y} = \frac{\partial Q}{\partial x} \qquad \text{throughout } D$$
>
> Then $\mathbf{F}$ is conservative.

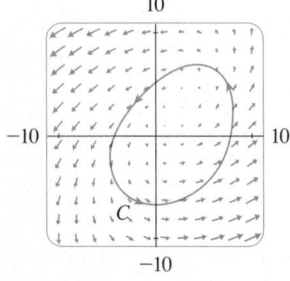

FIGURE 8

|||| Figures 8 and 9 show the vector fields in Examples 2 and 3, respectively. The vectors in Figure 8 that start on the closed curve C all appear to point in roughly the same direction as C. So it looks as if $\int_C \mathbf{F} \cdot d\mathbf{r} > 0$ and therefore $\mathbf{F}$ is not conservative. The calculation in Example 2 confirms this impression. Some of the vectors near the curves C_1 and C_2 in Figure 9 point in approximately the same direction as the curves, whereas others point in the opposite direction. So it appears plausible that line integrals around all closed paths are 0. Example 3 shows that $\mathbf{F}$ is indeed conservative.

FIGURE 9

EXAMPLE 2 Determine whether or not the vector field

$$\mathbf{F}(x, y) = (x - y)\,\mathbf{i} + (x - 2)\,\mathbf{j}$$

is conservative.

SOLUTION Let $P(x, y) = x - y$ and $Q(x, y) = x - 2$. Then

$$\frac{\partial P}{\partial y} = -1 \qquad \frac{\partial Q}{\partial x} = 1$$

Since $\partial P/\partial y \neq \partial Q/\partial x$, $\mathbf{F}$ is not conservative by Theorem 5.

EXAMPLE 3 Determine whether or not the vector field

$$\mathbf{F}(x, y) = (3 + 2xy)\,\mathbf{i} + (x^2 - 3y^2)\,\mathbf{j}$$

is conservative.

SOLUTION Let $P(x, y) = 3 + 2xy$ and $Q(x, y) = x^2 - 3y^2$. Then

$$\frac{\partial P}{\partial y} = 2x = \frac{\partial Q}{\partial x}$$

Also, the domain of $\mathbf{F}$ is the entire plane ($D = \mathbb{R}^2$), which is open and simply-connected. Therefore, we can apply Theorem 6 and conclude that $\mathbf{F}$ is conservative.

In Example 3, Theorem 6 told us that $\mathbf{F}$ is conservative, but it did not tell us how to find the (potential) function f such that $\mathbf{F} = \nabla f$. The proof of Theorem 4 gives us a clue as to how to find f. We use "partial integration" as in the following example.

EXAMPLE 4
(a) If $\mathbf{F}(x, y) = (3 + 2xy)\,\mathbf{i} + (x^2 - 3y^2)\,\mathbf{j}$, find a function f such that $\mathbf{F} = \nabla f$.
(b) Evaluate the line integral $\int_C \mathbf{F} \cdot d\mathbf{r}$, where C is the curve given by $\mathbf{r}(t) = e^t \sin t\,\mathbf{i} + e^t \cos t\,\mathbf{j}$, $0 \leq t \leq \pi$.

SOLUTION

(a) From Example 3 we know that $\mathbf{F}$ is conservative and so there exists a function f with $\nabla f = \mathbf{F}$, that is,

$$\boxed{7} \qquad\qquad f_x(x, y) = 3 + 2xy$$

$$\boxed{8} \qquad\qquad f_y(x, y) = x^2 - 3y^2$$

Integrating (7) with respect to x, we obtain

$$\boxed{9} \qquad\qquad f(x, y) = 3x + x^2y + g(y)$$

Notice that the constant of integration is a constant with respect to x, that is, a function of y, which we have called $g(y)$. Next we differentiate both sides of (9) with respect to y:

$$\boxed{10} \qquad\qquad f_y(x, y) = x^2 + g'(y)$$

Comparing (8) and (10), we see that

$$g'(y) = -3y^2$$

Integrating with respect to y, we have

$$g(y) = -y^3 + K$$

where K is a constant. Putting this in (9), we have

$$f(x, y) = 3x + x^2y - y^3 + K$$

as the desired potential function.

(b) To use Theorem 2 all we have to know are the initial and terminal points of C, namely, $\mathbf{r}(0) = (0, 1)$ and $\mathbf{r}(\pi) = (0, -e^\pi)$. In the expression for $f(x, y)$ in part (a), any value of the constant K will do, so let's choose $K = 0$. Then we have

$$\int_C \mathbf{F} \cdot d\mathbf{r} = \int_C \nabla f \cdot d\mathbf{r} = f(0, -e^\pi) - f(0, 1)$$

$$= e^{3\pi} - (-1) = e^{3\pi} + 1$$

This method is much shorter than the straightforward method for evaluating line integrals that we learned in Section 17.2.

A criterion for determining whether or not a vector field $\mathbf{F}$ on $\mathbb{R}^3$ is conservative is given in Section 17.5. Meanwhile, the next example shows that the technique for finding the potential function is much the same as for vector fields on $\mathbb{R}^2$.

EXAMPLE 5 If $\mathbf{F}(x, y, z) = y^2\mathbf{i} + (2xy + e^{3z})\mathbf{j} + 3ye^{3z}\mathbf{k}$, find a function f such that $\nabla f = \mathbf{F}$.

SOLUTION If there is such a function f, then

$$\boxed{11} \qquad\qquad f_x(x, y, z) = y^2$$

$$\boxed{12} \qquad\qquad f_y(x, y, z) = 2xy + e^{3z}$$

$$\boxed{13} \qquad\qquad f_z(x, y, z) = 3ye^{3z}$$

Integrating (11) with respect to x, we get

14
$$f(x, y, z) = xy^2 + g(y, z)$$

where $g(y, z)$ is a constant with respect to x. Then differentiating (14) with respect to y, we have

$$f_y(x, y, z) = 2xy + g_y(y, z)$$

and comparison with (12) gives

$$g_y(y, z) = e^{3z}$$

Thus, $g(y, z) = ye^{3z} + h(z)$ and we rewrite (14) as

$$f(x, y, z) = xy^2 + ye^{3z} + h(z)$$

Finally, differentiating with respect to z and comparing with (13), we obtain $h'(z) = 0$ and, therefore, $h(z) = K$, a constant. The desired function is

$$f(x, y, z) = xy^2 + ye^{3z} + K$$

It is easily verified that $\nabla f = \mathbf{F}$.

||||| **Conservation of Energy**

Let's apply the ideas of this chapter to a continuous force field $\mathbf{F}$ that moves an object along a path C given by $\mathbf{r}(t)$, $a \leqslant t \leqslant b$, where $\mathbf{r}(a) = A$ is the initial point and $\mathbf{r}(b) = B$ is the terminal point of C. According to Newton's Second Law of Motion (see Section 14.4), the force $\mathbf{F}(\mathbf{r}(t))$ at a point on C is related to the acceleration $\mathbf{a}(t) = \mathbf{r}''(t)$ by the equation

$$\mathbf{F}(\mathbf{r}(t)) = m\mathbf{r}''(t)$$

So the work done by the force on the object is

$$W = \int_C \mathbf{F} \cdot d\mathbf{r} = \int_a^b \mathbf{F}(\mathbf{r}(t)) \cdot \mathbf{r}'(t)\, dt$$

$$= \int_a^b m\mathbf{r}''(t) \cdot \mathbf{r}'(t)\, dt$$

$$= \frac{m}{2} \int_a^b \frac{d}{dt}[\mathbf{r}'(t) \cdot \mathbf{r}'(t)]\, dt \qquad \text{(Theorem 14.2.3, Formula 4)}$$

$$= \frac{m}{2} \int_a^b \frac{d}{dt}|\mathbf{r}'(t)|^2\, dt$$

$$= \frac{m}{2} \left[|\mathbf{r}'(t)|^2\right]_a^b \qquad \text{(Fundamental Theorem of Calculus)}$$

$$= \frac{m}{2} \left(|\mathbf{r}'(b)|^2 - |\mathbf{r}'(a)|^2\right)$$

Therefore

$$\boxed{15} \qquad W = \tfrac{1}{2}m\,|\mathbf{v}(b)|^2 - \tfrac{1}{2}m\,|\mathbf{v}(a)|^2$$

where $\mathbf{v} = \mathbf{r}'$ is the velocity.

The quantity $\tfrac{1}{2}m\,|\mathbf{v}(t)|^2$, that is, half the mass times the square of the speed, is called the **kinetic energy** of the object. Therefore, we can rewrite Equation 15 as

$$\boxed{16} \qquad W = K(B) - K(A)$$

which says that the work done by the force field along C is equal to the change in kinetic energy at the endpoints of C.

Now let's further assume that $\mathbf{F}$ is a conservative force field; that is, we can write $\mathbf{F} = \nabla f$. In physics, the **potential energy** of an object at the point (x, y, z) is defined as $P(x, y, z) = -f(x, y, z)$, so we have $\mathbf{F} = -\nabla P$. Then by Theorem 2 we have

$$W = \int_C \mathbf{F} \cdot d\mathbf{r} = -\int_C \nabla P \cdot d\mathbf{r}$$

$$= -[P(\mathbf{r}(b)) - P(\mathbf{r}(a))]$$

$$= P(A) - P(B)$$

Comparing this equation with Equation 16, we see that

$$P(A) + K(A) = P(B) + K(B)$$

which says that if an object moves from one point A to another point B under the influence of a conservative force field, then the sum of its potential energy and its kinetic energy remains constant. This is called the **Law of Conservation of Energy** and it is the reason the vector field is called *conservative*.

17.3 Exercises

1. The figure shows a curve C and a contour map of a function f whose gradient is continuous. Find $\int_C \nabla f \cdot d\mathbf{r}$.

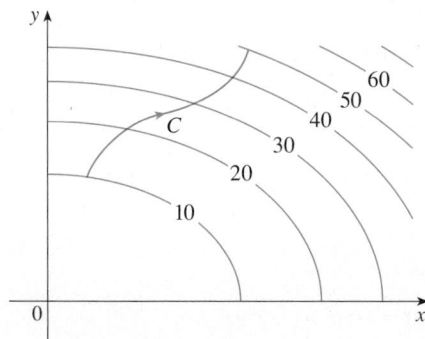

2. A table of values of a function f with continuous gradient is given. Find $\int_C \nabla f \cdot d\mathbf{r}$, where C has parametric equations $x = t^2 + 1,\ y = t^3 + t,\ 0 \le t \le 1$.

x \ y	0	1	2
0	1	6	4
1	3	5	7
2	8	2	9

3–10 ||||| Determine whether or not $\mathbf{F}$ is a conservative vector field. If it is, find a function f such that $\mathbf{F} = \nabla f$.

3. $\mathbf{F}(x, y) = (6x + 5y)\,\mathbf{i} + (5x + 4y)\,\mathbf{j}$

4. $\mathbf{F}(x, y) = (x^3 + 4xy)\,\mathbf{i} + (4xy - y^3)\,\mathbf{j}$

5. $\mathbf{F}(x, y) = xe^y\,\mathbf{i} + ye^x\,\mathbf{j}$

6. $\mathbf{F}(x, y) = e^y\,\mathbf{i} + xe^y\,\mathbf{j}$

7. $\mathbf{F}(x, y) = (2x \cos y - y \cos x)\,\mathbf{i} + (-x^2 \sin y - \sin x)\,\mathbf{j}$

8. $\mathbf{F}(x, y) = (1 + 2xy + \ln x)\,\mathbf{i} + x^2\,\mathbf{j}$

9. $\mathbf{F}(x, y) = (ye^x + \sin y)\,\mathbf{i} + (e^x + x \cos y)\,\mathbf{j}$

10. $\mathbf{F}(x, y) = (xy \cosh xy + \sinh xy)\mathbf{i} + (x^2 \cosh xy)\mathbf{j}$

11. The figure shows the vector field $\mathbf{F}(x, y) = \langle 2xy, x^2 \rangle$ and three curves that start at $(1, 2)$ and end at $(3, 2)$.
(a) Explain why $\int_C \mathbf{F} \cdot d\mathbf{r}$ has the same value for all three curves.
(b) What is this common value?

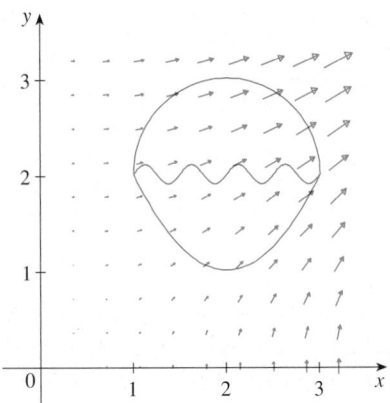

12–18 ▓ (a) Find a function f such that $\mathbf{F} = \nabla f$ and (b) use part (a) to evaluate $\int_C \mathbf{F} \cdot d\mathbf{r}$ along the given curve C.

12. $\mathbf{F}(x, y) = y\mathbf{i} + (x + 2y)\mathbf{j}$,
C is the upper semicircle that starts at $(0, 1)$ and ends at $(2, 1)$

13. $\mathbf{F}(x, y) = x^3 y^4 \mathbf{i} + x^4 y^3 \mathbf{j}$,
C: $\mathbf{r}(t) = \sqrt{t}\,\mathbf{i} + (1 + t^3)\mathbf{j}$, $0 \leqslant t \leqslant 1$

14. $\mathbf{F}(x, y) = \dfrac{y^2}{1 + x^2}\mathbf{i} + 2y \arctan x\,\mathbf{j}$,
C: $\mathbf{r}(t) = t^2 \mathbf{i} + 2t\,\mathbf{j}$, $0 \leqslant t \leqslant 1$

15. $\mathbf{F}(x, y, z) = yz\mathbf{i} + xz\mathbf{j} + (xy + 2z)\mathbf{k}$,
C is the line segment from $(1, 0, -2)$ to $(4, 6, 3)$

16. $\mathbf{F}(x, y, z) = (2xz + y^2)\mathbf{i} + 2xy\mathbf{j} + (x^2 + 3z^2)\mathbf{k}$,
C: $x = t^2$, $y = t + 1$, $z = 2t - 1$, $0 \leqslant t \leqslant 1$

17. $\mathbf{F}(x, y, z) = y^2 \cos z\,\mathbf{i} + 2xy \cos z\,\mathbf{j} - xy^2 \sin z\,\mathbf{k}$,
C: $\mathbf{r}(t) = t^2 \mathbf{i} + \sin t\,\mathbf{j} + t\,\mathbf{k}$, $0 \leqslant t \leqslant \pi$

18. $\mathbf{F}(x, y, z) = e^y \mathbf{i} + xe^y \mathbf{j} + (z + 1)e^z \mathbf{k}$,
C: $\mathbf{r}(t) = t\mathbf{i} + t^2 \mathbf{j} + t^3 \mathbf{k}$, $0 \leqslant t \leqslant 1$

19–20 ▓ Show that the line integral is independent of path and evaluate the integral.

19. $\int_C \tan y\,dx + x \sec^2 y\,dy$, C is any path from $(1, 0)$ to $(2, \pi/4)$

20. $\int_C (1 - ye^{-x})\,dx + e^{-x}\,dy$, C is any path from $(0, 1)$ to $(1, 2)$

21–22 ▓ Find the work done by the force field $\mathbf{F}$ in moving an object from P to Q.

21. $\mathbf{F}(x, y) = 2y^{3/2}\mathbf{i} + 3x\sqrt{y}\,\mathbf{j}$; $P(1, 1)$, $Q(2, 4)$

22. $\mathbf{F}(x, y) = (y^2/x^2)\mathbf{i} - (2y/x)\mathbf{j}$; $P(1, 1)$, $Q(4, -2)$

23. Is the vector field shown in the figure conservative? Explain.

[CAS] **24–25** ▓ From a plot of $\mathbf{F}$ guess whether it is conservative. Then determine whether your guess is correct.

24. $\mathbf{F}(x, y) = (2xy + \sin y)\mathbf{i} + (x^2 + x \cos y)\mathbf{j}$

25. $\mathbf{F}(x, y) = \dfrac{(x - 2y)\mathbf{i} + (x - 2)\mathbf{j}}{\sqrt{1 + x^2 + y^2}}$

26. Let $\mathbf{F} = \nabla f$, where $f(x, y) = \sin(x - 2y)$. Find curves C_1 and C_2 that are not closed and satisfy the equation.
(a) $\int_{C_1} \mathbf{F} \cdot d\mathbf{r} = 0$ (b) $\int_{C_2} \mathbf{F} \cdot d\mathbf{r} = 1$

27. Show that if the vector field $\mathbf{F} = P\mathbf{i} + Q\mathbf{j} + R\mathbf{k}$ is conservative and P, Q, R have continuous first-order partial derivatives, then

$$\frac{\partial P}{\partial y} = \frac{\partial Q}{\partial x} \qquad \frac{\partial P}{\partial z} = \frac{\partial R}{\partial x} \qquad \frac{\partial Q}{\partial z} = \frac{\partial R}{\partial y}$$

28. Use Exercise 27 to show that the line integral $\int_C y\,dx + x\,dy + xyz\,dz$ is not independent of path.

29–32 ▓ Determine whether or not the given set is (a) open, (b) connected, and (c) simply-connected.

29. $\{(x, y) \mid x > 0,\ y > 0\}$ **30.** $\{(x, y) \mid x \neq 0\}$

31. $\{(x, y) \mid 1 < x^2 + y^2 < 4\}$

32. $\{(x, y) \mid x^2 + y^2 \leqslant 1 \text{ or } 4 \leqslant x^2 + y^2 \leqslant 9\}$

33. Let $\mathbf{F}(x, y) = \dfrac{-y\mathbf{i} + x\mathbf{j}}{x^2 + y^2}$.
(a) Show that $\partial P/\partial y = \partial Q/\partial x$.
(b) Show that $\int_C \mathbf{F} \cdot d\mathbf{r}$ is not independent of path.
[Hint: Compute $\int_{C_1} \mathbf{F} \cdot d\mathbf{r}$ and $\int_{C_2} \mathbf{F} \cdot d\mathbf{r}$, where C_1 and C_2 are the upper and lower halves of the circle $x^2 + y^2 = 1$ from $(1, 0)$ to $(-1, 0)$.] Does this contradict Theorem 6?

34. (a) Suppose that $\mathbf{F}$ is an inverse square force field, that is,

$$\mathbf{F}(\mathbf{r}) = \frac{c\mathbf{r}}{|\mathbf{r}|^3}$$

for some constant c, where $\mathbf{r} = x\,\mathbf{i} + y\,\mathbf{j} + z\,\mathbf{k}$. Find the work done by $\mathbf{F}$ in moving an object from a point P_1 along a path to a point P_2 in terms of the distances d_1 and d_2 from these points to the origin.

(b) An example of an inverse square field is the gravitational field $\mathbf{F} = -(mMG)\mathbf{r}/|\mathbf{r}|^3$ discussed in Example 4 in Section 17.1. Use part (a) to find the work done by the gravitational field when the Earth moves from aphelion

(at a maximum distance of 1.52×10^8 km from the Sun) to perihelion (at a minimum distance of 1.47×10^8 km). (Use the values $m = 5.97 \times 10^{24}$ kg, $M = 1.99 \times 10^{30}$ kg, and $G = 6.67 \times 10^{-11}$ N·m²/kg².)

(c) Another example of an inverse square field is the electric force field $\mathbf{F} = \varepsilon qQ\mathbf{r}/|\mathbf{r}|^3$ discussed in Example 5 in Section 17.1. Suppose that an electron with a charge of -1.6×10^{-19} C is located at the origin. A positive unit charge is positioned a distance 10^{-12} m from the electron and moves to a position half that distance from the electron. Use part (a) to find the work done by the electric field. (Use the value $\varepsilon = 8.985 \times 10^9$.)

17.4 Green's Theorem

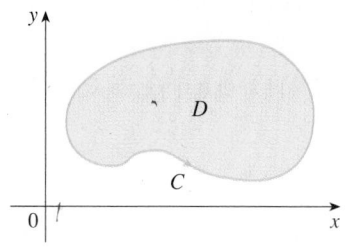

FIGURE 1

Green's Theorem gives the relationship between a line integral around a simple closed curve C and a double integral over the plane region D bounded by C. (See Figure 1. We assume that D consists of all points inside C as well as all points on C.) In stating Green's Theorem we use the convention that the **positive orientation** of a simple closed curve C refers to a single *counterclockwise* traversal of C. Thus, if C is given by the vector function $\mathbf{r}(t)$, $a \leqslant t \leqslant b$, then the region D is always on the left as the point $\mathbf{r}(t)$ traverses C. (See Figure 2.)

FIGURE 2

(a) Positive orientation

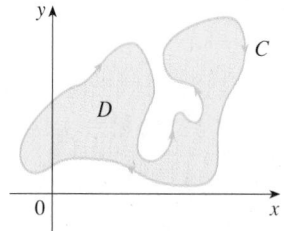

(b) Negative orientation

Green's Theorem Let C be a positively oriented, piecewise-smooth, simple closed curve in the plane and let D be the region bounded by C. If P and Q have continuous partial derivatives on an open region that contains D, then

$$\int_C P\,dx + Q\,dy = \iint_D \left(\frac{\partial Q}{\partial x} - \frac{\partial P}{\partial y} \right) dA$$

|||| Recall that the left side of this equation is another way of writing $\int_C \mathbf{F} \cdot d\mathbf{r}$, where $\mathbf{F} = P\,\mathbf{i} + Q\,\mathbf{j}$.

NOTE ▫ The notation

$$\oint_C P\,dx + Q\,dy \quad \text{or} \quad \oint_C P\,dx + Q\,dy$$

is sometimes used to indicate that the line integral is calculated using the positive orientation of the closed curve C. Another notation for the positively oriented boundary curve of

D is ∂D, so the equation in Green's Theorem can be written as

$$\boxed{1} \qquad \iint_D \left(\frac{\partial Q}{\partial x} - \frac{\partial P}{\partial y} \right) dA = \int_{\partial D} P\, dx + Q\, dy$$

Green's Theorem should be regarded as the counterpart of the Fundamental Theorem of Calculus for double integrals. Compare Equation 1 with the statement of the Fundamental Theorem of Calculus, Part 2, in the following equation:

$$\int_a^b F'(x)\, dx = F(b) - F(a)$$

In both cases there is an integral involving derivatives (F', $\partial Q/\partial x$, and $\partial P/\partial y$) on the left side of the equation. And in both cases the right side involves the values of the original functions (F, Q, and P) only on the *boundary* of the domain. (In the one-dimensional case, the domain is an interval $[a, b]$ whose boundary consists of just two points, a and b.)

Green's Theorem is not easy to prove in the generality stated in Theorem 1, but we can give a proof for the special case where the region is both of type I and of type II (see Section 16.3). Let's call such regions **simple regions**.

Proof of Green's Theorem for the Case in Which D Is a Simple Region Notice that Green's Theorem will be proved if we can show that

$$\boxed{2} \qquad \int_C P\, dx = -\iint_D \frac{\partial P}{\partial y}\, dA$$

and

$$\boxed{3} \qquad \int_C Q\, dy = \iint_D \frac{\partial Q}{\partial x}\, dA$$

We prove Equation 2 by expressing D as a type I region:

$$D = \{(x, y) \mid a \leq x \leq b,\ g_1(x) \leq y \leq g_2(x)\}$$

where g_1 and g_2 are continuous functions. This enables us to compute the double integral on the right side of Equation 2 as follows:

$$\boxed{4} \qquad \iint_D \frac{\partial P}{\partial y}\, dA = \int_a^b \int_{g_1(x)}^{g_2(x)} \frac{\partial P}{\partial y}(x, y)\, dy\, dx = \int_a^b [P(x, g_2(x)) - P(x, g_1(x))]\, dx$$

where the last step follows from the Fundamental Theorem of Calculus.

Now we compute the left side of Equation 2 by breaking up C as the union of the four curves C_1, C_2, C_3, and C_4 shown in Figure 3. On C_1 we take x as the parameter and write the parametric equations as $x = x$, $y = g_1(x)$, $a \leq x \leq b$. Thus

$$\int_{C_1} P(x, y)\, dx = \int_a^b P(x, g_1(x))\, dx$$

Observe that C_3 goes from right to left but $-C_3$ goes from left to right, so we can write the parametric equations of $-C_3$ as $x = x$, $y = g_2(x)$, $a \leq x \leq b$. Therefore

$$\int_{C_3} P(x, y)\, dx = -\int_{-C_3} P(x, y)\, dx = -\int_a^b P(x, g_2(x))\, dx$$

|||| Green's Theorem is named after the self-taught English scientist George Green (1793–1841). He worked full-time in his father's bakery from the age of nine and taught himself mathematics from library books. In 1828 he published privately *An Essay on the Application of Mathematical Analysis to the Theories of Electricity and Magnetism*, but only 100 copies were printed and most of those went to his friends. This pamphlet contained a theorem that is equivalent to what we know as Green's Theorem, but it didn't become widely known at that time. Finally, at age 40, Green entered Cambridge University as an undergraduate but died four years after graduation. In 1846 William Thomson (Lord Kelvin) located a copy of Green's essay, realized its significance, and had it reprinted. Green was the first person to try to formulate a mathematical theory of electricity and magnetism. His work was the basis for the subsequent electromagnetic theories of Thomson, Stokes, Rayleigh, and Maxwell.

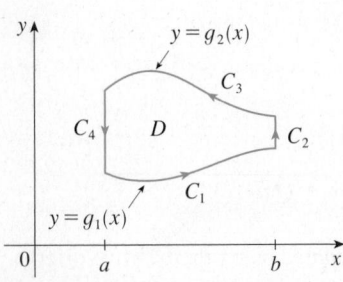

FIGURE 3

On C_2 or C_4 (either of which might reduce to just a single point), x is constant, so $dx = 0$ and

$$\int_{C_2} P(x, y)\, dx = 0 = \int_{C_4} P(x, y)\, dx$$

Hence

$$\int_C P(x, y)\, dx = \int_{C_1} P(x, y)\, dx + \int_{C_2} P(x, y)\, dx + \int_{C_3} P(x, y)\, dx + \int_{C_4} P(x, y)\, dx$$

$$= \int_a^b P(x, g_1(x))\, dx - \int_a^b P(x, g_2(x))\, dx$$

Comparing this expression with the one in Equation 4, we see that

$$\int_C P(x, y)\, dx = -\iint_D \frac{\partial P}{\partial y}\, dA$$

Equation 3 can be proved in much the same way by expressing D as a type II region (see Exercise 28). Then, by adding Equations 2 and 3, we obtain Green's Theorem.

EXAMPLE 1 Evaluate $\int_C x^4\, dx + xy\, dy$, where C is the triangular curve consisting of the line segments from $(0, 0)$ to $(1, 0)$, from $(1, 0)$ to $(0, 1)$, and from $(0, 1)$ to $(0, 0)$.

SOLUTION Although the given line integral could be evaluated as usual by the methods of Section 17.2, that would involve setting up three separate integrals along the three sides of the triangle, so let's use Green's Theorem instead. Notice that the region D enclosed by C is simple and C has positive orientation (see Figure 4). If we let $P(x, y) = x^4$ and $Q(x, y) = xy$, then we have

$$\int_C x^4\, dx + xy\, dy = \iint_D \left(\frac{\partial Q}{\partial x} - \frac{\partial P}{\partial y}\right) dA = \int_0^1 \int_0^{1-x} (y - 0)\, dy\, dx$$

$$= \int_0^1 \left[\tfrac{1}{2}y^2\right]_{y=0}^{y=1-x} dx = \tfrac{1}{2}\int_0^1 (1 - x)^2\, dx$$

$$= -\tfrac{1}{6}(1 - x)^3\Big]_0^1 = \tfrac{1}{6}$$

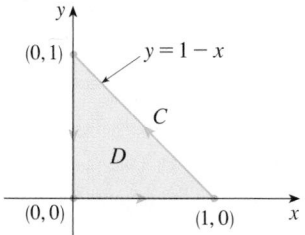

FIGURE 4

EXAMPLE 2 Evaluate $\oint_C (3y - e^{\sin x})\, dx + \left(7x + \sqrt{y^4 + 1}\right) dy$, where C is the circle $x^2 + y^2 = 9$.

SOLUTION The region D bounded by C is the disk $x^2 + y^2 \leqslant 9$, so let's change to polar coordinates after applying Green's Theorem:

$$\oint_C (3y - e^{\sin x})\, dx + \left(7x + \sqrt{y^4 + 1}\right) dy$$

$$= \iint_D \left[\frac{\partial}{\partial x}\left(7x + \sqrt{y^4 + 1}\right) - \frac{\partial}{\partial y}(3y - e^{\sin x})\right] dA$$

$$= \int_0^{2\pi} \int_0^3 (7 - 3)\, r\, dr\, d\theta$$

$$= 4\int_0^{2\pi} d\theta \int_0^3 r\, dr = 36\pi$$

▪▪▪▪ Instead of using polar coordinates, we could simply use the fact that D is a disk of radius 3 and write

$$\iint_D 4\, dA = 4 \cdot \pi(3)^2 = 36\pi$$

In Examples 1 and 2 we found that the double integral was easier to evaluate than the line integral. (Try setting up the line integral in Example 2 and you'll soon be convinced!) But sometimes it's easier to evaluate the line integral, and Green's Theorem is used in the reverse direction. For instance, if it is known that $P(x, y) = Q(x, y) = 0$ on the curve C, then Green's Theorem gives

$$\iint_D \left(\frac{\partial Q}{\partial x} - \frac{\partial P}{\partial y} \right) dA = \int_C P \, dx + Q \, dy = 0$$

no matter what values P and Q assume in the region D.

Another application of the reverse direction of Green's Theorem is in computing areas. Since the area of D is $\iint_D 1 \, dA$, we wish to choose P and Q so that

$$\frac{\partial Q}{\partial x} - \frac{\partial P}{\partial y} = 1$$

There are several possibilities:

$$P(x, y) = 0 \qquad P(x, y) = -y \qquad P(x, y) = -\tfrac{1}{2}y$$

$$Q(x, y) = x \qquad Q(x, y) = 0 \qquad Q(x, y) = \tfrac{1}{2}x$$

Then Green's Theorem gives the following formulas for the area of D:

[5]
$$A = \oint_C x \, dy = -\oint_C y \, dx = \tfrac{1}{2}\oint_C x \, dy - y \, dx$$

EXAMPLE 3 Find the area enclosed by the ellipse $\dfrac{x^2}{a^2} + \dfrac{y^2}{b^2} = 1$.

SOLUTION The ellipse has parametric equations $x = a \cos t$ and $y = b \sin t$, where $0 \le t \le 2\pi$. Using the third formula in Equation 5, we have

$$A = \tfrac{1}{2}\int_C x \, dy - y \, dx$$

$$= \tfrac{1}{2}\int_0^{2\pi} (a \cos t)(b \cos t) \, dt - (b \sin t)(-a \sin t) \, dt$$

$$= \frac{ab}{2} \int_0^{2\pi} dt = \pi ab$$

Although we have proved Green's Theorem only for the case where D is simple, we can now extend it to the case where D is a finite union of simple regions. For example, if D is the region shown in Figure 5, then we can write $D = D_1 \cup D_2$, where D_1 and D_2 are both simple. The boundary of D_1 is $C_1 \cup C_3$ and the boundary of D_2 is $C_2 \cup (-C_3)$ so, applying Green's Theorem to D_1 and D_2 separately, we get

$$\int_{C_1 \cup C_3} P \, dx + Q \, dy = \iint_{D_1} \left(\frac{\partial Q}{\partial x} - \frac{\partial P}{\partial y} \right) dA$$

$$\int_{C_2 \cup (-C_3)} P \, dx + Q \, dy = \iint_{D_2} \left(\frac{\partial Q}{\partial x} - \frac{\partial P}{\partial y} \right) dA$$

FIGURE 5

FIGURE 6

FIGURE 7

FIGURE 8

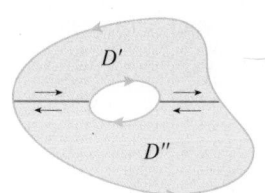

FIGURE 9

If we add these two equations, the line integrals along C_3 and $-C_3$ cancel, so we get

$$\int_{C_1 \cup C_2} P\,dx + Q\,dy = \iint_D \left(\frac{\partial Q}{\partial x} - \frac{\partial P}{\partial y} \right) dA$$

which is Green's Theorem for $D = D_1 \cup D_2$, since its boundary is $C = C_1 \cup C_2$.

The same sort of argument allows us to establish Green's Theorem for any finite union of nonoverlapping simple regions (see Figure 6).

EXAMPLE 4 Evaluate $\oint_C y^2\,dx + 3xy\,dy$, where C is the boundary of the semiannular region D in the upper half-plane between the circles $x^2 + y^2 = 1$ and $x^2 + y^2 = 4$.

SOLUTION Notice that although D is not simple, the y-axis divides it into two simple regions (see Figure 7). In polar coordinates we can write

$$D = \{(r, \theta) \mid 1 \leqslant r \leqslant 2,\ 0 \leqslant \theta \leqslant \pi\}$$

Therefore, Green's Theorem gives

$$\oint_C y^2\,dx + 3xy\,dy = \iint_D \left[\frac{\partial}{\partial x}(3xy) - \frac{\partial}{\partial y}(y^2) \right] dA$$

$$= \iint_D y\,dA = \int_0^\pi \int_1^2 (r \sin \theta)\, r\,dr\,d\theta$$

$$= \int_0^\pi \sin \theta\,d\theta \int_1^2 r^2\,dr = \left[-\cos \theta \right]_0^\pi \left[\tfrac{1}{3} r^3 \right]_1^2 = \frac{14}{3}$$

Green's Theorem can be extended to apply to regions with holes, that is, regions that are not simply-connected. Observe that the boundary C of the region D in Figure 8 consists of two simple closed curves C_1 and C_2. We assume that these boundary curves are oriented so that the region D is always on the left as the curve C is traversed. Thus, the positive direction is counterclockwise for the outer curve C_1 but clockwise for the inner curve C_2. If we divide D into two regions D' and D'' by means of the lines shown in Figure 9 and then apply Green's Theorem to each of D' and D'', we get

$$\iint_D \left(\frac{\partial Q}{\partial x} - \frac{\partial P}{\partial y} \right) dA = \iint_{D'} \left(\frac{\partial Q}{\partial x} - \frac{\partial P}{\partial y} \right) dA + \iint_{D''} \left(\frac{\partial Q}{\partial x} - \frac{\partial P}{\partial y} \right) dA$$

$$= \int_{\partial D'} P\,dx + Q\,dy + \int_{\partial D''} P\,dx + Q\,dy$$

Since the line integrals along the common boundary lines are in opposite directions, they cancel and we get

$$\iint_D \left(\frac{\partial Q}{\partial x} - \frac{\partial P}{\partial y} \right) dA = \int_{C_1} P\,dx + Q\,dy + \int_{C_2} P\,dx + Q\,dy = \int_C P\,dx + Q\,dy$$

which is Green's Theorem for the region D.

EXAMPLE 5 If $\mathbf{F}(x, y) = (-y\,\mathbf{i} + x\,\mathbf{j})/(x^2 + y^2)$, show that $\int_C \mathbf{F} \cdot d\mathbf{r} = 2\pi$ for every positively oriented simple closed path that encloses the origin.

SOLUTION Since C is an *arbitrary* closed path that encloses the origin, it's difficult to compute the given integral directly. So let's consider a counterclockwise-oriented circle

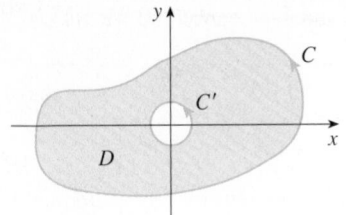

FIGURE 10

C' with center the origin and radius a, where a is chosen to be small enough that C' lies inside C. (See Figure 10.) Let D be the region bounded by C and C'. Then its positively oriented boundary is $C \cup (-C')$ and so the general version of Green's Theorem gives

$$\int_C P\,dx + Q\,dy + \int_{-C'} P\,dx + Q\,dy = \iint_D \left(\frac{\partial Q}{\partial x} - \frac{\partial P}{\partial y} \right) dA$$

$$= \iint_D \left[\frac{y^2 - x^2}{(x^2 + y^2)^2} - \frac{y^2 - x^2}{(x^2 + y^2)^2} \right] dA$$

$$= 0$$

Therefore

$$\int_C P\,dx + Q\,dy = \int_{C'} P\,dx + Q\,dy$$

that is,

$$\int_C \mathbf{F} \cdot d\mathbf{r} = \int_{C'} \mathbf{F} \cdot d\mathbf{r}$$

We now easily compute this last integral using the parametrization given by $\mathbf{r}(t) = a \cos t\,\mathbf{i} + a \sin t\,\mathbf{j}$, $0 \leqslant t \leqslant 2\pi$. Thus

$$\int_C \mathbf{F} \cdot d\mathbf{r} = \int_{C'} \mathbf{F} \cdot d\mathbf{r} = \int_0^{2\pi} \mathbf{F}(\mathbf{r}(t)) \cdot \mathbf{r}'(t)\, dt$$

$$= \int_0^{2\pi} \frac{(-a \sin t)(-a \sin t) + (a \cos t)(a \cos t)}{a^2 \cos^2 t + a^2 \sin^2 t}\, dt$$

$$= \int_0^{2\pi} dt = 2\pi$$

We end this section by using Green's Theorem to discuss a result that was stated in the preceding section.

Sketch of Proof of Theorem 17.3.6 We're assuming that $\mathbf{F} = P\,\mathbf{i} + Q\,\mathbf{j}$ is a vector field on an open simply-connected region D, that P and Q have continuous first-order partial derivatives, and that

$$\frac{\partial P}{\partial y} = \frac{\partial Q}{\partial x} \qquad \text{throughout } D$$

If C is any simple closed path in D and R is the region that C encloses, then Green's Theorem gives

$$\oint_C \mathbf{F} \cdot d\mathbf{r} = \oint_C P\,dx + Q\,dy = \iint_R \left(\frac{\partial Q}{\partial x} - \frac{\partial P}{\partial y} \right) dA = \iint_R 0\, dA = 0$$

A curve that is not simple crosses itself at one or more points and can be broken up into a number of simple curves. We have shown that the line integrals of $\mathbf{F}$ around these simple curves are all 0 and, adding these integrals, we see that $\int_C \mathbf{F} \cdot d\mathbf{r} = 0$ for any closed curve C. Therefore, $\int_C \mathbf{F} \cdot d\mathbf{r}$ is independent of path in D by Theorem 17.3.3. It follows that $\mathbf{F}$ is a conservative vector field.

17.4 Exercises

1–4 ▓ Evaluate the line integral by two methods: (a) directly and (b) using Green's Theorem.

1. $\oint_C xy^2\,dx + x^3\,dy$,
 C is the rectangle with vertices $(0, 0)$, $(2, 0)$, $(2, 3)$, and $(0, 3)$

2. $\oint_C y\,dx - x\,dy$,
 C is the circle with center the origin and radius 1

3. $\oint_C xy\,dx + x^2 y^3\,dy$,
 C is the triangle with vertices $(0, 0)$, $(1, 0)$, and $(1, 2)$

4. $\oint_C x\,dx + y\,dy$, C consists of the line segments from $(0, 1)$ to $(0, 0)$ and from $(0, 0)$ to $(1, 0)$ and the parabola $y = 1 - x^2$ from $(1, 0)$ to $(0, 1)$

CAS **5–6** ▓ Verify Green's Theorem by using a computer algebra system to evaluate both the line integral and the double integral.

5. $P(x, y) = x^4 y^5$, $Q(x, y) = -x^7 y^6$,
 C is the circle $x^2 + y^2 = 1$

6. $P(x, y) = y^2 \sin x$, $Q(x, y) = x^2 \sin y$,
 C consists of the arc of the parabola $y = x^2$ from $(0, 0)$ to $(1, 1)$ followed by the line segment from $(1, 1)$ to $(0, 0)$

7–12 ▓ Use Green's Theorem to evaluate the line integral along the given positively oriented curve.

7. $\int_C e^y\,dx + 2xe^y\,dy$,
 C is the square with sides $x = 0$, $x = 1$, $y = 0$, and $y = 1$

8. $\int_C x^2 y^2\,dx + 4xy^3\,dy$,
 C is the triangle with vertices $(0, 0)$, $(1, 3)$, and $(0, 3)$

9. $\int_C \left(y + e^{\sqrt{x}}\right)dx + (2x + \cos y^2)\,dy$,
 C is the boundary of the region enclosed by the parabolas $y = x^2$ and $x = y^2$

10. $\int_C xe^{-2x}\,dx + (x^4 + 2x^2 y^2)\,dy$,
 C is the boundary of the region between the circles $x^2 + y^2 = 1$ and $x^2 + y^2 = 4$

11. $\int_C y^3\,dx - x^3\,dy$, C is the circle $x^2 + y^2 = 4$

12. $\int_C \sin y\,dx + x \cos y\,dy$, C is the ellipse $x^2 + xy + y^2 = 1$

13–16 ▓ Use Green's Theorem to evaluate $\int_C \mathbf{F} \cdot d\mathbf{r}$. (Check the orientation of the curve before applying the theorem.)

13. $\mathbf{F}(x, y) = \langle \sqrt{x} + y^3, x^2 + \sqrt{y}\rangle$,
 C consists of the arc of the curve $y = \sin x$ from $(0, 0)$ to $(\pi, 0)$ and the line segment from $(\pi, 0)$ to $(0, 0)$

14. $\mathbf{F}(x, y) = \langle y^2 \cos x, x^2 + 2y \sin x\rangle$,
 C is the triangle from $(0, 0)$ to $(2, 6)$ to $(2, 0)$ to $(0, 0)$

15. $\mathbf{F}(x, y) = \langle e^x + x^2 y, e^y - xy^2\rangle$,
 C is the circle $x^2 + y^2 = 25$ oriented clockwise

16. $\mathbf{F}(x, y) = \langle y - \ln(x^2 + y^2), 2\tan^{-1}(y/x)\rangle$, C is the circle $(x - 2)^2 + (y - 3)^2 = 1$ oriented counterclockwise

17. Use Green's Theorem to find the work done by the force $\mathbf{F}(x, y) = x(x + y)\,\mathbf{i} + xy^2\,\mathbf{j}$ in moving a particle from the origin along the x-axis to $(1, 0)$, then along the line segment to $(0, 1)$, and then back to the origin along the y-axis.

18. A particle starts at the point $(-2, 0)$, moves along the x-axis to $(2, 0)$, and then along the semicircle $y = \sqrt{4 - x^2}$ to the starting point. Use Green's Theorem to find the work done on this particle by the force field $\mathbf{F}(x, y) = \langle x, x^3 + 3xy^2\rangle$.

19. Use one of the formulas in (5) to find the area under one arch of the cycloid $x = t - \sin t$, $y = 1 - \cos t$.

20. If a circle C with radius 1 rolls along the outside of the circle $x^2 + y^2 = 16$, a fixed point P on C traces out a curve called an epicycloid, with parametric equations $x = 5\cos t - \cos 5t$, $y = 5\sin t - \sin 5t$. Graph the epicycloid and use (5) to find the area it encloses.

21. (a) If C is the line segment connecting the point (x_1, y_1) to the point (x_2, y_2), show that
$$\int_C x\,dy - y\,dx = x_1 y_2 - x_2 y_1$$
(b) If the vertices of a polygon, in counterclockwise order, are (x_1, y_1), (x_2, y_2), \ldots, (x_n, y_n), show that the area of the polygon is
$$A = \tfrac{1}{2}[(x_1 y_2 - x_2 y_1) + (x_2 y_3 - x_3 y_2) + \cdots$$
$$+ (x_{n-1} y_n - x_n y_{n-1}) + (x_n y_1 - x_1 y_n)]$$
(c) Find the area of the pentagon with vertices $(0, 0)$, $(2, 1)$, $(1, 3)$, $(0, 2)$, and $(-1, 1)$.

22. Let D be a region bounded by a simple closed path C in the xy-plane. Use Green's Theorem to prove that the coordinates of the centroid $(\bar{x}, \bar{y})$ of D are
$$\bar{x} = \frac{1}{2A}\oint_C x^2\,dy \qquad \bar{y} = -\frac{1}{2A}\oint_C y^2\,dx$$
where A is the area of D.

23. Use Exercise 22 to find the centroid of the triangle with vertices $(0, 0)$, $(1, 0)$, and $(0, 1)$.

24. Use Exercise 22 to find the centroid of a semicircular region of radius a.

25. A plane lamina with constant density $\rho(x, y) = \rho$ occupies a region in the xy-plane bounded by a simple closed path C. Show that its moments of inertia about the axes are
$$I_x = -\frac{\rho}{3}\oint_C y^3\,dx \qquad I_y = \frac{\rho}{3}\oint_C x^3\,dy$$

26. Use Exercise 25 to find the moment of inertia of a circular disk of radius a with constant density ρ about a diameter. (Compare with Example 4 in Section 16.5.)

27. If **F** is the vector field of Example 5, show that $\int_C \mathbf{F} \cdot d\mathbf{r} = 0$ for every simple closed path that does not pass through or enclose the origin.

28. Complete the proof of the special case of Green's Theorem by proving Equation 3.

29. Use Green's Theorem to prove the change of variables formula for a double integral (Formula 16.9.9) for the case

where $f(x, y) = 1$:

$$\iint_R dx\, dy = \iint_S \left| \frac{\partial(x, y)}{\partial(u, v)} \right| du\, dv$$

Here R is the region in the xy-plane that corresponds to the region S in the uv-plane under the transformation given by $x = g(u, v)$, $y = h(u, v)$.

[*Hint:* Note that the left side is $A(R)$ and apply the first part of Equation 5. Convert the line integral over ∂R to a line integral over ∂S and apply Green's Theorem in the uv-plane.]

17.5 Curl and Divergence

In this section we define two operations that can be performed on vector fields and that play a basic role in the applications of vector calculus to fluid flow and electricity and magnetism. Each operation resembles differentiation, but one produces a vector field whereas the other produces a scalar field.

Curl

If $\mathbf{F} = P\,\mathbf{i} + Q\,\mathbf{j} + R\,\mathbf{k}$ is a vector field on $\mathbb{R}^3$ and the partial derivatives of P, Q, and R all exist, then the **curl** of **F** is the vector field on $\mathbb{R}^3$ defined by

$$\boxed{1} \qquad \operatorname{curl} \mathbf{F} = \left(\frac{\partial R}{\partial y} - \frac{\partial Q}{\partial z} \right) \mathbf{i} + \left(\frac{\partial P}{\partial z} - \frac{\partial R}{\partial x} \right) \mathbf{j} + \left(\frac{\partial Q}{\partial x} - \frac{\partial P}{\partial y} \right) \mathbf{k}$$

As an aid to our memory, let's rewrite Equation 1 using operator notation. We introduce the vector differential operator ∇ ("del") as

$$\nabla = \mathbf{i}\,\frac{\partial}{\partial x} + \mathbf{j}\,\frac{\partial}{\partial y} + \mathbf{k}\,\frac{\partial}{\partial z}$$

It has meaning when it operates on a scalar function to produce the gradient of f:

$$\nabla f = \mathbf{i}\,\frac{\partial f}{\partial x} + \mathbf{j}\,\frac{\partial f}{\partial y} + \mathbf{k}\,\frac{\partial f}{\partial z} = \frac{\partial f}{\partial x}\mathbf{i} + \frac{\partial f}{\partial y}\mathbf{j} + \frac{\partial f}{\partial z}\mathbf{k}$$

If we think of ∇ as a vector with components $\partial/\partial x$, $\partial/\partial y$, and $\partial/\partial z$, we can also consider the formal cross product of ∇ with the vector field **F** as follows:

$$\nabla \times \mathbf{F} = \begin{vmatrix} \mathbf{i} & \mathbf{j} & \mathbf{k} \\ \dfrac{\partial}{\partial x} & \dfrac{\partial}{\partial y} & \dfrac{\partial}{\partial z} \\ P & Q & R \end{vmatrix}$$

$$= \left(\frac{\partial R}{\partial y} - \frac{\partial Q}{\partial z} \right) \mathbf{i} + \left(\frac{\partial P}{\partial z} - \frac{\partial R}{\partial x} \right) \mathbf{j} + \left(\frac{\partial Q}{\partial x} - \frac{\partial P}{\partial y} \right) \mathbf{k}$$

$$= \operatorname{curl} \mathbf{F}$$

Thus, the easiest way to remember Definition 1 is by means of the symbolic expression

$$\boxed{2} \qquad \text{curl } \mathbf{F} = \nabla \times \mathbf{F}$$

EXAMPLE 1 If $\mathbf{F}(x, y, z) = xz\,\mathbf{i} + xyz\,\mathbf{j} - y^2\,\mathbf{k}$, find curl $\mathbf{F}$.

SOLUTION Using Equation 2, we have

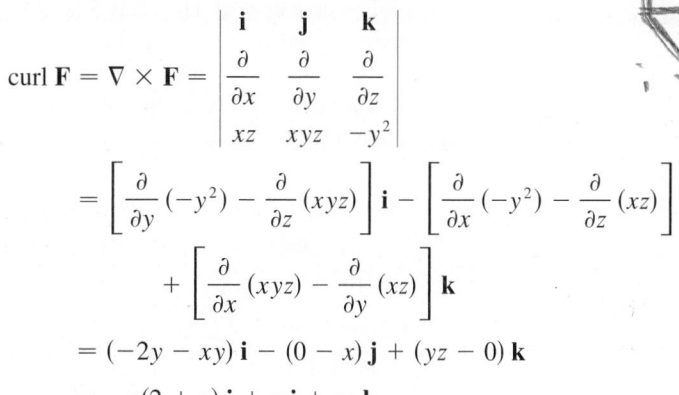

$$\text{curl } \mathbf{F} = \nabla \times \mathbf{F} = \begin{vmatrix} \mathbf{i} & \mathbf{j} & \mathbf{k} \\ \dfrac{\partial}{\partial x} & \dfrac{\partial}{\partial y} & \dfrac{\partial}{\partial z} \\ xz & xyz & -y^2 \end{vmatrix}$$

$$= \left[\frac{\partial}{\partial y}(-y^2) - \frac{\partial}{\partial z}(xyz) \right] \mathbf{i} - \left[\frac{\partial}{\partial x}(-y^2) - \frac{\partial}{\partial z}(xz) \right] \mathbf{j}$$

$$+ \left[\frac{\partial}{\partial x}(xyz) - \frac{\partial}{\partial y}(xz) \right] \mathbf{k}$$

$$= (-2y - xy)\,\mathbf{i} - (0 - x)\,\mathbf{j} + (yz - 0)\,\mathbf{k}$$

$$= -y(2 + x)\,\mathbf{i} + x\,\mathbf{j} + yz\,\mathbf{k}$$

|||| Most computer algebra systems have commands that compute the curl and divergence of vector fields. If you have access to a CAS, use these commands to check the answers to the examples and exercises in this section.

Recall that the gradient of a function f of three variables is a vector field on $\mathbb{R}^3$ and so we can compute its curl. The following theorem says that the curl of a gradient vector field is $\mathbf{0}$.

> **3 Theorem** If f is a function of three variables that has continuous second-order partial derivatives, then
>
> $$\text{curl}(\nabla f) = \mathbf{0}$$

Proof We have

|||| Notice the similarity to what we know from Section 13.4: $\mathbf{a} \times \mathbf{a} = \mathbf{0}$ for every three-dimensional vector $\mathbf{a}$.

$$\text{curl}(\nabla f) = \nabla \times (\nabla f) = \begin{vmatrix} \mathbf{i} & \mathbf{j} & \mathbf{k} \\ \dfrac{\partial}{\partial x} & \dfrac{\partial}{\partial y} & \dfrac{\partial}{\partial z} \\ \dfrac{\partial f}{\partial x} & \dfrac{\partial f}{\partial y} & \dfrac{\partial f}{\partial z} \end{vmatrix}$$

$$= \left(\frac{\partial^2 f}{\partial y\, \partial z} - \frac{\partial^2 f}{\partial z\, \partial y} \right) \mathbf{i} + \left(\frac{\partial^2 f}{\partial z\, \partial x} - \frac{\partial^2 f}{\partial x\, \partial z} \right) \mathbf{j} + \left(\frac{\partial^2 f}{\partial x\, \partial y} - \frac{\partial^2 f}{\partial y\, \partial x} \right) \mathbf{k}$$

$$= 0\,\mathbf{i} + 0\,\mathbf{j} + 0\,\mathbf{k} = \mathbf{0}$$

by Clairaut's Theorem.

|||| Compare this with Exercise 27 in Section 17.3.

Since a conservative vector field is one for which $\mathbf{F} = \nabla f$, Theorem 3 can be rephrased as follows:

> If $\mathbf{F}$ is conservative, then curl $\mathbf{F} = \mathbf{0}$.

This gives us a way of verifying that a vector field is not conservative.

EXAMPLE 2 Show that the vector field $\mathbf{F}(x, y, z) = xz\,\mathbf{i} + xyz\,\mathbf{j} - y^2\,\mathbf{k}$ is not conservative.

SOLUTION In Example 1 we showed that

$$\operatorname{curl}\mathbf{F} = -y(2 + x)\,\mathbf{i} + x\,\mathbf{j} + yz\,\mathbf{k}$$

This shows that curl $\mathbf{F} \neq \mathbf{0}$ and so, by Theorem 3, $\mathbf{F}$ is not conservative.

The converse of Theorem 3 is not true in general, but the following theorem says the converse is true if $\mathbf{F}$ is defined everywhere. (More generally it is true if the domain is simply-connected, that is, "has no hole.") Theorem 4 is the three-dimensional version of Theorem 17.3.6. Its proof requires Stokes' Theorem and is sketched at the end of Section 17.8.

> **4 Theorem** If $\mathbf{F}$ is a vector field defined on all of $\mathbb{R}^3$ whose component functions have continuous partial derivatives and curl $\mathbf{F} = \mathbf{0}$, then $\mathbf{F}$ is a conservative vector field.

EXAMPLE 3
(a) Show that $\mathbf{F}(x, y, z) = y^2z^3\,\mathbf{i} + 2xyz^3\,\mathbf{j} + 3xy^2z^2\,\mathbf{k}$ is a conservative vector field.
(b) Find a function f such that $\mathbf{F} = \nabla f$.

SOLUTION
(a) We compute the curl of $\mathbf{F}$:

$$\operatorname{curl}\mathbf{F} = \nabla \times \mathbf{F} = \begin{vmatrix} \mathbf{i} & \mathbf{j} & \mathbf{k} \\ \dfrac{\partial}{\partial x} & \dfrac{\partial}{\partial y} & \dfrac{\partial}{\partial z} \\ y^2z^3 & 2xyz^3 & 3xy^2z^2 \end{vmatrix}$$

$$= (6xyz^2 - 6xyz^2)\,\mathbf{i} - (3y^2z^2 - 3y^2z^2)\,\mathbf{j} + (2yz^3 - 2yz^3)\,\mathbf{k}$$

$$= \mathbf{0}$$

Since curl $\mathbf{F} = \mathbf{0}$ and the domain of $\mathbf{F}$ is $\mathbb{R}^3$, $\mathbf{F}$ is a conservative vector field by Theorem 4.

(b) The technique for finding f was given in Section 17.3. We have

$$\boxed{5} \qquad\qquad f_x(x, y, z) = y^2z^3$$

$$\boxed{6} \qquad\qquad f_y(x, y, z) = 2xyz^3$$

$$\boxed{7} \qquad\qquad f_z(x, y, z) = 3xy^2z^2$$

Integrating (5) with respect to x, we obtain

$$\boxed{8} \qquad\qquad f(x, y, z) = xy^2z^3 + g(y, z)$$

Differentiating (8) with respect to y, we get $f_y(x, y, z) = 2xyz^3 + g_y(y, z)$, so comparison with (6) gives $g_y(y, z) = 0$. Thus, $g(y, z) = h(z)$ and

$$f_z(x, y, z) = 3xy^2z^2 + h'(z)$$

Then (7) gives $h'(z) = 0$. Therefore

$$f(x, y, z) = xy^2z^3 + K$$

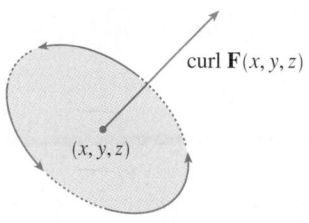

curl $\mathbf{F}(x, y, z)$

(x, y, z)

FIGURE 1

The reason for the name *curl* is that the curl vector is associated with rotations. One connection is explained in Exercise 35. Another occurs when $\mathbf{F}$ represents the velocity field in fluid flow (see Example 3 in Section 17.1). Particles near (x, y, z) in the fluid tend to rotate about the axis that points in the direction of curl $\mathbf{F}(x, y, z)$ and the length of this curl vector is a measure of how quickly the particles move around the axis (see Figure 1). If curl $\mathbf{F} = \mathbf{0}$ at a point P, then the fluid is free from rotations at P and $\mathbf{F}$ is called **irrotational** at P. In other words, there is no whirlpool or eddy at P. If curl $\mathbf{F} = \mathbf{0}$, then a tiny paddle wheel moves with the fluid but doesn't rotate about its axis. If curl $\mathbf{F} \neq \mathbf{0}$, the paddle wheel rotates about its axis. We give a more detailed explanation in Section 17.8 as a consequence of Stokes' Theorem.

‖‖ Divergence

If $\mathbf{F} = P\mathbf{i} + Q\mathbf{j} + R\mathbf{k}$ is a vector field on $\mathbb{R}^3$ and $\partial P/\partial x$, $\partial Q/\partial y$, and $\partial R/\partial z$ exist, then the **divergence of F** is the function of three variables defined by

$\boxed{9}$
$$\text{div } \mathbf{F} = \frac{\partial P}{\partial x} + \frac{\partial Q}{\partial y} + \frac{\partial R}{\partial z}$$

Observe that curl $\mathbf{F}$ is a vector field but div $\mathbf{F}$ is a scalar field. In terms of the gradient operator $\nabla = (\partial/\partial x)\,\mathbf{i} + (\partial/\partial y)\,\mathbf{j} + (\partial/\partial z)\,\mathbf{k}$, the divergence of $\mathbf{F}$ can be written symbolically as the dot product of ∇ and $\mathbf{F}$:

$\boxed{10}$
$$\text{div } \mathbf{F} = \nabla \cdot \mathbf{F}$$

EXAMPLE 4 If $\mathbf{F}(x, y, z) = xz\,\mathbf{i} + xyz\,\mathbf{j} - y^2\,\mathbf{k}$, find div $\mathbf{F}$.

SOLUTION By the definition of divergence (Equation 9 or 10) we have

$$\text{div } \mathbf{F} = \nabla \cdot \mathbf{F} = \frac{\partial}{\partial x}\,(xz) + \frac{\partial}{\partial y}\,(xyz) + \frac{\partial}{\partial z}\,(-y^2)$$

$$= z + xz$$

If $\mathbf{F}$ is a vector field on $\mathbb{R}^3$, then curl $\mathbf{F}$ is also a vector field on $\mathbb{R}^3$. As such, we can compute its divergence. The next theorem shows that the result is 0.

$\boxed{11}$ **Theorem** If $\mathbf{F} = P\mathbf{i} + Q\mathbf{j} + R\mathbf{k}$ is a vector field on $\mathbb{R}^3$ and P, Q, and R have continuous second-order partial derivatives, then

$$\text{div curl } \mathbf{F} = 0$$

|||| Note the analogy with the scalar triple product: $\mathbf{a} \cdot (\mathbf{a} \times \mathbf{b}) = 0$.

Proof Using the definitions of divergence and curl, we have

$$\text{div curl } \mathbf{F} = \nabla \cdot (\nabla \times \mathbf{F})$$

$$= \frac{\partial}{\partial x}\left(\frac{\partial R}{\partial y} - \frac{\partial Q}{\partial z}\right) + \frac{\partial}{\partial y}\left(\frac{\partial P}{\partial z} - \frac{\partial R}{\partial x}\right) + \frac{\partial}{\partial z}\left(\frac{\partial Q}{\partial x} - \frac{\partial P}{\partial y}\right)$$

$$= \frac{\partial^2 R}{\partial x\,\partial y} - \frac{\partial^2 Q}{\partial x\,\partial z} + \frac{\partial^2 P}{\partial y\,\partial z} - \frac{\partial^2 R}{\partial y\,\partial x} + \frac{\partial^2 Q}{\partial z\,\partial x} - \frac{\partial^2 P}{\partial z\,\partial y}$$

$$= 0$$

because the terms cancel in pairs by Clairaut's Theorem.

EXAMPLE 5 Show that the vector field $\mathbf{F}(x, y, z) = xz\,\mathbf{i} + xyz\,\mathbf{j} - y^2\,\mathbf{k}$ can't be written as the curl of another vector field, that is, $\mathbf{F} \neq \text{curl } \mathbf{G}$.

SOLUTION In Example 4 we showed that

$$\text{div } \mathbf{F} = z + xz$$

and therefore div $\mathbf{F} \neq 0$. If it were true that $\mathbf{F} = \text{curl } \mathbf{G}$, then Theorem 11 would give

$$\text{div } \mathbf{F} = \text{div curl } \mathbf{G} = 0$$

which contradicts div $\mathbf{F} \neq 0$. Therefore, $\mathbf{F}$ is not the curl of another vector field.

|||| The reason for this interpretation of div $\mathbf{F}$ will be explained at the end of Section 17.9 as a consequence of the Divergence Theorem.

Again, the reason for the name *divergence* can be understood in the context of fluid flow. If $\mathbf{F}(x, y, z)$ is the velocity of a fluid (or gas), then div $\mathbf{F}(x, y, z)$ represents the net rate of change (with respect to time) of the mass of fluid (or gas) flowing from the point (x, y, z) per unit volume. In other words, div $\mathbf{F}(x, y, z)$ measures the tendency of the fluid to diverge from the point (x, y, z). If div $\mathbf{F} = 0$, then $\mathbf{F}$ is said to be **incompressible**.

Another differential operator occurs when we compute the divergence of a gradient vector field ∇f. If f is a function of three variables, we have

$$\text{div}(\nabla f) = \nabla \cdot (\nabla f) = \frac{\partial^2 f}{\partial x^2} + \frac{\partial^2 f}{\partial y^2} + \frac{\partial^2 f}{\partial z^2}$$

and this expression occurs so often that we abbreviate it as $\nabla^2 f$. The operator

$$\nabla^2 = \nabla \cdot \nabla$$

is called the **Laplace operator** because of its relation to **Laplace's equation**

$$\nabla^2 f = \frac{\partial^2 f}{\partial x^2} + \frac{\partial^2 f}{\partial y^2} + \frac{\partial^2 f}{\partial z^2} = 0$$

We can also apply the Laplace operator ∇^2 to a vector field

$$\mathbf{F} = P\,\mathbf{i} + Q\,\mathbf{j} + R\,\mathbf{k}$$

in terms of its components:

$$\nabla^2 \mathbf{F} = \nabla^2 P\,\mathbf{i} + \nabla^2 Q\,\mathbf{j} + \nabla^2 R\,\mathbf{k}$$

‖‖ Vector Forms of Green's Theorem

The curl and divergence operators allow us to rewrite Green's Theorem in versions that will be useful in our later work. We suppose that the plane region D, its boundary curve C, and the functions P and Q satisfy the hypotheses of Green's Theorem. Then we consider the vector field $\mathbf{F} = P\,\mathbf{i} + Q\,\mathbf{j}$. Its line integral is

$$\oint_C \mathbf{F} \cdot d\mathbf{r} = \oint_C P\,dx + Q\,dy$$

and, regarding $\mathbf{F}$ as a vector field on $\mathbb{R}^3$ with third component 0, we have

$$\operatorname{curl} \mathbf{F} = \begin{vmatrix} \mathbf{i} & \mathbf{j} & \mathbf{k} \\ \dfrac{\partial}{\partial x} & \dfrac{\partial}{\partial y} & \dfrac{\partial}{\partial z} \\ P(x, y) & Q(x, y) & 0 \end{vmatrix} = \left(\frac{\partial Q}{\partial x} - \frac{\partial P}{\partial y} \right) \mathbf{k}$$

Therefore $\qquad (\operatorname{curl} \mathbf{F}) \cdot \mathbf{k} = \left(\dfrac{\partial Q}{\partial x} - \dfrac{\partial P}{\partial y} \right) \mathbf{k} \cdot \mathbf{k} = \dfrac{\partial Q}{\partial x} - \dfrac{\partial P}{\partial y}$

and we can now rewrite the equation in Green's Theorem in the vector form

$$\boxed{12} \qquad \boxed{\oint_C \mathbf{F} \cdot d\mathbf{r} = \iint_D (\operatorname{curl} \mathbf{F}) \cdot \mathbf{k}\, dA}$$

Equation 12 expresses the line integral of the tangential component of $\mathbf{F}$ along C as the double integral of the vertical component of curl $\mathbf{F}$ over the region D enclosed by C. We now derive a similar formula involving the *normal* component of $\mathbf{F}$.

If C is given by the vector equation

$$\mathbf{r}(t) = x(t)\,\mathbf{i} + y(t)\,\mathbf{j} \qquad a \le t \le b$$

then the unit tangent vector (see Section 14.2) is

$$\mathbf{T}(t) = \frac{x'(t)}{|\mathbf{r}'(t)|}\,\mathbf{i} + \frac{y'(t)}{|\mathbf{r}'(t)|}\,\mathbf{j}$$

You can verify that the outward unit normal vector to C is given by

$$\mathbf{n}(t) = \frac{y'(t)}{|\mathbf{r}'(t)|}\,\mathbf{i} - \frac{x'(t)}{|\mathbf{r}'(t)|}\,\mathbf{j}$$

(See Figure 2.) Then, from Equation 17.2.3, we have

$$\oint_C \mathbf{F} \cdot \mathbf{n}\, ds = \int_a^b (\mathbf{F} \cdot \mathbf{n})(t)\, |\mathbf{r}'(t)|\, dt$$

$$= \int_a^b \left[\frac{P(x(t), y(t))\, y'(t)}{|\mathbf{r}'(t)|} - \frac{Q(x(t), y(t))\, x'(t)}{|\mathbf{r}'(t)|} \right] |\mathbf{r}'(t)|\, dt$$

$$= \int_a^b P(x(t), y(t))\, y'(t)\, dt - Q(x(t), y(t))\, x'(t)\, dt$$

$$= \int_C P\,dy - Q\,dx = \iint_D \left(\frac{\partial P}{\partial x} + \frac{\partial Q}{\partial y} \right) dA$$

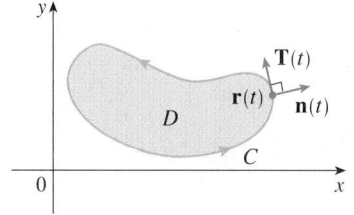

FIGURE 2

by Green's Theorem. But the integrand in this double integral is just the divergence of **F**. So we have a second vector form of Green's Theorem.

$$\boxed{13} \qquad \oint_C \mathbf{F} \cdot \mathbf{n}\, ds = \iint_D \operatorname{div} \mathbf{F}(x, y)\, dA$$

This version says that the line integral of the normal component of **F** along C is equal to the double integral of the divergence of **F** over the region D enclosed by C.

17.5 Exercises

1–8 ▏▎▍ Find (a) the curl and (b) the divergence of the vector field.

1. $\mathbf{F}(x, y, z) = xyz\,\mathbf{i} - x^2 y\,\mathbf{k}$

2. $\mathbf{F}(x, y, z) = x^2 yz\,\mathbf{i} + xy^2 z\,\mathbf{j} + xyz^2\,\mathbf{k}$

3. $\mathbf{F}(x, y, z) = \mathbf{i} + (x + yz)\,\mathbf{j} + (xy - \sqrt{z})\,\mathbf{k}$

4. $\mathbf{F}(x, y, z) = \cos xz\,\mathbf{j} - \sin xy\,\mathbf{k}$

5. $\mathbf{F}(x, y, z) = e^x \sin y\,\mathbf{i} + e^x \cos y\,\mathbf{j} + z\,\mathbf{k}$

6. $\mathbf{F}(x, y, z) = \dfrac{x}{x^2 + y^2 + z^2}\,\mathbf{i} + \dfrac{y}{x^2 + y^2 + z^2}\,\mathbf{j} + \dfrac{z}{x^2 + y^2 + z^2}\,\mathbf{k}$

7. $\mathbf{F}(x, y, z) = \langle \ln x, \ln(xy), \ln(xyz) \rangle$

8. $\mathbf{F}(x, y, z) = \langle xe^{-y}, xz, ze^{y} \rangle$

9–11 ▏▎▍ The vector field **F** is shown in the xy-plane and looks the same in all other horizontal planes. (In other words, **F** is independent of z and its z-component is 0.)
(a) Is div **F** positive, negative, or zero? Explain.
(b) Determine whether curl **F** = **0**. If not, in which direction does curl **F** point?

9.

10.

11.

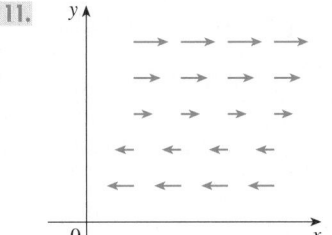

12. Let f be a scalar field and **F** a vector field. State whether each expression is meaningful. If not, explain why. If so, state whether it is a scalar field or a vector field.
(a) curl f (b) grad f
(c) div **F**   (d) curl(grad f)
(e) grad **F**   (f) grad(div **F**)
(g) div(grad f)   (h) grad(div f)
(i) curl(curl **F**)   (j) div(div **F**)
(k) (grad f) × (div **F**)   (l) div(curl(grad f))

13–18 ▏▎▍ Determine whether or not the vector field is conservative. If it is conservative, find a function f such that $\mathbf{F} = \nabla f$.

13. $\mathbf{F}(x, y, z) = yz\,\mathbf{i} + xz\,\mathbf{j} + xy\,\mathbf{k}$

14. $\mathbf{F}(x, y, z) = 3z^2\,\mathbf{i} + \cos y\,\mathbf{j} + 2xz\,\mathbf{k}$

15. $\mathbf{F}(x, y, z) = 2xy\,\mathbf{i} + (x^2 + 2yz)\,\mathbf{j} + y^2\,\mathbf{k}$

16. $\mathbf{F}(x, y, z) = e^z\,\mathbf{i} + \mathbf{j} + xe^z\,\mathbf{k}$

17. $\mathbf{F}(x, y, z) = ye^{-x}\,\mathbf{i} + e^{-x}\,\mathbf{j} + 2z\,\mathbf{k}$

18. $\mathbf{F}(x, y, z) = y \cos xy\,\mathbf{i} + x \cos xy\,\mathbf{j} - \sin z\,\mathbf{k}$

19. Is there a vector field **G** on $\mathbb{R}^3$ such that curl $\mathbf{G} = xy^2\,\mathbf{i} + yz^2\,\mathbf{j} + zx^2\,\mathbf{k}$? Explain.

20. Is there a vector field **G** on $\mathbb{R}^3$ such that curl $\mathbf{G} = yz\,\mathbf{i} + xyz\,\mathbf{j} + xy\,\mathbf{k}$? Explain.

21. Show that any vector field of the form
$$\mathbf{F}(x, y, z) = f(x)\,\mathbf{i} + g(y)\,\mathbf{j} + h(z)\,\mathbf{k}$$
where f, g, h are differentiable functions, is irrotational.

22. Show that any vector field of the form

$$\mathbf{F}(x, y, z) = f(y, z)\,\mathbf{i} + g(x, z)\,\mathbf{j} + h(x, y)\,\mathbf{k}$$

is incompressible.

23–29 |||| Prove the identity, assuming that the appropriate partial derivatives exist and are continuous. If f is a scalar field and $\mathbf{F}$, $\mathbf{G}$ are vector fields, then $f\mathbf{F}$, $\mathbf{F} \cdot \mathbf{G}$, and $\mathbf{F} \times \mathbf{G}$ are defined by

$$(f\mathbf{F})(x, y, z) = f(x, y, z)\mathbf{F}(x, y, z)$$

$$(\mathbf{F} \cdot \mathbf{G})(x, y, z) = \mathbf{F}(x, y, z) \cdot \mathbf{G}(x, y, z)$$

$$(\mathbf{F} \times \mathbf{G})(x, y, z) = \mathbf{F}(x, y, z) \times \mathbf{G}(x, y, z)$$

23. $\operatorname{div}(\mathbf{F} + \mathbf{G}) = \operatorname{div}\mathbf{F} + \operatorname{div}\mathbf{G}$

24. $\operatorname{curl}(\mathbf{F} + \mathbf{G}) = \operatorname{curl}\mathbf{F} + \operatorname{curl}\mathbf{G}$

25. $\operatorname{div}(f\mathbf{F}) = f\operatorname{div}\mathbf{F} + \mathbf{F} \cdot \nabla f$

26. $\operatorname{curl}(f\mathbf{F}) = f\operatorname{curl}\mathbf{F} + (\nabla f) \times \mathbf{F}$

27. $\operatorname{div}(\mathbf{F} \times \mathbf{G}) = \mathbf{G} \cdot \operatorname{curl}\mathbf{F} - \mathbf{F} \cdot \operatorname{curl}\mathbf{G}$

28. $\operatorname{div}(\nabla f \times \nabla g) = 0$

29. $\operatorname{curl}(\operatorname{curl}\mathbf{F}) = \operatorname{grad}(\operatorname{div}\mathbf{F}) - \nabla^2\mathbf{F}$

30–32 |||| Let $\mathbf{r} = x\,\mathbf{i} + y\,\mathbf{j} + z\,\mathbf{k}$ and $r = |\mathbf{r}|$.

30. Verify each identity.
(a) $\nabla \cdot \mathbf{r} = 3$ (b) $\nabla \cdot (r\mathbf{r}) = 4r$
(c) $\nabla^2 r^3 = 12r$

31. Verify each identity.
(a) $\nabla r = \mathbf{r}/r$ (b) $\nabla \times \mathbf{r} = \mathbf{0}$
(c) $\nabla(1/r) = -\mathbf{r}/r^3$ (d) $\nabla \ln r = \mathbf{r}/r^2$

32. If $\mathbf{F} = \mathbf{r}/r^p$, find div $\mathbf{F}$. Is there a value of p for which div $\mathbf{F} = 0$?

33. Use Green's Theorem in the form of Equation 13 to prove **Green's first identity**:

$$\iint_D f\nabla^2 g\, dA = \oint_C f(\nabla g) \cdot \mathbf{n}\,ds - \iint_D \nabla f \cdot \nabla g\, dA$$

where D and C satisfy the hypotheses of Green's Theorem and the appropriate partial derivatives of f and g exist and are continuous. (The quantity $\nabla g \cdot \mathbf{n} = D_{\mathbf{n}}g$ occurs in the line integral. This is the directional derivative in the direction of the normal vector $\mathbf{n}$ and is called the **normal derivative** of g.)

34. Use Green's first identity (Exercise 33) to prove **Green's second identity**:

$$\iint_D (f\nabla^2 g - g\nabla^2 f)\, dA = \oint_C (f\nabla g - g\nabla f) \cdot \mathbf{n}\, ds$$

where D and C satisfy the hypotheses of Green's Theorem and the appropriate partial derivatives of f and g exist and are continuous.

35. This exercise demonstrates a connection between the curl vector and rotations. Let B be a rigid body rotating about the

z-axis. The rotation can be described by the vector $\mathbf{w} = \omega\mathbf{k}$, where ω is the angular speed of B, that is, the tangential speed of any point P in B divided by the distance d from the axis of rotation. Let $\mathbf{r} = \langle x, y, z \rangle$ be the position vector of P.
(a) By considering the angle θ in the figure, show that the velocity field of B is given by $\mathbf{v} = \mathbf{w} \times \mathbf{r}$.
(b) Show that $\mathbf{v} = -\omega y\,\mathbf{i} + \omega x\,\mathbf{j}$.
(c) Show that curl $\mathbf{v} = 2\mathbf{w}$.

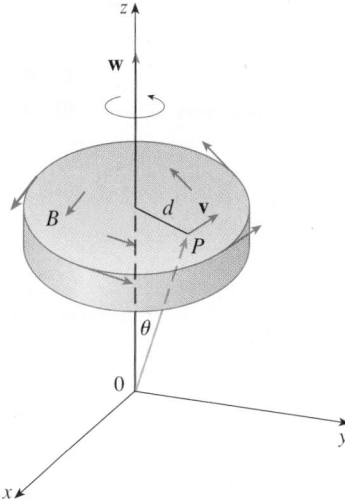

36. Maxwell's equations relating the electric field $\mathbf{E}$ and magnetic field $\mathbf{H}$ as they vary with time in a region containing no charge and no current can be stated as follows:

$$\operatorname{div}\mathbf{E} = 0 \qquad\qquad \operatorname{div}\mathbf{H} = 0$$

$$\operatorname{curl}\mathbf{E} = -\frac{1}{c}\frac{\partial\mathbf{H}}{\partial t} \qquad \operatorname{curl}\mathbf{H} = \frac{1}{c}\frac{\partial\mathbf{E}}{\partial t}$$

where c is the speed of light. Use these equations to prove the following:

(a) $\nabla \times (\nabla \times \mathbf{E}) = -\dfrac{1}{c^2}\dfrac{\partial^2\mathbf{E}}{\partial t^2}$

(b) $\nabla \times (\nabla \times \mathbf{H}) = -\dfrac{1}{c^2}\dfrac{\partial^2\mathbf{H}}{\partial t^2}$

(c) $\nabla^2\mathbf{E} = \dfrac{1}{c^2}\dfrac{\partial^2\mathbf{E}}{\partial t^2}$ [*Hint:* Use Exercise 29.]

(d) $\nabla^2\mathbf{H} = \dfrac{1}{c^2}\dfrac{\partial^2\mathbf{H}}{\partial t^2}$

37. We have seen that all vector fields of the form $\mathbf{F} = \nabla g$ satisfy the equation curl $\mathbf{F} = \mathbf{0}$ and that all vector fields of the form $\mathbf{F} = \operatorname{curl}\mathbf{G}$ satisfy the equation div $\mathbf{F} = 0$ (assuming continuity of the appropriate partial derivatives). This suggests the question: Are there any equations that all functions of the form $f = \operatorname{div}\mathbf{G}$ must satisfy? Show that the answer to this question is "No" by proving that *every* continuous function f on $\mathbb{R}^3$ is the divergence of some vector field. [*Hint:* Let $\mathbf{G}(x, y, z) = \langle g(x, y, z), 0, 0 \rangle$, where $g(x, y, z) = \int_0^x f(t, y, z)\, dt$.]

17.6 Parametric Surfaces and Their Areas

In Section 9.2 we found the area of a surface of revolution and in Section 16.6 we found the area of a surface with the equation $z = f(x, y)$. Here we discuss more general surfaces, called *parametric surfaces*, and compute their areas.

Parametric Surfaces

In much the same way that we describe a space curve by a vector function $\mathbf{r}(t)$ of a single parameter t, we can describe a surface by a vector function $\mathbf{r}(u, v)$ of two parameters u and v. We suppose that

$$\boxed{1} \qquad \mathbf{r}(u, v) = x(u, v)\,\mathbf{i} + y(u, v)\,\mathbf{j} + z(u, v)\,\mathbf{k}$$

is a vector-valued function defined on a region D in the uv-plane. So x, y, and z, the component functions of $\mathbf{r}$, are functions of the two variables u and v with domain D. The set of all points (x, y, z) in $\mathbb{R}^3$ such that

$$\boxed{2} \qquad x = x(u, v) \qquad y = y(u, v) \qquad z = z(u, v)$$

and (u, v) varies throughout D, is called a **parametric surface** S and Equations 2 are called **parametric equations** of S. Each choice of u and v gives a point on S; by making all choices, we get all of S. In other words, the surface S is traced out by the tip of the position vector $\mathbf{r}(u, v)$ as (u, v) moves throughout the region D. (See Figure 1.)

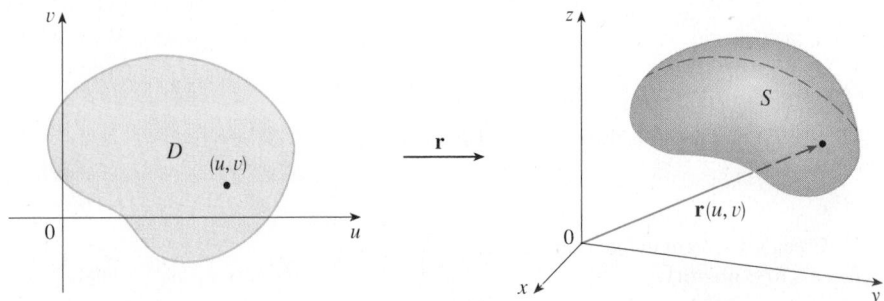

FIGURE 1
A parametric surface

EXAMPLE 1 Identify and sketch the surface with vector equation

$$\mathbf{r}(u, v) = 2 \cos u\,\mathbf{i} + v\,\mathbf{j} + 2 \sin u\,\mathbf{k}$$

SOLUTION The parametric equations for this surface are

$$x = 2 \cos u \qquad y = v \qquad z = 2 \sin u$$

So for any point (x, y, z) on the surface, we have

$$x^2 + z^2 = 4 \cos^2 u + 4 \sin^2 u = 4$$

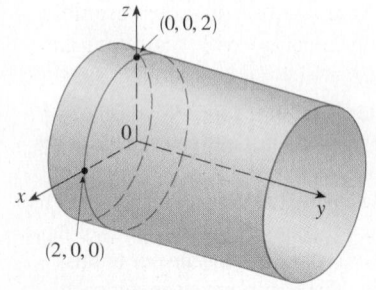

FIGURE 2

This means that vertical cross-sections parallel to the xz-plane (that is, with y constant) are all circles with radius 2. Since $y = v$ and no restriction is placed on v, the surface is a circular cylinder with radius 2 whose axis is the y-axis (see Figure 2). ▬

FIGURE 3

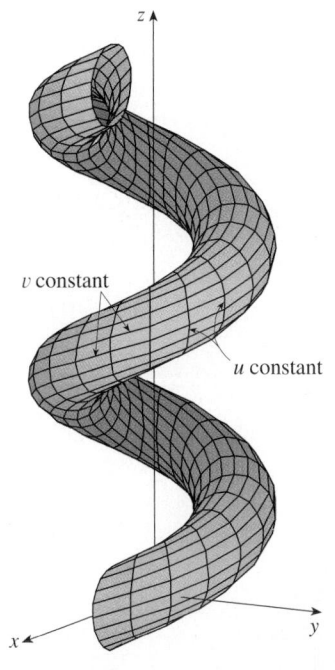

v constant

u constant

FIGURE 5

In Example 1 we placed no restrictions on the parameters u and v and so we obtained the entire cylinder. If, for instance, we restrict u and v by writing the parameter domain as

$$0 \leqslant u \leqslant \pi/2 \qquad 0 \leqslant v \leqslant 3$$

then $x \geqslant 0$, $z \geqslant 0$, $0 \leqslant y \leqslant 3$, and we get the quarter-cylinder with length 3 illustrated in Figure 3.

If a parametric surface S is given by a vector function $\mathbf{r}(u, v)$, then there are two useful families of curves that lie on S, one family with u constant and the other with v constant. These families correspond to vertical and horizontal lines in the uv-plane. If we keep u constant by putting $u = u_0$, then $\mathbf{r}(u_0, v)$ becomes a vector function of the single parameter v and defines a curve C_1 lying on S. (See Figure 4.)

Visual 17.6 shows animated versions of Figures 4 and 5, with moving grid curves, for several parametric surfaces.

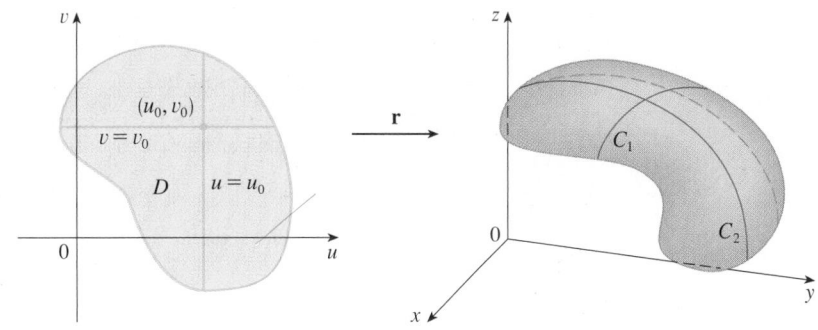

FIGURE 4

Similarly, if we keep v constant by putting $v = v_0$, we get a curve C_2 given by $\mathbf{r}(u, v_0)$ that lies on S. We call these curves **grid curves**. (In Example 1, for instance, the grid curves obtained by letting u be constant are horizontal lines whereas the grid curves with v constant are circles.) In fact, when a computer graphs a parametric surface, it usually depicts the surface by plotting these grid curves, as we see in the following example.

EXAMPLE 2 Use a computer algebra system to graph the surface

$$\mathbf{r}(u, v) = \langle (2 + \sin v) \cos u, (2 + \sin v) \sin u, u + \cos v \rangle$$

Which grid curves have u constant? Which have v constant?

SOLUTION We graph the portion of the surface with parameter domain $0 \leqslant u \leqslant 4\pi$, $0 \leqslant v \leqslant 2\pi$ in Figure 5. It has the appearance of a spiral tube. To identify the grid curves, we write the corresponding parametric equations:

$$x = (2 + \sin v) \cos u \qquad y = (2 + \sin v) \sin u \qquad z = u + \cos v$$

If v is constant, then $\sin v$ and $\cos v$ are constant, so the parametric equations resemble those of the helix in Example 4 in Section 14.1. So the grid curves with v constant are the spiral curves in Figure 5. We deduce that the grid curves with u constant must be the curves that look like circles in the figure. Further evidence for this assertion is that if u is kept constant, $u = u_0$, then the equation $z = u_0 + \cos v$ shows that the z-values vary from $u_0 - 1$ to $u_0 + 1$. ▬

In Examples 1 and 2 we were given a vector equation and asked to graph the corresponding parametric surface. In the following examples, however, we are given the more challenging problem of finding a vector function to represent a given surface. In the rest of this chapter we will often need to do exactly that.

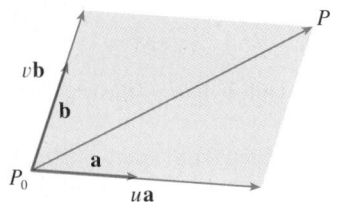

FIGURE 6

EXAMPLE 3 Find a vector function that represents the plane that passes through the point P_0 with position vector $\mathbf{r}_0$ and that contains two nonparallel vectors $\mathbf{a}$ and $\mathbf{b}$.

SOLUTION If P is any point in the plane, we can get from P_0 to P by moving a certain distance in the direction of $\mathbf{a}$ and another distance in the direction of $\mathbf{b}$. So there are scalars u and v such that $\overrightarrow{P_0P} = u\mathbf{a} + v\mathbf{b}$. (Figure 6 illustrates how this works, by means of the Parallelogram Law, for the case where u and v are positive. See also Exercise 38 in Section 13.2.) If $\mathbf{r}$ is the position vector of P, then

$$\mathbf{r} = \overrightarrow{OP_0} + \overrightarrow{P_0P} = \mathbf{r}_0 + u\mathbf{a} + v\mathbf{b}$$

So the vector equation of the plane can be written as

$$\mathbf{r}(u, v) = \mathbf{r}_0 + u\mathbf{a} + v\mathbf{b}$$

where u and v are real numbers.

If we write $\mathbf{r} = \langle x, y, z \rangle$, $\mathbf{r}_0 = \langle x_0, y_0, z_0 \rangle$, $\mathbf{a} = \langle a_1, a_2, a_3 \rangle$, and $\mathbf{b} = \langle b_1, b_2, b_3 \rangle$, then we can write the parametric equations of the plane through the point (x_0, y_0, z_0) as follows:

$$x = x_0 + ua_1 + vb_1 \qquad y = y_0 + ua_2 + vb_2 \qquad z = z_0 + ua_3 + vb_3$$

EXAMPLE 4 Find a parametric representation of the sphere

$$x^2 + y^2 + z^2 = a^2$$

SOLUTION The sphere has a simple representation $\rho = a$ in spherical coordinates, so let's choose the angles ϕ and θ in spherical coordinates as the parameters (see Section 13.7). Then, putting $\rho = a$ in the equations for conversion from spherical to rectangular coordinates (Equations 13.7.3), we obtain

$$x = a \sin \phi \cos \theta \qquad y = a \sin \phi \sin \theta \qquad z = a \cos \phi$$

as the parametric equations of the sphere. The corresponding vector equation is

$$\mathbf{r}(\phi, \theta) = a \sin \phi \cos \theta \, \mathbf{i} + a \sin \phi \sin \theta \, \mathbf{j} + a \cos \phi \, \mathbf{k}$$

We have $0 \leqslant \phi \leqslant \pi$ and $0 \leqslant \theta \leqslant 2\pi$, so the parameter domain is the rectangle $D = [0, \pi] \times [0, 2\pi]$. The grid curves with ϕ constant are the circles of constant latitude (including the equator). The grid curves with θ constant are the meridians (semicircles), which connect the north and south poles.

|||| One of the uses of parametric surfaces is in computer graphics. Figure 7 shows the result of trying to graph the sphere $x^2 + y^2 + z^2 = 1$ by solving the equation for z and graphing the top and bottom hemispheres separately. Part of the sphere appears to be missing because of the rectangular grid system used by the computer. The much better picture in Figure 8 was produced by a computer using the parametric equations found in Example 4.

FIGURE 7

FIGURE 8

EXAMPLE 5 Find a parametric representation for the cylinder

$$x^2 + y^2 = 4 \qquad 0 \le z \le 1$$

SOLUTION The cylinder has a simple representation $r = 2$ in cylindrical coordinates, so we choose as parameters θ and z in cylindrical coordinates. Then the parametric equations of the cylinder are

$$x = 2\cos\theta \qquad y = 2\sin\theta \qquad z = z$$

where $0 \le \theta \le 2\pi$ and $0 \le z \le 1$.

EXAMPLE 6 Find a vector function that represents the elliptic paraboloid $z = x^2 + 2y^2$.

SOLUTION If we regard x and y as parameters, then the parametric equations are simply

$$x = x \qquad y = y \qquad z = x^2 + 2y^2$$

and the vector equation is

$$\mathbf{r}(x, y) = x\,\mathbf{i} + y\,\mathbf{j} + (x^2 + 2y^2)\,\mathbf{k}$$

<table><tr><td>TEC</td><td>In Module 17.6 you can investigate several families of parametric surfaces.</td></tr></table>

In general, a surface given as the graph of a function of x and y, that is, with an equation of the form $z = f(x, y)$, can always be regarded as a parametric surface by taking x and y as parameters and writing the parametric equations as

$$x = x \qquad y = y \qquad z = f(x, y)$$

Parametric representations (also called parametrizations) of surfaces are not unique. The next example shows two ways to parametrize a cone.

EXAMPLE 7 Find a parametric representation for the surface $z = 2\sqrt{x^2 + y^2}$, that is, the top half of the cone $z^2 = 4x^2 + 4y^2$.

SOLUTION 1 One possible representation is obtained by choosing x and y as parameters:

$$x = x \qquad y = y \qquad z = 2\sqrt{x^2 + y^2}$$

So the vector equation is

$$\mathbf{r}(x, y) = x\,\mathbf{i} + y\,\mathbf{j} + 2\sqrt{x^2 + y^2}\,\mathbf{k}$$

|||| For some purposes the parametric representations in Solutions 1 and 2 are equally good, but Solution 2 might be preferable in certain situations. If we are interested only in the part of the cone that lies below the plane $z = 1$, for instance, all we have to do in Solution 2 is change the parameter domain to

$$0 \le r \le \tfrac{1}{2} \qquad 0 \le \theta \le 2\pi$$

SOLUTION 2 Another representation results from choosing as parameters the polar coordinates r and θ. A point (x, y, z) on the cone satisfies $x = r\cos\theta$, $y = r\sin\theta$, and $z = 2\sqrt{x^2 + y^2} = 2r$. So a vector equation for the cone is

$$\mathbf{r}(r, \theta) = r\cos\theta\,\mathbf{i} + r\sin\theta\,\mathbf{j} + 2r\,\mathbf{k}$$

where $r \ge 0$ and $0 \le \theta \le 2\pi$.

|||| **Surfaces of Revolution**

Surfaces of revolution can be represented parametrically and thus graphed using a computer. For instance, let's consider the surface S obtained by rotating the curve $y = f(x)$, $a \le x \le b$, about the x-axis, where $f(x) \ge 0$. Let θ be the angle of rotation as shown in

FIGURE 9

FIGURE 10

Figure 9. If (x, y, z) is a point on S, then

$$\boxed{3} \qquad x = x \qquad y = f(x) \cos \theta \qquad z = f(x) \sin \theta$$

Therefore, we take x and θ as parameters and regard Equations 3 as parametric equations of S. The parameter domain is given by $a \leqslant x \leqslant b$, $0 \leqslant \theta \leqslant 2\pi$.

EXAMPLE 8 Find parametric equations for the surface generated by rotating the curve $y = \sin x$, $0 \leqslant x \leqslant 2\pi$, about the x-axis. Use these equations to graph the surface of revolution.

SOLUTION From Equations 3, the parametric equations are

$$x = x \qquad y = \sin x \cos \theta \qquad z = \sin x \sin \theta$$

and the parameter domain is $0 \leqslant x \leqslant 2\pi$, $0 \leqslant \theta \leqslant 2\pi$. Using a computer to plot these equations and rotate the image, we obtain the graph in Figure 10.

We can adapt Equations 3 to represent a surface obtained through revolution about the y- or z-axis. (See Exercise 28.)

||||| **Tangent Planes**

We now find the tangent plane to a parametric surface S traced out by a vector function

$$\mathbf{r}(u, v) = x(u, v)\,\mathbf{i} + y(u, v)\,\mathbf{j} + z(u, v)\,\mathbf{k}$$

at a point P_0 with position vector $\mathbf{r}(u_0, v_0)$. If we keep u constant by putting $u = u_0$, then $\mathbf{r}(u_0, v)$ becomes a vector function of the single parameter v and defines a grid curve C_1 lying on S. (See Figure 11.) The tangent vector to C_1 at P_0 is obtained by taking the partial derivative of $\mathbf{r}$ with respect to v:

$$\boxed{4} \qquad \mathbf{r}_v = \frac{\partial x}{\partial v}(u_0, v_0)\,\mathbf{i} + \frac{\partial y}{\partial v}(u_0, v_0)\,\mathbf{j} + \frac{\partial z}{\partial v}(u_0, v_0)\,\mathbf{k}$$

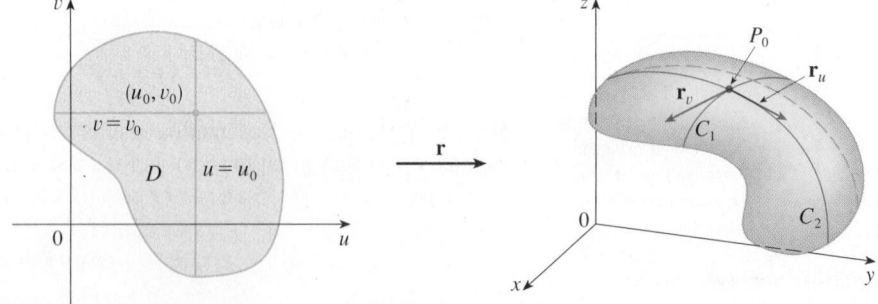

FIGURE 11

Similarly, if we keep v constant by putting $v = v_0$, we get a grid curve C_2 given by $\mathbf{r}(u, v_0)$ that lies on S, and its tangent vector at P_0 is

$$\boxed{5} \qquad \mathbf{r}_u = \frac{\partial x}{\partial u}(u_0, v_0)\,\mathbf{i} + \frac{\partial y}{\partial u}(u_0, v_0)\,\mathbf{j} + \frac{\partial z}{\partial u}(u_0, v_0)\,\mathbf{k}$$

If $\mathbf{r}_u \times \mathbf{r}_v$ is not $\mathbf{0}$, then the surface S is called **smooth** (it has no "corners"). For a smooth surface, the **tangent plane** is the plane that contains the tangent vectors $\mathbf{r}_u$ and $\mathbf{r}_v$, and the vector $\mathbf{r}_u \times \mathbf{r}_v$ is a normal vector to the tangent plane.

|||| Figure 12 shows the self-intersecting surface in Example 9 and its tangent plane at $(1, 1, 3)$.

EXAMPLE 9 Find the tangent plane to the surface with parametric equations $x = u^2$, $y = v^2$, $z = u + 2v$ at the point $(1, 1, 3)$.

SOLUTION We first compute the tangent vectors:

$$\mathbf{r}_u = \frac{\partial x}{\partial u}\mathbf{i} + \frac{\partial y}{\partial u}\mathbf{j} + \frac{\partial z}{\partial u}\mathbf{k} = 2u\,\mathbf{i} + \mathbf{k}$$

$$\mathbf{r}_v = \frac{\partial x}{\partial v}\mathbf{i} + \frac{\partial y}{\partial v}\mathbf{j} + \frac{\partial z}{\partial v}\mathbf{k} = 2v\,\mathbf{j} + 2\,\mathbf{k}$$

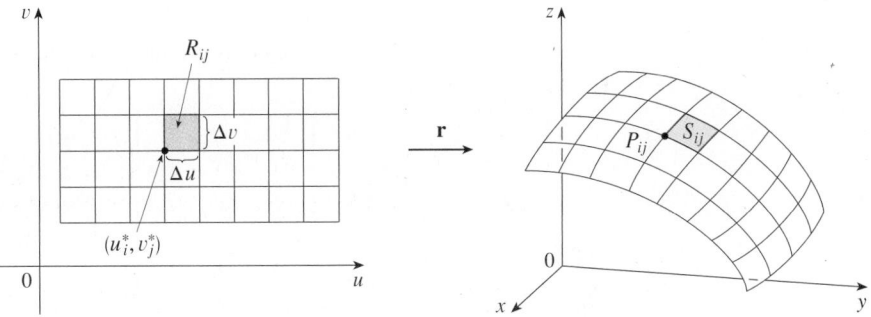

FIGURE 12

Thus, a normal vector to the tangent plane is

$$\mathbf{r}_u \times \mathbf{r}_v = \begin{vmatrix} \mathbf{i} & \mathbf{j} & \mathbf{k} \\ 2u & 0 & 1 \\ 0 & 2v & 2 \end{vmatrix} = -2v\,\mathbf{i} - 4u\,\mathbf{j} + 4uv\,\mathbf{k}$$

Notice that the point $(1, 1, 3)$ corresponds to the parameter values $u = 1$ and $v = 1$, so the normal vector there is

$$-2\,\mathbf{i} - 4\,\mathbf{j} + 4\,\mathbf{k}$$

Therefore, an equation of the tangent plane at $(1, 1, 3)$ is

$$-2(x - 1) - 4(y - 1) + 4(z - 3) = 0$$

or

$$x + 2y - 2z + 3 = 0$$

|||| Surface Area

Now we define the surface area of a general parametric surface given by Equation 1. For simplicity we start by considering a surface whose parameter domain D is a rectangle, and we divide it into subrectangles R_{ij}. Let's choose (u_i^*, v_j^*) to be the lower left corner of R_{ij}. (See Figure 13.) The part S_{ij} of the surface S that corresponds to R_{ij} is called a *patch* and has the point P_{ij} with position vector $\mathbf{r}(u_i^*, v_j^*)$ as one of its corners. Let

$$\mathbf{r}_u^* = \mathbf{r}_u(u_i^*, v_j^*) \qquad \text{and} \qquad \mathbf{r}_v^* = \mathbf{r}_v(u_i^*, v_j^*)$$

be the tangent vectors at P_{ij} as given by Equations 5 and 4.

FIGURE 13

The image of the subrectangle R_{ij} is the patch S_{ij}.

(a)

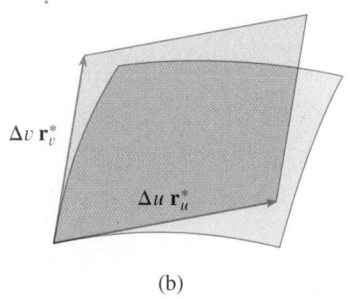

$\Delta v\ \mathbf{r}_v^*$

$\Delta u\ \mathbf{r}_u^*$

(b)

FIGURE 14

Approximating a patch
by a parallelogram

Figure 14(a) shows how the two edges of the patch that meet at P_{ij} can be approximated by vectors. These vectors, in turn, can be approximated by the vectors $\Delta u\ \mathbf{r}_u^*$ and $\Delta v\ \mathbf{r}_v^*$ because partial derivatives can be approximated by difference quotients. So we approximate S_{ij} by the parallelogram determined by the vectors $\Delta u\ \mathbf{r}_u^*$ and $\Delta v\ \mathbf{r}_v^*$. This parallelogram is shown in Figure 14(b) and lies in the tangent plane to S at P_{ij}. The area of this parallelogram is

$$\left|(\Delta u\ \mathbf{r}_u^*) \times (\Delta v\ \mathbf{r}_v^*)\right| = \left|\mathbf{r}_u^* \times \mathbf{r}_v^*\right| \Delta u\ \Delta v$$

and so an approximation to the area of S is

$$\sum_{i=1}^{m} \sum_{j=1}^{n} \left|\mathbf{r}_u^* \times \mathbf{r}_v^*\right| \Delta u\ \Delta v$$

Our intuition tells us that this approximation gets better as we increase the number of subrectangles, and we recognize the double sum as a Riemann sum for the double integral $\iint_D \left|\mathbf{r}_u \times \mathbf{r}_v\right| du\ dv$. This motivates the following definition.

6 **Definition** If a smooth parametric surface S is given by the equation

$$\mathbf{r}(u, v) = x(u, v)\ \mathbf{i} + y(u, v)\ \mathbf{j} + z(u, v)\ \mathbf{k} \qquad (u, v) \in D$$

and S is covered just once as (u, v) ranges throughout the parameter domain D, then the **surface area** of S is

$$A(S) = \iint_D \left|\mathbf{r}_u \times \mathbf{r}_v\right| dA$$

where $\quad \mathbf{r}_u = \dfrac{\partial x}{\partial u}\mathbf{i} + \dfrac{\partial y}{\partial u}\mathbf{j} + \dfrac{\partial z}{\partial u}\mathbf{k} \qquad \mathbf{r}_v = \dfrac{\partial x}{\partial v}\mathbf{i} + \dfrac{\partial y}{\partial v}\mathbf{j} + \dfrac{\partial z}{\partial v}\mathbf{k}$

EXAMPLE 10 Find the surface area of a sphere of radius a.

SOLUTION In Example 4 we found the parametric representation

$$x = a \sin \phi\ \cos \theta \qquad y = a \sin \phi\ \sin \theta \qquad z = a \cos \phi$$

where the parameter domain is

$$D = \{(\phi, \theta) \mid 0 \le \phi \le \pi,\ 0 \le \theta \le 2\pi\}$$

We first compute the cross product of the tangent vectors:

$$\mathbf{r}_\phi \times \mathbf{r}_\theta = \begin{vmatrix} \mathbf{i} & \mathbf{j} & \mathbf{k} \\ \dfrac{\partial x}{\partial \phi} & \dfrac{\partial y}{\partial \phi} & \dfrac{\partial z}{\partial \phi} \\ \dfrac{\partial x}{\partial \theta} & \dfrac{\partial y}{\partial \theta} & \dfrac{\partial z}{\partial \theta} \end{vmatrix} = \begin{vmatrix} \mathbf{i} & \mathbf{j} & \mathbf{k} \\ a \cos \phi\ \cos \theta & a \cos \phi\ \sin \theta & -a \sin \phi \\ -a \sin \phi\ \sin \theta & a \sin \phi\ \cos \theta & 0 \end{vmatrix}$$

$$= a^2 \sin^2\phi\ \cos \theta\ \mathbf{i} + a^2 \sin^2\phi\ \sin \theta\ \mathbf{j} + a^2 \sin \phi\ \cos \phi\ \mathbf{k}$$

Thus

$$|\mathbf{r}_\phi \times \mathbf{r}_\theta| = \sqrt{a^4 \sin^4\phi \, \cos^2\theta + a^4 \sin^4\phi \, \sin^2\theta + a^4 \sin^2\phi \, \cos^2\phi}$$

$$= \sqrt{a^4 \sin^4\phi + a^4 \sin^2\phi \, \cos^2\phi} = a^2\sqrt{\sin^2\phi} = a^2 \sin\phi$$

since $\sin\phi \geq 0$ for $0 \leq \phi \leq \pi$. Therefore, by Definition 6, the area of the sphere is

$$A = \iint_D |\mathbf{r}_\phi \times \mathbf{r}_\theta|\, dA = \int_0^{2\pi} \int_0^\pi a^2 \sin\phi \, d\phi \, d\theta$$

$$= a^2 \int_0^{2\pi} d\theta \int_0^\pi \sin\phi \, d\phi = a^2(2\pi)2 = 4\pi a^2$$

▓ Surface Area of the Graph of a Function

For the special case of a surface S with equation $z = f(x, y)$, where (x, y) lies in D and f has continuous partial derivatives, we take x and y as parameters. The parametric equations are

$$x = x \qquad y = y \qquad z = f(x, y)$$

so

$$\mathbf{r}_x = \mathbf{i} + \left(\frac{\partial f}{\partial x}\right)\mathbf{k} \qquad \mathbf{r}_y = \mathbf{j} + \left(\frac{\partial f}{\partial y}\right)\mathbf{k}$$

and

$$\boxed{7} \qquad \mathbf{r}_x \times \mathbf{r}_y = \begin{vmatrix} \mathbf{i} & \mathbf{j} & \mathbf{k} \\ 1 & 0 & \dfrac{\partial f}{\partial x} \\ 0 & 1 & \dfrac{\partial f}{\partial y} \end{vmatrix} = -\frac{\partial f}{\partial x}\mathbf{i} - \frac{\partial f}{\partial y}\mathbf{j} + \mathbf{k}$$

Thus, we have

$$\boxed{8} \qquad |\mathbf{r}_x \times \mathbf{r}_y| = \sqrt{\left(\frac{\partial f}{\partial x}\right)^2 + \left(\frac{\partial f}{\partial y}\right)^2 + 1} = \sqrt{1 + \left(\frac{\partial z}{\partial x}\right)^2 + \left(\frac{\partial z}{\partial y}\right)^2}$$

▓ Notice the similarity between the surface area formula in Equation 9 and the arc length formula

$$L = \int_a^b \sqrt{1 + \left(\frac{dy}{dx}\right)^2}\, dx$$

from Section 9.1.

and the surface area formula in Definition 6 becomes

$$\boxed{9} \qquad A(S) = \iint_D \sqrt{1 + \left(\frac{\partial z}{\partial x}\right)^2 + \left(\frac{\partial z}{\partial y}\right)^2}\, dA$$

EXAMPLE 11 Find the area of the part of the paraboloid $z = x^2 + y^2$ that lies under the plane $z = 9$.

SOLUTION The plane intersects the paraboloid in the circle $x^2 + y^2 = 9$, $z = 9$. Therefore, the given surface lies above the disk D with center the origin and radius 3. (See Figure 15.) Using Formula 9, we have

$$A = \iint_D \sqrt{1 + \left(\frac{\partial z}{\partial x}\right)^2 + \left(\frac{\partial z}{\partial y}\right)^2}\, dA = \iint_D \sqrt{1 + (2x)^2 + (2y)^2}\, dA$$

$$= \iint_D \sqrt{1 + 4(x^2 + y^2)}\, dA$$

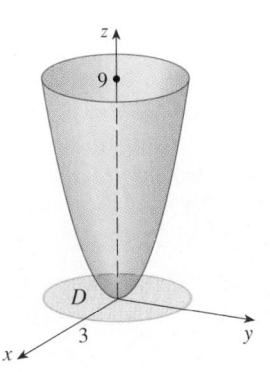

FIGURE 15

Converting to polar coordinates, we obtain

$$A = \int_0^{2\pi} \int_0^3 \sqrt{1 + 4r^2}\, r\, dr\, d\theta = \int_0^{2\pi} d\theta \int_0^3 r\sqrt{1 + 4r^2}\, dr$$

$$= 2\pi \left(\tfrac{1}{8}\right)\tfrac{2}{3}(1 + 4r^2)^{3/2}\Big]_0^3 = \frac{\pi}{6}\left(37\sqrt{37} - 1\right)$$

The question remains whether our definition of surface area (6) is consistent with the surface area formula from single-variable calculus (9.2.4).

We consider the surface S obtained by rotating the curve $y = f(x)$, $a \le x \le b$, about the x-axis, where $f(x) \ge 0$ and f' is continuous. From Equations 3 we know that parametric equations of S are

$$x = x \qquad y = f(x)\cos\theta \qquad z = f(x)\sin\theta \qquad a \le x \le b \qquad 0 \le \theta \le 2\pi$$

To compute the surface area of S we need the tangent vectors

$$\mathbf{r}_x = \mathbf{i} + f'(x)\cos\theta\,\mathbf{j} + f'(x)\sin\theta\,\mathbf{k}$$

$$\mathbf{r}_\theta = -f(x)\sin\theta\,\mathbf{j} + f(x)\cos\theta\,\mathbf{k}$$

Thus

$$\mathbf{r}_x \times \mathbf{r}_\theta = \begin{vmatrix} \mathbf{i} & \mathbf{j} & \mathbf{k} \\ 1 & f'(x)\cos\theta & f'(x)\sin\theta \\ 0 & -f(x)\sin\theta & f(x)\cos\theta \end{vmatrix}$$

$$= f(x)f'(x)\,\mathbf{i} - f(x)\cos\theta\,\mathbf{j} - f(x)\sin\theta\,\mathbf{k}$$

and so
$$|\mathbf{r}_x \times \mathbf{r}_\theta| = \sqrt{[f(x)]^2[f'(x)]^2 + [f(x)]^2\cos^2\theta + [f(x)]^2\sin^2\theta}$$

$$= \sqrt{[f(x)]^2[1 + (f'(x))^2]} = f(x)\sqrt{1 + [f'(x)]^2}$$

because $f(x) \ge 0$. Therefore, the area of S is

$$A = \iint_D |\mathbf{r}_x \times \mathbf{r}_\theta|\, dA = \int_0^{2\pi}\int_a^b f(x)\sqrt{1 + [f'(x)]^2}\, dx\, d\theta$$

$$= 2\pi \int_a^b f(x)\sqrt{1 + [f'(x)]^2}\, dx$$

This is precisely the formula that was used to define the area of a surface of revolution in single-variable calculus (9.2.4).

17.6 Exercises

1–4 ▐▐▐▐ Identify the surface with the given vector equation.

1. $\mathbf{r}(u, v) = u\cos v\,\mathbf{i} + u\sin v\,\mathbf{j} + u^2\,\mathbf{k}$

2. $\mathbf{r}(u, v) = (1 + 2u)\,\mathbf{i} + (-u + 3v)\,\mathbf{j} + (2 + 4u + 5v)\,\mathbf{k}$

3. $\mathbf{r}(x, \theta) = \langle x, \cos\theta, \sin\theta \rangle$

4. $\mathbf{r}(x, \theta) = \langle x, x\cos\theta, x\sin\theta \rangle$

5–10 ▐▐▐▐ Use a computer to graph the parametric surface. Get a printout and indicate on it which grid curves have u constant and which have v constant.

5. $\mathbf{r}(u, v) = \langle u^2 + 1, v^3 + 1, u + v \rangle$,
$-1 \le u \le 1$, $-1 \le v \le 1$

6. $\mathbf{r}(u, v) = \langle u + v, u^2, v^2 \rangle$,
$-1 \le u \le 1$, $-1 \le v \le 1$

7. $\mathbf{r}(u, v) = \langle \cos^3 u \, \cos^3 v, \sin^3 u \, \cos^3 v, \sin^3 v \rangle$,
$0 \leqslant u \leqslant \pi, \ 0 \leqslant v \leqslant 2\pi$

8. $\mathbf{r}(u, v) = \langle \cos u \sin v, \sin u \sin v, \cos v + \ln \tan(v/2) \rangle$,
$0 \leqslant u \leqslant 2\pi, \ 0.1 \leqslant v \leqslant 6.2$

9. $x = \cos u \sin 2v, \quad y = \sin u \sin 2v, \quad z = \sin v$

10. $x = u \sin u \cos v, \quad y = u \cos u \cos v, \quad z = u \sin v$

11–16 ▓ Match the equations with the graphs labeled I–VI and give reasons for your answers. Determine which families of grid curves have u constant and which have v constant.

11. $\mathbf{r}(u, v) = \cos v \, \mathbf{i} + \sin v \, \mathbf{j} + u \, \mathbf{k}$

12. $\mathbf{r}(u, v) = u \cos v \, \mathbf{i} + u \sin v \, \mathbf{j} + u \, \mathbf{k}$

13. $\mathbf{r}(u, v) = u \cos v \, \mathbf{i} + u \sin v \, \mathbf{j} + v \, \mathbf{k}$

14. $x = u^3, \quad y = u \sin v, \quad z = u \cos v$

15. $x = (u - \sin u) \cos v, \quad y = (1 - \cos u) \sin v, \quad z = u$

16. $x = (1 - u)(3 + \cos v) \cos 4\pi u$,
$y = (1 - u)(3 + \cos v) \sin 4\pi u$,
$z = 3u + (1 - u) \sin v$

17–24 ▓ Find a parametric representation for the surface.

17. The plane that passes through the point $(1, 2, -3)$ and contains the vectors $\mathbf{i} + \mathbf{j} - \mathbf{k}$ and $\mathbf{i} - \mathbf{j} + \mathbf{k}$.

18. The lower half of the ellipsoid $2x^2 + 4y^2 + z^2 = 1$

19. The part of the hyperboloid $x^2 + y^2 - z^2 = 1$ that lies to the right of the xz-plane

20. The part of the elliptic paraboloid $x + y^2 + 2z^2 = 4$ that lies in front of the plane $x = 0$

21. The part of the sphere $x^2 + y^2 + z^2 = 4$ that lies above the cone $z = \sqrt{x^2 + y^2}$

22. The part of the sphere $x^2 + y^2 + z^2 = 16$ that lies between the planes $z = -2$ and $z = 2$

23. The part of the cylinder $y^2 + z^2 = 16$ that lies between the planes $x = 0$ and $x = 5$

24. The part of the plane $z = x + 3$ that lies inside the cylinder $x^2 + y^2 = 1$

CAS **25–26** ▓ Use a computer algebra system to produce a graph that looks like the given one.

25.

26.

I

II

III

IV

V

VI

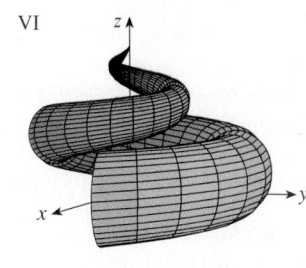

27. Find parametric equations for the surface obtained by rotating the curve $y = e^{-x}$, $0 \leqslant x \leqslant 3$, about the x-axis and use them to graph the surface.

28. Find parametric equations for the surface obtained by rotating the curve $x = 4y^2 - y^4$, $-2 \leqslant y \leqslant 2$, about the y-axis and use them to graph the surface.

29. (a) What happens to the spiral tube in Example 2 (see Figure 5) if we replace $\cos u$ by $\sin u$ and $\sin u$ by $\cos u$?
(b) What happens if we replace $\cos u$ by $\cos 2u$ and $\sin u$ by $\sin 2u$?

30. The surface with parametric equations

$$x = 2\cos\theta + r\cos(\theta/2)$$
$$y = 2\sin\theta + r\cos(\theta/2)$$
$$z = r\sin(\theta/2)$$

where $-\frac{1}{2} \le r \le \frac{1}{2}$ and $0 \le \theta \le 2\pi$, is called a **Möbius strip**. Graph this surface with several viewpoints. What is unusual about it?

31–34 ▓ Find an equation of the tangent plane to the given parametric surface at the specified point. If you have software that graphs parametric surfaces, use a computer to graph the surface and the tangent plane.

31. $x = u + v$, $y = 3u^2$, $z = u - v$; (2, 3, 0)

32. $x = u^2$, $y = v^2$, $z = uv$; $u = 1, v = 1$

33. $\mathbf{r}(u, v) = u^2\,\mathbf{i} + 2u\sin v\,\mathbf{j} + u\cos v\,\mathbf{k}$; $u = 1, v = 0$

34. $\mathbf{r}(u, v) = uv\,\mathbf{i} + u\sin v\,\mathbf{j} + v\cos u\,\mathbf{k}$; $u = 0, v = \pi$

35–45 ▓ Find the area of the surface.

35. The part of the plane $x + 2y + z = 4$ that lies inside the cylinder $x^2 + y^2 = 4$

36. The part of the plane with vector equation $\mathbf{r}(u, v) = \langle 1 + v, u - 2v, 3 - 5u + v \rangle$ that is given by $0 \le u \le 1, 0 \le v \le 1$

37. The part of the surface $z = xy$ that lies within the cylinder $x^2 + y^2 = 1$

38. The part of the surface $z = 1 + 3x + 2y^2$ that lies above the triangle with vertices (0, 0), (0, 1), and (2, 1)

39. The part of the hyperbolic paraboloid $z = y^2 - x^2$ that lies between the cylinders $x^2 + y^2 = 1$ and $x^2 + y^2 = 4$

40. The part of the paraboloid $x = y^2 + z^2$ that lies inside the cylinder $y^2 + z^2 = 9$

41. The part of the surface $y = 4x + z^2$ that lies between the planes $x = 0, x = 1, z = 0$, and $z = 1$

42. The part of the cylinder $x^2 + z^2 = a^2$ that lies inside the cylinder $x^2 + y^2 = a^2$

43. The part of the sphere $x^2 + y^2 + z^2 = a^2$ that lies inside the cylinder $x^2 + y^2 = ax$

44. The *helicoid* (or spiral ramp) with vector equation $\mathbf{r}(u, v) = u\cos v\,\mathbf{i} + u\sin v\,\mathbf{j} + v\,\mathbf{k}, 0 \le u \le 1, 0 \le v \le \pi$

45. The surface with parametric equations $x = uv, y = u + v, z = u - v, u^2 + v^2 \le 1$

46–47 ▓ Find the area of the surface correct to four decimal places by expressing the area in terms of a single integral and using your calculator to estimate the integral.

46. The part of the surface $z = \cos(x^2 + y^2)$ that lies inside the cylinder $x^2 + y^2 = 1$

47. The part of the surface $z = e^{-x^2-y^2}$ that lies above the disk $x^2 + y^2 \le 4$

48. Find, to four decimal places, the area of the part of the surface $z = (1 + x^2)/(1 + y^2)$ that lies above the square $|x| + |y| \le 1$. Illustrate by graphing this part of the surface.

49. (a) Use the Midpoint Rule for double integrals (see Section 16.1) with four squares to estimate the surface area of the portion of the paraboloid $z = x^2 + y^2$ that lies above the square $[0, 1] \times [0, 1]$.
  (b) Use a computer algebra system to approximate the surface area in part (a) to four decimal places. Compare with the answer to part (a).

50. Find the area of the surface with vector equation $\mathbf{r}(u, v) = \langle\cos^3u\cos^3v, \sin^3u\cos^3v, \sin^3v\rangle, 0 \le u \le \pi, 0 \le v \le 2\pi$. State your answer correct to four decimal places.

51. Find the exact area of the surface $z = 1 + 2x + 3y + 4y^2, 1 \le x \le 4, 0 \le y \le 1$.

52. (a) Set up, but do not evaluate, a double integral for the area of the surface with parametric equations $x = au\cos v$, $y = bu\sin v, z = u^2, 0 \le u \le 2, 0 \le v \le 2\pi$.
  (b) Eliminate the parameters to show that the surface is an elliptic paraboloid and set up another double integral for the surface area.
  (c) Use the parametric equations in part (a) with $a = 2$ and $b = 3$ to graph the surface.
  (d) For the case $a = 2, b = 3$, use a computer algebra system to find the surface area correct to four decimal places.

53. (a) Show that the parametric equations $x = a\sin u\cos v$, $y = b\sin u\sin v, z = c\cos u, 0 \le u \le \pi, 0 \le v \le 2\pi$, represent an ellipsoid.
  (b) Use the parametric equations in part (a) to graph the ellipsoid for the case $a = 1, b = 2, c = 3$.
  (c) Set up, but do not evaluate, a double integral for the surface area of the ellipsoid in part (b).

54. (a) Show that the parametric equations $x = a\cosh u\cos v$, $y = b\cosh u\sin v, z = c\sinh u$, represent a hyperboloid of one sheet.
  (b) Use the parametric equations in part (a) to graph the hyperboloid for the case $a = 1, b = 2, c = 3$.
  (c) Set up, but do not evaluate, a double integral for the surface area of the part of the hyperboloid in part (b) that lies between the planes $z = -3$ and $z = 3$.

CAS **55.** Find the area of the surface in Exercise 7 correct to four decimal places.

56. (a) Find a parametric representation for the torus obtained by rotating about the z-axis the circle in the xz-plane with center $(b, 0, 0)$ and radius $a < b$. [*Hint:* Take as parameters the angles θ and α shown in the figure.]

(b) Use the parametric equations found in part (a) to graph the torus for several values of a and b.

(c) Use the parametric representation from part (a) to find the surface area of the torus.

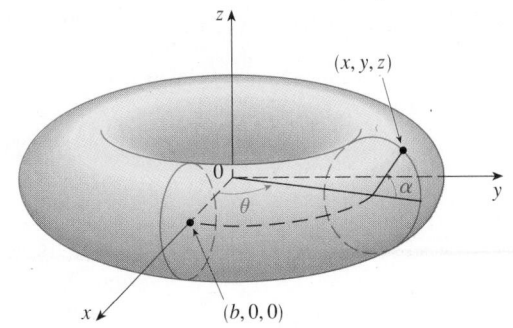

17.7 Surface Integrals

The relationship between surface integrals and surface area is much the same as the relationship between line integrals and arc length. Suppose f is a function of three variables whose domain includes a surface S. We divide S into patches S_{ij} with area ΔS_{ij}. We evaluate f at a point P_{ij}^* in each patch, multiply by the area ΔS_{ij}, and form the sum

$$\sum_{i=1}^{m} \sum_{j=1}^{n} f(P_{ij}^*) \, \Delta S_{ij}$$

Then we take the limit as the patch size approaches 0 and define the **surface integral of f over the surface S** as

$$\boxed{1} \qquad \iint_S f(x, y, z) \, dS = \lim_{m, n \to \infty} \sum_{i=1}^{m} \sum_{j=1}^{n} f(P_{ij}^*) \, \Delta S_{ij}$$

Notice the analogy with the definition of a line integral (17.2.2) and also the analogy with the definition of a double integral (16.1.5).

To evaluate the surface integral in Equation 1 we approximate the patch area ΔS_{ij} by the area ΔT_{ij} of an approximating parallelogram in the tangent plane, and the limit becomes a double integral. We now explain the details for two types of surfaces, graphs and parametric surfaces.

||| **Graphs** If the surface S is a graph of a function of two variables, then it has an equation of the form $z = g(x, y)$, $(x, y) \in D$, and is illustrated in Figure 1. We first assume that the parameter domain D is a rectangle and we divide it into smaller rectangles R_{ij} of equal size. The patch S_{ij} lies directly above the rectangle R_{ij} and the point P_{ij}^* in S_{ij} is of the form $(x_i^*, y_j^*, g(x_i^*, y_j^*))$. As with surface area in Section 16.6, we use the approximation

$$\Delta S_{ij} \approx \Delta T_{ij} = \sqrt{[g_x(x_i, y_j)]^2 + [g_y(x_i, y_j)]^2 + 1} \; \Delta A$$

In fact, it can be shown that, if f is continuous on S and g has continuous derivatives, then Definition 1 becomes

$$\iint_S f(x, y, z) \, dS = \lim_{m, n \to \infty} \sum_{i=1}^{m} \sum_{j=1}^{n} f(x_i^*, y_j^*, g(x_i^*, y_j^*)) \sqrt{[g_x(x_i, y_j)]^2 + [g_y(x_i, y_j)]^2 + 1} \; \Delta A$$

$$= \iint_D f(x, y, g(x, y)) \sqrt{[g_x(x, y)]^2 + [g_y(x, y)]^2 + 1} \; dA$$

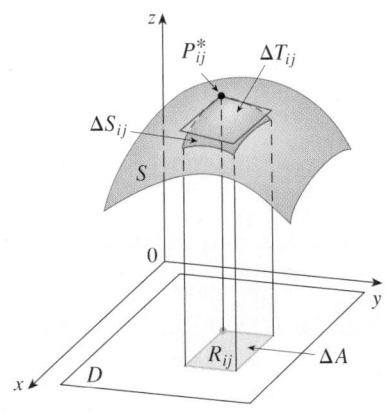

FIGURE 1

This formula is true even when D isn't a rectangle and is usually written in the following form.

$$\boxed{\; \fbox{2} \qquad \iint_S f(x, y, z)\, dS = \iint_D f(x, y, g(x, y)) \sqrt{\left(\frac{\partial z}{\partial x}\right)^2 + \left(\frac{\partial z}{\partial y}\right)^2 + 1}\; dA \;}$$

Similar formulas apply when it is more convenient to project S onto the yz-plane or xz-plane. For instance, if S is a surface with equation $y = h(x, z)$ and D is its projection on the xz-plane, then

$$\iint_S f(x, y, z)\, dS = \iint_D f(x, h(x, z), z) \sqrt{\left(\frac{\partial y}{\partial x}\right)^2 + \left(\frac{\partial y}{\partial z}\right)^2 + 1}\; dA$$

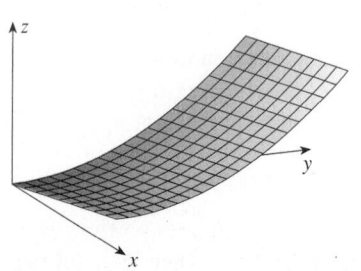

FIGURE 2

EXAMPLE 1 Evaluate $\iint_S y\, dS$, where S is the surface $z = x + y^2$, $0 \leqslant x \leqslant 1$, $0 \leqslant y \leqslant 2$. (See Figure 2.)

SOLUTION Since

$$\frac{\partial z}{\partial x} = 1 \qquad \text{and} \qquad \frac{\partial z}{\partial y} = 2y$$

Formula 2 gives

$$\iint_S y\, dS = \iint_D y \sqrt{1 + \left(\frac{\partial z}{\partial x}\right)^2 + \left(\frac{\partial z}{\partial y}\right)^2}\; dA$$

$$= \int_0^1 \int_0^2 y\sqrt{1 + 1 + 4y^2}\; dy\, dx$$

$$= \int_0^1 dx\, \sqrt{2} \int_0^2 y\sqrt{1 + 2y^2}\; dy$$

$$= \sqrt{2}\left(\tfrac{1}{4}\right)\tfrac{2}{3}(1 + 2y^2)^{3/2}\big]_0^2 = \frac{13\sqrt{2}}{3}$$

Surface integrals have applications similar to those for the integrals we have previously considered. For example, if a thin sheet (say, of aluminum foil) has the shape of a surface S and the density (mass per unit area) at the point (x, y, z) is $\rho(x, y, z)$, then the total **mass** of the sheet is

$$m = \iint_S \rho(x, y, z)\, dS$$

and the **center of mass** is $(\bar{x}, \bar{y}, \bar{z})$, where

$$\bar{x} = \frac{1}{m}\iint_S x\rho(x, y, z)\, dS \qquad \bar{y} = \frac{1}{m}\iint_S y\rho(x, y, z)\, dS \qquad \bar{z} = \frac{1}{m}\iint_S z\rho(x, y, z)\, dS$$

Moments of inertia can also be defined as before (see Exercise 37).

|||| **Parametric Surfaces** Suppose that a surface S has a vector equation

$$\mathbf{r}(u, v) = x(u, v)\, \mathbf{i} + y(u, v)\, \mathbf{j} + z(u, v)\, \mathbf{k} \qquad (u, v) \in D$$

We first assume that the parameter domain D is a rectangle and we divide it into subrectangles R_{ij} with dimensions Δu and Δv. Then the surface is divided into corresponding patches S_{ij} with areas ΔS_{ij}, as in Figure 3.

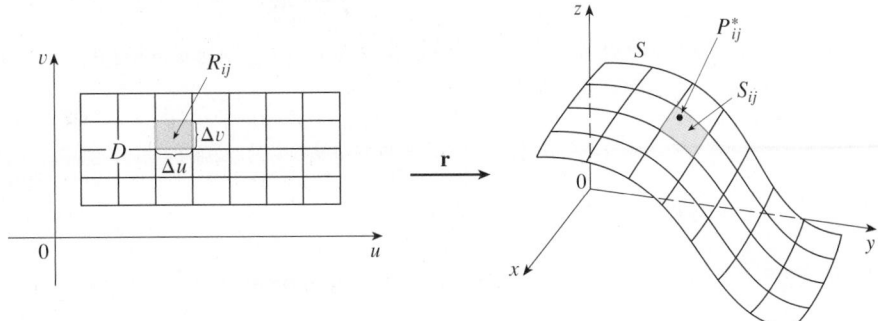

FIGURE 3

In our discussion of surface area in Section 17.6 we made the approximation

$$\Delta S_{ij} \approx \left| \mathbf{r}_u \times \mathbf{r}_v \right| \Delta u\, \Delta v$$

where

$$\mathbf{r}_u = \frac{\partial x}{\partial u}\mathbf{i} + \frac{\partial y}{\partial u}\mathbf{j} + \frac{\partial z}{\partial u}\mathbf{k} \qquad \mathbf{r}_v = \frac{\partial x}{\partial v}\mathbf{i} + \frac{\partial y}{\partial v}\mathbf{j} + \frac{\partial z}{\partial v}\mathbf{k}$$

are the tangent vectors at a corner of S_{ij}. If the components are continuous and $\mathbf{r}_u$ and $\mathbf{r}_v$ are nonzero and nonparallel in the interior of D, it can be shown from Definition 1, even when D is not a rectangle, that

|||| We assume that the surface is covered only once as (u, v) ranges throughout D. The value of the surface integral does not depend on the parametrization that is used.

$\boxed{3}$

$$\iint_S f(x, y, z)\, dS = \iint_D f(\mathbf{r}(u, v))\left| \mathbf{r}_u \times \mathbf{r}_v \right| dA$$

This should be compared with the formula for a line integral:

$$\int_C f(x, y, z)\, ds = \int_a^b f(\mathbf{r}(t))\left| \mathbf{r}'(t) \right| dt$$

Observe also that

$$\iint_S 1\, dS = \iint_D \left| \mathbf{r}_u \times \mathbf{r}_v \right| dA \doteq A(S)$$

Formula 3 allows us to compute a surface integral by converting it into a double integral over the parameter domain D. When using this formula, remember that $f(\mathbf{r}(u, v))$ is evaluated by writing $x = x(u, v)$, $y = y(u, v)$, and $z = z(u, v)$ in the formula for $f(x, y, z)$.

Any surface S with equation $z = g(x, y)$ can be regarded as a parametric surface with parametric equations

$$x = x \qquad y = y \qquad z = g(x, y)$$

and from Equation 17.6.8 we have

$$\left| \mathbf{r}_x \times \mathbf{r}_y \right| = \sqrt{1 + \left(\frac{\partial z}{\partial x} \right)^2 + \left(\frac{\partial z}{\partial y} \right)^2}$$

Therefore, in this case, Formula 3 becomes Formula 2.

EXAMPLE 2 Compute the surface integral $\iint_S x^2\, dS$, where S is the unit sphere $x^2 + y^2 + z^2 = 1$.

SOLUTION As in Example 4 in Section 17.6, we use the parametric representation

$$x = \sin \phi \cos \theta \quad y = \sin \phi \sin \theta \quad z = \cos \phi \quad 0 \le \phi \le \pi \quad 0 \le \theta \le 2\pi$$

that is, $\quad \mathbf{r}(\phi, \theta) = \sin \phi \cos \theta\, \mathbf{i} + \sin \phi \sin \theta\, \mathbf{j} + \cos \phi\, \mathbf{k}$

As in Example 10 in Section 17.6, we can compute that

$$|\mathbf{r}_\phi \times \mathbf{r}_\theta| = \sin \phi$$

Therefore, by Formula 3,

$$\iint_S x^2\, dS = \iint_D (\sin \phi \cos \theta)^2 \,|\mathbf{r}_\phi \times \mathbf{r}_\theta|\, dA$$

$$= \int_0^{2\pi} \int_0^\pi \sin^2\phi \cos^2\theta \sin \phi\, d\phi\, d\theta = \int_0^{2\pi} \cos^2\theta\, d\theta \int_0^\pi \sin^3\phi\, d\phi$$

$$= \int_0^{2\pi} \tfrac{1}{2}(1 + \cos 2\theta)\, d\theta \int_0^\pi (\sin \phi - \sin \phi \cos^2\phi)\, d\phi$$

$$= \tfrac{1}{2}\Big[\theta + \tfrac{1}{2}\sin 2\theta\Big]_0^{2\pi} \Big[-\cos \phi + \tfrac{1}{3}\cos^3\phi\Big]_0^\pi = \frac{4\pi}{3}$$

If S is a piecewise-smooth surface, that is, a finite union of smooth surfaces $S_1, S_2, \ldots,$ S_n that intersect only along their boundaries, then the surface integral of f over S is defined by

$$\iint_S f(x, y, z)\, dS = \iint_{S_1} f(x, y, z)\, dS + \cdots + \iint_{S_n} f(x, y, z)\, dS$$

EXAMPLE 3 Evaluate $\iint_S z\, dS$, where S is the surface whose sides S_1 are given by the cylinder $x^2 + y^2 = 1$, whose bottom S_2 is the disk $x^2 + y^2 \le 1$ in the plane $z = 0$, and whose top S_3 is the part of the plane $z = 1 + x$ that lies above S_2.

SOLUTION The surface S is shown in Figure 4. (We have changed the usual position of the axes to get a better look at S.) For S_1 we use θ and z as parameters (see Example 5 in Section 17.6) and write its parametric equations as

$$x = \cos \theta \quad y = \sin \theta \quad z = z$$

where $\quad 0 \le \theta \le 2\pi \quad$ and $\quad 0 \le z \le 1 + x = 1 + \cos \theta$

Therefore

$$\mathbf{r}_\theta \times \mathbf{r}_z = \begin{vmatrix} \mathbf{i} & \mathbf{j} & \mathbf{k} \\ -\sin \theta & \cos \theta & 0 \\ 0 & 0 & 1 \end{vmatrix} = \cos \theta\, \mathbf{i} + \sin \theta\, \mathbf{j}$$

and $\quad |\mathbf{r}_\theta \times \mathbf{r}_z| = \sqrt{\cos^2\theta + \sin^2\theta} = 1$

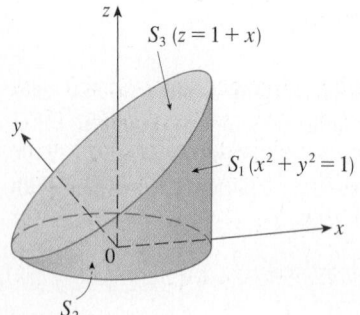

$S_3 \ (z = 1 + x)$

$S_1 \ (x^2 + y^2 = 1)$

S_2

FIGURE 4

Thus, the surface integral over S_1 is

$$\iint\limits_{S_1} z \, dS = \iint\limits_{D} z \, |\mathbf{r}_\theta \times \mathbf{r}_z| \, dA$$

$$= \int_0^{2\pi} \int_0^{1+\cos\theta} z \, dz \, d\theta = \int_0^{2\pi} \tfrac{1}{2}(1 + \cos\theta)^2 \, d\theta$$

$$= \tfrac{1}{2} \int_0^{2\pi} \left[1 + 2\cos\theta + \tfrac{1}{2}(1 + \cos 2\theta) \right] d\theta$$

$$= \tfrac{1}{2} \left[\tfrac{3}{2}\theta + 2\sin\theta + \tfrac{1}{4}\sin 2\theta \right]_0^{2\pi} = \frac{3\pi}{2}$$

Since S_2 lies in the plane $z = 0$, we have

$$\iint\limits_{S_2} z \, dS = \iint\limits_{S_2} 0 \, dS = 0$$

The top surface S_3 lies above the unit disk D and is part of the plane $z = 1 + x$. So, taking $g(x, y) = 1 + x$ in Formula 2 and converting to polar coordinates, we have

$$\iint\limits_{S_3} z \, dS = \iint\limits_{D} (1 + x) \sqrt{1 + \left(\frac{\partial z}{\partial x} \right)^2 + \left(\frac{\partial z}{\partial y} \right)^2} \, dA$$

$$= \int_0^{2\pi} \int_0^1 (1 + r\cos\theta) \sqrt{1 + 1 + 0} \, r \, dr \, d\theta$$

$$= \sqrt{2} \int_0^{2\pi} \int_0^1 (r + r^2 \cos\theta) \, dr \, d\theta$$

$$= \sqrt{2} \int_0^{2\pi} \left(\tfrac{1}{2} + \tfrac{1}{3}\cos\theta \right) d\theta = \sqrt{2} \left[\frac{\theta}{2} + \frac{\sin\theta}{3} \right]_0^{2\pi} = \sqrt{2}\,\pi$$

Therefore
$$\iint\limits_{S} z \, dS = \iint\limits_{S_1} z \, dS + \iint\limits_{S_2} z \, dS + \iint\limits_{S_3} z \, dS$$

$$= \frac{3\pi}{2} + 0 + \sqrt{2}\,\pi = \left(\tfrac{3}{2} + \sqrt{2} \right)\pi$$

||||| Oriented Surfaces

In order to define surface integrals of vector fields, we need to rule out nonorientable surfaces such as the Möbius strip shown in Figure 5. [It is named after the German geometer August Möbius (1790–1868).] You can construct one for yourself by taking a long rectangular strip of paper, giving it a half-twist, and taping the short edges together as in Figure 6. If an ant were to crawl along the Möbius strip starting at a point P, it would end up on the "other side" of the strip (that is, with its upper side pointing in the opposite direction). Then, if the ant continued to crawl in the same direction, it would end up back

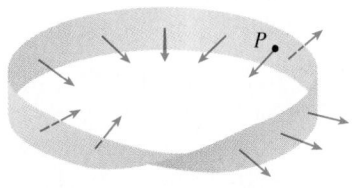

FIGURE 5

A Möbius strip

Visual 17.7 shows a Möbius strip with a normal vector that can be moved along the surface.

FIGURE 6

Constructing a Möbius strip

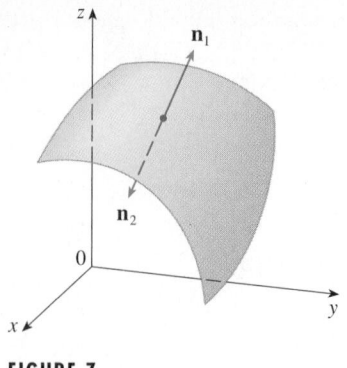

FIGURE 7

at the same point P without ever having crossed an edge. (If you have constructed a Möbius strip, try drawing a pencil line down the middle.) Therefore, a Möbius strip really has only one side. You can graph the Möbius strip using the parametric equations in Exercise 30 in Section 17.6.

From now on we consider only orientable (two-sided) surfaces. We start with a surface S that has a tangent plane at every point (x, y, z) on S (except at any boundary points). There are two unit normal vectors $\mathbf{n}_1$ and $\mathbf{n}_2 = -\mathbf{n}_1$ at (x, y, z). (See Figure 7.) If it is possible to choose a unit normal vector $\mathbf{n}$ at every such point (x, y, z) so that $\mathbf{n}$ varies continuously over S, then S is called an **oriented surface** and the given choice of $\mathbf{n}$ provides S with an **orientation**. There are two possible orientations for any orientable surface (see Figure 8).

FIGURE 8

The two orientations of an orientable surface

 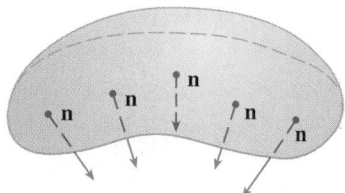

For a surface $z = g(x, y)$ given as the graph of g, we use Equation 17.6.7 and see that the induced orientation is given by the unit normal vector

$$\boxed{4} \qquad \mathbf{n} = \frac{-\dfrac{\partial g}{\partial x}\,\mathbf{i} - \dfrac{\partial g}{\partial y}\,\mathbf{j} + \mathbf{k}}{\sqrt{1 + \left(\dfrac{\partial g}{\partial x}\right)^2 + \left(\dfrac{\partial g}{\partial y}\right)^2}}$$

Since the $\mathbf{k}$-component is positive, this gives the *upward* orientation of the surface.

If S is a smooth orientable surface given in parametric form by a vector function $\mathbf{r}(u, v)$, then it is automatically supplied with the orientation of the unit normal vector

$$\boxed{5} \qquad \mathbf{n} = \frac{\mathbf{r}_u \times \mathbf{r}_v}{|\mathbf{r}_u \times \mathbf{r}_v|}$$

and the opposite orientation is given by $-\mathbf{n}$. For instance, in Example 4 in Section 17.6 we found the parametric representation

$$\mathbf{r}(\phi, \theta) = a \sin \phi \cos \theta\, \mathbf{i} + a \sin \phi \sin \theta\, \mathbf{j} + a \cos \phi\, \mathbf{k}$$

for the sphere $x^2 + y^2 + z^2 = a^2$. Then in Example 10 in Section 17.6 we found that

$$\mathbf{r}_\phi \times \mathbf{r}_\theta = a^2 \sin^2\phi \cos \theta\, \mathbf{i} + a^2 \sin^2\phi \sin \theta\, \mathbf{j} + a^2 \sin \phi \cos \phi\, \mathbf{k}$$

and

$$|\mathbf{r}_\phi \times \mathbf{r}_\theta| = a^2 \sin \phi$$

So the orientation induced by $\mathbf{r}(\phi, \theta)$ is defined by the unit normal vector

$$\mathbf{n} = \frac{\mathbf{r}_\phi \times \mathbf{r}_\theta}{|\mathbf{r}_\phi \times \mathbf{r}_\theta|} = \sin \phi \cos \theta\, \mathbf{i} + \sin \phi \sin \theta\, \mathbf{j} + \cos \phi\, \mathbf{k} = \frac{1}{a}\mathbf{r}(\phi, \theta)$$

Observe that $\mathbf{n}$ points in the same direction as the position vector, that is, outward from the sphere (see Figure 9). The opposite (inward) orientation would have been obtained (see Figure 10) if we had reversed the order of the parameters because $\mathbf{r}_\theta \times \mathbf{r}_\phi = -\mathbf{r}_\phi \times \mathbf{r}_\theta$.

FIGURE 9

Positive orientation

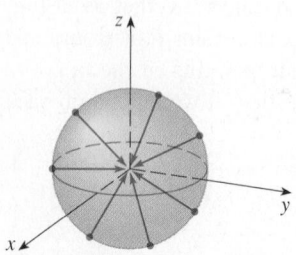

FIGURE 10

Negative orientation

For a **closed surface**, that is, a surface that is the boundary of a solid region E, the convention is that the **positive orientation** is the one for which the normal vectors point *outward* from E, and inward-pointing normals give the negative orientation (see Figures 9 and 10).

||| Surface Integrals of Vector Fields

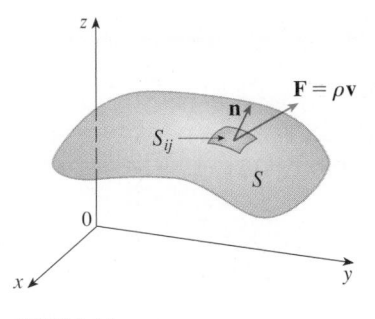

FIGURE 11

Suppose that S is an oriented surface with unit normal vector $\mathbf{n}$, and imagine a fluid with density $\rho(x, y, z)$ and velocity field $\mathbf{v}(x, y, z)$ flowing through S. (Think of S as an imaginary surface that doesn't impede the fluid flow, like a fishing net across a stream.) Then the rate of flow (mass per unit time) per unit area is $\rho\mathbf{v}$. If we divide S into small patches S_{ij}, as in Figure 11 (compare with Figures 1 and 3), then S_{ij} is nearly planar and so we can approximate the mass of fluid crossing S_{ij} in the direction of the normal $\mathbf{n}$ per unit time by the quantity

$$(\rho\mathbf{v} \cdot \mathbf{n})A(S_{ij})$$

where ρ, $\mathbf{v}$, and $\mathbf{n}$ are evaluated at some point on S_{ij}. (Recall that the component of the vector $\rho\mathbf{v}$ in the direction of the unit vector $\mathbf{n}$ is $\rho\mathbf{v} \cdot \mathbf{n}$.) By summing these quantities and taking the limit we get, according to Definition 1, the surface integral of the function $\rho\mathbf{v} \cdot \mathbf{n}$ over S:

$$\boxed{6} \qquad \iint_S \rho\mathbf{v} \cdot \mathbf{n} \, dS = \iint_S \rho(x, y, z)\mathbf{v}(x, y, z) \cdot \mathbf{n}(x, y, z) \, dS$$

and this is interpreted physically as the rate of flow through S.

If we write $\mathbf{F} = \rho\mathbf{v}$, then $\mathbf{F}$ is also a vector field on $\mathbb{R}^3$ and the integral in Equation 6 becomes

$$\iint_S \mathbf{F} \cdot \mathbf{n} \, dS$$

A surface integral of this form occurs frequently in physics, even when $\mathbf{F}$ is not $\rho\mathbf{v}$, and is called the *surface integral* (or *flux integral*) of $\mathbf{F}$ over S.

---

7 Definition If $\mathbf{F}$ is a continuous vector field defined on an oriented surface S with unit normal vector $\mathbf{n}$, then the **surface integral of F over** S is

$$\iint_S \mathbf{F} \cdot d\mathbf{S} = \iint_S \mathbf{F} \cdot \mathbf{n} \, dS$$

This integral is also called the **flux** of $\mathbf{F}$ across S.

In words, Definition 7 says that the surface integral of a vector field over S is equal to the surface integral of its normal component over S (as previously defined).

||| **Graphs** In the case of a surface S given by a graph $z = g(x, y)$, we can find $\mathbf{n}$ by noting that S is also the level surface $f(x, y, z) = z - g(x, y) = 0$. We know that the gradient $\nabla f(x, y, z)$ is normal to this surface at (x, y, z) and so a unit normal vector is

$$\mathbf{n} = \frac{\nabla f(x, y, z)}{|\nabla f(x, y, z)|} = \frac{-g_x(x, y)\,\mathbf{i} - g_y(x, y)\,\mathbf{j} + \mathbf{k}}{\sqrt{[g_x(x, y)]^2 + [g_y(x, y)]^2 + 1}}$$

Since the **k**-component is positive, this is the upward unit normal. If we now use Formula 2 to evaluate the surface integral (7) with

$$\mathbf{F}(x, y, z) = P(x, y, z)\,\mathbf{i} + Q(x, y, z)\,\mathbf{j} + R(x, y, z)\,\mathbf{k}$$

we get

$$\iint_S \mathbf{F} \cdot d\mathbf{S} = \iint_S \mathbf{F} \cdot \mathbf{n}\, dS$$

$$= \iint_D (P\,\mathbf{i} + Q\,\mathbf{j} + R\,\mathbf{k}) \cdot \frac{-\dfrac{\partial g}{\partial x}\,\mathbf{i} - \dfrac{\partial g}{\partial y}\,\mathbf{j} + \mathbf{k}}{\sqrt{\left(\dfrac{\partial g}{\partial x}\right)^2 + \left(\dfrac{\partial g}{\partial y}\right)^2 + 1}} \sqrt{\left(\dfrac{\partial g}{\partial x}\right)^2 + \left(\dfrac{\partial g}{\partial y}\right)^2 + 1}\; dA$$

or

$$\boxed{8} \qquad \iint_S \mathbf{F} \cdot d\mathbf{S} = \iint_D \left(-P\,\frac{\partial g}{\partial x} - Q\,\frac{\partial g}{\partial y} + R\right) dA$$

For a downward unit normal we multiply by -1. Similar formulas can be worked out if S is given by $y = h(x, z)$ or $x = k(y, z)$. (See Exercises 33 and 34.)

EXAMPLE 4 Evaluate $\iint_S \mathbf{F} \cdot d\mathbf{S}$, where $\mathbf{F}(x, y, z) = y\,\mathbf{i} + x\,\mathbf{j} + z\,\mathbf{k}$ and S is the boundary of the solid region E enclosed by the paraboloid $z = 1 - x^2 - y^2$ and the plane $z = 0$.

SOLUTION S consists of a parabolic top surface S_1 and a circular bottom surface S_2. (See Figure 12.) Since S is a closed surface, we use the convention of positive (outward) orientation. This means that S_1 is oriented upward and we can use Equation 8 with D being the projection of S_1 on the xy-plane, namely, the disk $x^2 + y^2 \leq 1$. Since

$$P(x, y, z) = y \qquad Q(x, y, z) = x \qquad R(x, y, z) = z = 1 - x^2 - y^2$$

on S_1 and

$$\frac{\partial g}{\partial x} = -2x \qquad \frac{\partial g}{\partial y} = -2y$$

we have

$$\iint_{S_1} \mathbf{F} \cdot d\mathbf{S} = \iint_D \left(-P\,\frac{\partial g}{\partial x} - Q\,\frac{\partial g}{\partial y} + R\right) dA$$

$$= \iint_D [-y(-2x) - x(-2y) + 1 - x^2 - y^2]\, dA$$

$$= \iint_D (1 + 4xy - x^2 - y^2)\, dA$$

$$= \int_0^{2\pi} \int_0^1 (1 + 4r^2 \cos\theta \sin\theta - r^2)\, r\, dr\, d\theta$$

$$= \int_0^{2\pi} \int_0^1 (r - r^3 + 4r^3 \cos\theta \sin\theta)\, dr\, d\theta$$

$$= \int_0^{2\pi} \left(\tfrac{1}{4} + \cos\theta \sin\theta\right) d\theta = \tfrac{1}{4}(2\pi) + 0 = \frac{\pi}{2}$$

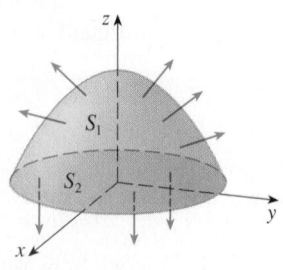

FIGURE 12

The disk S_2 is oriented downward, so its unit normal vector is $\mathbf{n} = -\mathbf{k}$ and we have

$$\iint_{S_2} \mathbf{F} \cdot d\mathbf{S} = \iint_{S_2} \mathbf{F} \cdot (-\mathbf{k})\, dS = \iint_D (-z)\, dA = \iint_D 0\, dA = 0$$

since $z = 0$ on S_2. Finally, we compute, by definition, $\iint_S \mathbf{F} \cdot d\mathbf{S}$ as the sum of the surface integrals of $\mathbf{F}$ over the pieces S_1 and S_2:

$$\iint_S \mathbf{F} \cdot d\mathbf{S} = \iint_{S_1} \mathbf{F} \cdot d\mathbf{S} + \iint_{S_2} \mathbf{F} \cdot d\mathbf{S} = \frac{\pi}{2} + 0 = \frac{\pi}{2}$$

▓ **Parametric Surfaces** If S is given by a vector function $\mathbf{r}(u, v)$, then $\mathbf{n}$ is given by Equation 5, and from Definition 7 and Equation 3 we have

$$\iint_S \mathbf{F} \cdot d\mathbf{S} = \iint_S \mathbf{F} \cdot \frac{\mathbf{r}_u \times \mathbf{r}_v}{|\mathbf{r}_u \times \mathbf{r}_v|}\, dS$$

$$= \iint_D \left[\mathbf{F}(\mathbf{r}(u, v)) \cdot \frac{\mathbf{r}_u \times \mathbf{r}_v}{|\mathbf{r}_u \times \mathbf{r}_v|} \right] |\mathbf{r}_u \times \mathbf{r}_v|\, dA$$

where D is the parameter domain. Thus, we have

▓ Compare Equation 9 to the similar expression for evaluating line integrals of vector fields in Definition 17.2.13:

$$\int_C \mathbf{F} \cdot d\mathbf{r} = \int_a^b \mathbf{F}(\mathbf{r}(t)) \cdot \mathbf{r}'(t)\, dt$$

$$\boxed{9 \qquad \iint_S \mathbf{F} \cdot d\mathbf{S} = \iint_D \mathbf{F} \cdot (\mathbf{r}_u \times \mathbf{r}_v)\, dA}$$

Notice that, in view of Equation 17.6.7, we have

$$\mathbf{r}_x \times \mathbf{r}_y = -\frac{\partial g}{\partial x}\mathbf{i} - \frac{\partial g}{\partial y}\mathbf{j} + \mathbf{k}$$

and so Formula 8 is just a special case of Formula 9.

EXAMPLE 5 Find the flux of the vector field $\mathbf{F}(x, y, z) = z\,\mathbf{i} + y\,\mathbf{j} + x\,\mathbf{k}$ across the unit sphere $x^2 + y^2 + z^2 = 1$.

▓ Figure 13 shows the vector field $\mathbf{F}$ in Example 5 at points on the unit sphere.

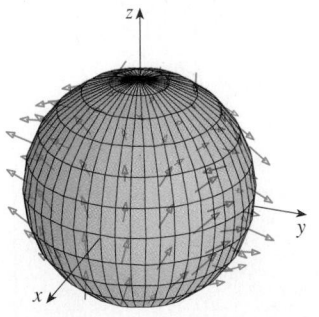

FIGURE 13

SOLUTION Using the parametric representation

$$\mathbf{r}(\phi, \theta) = \sin\phi \cos\theta\,\mathbf{i} + \sin\phi \sin\theta\,\mathbf{j} + \cos\phi\,\mathbf{k} \qquad 0 \leq \phi \leq \pi \qquad 0 \leq \theta \leq 2\pi$$

we have

$$\mathbf{F}(\mathbf{r}(\phi, \theta)) = \cos\phi\,\mathbf{i} + \sin\phi \sin\theta\,\mathbf{j} + \sin\phi \cos\theta\,\mathbf{k}$$

and, from Example 10 in Section 17.6,

$$\mathbf{r}_\phi \times \mathbf{r}_\theta = \sin^2\phi \cos\theta\,\mathbf{i} + \sin^2\phi \sin\theta\,\mathbf{j} + \sin\phi \cos\phi\,\mathbf{k}$$

Therefore

$$\mathbf{F}(\mathbf{r}(\phi, \theta)) \cdot (\mathbf{r}_\phi \times \mathbf{r}_\theta) = \cos\phi \sin^2\phi \cos\theta + \sin^3\phi \sin^2\theta + \sin^2\phi \cos\phi \cos\theta$$

and, by Formula 9, the flux is

$$\iint\limits_{S} \mathbf{F} \cdot d\mathbf{S} = \iint\limits_{D} \mathbf{F} \cdot (\mathbf{r}_{\phi} \times \mathbf{r}_{\theta}) \, dA$$

$$= \int_{0}^{2\pi} \int_{0}^{\pi} (2 \sin^{2}\phi \cos \phi \cos \theta + \sin^{3}\phi \sin^{2}\theta) \, d\phi \, d\theta$$

$$= 2 \int_{0}^{\pi} \sin^{2}\phi \cos \phi \, d\phi \int_{0}^{2\pi} \cos \theta \, d\theta + \int_{0}^{\pi} \sin^{3}\phi \, d\phi \int_{0}^{2\pi} \sin^{2}\theta \, d\theta$$

$$= 0 + \int_{0}^{\pi} \sin^{3}\phi \, d\phi \int_{0}^{2\pi} \sin^{2}\theta \, d\theta \quad \left(\text{since } \int_{0}^{2\pi} \cos \theta \, d\theta = 0 \right)$$

$$= \frac{4\pi}{3}$$

by the same calculation as in Example 2.

If, for instance, the vector field in Example 5 is a velocity field describing the flow of a fluid with density 1, then the answer, $4\pi/3$, represents the rate of flow through the unit sphere in units of mass per unit time.

Although we motivated the surface integral of a vector field using the example of fluid flow, this concept also arises in other physical situations. For instance, if $\mathbf{E}$ is an electric field (see Example 5 in Section 17.1), then the surface integral

$$\iint\limits_{S} \mathbf{E} \cdot d\mathbf{S}$$

is called the **electric flux** of $\mathbf{E}$ through the surface S. One of the important laws of electrostatics is **Gauss's Law**, which says that the net charge enclosed by a closed surface S is

$$\boxed{10} \qquad\qquad Q = \varepsilon_{0} \iint\limits_{S} \mathbf{E} \cdot d\mathbf{S}$$

where ε_{0} is a constant (called the permittivity of free space) that depends on the units used. (In the SI system, $\varepsilon_{0} \approx 8.8542 \times 10^{-12} \, C^{2}/N \cdot m^{2}$.) Therefore, if the vector field $\mathbf{F}$ in Example 5 represents an electric field, we can conclude that the charge enclosed by S is $Q = 4\pi\varepsilon_{0}/3$.

Another application of surface integrals occurs in the study of heat flow. Suppose the temperature at a point (x, y, z) in a body is $u(x, y, z)$. Then the **heat flow** is defined as the vector field

$$\mathbf{F} = -K \nabla u$$

where K is an experimentally determined constant called the **conductivity** of the substance. The rate of heat flow across the surface S in the body is then given by the surface integral

$$\iint\limits_{S} \mathbf{F} \cdot d\mathbf{S} = -K \iint\limits_{S} \nabla u \cdot d\mathbf{S}$$

EXAMPLE 6 The temperature u in a metal ball is proportional to the square of the distance from the center of the ball. Find the rate of heat flow across a sphere S of radius a with center at the center of the ball.

SOLUTION Taking the center of the ball to be at the origin, we have

$$u(x, y, z) = C(x^2 + y^2 + z^2)$$

where C is the proportionality constant. Then the heat flow is

$$\mathbf{F}(x, y, z) = -K \nabla u = -KC(2x\,\mathbf{i} + 2y\,\mathbf{j} + 2z\,\mathbf{k})$$

where K is the conductivity of the metal. Instead of using the usual parametrization of the sphere as in Example 5, we observe that the outward unit normal to the sphere $x^2 + y^2 + z^2 = a^2$ at the point (x, y, z) is

$$\mathbf{n} = \frac{1}{a}(x\,\mathbf{i} + y\,\mathbf{j} + z\,\mathbf{k})$$

and so $$\mathbf{F} \cdot \mathbf{n} = -\frac{2KC}{a}(x^2 + y^2 + z^2)$$

But on S we have $x^2 + y^2 + z^2 = a^2$, so $\mathbf{F} \cdot \mathbf{n} = -2aKC$. Therefore, the rate of heat flow across S is

$$\iint_S \mathbf{F} \cdot d\mathbf{S} = \iint_S \mathbf{F} \cdot \mathbf{n}\, dS = -2aKC \iint_S dS$$

$$= -2aKCA(S) = -2aKC(4\pi a^2) = -8KC\pi a^3$$

17.7 Exercises

1. Let S be the cube with vertices $(\pm 1, \pm 1, \pm 1)$. Approximate $\iint_S \sqrt{x^2 + 2y^2 + 3z^2}\, dS$ by using a Riemann sum as in Definition 1, taking the patches S_{ij} to be the squares that are the faces of the cube and the points P_{ij}^* to be the centers of the squares.

2. A surface S consists of the cylinder $x^2 + y^2 = 1$, $-1 \le z \le 1$, together with its top and bottom disks. Suppose you know that f is a continuous function with $f(\pm 1, 0, 0) = 2$, $f(0, \pm 1, 0) = 3$, and $f(0, 0, \pm 1) = 4$. Estimate the value of $\iint_S f(x, y, z)\, dS$ by using a Riemann sum, taking the patches S_{ij} to be four quarter-cylinders and the top and bottom disks.

3. Let H be the hemisphere $x^2 + y^2 + z^2 = 50$, $z \ge 0$, and suppose f is a continuous function with $f(3, 4, 5) = 7$, $f(3, -4, 5) = 8$, $f(-3, 4, 5) = 9$, and $f(-3, -4, 5) = 12$. By dividing H into four patches, estimate the value of $\iint_H f(x, y, z)\, dS$.

4. Suppose that $f(x, y, z) = g(\sqrt{x^2 + y^2 + z^2})$, where g is a function of one variable such that $g(2) = -5$. Evaluate $\iint_S f(x, y, z)\, dS$, where S is the sphere $x^2 + y^2 + z^2 = 4$.

5–18 ▥ Evaluate the surface integral.

5. $\iint_S x^2yz\, dS$,
S is the part of the plane $z = 1 + 2x + 3y$ that lies above the rectangle $[0, 3] \times [0, 2]$

6. $\iint_S xy\, dS$,
S is the triangular region with vertices $(1, 0, 0)$, $(0, 2, 0)$, and $(0, 0, 2)$

7. $\iint_S yz\, dS$,
S is the part of the plane $x + y + z = 1$ that lies in the first octant

8. $\iint_S y\, dS$,
S is the surface $z = \frac{2}{3}(x^{3/2} + y^{3/2})$, $0 \le x \le 1$, $0 \le y \le 1$

9. $\iint_S x^2z^2\, dS$,
S is the part of the cone $z^2 = x^2 + y^2$ that lies between the planes $z = 1$ and $z = 3$

10. $\iint_S z\, dS$,
S is the surface $x = y + 2z^2$, $0 \le y \le 1$, $0 \le z \le 1$

11. $\iint_S y\, dS$,
S is the part of the paraboloid $y = x^2 + z^2$ that lies inside the cylinder $x^2 + z^2 = 4$

12. $\iint_S xy\, dS$,
S is the boundary of the region enclosed by the cylinder $x^2 + z^2 = 1$ and the planes $y = 0$ and $x + y = 2$

13. $\iint_S (x^2z + y^2z)\, dS$,
S is the hemisphere $x^2 + y^2 + z^2 = 4$, $z \ge 0$

14. $\iint_S xyz \, dS$,
S is the part of the sphere $x^2 + y^2 + z^2 = 1$ that lies above the cone $z = \sqrt{x^2 + y^2}$

15. $\iint_S (x^2 y + z^2) \, dS$,
S is the part of the cylinder $x^2 + y^2 = 9$ between the planes $z = 0$ and $z = 2$

16. $\iint_S (x^2 + y^2 + z^2) \, dS$,
S consists of the cylinder in Exercise 15 together with its top and bottom disks

17. $\iint_S yz \, dS$,
S is the surface with parametric equations $x = u^2$, $y = u \sin v$, $z = u \cos v$, $0 \leqslant u \leqslant 1$, $0 \leqslant v \leqslant \pi/2$

18. $\iint_S \sqrt{1 + x^2 + y^2} \, dS$,
S is the helicoid with vector equation
$\mathbf{r}(u, v) = u \cos v \, \mathbf{i} + u \sin v \, \mathbf{j} + v \, \mathbf{k}$, $0 \leqslant u \leqslant 1$, $0 \leqslant v \leqslant \pi$

19–28 |||| Evaluate the surface integral $\iint_S \mathbf{F} \cdot d\mathbf{S}$ for the given vector field $\mathbf{F}$ and the oriented surface S. In other words, find the flux of $\mathbf{F}$ across S. For closed surfaces, use the positive (outward) orientation.

19. $\mathbf{F}(x, y, z) = xy \, \mathbf{i} + yz \, \mathbf{j} + zx \, \mathbf{k}$, S is the part of the parabo-loid $z = 4 - x^2 - y^2$ that lies above the square $0 \leqslant x \leqslant 1$, $0 \leqslant y \leqslant 1$, and has upward orientation

20. $\mathbf{F}(x, y, z) = xy \, \mathbf{i} + 4x^2 \, \mathbf{j} + yz \, \mathbf{k}$, S is the surface $z = xe^y$, $0 \leqslant x \leqslant 1$, $0 \leqslant y \leqslant 1$, with upward orientation

21. $\mathbf{F}(x, y, z) = xze^y \, \mathbf{i} - xze^y \, \mathbf{j} + z \, \mathbf{k}$,
S is the part of the plane $x + y + z = 1$ in the first octant and has downward orientation

22. $\mathbf{F}(x, y, z) = x \, \mathbf{i} + y \, \mathbf{j} + z^4 \, \mathbf{k}$,
S is the part of the cone $z = \sqrt{x^2 + y^2}$ beneath the plane $z = 1$ with downward orientation

23. $\mathbf{F}(x, y, z) = x \, \mathbf{i} - z \, \mathbf{j} + y \, \mathbf{k}$,
S is the part of the sphere $x^2 + y^2 + z^2 = 4$ in the first octant, with orientation toward the origin

24. $\mathbf{F}(x, y, z) = xz \, \mathbf{i} + x \, \mathbf{j} + y \, \mathbf{k}$,
S is the hemisphere $x^2 + y^2 + z^2 = 25$, $y \geqslant 0$, oriented in the direction of the positive y-axis

25. $\mathbf{F}(x, y, z) = y \, \mathbf{j} - z \, \mathbf{k}$,
S consists of the paraboloid $y = x^2 + z^2$, $0 \leqslant y \leqslant 1$, and the disk $x^2 + z^2 \leqslant 1$, $y = 1$

26. $\mathbf{F}(x, y, z) = x \, \mathbf{i} + y \, \mathbf{j} + 5 \, \mathbf{k}$, S is the surface of Exercise 12

27. $\mathbf{F}(x, y, z) = x \, \mathbf{i} + 2y \, \mathbf{j} + 3z \, \mathbf{k}$,
S is the cube with vertices $(\pm 1, \pm 1, \pm 1)$

28. $\mathbf{F}(x, y, z) = y \, \mathbf{i} + x \, \mathbf{j} + z^2 \, \mathbf{k}$,
S is the helicoid of Exercise 18 with upward orientation

29. Evaluate $\iint_S xyz \, dS$ correct to four decimal places, where S is the surface $z = xy$, $0 \leqslant x \leqslant 1$, $0 \leqslant y \leqslant 1$.

30. Find the exact value of $\iint_S x^2 yz \, dS$, where S is the surface in Exercise 29.

31. Find the value of $\iint_S x^2 y^2 z^2 \, dS$ correct to four decimal places, where S is the part of the paraboloid $z = 3 - 2x^2 - y^2$ that lies above the xy-plane.

32. Find the flux of $\mathbf{F}(x, y, z) = \sin(xyz) \, \mathbf{i} + x^2 y \, \mathbf{j} + z^2 e^{x/5} \, \mathbf{k}$ across the part of the cylinder $4y^2 + z^2 = 4$ that lies above the xy-plane and between the planes $x = -2$ and $x = 2$ with upward orientation. Illustrate by using a computer algebra system to draw the cylinder and the vector field on the same screen.

33. Find a formula for $\iint_S \mathbf{F} \cdot d\mathbf{S}$ similar to Formula 8 for the case where S is given by $y = h(x, z)$ and $\mathbf{n}$ is the unit normal that points toward the left.

34. Find a formula for $\iint_S \mathbf{F} \cdot d\mathbf{S}$ similar to Formula 8 for the case where S is given by $x = k(y, z)$ and $\mathbf{n}$ is the unit normal that points forward (that is, toward the viewer when the axes are drawn in the usual way).

35. Find the center of mass of the hemisphere $x^2 + y^2 + z^2 = a^2$, $z \geqslant 0$, if it has constant density.

36. Find the mass of a thin funnel in the shape of a cone $z = \sqrt{x^2 + y^2}$, $1 \leqslant z \leqslant 4$, if its density function is $\rho(x, y, z) = 10 - z$.

37. (a) Give an integral expression for the moment of inertia I_z about the z-axis of a thin sheet in the shape of a surface S if the density function is ρ.
(b) Find the moment of inertia about the z-axis of the funnel in Exercise 36.

38. The conical surface $z^2 = x^2 + y^2$, $0 \leqslant z \leqslant a$, has constant density k. Find (a) the center of mass and (b) the moment of inertia about the z-axis.

39. A fluid with density 1200 flows with velocity $\mathbf{v} = y \, \mathbf{i} + \mathbf{j} + z \, \mathbf{k}$. Find the rate of flow upward through the paraboloid $z = 9 - \frac{1}{4}(x^2 + y^2)$, $x^2 + y^2 \leqslant 36$.

40. A fluid has density 1500 and velocity field $\mathbf{v} = -y \, \mathbf{i} + x \, \mathbf{j} + 2z \, \mathbf{k}$. Find the rate of flow outward through the sphere $x^2 + y^2 + z^2 = 25$.

41. Use Gauss's Law to find the charge contained in the solid hemisphere $x^2 + y^2 + z^2 \leqslant a^2$, $z \geqslant 0$, if the electric field is $\mathbf{E}(x, y, z) = x \, \mathbf{i} + y \, \mathbf{j} + 2z \, \mathbf{k}$.

42. Use Gauss's Law to find the charge enclosed by the cube with vertices $(\pm 1, \pm 1, \pm 1)$ if the electric field is $\mathbf{E}(x, y, z) = x \, \mathbf{i} + y \, \mathbf{j} + z \, \mathbf{k}$.

43. The temperature at the point (x, y, z) in a substance with con-ductivity $K = 6.5$ is $u(x, y, z) = 2y^2 + 2z^2$. Find the rate of heat flow inward across the cylindrical surface $y^2 + z^2 = 6$, $0 \leqslant x \leqslant 4$.

44. The temperature at a point in a ball with conductivity K is inversely proportional to the distance from the center of the ball. Find the rate of heat flow across a sphere S of radius a with center at the center of the ball.

17.8 Stokes' Theorem

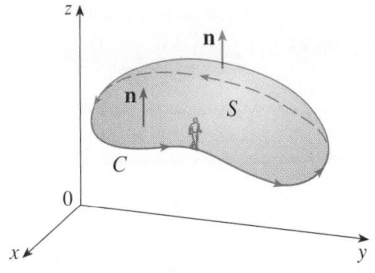

FIGURE 1

|||| Stokes' Theorem is named after the Irish mathematical physicist Sir George Stokes (1819–1903). Stokes was a professor at Cambridge University (in fact he held the same position as Newton, Lucasian Professor of Mathematics) and was especially noted for his studies of fluid flow and light. What we call Stokes' Theorem was actually discovered by the Scottish physicist Sir William Thomson (1824–1907, known as Lord Kelvin). Stokes learned of this theorem in a letter from Thomson in 1850 and asked students to prove it on an examination at Cambridge University in 1854. We don't know if any of those students was able to do so.

Stokes' Theorem can be regarded as a higher-dimensional version of Green's Theorem. Whereas Green's Theorem relates a double integral over a plane region D to a line integral around its plane boundary curve, Stokes' Theorem relates a surface integral over a surface S to a line integral around the boundary curve of S (which is a space curve). Figure 1 shows an oriented surface with unit normal vector $\mathbf{n}$. The orientation of S induces the **positive orientation of the boundary curve C** shown in the figure. This means that if you walk in the positive direction around C with your head pointing in the direction of $\mathbf{n}$, then the surface will always be on your left.

> **Stokes' Theorem** Let S be an oriented piecewise-smooth surface that is bounded by a simple, closed, piecewise-smooth boundary curve C with positive orientation. Let $\mathbf{F}$ be a vector field whose components have continuous partial derivatives on an open region in $\mathbb{R}^3$ that contains S. Then
>
> $$\int_C \mathbf{F} \cdot d\mathbf{r} = \iint_S \operatorname{curl} \mathbf{F} \cdot d\mathbf{S}$$

Since

$$\int_C \mathbf{F} \cdot d\mathbf{r} = \int_C \mathbf{F} \cdot \mathbf{T}\, ds \qquad \text{and} \qquad \iint_S \operatorname{curl} \mathbf{F} \cdot d\mathbf{S} = \iint_S \operatorname{curl} \mathbf{F} \cdot \mathbf{n}\, dS$$

Stokes' Theorem says that the line integral around the boundary curve of S of the tangential component of $\mathbf{F}$ is equal to the surface integral of the normal component of the curl of $\mathbf{F}$.

The positively oriented boundary curve of the oriented surface S is often written as ∂S, so Stokes' Theorem can be expressed as

$$\boxed{1} \qquad \iint_S \operatorname{curl} \mathbf{F} \cdot d\mathbf{S} = \int_{\partial S} \mathbf{F} \cdot d\mathbf{r}$$

There is an analogy among Stokes' Theorem, Green's Theorem, and the Fundamental Theorem of Calculus. As before, there is an integral involving derivatives on the left side of Equation 1 (recall that curl $\mathbf{F}$ is a sort of derivative of $\mathbf{F}$) and the right side involves the values of $\mathbf{F}$ only on the *boundary* of S.

In fact, in the special case where the surface S is flat and lies in the xy-plane with upward orientation, the unit normal is $\mathbf{k}$, the surface integral becomes a double integral, and Stokes' Theorem becomes

$$\int_C \mathbf{F} \cdot d\mathbf{r} = \iint_S \operatorname{curl} \mathbf{F} \cdot d\mathbf{S} = \iint_S (\operatorname{curl} \mathbf{F}) \cdot \mathbf{k}\, dA$$

This is precisely the vector form of Green's Theorem given in Equation 17.5.12. Thus, we see that Green's Theorem is really a special case of Stokes' Theorem.

Although Stokes' Theorem is too difficult for us to prove in its full generality, we can give a proof when S is a graph and $\mathbf{F}$, S, and C are well behaved.

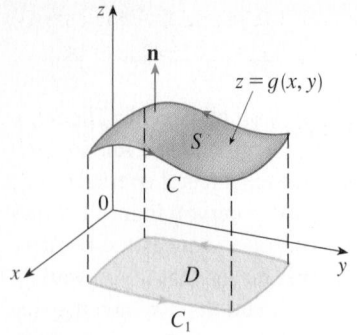

FIGURE 2

Proof of a Special Case of Stokes' Theorem   We assume that the equation of S is $z = g(x, y)$, $(x, y) \in D$, where g has continuous second-order partial derivatives and D is a simple plane region whose boundary curve C_1 corresponds to C. If the orientation of S is upward, then the positive orientation of C corresponds to the positive orientation of C_1. (See Figure 2.) We are given that $\mathbf{F} = P\,\mathbf{i} + Q\,\mathbf{j} + R\,\mathbf{k}$, where the partial derivatives of P, Q, and R are continuous.

Since S is a graph of a function, we can apply Formula 17.7.8 with $\mathbf{F}$ replaced by curl $\mathbf{F}$. The result is

$$\boxed{2} \iint_S \text{curl } \mathbf{F} \cdot d\mathbf{S}$$

$$= \iint_D \left[-\left(\frac{\partial R}{\partial y} - \frac{\partial Q}{\partial z} \right) \frac{\partial z}{\partial x} - \left(\frac{\partial P}{\partial z} - \frac{\partial R}{\partial x} \right) \frac{\partial z}{\partial y} + \left(\frac{\partial Q}{\partial x} - \frac{\partial P}{\partial y} \right) \right] dA$$

where the partial derivatives of P, Q, and R are evaluated at $(x, y, g(x, y))$. If

$$x = x(t) \qquad y = y(t) \qquad a \leqslant t \leqslant b$$

is a parametric representation of C_1, then a parametric representation of C is

$$x = x(t) \qquad y = y(t) \qquad z = g(x(t), y(t)) \qquad a \leqslant t \leqslant b$$

This allows us, with the aid of the Chain Rule, to evaluate the line integral as follows:

$$\int_C \mathbf{F} \cdot d\mathbf{r} = \int_a^b \left(P \frac{dx}{dt} + Q \frac{dy}{dt} + R \frac{dz}{dt} \right) dt$$

$$= \int_a^b \left[P \frac{dx}{dt} + Q \frac{dy}{dt} + R \left(\frac{\partial z}{\partial x} \frac{dx}{dt} + \frac{\partial z}{\partial y} \frac{dy}{dt} \right) \right] dt$$

$$= \int_a^b \left[\left(P + R \frac{\partial z}{\partial x} \right) \frac{dx}{dt} + \left(Q + R \frac{\partial z}{\partial y} \right) \frac{dy}{dt} \right] dt$$

$$= \int_{C_1} \left(P + R \frac{\partial z}{\partial x} \right) dx + \left(Q + R \frac{\partial z}{\partial y} \right) dy$$

$$= \iint_D \left[\frac{\partial}{\partial x} \left(Q + R \frac{\partial z}{\partial y} \right) - \frac{\partial}{\partial y} \left(P + R \frac{\partial z}{\partial x} \right) \right] dA$$

where we have used Green's Theorem in the last step. Then, using the Chain Rule again and remembering that P, Q, and R are functions of x, y, and z and that z is itself a function of x and y, we get

$$\int_C \mathbf{F} \cdot d\mathbf{r} = \iint_D \left[\left(\frac{\partial Q}{\partial x} + \frac{\partial Q}{\partial z} \frac{\partial z}{\partial x} + \frac{\partial R}{\partial x} \frac{\partial z}{\partial y} + \frac{\partial R}{\partial z} \frac{\partial z}{\partial x} \frac{\partial z}{\partial y} + R \frac{\partial^2 z}{\partial x \, \partial y} \right) \right.$$

$$\left. - \left(\frac{\partial P}{\partial y} + \frac{\partial P}{\partial z} \frac{\partial z}{\partial y} + \frac{\partial R}{\partial y} \frac{\partial z}{\partial x} + \frac{\partial R}{\partial z} \frac{\partial z}{\partial y} \frac{\partial z}{\partial x} + R \frac{\partial^2 z}{\partial y \, \partial x} \right) \right] dA$$

Four of the terms in this double integral cancel and the remaining six terms can be arranged to coincide with the right side of Equation 2. Therefore

$$\int_C \mathbf{F} \cdot d\mathbf{r} = \iint_S \text{curl } \mathbf{F} \cdot d\mathbf{S}$$

EXAMPLE 1 Evaluate $\int_C \mathbf{F} \cdot d\mathbf{r}$, where $\mathbf{F}(x, y, z) = -y^2\,\mathbf{i} + x\,\mathbf{j} + z^2\,\mathbf{k}$ and C is the curve of intersection of the plane $y + z = 2$ and the cylinder $x^2 + y^2 = 1$. (Orient C to be counterclockwise when viewed from above.)

SOLUTION The curve C (an ellipse) is shown in Figure 3. Although $\int_C \mathbf{F} \cdot d\mathbf{r}$ could be evaluated directly, it's easier to use Stokes' Theorem. We first compute

$$\text{curl } \mathbf{F} = \begin{vmatrix} \mathbf{i} & \mathbf{j} & \mathbf{k} \\ \dfrac{\partial}{\partial x} & \dfrac{\partial}{\partial y} & \dfrac{\partial}{\partial z} \\ -y^2 & x & z^2 \end{vmatrix} = (1 + 2y)\,\mathbf{k}$$

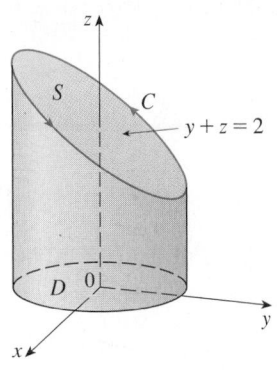

FIGURE 3

Although there are many surfaces with boundary C, the most convenient choice is the elliptical region S in the plane $y + z = 2$ that is bounded by C. If we orient S upward, then C has the induced positive orientation. The projection D of S on the xy-plane is the disk $x^2 + y^2 \le 1$ and so using Equation 17.7.8 with $z = g(x, y) = 2 - y$, we have

$$\int_C \mathbf{F} \cdot d\mathbf{r} = \iint_S \text{curl } \mathbf{F} \cdot d\mathbf{S} = \iint_D (1 + 2y)\,dA$$

$$= \int_0^{2\pi} \int_0^1 (1 + 2r \sin \theta)\, r\, dr\, d\theta$$

$$= \int_0^{2\pi} \left[\frac{r^2}{2} + 2\frac{r^3}{3} \sin \theta \right]_0^1 d\theta = \int_0^{2\pi} \left(\tfrac{1}{2} + \tfrac{2}{3} \sin \theta \right) d\theta$$

$$= \tfrac{1}{2}(2\pi) + 0 = \pi$$

EXAMPLE 2 Use Stokes' Theorem to compute the integral $\iint_S \text{curl } \mathbf{F} \cdot d\mathbf{S}$, where $\mathbf{F}(x, y, z) = xz\,\mathbf{i} + yz\,\mathbf{j} + xy\,\mathbf{k}$ and S is the part of the sphere $x^2 + y^2 + z^2 = 4$ that lies inside the cylinder $x^2 + y^2 = 1$ and above the xy-plane. (See Figure 4.)

SOLUTION To find the boundary curve C we solve the equations $x^2 + y^2 + z^2 = 4$ and $x^2 + y^2 = 1$. Subtracting, we get $z^2 = 3$ and so $z = \sqrt{3}$ (since $z > 0$). Thus, C is the circle given by the equations $x^2 + y^2 = 1$, $z = \sqrt{3}$. A vector equation of C is

$$\mathbf{r}(t) = \cos t\,\mathbf{i} + \sin t\,\mathbf{j} + \sqrt{3}\,\mathbf{k} \qquad 0 \le t \le 2\pi$$

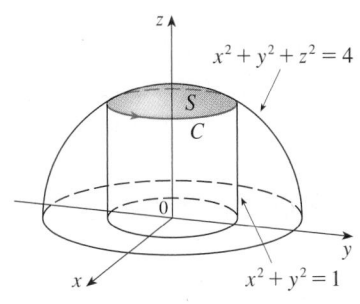

FIGURE 4

so
$$\mathbf{r}'(t) = -\sin t\,\mathbf{i} + \cos t\,\mathbf{j}$$

Also, we have

$$\mathbf{F}(\mathbf{r}(t)) = \sqrt{3} \cos t\,\mathbf{i} + \sqrt{3} \sin t\,\mathbf{j} + \cos t \sin t\,\mathbf{k}$$

Therefore, by Stokes' Theorem,

$$\iint_S \text{curl } \mathbf{F} \cdot d\mathbf{S} = \int_C \mathbf{F} \cdot d\mathbf{r} = \int_0^{2\pi} \mathbf{F}(\mathbf{r}(t)) \cdot \mathbf{r}'(t)\, dt$$

$$= \int_0^{2\pi} \left(-\sqrt{3} \cos t \sin t + \sqrt{3} \sin t \cos t \right) dt$$

$$= \sqrt{3} \int_0^{2\pi} 0\, dt = 0$$

Note that in Example 2 we computed a surface integral simply by knowing the values of **F** on the boundary curve C. This means that if we have another oriented surface with the same boundary curve C, then we get exactly the same value for the surface integral!

In general, if S_1 and S_2 are oriented surfaces with the same oriented boundary curve C and both satisfy the hypotheses of Stokes' Theorem, then

$$\boxed{3} \qquad \iint_{S_1} \text{curl } \mathbf{F} \cdot d\mathbf{S} = \int_C \mathbf{F} \cdot d\mathbf{r} = \iint_{S_2} \text{curl } \mathbf{F} \cdot d\mathbf{S}$$

This fact is useful when it is difficult to integrate over one surface but easy to integrate over the other.

We now use Stokes' Theorem to throw some light on the meaning of the curl vector. Suppose that C is an oriented closed curve and **v** represents the velocity field in fluid flow. Consider the line integral

$$\int_C \mathbf{v} \cdot d\mathbf{r} = \int_C \mathbf{v} \cdot \mathbf{T}\, ds$$

(a) $\int_C \mathbf{v} \cdot d\mathbf{r} > 0$, positive circulation

and recall that $\mathbf{v} \cdot \mathbf{T}$ is the component of **v** in the direction of the unit tangent vector **T**. This means that the closer the direction of **v** is to the direction of **T**, the larger the value of $\mathbf{v} \cdot \mathbf{T}$. Thus, $\int_C \mathbf{v} \cdot d\mathbf{r}$ is a measure of the tendency of the fluid to move around C and is called the **circulation** of **v** around C. (See Figure 5.)

Now let $P_0(x_0, y_0, z_0)$ be a point in the fluid and let S_a be a small disk with radius a and center P_0. Then $(\text{curl } \mathbf{F})(P) \approx (\text{curl } \mathbf{F})(P_0)$ for all points P on S_a because curl **F** is continuous. Thus, by Stokes' Theorem, we get the following approximation to the circulation around the boundary circle C_a:

(b) $\int_C \mathbf{v} \cdot d\mathbf{r} < 0$, negative circulation

FIGURE 5

$$\int_{C_a} \mathbf{v} \cdot d\mathbf{r} = \iint_{S_a} \text{curl } \mathbf{v} \cdot d\mathbf{S} = \iint_{S_a} \text{curl } \mathbf{v} \cdot \mathbf{n}\, dS$$

$$\approx \iint_{S_a} \text{curl } \mathbf{v}(P_0) \cdot \mathbf{n}(P_0)\, dS = \text{curl } \mathbf{v}(P_0) \cdot \mathbf{n}(P_0)\pi a^2$$

▓▓▓▓ Imagine a tiny paddle wheel placed in the fluid at a point P, as in Figure 6; the paddle wheel rotates fastest when its axis is parallel to curl **v**.

This approximation becomes better as $a \to 0$ and we have

$$\boxed{4} \qquad \text{curl } \mathbf{v}(P_0) \cdot \mathbf{n}(P_0) = \lim_{a \to 0} \frac{1}{\pi a^2} \int_{C_a} \mathbf{v} \cdot d\mathbf{r}$$

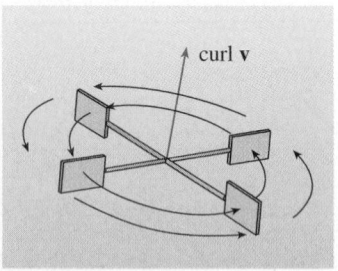

Equation 4 gives the relationship between the curl and the circulation. It shows that curl $\mathbf{v} \cdot \mathbf{n}$ is a measure of the rotating effect of the fluid about the axis **n**. The curling effect is greatest about the axis parallel to curl **v**.

Finally, we mention that Stokes' Theorem can be used to prove Theorem 17.5.4 (which states that if curl $\mathbf{F} = \mathbf{0}$ on all of $\mathbb{R}^3$, then **F** is conservative). From our previous work (Theorems 17.3.3 and 17.3.4), we know that **F** is conservative if $\int_C \mathbf{F} \cdot d\mathbf{r} = 0$ for every closed path C. Given C, suppose we can find an orientable surface S whose boundary is C. (This can be done, but the proof requires advanced techniques.) Then Stokes' Theorem gives

FIGURE 6

$$\int_C \mathbf{F} \cdot d\mathbf{r} = \iint_S \text{curl } \mathbf{F} \cdot d\mathbf{S} = \iint_S \mathbf{0} \cdot d\mathbf{S} = 0$$

A curve that is not simple can be broken into a number of simple curves, and the integrals around these simple curves are all 0. Adding these integrals, we obtain $\int_C \mathbf{F} \cdot d\mathbf{r} = 0$ for any closed curve C.

17.8 Exercises

1. A hemisphere H and a portion P of a paraboloid are shown. Suppose $\mathbf{F}$ is a vector field on $\mathbb{R}^3$ whose components have continuous partial derivatives. Explain why

$$\iint_H \operatorname{curl} \mathbf{F} \cdot d\mathbf{S} = \iint_P \operatorname{curl} \mathbf{F} \cdot d\mathbf{S}$$

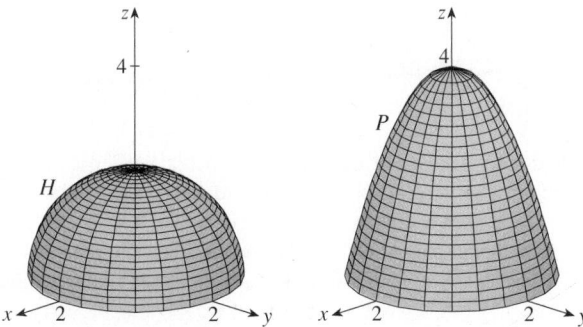

2–6 ▍▍ Use Stokes' Theorem to evaluate $\iint_S \operatorname{curl} \mathbf{F} \cdot d\mathbf{S}$.

2. $\mathbf{F}(x, y, z) = yz\,\mathbf{i} + xz\,\mathbf{j} + xy\,\mathbf{k}$,
S is the part of the paraboloid $z = 9 - x^2 - y^2$ that lies above the plane $z = 5$, oriented upward

3. $\mathbf{F}(x, y, z) = x^2 e^{yz}\,\mathbf{i} + y^2 e^{xz}\,\mathbf{j} + z^2 e^{xy}\,\mathbf{k}$,
S is the hemisphere $x^2 + y^2 + z^2 = 4$, $z \geqslant 0$,
oriented upward

4. $\mathbf{F}(x, y, z) = x^2 y^3 z\,\mathbf{i} + \sin(xyz)\,\mathbf{j} + xyz\,\mathbf{k}$,
S is the part of the cone $y^2 = x^2 + z^2$ that lies between the planes $y = 0$ and $y = 3$, oriented in the direction of the positive y-axis

5. $\mathbf{F}(x, y, z) = xyz\,\mathbf{i} + xy\,\mathbf{j} + x^2 yz\,\mathbf{k}$,
S consists of the top and the four sides (but not the bottom) of the cube with vertices $(\pm 1, \pm 1, \pm 1)$, oriented outward
[*Hint:* Use Equation 3.]

6. $\mathbf{F}(x, y, z) = e^{xy} \cos z\,\mathbf{i} + x^2 z\,\mathbf{j} + xy\,\mathbf{k}$,
S is the hemisphere $x = \sqrt{1 - y^2 - z^2}$, oriented in the direction of the positive x-axis   [*Hint:* Use Equation 3.]

7–10 ▍▍ Use Stokes' Theorem to evaluate $\int_C \mathbf{F} \cdot d\mathbf{r}$. In each case C is oriented counterclockwise as viewed from above.

7. $\mathbf{F}(x, y, z) = (x + y^2)\,\mathbf{i} + (y + z^2)\,\mathbf{j} + (z + x^2)\,\mathbf{k}$,
C is the triangle with vertices $(1, 0, 0)$, $(0, 1, 0)$, and $(0, 0, 1)$

8. $\mathbf{F}(x, y, z) = e^{-x}\,\mathbf{i} + e^x\,\mathbf{j} + e^z\,\mathbf{k}$,
C is the boundary of the part of the plane $2x + y + 2z = 2$ in the first octant

9. $\mathbf{F}(x, y, z) = yz\,\mathbf{i} + 2xz\,\mathbf{j} + e^{xy}\,\mathbf{k}$,
C is the circle $x^2 + y^2 = 16$, $z = 5$

10. $\mathbf{F}(x, y, z) = x\,\mathbf{i} + y\,\mathbf{j} + (x^2 + y^2)\,\mathbf{k}$,
C is the boundary of the part of the paraboloid $z = 1 - x^2 - y^2$ in the first octant

11. (a) Use Stokes' Theorem to evaluate $\int_C \mathbf{F} \cdot d\mathbf{r}$, where

$$\mathbf{F}(x, y, z) = x^2 z\,\mathbf{i} + xy^2\,\mathbf{j} + z^2\,\mathbf{k}$$

and C is the curve of intersection of the plane $x + y + z = 1$ and the cylinder $x^2 + y^2 = 9$ oriented counterclockwise as viewed from above.

(b) Graph both the plane and the cylinder with domains chosen so that you can see the curve C and the surface that you used in part (a).

(c) Find parametric equations for C and use them to graph C.

12. (a) Use Stokes' Theorem to evaluate $\int_C \mathbf{F} \cdot d\mathbf{r}$, where
$\mathbf{F}(x, y, z) = x^2 y\,\mathbf{i} + \frac{1}{3}x^3\,\mathbf{j} + xy\,\mathbf{k}$ and C is the curve of intersection of the hyperbolic paraboloid $z = y^2 - x^2$ and the cylinder $x^2 + y^2 = 1$ oriented counterclockwise as viewed from above.

(b) Graph both the hyperbolic paraboloid and the cylinder with domains chosen so that you can see the curve C and the surface that you used in part (a).

(c) Find parametric equations for C and use them to graph C.

13–15 ▍▍ Verify that Stokes' Theorem is true for the given vector field $\mathbf{F}$ and surface S.

13. $\mathbf{F}(x, y, z) = y^2\,\mathbf{i} + x\,\mathbf{j} + z^2\,\mathbf{k}$,
S is the part of the paraboloid $z = x^2 + y^2$ that lies below the plane $z = 1$, oriented upward

14. $\mathbf{F}(x, y, z) = x\,\mathbf{i} + y\,\mathbf{j} + xyz\,\mathbf{k}$,
S is the part of the plane $2x + y + z = 2$ that lies in the first octant, oriented upward

15. $\mathbf{F}(x, y, z) = y\,\mathbf{i} + z\,\mathbf{j} + x\,\mathbf{k}$,
S is the hemisphere $x^2 + y^2 + z^2 = 1$, $y \geqslant 0$, oriented in the direction of the positive y-axis

16. Let

$$\mathbf{F}(x, y, z) = \langle ax^3 - 3xz^2, x^2 y + by^3, cz^3 \rangle$$

Let C be the curve in Exercise 12 and consider all possible smooth surfaces S whose boundary curve is C. Find the values of a, b, and c for which $\iint_S \mathbf{F} \cdot d\mathbf{S}$ is independent of the choice of S.

17. Calculate the work done by the force field

$$\mathbf{F}(x, y, z) = (x^x + z^2)\,\mathbf{i} + (y^y + x^2)\,\mathbf{j} + (z^z + y^2)\,\mathbf{k}$$

when a particle moves under its influence around the edge of the part of the sphere $x^2 + y^2 + z^2 = 4$ that lies in the first octant, in a counterclockwise direction as viewed from above.

18. Evaluate $\int_C (y + \sin x)\, dx + (z^2 + \cos y)\, dy + x^3\, dz$, where C is the curve $\mathbf{r}(t) = \langle \sin t, \cos t, \sin 2t \rangle$, $0 \le t \le 2\pi$. [*Hint:* Observe that C lies on the surface $z = 2xy$.]

19. If S is a sphere and $\mathbf{F}$ satisfies the hypotheses of Stokes' Theorem, show that $\iint_S \operatorname{curl} \mathbf{F} \cdot d\mathbf{S} = 0$.

20. Suppose S and C satisfy the hypotheses of Stokes' Theorem and f, g have continuous second-order partial derivatives. Use Exercises 24 and 26 in Section 17.5 to show the following.

(a) $\int_C (f \nabla g) \cdot d\mathbf{r} = \iint_S (\nabla f \times \nabla g) \cdot d\mathbf{S}$

(b) $\int_C (f \nabla f) \cdot d\mathbf{r} = 0$

(c) $\int_C (f \nabla g + g \nabla f) \cdot d\mathbf{r} = 0$

▚▚ WRITING PROJECT

Three Men and Two Theorems

Although two of the most important theorems in vector calculus are named after George Green and George Stokes, a third man, William Thomson (also known as Lord Kelvin), played a large role in the formulation, dissemination, and application of both of these results. All three men were interested in how the two theorems could help to explain and predict physical phenomena in electricity and magnetism and fluid flow. The basic facts of the story are given in the margin notes on pages 1120 and 1157.

Write a report on the historical origins of Green's Theorem and Stokes' Theorem. Explain the similarities and relationship between the theorems. Discuss the roles that Green, Thomson, and Stokes played in discovering these theorems and making them widely known. Show how both theorems arose from the investigation of electricity and magnetism and were later used to study a variety of physical problems.

The dictionary edited by Gillispie [2] is a good source for both biographical and scientific information. The book by Hutchinson [5] gives an account of Stokes' life and the book by Thompson [8] is a biography of Lord Kelvin. The articles by Grattan-Guinness [3] and Gray [4] and the book by Cannell [1] give background on the extraordinary life and works of Green. Additional historical and mathematical information is found in the books by Katz [6] and Kline [7].

▚▚ The photograph shows a stained-glass window at Cambridge University in honor of George Green.

Courtesy of the Masters and Fellows of Gonville and Caius College, University of Cambridge, England

1. D. M. Cannell, *George Green, Mathematician and Physicist 1793–1841: The Background to His Life and Work* (Philadelphia: Society for Industrial and Applied Mathematics, 2001).

2. C. C. Gillispie, ed., *Dictionary of Scientific Biography* (New York: Scribner's, 1974). See the article on Green by P. J. Wallis in Volume XV and the articles on Thomson by Jed Buchwald and on Stokes by E. M. Parkinson in Volume XIII.

3. I. Grattan-Guinness, "Why did George Green write his essay of 1828 on electricity and magnetism?" *Amer. Math. Monthly*, Vol. 102 (1995), pp. 387–396.

4. J. Gray, "There was a jolly miller." *The New Scientist*, Vol. 139 (1993), pp. 24–27.

5. G. E. Hutchinson, *The Enchanted Voyage and Other Studies* (Westport Conn.: Greenwood Press, 1978).

6. Victor Katz, *A History of Mathematics: An Introduction* (New York: HarperCollins, 1993), pp. 678–680.

7. Morris Kline, *Mathematical Thought from Ancient to Modern Times* (New York: Oxford University Press, 1972), pp. 683–685.

8. Sylvanus P. Thompson, *The Life of Lord Kelvin* (New York: Chelsea, 1976).

17.9 The Divergence Theorem

In Section 17.5 we rewrote Green's Theorem in a vector version as

$$\int_C \mathbf{F} \cdot \mathbf{n}\, ds = \iint_D \operatorname{div} \mathbf{F}(x, y)\, dA$$

where C is the positively oriented boundary curve of the plane region D. If we were seeking to extend this theorem to vector fields on $\mathbb{R}^3$, we might make the guess that

$$\boxed{1} \qquad \iint_S \mathbf{F} \cdot \mathbf{n}\, dS = \iiint_E \operatorname{div} \mathbf{F}(x, y, z)\, dV$$

where S is the boundary surface of the solid region E. It turns out that Equation 1 is true, under appropriate hypotheses, and is called the Divergence Theorem. Notice its similarity to Green's Theorem and Stokes' Theorem in that it relates the integral of a derivative of a function ($\operatorname{div} \mathbf{F}$ in this case) over a region to the integral of the original function $\mathbf{F}$ over the boundary of the region.

At this stage you may wish to review the various types of regions over which we were able to evaluate triple integrals in Section 16.7. We state and prove the Divergence Theorem for regions E that are simultaneously of types 1, 2, and 3 and we call such regions **simple solid regions**. (For instance, regions bounded by ellipsoids or rectangular boxes are simple solid regions.) The boundary of E is a closed surface, and we use the convention, introduced in Section 17.7, that the positive orientation is outward; that is, the unit normal vector $\mathbf{n}$ is directed outward from E.

|||| The Divergence Theorem is sometimes called Gauss's Theorem after the great German mathematician Karl Friedrich Gauss (1777–1855), who discovered this theorem during his investigation of electrostatics. In Eastern Europe the Divergence Theorem is known as Ostrogradsky's Theorem after the Russian mathematician Mikhail Ostrogradsky (1801–1862), who published this result in 1826.

> **The Divergence Theorem** Let E be a simple solid region and let S be the boundary surface of E, given with positive (outward) orientation. Let $\mathbf{F}$ be a vector field whose component functions have continuous partial derivatives on an open region that contains E. Then
>
> $$\iint_S \mathbf{F} \cdot d\mathbf{S} = \iiint_E \operatorname{div} \mathbf{F}\, dV$$

Proof Let $\mathbf{F} = P\,\mathbf{i} + Q\,\mathbf{j} + R\,\mathbf{k}$. Then

$$\operatorname{div} \mathbf{F} = \frac{\partial P}{\partial x} + \frac{\partial Q}{\partial y} + \frac{\partial R}{\partial z}$$

so

$$\iiint_E \operatorname{div} \mathbf{F}\, dV = \iiint_E \frac{\partial P}{\partial x}\, dV + \iiint_E \frac{\partial Q}{\partial y}\, dV + \iiint_E \frac{\partial R}{\partial z}\, dV$$

If $\mathbf{n}$ is the unit outward normal of S, then the surface integral on the left side of the Divergence Theorem is

$$\iint_S \mathbf{F} \cdot d\mathbf{S} = \iint_S \mathbf{F} \cdot \mathbf{n}\, dS = \iint_S (P\,\mathbf{i} + Q\,\mathbf{j} + R\,\mathbf{k}) \cdot \mathbf{n}\, dS$$

$$= \iint_S P\,\mathbf{i} \cdot \mathbf{n}\, dS + \iint_S Q\,\mathbf{j} \cdot \mathbf{n}\, dS + \iint_S R\,\mathbf{k} \cdot \mathbf{n}\, dS$$

Therefore, to prove the Divergence Theorem, it suffices to prove the following three equations:

$$\boxed{2} \qquad \iint_S P\,\mathbf{i}\cdot\mathbf{n}\,dS = \iiint_E \frac{\partial P}{\partial x}\,dV$$

$$\boxed{3} \qquad \iint_S Q\,\mathbf{j}\cdot\mathbf{n}\,dS = \iiint_E \frac{\partial Q}{\partial y}\,dV$$

$$\boxed{4} \qquad \iint_S R\,\mathbf{k}\cdot\mathbf{n}\,dS = \iiint_E \frac{\partial R}{\partial z}\,dV$$

To prove Equation 4 we use the fact that E is a type 1 region:

$$E = \{(x, y, z)\,|\,(x, y) \in D,\ u_1(x, y) \leq z \leq u_2(x, y)\}$$

where D is the projection of E onto the xy-plane. By Equation 16.7.6, we have

$$\iiint_E \frac{\partial R}{\partial z}\,dV = \iint_D \left[\int_{u_1(x,\,y)}^{u_2(x,\,y)} \frac{\partial R}{\partial z}(x, y, z)\,dz \right] dA$$

and, therefore, by the Fundamental Theorem of Calculus,

$$\boxed{5} \qquad \iiint_E \frac{\partial R}{\partial z}\,dV = \iint_D \left[R(x, y, u_2(x, y)) - R(x, y, u_1(x, y)) \right] dA$$

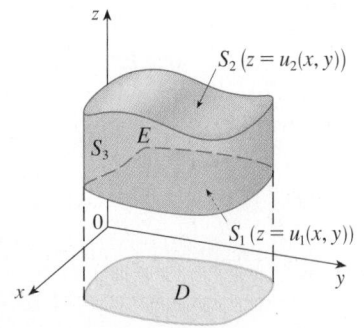

FIGURE 1

The boundary surface S consists of three pieces: the bottom surface S_1, the top surface S_2, and possibly a vertical surface S_3, which lies above the boundary curve of D. (See Figure 1. It might happen that S_3 doesn't appear, as in the case of a sphere.) Notice that on S_3 we have $\mathbf{k}\cdot\mathbf{n} = 0$, because $\mathbf{k}$ is vertical and $\mathbf{n}$ is horizontal, and so

$$\iint_{S_3} R\,\mathbf{k}\cdot\mathbf{n}\,dS = \iint_{S_3} 0\,dS = 0$$

Thus, regardless of whether there is a vertical surface, we can write

$$\boxed{6} \qquad \iint_S R\,\mathbf{k}\cdot\mathbf{n}\,dS = \iint_{S_1} R\,\mathbf{k}\cdot\mathbf{n}\,dS + \iint_{S_2} R\,\mathbf{k}\cdot\mathbf{n}\,dS$$

The equation of S_2 is $z = u_2(x, y)$, $(x, y) \in D$, and the outward normal $\mathbf{n}$ points upward, so from Equation 17.7.8 (with $\mathbf{F}$ replaced by $R\,\mathbf{k}$) we have

$$\iint_{S_2} R\,\mathbf{k}\cdot\mathbf{n}\,dS = \iint_D R(x, y, u_2(x, y))\,dA$$

On S_1 we have $z = u_1(x, y)$, but here the outward normal $\mathbf{n}$ points downward, so we multiply by -1:

$$\iint_{S_1} R\,\mathbf{k}\cdot\mathbf{n}\,dS = -\iint_D R(x, y, u_1(x, y))\,dA$$

Therefore, Equation 6 gives

$$\iint_S R\,\mathbf{k}\cdot\mathbf{n}\,dS = \iint_D [R(x, y, u_2(x, y)) - R(x, y, u_1(x, y))]\,dA$$

Comparison with Equation 5 shows that

$$\iint_S R\,\mathbf{k}\cdot\mathbf{n}\,dS = \iiint_E \frac{\partial R}{\partial z}\,dV$$

▓ Notice that the method of proof of the Divergence Theorem is very similar to that of Green's Theorem.

Equations 2 and 3 are proved in a similar manner using the expressions for E as a type 2 or type 3 region, respectively. ▬

EXAMPLE 1 Find the flux of the vector field $\mathbf{F}(x, y, z) = z\,\mathbf{i} + y\,\mathbf{j} + x\,\mathbf{k}$ over the unit sphere $x^2 + y^2 + z^2 = 1$.

SOLUTION First we compute the divergence of $\mathbf{F}$:

$$\operatorname{div}\mathbf{F} = \frac{\partial}{\partial x}(z) + \frac{\partial}{\partial y}(y) + \frac{\partial}{\partial z}(x) = 1$$

The unit sphere S is the boundary of the unit ball B given by $x^2 + y^2 + z^2 \leqslant 1$. Thus, the Divergence Theorem gives the flux as

▓ The solution in Example 1 should be compared with the solution in Example 5 in Section 17.7.

$$\iint_S \mathbf{F}\cdot d\mathbf{S} = \iiint_B \operatorname{div}\mathbf{F}\,dV = \iiint_B 1\,dV$$

$$= V(B) = \tfrac{4}{3}\pi(1)^3 = \frac{4\pi}{3}$$ ▬

EXAMPLE 2 Evaluate $\displaystyle\iint_S \mathbf{F}\cdot d\mathbf{S}$, where

$$\mathbf{F}(x, y, z) = xy\,\mathbf{i} + \left(y^2 + e^{xz^2}\right)\mathbf{j} + \sin(xy)\,\mathbf{k}$$

and S is the surface of the region E bounded by the parabolic cylinder $z = 1 - x^2$ and the planes $z = 0$, $y = 0$, and $y + z = 2$. (See Figure 2.)

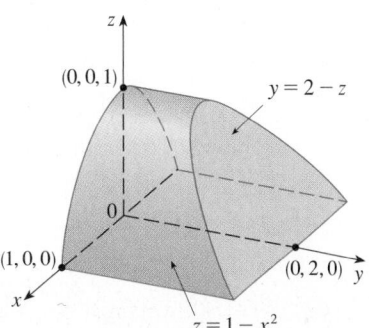

FIGURE 2

SOLUTION It would be extremely difficult to evaluate the given surface integral directly. (We would have to evaluate four surface integrals corresponding to the four pieces of S.)

Furthermore, the divergence of $\mathbf{F}$ is much less complicated than $\mathbf{F}$ itself:

$$\text{div } \mathbf{F} = \frac{\partial}{\partial x}(xy) + \frac{\partial}{\partial y}\left(y^2 + e^{xz^2}\right) + \frac{\partial}{\partial z}(\sin xy)$$

$$= y + 2y = 3y$$

Therefore, we use the Divergence Theorem to transform the given surface integral into a triple integral. The easiest way to evaluate the triple integral is to express E as a type 3 region:

$$E = \{(x, y, z) \mid -1 \leqslant x \leqslant 1,\ 0 \leqslant z \leqslant 1 - x^2,\ 0 \leqslant y \leqslant 2 - z\}$$

Then we have

$$\iint_S \mathbf{F} \cdot d\mathbf{S} = \iiint_E \text{div } \mathbf{F}\, dV = \iiint_E 3y\, dV$$

$$= 3 \int_{-1}^{1} \int_0^{1-x^2} \int_0^{2-z} y\, dy\, dz\, dx$$

$$= 3 \int_{-1}^{1} \int_0^{1-x^2} \frac{(2-z)^2}{2}\, dz\, dx$$

$$= \frac{3}{2} \int_{-1}^{1} \left[-\frac{(2-z)^3}{3} \right]_0^{1-x^2} dx$$

$$= -\tfrac{1}{2} \int_{-1}^{1} \left[(x^2 + 1)^3 - 8 \right] dx$$

$$= -\int_0^1 (x^6 + 3x^4 + 3x^2 - 7)\, dx = \tfrac{184}{35}$$

Although we have proved the Divergence Theorem only for simple solid regions, it can be proved for regions that are finite unions of simple solid regions. (The procedure is similar to the one we used in Section 17.4 to extend Green's Theorem.)

For example, let's consider the region E that lies between the closed surfaces S_1 and S_2, where S_1 lies inside S_2. Let $\mathbf{n}_1$ and $\mathbf{n}_2$ be outward normals of S_1 and S_2. Then the boundary surface of E is $S = S_1 \cup S_2$ and its normal $\mathbf{n}$ is given by $\mathbf{n} = -\mathbf{n}_1$ on S_1 and $\mathbf{n} = \mathbf{n}_2$ on S_2. (See Figure 3.) Applying the Divergence Theorem to S, we get

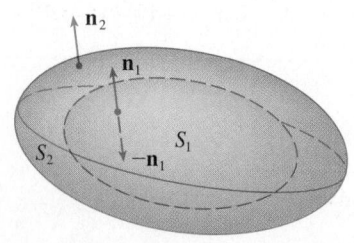

FIGURE 3

$$\boxed{7} \qquad \iiint_E \text{div } \mathbf{F}\, dV = \iint_S \mathbf{F} \cdot d\mathbf{S} = \iint_S \mathbf{F} \cdot \mathbf{n}\, dS$$

$$= \iint_{S_1} \mathbf{F} \cdot (-\mathbf{n}_1)\, dS + \iint_{S_2} \mathbf{F} \cdot \mathbf{n}_2\, dS$$

$$= -\iint_{S_1} \mathbf{F} \cdot d\mathbf{S} + \iint_{S_2} \mathbf{F} \cdot d\mathbf{S}$$

Let's apply this to the electric field (see Example 5 in Section 17.1):

$$\mathbf{E}(\mathbf{x}) = \frac{\varepsilon Q}{|\mathbf{x}|^3}\, \mathbf{x}$$

where S_1 is a small sphere with radius a and center the origin. You can verify that div $\mathbf{E} = 0$. (See Exercise 21.) Therefore, Equation 7 gives

$$\iint_{S_2} \mathbf{E} \cdot d\mathbf{S} = \iint_{S_1} \mathbf{E} \cdot d\mathbf{S} + \iiint_E \operatorname{div} \mathbf{E}\, dV$$

$$= \iint_{S_1} \mathbf{E} \cdot d\mathbf{S} = \iint_{S_1} \mathbf{E} \cdot \mathbf{n}\, dS$$

The point of this calculation is that we can compute the surface integral over S_1 because S_1 is a sphere. The normal vector at $\mathbf{x}$ is $\mathbf{x}/|\mathbf{x}|$. Therefore

$$\mathbf{E} \cdot \mathbf{n} = \frac{\varepsilon Q}{|\mathbf{x}|^3} \mathbf{x} \cdot \left(\frac{\mathbf{x}}{|\mathbf{x}|}\right) = \frac{\varepsilon Q}{|\mathbf{x}|^4} \mathbf{x} \cdot \mathbf{x}$$

$$= \frac{\varepsilon Q}{|\mathbf{x}|^2} = \frac{\varepsilon Q}{a^2}$$

since the equation of S_1 is $|\mathbf{x}| = a$. Thus, we have

$$\iint_{S_2} \mathbf{E} \cdot d\mathbf{S} = \iint_{S_1} \mathbf{E} \cdot \mathbf{n}\, dS$$

$$= \frac{\varepsilon Q}{a^2} \iint_{S_1} dS = \frac{\varepsilon Q}{a^2} A(S_1)$$

$$= \frac{\varepsilon Q}{a^2} 4\pi a^2 = 4\pi \varepsilon Q$$

This shows that the electric flux of $\mathbf{E}$ is $4\pi\varepsilon Q$ through *any* closed surface S_2 that contains the origin. [This is a special case of Gauss's Law (Equation 17.7.10) for a single charge. The relationship between ε and ε_0 is $\varepsilon = 1/(4\pi\varepsilon_0)$.]

Another application of the Divergence Theorem occurs in fluid flow. Let $\mathbf{v}(x, y, z)$ be the velocity field of a fluid with constant density ρ. Then $\mathbf{F} = \rho \mathbf{v}$ is the rate of flow per unit area. If $P_0(x_0, y_0, z_0)$ is a point in the fluid and B_a is a ball with center P_0 and very small radius a, then div $\mathbf{F}(P) \approx$ div $\mathbf{F}(P_0)$ for all points in B_a since div $\mathbf{F}$ is continuous. We approximate the flux over the boundary sphere S_a as follows:

$$\iint_{S_a} \mathbf{F} \cdot d\mathbf{S} = \iiint_{B_a} \operatorname{div} \mathbf{F}\, dV$$

$$\approx \iiint_{B_a} \operatorname{div} \mathbf{F}(P_0)\, dV$$

$$= \operatorname{div} \mathbf{F}(P_0) V(B_a)$$

This approximation becomes better as $a \to 0$ and suggests that

$$\boxed{8} \qquad \operatorname{div} \mathbf{F}(P_0) = \lim_{a \to 0} \frac{1}{V(B_a)} \iint_{S_a} \mathbf{F} \cdot d\mathbf{S}$$

Equation 8 says that div $\mathbf{F}(P_0)$ is the net rate of outward flux per unit volume at P_0. (This is the reason for the name *divergence*.) If div $\mathbf{F}(P) > 0$, the net flow is outward near P and P is called a **source**. If div $\mathbf{F}(P) < 0$, the net flow is inward near P and P is called a **sink**.

For the vector field in Figure 4, it appears that the vectors that end near P_1 are shorter than the vectors that start near P_1. Thus, the net flow is outward near P_1, so div $\mathbf{F}(P_1) > 0$ and P_1 is a source. Near P_2, on the other hand, the incoming arrows are longer than the outgoing arrows. Here the net flow is inward, so div $\mathbf{F}(P_2) < 0$ and P_2 is a sink. We can use the formula for $\mathbf{F}$ to confirm this impression. Since $\mathbf{F} = x^2\mathbf{i} + y^2\mathbf{j}$, we have div $\mathbf{F} = 2x + 2y$, which is positive when $y > -x$. So the points above the line $y = -x$ are sources and those below are sinks.

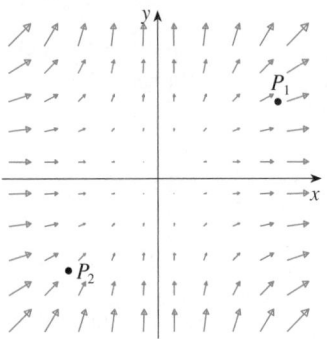

FIGURE 4
The vector field $\mathbf{F} = x^2\mathbf{i} + y^2\mathbf{j}$

17.9 Exercises

1. A vector field $\mathbf{F}$ is shown. Use the interpretation of divergence derived in this section to determine whether div $\mathbf{F}$ is positive or negative at P_1 and at P_2.

2. (a) Are the points P_1 and P_2 sources or sinks for the vector field $\mathbf{F}$ shown in the figure? Give an explanation based solely on the picture.
   (b) Given that $\mathbf{F}(x, y) = \langle x, y^2 \rangle$, use the definition of divergence to verify your answer to part (a).

3–6 |||| Verify that the Divergence Theorem is true for the vector field $\mathbf{F}$ on the region E.

3. $\mathbf{F}(x, y, z) = 3x\mathbf{i} + xy\mathbf{j} + 2xz\mathbf{k}$,
E is the cube bounded by the planes $x = 0$, $x = 1$, $y = 0$, $y = 1$, $z = 0$, and $z = 1$

4. $\mathbf{F}(x, y, z) = x^2\mathbf{i} + xy\mathbf{j} + z\mathbf{k}$,
E is the solid bounded by the paraboloid $z = 4 - x^2 - y^2$ and the xy-plane

5. $\mathbf{F}(x, y, z) = xy\mathbf{i} + yz\mathbf{j} + zx\mathbf{k}$,
E is the solid cylinder $x^2 + y^2 \leq 1$, $0 \leq z \leq 1$

6. $\mathbf{F}(x, y, z) = x\mathbf{i} + y\mathbf{j} + z\mathbf{k}$,
E is the unit ball $x^2 + y^2 + z^2 \leq 1$

7–17 |||| Use the Divergence Theorem to calculate the surface integral $\iint_S \mathbf{F} \cdot d\mathbf{S}$; that is, calculate the flux of $\mathbf{F}$ across S.

7. $\mathbf{F}(x, y, z) = e^x \sin y\,\mathbf{i} + e^x \cos y\,\mathbf{j} + yz^2\,\mathbf{k}$,
S is the surface of the box bounded by the planes $x = 0$, $x = 1$, $y = 0$, $y = 1$, $z = 0$, and $z = 2$

8. $\mathbf{F}(x, y, z) = x^2z^3\,\mathbf{i} + 2xyz^3\,\mathbf{j} + xz^4\,\mathbf{k}$,
S is the surface of the box with vertices $(\pm1, \pm2, \pm3)$

9. $\mathbf{F}(x, y, z) = 3xy^2\,\mathbf{i} + xe^z\,\mathbf{j} + z^3\,\mathbf{k}$,
S is the surface of the solid bounded by the cylinder $y^2 + z^2 = 1$ and the planes $x = -1$ and $x = 2$

10. $\mathbf{F}(x, y, z) = x^3y\,\mathbf{i} - x^2y^2\,\mathbf{j} - x^2yz\,\mathbf{k}$,
S is the surface of the solid bounded by the hyperboloid $x^2 + y^2 - z^2 = 1$ and the planes $z = -2$ and $z = 2$

11. $\mathbf{F}(x, y, z) = xy \sin z\,\mathbf{i} + \cos(xz)\,\mathbf{j} + y \cos z\,\mathbf{k}$,
S is the ellipsoid $x^2/a^2 + y^2/b^2 + z^2/c^2 = 1$

12. $\mathbf{F}(x, y, z) = x^2 y\,\mathbf{i} + xy^2\,\mathbf{j} + 2xyz\,\mathbf{k}$,
S is the surface of the tetrahedron bounded by the planes
$x = 0$, $y = 0$, $z = 0$, and $x + 2y + z = 2$

13. $\mathbf{F}(x, y, z) = (\cos z + xy^2)\,\mathbf{i} + xe^{-z}\,\mathbf{j} + (\sin y + x^2 z)\,\mathbf{k}$,
S is the surface of the solid bounded by the paraboloid
$z = x^2 + y^2$ and the plane $z = 4$

14. $\mathbf{F}(x, y, z) = x^4\,\mathbf{i} - x^3 z^2\,\mathbf{j} + 4xy^2 z\,\mathbf{k}$,
S is the surface of the solid bounded by the cylinder
$x^2 + y^2 = 1$ and the planes $z = x + 2$ and $z = 0$

15. $\mathbf{F}(x, y, z) = 4x^3 z\,\mathbf{i} + 4y^3 z\,\mathbf{j} + 3z^4\,\mathbf{k}$,
S is the sphere with radius R and center the origin

16. $\mathbf{F}(x, y, z) = (x^3 + y \sin z)\,\mathbf{i} + (y^3 + z \sin x)\,\mathbf{j} + 3z\,\mathbf{k}$,
S is the surface of the solid bounded by the hemispheres
$z = \sqrt{4 - x^2 - y^2}$, $z = \sqrt{1 - x^2 - y^2}$ and the plane $z = 0$

CAS 17. $\mathbf{F}(x, y, z) = e^y \tan z\,\mathbf{i} + y\sqrt{3 - x^2}\,\mathbf{j} + x \sin y\,\mathbf{k}$,
S is the surface of the solid that lies above the xy-plane
and below the surface $z = 2 - x^4 - y^4$, $-1 \leq x \leq 1$,
$-1 \leq y \leq 1$

CAS 18. Use a computer algebra system to plot the vector field
$\mathbf{F}(x, y, z) = \sin x \cos^2 y\,\mathbf{i} + \sin^3 y \cos^4 z\,\mathbf{j} + \sin^5 z \cos^6 x\,\mathbf{k}$
in the cube cut from the first octant by the planes $x = \pi/2$,
$y = \pi/2$, and $z = \pi/2$. Then compute the flux across the
surface of the cube.

19. Use the Divergence Theorem to evaluate $\iint_S \mathbf{F} \cdot d\mathbf{S}$, where
$$\mathbf{F}(x, y, z) = z^2 x\,\mathbf{i} + \left(\tfrac{1}{3}y^3 + \tan z\right)\mathbf{j} + (x^2 z + y^2)\,\mathbf{k}$$
and S is the top half of the sphere $x^2 + y^2 + z^2 = 1$.
[*Hint:* Note that S is not a closed surface. First compute
integrals over S_1 and S_2, where S_1 is the disk $x^2 + y^2 \leq 1$,
oriented downward, and $S_2 = S \cup S_1$.]

20. Let $\mathbf{F}(x, y, z) = z \tan^{-1}(y^2)\,\mathbf{i} + z^3 \ln(x^2 + 1)\,\mathbf{j} + z\,\mathbf{k}$. Find the
flux of $\mathbf{F}$ across the part of the paraboloid $x^2 + y^2 + z = 2$
that lies above the plane $z = 1$ and is oriented upward.

21. Verify that div $\mathbf{E} = 0$ for the electric field
$$\mathbf{E}(\mathbf{x}) = \frac{\varepsilon Q}{|\mathbf{x}|^3}\,\mathbf{x}$$

22. Use the Divergence Theorem to evaluate
$$\iint_S (2x + 2y + z^2)\,dS$$
where S is the sphere $x^2 + y^2 + z^2 = 1$.

23–28 |||| Prove each identity, assuming that S and E satisfy the
conditions of the Divergence Theorem and the scalar functions
and components of the vector fields have continuous second-order
partial derivatives.

23. $\iint_S \mathbf{a} \cdot \mathbf{n}\,dS = 0$, where $\mathbf{a}$ is a constant vector

24. $V(E) = \tfrac{1}{3}\iint_S \mathbf{F} \cdot d\mathbf{S}$, where $\mathbf{F}(x, y, z) = x\,\mathbf{i} + y\,\mathbf{j} + z\,\mathbf{k}$

25. $\iint_S \text{curl } \mathbf{F} \cdot d\mathbf{S} = 0$

26. $\iint_S D_n f\,dS = \iiint_E \nabla^2 f\,dV$

27. $\iint_S (f\nabla g) \cdot \mathbf{n}\,dS = \iiint_E (f\nabla^2 g + \nabla f \cdot \nabla g)\,dV$

28. $\iint_S (f\nabla g - g\nabla f) \cdot \mathbf{n}\,dS = \iiint_E (f\nabla^2 g - g\nabla^2 f)\,dV$

29. Suppose S and E satisfy the conditions of the Divergence Theorem and f is a scalar function with continuous partial derivatives. Prove that
$$\iint_S f\mathbf{n}\,dS = \iiint_E \nabla f\,dV$$
These surface and triple integrals of vector functions are
vectors defined by integrating each component function.
[*Hint:* Start by applying the Divergence Theorem to $\mathbf{F} = f\mathbf{c}$,
where $\mathbf{c}$ is an arbitrary constant vector.]

30. A solid occupies a region E with surface S and is immersed in
a liquid with constant density ρ. We set up a coordinate system
so that the xy-plane coincides with the surface of the liquid and
positive values of z are measured downward into the liquid.
Then the pressure at depth z is $p = \rho g z$, where g is the acceleration due to gravity (see Section 9.3). The total buoyant force
on the solid due to the pressure distribution is given by the surface integral
$$\mathbf{F} = -\iint_S p\mathbf{n}\,dS$$
where $\mathbf{n}$ is the outer unit normal. Use the result of Exercise 29
to show that $\mathbf{F} = -W\mathbf{k}$, where W is the weight of the liquid
displaced by the solid. (Note that $\mathbf{F}$ is directed upward because
z is directed downward.) The result is *Archimedes' principle:*
The buoyant force on an object equals the weight of the displaced liquid.

17.10 Summary

The main results of this chapter are all higher-dimensional versions of the Fundamental Theorem of Calculus. To help you remember them, we collect them together here (without hypotheses) so that you can see more easily their essential similarity. Notice that in each case we have an integral of a "derivative" over a region on the left side, and the right side involves the values of the original function only on the *boundary* of the region.

Fundamental Theorem of Calculus

$$\int_a^b F'(x)\,dx = F(b) - F(a)$$

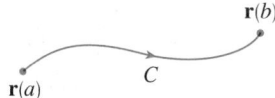

Fundamental Theorem for Line Integrals

$$\int_C \nabla f \cdot d\mathbf{r} = f(\mathbf{r}(b)) - f(\mathbf{r}(a))$$

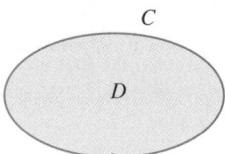

Green's Theorem

$$\iint_D \left(\frac{\partial Q}{\partial x} - \frac{\partial P}{\partial y} \right) dA = \int_C P\,dx + Q\,dy$$

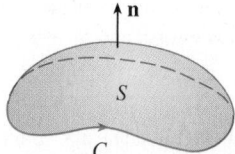

Stokes' Theorem

$$\iint_S \operatorname{curl} \mathbf{F} \cdot d\mathbf{S} = \int_C \mathbf{F} \cdot d\mathbf{r}$$

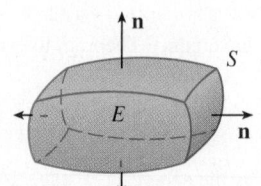

Divergence Theorem

$$\iiint_E \operatorname{div} \mathbf{F}\,dV = \iint_S \mathbf{F} \cdot d\mathbf{S}$$

17 Review

1. What is a vector field? Give three examples that have physical meaning.

2. (a) What is a conservative vector field?
   (b) What is a potential function?

3. (a) Write the definition of the line integral of a scalar function f along a smooth curve C with respect to arc length.
   (b) How do you evaluate such a line integral?
   (c) Write expressions for the mass and center of mass of a thin wire shaped like a curve C if the wire has linear density function $\rho(x, y)$.
   (d) Write the definitions of the line integrals along C of a scalar function f with respect to x, y, and z.
   (e) How do you evaluate these line integrals?

4. (a) Define the line integral of a vector field $\mathbf{F}$ along a smooth curve C given by a vector function $\mathbf{r}(t)$.
   (b) If $\mathbf{F}$ is a force field, what does this line integral represent?
   (c) If $\mathbf{F} = \langle P, Q, R \rangle$, what is the connection between the line integral of $\mathbf{F}$ and the line integrals of the component functions P, Q, and R?

5. State the Fundamental Theorem for Line Integrals.

6. (a) What does it mean to say that $\int_C \mathbf{F} \cdot d\mathbf{r}$ is independent of path?
   (b) If you know that $\int_C \mathbf{F} \cdot d\mathbf{r}$ is independent of path, what can you say about $\mathbf{F}$?

7. State Green's Theorem.

8. Write expressions for the area enclosed by a curve C in terms of line integrals around C.

9. Suppose $\mathbf{F}$ is a vector field on $\mathbb{R}^3$.
   (a) Define curl $\mathbf{F}$.
   (b) Define div $\mathbf{F}$.

(c) If $\mathbf{F}$ is a velocity field in fluid flow, what are the physical interpretations of curl $\mathbf{F}$ and div $\mathbf{F}$?

10. If $\mathbf{F} = P\,\mathbf{i} + Q\,\mathbf{j}$, how do you test to determine whether $\mathbf{F}$ is conservative? What if $\mathbf{F}$ is a vector field on $\mathbb{R}^3$?

11. (a) What is a parametric surface? What are its grid curves?
    (b) Write an expression for the area of a parametric surface.
    (c) What is the area of a surface given by an equation $z = g(x, y)$?

12. (a) Write the definition of the surface integral of a scalar function f over a surface S.
    (b) How do you evaluate such an integral if S is a parametric surface given by a vector function $\mathbf{r}(u, v)$?
    (c) What if S is given by an equation $z = g(x, y)$?
    (d) If a thin sheet has the shape of a surface S, and the density at (x, y, z) is $\rho(x, y, z)$, write expressions for the mass and center of mass of the sheet.

13. (a) What is an oriented surface? Give an example of a non-orientable surface.
    (b) Define the surface integral (or flux) of a vector field $\mathbf{F}$ over an oriented surface S with unit normal vector $\mathbf{n}$.
    (c) How do you evaluate such an integral if S is a parametric surface given by a vector function $\mathbf{r}(u, v)$?
    (d) What if S is given by an equation $z = g(x, y)$?

14. State Stokes' Theorem.

15. State the Divergence Theorem.

16. In what ways are the Fundamental Theorem for Line Integrals, Green's Theorem, Stokes' Theorem, and the Divergence Theorem similar?

Determine whether the statement is true or false. If it is true, explain why. If it is false, explain why or give an example that disproves the statement.

1. If $\mathbf{F}$ is a vector field, then div $\mathbf{F}$ is a vector field.

2. If $\mathbf{F}$ is a vector field, then curl $\mathbf{F}$ is a vector field.

3. If f has continuous partial derivatives of all orders on $\mathbb{R}^3$, then $\operatorname{div}(\operatorname{curl} \nabla f) = 0$.

4. If f has continuous partial derivatives on $\mathbb{R}^3$ and C is any circle, then $\int_C \nabla f \cdot d\mathbf{r} = 0$.

5. If $\mathbf{F} = P\,\mathbf{i} + Q\,\mathbf{j}$ and $P_y = Q_x$ in an open region D, then $\mathbf{F}$ is conservative.

6. $\int_{-C} f(x, y) \, ds = -\int_C f(x, y) \, ds$

7. If S is a sphere and $\mathbf{F}$ is a constant vector field, then $\iint_S \mathbf{F} \cdot d\mathbf{S} = 0$.

8. There is a vector field $\mathbf{F}$ such that
$$\operatorname{curl} \mathbf{F} = x\,\mathbf{i} + y\,\mathbf{j} + z\,\mathbf{k}$$

— ◦ EXERCISES ◦ —

1. A vector field **F**, a curve C, and a point P are shown.
   (a) Is $\int_C \mathbf{F} \cdot d\mathbf{r}$ positive, negative, or zero? Explain.
   (b) Is div $\mathbf{F}(P)$ positive, negative, or zero? Explain.

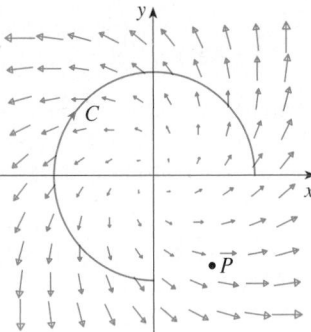

2–9 ▏▎▎ Evaluate the line integral.

2. $\int_C x \, ds$,
   C is the arc of the parabola $y = x^2$ from $(0, 0)$ to $(1, 1)$

3. $\int_C x^3 z \, ds$,
   C: $x = 2 \sin t$, $y = t$, $z = 2 \cos t$, $0 \le t \le \pi/2$

4. $\int_C xy \, dx + y \, dy$,
   C is the sine curve $y = \sin x$, $0 \le x \le \pi/2$

5. $\int_C x^3 y \, dx - x \, dy$,
   C is the circle $x^2 + y^2 = 1$ with counterclockwise
   orientation

6. $\int_C \sqrt{xy} \, dx + e^y \, dy + xz \, dz$,
   C is given by $\mathbf{r}(t) = t^4 \mathbf{i} + t^2 \mathbf{j} + t^3 \mathbf{k}$, $0 \le t \le 1$

7. $\int_C y \, dx + z \, dy + x \, dz$,
   C consists of the line segments from $(0, 0, 0)$ to $(1, 1, 2)$ and
   from $(1, 1, 2)$ to $(3, 1, 4)$

8. $\int_C \mathbf{F} \cdot d\mathbf{r}$, where $\mathbf{F}(x, y) = xy \, \mathbf{i} + x^2 \mathbf{j}$ and C is given by
   $\mathbf{r}(t) = \sin t \, \mathbf{i} + (1 + t) \mathbf{j}$, $0 \le t \le \pi$

9. $\int_C \mathbf{F} \cdot d\mathbf{r}$, where $\mathbf{F}(x, y, z) = e^z \mathbf{i} + xz \, \mathbf{j} + (x + y) \mathbf{k}$ and
   C is given by $\mathbf{r}(t) = t^2 \mathbf{i} + t^3 \mathbf{j} - t \, \mathbf{k}$, $0 \le t \le 1$

10. Find the work done by the force field

$$\mathbf{F}(x, y, z) = z \, \mathbf{i} + x \, \mathbf{j} + y \, \mathbf{k}$$

   in moving a particle from the point $(3, 0, 0)$ to the point
   $(0, \pi/2, 3)$ along
   (a) A straight line
   (b) The helix $x = 3 \cos t$, $y = t$, $z = 3 \sin t$

11–12 ▏▎▎ Show that **F** is a conservative vector field. Then find a
function f such that $\mathbf{F} = \nabla f$.

11. $\mathbf{F}(x, y) = (1 + xy)e^{xy} \mathbf{i} + (e^y + x^2 e^{xy}) \mathbf{j}$

12. $\mathbf{F}(x, y, z) = \sin y \, \mathbf{i} + x \cos y \, \mathbf{j} - \sin z \, \mathbf{k}$

13–14 ▏▎▎ Show that **F** is conservative and use this fact to evaluate
$\int_C \mathbf{F} \cdot d\mathbf{r}$ along the given curve.

13. $\mathbf{F}(x, y) = (4x^3 y^2 - 2xy^3) \mathbf{i} + (2x^4 y - 3x^2 y^2 + 4y^3) \mathbf{j}$,
   C: $\mathbf{r}(t) = (t + \sin \pi t) \mathbf{i} + (2t + \cos \pi t) \mathbf{j}$, $0 \le t \le 1$

14. $\mathbf{F}(x, y, z) = e^y \mathbf{i} + (xe^y + e^z) \mathbf{j} + ye^z \mathbf{k}$,
   C is the line segment from $(0, 2, 0)$ to $(4, 0, 3)$

15. Verify that Green's Theorem is true for the line integral
   $\int_C xy^2 \, dx - x^2 y \, dy$, where C consists of the parabola $y = x^2$
   from $(-1, 1)$ to $(1, 1)$ and the line segment from $(1, 1)$ to
   $(-1, 1)$.

16. Use Green's Theorem to evaluate

$$\int_C \sqrt{1 + x^3} \, dx + 2xy \, dy$$

   where C is the triangle with vertices $(0, 0)$, $(1, 0)$, and $(1, 3)$.

17. Use Green's Theorem to evaluate $\int_C x^2 y \, dx - xy^2 \, dy$, where C
   is the circle $x^2 + y^2 = 4$ with counterclockwise orientation.

18. Find curl **F** and div **F** if

$$\mathbf{F}(x, y, z) = e^{-x} \sin y \, \mathbf{i} + e^{-y} \sin z \, \mathbf{j} + e^{-z} \sin x \, \mathbf{k}$$

19. Show that there is no vector field **G** such that

$$\text{curl } \mathbf{G} = 2x \, \mathbf{i} + 3yz \, \mathbf{j} - xz^2 \mathbf{k}$$

20. Show that, under conditions to be stated on the vector fields **F**
   and **G**,

$$\text{curl}(\mathbf{F} \times \mathbf{G}) = \mathbf{F} \text{ div } \mathbf{G} - \mathbf{G} \text{ div } \mathbf{F} + (\mathbf{G} \cdot \nabla)\mathbf{F} - (\mathbf{F} \cdot \nabla)\mathbf{G}$$

21. If C is any piecewise-smooth simple closed plane curve and f
   and g are differentiable functions, show that

$$\int_C f(x) \, dx + g(y) \, dy = 0$$

22. If f and g are twice differentiable functions, show that

$$\nabla^2(fg) = f\nabla^2 g + g\nabla^2 f + 2\nabla f \cdot \nabla g$$

23. If f is a harmonic function, that is, $\nabla^2 f = 0$, show that the line
   integral $\int f_y \, dx - f_x \, dy$ is independent of path in any simple
   region D.

24. (a) Sketch the curve C with parametric equations

$$x = \cos t \qquad y = \sin t \qquad z = \sin t \qquad 0 \le t \le 2\pi$$

   (b) Find $\int_C 2xe^{2y} \, dx + (2x^2 e^{2y} + 2y \cot z) \, dy - y^2 \csc^2 z \, dz$.

25. Find the area of the part of the surface $z = x^2 + 2y$ that lies
   above the triangle with vertices $(0, 0)$, $(1, 0)$, and $(1, 2)$.

26. (a) Find an equation of the tangent plane at the point $(4, -2, 1)$
   to the parametric surface S given by

$$\mathbf{r}(u, v) = v^2 \mathbf{i} - uv \, \mathbf{j} + u^2 \mathbf{k} \qquad 0 \le u \le 3, \, -3 \le v \le 3$$

(b) Use a computer to graph the surface S and the tangent plane found in part (a).

(c) Set up, but do not evaluate, an integral for the surface area of S.

(d) If

$$F(x, y, z) = \frac{z^2}{1 + x^2}\,i + \frac{x^2}{1 + y^2}\,j + \frac{y^2}{1 + z^2}\,k$$

find $\iint_S F \cdot dS$ correct to four decimal places.

27–30 ▥ Evaluate the surface integral.

27. $\iint_S z\,dS$, where S is the part of the paraboloid $z = x^2 + y^2$ that lies under the plane $z = 4$

28. $\iint_S (x^2 z + y^2 z)\,dS$, where S is the part of the plane $z = 4 + x + y$ that lies inside the cylinder $x^2 + y^2 = 4$

29. $\iint_S F \cdot dS$, where $F(x, y, z) = xz\,i - 2y\,j + 3x\,k$ and S is the sphere $x^2 + y^2 + z^2 = 4$ with outward orientation

30. $\iint_S F \cdot dS$, where $F(x, y, z) = x^2\,i + xy\,j + z\,k$ and S is the part of the paraboloid $z = x^2 + y^2$ below the plane $z = 1$ with upward orientation

⎯ ⎯ ⎯ ⎯ ⎯ ⎯ ⎯ ⎯ ⎯ ⎯ ⎯ ⎯

31. Verify that Stokes' Theorem is true for the vector field

$$F(x, y, z) = x^2\,i + y^2\,j + z^2\,k$$

where S is the part of the paraboloid $z = 1 - x^2 - y^2$ that lies above the xy-plane and S has upward orientation.

32. Use Stokes' Theorem to evaluate $\iint_S$ curl $F \cdot dS$, where $F(x, y, z) = x^2 yz\,i + yz^2\,j + z^3 e^{xy}\,k$, S is the part of the sphere $x^2 + y^2 + z^2 = 5$ that lies above the plane $z = 1$, and S is oriented upward.

33. Use Stokes' Theorem to evaluate $\int_C F \cdot dr$, where $F(x, y, z) = xy\,i + yz\,j + zx\,k$ and C is the triangle with vertices $(1, 0, 0)$, $(0, 1, 0)$, and $(0, 0, 1)$, oriented counterclockwise as viewed from above.

34. Use the Divergence Theorem to calculate the surface integral $\iint_S F \cdot dS$, where $F(x, y, z) = x^3\,i + y^3\,j + z^3\,k$ and S is the surface of the solid bounded by the cylinder $x^2 + y^2 = 1$ and the planes $z = 0$ and $z = 2$.

35. Verify that the Divergence Theorem is true for the vector field

$$F(x, y, z) = x\,i + y\,j + z\,k$$

where E is the unit ball $x^2 + y^2 + z^2 \leqslant 1$.

36. Compute the outward flux of

$$F(x, y, z) = \frac{x\,i + y\,j + z\,k}{(x^2 + y^2 + z^2)^{3/2}}$$

through the ellipsoid $4x^2 + 9y^2 + 6z^2 = 36$.

37. Let

$$F(x, y, z) = (3x^2 yz - 3y)\,i + (x^3 z - 3x)\,j + (x^3 y + 2z)\,k$$

Evaluate $\int_C F \cdot dr$, where C is the curve with initial point $(0, 0, 2)$ and terminal point $(0, 3, 0)$ shown in the figure.

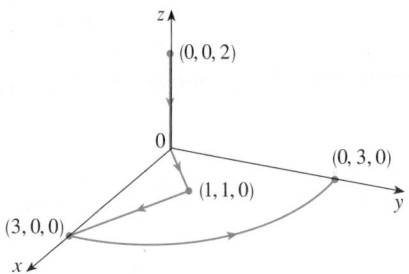

38. Let

$$F(x, y) = \frac{(2x^3 + 2xy^2 - 2y)\,i + (2y^3 + 2x^2 y + 2x)\,j}{x^2 + y^2}$$

Evaluate $\oint_C F \cdot dr$, where C is shown in the figure.

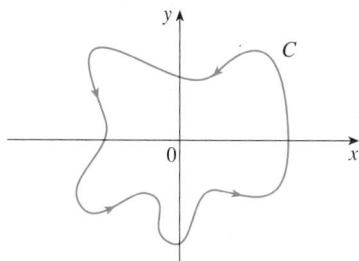

39. Find $\iint_S F \cdot n\,dS$, where $F(x, y, z) = x\,i + y\,j + z\,k$ and S is the outwardly oriented surface shown in the figure (the boundary surface of a cube with a unit corner cube removed).

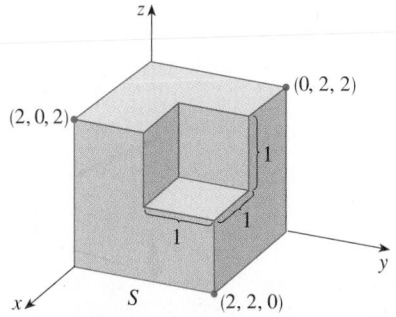

40. If the components of F have continuous second partial derivatives and S is the boundary surface of a simple solid region, show that $\iint_S$ curl $F \cdot dS = 0$.

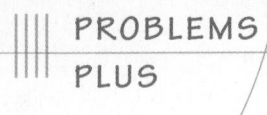
1. Let S be a smooth parametric surface and let P be a point such that each line that starts at P intersects S at most once. The **solid angle** $\Omega(S)$ subtended by S at P is the set of lines starting at P and passing through S. Let $S(a)$ be the intersection of $\Omega(S)$ with the surface of the sphere with center P and radius a. Then the measure of the solid angle (in *steradians*) is defined to be

$$|\Omega(S)| = \frac{\text{area of } S(a)}{a^2}$$

Apply the Divergence Theorem to the part of $\Omega(S)$ between $S(a)$ and S to show that

$$|\Omega(S)| = \iint\limits_{S} \frac{\mathbf{r} \cdot \mathbf{n}}{r^3}\, dS$$

where $\mathbf{r}$ is the radius vector from P to any point on S, $r = |\mathbf{r}|$, and the unit normal vector $\mathbf{n}$ is directed away from P.

   This shows that the definition of the measure of a solid angle is independent of the radius a of the sphere. Thus, the measure of the solid angle is equal to the area subtended on a *unit* sphere. (Note the analogy with the definition of radian measure.) The total solid angle subtended by a sphere at its center is thus 4π steradians.

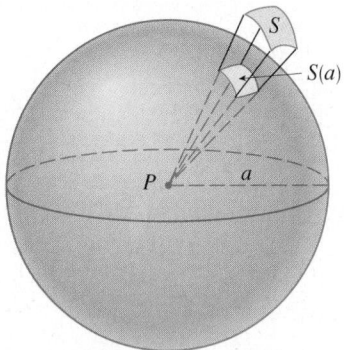

2. Find the positively oriented simple closed curve C for which the value of the line integral

$$\int_C (y^3 - y)\, dx - 2x^3\, dy$$

   is a maximum.

3. Let C be a simple closed piecewise-smooth space curve that lies in a plane with unit normal vector $\mathbf{n} = \langle a, b, c \rangle$ and has positive orientation with respect to $\mathbf{n}$. Show that the plane area enclosed by C is

$$\tfrac{1}{2}\int_C (bz - cy)\, dx + (cx - az)\, dy + (ay - bx)\, dz$$

4. The figure depicts the sequence of events in each cylinder of a four-cylinder internal combustion engine. Each piston moves up and down and is connected by a pivoted arm to a rotating crankshaft. Let $P(t)$ and $V(t)$ be the pressure and volume within a cylinder at time t, where $a \leqslant t \leqslant b$ gives the time required for a complete cycle. The graph shows how P and V vary through one cycle of a four-stroke engine.

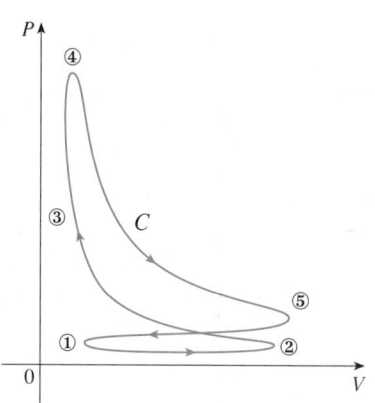

During the intake stroke (from ① to ②) a mixture of air and gasoline at atmospheric pressure is drawn into a cylinder through the intake valve as the piston moves downward. Then the piston rapidly compresses the mix with the valves closed in the compression stroke (from ② to ③) during which the pressure rises and the volume decreases. At ③ the sparkplug ignites the fuel, raising the temperature and pressure at almost constant volume to ④. Then, with valves closed, the rapid expansion forces the piston downward during the power stroke (from ④ to ⑤). The exhaust valve opens, temperature and pressure drop, and mechanical energy stored in a rotating flywheel pushes the piston upward, forcing the waste products out of the exhaust valve in the exhaust stroke. The exhaust valve closes and the intake valve opens. We're now back at ① and the cycle starts again.

(a) Show that the work done on the piston during one cycle of a four-stroke engine is
$W = \int_C P\, dV$, where C is the curve in the PV-plane shown in the figure.

[*Hint:* Let $x(t)$ be the distance from the piston to the top of the cylinder and note that the force on the piston is $\mathbf{F} = AP(t)\,\mathbf{i}$, where A is the area of the top of the piston. Then $W = \int_{C_1} \mathbf{F} \cdot d\mathbf{r}$, where C_1 is given by $\mathbf{r}(t) = x(t)\,\mathbf{i}$, $a \leqslant t \leqslant b$. An alternative approach is to work directly with Riemann sums.]

(b) Use Formula 17.4.5 to show that the work is the difference of the areas enclosed by the two loops of C.

CHAPTER 18

The charge in an electric circuit is governed by the differential equations that we solve in Section 18.3.

Dia Max / Getty Images

Second-Order Differential Equations

The basic ideas of differential equations were explained in Chapter 10; there we concentrated on first-order equations. In this chapter we study second-order linear differential equations and learn how they can be applied to solve problems concerning the vibrations of springs and electric circuits. We will also see how infinite series can be used to solve differential equations.

18.1 Second-Order Linear Equations

A **second-order linear differential equation** has the form

$$\boxed{1} \qquad P(x)\frac{d^2y}{dx^2} + Q(x)\frac{dy}{dx} + R(x)y = G(x)$$

where P, Q, R, and G are continuous functions. We saw in Section 10.1 that equations of this type arise in the study of the motion of a spring. In Section 18.3 we will further pursue this application as well as the application to electric circuits.

In this section we study the case where $G(x) = 0$, for all x, in Equation 1. Such equations are called **homogeneous** linear equations. Thus, the form of a second-order linear homogeneous differential equation is

$$\boxed{2} \qquad P(x)\frac{d^2y}{dx^2} + Q(x)\frac{dy}{dx} + R(x)y = 0$$

If $G(x) \neq 0$ for some x, Equation 1 is **nonhomogeneous** and is discussed in Section 18.2.

Two basic facts enable us to solve homogeneous linear equations. The first of these says that if we know two solutions y_1 and y_2 of such an equation, then the **linear combination** $y = c_1y_1 + c_2y_2$ is also a solution.

> **3 Theorem** If $y_1(x)$ and $y_2(x)$ are both solutions of the linear homogeneous equation (2) and c_1 and c_2 are any constants, then the function
>
> $$y(x) = c_1y_1(x) + c_2y_2(x)$$
>
> is also a solution of Equation 2.

Proof Since y_1 and y_2 are solutions of Equation 2, we have

$$P(x)y_1'' + Q(x)y_1' + R(x)y_1 = 0$$

and

$$P(x)y_2'' + Q(x)y_2' + R(x)y_2 = 0$$

Therefore, using the basic rules for differentiation, we have

$$P(x)y'' + Q(x)y' + R(x)y$$

$$= P(x)(c_1y_1 + c_2y_2)'' + Q(x)(c_1y_1 + c_2y_2)' + R(x)(c_1y_1 + c_2y_2)$$

$$= P(x)(c_1y_1'' + c_2y_2'') + Q(x)(c_1y_1' + c_2y_2') + R(x)(c_1y_1 + c_2y_2)$$

$$= c_1[P(x)y_1'' + Q(x)y_1' + R(x)y_1] + c_2[P(x)y_2'' + Q(x)y_2' + R(x)y_2]$$

$$= c_1(0) + c_2(0) = 0$$

Thus, $y = c_1y_1 + c_2y_2$ is a solution of Equation 2.

The other fact we need is given by the following theorem, which is proved in more advanced courses. It says that the general solution is a linear combination of two **linearly independent** solutions y_1 and y_2. This means that neither y_1 nor y_2 is a constant multiple of the other. For instance, the functions $f(x) = x^2$ and $g(x) = 5x^2$ are linearly dependent, but $f(x) = e^x$ and $g(x) = xe^x$ are linearly independent.

> **4** **Theorem** If y_1 and y_2 are linearly independent solutions of Equation 2, and $P(x)$ is never 0, then the general solution is given by
>
> $$y(x) = c_1y_1(x) + c_2y_2(x)$$
>
> where c_1 and c_2 are arbitrary constants.

Theorem 4 is very useful because it says that if we know *two* particular linearly independent solutions, then we know *every* solution.

In general, it is not easy to discover particular solutions to a second-order linear equation. But it is always possible to do so if the coefficient functions P, Q, and R are constant functions, that is, if the differential equation has the form

5
$$ay'' + by' + cy = 0$$

where a, b, and c are constants and $a \neq 0$.

It's not hard to think of some likely candidates for particular solutions of Equation 5 if we state the equation verbally. We are looking for a function y such that a constant times its second derivative y'' plus another constant times y' plus a third constant times y is equal to 0. We know that the exponential function $y = e^{rx}$ (where r is a constant) has the property that its derivative is a constant multiple of itself: $y' = re^{rx}$. Furthermore, $y'' = r^2e^{rx}$. If we substitute these expressions into Equation 5, we see that $y = e^{rx}$ is a solution if

$$ar^2e^{rx} + bre^{rx} + ce^{rx} = 0$$

or

$$(ar^2 + br + c)e^{rx} = 0$$

But e^{rx} is never 0. Thus, $y = e^{rx}$ is a solution of Equation 5 if r is a root of the equation

6
$$ar^2 + br + c = 0$$

Equation 6 is called the **auxiliary equation** (or **characteristic equation**) of the differential equation $ay'' + by' + cy = 0$. Notice that it is an algebraic equation that is obtained from the differential equation by replacing y'' by r^2, y' by r, and y by 1.

Sometimes the roots r_1 and r_2 of the auxiliary equation can be found by factoring. In other cases they are found by using the quadratic formula:

$$\boxed{7} \qquad r_1 = \frac{-b + \sqrt{b^2 - 4ac}}{2a} \qquad r_2 = \frac{-b - \sqrt{b^2 - 4ac}}{2a}$$

We distinguish three cases according to the sign of the discriminant $b^2 - 4ac$.

CASE I ▢ $b^2 - 4ac > 0$

In this case the roots r_1 and r_2 of the auxiliary equation are real and distinct, so $y_1 = e^{r_1 x}$ and $y_2 = e^{r_2 x}$ are two linearly independent solutions of Equation 5. (Note that $e^{r_2 x}$ is not a constant multiple of $e^{r_1 x}$.) Therefore, by Theorem 4, we have the following fact.

> $\boxed{8}$ If the roots r_1 and r_2 of the auxiliary equation $ar^2 + br + c = 0$ are real and unequal, then the general solution of $ay'' + by' + cy = 0$ is
> $$y = c_1 e^{r_1 x} + c_2 e^{r_2 x}$$

▐▐ In Figure 1 the graphs of the basic solutions $f(x) = e^{2x}$ and $g(x) = e^{-3x}$ of the differential equation in Example 1 are shown in black and red, respectively. Some of the other solutions, linear combinations of f and g, are shown in blue.

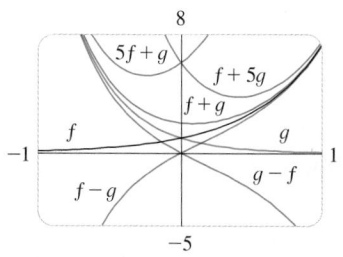

FIGURE 1

EXAMPLE 1 Solve the equation $y'' + y' - 6y = 0$.

SOLUTION The auxiliary equation is

$$r^2 + r - 6 = (r - 2)(r + 3) = 0$$

whose roots are $r = 2, -3$. Therefore, by (8) the general solution of the given differential equation is

$$y = c_1 e^{2x} + c_2 e^{-3x}$$

We could verify that this is indeed a solution by differentiating and substituting into the differential equation.

EXAMPLE 2 Solve $3\dfrac{d^2 y}{dx^2} + \dfrac{dy}{dx} - y = 0$.

SOLUTION To solve the auxiliary equation $3r^2 + r - 1 = 0$ we use the quadratic formula:

$$r = \frac{-1 \pm \sqrt{13}}{6}$$

Since the roots are real and distinct, the general solution is

$$y = c_1 e^{(-1+\sqrt{13})x/6} + c_2 e^{(-1-\sqrt{13})x/6}$$

CASE II ▢ $b^2 - 4ac = 0$

In this case $r_1 = r_2$; that is, the roots of the auxiliary equation are real and equal. Let's denote by r the common value of r_1 and r_2. Then, from Equations 7, we have

$$\boxed{9} \qquad r = -\frac{b}{2a} \qquad \text{so} \quad 2ar + b = 0$$

We know that $y_1 = e^{rx}$ is one solution of Equation 5. We now verify that $y_2 = xe^{rx}$ is also a solution:

$$ay_2'' + by_2' + cy_2 = a(2re^{rx} + r^2xe^{rx}) + b(e^{rx} + rxe^{rx}) + cxe^{rx}$$
$$= (2ar + b)e^{rx} + (ar^2 + br + c)xe^{rx}$$
$$= 0(e^{rx}) + 0(xe^{rx}) = 0$$

The first term is 0 by Equations 9; the second term is 0 because r is a root of the auxiliary equation. Since $y_1 = e^{rx}$ and $y_2 = xe^{rx}$ are linearly independent solutions, Theorem 4 provides us with the general solution.

> **10** If the auxiliary equation $ar^2 + br + c = 0$ has only one real root r, then the general solution of $ay'' + by' + cy = 0$ is
>
> $$y = c_1e^{rx} + c_2xe^{rx}$$

▨▨ Figure 2 shows the basic solutions $f(x) = e^{-3x/2}$ and $g(x) = xe^{-3x/2}$ in Example 3 and some other members of the family of solutions. Notice that all of them approach 0 as $x \to \infty$.

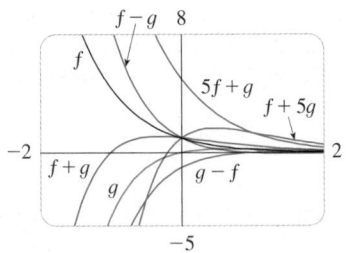

FIGURE 2

EXAMPLE 3 Solve the equation $4y'' + 12y' + 9y = 0$.

SOLUTION The auxiliary equation $4r^2 + 12r + 9 = 0$ can be factored as

$$(2r + 3)^2 = 0$$

so the only root is $r = -\frac{3}{2}$. By (10) the general solution is

$$y = c_1e^{-3x/2} + c_2xe^{-3x/2}$$

CASE III ▫ $b^2 - 4ac < 0$

In this case the roots r_1 and r_2 of the auxiliary equation are complex numbers. (See Appendix G for information about complex numbers.) We can write

$$r_1 = \alpha + i\beta \qquad r_2 = \alpha - i\beta$$

where α and β are real numbers. [In fact, $\alpha = -b/(2a)$, $\beta = \sqrt{4ac - b^2}/(2a)$.] Then, using Euler's equation

$$e^{i\theta} = \cos\theta + i\sin\theta$$

from Appendix G, we write the solution of the differential equation as

$$y = C_1e^{r_1x} + C_2e^{r_2x} = C_1e^{(\alpha+i\beta)x} + C_2e^{(\alpha-i\beta)x}$$
$$= C_1e^{\alpha x}(\cos\beta x + i\sin\beta x) + C_2e^{\alpha x}(\cos\beta x - i\sin\beta x)$$
$$= e^{\alpha x}[(C_1 + C_2)\cos\beta x + i(C_1 - C_2)\sin\beta x]$$
$$= e^{\alpha x}(c_1\cos\beta x + c_2\sin\beta x)$$

where $c_1 = C_1 + C_2$, $c_2 = i(C_1 - C_2)$. This gives all solutions (real or complex) of the differential equation. The solutions are real when the constants c_1 and c_2 are real. We summarize the discussion as follows.

> **11** If the roots of the auxiliary equation $ar^2 + br + c = 0$ are the complex numbers $r_1 = \alpha + i\beta$, $r_2 = \alpha - i\beta$, then the general solution of $ay'' + by' + cy = 0$ is
>
> $$y = e^{\alpha x}(c_1 \cos \beta x + c_2 \sin \beta x)$$

‖‖ Figure 3 shows the graphs of the solutions in Example 4, $f(x) = e^{3x} \cos 2x$ and $g(x) = e^{3x} \sin 2x$, together with some linear combinations. All solutions approach 0 as $x \to -\infty$.

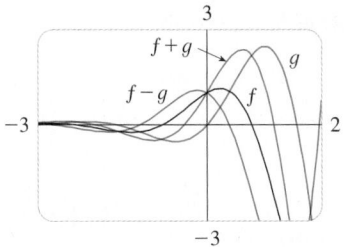

FIGURE 3

EXAMPLE 4 Solve the equation $y'' - 6y' + 13y = 0$.

SOLUTION The auxiliary equation is $r^2 - 6r + 13 = 0$. By the quadratic formula, the roots are

$$r = \frac{6 \pm \sqrt{36 - 52}}{2} = \frac{6 \pm \sqrt{-16}}{2} = 3 \pm 2i$$

By (11) the general solution of the differential equation is

$$y = e^{3x}(c_1 \cos 2x + c_2 \sin 2x)$$

‖‖‖‖ **Initial-Value and Boundary-Value Problems**

An **initial-value problem** for the second-order Equation 1 or 2 consists of finding a solution y of the differential equation that also satisfies initial conditions of the form

$$y(x_0) = y_0 \qquad y'(x_0) = y_1$$

where y_0 and y_1 are given constants. If P, Q, R, and G are continuous on an interval and $P(x) \neq 0$ there, then a theorem found in more advanced books guarantees the existence and uniqueness of a solution to this initial-value problem. Examples 5 and 6 illustrate the technique for solving such a problem.

EXAMPLE 5 Solve the initial-value problem

$$y'' + y' - 6y = 0 \qquad y(0) = 1 \qquad y'(0) = 0$$

‖‖ Figure 4 shows the graph of the solution of the initial-value problem in Example 5. Compare with Figure 1.

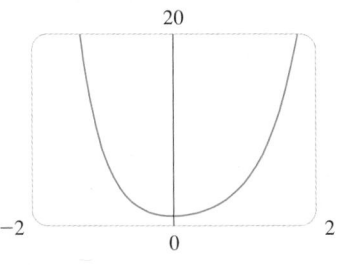

FIGURE 4

SOLUTION From Example 1 we know that the general solution of the differential equation is

$$y(x) = c_1 e^{2x} + c_2 e^{-3x}$$

Differentiating this solution, we get

$$y'(x) = 2c_1 e^{2x} - 3c_2 e^{-3x}$$

To satisfy the initial conditions we require that

12 $$y(0) = c_1 + c_2 = 1$$

13 $$y'(0) = 2c_1 - 3c_2 = 0$$

From (13) we have $c_2 = \frac{2}{3}c_1$ and so (12) gives

$$c_1 + \tfrac{2}{3}c_1 = 1 \qquad c_1 = \tfrac{3}{5} \qquad c_2 = \tfrac{2}{5}$$

Thus, the required solution of the initial-value problem is

$$y = \tfrac{3}{5}e^{2x} + \tfrac{2}{5}e^{-3x}$$

□ The solution to Example 6 is graphed in Figure 5. It appears to be a shifted sine curve and, indeed, you can verify that another way of writing the solution is

$$y = \sqrt{13} \sin(x + \phi) \quad \text{where } \tan \phi = \tfrac{2}{3}$$

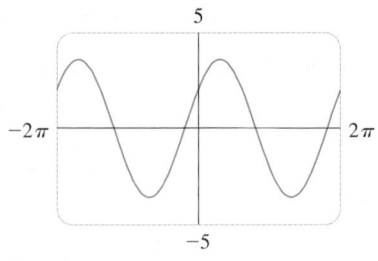

FIGURE 5

EXAMPLE 6 Solve the initial-value problem

$$y'' + y = 0 \qquad y(0) = 2 \qquad y'(0) = 3$$

SOLUTION The auxiliary equation is $r^2 + 1 = 0$, or $r^2 = -1$, whose roots are $\pm i$. Thus $\alpha = 0$, $\beta = 1$, and since $e^{0x} = 1$, the general solution is

$$y(x) = c_1 \cos x + c_2 \sin x$$

Since

$$y'(x) = -c_1 \sin x + c_2 \cos x$$

the initial conditions become

$$y(0) = c_1 = 2 \qquad y'(0) = c_2 = 3$$

Therefore, the solution of the initial-value problem is

$$y(x) = 2 \cos x + 3 \sin x$$

A **boundary-value problem** for Equation 1 consists of finding a solution y of the differential equation that also satisfies boundary conditions of the form

$$y(x_0) = y_0 \qquad y(x_1) = y_1$$

In contrast with the situation for initial-value problems, a boundary-value problem does not always have a solution.

EXAMPLE 7 Solve the boundary-value problem

$$y'' + 2y' + y = 0 \qquad y(0) = 1 \qquad y(1) = 3$$

SOLUTION The auxiliary equation is

$$r^2 + 2r + 1 = 0 \qquad \text{or} \qquad (r + 1)^2 = 0$$

whose only root is $r = -1$. Therefore, the general solution is

$$y(x) = c_1 e^{-x} + c_2 x e^{-x}$$

The boundary conditions are satisfied if

$$y(0) = c_1 = 1$$

$$y(1) = c_1 e^{-1} + c_2 e^{-1} = 3$$

The first condition gives $c_1 = 1$, so the second condition becomes

$$e^{-1} + c_2 e^{-1} = 3$$

Solving this equation for c_2 by first multiplying through by e, we get

$$1 + c_2 = 3e \qquad \text{so} \qquad c_2 = 3e - 1$$

|||| Figure 6 shows the graph of the solution of the boundary-value problem in Example 7.

FIGURE 6

Thus, the solution of the boundary-value problem is

$$y = e^{-x} + (3e - 1)x e^{-x}$$

Summary: Solutions of $ay'' + by' + c = 0$

Roots of $ar^2 + br + c = 0$	General solution
r_1, r_2 real and distinct	$y = c_1 e^{r_1 x} + c_2 e^{r_2 x}$
$r_1 = r_2 = r$	$y = c_1 e^{rx} + c_2 x e^{rx}$
r_1, r_2 complex: $\alpha \pm i\beta$	$y = e^{\alpha x}(c_1 \cos \beta x + c_2 \sin \beta x)$

18.1 Exercises

1–13 ▥ Solve the differential equation.

1. $y'' - 6y' + 8y = 0$

2. $y'' - 4y' + 8y = 0$

3. $y'' + 8y' + 41y = 0$

4. $2y'' - y' - y = 0$

5. $y'' - 2y' + y = 0$

6. $3y'' = 5y'$

7. $4y'' + y = 0$

8. $16y'' + 24y' + 9y = 0$

9. $4y'' + y' = 0$

10. $9y'' + 4y = 0$

11. $\dfrac{d^2 y}{dt^2} - 2\dfrac{dy}{dt} - y = 0$

12. $\dfrac{d^2 y}{dt^2} - 6\dfrac{dy}{dt} + 4y = 0$

13. $\dfrac{d^2 y}{dt^2} + \dfrac{dy}{dt} + y = 0$

14–16 ▥ Graph the two basic solutions of the differential equation and several other solutions. What features do the solutions have in common?

14. $6\dfrac{d^2 y}{dx^2} - \dfrac{dy}{dx} - 2y = 0$

15. $\dfrac{d^2 y}{dx^2} - 8\dfrac{dy}{dx} + 16y = 0$

16. $\dfrac{d^2 y}{dx^2} - 2\dfrac{dy}{dx} + 5y = 0$

17–24 ▥ Solve the initial-value problem.

17. $2y'' + 5y' + 3y = 0$, $y(0) = 3$, $y'(0) = -4$

18. $y'' + 3y = 0$, $y(0) = 1$, $y'(0) = 3$

19. $4y'' - 4y' + y = 0$, $y(0) = 1$, $y'(0) = -1.5$

20. $2y'' + 5y' - 3y = 0$, $y(0) = 1$, $y'(0) = 4$

21. $y'' + 16y = 0$, $y(\pi/4) = -3$, $y'(\pi/4) = 4$

22. $y'' - 2y' + 5y = 0$, $y(\pi) = 0$, $y'(\pi) = 2$

23. $y'' + 2y' + 2y = 0$, $y(0) = 2$, $y'(0) = 1$

24. $y'' + 12y' + 36y = 0$, $y(1) = 0$, $y'(1) = 1$

25–32 ▥ Solve the boundary-value problem, if possible.

25. $4y'' + y = 0$, $y(0) = 3$, $y(\pi) = -4$

26. $y'' + 2y' = 0$, $y(0) = 1$, $y(1) = 2$

27. $y'' - 3y' + 2y = 0$, $y(0) = 1$, $y(3) = 0$

28. $y'' + 100y = 0$, $y(0) = 2$, $y(\pi) = 5$

29. $y'' - 6y' + 25y = 0$, $y(0) = 1$, $y(\pi) = 2$

30. $y'' - 6y' + 9y = 0$, $y(0) = 1$, $y(1) = 0$

31. $y'' + 4y' + 13y = 0$, $y(0) = 2$, $y(\pi/2) = 1$

32. $9y'' - 18y' + 10y = 0$, $y(0) = 0$, $y(\pi) = 1$

33. Let L be a nonzero real number.
   (a) Show that the boundary-value problem $y'' + \lambda y = 0$, $y(0) = 0$, $y(L) = 0$ has only the trivial solution $y = 0$ for the cases $\lambda = 0$ and $\lambda < 0$.
   (b) For the case $\lambda > 0$, find the values of λ for which this problem has a nontrivial solution and give the corresponding solution.

34. If a, b, and c are all positive constants and $y(x)$ is a solution of the differential equation $ay'' + by' + cy = 0$, show that $\lim_{x \to \infty} y(x) = 0$.

18.2 Nonhomogeneous Linear Equations

In this section we learn how to solve second-order nonhomogeneous linear differential equations with constant coefficients, that is, equations of the form

⊡1

$$ay'' + by' + cy = G(x)$$

where a, b, and c are constants and G is a continuous function. The related homogeneous equation

$$\boxed{2} \qquad ay'' + by' + cy = 0$$

is called the **complementary equation** and plays an important role in the solution of the original nonhomogeneous equation (1).

> $\boxed{3}$ **Theorem** The general solution of the nonhomogeneous differential equation (1) can be written as
>
> $$y(x) = y_p(x) + y_c(x)$$
>
> where y_p is a particular solution of Equation 1 and y_c is the general solution of the complementary Equation 2.

Proof All we have to do is verify that if y is any solution of Equation 1, then $y - y_p$ is a solution of the complementary Equation 2. Indeed

$$
\begin{aligned}
a(y - y_p)'' + b(y - y_p)' + c(y - y_p) &= ay'' - ay_p'' + by' - by_p' + cy - cy_p \\
&= (ay'' + by' + cy) - (ay_p'' + by_p' + cy_p) \\
&= g(x) - g(x) = 0
\end{aligned}
$$

We know from Section 18.1 how to solve the complementary equation. (Recall that the solution is $y_c = c_1 y_1 + c_2 y_2$, where y_1 and y_2 are linearly independent solutions of Equation 2.) Therefore, Theorem 3 says that we know the general solution of the nonhomogeneous equation as soon as we know a particular solution y_p. There are two methods for finding a particular solution: The method of undetermined coefficients is straightforward but works only for a restricted class of functions G. The method of variation of parameters works for every function G but is usually more difficult to apply in practice.

The Method of Undetermined Coefficients

We first illustrate the method of undetermined coefficients for the equation

$$ay'' + by' + cy = G(x)$$

where $G(x)$ is a polynomial. It is reasonable to guess that there is a particular solution y_p that is a polynomial of the same degree as G because if y is a polynomial, then $ay'' + by' + cy$ is also a polynomial. We therefore substitute $y_p(x) = $ a polynomial (of the same degree as G) into the differential equation and determine the coefficients.

EXAMPLE 1 Solve the equation $y'' + y' - 2y = x^2$.

SOLUTION The auxiliary equation of $y'' + y' - 2y = 0$ is

$$r^2 + r - 2 = (r - 1)(r + 2) = 0$$

with roots $r = 1, -2$. So the solution of the complementary equation is

$$y_c = c_1 e^x + c_2 e^{-2x}$$

Since $G(x) = x^2$ is a polynomial of degree 2, we seek a particular solution of the form

$$y_p(x) = Ax^2 + Bx + C$$

Then $y_p' = 2Ax + B$ and $y_p'' = 2A$ so, substituting into the given differential equation, we have

$$(2A) + (2Ax + B) - 2(Ax^2 + Bx + C) = x^2$$

or

$$-2Ax^2 + (2A - 2B)x + (2A + B - 2C) = x^2$$

Polynomials are equal when their coefficients are equal. Thus

$$-2A = 1 \qquad 2A - 2B = 0 \qquad 2A + B - 2C = 0$$

The solution of this system of equations is

$$A = -\tfrac{1}{2} \qquad B = -\tfrac{1}{2} \qquad C = -\tfrac{3}{4}$$

A particular solution is therefore

$$y_p(x) = -\tfrac{1}{2}x^2 - \tfrac{1}{2}x - \tfrac{3}{4}$$

and, by Theorem 3, the general solution is

$$y = y_c + y_p = c_1 e^x + c_2 e^{-2x} - \tfrac{1}{2}x^2 - \tfrac{1}{2}x - \tfrac{3}{4}$$

|||| Figure 1 shows four solutions of the differential equation in Example 1 in terms of the particular solution y_p and the functions $f(x) = e^x$ and $g(x) = e^{-2x}$.

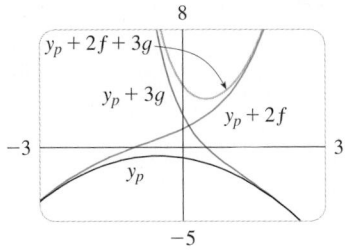

FIGURE 1

If $G(x)$ (the right side of Equation 1) is of the form Ce^{kx}, where C and k are constants, then we take as a trial solution a function of the same form, $y_p(x) = Ae^{kx}$, because the derivatives of e^{kx} are constant multiples of e^{kx}.

EXAMPLE 2 Solve $y'' + 4y = e^{3x}$.

SOLUTION The auxiliary equation is $r^2 + 4 = 0$ with roots $\pm 2i$, so the solution of the complementary equation is

$$y_c(x) = c_1 \cos 2x + c_2 \sin 2x$$

For a particular solution we try $y_p(x) = Ae^{3x}$. Then $y_p' = 3Ae^{3x}$ and $y_p'' = 9Ae^{3x}$. Substituting into the differential equation, we have

$$9Ae^{3x} + 4(Ae^{3x}) = e^{3x}$$

so $13Ae^{3x} = e^{3x}$ and $A = \tfrac{1}{13}$. Thus, a particular solution is

$$y_p(x) = \tfrac{1}{13}e^{3x}$$

and the general solution is

$$y(x) = c_1 \cos 2x + c_2 \sin 2x + \tfrac{1}{13}e^{3x}$$

|||| Figure 2 shows solutions of the differential equation in Example 2 in terms of y_p and the functions $f(x) = \cos 2x$ and $g(x) = \sin 2x$. Notice that all solutions approach ∞ as $x \to \infty$ and all solutions resemble sine functions when x is negative.

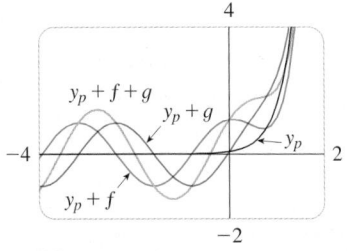

FIGURE 2

If $G(x)$ is either $C \cos kx$ or $C \sin kx$, then, because of the rules for differentiating the sine and cosine functions, we take as a trial particular solution a function of the form

$$y_p(x) = A \cos kx + B \sin kx$$

EXAMPLE 3 Solve $y'' + y' - 2y = \sin x$.

SOLUTION We try a particular solution

$$y_p(x) = A \cos x + B \sin x$$

Then $\qquad y_p' = -A \sin x + B \cos x \qquad y_p'' = -A \cos x - B \sin x$

so substitution in the differential equation gives

$$(-A \cos x - B \sin x) + (-A \sin x + B \cos x) - 2(A \cos x + B \sin x) = \sin x$$

or $\qquad\qquad\qquad\qquad (-3A + B) \cos x + (-A - 3B) \sin x = \sin x$

This is true if

$$-3A + B = 0 \qquad \text{and} \qquad -A - 3B = 1$$

The solution of this system is

$$A = -\tfrac{1}{10} \qquad\qquad B = -\tfrac{3}{10}$$

so a particular solution is

$$y_p(x) = -\tfrac{1}{10} \cos x - \tfrac{3}{10} \sin x$$

In Example 1 we determined that the solution of the complementary equation is $y_c = c_1 e^x + c_2 e^{-2x}$. Thus, the general solution of the given equation is

$$y(x) = c_1 e^x + c_2 e^{-2x} - \tfrac{1}{10}(\cos x + 3 \sin x)$$

If $G(x)$ is a product of functions of the preceding types, then we take the trial solution to be a product of functions of the same type. For instance, in solving the differential equation

$$y'' + 2y' + 4y = x \cos 3x$$

we would try

$$y_p(x) = (Ax + B) \cos 3x + (Cx + D) \sin 3x$$

If $G(x)$ is a sum of functions of these types, we use the easily verified *principle of superposition*, which says that if y_{p_1} and y_{p_2} are solutions of

$$ay'' + by' + cy = G_1(x) \qquad\qquad ay'' + by' + cy = G_2(x)$$

respectively, then $y_{p_1} + y_{p_2}$ is a solution of

$$ay'' + by' + cy = G_1(x) + G_2(x)$$

EXAMPLE 4 Solve $y'' - 4y = xe^x + \cos 2x$.

SOLUTION The auxiliary equation is $r^2 - 4 = 0$ with roots ± 2, so the solution of the complementary equation is $y_c(x) = c_1 e^{2x} + c_2 e^{-2x}$. For the equation $y'' - 4y = xe^x$ we try

$$y_{p_1}(x) = (Ax + B)e^x$$

Then $y'_{p_1} = (Ax + A + B)e^x$, $y''_{p_1} = (Ax + 2A + B)e^x$, so substitution in the equation gives

$$(Ax + 2A + B)e^x - 4(Ax + B)e^x = xe^x$$

or

$$(-3Ax + 2A - 3B)e^x = xe^x$$

Thus, $-3A = 1$ and $2A - 3B = 0$, so $A = -\frac{1}{3}$, $B = -\frac{2}{9}$, and

$$y_{p_1}(x) = \left(-\tfrac{1}{3}x - \tfrac{2}{9}\right)e^x$$

For the equation $y'' - 4y = \cos 2x$, we try

$$y_{p_2}(x) = C\cos 2x + D\sin 2x$$

Substitution gives

$$-4C\cos 2x - 4D\sin 2x - 4(C\cos 2x + D\sin 2x) = \cos 2x$$

or

$$-8C\cos 2x - 8D\sin 2x = \cos 2x$$

Therefore, $-8C = 1$, $-8D = 0$, and

$$y_{p_2}(x) = -\tfrac{1}{8}\cos 2x$$

By the superposition principle, the general solution is

$$y = y_c + y_{p_1} + y_{p_2} = c_1 e^{2x} + c_2 e^{-2x} - \left(\tfrac{1}{3}x + \tfrac{2}{9}\right)e^x - \tfrac{1}{8}\cos 2x$$

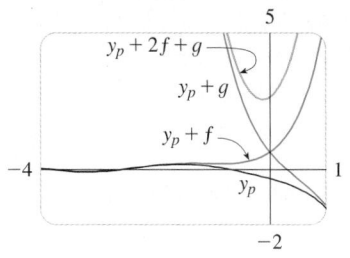

FIGURE 3

Finally we note that the recommended trial solution y_p sometimes turns out to be a solution of the complementary equation and therefore can't be a solution of the nonhomogeneous equation. In such cases we multiply the recommended trial solution by x (or by x^2 if necessary) so that no term in $y_p(x)$ is a solution of the complementary equation.

EXAMPLE 5 Solve $y'' + y = \sin x$.

SOLUTION The auxiliary equation is $r^2 + 1 = 0$ with roots $\pm i$, so the solution of the complementary equation is

$$y_c(x) = c_1 \cos x + c_2 \sin x$$

Ordinarily, we would use the trial solution

$$y_p(x) = A\cos x + B\sin x$$

but we observe that it is a solution of the complementary equation, so instead we try

$$y_p(x) = Ax\cos x + Bx\sin x$$

Then

$$y'_p(x) = A\cos x - Ax\sin x + B\sin x + Bx\cos x$$

$$y''_p(x) = -2A\sin x - Ax\cos x + 2B\cos x - Bx\sin x$$

‖‖ The graphs of four solutions of the differential equation in Example 5 are shown in Figure 4.

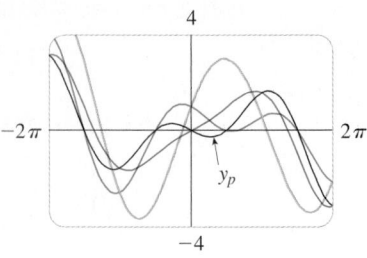

FIGURE 4

Substitution in the differential equation gives

$$y_p'' + y_p = -2A \sin x + 2B \cos x = \sin x$$

so $A = -\frac{1}{2}$, $B = 0$, and

$$y_p(x) = -\tfrac{1}{2}x \cos x$$

The general solution is

$$y(x) = c_1 \cos x + c_2 \sin x - \tfrac{1}{2}x \cos x$$

We summarize the method of undetermined coefficients as follows:

1. If $G(x) = e^{kx}P(x)$, where P is a polynomial of degree n, then try $y_p(x) = e^{kx}Q(x)$, where $Q(x)$ is an nth-degree polynomial (whose coefficients are determined by substituting in the differential equation.)

2. If $G(x) = e^{kx}P(x) \cos mx$ or $G(x) = e^{kx}P(x) \sin mx$, where P is an nth-degree polynomial, then try

$$y_p(x) = e^{kx}Q(x) \cos mx + e^{kx}R(x) \sin mx$$

where Q and R are nth-degree polynomials.

Modification: If any term of y_p is a solution of the complementary equation, multiply y_p by x (or by x^2 if necessary).

EXAMPLE 6 Determine the form of the trial solution for the differential equation $y'' - 4y' + 13y = e^{2x} \cos 3x$.

SOLUTION Here $G(x)$ has the form of part 2 of the summary, where $k = 2$, $m = 3$, and $P(x) = 1$. So, at first glance, the form of the trial solution would be

$$y_p(x) = e^{2x}(A \cos 3x + B \sin 3x)$$

But the auxiliary equation is $r^2 - 4r + 13 = 0$, with roots $r = 2 \pm 3i$, so the solution of the complementary equation is

$$y_c(x) = e^{2x}(c_1 \cos 3x + c_2 \sin 3x)$$

This means that we have to multiply the suggested trial solution by x. So, instead, we use

$$y_p(x) = xe^{2x}(A \cos 3x + B \sin 3x)$$

‖‖ **The Method of Variation of Parameters**

Suppose we have already solved the homogeneous equation $ay'' + by' + cy = 0$ and written the solution as

$$\boxed{4} \qquad y(x) = c_1 y_1(x) + c_2 y_2(x)$$

where y_1 and y_2 are linearly independent solutions. Let's replace the constants (or parameters) c_1 and c_2 in Equation 4 by arbitrary functions $u_1(x)$ and $u_2(x)$. We look for a particular solution of the nonhomogeneous equation $ay'' + by' + cy = G(x)$ of the form

$$\boxed{5} \qquad y_p(x) = u_1(x)\,y_1(x) + u_2(x)\,y_2(x)$$

(This method is called **variation of parameters** because we have varied the parameters c_1 and c_2 to make them functions.) Differentiating Equation 5, we get

$$\boxed{6} \qquad y_p' = (u_1'\,y_1 + u_2'\,y_2) + (u_1\,y_1' + u_2\,y_2')$$

Since u_1 and u_2 are arbitrary functions, we can impose two conditions on them. One condition is that y_p is a solution of the differential equation; we can choose the other condition so as to simplify our calculations. In view of the expression in Equation 6, let's impose the condition that

$$\boxed{7} \qquad u_1'\,y_1 + u_2'\,y_2 = 0$$

Then $\qquad\qquad y_p'' = u_1'\,y_1' + u_2'\,y_2' + u_1\,y_1'' + u_2\,y_2''$

Substituting in the differential equation, we get

$$a(u_1'\,y_1' + u_2'\,y_2' + u_1\,y_1'' + u_2\,y_2'') + b(u_1\,y_1' + u_2\,y_2') + c(u_1\,y_1 + u_2\,y_2) = G$$

or

$$\boxed{8} \qquad u_1(ay_1'' + by_1' + cy_1) + u_2(ay_2'' + by_2' + cy_2) + a(u_1'\,y_1' + u_2'\,y_2') = G$$

But y_1 and y_2 are solutions of the complementary equation, so

$$ay_1'' + by_1' + cy_1 = 0 \qquad \text{and} \qquad ay_2'' + by_2' + cy_2 = 0$$

and Equation 8 simplifies to

$$\boxed{9} \qquad a(u_1'\,y_1' + u_2'\,y_2') = G$$

Equations 7 and 9 form a system of two equations in the unknown functions u_1' and u_2'. After solving this system we may be able to integrate to find u_1 and u_2 and then the particular solution is given by Equation 5.

EXAMPLE 7 Solve the equation $y'' + y = \tan x$, $0 < x < \pi/2$.

SOLUTION The auxiliary equation is $r^2 + 1 = 0$ with roots $\pm i$, so the solution of $y'' + y = 0$ is $c_1 \sin x + c_2 \cos x$. Using variation of parameters, we seek a solution of the form

$$y_p(x) = u_1(x) \sin x + u_2(x) \cos x$$

Then $\qquad\qquad y_p' = (u_1' \sin x + u_2' \cos x) + (u_1 \cos x - u_2 \sin x)$

Set

$$\boxed{10} \qquad u_1' \sin x + u_2' \cos x = 0$$

Then $$y_p'' = u_1' \cos x - u_2' \sin x - u_1 \sin x - u_2 \cos x$$

For y_p to be a solution we must have

[11] $$y_p'' + y_p = u_1' \cos x - u_2' \sin x = \tan x$$

Solving Equations 10 and 11, we get

$$u_1'(\sin^2 x + \cos^2 x) = \cos x \tan x$$

$$u_1' = \sin x \qquad u_1(x) = -\cos x$$

(We seek a particular solution, so we don't need a constant of integration here.) Then, from Equation 10, we obtain

$$u_2' = -\frac{\sin x}{\cos x} u_1' = -\frac{\sin^2 x}{\cos x} = \frac{\cos^2 x - 1}{\cos x} = \cos x - \sec x$$

So $$u_2(x) = \sin x - \ln(\sec x + \tan x)$$

(Note that $\sec x + \tan x > 0$ for $0 < x < \pi/2$.) Therefore

$$y_p(x) = -\cos x \sin x + [\sin x - \ln(\sec x + \tan x)] \cos x$$

$$= -\cos x \ln(\sec x + \tan x)$$

and the general solution is

$$y(x) = c_1 \sin x + c_2 \cos x - \cos x \ln(\sec x + \tan x)$$

‖‖ Figure 5 shows four solutions of the differential equation in Example 7.

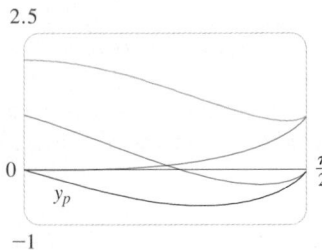

FIGURE 5

18.2 Exercises

1–10 ‖‖ Solve the differential equation or initial-value problem using the method of undetermined coefficients.

1. $y'' + 3y' + 2y = x^2$

2. $y'' + 9y = e^{3x}$

3. $y'' - 2y' = \sin 4x$

4. $y'' + 6y' + 9y = 1 + x$

5. $y'' - 4y' + 5y = e^{-x}$

6. $y'' + 2y' + y = xe^{-x}$

7. $y'' + y = e^x + x^3$, $\quad y(0) = 2$, $\quad y'(0) = 0$

8. $y'' - 4y = e^x \cos x$, $\quad y(0) = 1$, $\quad y'(0) = 2$

9. $y'' - y' = xe^x$, $\quad y(0) = 2$, $\quad y'(0) = 1$

10. $y'' + y' - 2y = x + \sin 2x$, $\quad y(0) = 1$, $\quad y'(0) = 0$

⌂ **11–12** ‖‖ Graph the particular solution and several other solutions. What characteristics do these solutions have in common?

11. $4y'' + 5y' + y = e^x$

12. $2y'' + 3y' + y = 1 + \cos 2x$

13–18 ‖‖ Write a trial solution for the method of undetermined coefficients. Do not determine the coefficients.

13. $y'' + 9y = e^{2x} + x^2 \sin x$

14. $y'' + 9y = xe^{-x} \cos \pi x$

15. $y'' + 9y = 1 + xe^{9x}$

16. $y'' + 3y' - 4y = (x^3 + x)e^x$

17. $y'' + 2y' + 10y = x^2 e^{-x} \cos 3x$

18. $y'' + 4y = e^{3x} + x \sin 2x$

19–22 ‖‖ Solve the differential equation using (a) undetermined coefficients and (b) variation of parameters.

19. $y'' + 4y = x$

20. $y'' - 3y' + 2y = \sin x$

21. $y'' - 2y' + y = e^{2x}$

22. $y'' - y' = e^x$

23–28 ⫿⫿⫿⫿ Solve the differential equation using the method of variation of parameters.

23. $y'' + y = \sec x, \ 0 < x < \pi/2$

24. $y'' + y = \cot x, \ 0 < x < \pi/2$

25. $y'' - 3y' + 2y = \dfrac{1}{1 + e^{-x}}$

26. $y'' + 3y' + 2y = \sin(e^x)$

27. $y'' - y = \dfrac{1}{x}$

28. $y'' + 4y' + 4y = \dfrac{e^{-2x}}{x^3}$

18.3 Applications of Second-Order Differential Equations

Second-order linear differential equations have a variety of applications in science and engineering. In this section we explore two of them: the vibration of springs and electric circuits.

Vibrating Springs

We consider the motion of an object with mass m at the end of a spring that is either vertical (as in Figure 1) or horizontal on a level surface (as in Figure 2).

In Section 6.4 we discussed Hooke's Law, which says that if the spring is stretched (or compressed) x units from its natural length, then it exerts a force that is proportional to x:

$$\text{restoring force} = -kx$$

where k is a positive constant (called the **spring constant**). If we ignore any external resisting forces (due to air resistance or friction) then, by Newton's Second Law (force equals mass times acceleration), we have

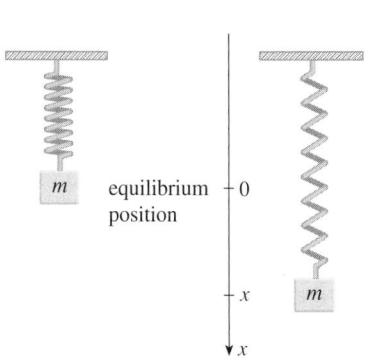

FIGURE 1

1

$$m\frac{d^2x}{dt^2} = -kx \qquad \text{or} \qquad m\frac{d^2x}{dt^2} + kx = 0$$

This is a second-order linear differential equation. Its auxiliary equation is $mr^2 + k = 0$ with roots $r = \pm\omega i$, where $\omega = \sqrt{k/m}$. Thus, the general solution is

$$x(t) = c_1 \cos \omega t + c_2 \sin \omega t$$

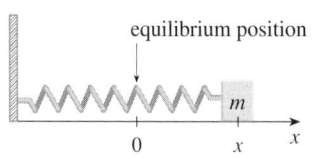

FIGURE 2

which can also be written as

$$x(t) = A\cos(\omega t + \delta)$$

where

$$\omega = \sqrt{k/m} \quad \text{(frequency)}$$

$$A = \sqrt{c_1^2 + c_2^2} \quad \text{(amplitude)}$$

$$\cos \delta = \frac{c_1}{A} \qquad \sin \delta = -\frac{c_2}{A} \quad (\delta \text{ is the phase angle})$$

(See Exercise 17.) This type of motion is called **simple harmonic motion**.

EXAMPLE 1 A spring with a mass of 2 kg has natural length 0.5 m. A force of 25.6 N is required to maintain it stretched to a length of 0.7 m. If the spring is stretched to a length of 0.7 m and then released with initial velocity 0, find the position of the mass at any time t.

SOLUTION From Hooke's Law, the force required to stretch the spring is

$$k(0.2) = 25.6$$

so $k = 25.6/0.2 = 128$. Using this value of the spring constant k, together with $m = 2$ in Equation 1, we have

$$2\frac{d^2x}{dt^2} + 128x = 0$$

As in the earlier general discussion, the solution of this equation is

$\boxed{2}$ $$x(t) = c_1 \cos 8t + c_2 \sin 8t$$

We are given the initial condition that $x(0) = 0.2$. But, from Equation 2, $x(0) = c_1$. Therefore, $c_1 = 0.2$. Differentiating Equation 2, we get

$$x'(t) = -8c_1 \sin 8t + 8c_2 \cos 8t$$

Since the initial velocity is given as $x'(0) = 0$, we have $c_2 = 0$ and so the solution is

$$x(t) = \tfrac{1}{5} \cos 8t$$

▌▌▌ Damped Vibrations

We next consider the motion of a spring that is subject to a frictional force (in the case of the horizontal spring of Figure 2) or a damping force (in the case where a vertical spring moves through a fluid as in Figure 3). An example is the damping force supplied by a shock absorber in a car or a bicycle.

We assume that the damping force is proportional to the velocity of the mass and acts in the direction opposite to the motion. (This has been confirmed, at least approximately, by some physical experiments.) Thus

$$\text{damping force} = -c\,\frac{dx}{dt}$$

where c is a positive constant, called the **damping constant**. Thus, in this case, Newton's Second Law gives

$$m\frac{d^2x}{dt^2} = \text{restoring force} + \text{damping force} = -kx - c\,\frac{dx}{dt}$$

or

$\boxed{3}$ $$m\frac{d^2x}{dt^2} + c\,\frac{dx}{dt} + kx = 0$$

FIGURE 3

Equation 3 is a second-order linear differential equation and its auxiliary equation is $mr^2 + cr + k = 0$. The roots are

$$\boxed{4} \qquad r_1 = \frac{-c + \sqrt{c^2 - 4mk}}{2m} \qquad r_2 = \frac{-c - \sqrt{c^2 - 4mk}}{2m}$$

According to Section 18.1 we need to discuss three cases.

CASE I □ $c^2 - 4mk > 0$ (**overdamping**)
In this case r_1 and r_2 are distinct real roots and

$$x = c_1 e^{r_1 t} + c_2 e^{r_2 t}$$

Since c, m, and k are all positive, we have $\sqrt{c^2 - 4mk} < c$, so the roots r_1 and r_2 given by Equations 4 must both be negative. This shows that $x \to 0$ as $t \to \infty$. Typical graphs of x as a function of t are shown in Figure 4. Notice that oscillations do not occur. (It's possible for the mass to pass through the equilibrium position once, but only once.) This is because $c^2 > 4mk$ means that there is a strong damping force (high-viscosity oil or grease) compared with a weak spring or small mass.

CASE II □ $c^2 - 4mk = 0$ (**critical damping**)
This case corresponds to equal roots

$$r_1 = r_2 = -\frac{c}{2m}$$

and the solution is given by

$$x = (c_1 + c_2 t)e^{-(c/2m)t}$$

It is similar to Case I, and typical graphs resemble those in Figure 4 (see Exercise 12), but the damping is just sufficient to suppress vibrations. Any decrease in the viscosity of the fluid leads to the vibrations of the following case.

CASE III □ $c^2 - 4mk < 0$ (**underdamping**)
Here the roots are complex:

$$\left.\begin{array}{c} r_1 \\ r_2 \end{array}\right\} = -\frac{c}{2m} \pm \omega i$$

where

$$\omega = \frac{\sqrt{4mk - c^2}}{2m}$$

The solution is given by

$$x = e^{-(c/2m)t}(c_1 \cos \omega t + c_2 \sin \omega t)$$

We see that there are oscillations that are damped by the factor $e^{-(c/2m)t}$. Since $c > 0$ and $m > 0$, we have $-(c/2m) < 0$ so $e^{-(c/2m)t} \to 0$ as $t \to \infty$. This implies that $x \to 0$ as $t \to \infty$; that is, the motion decays to 0 as time increases. A typical graph is shown in Figure 5.

FIGURE 4
Overdamping

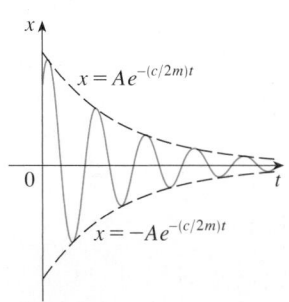

FIGURE 5
Underdamping

EXAMPLE 2 Suppose that the spring of Example 1 is immersed in a fluid with damping constant $c = 40$. Find the position of the mass at any time t if it starts from the equilibrium position and is given a push to start it with an initial velocity of 0.6 m/s.

SOLUTION From Example 1 the mass is $m = 2$ and the spring constant is $k = 128$, so the differential equation (3) becomes

$$2\frac{d^2x}{dt^2} + 40\frac{dx}{dt} + 128x = 0$$

or

$$\frac{d^2x}{dt^2} + 20\frac{dx}{dt} + 64x = 0$$

The auxiliary equation is $r^2 + 20r + 64 = (r + 4)(r + 16) = 0$ with roots -4 and -16, so the motion is overdamped and the solution is

$$x(t) = c_1 e^{-4t} + c_2 e^{-16t}$$

||| Figure 6 shows the graph of the position function for the overdamped motion in Example 2.

We are given that $x(0) = 0$, so $c_1 + c_2 = 0$. Differentiating, we get

$$x'(t) = -4c_1 e^{-4t} - 16c_2 e^{-16t}$$

so

$$x'(0) = -4c_1 - 16c_2 = 0.6$$

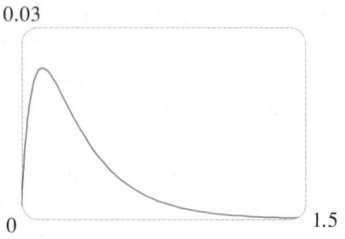

0.03

0

1.5

FIGURE 6

Since $c_2 = -c_1$, this gives $12c_1 = 0.6$ or $c_1 = 0.05$. Therefore

$$x = 0.05(e^{-4t} - e^{-16t})$$

||| **Forced Vibrations**

Suppose that, in addition to the restoring force and the damping force, the motion of the spring is affected by an external force $F(t)$. Then Newton's Second Law gives

$$m\frac{d^2x}{dt^2} = \text{restoring force} + \text{damping force} + \text{external force}$$

$$= -kx - c\frac{dx}{dt} + F(t)$$

Thus, instead of the homogeneous equation (3), the motion of the spring is now governed by the following nonhomogeneous differential equation:

5
$$\boxed{m\frac{d^2x}{dt^2} + c\frac{dx}{dt} + kx = F(t)}$$

The motion of the spring can be determined by the methods of Section 18.2.

A commonly occurring type of external force is a periodic force function

$$F(t) = F_0 \cos \omega_0 t \qquad \text{where} \quad \omega_0 \ne \omega = \sqrt{k/m}$$

In this case, and in the absence of a damping force ($c = 0$), you are asked in Exercise 9 to use the method of undetermined coefficients to show that

$$\boxed{6} \qquad x(t) = c_1 \cos \omega t + c_2 \sin \omega t + \frac{F_0}{m(\omega^2 - \omega_0^2)} \cos \omega_0 t$$

If $\omega_0 = \omega$, then the applied frequency reinforces the natural frequency and the result is vibrations of large amplitude. This is the phenomenon of **resonance** (see Exercise 10).

Electric Circuits

FIGURE 7

In Sections 10.3 and 10.6 we were able to use first-order separable and linear equations to analyze electric circuits that contain a resistor and inductor (see Figure 5 on page 639 or Figure 4 on page 671) or a resistor and capacitor (see Exercise 29 on page 673). Now that we know how to solve second-order linear equations, we are in a position to analyze the circuit shown in Figure 7. It contains an electromotive force E (supplied by a battery or generator), a resistor R, an inductor L, and a capacitor C, in series. If the charge on the capacitor at time t is $Q = Q(t)$, then the current is the rate of change of Q with respect to t: $I = dQ/dt$. As in Section 10.6, it is known from physics that the voltage drops across the resistor, inductor, and capacitor are

$$RI \qquad L\frac{dI}{dt} \qquad \frac{Q}{C}$$

respectively. Kirchhoff's voltage law says that the sum of these voltage drops is equal to the supplied voltage:

$$L\frac{dI}{dt} + RI + \frac{Q}{C} = E(t)$$

Since $I = dQ/dt$, this equation becomes

$$\boxed{7} \qquad L\frac{d^2Q}{dt^2} + R\frac{dQ}{dt} + \frac{1}{C}Q = E(t)$$

which is a second-order linear differential equation with constant coefficients. If the charge Q_0 and the current I_0 are known at time 0, then we have the initial conditions

$$Q(0) = Q_0 \qquad Q'(0) = I(0) = I_0$$

and the initial-value problem can be solved by the methods of Section 18.2.

A differential equation for the current can be obtained by differentiating Equation 7 with respect to t and remembering that $I = dQ/dt$:

$$L \frac{d^2I}{dt^2} + R \frac{dI}{dt} + \frac{1}{C} I = E'(t)$$

EXAMPLE 3 Find the charge and current at time t in the circuit of Figure 7 if $R = 40 \ \Omega$, $L = 1 \ H$, $C = 16 \times 10^{-4} \ F$, $E(t) = 100 \cos 10t$, and the initial charge and current are both 0.

SOLUTION With the given values of L, R, C, and $E(t)$, Equation 7 becomes

8

$$\frac{d^2Q}{dt^2} + 40 \frac{dQ}{dt} + 625Q = 100 \cos 10t$$

The auxiliary equation is $r^2 + 40r + 625 = 0$ with roots

$$r = \frac{-40 \pm \sqrt{-900}}{2} = -20 \pm 15i$$

so the solution of the complementary equation is

$$Q_c(t) = e^{-20t}(c_1 \cos 15t + c_2 \sin 15t)$$

For the method of undetermined coefficients we try the particular solution

$$Q_p(t) = A \cos 10t + B \sin 10t$$

Then $\qquad\qquad Q_p'(t) = -10A \sin 10t + 10B \cos 10t$

$$Q_p''(t) = -100A \cos 10t - 100B \sin 10t$$

Substituting into Equation 8, we have

$$(-100A \cos 10t - 100B \sin 10t) + 40(-10A \sin 10t + 10B \cos 10t)$$
$$+ 625(A \cos 10t + B \sin 10t) = 100 \cos 10t$$

or $\qquad (525A + 400B) \cos 10t + (-400A + 525B) \sin 10t = 100 \cos 10t$

Equating coefficients, we have

$$525A + 400B = 100 \qquad\qquad 21A + 16B = 4$$
or
$$-400A + 525B = 0 \qquad\qquad -16A + 21B = 0$$

The solution of this system is $A = \frac{84}{697}$ and $B = \frac{64}{697}$, so a particular solution is

$$Q_p(t) = \frac{1}{697}(84 \cos 10t + 64 \sin 10t)$$

and the general solution is

$$Q(t) = Q_c(t) + Q_p(t) = e^{-20t}(c_1 \cos 15t + c_2 \sin 15t) + \frac{4}{697}(21 \cos 10t + 16 \sin 10t)$$

Imposing the initial condition $Q(0) = 0$, we get

$$Q(0) = c_1 + \tfrac{84}{697} = 0 \qquad c_1 = -\tfrac{84}{697}$$

To impose the other initial condition we first differentiate to find the current:

$$I = \frac{dQ}{dt} = e^{-20t}[(-20c_1 + 15c_2)\cos 15t + (-15c_1 - 20c_2)\sin 15t]$$

$$+ \tfrac{40}{697}(-21\sin 10t + 16\cos 10t)$$

$$I(0) = -20c_1 + 15c_2 + \tfrac{640}{697} = 0 \qquad c_2 = -\tfrac{464}{2091}$$

Thus, the formula for the charge is

$$Q(t) = \frac{4}{697}\left[\frac{e^{-20t}}{3}(-63\cos 15t - 116\sin 15t) + (21\cos 10t + 16\sin 10t)\right]$$

and the expression for the current is

$$I(t) = \tfrac{1}{2091}\left[e^{-20t}(-1920\cos 15t + 13{,}060\sin 15t) + 120(-21\sin 10t + 16\cos 10t)\right]$$

NOTE 1 ▫ In Example 3 the solution for $Q(t)$ consists of two parts. Since $e^{-20t} \to 0$ as $t \to \infty$ and both $\cos 15t$ and $\sin 15t$ are bounded functions,

$$Q_c(t) = \tfrac{4}{2091}e^{-20t}(-63\cos 15t - 116\sin 15t) \to 0 \qquad \text{as } t \to \infty$$

So, for large values of t,

$$Q(t) \approx Q_p(t) = \tfrac{4}{697}(21\cos 10t + 16\sin 10t)$$

and, for this reason, $Q_p(t)$ is called the **steady state solution**. Figure 8 shows how the graph of the steady state solution compares with the graph of Q in this case.

NOTE 2 ▫ Comparing Equations 5 and 7, we see that mathematically they are identical. This suggests the analogies given in the following chart between physical situations that, at first glance, are very different.

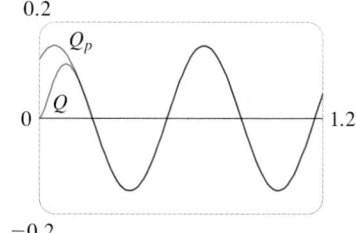

0.2

0

−0.2

1.2

Q_p

Q

FIGURE 8

$$\boxed{5} \quad m\frac{d^2x}{dt^2} + c\frac{dx}{dt} + kx = F(t)$$

$$\boxed{7} \quad L\frac{d^2Q}{dt^2} + R\frac{dQ}{dt} + \frac{1}{C}Q = E(t)$$

Spring system		Electric circuit	
x	displacement	Q	charge
dx/dt	velocity	$I = dQ/dt$	current
m	mass	L	inductance
c	damping constant	R	resistance
k	spring constant	$1/C$	elastance
$F(t)$	external force	$E(t)$	electromotive force

We can also transfer other ideas from one situation to the other. For instance, the steady state solution discussed in Note 1 makes sense in the spring system. And the phenomenon of resonance in the spring system can be usefully carried over to electric circuits as electrical resonance.

18.3 Exercises

1. A spring with a 3-kg mass is held stretched 0.6 m beyond its natural length by a force of 20 N. If the spring begins at its equilibrium position but a push gives it an initial velocity of 1.2 m/s, find the position of the mass after t seconds.

2. A spring with a 4-kg mass has natural length 1 m and is maintained stretched to a length of 1.3 m by a force of 24.3 N. If the spring is compressed to a length of 0.8 m and then released with zero velocity, find the position of the mass at any time t.

3. A spring with a mass of 2 kg has damping constant 14, and a force of 6 N is required to keep the spring stretched 0.5 m beyond its natural length. The spring is stretched 1 m beyond its natural length and then released with zero velocity. Find the position of the mass at any time t.

4. A spring with a mass of 3 kg has damping constant 30 and spring constant 123.
   (a) Find the position of the mass at time t if it starts at the equilibrium position with a velocity of 2 m/s.
   (b) Graph the position function of the mass.

5. For the spring in Exercise 3, find the mass that would produce critical damping.

6. For the spring in Exercise 4, find the damping constant that would produce critical damping.

7. A spring has a mass of 1 kg and its spring constant is $k = 100$. The spring is released at a point 0.1 m above its equilibrium position. Graph the position function for the following values of the damping constant c: 10, 15, 20, 25, 30. What type of damping occurs in each case?

8. A spring has a mass of 1 kg and its damping constant is $c = 10$. The spring starts from its equilibrium position with a velocity of 1 m/s. Graph the position function for the following values of the spring constant k: 10, 20, 25, 30, 40. What type of damping occurs in each case?

9. Suppose a spring has mass m and spring constant k and let $\omega = \sqrt{k/m}$. Suppose that the damping constant is so small that the damping force is negligible. If an external force $F(t) = F_0 \cos \omega_0 t$ is applied, where $\omega_0 \neq \omega$, use the method of undetermined coefficients to show that the motion of the mass is described by Equation 6.

10. As in Exercise 9, consider a spring with mass m, spring constant k, and damping constant $c = 0$, and let $\omega = \sqrt{k/m}$. If an external force $F(t) = F_0 \cos \omega t$ is applied (the applied frequency equals the natural frequency), use the method of undetermined coefficients to show that the motion of the mass is given by $x(t) = c_1 \cos \omega t + c_2 \sin \omega t + (F_0/(2m\omega))t \sin \omega t$.

11. Show that if $\omega_0 \neq \omega$, but ω/ω_0 is a rational number, then the motion described by Equation 6 is periodic.

12. Consider a spring subject to a frictional or damping force.
    (a) In the critically damped case, the motion is given by $x = c_1 e^{rt} + c_2 t e^{rt}$. Show that the graph of x crosses the t-axis whenever c_1 and c_2 have opposite signs.
    (b) In the overdamped case, the motion is given by $x = c_1 e^{r_1 t} + c_2 e^{r_2 t}$, where $r_1 > r_2$. Determine a condition on the relative magnitudes of c_1 and c_2 under which the graph of x crosses the t-axis at a positive value of t.

13. A series circuit consists of a resistor with $R = 20\ \Omega$, an inductor with $L = 1$ H, a capacitor with $C = 0.002$ F, and a 12-V battery. If the initial charge and current are both 0, find the charge and current at time t.

14. A series circuit contains a resistor with $R = 24\ \Omega$, an inductor with $L = 2$ H, a capacitor with $C = 0.005$ F, and a 12-V battery. The initial charge is $Q = 0.001$ C and the initial current is 0.
    (a) Find the charge and current at time t.
    (b) Graph the charge and current functions.

15. The battery in Exercise 13 is replaced by a generator producing a voltage of $E(t) = 12 \sin 10t$. Find the charge at time t.

16. The battery in Exercise 14 is replaced by a generator producing a voltage of $E(t) = 12 \sin 10t$.
    (a) Find the charge at time t.
    (b) Graph the charge function.

17. Verify that the solution to Equation 1 can be written in the form $x(t) = A \cos(\omega t + \delta)$.

18. The figure shows a pendulum with length L and the angle θ from the vertical to the pendulum. It can be shown that θ, as a function of time, satisfies the nonlinear differential equation

    $$\frac{d^2\theta}{dt^2} + \frac{g}{L}\sin\theta = 0$$

    where g is the acceleration due to gravity. For small values of θ we can use the linear approximation $\sin\theta \approx \theta$ and then the differential equation becomes linear.
    (a) Find the equation of motion of a pendulum with length 1 m if θ is initially 0.2 rad and the initial angular velocity is $d\theta/dt = 1$ rad/s.
    (b) What is the maximum angle from the vertical?
    (c) What is the period of the pendulum (that is, the time to complete one back-and-forth swing)?
    (d) When will the pendulum first be vertical?
    (e) What is the angular velocity when the pendulum is vertical?

18.4 Series Solutions

Many differential equations can't be solved explicitly in terms of finite combinations of simple familiar functions. This is true even for a simple-looking equation like

$$y'' - 2xy' + y = 0 \tag{1}$$

But it is important to be able to solve equations such as Equation 1 because they arise from physical problems and, in particular, in connection with the Schrödinger equation in quantum mechanics. In such a case we use the method of power series; that is, we look for a solution of the form

$$y = f(x) = \sum_{n=0}^{\infty} c_n x^n = c_0 + c_1 x + c_2 x^2 + c_3 x^3 + \cdots$$

The method is to substitute this expression into the differential equation and determine the values of the coefficients $c_0, c_1, c_2, \ldots$. This technique resembles the method of undetermined coefficients discussed in Section 18.2.

Before using power series to solve Equation 1, we illustrate the method on the simpler equation $y'' + y = 0$ in Example 1. It's true that we already know how to solve this equation by the techniques of Section 18.1, but it's easier to understand the power series method when it is applied to this simpler equation.

EXAMPLE 1 Use power series to solve the equation $y'' + y = 0$.

SOLUTION We assume there is a solution of the form

$$y = c_0 + c_1 x + c_2 x^2 + c_3 x^3 + \cdots = \sum_{n=0}^{\infty} c_n x^n \tag{2}$$

We can differentiate power series term by term, so

$$y' = c_1 + 2c_2 x + 3c_3 x^2 + \cdots = \sum_{n=1}^{\infty} n c_n x^{n-1}$$

$$y'' = 2c_2 + 2 \cdot 3c_3 x + \cdots = \sum_{n=2}^{\infty} n(n-1) c_n x^{n-2} \tag{3}$$

In order to compare the expressions for y and y'' more easily, we rewrite y'' as follows:

‖‖‖ By writing out the first few terms of (4), you can see that it is the same as (3). To obtain (4) we replaced n by $n + 2$ and began the summation at 0 instead of 2.

$$y'' = \sum_{n=0}^{\infty} (n+2)(n+1) c_{n+2} x^n \tag{4}$$

Substituting the expressions in Equations 2 and 4 into the differential equation, we obtain

$$\sum_{n=0}^{\infty} (n+2)(n+1) c_{n+2} x^n + \sum_{n=0}^{\infty} c_n x^n = 0$$

or

$$\sum_{n=0}^{\infty} [(n+2)(n+1) c_{n+2} + c_n] x^n = 0 \tag{5}$$

If two power series are equal, then the corresponding coefficients must be equal. Therefore, the coefficients of x^n in Equation 5 must be 0:

$$(n + 2)(n + 1)c_{n+2} + c_n = 0$$

$$\boxed{6} \qquad c_{n+2} = -\frac{c_n}{(n + 1)(n + 2)} \qquad n = 0, 1, 2, 3, \ldots$$

Equation 6 is called a *recursion relation*. If c_0 and c_1 are known, this equation allows us to determine the remaining coefficients recursively by putting $n = 0, 1, 2, 3, \ldots$ in succession.

$$\text{Put } n = 0: \qquad c_2 = -\frac{c_0}{1 \cdot 2}$$

$$\text{Put } n = 1: \qquad c_3 = -\frac{c_1}{2 \cdot 3}$$

$$\text{Put } n = 2: \qquad c_4 = -\frac{c_2}{3 \cdot 4} = \frac{c_0}{1 \cdot 2 \cdot 3 \cdot 4} = \frac{c_0}{4!}$$

$$\text{Put } n = 3: \qquad c_5 = -\frac{c_3}{4 \cdot 5} = \frac{c_1}{2 \cdot 3 \cdot 4 \cdot 5} = \frac{c_1}{5!}$$

$$\text{Put } n = 4: \qquad c_6 = -\frac{c_4}{5 \cdot 6} = -\frac{c_0}{4! \, 5 \cdot 6} = -\frac{c_0}{6!}$$

$$\text{Put } n = 5: \qquad c_7 = -\frac{c_5}{6 \cdot 7} = -\frac{c_1}{5! \, 6 \cdot 7} = -\frac{c_1}{7!}$$

By now we see the pattern:

$$\text{For the even coefficients, } \quad c_{2n} = (-1)^n \frac{c_0}{(2n)!}$$

$$\text{For the odd coefficients, } \quad c_{2n+1} = (-1)^n \frac{c_1}{(2n + 1)!}$$

Putting these values back into Equation 2, we write the solution as

$$y = c_0 + c_1 x + c_2 x^2 + c_3 x^3 + c_4 x^4 + c_5 x^5 + \cdots$$

$$= c_0\left(1 - \frac{x^2}{2!} + \frac{x^4}{4!} - \frac{x^6}{6!} + \cdots + (-1)^n \frac{x^{2n}}{(2n)!} + \cdots\right)$$

$$+ c_1\left(x - \frac{x^3}{3!} + \frac{x^5}{5!} - \frac{x^7}{7!} + \cdots + (-1)^n \frac{x^{2n+1}}{(2n + 1)!} + \cdots\right)$$

$$= c_0 \sum_{n=0}^{\infty} (-1)^n \frac{x^{2n}}{(2n)!} + c_1 \sum_{n=0}^{\infty} (-1)^n \frac{x^{2n+1}}{(2n + 1)!}$$

Notice that there are two arbitrary constants, c_0 and c_1.

NOTE 1 ▫ We recognize the series obtained in Example 1 as being the Maclaurin series for $\cos x$ and $\sin x$. (See Equations 12.10.16 and 12.10.15.) Therefore, we could write the solution as

$$y(x) = c_0 \cos x + c_1 \sin x$$

But we are not usually able to express power series solutions of differential equations in terms of known functions.

EXAMPLE 2 Solve $y'' - 2xy' + y = 0$.

SOLUTION We assume there is a solution of the form

$$y = \sum_{n=0}^{\infty} c_n x^n$$

Then

$$y' = \sum_{n=1}^{\infty} n c_n x^{n-1}$$

and

$$y'' = \sum_{n=2}^{\infty} n(n-1) c_n x^{n-2} = \sum_{n=0}^{\infty} (n+2)(n+1) c_{n+2} x^n$$

as in Example 1. Substituting in the differential equation, we get

$$\sum_{n=0}^{\infty} (n+2)(n+1) c_{n+2} x^n - 2x \sum_{n=1}^{\infty} n c_n x^{n-1} + \sum_{n=0}^{\infty} c_n x^n = 0$$

$$\sum_{n=0}^{\infty} (n+2)(n+1) c_{n+2} x^n - \sum_{n=1}^{\infty} 2n c_n x^n + \sum_{n=0}^{\infty} c_n x^n = 0$$

$$\sum_{n=1}^{\infty} 2n c_n x^n = \sum_{n=0}^{\infty} 2n c_n x^n \qquad \sum_{n=0}^{\infty} [(n+2)(n+1) c_{n+2} - (2n-1) c_n] x^n = 0$$

This equation is true if the coefficient of x^n is 0:

$$(n+2)(n+1) c_{n+2} - (2n-1) c_n = 0$$

7
$$c_{n+2} = \frac{2n-1}{(n+1)(n+2)} c_n \qquad n = 0, 1, 2, 3, \ldots$$

We solve this recursion relation by putting $n = 0, 1, 2, 3, \ldots$ successively in Equation 7:

Put $n = 0$: $\quad c_2 = \dfrac{-1}{1 \cdot 2} c_0$

Put $n = 1$: $\quad c_3 = \dfrac{1}{2 \cdot 3} c_1$

Put $n = 2$: $\quad c_4 = \dfrac{3}{3 \cdot 4} c_2 = -\dfrac{3}{1 \cdot 2 \cdot 3 \cdot 4} c_0 = -\dfrac{3}{4!} c_0$

Put $n = 3$: $\quad c_5 = \dfrac{5}{4 \cdot 5} c_3 = \dfrac{1 \cdot 5}{2 \cdot 3 \cdot 4 \cdot 5} c_1 = \dfrac{1 \cdot 5}{5!} c_1$

Put $n = 4$: $\quad c_6 = \dfrac{7}{5 \cdot 6} c_4 = -\dfrac{3 \cdot 7}{4! \, 5 \cdot 6} c_0 = -\dfrac{3 \cdot 7}{6!} c_0$

Put $n = 5$: $\quad c_7 = \dfrac{9}{6 \cdot 7} c_5 = \dfrac{1 \cdot 5 \cdot 9}{5! \, 6 \cdot 7} c_1 = \dfrac{1 \cdot 5 \cdot 9}{7!} c_1$

Put $n = 6$: $\quad c_8 = \dfrac{11}{7 \cdot 8} c_6 = -\dfrac{3 \cdot 7 \cdot 11}{8!} c_0$

Put $n = 7$: $\quad c_9 = \dfrac{13}{8 \cdot 9} c_7 = \dfrac{1 \cdot 5 \cdot 9 \cdot 13}{9!} c_1$

In general, the even coefficients are given by

$$c_{2n} = -\frac{3 \cdot 7 \cdot 11 \cdot \cdots \cdot (4n - 5)}{(2n)!} c_0$$

and the odd coefficients are given by

$$c_{2n+1} = \frac{1 \cdot 5 \cdot 9 \cdot \cdots \cdot (4n - 3)}{(2n + 1)!} c_1$$

The solution is

$$y = c_0 + c_1 x + c_2 x^2 + c_3 x^3 + c_4 x^4 + \cdots$$

$$= c_0 \left(1 - \frac{1}{2!} x^2 - \frac{3}{4!} x^4 - \frac{3 \cdot 7}{6!} x^6 - \frac{3 \cdot 7 \cdot 11}{8!} x^8 - \cdots \right)$$

$$+ c_1 \left(x + \frac{1}{3!} x^3 + \frac{1 \cdot 5}{5!} x^5 + \frac{1 \cdot 5 \cdot 9}{7!} x^7 + \frac{1 \cdot 5 \cdot 9 \cdot 13}{9!} x^9 + \cdots \right)$$

or

$$\boxed{8} \qquad y = c_0 \left(1 - \frac{1}{2!} x^2 - \sum_{n=2}^{\infty} \frac{3 \cdot 7 \cdot \cdots \cdot (4n - 5)}{(2n)!} x^{2n} \right)$$

$$+ c_1 \left(x + \sum_{n=1}^{\infty} \frac{1 \cdot 5 \cdot 9 \cdot \cdots \cdot (4n - 3)}{(2n + 1)!} x^{2n+1} \right)$$

NOTE 2 ▫ In Example 2 we had to assume that the differential equation had a series solution. But now we could verify directly that the function given by Equation 8 is indeed a solution.

NOTE 3 ▫ Unlike the situation of Example 1, the power series that arise in the solution of Example 2 do not define elementary functions. The functions

$$y_1(x) = 1 - \frac{1}{2!} x^2 - \sum_{n=2}^{\infty} \frac{3 \cdot 7 \cdot \cdots \cdot (4n - 5)}{(2n)!} x^{2n}$$

and

$$y_2(x) = x + \sum_{n=1}^{\infty} \frac{1 \cdot 5 \cdot 9 \cdot \cdots \cdot (4n - 3)}{(2n + 1)!} x^{2n+1}$$

FIGURE 1

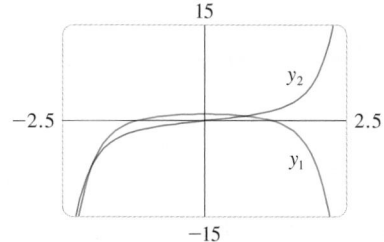

FIGURE 2

are perfectly good functions but they can't be expressed in terms of familiar functions. We can use these power series expressions for y_1 and y_2 to compute approximate values of the functions and even to graph them. Figure 1 shows the first few partial sums $T_0, T_2, T_4, \ldots$ (Taylor polynomials) for $y_1(x)$, and we see how they converge to y_1. In this way we can graph both y_1 and y_2 in Figure 2.

NOTE 4 ▫ If we were asked to solve the initial-value problem

$$y'' - 2xy' + y = 0 \qquad y(0) = 0 \qquad y'(0) = 1$$

we would observe from Theorem 11.10.5 that

$$c_0 = y(0) = 0 \qquad c_1 = y'(0) = 1$$

This would simplify the calculations in Example 2, since all of the even coefficients would be 0. The solution to the initial-value problem is

$$y(x) = x + \sum_{n=1}^{\infty} \frac{1 \cdot 5 \cdot 9 \cdot \cdots \cdot (4n - 3)}{(2n + 1)!} x^{2n+1}$$

18.4 Exercises

1–11 ▊▊ Use power series to solve the differential equation.

1. $y' - y = 0$

2. $y' = xy$

3. $y' = x^2 y$

4. $(x - 3)y' + 2y = 0$

5. $y'' + xy' + y = 0$

6. $y'' = y$

7. $(x^2 + 1)y'' + xy' - y = 0$

8. $y'' = xy$

9. $y'' - xy' - y = 0$, $y(0) = 1$, $y'(0) = 0$

10. $y'' + x^2 y = 0$, $y(0) = 1$, $y'(0) = 0$

11. $y'' + x^2 y' + xy = 0$, $y(0) = 0$, $y'(0) = 1$

▫   ▫   ▫   ▫   ▫   ▫   ▫   ▫   ▫   ▫   ▫   ▫

12. The solution of the initial-value problem

$$x^2 y'' + xy' + x^2 y = 0 \qquad y(0) = 1 \qquad y'(0) = 0$$

is called a Bessel function of order 0.
(a) Solve the initial-value problem to find a power series expansion for the Bessel function.
(b) Graph several Taylor polynomials until you reach one that looks like a good approximation to the Bessel function on the interval $[-5, 5]$.

18 Review
═ CONCEPT CHECK ═

1. (a) Write the general form of a second-order homogeneous linear differential equation with constant coefficients.
  (b) Write the auxiliary equation.
  (c) How do you use the roots of the auxiliary equation to solve the differential equation? Write the form of the solution for each of the three cases that can occur.

2. (a) What is an initial-value problem for a second-order differential equation?
  (b) What is a boundary-value problem for such an equation?

3. (a) Write the general form of a second-order nonhomogeneous linear differential equation with constant coefficients.

  (b) What is the complementary equation? How does it help solve the original differential equation?
  (c) Explain how the method of undetermined coefficients works.
  (d) Explain how the method of variation of parameters works.

4. Discuss two applications of second-order linear differential equations.

5. How do you use power series to solve a differential equation?

──────────────── ○ TRUE-FALSE QUIZ ○ ────────────────

Determine whether the statement is true or false. If it is true, explain why. If it is false, explain why or give an example that disproves the statement.

1. If y_1 and y_2 are solutions of $y'' + y = 0$, then $y_1 + y_2$ is also a solution of the equation.

2. If y_1 and y_2 are solutions of $y'' + 6y' + 5y = x$, then $c_1 y_1 + c_2 y_2$ is also a solution of the equation.

3. The general solution of $y'' - y = 0$ can be written as

$$y = c_1 \cosh x + c_2 \sinh x$$

4. The equation $y'' - y = e^x$ has a particular solution of the form

$$y_p = A e^x$$

──────────────── ○ EXERCISES ○ ────────────────

1–10 ▐▐ Solve the differential equation.

1. $y'' - 2y' - 15y = 0$

2. $y'' + 4y' + 13y = 0$

3. $y'' + 3y = 0$

4. $4y'' + 4y' + y = 0$

5. $\dfrac{d^2 y}{dx^2} - 4\dfrac{dy}{dx} + 5y = e^{2x}$

6. $\dfrac{d^2 y}{dx^2} + \dfrac{dy}{dx} - 2y = x^2$

7. $\dfrac{d^2 y}{dx^2} - 2\dfrac{dy}{dx} + y = x \cos x$

8. $\dfrac{d^2 y}{dx^2} + 4y = \sin 2x$

9. $\dfrac{d^2 y}{dx^2} - \dfrac{dy}{dx} - 6y = 1 + e^{-2x}$

10. $\dfrac{d^2 y}{dx^2} + y = \csc x, \quad 0 < x < \pi/2$

11–14 ▐▐ Solve the initial-value problem.

11. $y'' + 6y' = 0, \quad y(1) = 3, \quad y'(1) = 12$

12. $y'' - 6y' + 25y = 0, \quad y(0) = 2, \quad y'(0) = 1$

13. $y'' - 5y' + 4y = 0, \quad y(0) = 0, \quad y'(0) = 1$

14. $9y'' + y = 3x + e^{-x}, \quad y(0) = 1, \quad y'(0) = 2$

15. Use power series to solve the initial-value problem

$$y'' + xy' + y = 0 \qquad y(0) = 0 \qquad y'(0) = 1$$

16. Use power series to solve the equation

$$y'' - xy' - 2y = 0$$

17. A series circuit contains a resistor with $R = 40\ \Omega$, an inductor with $L = 2$ H, a capacitor with $C = 0.0025$ F, and a 12-V battery. The initial charge is $Q = 0.01$ C and the initial current is 0. Find the charge at time t.

18. A spring with a mass of 2 kg has damping constant 16, and a force of 12.8 N keeps the spring stretched 0.2 m beyond its natural length. Find the position of the mass at time t if it starts at the equilibrium position with a velocity of 2.4 m/s.

19. Assume that the earth is a solid sphere of uniform density with mass M and radius $R = 3960$ mi. For a particle of mass m within the earth at a distance r from the earth's center, the gravitational force attracting the particle to the center is

$$F_r = \frac{-GM_r m}{r^2}$$

where G is the gravitational constant and M_r is the mass of the earth within the sphere of radius r.

(a) Show that $F_r = \dfrac{-GMm}{R^3} r$.

(b) Suppose a hole is drilled through the earth along a diameter. Show that if a particle of mass m is dropped from rest, at the surface, into the hole, then the distance $y = y(t)$ of the particle from the center of the earth at time t is given by

$$y''(t) = -k^2 y(t)$$

where $k^2 = GM/R^3 = g/R$.

(c) Conclude from part (b) that the particle undergoes simple harmonic motion. Find the period T.

(d) With what speed does the particle pass through the center of the earth?

APPENDIXES

▏▏▏▏ **A Numbers, Inequalities, and Absolute Values**

Calculus is based on the real number system. We start with the **integers**:

$$\ldots, \quad -3, \quad -2, \quad -1, \quad 0, \quad 1, \quad 2, \quad 3, \quad 4, \quad \ldots$$

Then we construct the **rational numbers**, which are ratios of integers. Thus, any rational number r can be expressed as

$$r = \frac{m}{n} \qquad \text{where } m \text{ and } n \text{ are integers and } n \neq 0$$

Examples are

$$\tfrac{1}{2} \qquad -\tfrac{3}{7} \qquad 46 = \tfrac{46}{1} \qquad 0.17 = \tfrac{17}{100}$$

(Recall that division by 0 is always ruled out, so expressions like $\frac{3}{0}$ and $\frac{0}{0}$ are undefined.) Some real numbers, such as $\sqrt{2}$, can't be expressed as a ratio of integers and are therefore called **irrational numbers**. It can be shown, with varying degrees of difficulty, that the following are also irrational numbers:

$$\sqrt{3} \qquad \sqrt{5} \qquad \sqrt[3]{2} \qquad \pi \qquad \sin 1° \qquad \log_{10} 2$$

The set of all real numbers is usually denoted by the symbol $\mathbb{R}$. When we use the word *number* without qualification, we mean "real number."

Every number has a decimal representation. If the number is rational, then the corresponding decimal is repeating. For example,

$$\tfrac{1}{2} = 0.5000\ldots = 0.5\overline{0} \qquad\qquad \tfrac{2}{3} = 0.66666\ldots = 0.\overline{6}$$

$$\tfrac{157}{495} = 0.317171717\ldots = 0.3\overline{17} \qquad \tfrac{9}{7} = 1.285714285714\ldots = 1.\overline{285714}$$

(The bar indicates that the sequence of digits repeats forever.) On the other hand, if the number is irrational, the decimal is nonrepeating:

$$\sqrt{2} = 1.414213562373095\ldots \qquad \pi = 3.141592653589793\ldots$$

If we stop the decimal expansion of any number at a certain place, we get an approximation to the number. For instance, we can write

$$\pi \approx 3.14159265$$

where the symbol $\approx$ is read "is approximately equal to." The more decimal places we retain, the better the approximation we get.

The real numbers can be represented by points on a line as in Figure 1. The positive direction (to the right) is indicated by an arrow. We choose an arbitrary reference point O, called the **origin**, which corresponds to the real number 0. Given any convenient unit of measurement, each positive number x is represented by the point on the line a distance of x units to the right of the origin, and each negative number $-x$ is represented by the point x units to the left of the origin. Thus, every real number is represented by a point on the line, and every point P on the line corresponds to exactly one real number. The number associated with the point P is called the **coordinate** of P and the line is then called a **coor-**

dinate line, or a **real number line**, or simply a **real line**. Often we identify the point with its coordinate and think of a number as being a point on the real line.

FIGURE 1

$$-2.63 \qquad -\tfrac{3}{7} \qquad \tfrac{1}{2} \qquad \sqrt{2} \qquad \pi$$

The real numbers are ordered. We say *a is less than b* and write $a < b$ if $b - a$ is a positive number. Geometrically, this means that a lies to the left of b on the number line. (Equivalently, we say *b is greater than a* and write $b > a$.) The symbol $a \leq b$ (or $b \geq a$) means that either $a < b$ or $a = b$ and is read "*a is less than or equal to b*." For instance, the following are true inequalities:

$$7 < 7.4 < 7.5 \qquad -3 > -\pi \qquad \sqrt{2} < 2 \qquad \sqrt{2} \leq 2 \qquad 2 \leq 2$$

In what follows we need to use *set notation*. A **set** is a collection of objects, and these objects are called the **elements** of the set. If S is a set, the notation $a \in S$ means that a is an element of S, and $a \notin S$ means that a is not an element of S. For example, if Z represents the set of integers, then $-3 \in Z$ but $\pi \notin Z$. If S and T are sets, then their **union** $S \cup T$ is the set consisting of all elements that are in S or T (or in both S and T). The **intersection** of S and T is the set $S \cap T$ consisting of all elements that are in both S and T. In other words, $S \cap T$ is the common part of S and T. The empty set, denoted by $\varnothing$, is the set that contains no element.

Some sets can be described by listing their elements between braces. For instance, the set A consisting of all positive integers less than 7 can be written as

$$A = \{1, 2, 3, 4, 5, 6\}$$

We could also write A in *set-builder notation* as

$$A = \{x \mid x \text{ is an integer and } 0 < x < 7\}$$

which is read "A is the set of x such that x is an integer and $0 < x < 7$."

‖‖‖‖ Intervals

Certain sets of real numbers, called **intervals,** occur frequently in calculus and correspond geometrically to line segments. For example, if $a < b$, the **open interval** from a to b consists of all numbers between a and b and is denoted by the symbol (a, b). Using set-builder notation, we can write

$$(a, b) = \{x \mid a < x < b\}$$

FIGURE 2

Open interval (a, b)

Notice that the endpoints of the interval—namely, a and b—are excluded. This is indicated by the round brackets ( ) and by the open dots in Figure 2. The **closed interval** from a to b is the set

$$[a, b] = \{x \mid a \leq x \leq b\}$$

FIGURE 3

Closed interval $[a, b]$

Here the endpoints of the interval are included. This is indicated by the square brackets [ ] and by the solid dots in Figure 3. It is also possible to include only one endpoint in an interval, as shown in Table 1.

1 **Table of Intervals**

Notation	Set description	Picture
(a, b)	$\{x \mid a < x < b\}$	
$[a, b]$	$\{x \mid a \leq x \leq b\}$	
$[a, b)$	$\{x \mid a \leq x < b\}$	
$(a, b]$	$\{x \mid a < x \leq b\}$	
(a, ∞)	$\{x \mid x > a\}$	
$[a, \infty)$	$\{x \mid x \geq a\}$	
$(-\infty, b)$	$\{x \mid x < b\}$	
$(-\infty, b]$	$\{x \mid x \leq b\}$	
$(-\infty, \infty)$	$\mathbb{R}$ (set of all real numbers)	

||| Table 1 lists the nine possible types of intervals. When these intervals are discussed, it is always assumed that $a < b$.

We also need to consider infinite intervals such as

$$(a, \infty) = \{x \mid x > a\}$$

This does not mean that ∞ ("infinity") is a number. The notation (a, ∞) stands for the set of all numbers that are greater than a, so the symbol ∞ simply indicates that the interval extends indefinitely far in the positive direction.

||| **Inequalities**

When working with inequalities, note the following rules.

2 **Rules for Inequalities**

1. If $a < b$, then $a + c < b + c$.

2. If $a < b$ and $c < d$, then $a + c < b + d$.

3. If $a < b$ and $c > 0$, then $ac < bc$.

4. If $a < b$ and $c < 0$, then $ac > bc$.

5. If $0 < a < b$, then $1/a > 1/b$.

Rule 1 says that we can add any number to both sides of an inequality, and Rule 2 says that two inequalities can be added. However, we have to be careful with multiplication. Rule 3 says that we can multiply both sides of an inequality by a *positive* number, but ⊘ Rule 4 says that if we multiply both sides of an inequality by a negative number, then we reverse the direction of the inequality. For example, if we take the inequality $3 < 5$ and multiply by 2, we get $6 < 10$, but if we multiply by -2, we get $-6 > -10$. Finally, Rule 5 says that if we take reciprocals, then we reverse the direction of an inequality (provided the numbers are positive).

EXAMPLE 1 Solve the inequality $1 + x < 7x + 5$.

SOLUTION The given inequality is satisfied by some values of x but not by others. To *solve* an inequality means to determine the set of numbers x for which the inequality is true. This is called the *solution set*.

First we subtract 1 from each side of the inequality (using Rule 1 with $c = -1$):

$$x < 7x + 4$$

Then we subtract $7x$ from both sides (Rule 1 with $c = -7x$):

$$-6x < 4$$

Now we divide both sides by -6 $\left(\text{Rule 4 with } c = -\tfrac{1}{6}\right)$:

$$x > -\tfrac{4}{6} = -\tfrac{2}{3}$$

These steps can all be reversed, so the solution set consists of all numbers greater than $-\tfrac{2}{3}$. In other words, the solution of the inequality is the interval $\left(-\tfrac{2}{3}, \infty\right)$.

EXAMPLE 2 Solve the inequalities $4 \leqslant 3x - 2 < 13$.

SOLUTION Here the solution set consists of all values of x that satisfy both inequalities. Using the rules given in (2), we see that the following inequalities are equivalent:

$$4 \leqslant 3x - 2 < 13$$

$$6 \leqslant 3x < 15 \qquad \text{(add 2)}$$

$$2 \leqslant x < 5 \qquad \text{(divide by 3)}$$

Therefore, the solution set is $[2, 5)$.

EXAMPLE 3 Solve the inequality $x^2 - 5x + 6 \leqslant 0$.

SOLUTION First we factor the left side:

$$(x - 2)(x - 3) \leqslant 0$$

We know that the corresponding equation $(x - 2)(x - 3) = 0$ has the solutions 2 and 3. The numbers 2 and 3 divide the real line into three intervals:

$$(-\infty, 2) \qquad (2, 3) \qquad (3, \infty)$$

On each of these intervals we determine the signs of the factors. For instance,

$$x \in (-\infty, 2) \quad \Rightarrow \quad x < 2 \quad \Rightarrow \quad x - 2 < 0$$

Then we record these signs in the following chart:

Interval	$x - 2$	$x - 3$	$(x - 2)(x - 3)$
$x < 2$	$-$	$-$	$+$
$2 < x < 3$	$+$	$-$	$-$
$x > 3$	$+$	$+$	$+$

▏ A visual method for solving Example 3 is to use a graphing device to graph the parabola $y = x^2 - 5x + 6$ (as in Figure 4) and observe that the curve lies on or below the x-axis when $2 \leqslant x \leqslant 3$.

FIGURE 4

Another method for obtaining the information in the chart is to use *test values*. For instance, if we use the test value $x = 1$ for the interval $(-\infty, 2)$, then substitution in $x^2 - 5x + 6$ gives

$$1^2 - 5(1) + 6 = 2$$

The polynomial $x^2 - 5x + 6$ doesn't change sign inside any of the three intervals, so we conclude that it is positive on $(-\infty, 2)$.

Then we read from the chart that $(x - 2)(x - 3)$ is negative when $2 < x < 3$. Thus, the solution of the inequality $(x - 2)(x - 3) \leq 0$ is

$$\{x \mid 2 \leq x \leq 3\} = [2, 3]$$

Notice that we have included the endpoints 2 and 3 because we are looking for values of x such that the product is either negative or zero. The solution is illustrated in Figure 5.

FIGURE 5

EXAMPLE 4 Solve $x^3 + 3x^2 > 4x$.

SOLUTION First we take all nonzero terms to one side of the inequality sign and factor the resulting expression:

$$x^3 + 3x^2 - 4x > 0 \qquad \text{or} \qquad x(x - 1)(x + 4) > 0$$

As in Example 3 we solve the corresponding equation $x(x - 1)(x + 4) = 0$ and use the solutions $x = -4$, $x = 0$, and $x = 1$ to divide the real line into four intervals $(-\infty, -4)$, $(-4, 0)$, $(0, 1)$, and $(1, \infty)$. On each interval the product keeps a constant sign as shown in the following chart:

Interval	x	$x - 1$	$x + 4$	$x(x - 1)(x + 4)$
$x < -4$	$-$	$-$	$-$	$-$
$-4 < x < 0$	$-$	$-$	$+$	$+$
$0 < x < 1$	$+$	$-$	$+$	$-$
$x > 1$	$+$	$+$	$+$	$+$

Then we read from the chart that the solution set is

$$\{x \mid -4 < x < 0 \ \text{ or } \ x > 1\} = (-4, 0) \cup (1, \infty)$$

FIGURE 6

The solution is illustrated in Figure 6.

|||| **Absolute Value**

The **absolute value** of a number a, denoted by $|a|$, is the distance from a to 0 on the real number line. Distances are always positive or 0, so we have

$$|a| \geq 0 \qquad \text{for every number } a$$

For example,

$$|3| = 3 \qquad |-3| = 3 \qquad |0| = 0 \qquad |\sqrt{2} - 1| = \sqrt{2} - 1 \qquad |3 - \pi| = \pi - 3$$

In general, we have

|||| Remember that if a is negative, then $-a$ is positive.

 3

$$|a| = a \qquad \text{if } a \geq 0$$

$$|a| = -a \qquad \text{if } a < 0$$

EXAMPLE 5 Express $|3x - 2|$ without using the absolute-value symbol.

SOLUTION

$$|3x - 2| = \begin{cases} 3x - 2 & \text{if } 3x - 2 \geqslant 0 \\ -(3x - 2) & \text{if } 3x - 2 < 0 \end{cases}$$

$$= \begin{cases} 3x - 2 & \text{if } x \geqslant \frac{2}{3} \\ 2 - 3x & \text{if } x < \frac{2}{3} \end{cases}$$

Recall that the symbol $\sqrt{\;}$ means "the positive square root of." Thus, $\sqrt{r} = s$ means $s^2 = r$ and $s \geqslant 0$. Therefore, the equation $\sqrt{a^2} = a$ is not always true. It is true only when $a \geqslant 0$. If $a < 0$, then $-a > 0$, so we have $\sqrt{a^2} = -a$. In view of (3), we then have the equation

4

$$\sqrt{a^2} = |a|$$

which is true for all values of a.

Hints for the proofs of the following properties are given in the exercises.

---

5 **Properties of Absolute Values** Suppose a and b are any real numbers and n is an integer. Then

1. $|ab| = |a||b|$ **2.** $\left|\dfrac{a}{b}\right| = \dfrac{|a|}{|b|}$ $(b \neq 0)$ **3.** $|a^n| = |a|^n$

For solving equations or inequalities involving absolute values, it's often very helpful to use the following statements.

---

6 Suppose $a > 0$. Then

4. $|x| = a$ if and only if $x = \pm a$

5. $|x| < a$ if and only if $-a < x < a$

6. $|x| > a$ if and only if $x > a$ or $x < -a$

FIGURE 7

FIGURE 8
Length of a line segment $= |a - b|$

For instance, the inequality $|x| < a$ says that the distance from x to the origin is less than a, and you can see from Figure 7 that this is true if and only if x lies between $-a$ and a.

If a and b are any real numbers, then the distance between a and b is the absolute value of the difference, namely, $|a - b|$, which is also equal to $|b - a|$. (See Figure 8.)

EXAMPLE 6 Solve $|2x - 5| = 3$.

SOLUTION By Property 4 of (6), $|2x - 5| = 3$ is equivalent to

$$2x - 5 = 3 \quad \text{or} \quad 2x - 5 = -3$$

So $2x = 8$ or $2x = 2$. Thus, $x = 4$ or $x = 1$.

EXAMPLE 7 Solve $|x - 5| < 2$.

SOLUTION 1 By Property 5 of (6), $|x - 5| < 2$ is equivalent to

$$-2 < x - 5 < 2$$

Therefore, adding 5 to each side, we have

$$3 < x < 7$$

and the solution set is the open interval $(3, 7)$.

FIGURE 9

SOLUTION 2 Geometrically, the solution set consists of all numbers x whose distance from 5 is less than 2. From Figure 9 we see that this is the interval $(3, 7)$.

EXAMPLE 8 Solve $|3x + 2| \geqslant 4$.

SOLUTION By Properties 4 and 6 of (6), $|3x + 2| \geqslant 4$ is equivalent to

$$3x + 2 \geqslant 4 \qquad \text{or} \qquad 3x + 2 \leqslant -4$$

In the first case $3x \geqslant 2$, which gives $x \geqslant \frac{2}{3}$. In the second case $3x \leqslant -6$, which gives $x \leqslant -2$. So the solution set is

$$\left\{ x \mid x \leqslant -2 \ \text{or} \ x \geqslant \tfrac{2}{3} \right\} = (-\infty, -2] \cup \left[\tfrac{2}{3}, \infty \right)$$

Another important property of absolute value, called the Triangle Inequality, is used frequently not only in calculus but throughout mathematics in general.

---

7 **The Triangle Inequality** If a and b are any real numbers, then

$$|a + b| \leqslant |a| + |b|$$

Observe that if the numbers a and b are both positive or both negative, then the two sides in the Triangle Inequality are actually equal. But if a and b have opposite signs, the left side involves a subtraction and the right side does not. This makes the Triangle Inequality seem reasonable, but we can prove it as follows.

Notice that

$$-|a| \leqslant a \leqslant |a|$$

is always true because a equals either $|a|$ or $-|a|$. The corresponding statement for b is

$$-|b| \leqslant b \leqslant |b|$$

Adding these inequalities, we get

$$-(|a| + |b|) \leqslant a + b \leqslant |a| + |b|$$

If we now apply Properties 4 and 5 (with x replaced by $a + b$ and a by $|a| + |b|$), we obtain

$$|a + b| \leqslant |a| + |b|$$

which is what we wanted to show.

EXAMPLE 9 If $|x - 4| < 0.1$ and $|y - 7| < 0.2$, use the Triangle Inequality to estimate $|(x + y) - 11|$.

SOLUTION In order to use the given information, we use the Triangle Inequality with $a = x - 4$ and $b = y - 7$:

$$|(x + y) - 11| = |(x - 4) + (y - 7)|$$
$$\leq |x - 4| + |y - 7|$$
$$< 0.1 + 0.2 = 0.3$$

Thus $\qquad |(x + y) - 11| < 0.3$

A Exercises

1–12 $\parallel$ Rewrite the expression without using the absolute value symbol.

1. $|5 - 23|$

2. $|5| - |-23|$

3. $|-\pi|$

4. $|\pi - 2|$

5. $|\sqrt{5} - 5|$

6. $||-2| - |-3||$

7. $|x - 2|$ if $x < 2$

8. $|x - 2|$ if $x > 2$

9. $|x + 1|$

10. $|2x - 1|$

11. $|x^2 + 1|$

12. $|1 - 2x^2|$

13–38 $\parallel$ Solve the inequality in terms of intervals and illustrate the solution set on the real number line.

13. $2x + 7 > 3$

14. $3x - 11 < 4$

15. $1 - x \leq 2$

16. $4 - 3x \geq 6$

17. $2x + 1 < 5x - 8$

18. $1 + 5x > 5 - 3x$

19. $-1 < 2x - 5 < 7$

20. $1 < 3x + 4 \leq 16$

21. $0 \leq 1 - x < 1$

22. $-5 \leq 3 - 2x \leq 9$

23. $4x < 2x + 1 \leq 3x + 2$

24. $2x - 3 < x + 4 < 3x - 2$

25. $(x - 1)(x - 2) > 0$

26. $(2x + 3)(x - 1) \geq 0$

27. $2x^2 + x \leq 1$

28. $x^2 < 2x + 8$

29. $x^2 + x + 1 > 0$

30. $x^2 + x > 1$

31. $x^2 < 3$

32. $x^2 \geq 5$

33. $x^3 - x^2 \leq 0$

34. $(x + 1)(x - 2)(x + 3) \geq 0$

35. $x^3 > x$

36. $x^3 + 3x < 4x^2$

37. $\dfrac{1}{x} < 4$

38. $-3 < \dfrac{1}{x} \leq 1$

39. The relationship between the Celsius and Fahrenheit temperature scales is given by $C = \frac{5}{9}(F - 32)$, where C is the tempera-ture in degrees Celsius and F is the temperature in degrees Fahrenheit. What interval on the Celsius scale corresponds to the temperature range $50 \leq F \leq 95$?

40. Use the relationship between C and F given in Exercise 39 to find the interval on the Fahrenheit scale corresponding to the temperature range $20 \leq C \leq 30$.

41. As dry air moves upward, it expands and in so doing cools at a rate of about 1°C for each 100-m rise, up to about 12 km.
 (a) If the ground temperature is 20°C, write a formula for the temperature at height h.
 (b) What range of temperature can be expected if a plane takes off and reaches a maximum height of 5 km?

42. If a ball is thrown upward from the top of a building 128 ft high with an initial velocity of 16 ft/s, then the height h above the ground t seconds later will be

$$h = 128 + 16t - 16t^2$$

During what time interval will the ball be at least 32 ft above the ground?

43–46 $\parallel$ Solve the equation for x.

43. $|2x| = 3$

44. $|3x + 5| = 1$

45. $|x + 3| = |2x + 1|$

46. $\left|\dfrac{2x - 1}{x + 1}\right| = 3$

47–56 $\parallel$ Solve the inequality.

47. $|x| < 3$

48. $|x| \geq 3$

49. $|x - 4| < 1$

50. $|x - 6| < 0.1$

51. $|x + 5| \geq 2$

52. $|x + 1| \geq 3$

53. $|2x - 3| \leq 0.4$

54. $|5x - 2| < 6$

55. $1 \leq |x| \leq 4$

56. $0 < |x - 5| < \frac{1}{2}$

57–58 ▏▏▏▏ Solve for x, assuming a, b, and c are positive constants.

57. $a(bx - c) \geq bc$

58. $a \leq bx + c < 2a$

59–60 ▏▏▏▏ Solve for x, assuming a, b, and c are negative constants.

59. $ax + b < c$

60. $\dfrac{ax + b}{c} \leq b$

61. Suppose that $|x - 2| < 0.01$ and $|y - 3| < 0.04$. Use the Triangle Inequality to show that $|(x + y) - 5| < 0.05$.

62. Show that if $|x + 3| < \frac{1}{2}$, then $|4x + 13| < 3$.

63. Show that if $a < b$, then $a < \dfrac{a + b}{2} < b$.

64. Use Rule 3 to prove Rule 5 of (2).

65. Prove that $|ab| = |a||b|$. [*Hint:* Use Equation 4.]

66. Prove that $\left|\dfrac{a}{b}\right| = \dfrac{|a|}{|b|}$.

67. Show that if $0 < a < b$, then $a^2 < b^2$.

68. Prove that $|x - y| \geq |x| - |y|$. [*Hint:* Use the Triangle Inequality with $a = x - y$ and $b = y$.]

69. Show that the sum, difference, and product of rational numbers are rational numbers.

70. (a) Is the sum of two irrational numbers always an irrational number?
(b) Is the product of two irrational numbers always an irrational number?

▏▏▏▏ **B** **Coordinate Geometry and Lines**

Just as the points on a line can be identified with real numbers by assigning them coordinates, as described in Appendix A, so the points in a plane can be identified with ordered pairs of real numbers. We start by drawing two perpendicular coordinate lines that intersect at the origin O on each line. Usually one line is horizontal with positive direction to the right and is called the *x*-axis; the other line is vertical with positive direction upward and is called the *y*-axis.

Any point P in the plane can be located by a unique ordered pair of numbers as follows. Draw lines through P perpendicular to the *x*- and *y*-axes. These lines intersect the axes in points with coordinates a and b as shown in Figure 1. Then the point P is assigned the ordered pair (a, b). The first number a is called the **x-coordinate** of P; the second number b is called the **y-coordinate** of P. We say that P is the point with coordinates (a, b), and we denote the point by the symbol $P(a, b)$. Several points are labeled with their coordinates in Figure 2.

FIGURE 1

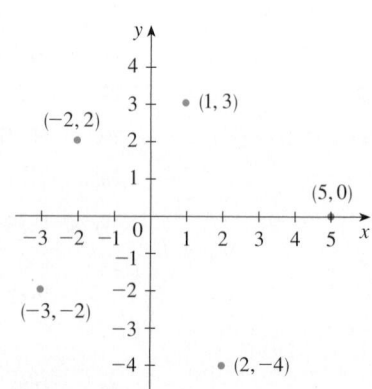

FIGURE 2

By reversing the preceding process we can start with an ordered pair (a, b) and arrive at the corresponding point P. Often we identify the point P with the ordered pair (a, b) and refer to "the point (a, b)." [Although the notation used for an open interval (a, b) is the same as the notation used for a point (a, b), you will be able to tell from the context which meaning is intended.]

This coordinate system is called the **rectangular coordinate system** or the **Cartesian coordinate system** in honor of the French mathematician René Descartes (1596–1650), even though another Frenchman, Pierre Fermat (1601–1665), invented the principles of analytic geometry at about the same time as Descartes. The plane supplied with this coordinate system is called the **coordinate plane** or the **Cartesian plane** and is denoted by $\mathbb{R}^2$.

The x- and y-axes are called the **coordinate axes** and divide the Cartesian plane into four quadrants, which are labeled I, II, III, and IV in Figure 1. Notice that the first quadrant consists of those points whose x- and y-coordinates are both positive.

EXAMPLE 1 Describe and sketch the regions given by the following sets.

(a) $\{(x, y) \mid x \geq 0\}$ (b) $\{(x, y) \mid y = 1\}$ (c) $\{(x, y) \mid |y| < 1\}$

SOLUTION

(a) The points whose x-coordinates are 0 or positive lie on the y-axis or to the right of it as indicated by the shaded region in Figure 3(a).

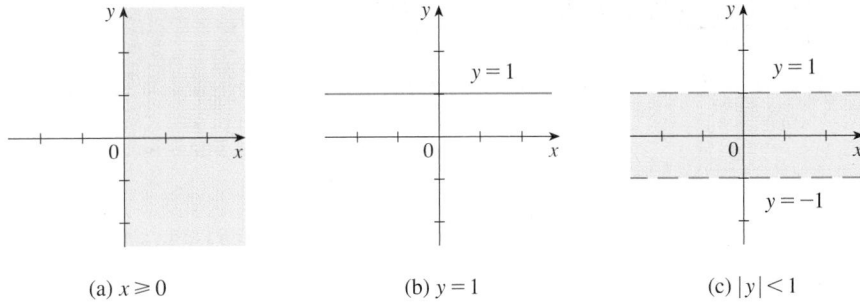

FIGURE 3

(a) $x \geq 0$ (b) $y = 1$ (c) $|y| < 1$

(b) The set of all points with y-coordinate 1 is a horizontal line one unit above the x-axis [see Figure 3(b)].

(c) Recall from Appendix A that

$$|y| < 1 \qquad \text{if and only if} \qquad -1 < y < 1$$

The given region consists of those points in the plane whose y-coordinates lie between -1 and 1. Thus, the region consists of all points that lie between (but not on) the horizontal lines $y = 1$ and $y = -1$. [These lines are shown as dashed lines in Figure 3(c) to indicate that the points on these lines don't lie in the set.]

Recall from Appendix A that the distance between points a and b on a number line is $|a - b| = |b - a|$. Thus, the distance between points $P_1(x_1, y_1)$ and $P_3(x_2, y_1)$ on a horizontal line must be $|x_2 - x_1|$ and the distance between $P_2(x_2, y_2)$ and $P_3(x_2, y_1)$ on a vertical line must be $|y_2 - y_1|$. (See Figure 4.)

To find the distance $|P_1P_2|$ between any two points $P_1(x_1, y_1)$ and $P_2(x_2, y_2)$, we note that triangle $P_1P_2P_3$ in Figure 4 is a right triangle, and so by the Pythagorean Theorem we have

$$|P_1P_2| = \sqrt{|P_1P_3|^2 + |P_2P_3|^2} = \sqrt{|x_2 - x_1|^2 + |y_2 - y_1|^2}$$

$$= \sqrt{(x_2 - x_1)^2 + (y_2 - y_1)^2}$$

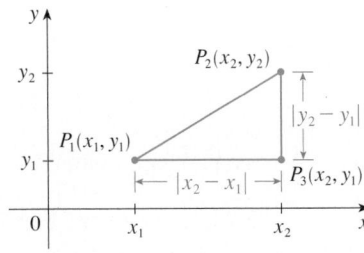

FIGURE 4

> **1 Distance Formula** The distance between the points $P_1(x_1, y_1)$ and $P_2(x_2, y_2)$ is
>
> $$|P_1P_2| = \sqrt{(x_2 - x_1)^2 + (y_2 - y_1)^2}$$

EXAMPLE 2 The distance between $(1, -2)$ and $(5, 3)$ is

$$\sqrt{(5 - 1)^2 + [3 - (-2)]^2} = \sqrt{4^2 + 5^2} = \sqrt{41}$$

▓ Lines

We want to find an equation of a given line L; such an equation is satisfied by the coordinates of the points on L and by no other point. To find the equation of L we use its *slope,* which is a measure of the steepness of the line.

FIGURE 5

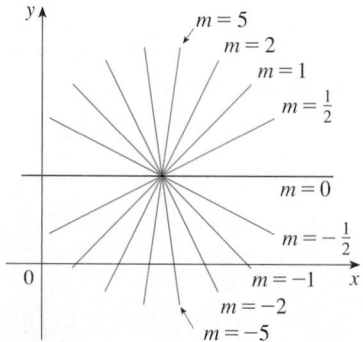

FIGURE 6

> **2 Definition** The **slope** of a nonvertical line that passes through the points $P_1(x_1, y_1)$ and $P_2(x_2, y_2)$ is
>
> $$m = \frac{\Delta y}{\Delta x} = \frac{y_2 - y_1}{x_2 - x_1}$$
>
> The slope of a vertical line is not defined.

Thus, the slope of a line is the ratio of the change in y, Δy, to the change in x, Δx. (See Figure 5.) The slope is therefore the rate of change of y with respect to x. The fact that the line is straight means that the rate of change is constant.

Figure 6 shows several lines labeled with their slopes. Notice that lines with positive slope slant upward to the right, whereas lines with negative slope slant downward to the right. Notice also that the steepest lines are the ones for which the absolute value of the slope is largest, and a horizontal line has slope 0.

Now let's find an equation of the line that passes through a given point $P_1(x_1, y_1)$ and has slope m. A point $P(x, y)$ with $x \neq x_1$ lies on this line if and only if the slope of the line through P_1 and P is equal to m; that is,

$$\frac{y - y_1}{x - x_1} = m$$

This equation can be rewritten in the form

$$y - y_1 = m(x - x_1)$$

and we observe that this equation is also satisfied when $x = x_1$ and $y = y_1$. Therefore, it is an equation of the given line.

> **3 Point-Slope Form of the Equation of a Line** An equation of the line passing through the point $P_1(x_1, y_1)$ and having slope m is
>
> $$y - y_1 = m(x - x_1)$$

EXAMPLE 3 Find an equation of the line through $(1, -7)$ with slope $-\frac{1}{2}$.

SOLUTION Using (3) with $m = -\frac{1}{2}$, $x_1 = 1$, and $y_1 = -7$, we obtain an equation of the line as

$$y + 7 = -\tfrac{1}{2}(x - 1)$$

which we can rewrite as

$$2y + 14 = -x + 1 \qquad \text{or} \qquad x + 2y + 13 = 0$$

EXAMPLE 4 Find an equation of the line through the points $(-1, 2)$ and $(3, -4)$.

SOLUTION By Definition 2 the slope of the line is

$$m = \frac{-4 - 2}{3 - (-1)} = -\frac{3}{2}$$

Using the point-slope form with $x_1 = -1$ and $y_1 = 2$, we obtain

$$y - 2 = -\tfrac{3}{2}(x + 1)$$

which simplifies to $\qquad\qquad\qquad 3x + 2y = 1$

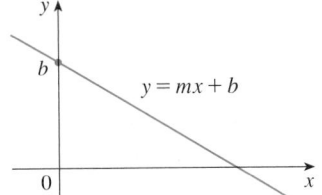

FIGURE 7

Suppose a nonvertical line has slope m and y-intercept b. (See Figure 7.) This means it intersects the y-axis at the point $(0, b)$, so the point-slope form of the equation of the line, with $x_1 = 0$ and $y_1 = b$, becomes

$$y - b = m(x - 0)$$

This simplifies as follows.

> **4** **Slope-Intercept Form of the Equation of a Line**   An equation of the line with slope m and y-intercept b is
>
> $$y = mx + b$$

In particular, if a line is horizontal, its slope is $m = 0$, so its equation is $y = b$, where b is the y-intercept (see Figure 8). A vertical line does not have a slope, but we can write its equation as $x = a$, where a is the x-intercept, because the x-coordinate of every point on the line is a.

Observe that the equation of every line can be written in the form

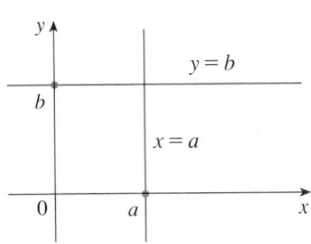

FIGURE 8

5 $\qquad\qquad Ax + By + C = 0$

because a vertical line has the equation $x = a$ or $x - a = 0$ ($A = 1$, $B = 0$, $C = -a$) and a nonvertical line has the equation $y = mx + b$ or $-mx + y - b = 0$ ($A = -m$, $B = 1$, $C = -b$). Conversely, if we start with a general first-degree equation, that is, an equation of the form (5), where A, B, and C are constants and A and B are not both 0, then we can show that it is the equation of a line. If $B = 0$, the equation becomes $Ax + C = 0$ or $x = -C/A$, which represents a vertical line with x-intercept $-C/A$. If $B \neq 0$, the equation can be rewritten by solving for y:

$$y = -\frac{A}{B}x - \frac{C}{B}$$

and we recognize this as being the slope-intercept form of the equation of a line ($m = -A/B$, $b = -C/B$). Therefore, an equation of the form (5) is called a **linear equation** or the **general equation of a line**. For brevity, we often refer to "the line $Ax + By + C = 0$" instead of "the line whose equation is $Ax + By + C = 0$."

EXAMPLE 5 Sketch the graph of the equation $3x - 5y = 15$.

SOLUTION Since the equation is linear, its graph is a line. To draw the graph, we can simply find two points on the line. It's easiest to find the intercepts. Substituting $y = 0$ (the equation of the x-axis) in the given equation, we get $3x = 15$, so $x = 5$ is the x-intercept. Substituting $x = 0$ in the equation, we see that the y-intercept is -3. This allows us to sketch the graph as in Figure 9.

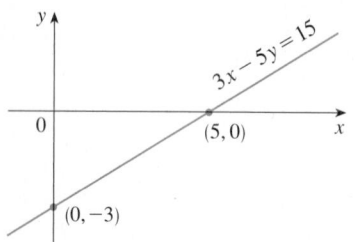

FIGURE 9

EXAMPLE 6 Graph the inequality $x + 2y > 5$.

SOLUTION We are asked to sketch the graph of the set $\{(x, y) \mid x + 2y > 5\}$ and we do so by solving the inequality for y:

$$x + 2y > 5$$

$$2y > -x + 5$$

$$y > -\tfrac{1}{2}x + \tfrac{5}{2}$$

Compare this inequality with the equation $y = -\tfrac{1}{2}x + \tfrac{5}{2}$, which represents a line with slope $-\tfrac{1}{2}$ and y-intercept $\tfrac{5}{2}$. We see that the given graph consists of points whose y-coordinates are *larger* than those on the line $y = -\tfrac{1}{2}x + \tfrac{5}{2}$. Thus, the graph is the region that lies *above* the line, as illustrated in Figure 10.

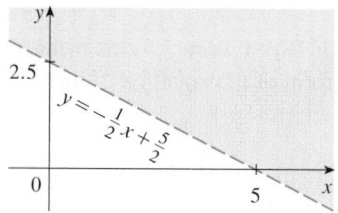

FIGURE 10

▏▏▏ **Parallel and Perpendicular Lines**

Slopes can be used to show that lines are parallel or perpendicular. The following facts are proved, for instance, in *Precalculus: Mathematics for Calculus, Fourth Edition* by Stewart, Redlin, and Watson (Brooks/Cole Publishing Co., Pacific Grove, CA, 2002).

---

6 **Parallel and Perpendicular Lines**

1. Two nonvertical lines are parallel if and only if they have the same slope.

2. Two lines with slopes m_1 and m_2 are perpendicular if and only if $m_1m_2 = -1$; that is, their slopes are negative reciprocals:

$$m_2 = -\frac{1}{m_1}$$

EXAMPLE 7 Find an equation of the line through the point $(5, 2)$ that is parallel to the line $4x + 6y + 5 = 0$.

SOLUTION The given line can be written in the form

$$y = -\tfrac{2}{3}x - \tfrac{5}{6}$$

which is in slope-intercept form with $m = -\frac{2}{3}$. Parallel lines have the same slope, so the required line has slope $-\frac{2}{3}$ and its equation in point-slope form is

$$y - 2 = -\frac{2}{3}(x - 5)$$

We can write this equation as $2x + 3y = 16$.

EXAMPLE 8 Show that the lines $2x + 3y = 1$ and $6x - 4y - 1 = 0$ are perpendicular.

SOLUTION The equations can be written as

$$y = -\frac{2}{3}x + \frac{1}{3} \qquad \text{and} \qquad y = \frac{3}{2}x - \frac{1}{4}$$

from which we see that the slopes are

$$m_1 = -\frac{2}{3} \qquad \text{and} \qquad m_2 = \frac{3}{2}$$

Since $m_1 m_2 = -1$, the lines are perpendicular.

|||| B Exercises

1–6 |||| Find the distance between the points.

1. $(1, 1)$, $(4, 5)$

2. $(1, -3)$, $(5, 7)$

3. $(6, -2)$, $(-1, 3)$

4. $(1, -6)$, $(-1, -3)$

5. $(2, 5)$, $(4, -7)$

6. (a, b), (b, a)

7–10 |||| Find the slope of the line through P and Q.

7. $P(1, 5)$, $Q(4, 11)$

8. $P(-1, 6)$, $Q(4, -3)$

9. $P(-3, 3)$, $Q(-1, -6)$

10. $P(-1, -4)$, $Q(6, 0)$

11. Show that the triangle with vertices $A(0, 2)$, $B(-3, -1)$, and $C(-4, 3)$ is isosceles.

12. (a) Show that the triangle with vertices $A(6, -7)$, $B(11, -3)$, and $C(2, -2)$ is a right triangle using the converse of the Pythagorean Theorem.
(b) Use slopes to show that ABC is a right triangle.
(c) Find the area of the triangle.

13. Show that the points $(-2, 9)$, $(4, 6)$, $(1, 0)$, and $(-5, 3)$ are the vertices of a square.

14. (a) Show that the points $A(-1, 3)$, $B(3, 11)$, and $C(5, 15)$ are collinear (lie on the same line) by showing that $|AB| + |BC| = |AC|$.
(b) Use slopes to show that A, B, and C are collinear.

15. Show that $A(1, 1)$, $B(7, 4)$, $C(5, 10)$, and $D(-1, 7)$ are vertices of a parallelogram.

16. Show that $A(1, 1)$, $B(11, 3)$, $C(10, 8)$, and $D(0, 6)$ are vertices of a rectangle.

17–20 |||| Sketch the graph of the equation.

17. $x = 3$

18. $y = -2$

19. $xy = 0$

20. $|y| = 1$

21–36 |||| Find an equation of the line that satisfies the given conditions.

21. Through $(2, -3)$, slope 6

22. Through $(-1, 4)$, slope -3

23. Through $(1, 7)$, slope $\frac{2}{3}$

24. Through $(-3, -5)$, slope $-\frac{7}{2}$

25. Through $(2, 1)$ and $(1, 6)$

26. Through $(-1, -2)$ and $(4, 3)$

27. Slope 3, y-intercept -2

28. Slope $\frac{2}{5}$, y-intercept 4

29. x-intercept 1, y-intercept -3

30. x-intercept -8, y-intercept 6

31. Through $(4, 5)$, parallel to the x-axis

32. Through $(4, 5)$, parallel to the y-axis

33. Through $(1, -6)$, parallel to the line $x + 2y = 6$

34. y-intercept 6, parallel to the line $2x + 3y + 4 = 0$

35. Through $(-1, -2)$, perpendicular to the line $2x + 5y + 8 = 0$

36. Through $\left(\frac{1}{2}, -\frac{2}{3}\right)$, perpendicular to the line $4x - 8y = 1$

37–42 |||| Find the slope and y-intercept of the line and draw its graph.

37. $x + 3y = 0$

38. $2x - 5y = 0$

39. $y = -2$

40. $2x - 3y + 6 = 0$

41. $3x - 4y = 12$

42. $4x + 5y = 10$

43–52 |||| Sketch the region in the xy-plane.

43. $\{(x, y) \mid x < 0\}$

44. $\{(x, y) \mid y > 0\}$

45. $\{(x, y) \mid xy < 0\}$

46. $\{(x, y) \mid x \geq 1 \text{ and } y < 3\}$

47. $\{(x, y) \mid |x| \leq 2\}$

48. $\{(x, y) \mid |x| < 3 \text{ and } |y| < 2\}$

49. $\{(x, y) \mid 0 \leq y \leq 4 \text{ and } x \leq 2\}$

50. $\{(x, y) \mid y > 2x - 1\}$

51. $\{(x, y) \mid 1 + x \leq y \leq 1 - 2x\}$

52. $\{(x, y) \mid -x \leq y < \frac{1}{2}(x + 3)\}$

53. Find a point on the y-axis that is equidistant from $(5, -5)$ and $(1, 1)$.

54. Show that the midpoint of the line segment from $P_1(x_1, y_1)$ to $P_2(x_2, y_2)$ is

$$\left(\frac{x_1 + x_2}{2}, \frac{y_1 + y_2}{2} \right)$$

55. Find the midpoint of the line segment joining the given points.
(a) $(1, 3)$ and $(7, 15)$ (b) $(-1, 6)$ and $(8, -12)$

56. Find the lengths of the medians of the triangle with vertices $A(1, 0)$, $B(3, 6)$, and $C(8, 2)$. (A median is a line segment from a vertex to the midpoint of the opposite side.)

57. Show that the lines $2x - y = 4$ and $6x - 2y = 10$ are not parallel and find their point of intersection.

58. Show that the lines $3x - 5y + 19 = 0$ and $10x + 6y - 50 = 0$ are perpendicular and find their point of intersection.

59. Find an equation of the perpendicular bisector of the line segment joining the points $A(1, 4)$ and $B(7, -2)$.

60. (a) Find equations for the sides of the triangle with vertices $P(1, 0)$, $Q(3, 4)$, and $R(-1, 6)$.
(b) Find equations for the medians of this triangle. Where do they intersect?

61. (a) Show that if the x- and y-intercepts of a line are nonzero numbers a and b, then the equation of the line can be put in the form

$$\frac{x}{a} + \frac{y}{b} = 1$$

This equation is called the **two-intercept form** of an equation of a line.
(b) Use part (a) to find an equation of the line whose x-intercept is 6 and whose y-intercept is -8.

62. A car leaves Detroit at 2:00 P.M., traveling at a constant speed west along I-96. It passes Ann Arbor, 40 mi from Detroit, at 2:50 P.M.
(a) Express the distance traveled in terms of the time elapsed.
(b) Draw the graph of the equation in part (a).
(c) What is the slope of this line? What does it represent?

||| C   Graphs of Second-Degree Equations

In Appendix B we saw that a first-degree, or linear, equation $Ax + By + C = 0$ represents a line. In this section we discuss second-degree equations such as

$$x^2 + y^2 = 1 \qquad y = x^2 + 1 \qquad \frac{x^2}{9} + \frac{y^2}{4} = 1 \qquad x^2 - y^2 = 1$$

which represent a circle, a parabola, an ellipse, and a hyperbola, respectively.

The graph of such an equation in x and y is the set of all points (x, y) that satisfy the equation; it gives a visual representation of the equation. Conversely, given a curve in the xy-plane, we may have to find an equation that represents it, that is, an equation satisfied by the coordinates of the points on the curve and by no other point. This is the other half of the basic principle of analytic geometry as formulated by Descartes and Fermat. The idea is that if a geometric curve can be represented by an algebraic equation, then the rules of algebra can be used to analyze the geometric problem.

||| Circles

As an example of this type of problem, let's find an equation of the circle with radius r and center (h, k). By definition, the circle is the set of all points $P(x, y)$ whose distance from

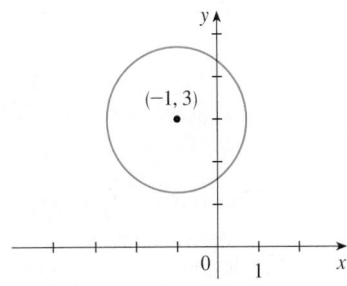

FIGURE 1

the center $C(h, k)$ is r. (See Figure 1.) Thus, P is on the circle if and only if $|PC| = r$. From the distance formula, we have

$$\sqrt{(x - h)^2 + (y - k)^2} = r$$

or equivalently, squaring both sides, we get

$$(x - h)^2 + (y - k)^2 = r^2$$

This is the desired equation.

> **1 Equation of a Circle** An equation of the circle with center (h, k) and radius r is
>
> $$(x - h)^2 + (y - k)^2 = r^2$$
>
> In particular, if the center is the origin $(0, 0)$, the equation is
>
> $$x^2 + y^2 = r^2$$

EXAMPLE 1 Find an equation of the circle with radius 3 and center $(2, -5)$.

SOLUTION From Equation 1 with $r = 3$, $h = 2$, and $k = -5$, we obtain

$$(x - 2)^2 + (y + 5)^2 = 9$$

EXAMPLE 2 Sketch the graph of the equation $x^2 + y^2 + 2x - 6y + 7 = 0$ by first showing that it represents a circle and then finding its center and radius.

SOLUTION We first group the x-terms and y-terms as follows:

$$(x^2 + 2x) + (y^2 - 6y) = -7$$

Then we complete the square within each grouping, adding the appropriate constants to both sides of the equation:

$$(x^2 + 2x + 1) + (y^2 - 6y + 9) = -7 + 1 + 9$$

or

$$(x + 1)^2 + (y - 3)^2 = 3$$

Comparing this equation with the standard equation of a circle (1), we see that $h = -1$, $k = 3$, and $r = \sqrt{3}$, so the given equation represents a circle with center $(-1, 3)$ and radius $\sqrt{3}$. It is sketched in Figure 2.

FIGURE 2
$x^2 + y^2 + 2x - 6y + 7 = 0$

|||| **Parabolas**

The geometric properties of parabolas are reviewed in Section 11.5. Here we regard a parabola as a graph of an equation of the form $y = ax^2 + bx + c$.

EXAMPLE 3 Draw the graph of the parabola $y = x^2$.

SOLUTION We set up a table of values, plot points, and join them by a smooth curve to obtain the graph in Figure 3.

x	$y = x^2$
0	0
$\pm\frac{1}{2}$	$\frac{1}{4}$
± 1	1
± 2	4
± 3	9

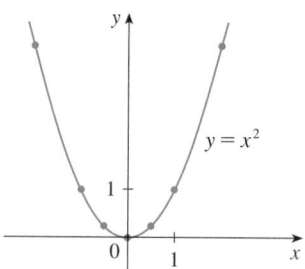

FIGURE 3

Figure 4 shows the graphs of several parabolas with equations of the form $y = ax^2$ for various values of the number a. In each case the *vertex*, the point where the parabola changes direction, is the origin. We see that the parabola $y = ax^2$ opens upward if $a > 0$ and downward if $a < 0$ (as in Figure 5).

FIGURE 4

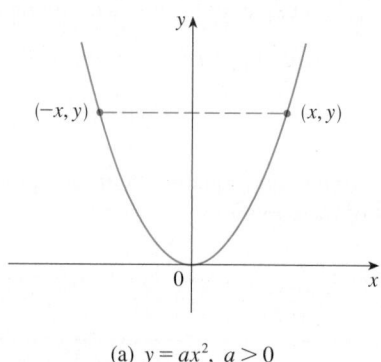

(a) $y = ax^2$, $a > 0$

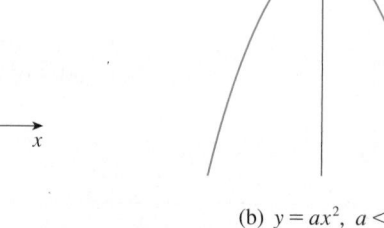

(b) $y = ax^2$, $a < 0$

FIGURE 5

Notice that if (x, y) satisfies $y = ax^2$, then so does $(-x, y)$. This corresponds to the geometric fact that if the right half of the graph is reflected about the y-axis, then the left half of the graph is obtained. We say that the graph is **symmetric with respect to the y-axis**.

> The graph of an equation is symmetric with respect to the y-axis if the equation is unchanged when x is replaced by $-x$.

If we interchange x and y in the equation $y = ax^2$, the result is $x = ay^2$, which also represents a parabola. (Interchanging x and y amounts to reflecting about the diagonal line $y = x$.) The parabola $x = ay^2$ opens to the right if $a > 0$ and to the left if $a < 0$. (See

Figure 6.) This time the parabola is symmetric with respect to the x-axis because if (x, y) satisfies $x = ay^2$, then so does $(x, -y)$.

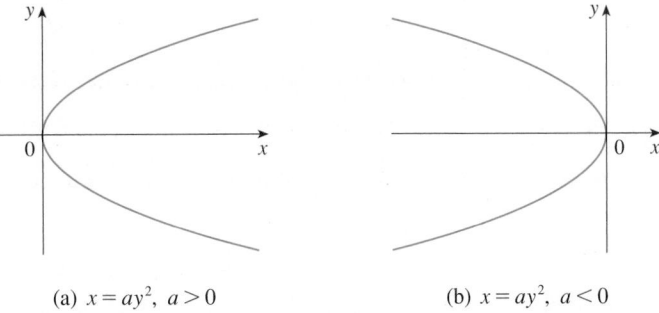

FIGURE 6
(a) $x = ay^2$, $a > 0$
(b) $x = ay^2$, $a < 0$

> The graph of an equation is symmetric with respect to the x-axis if the equation is unchanged when y is replaced by $-y$.

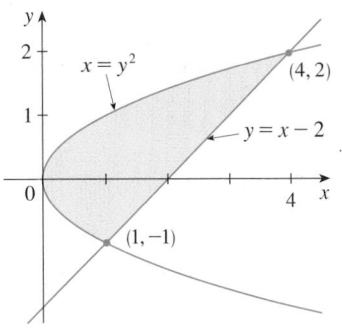

FIGURE 7

EXAMPLE 4 Sketch the region bounded by the parabola $x = y^2$ and the line $y = x - 2$.

SOLUTION First we find the points of intersection by solving the two equations. Substituting $x = y + 2$ into the equation $x = y^2$, we get $y + 2 = y^2$, which gives

$$0 = y^2 - y - 2 = (y - 2)(y + 1)$$

so $y = 2$ or -1. Thus, the points of intersection are $(4, 2)$ and $(1, -1)$, and we draw the line $y = x - 2$ passing through these points. We then sketch the parabola $x = y^2$ by referring to Figure 6(a) and having the parabola pass through $(4, 2)$ and $(1, -1)$. The region bounded by $x = y^2$ and $y = x - 2$ means the finite region whose boundaries are these curves. It is sketched in Figure 7.

||| Ellipses

The curve with equation

2
$$\frac{x^2}{a^2} + \frac{y^2}{b^2} = 1$$

where a and b are positive numbers, is called an **ellipse** in standard position. (Geometric properties of ellipses are discussed in Section 11.5.) Observe that Equation 2 is unchanged if x is replaced by $-x$ or y is replaced by $-y$, so the ellipse is symmetric with respect to both axes. As a further aid to sketching the ellipse, we find its intercepts.

> The **x-intercepts** of a graph are the x-coordinates of the points where the graph intersects the x-axis. They are found by setting $y = 0$ in the equation of the graph.
>
> The **y-intercepts** are the y-coordinates of the points where the graph intersects the y-axis. They are found by setting $x = 0$ in its equation.

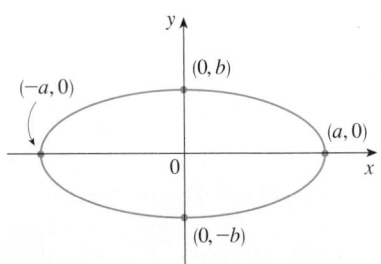

FIGURE 8
$$\frac{x^2}{a^2} + \frac{y^2}{b^2} = 1$$

If we set $y = 0$ in Equation 2, we get $x^2 = a^2$ and so the x-intercepts are $\pm a$. Setting $x = 0$, we get $y^2 = b^2$, so the y-intercepts are $\pm b$. Using this information, together with symmetry, we sketch the ellipse in Figure 8. If $a = b$, the ellipse is a circle with radius a.

EXAMPLE 5 Sketch the graph of $9x^2 + 16y^2 = 144$.

SOLUTION We divide both sides of the equation by 144:

$$\frac{x^2}{16} + \frac{y^2}{9} = 1$$

The equation is now in the standard form for an ellipse (2), so we have $a^2 = 16$, $b^2 = 9$, $a = 4$, and $b = 3$. The x-intercepts are ± 4; the y-intercepts are ± 3. The graph is sketched in Figure 9.

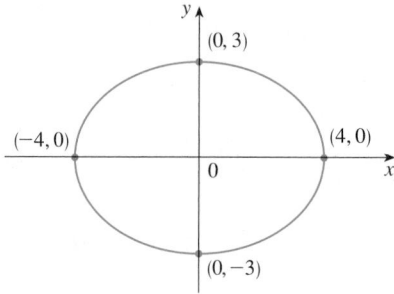

FIGURE 9

$9x^2 + 16y^2 = 144$

▏▏▏▏ **Hyperbolas**

The curve with equation

$$\boxed{3} \qquad \frac{x^2}{a^2} - \frac{y^2}{b^2} = 1$$

is called a **hyperbola** in standard position. Again, Equation 3 is unchanged when x is replaced by $-x$ or y is replaced by $-y$, so the hyperbola is symmetric with respect to both axes. To find the x-intercepts we set $y = 0$ and obtain $x^2 = a^2$ and $x = \pm a$. However, if we put $x = 0$ in Equation 3, we get $y^2 = -b^2$, which is impossible, so there is no y-intercept. In fact, from Equation 3 we obtain

$$\frac{x^2}{a^2} = 1 + \frac{y^2}{b^2} \geq 1$$

which shows that $x^2 \geq a^2$ and so $|x| = \sqrt{x^2} \geq a$. Therefore, we have $x \geq a$ or $x \leq -a$. This means that the hyperbola consists of two parts, called its *branches*. It is sketched in Figure 10.

In drawing a hyperbola it is useful to draw first its *asymptotes*, which are the lines $y = (b/a)x$ and $y = -(b/a)x$ shown in Figure 10. Both branches of the hyperbola approach the asymptotes; that is, they come arbitrarily close to the asymptotes. This involves the idea of a limit, which is discussed in Chapter 2. (See also Exercise 55 in Section 4.5.)

By interchanging the roles of x and y we get an equation of the form

$$\frac{y^2}{a^2} - \frac{x^2}{b^2} = 1$$

which also represents a hyperbola and is sketched in Figure 11.

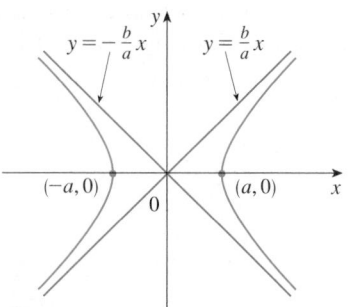

FIGURE 10

The hyperbola $\dfrac{x^2}{a^2} - \dfrac{y^2}{b^2} = 1$

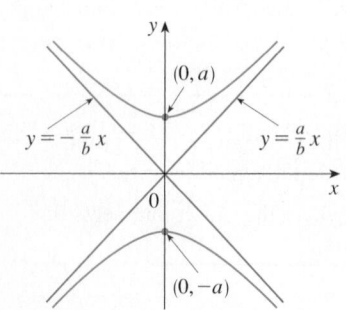

FIGURE 11

The hyperbola $\dfrac{y^2}{a^2} - \dfrac{x^2}{b^2} = 1$

EXAMPLE 6 Sketch the curve $9x^2 - 4y^2 = 36$.

SOLUTION Dividing both sides by 36, we obtain

$$\frac{x^2}{4} - \frac{y^2}{9} = 1$$

which is the standard form of the equation of a hyperbola (Equation 3). Since $a^2 = 4$, the x-intercepts are ± 2. Since $b^2 = 9$, we have $b = 3$ and the asymptotes are $y = \pm\left(\frac{3}{2}\right)x$. The hyperbola is sketched in Figure 12.

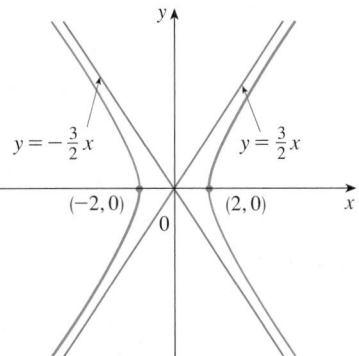

FIGURE 12

The hyperbola $9x^2 - 4y^2 = 36$

If $b = a$, a hyperbola has the equation $x^2 - y^2 = a^2$ (or $y^2 - x^2 = a^2$) and is called an *equilateral hyperbola* [see Figure 13(a)]. Its asymptotes are $y = \pm x$, which are perpendicular. If an equilateral hyperbola is rotated by $45°$, the asymptotes become the x- and y-axes, and it can be shown that the new equation of the hyperbola is $xy = k$, where k is a constant [see Figure 13(b)].

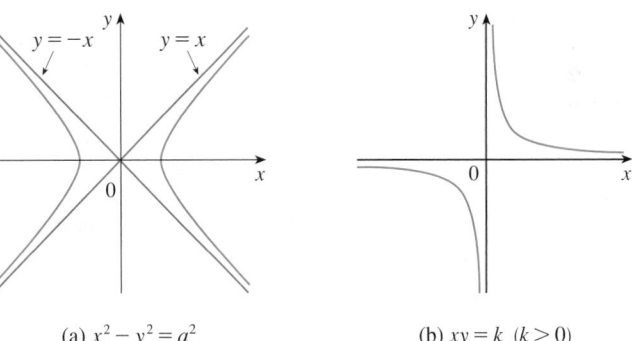

FIGURE 13

Equilateral hyperbolas

(a) $x^2 - y^2 = a^2$ (b) $xy = k$ $(k > 0)$

||||| **Shifted Conics**

Recall that an equation of the circle with center the origin and radius r is $x^2 + y^2 = r^2$, but if the center is the point (h, k), then the equation of the circle becomes

$$(x - h)^2 + (y - k)^2 = r^2$$

Similarly, if we take the ellipse with equation

4

$$\frac{x^2}{a^2} + \frac{y^2}{b^2} = 1$$

and translate it (shift it) so that its center is the point (h, k), then its equation becomes

5
$$\frac{(x - h)^2}{a^2} + \frac{(y - k)^2}{b^2} = 1$$

(See Figure 14.)

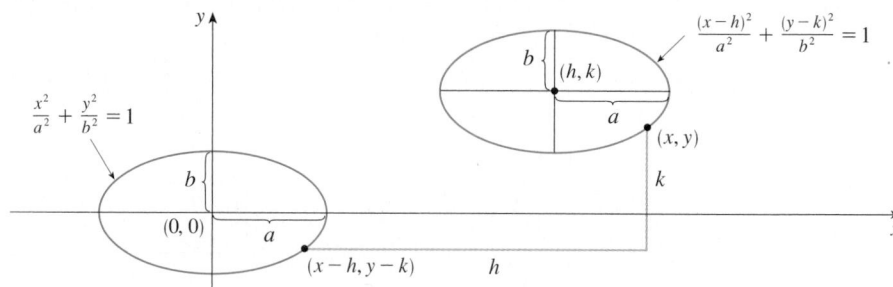

FIGURE 14

Notice that in shifting the ellipse, we replaced x by $x - h$ and y by $y - k$ in Equation 4 to obtain Equation 5. We use the same procedure to shift the parabola $y = ax^2$ so that its vertex (the origin) becomes the point (h, k) as in Figure 15. Replacing x by $x - h$ and y by $y - k$, we see that the new equation is

$$y - k = a(x - h)^2 \qquad \text{or} \qquad y = a(x - h)^2 + k$$

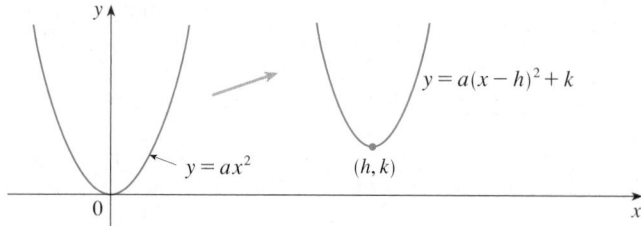

FIGURE 15

EXAMPLE 7 Sketch the graph of the equation $y = 2x^2 - 4x + 1$.

SOLUTION First we complete the square:

$$y = 2(x^2 - 2x) + 1 = 2(x - 1)^2 - 1$$

In this form we see that the equation represents the parabola obtained by shifting $y = 2x^2$ so that its vertex is at the point $(1, -1)$. The graph is sketched in Figure 16.

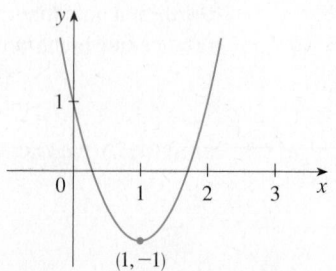

FIGURE 16
$y = 2x^2 - 4x + 1$

EXAMPLE 8 Sketch the curve $x = 1 - y^2$.

SOLUTION This time we start with the parabola $x = -y^2$ (as in Figure 6 with $a = -1$) and shift one unit to the right to get the graph of $x = 1 - y^2$. (See Figure 17.)

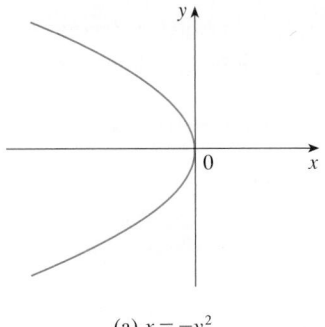

FIGURE 17

(a) $x = -y^2$

(b) $x = 1 - y^2$

‖‖‖ **C Exercises**

1–4 ‖‖‖ Find an equation of a circle that satisfies the given conditions.

1. Center $(3, -1)$, radius 5

2. Center $(-2, -8)$, radius 10

3. Center at the origin, passes through $(4, 7)$

4. Center $(-1, 5)$, passes through $(-4, -6)$

5–9 ‖‖‖ Show that the equation represents a circle and find the center and radius.

5. $x^2 + y^2 - 4x + 10y + 13 = 0$

6. $x^2 + y^2 + 6y + 2 = 0$

7. $x^2 + y^2 + x = 0$

8. $16x^2 + 16y^2 + 8x + 32y + 1 = 0$

9. $2x^2 + 2y^2 - x + y = 1$

10. Under what condition on the coefficients a, b, and c does the equation $x^2 + y^2 + ax + by + c = 0$ represent a circle? When that condition is satisfied, find the center and radius of the circle.

11–32 ‖‖‖ Identify the type of curve and sketch the graph. Do not plot points. Just use the standard graphs given in Figures 5, 6, 8, 10, and 11 and shift if necessary.

11. $y = -x^2$

12. $y^2 - x^2 = 1$

13. $x^2 + 4y^2 = 16$

14. $x = -2y^2$

15. $16x^2 - 25y^2 = 400$

16. $25x^2 + 4y^2 = 100$

17. $4x^2 + y^2 = 1$

18. $y = x^2 + 2$

19. $x = y^2 - 1$

20. $9x^2 - 25y^2 = 225$

21. $9y^2 - x^2 = 9$

22. $2x^2 + 5y^2 = 10$

23. $xy = 4$

24. $y = x^2 + 2x$

25. $9(x - 1)^2 + 4(y - 2)^2 = 36$

26. $16x^2 + 9y^2 - 36y = 108$

27. $y = x^2 - 6x + 13$

28. $x^2 - y^2 - 4x + 3 = 0$

29. $x = 4 - y^2$

30. $y^2 - 2x + 6y + 5 = 0$

31. $x^2 + 4y^2 - 6x + 5 = 0$

32. $4x^2 + 9y^2 - 16x + 54y + 61 = 0$

33–34 ‖‖‖ Sketch the region bounded by the curves.

33. $y = 3x$, $y = x^2$

34. $y = 4 - x^2$, $x - 2y = 2$

35. Find an equation of the parabola with vertex $(1, -1)$ that passes through the points $(-1, 3)$ and $(3, 3)$.

36. Find an equation of the ellipse with center at the origin that passes through the points $\left(1, -10\sqrt{2}/3\right)$ and $\left(-2, 5\sqrt{5}/3\right)$.

37–40 ‖‖‖ Sketch the graph of the set.

37. $\{(x, y) \mid x^2 + y^2 \leqslant 1\}$

38. $\{(x, y) \mid x^2 + y^2 > 4\}$

39. $\{(x, y) \mid y \geqslant x^2 - 1\}$

40. $\{(x, y) \mid x^2 + 4y^2 \leqslant 4\}$

D Trigonometry

Angles

Angles can be measured in degrees or in radians (abbreviated as rad). The angle given by a complete revolution contains 360°, which is the same as 2π rad. Therefore

$$\boxed{1} \qquad \pi \text{ rad} = 180°$$

and

$$\boxed{2} \qquad 1 \text{ rad} = \left(\frac{180}{\pi}\right)^{\circ} \approx 57.3° \qquad 1° = \frac{\pi}{180} \text{ rad} \approx 0.017 \text{ rad}$$

EXAMPLE 1
(a) Find the radian measure of 60°.   (b) Express $5\pi/4$ rad in degrees.

SOLUTION
(a) From Equation 1 or 2 we see that to convert from degrees to radians we multiply by $\pi/180$. Therefore

$$60° = 60\left(\frac{\pi}{180}\right) = \frac{\pi}{3} \text{ rad}$$

(b) To convert from radians to degrees we multiply by $180/\pi$. Thus

$$\frac{5\pi}{4} \text{ rad} = \frac{5\pi}{4}\left(\frac{180}{\pi}\right) = 225°$$

In calculus we use radians to measure angles except when otherwise indicated. The following table gives the correspondence between degree and radian measures of some common angles.

Degrees	0°	30°	45°	60°	90°	120°	135°	150°	180°	270°	360°
Radians	0	$\frac{\pi}{6}$	$\frac{\pi}{4}$	$\frac{\pi}{3}$	$\frac{\pi}{2}$	$\frac{2\pi}{3}$	$\frac{3\pi}{4}$	$\frac{5\pi}{6}$	π	$\frac{3\pi}{2}$	2π

Figure 1 shows a sector of a circle with central angle θ and radius r subtending an arc with length a. Since the length of the arc is proportional to the size of the angle, and since the entire circle has circumference $2\pi r$ and central angle 2π, we have

$$\frac{\theta}{2\pi} = \frac{a}{2\pi r}$$

Solving this equation for θ and for a, we obtain

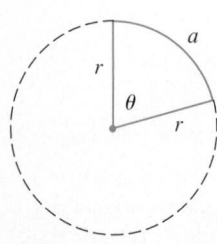

FIGURE 1

$$\boxed{3} \qquad \theta = \frac{a}{r} \qquad\qquad a = r\theta$$

Remember that Equations 3 are valid only when θ is measured in radians.

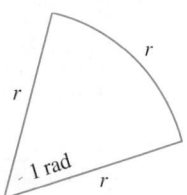

FIGURE 2

In particular, putting $a = r$ in Equation 3, we see that an angle of 1 rad is the angle subtended at the center of a circle by an arc equal in length to the radius of the circle (see Figure 2).

EXAMPLE 2
(a) If the radius of a circle is 5 cm, what angle is subtended by an arc of 6 cm?
(b) If a circle has radius 3 cm, what is the length of an arc subtended by a central angle of $3\pi/8$ rad?

SOLUTION
(a) Using Equation 3 with $a = 6$ and $r = 5$, we see that the angle is

$$\theta = \tfrac{6}{5} = 1.2 \text{ rad}$$

(b) With $r = 3$ cm and $\theta = 3\pi/8$ rad, the arc length is

$$a = r\theta = 3\left(\frac{3\pi}{8}\right) = \frac{9\pi}{8} \text{ cm}$$

The **standard position** of an angle occurs when we place its vertex at the origin of a coordinate system and its initial side on the positive x-axis as in Figure 3. A **positive** angle is obtained by rotating the initial side counterclockwise until it coincides with the terminal side. Likewise, **negative** angles are obtained by clockwise rotation as in Figure 4.

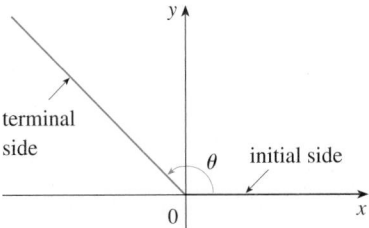

FIGURE 3 $\theta \geqslant 0$

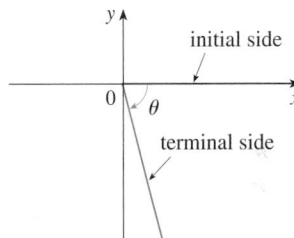

FIGURE 4 $\theta < 0$

Figure 5 shows several examples of angles in standard position. Notice that different angles can have the same terminal side. For instance, the angles $3\pi/4$, $-5\pi/4$, and $11\pi/4$ have the same initial and terminal sides because

$$\frac{3\pi}{4} - 2\pi = -\frac{5\pi}{4} \qquad \frac{3\pi}{4} + 2\pi = \frac{11\pi}{4}$$

and 2π rad represents a complete revolution.

FIGURE 5
Angles in standard position

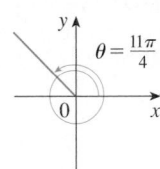

||| **The Trigonometric Functions**

For an acute angle θ the six trigonometric functions are defined as ratios of lengths of sides of a right triangle as follows (see Figure 6).

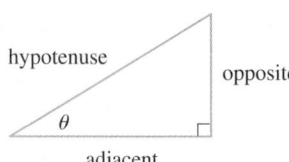

FIGURE 6

$$\boxed{4} \qquad \sin\theta = \frac{\text{opp}}{\text{hyp}} \qquad \csc\theta = \frac{\text{hyp}}{\text{opp}}$$

$$\cos\theta = \frac{\text{adj}}{\text{hyp}} \qquad \sec\theta = \frac{\text{hyp}}{\text{adj}}$$

$$\tan\theta = \frac{\text{opp}}{\text{adj}} \qquad \cot\theta = \frac{\text{adj}}{\text{opp}}$$

This definition doesn't apply to obtuse or negative angles, so for a general angle θ in standard position we let $P(x, y)$ be any point on the terminal side of θ and we let r be the distance $|OP|$ as in Figure 7. Then we define

FIGURE 7

$$\boxed{5} \qquad \sin\theta = \frac{y}{r} \qquad \csc\theta = \frac{r}{y}$$

$$\cos\theta = \frac{x}{r} \qquad \sec\theta = \frac{r}{x}$$

$$\tan\theta = \frac{y}{x} \qquad \cot\theta = \frac{x}{y}$$

Since division by 0 is not defined, $\tan\theta$ and $\sec\theta$ are undefined when $x = 0$ and $\csc\theta$ and $\cot\theta$ are undefined when $y = 0$. Notice that the definitions in (4) and (5) are consistent when θ is an acute angle.

If θ is a number, the convention is that $\sin\theta$ means the sine of the angle whose *radian* measure is θ. For example, the expression $\sin 3$ implies that we are dealing with an angle of 3 rad. When finding a calculator approximation to this number we must remember to set our calculator in radian mode, and then we obtain

$$\sin 3 \approx 0.14112$$

If we want to know the sine of the angle 3° we would write $\sin 3°$ and, with our calculator in degree mode, we find that

$$\sin 3° \approx 0.05234$$

The exact trigonometric ratios for certain angles can be read from the triangles in Figure 8. For instance,

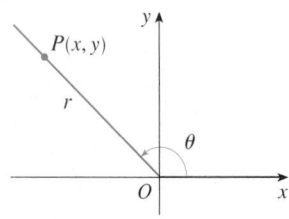

FIGURE 8

$$\sin\frac{\pi}{4} = \frac{1}{\sqrt{2}} \qquad \sin\frac{\pi}{6} = \frac{1}{2} \qquad \sin\frac{\pi}{3} = \frac{\sqrt{3}}{2}$$

$$\cos\frac{\pi}{4} = \frac{1}{\sqrt{2}} \qquad \cos\frac{\pi}{6} = \frac{\sqrt{3}}{2} \qquad \cos\frac{\pi}{3} = \frac{1}{2}$$

$$\tan\frac{\pi}{4} = 1 \qquad \tan\frac{\pi}{6} = \frac{1}{\sqrt{3}} \qquad \tan\frac{\pi}{3} = \sqrt{3}$$

FIGURE 9

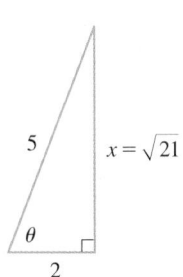

FIGURE 10

The signs of the trigonometric functions for angles in each of the four quadrants can be remembered by means of the rule "All Students Take Calculus" shown in Figure 9.

EXAMPLE 3 Find the exact trigonometric ratios for $\theta = 2\pi/3$.

SOLUTION From Figure 10 we see that a point on the terminal line for $\theta = 2\pi/3$ is $P(-1, \sqrt{3})$. Therefore, taking

$$x = -1 \qquad y = \sqrt{3} \qquad r = 2$$

in the definitions of the trigonometric ratios, we have

$$\sin \frac{2\pi}{3} = \frac{\sqrt{3}}{2} \qquad \cos \frac{2\pi}{3} = -\frac{1}{2} \qquad \tan \frac{2\pi}{3} = -\sqrt{3}$$

$$\csc \frac{2\pi}{3} = \frac{2}{\sqrt{3}} \qquad \sec \frac{2\pi}{3} = -2 \qquad \cot \frac{2\pi}{3} = -\frac{1}{\sqrt{3}}$$

The following table gives some values of $\sin \theta$ and $\cos \theta$ found by the method of Example 3.

θ	0	$\frac{\pi}{6}$	$\frac{\pi}{4}$	$\frac{\pi}{3}$	$\frac{\pi}{2}$	$\frac{2\pi}{3}$	$\frac{3\pi}{4}$	$\frac{5\pi}{6}$	π	$\frac{3\pi}{2}$	2π
$\sin \theta$	0	$\frac{1}{2}$	$\frac{1}{\sqrt{2}}$	$\frac{\sqrt{3}}{2}$	1	$\frac{\sqrt{3}}{2}$	$\frac{1}{\sqrt{2}}$	$\frac{1}{2}$	0	-1	0
$\cos \theta$	1	$\frac{\sqrt{3}}{2}$	$\frac{1}{\sqrt{2}}$	$\frac{1}{2}$	0	$-\frac{1}{2}$	$-\frac{1}{\sqrt{2}}$	$-\frac{\sqrt{3}}{2}$	-1	0	1

EXAMPLE 4 If $\cos \theta = \frac{2}{5}$ and $0 < \theta < \pi/2$, find the other five trigonometric functions of θ.

SOLUTION Since $\cos \theta = \frac{2}{5}$, we can label the hypotenuse as having length 5 and the adjacent side as having length 2 in Figure 11. If the opposite side has length x, then the Pythagorean Theorem gives $x^2 + 4 = 25$ and so $x^2 = 21$, $x = \sqrt{21}$. We can now use the diagram to write the other five trigonometric functions:

$$\sin \theta = \frac{\sqrt{21}}{5} \qquad \tan \theta = \frac{\sqrt{21}}{2}$$

$$\csc \theta = \frac{5}{\sqrt{21}} \qquad \sec \theta = \frac{5}{2} \qquad \cot \theta = \frac{2}{\sqrt{21}}$$

FIGURE 11

EXAMPLE 5 Use a calculator to approximate the value of x in Figure 12.

SOLUTION From the diagram we see that

$$\tan 40° = \frac{16}{x}$$

Therefore

$$x = \frac{16}{\tan 40°} \approx 19.07$$

FIGURE 12

⫴ **Trigonometric Identities**

A trigonometric identity is a relationship among the trigonometric functions. The most elementary are the following, which are immediate consequences of the definitions of the trigonometric functions.

$$\boxed{6} \qquad \csc\theta = \frac{1}{\sin\theta} \qquad \sec\theta = \frac{1}{\cos\theta} \qquad \cot\theta = \frac{1}{\tan\theta}$$

$$\tan\theta = \frac{\sin\theta}{\cos\theta} \qquad \cot\theta = \frac{\cos\theta}{\sin\theta}$$

For the next identity we refer back to Figure 7. The distance formula (or, equivalently, the Pythagorean Theorem) tells us that $x^2 + y^2 = r^2$. Therefore

$$\sin^2\theta + \cos^2\theta = \frac{y^2}{r^2} + \frac{x^2}{r^2} = \frac{x^2 + y^2}{r^2} = \frac{r^2}{r^2} = 1$$

We have therefore proved one of the most useful of all trigonometric identities:

$$\boxed{7} \qquad \sin^2\theta + \cos^2\theta = 1$$

If we now divide both sides of Equation 7 by $\cos^2\theta$ and use Equations 6, we get

$$\boxed{8} \qquad \tan^2\theta + 1 = \sec^2\theta$$

Similarly, if we divide both sides of Equation 7 by $\sin^2\theta$, we get

$$\boxed{9} \qquad 1 + \cot^2\theta = \csc^2\theta$$

The identities

$$\boxed{10a} \qquad \sin(-\theta) = -\sin\theta$$

$$\boxed{10b} \qquad \cos(-\theta) = \cos\theta$$

⫴ Odd functions and even functions are discussed in Section 1.1.

show that sin is an odd function and cos is an even function. They are easily proved by drawing a diagram showing θ and $-\theta$ in standard position (see Exercise 39).

Since the angles θ and $\theta + 2\pi$ have the same terminal side, we have

$$\boxed{11} \qquad \sin(\theta + 2\pi) = \sin\theta \qquad \cos(\theta + 2\pi) = \cos\theta$$

These identities show that the sine and cosine functions are periodic with period 2π.

The remaining trigonometric identities are all consequences of two basic identities called the **addition formulas**:

12a
$$\sin(x + y) = \sin x \cos y + \cos x \sin y$$

12b
$$\cos(x + y) = \cos x \cos y - \sin x \sin y$$

The proofs of these addition formulas are outlined in Exercises 85, 86, and 87.

By substituting $-y$ for y in Equations 12a and 12b and using Equations 10a and 10b, we obtain the following **subtraction formulas**:

13a
$$\sin(x - y) = \sin x \cos y - \cos x \sin y$$

13b
$$\cos(x - y) = \cos x \cos y + \sin x \sin y$$

Then, by dividing the formulas in Equations 12 or Equations 13, we obtain the corresponding formulas for $\tan(x \pm y)$:

14a
$$\tan(x + y) = \frac{\tan x + \tan y}{1 - \tan x \tan y}$$

14b
$$\tan(x - y) = \frac{\tan x - \tan y}{1 + \tan x \tan y}$$

If we put $y = x$ in the addition formulas (12), we get the **double-angle formulas**:

15a
$$\sin 2x = 2 \sin x \cos x$$

15b
$$\cos 2x = \cos^2 x - \sin^2 x$$

Then, by using the identity $\sin^2 x + \cos^2 x = 1$, we obtain the following alternate forms of the double-angle formulas for $\cos 2x$:

16a
$$\cos 2x = 2 \cos^2 x - 1$$

16b
$$\cos 2x = 1 - 2 \sin^2 x$$

If we now solve these equations for $\cos^2 x$ and $\sin^2 x$, we get the following **half-angle formulas**, which are useful in integral calculus:

17a
$$\cos^2 x = \frac{1 + \cos 2x}{2}$$

17b
$$\sin^2 x = \frac{1 - \cos 2x}{2}$$

Finally, we state the **product formulas**, which can be deduced from Equations 12 and 13:

18a	$\sin x \cos y = \frac{1}{2}[\sin(x+y) + \sin(x-y)]$
18b	$\cos x \cos y = \frac{1}{2}[\cos(x+y) + \cos(x-y)]$
18c	$\sin x \sin y = \frac{1}{2}[\cos(x-y) - \cos(x+y)]$

There are many other trigonometric identities, but those we have stated are the ones used most often in calculus. If you forget any of them, remember that they can all be deduced from Equations 12a and 12b.

EXAMPLE 6 Find all values of x in the interval $[0, 2\pi]$ such that $\sin x = \sin 2x$.

SOLUTION Using the double-angle formula (15a), we rewrite the given equation as

$$\sin x = 2 \sin x \cos x \qquad \text{or} \qquad \sin x(1 - 2\cos x) = 0$$

Therefore, there are two possibilities:

$$\sin x = 0 \qquad \text{or} \qquad 1 - 2\cos x = 0$$

$$x = 0, \pi, 2\pi \qquad\qquad \cos x = \tfrac{1}{2}$$

$$x = \frac{\pi}{3}, \frac{5\pi}{3}$$

The given equation has five solutions: 0, $\pi/3$, π, $5\pi/3$, and 2π.

▬

▓ Graphs of Trigonometric Functions

The graph of the function $f(x) = \sin x$, shown in Figure 13(a), is obtained by plotting points for $0 \le x \le 2\pi$ and then using the periodic nature of the function (from Equation 11) to complete the graph. Notice that the zeros of the sine function occur at the

(a) $f(x) = \sin x$

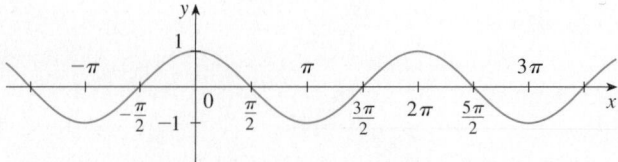

FIGURE 13

(b) $g(x) = \cos x$

integer multiples of π, that is,

$$\sin x = 0 \qquad \text{whenever } x = n\pi, \quad n \text{ an integer}$$

Because of the identity

$$\cos x = \sin\left(x + \frac{\pi}{2}\right)$$

(which can be verified using Equation 12a), the graph of cosine is obtained by shifting the graph of sine by an amount $\pi/2$ to the left [see Figure 13(b)]. Note that for both the sine and cosine functions the domain is $(-\infty, \infty)$ and the range is the closed interval $[-1, 1]$. Thus, for all values of x, we have

$$-1 \leqslant \sin x \leqslant 1 \qquad -1 \leqslant \cos x \leqslant 1$$

The graphs of the remaining four trigonometric functions are shown in Figure 14 and their domains are indicated there. Notice that tangent and cotangent have range $(-\infty, \infty)$, whereas cosecant and secant have range $(-\infty, -1] \cup [1, \infty)$. All four functions are periodic: tangent and cotangent have period π, whereas cosecant and secant have period 2π.

(a) $y = \tan x$

(b) $y = \cot x$

(c) $y = \csc x$

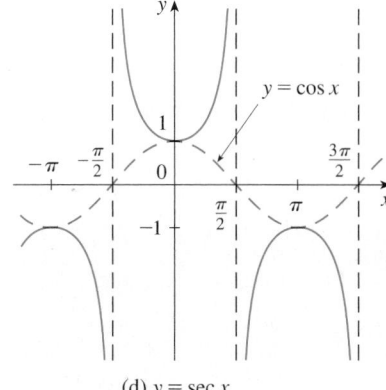

(d) $y = \sec x$

FIGURE 14

▥ D Exercises

1–6 ▥▥ Convert from degrees to radians.

1. 210°

2. 300°

3. 9°

4. −315°

5. 900°

6. 36°

7–12 ▥▥ Convert from radians to degrees.

7. 4π

8. $-\dfrac{7\pi}{2}$

9. $\dfrac{5\pi}{12}$

10. $\dfrac{8\pi}{3}$

11. $-\dfrac{3\pi}{8}$

12. 5

13. Find the length of a circular arc subtended by an angle of $\pi/12$ rad if the radius of the circle is 36 cm.

14. If a circle has radius 10 cm, find the length of the arc subtended by a central angle of 72°.

15. A circle has radius 1.5 m. What angle is subtended at the center of the circle by an arc 1 m long?

16. Find the radius of a circular sector with angle $3\pi/4$ and arc length 6 cm.

17–22 ▥▥ Draw, in standard position, the angle whose measure is given.

17. 315°

18. −150°

19. $-\dfrac{3\pi}{4}$ rad

20. $\dfrac{7\pi}{3}$ rad

21. 2 rad

22. −3 rad

23–28 ▥▥ Find the exact trigonometric ratios for the angle whose radian measure is given.

23. $\dfrac{3\pi}{4}$

24. $\dfrac{4\pi}{3}$

25. $\dfrac{9\pi}{2}$

26. -5π

27. $\dfrac{5\pi}{6}$

28. $\dfrac{11\pi}{4}$

29–34 ▥▥ Find the remaining trigonometric ratios.

29. $\sin\theta = \dfrac{3}{5}, \quad 0 < \theta < \dfrac{\pi}{2}$

30. $\tan\alpha = 2, \quad 0 < \alpha < \dfrac{\pi}{2}$

31. $\sec\phi = -1.5, \quad \dfrac{\pi}{2} < \phi < \pi$

32. $\cos x = -\dfrac{1}{3}, \quad \pi < x < \dfrac{3\pi}{2}$

33. $\cot\beta = 3, \quad \pi < \beta < 2\pi$

34. $\csc\theta = -\dfrac{4}{3}, \quad \dfrac{3\pi}{2} < \theta < 2\pi$

35–38 ▥▥ Find, correct to five decimal places, the length of the side labeled x.

35.

36.

37.

38.

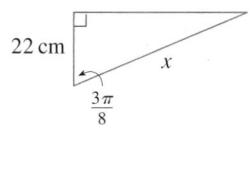

39–41 ▥▥ Prove each equation.

39. (a) Equation 10a   (b) Equation 10b

40. (a) Equation 14a   (b) Equation 14b

41. (a) Equation 18a   (b) Equation 18b
      (c) Equation 18c

42–58 ▥▥ Prove the identity.

42. $\cos\left(\dfrac{\pi}{2} - x\right) = \sin x$

43. $\sin\left(\dfrac{\pi}{2} + x\right) = \cos x$ **44.** $\sin(\pi - x) = \sin x$

45. $\sin\theta \cot\theta = \cos\theta$ **46.** $(\sin x + \cos x)^2 = 1 + \sin 2x$

47. $\sec y - \cos y = \tan y \sin y$

48. $\tan^2\alpha - \sin^2\alpha = \tan^2\alpha \sin^2\alpha$

49. $\cot^2\theta + \sec^2\theta = \tan^2\theta + \csc^2\theta$

50. $2 \csc 2t = \sec t \csc t$ **51.** $\tan 2\theta = \dfrac{2\tan\theta}{1 - \tan^2\theta}$

52. $\dfrac{1}{1 - \sin\theta} + \dfrac{1}{1 + \sin\theta} = 2\sec^2\theta$

53. $\sin x \sin 2x + \cos x \cos 2x = \cos x$

54. $\sin^2 x - \sin^2 y = \sin(x + y)\sin(x - y)$

55. $\dfrac{\sin\phi}{1 - \cos\phi} = \csc\phi + \cot\phi$

56. $\tan x + \tan y = \dfrac{\sin(x + y)}{\cos x \cos y}$

57. $\sin 3\theta + \sin \theta = 2 \sin 2\theta \cos \theta$

58. $\cos 3\theta = 4 \cos^3\theta - 3 \cos \theta$

59–64 ▓ If $\sin x = \frac{1}{3}$ and $\sec y = \frac{5}{4}$, where x and y lie between 0 and $\pi/2$, evaluate the expression.

59. $\sin(x + y)$ **60.** $\cos(x + y)$

61. $\cos(x - y)$ **62.** $\sin(x - y)$

63. $\sin 2y$ **64.** $\cos 2y$

65–72 ▓ Find all values of x in the interval $[0, 2\pi]$ that satisfy the equation.

65. $2 \cos x - 1 = 0$ **66.** $3 \cot^2 x = 1$

67. $2 \sin^2 x = 1$ **68.** $|\tan x| = 1$

69. $\sin 2x = \cos x$ **70.** $2 \cos x + \sin 2x = 0$

71. $\sin x = \tan x$ **72.** $2 + \cos 2x = 3 \cos x$

73–76 ▓ Find all values of x in the interval $[0, 2\pi]$ that satisfy the inequality.

73. $\sin x \leq \frac{1}{2}$ **74.** $2 \cos x + 1 > 0$

75. $-1 < \tan x < 1$ **76.** $\sin x > \cos x$

77–82 ▓ Graph the function by starting with the graphs in Figures 13 and 14 and applying the transformations of Section 1.3 where appropriate.

77. $y = \cos\left(x - \dfrac{\pi}{3}\right)$ **78.** $y = \tan 2x$

79. $y = \dfrac{1}{3} \tan\left(x - \dfrac{\pi}{2}\right)$ **80.** $y = 1 + \sec x$

81. $y = |\sin x|$ **82.** $y = 2 + \sin\left(x + \dfrac{\pi}{4}\right)$

83. Prove the **Law of Cosines**: If a triangle has sides with lengths a, b, and c, and θ is the angle between the sides with lengths a and b, then
$$c^2 = a^2 + b^2 - 2ab \cos \theta$$

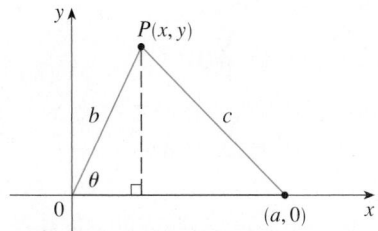

[*Hint:* Introduce a coordinate system so that θ is in standard position as in the figure. Express x and y in terms of θ and then use the distance formula to compute c.]

84. In order to find the distance $|AB|$ across a small inlet, a point C is located as in the figure and the following measurements were recorded:
$$\angle C = 103° \qquad |AC| = 820 \text{ m} \qquad |BC| = 910 \text{ m}$$

Use the Law of Cosines from Exercise 83 to find the required distance.

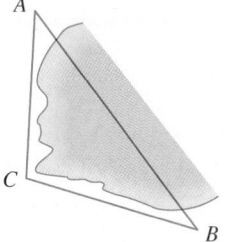

85. Use the figure to prove the subtraction formula
$$\cos(\alpha - \beta) = \cos \alpha \cos \beta + \sin \alpha \sin \beta$$

[*Hint:* Compute c^2 in two ways (using the Law of Cosines from Exercise 83 and also using the distance formula) and compare the two expressions.]

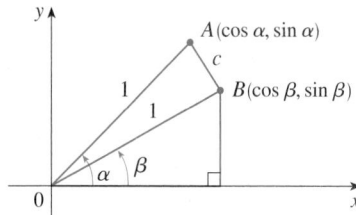

86. Use the formula in Exercise 85 to prove the addition formula for cosine (12b).

87. Use the addition formula for cosine and the identities
$$\cos\left(\dfrac{\pi}{2} - \theta\right) = \sin \theta \qquad \sin\left(\dfrac{\pi}{2} - \theta\right) = \cos \theta$$

to prove the subtraction formula for the sine function.

88. Show that the area of a triangle with sides of lengths a and b and with included angle θ is
$$A = \tfrac{1}{2}ab \sin \theta$$

89. Find the area of triangle ABC, correct to five decimal places, if
$$|AB| = 10 \text{ cm} \qquad |BC| = 3 \text{ cm} \qquad \angle ABC = 107°$$

E Sigma Notation

A convenient way of writing sums uses the Greek letter Σ (capital sigma, corresponding to our letter S) and is called **sigma notation**.

This tells us to end with $i = n$.

This tells us to add.

$$\sum_{i=m}^{n} a_i$$

This tells us to start with $i = m$.

> **1 Definition** If $a_m, a_{m+1}, \ldots, a_n$ are real numbers and m and n are integers such that $m \leq n$, then
>
> $$\sum_{i=m}^{n} a_i = a_m + a_{m+1} + a_{m+2} + \cdots + a_{n-1} + a_n$$

With function notation, Definition 1 can be written as

$$\sum_{i=m}^{n} f(i) = f(m) + f(m + 1) + f(m + 2) + \cdots + f(n - 1) + f(n)$$

Thus, the symbol $\sum_{i=m}^{n}$ indicates a summation in which the letter i (called the **index of summation**) takes on consecutive integer values beginning with m and ending with n, that is, $m, m + 1, \ldots, n$. Other letters can also be used as the index of summation.

EXAMPLE 1

(a) $\displaystyle\sum_{i=1}^{4} i^2 = 1^2 + 2^2 + 3^2 + 4^2 = 30$

(b) $\displaystyle\sum_{i=3}^{n} i = 3 + 4 + 5 + \cdots + (n - 1) + n$

(c) $\displaystyle\sum_{j=0}^{5} 2^j = 2^0 + 2^1 + 2^2 + 2^3 + 2^4 + 2^5 = 63$

(d) $\displaystyle\sum_{k=1}^{n} \frac{1}{k} = 1 + \frac{1}{2} + \frac{1}{3} + \cdots + \frac{1}{n}$

(e) $\displaystyle\sum_{i=1}^{3} \frac{i - 1}{i^2 + 3} = \frac{1 - 1}{1^2 + 3} + \frac{2 - 1}{2^2 + 3} + \frac{3 - 1}{3^2 + 3} = 0 + \frac{1}{7} + \frac{1}{6} = \frac{13}{42}$

(f) $\displaystyle\sum_{i=1}^{4} 2 = 2 + 2 + 2 + 2 = 8$

EXAMPLE 2 Write the sum $2^3 + 3^3 + \cdots + n^3$ in sigma notation.

SOLUTION There is no unique way of writing a sum in sigma notation. We could write

$$2^3 + 3^3 + \cdots + n^3 = \sum_{i=2}^{n} i^3$$

or

$$2^3 + 3^3 + \cdots + n^3 = \sum_{j=1}^{n-1} (j + 1)^3$$

or

$$2^3 + 3^3 + \cdots + n^3 = \sum_{k=0}^{n-2} (k + 2)^3$$

The following theorem gives three simple rules for working with sigma notation.

$\boxed{2}$ **Theorem** If c is any constant (that is, it does not depend on i), then

(a) $\displaystyle\sum_{i=m}^{n} ca_i = c \sum_{i=m}^{n} a_i$ (b) $\displaystyle\sum_{i=m}^{n} (a_i + b_i) = \sum_{i=m}^{n} a_i + \sum_{i=m}^{n} b_i$

(c) $\displaystyle\sum_{i=m}^{n} (a_i - b_i) = \sum_{i=m}^{n} a_i - \sum_{i=m}^{n} b_i$

Proof To see why these rules are true, all we have to do is write both sides in expanded form. Rule (a) is just the distributive property of real numbers:

$$ca_m + ca_{m+1} + \cdots + ca_n = c(a_m + a_{m+1} + \cdots + a_n)$$

Rule (b) follows from the associative and commutative properties:

$$(a_m + b_m) + (a_{m+1} + b_{m+1}) + \cdots + (a_n + b_n)$$
$$= (a_m + a_{m+1} + \cdots + a_n) + (b_m + b_{m+1} + \cdots + b_n)$$

Rule (c) is proved similarly.

EXAMPLE 3 Find $\displaystyle\sum_{i=1}^{n} 1$.

SOLUTION
$$\sum_{i=1}^{n} 1 = \underbrace{1 + 1 + \cdots + 1}_{n \text{ terms}} = n$$

EXAMPLE 4 Prove the formula for the sum of the first n positive integers:

$$\sum_{i=1}^{n} i = 1 + 2 + 3 + \cdots + n = \frac{n(n + 1)}{2}$$

SOLUTION This formula can be proved by mathematical induction (see page 59) or by the following method used by the German mathematician Karl Friedrich Gauss (1777–1855) when he was ten years old.

Write the sum S twice, once in the usual order and once in reverse order:

$$S = 1 + \quad 2 \quad + \quad 3 \quad + \cdots + (n - 1) + n$$
$$S = n + (n - 1) + (n - 2) + \cdots + \quad 2 \quad + 1$$

Adding all columns vertically, we get

$$2S = (n + 1) + (n + 1) + (n + 1) + \cdots + (n + 1) + (n + 1)$$

On the right side there are n terms, each of which is $n + 1$, so

$$2S = n(n + 1) \qquad \text{or} \qquad S = \frac{n(n + 1)}{2}$$

EXAMPLE 5 Prove the formula for the sum of the squares of the first n positive integers:

$$\sum_{i=1}^{n} i^2 = 1^2 + 2^2 + 3^2 + \cdots + n^2 = \frac{n(n + 1)(2n + 1)}{6}$$

SOLUTION 1 Let S be the desired sum. We start with the *telescoping sum* (or collapsing sum):

Most terms cancel in pairs.

$$\sum_{i=1}^{n} [(1+i)^3 - i^3] = (2^3 - 1^3) + (3^3 - 2^3) + (4^3 - 3^3) + \cdots + [(n+1)^3 - n^3]$$

$$= (n+1)^3 - 1^3 = n^3 + 3n^2 + 3n$$

On the other hand, using Theorem 2 and Examples 3 and 4, we have

$$\sum_{i=1}^{n} [(1+i)^3 - i^3] = \sum_{i=1}^{n} [3i^2 + 3i + 1] = 3\sum_{i=1}^{n} i^2 + 3\sum_{i=1}^{n} i + \sum_{i=1}^{n} 1$$

$$= 3S + 3\frac{n(n+1)}{2} + n = 3S + \tfrac{3}{2}n^2 + \tfrac{5}{2}n$$

Thus, we have

$$n^3 + 3n^2 + 3n = 3S + \tfrac{3}{2}n^2 + \tfrac{5}{2}n$$

Solving this equation for S, we obtain

$$3S = n^3 + \tfrac{3}{2}n^2 + \tfrac{1}{2}n$$

or

$$S = \frac{2n^3 + 3n^2 + n}{6} = \frac{n(n+1)(2n+1)}{6}$$

▏▏▏ PRINCIPLE OF MATHEMATICAL INDUCTION

Let S_n be a statement involving the positive integer n. Suppose that

1. S_1 is true.
2. If S_k is true, then S_{k+1} is true.

Then S_n is true for all positive integers n.

▏▏▏ See pages 59 and 61 for a more thorough discussion of mathematical induction.

SOLUTION 2 Let S_n be the given formula.

1. S_1 is true because
$$1^2 = \frac{1(1+1)(2 \cdot 1 + 1)}{6}$$

2. Assume that S_k is true; that is,
$$1^2 + 2^2 + 3^2 + \cdots + k^2 = \frac{k(k+1)(2k+1)}{6}$$

Then

$$1^2 + 2^2 + 3^2 + \cdots + (k+1)^2 = (1^2 + 2^2 + 3^2 + \cdots + k^2) + (k+1)^2$$

$$= \frac{k(k+1)(2k+1)}{6} + (k+1)^2$$

$$= (k+1)\frac{k(2k+1) + 6(k+1)}{6}$$

$$= (k+1)\frac{2k^2 + 7k + 6}{6}$$

$$= \frac{(k+1)(k+2)(2k+3)}{6}$$

$$= \frac{(k+1)[(k+1)+1][2(k+1)+1]}{6}$$

So S_{k+1} is true.

By the Principle of Mathematical Induction, S_n is true for all n.

We list the results of Examples 3, 4, and 5 together with a similar result for cubes (see Exercises 37–40) as Theorem 3. These formulas are needed for finding areas and evaluating integrals in Chapter 5.

> **3 Theorem** Let c be a constant and n a positive integer. Then
>
> (a) $\displaystyle\sum_{i=1}^{n} 1 = n$ 　　　　　　 (b) $\displaystyle\sum_{i=1}^{n} c = nc$
>
> (c) $\displaystyle\sum_{i=1}^{n} i = \frac{n(n+1)}{2}$ 　　　 (d) $\displaystyle\sum_{i=1}^{n} i^2 = \frac{n(n+1)(2n+1)}{6}$
>
> (e) $\displaystyle\sum_{i=1}^{n} i^3 = \left[\frac{n(n+1)}{2}\right]^2$

EXAMPLE 6 Evaluate $\displaystyle\sum_{i=1}^{n} i(4i^2 - 3)$.

SOLUTION Using Theorems 2 and 3, we have

$$\sum_{i=1}^{n} i(4i^2-3) = \sum_{i=1}^{n}(4i^3-3i) = 4\sum_{i=1}^{n} i^3 - 3\sum_{i=1}^{n} i$$

$$= 4\left[\frac{n(n+1)}{2}\right]^2 - 3\frac{n(n+1)}{2}$$

$$= \frac{n(n+1)[2n(n+1)-3]}{2}$$

$$= \frac{n(n+1)(2n^2+2n-3)}{2}$$

‖‖ The type of calculation in Example 7 arises in Chapter 5 when we compute areas.

EXAMPLE 7 Find $\displaystyle\lim_{n\to\infty}\sum_{i=1}^{n}\frac{3}{n}\left[\left(\frac{i}{n}\right)^2+1\right]$.

SOLUTION

$$\lim_{n\to\infty}\sum_{i=1}^{n}\frac{3}{n}\left[\left(\frac{i}{n}\right)^2+1\right] = \lim_{n\to\infty}\sum_{i=1}^{n}\left[\frac{3}{n^3}i^2+\frac{3}{n}\right]$$

$$= \lim_{n\to\infty}\left[\frac{3}{n^3}\sum_{i=1}^{n}i^2+\frac{3}{n}\sum_{i=1}^{n}1\right]$$

$$= \lim_{n\to\infty}\left[\frac{3}{n^3}\frac{n(n+1)(2n+1)}{6}+\frac{3}{n}\cdot n\right]$$

$$= \lim_{n\to\infty}\left[\frac{1}{2}\cdot\frac{n}{n}\cdot\left(\frac{n+1}{n}\right)\left(\frac{2n+1}{n}\right)+3\right]$$

$$= \lim_{n\to\infty}\left[\frac{1}{2}\cdot1\left(1+\frac{1}{n}\right)\left(2+\frac{1}{n}\right)+3\right]$$

$$= \tfrac{1}{2}\cdot1\cdot1\cdot2+3 = 4$$

IIII E Exercises

1–10 IIII Write the sum in expanded form.

1. $\sum_{i=1}^{5} \sqrt{i}$

2. $\sum_{i=1}^{6} \frac{1}{i+1}$

3. $\sum_{i=4}^{6} 3^i$

4. $\sum_{i=4}^{6} i^3$

5. $\sum_{k=0}^{4} \frac{2k-1}{2k+1}$

6. $\sum_{k=5}^{8} x^k$

7. $\sum_{i=1}^{n} i^{10}$

8. $\sum_{j=n}^{n+3} j^2$

9. $\sum_{j=0}^{n-1} (-1)^j$

10. $\sum_{i=1}^{n} f(x_i)\,\Delta x_i$

11–20 IIII Write the sum in sigma notation.

11. $1 + 2 + 3 + 4 + \cdots + 10$

12. $\sqrt{3} + \sqrt{4} + \sqrt{5} + \sqrt{6} + \sqrt{7}$

13. $\frac{1}{2} + \frac{2}{3} + \frac{3}{4} + \frac{4}{5} + \cdots + \frac{19}{20}$

14. $\frac{3}{7} + \frac{4}{8} + \frac{5}{9} + \frac{6}{10} + \cdots + \frac{23}{27}$

15. $2 + 4 + 6 + 8 + \cdots + 2n$

16. $1 + 3 + 5 + 7 + \cdots + (2n-1)$

17. $1 + 2 + 4 + 8 + 16 + 32$

18. $\frac{1}{1} + \frac{1}{4} + \frac{1}{9} + \frac{1}{16} + \frac{1}{25} + \frac{1}{36}$

19. $x + x^2 + x^3 + \cdots + x^n$

20. $1 - x + x^2 - x^3 + \cdots + (-1)^n x^n$

21–35 IIII Find the value of the sum.

21. $\sum_{i=4}^{8} (3i-2)$

22. $\sum_{i=3}^{6} i(i+2)$

23. $\sum_{j=1}^{6} 3^{j+1}$

24. $\sum_{k=0}^{8} \cos k\pi$

25. $\sum_{n=1}^{20} (-1)^n$

26. $\sum_{i=1}^{100} 4$

27. $\sum_{i=0}^{4} (2^i + i^2)$

28. $\sum_{i=-2}^{4} 2^{3-i}$

29. $\sum_{i=1}^{n} 2i$

30. $\sum_{i=1}^{n} (2 - 5i)$

31. $\sum_{i=1}^{n} (i^2 + 3i + 4)$

32. $\sum_{i=1}^{n} (3 + 2i)^2$

33. $\sum_{i=1}^{n} (i+1)(i+2)$

34. $\sum_{i=1}^{n} i(i+1)(i+2)$

35. $\sum_{i=1}^{n} (i^3 - i - 2)$

36. Find the number n such that $\sum_{i=1}^{n} i = 78$.

37. Prove formula (b) of Theorem 3.

38. Prove formula (e) of Theorem 3 using mathematical induction.

39. Prove formula (e) of Theorem 3 using a method similar to that of Example 5, Solution 1 [start with $(1+i)^4 - i^4$].

40. Prove formula (e) of Theorem 3 using the following method published by Abu Bekr Mohammed ibn Alhusain Alkarchi in about A.D. 1010. The figure shows a square $ABCD$ in which sides AB and AD have been divided into segments of lengths 1, 2, 3, ..., n. Thus, the side of the square has length $n(n+1)/2$ so the area is $[n(n+1)/2]^2$. But the area is also the sum of the areas of the n "gnomons" $G_1, G_2, \ldots, G_n$ shown in the figure. Show that the area of G_i is i^3 and conclude that formula (e) is true.

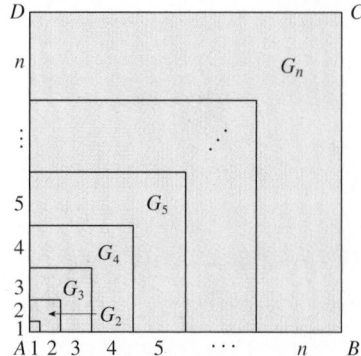

41. Evaluate each telescoping sum.

(a) $\sum_{i=1}^{n} [i^4 - (i-1)^4]$

(b) $\sum_{i=1}^{100} (5^i - 5^{i-1})$

(c) $\sum_{i=3}^{99} \left(\frac{1}{i} - \frac{1}{i+1} \right)$

(d) $\sum_{i=1}^{n} (a_i - a_{i-1})$

42. Prove the generalized triangle inequality

$$\left| \sum_{i=1}^{n} a_i \right| \le \sum_{i=1}^{n} |a_i|$$

43–46 IIII Find each limit.

43. $\lim_{n \to \infty} \sum_{i=1}^{n} \frac{1}{n} \left(\frac{i}{n} \right)^2$

44. $\lim_{n \to \infty} \sum_{i=1}^{n} \frac{1}{n} \left[\left(\frac{i}{n} \right)^3 + 1 \right]$

45. $\lim_{n \to \infty} \sum_{i=1}^{n} \frac{2}{n} \left[\left(\frac{2i}{n} \right)^3 + 5 \left(\frac{2i}{n} \right) \right]$

46. $\lim\limits_{n\to\infty} \sum\limits_{i=1}^{n} \dfrac{3}{n}\left[\left(1 + \dfrac{3i}{n}\right)^3 - 2\left(1 + \dfrac{3i}{n}\right)\right]$

□ □ □ □ □ □ □ □ □ □ □ □

47. Prove the formula for the sum of a finite geometric series with first term a and common ratio $r \neq 1$:

$$\sum_{i=1}^{n} ar^{i-1} = a + ar + ar^2 + \cdots + ar^{n-1} = \frac{a(r^n - 1)}{r - 1}$$

48. Evaluate $\sum\limits_{i=1}^{n} \dfrac{3}{2^{i-1}}$.

49. Evaluate $\sum\limits_{i=1}^{n} (2i + 2^i)$.

50. Evaluate $\sum\limits_{i=1}^{m}\left[\sum\limits_{j=1}^{n}(i + j)\right]$.

‖‖ F Proofs of Theorems

In this appendix we present proofs of several theorems that are stated in the main body of the text. The sections in which they occur are indicated in the margin.

SECTION 2.3

> **Limit Laws** Suppose that c is a constant and the limits
>
> $$\lim_{x\to a} f(x) = L \qquad \text{and} \qquad \lim_{x\to a} g(x) = M$$
>
> exist. Then
>
> **1.** $\lim\limits_{x\to a}[f(x) + g(x)] = L + M$ **2.** $\lim\limits_{x\to a}[f(x) - g(x)] = L - M$
>
> **3.** $\lim\limits_{x\to a}[cf(x)] = cL$ **4.** $\lim\limits_{x\to a}[f(x)g(x)] = LM$
>
> **5.** $\lim\limits_{x\to a}\dfrac{f(x)}{g(x)} = \dfrac{L}{M}$ if $M \neq 0$

Proof of Law 4 Let $\varepsilon > 0$ be given. We want to find $\delta > 0$ such that

$$|f(x)g(x) - LM| < \varepsilon \qquad \text{whenever} \qquad 0 < |x - a| < \delta$$

In order to get terms that contain $|f(x) - L|$ and $|g(x) - M|$, we add and subtract $Lg(x)$ as follows:

$$\begin{aligned}
|f(x)g(x) - LM| &= |f(x)g(x) - Lg(x) + Lg(x) - LM| \\
&= |[f(x) - L]g(x) + L[g(x) - M]| \\
&\leq |[f(x) - L]g(x)| + |L[g(x) - M]| \qquad \text{(Triangle Inequality)} \\
&= |f(x) - L||g(x)| + |L||g(x) - M|
\end{aligned}$$

We want to make each of these terms less than $\varepsilon/2$.

Since $\lim_{x\to a} g(x) = M$, there is a number $\delta_1 > 0$ such that

$$|g(x) - M| < \frac{\varepsilon}{2(1 + |L|)} \qquad \text{whenever} \qquad 0 < |x - a| < \delta_1$$

Also, there is a number $\delta_2 > 0$ such that if $0 < |x - a| < \delta_2$, then

$$|g(x) - M| < 1$$

and therefore

$$|g(x)| = |g(x) - M + M| \leq |g(x) - M| + |M| < 1 + |M|$$

Since $\lim_{x \to a} f(x) = L$, there is a number $\delta_3 > 0$ such that

$$|f(x) - L| < \frac{\varepsilon}{2(1 + |M|)} \qquad \text{whenever} \qquad 0 < |x - a| < \delta_3$$

Let $\delta = \min\{\delta_1, \delta_2, \delta_3\}$. If $0 < |x - a| < \delta$, then we have $0 < |x - a| < \delta_1$, $0 < |x - a| < \delta_2$, and $0 < |x - a| < \delta_3$, so we can combine the inequalities to obtain

$$|f(x)g(x) - LM| \leq |f(x) - L||g(x)| + |L||g(x) - M|$$

$$< \frac{\varepsilon}{2(1 + |M|)}(1 + |M|) + |L|\frac{\varepsilon}{2(1 + |L|)}$$

$$< \frac{\varepsilon}{2} + \frac{\varepsilon}{2} = \varepsilon$$

This shows that $\lim_{x \to a} f(x)g(x) = LM$.

Proof of Law 3 If we take $g(x) = c$ in Law 4, we get

$$\lim_{x \to a}[cf(x)] = \lim_{x \to a}[g(x)f(x)] = \lim_{x \to a} g(x) \cdot \lim_{x \to a} f(x)$$

$$= \lim_{x \to a} c \cdot \lim_{x \to a} f(x)$$

$$= c \lim_{x \to a} f(x) \qquad \text{(by Law 7)}$$

Proof of Law 2 Using Law 1 and Law 3 with $c = -1$, we have

$$\lim_{x \to a}[f(x) - g(x)] = \lim_{x \to a}[f(x) + (-1)g(x)] = \lim_{x \to a} f(x) + \lim_{x \to a}(-1)g(x)$$

$$= \lim_{x \to a} f(x) + (-1)\lim_{x \to a} g(x) = \lim_{x \to a} f(x) - \lim_{x \to a} g(x)$$

Proof of Law 5 First let us show that

$$\lim_{x \to a} \frac{1}{g(x)} = \frac{1}{M}$$

To do this we must show that, given $\varepsilon > 0$, there exists $\delta > 0$ such that

$$\left| \frac{1}{g(x)} - \frac{1}{M} \right| < \varepsilon \qquad \text{whenever} \qquad 0 < |x - a| < \delta$$

Observe that
$$\left| \frac{1}{g(x)} - \frac{1}{M} \right| = \frac{|M - g(x)|}{|Mg(x)|}$$

We know that we can make the numerator small. But we also need to know that the denominator is not small when x is near a. Since $\lim_{x \to a} g(x) = M$, there is a number $\delta_1 > 0$ such that, whenever $0 < |x - a| < \delta_1$, we have

$$|g(x) - M| < \frac{|M|}{2}$$

and therefore $|M| = |M - g(x) + g(x)| \leq |M - g(x)| + |g(x)|$

$$< \frac{|M|}{2} + |g(x)|$$

This shows that

$$|g(x)| > \frac{|M|}{2} \qquad \text{whenever} \qquad 0 < |x - a| < \delta_1$$

and so, for these values of x,

$$\frac{1}{|Mg(x)|} = \frac{1}{|M||g(x)|} < \frac{1}{|M|} \cdot \frac{2}{|M|} = \frac{2}{M^2}$$

Also, there exists $\delta_2 > 0$ such that

$$|g(x) - M| < \frac{M^2}{2} \varepsilon \qquad \text{whenever} \qquad 0 < |x - a| < \delta_2$$

Let $\delta = \min\{\delta_1, \delta_2\}$. Then, for $0 < |x - a| < \delta$, we have

$$\left| \frac{1}{g(x)} - \frac{1}{M} \right| = \frac{|M - g(x)|}{|Mg(x)|} < \frac{2}{M^2} \frac{M^2}{2} \varepsilon = \varepsilon$$

It follows that $\lim_{x \to a} 1/g(x) = 1/M$. Finally, using Law 4, we obtain

$$\lim_{x \to a} \frac{f(x)}{g(x)} = \lim_{x \to a} f(x) \left(\frac{1}{g(x)} \right)$$

$$= \lim_{x \to a} f(x) \lim_{x \to a} \frac{1}{g(x)} = L \cdot \frac{1}{M} = \frac{L}{M}$$

---

2 Theorem If $f(x) \le g(x)$ for all x in an open interval that contains a (except possibly at a) and

$$\lim_{x \to a} f(x) = L \qquad \text{and} \qquad \lim_{x \to a} g(x) = M$$

then $L \le M$.

Proof We use the method of proof by contradiction. Suppose, if possible, that $L > M$. Law 2 of limits says that

$$\lim_{x \to a} [g(x) - f(x)] = M - L$$

Therefore, for any $\varepsilon > 0$, there exists $\delta > 0$ such that

$$|[g(x) - f(x)] - (M - L)| < \varepsilon \qquad \text{whenever} \qquad 0 < |x - a| < \delta$$

In particular, taking $\varepsilon = L - M$ (noting that $L - M > 0$ by hypothesis), we have a number $\delta > 0$ such that

$$|[g(x) - f(x)] - (M - L)| < L - M \qquad \text{whenever} \qquad 0 < |x - a| < \delta$$

Since $a \le |a|$ for any number a, we have

$$[g(x) - f(x)] - (M - L) < L - M \qquad \text{whenever} \qquad 0 < |x - a| < \delta$$

which simplifies to

$$g(x) < f(x) \qquad \text{whenever} \qquad 0 < |x - a| < \delta$$

But this contradicts $f(x) \leq g(x)$. Thus, the inequality $L > M$ must be false. Therefore, $L \leq M$.

---

3 **The Squeeze Theorem** If $f(x) \leq g(x) \leq h(x)$ for all x in an open interval that contains a (except possibly at a) and

$$\lim_{x \to a} f(x) = \lim_{x \to a} h(x) = L$$

then

$$\lim_{x \to a} g(x) = L$$

Proof Let $\varepsilon > 0$ be given. Since $\lim_{x \to a} f(x) = L$, there is a number $\delta_1 > 0$ such that

$$|f(x) - L| < \varepsilon \qquad \text{whenever} \qquad 0 < |x - a| < \delta_1$$

that is, $L - \varepsilon < f(x) < L + \varepsilon$ whenever $0 < |x - a| < \delta_1$

Since $\lim_{x \to a} h(x) = L$, there is a number $\delta_2 > 0$ such that

$$|h(x) - L| < \varepsilon \qquad \text{whenever} \qquad 0 < |x - a| < \delta_2$$

that is, $L - \varepsilon < h(x) < L + \varepsilon$ whenever $0 < |x - a| < \delta_2$

Let $\delta = \min\{\delta_1, \delta_2\}$. If $0 < |x - a| < \delta$, then $0 < |x - a| < \delta_1$ and $0 < |x - a| < \delta_2$, so

$$L - \varepsilon < f(x) \leq g(x) \leq h(x) < L + \varepsilon$$

In particular, $L - \varepsilon < g(x) < L + \varepsilon$

and so $|g(x) - L| < \varepsilon$. Therefore, $\lim_{x \to a} g(x) = L$.

SECTION 2.5

8 **Theorem** If f is continuous at b and $\lim_{x \to a} g(x) = b$, then

$$\lim_{x \to a} f(g(x)) = f(b)$$

Proof Let $\varepsilon > 0$ be given. We want to find a number $\delta > 0$ such that

$$|f(g(x)) - f(b)| < \varepsilon \qquad \text{whenever} \qquad 0 < |x - a| < \delta$$

Since f is continuous at b, we have

$$\lim_{y \to b} f(y) = f(b)$$

and so there exists $\delta_1 > 0$ such that

$$|f(y) - f(b)| < \varepsilon \qquad \text{whenever} \qquad 0 < |y - b| < \delta_1$$

Since $\lim_{x \to a} g(x) = b$, there exists $\delta > 0$ such that

$$|g(x) - b| < \delta_1 \qquad \text{whenever} \qquad 0 < |x - a| < \delta$$

Combining these two statements, we see that whenever $0 < |x - a| < \delta$ we have $|g(x) - b| < \delta_1$, which implies that $|f(g(x)) - f(b)| < \varepsilon$. Therefore, we have proved that $\lim_{x \to a} f(g(x)) = f(b)$.

SECTION 3.5

The proof of the following result was promised when we proved that $\lim\limits_{\theta \to 0} \dfrac{\sin \theta}{\theta} = 1$.

> **Theorem** If $0 < \theta < \pi/2$, then $\theta \leqslant \tan \theta$.

Proof Figure 1 shows a sector of a circle with center O, central angle θ, and radius 1. Then

$$|AD| = |OA| \tan \theta = \tan \theta$$

We approximate the arc AB by an inscribed polygon consisting of n equal line segments and we look at a typical segment PQ. We extend the lines OP and OQ to meet AD in the points R and S. Then we draw $RT \parallel PQ$ as in Figure 1. Observe that

$$\angle RTO = \angle PQO < 90°$$

and so $\angle RTS > 90°$. Therefore, we have

$$|PQ| < |RT| < |RS|$$

If we add n such inequalities, we get

$$L_n < |AD| = \tan \theta$$

where L_n is the length of the inscribed polygon. Thus, by Theorem 2.3.2, we have

$$\lim_{n \to \infty} L_n \leqslant \tan \theta$$

But the arc length was defined in Equation 9.1.1 as the limit of the lengths of inscribed polygons, so

$$\theta = \lim_{n \to \infty} L_n \leqslant \tan \theta$$

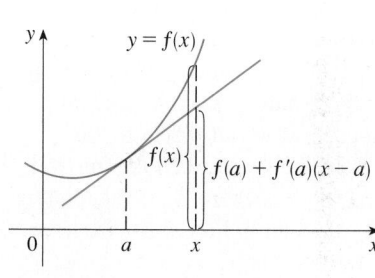

FIGURE 1

SECTION 4.3

> **Concavity Test**
> (a) If $f''(x) > 0$ for all x in I, then the graph of f is concave upward on I.
> (b) If $f''(x) < 0$ for all x in I, then the graph of f is concave downward on I.

Proof of (a) Let a be any number in I. We must show that the curve $y = f(x)$ lies above the tangent line at the point $(a, f(a))$. The equation of this tangent is

$$y = f(a) + f'(a)(x - a)$$

So we must show that

$$f(x) > f(a) + f'(a)(x - a)$$

FIGURE 2

whenever $x \in I$ $(x \neq a)$. (See Figure 2.)

First let us take the case where $x > a$. Applying the Mean Value Theorem to f on the interval $[a, x]$, we get a number c, with $a < c < x$, such that

$$\boxed{1} \qquad f(x) - f(a) = f'(c)(x - a)$$

Since $f'' > 0$ on I we know from the Increasing/Decreasing Test that f' is increasing on I. Thus, since $a < c$, we have

$$f'(a) < f'(c)$$

and so, multiplying this inequality by the positive number $x - a$, we get

$$\boxed{2} \qquad f'(a)(x - a) < f'(c)(x - a)$$

Now we add $f(a)$ to both sides of this inequality:

$$f(a) + f'(a)(x - a) < f(a) + f'(c)(x - a)$$

But from Equation 1 we have $f(x) = f(a) + f'(c)(x - a)$. So this inequality becomes

$$\boxed{3} \qquad f(x) > f(a) + f'(a)(x - a)$$

which is what we wanted to prove.

For the case where $x < a$ we have $f'(c) < f'(a)$, but multiplication by the negative number $x - a$ reverses the inequality, so we get (2) and (3) as before.

SECTION 7.1

> $\boxed{6}$ **Theorem** If f is a one-to-one continuous function defined on an interval (a, b), then its inverse function f^{-1} is also continuous.

Proof First we show that if f is both one-to-one and continuous on (a, b), then it must be either increasing or decreasing on (a, b). If it were neither increasing nor decreasing, then there would exist numbers x_1, x_2, and x_3 in (a, b) with $x_1 < x_2 < x_3$ such that $f(x_2)$ does not lie between $f(x_1)$ and $f(x_3)$. There are two possibilities: either (1) $f(x_3)$ lies between $f(x_1)$ and $f(x_2)$ or (2) $f(x_1)$ lies between $f(x_2)$ and $f(x_3)$. (Draw a picture.) In case (1) we apply the Intermediate Value Theorem to the continuous function f to get a number c between x_1 and x_2 such that $f(c) = f(x_3)$. In case (2) the Intermediate Value Theorem gives a number c between x_2 and x_3 such that $f(c) = f(x_1)$. In either case we have contradicted the fact that f is one-to-one.

Let us assume, for the sake of definiteness, that f is increasing on (a, b). We take any number y_0 in the domain of f^{-1} and we let $f^{-1}(y_0) = x_0$; that is, x_0 is the number in (a, b) such that $f(x_0) = y_0$. To show that f^{-1} is continuous at y_0 we take any $\varepsilon > 0$ such that the interval $(x_0 - \varepsilon, x_0 + \varepsilon)$ is contained in the interval (a, b). Since f is increasing, it maps the numbers in the interval $(x_0 - \varepsilon, x_0 + \varepsilon)$ onto the numbers in the interval $(f(x_0 - \varepsilon), f(x_0 + \varepsilon))$ and f^{-1} reverses the correspondence. If we let δ denote the smaller of the numbers $\delta_1 = y_0 - f(x_0 - \varepsilon)$ and $\delta_2 = f(x_0 + \varepsilon) - y_0$, then the interval $(y_0 - \delta, y_0 + \delta)$ is contained in the interval $(f(x_0 - \varepsilon), f(x_0 + \varepsilon))$ and so is mapped into the interval $(x_0 - \varepsilon, x_0 + \varepsilon)$ by f^{-1}. (See the arrow diagram in Figure 3.) We have therefore found a number $\delta > 0$ such that

$$|f^{-1}(y) - f^{-1}(y_0)| < \varepsilon \qquad \text{whenever} \qquad |y - y_0| < \delta$$

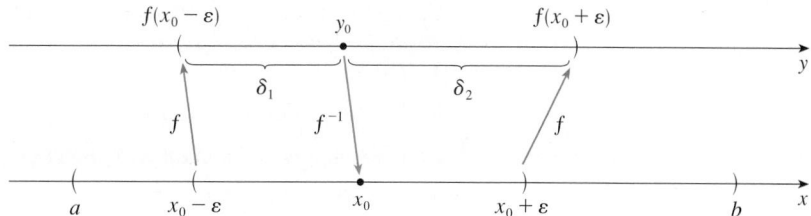

FIGURE 3

This shows that $\lim_{y \to y_0} f^{-1}(y) = f^{-1}(y_0)$ and so f^{-1} is continuous at any number y_0 in its domain.

SECTION 12.8

In order to prove Theorem 12.8.3 we first need the following results.

Theorem

1. If a power series $\Sigma \, c_n x^n$ converges when $x = b$ (where $b \neq 0$), then it converges whenever $|x| < |b|$.

2. If a power series $\Sigma \, c_n x^n$ diverges when $x = d$ (where $d \neq 0$), then it diverges whenever $|x| > |d|$.

Proof of 1   Suppose that $\Sigma \, c_n b^n$ converges. Then, by Theorem 12.2.6, we have $\lim_{n \to \infty} c_n b^n = 0$. According to Definition 12.1.2 with $\varepsilon = 1$, there is a positive integer N such that $|c_n b^n| < 1$ whenever $n \geq N$. Thus, for $n \geq N$, we have

$$|c_n x^n| = \left| \frac{c_n b^n x^n}{b^n} \right| = |c_n b^n| \left| \frac{x}{b} \right|^n < \left| \frac{x}{b} \right|^n$$

If $|x| < |b|$, then $|x/b| < 1$, so $\Sigma \, |x/b|^n$ is a convergent geometric series. Therefore, by the Comparison Test, the series $\Sigma_{n=N}^{\infty} |c_n x^n|$ is convergent. Thus, the series $\Sigma \, c_n x^n$ is absolutely convergent and therefore convergent.

Proof of 2   Suppose that $\Sigma \, c_n d^n$ diverges. If x is any number such that $|x| > |d|$, then $\Sigma \, c_n x^n$ cannot converge because, by part 1, the convergence of $\Sigma \, c_n x^n$ would imply the convergence of $\Sigma \, c_n d^n$. Therefore, $\Sigma \, c_n x^n$ diverges whenever $|x| > |d|$.

Theorem   For a power series $\Sigma \, c_n x^n$ there are only three possibilities:

1. The series converges only when $x = 0$.

2. The series converges for all x.

3. There is a positive number R such that the series converges if $|x| < R$ and diverges if $|x| > R$.

Proof   Suppose that neither case 1 nor case 2 is true. Then there are nonzero numbers b and d such that $\Sigma \, c_n x^n$ converges for $x = b$ and diverges for $x = d$. Therefore, the set $S = \{x \mid \Sigma \, c_n x^n \text{ converges}\}$ is not empty. By the preceding theorem, the series diverges if $|x| > |d|$, so $|x| \leq |d|$ for all $x \in S$. This says that $|d|$ is an upper bound for the set S. Thus, by the Completeness Axiom (see Section 12.1), S has a least upper bound R. If $|x| > R$, then $x \notin S$, so $\Sigma \, c_n x^n$ diverges. If $|x| < R$, then $|x|$ is not an upper bound for S and so there exists $b \in S$ such that $b > |x|$. Since $b \in S$, $\Sigma \, c_n b^n$ converges, so by the preceding theorem $\Sigma \, c_n x^n$ converges.

> **3** **Theorem** For a power series $\Sigma\, c_n(x - a)^n$ there are only three possibilities:
>
> **1.** The series converges only when $x = a$.
>
> **2.** The series converges for all x.
>
> **3.** There is a positive number R such that the series converges if $|x - a| < R$ and diverges if $|x - a| > R$.

Proof If we make the change of variable $u = x - a$, then the power series becomes $\Sigma\, c_n u^n$ and we can apply the preceding theorem to this series. In case 3 we have convergence for $|u| < R$ and divergence for $|u| > R$. Thus, we have convergence for $|x - a| < R$ and divergence for $|x - a| > R$.

SECTION 15.3

> **Clairaut's Theorem** Suppose f is defined on a disk D that contains the point (a, b). If the functions f_{xy} and f_{yx} are both continuous on D, then $f_{xy}(a, b) = f_{yx}(a, b)$.

Proof For small values of h, $h \neq 0$, consider the difference

$$\Delta(h) = [f(a + h, b + h) - f(a + h, b)] - [f(a, b + h) - f(a, b)]$$

Notice that if we let $g(x) = f(x, b + h) - f(x, b)$, then

$$\Delta(h) = g(a + h) - g(a)$$

By the Mean Value Theorem, there is a number c between a and $a + h$ such that

$$g(a + h) - g(a) = g'(c)h = h[f_x(c, b + h) - f_x(c, b)]$$

Applying the Mean Value Theorem again, this time to f_x, we get a number d between b and $b + h$ such that

$$f_x(c, b + h) - f_x(c, b) = f_{xy}(c, d)h$$

Combining these equations, we obtain

$$\Delta(h) = h^2 f_{xy}(c, d)$$

If $h \to 0$, then $(c, d) \to (a, b)$, so the continuity of f_{xy} at (a, b) gives

$$\lim_{h \to 0} \frac{\Delta(h)}{h^2} = \lim_{(c, d) \to (a, b)} f_{xy}(c, d) = f_{xy}(a, b)$$

Similarly, by writing

$$\Delta(h) = [f(a + h, b + h) - f(a, b + h)] - [f(a + h, b) - f(a, b)]$$

and using the Mean Value Theorem twice and the continuity of f_{yx} at (a, b), we obtain

$$\lim_{h \to 0} \frac{\Delta(h)}{h^2} = f_{yx}(a, b)$$

It follows that $f_{xy}(a, b) = f_{yx}(a, b)$.

SECTION 15.4

> [8] **Theorem** If the partial derivatives f_x and f_y exist near (a, b) and are continuous at (a, b), then f is differentiable at (a, b).

Proof Let

$$\Delta z = f(a + \Delta x, b + \Delta y) - f(a, b)$$

According to (15.4.7), to prove that f is differentiable at (a, b) we have to show that we can write Δz in the form

$$\Delta z = f_x(a, b)\,\Delta x + f_y(a, b)\,\Delta y + \varepsilon_1\,\Delta x + \varepsilon_2\,\Delta y$$

where ε_1 and $\varepsilon_2 \to 0$ as $(\Delta x, \Delta y) \to (0, 0)$.

Referring to Figure 4, we write

$$\boxed{1} \quad \Delta z = [f(a + \Delta x, b + \Delta y) - f(a, b + \Delta y)] + [f(a, b + \Delta y) - f(a, b)]$$

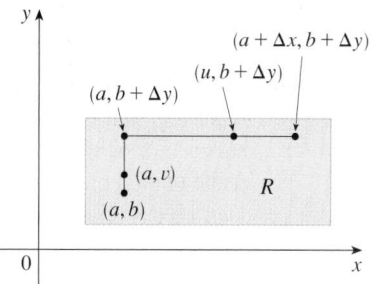

FIGURE 4

Observe that the function of a single variable

$$g(x) = f(x, b + \Delta y)$$

is defined on the interval $[a, a + \Delta x]$ and $g'(x) = f_x(x, b + \Delta y)$. If we apply the Mean Value Theorem to g, we get

$$g(a + \Delta x) - g(a) = g'(u)\,\Delta x$$

where u is some number between a and $a + \Delta x$. In terms of f, this equation becomes

$$f(a + \Delta x, b + \Delta y) - f(a, b + \Delta y) = f_x(u, b + \Delta y)\,\Delta x$$

This gives us an expression for the first part of the right side of Equation 1. For the second part we let $h(y) = f(a, y)$. Then h is a function of a single variable defined on the interval $[b, b + \Delta y]$ and $h'(y) = f_y(a, y)$. A second application of the Mean Value Theorem then gives

$$h(b + \Delta y) - h(b) = h'(v)\,\Delta y$$

where v is some number between b and $b + \Delta y$. In terms of f, this becomes

$$f(a, b + \Delta y) - f(a, b) = f_y(a, v)\,\Delta y$$

We now substitute these expressions into Equation 3 and obtain

$$\Delta z = f_x(u, b + \Delta y)\, \Delta x + f_y(a, v)\, \Delta y$$

$$= f_x(a, b)\, \Delta x + [f_x(u, b + \Delta y) - f_x(a, b)]\, \Delta x + f_y(a, b)\, \Delta y$$

$$+ [f_y(a, v) - f_y(a, b)]\, \Delta y$$

$$= f_x(a, b)\, \Delta x + f_y(a, b)\, \Delta y + \varepsilon_1\, \Delta x + \varepsilon_2\, \Delta y$$

where
$$\varepsilon_1 = f_x(u, b + \Delta y) - f_x(a, b)$$

$$\varepsilon_2 = f_y(a, v) - f_y(a, b)$$

Since $(u, b + \Delta y) \to (a, b)$ and $(a, v) \to (a, b)$ as $(\Delta x, \Delta y) \to (0, 0)$ and since f_x and f_y are continuous at (a, b), we see that $\varepsilon_1 \to 0$ and $\varepsilon_2 \to 0$ as $(\Delta x, \Delta y) \to (0, 0)$.

Therefore, f is differentiable at (a, b). ▬

▌▌▌ G Complex Numbers

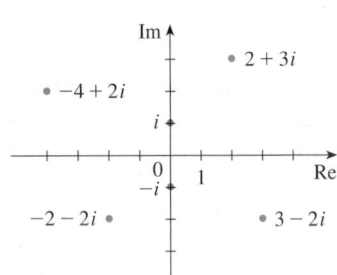

FIGURE 1

Complex numbers as points in the Argand plane

A **complex number** can be represented by an expression of the form $a + bi$, where a and b are real numbers and i is a symbol with the property that $i^2 = -1$. The complex number $a + bi$ can also be represented by the ordered pair (a, b) and plotted as a point in a plane (called the Argand plane) as in Figure 1. Thus, the complex number $i = 0 + 1 \cdot i$ is identified with the point $(0, 1)$.

The **real part** of the complex number $a + bi$ is the real number a and the **imaginary part** is the real number b. Thus, the real part of $4 - 3i$ is 4 and the imaginary part is -3. Two complex numbers $a + bi$ and $c + di$ are **equal** if $a = c$ and $b = d$, that is, their real parts are equal and their imaginary parts are equal. In the Argand plane the horizontal axis is called the real axis and the vertical axis is called the imaginary axis.

The sum and difference of two complex numbers are defined by adding or subtracting their real parts and their imaginary parts:

$$(a + bi) + (c + di) = (a + c) + (b + d)i$$

$$(a + bi) - (c + di) = (a - c) + (b - d)i$$

For instance,

$$(1 - i) + (4 + 7i) = (1 + 4) + (-1 + 7)i = 5 + 6i$$

The product of complex numbers is defined so that the usual commutative and distributive laws hold:

$$(a + bi)(c + di) = a(c + di) + (bi)(c + di)$$

$$= ac + adi + bci + bdi^2$$

Since $i^2 = -1$, this becomes

$$(a + bi)(c + di) = (ac - bd) + (ad + bc)i$$

EXAMPLE 1

$$(-1 + 3i)(2 - 5i) = (-1)(2 - 5i) + 3i(2 - 5i)$$

$$= -2 + 5i + 6i - 15(-1) = 13 + 11i$$ ▬

Division of complex numbers is much like rationalizing the denominator of a rational expression. For the complex number $z = a + bi$, we define its **complex conjugate** to be $\bar{z} = a - bi$. To find the quotient of two complex numbers we multiply numerator and denominator by the complex conjugate of the denominator.

EXAMPLE 2 Express the number $\dfrac{-1 + 3i}{2 + 5i}$ in the form $a + bi$.

SOLUTION We multiply numerator and denominator by the complex conjugate of $2 + 5i$, namely $2 - 5i$, and we take advantage of the result of Example 1:

$$\frac{-1 + 3i}{2 + 5i} = \frac{-1 + 3i}{2 + 5i} \cdot \frac{2 - 5i}{2 - 5i} = \frac{13 + 11i}{2^2 + 5^2} = \frac{13}{29} + \frac{11}{29}\,i$$

The geometric interpretation of the complex conjugate is shown in Figure 2: $\bar{z}$ is the reflection of z in the real axis. We list some of the properties of the complex conjugate in the following box. The proofs follow from the definition and are requested in Exercise 18.

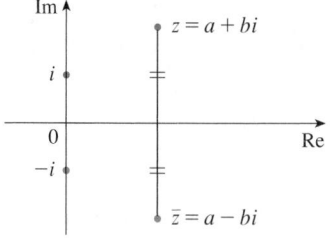

FIGURE 2

> **Properties of Conjugates**
>
> $$\overline{z + w} = \bar{z} + \bar{w} \qquad \overline{zw} = \bar{z}\,\bar{w} \qquad \overline{z^n} = \bar{z}^{\,n}$$

The **modulus**, or **absolute value**, $|z|$ of a complex number $z = a + bi$ is its distance from the origin. From Figure 3 we see that if $z = a + bi$, then

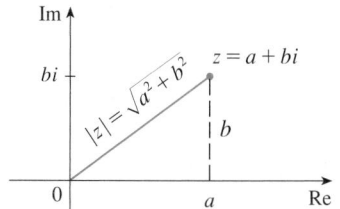

FIGURE 3

$$\boxed{\,|z| = \sqrt{a^2 + b^2}\,}$$

Notice that

$$z\bar{z} = (a + bi)(a - bi) = a^2 + abi - abi - b^2i^2 = a^2 + b^2$$

and so

$$\boxed{\,z\bar{z} = |z|^2\,}$$

This explains why the division procedure in Example 2 works in general:

$$\frac{z}{w} = \frac{z\bar{w}}{w\bar{w}} = \frac{z\bar{w}}{|w|^2}$$

Since $i^2 = -1$, we can think of i as a square root of -1. But notice that we also have $(-i)^2 = i^2 = -1$ and so $-i$ is also a square root of -1. We say that i is the **principal square root** of -1 and write $\sqrt{-1} = i$. In general, if c is any positive number, we write

$$\sqrt{-c} = \sqrt{c}\,i$$

With this convention, the usual derivation and formula for the roots of the quadratic equation $ax^2 + bx + c = 0$ are valid even when $b^2 - 4ac < 0$:

$$x = \frac{-b \pm \sqrt{b^2 - 4ac}}{2a}$$

EXAMPLE 3 Find the roots of the equation $x^2 + x + 1 = 0$.

SOLUTION Using the quadratic formula, we have

$$x = \frac{-1 \pm \sqrt{1^2 - 4 \cdot 1}}{2} = \frac{-1 \pm \sqrt{-3}}{2} = \frac{-1 \pm \sqrt{3}i}{2}$$

We observe that the solutions of the equation in Example 3 are complex conjugates of each other. In general, the solutions of any quadratic equation $ax^2 + bx + c = 0$ with real coefficients a, b, and c are always complex conjugates. (If z is real, $\bar{z} = z$, so z is its own conjugate.)

We have seen that if we allow complex numbers as solutions, then every quadratic equation has a solution. More generally, it is true that every polynomial equation

$$a_n x^n + a_{n-1} x^{n-1} + \cdots + a_1 x + a_0 = 0$$

of degree at least one has a solution among the complex numbers. This fact is known as the Fundamental Theorem of Algebra and was proved by Gauss.

‖‖ Polar Form

We know that any complex number $z = a + bi$ can be considered as a point (a, b) and that any such point can be represented by polar coordinates (r, θ) with $r \geqslant 0$. In fact,

$$a = r \cos \theta \qquad b = r \sin \theta$$

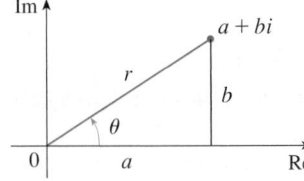

FIGURE 4

as in Figure 4. Therefore, we have

$$z = a + bi = (r \cos \theta) + (r \sin \theta)i$$

Thus, we can write any complex number z in the form

$$z = r(\cos \theta + i \sin \theta)$$

where $$r = |z| = \sqrt{a^2 + b^2} \qquad \text{and} \qquad \tan \theta = \frac{b}{a}$$

The angle θ is called the **argument** of z and we write $\theta = \arg(z)$. Note that $\arg(z)$ is not unique; any two arguments of z differ by an integer multiple of 2π.

EXAMPLE 4 Write the following numbers in polar form.
(a) $z = 1 + i$ \hfill (b) $w = \sqrt{3} - i$

SOLUTION
(a) We have $r = |z| = \sqrt{1^2 + 1^2} = \sqrt{2}$ and $\tan \theta = 1$, so we can take $\theta = \pi/4$. Therefore, the polar form is

$$z = \sqrt{2}\left(\cos \frac{\pi}{4} + i \sin \frac{\pi}{4}\right)$$

(b) Here we have $r = |w| = \sqrt{3 + 1} = 2$ and $\tan \theta = -1/\sqrt{3}$. Since w lies in the

FIGURE 5

FIGURE 6

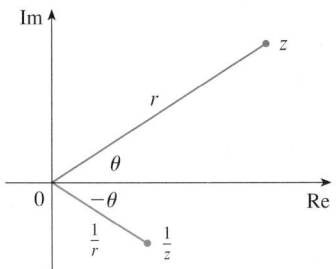

FIGURE 7

fourth quadrant, we take $\theta = -\pi/6$ and

$$w = 2\left[\cos\left(-\frac{\pi}{6}\right) + i \sin\left(-\frac{\pi}{6}\right)\right]$$

The numbers z and w are shown in Figure 5.

The polar form of complex numbers gives insight into multiplication and division. Let

$$z_1 = r_1(\cos\theta_1 + i \sin\theta_1) \qquad z_2 = r_2(\cos\theta_2 + i \sin\theta_2)$$

be two complex numbers written in polar form. Then

$$z_1 z_2 = r_1 r_2(\cos\theta_1 + i \sin\theta_1)(\cos\theta_2 + i \sin\theta_2)$$
$$= r_1 r_2[(\cos\theta_1 \cos\theta_2 - \sin\theta_1 \sin\theta_2) + i(\sin\theta_1 \cos\theta_2 + \cos\theta_1 \sin\theta_2)]$$

Therefore, using the addition formulas for cosine and sine, we have

$$\boxed{1} \qquad \boxed{z_1 z_2 = r_1 r_2[\cos(\theta_1 + \theta_2) + i \sin(\theta_1 + \theta_2)]}$$

This formula says that *to multiply two complex numbers we multiply the moduli and add the arguments.* (See Figure 6.)

A similar argument using the subtraction formulas for sine and cosine shows that *to divide two complex numbers we divide the moduli and subtract the arguments.*

$$\frac{z_1}{z_2} = \frac{r_1}{r_2}[\cos(\theta_1 - \theta_2) + i \sin(\theta_1 - \theta_2)] \qquad z_2 \neq 0$$

In particular, taking $z_1 = 1$ and $z_2 = z$ (and therefore $\theta_1 = 0$ and $\theta_2 = \theta$), we have the following, which is illustrated in Figure 7.

$$\text{If} \quad z = r(\cos\theta + i \sin\theta), \quad \text{then} \quad \frac{1}{z} = \frac{1}{r}(\cos\theta - i \sin\theta).$$

EXAMPLE 5 Find the product of the complex numbers $1 + i$ and $\sqrt{3} - i$ in polar form.

SOLUTION From Example 4 we have

$$1 + i = \sqrt{2}\left(\cos\frac{\pi}{4} + i \sin\frac{\pi}{4}\right)$$

and

$$\sqrt{3} - i = 2\left[\cos\left(-\frac{\pi}{6}\right) + i \sin\left(-\frac{\pi}{6}\right)\right]$$

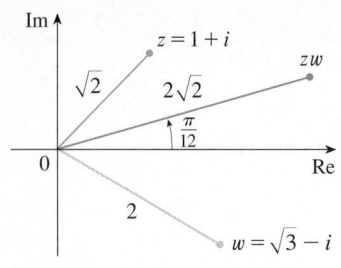

FIGURE 8

So, by Equation 1,

$$(1 + i)(\sqrt{3} - i) = 2\sqrt{2}\left[\cos\left(\frac{\pi}{4} - \frac{\pi}{6}\right) + i\sin\left(\frac{\pi}{4} - \frac{\pi}{6}\right)\right]$$

$$= 2\sqrt{2}\left(\cos\frac{\pi}{12} + i\sin\frac{\pi}{12}\right)$$

This is illustrated in Figure 8.

Repeated use of Formula 1 shows how to compute powers of a complex number. If

$$z = r(\cos\theta + i\sin\theta)$$

then

$$z^2 = r^2(\cos 2\theta + i\sin 2\theta)$$

and

$$z^3 = zz^2 = r^3(\cos 3\theta + i\sin 3\theta)$$

In general, we obtain the following result, which is named after the French mathematician Abraham De Moivre (1667–1754).

> **2 De Moivre's Theorem** If $z = r(\cos\theta + i\sin\theta)$ and n is a positive integer, then
>
> $$z^n = [r(\cos\theta + i\sin\theta)]^n = r^n(\cos n\theta + i\sin n\theta)$$

This says that *to take the nth power of a complex number we take the nth power of the modulus and multiply the argument by n.*

EXAMPLE 6 Find $\left(\frac{1}{2} + \frac{1}{2}i\right)^{10}$.

SOLUTION Since $\frac{1}{2} + \frac{1}{2}i = \frac{1}{2}(1 + i)$, it follows from Example 4(a) that $\frac{1}{2} + \frac{1}{2}i$ has the polar form

$$\frac{1}{2} + \frac{1}{2}i = \frac{\sqrt{2}}{2}\left(\cos\frac{\pi}{4} + i\sin\frac{\pi}{4}\right)$$

So by De Moivre's Theorem,

$$\left(\frac{1}{2} + \frac{1}{2}i\right)^{10} = \left(\frac{\sqrt{2}}{2}\right)^{10}\left(\cos\frac{10\pi}{4} + i\sin\frac{10\pi}{4}\right)$$

$$= \frac{2^5}{2^{10}}\left(\cos\frac{5\pi}{2} + i\sin\frac{5\pi}{2}\right) = \frac{1}{32}i$$

De Moivre's Theorem can also be used to find the nth roots of complex numbers. An nth root of the complex number z is a complex number w such that

$$w^n = z$$

Writing these two numbers in trigonometric form as

$$w = s(\cos\phi + i\sin\phi) \qquad \text{and} \qquad z = r(\cos\theta + i\sin\theta)$$

and using De Moivre's Theorem, we get

$$s^n(\cos n\phi + i \sin n\phi) = r(\cos \theta + i \sin \theta)$$

The equality of these two complex numbers shows that

$$s^n = r \quad \text{or} \quad s = r^{1/n}$$

and $\qquad\qquad \cos n\phi = \cos \theta \quad \text{and} \quad \sin n\phi = \sin \theta$

From the fact that sine and cosine have period 2π it follows that

$$n\phi = \theta + 2k\pi \quad \text{or} \quad \phi = \frac{\theta + 2k\pi}{n}$$

Thus $\qquad\qquad w = r^{1/n}\left[\cos\left(\frac{\theta + 2k\pi}{n}\right) + i \sin\left(\frac{\theta + 2k\pi}{n}\right)\right]$

Since this expression gives a different value of w for $k = 0, 1, 2, \ldots, n - 1$, we have the following.

> **3** **Roots of a Complex Number** Let $z = r(\cos \theta + i \sin \theta)$ and let n be a positive integer. Then z has the n distinct nth roots
>
> $$w_k = r^{1/n}\left[\cos\left(\frac{\theta + 2k\pi}{n}\right) + i \sin\left(\frac{\theta + 2k\pi}{n}\right)\right]$$
>
> where $k = 0, 1, 2, \ldots, n - 1$.

Notice that each of the nth roots of z has modulus $|w_k| = r^{1/n}$. Thus, all the nth roots of z lie on the circle of radius $r^{1/n}$ in the complex plane. Also, since the argument of each successive nth root exceeds the argument of the previous root by $2\pi/n$, we see that the nth roots of z are equally spaced on this circle.

EXAMPLE 7 Find the six sixth roots of $z = -8$ and graph these roots in the complex plane.

SOLUTION In trigonometric form, $z = 8(\cos \pi + i \sin \pi)$. Applying Equation 3 with $n = 6$, we get

$$w_k = 8^{1/6}\left(\cos \frac{\pi + 2k\pi}{6} + i \sin \frac{\pi + 2k\pi}{6}\right)$$

We get the six sixth roots of -8 by taking $k = 0, 1, 2, 3, 4, 5$ in this formula:

$$w_0 = 8^{1/6}\left(\cos \frac{\pi}{6} + i \sin \frac{\pi}{6}\right) = \sqrt{2}\left(\frac{\sqrt{3}}{2} + \frac{1}{2}i\right)$$

$$w_1 = 8^{1/6}\left(\cos \frac{\pi}{2} + i \sin \frac{\pi}{2}\right) = \sqrt{2}\,i$$

$$w_2 = 8^{1/6}\left(\cos \frac{5\pi}{6} + i \sin \frac{5\pi}{6}\right) = \sqrt{2}\left(-\frac{\sqrt{3}}{2} + \frac{1}{2}i\right)$$

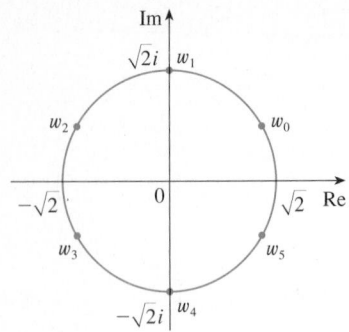

FIGURE 9
The six sixth roots of $z = -8$

$$w_3 = 8^{1/6}\left(\cos\frac{7\pi}{6} + i\sin\frac{7\pi}{6}\right) = \sqrt{2}\left(-\frac{\sqrt{3}}{2} - \frac{1}{2}i\right)$$

$$w_4 = 8^{1/6}\left(\cos\frac{3\pi}{2} + i\sin\frac{3\pi}{2}\right) = -\sqrt{2}\,i$$

$$w_5 = 8^{1/6}\left(\cos\frac{11\pi}{6} + i\sin\frac{11\pi}{6}\right) = \sqrt{2}\left(\frac{\sqrt{3}}{2} - \frac{1}{2}i\right)$$

All these points lie on the circle of radius $\sqrt{2}$ as shown in Figure 9.

||| **Complex Exponentials**

We also need to give a meaning to the expression e^z when $z = x + iy$ is a complex number. The theory of infinite series as developed in Chapter 12 can be extended to the case where the terms are complex numbers. Using the Taylor series for e^x (12.10.11) as our guide, we define

$$\boxed{4} \qquad e^z = \sum_{n=0}^{\infty} \frac{z^n}{n!} = 1 + z + \frac{z^2}{2!} + \frac{z^3}{3!} + \cdots$$

and it turns out that this complex exponential function has the same properties as the real exponential function. In particular, it is true that

$$\boxed{5} \qquad e^{z_1+z_2} = e^{z_1}e^{z_2}$$

If we put $z = iy$, where y is a real number, in Equation 4, and use the facts that

$$i^2 = -1, \quad i^3 = i^2 i = -i, \quad i^4 = 1, \quad i^5 = i, \quad \ldots$$

we get

$$e^{iy} = 1 + iy + \frac{(iy)^2}{2!} + \frac{(iy)^3}{3!} + \frac{(iy)^4}{4!} + \frac{(iy)^5}{5!} + \cdots$$

$$= 1 + iy - \frac{y^2}{2!} - i\frac{y^3}{3!} + \frac{y^4}{4!} + i\frac{y^5}{5!} + \cdots$$

$$= \left(1 - \frac{y^2}{2!} + \frac{y^4}{4!} - \frac{y^6}{6!} + \cdots\right) + i\left(y - \frac{y^3}{3!} + \frac{y^5}{5!} - \cdots\right)$$

$$= \cos y + i\sin y$$

Here we have used the Taylor series for $\cos y$ and $\sin y$ (Equations 12.10.16 and 12.10.15). The result is a famous formula called **Euler's formula**:

$$\boxed{6} \qquad \boxed{e^{iy} = \cos y + i\sin y}$$

Combining Euler's formula with Equation 5, we get

$$\boxed{7} \qquad e^{x+iy} = e^x e^{iy} = e^x(\cos y + i\sin y)$$

EXAMPLE 8 Evaluate: (a) $e^{i\pi}$ (b) $e^{-1+i\pi/2}$

SOLUTION

IIII We could write the result of Example 8(a) as

$$e^{i\pi} + 1 = 0$$

This equation relates the five most famous numbers in all of mathematics: 0, 1, e, i, and π.

(a) From Euler's equation (6) we have

$$e^{i\pi} = \cos \pi + i \sin \pi = -1 + i(0) = -1$$

(b) Using Equation 7 we get

$$e^{-1+i\pi/2} = e^{-1}\left(\cos \frac{\pi}{2} + i \sin \frac{\pi}{2}\right) = \frac{1}{e}[0 + i(1)] = \frac{i}{e}$$

Finally, we note that Euler's equation provides us with an easier method of proving De Moivre's Theorem:

$$[r(\cos \theta + i \sin \theta)]^n = (re^{i\theta})^n = r^n e^{in\theta} = r^n(\cos n\theta + i \sin n\theta)$$

G Exercises

1–14 ▓ Evaluate the expression and write your answer in the form $a + bi$.

1. $(5 - 6i) + (3 + 2i)$

2. $(4 - \frac{1}{2}i) - (9 + \frac{5}{2}i)$

3. $(2 + 5i)(4 - i)$

4. $(1 - 2i)(8 - 3i)$

5. $\overline{12 + 7i}$

6. $2i(\frac{1}{2} - i)$

7. $\dfrac{1 + 4i}{3 + 2i}$

8. $\dfrac{3 + 2i}{1 - 4i}$

9. $\dfrac{1}{1 + i}$

10. $\dfrac{3}{4 - 3i}$

11. i^3

12. i^{100}

13. $\sqrt{-25}$

14. $\sqrt{-3}\sqrt{-12}$

15–17 ▓ Find the complex conjugate and the modulus of the number.

15. $12 - 5i$

16. $-1 + 2\sqrt{2}\,i$

17. $-4i$

18. Prove the following properties of complex numbers.
(a) $\overline{z + w} = \bar{z} + \bar{w}$ (b) $\overline{zw} = \bar{z}\,\bar{w}$
(c) $\overline{z^n} = \bar{z}^n$, where n is a positive integer
    [*Hint:* Write $z = a + bi$, $w = c + di$.]

19–24 ▓ Find all solutions of the equation.

19. $4x^2 + 9 = 0$

20. $x^4 = 1$

21. $x^2 + 2x + 5 = 0$

22. $2x^2 - 2x + 1 = 0$

23. $z^2 + z + 2 = 0$

24. $z^2 + \frac{1}{2}z + \frac{1}{4} = 0$

25–28 ▓ Write the number in polar form with argument between 0 and 2π.

25. $-3 + 3i$ **26.** $1 - \sqrt{3}i$ **27.** $3 + 4i$ **28.** $8i$

29–32 ▓ Find polar forms for zw, z/w, and $1/z$ by first putting z and w into polar form.

29. $z = \sqrt{3} + i$, $w = 1 + \sqrt{3}i$

30. $z = 4\sqrt{3} - 4i$, $w = 8i$

31. $z = 2\sqrt{3} - 2i$, $w = -1 + i$

32. $z = 4(\sqrt{3} + i)$, $w = -3 - 3i$

33–36 ▓ Find the indicated power using De Moivre's Theorem.

33. $(1 + i)^{20}$ **34.** $(1 - \sqrt{3}i)^5$ **35.** $(2\sqrt{3} + 2i)^5$ **36.** $(1 - i)^8$

37–40 ▓ Find the indicated roots. Sketch the roots in the complex plane.

37. The eighth roots of 1   **38.** The fifth roots of 32

39. The cube roots of i **40.** The cube roots of $1 + i$

41–46 ▓ Write the number in the form $a + bi$.

41. $e^{i\pi/2}$ **42.** $e^{2\pi i}$ **43.** $e^{i\pi/3}$

44. $e^{-i\pi}$ **45.** $e^{2+i\pi}$ **46.** $e^{\pi+i}$

47. If $u(x) = f(x) + ig(x)$ is a complex-valued function of a real variable x and the real and imaginary parts $f(x)$ and $g(x)$ are differentiable functions of x, then the derivative of u is defined to be $u'(x) = f'(x) + ig'(x)$. Use this together with Equation 7 to prove that if $F(x) = e^{rx}$, then $F'(x) = re^{rx}$ when $r = a + bi$ is a complex number.

48. (a) If u is a complex-valued function of a real variable, its indefinite integral $\int u(x)\, dx$ is an antiderivative of u. Evaluate

$$\int e^{(1+i)x}\, dx$$

(b) By considering the real and imaginary parts of the integral in part (a), evaluate the real integrals

$$\int e^x \cos x\, dx \quad \text{and} \quad \int e^x \sin x\, dx$$

(c) Compare with the method used in Example 4 in Section 8.1.

27. A. $\mathbb{R}$ **B.** y-int. -2
C. About y-axis, period 2π **D.** None
E. Inc. on $(2n\pi, (2n + 1)\pi)$, n an integer; dec. on $((2n - 1)\pi, 2n\pi)$
F. Loc. max. $f((2n + 1)\pi) = 2$; loc. min. $f(2n\pi) = -2$
G. CU on $(2n\pi - (\pi/3), 2n\pi + (\pi/3))$;
CD on $(2n\pi + (\pi/3), 2n\pi + (5\pi/3))$; IP $\left(2n\pi \pm (\pi/3), -\frac{1}{4}\right)$
H.

29. Inc. on $(-\sqrt{3}, 0)$, $(0, \sqrt{3})$;
dec. on $(-\infty, -\sqrt{3})$, $(\sqrt{3}, \infty)$;
loc. max. $f(\sqrt{3}) = \frac{2}{9}\sqrt{3}$,
loc. min. $f(-\sqrt{3}) = -\frac{2}{9}\sqrt{3}$;
CU on $(-\sqrt{6}, 0)$, $(\sqrt{6}, \infty)$;
CD on $(-\infty, -\sqrt{6})$, $(0, \sqrt{6})$;
IP $\left(\sqrt{6}, \frac{5}{36}\sqrt{6}\right)$, $\left(-\sqrt{6}, -\frac{5}{36}\sqrt{6}\right)$

31. Inc. on $(-0.23, 0)$, $(1.62, \infty)$; dec. on $(-\infty, -0.23)$, $(0, 1.62)$;
loc. max. $f(0) = 2$; loc. min. $f(-0.23) \approx 1.96$, $f(1.62) \approx -19.2$;
CU on $(-\infty, -0.12)$, $(1.24, \infty)$; CD on $(-0.12, 1.24)$;
IP $(-0.12, 1.98)$, $(1.24, -12.1)$

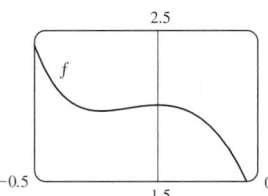

37. (a) 0   (b) CU on $\mathbb{R}$
41. $3\sqrt{3}\,r^2$ **43.** $4/\sqrt{3}$ cm from D **45.** $L = C$
47. $11.50   **49.** 1.297383   **51.** 1.16718557
53. $f(x) = \frac{2}{7}x^{7/2} - 5x^{4/5} + C$
55. $f(t) = t^2 + 3\cos t + 2$
57. $f(x) = \frac{1}{2}x^2 - x^3 + 4x^4 + 2x + 1$
59.

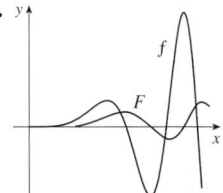

61. No
63. (a) $20\sqrt{2} \approx 28$ ft   (b) $\dfrac{dI}{dt} = \dfrac{-480k(h - 4)}{[(h - 4)^2 + 1600]^{5/2}}$, where k is the constant of proportionality

Problems Plus □ **page 312**

5. $(-2, 4)$, $(2, -4)$ **7.** $\frac{4}{3}$ **9.** $(m/2, m^2/4)$
11. $-3.5 < a < -2.5$ **13.** (a) $x/(x^2 + 1)$ (b) $\frac{1}{2}$

15. (a) $-\tan\theta\left[\dfrac{1}{c}\dfrac{dc}{dt} + \dfrac{1}{b}\dfrac{db}{dt}\right]$

(b) $\dfrac{b\dfrac{db}{dt} + c\dfrac{dc}{dt} - \left(b\dfrac{dc}{dt} + c\dfrac{db}{dt}\right)\sec\theta}{\sqrt{b^2 + c^2 - 2bc\cos\theta}}$

17. (a) $T_1 = D/c_1$, $T_2 = (2h\sec\theta)/c_1 + (D - 2h\tan\theta)/c_2$,
$T_3 = \sqrt{4h^2 + D^2}/c_1$
(c) $c_1 \approx 3.85$ km/s, $c_2 \approx 7.66$ km/s, $h \approx 0.42$ km
21. $3/(\sqrt[3]{2} - 1) \approx 11\frac{1}{2}$ h

▏▏▏ **Chapter 5**

Exercises 5.1 □ **page 324**
1. (a) 40, 52

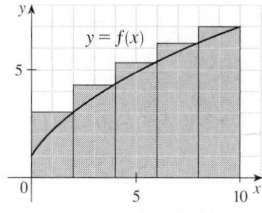

(b) 43.2, 49.2

3. (a) $\frac{77}{60}$, underestimate   (b) $\frac{25}{12}$, overestimate

5. (a) 8, 6.875

(b) 5, 5.375

(c) 5.75, 5.9375

(d) M_6

7. 1.9835, 1.9982, 1.9993; 2

9. (a) Left: 4.5148, 4.6165, 4.6366; right: 4.8148, 4.7165, 4.6966

11. 34.7 ft, 44.8 ft   **13.** 63.2 L, 70 L   **15.** 155 ft

17. $\lim\limits_{n\to\infty} \sum\limits_{i=1}^{n} \sqrt[4]{1 + 15i/n} \cdot (15/n)$

19. $\lim\limits_{n\to\infty} \sum\limits_{i=1}^{n} \left(\dfrac{i\pi}{2n} \cos \dfrac{i\pi}{2n}\right) \dfrac{\pi}{2n}$

21. The region under the graph of $y = \tan x$ from 0 to $\pi/4$

23. (a) $\lim\limits_{n\to\infty} \dfrac{64}{n^6} \sum\limits_{i=1}^{n} i^5$ (b) $\dfrac{n^2(n+1)^2(2n^2+2n-1)}{12}$ (c) $\dfrac{32}{3}$

25. $\sin b$, 1

Exercises 5.2 □ **page 390**

1. 0.25

The Riemann sum represents
the sum of the areas of the
two rectangles above the
x-axis minus the sum of the
areas of the two rectangles
below the x-axis.

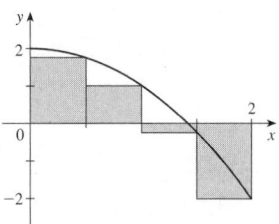

3. -0.856759

The Riemann sum represents
the sum of the areas of the
two rectangles above the
x-axis minus the sum of the
areas of the three rectangles
below the x-axis.

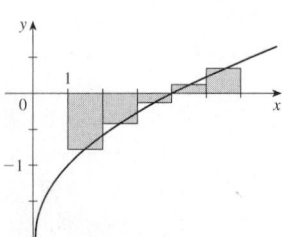

5. (a) 4   (b) 6   (c) 10   **7.** $-475, -85$ **9.** 124.1644

11. 0.3084   **13.** 0.30843908, 0.30981629, 0.31015563

15.

n	R_n
5	1.933766
10	1.983524
50	1.999342
100	1.999836

The values of R_n appear to be approaching 2.

17. $\int_0^\pi x \sin x\, dx$ **19.** $\int_1^8 \sqrt{2x + x^2}\, dx$ **21.** 42   **23.** $\frac{4}{3}$

25. 3.75   **29.** $\lim\limits_{n\to\infty} \sum\limits_{i=1}^{n} \dfrac{2 + 4i/n}{1 + (2 + 4i/n)^5} \cdot \dfrac{4}{n}$

31. $\lim\limits_{n\to\infty} \sum\limits_{i=1}^{n} \left(\sin \dfrac{5\pi i}{n}\right) \dfrac{\pi}{n} = \dfrac{2}{5}$

33. (a) 4   (b) 10   (c) -3 (d) 2   **35.** $-\frac{3}{4}$

37. $3 + \frac{9}{4}\pi$ **39.** 2.5   **41.** $-\frac{38}{3}$

43. 3   **45.** 22.5

47. $\int_{-1}^{5} f(x)\, dx$ **49.** 122   **55.** $\frac{1}{2} \le \int_1^2 dx/x \le 1$

57. $\dfrac{\pi}{12} \le \int_{\pi/4}^{\pi/3} \tan x\, dx \le \dfrac{\pi}{12}\sqrt{3}$

59. $2 \le \int_{-1}^{1} \sqrt{1 + x^4}\, dx \le 2\sqrt{2}$ **67.** $\int_0^1 x^4\, dx$ **69.** $\frac{1}{2}$

Exercises 5.3 □ **page 347**

1. One process undoes what the other one does. See the
Fundamental Theorem of Calculus, page 347.

3. (a) 0, 2, 5, 7, 3   (d)
(b) (0, 3)
(c) $x = 3$

5.   (a), (b) x^2

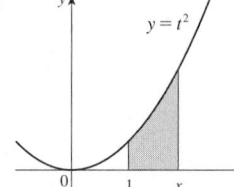

7. $g'(x) = \sqrt{1 + 2x}$ **9.** $g'(y) = y^2 \sin y$

11. $F'(x) = -\cos(x^2)$ **13.** $h'(x) = -\sin^4(1/x)/x^2$

15. $y' = \dfrac{\cos\sqrt{x}}{2x}$ **17.** $y' = \dfrac{3(1 - 3x)^3}{1 + (1 - 3x)^2}$ **19.** $\frac{364}{3}$

21. 138   **23.** $\frac{5}{9}$ **25.** $\frac{7}{8}$ **27.** Does not exist

29. $\frac{156}{7}$ **31.** 1   **33.** Does not exist   **35.** 10.7

37. $\frac{243}{4}$ **39.** 2   **41.** 3.75

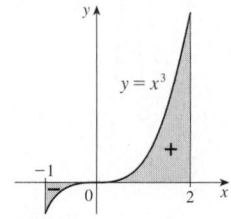

43. $g'(x) = \dfrac{-2(4x^2 - 1)}{4x^2 + 1} + \dfrac{3(9x^2 - 1)}{9x^2 + 1}$

45. $y' = 3x^{7/2} \sin(x^3) - (\sin\sqrt{x})/(2\sqrt[4]{x})$ **47.** $\sqrt{257}$

49. (a) $-2\sqrt{n}$, $\sqrt{4n - 2}$, n an integer > 0
(b) (0, 1), $\left(-\sqrt{4n-1}, -\sqrt{4n-3}\right)$, and $\left(\sqrt{4n-1}, \sqrt{4n+1}\right)$,
n an integer > 0
(c) 0.74

51. (a) Loc. max. at 1 and 5;
loc. min. at 3 and 7

(b) 9

(c) $\left(\frac{1}{2}, 2\right)$, $(4, 6)$, $(8, 9)$

(d) See graph at right.

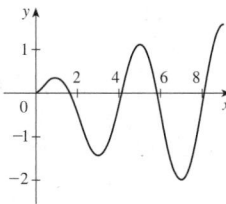

53. $\frac{1}{4}$ **59.** $f(x) = x^{3/2}, a = 9$
61. (b) Average expenditure over $[0, t]$; minimize average
expenditure
63. ln 3 **65.** π **67.** $e^2 - 1$

Exercises 5.4 □ page 356

5. $4x^{1/4} + C$ **7.** $\frac{1}{4}x^4 + 3x^2 + x + C$
9. $2t - t^2 + \frac{1}{3}t^3 - \frac{1}{4}t^4 + C$
11. $4x - \frac{8}{3}x^{3/2} + \frac{1}{2}x^2 + C$ **13.** $\sec x + C$
15. $\frac{2}{5}x^{5/2} + C$

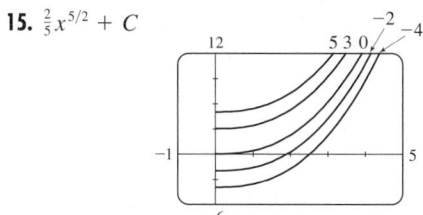

17. 18 **19.** 231 **21.** 52 **23.** $\frac{256}{15}$ **25.** $-\frac{63}{4}$
27. $\frac{55}{63}$ **29.** $2\sqrt{5}$ **31.** 8 **33.** $1 + \frac{1}{4}\pi$ **35.** $\frac{256}{5}$
37. 1 **39.** -3.5 **41.** 0, 1.32; 0.84 **43.** $\frac{4}{3}$
45. The increase in the child's weight (in pounds) between the
ages of 5 and 10
47. Number of gallons of oil leaked in the first 2 hours
49. Increase in revenue when production is increased from 1000
to 5000 units
51. Newton-meters (or joules) **53.** (a) $-\frac{3}{2}$ m (b) $\frac{41}{6}$ m
55. (a) $v(t) = \frac{1}{2}t^2 + 4t + 5$ m/s (b) $416\frac{2}{3}$ m
57. $46\frac{2}{3}$ kg **59.** 1.4 mi **61.** \$58,000
63. (b) At most 40%; $\frac{5}{36}$ **65.** $\frac{1}{2}e^2 + e - \frac{1}{2}$
67. $\frac{1}{3}x^3 + x + \tan^{-1}x + C$

Exercises 5.5 □ page 365

1. $\frac{1}{3}\sin 3x + C$ **3.** $\frac{2}{9}(x^3 + 1)^{3/2} + C$
5. $-1/(1 + 2x)^2 + C$ **7.** $\frac{1}{5}(x^2 + 3)^5 + C$
9. $\frac{1}{63}(3x - 2)^{21} + C$ **11.** $2\sqrt{1 + x + 2x^2} + C$
13. $\dfrac{-3}{8(2y + 1)^4} + C$ **15.** $-\frac{2}{3}(4 - t)^{3/2} + C$
17. $-(1/\pi)\cos \pi t + C$ **19.** $2\sin\sqrt{t} + C$
21. $\frac{1}{7}\sin^7\theta + C$ **23.** $\frac{1}{2}(1 + z^3)^{2/3} + C$
25. $-\frac{2}{3}(\cot x)^{3/2} + C$ **27.** $\frac{1}{3}\sec^3 x + C$
29. $\dfrac{2(b + cx^{a+1})^{3/2}}{3c(a + 1)} + C$
31. $\frac{4}{7}(x + 2)^{7/4} - \frac{8}{3}(x + 2)^{3/4} + C$

33. $\dfrac{-1}{6(3x^2 - 2x + 1)^3} + C$ **35.** $\frac{1}{4}\sin^4 x + C$

  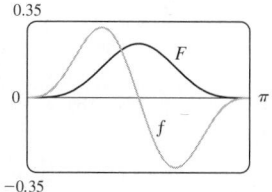

37. 0 **39.** $\frac{182}{9}$ **41.** 4 **43.** 0 **45.** 1 **47.** 3
49. $\frac{16}{15}$ **51.** Does not exist **53.** $\frac{1}{3}(2\sqrt{2} - 1)a^3$

55. $\sqrt{3} - \frac{1}{3}$ **57.** 6π **59.** $\dfrac{5}{4\pi}\left(1 - \cos\dfrac{2\pi t}{5}\right)$ L

61. 5 **67.** $-\frac{1}{3}\ln|5 - 3x| + C$ **69.** $\frac{1}{3}(\ln x)^3 + C$
71. $\frac{2}{3}(1 + e^x)^{3/2} + C$ **73.** $\ln|\ln x| + C$
75. $\ln|\sin x| + C$ **77.** $\tan^{-1}x + \frac{1}{2}\ln(1 + x^2) + C$
79. $e - \sqrt{e}$ **81.** 2 **83.** $\pi^2/4$

Chapter 5 Review □ page 368

True-False Quiz

1. True **3.** True **5.** False **7.** True **9.** True
11. False **13.** False

Exercises

1. (a) 8 (b) 5.7

  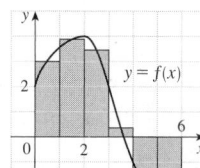

3. $\frac{1}{2} + \pi/4$ **5.** 3 **7.** $f = c, f' = b, \int_0^x f(t)\,dt = a$
9. 37 **11.** $\frac{9}{10}$ **13.** -76 **15.** $\frac{21}{4}$ **17.** Does not exist
19. $\frac{1}{3}\sin 1$ **21.** $\sqrt{x^2 + 4x} + C$ **23.** $[1/(2\pi)]\sin^2\pi t + C$
25. $\frac{1}{2}\sqrt{2} - \frac{1}{2}$ **27.** $\frac{23}{3}$ **29.** $2\sqrt{1 + \sin x} + C$ **31.** $\frac{64}{5}$
33. $F'(x) = \sqrt{1 + x^4}$ **35.** $g'(x) = 3x^5/\sqrt{1 + x^9}$
37. $y' = (2\cos x - \cos\sqrt{x})/(2x)$
39. $4 \le \int_1^3 \sqrt{x^2 + 3}\,dx \le 4\sqrt{3}$ **43.** 1.11
45. Number of barrels of oil consumed from Jan. 1, 2000, through
Jan. 1, 2003
47. 72,400 **49.** $F(x) = \int_1^x t^2 \sin(t^2)\,dt$
51. $(1 + x^2)(x\cos x + \sin x)/x^2$

Problems Plus □ page 373

1. $\pi/2$ **5.** Does not exist **7.** -1 **9.** $[-1, 2]$
11. (a) $(n - 1)n/2$
(b) $\frac{1}{2}[\![b]\!](2b - [\![b]\!] - 1) - \frac{1}{2}[\![a]\!](2a - [\![a]\!] - 1)$
13. $f(x) = \frac{1}{2}x$ or $f(x) = 0$ **17.** $2(\sqrt{2} - 1)$

Chapter 6

Exercises 6.1 □ page 380

1. $\frac{32}{3}$ **3.** $\frac{4}{3}$ **5.** 19.5   **7.** $\frac{1}{6}$ **9.** $\frac{4}{3}$ **11.** $\frac{1}{3}$ **13.** 72
15. $\frac{59}{12}$ **17.** $\frac{9}{8}$ **19.** $\frac{8}{3}$ **21.** $\frac{1}{2}$ **23.** $2 - \pi/2$ **25.** $\frac{3}{2}$
27. 6.5   **29.** $\frac{1}{2}$

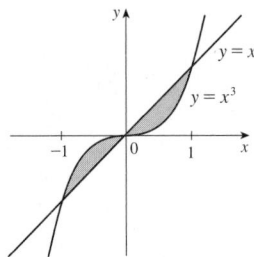

31. 0.6407   **33.** ± 1.02; 2.70   **35.** -0.72, 1.22; 1.38
37. $12\sqrt{6} - 9$ **39.** $117\frac{1}{3}$ ft
41. (a) Car A (b) The distance by which A is ahead of B after
1 minute   (c) Car A (d) $t \approx 2.2$ min
43. $24\sqrt{3}/5$ **45.** $4^{2/3}$ **47.** ± 6
49. $\ln 2 - \frac{1}{2}$ **51.** $\pi - \frac{2}{3}$

Exercises 6.2 □ page 391

1. $\pi/5$

3. $\pi/2$

5. 8π

7. $3\pi/10$

9. $64\pi/15$

11. $\pi/6$

13. $208\pi/45$

15. $16\pi/15$

17. $29\pi/30$

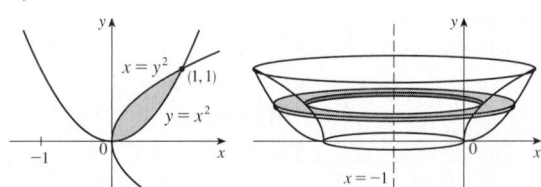

19. $\pi/7$ **21.** $\pi/10$ **23.** $\pi/2$ **25.** $7\pi/15$
27. $5\pi/14$ **29.** $13\pi/30$ **31.** $\pi \int_0^{\pi/4} (1 - \tan^3 x)^2 \, dx$
33. $\pi \int_0^\pi [1^2 - (1 - \sin x)^2] \, dx$
35. $\pi \int_{-\sqrt{8}}^{\sqrt{8}} \{[3 - (-2)]^2 - [\sqrt{y^2 + 1} - (-2)]^2\} \, dy$
37. -0.72, 1.22; 5.80   **39.** $\frac{11}{8}\pi^2$
41. Solid obtained by rotating the region $0 \leqslant y \leqslant \cos x$,
$0 \leqslant x \leqslant \pi/2$ about the x-axis
43. Solid obtained by rotating the region $y^4 \leqslant x \leqslant y^2$, $0 \leqslant y \leqslant 1$
about the y-axis
45. 1110 cm^3 **47.** $\pi r^2 h/3$ **49.** $\pi h^2[r - (h/3)]$
51. $2b^2 h/3$ **53.** 10 cm^3 **55.** 24   **57.** 2   **59.** 3
61. (a) $8\pi R \int_0^r \sqrt{r^2 - y^2} \, dy$ (b) $2\pi^2 r^2 R$
63. (b) $\pi r^2 h$ **65.** $\frac{5}{12}\pi r^3$ **67.** $8 \int_0^r \sqrt{R^2 - y^2}\sqrt{r^2 - y^2} \, dy$

Exercises 6.3 □ page 396

1. Circumference $= 2\pi x$, height $= x(x - 1)^2$; $\pi/15$

3. 2π

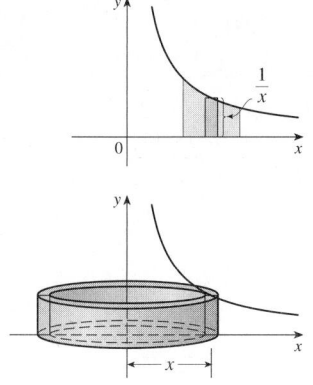

5. 8π **7.** 16π

9. $21\pi/2$

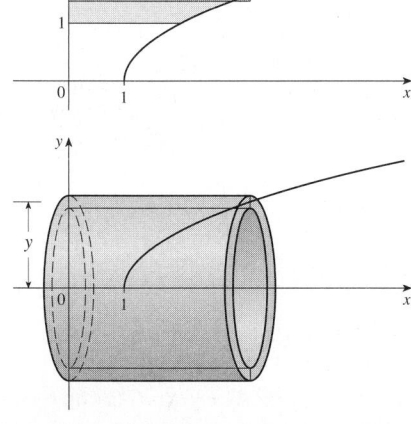

11. $768\pi/7$ **13.** $250\pi/3$

15. $17\pi/6$ **17.** $67\pi/6$ **19.** 24π **21.** $\int_{2\pi}^{3\pi} 2\pi x \sin x \, dx$

23. $\int_0^1 2\pi(x + 1)[\sin(\pi x/2) - x^4] \, dx$

25. $\int_0^\pi 2\pi(4 - y)\sqrt{\sin y} \, dy$ **27.** 1.142

29. Solid obtained by rotating the region $0 \le y \le x^4$, $0 \le x \le 3$ about the y-axis

31. Solid obtained by rotating the region bounded by
(i) $x = 1 - y^2$, $x = 0$, and $y = 0$, or (ii) $x = y^2$, $x = 1$, and $y = 0$ about the line $y = 3$

33. 0, 1.32; 4.05   **35.** $\frac{1}{32}\pi^3$ **37.** $81\pi/10$ **39.** $63\pi/2$

41. $4\pi/3$ **43.** $\frac{4}{3}\pi r^3$ **45.** $\frac{1}{3}\pi r^2 h$

Exercises 6.4 □ page 401

1. 7200 J   **3.** 9 ft-lb   **5.** 180 J

7. $\frac{15}{4}$ ft-lb   **9.** $\frac{25}{24} \approx 1.04$ J   **11.** 10.8 cm

13. (a) 625 ft-lb   (b) $\frac{1875}{4}$ ft-lb   **15.** 650,000 ft-lb

17. 3857 J   **19.** 2450 J   **21.** $\approx 1.06 \times 10^6$ J

23. $\approx 5.8 \times 10^3$ ft-lb   **25.** 2.0 m   **29.** $Gm_1 m_2[(1/a) - (1/b)]$

Exercises 6.5 □ page 405

1. $\frac{1}{3}$ **3.** $2/\pi$ **5.** $\frac{1}{15}(26^{3/2} - 1)$ **7.** $2/(5\pi)$

9. (a) 1   (b) 2, 4   (c)

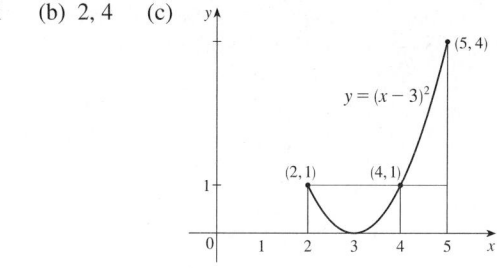

11. (a) $4/\pi$ (b) ≈ 1.24, 2.81

(c)

15. $38\frac{1}{3}$ **17.** $(50 + 28/\pi)°F \approx 59°F$

19. 6 kg/m   **21.** $5/(4\pi) \approx 0.4$ L

Chapter 6 Review □ page 406

Exercises

1. $\frac{125}{6}$ **3.** $\frac{1}{3}$ **5.** $\frac{4}{3} + 4/\pi$ **7.** $64\pi/15$ **9.** $1656\pi/5$

11. $\frac{4}{3}\pi(2ah + h^2)^{3/2}$ **13.** $\int_0^1 \pi[(1 - x^3)^2 - (1 - x^2)^2] \, dx$

15. (a) $2\pi/15$ (b) $\pi/6$ (c) $8\pi/15$

17. (a) 0.38   (b) 0.87

19. Solid obtained by rotating the region $0 \le y \le \cos x$, $0 \le x \le \pi/2$ about the y-axis

21. Solid obtained by rotating the region in the first quadrant bounded by $x = 4 - y^2$ and the axes about the x-axis

23. 36   **25.** $125\sqrt{3}/3$ m³   **27.** 3.2 J

29. (a) $8000\pi/3 \approx 8378$ ft-lb   (b) 2.1 ft   **31.** $f(x)$

Problems Plus □ **page 408**

1. (a) $f(t) = 3t^2$ (b) $f(x) = \sqrt{2x/\pi}$ **3.** $\frac{32}{27}$
5. (b) 0.2261   (c) 0.6736 m
(d) (i) $1/(105\pi) \approx 0.003$ in/s   (ii) $370\pi/3$ s ≈ 6.5 min
9. $y = \frac{32}{9}x^2$
11. (a) $V = \int_0^h \pi[f(y)]^2\, dy$
(c) $f(y) = \sqrt{kA/(\pi C)}\, y^{1/4}$
Advantage: the markings on the container are equally spaced.
13. $B = 16A$

|||| **Chapter 7**

Exercises 7.1 □ **page 420**

1. (a) See Definition 1.
(b) It must pass the Horizontal Line Test.
3. No   **5.** Yes   **7.** No   **9.** Yes   **11.** Yes   **13.** No
15. No   **17.** No   **19.** 2   **21.** 4
23. $F = \frac{9}{5}C + 32$; the Fahrenheit temperature as a function of the Celsius temperature; $[-273.15, \infty)$
25. $f^{-1}(x) = \frac{3}{2} - \frac{1}{2}x$ **27.** $f^{-1}(x) = -\frac{1}{3}x^2 + \frac{10}{3}$, $x \geq 0$
29. $y = \left(\dfrac{1-x}{1+x}\right)^2$, $-1 < x \leq 1$
31. $f^{-1}(x) = \sqrt{2/(1-x)}$ **33.**

35. (b) $\frac{1}{12}$
(c) $g(x) = \sqrt[3]{x}$,
domain $= \mathbb{R} =$ range
(e)

37. (b) $-\frac{1}{2}$
(c) $g(x) = \sqrt{9-x}$,
domain $= [0, 9]$,
range $= [0, 3]$
(e)

39. 1   **41.** $2/\pi$ **43.** $\frac{3}{2}$
45. $f^{-1}(x) =$
$-(\sqrt[3]{4}/6)(\sqrt[3]{D - 27x^2 + 20} - \sqrt[3]{D + 27x^2 - 20} + \sqrt[3]{2})$,
where $D = 3\sqrt{3}\sqrt{27x^4 - 40x^2 + 16}$; two of the expressions are complex.
47. (a) $g^{-1}(x) = f^{-1}(x) - c$ (b) $h^{-1}(x) = (1/c)f^{-1}(x)$

Exercises 7.2 □ **page 431**

1. (a) $f(x) = a^x, a > 0$ (b) $\mathbb{R}$ (c) $(0, \infty)$
(d) See Figures 4(c), 4(b), and 4(a), respectively.
3.

All approach 0 as $x \to -\infty$, all pass through $(0, 1)$, and all are increasing. The larger the base, the faster the rate of increase.

5.

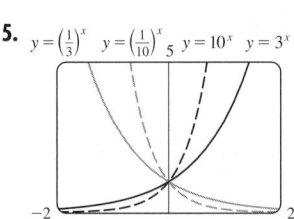

The functions with base greater than 1 are increasing and those with base less than 1 are decreasing. The latter are reflections of the former about the y-axis.

7.

9.

11.

13. (a) $y = e^x - 2$ (b) $y = e^{x-2}$ (c) $y = -e^x$
(d) $y = e^{-x}$ (e) $y = -e^{-x}$
15. (a) $(-\infty, \infty)$ (b) $(-\infty, 0) \cup (0, \infty)$
17. $f(x) = 3 \cdot 2^x$ **21.** At $x \approx 35.8$ **23.** ∞ **25.** 1
27. 0   **29.** $f'(x) = x(x+2)e^x$ **31.** $y' = 3ax^2 e^{ax^3}$
33. $f'(u) = (-1/u^2)e^{1/u}$ **35.** $F'(t) = e^{t\sin 2t}(2t\cos 2t + \sin 2t)$
37. $y' = 3e^{3x}/\sqrt{1 + 2e^{3x}}$ **39.** $y' = e^{e^x}e^x$
41. $y' = \dfrac{(ad - bc)e^x}{(ce^x + d)^2}$ **43.** $y = 2x + 1$
45. $y' = (1 - 2xye^{x^2y})/(x^2e^{x^2y} - 1)$ **49.** $-4, -2$
51. $f^{(n)}(x) = 2^n e^{2x}$ **53.** (b) -0.567143
55. (a) 7.92 mg   (b) -0.22 mg/yr   (c) 56.6 yr
57. (a) 1   (b) $kae^{-kt}/(1 + ae^{-kt})^2$
(c)

$t \approx 7.4$ h

59. (a) $y \approx 100.012437e^{-10.005531t}$ (b) $-670.63 \ \mu A$

61. -1

63. (a) Inc. on $(-1, \infty)$; dec. on $(-\infty, -1)$
(b) CU on $(-2, \infty)$; CD on $(-\infty, -2)$ (c) $(-2, -2e^{-2})$

65. A. $\{x \mid x \neq -1\}$
B. y-int. $1/e$ C. None
D. HA $y = 1$; VA $x = -1$
E. Inc. on $(-\infty, -1), (-1, \infty)$
F. None
G. CU on $(-\infty, -1), \left(-1, -\frac{1}{2}\right)$;
CD on $\left(-\frac{1}{2}, \infty\right)$; IP $\left(-\frac{1}{2}, 1/e^2\right)$
H. See graph at right

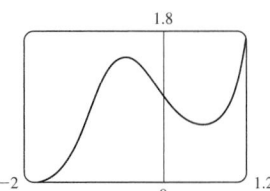

67. A. $\mathbb{R}$ B. y-int. 2   C. None
D. None
E. Inc. on $\left(\frac{1}{5} \ln \frac{2}{3}, \infty\right)$;
dec. on $\left(-\infty, \frac{1}{5} \ln \frac{2}{3}\right)$
F. Loc. min.
$f\left(\frac{1}{5} \ln \frac{2}{3}\right) = \left(\frac{2}{3}\right)^{3/5} + \left(\frac{2}{3}\right)^{-2/5}$
G. CU on $(-\infty, \infty)$
H. See graph at right.

local minimum (0, 2)

69. Loc. max. $f(-1/\sqrt{3}) = e^{2\sqrt{3}/9} \approx 1.5$;
loc. min. $f(1/\sqrt{3}) = e^{-2\sqrt{3}/9} \approx 0.7$;
IP $(-0.15, 1.15), (-1.09, 0.82)$

71. $\frac{1}{3}(1 - e^{-15})$ **73.** $\frac{2}{3}(1 + e^x)^{3/2} + C$ **75.** $x - e^{-x} + C$
77. $2e^{\sqrt{x}} + C$ **79.** 4.644   **81.** $\pi(e^2 - 1)/2$ **83.** $\frac{1}{2}$

Exercises 7.3 □ page 439

1. (a) It's defined as the inverse of the exponential function with base a, that is, $\log_a x = y \iff a^y = x$.
(b) $(0, \infty)$ (c) $\mathbb{R}$ (d) See Figure 1.
3. (a) 3   (b) $\frac{1}{2}$ **5.** (a) -2 (b) 15   **7.** (a) 2   (b) -1
9. $3 \log_2 x + \log_2 y - 2 \log_2 z$ **11.** $10 \ln u + 10 \ln v$
13. $\log_{10}(ac/b)$ **15.** $\ln 8$ **17.** $\ln \left[\sqrt{x}/(x^2 + 1)^5\right]$
19. (a) 0.402430   (b) 1.454240   (c) 1.651496
21.

$y = \log_{1.5} x$
$y = \ln x$
$y = \log_{10} x$
$y = \log_{50} x$

All graphs approach $-\infty$ as $x \to 0^+$, all pass through $(1, 0)$, and all are increasing. The larger the base, the slower the rate of increase.

23.

25.

27.

$(3, 5)$

29. (a) $\sqrt{e}$ (b) $-\ln 5$ **31.** (a) $3 + 1/\log_{10} 5$ (b) 9999
33. e^e **35.** 2, 4   **37.** $(\ln C)/(a - b)$ **39.** 0.5210
41. 3.0949   **43.** (a) $x < \ln 10$ (b) $x > 1/e$
45. About 1,084,588 mi   **47.** 8.3
49. (a) $f^{-1}(n) = (3/\ln 2) \ln(n/100)$; the time elapsed when there are n bacteria   (b) After about 26.9 h
51. $-\infty$ **53.** 0   **55.** ∞ **57.** $\left(\frac{3}{5}, \infty\right), \mathbb{R}$
59. (a) $\left(-\infty, \frac{1}{2} \ln 3\right]$ (b) $f^{-1}(x) = \frac{1}{2} \ln(3 - x^2), [0, \sqrt{3})$
61. $y = e^x - 3$ **63.** $f^{-1}(x) = \sqrt[3]{\ln x}$
65. $y = \log_{10}[x/(1 - x)]$ **67.** $\left(-\frac{1}{2} \ln 3, \infty\right)$
69. (b) $f^{-1}(x) = \frac{1}{2}(e^x - e^{-x})$ **71.** f is a constant function
75. $-1 \leq x < 1 - \sqrt{3}$ or $1 + \sqrt{3} < x \leq 3$

Exercises 7.4 □ page 449

1. The differentiation formula is simplest.
3. $f'(\theta) = -\tan \theta$ **5.** $f'(x) = 3/[(3x - 1) \ln 2]$
7. $f'(x) = 1/\left[5x \sqrt[5]{(\ln x)^4}\right]$ **9.** $f'(x) = (2 + \ln x)/(2\sqrt{x})$
11. $F'(t) = 6/(2t + 1) - 12/(3t - 1)$
13. $g'(x) = -2a/(a^2 - x^2)$
15. $f'(u) = \dfrac{1 + \ln 2}{u[1 + \ln(2u)]^2}$ **17.** $h'(t) = 3t^2 - 3^t \ln 3$
19. $y' = (10x + 1)/(5x^2 + x - 2)$ **21.** $y' = -x/(1 + x)$
23. $y' = 5^{-1/x}(\ln 5)/x^2$ **25.** $y' = \ln x + 1, y'' = 1/x$
27. $y' = 1/(x \ln 10), y'' = -1/(x^2 \ln 10)$
29. $f'(x) = \dfrac{2x - 1 - (x - 1) \ln(x - 1)}{(x - 1)[1 - \ln(x - 1)]^2}; (1, 1 + e) \cup (1 + e, \infty)$
31. $f'(x) = 2x \ln(1 - x^2) - 2x^3/(1 - x^2), (-1, 1)$ **33.** 0
35. $x - ey = e$ **37.** $f'(x) = \cos x + 1/x$
39. $y' = (2x + 1)^5(x^4 - 3)^6\left(\dfrac{10}{2x + 1} + \dfrac{24x^3}{x^4 - 3}\right)$
41. $y' = \dfrac{\sin^2 x \tan^4 x}{(x^2 + 1)^2}\left(2 \cot x + \dfrac{4 \sec^2 x}{\tan x} - \dfrac{4x}{x^2 + 1}\right)$
43. $y' = x^x(1 + \ln x)$ **45.** $y' = x^{\sin x}[(\sin x)/x + \ln x \cos x]$
47. $y' = (\ln x)^x(1/\ln x + \ln \ln x)$ **49.** $y' = e^x x^{e^x}(\ln x + 1/x)$
51. $y' = 2x/(x^2 + y^2 - 2y)$
53. $f^{(n)}(x) = (-1)^{n-1}(n - 1)!/(x - 1)^n$
55. 2.958516, 5.290718

57. CU on $(e^{8/3}, \infty)$, CD on $(0, e^{8/3})$, IP $\left(e^{8/3}, \frac{8}{3}e^{-4/3}\right)$
59. A. All x in $(2n\pi, (2n + 1)\pi)$ (n an integer)
B. x-int. $\pi/2 + 2n\pi$ C. Period 2π D. VA $x = n\pi$
E. Inc. on $(2n\pi, \pi/2 + 2n\pi)$; dec. on $(\pi/2 + 2n\pi, (2n + 1)\pi)$
F. Loc. max. $f(\pi/2 + 2n\pi) = 0$
G. CD on $(2n\pi, (2n + 1)\pi)$
H.

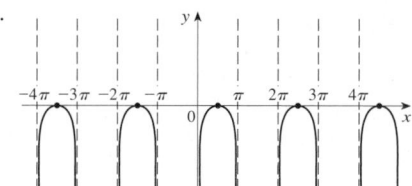

61. A. $\mathbb{R}$ B. y-int 0; x-int. 0
C. About y-axis   D. None
E. Inc. on $(0, \infty)$; dec. on $(-\infty, 0)$
F. Loc. min. $f(0) = 0$
G. CU on $(-1, 1)$; CD on $(-\infty, -1)$, $(1, \infty)$;
IP $(\pm1, \ln 2)$ H. See graph at right.

63. Inc. on $(0, 2.7)$, $(4.5, 8.2)$, $(10.9, 14.3)$;
IP $(3.8, 1.7)$, $(5.7, 2.1)$, $(10.0, 2.7)$, $(12.0, 2.9)$
65. $3 \ln 2$ **67.** $\frac{1}{3} \ln \frac{5}{2}$ **69.** $\frac{1}{2}e^2 + e - \frac{1}{2}$
71. $\frac{1}{3} \ln |6x - x^3| + C$ **73.** $\frac{1}{3}(\ln x)^3 + C$
75. $90/(\ln 10)$ **79.** $\pi \ln 2$ **81.** 45,974 J   **83.** $\frac{1}{3}$
85. $0 < m < 1$, $m - 1 - \ln m$

Exercises 7.2* □ page 458

1. $3 \ln x + \ln y - 2 \ln z$ **3.** $10 \ln u + 10 \ln v$
5. $\ln 8$ **7.** $\ln \left[\sqrt{x}/(x^2 + 1)^5\right]$
9.

11.

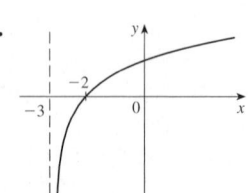

13. $f'(x) = (2 + \ln x)/(2\sqrt{x})$ **15.** $f'(\theta) = -\tan\theta$
17. $f'(x) = 1/\left[5x \sqrt[5]{(\ln x)^4}\right]$ **19.** $g'(x) = -2a/(a^2 - x^2)$
21. $f'(u) = \dfrac{1 + \ln 2}{u[1 + \ln(2u)]^2}$
23. $F'(t) = 6/(2t + 1) - 12/(3t - 1)$
25. $y' = (10x + 1)/(5x^2 + x - 2)$ **27.** $y' = -6/[5(x^2 - 1)]$
29. $y' = \sec^2(\ln(ax + b)) \dfrac{a}{ax + b}$
31. $y' = \dfrac{1}{x \ln x}$, $y'' = -\dfrac{1 + \ln x}{(x \ln x)^2}$
33. $f'(x) = \dfrac{2x - 1 - (x - 1)\ln(x - 1)}{(x - 1)[1 - \ln(x - 1)]^2}$; $(1, 1 + e) \cup (1 + e, \infty)$
35. $f'(x) = -\dfrac{1}{2x\sqrt{1 - \ln x}}$; $(0, e]$
37. 0   **39.** $f'(x) = \cos x + 1/x$ **41.** $y = 2x - 2$
43. $y' = 2x/(x^2 + y^2 - 2y)$

45. $f^{(n)}(x) = (-1)^{n-1}(n - 1)!/(x - 1)^n$
47. 2.958516, 5.290718
49. A. All x in $(2n\pi, (2n + 1)\pi)$ (n an integer)
B. x-int. $\pi/2 + 2n\pi$ C. Period 2π D. VA $x = n\pi$
E. Inc. on $(2n\pi, \pi/2 + 2n\pi)$; dec. on $(\pi/2 + 2n\pi, (2n + 1)\pi)$
F. Loc. max. $f(\pi/2 + 2n\pi) = 0$ G. CD on $(2n\pi, (2n + 1)\pi)$
H.

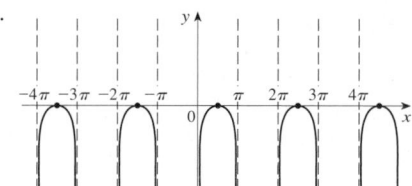

51. A. $\mathbb{R}$ B. y-int 0; x-int. 0
C. About y-axis   D. None
E. Inc. on $(0, \infty)$; dec. on $(-\infty, 0)$
F. Loc. min. $f(0) = 0$
G. CU on $(-1, 1)$; CD on $(-\infty, -1)$, $(1, \infty)$;
IP $(\pm1, \ln 2)$ H. See graph at right.
53. Inc. on $(0, 2.7)$, $(4.5, 8.2)$, $(10.9, 14.3)$;
IP $(3.8, 1.7)$, $(5.7, 2.1)$, $(10.0, 2.7)$, $(12.0, 2.9)$

55. $y' = (2x + 1)^5(x^4 - 3)^6\left(\dfrac{10}{2x + 1} + \dfrac{24x^3}{x^4 - 3}\right)$
57. $y' = \dfrac{\sin^2 x \tan^4 x}{(x^2 + 1)^2}\left(2 \cot x + \dfrac{4 \sec^2 x}{\tan x} - \dfrac{4x}{x^2 + 1}\right)$
59. $3 \ln 2$ **61.** $\frac{1}{3} \ln \frac{5}{2}$ **63.** $\frac{1}{2}e^2 + e - \frac{1}{2}$
65. $\frac{1}{3} \ln |6x - x^3| + C$ **67.** $\frac{1}{3}(\ln x)^3 + C$ **71.** $\pi \ln 2$
73. 45,974 J   **75.** $\frac{1}{3}$ **77.** (b) 0.405
81. $0 < m < 1$, $m - 1 - \ln m$

Exercises 7.3* □ page 465

1. (a) e is the number such that $\ln e = 1$.
(b) $e \approx 2.71828$
(c)   If $f(x) = e^x$, then $f'(0) = 1$.

3. (a) $\sqrt{2}$ (b) 8   **5.** (a) $\sqrt{e}$ (b) $-\ln 5$ **7.** e^e
9. 2, 4   **11.** $(\ln C)/(a - b)$ **13.** 0.5210   **15.** 3.0949
17. (a) $x < \ln 10$ (b) $x > 1/e$
19.   **21.**

23. (a) $y = e^x - 2$ (b) $y = e^{x-2}$ (c) $y = -e^x$
(d) $y = e^{-x}$ (e) $y = -e^{-x}$
25. 0   **27.** 1   **29.** 0   **31.** $f'(x) = x(x + 2)e^x$
33. $y' = 3ax^2 e^{ax^3}$ **35.** $f'(u) = (-1/u^2)e^{1/u}$
37. $F'(t) = e^{t\sin 2t}(2t\cos 2t + \sin 2t)$
39. $y' = 3e^{3x}/\sqrt{1 + 2e^{3x}}$ **41.** $y' = e^{e^x}e^x$
43. $y' = \dfrac{(ad - bc)e^x}{(ce^x + d)^2}$ **45.** $y = 2x + 1$
47. $y' = (1 - 2xye^{x^2y})/(x^2 e^{x^2y} - 1)$ **49.** $-4, -2$
51. $f^{(n)}(x) = 2^n e^{2x}$ **53.** (b) -0.567143
55. (a) 7.92 mg   (b) -0.22 mg/yr   (c) 56.6 yr
57. (a) 1   (b) $kae^{-kt}/(1 + ae^{-kt})^2$
(c) $t \approx 7.4$ h

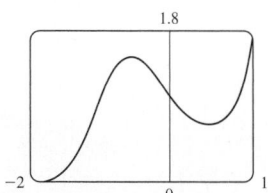

59. -1 **61.** $\left(-\frac{2}{3}, \infty\right)$
63. A. $\{x \mid x \neq -1\}$ B. y-int. $1/e$ C. None
D. HA $y = 1$; VA $x = -1$
E. Inc. on $(-\infty, -1), (-1, \infty)$
F. None
G. CU on $(-\infty, -1), \left(-1, -\frac{1}{2}\right)$;
CD on $\left(-\frac{1}{2}, \infty\right)$; IP $\left(-\frac{1}{2}, 1/e^2\right)$
H. See graph at right

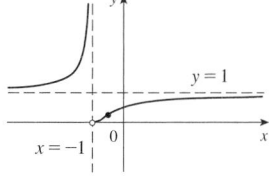

65. A. $\mathbb{R}$ B. y-int. 2   C. None
D. None
E. Inc. on $\left(\frac{1}{5}\ln\frac{2}{3}, \infty\right)$;
dec. on $\left(-\infty, \frac{1}{5}\ln\frac{2}{3}\right)$
F. Loc. min.
$f\left(\frac{1}{5}\ln\frac{2}{3}\right) = \left(\frac{2}{3}\right)^{3/5} + \left(\frac{2}{3}\right)^{-2/5}$
G. CU on $(-\infty, \infty)$
H. See graph at right.

67. Loc. max. $f\left(-1/\sqrt{3}\right) = e^{2\sqrt{3}/9} \approx 1.5$;
loc. min. $f\left(1/\sqrt{3}\right) = e^{-2\sqrt{3}/9} \approx 0.7$;
IP $(-0.15, 1.15), (-1.09, 0.82)$

69. $\frac{1}{3}(1 - e^{-15})$ **71.** $\frac{2}{3}(1 + e^x)^{3/2} + C$ **73.** $x - e^{-x} + C$
75. $2e^{\sqrt{x}} + C$ **77.** 4.644   **79.** $\pi(e^2 - 1)/2$
81. $f^{-1}(x) = e^x - 3$ **83.** $\frac{1}{2}$

Exercises 7.4* ◻ **page 475**

1. (a) $a^x = e^{x\ln a}$ (b) $(-\infty, \infty)$ (c) $(0, \infty)$
(d) See Figures 1, 2, and 3.   **3.** $e^{\sqrt{7}\ln 5}$ **5.** $e^{x\ln\cos x}$
7. (a) 3   (b) -4
9. (a) 2   (b) $\sqrt{2}$
11.

All approach 0 as $x \to -\infty$, all pass through $(0, 1)$, and all are increasing. The larger the base, the faster the rate of increase.

13. (a) 0.402430   (b) 1.454240   (c) 1.651496
15.

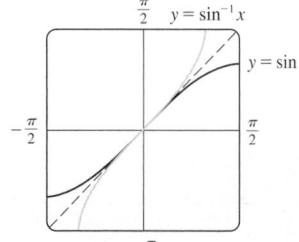

All graphs approach $-\infty$ as $x \to 0^+$, all pass through $(1, 0)$, and all are increasing. The larger the base, the slower the rate of increase.
17. $f(x) = 3 \cdot 2^x$ **19.** (b) About 1,084,588 mi   **21.** 0
23. $h'(t) = 3t^2 - 3^t \ln 3$ **25.** $y' = 5^{-1/x}(\ln 5)/x^2$
27. $f'(u) = 10 \ln 2(2^u + 2^{-u})^9(2^u - 2^{-u})$
29. $f'(x) = 2x/[(x^2 - 4)\ln 3]$ **31.** $y' = x^x(\ln x + 1)$
33. $y' = x^{\sin x}[\cos x \ln x + (\sin x)/x]$
35. $y' = (\ln x)^x(\ln \ln x + 1/\ln x)$ **37.** $y' = x^{e^x}e^x(\ln x + 1/x)$
39. $y = (10 \ln 10)x + 10(1 - \ln 10)$ **41.** $90/(\ln 10)$
43. $(\ln x)^2/(2 \ln 10) + C$ $\left[\text{or } \frac{1}{2}(\ln 10)(\log_{10} x)^2 + C\right]$
45. $3^{\sin\theta}/\ln 3 + C$ **47.** $16/(5 \ln 5) - 1/(2 \ln 2)$
49. 0.600967   **51.** $y = \log_{10} x - \log_{10}(1 - x)$ **53.** 8.3
55. $10^8/\ln 10$ dB/(watt/m^2)
57. (a) $y \approx 100.012437e^{-10.005531t}$ (b) -670.63 μA

Exercises 7.5 ◻ **page 483**

1. (a) $\pi/3$ (b) π **3.** (a) $\pi/3$ (b) $-\pi/4$
5. (a) 0   (b) 5   **7.** $2/\sqrt{5}$ **9.** $\frac{2}{3}\sqrt{2}$ **13.** $x/\sqrt{1 + x^2}$
15.

The second graph is the reflection of the first graph about the line $y = x$.

23. $y' = 1/\left[2\sqrt{x}(1 + x)\right]$ **25.** $y' = 1/\sqrt{-x^2 - x}$
27. $H'(x) = 1 + 2x \arctan x$ **29.** $y' = -2e^{2x}/\sqrt{1 - e^{4x}}$
31. $y' = -(\sin\theta)/(1 + \cos^2\theta)$ **33.** $h'(t) = 0$

35. $y' = \sqrt{a^2 - b^2}/(a + b\cos x)$
37. $g'(x) = 2/\sqrt{1 - (3 - 2x)^2};\ [1, 2],\ (1, 2)$ **39.** $\pi/6$
41. $f'(x) = \dfrac{e^{-x}}{1 + x^2} - e^{-x}\arctan x$ **43.** $-\pi/2$ **45.** $\pi/2$
47. At a distance $5 - 2\sqrt{5}$ from A **49.** $\frac{1}{4}$ rad/s
51. A. $\left[-\frac{1}{2}, \infty\right)$
B. y-int. 0; x-int. 0
C. None
D. HA $y = \pi/2$
E. Inc. on $\left(-\frac{1}{2}, \infty\right)$
F. None
G. CD on $\left(-\frac{1}{2}, \infty\right)$
H. See graph at right

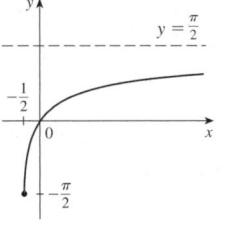

53. A. $\mathbb{R}$
B. y-int. 0; x-int. 0
C. About $(0, 0)$
D. SA $y = x \pm \pi/2$
E. Inc. on $\mathbb{R}$ F. None
G. CU on $(0, \infty)$; CD on $(-\infty, 0)$;
IP $(0, 0)$
H. See graph at right.

55. Max. at $x = 0$, min. at $x \approx \pm 0.87$, IP at $x \approx \pm 0.52$
57. $x^2 + 5\sin^{-1}x + C$ **59.** π **61.** $\pi/12$ **63.** $\pi^2/72$
65. $\frac{1}{2}\ln(x^2 + 9) + 3\tan^{-1}(x/3) + C$ **67.** $\frac{1}{3}\sin^{-1}t^3 + C$
69. $2\tan^{-1}\sqrt{x} + C$ **73.** $\pi/2 - 1$

Exercises 7.6 □ page 491

1. (a) 0 (b) 1 **3.** (a) $\frac{3}{4}$ (b) $\frac{1}{2}(e^2 - e^{-2}) \approx 3.62686$
5. (a) 1 (b) 0
21. $\coth x = \frac{5}{4}$, $\text{sech } x = \frac{3}{5}$, $\cosh x = \frac{5}{3}$, $\sinh x = \frac{4}{3}$, $\text{csch } x = \frac{3}{4}$
23. (a) 1 (b) -1 (c) ∞ (d) $-\infty$ (e) 0 (f) 1
(g) ∞ (h) $-\infty$ (i) 0
31. $f'(x) = x\sinh x + \cosh x$ **33.** $h'(x) = 2x\cosh(x^2)$
35. $G'(x) = -(2\sinh x)/(1 + \cosh x)^2$
37. $h'(t) = -\left(t\,\text{csch}^2\sqrt{1 + t^2}\right)/\sqrt{1 + t^2}$
39. $H'(t) = e^t\,\text{sech}^2(e^t)$
41. $y' = 3e^{\cosh 3x}\sinh 3x$ **43.** $y' = 1/\left[2\sqrt{x}\,(1 - x)\right]$
45. $y' = \sinh^{-1}(x/3)$ **47.** $y' = -1/\left(x\sqrt{x^2 + 1}\right)$
49. (a) 0.3572 (b) 70.34°
51. (b) $y = 2\sinh 3x - 4\cosh 3x$ **53.** $\left(\ln\left(1 + \sqrt{2}\right), \sqrt{2}\right)$
55. $\frac{1}{3}\cosh^3 x + C$ **57.** $2\cosh\sqrt{x} + C$ **59.** $-\text{csch } x + C$
61. $\ln\left(\dfrac{6 + 3\sqrt{3}}{4 + \sqrt{7}}\right)$ **63.** $\tanh^{-1}e^x + C$
65. (a) $0, 0.48$ (b) 0.04

Exercises 7.7 □ page 501

1. (a) Indeterminate (b) 0 (c) 0
(d) ∞, $-\infty$, or does not exist (e) Indeterminate
3. (a) $-\infty$ (b) Indeterminate (c) ∞ **5.** -2 **7.** $\frac{9}{5}$

9. $-\infty$ **11.** ∞ **13.** p/q **15.** 0 **17.** $-\infty$ **19.** $\ln\frac{5}{3}$
21. $\frac{1}{2}$ **23.** ∞ **25.** 1 **27.** $\frac{1}{2}$ **29.** 0
31. 1 **33.** $-1/\pi^2$ **35.** $a(a - 1)/2$ **37.** 0
39. 3 **41.** 0 **43.** $-2/\pi$ **45.** 0 **47.** $\frac{1}{2}$ **49.** ∞
51. 1 **53.** e^{-2} **55.** e^3 **57.** 1
59. $1/e$ **61.** $1/\sqrt{e}$ **63.** 5 **65.** $\frac{1}{4}$

67. A. $\mathbb{R}$ B. y-int. 0; x-int. 0
C. None D. HA $y = 0$
E. Inc. on $(-\infty, 1)$, dec. on $(1, \infty)$
F. Loc. max. $f(1) = 1/e$
G. CU on $(2, \infty)$; CD on $(-\infty, 2)$
IP $(2, 2/e^2)$
H. See graph at right.

69. A. $\mathbb{R}$ B. y-int. 0; x-int. 0
C. About $(0, 0)$ D. HA $y = 0$
E. Inc. on $\left(-1/\sqrt{2}, 1/\sqrt{2}\right)$; dec. on $\left(-\infty, -1/\sqrt{2}\right), \left(1/\sqrt{2}, \infty\right)$
F. Loc. min. $f\left(-1/\sqrt{2}\right) = -1/\sqrt{2e}$;
loc. max. $f\left(1/\sqrt{2}\right) = 1/\sqrt{2e}$
G. CU on $\left(-\sqrt{3/2}, 0\right), \left(\sqrt{3/2}, \infty\right)$; CD on $\left(-\infty, -\sqrt{3/2}\right)$,
$\left(0, \sqrt{3/2}\right)$; IP $\left(\pm\sqrt{3/2}, \pm\sqrt{3/2}e^{-3/2}\right)$, $(0, 0)$
H.

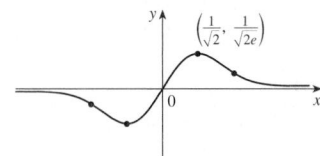

71. A. $(-1, \infty)$ B. y-int. 0; x-int. 0
C. None D. VA $x = -1$
E. Inc. on $(0, \infty)$; dec. on $(-1, 0)$
F. Loc. min. $f(0) = 0$
G. CU on $(-1, \infty)$
H. See graph at right.

73. (a)

(b) $\lim_{x \to 0^+} x^{-x} = 1$
(c) Max. value $f(1/e) = e^{1/e} \approx 1.44$ (d) 1.0

75. (a)

(b) $\lim_{x \to 0^+} x^{1/x} = 0$, $\lim_{x \to \infty} x^{1/x} = 1$
(c) Max. value $f(e) = e^{1/e} \approx 1.44$ (d) 0.58, 4.4

77.

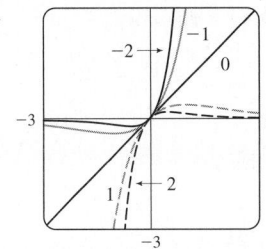

For $c > 0$, $\lim_{x \to \infty} f(x) = 0$ and $\lim_{x \to -\infty} f(x) = -\infty$. For $c < 0$, $\lim_{x \to \infty} f(x) = \infty$ and $\lim_{x \to -\infty} f(x) = 0$. As $|c|$ increases, the maximum and minimum points and the IPs get closer to the origin.
81. $\pi/6$ **83.** 56   **91.** $\frac{1}{3}$ **93.** (a) 0

Chapter 7 Review □ page 505

True-False Quiz

1. True   **3.** False   **5.** True   **7.** True   **9.** False
11. False   **13.** False   **15.** True   **17.** True

Exercises

1. No   **3.** (a) 7   (b) $\frac{1}{8}$
5.

7.

9.

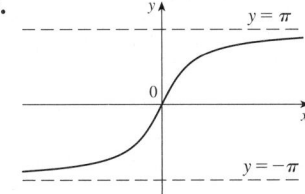

11. (a) 9   (b) 2   **13.** $e^{1/3}$
15. $\ln \ln 17$ **17.** $\sqrt{1 + e}$
19. $\tan 1$ **21.** $f'(t) = t + 2t \ln t$
23. $h'(\theta) = 2\sec^2(2\theta)e^{\tan 2\theta}$ **25.** $y' = 5 \sec 5x$
27. $y' = (1 + c^2)e^{cx} \sin x$ **29.** $y' = 2 \tan x$
31. $y' = e^{-1/x}(1 + 1/x)$ **33.** $y' = -(2 \ln 2)\, t2^{-t^2}$
35. $H'(v) = (v/(1 + v^2)) + \tan^{-1}v$
37. $y' = 2x^2 \cosh(x^2) + \sinh(x^2)$
39. $y' = \cot x - \sin x \cos x$
41. $y' = -(1/x)[1 + 1/(\ln x)^2]$
43. $y' = 3 \tanh 3x$
45. $y' = (\cosh x)/\sqrt{\sinh^2 x - 1}$
47. $f'(x) = \dfrac{6x}{x^2 + 1} \sin^2(\ln(x^2 + 1)) \cdot \cos(\ln(x^2 + 1)) \cdot e^{\sin^3(\ln(x^2+1))}$

49. $f'(x) = g'(x)e^{g(x)}$ **51.** $f'(x) = g'(x)/g(x)$ **53.** $2^x(\ln 2)^n$
57. $y = -x + 2$ **59.** $(-3, 0)$
61. (a) $y = \frac{1}{4}x + \frac{1}{4}(\ln 4 + 1)$ (b) $y = ex$
63. 0   **65.** 0   **67.** $-\infty$ **69.** -1
71. π **73.** 8   **75.** 0   **77.** $\frac{1}{2}$

79. A. $\{x \mid x \neq 0\}$ B. None
C. About $(0, 0)$ D. HA $y = 0$
E. Dec. on $(-\infty, 0)$ and $(0, \infty)$
F. None
G. CU on $(0, \infty)$; CD on $(-\infty, 0)$
H. See graph at right.

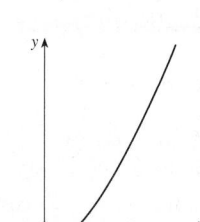

81. A. $(0, \infty)$ B. x-int. 1
C. None   D. None
E. Inc. on $(1/e, \infty)$; dec. on $(0, 1/e)$
F. Loc. min. $f(1/e) = -1/e$
G. CU on $(0, \infty)$
H. See graph at right.

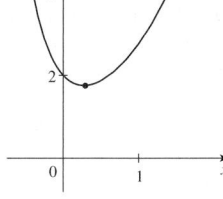

83. A. $\mathbb{R}$ B. y-int. 2
C. None   D. None
E. Inc. on $\left(\frac{1}{4}\ln 3, \infty\right)$, dec. on $\left(-\infty, \frac{1}{4}\ln 3\right)$
F. Loc. min. $f\left(\frac{1}{4}\ln 3\right) = 3^{1/4} + 3^{-3/4}$
G. CU on $(-\infty, \infty)$
H. See graph at right

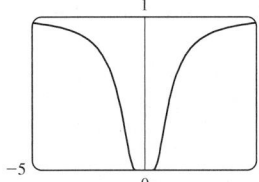

85.

$(\pm 0.82, 0.22)$; $\left(\pm\sqrt{2/3}, e^{-3/2}\right)$

87. $v(t) = -Ae^{-ct}[\omega \sin(\omega t + \delta) + c \cos(\omega t + \delta)]$,
$a(t) = Ae^{-ct}[(c^2 - \omega^2)\cos(\omega t + \delta) + 2c\omega \sin(\omega t + \delta)]$
89. 4.32 days   **91.** $\frac{1}{4}(1 - e^{-2})$ **93.** $\ln 2 - \frac{7}{4}$
95. $2e^{\sqrt{x}} + C$ **97.** $\frac{1}{2}\ln|x^2 + 2x| + C$
99. $-\frac{1}{2}[\ln(\cos x)]^2 + C$
101. $2^{\tan\theta}/\ln 2 + C$
103. $\ln|1 + \sec\theta| + C$
107. $e^{\sqrt{x}}/(2x)$ **109.** $\frac{1}{3}\ln 4$
111. $\pi^2/4$ **113.** $\frac{2}{3}$
115. $2/e$ **119.** $f(x) = e^{2x}(2x + 1)/(1 - e^{-x})$

Problems Plus □ page 509

7. $1/\sqrt{2}$ **9.** $\frac{1}{2}$ **13.** $2\sqrt{e}$ **15.** $a \leq e^{1/e}$

Chapter 8

Exercises 8.1 □ page 516

1. $\frac{1}{2}x^2 \ln x - \frac{1}{4}x^2 + C$ **3.** $\frac{1}{5}x \sin 5x + \frac{1}{25} \cos 5x + C$

5. $2(r-2)e^{r/2} + C$

7. $-\frac{1}{\pi}x^2 \cos \pi x + \frac{2}{\pi^2}x \sin \pi x + \frac{2}{\pi^3} \cos \pi x + C$

9. $\frac{1}{2}(2x+1) \ln(2x+1) - x + C$

11. $t \arctan 4t - \frac{1}{8}\ln(1 + 16t^2) + C$

13. $x(\ln x)^2 - 2x \ln x + 2x + C$

15. $\frac{1}{13}e^{2\theta}(2 \sin 3\theta - 3 \cos 3\theta) + C$

17. $y \cosh y - \sinh y + C$

19. $\pi/3$ **21.** $\frac{1}{2} - \frac{1}{2}\ln 2$ **23.** $\frac{1}{4} - \frac{3}{4}e^{-2}$

25. $(\pi + 6 - 3\sqrt{3})/6$ **27.** $\sin x (\ln \sin x - 1) + C$

29. $\frac{1}{2}x(\cos \ln x + \sin \ln x) + C$ **31.** $\frac{32}{5}(\ln 2)^2 - \frac{64}{25}\ln 2 + \frac{62}{125}$

33. $2(\sin \sqrt{x} - \sqrt{x} \cos \sqrt{x}) + C$ **35.** $-\frac{1}{2} - \pi/4$

37. $(x \sin \pi x)/\pi + (\cos \pi x)/\pi^2 + C$

39. $(2x+1)e^x + C$

41. (b) $-\frac{1}{4}\cos x \sin^3 x + \frac{3}{8}x - \frac{3}{16}\sin 2x + C$

43. (b) $\frac{2}{3}, \frac{8}{15}$ **49.** $x[(\ln x)^3 - 3(\ln x)^2 + 6 \ln x - 6] + C$

51. $\frac{25}{4} - \frac{75}{4}e^{-2}$ **53.** $1.0475, 2.8731; 2.1828$

55. $4 - 8/\pi$ **57.** $2\pi e$

59. $\frac{9}{2}\ln 3 - \frac{13}{9}$ **61.** $2 - e^{-t}(t^2 + 2t + 2)$ m   **63.** 2

Exercises 8.2 □ page 524

1. $\frac{1}{5}\cos^5 x - \frac{1}{3}\cos^3 x + C$ **3.** $-\frac{11}{384}$

5. $\frac{1}{5}\sin^5 x - \frac{2}{7}\sin^7 x + \frac{1}{9}\sin^9 x + C$ **7.** $\pi/4$ **9.** $3\pi/8$

11. $\frac{3}{2}\theta + 2 \sin \theta + \frac{1}{4}\sin 2\theta + C$ **13.** $(3\pi - 4)/192$

15. $\left(\frac{2}{7}\cos^3 x - \frac{2}{3}\cos x\right)\sqrt{\cos x} + C$

17. $\frac{1}{2}\cos^2 x - \ln|\cos x| + C$ **19.** $\ln(1 + \sin x) + C$

21. $\frac{1}{2}\tan^2 x + C$ **23.** $\tan x - x + C$

25. $\frac{1}{5}\tan^5 t + \frac{2}{3}\tan^3 t + \tan t + C$ **27.** $\frac{117}{8}$

29. $\frac{1}{3}\sec^3 x - \sec x + C$

31. $\frac{1}{4}\sec^4 x - \tan^2 x + \ln|\sec x| + C$

33. $\frac{1}{6}\tan^6 \theta + \frac{1}{4}\tan^4 \theta + C$ **35.** $\sqrt{3} - (\pi/3)$

37. $\frac{1}{3}\csc^3 \alpha - \frac{1}{5}\csc^5 \alpha + C$ **39.** $\ln|\csc x - \cot x| + C$

41. $\frac{1}{6}\sin 3x - \frac{1}{14}\sin 7x + C$ **43.** $\frac{1}{4}\sin 2\theta + \frac{1}{24}\sin 12\theta + C$

45. $\frac{1}{2}\sin 2x + C$ **47.** $\frac{1}{10}\tan^5(t^2) + C$

49. $-\frac{1}{5}\cos^5 x + \frac{2}{3}\cos^3 x - \cos x + C$

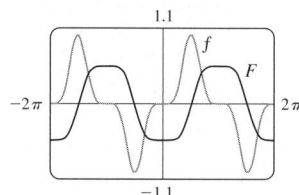

51. $\frac{1}{6}\sin 3x - \frac{1}{18}\sin 9x + C$

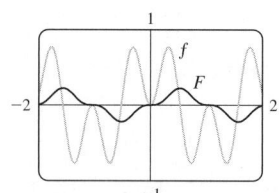

53. 0 **55.** $\frac{1}{3}$ **57.** 0 **59.** $\pi^2/4$ **61.** $2\pi + (\pi^2/4)$

63. $s = (1 - \cos^3 \omega t)/(3\omega)$

Exercises 8.3 □ page 530

1. $\sqrt{x^2 - 9}/(9x) + C$ **3.** $\frac{1}{3}(x^2 - 18)\sqrt{x^2 + 9} + C$

5. $\pi/24 + \sqrt{3}/8 - \frac{1}{4}$ **7.** $-\sqrt{25 - x^2}/(25x) + C$

9. $\ln(\sqrt{x^2 + 16} + x) + C$ **11.** $\frac{1}{4}\sin^{-1}(2x) + \frac{1}{2}x\sqrt{1 - 4x^2} + C$

13. $\frac{1}{6}\sec^{-1}(x/3) - \sqrt{x^2 - 9}/(2x^2) + C$

15. $(x/\sqrt{a^2 - x^2}) - \sin^{-1}(x/a) + C$ **17.** $\sqrt{x^2 - 7} + C$

19. $\ln\left|(\sqrt{1 + x^2} - 1)/x\right| + \sqrt{1 + x^2} + C$ **21.** $\frac{64}{1215}$

23. $\frac{9}{2}\sin^{-1}((x - 2)/3) + \frac{1}{2}(x - 2)\sqrt{5 + 4x - x^2} + C$

25. $\frac{1}{3}\ln|3x + 1 + \sqrt{9x^2 + 6x - 8}| + C$

27. $\frac{1}{2}[\tan^{-1}(x + 1) + (x + 1)/(x^2 + 2x + 2)] + C$

29. $\frac{1}{4}\sin^{-1}x^2 + \frac{1}{4}x^2\sqrt{1 - x^4} + C$

33. $\frac{1}{6}(\sqrt{48} - \sec^{-1} 7)$ **37.** $0.81, 2; 2.10$

39. $r\sqrt{R^2 - r^2} + \pi r^2/2 - R^2 \arcsin(r/R)$ **41.** $2\pi^2 R r^2$

Exercises 8.4 □ page 540

1. (a) $\dfrac{A}{x + 3} + \dfrac{B}{3x + 1}$ (b) $\dfrac{A}{x} + \dfrac{B}{x + 1} + \dfrac{C}{(x + 1)^2}$

3. (a) $\dfrac{A}{x + 4} + \dfrac{B}{x - 1}$ (b) $\dfrac{A}{x - 1} + \dfrac{Bx + C}{x^2 + x + 1}$

5. (a) $1 + \dfrac{A}{x - 1} + \dfrac{B}{x + 1} + \dfrac{Cx + D}{x^2 + 1}$

(b) $\dfrac{At + B}{t^2 + 1} + \dfrac{Ct + D}{t^2 + 4} + \dfrac{Et + F}{(t^2 + 4)^2}$

7. $x + 6 \ln|x - 6| + C$

9. $2 \ln|x + 5| - \ln|x - 2| + C$ **11.** $\frac{1}{2}\ln \frac{3}{2}$

13. $a \ln|x - b| + C$ **15.** $2 \ln 2 + \frac{1}{2}$

17. $\frac{27}{5}\ln 2 - \frac{9}{5}\ln 3 \left(\text{or } \frac{9}{5}\ln \frac{8}{3}\right)$

19. $-\frac{1}{36}\ln|x+5| + \frac{1}{6}\frac{1}{x+5} + \frac{1}{36}\ln|x-1| + C$

21. $2\ln|x| + 3\ln|x+2| + (1/x) + C$

23. $\ln|x+1| + 2/(x+1) - 1/[2(x+1)^2] + C$

25. $\ln|x-1| - \frac{1}{2}\ln(x^2+9) - \frac{1}{3}\tan^{-1}(x/3) + C$

27. $\frac{1}{2}\ln(x^2+1) + \left(1/\sqrt{2}\right)\tan^{-1}(x/\sqrt{2}) + C$

29. $\frac{1}{2}\ln(x^2+2x+5) + \frac{3}{2}\tan^{-1}((x+1)/2) + C$

31. $\frac{1}{3}\ln|x-1| - \frac{1}{6}\ln(x^2+x+1) - \frac{1}{\sqrt{3}}\tan^{-1}\frac{2x+1}{\sqrt{3}} + C$

33. $\frac{1}{3}\ln\frac{17}{2}$

35. $(1/x) + \frac{1}{2}\ln|(x-1)/(x+1)| + C$

37. $\dfrac{-1}{2(x^2+2x+4)} - \dfrac{2\sqrt{3}}{9}\tan^{-1}\left(\dfrac{x+1}{\sqrt{3}}\right) - \dfrac{2(x+1)}{3(x^2+2x+4)} + C$

39. $\ln|(\sqrt{x+1}-1)/(\sqrt{x+1}+1)| + C$

41. $2 + \ln\frac{25}{9}$ **43.** $\frac{3}{10}(x^2+1)^{5/3} - \frac{3}{4}(x^2+1)^{2/3} + C$

45. $2\sqrt{x} + 3\sqrt[3]{x} + 6\sqrt[6]{x} + 6\ln|\sqrt[6]{x}-1| + C$

47. $\ln[(e^x+2)^2/(e^x+1)] + C$

49. $\left(x-\frac{1}{2}\right)\ln(x^2-x+2) - 2x + \sqrt{7}\tan^{-1}((2x-1)/\sqrt{7}) + C$

51. $-\frac{1}{2}\ln 3 \approx -0.55$

53. $\frac{1}{2}\ln|(x-2)/x| + C$ **57.** $\frac{1}{5}\ln\left|\dfrac{2\tan(x/2)-1}{\tan(x/2)+2}\right| + C$

59. $\frac{1}{4}\ln|\tan(x/2)| + \frac{1}{8}\tan^2(x/2) + C$ **61.** $1 + 2\ln 2$

63. $t = -\ln P - \frac{1}{9}\ln(0.9P + 900) + C$, where $C \approx 10.23$

65. (a) $\dfrac{24{,}110}{4879}\dfrac{1}{5x+2} - \dfrac{668}{323}\dfrac{1}{2x+1} - \dfrac{9438}{80{,}155}\dfrac{1}{3x-7} +$

$\dfrac{1}{260{,}015}\dfrac{22{,}098x + 48{,}935}{x^2+x+5}$

(b) $\dfrac{4822}{4879}\ln|5x+2| - \dfrac{334}{323}\ln|2x+1| - \dfrac{3146}{80{,}155}\ln|3x-7| +$

$\dfrac{11{,}049}{260{,}015}\ln(x^2+x+5) + \dfrac{75{,}772}{260{,}015\sqrt{19}}\tan^{-1}\dfrac{2x+1}{\sqrt{19}} + C$

The CAS omits the absolute value signs and the constant of integration.

Exercises 8.5 □ page 546

1. $\sin x + \ln|\csc x - \cot x| + C$

3. $4 - \ln 9$ **5.** $e^{\pi/4} - e^{-\pi/4}$

7. $\frac{243}{5}\ln 3 - \frac{242}{25}$ **9.** $\frac{1}{2}\ln(x^2-4x+5) + \tan^{-1}(x-2) + C$

11. $\frac{1}{8}\cos^8\theta - \frac{1}{6}\cos^6\theta + C$ (or $\frac{1}{4}\sin^4\theta - \frac{1}{3}\sin^6\theta + \frac{1}{8}\sin^8\theta + C$)

13. $x/\sqrt{1-x^2} + C$ **15.** $1 - \frac{1}{2}\sqrt{3}$

17. $\frac{1}{4}x^2 - \frac{1}{2}x\sin x\cos x + \frac{1}{4}\sin^2 x + C$

(or $\frac{1}{4}x^2 - \frac{1}{4}x\sin 2x - \frac{1}{8}\cos 2x + C$)

19. $e^{e^x} + C$ **21.** $-\frac{1}{8}e^{-2t}(4t^3 + 6t^2 + 6t + 3) + C$

23. $\frac{4097}{45}$ **25.** $3x + \frac{23}{3}\ln|x-4| - \frac{5}{3}\ln|x+2| + C$

27. $\frac{1}{2}(\ln\sin x)^2 + C$ **29.** $15 + 7\ln\frac{2}{7}$

31. $\sin^{-1}x - \sqrt{1-x^2} + C$

33. $2\sin^{-1}((x+1)/2) + ((x+1)/2)\sqrt{3-2x-x^2} + C$

35. 0 **37.** $\pi/8 - \frac{1}{4}$ **39.** $-\ln(1 + \sqrt{1-x^2}) + C$

41. $\theta\tan\theta - \frac{1}{2}\theta^2 - \ln|\sec\theta| + C$ **43.** $\frac{2}{3}(1+e^x)^{3/2} + C$

45. $-\frac{1}{3}(x^3+1)e^{-x^3} + C$

47. $\ln\sqrt{x^2+a^2} + \tan^{-1}(x/a) + C$

49. $\ln\left|\dfrac{\sqrt{4x+1}-1}{\sqrt{4x+1}+1}\right| + C$ **51.** $-\ln\left|\dfrac{\sqrt{4x^2+1}+1}{2x}\right| + C$

53. $(1/m)x^2\cosh(mx) - (2/m^2)x\sinh(mx) + (2/m^3)\cosh(mx) + C$

55. $3\ln(\sqrt{x+1}+3) - \ln(\sqrt{x+1}+1) + C$

57. $\frac{3}{7}(x+c)^{7/3} - \frac{3}{4}c(x+c)^{4/3} + C$

59. $e^{-x} + \frac{1}{2}\ln|(e^x-1)/(e^x+1)| + C$

61. $\frac{1}{20}\tan^{-1}(\frac{1}{4}x^5) + C$ **63.** $2(x - 2\sqrt{x} + 2)e^{\sqrt{x}} + C$

65. $\frac{2}{3}[(x+1)^{3/2} - x^{3/2}] + C$

67. $\frac{2}{3}\sqrt{3}\pi - \frac{1}{2}\pi - \ln 2$ **69.** $e^x - \ln(1+e^x) + C$

71. $-\frac{1}{4}\ln(x^2+3) + \frac{1}{4}\ln(x^2+1) + C$

73. $\frac{1}{8}\ln|x-2| - \frac{1}{16}\ln(x^2+4) - \frac{1}{8}\tan^{-1}(x/2) + C$

75. $\frac{1}{24}\cos 6x - \frac{1}{16}\cos 4x - \frac{1}{8}\cos 2x + C$ **77.** $\frac{2}{3}\tan^{-1}(x^{3/2}) + C$

79. $\frac{1}{3}x\sin^3 x + \frac{1}{3}\cos x - \frac{1}{9}\cos^3 x + C$ **81.** $xe^{x^2} + C$

Exercises 8.6 □ page 551

1. $(-1/x)\sqrt{7-2x^2} - \sqrt{2}\sin^{-1}(\sqrt{2}x/\sqrt{7}) + C$

3. $(1/(2\pi))\sec(\pi x)\tan(\pi x) + (1/(2\pi))\ln|\sec(\pi x) + \tan(\pi x)| + C$

5. $\pi/4$ **7.** $\frac{1}{25}e^{-3x}(-3\cos 4x + 4\sin 4x) + C$

9. $-\sqrt{4x^2+9}/(9x) + C$ **11.** $e - 2$

13. $-\frac{1}{2}\tan^2(1/z) - \ln|\cos(1/z)| + C$ **15.** $\tan^{-1}(\sinh e^x) + C$

17. $((2y-1)/8)\sqrt{6+4y-4y^2} + \frac{7}{8}\sin^{-1}((2y-1)/\sqrt{7})$

$- \frac{1}{12}(6+4y-4y^2)^{3/2} + C$

19. $\frac{1}{9}\sin^3 x\,[3\ln(\sin x) - 1] + C$ **21.** $\dfrac{1}{2\sqrt{3}}\ln\left|\dfrac{e^x+\sqrt{3}}{e^x-\sqrt{3}}\right| + C$

23. $\frac{1}{4}\tan x\sec^3 x + \frac{3}{8}\tan x\sec x + \frac{3}{8}\ln|\sec x + \tan x| + C$

25. $\frac{1}{2}(\ln x)\sqrt{4+(\ln x)^2} + 2\ln[\ln x + \sqrt{4+(\ln x)^2}] + C$

27. $\sqrt{e^{2x}-1} - \cos^{-1}(e^{-x}) + C$

29. $\frac{1}{5}\ln|x^5 + \sqrt{x^{10}-2}| + C$ **31.** $2\pi^2$

35. $-\frac{1}{4}x(5-x^2)^{3/2} + \frac{5}{8}x\sqrt{5-x^2} + \frac{25}{8}\sin^{-1}(x/\sqrt{5}) + C$

37. $-\frac{1}{5}\sin^2 x\cos^3 x - \frac{2}{15}\cos^3 x + C$

39. $\frac{1}{10}(1+2x)^{5/2} - \frac{1}{6}(1+2x)^{3/2} + C$

41. $-\ln|\cos x| - \frac{1}{2}\tan^2 x + \frac{1}{4}\tan^4 x + C$

43. $\dfrac{2^{x-1}\sqrt{2^{2x}-1}}{\ln 2} - \dfrac{\ln(\sqrt{2^{2x}-1}+2^x)}{2\ln 2} + C$

45. $F(x) = \frac{1}{2}\ln(x^2-x+1) - \frac{1}{2}\ln(x^2+x+1)$;

max. at -1, min. at 1; IP at -1.7, 0, and 1.7

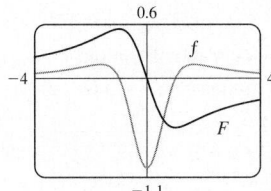

47. $F(x) = -\frac{1}{10}\sin^3 x \cos^7 x - \frac{3}{80}\sin x \cos^7 x + \frac{1}{160}\sin x \cos^5 x + \frac{1}{128}\sin x \cos^3 x + \frac{3}{256}\sin x \cos x + \frac{3}{256}x;$
max. at π, min. at 0; IP at 0.68, $\pi/2$, and 2.46

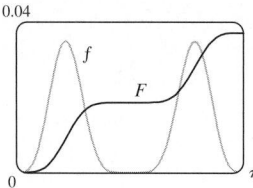

Exercises 8.7 □ page 563

1. (a) $L_2 = 6, R_2 = 12, M_2 \approx 9.6$
(b) L_2 is an underestimate, R_2 and M_2 are overestimates.
(c) $T_2 = 9 < I$ (d) $L_n < T_n < I < M_n < R_n$
3. (a) $T_4 \approx 0.895759$ (underestimate)
(b) $M_4 \approx 0.908907$ (overestimate)
$T_4 < I < M_4$
5. (a) 5.932957, $E_M \approx -0.063353$
(b) 5.869247, $E_S \approx 0.000357$
7. (a) 2.413790   (b) 2.411453   (c) 2.412232
9. (a) 0.146879   (b) 0.147391   (c) 0.147219
11. (a) 0.451948   (b) 0.451991   (c) 0.451976
13. (a) 2.031893   (b) 2.014207   (c) 2.020651
15. (a) -0.495333 (b) -0.543321 (c) -0.526123
17. (a) 1.064275   (b) 1.067416   (c) 1.074915
19. (a) $T_{10} \approx 0.881839, M_{10} \approx 0.882202$
(b) $|E_T| \le 0.01\overline{3}, |E_M| \le 0.00\overline{6}$
(c) $n = 366$ for T_n, $n = 259$ for M_n
21. (a) $T_{10} \approx 1.719713, E_T \approx -0.001432$;
$S_{10} \approx 1.718283, E_S \approx -0.000001$
(b) $|E_T| \le 0.002266, |E_S| \le 0.0000016$
(c) $n = 151$ for T_n, $n = 107$ for M_n, $n = 8$ for S_n
23. (a) 2.8   (b) 7.954926518   (c) 0.2894
(d) 7.954926521   (e) The actual error is much smaller.
(f) 10.9   (g) 7.953789422   (h) 0.0593
(i) The actual error is smaller.   (j) $n \ge 50$
25.

n	L_n	R_n	T_n	M_n
4	0.140625	0.390625	0.265625	0.242188
8	0.191406	0.316406	0.253906	0.248047
16	0.219727	0.282227	0.250977	0.249512

n	E_L	E_R	E_T	E_M
4	0.109375	-0.140625	-0.015625	0.007813
8	0.058594	-0.066406	-0.003906	0.001953
16	0.030273	-0.032227	-0.000977	0.000488

Observations same as after Example 1.

27.

n	T_n	M_n	S_n
6	4.661488	4.669245	4.666563
12	4.665367	4.667316	4.666659

n	E_T	E_M	E_S
6	0.005178	-0.002578	0.000104
12	0.001300	-0.000649	0.000007

Observations same as after Example 1.
29. (a) 11.5   (b) 12   (c) $11.\overline{6}$
31. (a) 23.44   (b) $0.341\overline{3}$ **33.** $37.7\overline{3}$ ft/s
35. 10,177 megawatt-hours   **37.** 828
39. 12.3251   **41.** 59.4
43.

Exercises 8.8 □ page 573

Abbreviations: C, convergent; D, divergent

1. (a) Infinite interval   (b) Infinite discontinuity
(c) Infinite discontinuity   (d) Infinite interval
3. $\frac{1}{2} - 1/(2t^2)$; 0.495, 0.49995, 0.4999995; 0.5
5. $\frac{1}{12}$ **7.** D   **9.** $2e^{-2}$ **11.** D   **13.** 0   **15.** D
17. D   **19.** $\frac{1}{25}$ **21.** D   **23.** $\pi/9$
25. 1   **27.** $2\sqrt{3}$ **29.** D   **31.** D   **33.** $\frac{75}{4}$
35. D   **37.** D   **39.** $\frac{8}{3}\ln 2 - \frac{8}{9}$
41. e **43.** $\frac{2\pi}{3}$

45. Infinite area

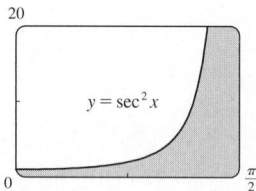

47. (a)

t	$\int_1^t [(\sin^2 x)/x^2]\, dx$
2	0.447453
5	0.577101
10	0.621306
100	0.668479
1,000	0.672957
10,000	0.673407

It appears that the integral is convergent.

(c)

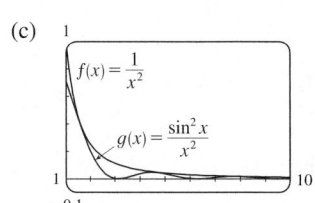

49. C   **51.** C   **53.** D   **55.** π **57.** $p < 1, 1/(1 - p)$
59. $p > -1, -1/(p + 1)^2$ **65.** $\sqrt{2GM/R}$
67. (a)

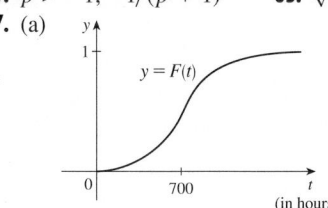

(b) The rate at which the fraction $F(t)$ increases as t increases
(c) 1; all bulbs burn out eventually
69. 1000
71. (a) $F(s) = 1/s, s > 0$ (b) $F(s) = 1/(s - 1), s > 1$
(c) $F(s) = 1/s^2, s > 0$
77. $C = 1$; ln 2

Chapter 8 Review □ page 576

True-False Quiz

1. False   **3.** False   **5.** False   **7.** False
9. (a) True   (b) False   **11.** False   **13.** False

Exercises

1. $5 + 10 \ln \frac{2}{3}$ **3.** ln 2
5. $\frac{1}{9} \sec^9 x - \frac{3}{7} \sec^7 x + \frac{3}{5} \sec^5 x - \frac{1}{3} \sec^3 x + C$
7. $-\cos(\ln t) + C$ **9.** $\frac{64}{5} \ln 4 - \frac{124}{25}$
11. $\sqrt{3} - (\pi/3)$ **13.** $\ln|x| - \frac{1}{2} \ln(x^2 + 1) + C$
15. $\frac{1}{3} \sin^3 \theta - \frac{2}{5} \sin^5 \theta + \frac{1}{7} \sin^7 \theta + C$
17. $x \sec x - \ln|\sec x + \tan x| + C$
19. $\frac{1}{18} \ln(9x^2 + 6x + 5) + \frac{1}{9} \tan^{-1}((3x + 1)/2) + C$
21. $\ln|x - 2 + \sqrt{x^2 - 4x}| + C$
23. $-\frac{1}{12}(\cot^3 4x + 3 \cot 4x) + C$
25. $\frac{3}{2} \ln(x^2 + 1) - 3 \tan^{-1} x + \sqrt{2} \tan^{-1}(x/\sqrt{2}) + C$
27. $\frac{2}{5}$ **29.** 0   **31.** $6 - 3\pi/2$
33. $(x/\sqrt{4 - x^2}) - \sin^{-1}(x/2) + C$
35. $4\sqrt{1 + \sqrt{x}} + C$ **37.** $\frac{1}{2} \sin 2x - \frac{1}{8} \cos 4x + C$
39. $\frac{1}{8} e - \frac{1}{4}$ **41.** $\frac{1}{36}$ **43.** D
45. $4 \ln 4 - 8$ **47.** D   **49.** $\pi/4$
51. $(x + 1) \ln(x^2 + 2x + 2) + 2 \arctan(x + 1) - 2x + C$
53. 0   **55.** $\frac{1}{2}[e^x \sqrt{1 - e^{2x}} + \sin^{-1}(e^x)] + C$
57. $\frac{1}{4}(2x + 1)\sqrt{x^2 + x + 1} + \frac{3}{8} \ln(x + \frac{1}{2} + \sqrt{x^2 + x + 1}) + C$
61. No
63. (a) 1.090608 (overestimate)
(b) 1.088840 (underestimate)
(c) 1.089429 (unknown)

65. (a) $0.00\bar{6}, n \geqslant 259$ (b) $0.00\bar{3}, n \geqslant 183$
67. 8.6 mi   **69.** (a) 3.8   (b) 1.7867, 0.000646   (c) $n \geqslant 30$
71. C   **73.** 2   **75.** $3\pi^2/16$

Problems Plus □ page 580

1. About 1.85 inches from the center   **3.** 0
5. $f(\pi) = -\pi/2$ **9.** $(b^b a^{-a})^{1/(b-a)} e^{-1}$
11. $2 - \sin^{-1}(2/\sqrt{5})$

▐▌▐▌ Chapter 9

Exercises 9.1 □ page 588

1. $3\sqrt{10}$ **3.** $\frac{46}{3}$ **5.** $\frac{2}{243}(82\sqrt{82} - 1)$ **7.** $\frac{1261}{240}$ **9.** $\frac{32}{3}$
11. $\ln(\sqrt{2} + 1)$ **13.** sinh 1
15. $\sqrt{1 + e^2} - \sqrt{2} + \ln(\sqrt{1 + e^2} - 1) - 1 - \ln(\sqrt{2} - 1)$
17. $\int_0^{2\pi} \sqrt{1 + \sin^2 x}\, dx$ **19.** $\int_1^4 \sqrt{9y^4 + 6y^2 + 2}\, dy$
21. 5.115840   **23.** 1.569619
25. (a), (b)

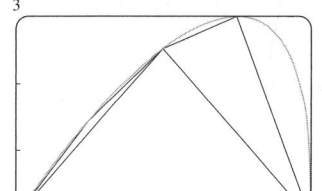

$L_1 = 4,$
$L_2 \approx 6.43,$
$L_4 \approx 7.50$

(c) $\int_0^4 \sqrt{1 + [4(3 - x)/(3(4 - x)^{2/3})]^2}\, dx$ (d) 7.7988
27. $\ln 3 - \frac{1}{2}$
29. 6

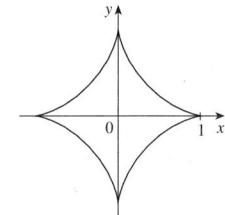

31. $s(x) = \frac{2}{27}[(1 + 9x)^{3/2} - 10\sqrt{10}]$
33. 209.1 m   **35.** 29.36 in.   **37.** 12.4

Exercises 9.2 □ page 595

1. $\int_1^3 2\pi \ln x \sqrt{1 + (1/x)^2}\, dx$

3. $\int_0^{\pi/4} 2\pi x \sqrt{1 + (\sec x \tan x)^2}\, dx$

5. $\pi(145\sqrt{145} - 1)/27$ **7.** $\pi(37\sqrt{37} - 17\sqrt{17})/6$
9. $\pi[1 + \frac{1}{4}(e^2 - e^{-2})]$ **11.** $21\pi/2$
13. $\pi(145\sqrt{145} - 10\sqrt{10})/27$ **15.** πa^2
17. 9.023754   **19.** 13.527296
21. $(\pi/4)[4 \ln(\sqrt{17} + 4) - 4 \ln(\sqrt{2} + 1) - \sqrt{17} + 4\sqrt{2}]$
23. $(\pi/6)[\ln(\sqrt{10} + 3) + 3\sqrt{10}]$

27. (a) $\pi a^2/3$ (b) $56\pi\sqrt{3}\,a^2/45$

29. $2\pi\left[b^2 + a^2b\,\sin^{-1}(\sqrt{a^2 - b^2}/a)/\sqrt{a^2 - b^2}\right]$

31. $\int_a^b 2\pi[c - f(x)]\sqrt{1 + [f'(x)]^2}\,dx$ **33.** $4\pi^2r^2$

Exercises 9.3 □ page 605

1. (a) 187.5 lb/ft^2 (b) 1875 lb (c) 562.5 lb

3. 6000 lb **5.** 6.5×10^6 N **7.** 3.5×10^4 lb

9. $1000g\pi r^3$ N **11.** 5.27×10^5 N

13. (a) 314 N (b) 353 N

15. (a) $\approx 5.63 \times 10^3$ lb (b) $\approx 5.06 \times 10^4$ lb

(c) $\approx 4.88 \times 10^4$ lb (d) $\approx 3.03 \times 10^5$ lb

17. 2.5×10^5 N **19.** $230; \frac{23}{7}$ **21.** $10; 1; \left(\frac{1}{21}, \frac{10}{21}\right)$

23. $(0, 1.6)$ **25.** $(1/(e - 1), (e + 1)/4)$ **27.** $\left(\frac{2}{5}, \frac{1}{2}\right)$

29. $\left((\pi\sqrt{2} - 4)/[4(\sqrt{2} - 1)], 1/[4(\sqrt{2} - 1)]\right)$

31. $(2, 0)$ **33.** $\frac{4}{3}, 0, \left(0, \frac{2}{3}\right)$ **35.** $(0.781, 1.330)$ **39.** $\left(0, \frac{1}{12}\right)$

41. $\frac{1}{3}\pi r^2 h$

Exercises 9.4 □ page 610

1. $\$38,000$ **3.** $\$43,866,933.33$ **5.** $\$407.25$

7. $\$12,000$ **9.** $3727; \$37,753$

11. $\frac{2}{3}(16\sqrt{2} - 8) \approx \$9.75$ million

13. 1.19×10^{-4} cm^3/s **15.** $\frac{1}{9}$ L/s

Exercises 9.5 □ page 617

1. (a) The probability that a randomly chosen tire will have a lifetime between 30,000 and 40,000 miles

(b) The probability that a randomly chosen tire will have a lifetime of at least 25,000 miles

3. (a) $f(x) \geq 0$ for all x and $\int_{-\infty}^{\infty} f(x)\,dx = 1$

(b) $1 - \frac{3}{8}\sqrt{3} \approx 0.35$

5. (a) $f(x) \geq 0$ for all x and $\int_{-\infty}^{\infty} f(x)\,dx = 1$ (b) 5

7. $5 \ln 2 \approx 3.47$ min

9. (a) $e^{-4/2.5} \approx 0.20$ (b) $1 - e^{-2/2.5} \approx 0.55$

(c) If you aren't served within 10 minutes, you get a free hamburger.

11. $\approx 44\%$ **13.** ≈ 0.9545

15. (b) $0; a_0$ (c) 1×10^{10}

(d) $1 - 41e^{-8} \approx 0.986$ (e) $\frac{3}{2}a_0$

Chapter 9 Review □ page 619

Exercises

1. $\frac{15}{2}$ **3.** (a) $\frac{21}{16}$ (b) $41\pi/10$ **5.** 3.292287 **7.** $\frac{124}{5}$

9. ≈ 458 lb **11.** $\left(-\frac{1}{2}, \frac{12}{5}\right)$ **13.** $\left(2, \frac{2}{3}\right)$

15. $2\pi^2$ **17.** $\$7166.67$

19. (a) $f(x) \geq 0$ for all x and $\int_{-\infty}^{\infty} f(x)\,dx = 1$

(b) ≈ 0.3455 (c) 5, yes

21. (a) $1 - e^{-3/8} \approx 0.31$ (b) $e^{-5/4} \approx 0.29$

(c) $8 \ln 2 \approx 5.55$ min

Problems Plus □ page 620

1. $2\pi/3 - \sqrt{3}/2$

3. (a) $2\pi r(r \pm d)$ (b) $\approx 3,360,000$ mi^2

(d) $\approx 78,400,000$ mi^2

5. (a) $P(z) = P_0 + g\int_0^z \rho(x)\,dx$

(b) $(P_0 - \rho_0 gH)(\pi r^2) + \rho_0 gHe^{L/H}\int_{-r}^r e^{x/H} \cdot 2\sqrt{r^2 - x^2}\,dx$

7. Height $\sqrt{2}\,b$, volume $\left(\frac{28}{27}\sqrt{6} - 2\right)\pi b^3$

9. 0.14 m **11.** $2/\pi, 1/\pi$

||| Chapter 10

Exercises 10.1 □ page 627

3. (a) ± 3 **5.** (b) and (c)

7. (a) It must be either 0 or decreasing

(c) $y = 0$ (d) $y = 1/(x + 2)$

9. (a) $0 < P < 4200$ (b) $P > 4200$

(c) $P = 0, P = 4200$

13. (a) At the beginning; stays positive, but decreases

(c)

Exercises 10.2 □ page 635

1. (a)

(b) $y = 0, y = 2,$ $y = -2$

3. IV **5.** III

7.

9.

11.

13.

15.

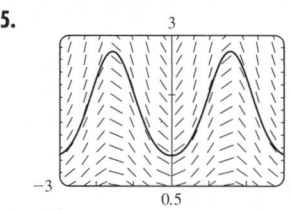

17. $-2 \le c \le 2$; $-2, 0, 2$

19. (a) (i) 1.4   (ii) 1.44   (iii) 1.4641

(b)

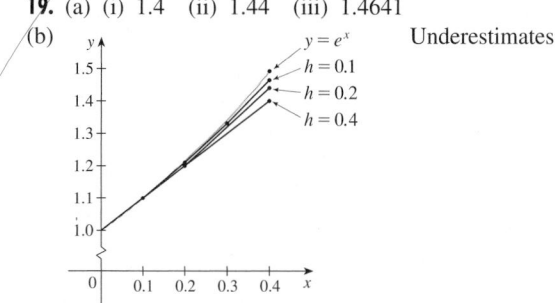

Underestimates

(c) (i) 0.0918   (ii) 0.0518   (iii) 0.0277
It appears that the error is also halved (approximately).
21. $-1, -3, -6.5, -12.25$ **23.** 1.7616
25. (a) (i) 3   (ii) 2.3928   (iii) 2.3701   (iv) 2.3681
(c) (i) -0.6321 (ii) -0.0249 (iii) -0.0022
(iv) -0.0002
It appears that the error is also divided by 10 (approximately).
27. (a), (d)   (b) 3
                                   (c) Yes; $Q = 3$
                                   (e) 2.77 C

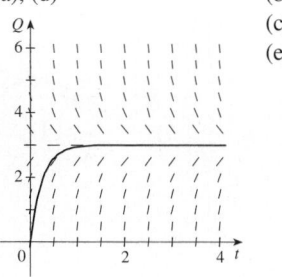

Exercises 10.3 □ page 643

Exercises 10.3 □ **page 643**
1. $y = Kx$ **3.** $y = K\sqrt{x^2 + 1}$
5. $y + \ln|\sec y| = \frac{1}{3}x^3 + x + C$
7. $y = \pm\sqrt{[3(te^t - e^t + C)]^{2/3} - 1}$
9. $u = Ae^{2t + t^2/2} - 1$ **11.** $y = \tan(x - 1)$
13. $\cos x + x \sin x = y^2 + \frac{1}{3}e^{3y} + \frac{2}{3}$
15. $u = -\sqrt{t^2 + \tan t + 25}$
17. $y = \dfrac{4a}{\sqrt{3}}\sin x - a$ **19.** $y = 7e^{x^4}$
21. (a) $\sin^{-1}y = x^2 + C$
(b) $y = \sin(x^2)$,
   $-\sqrt{\pi/2} \le x \le \sqrt{\pi/2}$

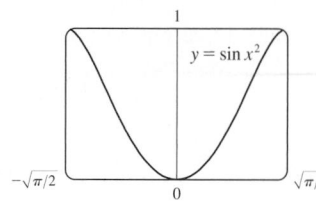

(c) No
23. $\cos y = \cos x - 1$

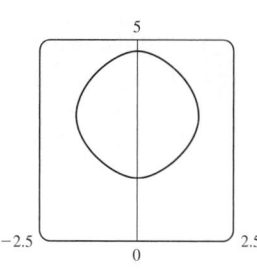

25. (a), (c)   (b) $y = \pm\sqrt{2(x + C)}$

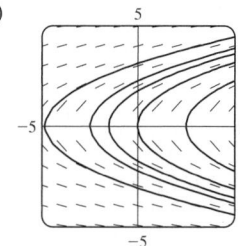

27. $x^2 + 2y^2 = C$ **29.** $y^3 = 3(x + C)$

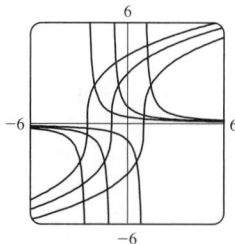

31. $Q(t) = 3 - 3e^{-4t}$; 3   **33.** $P(t) = M - Me^{-kt}$; M
35. (a) $x = a - 4/(kt + 2/\sqrt{a})^2$
(b) $t = \dfrac{2}{k\sqrt{a - b}}\left(\tan^{-1}\sqrt{\dfrac{b}{a - b}} - \tan^{-1}\sqrt{\dfrac{b - x}{a - b}}\right)$
37. (a) $C(t) = (C_0 - r/k)e^{-kt} + r/k$
(b) r/k; the concentration approaches r/k regardless of the value of C_0
21. (a) $\sin^{-1}y = x^2 + C$

39. (a) $15e^{-t/100}$ kg   (b) $15e^{-0.2} \approx 12.3$ kg   **41.** g/k
43. (a) $dA/dt = k\sqrt{A}\,(M - A)$
(b) $A(t) = M[(Ce^{\sqrt{M}kt} - 1)/(Ce^{\sqrt{M}kt} + 1)]^2$, where
$C = (\sqrt{M} + \sqrt{A_0})/(\sqrt{M} - \sqrt{A_0})$ and $A_0 = A(0)$

Exercises 10.4 □ page 656

1. About 235
3. (a) $500 \times 16^{t/3}$ (b) $\approx 20{,}159$
(c) $18{,}631$ cells/h   (d) $(3 \ln 60)/\ln 16 \approx 4.4$ h
5. (a) 1508 million, 1871 million   (b) 2161 million
(c) 3972 million; wars in the first half of century, increased life
expectancy in second half
7. (a) $Ce^{-0.0005t}$ (b) $-2000 \ln 0.9 \approx 211$ s
9. (a) $100 \times 2^{-t/30}$ mg   (b) ≈ 9.92 mg
(c) ≈ 199.3 years
11. ≈ 2500 years
13. (a) $\approx 137\,°F$ (b) ≈ 116 min
15. (a) $13.\overline{3}\,°C$ (b) ≈ 67.74 min
17. (a) ≈ 64.5 kPa   (b) ≈ 39.9 kPa
19. (a) (i) $\$3828.84$ (ii) $\$3840.25$ (iii) $\$3850.08$
(iv) $\$3851.61$ (v) $\$3852.01$ (vi) $\$3852.08$
(b) $dA/dt = 0.05A$, $A(0) = 3000$
21. (a) $P(t) = (m/k) + (P_0 - m/k)e^{kt}$ (b) $m < kP_0$
(c) $m = kP_0$, $m > kP_0$ (d) Declining

Exercises 10.5 □ page 665

1. (a) 100; 0.05
(b) Where P is close to 0 or 100; on the line $P = 50$;
$0 < P_0 < 100$; $P_0 > 100$
(c)

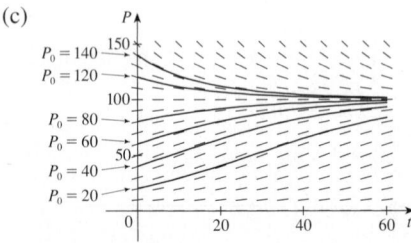

Solutions approach 100; some increase and some decrease, some
have an inflection point but others don't; solutions with $P_0 = 20$
and $P_0 = 40$ have inflection points at $P = 50$
(d) $P = 0$, $P = 100$; other solutions move away from $P = 0$ and
toward $P = 100$
3. (a) 3.23×10^7 kg   (b) ≈ 1.55 years
5. (a) $dP/dt = \frac{1}{265}P(1 - P/100)$, P in billions
(b) 5.49 billion   (c) In billions: 7.81, 27.72
(d) In billions: 5.48, 7.61, 22.41
7. (a) $dy/dt = ky(1 - y)$
(b) $y = y_0/[y_0 + (1 - y_0)e^{-kt}]$
(c) $3{:}36$ P.M.
11. (a) Fish are caught at a rate of 15 per week.
(b) See part (d)   (c) $P = 250$, $P = 750$

(d)

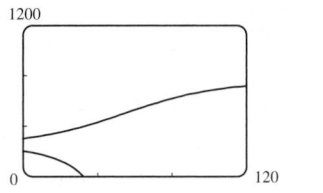

$0 < P_0 < 250$: $P \to 0$; $P_0 = 250$: $P \to 250$; $P_0 > 250$: $P \to 750$
(e) $P(t) = \dfrac{250 - 750ke^{t/25}}{1 - ke^{t/25}}$,   where $k = \frac{1}{11}, -\frac{1}{9}$

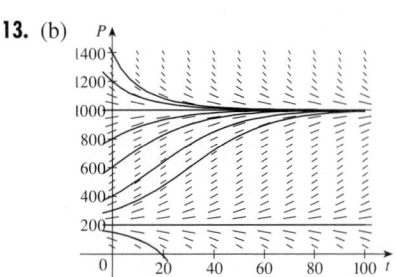

13. (b)

$0 < P_0 < 200$: $P \to 0$; $P_0 = 200$: $P \to 200$; $P_0 > 200$: $P \to 1000$
(c) $P(t) = \dfrac{m(K - P_0) + K(P_0 - m)e^{(K-m)(k/K)t}}{K - P_0 + (P_0 - m)e^{(K-m)(k/K)t}}$

15. (a) $P(t) = P_0 e^{(k/r)[\sin(rt - \phi) + \sin \phi]}$ (b) Does not exist

Exercises 10.6 □ page 672

1. No   **3.** Yes   **5.** $y = \frac{2}{3}e^x + Ce^{-2x}$
7. $y = x^2 \ln|x| + Cx^2$ **9.** $y = \frac{2}{3}\sqrt{x} + C/x$
11. $y = \frac{1}{2}x + Ce^{-x^2} - \frac{1}{2}e^{-x^2}\int e^{x^2}\,dx$
13. $u = (t^2 + 2t + 2C)/[2(t + 1)]$
15. $y = -x - 1 + 3e^x$ **17.** $v = t^3 e^{t^2} + 5e^{t^2}$
19. $y = -x \cos x - x$
21. $y = \sin x + (\cos x)/x + C/x$

25. $y = \pm[Cx^4 + 2/(5x)]^{-1/2}$
27. (a) $I(t) = 4 - 4e^{-5t}$ (b) $4 - 4e^{-1/2} \approx 1.57$ A
29. $Q(t) = 3(1 - e^{-4t})$, $I(t) = 12e^{-4t}$

31. $P(t) = M + Ce^{-kt}$

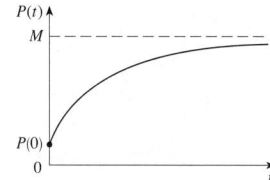

33. $y = \frac{2}{5}(100 + 2t) - 40{,}000(100 + 2t)^{-3/2}$; 0.2275 kg/L
35. (b) mg/c (c) $(mg/c)[t + (m/c)e^{-ct/m}] - m^2g/c^2$

Exercises 10.7 □ page 678

1. (a) x = predators, y = prey; growth is restricted only by predators, which feed only on prey.
(b) x = prey, y = predators; growth is restricted by carrying capacity and by predators, which feed only on prey.

3. (a) The rabbit population starts at about 300, increases to 2400, then decreases back to 300. The fox population starts at 100, decreases to about 20, increases to about 315, decreases to 100, and the cycle starts again.
(b)

5.

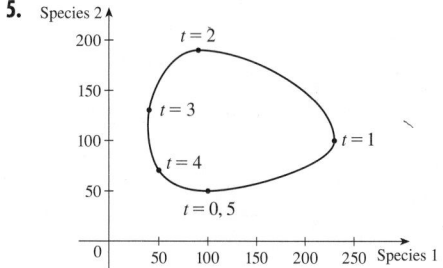

9. (a) Population stabilizes at 5000.
(b) (i) $W = 0$, $R = 0$: Zero populations
(ii) $W = 0$, $R = 5000$: In the absence of wolves, the rabbit population is always 5000.
(iii) $W = 64$, $R = 1000$: Both populations are stable.
(c) The populations stabilize at 1000 rabbits and 64 wolves.
(d)

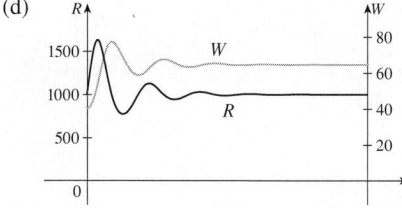

Chapter 10 Review □ page 684

True-False Quiz

1. True   **3.** False   **5.** True   **7.** True

Exercises

1. (a)

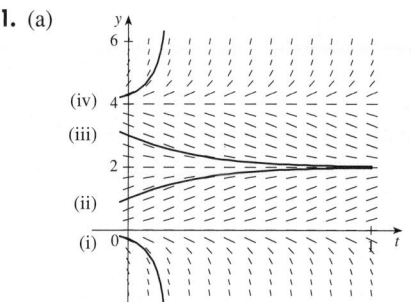

(b) $0 \le c \le 4$; $y = 0$, $y = 2$, $y = 4$

3. (a) $y(0.3) \approx 0.8$

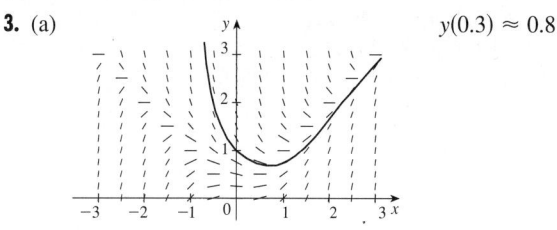

(b) 0.75676
(c) $y = x$ and $y = -x$; there is a local maximum or minimum
5. $y = \left(\frac{1}{2}x^2 + C\right)e^{-\sin x}$ **7.** $y^3 + y^2 = \cos x + x \sin x + C$
9. $y = \sqrt{(\ln x)^2 + 4}$ **11.** $y = e^{-x}\left(\frac{2}{3}x^{3/2} + 3\right)$
13. $y^2 - 2 \ln|y| + x^2 = C$
15. (a) 1000×3^t (b) 27,000
(c) $27{,}000 \ln 3 \approx 29{,}663$ bacteria per hour
(d) $(\ln 2)/\ln 3 \approx 0.63$ h
17. (a) $C_0 e^{-kt}$ (b) ≈ 100 h
19. (a) $L(t) = L_\infty - [L_\infty - L(0)]e^{-kt}$
(b) $L(t) = 53 - 43e^{-0.2t}$
21. 15 days   **23.** $k \ln h + h = (-R/V)t + C$
25. (a) Stabilizes at 200,000
(b) (i) $x = 0$, $y = 0$: Zero populations
(ii) $x = 200{,}000$, $y = 0$: In the absence of birds, the insect population is always 200,000.
(iii) $x = 25{,}000$, $y = 175$: Both populations are stable.
(c) The populations stabilize at 25,000 insects and 175 birds.
(d)

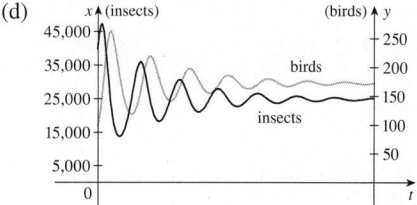

27. (a) $y = (1/k) \cosh kx + a - 1/k$ or
$y = (1/k) \cosh kx - (1/k) \cosh kb + h$ (b) $(2/k) \sinh kb$

Problems Plus □ **page 684**

1. $f(x) = \pm 10e^x$ **5.** 20°C
7. (b) $f(x) = (x^2 - L^2)/(4L) - (L/2) \ln(x/L)$ (c) No
9. (a) 9.8 h
(b) $31,900\pi \approx 100,000$ ft²; 6283 ft²/h
(c) 5.1 h
11. $x^2 + (y - 6)^2 = 25$

|||| **Chapter 11**

Exercises 11.1 □ **page 692**

1.

3.

5. (a)
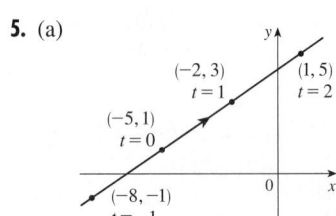
(b) $y = \frac{2}{3}x + \frac{13}{3}$

7. (a)

(b) $x = \frac{1}{4}(y - 5)^2 - 2$,
$-3 \leq y \leq 11$

9. (a)
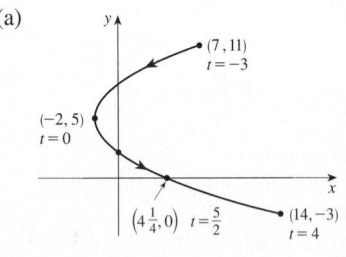
(b) $y = 1 - x^2, x \geq 0$

11. (a) $x^2 + y^2 = 1, x \geq 0$
(b)
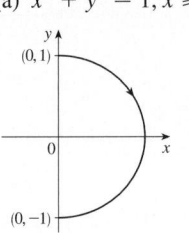

13. (a) $x + y = 1, 0 \leq x \leq 1$
(b)
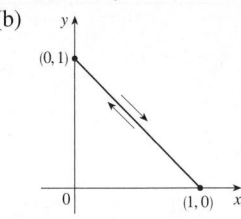

15. (a) $y = 1/x, x > 0$
(b)
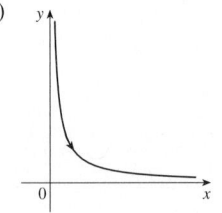

17. (a) $x^2 - y^2 = 1, x \geq 1$
(b)
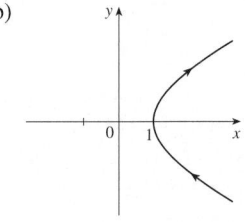

19. Moves counterclockwise along the circle $x^2 + y^2 = 1$ from $(-1, 0)$ to $(1, 0)$
21. Moves once clockwise around the ellipse $(x^2/4) + (y^2/9) = 1$, starting and ending at $(0, 3)$
23. It is contained in the rectangle described by $1 \leq x \leq 4$ and $2 \leq y \leq 3$.
25.

27.

29.
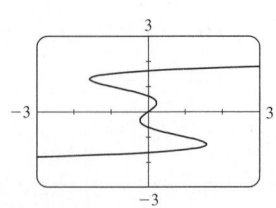

31. (b) $x = -2 + 5t, y = 7 - 8t, 0 \leq t \leq 1$
33. (a) $x = 2 \cos t, y = 1 - 2 \sin t, 0 \leq t \leq 2\pi$
(b) $x = 2 \cos t, y = 1 + 2 \sin t, 0 \leq t \leq 6\pi$
(c) $x = 2 \cos t, y = 1 + 2 \sin t, \pi/2 \leq t \leq 3\pi/2$
35. (a) $x = a \sin t, y = b \cos t, 0 \leq t \leq 2\pi$
(b)

(c) As b increases, the ellipse stretches vertically.

39. $x = a \cos \theta, y = b \sin \theta; (x^2/a^2) + (y^2/b^2) = 1$, ellipse

41.

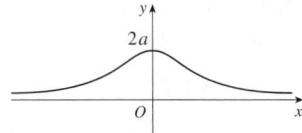

43. (a) Two points of intersection

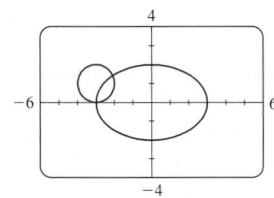

(b) One collision point at $(-3, 0)$ when $t = 3\pi/2$
(c) There are still two intersection points, but no collision point.
45. For $c = 0$, there is a cusp; for $c > 0$, there is a loop whose size increases as c increases.

 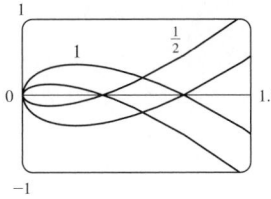

47. As n increases, the number of oscillations increases; a and b determine the width and height.

Exercises 11.2 ▫ **page 702**

1. $5/(3t^2 - 1)$ **3.** $y = -x$
5. $y = -(2/e)x + 3$ **7.** $y = -2x + 3$
9. $y = (\sqrt{3}/2)x - \frac{1}{2}$

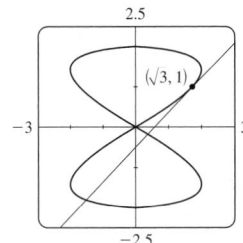

11. $1 + \frac{3}{2}t, 3/(4t), t > 0$ **13.** $-e^{-t}, e^{-t}/(1 - e^t), t < 0$
15. $-\frac{3}{2}\tan t, -\frac{3}{4}\sec^3 t, \frac{\pi}{2} < t < \frac{3\pi}{2}$
17. Horizontal at $(6, \pm 16)$, vertical at $(10, 0)$
19. Horizontal at $(\pm\sqrt{2}, \pm 1)$ (four points), vertical at $(\pm 2, 0)$
21. $(-0.25, 0.36), \left(-\frac{1}{4}, (1/\sqrt{2}) - \frac{1}{2}\ln 2\right)$
23.   **25.** $y = x, y = -x$

 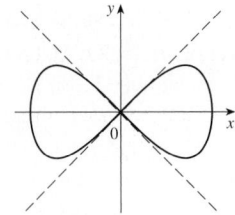

27. (a) $d\sin\theta/(r - d\cos\theta)$ **29.** $(-5, 6), \left(-\frac{208}{27}, \frac{32}{3}\right)$
31. πab **33.** $(e^{\pi/2} - 1)/2$ **35.** $2\pi r^2 + \pi d^2$
37. $\int_1^2 \sqrt{1 + 4t^2}\, dt$ **39.** $\int_0^{2\pi} \sqrt{3 - 2\sin t - 2\cos t}\, dt$
41. $4\sqrt{2} - 2$
43. $-\sqrt{10}/3 + \ln(3 + \sqrt{10}) + \sqrt{2} - \ln(1 + \sqrt{2})$
45. $\sqrt{2}(e^\pi - 1)$

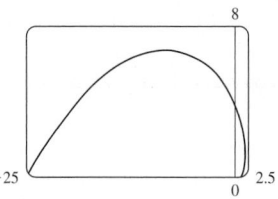

47. $e^3 + 11 - e^{-8}$

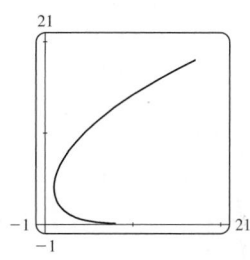

49. 612.3053   **51.** $6\sqrt{2}, \sqrt{2}$
55. (a) $t \in [0, 4\pi]$ (b) ≈ 294

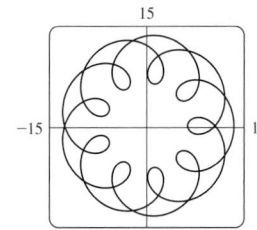

57. $\int_1^2 \frac{8}{3}\pi t^{3/2}\sqrt{1 + 4t^2}\, dt$ **59.** $2\pi(247\sqrt{13} + 64)/1215$
61. $6\pi a^2/5$ **63.** 59.101   **65.** $24\pi(949\sqrt{26} + 1)/5$
71. $\frac{1}{4}$

Exercises 11.3 ▫ **page 713**

1. (a)   (b)

 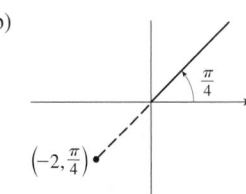

$(1, 5\pi/2), (-1, 3\pi/2)$ $(2, 5\pi/4), (-2, 9\pi/4)$

(c)

$(3, 2 + 2\pi), (-3, 2 + \pi)$

3. (a)

(b)

(0, 3)

$(-2, 2)$

(c)

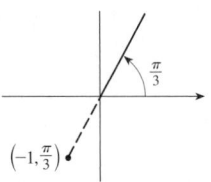

$\left(-\frac{1}{2}, -\sqrt{3}/2\right)$

5. (a) (i) $\left(\sqrt{2}, \pi/4\right)$ (ii) $\left(-\sqrt{2}, 5\pi/4\right)$
(b) (i) $(4, 11\pi/6)$ (ii) $(-4, 5\pi/6)$

7.

9.

11.

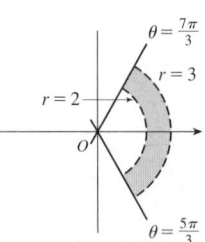

13. $\frac{1}{2}\sqrt{40 + 6\sqrt{6} - 6\sqrt{2}}$
15. Circle, center O, radius 2   **17.** Circle, center $\left(0, \frac{3}{2}\right)$, radius $\frac{3}{2}$
19. Horizontal line, 1 unit above the x-axis
21. $r = 3 \sec \theta$ **23.** $r = -\cot \theta \csc \theta$ **25.** $r = 2c \cos \theta$
27. (a) $\theta = \pi/6$ (b) $x = 3$
29.

31.

33.

35.

37.

39.

41.

43.

45.

47.

49.

51.

53. (a) For $c < -1$, the loop begins at $\theta = \sin^{-1}(-1/c)$ and ends
at $\theta = \pi - \sin^{-1}(-1/c)$; for $c > 1$, it begins at
$\theta = \pi + \sin^{-1}(1/c)$ and ends at $\theta = 2\pi - \sin^{-1}(1/c)$.
55. $\sqrt{3}$ **57.** $-\pi$ **59.** -1
61. Horizontal at $\left(3/\sqrt{2}, \pi/4\right)$, $\left(-3/\sqrt{2}, 3\pi/4\right)$;
vertical at $(3, 0)$, $(0, \pi/2)$
63. Horizontal at $\left(\frac{3}{2}, \pi/3\right)$, $\left(\frac{3}{2}, 5\pi/3\right)$, and the pole;
vertical at $(2, 0)$, $\left(\frac{1}{2}, 2\pi/3\right)$, $\left(\frac{1}{2}, 4\pi/3\right)$
65. Horizontal at $(-1, 3\pi/2)$, $(-1, \pi/2)$, $\left(\frac{2}{3}, \alpha\right)$, $\left(\frac{2}{3}, \pi - \alpha\right)$,
$\left(\frac{2}{3}, \pi + \alpha\right)$, $\left(\frac{2}{3}, 2\pi - \alpha\right)$, where $\alpha = \sin^{-1}\left(1/\sqrt{6}\right)$;
vertical at $(1, 0)$, $(1, \pi)$, $\left(-\frac{2}{3}, \beta\right)$, $\left(-\frac{2}{3}, \pi - \beta\right)$, $\left(-\frac{2}{3}, \pi + \beta\right)$,
$\left(-\frac{2}{3}, 2\pi - \beta\right)$, where $\beta = \cos^{-1}\left(1/\sqrt{6}\right)$
67. Center $(b/2, a/2)$, radius $\sqrt{a^2 + b^2}/2$

69.

71.

73.
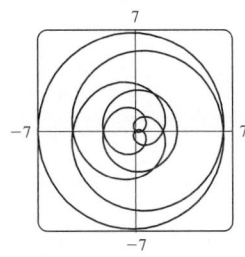

75. By counterclockwise rotation through angle $\pi/6$, $\pi/3$, or α about the origin

77. (a) A rose with n loops if n is odd and $2n$ loops if n is even
(b) Number of loops is always $2n$

79. For $0 < a < 1$, the curve is an oval, which develops a dimple as $a \to 1^-$. When $a > 1$, the curve splits into two parts, one of which has a loop.

Exercises 11.4 □ **page 719**

1. $\pi^2/64$ **3.** $\pi/12 + \sqrt{3}/8$ **5.** $\pi^3/6$ **7.** $41\pi/4$
9. $9\pi/4$ **11.** 4

13. π **15.** 3π

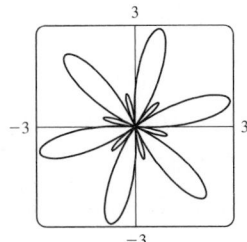

17. $\pi/8$ **19.** $9\pi/20$ **21.** $\pi - \left(3\sqrt{3}/2\right)$
23. $(4\pi/3) + 2\sqrt{3}$ **25.** $4\sqrt{3} - \frac{4}{3}\pi$ **27.** π
29. $\frac{1}{8}(\pi - 2)$ **31.** $(\pi/2) - 1$
33. $(19\pi/3) - \left(11\sqrt{3}/2\right)$
35. $\frac{1}{4}\left(\pi + 3\sqrt{3}\right)$ **37.** $\left(1/\sqrt{2}, \pi/4\right)$ and the pole
39. $\left(\frac{1}{2}, \pi/3\right), \left(\frac{1}{2}, 5\pi/3\right)$, and the pole
41. $\left(\sqrt{3}/2, \pi/3\right), \left(\sqrt{3}/2, 2\pi/3\right)$, and the pole
43. Intersection at $\theta \approx 0.89, 2.25$; area ≈ 3.46

45. π **47.** $\frac{8}{3}\left[(\pi^2 + 1)^{3/2} - 1\right]$ **49.** 29.0653
51. 9.6884
53. $\frac{16}{3}$ **55.** (b) $2\pi\left(2 - \sqrt{2}\right)$

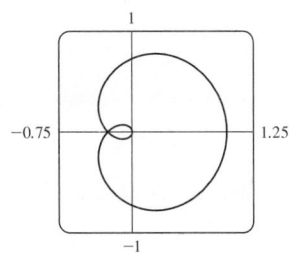

Exercises 11.5 □ **page 726**

1. $(0, 0), \left(\frac{1}{8}, 0\right), x = -\frac{1}{8}$ **3.** $(0, 0), \left(0, -\frac{1}{16}\right), y = \frac{1}{16}$

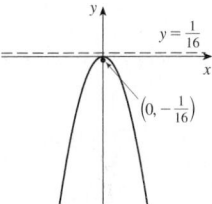

5. $(-2, 3), (-2, 5), y = 1$ **7.** $(-2, -1), (-5, -1), x = 1$

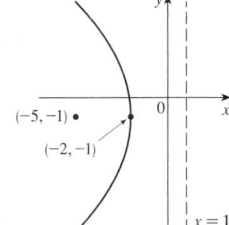

9. $x = -y^2$, focus $\left(-\frac{1}{4}, 0\right)$, directrix $x = \frac{1}{4}$
11. $(\pm 3, 0), (\pm 2, 0)$ **13.** $(0, \pm 4), \left(0, \pm 2\sqrt{3}\right)$

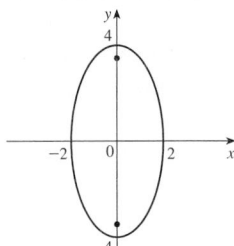

15. $(1, \pm 3), \left(1, \pm\sqrt{5}\right)$

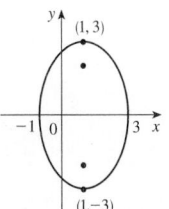

17. $\dfrac{x^2}{4} + \dfrac{y^2}{9} = 1$, foci $\left(0, \pm\sqrt{5}\right)$

19. $(\pm 12, 0)$, $(\pm 13, 0)$, $y = \pm\frac{5}{12}x$

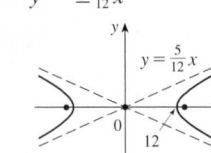

21. $(0, \pm 2)$, $(0, \pm 2\sqrt{2})$, $y = \pm x$

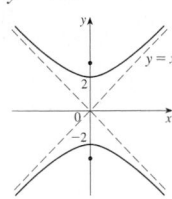

23. $(2 \pm \sqrt{6}, 1)$, $(2 \pm \sqrt{15}, 1)$, $y - 1 = \pm(\sqrt{6}/2)(x - 2)$

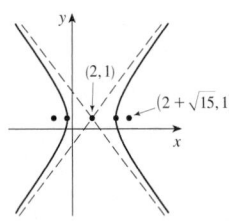

25. Parabola, $(0, -1)$, $\left(0, -\frac{3}{4}\right)$ **27.** Ellipse, $(\pm\sqrt{2}, 1)$, $(\pm 1, 1)$

29. Hyperbola, $(0, 1)$, $(0, 3)$; $(0, -1 \pm \sqrt{5})$

31. $x^2 = -8y$ **33.** $y^2 = -12(x + 1)$

35. $y^2 = 16x$ **37.** $(x^2/25) + (y^2/21) = 1$

39. $(x^2/12) + [(y - 4)^2/16] = 1$

41. $[(x - 2)^2/9] + [(y - 2)^2/5] = 1$ **43.** $y^2 - (x^2/8) = 1$

45. $[(x - 4)^2/4] - [(y - 3)^2/5] = 1$

47. $(x^2/9) - (y^2/36) = 1$

49. $(x^2/3{,}763{,}600) + (y^2/3{,}753{,}196) = 1$

51. (a) $(121x^2/1{,}500{,}625) - (121y^2/3{,}339{,}375) = 1$

(b) ≈ 248 mi

55. (a) Ellipse   (b) Hyperbola   (c) No curve   **57.** 9.69

Exercises 11.6 □ **page 731**

1. $r = 42/(4 + 7\sin\theta)$ **3.** $r = 15/(4 - 3\cos\theta)$

5. $r = 8/(1 - \sin\theta)$ **7.** $r = 4/(2 + \cos\theta)$

9. (a) 1   (b) Parabola   (c) $y = 1$

(d)

11. (a) $\frac{1}{4}$ (b) Ellipse   (c) $y = -12$

(d)

13. (a) $\frac{1}{3}$ (b) Ellipse   (c) $x = \frac{9}{2}$

(d)

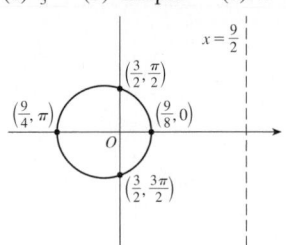

15. (a) 2   (b) Hyperbola   (c) $x = -\frac{3}{8}$

(d)

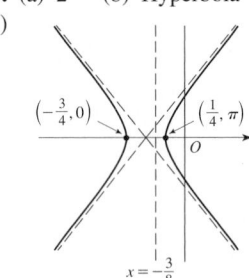

17. (a) $e = \frac{3}{4}$, directrix $x = -\frac{1}{3}$

(b) $r = 1/[4 - 3\cos(\theta - \pi/3)]$

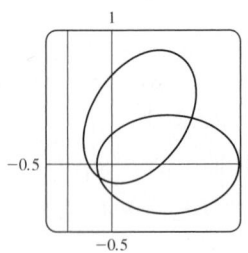

19. The ellipse is nearly circular when e is close to 0 and becomes more elongated as $e \to 1^-$. At $e = 1$, the curve becomes a parabola.

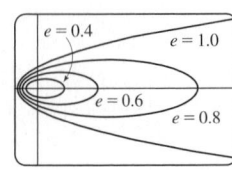

25. (b) $r = (1.49 \times 10^8)/(1 - 0.017\cos\theta)$

27. 35.64 AU

29. 7.0×10^7 km

31. 3.6×10^8 km

Chapter 11 Review □ **page 733**

True-False Quiz

1. False   **3.** False   **5.** True   **7.** False   **9.** True

Exercises

1. $x = y^2 - 8y + 12$ **3.** $y = 1/x$

5. $x = t$, $y = \sqrt{t}$, $t \geqslant 0$; $x = t^4$, $y = t^2$;
$x = \tan^2 t$, $y = \tan t$, $0 \leqslant t < \frac{\pi}{2}$

7.

9.

11.

13.

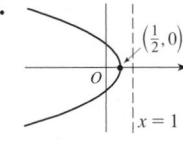

15. $r = 2/(\cos \theta + \sin \theta)$

17.

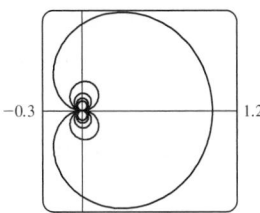

19. 2   **21.** -1
23. $(\sin t + t \cos t)/(\cos t - t \sin t)$, $(t^2 + 2)/(\cos t - t \sin t)^3$
25. $\left(\frac{11}{8}, \frac{3}{4}\right)$
27. Vertical tangent at
$\left(3a/2, \pm\sqrt{3}\, a/2\right)$, $(-3a, 0)$;
horizontal tangent at
$(a, 0)$, $\left(-a/2, \pm 3\sqrt{3}\, a/2\right)$

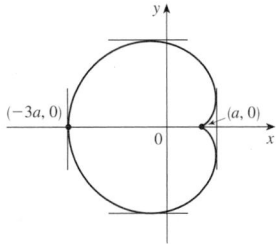

29. 18   **31.** $(2, \pm\pi/3)$ **33.** $(\pi - 1)/2$ **35.** $2\left(5\sqrt{5} - 1\right)$
37. $\dfrac{2\sqrt{\pi^2 + 1} - \sqrt{4\pi^2 + 1}}{2\pi} + \ln\left(\dfrac{2\pi + \sqrt{4\pi^2 + 1}}{\pi + \sqrt{\pi^2 + 1}}\right)$
39. $471{,}295\pi/1024$
41. All curves have the vertical asymptote $x = 1$. For $c < -1$, the curve bulges to the right. At $c = -1$, the curve is the line $x = 1$. For $-1 < c < 0$, it bulges to the left. At $c = 0$ there is a cusp at $(0, 0)$. For $c > 0$, there is a loop.
43. $(\pm 1, 0)$, $(\pm 3, 0)$ **45.** $\left(-\frac{25}{24}, 3\right)$, $(-1, 3)$

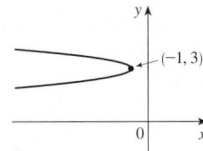

47. $x^2 = 8(y - 4)$
49. $5x^2 - 20y^2 = 36$
51. $(x^2/25) + ((8y - 399)^2/160{,}801) = 1$
53. $r = 4/(3 + \cos \theta)$
55. $x = a(\cot \theta + \sin \theta \cos \theta)$, $y = a(1 + \sin^2\theta)$

Problems Plus ▫ **page 735**

1. $\ln(\pi/2)$ **3.** $\left[-\frac{3}{4}\sqrt{3}, \frac{3}{4}\sqrt{3}\right] \times [-1, 2]$
5. (a) At $(0, 0)$ and $\left(\frac{3}{2}, \frac{3}{2}\right)$
(b) Horizontal tangents at $(0, 0)$ and $\left(\sqrt[3]{2}, \sqrt[3]{4}\right)$;
vertical tangents at $(0, 0)$ and $\left(\sqrt[3]{4}, \sqrt[3]{2}\right)$
(d)   (g) $\frac{3}{2}$

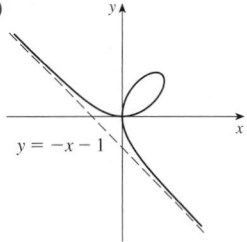

Chapter 12

Exercises 12.1 ▫ **page 746**

Abbreviations: C, convergent; D, divergent

1. (a) A sequence is an ordered list of numbers. It can also be defined as a function whose domain is the set of positive integers.
(b) The terms a_n approach 8 as n becomes large.
(c) The terms a_n become large as n becomes large.
3. 0.8, 0.96, 0.992, 0.9984, 0.99968   **5.** $-3, \frac{3}{2}, -\frac{1}{2}, \frac{1}{8}, -\frac{1}{40}$
7. 3, 5, 9, 17, 33
9. $a_n = 1/2^n$ **11.** $a_n = 5n - 3$ **13.** $a_n = \left(-\frac{2}{3}\right)^{n-1}$
15. D   **17.** 5   **19.** 0   **21.** 0
23. D   **25.** 0   **27.** 0   **29.** 0   **31.** 0
33. 1   **35.** 1   **37.** D   **39.** D   **41.** D
43. $\pi/4$ **45.** 0   **47.** 0
49. (a) 1060, 1123.60, 1191.02, 1262.48, 1338.23   (b) D
51. $-1 < r < 1$
53. Convergent by the Monotonic Sequence Theorem; $5 \leqslant L < 8$
55. Decreasing; yes   **57.** Not monotonic; yes
59. Decreasing; yes   **61.** 2   **63.** $(3 + \sqrt{5})/2$
65. (b) $\left(1 + \sqrt{5}\right)/2$ **67.** (a) 0   (b) 9, 11

Exercises 12.2 ▫ **page 756**

1. (a) A sequence is an ordered list of numbers whereas a series is the *sum* of a list of numbers.
(b) A series is convergent if the sequence of partial sums is a convergent sequence. A series is divergent if it is not convergent.

3. $-2.40000, -1.92000$
$-2.01600, -1.99680,$
$-2.00064, -1.99987$
$-2.00003, -1.99999$
$-2.00000, -2.00000$
Convergent, sum $= -2$

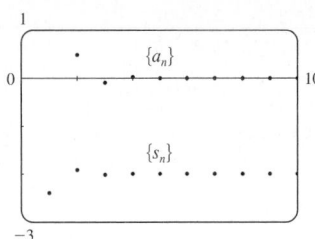

5. $1.55741, -0.62763,$
$-0.77018, 0.38764$
$-2.99287, -3.28388$
$-2.41243, -9.21214$
$-9.66446, -9.01610$
Divergent

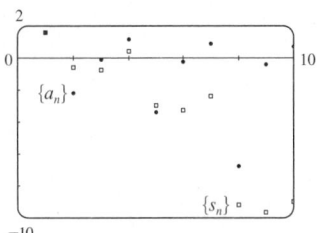

7. $0.64645, 0.80755,$
$0.87500, 0.91056,$
$0.93196, 0.94601,$
$0.95581, 0.96296,$
$0.96838, 0.97259$
Convergent, sum $= 1$

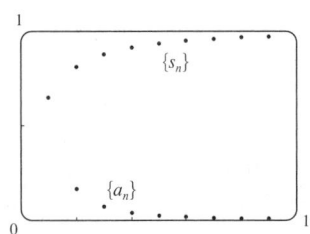

9. (a) C   (b) D
11. 9   **13.** D   **15.** 15   **17.** $\frac{1}{7}$ **19.** D   **21.** D
23. $\frac{3}{2}$ **25.** D   **27.** $\frac{3}{2}$ **29.** D   **31.** D   **33.** $\frac{7}{2}$
35. $\frac{2}{9}$ **37.** $\frac{1138}{333}$ **39.** $41,111/333,000$
41. $-3 < x < 3; x/(3 - x)$ **43.** $-\frac{1}{4} < x < \frac{1}{4}; 1/(1 - 4x)$
45. all x; $\dfrac{2}{2 - \cos x}$ **47.** $\frac{1}{4}$
49. $a_1 = 0, a_n = 2/[n(n + 1)]$ for $n > 1$, sum $= 1$
51. (a) $S_n = D(1 - c^n)/(1 - c)$ (b) 5
53. $(\sqrt{3} - 1)/2$ **55.** $1/[n(n + 1)]$
57. The series is divergent.
63. $\{s_n\}$ is bounded and increasing.
65. (a) $0, \frac{1}{9}, \frac{2}{9}, \frac{1}{3}, \frac{2}{3}, \frac{7}{9}, \frac{8}{9}, 1$
67. (a) $\frac{1}{2}, \frac{5}{6}, \frac{23}{24}, \frac{119}{120}; [(n + 1)! - 1]/(n + 1)!$ (c) 1

Exercises 12.3 □ **page 765**
1. C

3. C   **5.** D   **7.** C   **9.** D   **11.** C   **13.** C   **15.** C

17. D   **19.** C   **21.** D   **23.** C   **25.** $p > 1$
27. $p < -1$ **29.** $(1, \infty)$
31. (a) 1.54977, error $\leqslant 0.1$ (b) 1.64522, error $\leqslant 0.005$
(c) $n > 1000$
33. 2.61   **39.** $b < 1/e$

Exercises 12.4 □ **page 770**
1. (a) Nothing   (b) C
3. C   **5.** C   **7.** D
9. C   **11.** D   **13.** C   **15.** C   **17.** D   **19.** C
21. D   **23.** C   **25.** D   **27.** C   **29.** C   **31.** D
33. 0.567975, error $\leqslant 0.000\overline{3}$ **35.** 0.76352, error < 0.001
45. Yes

Exercises 12.5 □ **page 775**
1. (a) A series whose terms are alternately positive and negative
(b) $0 < b_{n+1} \leqslant b_n$ and $\lim_{n \to \infty} b_n = 0$, where $b_n = |a_n|$
(c) $|R_n| \leqslant b_{n+1}$
3. C   **5.** C   **7.** D   **9.** C   **11.** C   **13.** D
15. C   **17.** C   **19.** D
21. $1.0000, 0.6464,$
$0.8389, 0.7139, 0.8033,$
$0.7353, 0.7893, 0.7451, 0.7821,$
0.7505; error < 0.0275

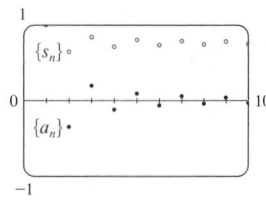

23. 10   **25.** 7   **27.** 0.9721   **29.** 0.0676
31. An underestimate   **33.** p is not a negative integer
35. $\{b_n\}$ is not decreasing

Exercises 12.6 □ **page 781**
Abbreviations: AC, absolutely convergent;
CC, conditionally convergent
1. (a) D   (b) C   (c) May converge or diverge
3. AC   **5.** CC   **7.** D   **9.** AC   **11.** AC   **13.** AC
15. AC   **17.** CC   **19.** AC   **21.** D   **23.** AC
25. AC   **27.** D   **29.** D   **31.** (a) and (d)
35. (a) $\frac{661}{960} \approx 0.68854$, error < 0.00521 (b) $n \geqslant 11, 0.693109$

Exercises 12.7 □ **page 784**
1. D   **3.** C   **5.** C   **7.** D   **9.** C   **11.** C   **13.** C
15. C   **17.** D   **19.** C   **21.** C   **23.** D   **25.** C
27. C   **29.** C   **31.** D   **33.** C   **35.** C   **37.** C

Exercises 12.8 □ **page 789**
1. A series of the form $\sum_{n=0}^{\infty} c_n(x - a)^n$, where x is a variable and a and the c_n's are constants
3. $1, [-1, 1)$ **5.** $1, [-1, 1]$ **7.** $\infty, (-\infty, \infty)$ **9.** $\frac{1}{4}, \left(-\frac{1}{4}, \frac{1}{4}\right)$
11. $\frac{1}{2}, \left(-\frac{1}{2}, \frac{1}{2}\right]$ **13.** $4, (-4, 4]$ **15.** $1, (0, 2)$
17. $2, (-4, 0]$ **19.** $\infty, (-\infty, \infty)$ **21.** $b, (a - b, a + b)$

23. $0, \left\{\frac{1}{2}\right\}$ **25.** $\frac{1}{4}, \left[-\frac{1}{2}, 0\right]$ **27.** $\infty, (-\infty, \infty)$
29. (a) Yes (b) No **31.** k^k
33. (a) $(-\infty, \infty)$
(b), (c)

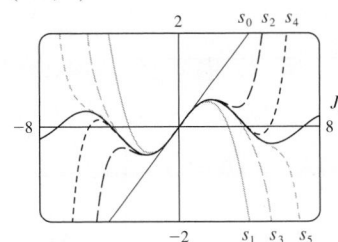

35. $(-1, 1), f(x) = (1 + 2x)/(1 - x^2)$ **39.** 2

Exercises 12.9 □ page 795

1. 10 **3.** $\sum_{n=0}^{\infty} (-1)^n x^n, (-1, 1)$ **5.** $\sum_{n=0}^{\infty} x^{3n}, (-1, 1)$

7. $-\sum_{n=0}^{\infty} \frac{1}{5^{n+1}} x^n, (-5, 5)$ **9.** $\sum_{n=0}^{\infty} (-1)^n \frac{1}{9^{n+1}} x^{2n+1}, (-3, 3)$

11. $\sum_{n=0}^{\infty} \left[\frac{(-1)^{n+1}}{2^{n+1}} - 1\right] x^n, (-1, 1)$

13. (a) $\sum_{n=0}^{\infty} (-1)^n (n + 1) x^n, R = 1$

(b) $\frac{1}{2} \sum_{n=0}^{\infty} (-1)^n (n + 2)(n + 1) x^n, R = 1$

(c) $\frac{1}{2} \sum_{n=2}^{\infty} (-1)^n n(n - 1) x^n, R = 1$

15. $\ln 5 - \sum_{n=1}^{\infty} \frac{x^n}{n 5^n}, R = 5$

17. $\sum_{n=3}^{\infty} \frac{n - 2}{2^{n-1}} x^n, R = 2$

19. $\ln 3 + \sum_{n=1}^{\infty} \frac{(-1)^{n-1}}{n 3^n} x^n, R = 3$

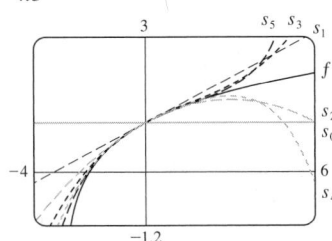

21. $\sum_{n=0}^{\infty} \frac{2x^{2n+1}}{2n + 1}, R = 1$

23. $C + \sum_{n=0}^{\infty} \frac{t^{8n+2}}{8n + 2}; 1$

25. $C + \sum_{n=1}^{\infty} (-1)^{n+1} \frac{x^{2n-1}}{4n^2 - 1}; 1$

27. 0.199989 **29.** 0.000065 **31.** 0.09531
33. (b) 0.920 **37.** $[-1, 1], [-1, 1), (-1, 1)$

Exercises 12.10 □ page 806

1. $b_8 = f^{(8)}(5)/8!$ **3.** $\sum_{n=0}^{\infty} (-1)^n \frac{x^{2n}}{(2n)!}, R = \infty$

5. $\sum_{n=0}^{\infty} (-1)^n \frac{(n + 1)(n + 2)}{2} x^n, R = 1$

7. $\sum_{n=0}^{\infty} \frac{5^n}{n!} x^n, R = \infty$

9. $\sum_{n=0}^{\infty} \frac{x^{2n+1}}{(2n + 1)!}, R = \infty$

11. $7 + 5(x - 2) + (x - 2)^2, R = \infty$

13. $\sum_{n=0}^{\infty} \frac{e^3}{n!} (x - 3)^n, R = \infty$

15. $\sum_{n=0}^{\infty} (-1)^{n+1} \frac{1}{(2n)!} (x - \pi)^{2n}, R = \infty$

17. $\sum_{n=0}^{\infty} (-1)^n \frac{1 \cdot 3 \cdot 5 \cdot \cdots \cdot (2n - 1)}{2^n \cdot 3^{2n+1} \cdot n!} (x - 9)^n, R = 9$

23. $\sum_{n=0}^{\infty} (-1)^n \frac{\pi^{2n}}{(2n)!} x^{2n}, R = \infty$

25. $\sum_{n=0}^{\infty} (-1)^n \frac{1}{2n + 1} x^{2n+2}, R = 1$

27. $\sum_{n=0}^{\infty} (-1)^n \frac{1}{n!} x^{n+2}, R = \infty$

29. $\sum_{n=1}^{\infty} \frac{(-1)^{n+1} 2^{2n-1} x^{2n}}{(2n)!}, R = \infty$

31. $\sum_{n=0}^{\infty} \frac{(-1)^n x^{2n}}{(2n + 1)!}, R = \infty$

33. $1 + \frac{x}{2} + \sum_{n=2}^{\infty} (-1)^{n-1} \frac{1 \cdot 3 \cdot 5 \cdot \cdots \cdot (2n - 3)}{2^n n!} x^n, R = 1$

35. $\sum_{n=0}^{\infty} (-1)^n \dfrac{1}{(2n)!} x^{4n}, R = \infty$

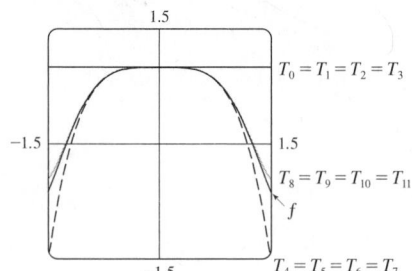

37. 0.81873

39. $C + \sum_{n=0}^{\infty} (-1)^n \dfrac{x^{6n+2}}{(6n+2)(2n)!}$

41. $C + x + \dfrac{x^4}{8} + \sum_{n=2}^{\infty} (-1)^{n-1} \dfrac{1 \cdot 3 \cdot 5 \cdot \cdots \cdot (2n-3)}{2^n n!(3n+1)} x^{3n+1}$

43. 0.440 **45.** 0.09998750 **47.** $\frac{1}{3}$ **49.** $\frac{1}{120}$

51. $1 - \frac{3}{2}x^2 + \frac{25}{24}x^4$ **53.** $1 + \frac{1}{6}x^2 + \frac{7}{360}x^4$

55. e^{-x^4} **57.** $1/\sqrt{2}$ **59.** $e^3 - 1$

Exercises 12.11 □ **page 811**

1. $1 + \dfrac{x}{2} + \sum_{n=2}^{\infty} (-1)^{n-1} \dfrac{1 \cdot 3 \cdot 5 \cdot \cdots \cdot (2n-3)}{2^n n!} x^n, R = 1$

3. $\sum_{n=0}^{\infty} (-1)^n \dfrac{(n+1)(n+2)}{2^{n+4}} x^n, R = 2$

5. $1 - 2x - \sum_{n=2}^{\infty} \dfrac{3 \cdot 7 \cdot \cdots \cdot (4n-5) \cdot 2^n}{n!} x^n, R = \frac{1}{8}$

7. $\frac{1}{2}x + \sum_{n=1}^{\infty} (-1)^n \dfrac{1 \cdot 3 \cdot 5 \cdot \cdots \cdot (2n-1)}{n! 2^{3n+1}} x^{2n+1}, R = 2$

9. $1 + \frac{3}{2}x, 1 + \frac{3}{2}x - \frac{3}{8}x^2, 1 + \frac{3}{2}x - \frac{3}{8}x^2 + \frac{5}{16}x^3$

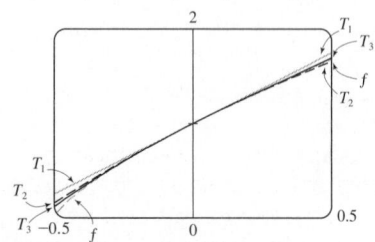

11. (a) $1 + \sum_{n=1}^{\infty} \dfrac{1 \cdot 3 \cdot 5 \cdot \cdots \cdot (2n-1)}{2^n n!} x^{2n}$

(b) $x + \sum_{n=1}^{\infty} \dfrac{1 \cdot 3 \cdot 5 \cdot \cdots \cdot (2n-1)}{(2n+1)2^n n!} x^{2n+1}$

13. (a) $1 + \dfrac{x}{3} + \sum_{n=2}^{\infty} (-1)^{n+1} \dfrac{2 \cdot 5 \cdot 8 \cdot \cdots \cdot (3n-4)}{3^n n!} x^n$

(b) 1.0033

15. (a) $\sum_{n=1}^{\infty} n x^n$ (b) 2

17. (a) $1 + \dfrac{x^2}{2} + \sum_{n=2}^{\infty} (-1)^{n-1} \dfrac{1 \cdot 3 \cdot 5 \cdot \cdots \cdot (2n-3)}{2^n n!} x^{2n}$

(b) 99,225

Exercises 12.12 □ **page 819**

1. (a) $T_0(x) = 1 = T_1(x), T_2(x) = 1 - \frac{1}{2}x^2 = T_3(x),$
$T_4(x) = 1 - \frac{1}{2}x^2 + \frac{1}{24}x^4 = T_5(x), T_6(x) = 1 - \frac{1}{2}x^2 + \frac{1}{24}x^4 - \frac{1}{720}x^6$

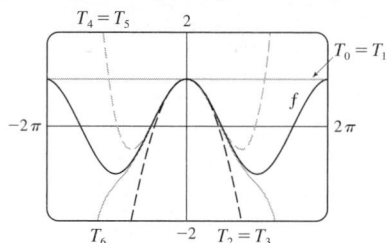

(b)

x	f	$T_0 = T_1$	$T_2 = T_3$	$T_4 = T_5$	T_6
$\dfrac{\pi}{4}$	0.7071	1	0.6916	0.7074	0.7071
$\dfrac{\pi}{2}$	0	1	−0.2337	0.0200	−0.0009
π	−1	1	−3.9348	0.1239	−1.2114

(c) As n increases, $T_n(x)$ is a good approximation to $f(x)$ on a larger and larger interval.

3. $(x - 1) - \frac{1}{2}(x-1)^2 + \frac{1}{3}(x-1)^3 - \frac{1}{4}(x-1)^4$

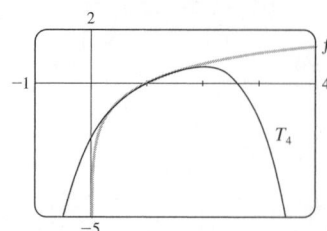

5. $\dfrac{1}{2} + \dfrac{\sqrt{3}}{2}\left(x - \dfrac{\pi}{6}\right) - \dfrac{1}{4}\left(x - \dfrac{\pi}{6}\right)^2 - \dfrac{\sqrt{3}}{12}\left(x - \dfrac{\pi}{6}\right)^3$

7. $x + \frac{1}{6}x^3$

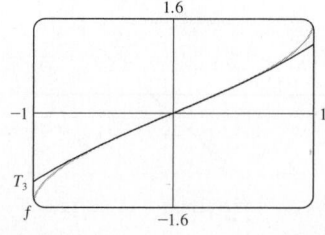

9. $x - 2x^2 + 2x^3$

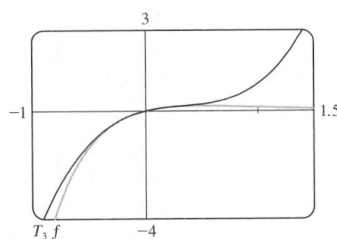

11. $T_8(x) = 1 + \frac{1}{2}x^2 + \frac{5}{24}x^4 + \frac{61}{720}x^6 + \frac{277}{8064}x^8$

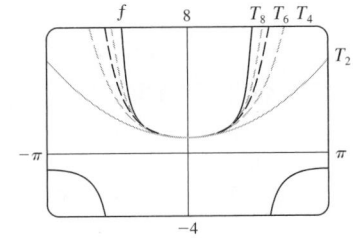

13. (a) $2 + \frac{1}{4}(x - 4) - \frac{1}{64}(x - 4)^2$ (b) 1.5625×10^{-5}
15. (a) $1 + \frac{2}{3}(x - 1) - \frac{1}{9}(x - 1)^2 + \frac{4}{81}(x - 1)^3$ (b) 0.000097
17. (a) $x + \frac{1}{3}x^3$ (b) 0.058
19. (a) $1 + x^2$ (b) 0.00006
21. (a) $x^2 - \frac{1}{6}x^4$ (b) 0.042
23. 0.57358   **25.** Four
27. $-1.037 < x < 1.037$ **29.** 21 m, no
35. (c) They differ by about 8×10^{-9} km.

Chapter 12 Review □ **page 822**

True-False Quiz

1. False   **3.** True   **5.** False   **7.** False   **9.** False
11. True   **13.** True   **15.** False   **17.** True

Exercises

1. $\frac{1}{2}$ **3.** D   **5.** 0   **7.** e^{12} **9.** 2   **11.** C   **13.** C
15. D   **17.** C   **19.** C   **21.** C   **23.** CC   **25.** AC
27. 8   **29.** $\pi/4$ **31.** e^{-e} **35.** 0.9721
37. 0.18976224, $|\text{error}| < 6.4 \times 10^{-7}$ **41.** $4, [-6, 2)$
43. 0.5, [2.5, 3.5)

45. $\frac{1}{2} \sum_{n=0}^{\infty} (-1)^n \left[\frac{1}{(2n)!} \left(x - \frac{\pi}{6} \right)^{2n} + \frac{\sqrt{3}}{(2n + 1)!} \left(x - \frac{\pi}{6} \right)^{2n+1} \right]$

47. $\sum_{n=0}^{\infty} (-1)^n x^{n+2}, R = 1$

49. $-\sum_{n=1}^{\infty} \frac{x^n}{n}, R = 1$

51. $\sum_{n=0}^{\infty} (-1)^n \frac{x^{8n+4}}{(2n + 1)!}, R = \infty$

53. $\frac{1}{2} + \sum_{n=1}^{\infty} \frac{1 \cdot 5 \cdot 9 \cdot \cdots \cdot (4n - 3)}{n! \, 2^{6n+1}} x^n, R = 16$

55. $C + \ln |x| + \sum_{n=1}^{\infty} \frac{x^n}{n \cdot n!}$

57. (a) $1 + \frac{1}{2}(x - 1) - \frac{1}{8}(x - 1)^2 + \frac{1}{16}(x - 1)^3$
(b)   (c) 0.000006

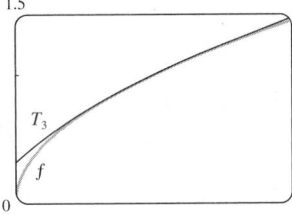

59. $-\frac{1}{6}$

Problems Plus □ **page 825**

1. $15!/5! = 10,897,286,400$
3. (b) 0 if $x = 0$, $(1/x) - \cot x$ if $x \neq k\pi$, k an integer
5. (a) $s_n = 3 \cdot 4^n$, $l_n = 1/3^n$, $p_n = 4^n/3^{n-1}$ (c) $2\sqrt{3}/5$
9. $(-1, 1)$, $(x^3 + 4x^2 + x)/(1 - x)^4$ **11.** $\ln \frac{1}{2}$

||| Chapter 13

Exercises 13.1 □ **page 833**

1. $(4, 0, -3)$ **3.** $Q; R$
5. A vertical plane that intersects the xy-plane in the line $y = 2 - x$, $z = 0$ (see graph at right)

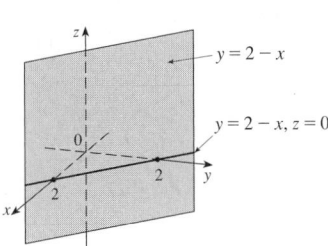

9. (a) Yes   (b) No
11. $(x - 1)^2 + (y + 4)^4 + (z - 3)^2 = 25$;
$(x - 1)^2 + (z - 3)^2 = 9$, $y = 0$ (a circle)
13. $(x - 3)^2 + (y - 8)^2 + (z - 1)^2 = 30$
15. $(3, -2, 1), 5$ **17.** $\left(\frac{1}{2}, \frac{1}{2}, \frac{1}{2}\right), \sqrt{3}/2$ **19.** (b) $\frac{5}{2}, \frac{1}{2}\sqrt{94}, \frac{1}{2}\sqrt{85}$
21. (a) $(x - 2)^2 + (y + 3)^2 + (z - 6)^2 = 36$
(b) $(x - 2)^2 + (y + 3)^2 + (z - 6)^2 = 4$
(c) $(x - 2)^2 + (y + 3)^2 + (z - 6)^2 = 9$
23. A plane parallel to the xz-plane and 4 units to the left of it
25. A half-space consisting of all points in front of the plane $x = 3$
27. All points on or between the horizontal planes $z = 0$ and $z = 6$
29. All points outside the sphere with radius 1 and center O
31. All points inside the sphere with radius 2 and center $(0, 0, 1)$
33. All points on or inside a circular cylinder of radius 3 with axis the y-axis
35. $y < 0$ **37.** $r^2 < x^2 + y^2 + z^2 < R^2$
39. (a) $(2, 1, 4)$ (b) L_1

41. $14x - 6y - 10z = 9$, a plane perpendicular to AB

Exercises 13.2 □ page 841

1. (a) Scalar (b) Vector (c) Vector (d) Scalar

3. $\vec{AB} = \vec{DC}, \vec{DA} = \vec{CB}, \vec{DE} = \vec{EB}, \vec{EA} = \vec{CE}$

5. (a)   (b)

(c)   (d)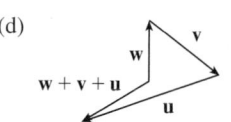

7. $\mathbf{a} = \langle -4, -2 \rangle$ **9.** $\mathbf{a} = \langle -2, 5 \rangle$

  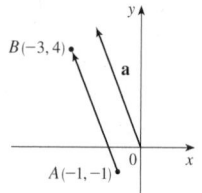

11. $\mathbf{a} = \langle 2, 0, -2 \rangle$ **13.** $\langle 1, 3 \rangle$

  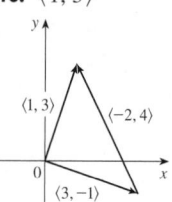

15. $\langle 0, 1, -1 \rangle$

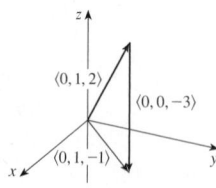

17. $5, \langle 2, 5 \rangle, \langle -10, 1 \rangle, \langle -8, 6 \rangle, \langle 12, 17 \rangle$

19. $7, \langle 5, 7, 1 \rangle, \langle 7, -3, 5 \rangle, \langle 12, 4, 6 \rangle, \langle 14, 26, 1 \rangle$

21. $\sqrt{6}, \mathbf{i} - \mathbf{j} + 3\mathbf{k}, \mathbf{i} - 3\mathbf{j} - \mathbf{k}, 2\mathbf{i} - 4\mathbf{j} + 2\mathbf{k}, 3\mathbf{i} - 2\mathbf{j} + 11\mathbf{k}$

23. $\langle 9/\sqrt{106}, -5/\sqrt{106} \rangle$ **25.** $\frac{8}{9}\mathbf{i} - \frac{1}{9}\mathbf{j} + \frac{4}{9}\mathbf{k}$ **27.** $\langle 2, 2\sqrt{3} \rangle$

29. $\mathbf{F} = (6\sqrt{3} - 5\sqrt{2})\mathbf{i} + (6 + 5\sqrt{2})\mathbf{j} \approx 3.32\mathbf{i} + 13.07\mathbf{j}$, $|\mathbf{F}| \approx 13.5$ lb, $\theta \approx 76°$

31. $\sqrt{493} \approx 22.2$ mi/h, N8°W

33. $\mathbf{T}_1 \approx -196\,\mathbf{i} + 3.92\,\mathbf{j}, \mathbf{T}_2 \approx 196\,\mathbf{i} + 3.92\,\mathbf{j}$ **35.** 0

37. (a), (b) 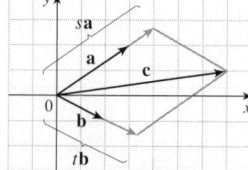 (d) $s = \frac{9}{7}, t = \frac{11}{7}$

39. A sphere with radius 1, centered at (x_0, y_0, z_0)

Exercises 13.3 □ page 848

1. (b), (c), (d) are meaningful **3.** 6 **5.** -5

7. 32 **9.** $90\sqrt{3}$ **11.** $\mathbf{u} \cdot \mathbf{v} = \frac{1}{2}, \mathbf{u} \cdot \mathbf{w} = -\frac{1}{2}$

15. $\cos^{-1}\left(\frac{63}{65}\right) \approx 14°$ **17.** $\cos^{-1}(1/\sqrt{238}) \approx 86°$

19. $\cos^{-1}\left(-1/(2\sqrt{7})\right) \approx 101°$ **21.** $45°, 45°, 90°$

23. (a) Neither (b) Orthogonal (c) Orthogonal (d) Parallel

25. Yes **27.** $(\mathbf{i} - \mathbf{j} - \mathbf{k})/\sqrt{3}$ [or $(-\mathbf{i} + \mathbf{j} + \mathbf{k})/\sqrt{3}$]

29. $\dfrac{3}{5\sqrt{2}}, \dfrac{4}{5\sqrt{2}}, \dfrac{1}{\sqrt{2}}$; $65°, 56°, 45°$

31. $\frac{2}{7}, \frac{3}{7}, -\frac{6}{7}$; $73°, 65°, 149°$

33. $1/\sqrt{3}, 1/\sqrt{3}, 1/\sqrt{3}$; $55°, 55°, 55°$ **35.** $3, \langle \frac{9}{5}, -\frac{12}{5} \rangle$

37. $3/\sqrt{5}, \langle \frac{6}{5}, \frac{3}{5}, 0 \rangle$ **39.** $1/\sqrt{2}, (\mathbf{i} + \mathbf{k})/2$

43. $\langle 0, 0, -2\sqrt{10} \rangle$ or any vector of the form $\langle s, t, 3s - 2\sqrt{10} \rangle, s, t \in \mathbb{R}$

45. 38 J **47.** $250 \cos 20° \approx 235$ ft-lb **49.** $\frac{13}{5}$

51. $\cos^{-1}(1/\sqrt{3}) \approx 55°$

Exercises 13.4 □ page 856

1. $2\mathbf{i} - \mathbf{j} + 3\mathbf{k}$ **3.** $3\mathbf{i} - 4\mathbf{j} + 2\mathbf{k}$

5. $2\mathbf{i} + 13\mathbf{j} - 8\mathbf{k}$ **7.** $t^4\mathbf{i} - 2t^3\mathbf{j} + t^2\mathbf{k}$

9. (a) Scalar (b) Meaningless (c) Vector (d) Meaningless (e) Meaningless (f) Scalar

11. 24; into the page

13. $\langle 5, -3, 1 \rangle, \langle -5, 3, -1 \rangle$

15. $\langle -2/\sqrt{6}, -1/\sqrt{6}, 1/\sqrt{6} \rangle, \langle 2/\sqrt{6}, 1/\sqrt{6}, -1/\sqrt{6} \rangle$

23. 16 **25.** (a) $\langle 6, 3, 2 \rangle$ (b) $\frac{7}{2}$

27. (a) $\langle 13, -14, 5 \rangle$ (b) $\frac{1}{2}\sqrt{390}$

29. 82 **31.** 3 **35.** $10.8 \sin 80° \approx 10.6$ J

37. ≈ 417 N **39.** (b) $\sqrt{97/3}$

45. (a) No (b) No (c) Yes

Exercises 13.5 □ page 865

1. (a) True (b) False (c) True (d) False (e) False (f) True (g) False (h) True (i) True (j) False (k) True

3. $\mathbf{r} = (-2\mathbf{i} + 4\mathbf{j} + 10\mathbf{k}) + t(3\mathbf{i} + \mathbf{j} - 8\mathbf{k})$; $x = -2 + 3t, y = 4 + t, z = 10 - 8t$

5. $\mathbf{r} = (\mathbf{i} + 6\mathbf{k}) + t(\mathbf{i} + 3\mathbf{j} + \mathbf{k})$; $x = 1 + t, y = 3t, z = 6 + t$

7. $x = 1 - 5t, y = 3, z = 2 - 2t$; $\dfrac{x - 1}{-5} = \dfrac{z - 2}{-2}, y = 3$

9. $x = 2 + 2t, y = 1 + \frac{1}{2}t, z = -3 - 4t$; $(x - 2)/2 = 2y - 2 = (z + 3)/(-4)$

11. $x = 1 + t, y = -1 + 2t, z = 1 + t$; $x - 1 = (y + 1)/2 = z - 1$

13. Yes

15. (a) $x/2 = (y - 2)/3 = (z + 1)/(-7)$ (b) $\left(-\frac{2}{7}, \frac{11}{7}, 0\right), \left(-\frac{4}{3}, 0, \frac{11}{3}\right), (0, 2, -1)$

17. $\mathbf{r}(t) = (2\mathbf{i} - \mathbf{j} + 4\mathbf{k}) + t(2\mathbf{i} + 7\mathbf{j} - 3\mathbf{k}), 0 \leq t \leq 1$

19. Parallel **21.** Skew

23. $-2x + y + 5z = 1$

25. $x + y - z = -1$

27. $2x - y + 3z = 0$ **29.** $3x - 7z = -9$
31. $x + y + z = 2$ **33.** $-13x + 17y + 7z = -42$
35. $33x + 10y + 4z = 190$ **37.** $x - 2y + 4z = -1$
39. $(2, 3, 5)$ **41.** $(2, 3, 1)$ **43.** $1, 0, -1$
45. Perpendicular   **47.** Neither, $\approx 70.5°$ **49.** Parallel
51. (a) $x - 2 = y/(-8) = z/(-7)$
(b) $\cos^{-1}(-\sqrt{6}/5) \approx 119°$ (or 61°)
53. $x = 6t, y = -\frac{1}{6} + t, z = -\frac{1}{6} + 7t$ **55.** $x = z$
57. $(x/a) + (y/b) + (z/c) = 1$
59. $x = 3t, y = 1 - t, z = 2 - 2t$
61. P_1 and P_3 are parallel, P_2 and P_4 are identical
63. $\sqrt{22/5}$ **65.** $\frac{25}{3}$ **67.** $7\sqrt{6}/18$ **71.** $1/\sqrt{6}$

Exercises 13.6 □ page 873

1. (a) Parabola
(b) Parabolic cylinder with rulings parallel to the z-axis
(c) Parabolic cylinder with rulings parallel to the x-axis
3. Elliptic cylinder   **5.** Parabolic cylinder

7. Cylindrical surface

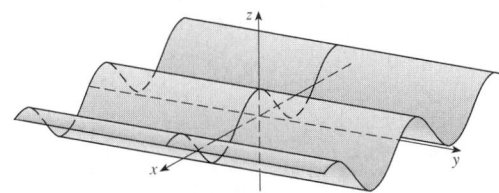

9. (a) $x = k, y^2 - z^2 = 1 - k^2$, hyperbola $(k \neq \pm 1)$;
$y = k, x^2 - z^2 = 1 - k^2$, hyperbola $(k \neq \pm 1)$;
$z = k, x^2 + z^2 = 1 + k^2$, circle
(b) The hyperboloid is rotated so that it has axis the y-axis
(c) The hyperboloid is shifted one unit in the negative y-direction
11. $x = k, y^2 + 4z^2 = 4 - 4k^2/9$, ellipse $(|k| < 3)$
$y = k, x^2 + 9z^2 = 9 - 9k^2/4$, ellipse $(|k| < 2)$
$z = k, 4x^2 + 9y^2 = 36(1 - k^2)$, ellipse $(|k| < 1)$

Ellipsoid

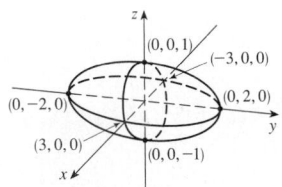

13. $x = k, y^2 - z^2 = k^2$, hyperbola $(k \neq 0)$
$y = k, x^2 + z^2 = k^2$, circle $(k \neq 0)$

$z = k, y^2 - x^2 = k^2$,
hyperbola $(k \neq 0)$
$x = 0, y = \pm z$, lines
$z = 0, y = \pm x$, lines

Cone

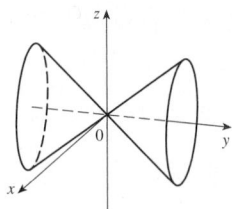

15. $x = k, 4y^2 - z^2 = 4 + k^2$, hyperbola
$y = k, x^2 + z^2 = 4k^2 - 4$,
circle $(|k| > 1)$
$z = k, 4y^2 - x^2 = 4 + k^2$,
hyperbola

Hyperboloid of two sheets

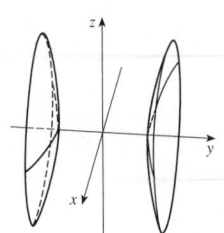

17. $x = k, y = 4z^2 + k^2$, parabola
$y = k, x^2 + 4z^2 = k$, ellipse $(k > 0)$
$z = k, y = x^2 + 4k^2$, parabola

Elliptic paraboloid with
axis the y-axis

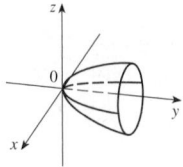

19. $x = k, y = z^2 - k^2$, parabola
$y = k, z^2 - x^2 = k$, hyperbola $(k \neq 0)$
$z = k, y = k^2 - x^2$, parabola

Hyperbolic paraboloid

21. VII   **23.** II   **25.** VI   **27.** VIII

29. $-\dfrac{x^2}{9} - \dfrac{y^2}{4} + \dfrac{z^2}{36} = 1$

Hyperboloid of two sheets
with axis the z-axis

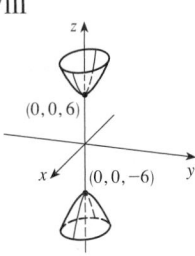

31. $\dfrac{x}{6} = \dfrac{y^2}{3} + \dfrac{z^2}{2}$

Elliptic paraboloid with vertex
$(0, 0, 0)$ and axis the x-axis

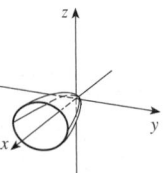

33. $x^2 + \dfrac{(y - 2)^2}{4} + (z - 3)^2 = 1$

Ellipsoid with center $(0, 2, 3)$

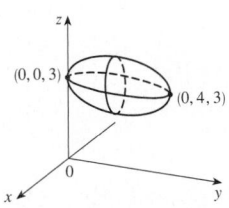

35. $(y + 1)^2 = (x - 2)^2 + (z - 1)^2$
Circular cone with vertex $(2, -1, 1)$
and axis parallel to the y-axis

37. **39.**

41.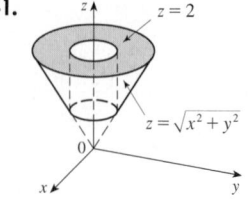

43. $y = x^2 + z^2$ **45.** $-4x = y^2 + z^2$, paraboloid

49.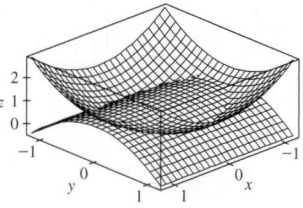

Exercises 13.7 □ **page 878**

1. See pages 839–40.
3. $\left(\sqrt{2}, \sqrt{2}, 1\right)$

5. **7.**

$(3, 0, -6)$ $\left(2, -2\sqrt{3}, 5\right)$

9. $\left(\sqrt{2}, 7\pi/4, 4\right)$ **11.** $(2, 4\pi/3, 2)$

13.

$(0, 0, 1)$

17.

15.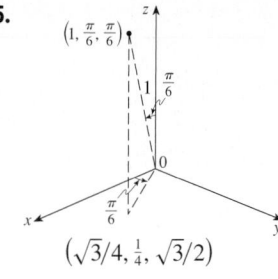

$\left(\sqrt{3}/4, \frac{1}{4}, \sqrt{3}/2\right)$
$\left(\frac{1}{2}\sqrt{2}, \frac{1}{2}\sqrt{6}, \sqrt{2}\right)$

19. $(4, \pi/3, \pi/6)$ **21.** $\left(\sqrt{2}, 3\pi/2, 3\pi/4\right)$
23. $(2, \pi/6, \pi/6)$ **25.** $(2, \pi/2, 2\pi/3)$
27. $(0, 0, 2)$ **29.** $(8, \pi/6, 0)$
31. Circular cylinder, radius 3, axis the z-axis
33. Positive z-axis
35. Half-cone **37.** Circular paraboloid
39. Horizontal plane
41. Circular cylinder, radius 1, axis parallel to the z-axis
43. Sphere, radius 5, center the origin
45. Circular cylinder, radius 2, axis the y-axis
47. Cylinder, radius 1, together with the z-axis
49. (a) $z = r^2$ (b) $\rho \sin^2\phi = \cos\phi$
51. (a) $r = 3 \sec\theta$ (b) $\rho \sin\phi \cos\theta = 3$
53. (a) $2z^2 = r^2 \cos 2\theta - 4$
(b) $\rho^2(\sin^2\phi \cos 2\theta - 2\cos^2\phi) = 4$
55. (a) $r = 2\sin\theta$ (b) $\rho \sin\phi = 2\sin\theta$
57. **59.**

61.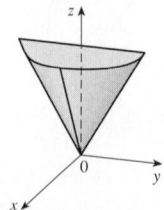

63. Cylindrical coordinates:
$6 \le r \le 7, 0 \le \theta \le 2\pi,$
$0 \le z \le 20$

65. $0 \le \phi \le \pi/4, 0 \le \rho \le \cos\phi$ **67.**

Chapter 13 Review □ page 881

True-False Quiz

1. True   **3.** True   **5.** True   **7.** True   **9.** True
11. False   **13.** False

Exercises

1. (a) $(x - 1)^2 + (y + 1)^2 + (z - 2)^2 = 9$
(b) $(-2, -3, 5), 6$
3. $\mathbf{u} \cdot \mathbf{v} = 3\sqrt{2}$; $|\mathbf{u} \times \mathbf{v}| = 3\sqrt{2}$; out of the page
5. $-2, -4$ **7.** (a) 2   (b) -2 (c) -2 (d) 0
9. $\cos^{-1}(\frac{1}{3}) \approx 71°$ **11.** (a) $\langle 4, -3, 4 \rangle$ (b) $\sqrt{41}/2$
13. 166 N, 114 N
15. $x = 4 - 3t, y = -1 + 2t, z = 2 + 3t$
17. $x = -2 + 2t, y = 2 - t, z = 4 + 5t$
19. $-4x + 3y + z = -14$ **21.** $(1, 4, 4)$
23. Skew   **25.** $22/\sqrt{26}$
27. Plane   **29.** Cone

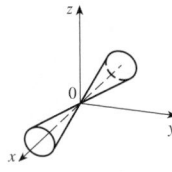

31. Hyperboloid of two sheets

33. Ellipsoid

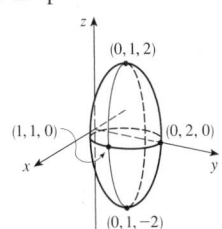

35. $4x^2 + y^2 + z^2 = 16$ **37.** $(\sqrt{3}, 3, 2), (4, \pi/3, \pi/3)$
39. $(2\sqrt{2}, 2\sqrt{2}, 4\sqrt{3}), (4, \pi/4, 4\sqrt{3})$
41. A half-plane   **43.** The horizontal plane $z = 3$
45. $r^2 + z^2 = 4, \rho = 2$ **47.** $z = 4r^2$

Problems Plus □ page 883

1. $(\sqrt{3} - 1.5)$ m
3. (a) $(x + 1)/(-2c) = (y - c)/(c^2 - 1) = (z - c)/(c^2 + 1)$
(b) $x^2 + y^2 = t^2 + 1, z = t$ (c) $4\pi/3$

Exercises 14.1 □ page 891

1. $[1, 5]$ **3.** $\langle 1, 0, 0 \rangle$ **5.** $2\mathbf{i} + \frac{1}{2}\mathbf{j} + (\tan 1)\mathbf{k}$
7.

9.

11.   **13.**

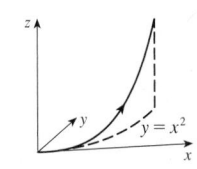

15. $\mathbf{r}(t) = \langle t, 2t, 3t \rangle, 0 \leq t \leq 1$;
$x = t, y = 2t, z = 3t, 0 \leq t \leq 1$
17. $\mathbf{r}(t) = \langle 3t + 1, 2t - 1, 5t + 2 \rangle, 0 \leq t \leq 1$;
$x = 3t + 1, y = 2t - 1, z = 5t + 2, 0 \leq t \leq 1$
19. VI   **21.** IV   **23.** V
25.   **27.**

29.

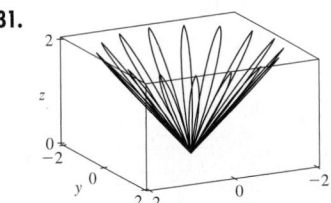

31.

35. $\mathbf{r}(t) = t\mathbf{i} + \frac{1}{2}(t^2 - 1)\mathbf{j} + \frac{1}{2}(t^2 + 1)\mathbf{k}$
37. $x = 2\cos t, y = 2\sin t, z = 4\cos^2 t$
39. Yes

Exercises 14.2 □ page 897

1. (a)

(b), (d)

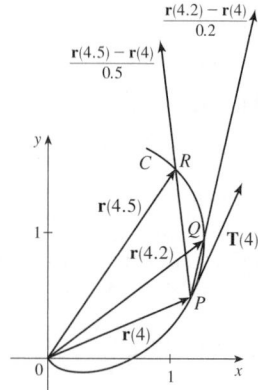

(c) $\mathbf{r}'(4) = \lim\limits_{h \to 0} \dfrac{\mathbf{r}(4+h) - \mathbf{r}(4)}{h}$; $\mathbf{T}(4) = \dfrac{\mathbf{r}'(4)}{|\mathbf{r}'(4)|}$

3. (a), (c)

(b) $\mathbf{r}'(t) = \langle -\sin t, \cos t \rangle$

5. (a), (c)

7. (a), (c)

(b) $\mathbf{r}'(t) = \mathbf{i} + 2t\,\mathbf{j}$ (b) $\mathbf{r}'(t) = e^t\mathbf{i} + 3e^{3t}\mathbf{j}$

9. $\mathbf{r}'(t) = \langle 2t, -1, 1/(2\sqrt{t}) \rangle$ **11.** $\mathbf{r}'(t) = 4e^{4t}\,\mathbf{k}$

13. $\mathbf{r}'(t) = 2te^{t^2}\mathbf{i} + [3/(1 + 3t)]\,\mathbf{k}$ **15.** $\mathbf{r}'(t) = \mathbf{b} + 2t\mathbf{c}$

17. $\langle 15/\sqrt{262}, 6/\sqrt{262}, 1/\sqrt{262} \rangle$ **19.** $\frac{3}{5}\mathbf{j} + \frac{4}{5}\mathbf{k}$

21. $\langle 1, 2t, 3t^2 \rangle$, $\langle 1/\sqrt{14}, 2/\sqrt{14}, 3/\sqrt{14} \rangle$, $\langle 0, 2, 6t \rangle$, $\langle 6t^2, -6t, 2 \rangle$

23. $x = 1 + 5t, y = 1 + 4t, z = 1 + 3t$

25. $x = 1 - t, y = t, z = 1 - t$

27. $x = \frac{1}{4}\pi + t, y = 1 - t, z = 1 + t$

29. (a) Not smooth   (b) Smooth   (c) Not smooth

31. $66°$ **33.** $4\mathbf{i} - 3\mathbf{j} + 5\mathbf{k}$ **35.** $\mathbf{i} + \mathbf{j} + \mathbf{k}$

37. $e^t\mathbf{i} + t^2\mathbf{j} + (t \ln t - t)\mathbf{k} + \mathbf{C}$

39. $\frac{1}{3}t^3\mathbf{i} + (t^4 + 1)\mathbf{j} - \frac{1}{3}t^3\mathbf{k}$

45. $1 - 4t \cos t + 11t^2 \sin t + 3t^3 \cos t$

Exercises 14.3 □ page 904

1. $20\sqrt{29}$ **3.** $e - e^{-1}$ **5.** $\frac{1}{27}(13^{3/2} - 8)$ **7.** 9.5706

9. $\mathbf{r}(t(s)) = \dfrac{2}{\sqrt{29}}s\,\mathbf{i} + \left(1 - \dfrac{3}{\sqrt{29}}s\right)\mathbf{j} + \left(5 + \dfrac{4}{\sqrt{29}}s\right)\mathbf{k}$

11. $\mathbf{r}(t(s)) = 3\sin(s/5)\mathbf{i} + (4s/5)\mathbf{j} + 3\cos(s/5)\mathbf{k}$

13. (a) $\langle (2/\sqrt{29})\cos t, 5/\sqrt{29}, (-2/\sqrt{29})\sin t \rangle$, $\langle -\sin t, 0, -\cos t \rangle$

(b) $\frac{2}{29}$

15. (a) $\dfrac{1}{e^{2t} + 1}\langle \sqrt{2}e^t, e^{2t}, -1 \rangle$, $\dfrac{1}{e^{2t} + 1}\langle 1 - e^{2t}, \sqrt{2}e^t, \sqrt{2}e^t \rangle$

(b) $\sqrt{2}e^{2t}/(e^{2t} + 1)^2$

17. $2/(4t^2 + 1)^{3/2}$ **19.** $\frac{4}{25}$ **21.** $\frac{1}{7}\sqrt{\frac{19}{14}}$

23. $6|x|/(1 + 9x^4)^{3/2}$ **25.** $15\sqrt{x}/(1 + 100x^3)^{3/2}$

27. $(-\frac{1}{2}\ln 2, 1/\sqrt{2})$; approaches 0   **29.** (a) P (b) $1.3, 0.7$

31.

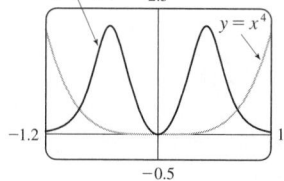

33. a is $y = f(x)$, b is $y = \kappa(x)$

35. $\kappa(t) = \dfrac{6\sqrt{4\cos^2 t - 12\cos t + 13}}{(17 - 12\cos t)^{3/2}}$

integer multiples of 2π

37. $1/(\sqrt{2}e^t)$ **39.** $\langle \frac{2}{3}, \frac{2}{3}, \frac{1}{3} \rangle, \langle -\frac{1}{3}, \frac{2}{3}, -\frac{2}{3} \rangle, \langle -\frac{2}{3}, \frac{1}{3}, \frac{2}{3} \rangle$

41. $y = 6x + \pi, x + 6y = 6\pi$

43. $\left(x + \frac{5}{2}\right)^2 + y^2 = \frac{81}{4}, x^2 + \left(y - \frac{5}{3}\right)^2 = \frac{16}{9}$

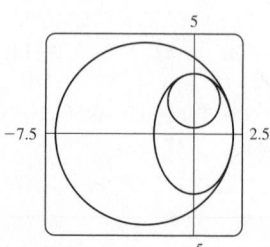

45. $(-1, -3, 1)$ **53.** $2/(t^4 + 4t^2 + 1)$

55. 2.07×10^{10} Å ≈ 2 m

Exercises 14.4 □ page 914

1. (a) $1.8\mathbf{i} - 3.8\mathbf{j} - 0.7\mathbf{k}$, $2.0\mathbf{i} - 2.4\mathbf{j} - 0.6\mathbf{k}$,
$2.8\mathbf{i} + 1.8\mathbf{j} - 0.3\mathbf{k}$, $2.8\mathbf{i} + 0.8\mathbf{j} - 0.4\mathbf{k}$
(b) $2.4\mathbf{i} - 0.8\mathbf{j} - 0.5\mathbf{k}$, 2.58
3. $\mathbf{v}(t) = \langle 2t, 1 \rangle$
$\mathbf{a}(t) = \langle 2, 0 \rangle$
$|\mathbf{v}(t)| = \sqrt{4t^2 + 1}$

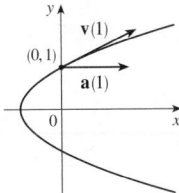

5. $\mathbf{v}(t) = e^t\mathbf{i} - e^{-t}\mathbf{j}$
$\mathbf{a}(t) = e^t\mathbf{i} + e^{-t}\mathbf{j}$
$|\mathbf{v}(t)| = \sqrt{e^{2t} + e^{-2t}}$

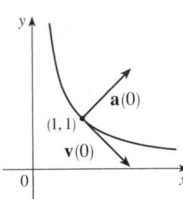

7. $\mathbf{v}(t) = \cos t\,\mathbf{i} + \mathbf{j} - \sin t\,\mathbf{k}$
$\mathbf{a}(t) = -\sin t\,\mathbf{i} - \cos t\,\mathbf{k}$
$|\mathbf{v}(t)| = \sqrt{2}$

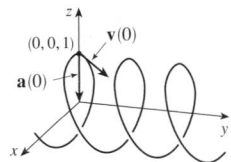

9. $\langle 2t, 3t^2, 2t \rangle$, $\langle 2, 6t, 2 \rangle$, $|t|\sqrt{9t^2 + 8}$
11. $\sqrt{2}\,\mathbf{i} + e^t\mathbf{j} - e^{-t}\mathbf{k}$, $e^t\mathbf{j} + e^{-t}\mathbf{k}$, $e^t + e^{-t}$
13. $e^t[(\cos t - \sin t)\mathbf{i} + (\sin t + \cos t)\mathbf{j} + (t + 1)\mathbf{k}]$,
$e^t[-2\sin t\,\mathbf{i} + 2\cos t\,\mathbf{j} + (t + 2)\mathbf{k}]$, $e^t\sqrt{t^2 + 2t + 3}$
15. $\mathbf{v}(t) = \mathbf{i} - \mathbf{j} + t\,\mathbf{k}$, $\mathbf{r}(t) = t\,\mathbf{i} - t\,\mathbf{j} + \frac{1}{2}t^2\mathbf{k}$
17. (a) $\mathbf{r}(t) = (1 + \frac{1}{2}t^2)\mathbf{i} + t^2\mathbf{j} + (1 + \frac{1}{3}t^3)\mathbf{k}$
(b)

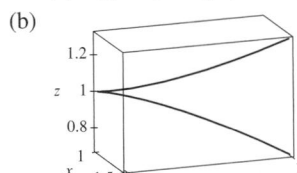

19. $t = 4$
21. $\mathbf{r}(t) = t\,\mathbf{i} - t\,\mathbf{j} + \frac{5}{2}t^2\,\mathbf{k}$, $|\mathbf{v}(t)| = \sqrt{25t^2 + 2}$
23. (a) ≈ 22 km   (b) ≈ 3.2 km   (c) 500 m/s
25. 30 m/s
27. $\approx 10.2°$, $\approx 79.8°$
29. (a) 16 m   (b) $\approx 23.6°$ upstream

31. $6t, 6$ **33.** $0, 1$ **35.** $e^t - e^{-t}, \sqrt{2}$
37. 4.5 cm/s^2, 9.0 cm/s^2 **39.** $t = 1$

Chapter 14 Review □ page 918

True-False Quiz

1. True   **3.** False   **5.** False   **7.** False   **9.** True

Exercises

1. (a)

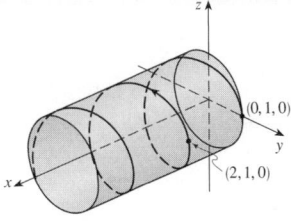

(b) $\mathbf{r}'(t) = \mathbf{i} - \pi\sin\pi t\,\mathbf{j} + \pi\cos\pi t\,\mathbf{k}$,
$\mathbf{r}''(t) = -\pi^2\cos\pi t\,\mathbf{j} - \pi^2\sin\pi t\,\mathbf{k}$
3. $\mathbf{r}(t) = 4\cos t\,\mathbf{i} + 4\sin t\,\mathbf{j} + (5 - 4\cos t)\mathbf{k}$, $0 \le t \le 2\pi$
5. $\frac{1}{3}\mathbf{i} - (2/\pi^2)\mathbf{j} + (2/\pi)\mathbf{k}$ **7.** 15.9241 **9.** $\pi/2$
11. (a) $\langle t^2, t, 1 \rangle / \sqrt{t^4 + t^2 + 1}$
(b) $\langle 2t, 1 - t^4, -2t^3 - t \rangle / \sqrt{t^8 + 4t^6 + 2t^4 + 5t^2}$
(c) $\sqrt{t^8 + 4t^6 + 2t^4 + 5t^2}/(t^4 + t^2 + 1)^2$
13. $12/17^{3/2}$ **15.** $x - 2y + 2\pi = 0$
17. $\mathbf{v}(t) = (1 + \ln t)\mathbf{i} + \mathbf{j} - e^{-t}\mathbf{k}$,
$|\mathbf{v}(t)| = \sqrt{2 + 2\ln t + (\ln t)^2 + e^{-2t}}$, $\mathbf{a}(t) = (1/t)\mathbf{i} + e^{-t}\mathbf{k}$
19. (a) About 3.8 ft above the ground, 60.8 ft from the athlete
(b) ≈ 21.4 ft   (c) ≈ 64.2 ft from the athlete
21. (c) $-2e^{-t}\mathbf{v}_d + e^{-t}\mathbf{R}$

Problems Plus □ page 920

1. (a) $\mathbf{v} = \omega R(-\sin\omega t\,\mathbf{i} + \cos\omega t\,\mathbf{j})$ (c) $\mathbf{a} = -\omega^2\mathbf{r}$
3. (a) $90°$, $v_0^2/(2g)$ **5.** (b) $\mathbf{R}(t) = (m/k)(1 - e^{-kt/m})\mathbf{v}_0 +$
$(gm/k)[(m/k)(1 - e^{-kt/m}) - t]\mathbf{j}$
7. (a) ≈ 0.94 ft to the right of the table's edge, ≈ 15 ft/s
(b) $\approx 7.6°$ (c) ≈ 2.13 ft to the right of the table's edge

‖ Chapter 15

Exercises 15.1 □ page 933

1. (a) -27; a temperature of $-15°$C with wind blowing at
40 km/h feels equivalent to about $-27°$C without wind.
(b) When the temperature is $-20°$C, what wind speed gives a wind
chill of $-30°$C?   20 km/h
(c) With a wind speed of 20 km/h, what temperature gives a wind
chill of $-49°$C? $-35°$C
(d) A function of wind speed that gives wind-chill values when the
temperature is $-5°$C
(e) A function of temperature that gives wind-chill values when
the wind speed is 50 km/h

3. Yes

5. (a) 25; a 40-knot wind blowing in the open sea for 15 h will create waves about 25 ft high.
(b) $f(30, t)$ is a function of t giving the wave heights produced by 30-knot winds blowing for t hours.
(c) $f(v, 30)$ is a function of v giving the wave heights produced by winds of speed v blowing for 30 hours.

7. (a) 4 (b) $\mathbb{R}^2$ (c) $[0, \infty)$

9. (a) e (b) $\{(x, y, z) \mid z \geqslant x^2 + y^2\}$ (c) $[1, \infty)$

11. $\{(x, y) \mid y \geqslant -x\}$

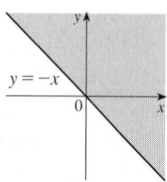

13. $\{(x, y) \mid \frac{1}{9}x^2 + y^2 < 1\}$

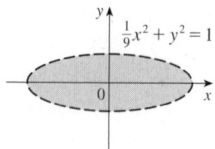

15. $\{(x, y) \mid x^2 + y^2 \neq 4\}$

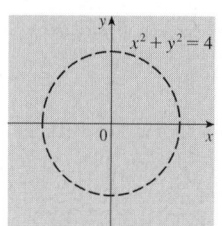

17. $\{(x, y) \mid y \geqslant x^2, x \neq \pm 1\}$

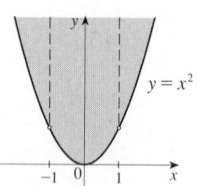

19. $\{(x, y, z) \mid x^2 + y^2 + z^2 \leqslant 1\}$

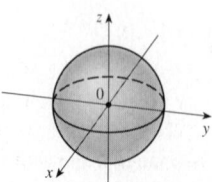

21. $z = 3$, horizontal plane **23.** $x + y + z = 1$, plane

  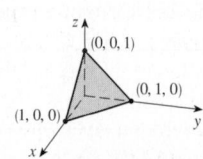

25. $z = 1 - x^2$
parabolic cylinder

27. $z = 4x^2 + y^2 + 1$
elliptic paraboloid

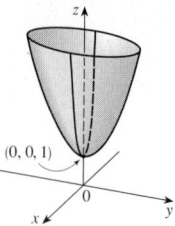

29. $z = \sqrt{x^2 + y^2}$,
top half of cone

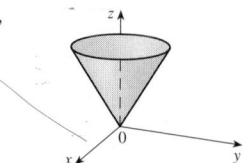

31. $\approx 56, \approx 35$ **33.** Steep; nearly flat

35. **37.** $xy = k$

39.

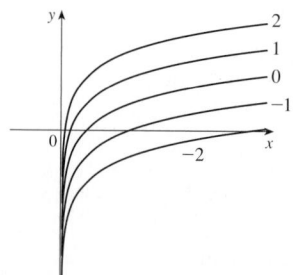

41. $\sqrt{x + y} = k$

43. $x = y^2 + k$

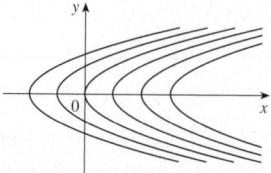

45. $x^2 + 9y^2 = k$

47.

49.   **51.**

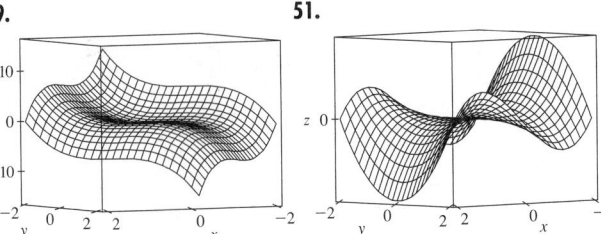

53. (a) B   (b) III
55. (a) F   (b) V
57. (a) D   (b) IV
59. Family of parallel planes
61. Family of hyperboloids of one or two sheets with axis the y-axis
63. (a) Shift the graph of f upward 2 units
(b) Stretch the graph of f vertically by a factor of 2
(c) Reflect the graph of f about the xy-plane
(d) Reflect the graph of f about the xy-plane and then shift it upward 2 units

65.

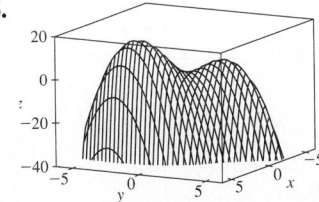

f appears to have a maximum value of about 15. There are two local maximum points but no local minimum point.

67.

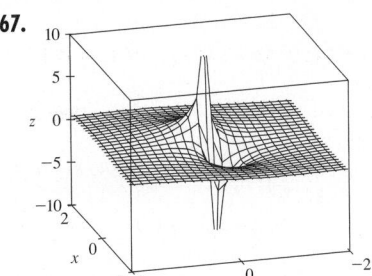

The function values approach 0 as x, y become large; as (x, y) approaches the origin, f approaches $\pm\infty$ or 0, depending on the direction of approach.
69. If $c = 0$, the graph is a cylindrical surface. For $c > 0$, the level curves are ellipses. The graph curves upward as we leave the origin, and the steepness increases as c increases. For $c < 0$, the level curves are hyperbolas. The graph curves upward in the y-direction and downward, approaching the xy-plane, in the x-direction giving a saddle-shaped appearance near $(0, 0, 1)$.
71. (b) $y = 0.75x + 0.01$

Exercises 15.2 □ page 944

1. Nothing; if f is continuous, $f(3, 1) = 6$ **3.** $-\frac{5}{2}$
5. 2025   **7.** Does not exist   **9.** Does not exist
11. 0   **13.** Does not exist   **15.** 2   **17.** 1
19. Does not exist
21. The graph shows that the function approaches different numbers along different lines.
23. $h(x, y) = (2x + 3y - 6)^2 + \sqrt{2x + 3y - 6}$;
$\{(x, y) \mid 2x + 3y \geqslant 6\}$
25. Along the line $y = x$
27. $\{(x, y) \mid y \neq \pm e^{x/2}\}$ **29.** $\{(x, y) \mid y \geqslant 0\}$
31. $\{(x, y) \mid x^2 + y^2 > 4\}$
33. $\{(x, y, z) \mid y \geqslant 0, y \neq \sqrt{x^2 + z^2}\}$
35. $\{(x, y) \mid (x, y) \neq (0, 0)\}$ **37.** 0   **39.** 0

Exercises 15.3 □ page 955

1. (a) The rate of change of temperature as longitude varies, with latitude and time fixed; the rate of change as only latitude varies; the rate of change as only time varies.
(b) Positive, negative, positive
3. (a) $f_T(-15, 30) \approx 1.3$; for a temperature of $-15°C$ and wind speed of 30 km/h, the wind-chill index rises by $1.3°C$ for each degree the temperature increases. $f_v(-15, 30) \approx -0.15$; for a temperature of $-15°C$ and wind speed of 30 km/h, the wind-chill index decreases by $0.15°C$ for each km/h the wind speed increases.
(b) Positive, negative   (c) 0
5. (a) Positive   (b) Negative
7. $c = f$, $b = f_x$, $a = f_y$

9. $f_x(1, 2) = -8 = $ slope of C_1, $f_y(1, 2) = -4 = $ slope of C_2

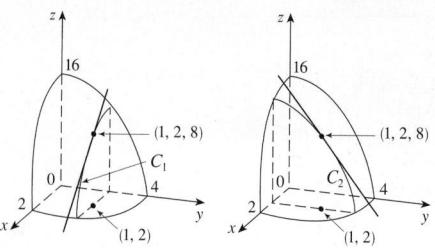

11. $f_x = 2x + 2xy$, $f_y = 2y + x^2$

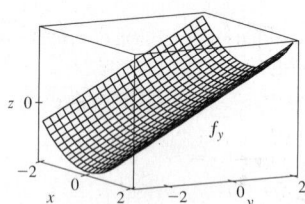

13. $f_x(x, y) = 3$, $f_y(x, y) = -8y^3$

15. $\partial z/\partial x = e^{3y}$, $\partial z/\partial y = 3xe^{3y}$

17. $f_x(x, y) = 2y/(x + y)^2$, $f_y(x, y) = -2x/(x + y)^2$

19. $\partial w/\partial \alpha = \cos \alpha \cos \beta$, $\partial w/\partial \beta = -\sin \alpha \sin \beta$

21. $f_r(r, s) = \dfrac{2r^2}{r^2 + s^2} + \ln(r^2 + s^2)$, $f_s(r, s) = \dfrac{2rs}{r^2 + s^2}$

23. $\partial u/\partial t = e^{w/t}(1 - w/t)$, $\partial u/\partial w = e^{w/t}$

25. $f_x = y^2z^3$, $f_y = 2xyz^3 + 3z$, $f_z = 3xy^2z^2 + 3y$

27. $\partial w/\partial x = 1/(x + 2y + 3z)$, $\partial w/\partial y = 2/(x + 2y + 3z)$, $\partial w/\partial z = 3/(x + 2y + 3z)$

29. $\partial u/\partial x = e^{-t} \sin \theta$, $\partial u/\partial t = -xe^{-t} \sin \theta$, $\partial u/\partial \theta = xe^{-t} \cos \theta$

31. $f_x = yz^2 \tan(yt)$, $f_y = xyz^2t \sec^2(yt) + xz^2 \tan(yt)$, $f_z = 2xyz \tan(yt)$, $f_t = xy^2z^2 \sec^2(yt)$

33. $\partial u/\partial x_i = x_i/\sqrt{x_1^2 + x_2^2 + \cdots + x_n^2}$ **35.** $\frac{3}{5}$ **37.** $-\frac{1}{3}$

39. $f_x(x, y) = 2x - y$, $f_y(x, y) = 4y - x$

41. $\dfrac{\partial z}{\partial x} = \dfrac{3yz - 2x}{2z - 3xy}$, $\dfrac{\partial z}{\partial y} = \dfrac{3xz - 2y}{2z - 3xy}$

43. $\dfrac{\partial z}{\partial x} = \dfrac{1 + y^2z^2}{1 + y + y^2z^2}$, $\dfrac{\partial z}{\partial y} = \dfrac{-z}{1 + y + y^2z^2}$.

45. (a) $f'(x), g'(y)$ (b) $f'(x + y), f'(x + y)$

47. $f_{xx} = 12x^2 - 6y^3$, $f_{xy} = -18xy^2 = f_{yx}$, $f_{yy} = -18x^2y$

49. $z_{xx} = -2y/(x + y)^3$, $z_{xy} = (x - y)/(x + y)^3 = z_{yx}$, $z_{yy} = 2x/(x + y)^3$

51. $u_{ss} = e^{-s} \sin t$, $u_{st} = -e^{-s} \cos t = u_{ts}$, $u_{tt} = -e^{-s} \sin t$

57. $12xy, 72xy$

59. $24 \sin(4x + 3y + 2z)$, $12 \sin(4x + 3y + 2z)$

61. $\theta e^{r\theta}(2 \sin \theta + \theta \cos \theta + r\theta \sin \theta)$

63. $4/(y + 2z)^3, 0$ **65.** $\approx 12.2, \approx 16.8, \approx 23.25$ **77.** R^2/R_1^2

83. No   **85.** $x = 1 + t, y = 2, z = 2 - 2t$ **89.** -2

91. (a)

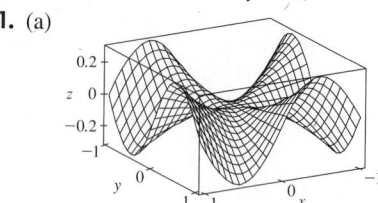

(b) $f_x(x, y) = \dfrac{x^4y + 4x^2y^3 - y^5}{(x^2 + y^2)^2}$, $f_y(x, y) = \dfrac{x^5 - 4x^3y^2 - xy^4}{(x^2 + y^2)^2}$

(c) $0, 0$ (e) No, since f_{xy} and f_{yx} are not continuous.

Exercises 15.4 □ page 966

1. $z = -8x - 2y$ **3.** $x - 2y + z = 4$ **5.** $z = y$

7.

9.

11. $2x + \frac{1}{4}y - 1$ **13.** $x + 1$ **15.** $\frac{1}{2}x + y + \frac{1}{4}\pi - \frac{1}{2}$

17. $-\frac{2}{3}x - \frac{7}{3}y + \frac{20}{3}; 2.846$ **19.** $\frac{3}{7}x + \frac{2}{7}y + \frac{6}{7}z; 6.9914$

21. $4T + H - 329; 129°F$

23. $dz = 3x^2 \ln(y^2)\,dx + (2x^3/y)\,dy$

25. $du = e^t \sin \theta\,dt + e^t \cos \theta\,d\theta$

27. $dw = (x^2 + y^2 + z^2)^{-1}(x\,dx + y\,dy + z\,dz)$

29. $\Delta z = 0.9225, dz = 0.9$ **31.** 5.4 cm^2 **33.** 16 cm^3

35. 150 **37.** $\frac{1}{17} \approx 0.059 \, \Omega$ **39.** $\varepsilon_1 = \Delta x, \varepsilon_2 = \Delta y$

Exercises 15.5 □ page 974

1. $4(2xy + y^2)t^3 - 3(x^2 + 2xy)t^2$

3. $\pi \cos x \cos y - (\sin x \sin y)/(2\sqrt{t})$

5. $e^{y/z}[2t - (x/z) - (2xy/z^2)]$

7. $\partial z/\partial s = 2x + y + xt + 2yt$, $\partial z/\partial t = 2x + y + xs + 2ys$

9. $\dfrac{\partial z}{\partial s} = \dfrac{4st + \ln t}{1 + (2x + y)^2}$, $\dfrac{\partial z}{\partial t} = \dfrac{2s^2 + s/t}{1 + (2x + y)^2}$

11. $\dfrac{\partial z}{\partial s} = e^r\left(t \cos \theta - \dfrac{s}{\sqrt{s^2 + t^2}} \sin \theta\right)$,

$\dfrac{\partial z}{\partial t} = e^r\left(s \cos \theta - \dfrac{t}{\sqrt{s^2 + t^2}} \sin \theta\right)$

13. 62   **15.** 7, 2

17. $\dfrac{\partial u}{\partial r} = \dfrac{\partial u}{\partial x}\dfrac{\partial x}{\partial r} + \dfrac{\partial u}{\partial y}\dfrac{\partial y}{\partial r}$, $\dfrac{\partial u}{\partial s} = \dfrac{\partial u}{\partial x}\dfrac{\partial x}{\partial s} + \dfrac{\partial u}{\partial y}\dfrac{\partial y}{\partial s}$,

$\dfrac{\partial u}{\partial t} = \dfrac{\partial u}{\partial x}\dfrac{\partial x}{\partial t} + \dfrac{\partial u}{\partial y}\dfrac{\partial y}{\partial t}$

19. $\dfrac{\partial v}{\partial x} = \dfrac{\partial v}{\partial p}\dfrac{\partial p}{\partial x} + \dfrac{\partial v}{\partial q}\dfrac{\partial q}{\partial x} + \dfrac{\partial v}{\partial r}\dfrac{\partial r}{\partial x}$,

$\dfrac{\partial v}{\partial y} = \dfrac{\partial v}{\partial p}\dfrac{\partial p}{\partial y} + \dfrac{\partial v}{\partial q}\dfrac{\partial q}{\partial y} + \dfrac{\partial v}{\partial r}\dfrac{\partial r}{\partial y}$,

$\dfrac{\partial v}{\partial z} = \dfrac{\partial v}{\partial p}\dfrac{\partial p}{\partial z} + \dfrac{\partial v}{\partial q}\dfrac{\partial q}{\partial z} + \dfrac{\partial v}{\partial r}\dfrac{\partial r}{\partial z}$

21. 85, 178, 54   **23.** $\frac{9}{7}, \frac{9}{7}$ **25.** 36, 24, 30

27. $\dfrac{4(xy)^{3/2} - y}{x - 2x^2\sqrt{xy}}$ **29.** $\dfrac{\sin(x - y) + e^y}{\sin(x - y) - xe^y}$

31. $\dfrac{3yz - 2x}{2z - 3xy}, \dfrac{3xz - 2y}{2z - 3xy}$

33. $\dfrac{1 + y^2z^2}{1 + y + y^2z^2}, -\dfrac{z}{1 + y + y^2z^2}$

35. 2°C/s

37. ≈ -0.33 m/s per minute

39. (a) 6 m³/s   (b) 10 m²/s   (c) 0 m/s   **41.** ≈ -0.27 L/s

43. (a) $\partial z/\partial r = (\partial z/\partial x)\cos \theta + (\partial z/\partial y)\sin \theta$,

$\partial z/\partial \theta = -(\partial z/\partial x)r \sin \theta + (\partial z/\partial y)r \cos \theta$

49. $4rs\,\partial^2 z/\partial x^2 + (4r^2 + 4s^2)\partial^2 z/\partial x\,\partial y + 4rs\,\partial^2 z/\partial y^2 + 2\,\partial z/\partial y$

Exercises 15.6 □ page 986

1. ≈ -0.1 millibar/mi   **3.** ≈ 0.778 **5.** $\frac{5}{16}\sqrt{3} + \frac{1}{4}$

7. (a) $\nabla f(x, y) = \langle 5y^2 - 12x^2y, 10xy - 4x^3\rangle$

(b) $\langle -4, 16\rangle$ (c) 172/13

9. (a) $\langle e^{2yz}, 2xze^{2yz}, 2xye^{2yz}\rangle$ (b) $\langle 1, 12, 0\rangle$ (c) $-\frac{22}{3}$

11. 23/10   **13.** $4\sqrt{2}$ **15.** 4/9

17. $9/(2\sqrt{5})$ **19.** 2/5   **21.** $4\sqrt{2}, \langle -1, 1\rangle$ **23.** 1, $\langle 0, 1\rangle$

25. $\sqrt{3}, \langle 1, -1, -1\rangle$ **27.** (b) $\langle -12, 92\rangle$

29. All points on the line $y = x + 1$ **31.** (a) $-40/(3\sqrt{3})$

33. (a) $32/\sqrt{3}$ (b) $\langle 38, 6, 12\rangle$ (c) $2\sqrt{406}$ **35.** $\frac{327}{13}$

39. (a) $4x - 2y + 3z = 21$ (b) $\dfrac{x - 4}{8} = \dfrac{y + 1}{-4} = \dfrac{z - 1}{6}$

41. (a) $4x - 5y - z = 4$ (b) $\dfrac{x - 2}{4} = \dfrac{y - 1}{-5} = \dfrac{z + 1}{-1}$

43. (a) $x + y - z = 1$ (b) $x - 1 = y = -z$

45.

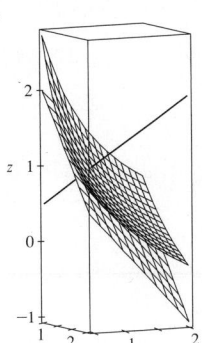

47. $\langle 4, 8\rangle$, $x + 2y = 4$

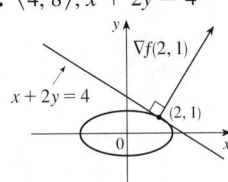

53. $\left(\pm\sqrt{6}/3, \mp 2\sqrt{6}/3, \pm\sqrt{6}/2\right)$

59. $x = -1 - 10t, y = 1 - 16t, z = 2 - 12t$

63. If $\mathbf{u} = \langle a, b\rangle$ and $\mathbf{v} = \langle c, d\rangle$, then $af_x + bf_y$ and $cf_x + df_y$ are known, so we solve linear equations for f_x and f_y.

Exercises 15.7 □ page 997

1. (a) f has a local minimum at $(1, 1)$.

(b) f has a saddle point at $(1, 1)$.

3. Local minimum at $(1, 1)$, saddle point at $(0, 0)$

5. Maximum $f(-1, \frac{1}{2}) = 11$

7. Minima $f(1, 1) = 0$, $f(-1, -1) = 0$, saddle point at $(0, 0)$

9. Saddle points at $(1, -1)$, $(-1, 1)$

11. f has a local maximum value of 1 at all points of the form (x_0, x_0).

13. None   **15.** Saddle points $(0, n\pi)$, n an integer

17. Minimum $f(0, 0) = 0$, saddle points at $(\pm 1, 0)$

19. Maximum $f(0, 0) = 2$, minimum $f(0, 2) = -2$, saddle points $(\pm 1, 1)$

21. Maximum $f(\pi/3, \pi/3) = 3\sqrt{3}/2$, minimum $f(5\pi/3, 5\pi/3) = -3\sqrt{3}/2$

23. Minima $f(-1.714, 0) \approx -9.200$, $f(1.402, 0) \approx 0.242$, saddle point $(0.312, 0)$, lowest point $(-1.714, 0, -9.200)$

25. Maxima $f(-1.267, 0) \approx 1.310$, $f(1.629, \pm 1.063) \approx 8.105$, saddle points $(-0.259, 0)$, $(1.526, 0)$, highest points $(1.629, \pm 1.063, 8.105)$

27. Maximum $f(2, 0) = 9$, minimum $f(0, 3) = -14$

29. Maximum $f(\pm 1, 1) = 7$, minimum $f(0, 0) = 4$

31. Maximum $f(3, 0) = 83$, minimum $f(1, 1) = 0$

33. Maximum $f(1, 0) = 2$, minimum $f(-1, 0) = -2$

35.

37. $\sqrt{3}$ **39.** $(0, 0, 1)$, $(0, 0, -1)$ **41.** $\frac{100}{3}, \frac{100}{3}, \frac{100}{3}$

43. $16/\sqrt{3}$ **45.** $\frac{4}{3}$ **47.** Cube, edge length $c/12$

49. Square base of side 40 cm, height 20 cm   **51.** $L^3/(3\sqrt{3})$

Exercises 15.8 □ page 1006

1. $\approx 59, 30$ **3.** Maxima $f(\pm1, 0) = 1$, minima $f(0, \pm1) = -1$
5. Maxima $f(\pm2, 1) = 4$, minima $f(\pm2, -1) = -4$
7. Maximum $f(1, 3, 5) = 70$, minimum $f(-1, -3, -5) = -70$
9. Maximum $2/\sqrt{3}$, minimum $-2/\sqrt{3}$
11. Maximum $\sqrt{3}$, minimum 1
13. Maximum $f(\frac{1}{2}, \frac{1}{2}, \frac{1}{2}, \frac{1}{2}) = 2$,
minimum $f(-\frac{1}{2}, -\frac{1}{2}, -\frac{1}{2}, -\frac{1}{2}) = -2$
15. Maximum $f(1, \sqrt{2}, -\sqrt{2}) = 1 + 2\sqrt{2}$,
minimum $f(1, -\sqrt{2}, \sqrt{2}) = 1 - 2\sqrt{2}$
17. Maximum $\frac{3}{2}$, minimum $\frac{1}{2}$
19. Maxima $f(\pm1/\sqrt{2}, \mp1/(2\sqrt{2})) = e^{1/4}$,
minima $f(\pm1/\sqrt{2}, \pm1/(2\sqrt{2})) = e^{-1/4}$
25–37. See Exercises 37–51 in Section 15.7.
39. Nearest $(\frac{1}{2}, \frac{1}{2}, \frac{1}{2})$, farthest $(-1, -1, 2)$
41. Maximum ≈ 9.7938, minimum ≈ -5.3506
43. (a) c/n (b) When $x_1 = x_2 = \cdots = x_n$

Chapter 15 Review □ page 1011

True-False Quiz

1. True **3.** False **5.** False **7.** True **9.** False
11. True

Exercises

1. $\{(x, y) \mid -1 \leqslant x \leqslant 1\}$ **3.**

5. **7.**

9. $\frac{2}{3}$
11. (a) $\approx 3.5°C/m$, $-3.0°C/m$ (b) $\approx 0.35°C/m$ by
Equation 15.6.9 (Definition 15.6.2 gives $\approx 1.1°C/m$.) (c) -0.25
13. $f_x = 1/\sqrt{2x + y^2}$, $f_y = y/\sqrt{2x + y^2}$
15. $g_u = \tan^{-1}v$, $g_v = u/(1 + v^2)$
17. $T_p = \ln(q + e^r)$, $T_q = p/(q + e^r)$, $T_r = pe^r/(q + e^r)$
19. $f_{xx} = 24x$, $f_{xy} = -2y = f_{yx}$, $f_{yy} = -2x$

21. $f_{xx} = k(k - 1)x^{k-2}y^l z^m$, $f_{xy} = klx^{k-1}y^{l-1}z^m = f_{yx}$,
$f_{xz} = kmx^{k-1}y^l z^{m-1} = f_{zx}$, $f_{yy} = l(l - 1)x^k y^{l-2}z^m$,
$f_{yz} = lmx^k y^{l-1}z^{m-1} = f_{zy}$, $f_{zz} = m(m - 1)x^k y^l z^{m-2}$
25. (a) $z = 8x + 4y + 1$ (b) $\dfrac{x - 1}{8} = \dfrac{y + 2}{4} = 1 - z$
27. (a) $2x - 2y - 3z = 3$ (b) $\dfrac{x - 2}{4} = \dfrac{y + 1}{-4} = \dfrac{z - 1}{-6}$
29. (a) $x + 2y + 5z = 0$ (b) $x - 2 = \dfrac{y + 1}{2} = \dfrac{z}{5}$
31. $(\pm\sqrt{2/7}, \pm1/\sqrt{14}, \mp3/\sqrt{14})$
33. $60x + \frac{24}{5}y + \frac{32}{5}z - 120$; 38.656
35. $e^t + 2(y/z)(3t^2 + 4) - 2t(y^2/z^2)$ **37.** $-47, 108$
43. $ze^{x\sqrt{y}}\langle z\sqrt{y}, xz/(2\sqrt{y}), 2\rangle$ **45.** $\frac{43}{5}$ **47.** $\sqrt{145}/2, \langle4, \frac{9}{2}\rangle$
49. $\approx \frac{5}{8}$ knot/mi **51.** Minimum $f(-4, 1) = -11$
53. Maximum $f(1, 1) = 1$; saddle points $(0, 0), (0, 3), (3, 0)$
55. Maximum $f(1, 2) = 4$, minimum $f(2, 4) = -64$
57. Maximum $f(-1, 0) = 2$, minima $f(1, \pm1) = -3$,
saddle points $(-1, \pm1), (1, 0)$
59. Maximum $f(\pm\sqrt{2/3}, 1/\sqrt{3}) = 2/(3\sqrt{3})$,
minimum $f(\pm\sqrt{2/3}, -1/\sqrt{3}) = -2/(3\sqrt{3})$
61. Maximum 1, minimum -1
63. $(\pm3^{-1/4}, 3^{-1/4}\sqrt{2}, \pm3^{1/4}), (\pm3^{-1/4}, -3^{-1/4}\sqrt{2}, \pm3^{1/4})$
65. $P(2 - \sqrt{3}), P(3 - \sqrt{3})/6, P(2\sqrt{3} - 3)/3$

Problems Plus □ page 1014

1. $L^2W^2, \frac{1}{4}L^2W^2$ **3.** (a) $x = w/3$, base $= w/3$ (b) Yes
9. $\sqrt{6}/2, 3\sqrt{2}/2$

||| Chapter 16

Exercises 16.1 □ page 1024

1. (a) 288 (b) 144 **3.** (a) $\pi^2/2 \approx 4.935$ (b) 0
5. (a) -6 (b) -3.5 **7.** $U < V < L$
9. (a) ≈ 248 (b) 15.5 **11.** 60
13. 3 **15.** 0.6065, 0.5694, 0.5606, 0.5585, 0.5579, 0.5578

Exercises 16.2 □ page 1030

1. $9 + 27y, 8x + 24x^2$ **3.** 10 **5.** 2 **7.** 261,632/45
9. $\frac{21}{2}\ln 2$ **11.** 6 **13.** $\frac{21}{2}$ **15.** $9\ln 2$
17. $[(\sqrt{3} - 1)/2] - (\pi/12)$ **19.** $\frac{1}{2}(e^2 - 3)$
21.

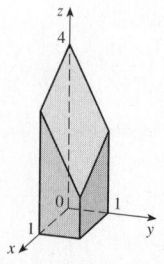

23. 47.5   **25.** $\frac{166}{27}$ **27.** $\frac{4}{15}(2\sqrt{2}-1)$ **29.** 36
31. $21e - 57$

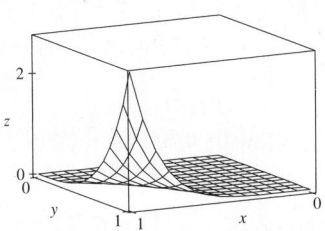

33. $\frac{5}{6}$
35. Fubini's Theorem does not apply. The integrand has an infinite discontinuity at the origin.

Exercises 16.3 □ page 1038

1. $\frac{9}{20}$ **3.** $\frac{4}{9}e^{3/2} - \frac{32}{45}$ **5.** $e-1$ **7.** $\frac{256}{21}$ **9.** $\frac{1}{2}\ln 2$
11. $\frac{1}{2}e^4 - 2e$ **13.** $\frac{1}{2}(1 - \cos 1)$ **15.** $\frac{147}{20}$ **17.** 0
19. $\frac{7}{18}$ **21.** $\frac{31}{8}$ **23.** $\frac{1}{6}$ **25.** $\frac{128}{15}$
27. $\frac{1}{3}$ **29.** 0, 1.213, 0.713   **31.** $\frac{64}{3}$
33. $13{,}984{,}735{,}616/14{,}549{,}535$ **35.** $\pi/2$
37. $\int_0^2 \int_{y^2}^4 f(x,y)\,dx\,dy$ **39.** $\int_{-3}^3 \int_0^{\sqrt{9-x^2}} f(x,y)\,dy\,dx$

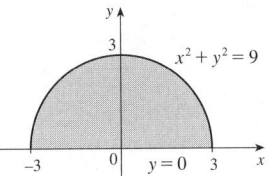

41. $\int_0^{\ln 2} \int_{e^y}^2 f(x,y)\,dx\,dy$

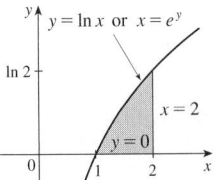

43. $\frac{1}{6}(e^9 - 1)$ **45.** $\frac{1}{4}\sin 81$ **47.** $\frac{1}{3}(2\sqrt{2}-1)$ **49.** 1
51. $0 \le \iint_D \sqrt{x^3 + y^3}\,dA \le \sqrt{2}$ **55.** 8π **57.** $2\pi/3$

Exercises 16.4 □ page 1044

1. $\int_0^{2\pi} \int_0^2 f(r\cos\theta, r\sin\theta)\,r\,dr\,d\theta$ **3.** $\int_{-2}^2 \int_x^2 f(x,y)\,dy\,dx$
5. $\int_0^{2\pi} \int_2^5 f(r\cos\theta, r\sin\theta)\,r\,dr\,d\theta$
7. $33\pi/2$

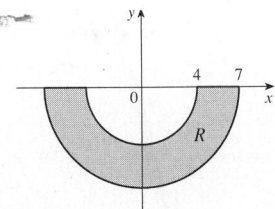

9. 0   **11.** $(\pi/2)\sin 9$ **13.** $(\pi/2)(1 - e^{-4})$
15. $\frac{3}{64}\pi^2$ **17.** $\pi/12$ **19.** $\frac{1}{8}(\pi - 2)$

21. $81\pi/2$ **23.** $\frac{4}{3}\pi a^3$ **25.** $(2\pi/3)[1 - (1/\sqrt{2})]$
27. $(8\pi/3)(64 - 24\sqrt{3})$ **29.** $(\pi/4)(e-1)$ **31.** $4\pi/3$
33. 1800π ft^3 **35.** $\frac{15}{16}$ **37.** (a) $\sqrt{\pi}/4$ (b) $\sqrt{\pi}/2$

Exercises 16.5 □ page 1054

1. $\frac{64}{3}$ C   **3.** $\frac{4}{3}, (\frac{4}{3}, 0)$ **5.** 6, $(\frac{3}{4}, \frac{3}{2})$
7. $\frac{1}{4}(e^2 - 1)$, $\left(\dfrac{e^2 + 1}{2(e^2 - 1)}, \dfrac{4(e^3 - 1)}{9(e^2 - 1)} \right)$
9. $\frac{27}{2}, (\frac{8}{5}, \frac{1}{2})$ **11.** $(\frac{3}{8}, 3\pi/16)$
13. $(2a/5, 2a/5)$ if vertex is $(0, 0)$ and sides are along positive axes
15. $\frac{1}{16}(e^4 - 1), \frac{1}{8}(e^2 - 1), \frac{1}{16}(e^4 + 2e^2 - 3)$ **17.** $\frac{189}{20}, \frac{1269}{28}, \frac{1917}{35}$
19. $m = \pi^2/8$, $(\bar{x}, \bar{y}) = \left(\dfrac{2\pi}{3} - \dfrac{1}{\pi}, \dfrac{16}{9\pi} \right)$, $I_x = \frac{3}{64}\pi^2$,
$I_y = \frac{1}{16}(\pi^4 - 3\pi^2), I_0 = \frac{1}{16}\pi^4 - \frac{9}{64}\pi^2$
21. $\rho a^4/3, \rho a^4/3; a/\sqrt{3}, a/\sqrt{3}$
23. (a) $\frac{1}{2}$ (b) 0.375   (c) $\frac{5}{48} \approx 0.1042$
25. (b) (i) $e^{-0.2} \approx 0.8187$
(ii) $1 + e^{-1.8} - e^{-0.8} - e^{-1} \approx 0.3481$ (c) 2, 5
27. (a) ≈ 0.500 (b) ≈ 0.632
29. (a) $\iint_D (k/20)[20 - \sqrt{(x - x_0)^2 + (y - y_0)^2}]\,dA$, where D is the disk with radius 10 mi centered at the center of the city
(b) $200\pi k/3 \approx 209k, 200(\pi/2 - \frac{8}{9})k \approx 136k$, on the edge

Exercises 16.6 □ page 1058

1. $15\sqrt{26}$ **3.** $3\sqrt{14}$ **5.** $12\sin^{-1}\frac{2}{3}$
7. $(\pi/6)(17\sqrt{17} - 5\sqrt{5})$ **9.** $(2\pi/3)(2\sqrt{2} - 1)$
11. $a^2(\pi - 2)$ **13.** 13.9783   **15.** (a) ≈ 1.83 (b) ≈ 1.8616
17. $\frac{45}{8}\sqrt{14} + \frac{15}{16}\ln[(11\sqrt{5} + 3\sqrt{70})/(3\sqrt{5} + \sqrt{70})]$
19. 3.3213   **23.** $(\pi/6)(101\sqrt{101} - 1)$

Exercises 16.7 □ page 1066

3. 1   **5.** $\frac{1}{3}(e^3 - 1)$ **7.** 4   **9.** $\frac{65}{28}$ **11.** $\frac{1}{10}$
13. $8/(3e)$ **15.** $16\pi/3$ **17.** $\frac{16}{3}$ **19.** 36π
21. (a) $\int_0^1 \int_0^x \int_0^{\sqrt{1-y^2}} dz\,dy\,dx$ (b) $\frac{1}{4}\pi - \frac{1}{3}$
23. 60.533   **25.**

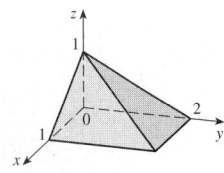

27. $\int_{-2}^2 \int_0^6 \int_{-\sqrt{4-x^2}}^{\sqrt{4-x^2}} f(x, y, z)\,dz\,dy\,dx$
$= \int_0^6 \int_{-2}^2 \int_{-\sqrt{4-x^2}}^{\sqrt{4-x^2}} f(x, y, z)\,dz\,dx\,dy$
$= \int_{-2}^2 \int_0^6 \int_{-\sqrt{4-z^2}}^{\sqrt{4-z^2}} f(x, y, z)\,dx\,dy\,dz$
$= \int_0^6 \int_{-2}^2 \int_{-\sqrt{4-z^2}}^{\sqrt{4-z^2}} f(x, y, z)\,dx\,dz\,dy$
$= \int_{-2}^2 \int_{-\sqrt{4-x^2}}^{\sqrt{4-x^2}} \int_0^6 f(x, y, z)\,dy\,dz\,dx$
$= \int_{-2}^2 \int_{-\sqrt{4-z^2}}^{\sqrt{4-z^2}} \int_0^6 f(x, y, z)\,dy\,dx\,dz$

29. $\int_{-1}^{1}\int_{0}^{1-x^2}\int_{0}^{y} f(x, y, z)\, dz\, dy\, dx$

$= \int_{0}^{1}\int_{-\sqrt{1-y}}^{\sqrt{1-y}}\int_{0}^{y} f(x, y, z)\, dz\, dx\, dy$

$= \int_{0}^{1}\int_{z}^{1}\int_{-\sqrt{1-y}}^{\sqrt{1-y}} f(x, y, z)\, dx\, dy\, dz$

$= \int_{0}^{1}\int_{0}^{y}\int_{-\sqrt{1-y}}^{\sqrt{1-y}} f(x, y, z)\, dx\, dz\, dy$

$= \int_{-1}^{1}\int_{0}^{1-x^2}\int_{z}^{1-x^2} f(x, y, z)\, dy\, dz\, dx$

$= \int_{0}^{1}\int_{-\sqrt{1-z}}^{\sqrt{1-z}}\int_{z}^{1-x^2} f(x, y, z)\, dy\, dx\, dz$

31. $\int_{0}^{1}\int_{\sqrt{x}}^{1}\int_{0}^{1-y} f(x, y, z)\, dz\, dy\, dx$

$= \int_{0}^{1}\int_{0}^{y^2}\int_{0}^{1-y} f(x, y, z)\, dz\, dx\, dy$

$= \int_{0}^{1}\int_{0}^{1-z}\int_{0}^{y^2} f(x, y, z)\, dx\, dy\, dz$

$= \int_{0}^{1}\int_{0}^{1-y}\int_{0}^{y^2} f(x, y, z)\, dx\, dz\, dy$

$= \int_{0}^{1}\int_{0}^{1-\sqrt{x}}\int_{\sqrt{x}}^{1-z} f(x, y, z)\, dy\, dz\, dx$

$= \int_{0}^{1}\int_{0}^{(1-z)^2}\int_{\sqrt{x}}^{1-z} f(x, y, z)\, dy\, dx\, dz$

33. $\int_{0}^{1}\int_{y}^{1}\int_{0}^{y} f(x, y, z)\, dz\, dx\, dy = \int_{0}^{1}\int_{0}^{x}\int_{0}^{y} f(x, y, z)\, dz\, dy\, dx$

$= \int_{0}^{1}\int_{z}^{1}\int_{y}^{1} f(x, y, z)\, dx\, dy\, dz = \int_{0}^{1}\int_{0}^{y}\int_{y}^{1} f(x, y, z)\, dx\, dz\, dy$

$= \int_{0}^{1}\int_{0}^{x}\int_{z}^{x} f(x, y, z)\, dy\, dz\, dx = \int_{0}^{1}\int_{z}^{1}\int_{z}^{x} f(x, y, z)\, dy\, dx\, dz$

35. $\frac{79}{30}, \left(\frac{358}{553}, \frac{33}{79}, \frac{571}{553}\right)$ **37.** $a^5, (7a/12, 7a/12, 7a/12)$

39. (a) $m = \int_{-3}^{3}\int_{-\sqrt{9-x^2}}^{\sqrt{9-x^2}}\int_{1}^{5-y} \sqrt{x^2 + y^2}\, dz\, dy\, dx$

(b) $(\bar{x}, \bar{y}, \bar{z})$, where

$\bar{x} = (1/m)\int_{-3}^{3}\int_{-\sqrt{9-x^2}}^{\sqrt{9-x^2}}\int_{1}^{5-y} x\sqrt{x^2 + y^2}\, dz\, dy\, dx$

$\bar{y} = (1/m)\int_{-3}^{3}\int_{-\sqrt{9-x^2}}^{\sqrt{9-x^2}}\int_{1}^{5-y} y\sqrt{x^2 + y^2}\, dz\, dy\, dx$

$\bar{z} = (1/m)\int_{-3}^{3}\int_{-\sqrt{9-x^2}}^{\sqrt{9-x^2}}\int_{1}^{5-y} z\sqrt{x^2 + y^2}\, dz\, dy\, dx$

(c) $\int_{-3}^{3}\int_{-\sqrt{9-x^2}}^{\sqrt{9-x^2}}\int_{1}^{5-y} (x^2 + y^2)^{3/2}\, dz\, dy\, dx$

41. (a) $\frac{3}{32}\pi + \frac{11}{24}$

(b) $(\bar{x}, \bar{y}, \bar{z}) = \left(\dfrac{28}{9\pi + 44}, \dfrac{30\pi + 128}{45\pi + 220}, \dfrac{45\pi + 208}{135\pi + 660}\right)$

(c) $\frac{1}{240}(68 + 15\pi)$

43. $I_x = I_y = I_z = \frac{2}{3}kL^5$ **45.** (a) $\frac{1}{8}$ (b) $\frac{1}{64}$ (c) $\frac{1}{5760}$

47. $L^3/8$

49. The region bounded by the ellipsoid $x^2 + 2y^2 + 3z^2 = 1$

Exercises 16.8 □ **page 1073**

1.

$64\pi/3$

3.

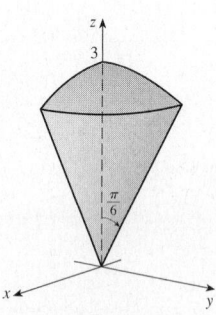

$(9\pi/4)(2 - \sqrt{3})$

5. $\int_{0}^{\pi/2}\int_{0}^{3}\int_{0}^{2} f(r\cos\theta, r\sin\theta, z)\, r\, dz\, dr\, d\theta$ **7.** 384π

9. $\pi(e^6 - e - 5)$ **11.** $2\pi/5$

13. (a) 162π (b) $(0, 0, 15)$

15. $\pi Ka^2/8, (0, 0, 2a/3)$ **17.** $4\pi/5$ **19.** $15\pi/16$

21. $(1562/15)\pi$ **23.** 10π **25.** $(0, \frac{525}{296}, 0)$

27. (a) $(0, 0, \frac{3}{8}a)$ (b) $4K\pi a^5/15$

29. $(2\pi/3)[1 - (1/\sqrt{2})], (0, 0, 3/[8(2 - \sqrt{2})])$ **31.** $5\pi/6$

33. $8\pi/35$ **35.** $243\pi/5$ **37.** $136\pi/99$

Exercises 16.9 □ **page 1084**

1. -14 **3.** 0 **5.** $2uvw$

7. The parallelogram with vertices $(0, 0)$, $(6, 3)$, $(12, 1)$, $(6, -2)$

9. The region bounded by the line $y = 1$, the y-axis, and $y = \sqrt{x}$

11. -3 **13.** 6π **15.** $2\ln 3$

17. (a) $\frac{4}{3}\pi abc$ (b) 1.083×10^{12} km^3

19. $\frac{8}{5}\ln 8$ **21.** $\frac{3}{2}\sin 1$ **23.** $e - e^{-1}$

Chapter 16 Review □ **page 1085**

True-False Quiz

1. True **3.** True **5.** True **7.** False

Exercises

1. ≈ 64.0 **3.** $4e^2 - 4e + 3$ **5.** $\frac{1}{2}\sin 1$ **7.** $\frac{2}{3}$

9. $\int_{0}^{\pi}\int_{2}^{4} f(r\cos\theta, r\sin\theta)\, r\, dr\, d\theta$

11. The region inside the loop of the four-leaved rose $r = \sin 2\theta$ in the first quadrant

13. $\frac{1}{2}\sin 1$ **15.** $\frac{1}{2}e^6 - \frac{7}{2}$ **17.** $\frac{1}{4}\ln 2$

19. 8 **21.** $81\pi/5$ **23.** 40.5 **25.** $\pi/96$

27. $\frac{64}{15}$ **29.** 176 **31.** $\frac{2}{3}$ **33.** $2ma^3/9$

35. (a) $\frac{1}{4}$ (b) $\left(\frac{1}{3}, \frac{8}{15}\right)$

(c) $I_x = \frac{1}{12}, I_y = \frac{1}{24}; \bar{\bar{y}} = 1/\sqrt{3}, \bar{\bar{x}} = 1/\sqrt{6}$

37. (a) $(0, 0, h/4)$ (b) $\pi a^4 h/10$ **39.** $\ln(\sqrt{2} + \sqrt{3}) + \sqrt{2}/3$

41. 97.2 **43.** 0.0512 **45.** (a) $\frac{1}{15}$ (b) $\frac{1}{3}$ (c) $\frac{1}{45}$

47. $\int_{0}^{1}\int_{0}^{1-z}\int_{-\sqrt{y}}^{\sqrt{y}} f(x, y, z)\, dx\, dy\, dz$ **49.** $-\ln 2$ **51.** 0

Problems Plus □ **page 1088**

1. 30 **3.** $\frac{1}{2}\sin 1$ **7.** (b) 0.90

|||| **Chapter 17**

Exercises 17.1 □ **page 1096**

1.

3.

5.

7.

9.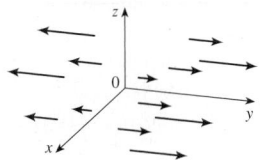

11. II   **13.** I   **15.** IV   **17.** III

19.

The line $y = 2x$

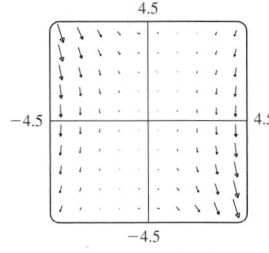

21. $\nabla f(x, y) = \dfrac{1}{x + 2y}\,\mathbf{i} + \dfrac{2}{x + 2y}\,\mathbf{j}$

23. $\nabla f(x, y, z) = \dfrac{x}{\sqrt{x^2 + y^2 + z^2}}\,\mathbf{i}$

$+ \dfrac{y}{\sqrt{x^2 + y^2 + z^2}}\,\mathbf{j} + \dfrac{z}{\sqrt{x^2 + y^2 + z^2}}\,\mathbf{k}$

25. $\nabla f(x, y) = (y - 2)\mathbf{i} + x\,\mathbf{j}$

27.

29. IV   **31.** II

33. (a) 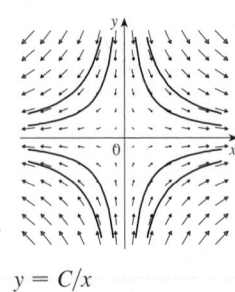   (b) $y = 1/x$, $x > 0$

$y = C/x$

Exercises 17.2 □ page 1107

1. $\frac{1}{2}(17\sqrt{17} - 1)$ **3.** 1638.4   **5.** $\frac{464}{5} + 9 \ln 3$ **7.** $\frac{17}{3}$
9. 320   **11.** $\frac{1}{12}\sqrt{14}(e^6 - 1)$ **13.** $\frac{1}{5}$ **15.** $\frac{97}{3}$
17. (a) Positive   (b) Negative   **19.** $-\frac{59}{105}$
21. $\frac{6}{5} - \cos 1 - \sin 1$
23. $3\pi + \frac{2}{3}$

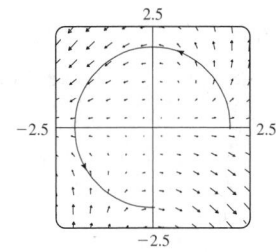

25. (a) $\frac{11}{8} - 1/e$ (b)

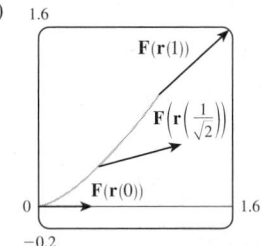

27. $\frac{945}{16,777,216}\,\pi$ **29.** 0.052   **31.** $2\pi k$, $(4/\pi, 0)$
33. (a) $\bar{x} = (1/m)\int_C x\rho(x, y, z)\,ds$,
$\bar{y} = (1/m)\int_C y\rho(x, y, z)\,ds$,
$\bar{z} = (1/m)\int_C z\rho(x, y, z)\,ds$, where $m = \int_C \rho(x, y, z)\,ds$
(b) $(0, 0, 3\pi)$
35. $I_x = k((\pi/2) - \frac{4}{3})$, $I_y = k((\pi/2) - \frac{2}{3})$
37. $2\pi^2$ **39.** 26   **41.** 1.67×10^4 ft-lb   **43.** (b) Yes
45. ≈ 22 J

Exercises 17.3 □ page 1117

1. 40   **3.** $f(x, y) = 3x^2 + 5xy + 2y^2 + K$
5. Not conservative   **7.** $f(x, y) = x^2 \cos y - y \sin x + K$
9. $f(x, y) = ye^x + x \sin y + K$ **11.** (b) 16
13. (a) $f(x, y) = \frac{1}{4}x^4 y^4$ (b) 4
15. (a) $f(x, y, z) = xyz + z^2$ (b) 77
17. (a) $f(x, y, z) = xy^2 \cos z$ (b) 0
19. 2   **21.** 30   **23.** No   **25.** No
29. (a) Yes   (b) Yes   (c) Yes
31. (a) Yes   (b) Yes   (c) No

Exercises 17.4 □ page 1125

1. 6   **3.** $\frac{2}{3}$ **7.** $e - 1$ **9.** $\frac{1}{3}$ **11.** -24π
13. $\frac{4}{3} - 2\pi$ **15.** $\frac{625}{2}\pi$ **17.** $-\frac{1}{12}$
19. 3π **21.** (c) $\frac{9}{2}$ **23.** $\left(\frac{1}{3}, \frac{1}{3}\right)$

Exercises 17.5 □ page 1132

1. (a) $-x^2\,\mathbf{i} + 3xy\,\mathbf{j} - xz\,\mathbf{k}$ (b) yz
3. (a) $(x - y)\,\mathbf{i} - y\,\mathbf{j} + \mathbf{k}$ (b) $z - 1/(2\sqrt{z})$
5. (a) $\mathbf{0}$ (b) 1
7. (a) $\langle 1/y, -1/x, 1/x \rangle$ (b) $1/x + 1/y + 1/z$
9. (a) Negative   (b) curl $\mathbf{F} = \mathbf{0}$
11. (a) Zero   (b) curl $\mathbf{F}$ points in the negative z-direction
13. $f(x, y, z) = xyz + K$ **15.** $f(x, y, z) = x^2y + y^2z + K$
17. Not conservative   **19.** No

Exercises 17.6 □ page 1142

1. Circular paraboloid with axis the z-axis
3. Circular cylinder with axis the x-axis
5.

7.

9.

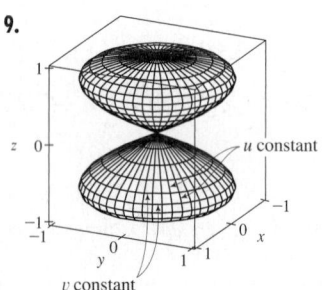

11. IV   **13.** I   **15.** II
17. $x = 1 + u + v, y = 2 + u - v, z = -3 - u + v$
19. $x = x, z = z, y = \sqrt{1 - x^2 + z^2}$
21. $x = 2\sin\phi\cos\theta, y = 2\sin\phi\sin\theta,$
$z = 2\cos\phi, 0 \le \phi \le \pi/4, 0 \le \theta \le 2\pi$
$\left[\text{or } x = x, y = y, z = \sqrt{4 - x^2 - y^2}, x^2 + y^2 \le 2\right]$
23. $x = x, y = 4\cos\theta, z = 4\sin\theta, 0 \le x \le 5, 0 \le \theta \le 2\pi$
27. $x = x, y = e^{-x}\cos\theta,$
$z = e^{-x}\sin\theta, 0 \le x \le 3,$
$0 \le \theta \le 2\pi$

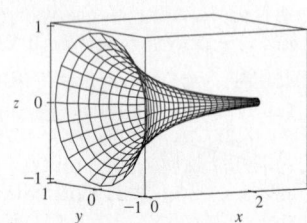

29. (a) Direction reverses   (b) Number of coils doubles
31. $3x - y + 3z = 3$ **33.** $-x + 2z = 1$ **35.** $4\sqrt{6}\,\pi$
37. $(2\pi/3)(2\sqrt{2} - 1)$ **39.** $(\pi/6)(17\sqrt{17} - 5\sqrt{5})$
41. $(\sqrt{21}/2) + \frac{17}{4}\left[\ln(2 + \sqrt{21}) - \ln\sqrt{17}\right]$ **43.** $2a^2(\pi - 2)$
45. $\pi\left(2\sqrt{6} - \frac{8}{3}\right)$ **47.** 13.9783
49. (a) ≈ 1.83 (b) ≈ 1.8616
51. $\frac{45}{8}\sqrt{14} + \frac{15}{16}\ln\left[(11\sqrt{5} + 3\sqrt{70})/(3\sqrt{5} + \sqrt{70})\right]$
53. (b)

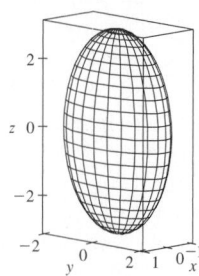

(c) $\int_0^{2\pi}\int_0^{\pi} \sqrt{36\sin^4u\cos^2v + 9\sin^4u\sin^2v + 4\cos^2u\sin^2u}\;du\,dv$
55. 4.4506

Exercises 17.7 □ page 1155

1. $8\left(1 + \sqrt{2} + \sqrt{3}\right) \approx 33.17$ **3.** 900π **5.** $171\sqrt{14}$
7. $\sqrt{3}/24$
9. $364\sqrt{2}\,\pi/3$ **11.** $(\pi/60)(391\sqrt{17} + 1)$
13. 16π **15.** 16π **17.** $5\sqrt{5}/48 + 1/240$
19. $\frac{713}{180}$ **21.** $-\frac{1}{6}$ **23.** $-\frac{4}{3}\pi$
25. 0   **27.** 48   **29.** 0.1642   **31.** 3.4895
33. $\iint_S \mathbf{F} \cdot d\mathbf{S} = \iint_D \left[P(\partial h/\partial x) - Q + R(\partial h/\partial z)\right] dA,$
where D = projection on xz-plane
35. $(0, 0, a/2)$
37. (a) $I_z = \iint_S (x^2 + y^2)\rho(x, y, z)\,dS$ (b) $4329\sqrt{2}\,\pi/5$
39. $194{,}400\pi$ **41.** $8\pi a^3\varepsilon_0/3$ **43.** 1248π

Exercises 17.8 □ page 1161

3. 0   **5.** 0   **7.** -1 **9.** 80π
11. (a) $81\pi/2$ (b)

(c) $x = 3\cos t, y = 3\sin t,$
$z = 1 - 3(\cos t + \sin t),$
$0 \le t \le 2\pi$

17. 16

Exercises 17.9 □ page 1168

1. Negative at P_1, positive at P_2 **7.** 2   **9.** $9\pi/2$
11. 0   **13.** $32\pi/3$ **15.** 0
17. $341\sqrt{2}/60 + \frac{81}{20}\arcsin(\sqrt{3}/3)$ **19.** $13\pi/20$

Chapter 17 Review □ page 1171

True-False Quiz

1. False   **3.** True   **5.** False   **7.** True

Exercises

1. (a) Negative   (b) Positive   **3.** $4\sqrt{5}$ **5.** $-\pi$
7. $\frac{17}{2}$ **9.** $\frac{11}{12} - 4/e$ **11.** $f(x, y) = e^y + xe^{xy}$ **13.** 0
17. -8π **25.** $\frac{1}{6}(27 - 5\sqrt{5})$ **27.** $\pi(391\sqrt{17} + 1)/60$
29. $-64\pi/3$ **33.** $-\frac{1}{2}$ **37.** -4 **39.** 21

▌▌▌ Chapter 18

Exercises 18.1 □ page 1183

1. $y = c_1 e^{4x} + c_2 e^{2x}$ **3.** $y = e^{-4x}(c_1 \cos 5x + c_2 \sin 5x)$
5. $y = c_1 e^x + c_2 x e^x$ **7.** $y = c_1 \cos(x/2) + c_2 \sin(x/2)$
9. $y = c_1 + c_2 e^{-x/4}$ **11.** $y = c_1 e^{(1+\sqrt{2})t} + c_2 e^{(1-\sqrt{2})t}$
13. $y = e^{-t/2}[c_1 \cos(\sqrt{3}t/2) + c_2 \sin(\sqrt{3}t/2)]$
15.

All solutions approach 0 as $x \to -\infty$ and approach $\pm\infty$ as $x \to \infty$.
17. $y = 2e^{-3x/2} + e^{-x}$ **19.** $y = e^{x/2} - 2xe^{x/2}$
21. $y = 3 \cos 4x - \sin 4x$ **23.** $y = e^{-x}(2 \cos x + 3 \sin x)$
25. $y = 3 \cos(\frac{1}{2}x) - 4 \sin(\frac{1}{2}x)$ **27.** $y = \dfrac{e^{x+3}}{e^3 - 1} + \dfrac{e^{2x}}{1 - e^3}$
29. No solution
31. $y = e^{-2x}(2 \cos 3x - e^\pi \sin 3x)$
33. (b) $\lambda = n^2\pi^2/L^2$, n a positive integer; $y = C \sin(n\pi x/L)$

Exercises 18.2 □ page 1190

1. $y = c_1 e^{-2x} + c_2 e^{-x} + \frac{1}{2}x^2 - \frac{3}{2}x + \frac{7}{4}$
3. $y = c_1 + c_2 e^{2x} + \frac{1}{40}\cos 4x - \frac{1}{20}\sin 4x$
5. $y = e^{2x}(c_1 \cos x + c_2 \sin x) + \frac{1}{10}e^{-x}$
7. $y = \frac{3}{2}\cos x + \frac{11}{2}\sin x + \frac{1}{2}e^x + x^3 - 6x$
9. $y = e^x(\frac{1}{2}x^2 - x + 2)$
11.

The solutions are all asymptotic to $y_p = e^x/10$ as $x \to \infty$. Except for y_p, all solutions approach either ∞ or $-\infty$ as $x \to -\infty$.

13. $y_p = Ae^{2x} + (Bx^2 + Cx + D) \cos x + (Ex^2 + Fx + G) \sin x$
15. $y_p = Ax + (Bx + C)e^{9x}$
17. $y_p = xe^{-x}[(Ax^2 + Bx + C) \cos 3x + (Dx^2 + Ex + F) \sin 3x]$
19. $y = c_1 \cos 2x + c_2 \sin 2x + \frac{1}{4}x$
21. $y = c_1 e^x + c_2 x e^x + e^{2x}$
23. $y = (c_1 + x) \sin x + (c_2 + \ln \cos x) \cos x$
25. $y = [c_1 + \ln(1 + e^{-x})]e^x + [c_2 - e^{-x} + \ln(1 + e^{-x})]e^{2x}$
27. $y = [c_1 - \frac{1}{2}\int (e^x/x)\,dx]e^{-x} + [c_2 + \frac{1}{2}\int (e^{-x}/x)\,dx]e^x$

Exercises 18.3 □ page 1198

1. $x = 0.36 \sin(10t/3)$ **3.** $x = -\frac{1}{5}e^{-6t} + \frac{6}{5}e^{-t}$ **5.** $\frac{49}{12}$ kg
7.

13. $Q(t) = (-e^{-10t}/250)(6 \cos 20t + 3 \sin 20t) + \frac{3}{125}$,
$I(t) = \frac{3}{5}e^{-10t} \sin 20t$
15. $Q(t) = e^{-10t}[\frac{3}{250}\cos 20t - \frac{3}{500}\sin 20t]$
$- \frac{3}{250}\cos 10t + \frac{3}{125}\sin 10t$

Exercises 18.4 □ page 1203

1. $c_0 \sum\limits_{n=0}^{\infty} \dfrac{x^n}{n!} = c_0 e^x$ **3.** $c_0 \sum\limits_{n=0}^{\infty} \dfrac{x^{3n}}{3^n n!} = c_0 e^{x^3/3}$

5. $c_0 \sum\limits_{n=0}^{\infty} \dfrac{(-1)^n}{2^n n!} x^{2n} + c_1 \sum\limits_{n=0}^{\infty} \dfrac{(-2)^n n!}{(2n+1)!} x^{2n+1}$

7. $c_0 + c_1 x + c_0 \dfrac{x^2}{2} + c_0 \sum\limits_{n=2}^{\infty} \dfrac{(-1)^{n-1}(2n-3)!}{2^{2n-2}n!(n-2)!} x^{2n}$

9. $\sum\limits_{n=0}^{\infty} \dfrac{x^{2n}}{2^n n!} = e^{x^2/2}$

11. $x + \sum\limits_{n=1}^{\infty} \dfrac{(-1)^n 2^2 5^2 \cdot\, \cdots\, \cdot (3n-1)^2}{(3n+1)!} x^{3n+1}$

Chapter 18 Review □ page 1204

True-False Quiz

1. True   **3.** True

Exercises

1. $y = c_1 e^{5x} + c_2 e^{-3x}$ **3.** $y = c_1 \cos(\sqrt{3}x) + c_2 \sin(\sqrt{3}x)$
5. $y = e^{2x}(c_1 \cos x + c_2 \sin x + 1)$
7. $y = c_1 e^x + c_2 x e^x - \frac{1}{2}\cos x - \frac{1}{2}(x+1) \sin x$
9. $y = c_1 e^{3x} + c_2 e^{-2x} - \frac{1}{6} - \frac{1}{5}xe^{-2x}$
11. $y = 5 - 2e^{-6(x-1)}$ **13.** $y = (e^{4x} - e^x)/3$

15. $\sum\limits_{n=0}^{\infty} \dfrac{(-2)^n n!}{(2n+1)!} x^{2n+1}$

17. $Q(t) = -0.02e^{-10t}(\cos 10t + \sin 10t) + 0.03$
19. (c) $2\pi/k \approx 85$ min   (d) $\approx 17{,}600$ mi/h

||| Appendixes

Exercises A □ page A9

1. 18 **3.** π **5.** $5 - \sqrt{5}$ **7.** $2 - x$

9. $|x + 1| = \begin{cases} x + 1 & \text{for } x \geq -1 \\ -x - 1 & \text{for } x < -1 \end{cases}$ **11.** $x^2 + 1$

13. $(-2, \infty)$

15. $[-1, \infty)$

17. $(3, \infty)$

19. $(2, 6)$

21. $(0, 1]$

23. $\left[-1, \frac{1}{2}\right)$

25. $(-\infty, 1) \cup (2, \infty)$

27. $\left[-1, \frac{1}{2}\right]$

29. $(-\infty, \infty)$

31. $\left(-\sqrt{3}, \sqrt{3}\right)$

33. $(-\infty, 1]$

35. $(-1, 0) \cup (1, \infty)$

37. $(-\infty, 0) \cup \left(\frac{1}{4}, \infty\right)$

39. $10 \leq C \leq 35$ **41.** (a) $T = 20 - 10h, 0 \leq h \leq 12$
(b) $-30°C \leq T \leq 20°C$ **43.** $\pm\frac{3}{2}$ **45.** $2, -\frac{4}{3}$
47. $(-3, 3)$ **49.** $(3, 5)$ **51.** $(-\infty, -7] \cup [-3, \infty)$
53. $[1.3, 1.7]$ **55.** $[-4, -1] \cup [1, 4]$
57. $x \geq (a + b)c/(ab)$ **59.** $x > (c - b)/a$

Exercises B □ page A15

1. 5 **3.** $\sqrt{74}$ **5.** $2\sqrt{37}$ **7.** 2 **9.** $-\frac{9}{2}$
17. **19.** **21.** $y = 6x - 15$

23. $2x - 3y + 19 = 0$ **25.** $5x + y = 11$ **27.** $y = 3x - 2$
29. $y = 3x - 3$ **31.** $y = 5$ **33.** $x + 2y + 11 = 0$
35. $5x - 2y + 1 = 0$
37. $m = -\frac{1}{3}$, **39.** $m = 0$, **41.** $m = \frac{3}{4}$,
$b = 0$ $b = -2$ $b = -3$

43. **45.**

47. **49.**

51.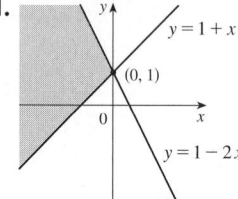

53. $(0, -4)$ **55.** (a) $(4, 9)$ (b) $(3.5, -3)$ **57.** $(1, -2)$
59. $y = x - 3$ **61.** (b) $4x - 3y - 24 = 0$

Exercises C □ page A23

1. $(x - 3)^2 + (y + 1)^2 = 25$ **3.** $x^2 + y^2 = 65$
5. $(2, -5), 4$ **7.** $\left(-\frac{1}{2}, 0\right), \frac{1}{2}$ **9.** $\left(\frac{1}{4}, -\frac{1}{4}\right), \sqrt{10}/4$
11. Parabola **13.** Ellipse

15. Hyperbola **17.** Ellipse

19. Parabola **21.** Hyperbola

23. Hyperbola

25. Ellipse

27. Parabola

29. Parabola

31. Ellipse

33.

35. $y = x^2 - 2x$

37.

39.

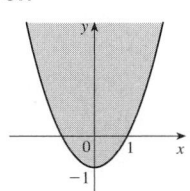

Exercises D □ **page A32**

1. $7\pi/6$ **3.** $\pi/20$ **5.** 5π **7.** $720°$ **9.** $75°$
11. $-67.5°$ **13.** 3π cm **15.** $\frac{2}{3}$ rad $= (120/\pi)°$
17.

19.

21.

23. $\sin(3\pi/4) = 1/\sqrt{2}$, $\cos(3\pi/4) = -1/\sqrt{2}$, $\tan(3\pi/4) = -1$,
$\csc(3\pi/4) = \sqrt{2}$, $\sec(3\pi/4) = -\sqrt{2}$, $\cot(3\pi/4) = -1$
25. $\sin(9\pi/2) = 1$, $\cos(9\pi/2) = 0$, $\csc(9\pi/2) = 1$, $\cot(9\pi/2) = 0$,
$\tan(9\pi/2)$ and $\sec(9\pi/2)$ undefined
27. $\sin(5\pi/6) = \frac{1}{2}$, $\cos(5\pi/6) = -\sqrt{3}/2$, $\tan(5\pi/6) = -1/\sqrt{3}$,
$\csc(5\pi/6) = 2$, $\sec(5\pi/6) = -2/\sqrt{3}$, $\cot(5\pi/6) = -\sqrt{3}$
29. $\cos\theta = \frac{4}{5}$, $\tan\theta = \frac{3}{4}$, $\csc\theta = \frac{5}{3}$, $\sec\theta = \frac{5}{4}$, $\cot\theta = \frac{4}{3}$
31. $\sin\phi = \sqrt{5}/3$, $\cos\phi = -\frac{2}{3}$, $\tan\phi = -\sqrt{5}/2$, $\csc\phi = 3/\sqrt{5}$,
$\cot\phi = -2/\sqrt{5}$
33. $\sin\beta = -1/\sqrt{10}$, $\cos\beta = -3/\sqrt{10}$, $\tan\beta = \frac{1}{3}$,
$\csc\beta = -\sqrt{10}$, $\sec\beta = -\sqrt{10}/3$
35. 5.73576 cm **37.** 24.62147 cm **59.** $(4 + 6\sqrt{2})/15$
61. $(3 + 8\sqrt{2})/15$ **63.** $\frac{24}{25}$
65. $\pi/3, 5\pi/3$ **67.** $\pi/4, 3\pi/4, 5\pi/4, 7\pi/4$
69. $\pi/6, \pi/2, 5\pi/6, 3\pi/2$ **71.** $0, \pi, 2\pi$
73. $0 \leq x \leq \pi/6$ and $5\pi/6 \leq x \leq 2\pi$
75. $0 \leq x < \pi/4, 3\pi/4 < x < 5\pi/4, 7\pi/4 < x \leq 2\pi$
77.

79.

81.

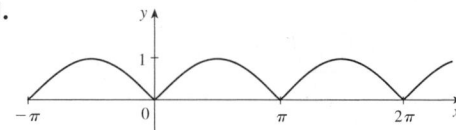

89. 14.34457 cm^2

Exercises E □ **page A38**

1. $\sqrt{1} + \sqrt{2} + \sqrt{3} + \sqrt{4} + \sqrt{5}$ **3.** $3^4 + 3^5 + 3^6$
5. $-1 + \frac{1}{3} + \frac{3}{5} + \frac{5}{7} + \frac{7}{9}$ **7.** $1^{10} + 2^{10} + 3^{10} + \cdots + n^{10}$
9. $1 - 1 + 1 - 1 + \cdots + (-1)^{n-1}$ **11.** $\sum_{i=1}^{10} i$
13. $\sum_{i=1}^{19} \frac{i}{i+1}$ **15.** $\sum_{i=1}^{n} 2i$ **17.** $\sum_{i=0}^{5} 2^i$ **19.** $\sum_{i=1}^{n} x^i$
21. 80 **23.** 3276 **25.** 0 **27.** 61 **29.** $n(n+1)$
31. $n(n^2 + 6n + 17)/3$ **33.** $n(n^2 + 6n + 11)/3$
35. $n(n^3 + 2n^2 - n - 10)/4$

41. (a) n^4 (b) $5^{100} - 1$ (c) $\frac{97}{300}$ (d) $a_n - a_0$

43. $\frac{1}{3}$ **45.** 14   **49.** $2^{n+1} + n^2 + n - 2$

Exercises G □ **page A55**

1. $8 - 4i$ **3.** $13 + 18i$ **5.** $12 - 7i$ **7.** $\frac{11}{13} + \frac{10}{13}i$

9. $\frac{1}{2} - \frac{1}{2}i$ **11.** $-i$ **13.** $5i$ **15.** $12 + 5i;\ 13$

17. $4i,\ 4$ **19.** $\pm\frac{3}{2}i$ **21.** $-1 \pm 2i$

23. $-\frac{1}{2} \pm (\sqrt{7}/2)i$ **25.** $3\sqrt{2}\,[\cos(3\pi/4) + i\sin(3\pi/4)]$

27. $5\{\cos[\tan^{-1}(\frac{4}{3})] + i\sin[\tan^{-1}(\frac{4}{3})]\}$

29. $4[\cos(\pi/2) + i\sin(\pi/2)],\ \cos(-\pi/6) + i\sin(-\pi/6),$
$\frac{1}{2}[\cos(-\pi/6) + i\sin(-\pi/6)]$

31. $4\sqrt{2}\,[\cos(7\pi/12) + i\sin(7\pi/12)],$
$(2\sqrt{2})[\cos(13\pi/12) + i\sin(13\pi/12)],\ \frac{1}{4}[\cos(\pi/6) + i\sin(\pi/6)]$

33. -1024 **35.** $-512\sqrt{3} + 512i$

37. $\pm 1,\ \pm i,\ (1/\sqrt{2})(\pm 1 \pm i)$ **39.** $\pm(\sqrt{3}/2) + \frac{1}{2}i,\ -i$

41. i **43.** $\frac{1}{2} + (\sqrt{3}/2)i$ **45.** $-e^2$

CREDITS

vi □ Brian C. Betsill

vii □ Brian C. Betsill
© Gregory D. Dimijian, M. D.

viii □ Brian C. Betsill

ix □ © Ron Lindsey / Phototake
© Gary Ladd 1984 / Photo Researchers, Inc.

x □ Brian C. Betsill

xi □ Brian C. Betsill;
NASA, STScI, and The Smithsonian Institution

xii □ Courtesy of dan clegg;
Brian C. Betsill

xiii □ *The Atmosphere 4/e. by Lutgens/Tarbuck*, © 1989. Reprinted by permission of Prentice-Hall, Inc., Upper Saddle River, NJ;
Dia Max / Getty Images;
Brian C. Betsill

2 □ (*clockwise from top*) © Gregory D. Dimijian, M. D.
© Gary Ladd 1984 / Photo Researchers, Inc.
© Jeff Lepore / Photo Researchers, Inc.
© Ron Lindsey / Phototake

10 □ Brian C. Betsill

24 □ (*photo*) © Catherine Karnow / Woodfin Camp & Associates

64 □ Brian C. Betsill

68 □ © 2003 Brand X Pictures

126 □ Brian C. Betsill

133 □ Figure for Exercise 33 adapted from *Environmental Science: Living Within the System of Nature, 2d ed., by Charles E. Kupchella*, © 1989. Reprinted by permission of Prentice-Hall, Inc., Upper Saddle River, NJ

222 □ © Gregory D. Dimijian, M. D.

229 □ NASA

287 □ (*photo*) © Manfred Kage / Peter Arnold

314 □ Brian C. Betsill

374 □ Brian C. Betsill

412 □ Brian C. Betsill

504 □ Title page courtesy of Thomas Fisher Rare Book Library.

510 □ © Ron Lindsey / Phototake

582 □ © Gary Ladd 1984 / Photo Researchers, Inc.
Brian C. Betsill

INDEX

|||| Special Functions

Power Functions $f(x) = x^a$

(i) $f(x) = x^n$, n a positive integer

n even

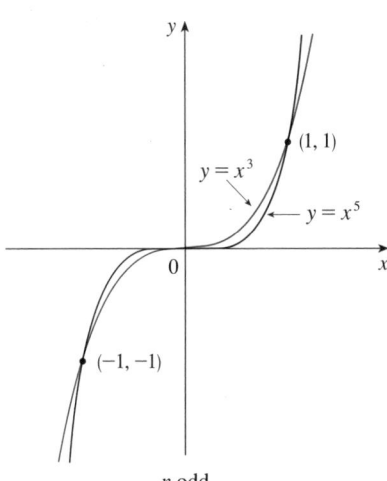

n odd

(ii) $f(x) = x^{1/n} = \sqrt[n]{x}$, n a positive integer

$f(x) = \sqrt{x}$

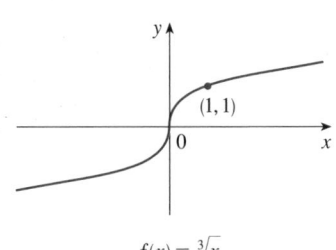

$f(x) = \sqrt[3]{x}$

(iii) $f(x) = x^{-1} = \dfrac{1}{x}$

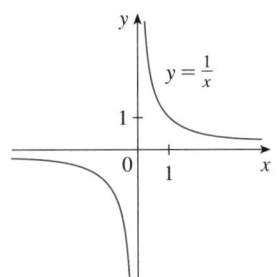

Inverse Trigonometric Functions

$\arcsin x = \sin^{-1}x = y \iff \sin y = x$ and $-\dfrac{\pi}{2} \leqslant y \leqslant \dfrac{\pi}{2}$

$\arccos x = \cos^{-1}x = y \iff \cos y = x$ and $0 \leqslant y \leqslant \pi$

$\arctan x = \tan^{-1}x = y \iff \tan y = x$ and $-\dfrac{\pi}{2} < y < \dfrac{\pi}{2}$

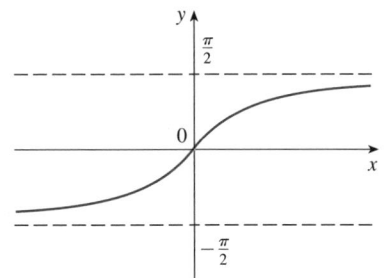

$y = \tan^{-1}x = \arctan x$

$\displaystyle \lim_{x \to -\infty} \tan^{-1}x = -\dfrac{\pi}{2}$

$\displaystyle \lim_{x \to \infty} \tan^{-1}x = \dfrac{\pi}{2}$

||| Special Functions

Exponential and Logarithmic Functions

$\log_a x = y \iff a^y = x$

$\ln x = \log_e x, \quad \text{where} \quad \ln e = 1$

$\ln x = y \iff e^y = x$

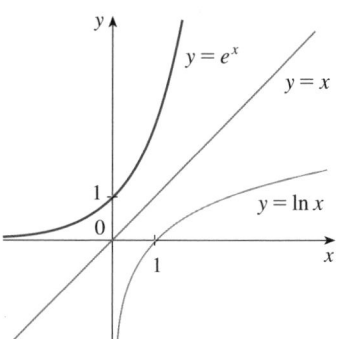

Cancellation Equations

$\log_a(a^x) = x \qquad a^{\log_a x} = x$

$\ln(e^x) = x \qquad e^{\ln x} = x$

Laws of Logarithms

1. $\log_a(xy) = \log_a x + \log_a y$

2. $\log_a\left(\dfrac{x}{y}\right) = \log_a x - \log_a y$

3. $\log_a(x^r) = r \log_a x$

$\lim_{x \to -\infty} e^x = 0 \qquad\qquad \lim_{x \to \infty} e^x = \infty$

$\lim_{x \to 0^+} \ln x = -\infty \qquad \lim_{x \to \infty} \ln x = \infty$

Exponential functions

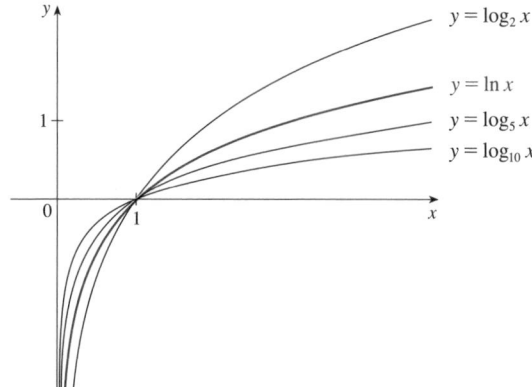

Logarithmic functions

Hyperbolic Functions

$\sinh x = \dfrac{e^x - e^{-x}}{2} \qquad\qquad \operatorname{csch} x = \dfrac{1}{\sinh x}$

$\cosh x = \dfrac{e^x + e^{-x}}{2} \qquad\qquad \operatorname{sech} x = \dfrac{1}{\cosh x}$

$\tanh x = \dfrac{\sinh x}{\cosh x} \qquad\qquad \coth x = \dfrac{\cosh x}{\sinh x}$

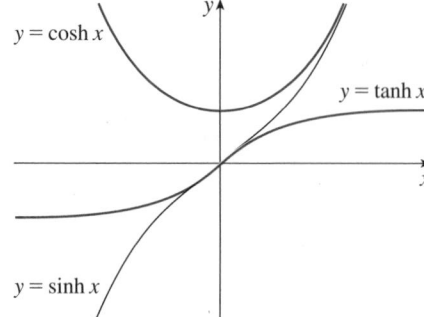

Inverse Hyperbolic Functions

$y = \sinh^{-1} x \iff \sinh y = x \qquad\qquad \sinh^{-1} x = \ln\left(x + \sqrt{x^2 + 1}\right)$

$y = \cosh^{-1} x \iff \cosh y = x \quad \text{and} \quad y \geq 0 \qquad \cosh^{-1} x = \ln\left(x + \sqrt{x^2 - 1}\right)$

$y = \tanh^{-1} x \iff \tanh y = x \qquad\qquad \tanh^{-1} x = \tfrac{1}{2} \ln\left(\dfrac{1 + x}{1 - x}\right)$

||| Differentiation Rules

General Formulas

1. $\dfrac{d}{dx}(c) = 0$

2. $\dfrac{d}{dx}[cf(x)] = cf'(x)$

3. $\dfrac{d}{dx}[f(x) + g(x)] = f'(x) + g'(x)$

4. $\dfrac{d}{dx}[f(x) - g(x)] = f'(x) - g'(x)$

5. $\dfrac{d}{dx}[f(x)g(x)] = f(x)g'(x) + g(x)f'(x)$ (Product Rule)

6. $\dfrac{d}{dx}\left[\dfrac{f(x)}{g(x)}\right] = \dfrac{g(x)f'(x) - f(x)g'(x)}{[g(x)]^2}$ (Quotient Rule)

7. $\dfrac{d}{dx}f(g(x)) = f'(g(x))g'(x)$ (Chain Rule)

8. $\dfrac{d}{dx}(x^n) = nx^{n-1}$ (Power Rule)

Exponential and Logarithmic Functions

9. $\dfrac{d}{dx}(e^x) = e^x$

10. $\dfrac{d}{dx}(a^x) = a^x \ln a$

11. $\dfrac{d}{dx}\ln|x| = \dfrac{1}{x}$

12. $\dfrac{d}{dx}(\log_a x) = \dfrac{1}{x \ln a}$

Trigonometric Functions

13. $\dfrac{d}{dx}(\sin x) = \cos x$

14. $\dfrac{d}{dx}(\cos x) = -\sin x$

15. $\dfrac{d}{dx}(\tan x) = \sec^2 x$

16. $\dfrac{d}{dx}(\csc x) = -\csc x \cot x$

17. $\dfrac{d}{dx}(\sec x) = \sec x \tan x$

18. $\dfrac{d}{dx}(\cot x) = -\csc^2 x$

Inverse Trigonometric Functions

19. $\dfrac{d}{dx}(\sin^{-1}x) = \dfrac{1}{\sqrt{1 - x^2}}$

20. $\dfrac{d}{dx}(\cos^{-1}x) = -\dfrac{1}{\sqrt{1 - x^2}}$

21. $\dfrac{d}{dx}(\tan^{-1}x) = \dfrac{1}{1 + x^2}$

22. $\dfrac{d}{dx}(\csc^{-1}x) = -\dfrac{1}{x\sqrt{x^2 - 1}}$

23. $\dfrac{d}{dx}(\sec^{-1}x) = \dfrac{1}{x\sqrt{x^2 - 1}}$

24. $\dfrac{d}{dx}(\cot^{-1}x) = -\dfrac{1}{1 + x^2}$

Hyperbolic Functions

25. $\dfrac{d}{dx}(\sinh x) = \cosh x$

26. $\dfrac{d}{dx}(\cosh x) = \sinh x$

27. $\dfrac{d}{dx}(\tanh x) = \operatorname{sech}^2 x$

28. $\dfrac{d}{dx}(\operatorname{csch} x) = -\operatorname{csch} x \coth x$

29. $\dfrac{d}{dx}(\operatorname{sech} x) = -\operatorname{sech} x \tanh x$

30. $\dfrac{d}{dx}(\coth x) = -\operatorname{csch}^2 x$

Inverse Hyperbolic Functions

31. $\dfrac{d}{dx}(\sinh^{-1}x) = \dfrac{1}{\sqrt{1 + x^2}}$

32. $\dfrac{d}{dx}(\cosh^{-1}x) = \dfrac{1}{\sqrt{x^2 - 1}}$

33. $\dfrac{d}{dx}(\tanh^{-1}x) = \dfrac{1}{1 - x^2}$

34. $\dfrac{d}{dx}(\operatorname{csch}^{-1}x) = -\dfrac{1}{|x|\sqrt{x^2 + 1}}$

35. $\dfrac{d}{dx}(\operatorname{sech}^{-1}x) = -\dfrac{1}{x\sqrt{1 - x^2}}$

36. $\dfrac{d}{dx}(\coth^{-1}x) = \dfrac{1}{1 - x^2}$

||| Table of Integrals

Basic Forms

1. $\int u \, dv = uv - \int v \, du$

2. $\int u^n \, du = \dfrac{u^{n+1}}{n+1} + C, \quad n \neq -1$

3. $\int \dfrac{du}{u} = \ln |u| + C$

4. $\int e^u \, du = e^u + C$

5. $\int a^u \, du = \dfrac{a^u}{\ln a} + C$

6. $\int \sin u \, du = -\cos u + C$

7. $\int \cos u \, du = \sin u + C$

8. $\int \sec^2 u \, du = \tan u + C$

9. $\int \csc^2 u \, du = -\cot u + C$

10. $\int \sec u \tan u \, du = \sec u + C$

11. $\int \csc u \cot u \, du = -\csc u + C$

12. $\int \tan u \, du = \ln |\sec u| + C$

13. $\int \cot u \, du = \ln |\sin u| + C$

14. $\int \sec u \, du = \ln |\sec u + \tan u| + C$

15. $\int \csc u \, du = \ln |\csc u - \cot u| + C$

16. $\int \dfrac{du}{\sqrt{a^2 - u^2}} = \sin^{-1} \dfrac{u}{a} + C$

17. $\int \dfrac{du}{a^2 + u^2} = \dfrac{1}{a} \tan^{-1} \dfrac{u}{a} + C$

18. $\int \dfrac{du}{u\sqrt{u^2 - a^2}} = \dfrac{1}{a} \sec^{-1} \dfrac{u}{a} + C$

19. $\int \dfrac{du}{a^2 - u^2} = \dfrac{1}{2a} \ln \left| \dfrac{u+a}{u-a} \right| + C$

20. $\int \dfrac{du}{u^2 - a^2} = \dfrac{1}{2a} \ln \left| \dfrac{u-a}{u+a} \right| + C$

Forms Involving $\sqrt{a^2 + u^2}$, $a > 0$

21. $\int \sqrt{a^2 + u^2} \, du = \dfrac{u}{2} \sqrt{a^2 + u^2} + \dfrac{a^2}{2} \ln\left(u + \sqrt{a^2 + u^2}\right) + C$

22. $\int u^2 \sqrt{a^2 + u^2} \, du = \dfrac{u}{8} (a^2 + 2u^2) \sqrt{a^2 + u^2} - \dfrac{a^4}{8} \ln\left(u + \sqrt{a^2 + u^2}\right) + C$

23. $\int \dfrac{\sqrt{a^2 + u^2}}{u} \, du = \sqrt{a^2 + u^2} - a \ln \left| \dfrac{a + \sqrt{a^2 + u^2}}{u} \right| + C$

24. $\int \dfrac{\sqrt{a^2 + u^2}}{u^2} \, du = -\dfrac{\sqrt{a^2 + u^2}}{u} + \ln\left(u + \sqrt{a^2 + u^2}\right) + C$

25. $\int \dfrac{du}{\sqrt{a^2 + u^2}} = \ln\left(u + \sqrt{a^2 + u^2}\right) + C$

26. $\int \dfrac{u^2 \, du}{\sqrt{a^2 + u^2}} = \dfrac{u}{2} \sqrt{a^2 + u^2} - \dfrac{a^2}{2} \ln\left(u + \sqrt{a^2 + u^2}\right) + C$

27. $\int \dfrac{du}{u\sqrt{a^2 + u^2}} = -\dfrac{1}{a} \ln \left| \dfrac{\sqrt{a^2 + u^2} + a}{u} \right| + C$

28. $\int \dfrac{du}{u^2 \sqrt{a^2 + u^2}} = -\dfrac{\sqrt{a^2 + u^2}}{a^2 u} + C$

29. $\int \dfrac{du}{(a^2 + u^2)^{3/2}} = \dfrac{u}{a^2 \sqrt{a^2 + u^2}} + C$

|||| Table of Integrals

Forms Involving $\sqrt{a^2 - u^2}$, $a > 0$

30. $\displaystyle \int \sqrt{a^2 - u^2}\, du = \frac{u}{2} \sqrt{a^2 - u^2} + \frac{a^2}{2} \sin^{-1} \frac{u}{a} + C$

31. $\displaystyle \int u^2 \sqrt{a^2 - u^2}\, du = \frac{u}{8} (2u^2 - a^2) \sqrt{a^2 - u^2} + \frac{a^4}{8} \sin^{-1} \frac{u}{a} + C$

32. $\displaystyle \int \frac{\sqrt{a^2 - u^2}}{u}\, du = \sqrt{a^2 - u^2} - a \ln \left| \frac{a + \sqrt{a^2 - u^2}}{u} \right| + C$

33. $\displaystyle \int \frac{\sqrt{a^2 - u^2}}{u^2}\, du = -\frac{1}{u} \sqrt{a^2 - u^2} - \sin^{-1} \frac{u}{a} + C$

34. $\displaystyle \int \frac{u^2\, du}{\sqrt{a^2 - u^2}} = -\frac{u}{2} \sqrt{a^2 - u^2} + \frac{a^2}{2} \sin^{-1} \frac{u}{a} + C$

35. $\displaystyle \int \frac{du}{u\sqrt{a^2 - u^2}} = -\frac{1}{a} \ln \left| \frac{a + \sqrt{a^2 - u^2}}{u} \right| + C$

36. $\displaystyle \int \frac{du}{u^2 \sqrt{a^2 - u^2}} = -\frac{1}{a^2 u} \sqrt{a^2 - u^2} + C$

37. $\displaystyle \int (a^2 - u^2)^{3/2}\, du = -\frac{u}{8} (2u^2 - 5a^2) \sqrt{a^2 - u^2} + \frac{3a^4}{8} \sin^{-1} \frac{u}{a} + C$

38. $\displaystyle \int \frac{du}{(a^2 - u^2)^{3/2}} = \frac{u}{a^2 \sqrt{a^2 - u^2}} + C$

Forms Involving $\sqrt{u^2 - a^2}$, $a > 0$

39. $\displaystyle \int \sqrt{u^2 - a^2}\, du = \frac{u}{2} \sqrt{u^2 - a^2} - \frac{a^2}{2} \ln \left| u + \sqrt{u^2 - a^2} \right| + C$

40. $\displaystyle \int u^2 \sqrt{u^2 - a^2}\, du = \frac{u}{8} (2u^2 - a^2) \sqrt{u^2 - a^2} - \frac{a^4}{8} \ln \left| u + \sqrt{u^2 - a^2} \right| + C$

41. $\displaystyle \int \frac{\sqrt{u^2 - a^2}}{u}\, du = \sqrt{u^2 - a^2} - a \cos^{-1} \frac{a}{|u|} + C$

42. $\displaystyle \int \frac{\sqrt{u^2 - a^2}}{u^2}\, du = -\frac{\sqrt{u^2 - a^2}}{u} + \ln \left| u + \sqrt{u^2 - a^2} \right| + C$

43. $\displaystyle \int \frac{du}{\sqrt{u^2 - a^2}} = \ln \left| u + \sqrt{u^2 - a^2} \right| + C$

44. $\displaystyle \int \frac{u^2\, du}{\sqrt{u^2 - a^2}} = \frac{u}{2} \sqrt{u^2 - a^2} + \frac{a^2}{2} \ln \left| u + \sqrt{u^2 - a^2} \right| + C$

45. $\displaystyle \int \frac{du}{u^2 \sqrt{u^2 - a^2}} = \frac{\sqrt{u^2 - a^2}}{a^2 u} + C$

46. $\displaystyle \int \frac{du}{(u^2 - a^2)^{3/2}} = -\frac{u}{a^2 \sqrt{u^2 - a^2}} + C$

|||| Table of Integrals

Forms Involving $a + bu$

47. $\displaystyle\int \frac{u\,du}{a + bu} = \frac{1}{b^2}\left(a + bu - a\ln|a + bu|\right) + C$

48. $\displaystyle\int \frac{u^2\,du}{a + bu} = \frac{1}{2b^3}\left[(a + bu)^2 - 4a(a + bu) + 2a^2\ln|a + bu|\right] + C$

49. $\displaystyle\int \frac{du}{u(a + bu)} = \frac{1}{a}\ln\left|\frac{u}{a + bu}\right| + C$

50. $\displaystyle\int \frac{du}{u^2(a + bu)} = -\frac{1}{au} + \frac{b}{a^2}\ln\left|\frac{a + bu}{u}\right| + C$

51. $\displaystyle\int \frac{u\,du}{(a + bu)^2} = \frac{a}{b^2(a + bu)} + \frac{1}{b^2}\ln|a + bu| + C$

52. $\displaystyle\int \frac{du}{u(a + bu)^2} = \frac{1}{a(a + bu)} - \frac{1}{a^2}\ln\left|\frac{a + bu}{u}\right| + C$

53. $\displaystyle\int \frac{u^2\,du}{(a + bu)^2} = \frac{1}{b^3}\left(a + bu - \frac{a^2}{a + bu} - 2a\ln|a + bu|\right) + C$

54. $\displaystyle\int u\sqrt{a + bu}\,du = \frac{2}{15b^2}(3bu - 2a)(a + bu)^{3/2} + C$

55. $\displaystyle\int \frac{u\,du}{\sqrt{a + bu}} = \frac{2}{3b^2}(bu - 2a)\sqrt{a + bu} + C$

56. $\displaystyle\int \frac{u^2\,du}{\sqrt{a + bu}} = \frac{2}{15b^3}(8a^2 + 3b^2u^2 - 4abu)\sqrt{a + bu} + C$

57. $\displaystyle\int \frac{du}{u\sqrt{a + bu}} = \frac{1}{\sqrt{a}}\ln\left|\frac{\sqrt{a + bu} - \sqrt{a}}{\sqrt{a + bu} + \sqrt{a}}\right| + C, \quad \text{if } a > 0$

$\displaystyle\qquad\qquad\quad = \frac{2}{\sqrt{-a}}\tan^{-1}\sqrt{\frac{a + bu}{-a}} + C, \qquad \text{if } a < 0$

58. $\displaystyle\int \frac{\sqrt{a + bu}}{u}\,du = 2\sqrt{a + bu} + a\int\frac{du}{u\sqrt{a + bu}}$

59. $\displaystyle\int \frac{\sqrt{a + bu}}{u^2}\,du = -\frac{\sqrt{a + bu}}{u} + \frac{b}{2}\int\frac{du}{u\sqrt{a + bu}}$

60. $\displaystyle\int u^n\sqrt{a + bu}\,du = \frac{2}{b(2n + 3)}\left[u^n(a + bu)^{3/2} - na\int u^{n-1}\sqrt{a + bu}\,du\right]$

61. $\displaystyle\int \frac{u^n\,du}{\sqrt{a + bu}} = \frac{2u^n\sqrt{a + bu}}{b(2n + 1)} - \frac{2na}{b(2n + 1)}\int\frac{u^{n-1}\,du}{\sqrt{a + bu}}$

62. $\displaystyle\int \frac{du}{u^n\sqrt{a + bu}} = -\frac{\sqrt{a + bu}}{a(n - 1)u^{n-1}} - \frac{b(2n - 3)}{2a(n - 1)}\int\frac{du}{u^{n-1}\sqrt{a + bu}}$

|||| Table of Integrals

Trigonometric Forms

63. $\displaystyle\int \sin^2u\, du = \tfrac{1}{2}u - \tfrac{1}{4}\sin 2u + C$

64. $\displaystyle\int \cos^2u\, du = \tfrac{1}{2}u + \tfrac{1}{4}\sin 2u + C$

65. $\displaystyle\int \tan^2u\, du = \tan u - u + C$

66. $\displaystyle\int \cot^2u\, du = -\cot u - u + C$

67. $\displaystyle\int \sin^3u\, du = -\tfrac{1}{3}(2 + \sin^2u)\cos u + C$

68. $\displaystyle\int \cos^3u\, du = \tfrac{1}{3}(2 + \cos^2u)\sin u + C$

69. $\displaystyle\int \tan^3u\, du = \tfrac{1}{2}\tan^2u + \ln|\cos u| + C$

70. $\displaystyle\int \cot^3u\, du = -\tfrac{1}{2}\cot^2u - \ln|\sin u| + C$

71. $\displaystyle\int \sec^3u\, du = \tfrac{1}{2}\sec u \tan u + \tfrac{1}{2}\ln|\sec u + \tan u| + C$

72. $\displaystyle\int \csc^3u\, du = -\tfrac{1}{2}\csc u \cot u + \tfrac{1}{2}\ln|\csc u - \cot u| + C$

73. $\displaystyle\int \sin^nu\, du = -\frac{1}{n}\sin^{n-1}u \cos u + \frac{n-1}{n}\int \sin^{n-2}u\, du$

74. $\displaystyle\int \cos^nu\, du = \frac{1}{n}\cos^{n-1}u \sin u + \frac{n-1}{n}\int \cos^{n-2}u\, du$

75. $\displaystyle\int \tan^nu\, du = \frac{1}{n-1}\tan^{n-1}u - \int \tan^{n-2}u\, du$

76. $\displaystyle\int \cot^nu\, du = \frac{-1}{n-1}\cot^{n-1}u - \int \cot^{n-2}u\, du$

77. $\displaystyle\int \sec^nu\, du = \frac{1}{n-1}\tan u \sec^{n-2}u + \frac{n-2}{n-1}\int \sec^{n-2}u\, du$

78. $\displaystyle\int \csc^nu\, du = \frac{-1}{n-1}\cot u \csc^{n-2}u + \frac{n-2}{n-1}\int \csc^{n-2}u\, du$

79. $\displaystyle\int \sin au \sin bu\, du = \frac{\sin(a-b)u}{2(a-b)} - \frac{\sin(a+b)u}{2(a+b)} + C$

80. $\displaystyle\int \cos au \cos bu\, du = \frac{\sin(a-b)u}{2(a-b)} + \frac{\sin(a+b)u}{2(a+b)} + C$

81. $\displaystyle\int \sin au \cos bu\, du = -\frac{\cos(a-b)u}{2(a-b)} - \frac{\cos(a+b)u}{2(a+b)} + C$

82. $\displaystyle\int u \sin u\, du = \sin u - u \cos u + C$

83. $\displaystyle\int u \cos u\, du = \cos u + u \sin u + C$

84. $\displaystyle\int u^n \sin u\, du = -u^n \cos u + n\int u^{n-1}\cos u\, du$

85. $\displaystyle\int u^n \cos u\, du = u^n \sin u - n\int u^{n-1}\sin u\, du$

86. $\displaystyle\int \sin^nu \cos^mu\, du = -\frac{\sin^{n-1}u \cos^{m+1}u}{n+m} + \frac{n-1}{n+m}\int \sin^{n-2}u \cos^mu\, du$

$\displaystyle\qquad\quad = \frac{\sin^{n+1}u \cos^{m-1}u}{n+m} + \frac{m-1}{n+m}\int \sin^nu \cos^{m-2}u\, du$

Inverse Trigonometric Forms

87. $\displaystyle\int \sin^{-1}u\, du = u \sin^{-1}u + \sqrt{1-u^2} + C$

88. $\displaystyle\int \cos^{-1}u\, du = u \cos^{-1}u - \sqrt{1-u^2} + C$

89. $\displaystyle\int \tan^{-1}u\, du = u \tan^{-1}u - \tfrac{1}{2}\ln(1+u^2) + C$

90. $\displaystyle\int u \sin^{-1}u\, du = \frac{2u^2-1}{4}\sin^{-1}u + \frac{u\sqrt{1-u^2}}{4} + C$

91. $\displaystyle\int u \cos^{-1}u\, du = \frac{2u^2-1}{4}\cos^{-1}u - \frac{u\sqrt{1-u^2}}{4} + C$

92. $\displaystyle\int u \tan^{-1}u\, du = \frac{u^2+1}{2}\tan^{-1}u - \frac{u}{2} + C$

93. $\displaystyle\int u^n \sin^{-1}u\, du = \frac{1}{n+1}\left[u^{n+1}\sin^{-1}u - \int \frac{u^{n+1}\, du}{\sqrt{1-u^2}}\right], \quad n \neq -1$

94. $\displaystyle\int u^n \cos^{-1}u\, du = \frac{1}{n+1}\left[u^{n+1}\cos^{-1}u + \int \frac{u^{n+1}\, du}{\sqrt{1-u^2}}\right], \quad n \neq -1$

95. $\displaystyle\int u^n \tan^{-1}u\, du = \frac{1}{n+1}\left[u^{n+1}\tan^{-1}u - \int \frac{u^{n+1}\, du}{1+u^2}\right], \quad n \neq -1$

Table of Integrals

Exponential and Logarithmic Forms

96. $\int ue^{au}\, du = \dfrac{1}{a^2}(au - 1)e^{au} + C$

97. $\int u^n e^{au}\, du = \dfrac{1}{a} u^n e^{au} - \dfrac{n}{a}\int u^{n-1}e^{au}\, du$

98. $\int e^{au} \sin bu\, du = \dfrac{e^{au}}{a^2 + b^2}(a \sin bu - b \cos bu) + C$

99. $\int e^{au} \cos bu\, du = \dfrac{e^{au}}{a^2 + b^2}(a \cos bu + b \sin bu) + C$

100. $\int \ln u\, du = u \ln u - u + C$

101. $\int u^n \ln u\, du = \dfrac{u^{n+1}}{(n+1)^2}[(n+1)\ln u - 1] + C$

102. $\int \dfrac{1}{u \ln u}\, du = \ln|\ln u| + C$

Hyperbolic Forms

103. $\int \sinh u\, du = \cosh u + C$

104. $\int \cosh u\, du = \sinh u + C$

105. $\int \tanh u\, du = \ln \cosh u + C$

106. $\int \coth u\, du = \ln|\sinh u| + C$

107. $\int \operatorname{sech} u\, du = \tan^{-1}|\sinh u| + C$

108. $\int \operatorname{csch} u\, du = \ln|\tanh \tfrac{1}{2}u| + C$

109. $\int \operatorname{sech}^2 u\, du = \tanh u + C$

110. $\int \operatorname{csch}^2 u\, du = -\coth u + C$

111. $\int \operatorname{sech} u \tanh u\, du = -\operatorname{sech} u + C$

112. $\int \operatorname{csch} u \coth u\, du = -\operatorname{csch} u + C$

Forms Involving $\sqrt{2au - u^2},\ a > 0$

113. $\int \sqrt{2au - u^2}\, du = \dfrac{u - a}{2}\sqrt{2au - u^2} + \dfrac{a^2}{2}\cos^{-1}\left(\dfrac{a - u}{a}\right) + C$

114. $\int u\sqrt{2au - u^2}\, du = \dfrac{2u^2 - au - 3a^2}{6}\sqrt{2au - u^2} + \dfrac{a^3}{2}\cos^{-1}\left(\dfrac{a - u}{a}\right) + C$

115. $\int \dfrac{\sqrt{2au - u^2}}{u}\, du = \sqrt{2au - u^2} + a\cos^{-1}\left(\dfrac{a - u}{a}\right) + C$

116. $\int \dfrac{\sqrt{2au - u^2}}{u^2}\, du = -\dfrac{2\sqrt{2au - u^2}}{u} - \cos^{-1}\left(\dfrac{a - u}{a}\right) + C$

117. $\int \dfrac{du}{\sqrt{2au - u^2}} = \cos^{-1}\left(\dfrac{a - u}{a}\right) + C$

118. $\int \dfrac{u\, du}{\sqrt{2au - u^2}} = -\sqrt{2au - u^2} + a\cos^{-1}\left(\dfrac{a - u}{a}\right) + C$

119. $\int \dfrac{u^2\, du}{\sqrt{2au - u^2}} = -\dfrac{(u + 3a)}{2}\sqrt{2au - u^2} + \dfrac{3a^2}{2}\cos^{-1}\left(\dfrac{a - u}{a}\right) + C$

120. $\int \dfrac{du}{u\sqrt{2au - u^2}} = -\dfrac{\sqrt{2au - u^2}}{au} + C$